Algebra

Exponents

$$c^r c^s = c^{r+s}$$

$$\frac{c^r}{c^s} = c^{r-s}$$

$$(c^r)^s = c^{rs}$$

$$(cd)^r = c^r d^r$$

$$\left(\frac{c}{d}\right)^r = \frac{c^r}{d^r} \quad (d \neq 0)$$

$$c^{-r} = \frac{1}{c^r} \quad (c \neq 0)$$

Multiplication & Factoring Patterns

Difference of Squares: $\quad u^2 - v^2 = (u + v)(u - v)$

Perfect Squares: $\quad (u + v)^2 = u^2 + 2uv + v^2$
$$(u - v)^2 = u^2 - 2uv + v^2$$

Difference of Cubes: $\quad u^3 - v^3 = (u - v)(u^2 + uv + v^2)$

Sum of Cubes: $\quad u^3 + v^3 = (u + v)(u^2 - uv + v^2)$

Perfect Cubes: $\quad (u + v)^3 = u^3 + 3u^2v + 3uv^2 + v^3$
$$(u - v)^3 = u^3 - 3u^2v + 3uv^2 - v^3$$

The Quadratic Formula

If $a \neq 0$, then the solutions of $ax^2 + bx + c = 0$ are $\quad x = \dfrac{-b \pm \sqrt{b^2 - 4ac}}{2a}$.

Equations and Graphs

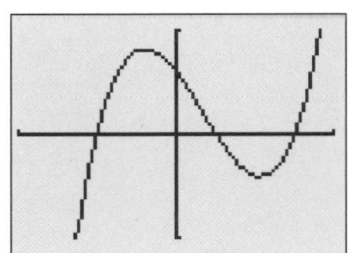

The solutions of the equation $f(x) = 0$ are the x-intercepts of the graph of $y = f(x)$.

Natural Logarithms

For $v, w > 0$ and any u:

$\ln v = u$ means $e^u = v$

$\ln(vw) = \ln v + \ln w$

$\ln\left(\dfrac{v}{w}\right) = \ln v - \ln w$

$\ln(v^k) = k(\ln v)$

Logarithms to Base b

For $v, w > 0$ and any u:

$\log_b v = u$ means $b^u = v$

$\log_b(vw) = \log_b v + \log_b w$

$\log_b\left(\dfrac{v}{w}\right) = \log_b v - \log_b w$

$\log_b(v^k) = k(\log_b v)$

Special Notation

$\ln v$ means $\log_e v$

$\log v$ means $\log_{10} v$

Change of Base Formula

$$\log_b v = \frac{\ln v}{\ln b}$$

Geometry

The Pythagorean Theorem

$$c^2 = a^2 + b^2$$

Area of a Triangle

$$A = \frac{1}{2}bh$$

Circle

Diameter $= 2r$

Circumference $= 2\pi r$

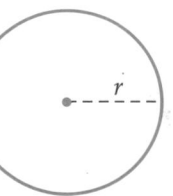

Area $= \pi r^2$

Distance Formula

Length of segment PQ

$$d = \sqrt{(x_1 - x_2)^2 + (y_1 - y_2)^2}$$

Midpoint Formula

Midpoint M of segment PQ

$$M\left(\frac{x_1 + x_2}{2}, \frac{y_1 + y_2}{2}\right)$$

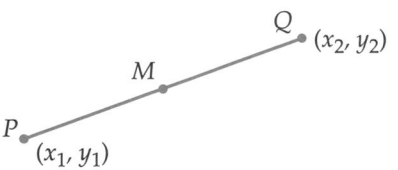

Slope

Slope of line PQ, $x_1 \neq x_2$

$$m = \frac{y_2 - y_1}{x_2 - x_1}$$

The equation of the straight line through (x_1, y_1) with slope m is $y - y_1 = m(x - x_1)$.
The equation of line with slope m and y-intercept b is $y = mx + b$.

Rectangular and Parametric Equations for Conic Sections

Circle
Center (h, k), radius r

$$(x - h)^2 + (y - k)^2 = r^2$$

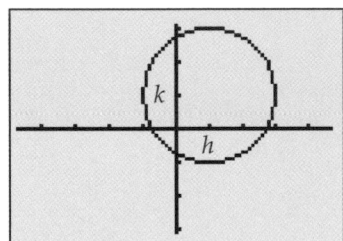

$$\begin{aligned} x &= r\cos t + h \\ y &= r\sin t + k \end{aligned} \quad (0 \leq t \leq 2\pi)$$

Ellipse
Center (h, k)

$$\frac{(x - h)^2}{a^2} + \frac{(y - k)^2}{b^2} = 1$$

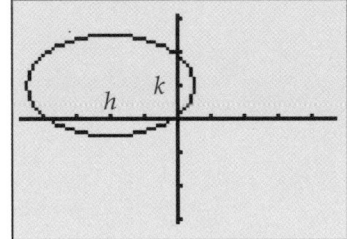

$$\begin{aligned} x &= a\cos t + h \\ y &= b\sin t + k \end{aligned} \quad (0 \leq t \leq 2\pi)$$

Parabola
Vertex (h, k)

$$(x - h)^2 = 4p(y - k)$$

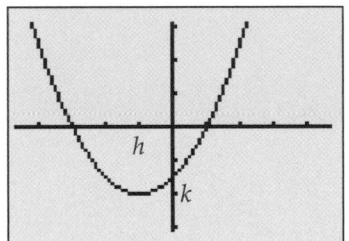

$$x = t \qquad (t \text{ any real})$$
$$y = \frac{(t - h)^2}{4p} + k$$

Parabola
Vertex (h, k)

$$(y - k)^2 = 4p(x - h)$$

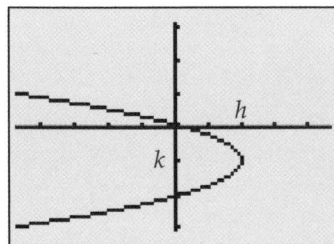

$$x = \frac{(t - k)^2}{4p} + h$$
$$y = t \qquad (t \text{ any real})$$

Hyperbola
Center (h, k)

$$\frac{(x - h)^2}{a^2} - \frac{(y - k)^2}{b^2} = 1$$

$$\begin{aligned} x &= \frac{a}{\cos t} + h \\ y &= b\tan t + k \end{aligned} \quad (0 \leq t \leq 2\pi)$$

Hyperbola
Center (h, k)

$$\frac{(y - k)^2}{a^2} - \frac{(x - h)^2}{b^2} = 1$$

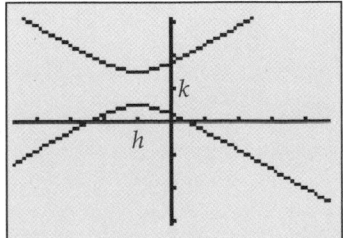

$$\begin{aligned} x &= b\tan t + h \\ y &= \frac{a}{\cos t} + k \end{aligned} \quad (0 \leq t \leq 2\pi)$$

Precalculus

A Graphing Approach

Support for Students

Objectives help students focus their learning.

Notes provide review and direct attention toward specific content.

Technology Tips and the **Technology Appendix** provide information and assistance for specific calculators, including the TI-84 Plus and Casio CFX-9850.

6.5 Basic Trigonometric Identities

Objectives

- Develop basic trigonometric identities

NOTE Most calculators automatically insert an opening parenthesis when a trigonometric function key is pushed. The display cos(5 + 3 is interpreted as cos(5 + 3). If you want cos 5 + 3, you must insert a parenthesis after the 5: cos(5) + 3 .

Technology Tip

- Calculators do not use the convention of writing an exponent between the trigonometric function and its argument. In order to obtain $\sin^3 4$, you must enter sin (4)^3.

The algebra of trigonometric functions is just like that of other functions. They may be added, subtracted, composed, etc. However, two notational conventions are normally used with trigonometric functions.

Parentheses can be omitted whenever no confusion can result.

Figure 6.5-1 shows, however, that parentheses *are* needed to distinguish

$$\cos(t + 3) \quad \text{and} \quad \cos t + 3.$$

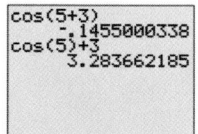

Figure 6.5-1

When dealing with powers of trigonometric functions,

exponents (other than −1) are written between the function symbol and the variable.

For example,

$$(\cos t)^3 \quad \text{is written} \quad \cos^3 t.$$

Furthermore,

$$\sin t^3 \quad \text{means } \sin(t^3) \quad \text{not } (\sin t)^3 \text{ or } \sin^3 t,$$

as illustrated in Figure 6.5-2.

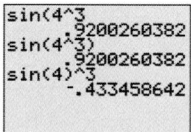

Figure 6.5-2

Identities

Trigonometric functions have numerous relationships that can be expressed as *identities*. An **identity** is an equation that is true for all val-

---

CHAPTER 5

can do calculus

Tangents to Exponential Functions

Tangent lines to a curve are important in calculus—where they are used to approximate function values close to a specific point and used for finding the zeros of general functions. The procedure developed in the Can Do Calculus for Chapter 3 will be used here to develop the equations of the tangent lines to exponential functions.

Slopes of Secant Lines and Tangent Lines

Recall that the difference quotient of f at the specific value $x = h$ is given by

$$\frac{f(b + h) - f(b)}{h}$$

where h is the amount of change in the x values from o[...]
The difference quotient can be interpreted as the slope [...]
that passes through the points $(b, f(b))$ and $(b + h, f(b +$ [...]
small, the value of $\dfrac{f(b + h) - f(b)}{h}$ approaches the va[...]
the tangent line at $(b, f(b))$.

Also, if f is any function, then the slope of the secant li[...]
and any other point $(x, f(x))$ on the graph of f is given[...]

$$\frac{f(x) - f(b)}{x - b}$$

Figure 5.C-1

Can Do Calculus connects calculus topics to chapter material as a preview to the world of calculus.

3.4.A *Excursion:* Symmetry

Objectives

- Determine whether a graph has *y*-axis, *x*-axis, or origin symmetry
- Determine whether a function is even, odd, or neither

This section presents three kinds of symmetry that a graph can have and ways to identify these symmetries both geometrically and algebraically.

y-Axis Symmetry

A graph of a function or relation is **symmetric with respect to the y-axis** if the part of the graph on the right side of the *y*-axis is the mirror image of the part on the left side of the *y*-axis, as shown in Figure 3.4.A-1.

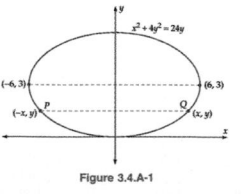

Figure 3.4.A-1

Excursions supplement material related to the previous section with high-interest, motivational topics.

Prepare students for calculus and trigonometry with the thorough support throughout the *Student Edition.*

ues of the variables for which every term of the equation is defined. For example,

$$(a + b)^2 = a^2 + 2ab + b^2$$

is an identity because it is true for all possible values of a and b.

The unit circle description of trigonometric functions (see the box on page 446) leads to the following **quotient identities.**

Quotient Identities

$$\tan t = \frac{\sin t}{\cos t} \qquad \cot t = \frac{\cos t}{\sin t}$$

Example 1   Quotient Identities

Simplify the expression below.

$$\tan t \cos t$$

Solution

By the quotient identity,

$$\tan t \cos t = \frac{\sin t}{\cos t}\cos t = \sin t$$

Reciprocal Identities

The **reciprocal identities** follow immediately from the definitions of the trigonometric functions.

Reciprocal Identities

$$\sin t = \frac{1}{\csc t} \qquad \cos t = \frac{1}{\sec t} \qquad \tan t = \frac{1}{\cot t}$$

$$\csc t = \frac{1}{\sin t} \qquad \sec t = \frac{1}{\cos t} \qquad \cot t = \frac{1}{\tan t}$$

CAUTION

An identity may not be true for a value of the variable that makes a term of the equation undefined. For example, if $t = 0$, then $\tan t = 0$ while $\cot t$ is undefined. Thus, $\tan t \neq \frac{1}{\cot t}$ for $t = 0$.

Example 2   Reciprocal Identities

Given that $\sin t = 0.28$ and $\cos t = 0.96$, find $\csc t$ and $\sec t$.

Solution

By the reciprocal identities,

$$\csc t = \frac{1}{\sin t} = \frac{1}{0.28} \approx 3.57 \qquad \sec t = \frac{1}{\cos t} = \frac{1}{0.96} \approx 1.04$$

Cautions
alert students
to common
errors and
misconceptions.

Examples
are completely
worked out
with clear
explanations.

Student Edition CD-ROM

Perfect for reducing the weight of books students carry home, the entire *Student Edition* is on one easy-to-navigate CD-ROM.

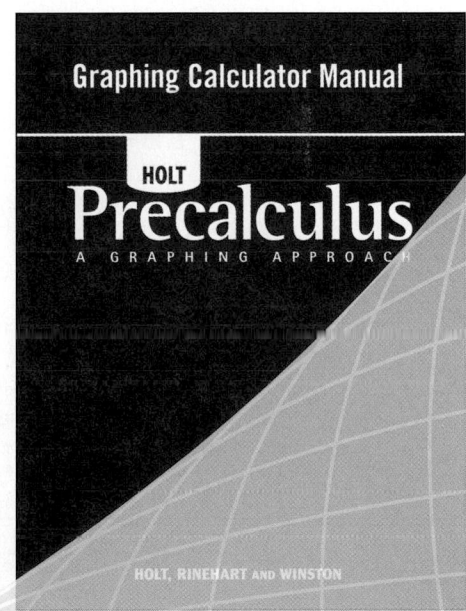

Graphing Calculator Manual

This booklet guides the student in the routine use of a graphing calculator.

Support for Teachers

Teaching Notes offer teaching suggestions pertinent to lesson concepts.

Math Background provides underlying information about a lesson, how the lesson fits into the program, or math history.

Example Notes present teaching tips and additional explanations.

Teaching Notes

For the sum $\sum_{i=1}^{9} u_i$, the letter i is called the **index** of the summation, the number 1 is the **lower limit** of the summation, and the number 9 is the **upper limit** of the summation.

Math Background

Summation notation represents an *iterative* process. An iterative process is a process that involves repetition of the same set of operations.

Example Notes

In **Example 5**, to find the nth term, you must find the common difference and use $u_n = u_1 + (n - 1)d$.

In **Example 6**, the method for finding d can be shown as follows:

$$d = \frac{u_{10} - u_6}{10 - 6} = \frac{93 - 57}{10 - 6} = \frac{36}{4} = 9$$

In **Example 7a**, the form $\sum_{n=1}^{5} (\ \ )$ indicates that the expression inside the grouping symbols is to appear 5 times, with appropriate changes based on the changing n-values. It may help to use color to show the changing n-values as follows:

$$\sum_{n=1}^{5} (-7 + 3n) = (-7 + 3 \cdot 1)$$
$$+ (-7 + 3 \cdot 2)$$
$$+ (-7 + 3 \cdot 3)$$
$$+ (-7 + 3 \cdot 4)$$
$$+ (-7 + 3 \cdot 5)$$

Real-World Application

The "break-even point" in business is when revenue equals cost.

In **Example 7**, you can find the number of cups that need to be produced in one week in order for the factory to break even by solving the equation $R(x) = C(x)$ for x.

To accomplish this, graph $R(x) = 1.95x$ and $C(x) = 0.80x + 12,000$ on a calculator and use a graphical intersection finder to find the point of intersection (See **Section 2.1**, page 82).

Real-World Applications spotlight occupations where concepts learned in precalculus are utilized in the real world, plus opportunities for further online research.

Example 5 Finding a Term of an Arithmetic Sequence

What is the 45th term of the arithmetic sequence whose first three terms are 5, 9, and 13?

Solution

The first three terms show that $u_1 = 5$ and that the common difference, d, is 4. Apply the formula with $n = 45$.

$$u_{45} = u_1 + (45 - 1)d = 5 + (44)(4) = 181$$

Example 6 Finding Explicit and Recursive Formulas

If $\{u_n\}$ is an arithmetic sequence with $u_6 = 57$ and $u_{10} = 93$, find u_1, a recursive formula, and an explicit formula for u_n.

Solution

The sequence can be written as

$$\dots, \underset{u_6}{57}, \underset{u_7}{\_\_}, \underset{u_8}{\_\_}, \underset{u_9}{\_\_}, \underset{u_{10}}{93}, \dots$$

The common difference, d, can be found by the difference between 93 and 57 divided by the number of times d must be added to 57 to produce 93 (i.e., the number of terms from 6 to 10).

$$d = \frac{93 - 57}{10 - 6} = \frac{36}{4} = 9$$

Note that $d = 9$ is the difference of the output values (terms of the sequence) divided by the difference of the input values (position of the terms of the sequence), which represents the change in output per unit change in input.

The value of u_1 can be found by using $n = 6$, $u_6 = 57$ and $d = 9$ in the equation

$$u_6 = u_1 + (n - 1)d$$
$$57 = u_1 + (6 - 1)9$$
$$u_1 = 57 - 5 \cdot 9 = 57 - 45 = 12$$

Because $u_1 = 12$ and $d = 9$, the recursive form of the arithmetic sequence is given by

$$u_1 = 12 \text{ and } u_n = u_{n-1} + 9, \text{ for } n \geq 2$$

The explicit form of the arithmetic sequence is given by

$$u_n = 12 + (n - 1)9$$
$$= 9n + 3, \text{ for } n \geq 1.$$

Wrap-around features offer a wealth of help where it's needed most.

Additional Examples accompany each **Example** in the *Student Edition*.

Common Error Alerts point out errors students may commonly make and suggest remedies.

NOTE If $u_1, u_2, u_3, \ldots$ is an arithmetic sequence, then an expression of the form $u_1 + u_2 + u_3 + \ldots$ (sometimes written as $\sum_{n=1}^{\infty} u_n$) is called an **arithmetic series**.

Summation Notation

It is sometimes necessary to find the sum of various terms in a sequence. For instance, we might want to find the sum of the first nine terms of the sequence $\{u_n\}$. Mathematicians often use the capital Greek letter sigma (Σ) to abbreviate such a sum as follows.

$$\sum_{i=1}^{9} u_i = u_1 + u_2 + u_3 + u_4 + u_5 + u_6 + u_7 + u_8 + u_9$$

Similarly, for any positive integer m and numbers $c_1, c_2, \ldots, c_m$,

Summation Notation

$$\sum_{k=1}^{m} c_k \quad \text{means} \quad c_1 + c_2 + c_3 + \cdots + c_m$$

Example 7 Sum of a Sequence

Compute each sum.

a. $\sum_{n=1}^{5}(-7 + 3n)$ **b.** $\sum_{n=1}^{4}[-3 + (n-1)4]$

Solution

a. Substitute 1, 2, 3, 4, and 5 for n in the expression $-7 + 3n$ and add the terms.

$\sum_{n=1}^{5}(-7 + 3n)$

$= (-7 + 3 \cdot 1) + (-7 + 3 \cdot 2) + (-7 + 3 \cdot 3)$
$\quad + (-7 + 3 \cdot 4) + (-7 + 3 \cdot 5)$
$= (-7 + 3) + (-7 + 6) + (-7 + 9) + (-7 + 12) + (-7 + 15)$
$= -4 - 1 + 2 + 5 + 8$
$= 10$

b. Substitute 1, 2, 3, and 4 for n in the expression $-3 + (n-1)4$, and add the terms.

$\sum_{n=1}^{4}[-3 + (n-1)4]$

$= [-3 + (1-1)4] + [-3 + (2-1)4]$
$\quad + [-3 + (3-1)4] + [-3 + (4-1)4]$
$= [-3 + 0 \cdot 4] + [-3 + 1 \cdot 4] + [-3 + 2 \cdot 4] + [-3 + 3 \cdot 4]$
$= -3 + (-3 + 4) + (-3 + 8) + (-3 + 12)$
$= -3 + 1 + 5 + 9$
$= 12$

ADDITIONAL EXAMPLES

Example 5

What is the 38th term of the arithmetic sequence whose first three terms are 15, 10, and 5? -170

Example 6

If $\{u_n\}$ is an arithmetic sequence with $u_5 = 22$ and $u_{11} = 64$, find u_1, a recursive formula, and an explicit formula.
$u_1 = -6$
$u_1 = -6$ and $u_n = u_{n-1} + 7$ for $n \geq 2$
$u_n = 7n - 13$ for $n \geq 1$

Example 7

Compute each sum.

a. $\sum_{i=1}^{4}(5 - 4n)$ -20

b. $\sum_{i=1}^{5}[-4 + (n-1)3]$ 10

COMMON ERROR ALERT

Students may use the wrong sign for a common difference. In **Additional Example 5**, remind students to subtract terms in the correct order to get the common difference.
$10 - 15 = -5$.

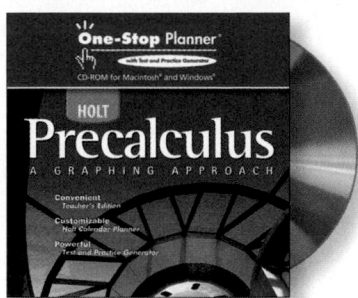

One-Stop Planner® CD-ROM with Test and Practice Generator

Plan and manage lessons with ease. Includes:
- Teacher's Edition
- Holt Calendar Planner
- ExamView® Test and Practice Generator

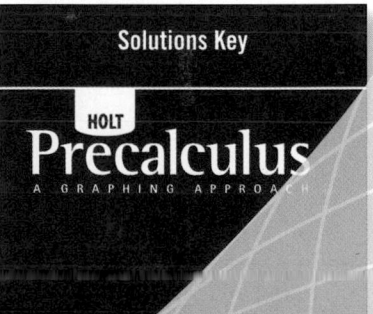

Math in Practice CD-ROM and Answer Key

This CD-ROM shows how situations involving precalculus concepts arise in real life. Over 20 engaging interviews with professionals in such fields as aviation, food service, banking, and environmental science are presented.

Solutions Key

Provides solutions to all exercises, chapter review problems, and other exercises including graphing calculator solutions.

TEACHER'S EDITION

HOLT
Precalculus
A GRAPHING APPROACH

HOLT, RINEHART AND WINSTON

A Harcourt Education Company

Orlando • **Austin** • New York • San Diego • Toronto • London

Acknowledgment: Portions of this text were previously published in *Contemporary Precalculus* by Thomas Hungerford, 2000, Saunders Publishing Co., and appear here with permission of the publisher.

Cover Photo: Richard Bryant/Alamy Images

(Acknowledgments appear on page 1053, which is an extension of the copyright page.)

ISBN: 0-03-041648-5

4 5 6 048 07

AUTHORS

Thomas W. Hungerford

Dr. Hungerford, a leading authority in the use of technology in advanced mathematics instruction, was Professor of Mathematics at Cleveland State University for many years. In addition to publishing numerous research articles, he has authored thirteen mathematics textbooks, ranging from the high school to the graduate level. Dr. Hungerford was one of the founders of the Cleveland Collaborative for Mathematics Education, a long-term project involving local universities, businesses, and mathematics teachers.

Irene "Sam" Jovell

An award winning teacher at Niskayuna High School, Niskayuna, New York, Ms. Jovell served on the writing team for the *New York State Mathematics, Science, and Technology Framework*. A popular presenter at state and national conferences, her workshops focus on technology-based innovative education. Ms. Jovell has served as president of the New York State Mathematics Teachers Association.

Betty Mayberry

Ms. Mayberry is the mathematics department chair at Pope John Paul II High School, Hendersonville, Tennessee. She has received the Presidential Award for Excellence in Teaching Mathematics and the Tandy Technology Scholar award. She is a Teachers Teaching with Technology instructor, is a popular speaker for the effective use of technology in mathematics instruction, and has served as president of the Tennessee Mathematics Teachers Association and Council of Presidential Awardees in Mathematics.

CONTENT CONSULTANT

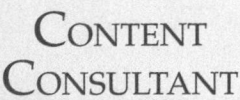

Martin Engelbrecht

A mathematics teacher at Culver Academies, Culver, Indiana, Mr. Engelbrecht also teaches statistics at Purdue University, North Central. An innovative teacher and writer, he integrates applied mathematics with technology to make mathematics accessible to all students.

PREFACE

This book is intended to provide the mathematical background needed for calculus, and it assumes that students have taken a geometry course and two courses in algebra. The text integrates graphing technology into the course without losing the underlying mathematics, which is the crucial issue. Mathematics is presented in an informal manner that stresses meaningful motivation, careful explanations, and numerous examples, with an ongoing focus on real-world problem solving.

Representations

The concepts that play a central role in calculus are explored from algebraic, graphical, and numerical perspectives. Students are expected to participate actively in the development of these concepts by using graphing calculators or computers with suitable software, as directed in the *Graphing Explorations* and *Calculator Explorations*, either to complete a particular discussion or to explore appropriate examples.

A variety of examples and exercises based on real-world data are included in the text. Additionally, sections have been included covering linear, polynomial, exponential, and logarithmic models, which can be constructed from data by using the regression capabilities of a calculator.

Organization of Beginning Chapters

Chapter 1 begins with a review of basic terminology. Numerical patterns are discussed that lead to arithmetic sequences, lines, and linear models. Geometric sequences are then introduced. Some of this material may be new to many students.

Chapter 2 introduces solving equations graphically and then reviews techniques for finding algebraic solutions of various types of equations and inequalities.

Chapter 3 discusses functions in detail and stresses transformations of parent functions. Function notation is reviewed and used throughout the text. The difference quotient, a basic building block of differential calculus, is introduced as a rate-of-change function; several examples are given. There is an optional section on iterative real-valued functions.

Chapter 4 reviews polynomial and rational functions, introduces complex numbers, and includes an optional section on the Mandelbrot set. Finally, the Fundamental Theorem of Algebra is introduced.

Chapter 5 reviews and extends topics on exponential and logarithmic functions.

Trigonometry

Five full chapters offer extensive coverage of trigonometry. Chapter 6 introduces trigonometry as ratios in right triangles, expands the discussion to include angle functions, and then presents trigonometric ratios as functions of real numbers. The basic trigonometric identities are given, and periodicity is discussed.

Chapter 7 introduces graphs of trigonometric functions and discusses amplitude and phase shift.

Chapter 8 deals with solving trigonometric equations by using graphical methods, as well as finding algebraic solutions by using inverse trigonometric functions. Algebraic methods for finding solutions to trigonometric equations are also discussed. The last section of Chapter 8 introduces simple harmonic motion and modeling.

Chapter 9 presents methods for proving identities and introduces other trigonometric identities.

Chapter 10 includes the Law of Cosines, the Law of Sines, polar form of complex numbers, de Moivre's theorem, and nth roots of complex numbers. Vectors in the plane and applications of vectors are also presented.

Organization of Ending Chapters

Chapters 11 through 14 are independent of each other and may be presented in any order. Topics covered in these chapters include analytic geometry, systems of equations, statistics and probability, and limits and continuity.

Features

Chapter Openers Each chapter begins with a brief example of an application of the mathematics treated in that chapter, together with a reference to an appropriate exercise. The opener also lists the titles of the sections in the chapter and provides a diagram showing their interdependence.

Excursions Each Excursion is a section that extends or supplements material related to the previous section. Some present topics that illustrate mathematics developed with the use of technology, some are high-interest topics that are motivational, and some present material that is used in other areas of mathematics. Exercises are included at the end of every Excursion. Clearly marked exercises reflecting material contained in each Excursion are also in corresponding Chapter Reviews. Each Excursion is independent of the rest of the book and should be considered an extension or enrichment.

Cautions Students are alerted to common errors and misconceptions, both mathematical and technological, by clearly marked Caution boxes.

Notes Students are reminded of review topics, or their attention is directed toward specific content.

Exercises Exercise sets proceed from routine calculations and drill to exercises requiring more complex thought, including graph interpretation and word problems. Problems labeled *Critical Thinking* present a question in a form different from what students may have seen before; a few of the *Critical Thinking* problems are quite challenging. Answers for selected problems are given in the back of the book.

Chapter Reviews Each chapter concludes with a list of important concepts (referenced by section and page number), a summary of important facts and formulas, and a set of review exercises.

Appendices

Algebra Review This Appendix reviews basic algebra. It can be omitted by well-prepared students or treated as an introductory chapter. Exercises are included.

Mathematical Induction and the Binomial Theorem Material relevant to these two topics is presented in an appendix with examples and exercises.

Geometry Review Frequently used facts from plane geometry are summarized, with examples, in this appendix.

Technology Appendix The technology appendix presents an overview of the use of the graphing calculator. It is recommended that students who are unfamiliar with the use of a graphing calculator complete all examples, explorations, investigations, and exercises in this appendix. All students may use the appendix for reference.

Technology

Minimal Technology Requirements It is assumed that each student has either a computer with appropriate software or a calculator at the level of a TI-82 or higher. Among current calculator models that meet or exceed this minimal requirement are TI-82 through TI-92, Sharp 9900, HP-39, and Casio 9850 and 9970. All students unfamiliar with graphing technology should complete the Technology Appendix before beginning the material.

Because either a graphing calculator or a computer with graphing software is required, several features are provided in the text to assist the student in the use of these tools.

Technology Tips Although the discussion of technology in the text is as generic as possible, some Technology Tips provide information and assistance in carrying out various procedures on specific calculators. Other Tips offer general information or helpful advice about performing a particular task on a calculator.

To avoid clutter, only a limited number of calculators are specifically mentioned in the Technology Tips. However, unless noted otherwise, observe the following guidelines.

- Technology Tips for TI apply to TI-84 Plus, TI-83 Plus, TI-83, and—except for some matrix operations—TI-82
- Technology Tips for TI-86 also apply to TI-85
- Technology Tips for Casio apply to Casio 9850GB-Plus, Casio 9850, and Casio 9970

Calculator Explorations Students are directed to use a calculator or computer with suitable software to complete a particular discussion or to explore certain examples.

Graphing Explorations Students may not be aware of the full capabilities—or limitations—of a calculator. The Graphing Explorations will help students to become familiar with the calculator and to maximize mathematical power. Even if the instructor does not assign these investigations, students may want to read through them for enrichment purposes.

Can Do Calculus Features

Each chapter has a Can Do Calculus feature that connects a calculus topic to material included in that chapter. This feature gives the student the opportunity to briefly step into the world of calculus. Many of these features include topics that are typically solved by using calculus but can be solved by using precalculus skills that the student has recently acquired. Other Can Do Calculus features conceptually develop calculus topics by using tables and graphs.

Interdependence of Chapters and Sections

The chart on the next page shows the interdependence of chapters. A similar chart appears at the beginning of each chapter, showing the interdependence of sections within the chapter.

INTERDEPENDENCE OF CHAPTERS

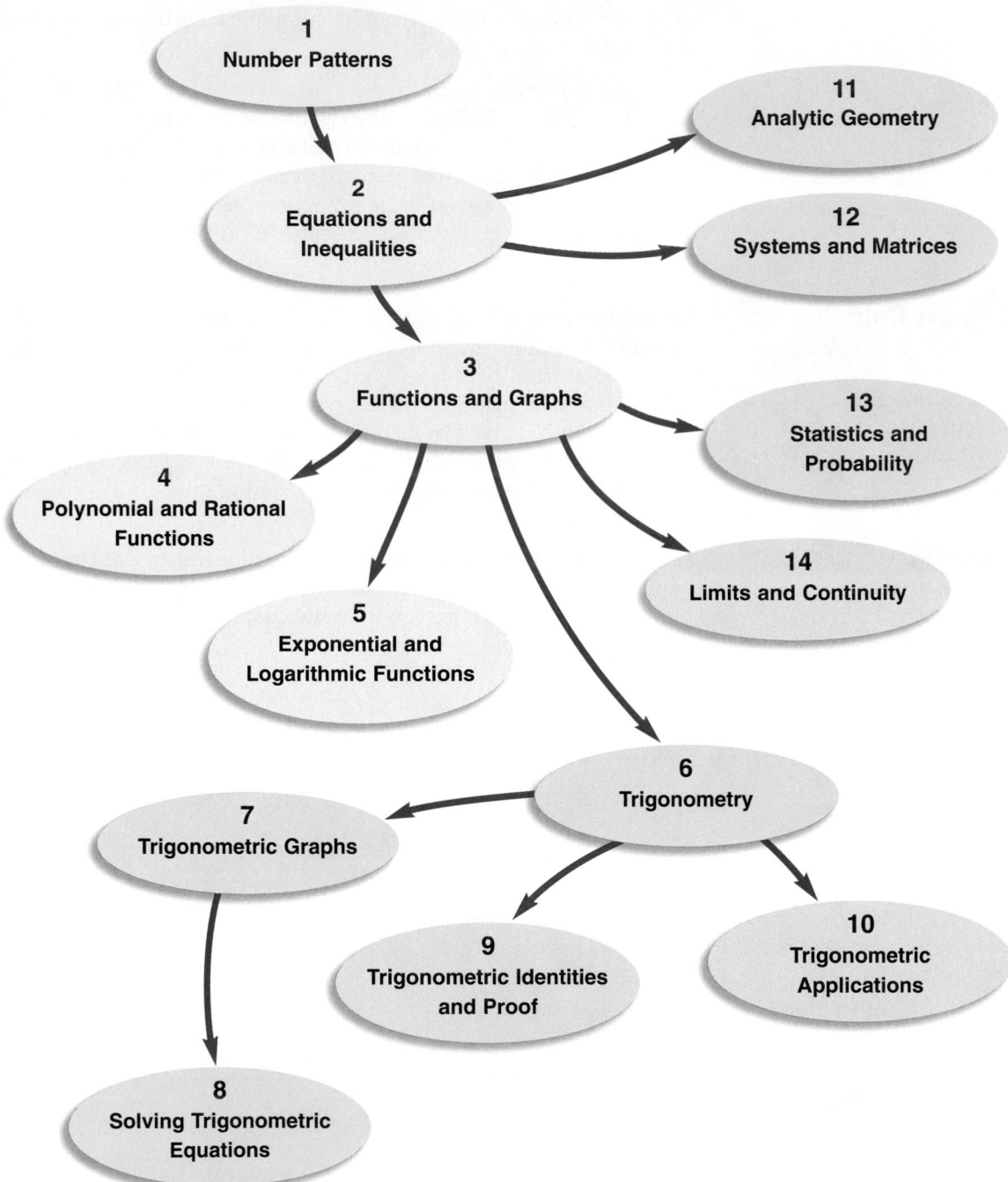

1
Number Patterns

2
Equations and
Inequalities

11
Analytic Geometry

12
Systems and Matrices

3
Functions and Graphs

4
Polynomial and Rational
Functions

5
Exponential and
Logarithmic Functions

13
Statistics and
Probability

14
Limits and Continuity

6
Trigonometry

7
Trigonometric Graphs

9
Trigonometric Identities
and Proof

10
Trigonometric
Applications

8
Solving Trigonometric
Equations

TABLE OF CONTENTS

APPLICATIONS

Biology and Life Science

Animal populations, 21, 223, 233, 342, 344, 355, 388, 407

Bacteria, 198, 259, 344, 350, 355, 388

Birth rates, 344, 397

Blood flow, 221

Illness, 42, 55, 88, 273, 362

Food, 844, 897

Food web, 810, 813

Forest fires, 635

Genealogy, 64

Infant mortality rates, 398

Life expectancy, 71, 344

Medicine, 223, 292

Murder rates, 258, 278

Plant growth, 355, 873, 889

Population growth, 340, 349, 355, 382-3, 388, 391, 395, 397-8, 404, 407, 565

Business and Manufacturing

Art galleries, 883

Cash flows, 44

Clothing design, 883

Computer speed, 864

Cost functions, 123, 125, 149, 181, 183, 292, 319, 325, 831

Depreciation, 35, 42, 64, 72

Farming, 51, 399-400

Food, 49, 54, 105, 790, 803, 813, 833, 851, 883, 897

Furniture, 803, 808

Gift boxes, 820

Gross Domestic Product (GDP), 53

Managerial jobs, 73

Manufacturing, 136, 216, 221

Merchandise production, 20, 42, 126, 135, 400, 789, 831

Profits, 30, 42, 146, 170, 220, 222, 233, 237

Revenue functions, 125, 146, 171, 824

Sales, 20, 41, 45, 126, 171-2, 221, 344, 363, 404, 790, 803, 812, 833, 837

Telemarketing, 848

Textbook publication, 42

Chemistry, Physics, and Geology

Antifreeze, 104-5

Atmospheric pressure, 388

Boiling points, 41, 335

Bouncing balls, 16, 62, 64

Carbon dioxide, 387

Evaporation, 195

Fahrenheit v. Celsius, 214

Floating balloons, 70

Gas pressure, 148

Gravitational acceleration, 293

Gravity, 677, 680, 687

Halley's Comet, 700, 754

Light, 117, 602

Mixtures, 104-5, 790, 835, 837

Orbits of astronomical objects, 393, 697, 700

Ozone, 387

Pendulums, 335, 556, 602

Photography, 293, 538

Purification, 350, 355

Radio waves, 500

Radioactive decay, 340, 352, 355-6, 381, 387, 404, 407

Richter Scale, 370, 407

Rotating wheels, 442-3, 550, 556

Sinkholes, 623

Sledding, 678, 687

Springs, 551-2, 564

Swimming pool chlorine levels, 20

Vacuum pumps, 64

Weather, 105, 116, 407, 485, 553, 557-8, 897, 903

Weather balloons, 198

Weight, 116

Whispering Gallery, 696

Construction

Antenna towers, 620

Building a ramp, 40

Bus shelters, 635

Equipment, 30, 106, 428, 431, 442, 469, 636

Fencing, 149, 292, 325, 635

Highway spotlights, 538

Lifting beams, 442

Monument construction, 30

Paving, 102, 105, 473

Pool heaters, 789

Rain gutters, 468

Sub-plots, 126

Surveying, 284

Tunnels, 623

Consumer Affairs

Campaign contributions, 5

Cars, 20, 126

Catalogs, 879

College, 10, 75, 87, 149, 320, 813

Credit cards, 64, 353, 800

Energy use, 57, 125

Expenditures per student, 355

Gas prices, 11

Health care, 42

Inflation, 355

Lawsuits, 864

Libraries, 883

Life insurance premiums, 53, 72

Loans, 56, 72, 105, 353, 803

Lotteries, 881, 886

Number Patterns

In this chapter, students will learn about the real number system, relations, and functions. They will study different number patterns, including arithmetic and geometric sequences, and review the concepts of lines and linear models.

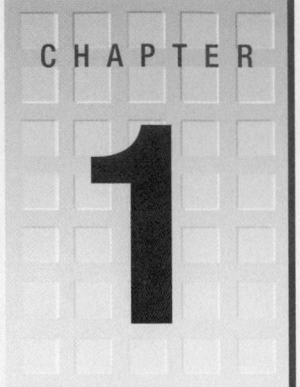

CHAPTER 1

Number Patterns

On a Clear Day

Hot-air balloons rise linearly as they ascend to the designated height. The distance they have traveled, as measured along the ground, is a function of time and can be found by using a linear function. See Exercise 58 in Chapter 1 Review.

2

Chapter Outline

Interdependence of Sections

$1.1 \longrightarrow 1.2 \longrightarrow 1.3 \longrightarrow 1.4 \longrightarrow 1.5$
$\searrow$
1.6

Mathematics is the study of quantity, order, and relationships. This chapter defines the real numbers and the coordinate plane, and it uses the vocabulary of relations and functions to begin the study of mathematical relationships. The number patterns in recursive, arithmetic, and geometric sequences are examined numerically, graphically, and algebraically. Lines and linear models are reviewed.

 ## Real Numbers, Relations, and Functions

Objectives

- Define key terms:
    sets of numbers
    the coordinate plane
    relation
    input and output
    domain and range
    function
- Use functional notation

Real number relationships, the points of a line, and the points of a plane are powerful tools in mathematics.

Real Numbers

You have been using **real numbers** most of your life. Some subsets of the real numbers are the **natural numbers,** $1, 2, 3, 4, \ldots$, and the **whole numbers,** which include 0 together with the set of natural numbers. The **integers** are the whole numbers and their opposites.

$$\ldots, -5, -4, -3, -2, -1, 0, 1, 2, 3, 4, 5, \ldots$$

The natural numbers are also referred to as the **counting numbers** and as the set of **positive integers,** and the whole numbers are also referred to as the set of **nonnegative integers.**

3

Section 1.1 Real Numbers, Relations, and Functions

Teaching Notes

Review with students some of the concepts from geometry and algebra that are used in the development of **Real Numbers, Relations, and Functions:**

A line consists of an infinite number of points, and if we use real numbers to correspond to those points, we have a *real number line.* Two intersecting lines determine a plane, and we can form a *coordinate plane* by using two *perpendicular* intersecting lines. *Ordered pairs* of numbers can be used to locate points in a coordinate plane. A *variable* is a letter used to represent a number; replacing the variable with different numbers can result in different values for a variable expression (to be used in function rules).

Teaching Notes

You may want to remind students that to express any fraction as a decimal, they can divide the numerator by the denominator.

To express a repeating decimal as a fraction, students can use the method shown below:

Change 1.666... to a fraction.
Let $a = 1.666...$.
Then, $10a = 16.666...$.

$$
\begin{array}{rcl}
10a &=& 16.666... \\
-a &=& -1.666... \\
\hline
9a &=& 15
\end{array}
$$

$$a = \frac{15}{9} = \frac{5}{3}$$

$$1.666... = \frac{5}{3}$$

Point out that a repeating block need not begin in the tenths place. For example, 0.0474747... is a repeating decimal.

Another method of changing a repeating decimal to a fraction is shown in the Chapter 1 Can Do Calculus Example 2 (pages 78–79).

Remind students of other irrational numbers such as $\sqrt{2}$ and $-\sqrt{3}$. You may want to challenge them to place these reasonably on a number line.

Math Background

The diagram showing the relationship between subsets of real numbers is called a Venn diagram. Venn diagrams were developed by English mathematician John Venn (1834–1923) to represent the relationships between sets of objects.

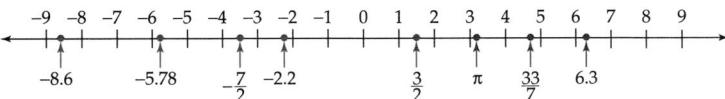

A real number is said to be a **rational number** if it can be expressed as a ratio, $\frac{r}{s}$, with r and s integers and $s \neq 0$. The following are rational numbers.

$$\frac{1}{2}, \quad -0.983 = -\frac{938}{1000}, \quad 47 = \frac{47}{1}, \quad \text{and} \quad 8\frac{3}{5} = \frac{43}{5}$$

Rational numbers may also be described as numbers that can be expressed as terminating decimals, such as $0.25 = \frac{1}{4}$, or as nonterminating repeating decimals in which a single digit or block of digits repeats, such as

$$\frac{5}{3} = 1.6666... \quad \text{or} \quad \frac{53}{333} = 0.159159...$$

A real number that cannot be expressed as a ratio with integer numerator and denominator is called an **irrational number.** Alternatively, an irrational number is one that can be expressed as a nonterminating, non-repeating decimal in which no single digit or block of digits repeats. For example, the number π, which is used to calculate the area of a circle, is irrational.

Although Figure 1.1-1 does not represent the size of each set of numbers, it shows the relationship between subsets of real numbers.

- All natural numbers are whole numbers.
- All whole numbers are integers.
- All integers are rational numbers.
- All rational numbers are real numbers.
- All irrational numbers are real numbers.

Figure 1.1-1

The Real Number Line

The real numbers are represented graphically as points on a number line, as shown in Figure 1.1-2. There is a one-to-one correspondence between the real numbers and the points of the line, which means that each real number corresponds to exactly one point on the line, and vice versa.

Figure 1.1-2

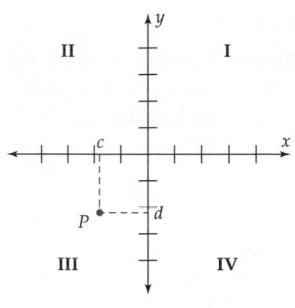

Figure 1.1-3

The Coordinate Plane

Just as real numbers correspond to points on a number line, ordered *pairs* of real numbers correspond to points in a plane. To sketch a coordinate plane, draw two number lines in the plane, one vertical and one horizontal, as shown in Figure 1.1-3.

The number lines, or **axes,** are often named the *x*-axis and the *y*-axis, but other letters may be used. The point where the axes intersect is the **origin,** and the axes divide the plane into four regions, called **quadrants,** indicated by Roman numerals in Figure 1.1-3. The plane is now said to have a **rectangular,** or **Cartesian, coordinate system.**

In Figure 1.1-3, point *P* is represented by an **ordered pair** that has **coordinates** (*c, d*), where *c* is the **x-coordinate** of *P*, and *d* is the **y-coordinate** of *P*.

Scatter Plots

In many application problems, data is plotted as points on the coordinate plane. This type of representation of data is called a **scatter plot.**

Example 1   Scatter Plot

Create a scatter plot of this data from the Federal Election Commission that shows the total amount of money, in millions of dollars, contributed to all congressional candidates in the years shown.

Year	1988	1990	1992	1994	1996
Amount	276	284	392	418	500

Solution

Let *x* be the number of years since 1988, so that $x = 0$ denotes 1988, $x = 2$ denotes 1990, and so on. Plot the points (0, 276), (2, 284), (4, 392), (6, 418), and (8, 500) to obtain a scatter plot. See Figure 1.1-4.

Figure 1.1-4

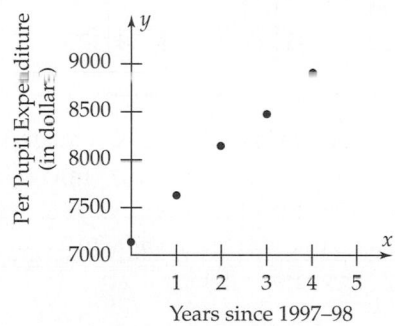

Teaching Notes

You may want to show your students the same relation represented numerically, graphically, and algebraically, along with identifying the domain and range. For example, $\{(0, 4), (1, 3), (-1, 3), (-2, 0), (2, 0)\}$

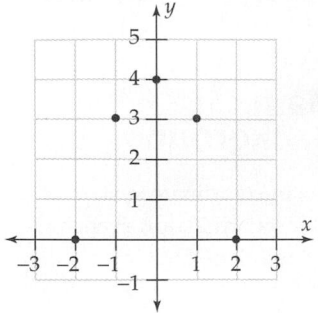

$y = 4 - x^2$ (for $x = -2, -1, 0, 1, 2$)

domain: $\{-2, -1, 0, 1, 2\}$

range: $\{0, 3, 4\}$

ADDITIONAL EXAMPLES

Example 2

The table below shows the height and arm span of twelve members of the cheerleading squad:

Height (cm)	178	189	158	169	195	188
Arm Span (cm)	180	180	163	169	189	182

Height (cm)	193	167	164	154	179	172
Arm Span (cm)	188	172	172	158	179	176

Find the relation's domain and range.

domain: {154, 158, 164, 167, 169, 172, 178, 179, 188, 189, 193, 195}

range: {158, 163, 169, 172, 176, 179, 180, 182, 188, 189}

A Relation and Its Domain and Range

Scientists and social scientists spend much time and money looking for how two quantities are related. These quantities might be a person's height and his shoe size or how much a person earns and how many years of college she has completed. In these examples, a **relation** exists between two variables. The first quantity, often called the x-variable, is said to be related to the second quantity, often called the y-variable. Mathematicians are interested in the types of relations that exist between two quantities, or how x and y are paired. Of interest is a relation's **domain,** or possible values that x can have, as well as a relation's **range,** possible values that y can have. Relations may be represented numerically by a set of ordered pairs, graphically by a scatter plot, or algebraically by an equation.

Example 2   Domain and Range of a Relation

The table below shows the heights and shoe sizes of twelve high school seniors.

Height (inches)	67	72	69	76	67	72
Shoe size	8.5	10	12	12	10	11

Height (inches)	67	62.5	64.5	64	62	62
Shoe Size	7.5	5.5	8	8.5	6.5	6

For convenience, the data table lists the height first, so the pairing (height, shoe size) is said to be ordered. Hence, the data is a relation. Find the relation's domain and range.

Solution

There are twelve ordered pairs.

$$(67, 8.5), (72, 10), (69, 12), (76, 12), (67, 10), (72, 11),$$
$$(67, 7.5), (62.5, 5.5), (64.5, 8), (64, 8.5), (62, 6.5), (62, 6)$$

Figure 1.1-5 shows the scatter plot of the relation.

The relation's domain is the set of x values: {62, 62.5, 64, 64.5, 67, 69, 72, 76}, and its range is the set of y values: {5.5, 6, 6.5, 7.5, 8, 8.5, 10, 11, 12}.

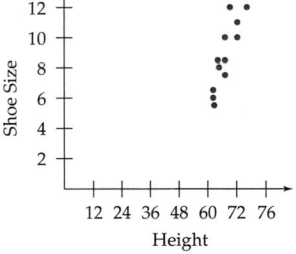

Figure 1.1-5

Sometimes a rule, which is a statement or an equation, expresses one quantity in a relation in terms of the other quantity.

Example 3   A Rule of a Relation

Given the relation

$$\{(0, 0), (1, 1), (1, -1), (4, 2), (4, -2), (9, 3), (9, -3)\},$$

state its domain and range. Create a scatter plot of the relation and find a rule that relates the value of the first coordinate to the value of the second coordinate.

Solution

The domain is {0, 1, 4, 9}, and the range is $\{-3, -2, -1, 0, 1, 2, 3\}$. The scatter plot is shown in Figure 1.1-6. One rule that relates the first coordinate to the second coordinate in each pair is $x = y^2$, where x is an integer. ∎

Figure 1.1-6

Functions

Much of mathematics focuses on special relations called **functions**. A **function** is a set of ordered pairs in which the first coordinate denotes the **input,** the second coordinate denotes the **output** that is obtained from the **rule of the function,** and

> each *input* corresponds to one and only one *output.*

Think of a function as a calculator with only one key that provides the solution for the *rule of the function.* A number is *input* into the calculator, the rule key (which represents a set of operations) is pushed, and a single answer is *output* to the display. On the special "function calculator," shown in Figure 1.1-7, if you press 9 then $2x^2 + 1$, the display screen will show 163—twice the square of 9 plus 1. The number 9 is the input, the rule is given by $2x^2 + 1$, and the output is 163.

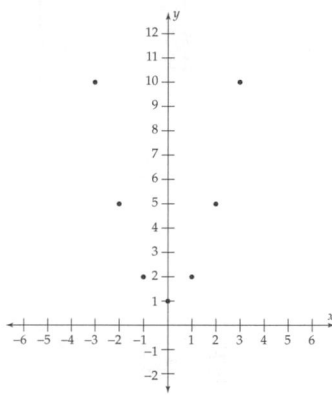

Figure 1.1-7

Example 4   Identifying a Function Represented Numerically

In each set of ordered pairs, the first coordinate represents input and the second coordinate represents its corresponding output. Explain why each set is, or is not, a function.

a. $\{(0, 0), (1, 1), (1, -1), (4, 2), (4, -2), (9, 3), (9, -3)\}$
b. $\{(0, 0), (1, 1), (-1, 1), (4, 2), (-4, 2), (9, 3), (-9, 3)\}$
c. $\{(0, 0), (1, 1), (-1, 1), (4, 2), (-4, -2), (9, 3), (-9, -3)\}$

Solution

The phrase "one and only one" in the definition of a function is the critical qualifier. To determine if a relation is a function, make sure that each input corresponds to exactly one output.

Example 3

Given the relation {(0, 1), (1, 2), (−1, 2), (2, 5), (−2, 5), (3, 10), (−3, 10)}, state its domain and range. Create a scatter plot of the relation and find a rule that relates the value of the first coordinate to the value of the second coordinate.

domain: {−3, −2, −1, 0, 1, 2, 3}

range: {1, 2, 5, 10}

One rule is $y = x^2 + 1$, where x is an integer between −3 and 3, inclusive.

Example 4

In each set of ordered pairs, the first coordinate represents input and the second coordinate represents its corresponding output. Explain why each set is, or is not, a function.

a. {(0, 1), (1, 5), (−1, 3), (2, 4), (2, −1), (5, 7), (−5, 3)} The set is not a function. The input 2 has two outputs, 4 and −1.

b. {(0, 0), (1, 0), (−1, 0), (2, 0), (−2, 0), (3, 0), (−3, 0)} The set is a function. Each input has one and only one output.

c. {(0, 0), (1, 1), (2, 2), (3, 3), (−2, −2), (−3, −3), (4, 4)} The set is a function. Each input has one and only one output.

Teaching Notes

The rule of a function is not always an equation involving an algebraic expression. For example, the rule that pairs each natural number with its number of positive factors would produce the function {(1, 1), (2, 2), (3, 2), (4, 3), (5, 2), (6, 4), ... }.

Teaching Notes

Solution to the **Calculator Exploration**:

4a.

4b.

4c.

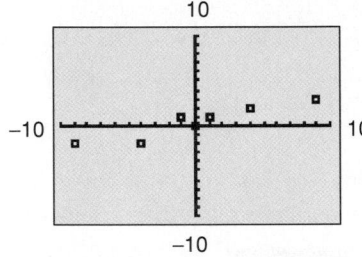

A graph represents a function if and only if no vertical line intersects more than one point. Parts **b** and **c** represent functions; part **a** does not.

ADDITIONAL EXAMPLES

Example 5

The graph in the figure below defines a function.

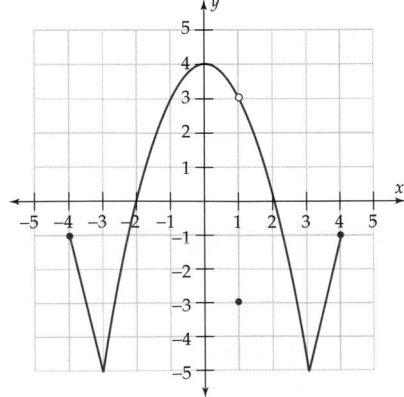

a. Find the output for the input 3. -5

b. Find the inputs whose output is 0.
   -2 and 2

a. $\{(0, 0), (1, 1), (1, -1), (4, 2), (4, -2), (9, 3), (9, -3)\}$ is not a function because the input 1 has two outputs, 1 and -1. Two other inputs, 4 and 9, also have more than one output.

b. $\{(0, 0), (1, 1), (-1, 1), (4, 2), (-4, 2), (9, 3), (-9, 3)\}$ is a function. Although 1 appears as an output twice, each input has one and only one output.

c. $\{(0, 0), (1, 1), (-1, 1), (4, 2), (-4, -2), (9, 3), (-9, -3)\}$ is a function because each input corresponds to one and only one output. ∎

Calculator Exploration ●

Make a scatter plot of each set of ordered pairs in Example 4. Examine each scatter plot to determine if there is a graphical test that can be used to determine if each input produces one and only one output, that is, if the set represents a function.

Example 5   Finding Function Values from a Graph

The graph in Figure 1.1-8 defines a function whose rule is:

> For input x, the output is the unique number y such that (x, y) is on the graph.

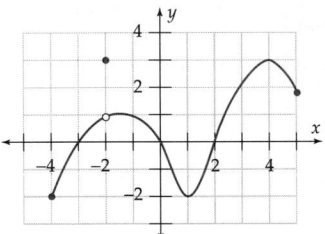

Figure 1.1-8

a. Find the output for the input 4.

b. Find the inputs whose output is 0.

c. Find the y-value that corresponds to $x = -2$.

d. State the domain and range of the function.

Solution

a. From the graph, if $x = 4$, then $y = 3$. Therefore, 3 is the output corresponding to the input 4.

b. When $y = 0$, $x = -3$ or $x = 0$ or $x = 2$. Therefore, $-3, 0$, and 2 are the inputs corresponding to the output 0.

c. The y-value that corresponds to $x = -2$ is $y = 3$.

d. The domain is all real numbers between -4 and 5, inclusive. The range is all real numbers between -2 and 3, inclusive. ■

Function Notation

Because functions are used throughout mathematics, **function notation** is a convenient shorthand developed to make their use and analysis easier. Function notation is easily adapted to mathematical settings, in which the particulars of a relationship are not mentioned. Suppose a function is given. Let f denote a given function and let a denote a number in the domain of f. Then

$f(a)$ denotes the output of the function f produced by input a.

For example, $f(6)$ denotes the output of the function f that corresponds to the input 6.

$$y \text{ is the output produced by input } x \text{ according to the rule of the function } f$$

is abbreviated

$$y = f(x),$$

which is read "y equals f of x."

In actual practice, functions are seldom presented in the style of domain-rule-range, as they have been here. Usually, a phrase, such as "the function $f(x) = \sqrt{x^2 + 1}$," will be given. It should be understood as a set of directions, as shown in the following diagram.

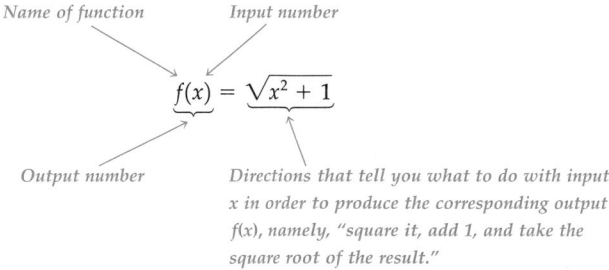

Name of function   *Input number*

$$f(x) = \sqrt{x^2 + 1}$$

Output number   *Directions that tell you what to do with input x in order to produce the corresponding output f(x), namely, "square it, add 1, and take the square root of the result."*

For example, to find $f(3)$, the output of the function f for input 3, simply replace x by 3 in the rule's directions.

$$f(x) = \sqrt{x^2 + 1}$$
$$f(3) = \sqrt{(3)^2 + 1} = \sqrt{9 + 1} = \sqrt{10}$$

Similarly, replacing x by -5 and 0 produces the respective outputs.

$$f(-5) = \sqrt{(-5)^2 + 1} = \sqrt{26} \quad \text{and} \quad f(0) = \sqrt{0^2 + 1} = 1$$

---

continued from page 8

c. Find the y-value that corresponds to $x = 1$. -3

d. State the domain and the range of the function.

domain: all real numbers between -4 and 4, inclusive; range: all real numbers between -5 and 4, inclusive

Teaching Notes

Point out that the equation $y = f(x)$ means that a function f has input x and output y. The familiar notation for a point on the graph of a function f is the ordered pair (x, y), but another notation is $(x, f(x))$. For the specific function $f(x) = \sqrt{x^2 + 1}$, an ordered pair on the graph can be indicated by (x, y), $(x, f(x))$, or $(x, \sqrt{x^2 + 1})$. If the input 3 is used for $f(x) = \sqrt{x^2 + 1}$, then $\sqrt{x^2 + 1} = \sqrt{3^2 + 1} = \sqrt{10}$, and a point on the graph is $(x, \sqrt{3^2 + 1})$, or $(x, \sqrt{10})$.

Different letters can be used to represent the same function. For example, the function $s(t) = \sqrt{t^2 + 1}$ is the same as $f(x) = \sqrt{x^2 + 1}$.

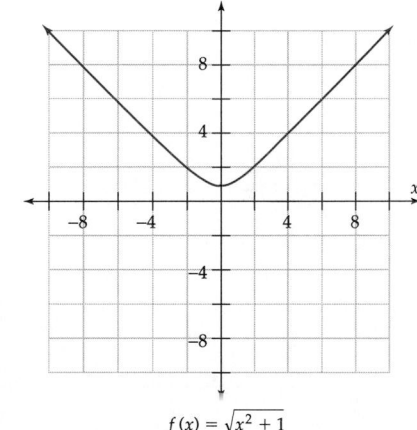

$f(x) = \sqrt{x^2 + 1}$

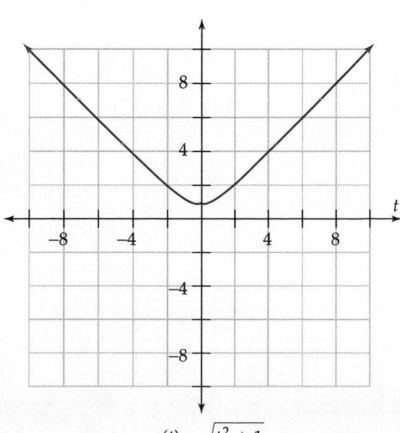

$s(t) = \sqrt{t^2 + 1}$

ADDITIONAL EXAMPLES

Example 6

For $g(x) = x^2 - 2x + 1$, find each of the following:

a. $g(\sqrt{2})$ $3 - 2\sqrt{2}$

b. $g(-3)$ 16

c. $g(-r)$ $r^2 + 2r + 1$

Exercises 1.1

ANSWERS

1. $A(-3, 3)$; $B(-1.5, 3)$; $C(-2.5, 0)$; $D(-1.5, -3)$; $E(0, 2)$; $F(0, 0)$; $G(2, 0)$; $H(3, 1)$; $I(3, -1)$

6.

7.

8.

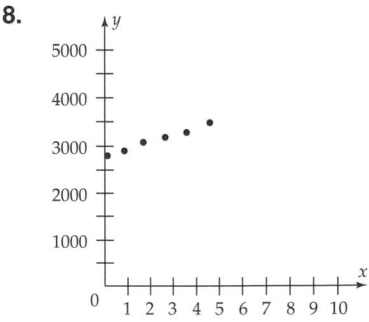

Technology Tip

One way to evaluate a function $f(x)$ is to enter its rule into the equation memory as $y = f(x)$ and use TABLE or EVAL. See the Technology Appendix for more detailed information.

NOTE Functions will be discussed in detail in Chapter 3.

Example 6   Function Notation

For $h(x) = x^2 + x - 2$, find each of the following:

a. $h(\sqrt{3})$ **b.** $h(-2)$ **c.** $h(-a)$

Solution

To find $h(\sqrt{3})$ and $h(-2)$, replace x by $\sqrt{3}$ and -2, respectively, in the rule of h.

a. $h(\sqrt{3}) = (\sqrt{3})^2 + \sqrt{3} - 2 = 3 + \sqrt{3} - 2 = 1 + \sqrt{3}$

b. $h(-2) = (-2)^2 + (-2) - 2 = 4 - 2 - 2 = 0$

The values of the function h at any quantity, such as $-a$, can be found by using the same procedure: *replace x in the formula for $h(x)$ by the quantity $-a$ and simplify.*

c. $h(-a) = (-a)^2 + (-a) - 2 = a^2 - a - 2$ ■

Exercises 1.1

1. Find the coordinates of points A–I.

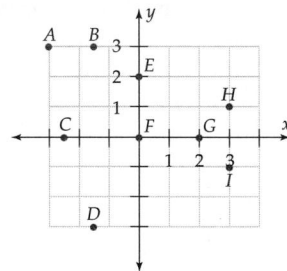

In Exercises 2–5, find the coordinates of the point P.

2. P lies 4 units to the left of the y-axis and 5 units below the x-axis. $P(-4, -5)$

3. P lies 3 units above the x-axis and on the same vertical line as $(-6, 7)$. $P(-6, 3)$

4. P lies 2 units below the x-axis and its x-coordinate is three times its y-coordinate. $P(-6, -2)$

5. P lies 4 units to the right of the y-axis and its y-coordinate is half its x-coordinate. $P(4, 2)$

In Exercises 6–8, sketch a scatter plot of the given data. In each case, let the x-axis run from 0 to 10.

6. The maximum yearly contribution to an individual retirement account in 2003 is $3000. The table shows the maximum contribution in fixed 2003 dollars. Let $x = 0$ correspond to 2000.

Year	2003	2004	2005	2006	2007	2008
Amount	3000	2910	3764	3651	3541	4294

7. The table shows projected sales, in thousands, of personal digital video recorders. Let $x = 0$ correspond to 2000. (Source: eBrain Market Research)

Year	2000	2001	2002	2003	2004	2005
Sales	257	129	143	214	315	485

8. The tuition and fees at public four-year colleges in the fall of each year are shown in the table. Let $x = 0$ correspond to 1995. (Source: The College Board)

Year	Tuition & fees	Year	Tuition & fees
1995	$2860	1998	$3247
1996	$2966	1999	$3356
1997	$3111	2000	$3510

9. The graph, which is based on data from the U.S. Department of Energy, shows approximate average gasoline prices (in cents per gallon) between 1985 and 1996, with $x = 0$ corresponding to 1985.

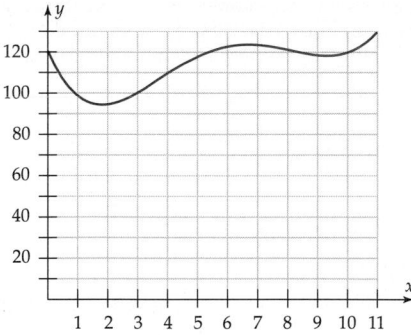

$0.94; $1.19
a. Estimate the average price in 1987 and in 1995.
b. What was the approximate percentage increase in the average price from 1987 to 1995? **≈26.6%**
c. In what year(s) was the average price at least $1.10 per gallon?
Early 1985 and 1989 onward
10. The graph, which is based on data from the U.S. Department of Commerce, shows the approximate amount of personal savings as a percent of disposable income between 1960 and 1995, with $x = 0$ corresponding to 1960.

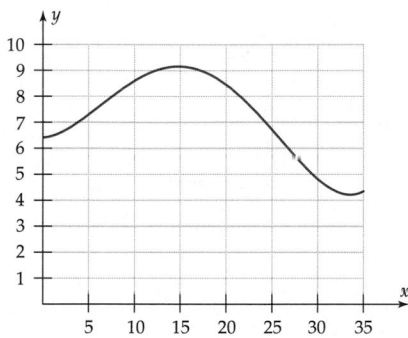

a. In what years during this period were personal savings largest and smallest (as a percent of disposable income)? **1975; 1993**
b. In what years were personal savings at least 7% of disposable income? **1964–1984**

11. a. If the first coordinate of a point is greater than 3 and its second coordinate is negative, in what quadrant does it lie?
b. What is the answer to part **a** if the first coordinate is less than 3?
a. Quadrant IV   b. Quadrants III or IV
12. In which possible quadrants does a point lie if the product of its coordinates is
a. positive?   **b.** negative?
a. Quadrants I or III   b. Quadrants II or IV
13. a. Plot the points $(3, 2)$, $(4, -1)$, $(-2, 3)$, and $(-5, -4)$.
b. Change the sign of the y-coordinate in each of the points in part **a**, and plot these new points.
c. Explain how the points (a, b) and $(a, -b)$ are related graphically.
Hint: What are their relative positions with respect to the x-axis?

14. a. Plot the points $(5, 3)$, $(4, -2)$, $(-1, 4)$, and $(-3, -5)$.
b. Change the sign of the x-coordinate in each of the points in part **a**, and plot these new points.
c. Explain how the points (a, b) and $(-a, b)$ are related graphically.
Hint: What are their relative positions with respect to the y-axis?

In Exercises 15–18, determine whether or not the given table could possibly be a table of values of a function. Give reasons for each answer.

15.

Input	-2	0	3	1	-5
Output	2	3	-2.5	2	14

Yes. Each input produces only one output.

16.

Input	-5	3	0	-3	5
Output	7	3	0	5	-3

Yes. Each input produces only one output.

17.

Input	-5	1	3	-5	7
Output	0	2	4	6	8

No. The value -5 produces two outputs.

18.

Input	1	-1	2	-2	3
Output	1	-2	±5	-6	8

No. The value 2 produces two outputs.

13. a.

b.

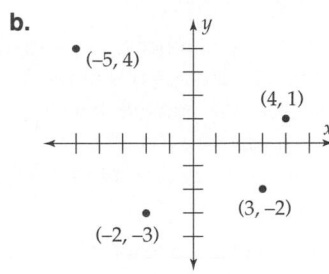

c. They are mirror images of each other, with the x-axis being the mirror. In other words, they lie on the same vertical line, on opposite sides of the x-axis, the same distance from the axis.

14. a.

b.

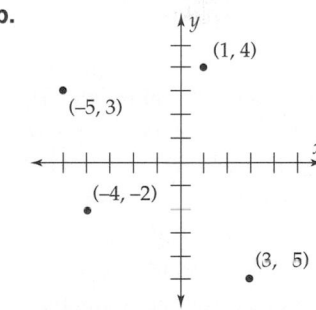

c. They are mirror images of each other, with the y-axis being the mirror. In other words, they lie on the same horizontal line, on opposite sides of the y-axis, the same distance from the axis.

19. (500, 0); (1509, 0); (3754, 35.08); (6783, 119.15); (12,500, 405); (55,342, 2547.10)

20. Many examples are possible. Any four incomes less than $2000 are all associated with the tax amount 0.

21. Each input (income) yields only one output (tax).

22. No. Every number greater than 2000 is associated with a different tax amount, since for incomes more than $2000, the more you earn, the more you pay.

23. Postage is a function of weight since each weight determines one and only one postage amount. But weight is *not* a function of postage since a given postage amount may apply to several different weights. For instance, *all* letters under 1 oz use just one first-class stamp.

24. This is not a function since for the input 25, the output could be either 5 or −5.

25. Domain: all real numbers between −3 and 3, inclusive; range: all real numbers between −4 and 3, inclusive

26. −2 is output of −2; 0 of −1; 1.2 of 0; and 2.5 of 1.

27. 2 is output of $\frac{1}{2}$; 0 of $\frac{5}{2}$; and −3 of $-\frac{5}{2}$.

28. Domain: all real numbers between −3 and 4, inclusive; range: all real numbers between −1.1 and 3, inclusive

29. −1 is output of −2; 3 of 0; 2 of 1; −1 of 2.5; and 0 of −1.5.

30. Domain: all real numbers between −2.2 and 2, inclusive; range: all real numbers between −3 and 3, inclusive

31. 1 is output of −2; −3 of −1; −1 of 0; 1 (approximately) of $\frac{1}{2}$; and 1.5 of 1.

32. a. $\sqrt{2} - 2$ **b.** 0   **c.** $\sqrt{8} - 2$
   d. 1   **e.** 2

---

12   Chapter 1   **Number Patterns**

Exercises 19–22 refer to the following state income tax table.

Annual income	Amount of tax
Less than $2000	0
$2000–$6000	2% of income over $2000
More than $6000	$80 plus 5% of income over $6000

19. Find the output (tax amount) that is produced by each of the following inputs (incomes):
  $500 $1509 $3754
  $6783 $12,500 $55,342

20. Find four different numbers in the domain of this function that produce the same output (number in the range).

21. Explain why your answer in Exercise 20 does not contradict the definition of a function.

22. Is it possible to do Exercise 20 if all four numbers in the domain are required to be greater than 2000? Why or why not?

23. The amount of postage required to mail a first-class letter is determined by its weight. In this situation, is weight a function of postage? Or vice versa? Or both?

24. Could the following statement ever be the rule of a function?

  For input x, the output is the number whose square is x.

  Why or why not? If there is a function with this rule, what is its domain and range?

Use the figure at the top of page 13 for Exercises 25–31. Each of the graphs in the figure defines a function.

25. State the domain and range of the function defined by graph **a**.

26. State the output (number in the range) that the function of Exercise 25 produces from the following inputs (numbers in the domain): −2, −1, 0, 1.

---

27. Do Exercise 26 for these numbers in the domain: $\frac{1}{2}, \frac{5}{2}, -\frac{5}{2}$.

28. State the domain and range of the function defined by graph **b**.

29. State the output (number in the range) that the function of Exercise 28 produces from the following inputs (numbers in the domain): −2, 0, 1, 2.5, −1.5.

30. State the domain and range of the function defined by graph **c**.

31. State the output (number in the range) that the function of Exercise 30 produces from the following inputs (numbers in the domain): −2, −1, 0, $\frac{1}{2}$, 1.

32. Find the indicated values of the function by hand and by using the table feature of a calculator.
  $g(x) = \sqrt{x + 4} - 2$
  a. $g(-2)$ **b.** $g(0)$ **c.** $g(4)$
  d. $g(5)$ **e.** $g(12)$

33. The rule of the function f is given by the graph. Find
  a. the domain of f
  b. the range of f
  c. $f(-3)$
  d. $f(-1)$
  e. $f(1)$
  f. $f(2)$

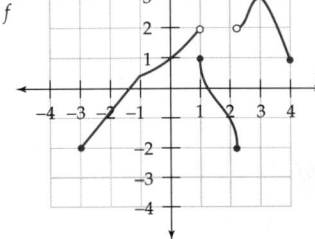

34. The rule of the function g is given by the graph. Find
  a. the domain of g
  b. the range of g
  c. $g(-3)$
  d. $g(-1)$
  e. $g(1)$
  f. $g(4)$

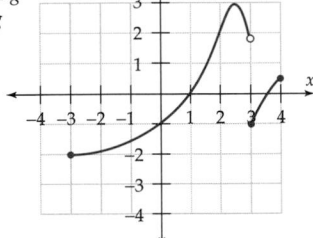

---

33. a. Domain: all real numbers between −3 and 4, inclusive
  b. Range: all real numbers between −2 and 3, inclusive
  c. −2
  d. 0.5
  e. 1
  f. −1

34. a. Domain: all real numbers between −3 and 4, inclusive
  b. Range: all real numbers between −2 and 3, inclusive
  c. −2
  d. approximately −1.6
  e. 0
  f. approximately 0.5

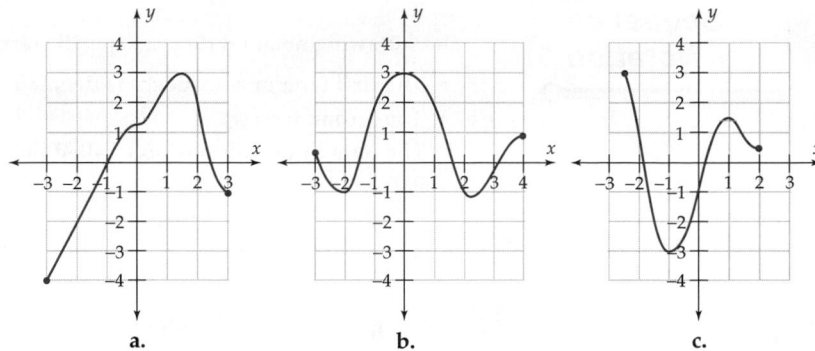

a. b. c.

1.2 Mathematical Patterns

Visual patterns exist all around us, and many inventions and discoveries began as ideas sparked by noticing patterns.

Consider the following lists of numbers.

$$-4, -1, 2, 5, 8, \underline{\ ?\ } \qquad -1, 10, -3, 73, \underline{\ ?\ }$$

Analyzing the lists above, many people would say that the next number in the list on the left is 11 because the pattern appears to be "add 3 to the previous term." In the list on the right, the next number is uncertain because there is no obvious pattern. Sequences may help in the visualization and understanding of patterns.

Definition of a Sequence

> A *sequence* is an ordered list of numbers.
> Each number in the list is called a *term* of the sequence.

An **infinite sequence** is a sequence with an infinite number of terms. Examples of infinite sequences are shown below.

$$2, 4, 6, 8, 10, 12, \ldots$$
$$1, -3, 5, -7, 9, -11, 13, \ldots$$
$$2, 1, \frac{2}{3}, \frac{2}{4}, \frac{2}{5}, \frac{2}{6}, \frac{2}{7}, \ldots$$

The three dots, or *points of ellipsis*, at the end of a sequence indicate that the same pattern continues for an infinite number of terms.

A special notation is used to represent a sequence.

Teaching Notes

Subscripts are used to denote the terms of a sequence. u_1 is read *u sub one*, u_n is read *u sub n*, and u_{n+1} is read *u sub n plus one*.

Example Notes

In **Example 2**, to graph this sequence on a calculator, the students can enter the points in their calculators and then create a scatter plot.

In **Example 3**, show the following pattern to help students understand the recursive rule.

$u_n = u_{n-1} + 3$:
$u_1 = -7$
$u_2 = u_1 + 3 = -7 + 3 = -4$
$u_3 = u_2 + 3 = -4 + 3 = -1$
$u_4 = u_3 + 3 = -1 + 3 = 2$
$\vdots$
$u_n = u_{n-1} + 3$

Sequence Notation

> The following notation denotes specific terms of a sequence:
> - **The first term of a sequence is denoted u_1.**
> - **The second term u_2.**
> - **The term in the nth position, called the nth term, is denoted by u_n.**
> - **The term before u_n is u_{n-1}.**

NOTE Any letter can be used to represent the terms of a sequence.

Example 1   Terms of a Sequence

Make observations about the pattern suggested by the diagrams below. Continue the pattern by drawing the next two diagrams, and write a sequence that represents the number of circles in each diagram.

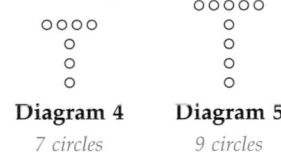

Diagram 1	Diagram 2	Diagram 3
1 circle	*3 circles*	*5 circles*

Solution

Adding two additional circles to the previous diagram forms each new diagram. If the pattern continues, then the number of circles in Diagram 4 will be two more than the number of circles in Diagram 3, and the number of circles in Diagram 5 will be two more than the number in Diagram 4.

Diagram 4	Diagram 5
7 circles	*9 circles*

The number of circles in the diagrams is represented by the sequence

$$\{1, 3, 5, 7, 9, \ldots\},$$

which can be expressed using sequence notation.

$$u_1 = 1 \qquad u_2 = 3 \qquad u_3 = 5 \qquad u_4 = 7 \qquad u_5 = 9 \quad \ldots \quad u_n = u_{n-1} + 2 \quad \blacksquare$$

Technology Tip

If needed, review how to create a scatter plot in the Technology Appendix.

Graphs of Sequences

A sequence is a function, because each input corresponds to exactly one output.

- The domain of a sequence is a subset of the integers.
- The range is the set of terms of the sequence.

Because the domain of a sequence is discrete, the graph of a sequence consists of points and is a scatter plot.

Example 2   **Graph of a Sequence**

Graph the first five terms of the sequence $\{1, 3, 5, 7, 9, \dots\}$.

Solution

The sequence can be written as a set of ordered pairs where the first coordinate is the position of the term in the sequence and the second coordinate is the term.

$$(1, 1) \qquad (2, 3) \qquad (3, 5) \qquad (4, 7) \qquad (5, 9)$$

The graph of the sequence is shown in Figure 1.2-1.

Figure 1.2-1

Recursive Form of a Sequence

In addition to being represented by a listing or a graph, a sequence can be denoted in recursive form.

Recursively Defined Sequence

> A sequence is defined *recursively* if the first term is given and there is a method of determining the nth term by using the terms that precede it.

Example 3   **Recursively Defined Sequence**

Define the sequence $\{-7, -4, -1, 2, 5, \dots\}$ recursively and graph it.

Solution

The sequence can be expressed as

$$u_1 = -7 \qquad u_2 = -4 \qquad u_3 = -1 \qquad u_4 = 2 \qquad u_5 = 5$$

The first term is given. The second term is obtained by adding 3 to the first term, and the third term is obtained by adding 3 to the second term. Therefore, the recursive form of the sequence is

$$u_1 = -7 \text{ and } u_n = u_{n-1} + 3 \text{ for } n \geq 2.$$

The ordered pairs that denote the sequence are

$$(1, -7) \qquad (2, -4) \qquad (3, -1) \qquad (4, 2) \qquad (5, 5)$$

The graph is shown in Figure 1.2-2.

Figure 1.2-2

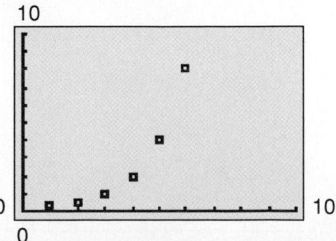

Example 4

A basketball is dropped from a height of 8 feet. It hits the floor and bounces to a height of 6 feet. It continues to bounce, and on each rebound it rises to $\frac{3}{4}$ the height of the previous bounce.

a. Write a recursive formula for the sequence that represents the height of the ball on each bounce.

$u_0 = 8$ and $u_n = \frac{3}{4} u_{n-1}$ for $n \geq 1$

b. Create a table and a graph showing the height of the ball on each bounce.

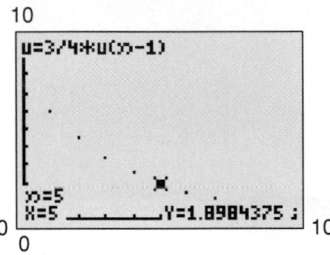

u(n)=1.8984375

c. Find the height of the ball on the fifth bounce. ≈ 1.8984 feet

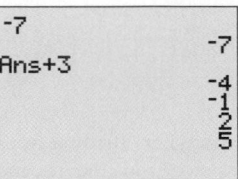

Figure 1.2-3

> **Technology Tip**
>
> The sequence graphing mode can be found in the TI MODE menu or the RECUR submenu of the Casio main menu. On such calculators, recursively defined function may be entered into the sequence memory, or Y = list. Check your instruction manual for the correct syntax and use.

> **Calculator Exploration**
>
> An alternative way to think about the sequence in Example 3 is
>
> Each answer = Preceding answer + 3.
>
> - Type -7 into your calculator and press ENTER. This establishes the first answer.
> - To calculate the second answer, press + to automatically place ANS + at the beginning of the next line of the display.
> - Now press 3 and ENTER to display the second answer.
> - Pressing ENTER repeatedly will display subsequent answers. See Figure 1.2-3.

Alternate Sequence Notation

Sometimes it is more convenient to begin numbering the terms of a sequence with a number other than 1, such as 0 or 4.

$$u_0, u_1, u_2, \ldots \text{ or } b_4, b_5, b_6, \ldots$$

Example 4 Using Alternate Sequence Notation

A ball is dropped from a height of 9 feet. It hits the ground and bounces to a height of 6 feet. It continues to bounce, and on each rebound it rises to $\frac{2}{3}$ the height of the previous bounce.

a. Write a recursive formula for the sequence that represents the height of the ball on each bounce.

b. Create a table and a graph showing the height of the ball on each bounce.

c. Find the height of the ball on the fourth bounce.

Solution

a. The initial height, u_0, is 9 feet. On the first bounce, the rebound height, u_1, is 6 feet, which is $\frac{2}{3}$ the initial height of 9 feet. The recursive form of the sequence is given by

$$u_0 = 9 \text{ and } u_n = \frac{2}{3} u_{n-1} \text{ for } n \geq 1$$

b. Set the mode of the calculator to Seq instead of Func and enter the function as shown on the next page in Figure 1.2-4a. Figure 1.2-4b displays the table of values of the function, and Figure 1.2-4c displays the graph of the function.

Figure 1.2-4a

Figure 1.2-4b

Figure 1.2-4c

c. As shown in Figures 1.2-4b and 1.2-4c, the height on the fourth bounce is approximately 1.7778 feet. ∎

Applications using Sequences

Example 5 **Salary Raise Sequence**

If the starting salary for a job is $20,000 and a raise of $2000 is earned at the end of each year of work, what will the salary be at the end of the sixth year? Find a recursive function to represent this problem and use a table and a graph to find the solution.

Solution

The initial term, u_0, is 20,000. The amount of money earned at the end of the first year, u_1, will be 2000 more than u_0. The recursive function

$$u_0 = 20,000 \text{ and } u_n = u_{n-1} + 2000 \text{ for } n \geq 1$$

will generate the sequence that represents the salaries for each year. As shown in Figures 1.2-5a and 1.2-5b, the salary at the end of the sixth year will be $32,000.

Figure 1.2-5a

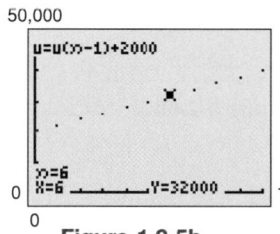

Figure 1.2-5b

In the previous examples, the recursive formulas were obtained by either adding a constant value to the previous term or by multiplying the previous term by a constant value. Recursive functions can also be obtained by adding different values that form a pattern.

Example 5

Rick owns an automobile dealership. Last year, he spent $16,000 on advertising. He plans to increase his advertising expenditures by $1200 this year and in each subsequent year. What will be the amount he spends on advertising in the sixth year? Find a recursive function to represent this problem and use a table and a graph to find the solution. $u_0 = 16,000$ and $u_n = u_{n-1} + 1200$ for $n \geq 1$

Amount spent on advertising in the 6th year: $23,200

🌍 Real-World Application

In **Example 5,** the starting salary for a job is $20,000 and the annual raise is $2000. In some cases, an annual raise is a percent increase. Suppose a company offers a starting salary of $18,000 and a 15% increase each year for the same job. The function for this offer is $v_0 = 18,000$ and $v_n = v_{n-1} + 0.15v_{n-1}$ for $n \geq 1$. The table shows the salary schedules for Example 5 (u_n) and this example (v_n).

Challenge students to find the year of employment during which the *cumulative* salary earned on the job in this example (v_n) would exceed the *cumulative* salary earned on the job in Example 5 (u_n). during the 3rd year

ADDITIONAL EXAMPLES

Example 6

Triangular numbers are numbers that can be represented geometrically as triangles of points, following the pattern shown below (each row has one more point than the row above it). Here are the first four triangular numbers.

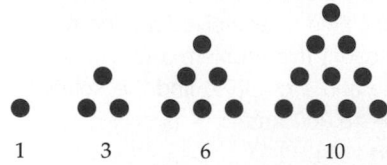

1   3   6   10

a. Find a recursive function to represent the nth triangular number.
$u_1 = 1$ and $u_n = u_{n-1} + n$ for $n \geq 2$

b. Use a table to find the 20th triangular number.

n	$u(n)$
14	105
15	120
16	136
17	153
18	171
19	190
20	210

$u(n)=210$

The 20th triangular number is 210.

Example 7

Ms. Long creates an endowment fund for her alma mater. She places $250,000 in the fund to start, and will add $50,000 to the fund each year. She states that 25% of the total amount in the fund shall be used each year for scholarships. How much will be in the fund at the end of the sixth year?

n	$u(n)$
0	250000
1	225000
2	206250
3	192188
4	181641
5	173730
6	167798

$u(n)=167797.8516$

$167,797.85

Example 6 Sequence Formed by Adding a Pattern of Values

A chord is a line segment joining two points of a circle. The following diagram illustrates the maximum number of regions that can be formed by 1, 2, 3, and 4 chords, where the regions are not required to have equal areas.

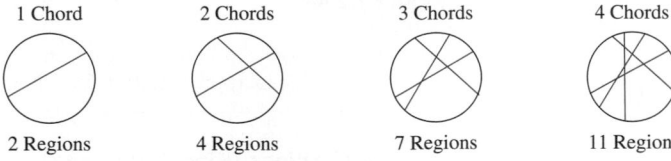

1 Chord   2 Chords   3 Chords   4 Chords

2 Regions   4 Regions   7 Regions   11 Regions

a. Find a recursive function to represent the maximum number of regions formed with n chords.

b. Use a table to find the maximum number of regions formed with 20 chords.

Solution

Let the initial number of regions occur with 1 chord, so $u_1 = 2$. The maximum number of regions formed for each number or chords is shown in the following table.

Number of chords	Maximum number of regions
1	$u_1 = 2$
2	$u_2 = 4 = u_1 + 2$
3	$u_3 = 7 = u_2 + 3$
4	$u_4 = 11 = u_3 + 4$
...	...
n	$u_n = u_{n-1} + n$

The recursive function is shown as the last entry in the listing above, and the table and graph, as shown in Figures 1.2-6a and 1.2-6b, identify the 20th term of the sequence as 211. Therefore, the maximum number of regions that can be formed with 20 chords is 211. ∎

Example 7 Adding Chlorine to a Pool

Dr. Miller starts with 3.4 gallons of chlorine in his pool. Each day he adds 0.25 gallons of chlorine and 15% evaporates. How much chlorine will be in his pool at the end of the sixth day?

Solution

The initial amount of chlorine is 3.4 gallons, so $u_0 = 3.4$ and each day 0.25 gallons of chlorine are added. Because 15% evaporates, 85% of the mixture remains.

---

n	$u(n)$
14	106
15	121
16	137
17	154
18	172
19	191
20	211

$u(n)=211$

Figure 1.2-6a

Figure 1.2-6b

Figure 1.2-7a

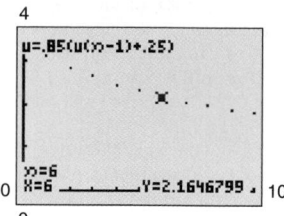

Figure 1.2-7b

The amount of chlorine in the pool at the end of the first day is obtained by adding 0.25 to 3.4 and then multiplying the result by 0.85.

$$0.85(3.4 + 0.25) = 3.1025$$

The procedure is repeated to yield the amount of chlorine in the pool at the end of the second day.

$$0.85(3.1025 + 0.25) = 2.85$$

Continuing with the same pattern, the recursive form for the sequence is

$$u_0 = 3.4 \text{ and } u_n = 0.85(u_{n-1} + 0.25) \text{ for } n \geq 1.$$

As shown in Figures 1.2-7a and 1.2-7b, approximately 2.165 gallons of chlorine will be in the pool at the end of the sixth day. ∎

Exercises 1.2

In Exercises 1–4, graph the first four terms of the sequence.

1. $\{2, 5, 8, 11, \ldots\}$

2. $\{3, 6, 12, 24, \ldots\}$

3. $\{4, 5, 8, 13, \ldots\}$

4. $\{4, 12, 36, 108, \ldots\}$

In Exercises 5–8, define the sequence recursively and graph the sequence.

5. $\{-6, -4, -2, 0, 2, \ldots\}$

6. $\{-4, -8, -16, -32, -64, \ldots\}$

7. $\{6, 11, 16, 21, 26, \ldots\}$

8. $\left\{8, 4, 2, 1, \frac{1}{2}, \frac{1}{4}, \ldots\right\}$

In Exercises 9–12, find the first five terms of the given sequence.

9. $u_1 = 4$ and $u_n = 2u_{n-1} + 3$ for $n \geq 2$

10. $u_1 = 5$ and $u_n = \frac{1}{3}u_{n-1} - 4$ for $n \geq 2$

11. $u_1 = 1, u_2 = -2, u_3 = 3$, and $u_n = u_{n-1} + u_{n-2} + u_{n-3}$ for $n \geq 4$

12. $u_0 = 1, u_1 = 1$ and $u_n = nu_{n-1}$ for $n \geq 2$

13. A really big rubber ball will rebound 80% of its height from which it is dropped. If the ball is dropped from 400 centimeters, how high will it bounce after the sixth bounce?

14. A tree in the Amazon rain forest grows an average of 2.3 cm per week. Write a sequence that represents the weekly height of the tree over the course of 1 year if it is 7 meters tall today. Write a recursive formula for the sequence and graph the sequence.

15. If two rays have a common endpoint, one angle is formed. If a third ray is added, three angles are formed. See the figure below.

Write a recursive formula for the number of angles formed with n rays if the same pattern continues. Graph the sequence. Use the formula to find the number of angles formed by 25 rays.

11. $u_1 = 1$
$u_2 = -2$
$u_3 = 3$
$u_4 = 1 - 2 + 3 = 2$
$u_5 = -2 + 3 + 2 = 3$

12. $u_0 = 1$
$u_1 = 1$
$u_2 = 2 \cdot 1 = 2$
$u_3 = 3 \cdot 2 = 6$
$u_4 = 4 \cdot 6 = 24$

13. $u_0 = 400; u_n = 0.8u_{n-1}; u_6 \approx 104.858$ cm

14–15. *For graphs, see p.* 1054.

14. $\{7, 7.023, 7.046, 7.069, \ldots\}$,
where $u_0 = 7$ and $u_{52} = 8.196$;
$u_0 = 7$ and $u_n = u_{n-1} + 0.023$

15. For 2 rays: $u_2 = 1$; for 3 rays:
$u_3 = 3$; for 4 rays: $u_4 = 6$;
$u_n = u_{n-1} + n - 1$ for $n \geq 3$

Exercises 1.2

ANSWERS

1.

2.

3.

4.

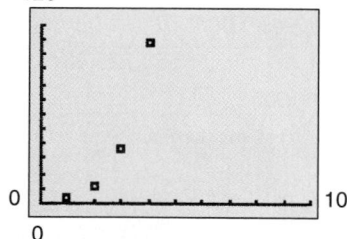

5–8. *For graphs, see p.* 1054.

5. $u_1 = -6$ and $u_n = u_{n-1} + 2$

6. $u_1 = -4$ and $u_n = 2u_{n-1}$

7. $u_1 = 6$ and $u_n = u_{n-1} + 5$

8. $u_1 = 8$ and $u_n = \frac{1}{2}u_{n-1}$

9. $u_1 = 4$
$u_2 = 2 \cdot 4 + 3 = 11$
$u_3 = 2 \cdot 11 + 3 = 25$
$u_4 = 2 \cdot 25 + 3 = 53$
$u_5 = 2 \cdot 53 + 3 = 109$

10. $u_1 = 5$
$u_2 = \frac{1}{3} \cdot 5 - 4 = -2\frac{1}{3}$
$u_3 = \frac{1}{3} \cdot \left(-2\frac{1}{3}\right) - 4 = -4\frac{7}{9}$
$u_4 = \frac{1}{3} \cdot \left(-4\frac{7}{9}\right) - 4 = -5\frac{16}{27}$
$u_5 = \frac{1}{3} \cdot \left(-5\frac{16}{27}\right) - 4 = -5\frac{70}{81}$

16. a. u_0 = original content and $u_n = 0.85u_{n-1}$. If $u_0 = 2.5$, then $u_6 \approx 0.943$ so the water will become cloudy in 6 days.

   b. If $u_0 = 2.5$ and $u_n = 0.85(u_{n-1} + 0.5)$, the concentration will eventually stabilize at approximately 2.833 ppm.

   c. If $u_0 = 2.5$ and $u_n = 0.85(u_{n-1} + 0.1)$, the concentration will eventually stabilize at approximately 0.567 ppm.

   d. By successive trials, if $u_0 = 2.5$ and $u_n = 0.85(u_{n-1} + 0.318)$, the concentration will eventually stabilize at approximately 1.8 ppm. Therefore, 0.318 ppm should be added each day.

17. $u_1 = 12$, $u_n = u_{n-1} + 2$ for $2 \leq n \leq 35$; $u_{30} = $ 70 seats

18. $u_3 = 17.50 + 5.50(2) = 28.50$, $u_5 = 17.50 + 5.50(4) = 39.50$, $u_8 = 17.50 + 5.50(7) = 56.00$; $u_1 = 17.50$ and $u_n = u_{n-1} + 5.50$ for $n \geq 2$

19. $u_0 = 30{,}000$, $u_n = 1.06u_{n-1}$ for $n \geq 1$; $u_{10} = \$53{,}725.43$

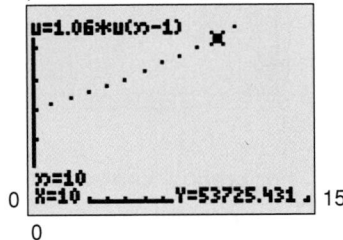

20. $\{15.8, 16.4, 17.0, 17.6\}$; $u_0 = 15.2$ and $u_n = u_{n-1} + 0.6$ for $n \geq 1$; $u_{13} = 23$ billion books

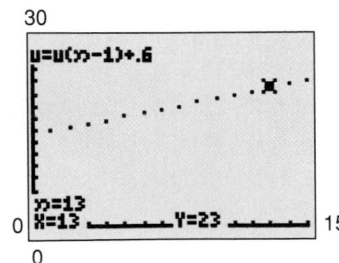

21. $u_8 = 26{,}901$ students

---

16. Swimming pool manufacturers recommend that the concentration of chlorine be kept between 1 and 2 parts per million (ppm). They also warn that if the concentration exceeds 3 ppm, swimmers experience burning eyes. If the concentration drops below 1 ppm, the water will become cloudy. If it drops below 0.5 ppm, algae will begin to grow. During a period of one day 15% of the chlorine present in the pool dissipates, mainly due to evaporation.

   a. If the chlorine content is currently 2.5 ppm and no additional chlorine is added, how long will it be before the water becomes cloudy?

   b. If the chlorine content is currently 2.5 ppm and 0.5 ppm of chlorine is added daily, what will the concentration eventually become?

   c. If the chlorine content is currently 2.5 ppm and 0.1 ppm of chlorine is added daily, what will the concentration eventually become?

   d. How much chlorine must be added daily for the chlorine level to stabilize at 1.8 ppm?

17. An auditorium has 12 seats in the front row. Each successive row, moving towards the back of the auditorium, has 2 additional seats. The last row has 80 seats.

Write a recursive formula for the number of seats in the nth row and use the formula to find the number of seats in the 30th row.

18. In 1991, the annual dividends per share of a stock were approximately $17.50. The dividends were increasing by $5.50 each year. What were the approximate dividends per share in 1993, 1995, and 1998? Write a recursive formula to represent this sequence.

19. A computer company offers you a job with a starting salary of $30,000 and promises a 6% raise each year. Find a recursive formula to represent the sequence, and find your salary ten years from now. Graph the sequence.

20. Book sales in the United States (in billions of dollars) were approximated at 15.2 in the year 1990. The book sales increased by 0.6 billion each year. Find a sequence to represent the book sales for the next four years, and write a recursive formula to represent the sequence. Graph the sequence and predict the number of book sales in 2003.

21. The enrollment at Tennessee State University is currently 35,000. Each year, the school will graduate 25% of its students and will enroll 6,500

22. a. $u_0 = 7000$ and
$$u_n = \left(1 + \frac{0.1325}{12}\right)u_{n-1} - 200$$
for $n \geq 1$

   b. $\{7000, 6877.29, 6753.23, 6627.80, 6500.98\}$

   c. $u_{12} = \$5434.70$

   d. approximately $626.04

---

new students. What will be the enrollment 8 years from now?

22. Suppose you want to buy a new car and finance it by borrowing $7,000. The 12-month loan has an annual interest rate of 13.25%.

   a. Write a recursive formula that provides the declining balances of the loan for a monthly payment of $200.

   b. Write out the first five terms of this sequence.

   c. What is the unpaid balance after 12 months?

   d. Make the necessary adjustments to the monthly payment so that the loan can be paid off in 12 equal payments. What monthly payment is needed?

23. Suppose a flower nursery manages 50,000 flowers and each year sells 10% of the flowers and plants 4,000 new ones. Determine the number of flowers after 20 years and 35 years.

24. Find the first ten terms of a sequence whose first two terms are $u_1 = 1$ and $u_2 = 1$ and whose nth term (for $n \geq 3$) is the sum of the two preceding terms.

Exercises 25–29 deal with prime numbers. A positive integer greater than 1 is prime if its only positive integer factors are itself and 1. For example, 7 is prime because its only factors are 7 and 1, but 15 is not prime because it has factors other than 15 and 1, namely, 3 and 5.

25. *Critical Thinking* **a.** Let $\{u_n\}$ be the sequence of prime integers in their usual ordering. Verify that the first ten terms are 2, 3, 5, 7, 11, 13, 17, 19, 23, 29.

   b. Find $u_{17}, u_{18}, u_{19}, u_{20}$.

In Exercises 26–29, find the first five terms of the sequence.

26. *Critical Thinking* u_n is the nth prime integer larger than 10.   **11, 13, 17, 19, 23**

27. *Critical Thinking* u_n is the square of the nth prime integer.   **4, 9, 25, 49, 121**

28. *Critical Thinking* u_n is the number of prime integers less than n.   **0, 0, 1, 2, 2**

29. *Critical Thinking* u_n is the largest prime integer less than $5n$.   **3, 7, 13, 19, 23**

Exercises 30–34 deal with the Fibonacci sequence $\{u_n\}$ which is defined as follows:

23. $u_{20} = 41{,}216$; $u_{35} = 40{,}250$

24. $\{1, 1, 2, 3, 5, 8, 13, 21, 34, 55\}$

25. a. The items listed are the first ten primes. Every other number less than 29 can be factored into a product of smaller integers.

   b. 59, 61, 67, 71

$u_1 = 1$, $u_2 = 1$, and for $n \geq 3$, u_n is the sum of the two preceding terms, $u_n = u_{n-1} + u_{n-2}$. That is,

$$u_1 = 1$$
$$u_2 = 1$$
$$u_3 = u_1 + u_2 = 1 + 1 = 2$$
$$u_4 = u_2 + u_3 = 1 + 2 = 3$$
$$u_5 = u_3 + u_4 = 2 + 3 = 5$$
and so on.

30. *Critical Thinking* Leonardo Fibonacci discovered the sequence in the thirteenth century in connection with the following problem: A rabbit colony begins with one pair of adult rabbits, one male and one female. Each adult pair produces one pair of babies, one male and one female, every month. Each pair of baby rabbits becomes adult and produces its first offspring at age two months. Assuming that no rabbits die, how many adult pairs of rabbits are in the colony at the end of n months, $n = 1, 2, 3, \ldots$? *Hint:* It may be helpful to make up a chart listing for each month the number of adult pairs, the number of one-month-old pairs, and the number of baby pairs.
$u_n = u_{n-2} + u_{n-1}$

31. *Critical Thinking* List the first ten terms of the Fibonacci sequence.
1, 1, 2, 3, 5, 8, 13, 21, 34, 55

32. *Critical Thinking* Verify that every positive integer less than or equal to 15 can be written as a Fibonacci number or as a sum of Fibonacci numbers, with none used more than once.

33. *Critical Thinking* Verify that $5(u_n)^2 + 4(-1)^n$ is a perfect square for $n = 1, 2, \ldots, 10$.

34. *Critical Thinking* Verify that $(u_n)^2 = u_{n+1} u_{n-1} + (-1)^{n-1}$ for $n = 2, 3, \ldots, 10$.

32. $1 = 1$, $2 = 2$, $3 = 1 + 2$,
$4 = 1 + 3$, $5 = 2 + 3$, $6 = 1 + 5$,
$7 = 2 + 5$, $8 = 3 + 5$,
$9 = 1 + 8$, $10 = 2 + 8$,
$11 = 3 + 8$, $12 = 1 + 3 + 8$,
$13 = 2 + 3 + 8$, $14 = 1 + 13$,
$15 = 2 + 13$

33. $n = 1: 5(1)^2 + 4(-1)^1 = 1 = 1^2$
$n = 2: 5(1)^2 + 4(-1)^2 = 9 = 3^2$
$n = 3: 5(2)^2 + 4(-1)^3 = 16 = 4^2$
$n = 4: 5(3)^2 + 4(-1)^4 = 49 = 7^2$
$n = 5: 5(5)^2 + 4(-1)^5 = 121 = 11^2$
$n = 6: 5(8)^2 + 4(-1)^6 = 324 = 18^2$
$n = 7: 5(13)^2 + 4(-1)^7 = 841 = 29^2$
$n = 8: 5(21)^2 + 4(-1)^8 = 2209 = 47^2$
$n = 9: 5(34)^2 + 4(-1)^9 = 5776 = 76^2$
$n = 10: 5(55)^2 + 4(-1)^{10} = 15{,}129$
$= 123^2$

1.3 Arithmetic Sequences

Objectives

- Identify and graph an arithmetic sequence
- Find a common difference
- Write an arithmetic sequence recursively and explicitly
- Use summation notation
- Find the nth term and the nth partial sum of an arithmetic sequence

An **arithmetic sequence**, which is sometimes called an *arithmetic progression*, is a sequence in which the difference between each term and the preceding term is always constant.

Example 1 — Arithmetic Sequence

Are the following sequences arithmetic? If so, what is the difference between each term and the term preceding it?

a. $\{14, 10, 6, 2, -2, -6, -10, \ldots\}$

b. $\{3, 5, 8, 12, 17, \ldots\}$

Solution

a. The difference between each term and the preceding term is -4. So this is an arithmetic sequence with a difference of -4.

b. The difference between the 1st and 2nd terms is 2 and the difference between the 2nd and 3rd terms is 3. The differences are not constant, therefore this is not an arithmetic sequence. ∎

If $\{u_n\}$ is an arithmetic sequence, then for each $n \geq 2$, the term preceding u_n is u_{n-1} and the difference $u_n - u_{n-1}$ is some constant—usually called d. Therefore, $u_n - u_{n-1} = d$.

34. $n = 2: 1^2 = 1; 2 \cdot 1 + (-1)^1 = 1$
$n = 3: 2^2 = 4; 3 \cdot 1 + (-1)^2 = 4$
$n = 4: 3^2 = 9; 5 \cdot 2 + (-1)^3 = 9$
$n = 5: 5^2 = 25; 8 \cdot 3 + (-1)^4 = 25$
$n = 6: 8^2 = 64; 13 \cdot 5 + (-1)^5 = 64$
$n = 7: 13^2 = 169; 21 \cdot 8 + (-1)^6 = 169$
$n = 8: 21^2 = 441; 34 \cdot 13 + (-1)^7 = 441$
$n = 9: 34^2 = 1156; 55 \cdot 21 + (-1)^8 = 1156$
$n = 10: 55^2 = 3025; 89 \cdot 34 + (-1)^9 = 3025$

Teaching Notes

Make sure that students know that to define an arithmetic sequence recursively, they must specify the first term u_1.

You may want to use **Example 3** to help develop the **Explicit Form of an Arithmetic Sequence.** Replace -7 with u_1 and 4 with d. For example, rewrite $u_3 = (-7 + 4) + 4 = -7 + 2 \cdot 4$ as $u_3 = (u_1 + d) + d = u_1 + 2d$.

ADDITIONAL EXAMPLES

Example 2

If $\{u_n\}$ is an arithmetic sequence with $u_1 = 2.5$ and $u_2 = 6$ as its first two terms,

a. find the common difference. 3.5

b. write the sequence as a recursive function.
$u_1 = 2.5$ and $u_n = u_{n-1} + 3.5$ for $n \geq 2$

c. give the first six terms of the sequence. 2.5, 6, 9.5, 13, 16.5, 20

d. graph the sequence.

Recursive Form of an Arithmetic Sequence

In an arithmetic sequence $\{u_n\}$
$$u_n = u_{n-1} + d$$
for some constant d and all $n \geq 2$.

Figure 1.3-1a

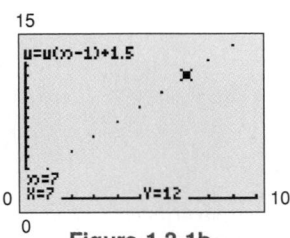

Figure 1.3-1b

The number d is called the **common difference** of the arithmetic sequence.

Example 2   Graph of an Arithmetic Sequence

If $\{u_n\}$ is an arithmetic sequence with $u_1 = 3$ and $u_2 = 4.5$ as its first two terms,

a. find the common difference.

b. write the sequence as a recursive function.

c. give the first seven terms of the sequence.

d. graph the sequence.

Solution

a. The sequence is arithmetic and has a common difference of
$$u_2 - u_1 = 4.5 - 3 = 1.5$$

b. The recursive function that describes the sequence is
$$u_1 = 3 \text{ and } u_n = u_{n-1} + 1.5 \text{ for } n \geq 2$$

c. The first seven terms are 3, 4.5, 6, 7.5, 9, 10.5, and 12, as shown in Figure 1.3-1a.

d. The graph of the sequence is shown in Figure 1.3-1b.

Explicit Form of an Arithmetic Sequence

Example 2 illustrated an arithmetic sequence expressed in recursive form in which a term is found by using preceding terms. Arithmetic sequences can also be expressed in a form in which a term of the sequence can be found based on its position in the sequence.

Example 3   Explicit Form of an Arithmetic Sequence

Confirm that the sequence $u_n = u_{n-1} + 4$ with $u_1 = -7$ can also be expressed as $u_n = -7 + (n - 1) \cdot 4$.

Solution

Use the recursive function to find the first few terms of the sequence.
$$u_1 = -7$$
$$u_2 = -7 + 4 = -3$$

Figure 1.3-2a

Figure 1.3-2b

$$u_3 = (-7 + 4) + 4 = -7 + 2 \cdot 4 = -7 + 8 = 1$$
$$u_4 = (-7 + 2 \cdot 4) + 4 = -7 + 3 \cdot 4 = -7 + 12 = 5$$
$$u_5 = (-7 + 3 \cdot 4) + 4 = -7 + 4 \cdot 4 = -7 + 16 = 9$$

Notice that u_3 is $-7 + 2 \cdot 4$, which is the first term of the sequence with the common difference of 4 added twice. Also, u_4 is $-7 + 3 \cdot 4$, which is the first term of the sequence with the common difference of 4 added three times. Because this pattern continues, $u_n = -7 + (n - 1) \cdot 4$. The table in Figure 1.3-2b confirms the equality of the two functions.

$$u_n = u_{n-1} + 4 \text{ with } u_1 = -7 \quad \text{and} \quad u_n = -7 + (n - 1) \cdot 4$$

As shown in Example 3, if $\{u_n\}$ is an arithmetic sequence with common difference d, then for each $n \geq 2$, $u_n = u_{n-1} + d$ can be written as a function in terms of n, the position of the term.

Applying the procedure shown in Example 3 to the general case shows that

$$u_2 = u_1 + d$$
$$u_3 = u_2 + d = (u_1 + d) + d = u_1 + 2d$$
$$u_4 = u_3 + d = (u_1 + 2d) + d = u_1 + 3d$$
$$u_5 = u_4 + d = (u_1 + 3d) + d = u_1 + 4d$$

Notice that $4d$ is added to u_1 to obtain u_5. In general, adding $(n - 1)d$ to u_1 yields u_n. So u_n is the sum of n numbers: u_1 and the common difference, d, added $(n - 1)$ times.

Explicit Form of an Arithmetic Sequence

> In an arithmetic sequence $\{u_n\}$ with common difference d,
>
> $$u_n = u_1 + (n - 1)d \qquad \text{for every } n \geq 1.$$

If the initial term of a sequence is denoted as u_0, the explicit form of an arithmetic sequence with common difference d is

$$u_n = u_0 + nd \qquad \text{for every } n \geq 0.$$

Example 4 **Explicit Form of an Arithmetic Sequence**

Find the nth term of an arithmetic sequence with first term -5 and common difference of 3. Sketch a graph of the sequence.

Solution

Because $u_1 = -5$ and $d = 3$, the formula in the box states that

$$u_n = u_1 + (n - 1)d = -5 + (n - 1)3 = 3n - 8$$

The graph of the sequence is shown in Figure 1.3-3.

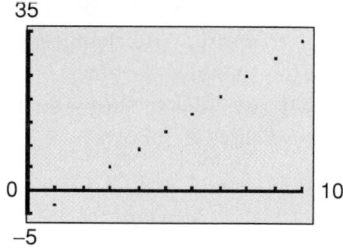

Figure 1.3-3

Example 3

Confirm that the sequence
$u_n = u_{n-1} + 3$ with $u_1 = -5$
can also be expressed as
$u_n = -5 + (n - 1) \cdot 3$.

Example 4

Find the nth term of an arithmetic sequence with first term -3 and common difference of 4. Sketch a graph of the sequence. $u_n = 4n - 7$

Example Notes

In **Example 4,** you can verify that $3n - 8$ is the correct expression for u_n. Use it to get several terms, and verify that $u_1 = -5$ and $d = 3$:
$$u_n - 3n - 8$$
$$u_1 = 3 \cdot 1 - 8 = 3 - 8 = -5 \checkmark$$
$$u_2 = 3 \cdot 2 - 8 = 6 - 8 = -2$$
$$u_3 = 3 \cdot 3 - 8 = 9 - 8 = 1$$

$$d - u_2 \quad u_1 - 2 \quad (-5) - 3 \checkmark$$

Teaching Notes

For the sum $\displaystyle\sum_{i=1}^{9} u_i$, the letter i is called the **index** of the summation, the number 1 is the **lower limit** of the summation, and the number 9 is the **upper limit** of the summation.

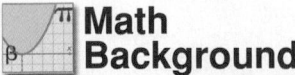 **Math Background**

Summation notation represents an *iterative* process. An iterative process is a process that involves repetition of the same set of operations.

Example Notes

In **Example 5,** to find the nth term, you must find the common difference and use $u_n = u_1 + (n-1)d$.

In **Example 6,** the method for finding d can be shown as follows:

$$d = \frac{u_{10} - u_6}{10 - 6} = \frac{93 - 57}{10 - 6} = \frac{36}{4} = 9$$

In **Example 7a,** the form $\displaystyle\sum_{n=1}^{5} (\quad)$ indicates that the expression inside the grouping symbols is to appear 5 times, with appropriate changes based on the changing n-values. It may help to use color to show the changing n-values as follows:

$$\sum_{n=1}^{5} (-7 + 3n) = (-7 + 3 \cdot 1)$$
$$+ (-7 + 3 \cdot 2)$$
$$+ (-7 + 3 \cdot 3)$$
$$+ (-7 + 3 \cdot 4)$$
$$+ (-7 + 3 \cdot 5)$$

Example 5 Finding a Term of an Arithmetic Sequence

What is the 45th term of the arithmetic sequence whose first three terms are 5, 9, and 13?

Solution

The first three terms show that $u_1 = 5$ and that the common difference, d, is 4. Apply the formula with $n = 45$.

$$u_{45} = u_1 + (45 - 1)d = 5 + (44)(4) = 181$$

Example 6 Finding Explicit and Recursive Formulas

If $\{u_n\}$ is an arithmetic sequence with $u_6 = 57$ and $u_{10} = 93$, find u_1, a recursive formula, and an explicit formula for u_n.

Solution

The sequence can be written as

$$\dots, \underset{u_6}{57}, \underset{u_7}{\rule{1em}{0.4pt}}, \underset{u_8}{\rule{1em}{0.4pt}}, \underset{u_9}{\rule{1em}{0.4pt}}, \underset{u_{10}}{93}, \dots$$

The common difference, d, can be found by the difference between 93 and 57 divided by the number of times d must be added to 57 to produce 93 (i.e., the number of terms from 6 to 10).

$$d = \frac{93 - 57}{10 - 6} = \frac{36}{4} = 9$$

Note that $d = 9$ is the difference of the output values (terms of the sequence) divided by the difference of the input values (position of the terms of the sequence), which represents the change in output per unit change in input.

The value of u_1 can be found by using $n = 6$, $u_6 = 57$ and $d = 9$ in the equation

$$u_6 = u_1 + (n - 1)d$$
$$57 = u_1 + (6 - 1)9$$
$$u_1 = 57 - 5 \cdot 9 = 57 - 45 = 12$$

Because $u_1 = 12$ and $d = 9$, the recursive form of the arithmetic sequence is given by

$$u_1 = 12 \text{ and } u_n = u_{n-1} + 9, \text{ for } n \geq 2$$

The explicit form of the arithmetic sequence is given by

$$u_n = 12 + (n - 1)9$$
$$= 9n + 3, \text{ for } n \geq 1.$$

ADDITIONAL EXAMPLES

Summation Notation

It is sometimes necessary to find the sum of various terms in a sequence. For instance, we might want to find the sum of the first nine terms of the sequence $\{u_n\}$. Mathematicians often use the capital Greek letter sigma (Σ) to abbreviate such a sum as follows.

$$\sum_{i=1}^{9} u_i = u_1 + u_2 + u_3 + u_4 + u_5 + u_6 + u_7 + u_8 + u_9$$

Similarly, for any positive integer m and numbers $c_1, c_2, \ldots, c_m$,

Summation Notation

$$\sum_{k=1}^{m} c_k \quad \text{means} \quad c_1 + c_2 + c_3 + \cdots + c_m$$

Example 7 **Sum of a Sequence**

Compute each sum.

a. $\sum\limits_{n=1}^{5}(-7 + 3n)$ **b.** $\sum\limits_{n=1}^{4}\left[-3 + (n-1)4\right]$

Solution

a. Substitute 1, 2, 3, 4, and 5 for n in the expression $-7 + 3n$ and add the terms.

$$\sum_{n=1}^{5}(-7 + 3n)$$

$= (-7 + 3 \cdot 1) + (-7 + 3 \cdot 2) + (-7 + 3 \cdot 3)$
$\quad + (-7 + 3 \cdot 4) + (-7 + 3 \cdot 5)$
$= (-7 + 3) + (-7 + 6) + (-7 + 9) + (-7 + 12) + (-7 + 15)$
$= -4 - 1 + 2 + 5 + 8$
$= 10$

b. Substitute 1, 2, 3, and 4 for n in the expression $-3 + (n-1)4$, and add the terms.

$$\sum_{n=1}^{4}\left[-3 + (n-1)4\right]$$

$= \left[-3 + (1-1)4\right] + \left[-3 + (2-1)4\right]$
$\quad + \left[-3 + (3-1)4\right] + \left[-3 + (4-1)4\right]$
$= \left[-3 + 0 \cdot 4\right] + \left[-3 + 1 \cdot 4\right] + \left[-3 + 2 \cdot 4\right] + \left[-3 + 3 \cdot 4\right]$
$= -3 + (-3 + 4) + (-3 + 8) + (-3 + 12)$
$= -3 + 1 + 5 + 9$
$= 12$

Example 5

What is the 38th term of the
arithmetic sequence whose first
three terms are 15, 10, and 5? -170

Example 6

If $\{u_n\}$ is an arithmetic sequence with
$u_5 = 22$ and $u_{11} = 64$, find u_1, a
recursive formula, and an explicit
formula.
$u_1 = -6$
$u_1 = -6$ and $u_n = u_{n-1} + 7$ for $n \geq 2$
$u_n = 7n - 13$ for $n \geq 1$

Example 7

Compute each sum.

a. $\sum\limits_{i=1}^{4}(5 - 4n)$ -20

b. $\sum\limits_{i=1}^{5}\left[-4 + (n-1)3\right]$ 10

COMMON ERROR
ALERT

Students may use the wrong sign for
a common difference. In **Additional
Example 5,** remind students to
subtract terms in the correct order
to get the common difference.
$10 - 15 = -5$.

Teaching Notes

Students already know the terms and the sum of the sequence in **Example 7a.** You may want to use that sequence to demonstrate **Using Calculators to Compute Sequences and Sums.** The screen display is shown below.

```
seq(-7+3n,n,1,5)
    {-4 -1 2 5 8}
sum(seq(-7+3n,n,
1,5))
            10
■
```

ADDITIONAL EXAMPLES

Example 8

Use a calculator to display the first 7 terms of the sequence $u_n = -5 + 6n$ and to compute the sum $\sum\limits_{n=1}^{100} -5 + 6n$.

```
seq(-5+6n,n,1,7)
{1 7 13 19 25 3...
```

```
seq(-5+6n,n,1,7)
...13 19 25 31 37}
```

{1, 7, 13, 19, 25, 31, 37}

```
sum(seq(-5+6n,n,
1,100))
        29800
```

$$\sum_{n=1}^{100} -5 + 6n = 29{,}800$$

SEQ is in the OPS submenu of the TI LIST menu and in the LIST submenu of the Casio OPTN menu.

SUM is in the MATH submenu of the TI LIST menu. SUM is in the LIST submenu of the Casio OPTN menu.

```
sum(seq(7-3n,n,1
,50))
        -3475
```

Figure 1.3-5

Using Calculators to Compute Sequences and Sums

Calculators can aid in computing sequences and sums of sequences. The SEQ (or MAKELIST) feature on most calculators has the following syntax.

SEQ(*expression, variable, begin, end, increment*)

The last parameter, *increment*, is usually optional. When omitted, *increment* defaults to 1. Refer to the Technology Tip about which menus contain SEQ and SUM for different calculators.

The syntax for the SUM (or ΣLIST) feature is

SUM(*list*[, *start, end*]), where *start* and *end* are optional. When *start* and *end* are omitted, the sum of the entire list is given.

Combining the two features of SUM and SEQ can produce sums of sequences.

SUM(SEQ(*expression, variable, begin, end*))

Example 8 Calculator Computation of a Sum

Use a calculator to display the first 8 terms of the sequence $u_n = 7 - 3n$ and to compute the sum $\sum\limits_{n=1}^{50} 7 - 3n$.

Solution

Using the Technology Tip, enter SEQ($7 - 3n, n, 1, 8$), which produces Figure 1.3-4. Additional terms can be viewed by using the right arrow key to scroll the display, as shown at right below.

```
seq(7-3n,n,1,8)         seq(7-3n,n,1,8)
{4 1 -2 -5 -8 -...      ...-8 -11 -14 -17}
```

Figure 1.3-4

The first 8 terms of the sequence are 4, 1, -2, -5, -8, -11, -14, and -17. To compute the sum of the first 50 terms of the sequence, enter SUM(SEQ($7 - 3n, n, 1, 50$)). Figure 1.3-5 shows the resulting display. Therefore, $\sum\limits_{n=1}^{50} 7 - 3n = -3475$. ■

Partial Sums

Suppose $\{u_n\}$ is a sequence and k is a positive integer. The sum of the first k terms of the sequence is called the **kth partial sum** of the sequence.

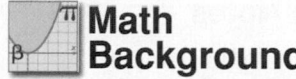

Math Background

Carl Friedrich Gauss (1777-1855) was a child prodigy. There is a story that when Carl was ten years old, his teacher assigned the class the task of finding the sum of the numbers 1 through 100. Carl found the sum almost immediately. Carl had noticed that the sum consists of 50 pairs: $1 + 100 = 101$, $2 + 99 = 101$, $3 + 98 = 101$, and so on. He reasoned that $50(101) = 5050$, so the sum of the first 100 counting numbers is 5050.

Teaching Notes

Solution to the **Calculator Exploration:** Here is one way to find the sum using a calculator:

The pattern is $1 + 100 = 101$, $2 + 99 = 101$, $3 + 98 = 101, \ldots$ There are $\frac{100}{2} = 50$ pairs, each with sum 101, so the formula is $50(101)$.

You may want to show how the proof of formula 1 in **Partial Sums of an Arithmetic Sequence** applies to a particular sequence. Consider the sequence $7, 12, 17, 22, 27, \ldots$. For this sequence, $S_4 = 7 + 12 + 17 + 22 = 58$. Using S_4 in place of S_k in the proof of the first formula, we have:

$$S_4 = 7 + 12 + 17 + 22$$
$$= 7 + [7 + 5] + [7 + 2 \cdot 5] + [7 + 3 \cdot 5]$$

$$S_4 = 22 + 17 + 12 + 7$$
$$= 22 + [22 - 5] + [22 - 2 \cdot 5] + [22 - 3 \cdot 5]$$

$$S_4 = 7 + [7 + 5] + [7 + 2 \cdot 5] + [7 + 3 \cdot 5]$$
$$\underline{S_4 = 22 + [22 - 5] + [22 - 2 \cdot 5] + [22 - 3 \cdot 5]}$$
$$2S_4 = (7 + 22) + (7 + 22) + (7 + 22) + (7 + 22)$$
$$= 4(7 + 22)$$

$$S_4 = \frac{4}{2}(7 + 22)$$

Calculator Exploration

Write the sum of the first 100 counting numbers. Then find a pattern to help find the sum by developing a formula using the terms in the sequence.

Partial Sums of an Arithmetic Sequence

If $\{u_n\}$ is an arithmetic sequence with common difference d, then for each positive integer k, the kth partial sum can be found by using either of the following formulas.

1. $\displaystyle\sum_{n=1}^{k} u_n = \frac{k}{2}(u_1 + u_k)$

2. $\displaystyle\sum_{n=1}^{k} u_n = ku_1 + \frac{k(k-1)}{2}d$

Proof Let S_k represent the kth partial sum $u_1 + u_2 + \cdots + u_k$. Write the terms of the arithmetic sequence in two ways. In the first representation of S_k, repeatedly add d to the first term.

$$S_k = u_1 + u_2 + u_3 + \cdots + u_{k-2} + u_{k-1} + u_k$$
$$= u_1 + [u_1 + d] + [u_1 + 2d] + \cdots + [u_1 + (k-1)d]$$

In the second representation of S_k, repeatedly subtract d from the kth term.

$$S_k = u_k + u_{k-1} + u_{k-2} + \cdots + u_3 + u_2 + u_1$$
$$= u_k + [u_k - d] + [u_k - 2d] + \cdots + [u_k - (k-1)d]$$

If the two representations of S_k are added, the multiples of d add to zero and the following representation of $2S_k$ is obtained.

$$S_k = u_1 + [u_1 + d] + [u_1 + 2d] + \cdots + [u_1 + (k-1)d]$$
$$\underline{S_k = u_k + [u_k - d] + [u_k - 2d] + \cdots + [u_k - (k-1)d]}$$

$$\overbrace{2S_k = (u_1 + u_k) + (u_1 + u_k) + \cdots + (u_1 + u_k)}^{k \text{ terms}} = k(u_1 + u_k)$$

$$S_k = \frac{k}{2}(u_1 + u_k) \qquad\qquad \textit{Divide by 2.}$$

The second formula is obtained by letting $u_k = u_1 + (k-1)d$ in the last equation.

$$S_k = \frac{k}{2}(u_1 + u_k) = \frac{k}{2}[u_1 + u_1 + (k-1)d] = \frac{k}{2}[2u_1 + (k-1)d]$$

$$= ku_1 + \frac{k(k-1)}{2}d$$

Example Notes

In **Example 9**, formula 1 from page 27 is used. Consider using formula 2 to check the answer, as shown below.

$$\sum_{n=1}^{k} u_n = ku_1 + \frac{k(k-1)}{2}d \quad \text{(formula 2)}$$

$$\sum_{n=1}^{12} u_n = 12(-8) + \frac{12(11)}{2}(5)$$

$$= -96 + 330 = 234 \checkmark$$

In **Example 10**, you need to form a sequence and then determine the appropriate partial sum of that sequence. Again, formula 1 from page 27 is used. If you use formula 2 to check the answer, the work will be:

$$\sum_{n-1}^{k} u_n = ku_1 + \frac{k(k-1)}{2}d \quad \text{(formula 2)}$$

$$\sum_{n=1}^{111} u_n = (111)(3) + \frac{(111)(110)}{2}(3)$$

$$= 333 + 18{,}315 = 18{,}648$$

ADDITIONAL EXAMPLES

Example 9

Find the 14th partial sum of the arithmetic sequence $21, 15, 9, 3, \ldots$. -252

Example 10

Find the sum of all multiples of 4 from 4 to 404. 20,604

Example 11

Larry owns an automobile dealership. He spends $18,000 on advertising during the first year, and he plans to increase his advertising expenditures by $1400 in each subsequent year. How much will Larry spend on advertising during the first 9 years? $212,400

Example 9 Partial Sum of a Sequence

Find the 12th partial sum of the arithmetic sequence below.

$$-8, -3, 2, 7, \ldots$$

Solution

First note that d, the common difference, is 5 and $u_1 = -8$.

$$u_{12} = u_1 + (12-1)d$$
$$= -8 + 11(5) = 47$$

Using formula **1** from the box on page 27 yields the 12th partial sum.

$$\sum_{n=1}^{12} u_n = \frac{12}{2}(-8+47) = 234$$

Example 10 Partial Sum of a Sequence

Find the sum of all multiples of 3 from 3 to 333.

Solution

Note that the desired sum is the partial sum of the arithmetic sequence $3, 6, 9, 12, \ldots$. The sequence can be written in the form

$$3 \cdot 1, 3 \cdot 2, 3 \cdot 3, 3 \cdot 4, \ldots,$$

where $333 = 3 \cdot 111$ is the 111th term. The 111th partial sum of the sequence can be found by using formula **1** from the box on page 27 with $k = 111$, $u_1 = 3$, and $u_{111} = 333$.

$$\sum_{n=1}^{111} u_n = \frac{111}{2}(3+333) = \frac{111}{2}(336) = 18{,}648$$

Example 11 Application of Partial Sums

If the starting salary for a job is $20,000 and you get a $2000 raise at the beginning of each subsequent year, how much will you earn during the first ten years?

Solution

The yearly salary rates form an arithmetic sequence.

$$20{,}000 \quad 22{,}000 \quad 24{,}000 \quad 26{,}000 \quad \ldots$$

The tenth-year salary is found using $u_1 = 20{,}000$ and $d = 2000$.

$$u_{10} = u_1 + (10-1)d$$
$$= 20{,}000 + 9(2000) = \$38{,}000$$

The ten-year total earnings are the tenth partial sum of the sequence.

$$\sum_{n=1}^{10} u_n = \frac{10}{2}(u_1 + u_{10}) = \frac{10}{2}(20{,}000 + 38{,}000)$$

$$= 5(58{,}000)$$

$$= \$290{,}000$$

Exercises 1.3

In Exercises 1–6, the first term, u_1, and the common difference, d, of an arithmetic sequence are given. Find the fifth term, the explicit form for the nth term, and sketch the graph of each sequence.

1. $u_1 = 5, d = 2$ **2.** $u_1 = -4, d = 5$

3. $u_1 = 4, d = \frac{1}{4}$ **4.** $u_1 = -6, d = \frac{2}{3}$

5. $u_1 = 10, d = -\frac{1}{2}$ **6.** $u_1 = \pi, d = \frac{1}{5}$

In Exercises 7–12, find the sum.

7. $\sum_{i=1}^{5} 3i$ **15**

8. $\sum_{i=1}^{4} \frac{1}{2^i}$ $\frac{15}{16}$

9. $\sum_{n=1}^{16} (2n - 3)$ **224**

10. $\sum_{n=1}^{75} (3n + 1)$ **8625**

11. $\sum_{n=15}^{36} (2n - 8)$ **946**

12. $\sum_{n=1}^{31} (300 + (n - 1)2)$ **10,230**

In Exercises 13–18, find the kth partial sum of the arithmetic sequence $\{u_n\}$ with common difference d.

13. $k = 6, u_1 = 2, d = 5$ **87**

14. $k = 8, u_1 = \frac{2}{3}, d = -\frac{4}{3}$ **−32**

15. $k = 7, u_1 = \frac{3}{4}, d = -\frac{1}{2}$ $-\frac{21}{4}$

16. $k = 9, u_1 = 6, u_9 = -24$ **−81**

17. $k = 6, u_1 = -4, u_6 = 14$ **30**

18. $k = 10, u_1 = 0, u_{10} = 30$ **150**

In Exercises 19–24, show that the sequence is arithmetic and find its common difference.

19. $\{3 - 2n\}$ **20.** $\left\{4 + \frac{n}{3}\right\}$

21. $\left\{\frac{5 + 3n}{2}\right\}$ **22.** $\left\{\frac{\pi - n}{2}\right\}$

23. $\{c + 2n\}$ (c constant)

24. $\{2b + 3nc\}$ (b, c constants)

In Exercises 25–30, use the given information about the arithmetic sequence with common difference d to find u_5 and a formula for u_n.

25. $u_4 = 12, d = 2$ **26.** $u_7 = -8, d = 3$
$u_5 = 14; u_n = 2n + 4$ $u_5 = -14, u_n = -29 + 3n$

27. $u_2 = 4, u_6 = 32$ **28.** $u_7 = 6, u_{12} = -4$
$u_5 = 25; u_n = 7n - 10$ $u_5 = 10, u_n = 20 - 2n$

29. $u_5 = 0, u_9 = 6$ **30.** $u_5 = -3, u_9 = -18$
$u_5 = 0; u_n = -\frac{15}{2} + \frac{3n}{2}$ $u_5 = -3, u_n = \frac{63}{4} - \frac{15}{4}n$

In Exercises 31–34, find the sum.

31. $\sum_{n=1}^{20} (3n + 4)$ **710** **32.** $\sum_{n=1}^{25} \left(\frac{n}{4} + 5\right)$ $\frac{825}{4}$

33. $\sum_{n=1}^{40} \frac{n + 3}{6}$ $156\frac{2}{3}$ **34.** $\sum_{n=1}^{30} \frac{4 - 6n}{3}$ **−890**

35. Find the sum of all the even integers from 2 to 100. **2550**

36. Find the sum of all the integer multiples of 7 from 7 to 700. **35,350**

37. Find the sum of the first 200 positive integers. **20,100**

38. Find the sum of the positive integers from 101 to 200 (inclusive). *Hint:* Recall the sum from 1 to 100. Use it and Exercise 37. **15,050**

6. $\pi + \frac{4}{5}; u_n = \pi + \frac{1}{5}(n - 1)$

19. $u_n - u_{n-1} = (3 - 2n) - [3 - 2(n - 1)]$
$= -2;$
arithmetic with $d = -2$

20. $u_n - u_{n-1} = \left(4 + \frac{n}{3}\right) - \left(4 + \frac{n - 1}{3}\right) = \frac{1}{3};$
arithmetic with $d = \frac{1}{3}$

21. $u_n - u_{n-1} = \frac{5 + 3n}{2} - \frac{5 + 3(n - 1)}{2} = \frac{3}{2};$
arithmetic with $d = \frac{3}{2}$

22–24. See p. 30.

1. 13; $u_n = 2n + 3$

2. 16; $u_n = 5n - 9$

3. 5; $u_n = \frac{n}{4} + \frac{15}{4}$

4. $-\frac{10}{3}; u_n = \frac{2}{3}n - \frac{20}{3}$

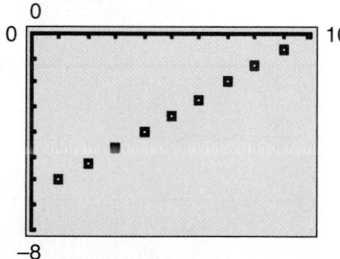

5. 8; $u_n = -\frac{n}{2} + \frac{21}{2}$

22. $u_n - u_{n-1} = \left(\dfrac{\pi - n}{2}\right) -$

$\left(\dfrac{\pi - (n-1)}{2}\right) = -\dfrac{1}{2};$

arithmetic with $d = -\dfrac{1}{2}$

23. $u_n - u_{n-1} = (c + 2n) -$

$[c + 2(n-1)]$

$= 2;$

arithmetic with $d = 2$

24. $u_n - u_{n-1} = (2b + 3nc) -$

$(2b + 3(n-1)c)$

$= 3c;$

arithmetic with $d = 3c$

39. A business makes a $10,000 profit during its first year. If the yearly profit increases by $7500 in each subsequent year, what will the profit be in the tenth year? What will be the total profit for the first ten years? **$77,500 in tenth year; $437,500 over ten years**

40. If a man's starting annual salary is $15,000 and he receives a $1000 increase to his annual salary every six months, what will he earn during the last six months of the sixth year? How much will he earn during the first six years? **$13,000 over six months; $123,000 over six years**

41. A lecture hall has 6 seats in the first row, 8 in the second, 10 in the third, and so on, through row 12. Rows 12 through 20 (the last row) all have the same number of seats. Find the number of seats in the lecture hall.   **428**

42. A monument is constructed by laying a row of 60 bricks at ground level. A second row, with two fewer bricks, is centered on that; a third row, with two fewer bricks, is centered on the second; and so on. The top row contains ten bricks. How many bricks are there in the monument? **910 bricks**

43. A ladder with nine rungs is to be built, with the bottom rung 24 inches wide and the top rung 18 inches wide. If the lengths of the rungs decrease uniformly from bottom to top, how long should each of the seven intermediate rungs be? **23.25, 22.5, 21.75, 21, 20.25, 19.5, 18.75**

44. Find the first eight numbers in an arithmetic sequence in which the sum of the first and seventh terms is 40 and the product of the first and fourth terms is 160. **8, 12, 16, 20, 24, 28, 32, 36**

1.4 Lines

Math Background

In an arithmetic sequence, when each term u_n is paired with its position n, the ordered pairs form a function whose domain is the set of counting numbers.

1.4 Lines

Objectives

- Find the slopes of lines, including parallel and perpendicular lines

- Describe the connection between arithmetic sequences and lines

- Graph lines

- Write the equations of lines, including horizontal and vertical lines

A **graph** is a set of points in a plane. Some graphs are based on data points, such as those shown in Section 1.3 where arithmetic sequences were graphed as scatter plots. Other graphs arise from equations.

A **solution of an equation** in two variables, say x and y, is a pair of numbers such that the substitution of the first number for x and the second for y produces a true statement. The **graph of an equation** in two variables is the set of points in a plane whose coordinates are solutions of the equation. Thus, the graph is a *geometric picture* of the solutions.

Recall that an arithmetic sequence is a sequence in which the difference between each term and the preceding term is constant.

For example, $\{3, 8, 13, 18, \dots\}$ is an arithmetic sequence.

Position (n)	1	2	3	4	5	...	n
Term (u_n)	3	8	13	18	23	...	$3 + (n-1) \cdot 5$

The graph of the sequence above has an infinite number of discrete points because the value of the sequence depends upon the term of the sequence, which must be a counting number. See Figure 1.4-1a. The graph of $y = 3 + (x - 1) \cdot 5$ is a continuous line that contains the discrete points of the arithmetic sequence, as shown in Figures 1.4-1a and 1.4-1b on page 31.

NOTE If needed, review graphing functions on a graphing calculator in the Technology Appendix.

Figure 1.4-1a

Figure 1.4-1b

As the positions within a sequence increase by one, the value of the terms increases by 5. Notice on the graph that as the x-values move to the right a distance of one, the y-values move up by a distance of 5. This common difference represents one of the most identifiable characteristics of a line, its slope.

Slope

When you move from a point P to a point Q on a line, two numbers are involved, as illustrated in Figure 1.4-2.

- The vertical distance you move is called the **change in y**, which is sometimes denoted Δy and read "delta y."

- The horizontal distance you move is called the **change in x**, which is sometimes denoted Δx and read "delta x."

$\dfrac{\text{Change in } y}{\text{Change in } x} = \dfrac{4}{6} = \dfrac{2}{3}$

a.

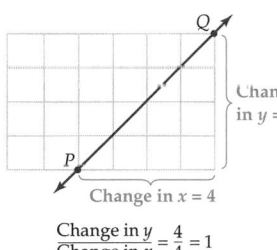

$\dfrac{\text{Change in } y}{\text{Change in } x} = \dfrac{4}{4} = 1$

b.

Figure 1.4-2

$\dfrac{\text{Change in } y}{\text{Change in } x} = \dfrac{4}{1} = 4$

c.

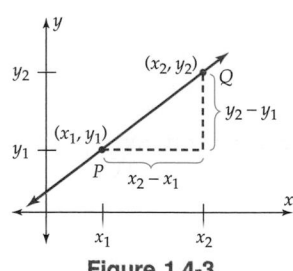

Figure 1.4-3

The fraction $\dfrac{\text{change in } y}{\text{change in } x} = \dfrac{\Delta y}{\Delta x}$ measures the steepness of the line. Suppose P has coordinates (x_1, y_1) and Q has coordinates (x_2, y_2), as shown in Figure 1.4-3.

- The change in y is the difference of the y-coordinates of P and Q.

$$\Delta y = y_2 - y_1$$

- The change in x is the difference of the x-coordinates of P and Q.

$$\Delta x = x_2 - x_1$$

Note that the graph of a sequence consists of discrete (separate and distinct) points. In Figure 1.4-1b, the line through the points is not the graph of the sequence.

In Figures 1.4-1a and 1.4-1b, point out that the tick marks on the x-axis are one unit apart and the tick marks on the y-axis are five units apart. If the scales for the x- and y-axes were the same, the line would be steeper.

You may want to show students that the *slope* is the same for any pair of points on a line by using a diagram like the one below.

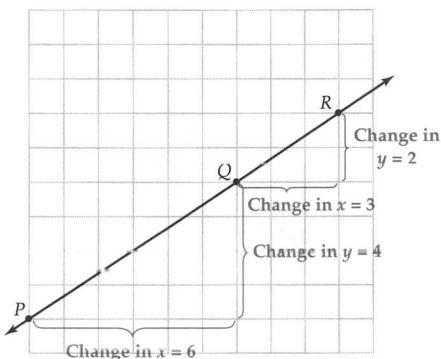

The fraction $\dfrac{\Delta y}{\Delta x}$ represents not only the steepness of a line, but also the direction. A line that rises left to right has a positive slope and a line that falls left to right has a negative slope. The line below has slope $-\dfrac{2}{3}$.

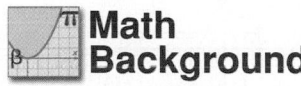

Math Background

The symbol Δ is the upper case Greek letter delta and is used to denote a change in a variable. The lower case delta is δ.

Teaching Notes

In the definition of **Slope of a Line**, stress the requirement that $x_1 \neq x_2$. If $x_1 = x_2$, the denominator of the ratio would be zero and the slope would be undefined. If $y_1 = y_2$, the slope equals zero.

ADDITIONAL EXAMPLES

Example 1

Find the slope of the line that passes through $(1, -2)$ and $(4, 1)$. See the figure below.

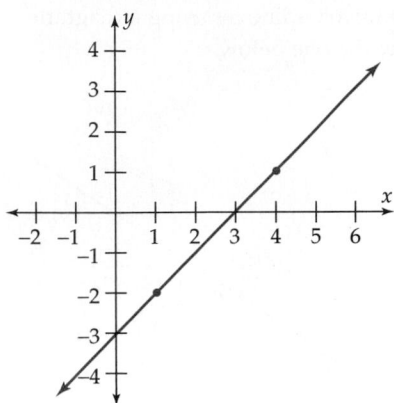

slope = 1

Example 2

Find the slope of each line shown below. The lines shown are determined by the following points:

$L_1: (0, 1)$ and $(-1, -3)$

$L_2: (0, 1)$ and $(2, 4)$

$L_3: (4, 1)$ and $(-3, 1)$

$L_4: (2, 0)$ and $(-2, 2)$

$L_5: (-2, 5)$ and $(2, -3)$

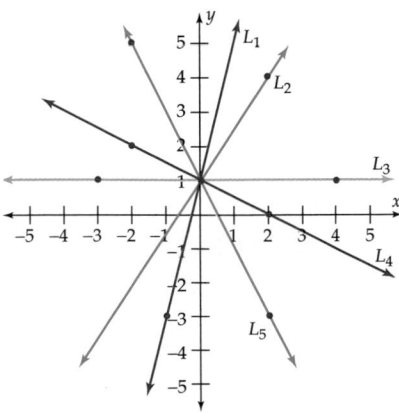

$L_1: 4, \; L_2: \dfrac{3}{2}, \; L_3: 0, \; L_4: -\dfrac{1}{2}, \; L_5: -2$

Slope of a Line

Consequently, slope is defined as follows.

> If (x_1, y_1) and (x_2, y_2) are points with $x_1 \neq x_2$, then the *slope* of the line through these points is the ratio
> $$\frac{\text{change in } y}{\text{change in } x} = \frac{\Delta y}{\Delta x} = \frac{y_2 - y_1}{x_2 - x_1}$$

Figure 1.4-4

Example 1 Finding Slope Given Two Points

Find the slope of the line that passes through $(0, -1)$ and $(4, 1)$. See Figure 1.4-4.

Solution

Apply the formula in the previous box with $x_1 = 0, y_1 = -1$ and $x_2 = 4, y_2 = 1$.

$$\text{Slope} = \frac{y_2 - y_1}{x_2 - x_1} = \frac{1 - (-1)}{4 - 0} = \frac{2}{4} = \frac{1}{2}$$

The order of the points makes no difference; if you use $(4, 1)$ for (x_1, y_1) and $(0, -1)$ for (x_2, y_2) in Example 1, the result is the same.

CAUTION

When finding slopes, you must subtract the y-coordinates and the x-coordinates in the same order. With the points $(3, 4)$ and $(1, 8)$, for instance, if you use $8 - 4$ in the numerator, you must write $1 - 3$ in the denominator, *not* $3 - 1$.

Example 2 Finding Slope From a Graph

Find the slope of each line shown in Figure 1.4-5. The lines shown are determined by the following points:

$L_1: (0, 2)$ and $(-1, -1)$ $L_2: (0, 2)$ and $(2, 4)$ $L_3: (-6, 2)$ and $(3, 2)$

$L_4: (-3, 5)$ and $(3, -1)$ $L_5: (1, 0)$ and $(2, -2)$

Solution

The slopes are as follows.

$L_1: \dfrac{2 - (-1)}{0 - (-1)} = \dfrac{3}{1} = 3$

$L_2: \dfrac{4 - 2}{2 - 0} = \dfrac{2}{2} = 1$

$L_3: \dfrac{2 - 2}{3 - (-6)} = \dfrac{0}{9} = 0$

$L_4: \dfrac{-1 - 5}{3 - (-3)} = \dfrac{-6}{6} = -1$

$L_5: \dfrac{-2 - 0}{2 - 1} = \dfrac{-2}{1} = -2$

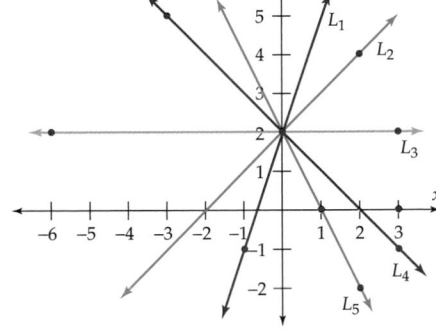

Figure 1.4-5

Example 2, page 32, illustrates how the slope measures the steepness of the line, summarized as follows. The lines referenced refer to Figure 1.4-5.

Properties of Slope

> The slope of a nonvertical line is a number m that measures how steeply the line rises or falls.
>
> - If $m > 0$, the line rises from left to right; the larger m is, the more steeply the line rises. [*Lines L_1 and L_2*]
> - If $m = 0$, the line is horizontal. [*Line L_3*]
> - If $m < 0$, the line falls from left to right; the larger $|m|$ is, the more steeply the line falls. [*Lines L_4 and L_5*]

Slope-Intercept Form

A nonvertical line intersects the y-axis at a point with coordinates $(0, b)$, because every point on the y-axis has first coordinate 0. The number b is called the y-intercept of the line. For example, the line in Figure 1.4-4 has y-intercept -1 because it crosses the y-axis at $(0, -1)$.

Let L be a nonvertical line with slope m and y-intercept b. Therefore, $(0, b)$ is a point on L. Let (x, y) be any other point on L, as shown in Figure 1.4-6. Use the points $(0, b)$ and (x, y) to compute the slope of L.

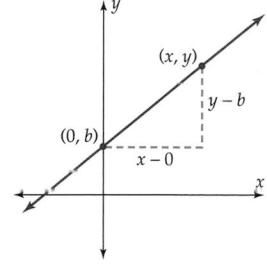

Figure 1.4-6

$$m = \frac{y - b}{x - 0} = \frac{y - b}{x}$$

Multiply both sides of the equation by x, and solve for y.

$$mx = y - b$$
$$y = mx + b$$

Thus, the coordinates of any point on L satisfy the equation $y = mx + b$, which leads to the following.

Slope-Intercept Form

> The line with slope m and y-intercept b is the graph of the equation
>
> $$y = mx + b.$$

Did you notice, as you recall your work with arithmetic sequences, that the explicit form of the sequence looks very similar to $y = mx + b$?

Example 2   Graphs of Arithmetic Sequences and Lines

The first three terms of an arithmetic sequence are $-2, 3,$ and 8. Use the explicit form of the sequence to express the nth term, and compare it to

---

Example 3

The first three terms of an arithmetic sequence are $-1, 2,$ and 5. Use the explicit form of the sequence to express the nth term, and compare it to the slope-intercept form of the equation of the line that passes through the points on the graph of the sequence. Graph both the sequence and the corresponding line on the same set of axes.

$u_n = 3n - 4$ has the form $y = mx + b$, with $m = d = 3$, $b = u_1 - d = -4$, and x corresponds to n.

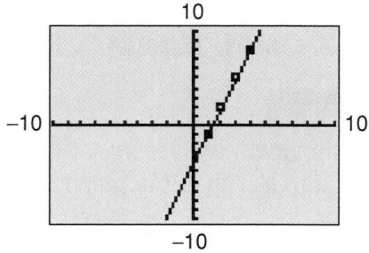

Teaching Notes

Try this useful exercise that requires very little time: Have a sketch prepared in advance (either on a transparency or the chalkboard) similar to Figure 1.4-5. Colors are not necessary. Show a list of pre-calculated slopes. Have students match the lines with their slopes.

Point out that the slope of a horizontal line is 0 and the slope of a vertical line is undefined. See **Common Error Alert** on page 38.

Make sure that students know that for any given line, m and b are constants in the equation $y = mx + b$.

Teaching Notes

You may want to show the algebraic steps that underlie the **Connection between Arithmetic Sequences and Lines.**

The graph of a sequence $\{u_n\}$ is the set of ordered pairs of the form (n, u_n).

$$u_n = u_1 + (n - 1)d$$
$$u_n = u_1 + dn - d$$
$$u_n = \underset{\updownarrow}{dn} + \underset{\updownarrow}{u_1 - d}$$
$$y = mx + b$$

The points of the sequence are a subset of the points (x, y) of the line $y = mx + b$, with $m = d$ and $b = u_1 - d$.

ADDITIONAL EXAMPLES

Example 4

Sketch the graph of $3y - 4x = 6$, and confirm your sketch with a graphing calculator.

$$y = \frac{4}{3}x + 2$$

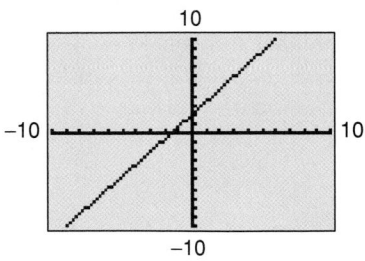

the slope-intercept form of the equation of a line that passes through the points on the graph of the sequence. Graph both the sequence and the corresponding line on the same set of axes.

Solution

The common difference for the sequence is 5 and $u_1 = -2$. Therefore, the explicit form is

$$u_n = u_1 + (n - 1)d$$
$$= -2 + (n - 1)5$$
$$= -2 + 5n - 5$$
$$= 5n - 7$$

The last equation, $u_n = 5n - 7$, has the form $y = mx + b$, where

$$m = d = 5 \qquad b = u_0 = u_1 - d = -7 \qquad \text{and} \qquad x \text{ corresponds to } n.$$

Figure 1.4-7 shows graphs of the sequence and the line.

25

-3   5

−10

Figure 1.4-7

Below is an important summary connecting the explicit form of an arithmetic sequence to the slope-intercept form of a line.

Connection between Arithmetic Sequences and Lines

> The connection between the explicit form of an arithmetic sequence, $u_n = u_1 + (n - 1)d$, and the slope-intercept form of a line, $y = mx + b$, is as follows.
>
> - The slope of the line corresponds to the common difference of the sequence, $m = d$.
>
> - The y-intercept represents the value of the first term of the sequence minus the difference, $b = u_1 - d$.

A linear equation expressed in slope-intercept form defines a relation for all the ordered pairs (x, y) on the line. The equation represents the rule and each x represents an input. For every input x there is one and only one output y, so y is a function of x. The graph of a linear function f is the graph of $y = f(x) = mx + b$.

Most graphing calculators are called *function graphers* because they graph a relation only if it can be expressed as a function $y = f(x)$. Thus, slope-intercept form is useful for graphing a line both on paper and with a graphing calculator.

Example 4   Graphing a Line

Sketch the graph of $2y - 5x = 2$, and confirm your sketch with a graphing calculator.

Figure 1.4-8a

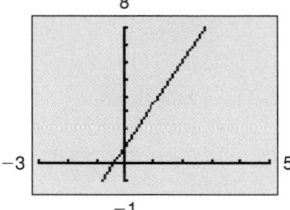

Figure 1.4-8b

Solution

Begin by solving the equation for y.

$$2y - 5x = 2$$
$$2y = 5x + 2$$
$$y = f(x) = \frac{5}{2}x + 1$$

Therefore, the graph is a line with slope $\frac{5}{2}$, the coefficient of x, and y-intercept 1, the constant term. Because the y-intercept is 1, the point $(0, 1)$ is on the line. When $x = 2$, then $f(2) = \frac{5}{2}(2) + 1 = 6$, so $(2, 6)$ is also on the line. Plotting and connecting the points $(0, 1)$ and $(2, 6)$ produces the line in Figure 1.4-8a. Figure 1.4-8b displays the same graph produced by a graphing calculator. ∎

| **Example 5** | **Linear Depreciation** |

An office buys a new computer system for $7000. Five years later its value is $800. Assume that the system depreciates linearly.

a. Write the equation that represents value as a function of years.

b. Find its value two years after it was purchased, that is, the y-value when $x = 2$.

c. Graph the equation.

d. Find how many years before the system is worthless, that is, the x-value that corresponds to a y-value of 0.

Solution

a. Linear depreciation means that the equation that gives the value y of the computer system in year x has the form $y = mx + b$ for some constants m and b. Because the system is worth $7000 new (when $x = 0$) the y-intercept is 7000 and the equation can be written as

$$y = mx + b$$
$$y = mx + 7000$$

Because the system is worth $800 after 5 years (i.e., $y = 800$ when $x = 5$),

$$y = mx + 7000$$
$$800 = m \cdot 5 + 7000$$
$$-6200 = 5m$$
$$m = \frac{-6200}{5} = -1240$$

The depreciation equation is $y = -1240x + 7000$, where y represents the value of the system after x years.

Example 5

An office buys a new color copier for $8000. Four years later its value is $2320. Assume that the copier depreciates linearly.

a. Write the equation that represents value as a function of years.
$y = -1420x + 8000$

b. Find its value three years after it was purchased, that is, the y-value when $x = 3$. $3740

c. Graph the equation.

10,000

d. Find how many years before the system is worthless, that is, the x-value that corresponds to a y-value of 0. approximately 5.63 years or 5 years 7.6 months

Example Notes

In **Example 5**, x represents time and cannot be negative; y represents the value of a computer system and must be between 0 and 8000, inclusive. Only ordered pairs in Quadrant I make sense for this application (See Figure 1.4-9 on page 36). The domain of the value function (depreciation equation) is [0, 5.645] and the range is [0, 8000].

Teaching Notes

Compare and contrast the **Point-Slope Form** on this page with the **Slope-Intercept Form** on page 33:

Point-Slope Form $y - y_1 = m(x - x_1)$

Slope-Intercept Form $y = mx + b$

For both forms, m is the slope of the line and (x, y) represents any point on the line.

For Point-Slope Form, b is the y-intercept. For Slope-Intercept Form, (x_1, y_1) represents a known point on the line.

ADDITIONAL EXAMPLES

Example 6

Sketch the graph and find the equation of the line that passes through the point $(-2, 5)$ with slope -3. Write the equation in slope-intercept form.

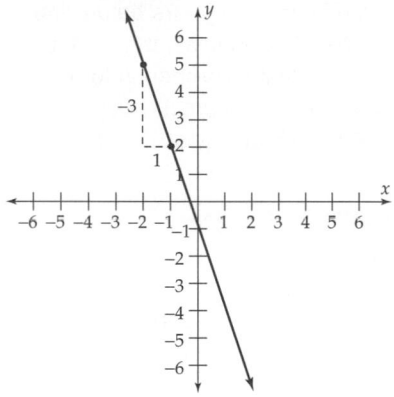

$y = -3x - 1$

Example 7

Describe and sketch the graph of the equation $y = -2$.

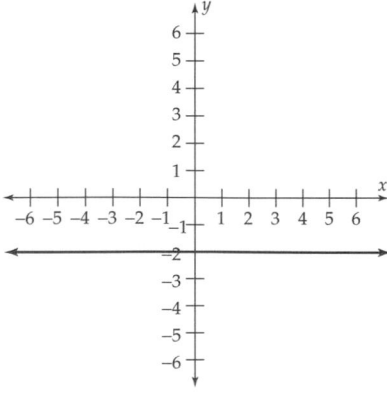

The graph is a line with slope 0 and y-intercept -2.

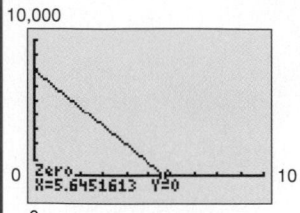

Figure 1.4-9

b. The value of the system after two years ($x = 2$) is

$$y = -1240(2) + 7000$$
$$= \$4520.$$

c. The graph of $y = -1240x + 7000$ is shown in Figure 1.4-9. Notice that the slope of the line, -1240, represents the depreciation of the system per year. That is, the value of the system decreases $1240 each year.

d. The trace feature or the zero feature of a graphing calculator shows that the x-value corresponding to $y = 0$ is $x \approx 5.6$, as shown in Figure 1.4-9. That is, the system will be worthless in 5 years and $0.6 \cdot 12 \approx 7.2$ months. ∎

The Point-Slope Form

Suppose the line L passes through the point (x_1, y_1) and has slope m. Let (x, y) be any other point on L. Use the fixed point (x_1, y_1) and the variable point (x, y) to compute the slope m of L, and it will generate another useful form of a line called the **point-slope form**. For $x \neq x_1$,

$$\frac{y - y_1}{x - x_1} = m \qquad \text{slope of } L$$

$$y - y_1 = m(x - x_1)$$

Thus, the coordinates of every point on L satisfy the equation

$$y - y_1 = m(x - x_1).$$

Point-Slope Form ○——

> The line with slope m through the point (x_1, y_1) is the graph of the equation
>
> $$y - y_1 = m(x - x_1).$$

There are two interesting observations about point-slope form.

1. Although slope-intercept form and point-slope form can be used to write the equation of a line, the point-slope form is easier to use, unless you know the y-intercept.

2. The point-slope form can also be used to graph a line because any point of the line can be used as the initial point and the remaining points can be found by using the equation's slope. The slope determines how to find a second point from the initial point by moving vertically an amount equal to the numerator of the slope, which represents Δy, and then moving horizontally an amount equal to the denominator of the slope, which represents Δx.

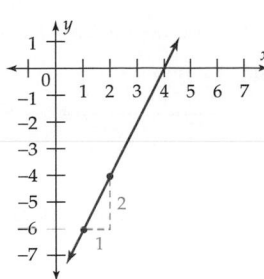

Figure 1.4-10

Example 6   Point-Slope Form of a Line

Sketch the graph and find the equation of the line that passes through the point $(1, -6)$ with slope 2. Write the equation in slope-intercept form.

Solution

To graph the line, start at the point $(1, -6)$ and identify another point on the line by moving 2 units vertically and 1 unit horizontally. The point $(2, -4)$ is also on the line. Because a unique line is determined by two points, connecting the points $(1, -6)$ and $(2, -4)$ produces the line, as shown in Figure 1.4-10.

To find the equation of the line, substitute 2 for m and $(1, -6)$ for (x_1, y_1) in the point-slope equation.

$$y - y_1 = m(x - x_1)$$
$$y - (-6) = 2(x - 1) \qquad \textit{Point-slope form}$$
$$y + 6 = 2x - 2$$
$$y = 2x - 8 \qquad \textit{Slope-intercept form}$$

Vertical and Horizontal Lines

When a line has 0 slope, it is called a **horizontal line,** and it can be written as $y = 0x + b = b$.

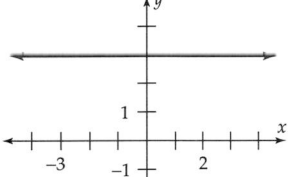

Figure 1.4-11

Example 7   Equation of a Horizontal Line

Describe and sketch the graph of the equation $y = 3$.

Solution

Because $y = 3$ can be written as $y = 0x + 3$, its graph is a line with slope 0 and y-intercept 3. This is sufficient information to obtain the graph shown in Figure 1.4-11.

Vertical Lines

The preceding discussion does not apply to vertical lines, whose equations have a different form than those examined earlier because a vertical line is not a function.

Example 8   Equation of a Vertical Line

Find the equation of the vertical line shown in Figure 1.4-12.

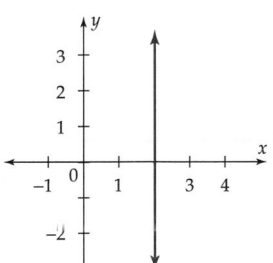

Figure 1.4-12

Solution

Every point on the vertical line in Figure 1.4-12 has first coordinate 2. Thus, every point on the line satisfies $x + 0y = 2$, and the line is the graph

---

ADDITIONAL EXAMPLES

Example 8

Find the equation of the vertical line shown below.

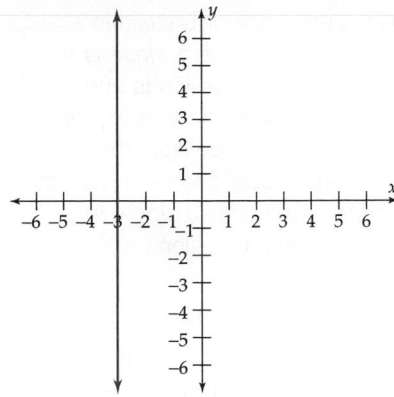

$x = -3$

COMMON ERROR ALERT

Students sometimes think that an equation with only the variable y is an equation of a vertical line and that an equation with only the variable x is an equation of a horizontal line. Suggest to students that they draw a horizontal line and label some points on it. They will see that all the points on the line have the same y-coordinate and therefore the equation must be of the form $y = \blacksquare$. The equation of the line below is $y = 2$.

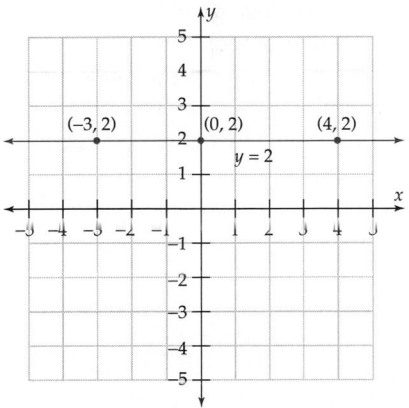

COMMON ERROR
ALERT

The phrase *no slope* is sometimes used for vertical lines. Because zero means none in everyday usage, students may forget whether no slope means zero slope or undefined slope. Remind students that a *slope is a number*. If an expression is undefined, there is *no number* for that expression. So, if a *slope is undefined*, there is *no slope*. Emphasize: A vertical line has no slope, or undefined slope. A horizontal line has a slope of 0.

Teaching Notes

The statements in the box at right are limited to nonvertical lines because the slope of vertical lines is not defined. Any two vertical lines are parallel. Every vertical line is perpendicular to every horizontal line.

The slopes of nonvertical perpendicular lines are negative reciprocals.

Example Notes

In **Example 9b**, to get the slope of the line perpendicular to the line with slope $\frac{3}{2}$, just invert the fraction and use the opposite sign.

COMMON ERROR
ALERT

Students sometimes use reciprocals for slopes of perpendicular lines, forgetting to use opposite signs. Remind them that the product must be -1, so the signs must be opposite.

---

of the equation $x = 2$. If you try to compute the slope of the line, say using $(2, 1)$ and $(2, 4)$, you obtain $\frac{4-1}{2-2} = \frac{3}{0}$, which is not defined.

Parallel and Perpendicular Lines

The slope of a line measures how steeply it rises or falls. Because parallel lines rise or fall equally steeply, their slopes are the same.

Two lines that meet in a right angle, that is, a 90° angle, are said to be **perpendicular**. There is a close relationship between the slopes of two perpendicular lines.

Parallel and Perpendicular Lines

> Two nonvertical lines are parallel when they have exactly the same slope.
>
> Two nonvertical lines are perpendicular when the product of their slopes is -1.

Example 9 Parallel and Perpendicular Lines

Given the line M whose equation is $3x - 2y + 6 = 0$, find the equation of the lines through the point $(2, -1)$

a. parallel to M.

b. perpendicular to M.

Solution

First find the slope of M by rewriting its equation in slope-intercept form.

$$3x - 2y + 6 = 0$$
$$-2y = -3x - 6$$
$$y = \frac{3}{2}x + 3$$

Therefore, M has slope $\frac{3}{2}$.

a. The line parallel to M must have the same slope, and because $(2, -1)$ is on the parallel line, use the point-slope form to find its equation.

$$y - y_1 = m(x - x_1)$$
$$y - (-1) = \frac{3}{2}(x - 2)$$
$$y + 1 = \frac{3}{2}x - 3$$
$$y = \frac{3}{2}x - 4$$

b. The line perpendicular to M must have slope $-\dfrac{1}{\frac{3}{2}} = -\dfrac{2}{3}$. Use point-slope form again to find the equation of the line perpendicular to M through $(2, -1)$.

$$y - (-1) = -\frac{2}{3}(x - 2)$$

$$y + 1 = -\frac{2}{3}x + \frac{4}{3}$$

$$y = -\frac{2}{3}x + \frac{1}{3}$$

Standard Form of a Line

> The *standard form of a line* is
>
> $$Ax + By = C,$$
>
> where A, B, and C are integers, $A \geq 0$, and A and B are not both 0.

NOTE The standard form of a line is sometimes called the *general form* of a line and may also be written as $Ax + By + C = 0$.

Any line, including vertical lines, can be written in this form. The last equation shown in Example 9, for the perpendicular line, $y = -\frac{2}{3}x + \frac{1}{3}$, can be written in standard form by multiplying both sides by 3, the least common denominator of all the terms, and then adding $2x$ to both sides. The resulting equation is $2x + 3y = 1$.

The following box summarizes the different forms of the equation of a line and when each form is best used.

Forms of Linear Equations

> The forms of the equation of a line are
>
> | | | |
> |---|---|---|
> | $Ax + By = C$ | *standard* form | |
> | $y = mx + b$ | *slope-intercept* form | **Graphing** |
> | $y - y_1 = m(x - x_1)$ | *point-slope* form | **Write equations** |
>
> A horizontal line has slope 0 and an equation of the form $y = b$.
>
> A vertical line has undefined slope and an equation of the form $x = c$.

Exercises 1.4

15.

$P(1, C)$

$(0, 0)$ $(1, 0)$

Slope of $L = \dfrac{C - 0}{1 - 0} = C$

16.

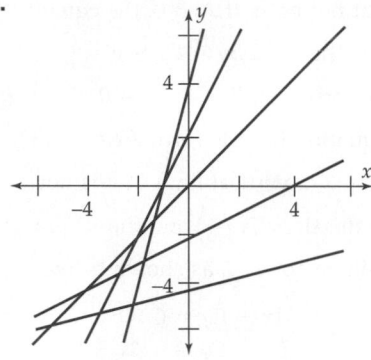

23. $y = -\dfrac{7}{3}x + \dfrac{34}{9}$

Exercises 1.4

1. For which of the line segments in the figure is the slope
  a. largest? **C**
  b. smallest? **B**
  c. largest in absolute value? **B**
  d. closest to zero? **D**

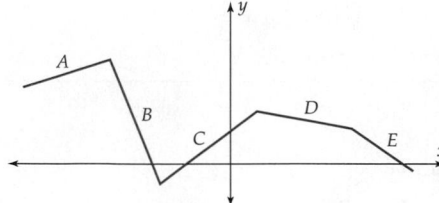

2. The doorsill of a campus building is 5 ft above ground level. To allow wheelchair access, the steps in front of the door are to be replaced by a straight ramp with constant slope $\dfrac{1}{12}$, as shown in the figure. How long must the ramp be? [The answer is not 60 ft.] $d = \sqrt{3625} \approx 60.2$ **feet**

In Exercises 3–6, find the slope and y-intercept of the line whose equation is given.

3. $2x - y + 5 = 0$ **2; 5**   **4.** $3x + 4y = 7$ $-\dfrac{3}{4}; \dfrac{7}{4}$

5. $3(x - 2) + y = 7 - 6(y + 4)$ $-\dfrac{3}{7}; -\dfrac{11}{7}$

6. $2(y - 3) + (x - 6) = 4(x + 1) - 2$
  $\dfrac{3}{2}; 7$

In Exercises 7–10, find the slope of the line through the given points.

7. $(1, 2); (3, 7)$ $\dfrac{5}{2}$ **8.** $(-1, -2); (2, -1)$ $\dfrac{1}{3}$

9. $\left(\dfrac{1}{4}, 0\right); \left(\dfrac{3}{4}, 2\right)$ **4**   **10.** $(\sqrt{2}, -1); (2, -9)$ $\dfrac{-8}{2 - \sqrt{2}}$

In Exercises 11–14, find a number t such that the line passing through the two given points has slope -2.

11. $(0, t); (9, 4)$ $t = 22$ **12.** $(1, t); (-3, 5)$
  $t = -3$

13. $(t + 1, 5); (6, -3t + 7)$ $t = \dfrac{12}{5}$ **14.** $(t, t); (5, 9)$ $t = \dfrac{19}{3}$

15. Let L be a nonvertical straight line through the origin. L intersects the vertical line through $(1, 0)$ at a point P. Show that the second coordinate of P is the slope of L.

16. On one graph, sketch five line segments, not all meeting at a single point, whose slopes are five different positive numbers.

In Exercises 17–20, find the equation of the line with slope m that passes through the given point.

17. $m = 1; (3, 5)$
  $y = x + 2$ **18.** $m = 2; (-2, 1)$
  $y = 2x + 5$
19. $m = -1; (6, 2)$
  $y = -x + 8$ **20.** $m = 0; (-4, -5)$
  $y = -5$

In Exercises 21–24, find the equation of the line through the given points.

21. $(0, -5)$ and $(-3, -2)$
  $y = -x - 5$ **22.** $(4, 3)$ and $(2, -1)$
  $y = 2x - 5$
23. $\left(\dfrac{4}{3}, \dfrac{2}{3}\right)$ and $\left(\dfrac{1}{3}, 3\right)$ **24.** $(6, 7)$ and $(6, 15)$
  $x = 6$

In Exercises 25–28, determine whether the line through P and Q is parallel or perpendicular to the line through R and S, or neither.

25. $P = (2, 5), Q = (-1, -1)$ and $R = (4, 2), S = (6, 1)$
  Perpendicular
26. $P = \left(0, \dfrac{3}{2}\right), Q = (1, 1)$ and $R = (2, 7), S = (3, 9)$
  Perpendicular
27. $P = \left(-3, \dfrac{1}{3}\right), Q = (1, -1)$ and $R = (2, 0),$
  $S = \left(4, -\dfrac{2}{3}\right)$
  Parallel
28. $P = (3, 3), Q = (-3, -1)$ and
  $R = (2, -2), S = (4, -5)$
  Perpendicular

In Exercises 29–31, determine whether the lines whose equations are given are parallel, perpendicular, or neither.

29. $2x + y - 2 = 0$ and $4x + 2y + 18 = 0$ **Parallel**

30. $3x + y - 3 = 0$ and $6x + 2y + 17 = 0$ **Parallel**

31. $y = 2x + 4$ and $0.5x + y = -3$ **Perpendicular**

32. Use slopes to show that the points $(-4, 6), (-1, 12)$, and $(-7, 0)$ all lie on the same straight line.

33. Use slopes to determine if $(9, 6), (-1, 2)$, and $(1, -3)$ are the vertices of a right triangle.

34. Use slopes to show that the points $(-5, -2) (-3, 1), (3, 0)$, and $(5, 3)$ are the vertices of a parallelogram.

In Exercises 35–42, find an equation for the line satisfying the given conditions.

35. through $(-2, 1)$ with slope 3 $\quad y = 3x + 7$

36. y-intercept -7 and slope 1 $\quad y = x - 7$

37. through $(2, 3)$ and parallel to $3x - 2y = 5$ $\quad y = \dfrac{3}{2}x$

38. through $(1, -2)$ and perpendicular to $y = 2x - 3$

39. x-intercept 5 and y-intercept -5 $\quad y = x - 5$

40. through $(-5, 2)$ and parallel to the line through $(1, 2)$ and $(4, 3)$ $\quad y = \dfrac{1}{3}x + \dfrac{11}{3}$

41. through $(-1, 3)$ and perpendicular to the line through $(0, 1)$ and $(2, 3)$ $\quad y = -x + 2$

42. y-intercept 3 and perpendicular to $2x - y + 6 = 0$

43. Find a real number k such that $(3, -2)$ is on the line $kx - 2y + 7 = 0$. $\quad k = -\dfrac{11}{3}$

44. Find a real number k such that the line $3x - ky + 2 = 0$ has y-intercept -3. $\quad k = -\dfrac{2}{3}$

45. Write the equation for the given arithmetic sequence in slope-intercept form.

1	2	3	4	5
-2	2	6	10	14

46. Write the equation for the given arithmetic sequence in slope-intercept form.

1	2	3	4	5
10	7	4	1	-2

47. The first three terms of an arithmetic sequence are 7, 1, and -5. Write the sequence's equation in slope-intercept form.

48. For a given arithmetic sequence, the common difference is -3 and $u_1 = 6$. Find the slope and y-intercept of the graph of this sequence.

49. For a given arithmetic sequence, the common difference is 8 and $u_1 = -2$. Find the slope and y-intercept of the graph of this sequence.

50. Let L be a line that is neither vertical nor horizontal and which does not pass through the origin. Show that L is the graph of $\dfrac{x}{a} + \dfrac{y}{b} = 1$, where a is the x-intercept and b is the y-intercept of L.

51. Let A, B, C, and D be nonzero real numbers. Show that the lines $Ax + By + C = 0$ and $Ax + By + D = 0$ are parallel.

52. Sales of a software company increased linearly from \$120,000 in 1996 to \$180,000 in 1999
  a. Find an equation that expresses the sales y in year x (where $x = 0$ corresponds to 1996).
  b. Estimate the sales in 2001.

53. The poverty level income for a family of four was \$9287 in 1981. Due to inflation and other factors, the poverty level income rose to approximately \$18,267 in 2001. (Source: U.S. Census Bureau)
  a. Find a linear equation that approximates the poverty level income y in year x (with $x = 0$ corresponding to 1981).
  b. Use the equation of part **a** to estimate the poverty level income in 1990 and 2005.

54. At sea level, water boils at 212° F. At a height of 1100 ft, water boils at 210° F. The relationship between boiling point and height is linear.
  a. Find an equation that gives the boiling point y of water at a height of x feet.

Find the boiling point of water in each of the following cities (whose altitudes are given).
  b. Cincinnati, OH (550 ft)
  c. Springfield, MO (1300 ft)
  d. Billings, MT (3120 ft)
  e. Flagstaff, AZ (6900 ft)

32. Yes. All 3 slopes are 2. The three points lie on the same straight line.

33. Yes. The slopes are $\dfrac{9}{8}, \dfrac{2}{5}$, and $-\dfrac{5}{2}$. Two sides perpendicular result in a right triangle.

34. Yes. The opposite sides have equal slopes and so are parallel. Therefore, this is a parallelogram.

38. $y = -\dfrac{1}{2}x - \dfrac{3}{2}$

42. $y = -\dfrac{1}{2}x + 3$

45. $y = 4x - 6$

46. $y = -3x + 13$

47. $y = -6x + 13$

48. The slope is $m = -3$ and the y-intercept is $b = 9$.

49. The slope is $m = 8$ and the y-intercept is $b = -10$.

50. Let $(a, 0)$ be the x-intercept and $(0, b)$ the y-intercept of the line.

Then $m = \dfrac{b - 0}{0 - a} = -\dfrac{b}{a}$.

$y = \dfrac{-b}{a}x + b$, $ay = -bx + ab$,

$bx + ay = ab$, $\dfrac{x}{a} + \dfrac{y}{b} = 1$

51. Both have slope $-\dfrac{A}{B}$ and different y-intercepts.

52. a. $y = 120,000 + 20,000x$

  b. \$220,000

53. a. $y = 449x + 9287$

  b. $x = 9$; $y = \$13,328$ (1990)

  $x = 24$; $y = \$20,063$ (2005)

54. a. $y = -\dfrac{1}{550}x + 212$

  b. 211 degrees

  c. 209.64 degrees

  d. 206.33 degrees

  e. 199.45 degrees

55. A small plane costs \$600,000 new. Ten years later, it is valued at \$150,000. Assuming linear depreciation, find the value of the plane when it is 5 years old and when it is 12 years old.
\$375,000; \$60,000

56. In 1950, the age-adjusted death rate from heart disease was about 307.2 per 100,000 people. In 1998, the rate had decreased to 126.6 per 100,000.
  a. Assuming the rate decreased linearly, find an equation that gives the number y of deaths per 100,000 from heart disease in year x, with $x = 0$ corresponding to 1950. Round the slope of the line to one decimal place. $y = -3.8x + 307.2$
  b. Use the equation in part **a** to estimate the death rate in 1995 and in 2005. **136.2; 98.2**

57. According to the Center of Science in the Public Interest, the maximum healthy weight for a person who is 5 ft 5 in. tall is 150 pounds and for someone 6 ft 3 in. tall is 200 pounds. The relationship between weight and height here is linear.
  a. Find a linear equation that gives the maximum healthy weight y for a person whose height is x inches over 5 ft 5 in. ($x = 0$ corresponds to 5 ft 5 in., $x = 2$ to 5 ft 7 in., etc.). $y = 5x + 150$
  b. Use the equation of part **a** to estimate the maximum healthy weight for a person whose height is 5 ft and for a person whose height is 6 ft. **125 lb; 185 lb**

58. The profit p (in thousands of dollars) on x thousand units of a specialty item is $p = 0.6x - 14.5$. The cost c of manufacturing x items is given by $c = 0.8x + 14.5$.
  a. Find an equation that gives the revenue r from selling x items. $r = 1.4x$
  b. How many items must be sold for the company to break even (i.e., for revenue to equal cost)? $x \approx$ **24.167 thousand units**

59. A publisher has fixed costs of \$110,000 for a mathematics text. The variable costs are \$50 per book. The book sells for \$72. Find equations that give the required information.
  a. the cost c of making x books $c(x) = 50x + 110,000$
  b. the revenue r from selling x books $r(x) = 72x$
  c. the profit p from selling x books $p(x) = 2x - 110,000$
  d. the publisher's break-even point (see Exercise 58b) $x = 5000$

60. If the fixed costs of a manufacturer are \$1000 and it costs \$2000 to produce 40 items, find a linear equation that gives the total cost of making x items. $y = 25x + 1000$

61. A hat company has fixed costs of \$50,000 and variable costs of \$8.50 per hat.
  a. Find an equation that gives the total cost y of producing x hats. $y = 8.50x + 50,000$
  b. What is the average cost per hat when 20,000 are made? 50,000? 100,000?
  \$11, \$9.50, \$9 per hat

Use the graph and the following information for Exercises 62–64. Rocky is an "independent" ticket dealer who markets choice tickets for Los Angeles Lakers home games (California currently has no laws against scalping). Each graph shows how many tickets will be demanded by buyers at a particular price. For instance, when the Lakers play the Chicago Bulls, the graph shows that at a price of \$160, no tickets are demanded. As the price (y-coordinate) gets lower, the number of tickets demanded (x-coordinate) increases.

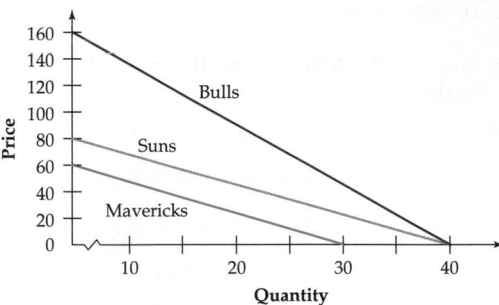

62. Write a linear equation expressing the quantity x of tickets demanded at price y when the Lakers play the indicated team.
  a. Dallas Mavericks $y = -2x + 60$
  b. Phoenix Suns $y = -2x + 80$
  c. Chicago Bulls $y = -4x + 160$
  Hint: In each case, use the points where the graph crosses the two axes to determine its slope.

63. Use the equations from Exercise 62 to find the number of tickets Rocky would sell at a price of \$40 for a game against the indicated team.
  a. Mavericks   **b.** Bulls
    $x = 10$ $x = 30$

64. Suppose Rocky has 20 tickets to sell. At what price could he sell them all when the Lakers play the indicated team.
  a. Mavericks   **b.** Suns
    \$20   \$40

1.5   Linear Models

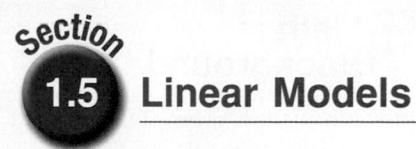

Objectives

• Algebraically fit a linear model

• Calculate finite differences and use residuals to determine the model of best fit

• Use a calculator to determine a linear model

• Find and interpret the correlation coefficient for a model

• Create and interpret a residual plot for a linear model

People working in business, medicine, agriculture, and other fields frequently want to know the relationship between two quantities. For instance,

> How does money spent on advertising affect sales?
>
> What effect does a fertilizer have on crop yield?
>
> How much do large doses of certain vitamins lengthen life expectancy?

In many such situations there is sufficient data available to construct a **mathematical model,** such as an equation or graph, which demonstrates the desired relationship or predicts the likely outcome in cases not included in the data. In this section applications are considered in which the data can be modeled by a linear equation. More complicated models will be considered in later sections.

When you are given a set of data points, you should first determine whether a straight line would be a good model for the data. This can be done graphically by making a scatter plot of the data, as shown in Figures 1.5-1a and 1.5-1b. Visual inspection suggests that the data points in Figure 1.5-1a are approximately linear but that those in Figure 1.5-1b are not. So a line would be a good model for the data points in Figure 1.5-1a, but for those in Figure 1.5-1b a line is not a good model.

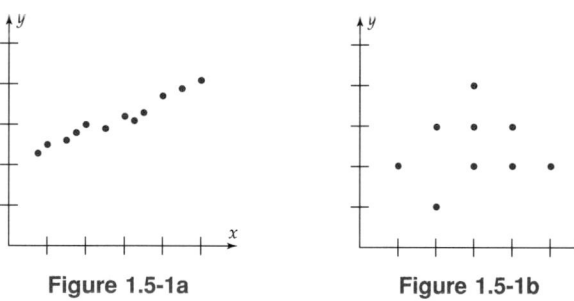

| Figure 1.5-1a | Figure 1.5-1b |

You can also determine whether a line is a good model for a given set of data points, without graphing, by using **finite differences.** To understand the idea, consider the equation $y = 3x - 1$, whose graph is known to be a line. Consider the table of values shown on the next page and look at the difference between each y-entry and the preceding one.

The differences are the same; all of them are equal to the slope of the line $y = 3x - 1$. This fact suggests that if the successive differences of the y-coordinates of the data points are approximately equal, then a line should be a good model for the data.

Teaching Notes

Mathematical models are created to represent real data. The models can then be analyzed to identify relationships and trends, and to make predictions and estimates. Models can be equations, inequalities, or graphs.

Math Background

Finite differences can be used to determine whether a polynomial function is a good model for a data set, and which type of polynomial function should be used. The differences at the top of page 44 are called first differences. When first differences are constant for a set of ordered pairs, the ordered pairs lie on the graph of a linear polynomial function. So, if first differences are *nearly constant*, a linear polynomial function is a good *model* for the data.

Second differences are successive differences of first differences. When first differences are not constant for a set of ordered pairs, but second differences are constant, the ordered pairs lie on the graph of a quadratic polynomial function.

Third differences are successive differences of second differences. When second differences are not constant, but third differences are constant, the ordered pairs lie on the graph of a cubic polynomial function.

Polynomial models are addressed in Chapter 4 (4.3.A Excursion), and other types of models are addressed in later chapters.

Math Background

In previous math courses, students may have estimated a line of fit by balancing data points above and below a line. Note that an estimated line of fit need not pass through any actual data points. This is also true of the least-squares regression line (line of *best* fit) for a data set, discussed on page 47.

ADDITIONAL EXAMPLES

Example 1

Estimated expenses for a company over the five-year period 1993–1997 are shown in the table below.

Year	1993	1994	1995	1996	1997
Expenses per share ($)	1.24	1.45	1.66	1.88	2.09

Determine whether a line would be a good model for this data. Use two different methods.

a. Calculate the finite differences for the data points. 0.21, 0.21, 0.22, 0.21

Because the differences are approximately equal, a line is a good model.

b. Draw a scatter plot of the data.

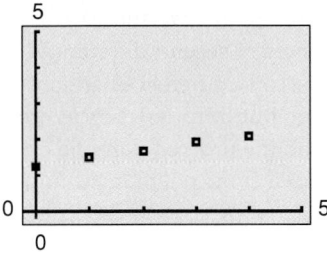

The points appear to be linear. A line is a good model.

x	$y = 3x - 1$	Difference
1	2	
2	5	$5 - 2 = 3$
3	8	$8 - 5 = 3$
4	11	$11 - 8 = 3$
5	14	$14 - 11 = 3$

Example 1 Linear Data

Estimated cash flows from a company over the five-year period 1988–1992 are shown in the table.

Year	1988	1989	1990	1991	1992
Cash flow per share ($)	2.38	2.79	3.23	3.64	4.06

Determine whether a line would be a good model for this data. Use two different methods.

a. Calculate the finite differences for the data points.

b. Draw a scatter plot of the data.

Solution

a. Subtract each cash flow from the preceding one and record the difference, as shown in Figure 1.5-2a.

Because the differences are approximately equal, a line is a good model for this data.

b. Let $x = 0$ correspond to 1988. The scatter plot for the data points is shown in Figure 1.5-2b, where the points appear to be linear. Therefore, a line is a reasonable model. ■

Figure 1.5-2a

Figure 1.5-2b

Once it has been determined that a line would be a good model for a set of data points, there are several ways to determine an appropriate model. The simplest way is to choose two of the data points and find the equation of the line that includes the points. This may require some experimenting to see which two points appear to produce a line that fits the data well. The number of data points above the line should balance with the number of data points below the line. Of course, there are many choices of two points and many possible lines that model the data. So there must be some way of determining which line fits the data best.

Modeling Terminology

Suppose (x, r) is a data point and that the corresponding point on the model is (x, y). Then the difference $r - y$ is called a **residual**. Residuals are a measure of the error between the actual value of the data, r, and the value y given by the model. Graphically, the residual is the vertical distance between the data point (x, r) and the model point (x, y), as shown in Figure 1.5-3.

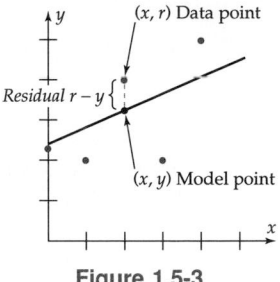

(x, r) Data point

Residual $r - y$ {

(x, y) Model point

Figure 1.5-3

The residual represents a directed distance that is positive when the data point is above the model point and negative when the data point is below the model point. When the sum of the residuals is 0, which indicates that the positive and negative errors cancel out each other, the model is probably a reasonable one. However, this is not always enough to determine which of several models is best because their residuals may all have the same sum.

Consequently, to find which model among several fits the data best, use the sum of the *squares* of the residuals because this sum has no negative terms and no canceling. Using the sum of the squares as a measure of accuracy has the effect of emphasizing large errors, those with absolute value greater than 1, because the square is greater than the residual. It minimizes small errors, those with absolute value less than 1, because the square is less than the residual.

Example 2   **Modeling Data**

The data below shows the weekly amount spent on advertising and the weekly sales revenue of a small store over a seven-week period.

Advertising Expenditure x (in hundreds of dollars)	0	1	2	3	4	5	6
Sales revenue (in thousands of dollars)	1	2	2	3	3	5	5

Find two models for the data, each determined by a pair of data points. Then use residuals to see which model best fits the data.

ADDITIONAL EXAMPLES

Example 2

The data below shows the monthly amount spent on marketing (in hundreds of dollars) x and the monthly sales revenue (in thousands of dollars) r of an online store over a seven-month period.

x	0	1	2	3	4	5	6
r	2	2	3	3	4	5	5

Find two models for the data, each determined by a pair of data points. For one model, use points $(1, 2)$ and $(4, 4)$. For the other model, use $(1, 2)$ and $(5, 5)$. Then use residuals to see which model best fits the data.

Model A (using $(1, 2)$ and $(4, 4)$):
Equation of model: $y = \frac{2}{3}x + \frac{4}{3}$.

(x, r)	(x, y)	$r - y$	$(r - y)^2$
$(0, 2)$	$(0, 1.33)$	0.67	0.45
$(1, 2)$	$(1, 2)$	0	0
$(2, 3)$	$(2, 2.67)$	0.33	0.11
$(3, 3)$	$(3, 3.33)$	-0.33	0.11
$(4, 4)$	$(4, 4)$	0	0
$(5, 5)$	$(5, 4.67)$	0.33	0.11
$(6, 5)$	$(6, 5.33)$	-0.33	0.11
		Sum	**0.89**

Sum of the squares of the residuals is 0.89.

Model B (using $(1, 2)$ and $(5, 5)$):
Equation of model: $y = \frac{3}{4}x + \frac{5}{4}$.

(x, r)	(x, y)	$r - y$	$(r - y)^2$
$(0, 2)$	$(0, 1.25)$	0.75	0.56
$(1, 2)$	$(1, 2)$	0	0
$(2, 3)$	$(2, 2.75)$	0.25	0.06
$(3, 3)$	$(3, 3.5)$	-0.5	0.25
$(4, 4)$	$(4, 4.25)$	-0.25	0.06
$(5, 5)$	$(5, 5)$	0	0
$(6, 5)$	$(6, 5.75)$	-0.75	0.56
		Sum	**1.24**

Sum of the squares of the residuals is 1.24.

Model A is the better of the two models because $0.89 < 1.24$.

Math Background

Historically, the concept of regression was developed by Sir Francis Galton (1822–1911) while studying the relationship between heights of parents and their children through generations. Galton published a paper "Regression towards Mediocrity in Hereditary Stature." The paper focused on how the physical traits of children are related to the physical traits of their parents. Galton found that children tend to "regress toward the mean." For example, tall parents tended to have children shorter than themselves, and short parents tended to have children taller than themselves.

For any set of data, the sum of the residuals of the **Least-Squares Regression Line** is zero. For example, the approximate least-squares regression line for the data in Example 2 is $y = 0.679x + 0.964$. The table below shows its residuals.

(x, r)	(x, y)	$r - y$
(0, 1)	(0, 0.964)	0.036
(1, 2)	(1, 1.643)	0.357
(2, 2)	(2, 2.322)	−0.322
(3, 3)	(3, 3.001)	−0.001
(4, 3)	(4, 3.68)	−0.68
(5, 5)	(5, 4.359)	0.641
(6, 5)	(6, 5.038)	−0.038
	Sum	**−0.007**

The sum is not exactly zero because the values 0.679 and 0.964 in the approximate regression line equation are rounded values.

Teaching Notes

Caution: the sum of the residuals may be 0 for lines other than the least squares regression line. For example, in Example 2, Model A, the sum of the residuals is 0.

Solution

Let the two models be denoted as A and B. For Model A, use the points (1, 2) and (3, 3). The slope of the line through these points is

$$m = \frac{3 - 2}{3 - 1} = \frac{1}{2} = 0.5$$

The equation of the line through (1, 2) and (3, 3) is

$$y - 2 = 0.5\,(x - 1)$$
$$y = 0.5x + 1.5$$

Model A is shown in Figure 1.5-4 and its residuals are shown in the table below. Notice that the sum of the squared residuals is 2.

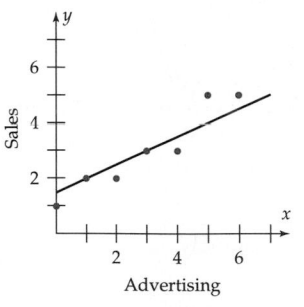

Figure 1.5-4

Data point (x, r)	Model point (x, y)	Residual $r - y$	Squared residual $(r - y)^2$
(0, 1)	(0, 1.5)	−0.5	0.25
(1, 2)	(1, 2)	0	0
(2, 2)	(2, 2.5)	−0.5	0.25
(3, 3)	(3, 3)	0	0
(4, 3)	(4, 3.5)	−0.5	0.25
(5, 5)	(5, 4)	1	1
(6, 5)	(6, 4.5)	0.5	0.25
	Sums	**0**	**2.00**

For Model B, use the point (1, 2) and (6, 5). The slope of the line through these points is $\frac{5 - 2}{6 - 1} = \frac{3}{5} = 0.6$ and its equation is

$$y - 2 = 0.6\,(x - 1) \quad \text{or} \quad y = 0.6\,x + 1.4$$

Figure 1.5-5 shows the graph of Model B and the table below shows its residuals. The sum of the squared residuals is 1.56.

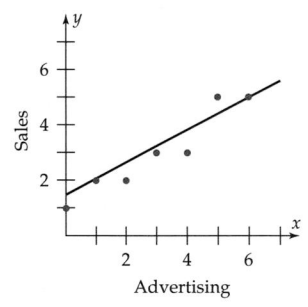

Figure 1.5-5

Data point (x, r)	Model point (x, y)	Residual $r - y$	Squared residual $(r - y)^2$
(0, 1)	(0, 1.4)	−0.4	0.16
(1, 2)	(1, 2)	0	0
(2, 2)	(2, 2.6)	−0.6	0.36
(3, 3)	(3, 3.2)	−0.2	.04
(4, 3)	(4, 3.8)	−0.8	0.64
(5, 5)	(5, 4.4)	0.6	0.36
(6, 5)	(6, 5)	0	0
	Sums	**−1.4**	**1.56**

Because this sum is smaller that the sum for Model A, conclude that Model B is the better of the two models. ∎

Least–Squares Regression Lines

> **NOTE** If needed, review how to compute linear regression equations in the Technology Appendix.

It can be proved that for any set of data there is one and only one line for which the sum of the squares of the residuals is as small as possible. Such a line is called the **least–squares regression line,** and the computational process for finding it is called **linear regression.** Most graphing calculators have the linear regression process built-in. For example, Figure 1.5-6 shows the approximate least–squares regression line for the data in Example 2.

$$y = 0.679x + 0.964$$

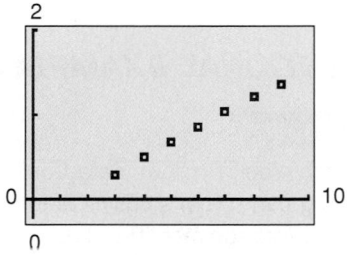

Figure 1.5-6

The sum of the squared residuals for this model is approximately 1.107, slightly less than the corresponding sum for Model *B* in Example 2.

The number *r* in Figure 1.5-6, which is called the **correlation coefficient,** is a statistical measure of how well the least–squares regression line fits the data points. The value of *r* is always between -1 and 1, the closer the absolute value of *r* is to 1, the better the fit. When $|r| = 1$, the fit is perfect: all the data points are on the regression line. Conversely, a correlation coefficient near 0 indicates a poor fit.

r^2 is called the **coefficient of determination.** It is the proportion of variation in *y* that can be attributed to a linear relationship between *x* and *y* in the data.

Example 3   Modeling Data

A circle can be circumscribed around any regular polygon. The lengths of the radii of the circumscribed circles around regular polygons whose sides have length of one unit are given as follows.

Number of sides	3	4	5	6	7	8	9
Radius	0.577	0.707	0.851	1.00	1.152	1.306	1.462

a. Draw a scatterplot.

b. Calculate the finite differences for the data points.

c. Find the model that best fits the data using the regression feature on a calculator.

d. What does the correlation coefficient indicate about the data?

> **Technology Tip**
>
> Many calculators have a ΔList command that can be entered into the label cell of a list. This will automatically calculate the differences between the items of the list specified. For example, ΔList(L2) produces a list of differences between the items of list L2.

Example 3

The lengths of the radii of the inscribed circles in regular polygons whose sides have length one unit are given as follows:

Number of sides	3	4	5	6
Radius	0.289	0.500	0.688	0.866

Number of sides	7	8	9
Radius	1.038	1.207	1.374

a. Draw a scatterplot.

b. Calculate the finite differences for the data points.

The differences, as shown in L3, are approximately equal.

c. Find the model that best fits the data using the regression feature on a calculator.

least-squares regression line:
$y = 0.18x - 0.22$

d. What does the correlation coefficient indicate about the data?
The correlation coefficient, $r = 0.9992152472$, is very close to 1, indicating that this linear model is a good fit for the data.

Example Notes

In **Example 4**, it may help to review two basic business principles:
- Profit = Revenue − Cost
- The break-even point is when the revenue equals the cost (the profit equals zero).

It may help to outline the tasks involved in solving Example 4:
- Find a linear model for the revenue and determine whether it is a good model.
- Find a linear model for the cost and determine whether it is a good model.
- Use the models of the revenue and the cost to find the break-even point.

ADDITIONAL EXAMPLES

Example 4

The table below shows data from a hot dog cart owner's business for Fridays last summer. The data includes the salaries S the workers were paid each day, the number of hot dogs H sold, the cost of materials M, and the total revenue R for each day. The owner also must spend $50 each operating day on rent for his location. Sales taxes have been ignored and amounts have been rounded to the nearest dollar.

Week	S ($)	H	M ($)	R ($)
1	81	134	66	242
2	72	105	50	142
3	79	97	39	150
4	75	130	58	225
5	75	104	45	176
6	70	126	54	190
7	68	139	63	245
8	73	146	64	250
9	76	120	57	231
10	69	96	43	134
11	78	115	50	189
12	68	129	62	194
13	76	111	56	199

Solution

a. A scatter plot of the data is shown in Figure 1.5-7a.

b. Subtract each radius from the preceding one and record the differences in a list. Notice that the differences are approximately equal, as shown in Figure 1.5-7b.

Figure 1.5-7a **Figure 1.5-7b**

Figure 1.5-7c

c. Use the linear regression feature to obtain Figure 1.5-7c, which shows that the least–squares regression line is approximately $y = 0.15x + 0.12$.

d. The correlation coefficient, $r = 0.9996308197$, is very close to 1, which indicates that this linear model is a very good fit for the data. ∎

Although only linear models are constructed in this section, you should always allow for the possibility that a linear model may not be the best choice for certain data. The least–squares regression line may give a reasonable model, which is the *line* that fits the data best, but there may be a nonlinear equation that is an even better model for the data. Polynomial models, for example, are presented in Chapter 4.

In addition to finding finite differences and a scatter plot of the data, another way to check that a linear model is appropriate is to construct a scatter plot of the residuals. In other words, plot the points $(x, r - y)$, where (x, r) is a data point and (x, y) is the corresponding point on the model. The general rule is two fold:

Use a linear model when the scatter plot of the residuals shows no obvious pattern, as shown in Figure 1.5-8.

Use a nonlinear model when the scatter plot of the residuals has a pattern, as shown in Figure 1.5-9.

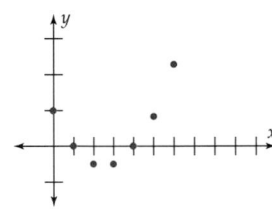

Figure 1.5-8 **Figure 1.5-9**

continued from page 48

a. Find a linear regression model for the daily revenue as a function of the number of hot dogs sold.

$y = 2.203x - 65.532$

b. Use a scatter plot of the residuals to determine if the linear model is a good fit for revenue.

no pattern; linear model is a good choice

c. Find a linear regression model for the daily cost as a function of the number of hot dogs sold. Be sure to include the pay for the workers, the fixed daily cost, and the cost of the material. $y = 0.446x + 124.996$

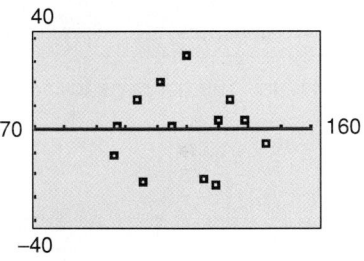

Technology Tip

The regression equation is stored in a variable that is usually called RegEQ each time the regression coefficients are calculated. The residuals are stored in a variable called RESID each time a regression is performed. See the Technology Appendix for specific instructions for graphing a regression line and residuals.

Example 4 Linear Regression and Residuals

A local resident owns an espresso cart and has asked you to provide an analysis based on last summer's data. To simplify things, only data for Mondays is provided. The data includes the amount the workers were paid each day, the number of cups sold, the cost of materials, and the total revenue for the day. The owner also must spend $40 each operating day on rent for her location and payment toward a business loan. Sales taxes have been removed from the data, so you need not consider them, and amounts have been rounded to the nearest dollar.

Date	Salaries ($)	Cups sold	Material cost ($)	Total revenue ($)
June 02	68	112	55	202
June 09	60	88	42	119
June 16	66	81	33	125
June 23	63	112	49	188
June 30	63	87	38	147
July 07	59	105	45	159
July 14	57	116	49	165
July 21	61	122	52	178
July 28	64	100	48	193
August 04	58	80	36	112
August 11	65	96	42	158
August 18	57	108	52	162
August 25	64	93	47	166

a. Find a linear regression model for the daily revenue as a function of the number of cups sold.

b. Use a scatter plot of the residuals to determine if the linear model is a good fit for revenue.

c. Find a linear regression model for the daily cost as a function of the number of cups sold. Be sure to include the pay for the workers, the fixed daily cost, and the cost of the material.

d. Draw a scatter plot of the residuals to determine if the proposed model is a good fit for cost.

e. Find the break-even point, that is, when revenue is equal to cost.

continued from page 49

d. Draw a scatter plot of the residuals to determine if the proposed model is a good fit for cost.

no pattern; linear model is a good choice

e. Find the break-even point, that is, when revenue is equal to cost.

must sell 109 hot dogs to break even

Solution

a. Enter two lists in your calculator, using the column labeled "Cups Sold" and "Total Revenue" in the chart. That is, the data points are (112, 202), (88, 119), and so on. Next, use the linear regression function on these lists to approximate the least–squares regression line.

$$y = 1.586x + 0.895$$

Store its equation as y_1 in the equation memory, as shown in Figure 1.5-10a and 1.5-10b.

Figure 1.5-10a

Figure 1.5-10b

b. To obtain a scatter plot of the residuals for the least squares regression line for revenue, plot the points whose first coordinates are given by the CUPS list and whose second coordinates are given by the RESID, the variable that holds the residuals each time a regression is performed.

Figure 1.5-11a

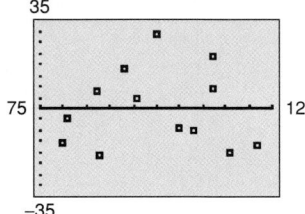
Figure 1.5-11b

c. First, create a new list that shows the total cost each day. For June 2,

Salaries + Material Cost + Rent/Loan Costs = Daily Cost

$68 + $55 + $40 = $163

Compute the total daily cost for each date, as shown in Figure 1.5-12a, where the salaries list is called PAY, the materials cost list is called COST, and TOTCO is the total daily cost list.

To find a model for the total daily cost as a function of cups sold, use the data points given by the lists CUPS and TOTCO with the regression feature. Find the closest approximate least–squares regression line.

$$y = 0.395x + 107.659$$

> **Technology Tip**
>
> Placing RESID into Ylist will use the last computed regression's residual values in a scatter plot.

Figure 1.5-12a

> **Technology Tip**
>
> A formula can be placed in the upper cell of a list to perform the operation on all the elements of the list.

Store this equation as y_2 in the equation memory, as shown in Figure 1.5-12b.

Figure 1.5-12b

d. Use the same procedure as in part **b** to obtain the scatter plot of the residuals for cost shown in Figure 1.5-12c. It shows no obvious pattern, which again indicates that a linear model is a good choice for this data.

 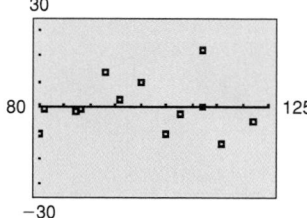

Figure 1.5-12c

e. The break-even point occurs when revenue is equal to cost. Plot the revenue equation found in part **a** and the cost equation found in part **c** on the same screen, and find the x-coordinate of their intersection (shown in Figure 1.5-13). Since 89.6 cups cannot be sold, 90 cups a day must be sold to break even.

Figure 1.5-13

Example 5 Prediction from a Model

The total number of farm workers (in millions) in selected years is shown in the following table.

Year	Workers	Year	Workers	Year	Workers
1900	29.030	1950	59.230	1985	106.210
1920	42.206	1960	67.990	1990	117.490
1930	48.686	1970	79.802	1994	120.380
1940	51.742	1980	105.060		

a. Use linear regression to find an equation that models the data. Use the equation to estimate the number of farm workers in 1975 and in 2000.

ADDITIONAL EXAMPLES

Example 5

The total number of farms (in millions) in selected years is shown in the table below.

Year	Farms	Year	Farms
1900	5.740	1960	3.963
1920	6.518	1970	2.949
1930	6.546	1985	2.293
1940	6.350	1990	2.146
1950	5.648	1995	2.196

a. Use linear regression to find an equation that models the data. Use the equation to estimate the number of farms in 1975 and in 2005. Let $x = 0$ correspond to 1900.
$$y = -0.0540x + 7.3507$$

1975: $\approx$3,300,700 farms
2005: $\approx$1,680,700 farms

b. According to the model, when will the number of farms be one million? There will be one million farms in approximately 2017.

c. Is a line the best model for the data?

The graph of the residuals seems to have a pattern, so there is a better, nonlinear model for the data.

Teaching Notes

For **Correlation and Slope**, remind students that the closer $|r|$ is to 1, the better the model fits the data. When $|r|$ is close to 1, the correlation is called strong. Point out that *positive* and *negative* do not describe the strength of the correlation; they simply describe whether the pattern of data points rises left to right or falls left to right. For example, $r = 0.9$ and $r = -0.9$ indicate correlations that are equally strong.

Math Background

The discussion about **Correlation and Slope** applies to linear models of data sets. For nonlinear models (such as the polynomial models in Excursion 4.3.A, pages 273–277), slope cannot be related to correlation.

Figure 1.5-14

Figure 1.5-15

b. According to the model, when will the number of workers be 150 million?

c. Is a line the best model for the data?

Solution

Let $x = 0$ correspond to 1900 and enter the data into two lists. Perform linear regression on the data, and display the scatter plot of the data together with the graph of the least–squares regression line.

$$y \approx 1.0116x + 18.3315$$

As suggested by Figure 1.5-14, the regression line provides a reasonable model for approximating the number of farm workers in a given year.

a. If $x = 75$, then $y \approx 1.0116(75) + 18.3315 = 94.202$.
  If $x = 100$, then $y \approx 1.0116(100) + 18.3315 = 119.492$.

  Therefore, there were approximately 94,202,000 farm workers in 1975 and 119,492,000 in 2000.

b. To determine when the number of workers will be 150 million, solve the regression equation when $y = 150$.

$$1.0116x + 18.3315 = 150$$
$$1.0116x = 131.6685$$
$$x = \frac{131.6685}{1.0116} \approx 130.159$$

  There will be 150 million farm workers in approximately 2030.

c. As shown in Figure 1.5-15, there seems to be a pattern in the residuals, so there is a better, nonlinear model for the data. Nonlinear models are discussed in Section 4.3.A. ∎

Correlation and Slope

The **correlation coefficient,** r, always has the same sign as the slope of the least squares regression line. So when r is negative, the regression line slants downward from left to right. In other words, as x increases, y decreases. In such cases, we say that the data has a **negative correlation.** When r is positive, the regression line slopes upward from left to right, and the data is said to have a **positive correlation.** As x increases, y also increases. When r is close to 0 (regardless of sign), there is **no correlation** between the quantities.

Exercises 1.5

1. a. In Example 2, find the equation of the line through the data points (1, 2) and (5, 5).
   b. Compute the sum of the squares of the errors for this line. Is it a better model than any of the models in the example? Why?

2. The linear model in Example 5 is the least squares regression line with coefficients rounded. Find the correlation coefficient for this model.

3. a. In Example 5, find the slope of the line through the data points for 1920 and 1994.
   b. Find the equation of the line through these two data points.
   c. Which model predicts the higher number of farm workers in 2010: the line in part **b** or the regression line found in Example 5?

In Exercises 4–7, determine whether the given scatter plot of the data indicates that there is a positive correlation, negative correlation, or very little correlation.

4.

positive correlation

5.

negative correlation

6.

negative correlation

7.

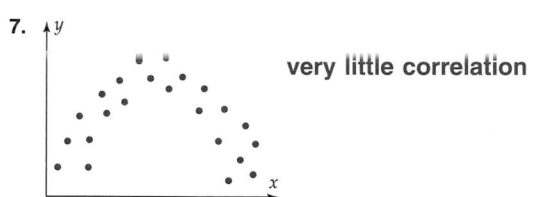

very little correlation

8. The U.S. gross domestic product (GDP) is the total value of all goods and services produced in the United States. The table shows the GDP in billions of 1996 dollars. Let $x = 0$ correspond to 1990. (Source: U.S. Bureau of Economic Analysis)
   a. Use a scatter plot to determine if the data appears to be linear.
   b. If so, is there a positive or negative correlation?

Year	GDP
1990	$6707.9
1992	$6880.0
1994	$7347.7
1996	$7813.2
1998	$8495.7
2000	$9318.5

In Exercises 9–13, construct a scatter plot for the data and answer these questions:
a. What are the finite differences for the data?
b. Do the finite differences confirm that the data is linear? If so, is there a positive or negative correlation?

9. The table shows the monthly premium (in dollars) for a term life insurance policy for a female nonsmoker. Let x represent age and y the amount of the premium.

Age	Premium
25	$11.57
30	$11.66
35	$11.83
40	$13.05
45	$16.18
50	$21.32
55	$29.58

10. The table shows the percent of persons in the United States below the U.S. poverty level in selected years. Let $x = 0$ correspond to 1960.

Exercises 1.5

ANSWERS

1. a. $y = \frac{3}{4}x + \frac{5}{4}$
   b. Sum of squares = 3
   Model B still has least error.

2. $r \approx 0.9694$

3. a. Slope = 1.0564054
   b. $y = 1.0564054x + 21.077892$
   c. Line described in **b** predicts a higher number of workers.

8. a.

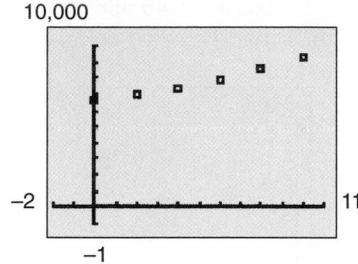

   b. The relationship appears to be linear and the correlation is positive.

9. a. 0.09, 0.17, 1.22, 3.13, 5.14, 8.26
   b. not linear;

10. a. −4.9, −4.7, −0.3, 0.7, 1.0, −0.5, 1.3, −0.3, −0.8, −0.4, −0.6, −0.9
   b. not linear;

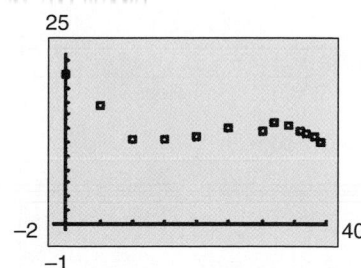

11. a. 4.6, 8.3, 14.3, 23.5, 37.2, 56.9, 84.3, 121.4, 170.7, 234.2

b. not linear

12. a. −234,560, −169,435, −56,116, −48,496

b. linear; negative correlation

13. a. 446.9, 405.2, 515.8, 785.3, 298, 413

b. linear; positive correlation

14. a.

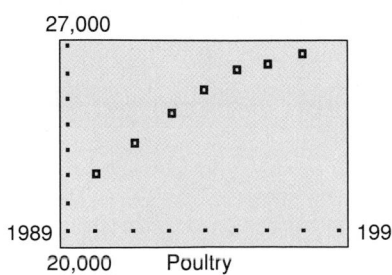

Year	Percent below poverty level
1960	22.2
1965	17.3
1970	12.6
1975	12.3
1980	13.0
1985	14.0
1990	13.5
1992	14.8
1994	14.5
1996	13.7
1997	13.3
1998	12.7
1999	11.8

11. The vapor pressure y of water depends on the temperature x, as given in the table.

Temperature (°C)	Pressure (mm Hg)
0	4.6
10	9.2
20	17.5
30	31.8
40	55.3
50	92.5
60	149.4
70	233.7
80	355.1
90	525.8
100	760.0

12. The table shows the U.S. Census Bureau's population data for St. Louis, Missouri in selected years. Let $x = 0$ correspond to 1950.

Year	Population
1950	856,796
1970	622,236
1980	452,801
1990	396,685
2000	348,189

13. The table shows the U.S. disposable income (personal income less personal taxes) in billions of dollars. (Source: Bureau of Economic Analysis, U.S. Dept. of Commerce). Let $x = 0$ correspond to 1990.

Year	Disposable personal income
1990	4166.8
1992	4613.7
1994	5018.9
1996	5534.7
1998	6320.0
1999	6618.0
2000	7031.0

14. The table gives the annual U.S. consumption of beef and poultry, in million of pounds. (Source: U.S. Dept. of Agriculture)

Year	Beef	Poultry
1990	24,031	22,151
1991	24,113	23,270
1992	24,261	24,394
1993	24,006	25,099
1994	25,125	25,754
1995	25,533	25,940
1996	25,875	26,614

b. $y_1 = 717.46x - 1{,}405{,}160$, poultry; $y_2 = 329.86x - 632{,}699$, beef

a. Make scatter plots for both beef and poultry consumption, using the actual years (1990, 1991, etc.) as x in each case.

b. Without graphing, use your knowledge of slopes to determine which of the following equations models beef consumption and which one models poultry consumption. Confirm your answer by graphing.

$$y_1 = 717.46x - 1,405,160$$
$$y_2 = 329.86x - 632,699$$

15. The table at the bottom of the page gives the median weekly earnings of full-time workers 25 years and older by their amount of education. (Source: U.S. Bureau of Labor Statistics)

a. Make four scatter plots, one for each educational group, using $x = 0$ to correspond to 1990.

b. Four linear models are given below. Match each model with the appropriate data set.

$$y_1 = 20.74x + 392 \qquad y_2 = 12.31x + 238$$
$$y_3 = 34.86x + 543 \qquad y_4 = 15.17x + 354$$

In Exercises 16–22, use the linear regression feature of your calculator to find the required model.

16. The table shows the number of deaths per 100,000 people from heart disease.

Year	1950	1960	1970	1980	1990	1999
Deaths	510.8	521.8	496.0	436.4	368.3	265.9

a. Find a linear model for this data, using $x = 0$ to correspond to 1950.

b. In the unlikely event that the linear model in part **a** remains valid far into the future, will there be a time when death from heart disease has been completely eliminated? If so, when would this occur?

17. The table shows the share of total U.S. household income earned by the poorest 20% of households and the share received by the wealthiest 5% of households. (Source: U.S. Census Bureau)

Year	Lowest 20%	Top 5%
1985	4	17.0
1990	3.9	18.6
1995	3.7	21.0
1996	3.7	21.4

a. Find a linear model for the income share of the poorest 20% of households.

b. Find a linear model for the income share of the wealthiest 5% of households.

c. What do the slopes of the two models suggest of each?

d. Assuming that these models remain accurate, will the income gap between the wealthy and the poor grow, stay about the same, or decline in the year 2000?

Median Weekly Earnings By Amount of Education

Year	No High School Diploma	High School Graduate	Some College	College Graduate
1996	$317	$443	$518	$758
1997	$321	$461	$535	$779
1998	$337	$479	$558	$821
1999	$346	$490	$580	$860
2000	$360	$506	$598	$896
2001	$378	$520	$621	$924

15. No High School Diploma
$y_2 = 12.31x + 238$

High School Graduate
$y_4 = 15.17x + 354$

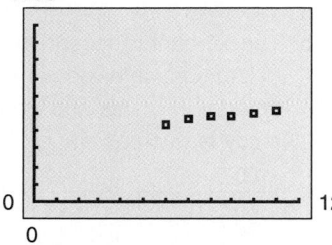

Some College
$y_1 = 20.74x + 392$

College Graduate
$y_3 = 34.86x + 543$

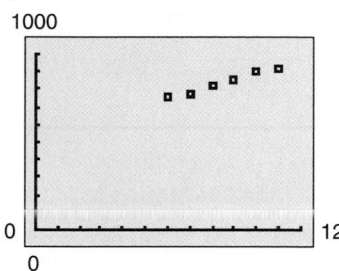

16. a. $y = -5.030298873x + 558.1190887$

b. Yes; 2060

17. a. $y = -0.0292x + 4.0149$
b. $y = 0.4078x + 16.8494$
c. The income of the rich is increasing faster than the income of the poor is decreasing.
d. The income gap will increase.

18. a. $y = 4x + 18$

b. The slope means that the percentage is increasing by 4 points each year. The y-intercept gives the percentage of loans in year 0, 1975.

c. 118%. Since over 100% doesn't make any sense in this context, we'd have to say 100%, as well as saying that the model is likely not valid out to the year 2000.

19. a. $y = -4x + 82$

b. The amount of federal money in loans is increasing and the amount in grants and work-study is decreasing.

■ Loan data
+ Grant/work-study data

c. 1983

20. a.

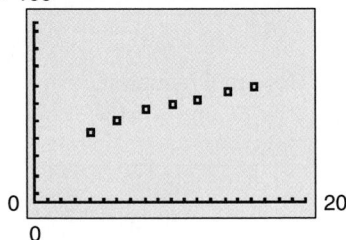

b. $y = 1.714285714x + 37.42857143$

c. 1993, $y \approx 60$; 2000, $y \approx 72$

21. a.

b. $y = -1.27x + 23.8318$

c. The model gives a negative median time for approval in 2009, and it will not be useful for data extrapolation.

---

18. The table shows what percent of federal aid is given in the form of loans to students at a particular college in selected years.

Year (in which school year begins)	Loans (%)
1975	18
1978	30
1984	54
1987	66
1990	78

a. Find a linear model for this data, with $x = 0$ corresponding to 1975.

b. Interpret the meaning of the slope and the y-intercept.

c. If the model remains accurate, what percentage of federal student aid were loans in 2000?

19. The table shows the percent of federal aid given in the form of grants or work-study programs to students at the college of Exercise 18.

Year (in which school year begins)	Grants and work-study (%)
1975	82
1978	70
1984	46
1987	34
1990	22

a. Find a linear model for this data, with $x = 0$ corresponding to 1975.

b. Graph the model from part **a** and the model from Exercise 18 on the same axes. What appears to be the trend in the federal share of financial aid to college students?

c. In what year is the percent of federal aid the same for loans as for grants and work-study?

20. The table gives the average number of takeout meals per person purchased at restaurants in selected years. (Source: NPD Group's Crest Service)

a. Make a scatter plot of the data, with $x = 0$ corresponding to 1980.

b. Find a linear model for the data.

c. According to the model, what was the average number of take-out meals purchased per person in 1993? in 2000?

Year	Average number of annual take-out meals per person
1984	43
1986	48
1988	53
1990	55
1992	57
1994	61
1996	65

21. The table shows the median time, in months, for the Food and Drug Administration to approve a new drug after the application has been made. (Source: U.S. Food and Drug Administration)

Year	Median time for approval
1990	24.3
1991	22.1
1992	22.6
1993	23.0
1994	17.5
1995	15.9
1996	14.3
1997	13.4
1998	12.0
1999	11.6
2000	15.6

a. Make a scatter plot of the data, with $x = 0$ corresponding to 1990.

b. Find a linear model for the data.

c. What are the limitations of this model? *Hint:* What does it say about approval time in the year 2009?

22. The ordered pairs below give production (x) and consumption (y) of primary energy in quadrillion BTUs for a sample of countries in 1995.

Australia (7.29, 4.43)   Mexico (8.15, 5.59)
Brazil (4.55, 6.76)   Poland (3.74, 3.75)
Canada (16.81, 11.72)   Russia (39.1, 26.75)
China (35.49, 35.67)   Saudi Arabia (20.34, 3.72)
France (4.92, 9.43)   South Africa (6.08, 5.51)
Germany (5.42, 13.71)   United States (69.1, 88.28)
India (8.33, 10.50)   United Kingdom (10.57,
Indonesia (6.65, 3.06)   9.85)
Iran (9.35, 3.90)   Venezuela (8.22, 2.53)
Japan (3.98, 21.42)

a. Make a scatter plot of the data.
b. Find a linear model for the data. Graph the model with the scatter plot.
c. In 1995, what three countries were the world's leading producers and consumers of energy?
d. As a general trend, what does it mean if a country's coordinates lie above the linear model?
e. As a general trend, what does it mean if a country's coordinates lie below the linear model?
f. Identify any countries whose coordinates appear to differ dramatically from most of the others.

23. The table shows the winning times, in minutes, for men's 1500-meter freestyle swimming at the Olympics in selected years.

Year	Time
1912	22.00
1924	20.11
1936	19.23
1948	19.31
1960	17.33
1972	15.88
1984	15.09
1996	14.94

a. Find a linear model for this data, with $x = 0$ corresponding to 1900.
b. Kieren Perkins of Australia set the Olympic record of 14.72 minutes in 1992. How accurately did your model estimate his time?
c. How long is this model likely to remain accurate? Why?
d. Find the correlation coefficient for the model.

e. Make a residual plot of the model. Is a linear model appropriate for the data?

24. The following table shows, for selected states, the percent of high school students in the class of 2001 who took the SAT and the average SAT math score.

State	Students who took SAT (%)	Average math score
Connecticut	82	510
Delaware	67	499
Georgia	63	489
Idaho	17	542
Indiana	60	501
Iowa	5	603
Montana	23	539
Nevada	33	515
New Jersey	81	513
New Mexico	13	542
North Dakota	4	599
Ohio	26	539
Pennsylvania	71	499
South Carolina	57	488
Washington	53	527

a. Make a scatter plot of the percent of students who took the SAT (x) versus the average SAT math score (y).
b. Find a linear model for the data.
c. What is the slope of your linear model? What does this mean in the context of the problem?
d. Below is the data on four additional states. How well does the model match the actual figures for these states?

State	Students taking SAT (%)	Average math score
Oklahoma	8	561
Arizona	34	525
Alaska	51	510
Hawaii	52	515

24. a.

b. $y = -1.058840x + 573.236019$

c. The slope is about -1.058840. This means that the average score decreases by about 1.06 points every time the percentage of students who takes the exam increases by 1.

d. Oklahoma: $y \approx 565$, pretty close to the actual value of 561; Arizona: $y \approx 537$ as compared to the actual value of 525; Alaska: $y \approx 519$, very close to the actual value of 510; Hawaii: $y \approx 518$, close to the actual value of 515

22. a.

b. $y = 1.089256088x - 1.413259148$

c. United States, Russia and China

d. A country for which consumption exceeds production, a net importer of energy.

e. A country for which production exceeds consumption, a net exporter of energy.

f. U.S., Japan, France; Russia, Saudi Arabia, and Iran

23. a. $y = -0.08586x + 22.62286$
b. ≈ 14.72 for 1992, a terrific prediction.
c. This model may not remain valid for any future dates. The rate of improvement seems to be slowing down.
d. $r \approx -0.9797$
e. The data appears to be linear because the residuals do not form a pattern.

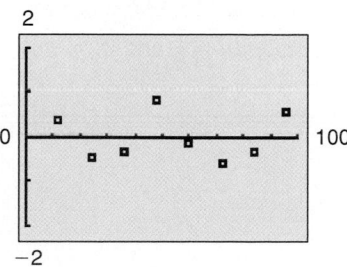

Teaching Notes

Remind students that for an *arithmetic sequence*, you *add a common difference d*.

Tell students that for a *geometric sequence*, you *multiply by a common ratio r*.

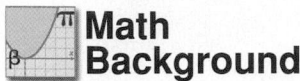

Math Background

For any three consecutive terms in a geometric sequence, the second term is the *geometric mean* of the first and third terms. (The geometric mean of two numbers a and b is $\sqrt{ab}$.)

In **Example 1a**, 9 is the geometric mean of 3 and 27: $\sqrt{3 \cdot 27} = \sqrt{81} = 9$.

In **Example 1b**, $\frac{5}{8}$ is the geometric mean of $\frac{5}{4}$ and $\frac{5}{16}$:

$$\sqrt{\frac{5}{4} \cdot \frac{5}{16}} = \sqrt{\frac{25}{64}} = \frac{5}{8}.$$

ADDITIONAL EXAMPLES

Example 1

Are the following sequences geometric? If so, what is the common ratio? Write each sequence as a recursive function.

a. $\{5, 10, 20, 40, \dots\}$ yes, it is a geometric sequence; common ratio: 2; $u_1 = 5$ and $u_n = 2u_{n-1}$ for $n \geq 2$

b. $\left\{\frac{7}{3}, \frac{7}{9}, \frac{7}{27}, \frac{7}{81}, \dots\right\}$ yes, it is a geometric sequence; common ratio: $\frac{1}{3}$; $u_1 = \frac{7}{3}$ and $u_n = \frac{1}{3}u_{n-1}$ for $n \geq 2$

1.6 Geometric Sequences

1.6 Geometric Sequences

Objectives

- Recognize a geometric sequence
- Find a common ratio
- Graph a geometric sequence
- Write a geometric sequence recursively and explicitly
- Find partial sums of a geometric sequence

Recall that in an arithmetic sequence, each term is obtained from the preceding term by adding a constant, d. A **geometric sequence**, which is sometimes called a *geometric progression*, is a sequence in which terms are found by multiplying a preceding term by a nonzero constant. Like an arithmetic sequence, where the difference between consecutive terms is the constant d, the quotient of consecutive terms in a geometric sequence is the constant r. The constant r is called the **common ratio** of the geometric sequence.

Example 1 Recognizing a Geometric Sequence

Are the following sequences geometric? If so, what is the common ratio? Write each sequence as a recursive function.

a. $\{3, 9, 27, 81, \dots\}$ **b.** $\left\{\frac{5}{2}, \frac{5}{4}, \frac{5}{8}, \frac{5}{16}, \dots\right\}$

Solution

a. The sequence $\{3, 9, 27, 81, \dots\}$ is geometric with a common ratio of 3.

$$\frac{u_2}{u_1} = \frac{9}{3} = 3 \qquad \frac{u_3}{u_2} = \frac{27}{9} = 3 \qquad \frac{u_4}{u_3} = \frac{81}{27} = 3$$

Because each term is obtained by multiplying the previous term by 3, the sequence may be denoted as a recursive function.

$$u_1 = 3 \text{ and } u_n = 3u_{n-1} \text{ for } n \geq 2$$

b. The sequence $\left\{\frac{5}{2}, \frac{5}{4}, \frac{5}{8}, \frac{5}{16}, \dots\right\}$ is geometric with a common ratio of $\frac{1}{2}$.

$$\frac{u_2}{u_1} = \frac{\frac{5}{4}}{\frac{5}{2}} = \frac{1}{2} \qquad \frac{u_3}{u_2} = \frac{\frac{5}{8}}{\frac{5}{4}} = \frac{1}{2} \qquad \frac{u_4}{u_3} = \frac{\frac{5}{16}}{\frac{5}{8}} = \frac{1}{2}$$

Each term is obtained by multiplying the previous term by $\frac{1}{2}$, which gives the following recursive function.

$$u_1 = \frac{5}{2} \text{ and } u_n = \frac{1}{2}u_{n-1} \text{ for } n \geq 2$$

If $\{u_n\}$ is a geometric sequence with common ratio r, then for each $n \geq 2$ the term preceding u_n is u_{n-1} and

$$\frac{u_n}{u_{n-1}} = r, \qquad \text{or equivalently,} \qquad u_n = ru_{n-1}.$$

Recursive Form of a Geometric Sequence

In a geometric sequence $\{u_n\}$,

$$u_n = r u_{n-1}$$

for some u_1 and some nonzero constant r and all $n \geq 2$.

Example 2   **Graph of a Geometric Sequence**

Find the common ratio of the geometric sequence with $u_1 = 2$ and $u_2 = 8$. List the first five terms of the sequence, write the sequence as a recursive function, and graph the function.

Solution

Because the sequence is geometric, the common ratio is $\dfrac{u_2}{u_1} = \dfrac{8}{2} = 4$.

Therefore, the sequence begins with $\{2, 8, 32, 128, 512, \dots\}$ and the recursive function is given below.

$$u_n = 4u_{n-1}, \text{ with } u_1 = 2$$

The graph of the function is shown in Figure 1.6-1.

Figure 1.6-1

Notice that the graph of the geometric sequence in Example 2 does not appear to be linear. If the points were connected, the graph would be an *exponential function*, which is discussed in Chapter 5.

Explicit Form of a Geometric Sequence

Geometric sequences can also be expressed in a form where the value of the sequence can be determined by the position of the term.

Example 3   **Writing a Geometric Sequence in Explicit Form**

Confirm that the sequence defined by $u_n = 2u_{n-1}$ with $u_1 = 7$ can also be expressed as $u_n = 7(2)^{n-1}$ by listing the first seven terms produced by each form.

Solution

Using the recursive function, the sequence is

$$u_1 = 7$$
$$u_2 = u_1 \cdot 2 = 7 \cdot 2 = 14$$
$$u_3 = u_2 \cdot 2 = (7 \cdot 2) \cdot 2 = 7(2)^2 = 28$$
$$u_4 = u_3 \cdot 2 = (7 \cdot 2^2) \cdot 2 = 7(2)^3 = 56$$
$$u_5 = u_4 \cdot 2 = (7 \cdot 2^3) \cdot 2 = 7(2)^4 = 112$$
$$u_6 = u_5 \cdot 2 = (7 \cdot 2^4) \cdot 2 = 7(2)^5 = 224$$
$$u_7 = u_6 \cdot 2 = (7 \cdot 2^5) \cdot 2 = 7(2)^6 = 448$$

Teaching Notes

Make sure that students know that in the **Explicit Form of a Geometric Sequence,** the common ratio r cannot be zero.

In **Example 4,** some students may get -5 for the common ratio by using $\dfrac{2}{-\frac{2}{5}}$. Remind students that to find the common ratio, divide any term by the preceding term.

Example Notes

In **Example 4,** point out how the signs can alternate in a geometric sequence. (Signs cannot alternate in an arithmetic sequence.)

In **Example 5,** an alternate way to find u_1 is to substitute -2 for r into the equation defining the ninth term:

$$u_1(-2)^8 = -640$$
$$u_1 = \frac{-640}{256} = -\frac{5}{2}$$

ADDITIONAL EXAMPLES

Example 4

Write the explicit form of a geometric sequence where the first two terms are 3 and $-\dfrac{3}{4}$, and find the first five terms of the sequence.

$$u_n = (3)\left(-\frac{1}{4}\right)^{n-1};$$

$$3, \ -\frac{3}{4}, \ \frac{3}{4^2}, \ -\frac{3}{4^3}, \ \frac{3}{4^4}, \ \dots$$

Example 5

The third and sixth terms of a geometric sequence are 80 and -5120. Find the explicit form of the sequence.

$$u_n = (5)(-4)^{n-1}$$

Figure 1.6-2a

Figure 1.6-2b

Explicit Form of a Geometric Sequence

Notice that u_3 is $7 \cdot 2^2$, which is the first term of the sequence multiplied by the common ratio twice, and that u_4 is $7 \cdot 2^3$, which is the first term of the sequence multiplied by the common ratio three times. u_n is the product of u_1 and the common ratio, r, raised to the $(n - 1)$ power. In general,

$$u_n = 7 \cdot 2^{n-1}.$$

The table in Figure 1.6-2b confirms the apparent equality of the two functions.

∎

The recursive formula for $n = 2, 3, 4, \dots$ implies that

$$u_2 = u_1 r$$
$$u_3 = u_2 r = (u_1 r)r = u_1 r^2$$
$$u_4 = u_3 r = (u_1 r^2)r = u_1 r^3$$
$$u_5 = u_4 r = (u_1 r^3)r = u_1 r^4$$

> If $\{u_n\}$ is a geometric sequence with common ratio r, then for all $n \geq 1$,
> $$u_n = u_1 r^{n-1}$$

Example 4   Explicit Form of a Geometric Sequence

Write the explicit form of a geometric sequence where the first two terms are 2 and $-\dfrac{2}{5}$, and find the first five terms of the sequence.

Solution

The common ratio is $r = \dfrac{-\frac{2}{5}}{2} = \dfrac{-2}{5} \cdot \dfrac{1}{2} = -\dfrac{1}{5}$.

Using the explicit form, the geometric sequence can be written as

$$u_n = u_1 r^{n-1} = (2)\left(-\frac{1}{5}\right)^{n-1}$$

The sequence begins $2, \ -\dfrac{2}{5}, \ \dfrac{2}{5^2}, \ -\dfrac{2}{5^3}, \ \dfrac{2}{5^4}, \dots$

∎

Example 5   Explicit Form of a Geometric Sequence

The fourth and ninth terms of a geometric sequence are 20 and -640. Find the explicit form of the sequence.

Solution

The fourth term can be written as $u_4 = u_1 r^{n-1}$, or $20 = u_1 r^3$.

The ninth term can be written as $u_9 = u_1 r^{n-1}$, or $-640 = u_1 r^8$.

The ratio of the ninth term to the fourth term can be used to find r.

$$\frac{u_1 r^8}{u_1 r^3} = \frac{-640}{20}$$
$$r^5 = -32$$
$$r = -2$$

Substitute -2 for r into the equation defining the fourth term.

$$u_1(-2)^3 = 20$$
$$u_1 = \frac{20}{-8} = -\frac{5}{2}$$

Thus, $u_n = u_1 \cdot r^{n-1} = -\frac{5}{2}(-2)^{n-1}$.

∎

Partial Sums

If the common ratio r of a geometric sequence is the number 1, then

$$u_n = 1^{n-1} u_1 \qquad \text{for every } n \geq 1.$$

Therefore, the sequence is just the constant sequence $u_1, u_2, u_3, \ldots$. For any positive integer k, the kth partial sum of this constant sequence is

$$\underbrace{u_1 + u_1 + \cdots + u_1}_{k \text{ terms}} = k u_1$$

In other words, the kth partial sum of a constant sequence is just k times the constant. If a geometric sequence is not constant (that is, $r \neq 1$), then its partial sums are given by the following formula.

Partial Sums of a Geometric Sequence

> The kth partial sum of the geometric sequence $\{u_n\}$ with common ratio $r \neq 1$ is
>
> $$\sum_{n=1}^{k} u_n = u_1\left(\frac{1-r^k}{1-r}\right)$$

Proof

If S denotes the kth partial sum, then using the formula for the nth term of a geometric sequence derives the expression for S.

$$S = u_1 + u_2 + \ldots + u_k = u_1 + u_1 r + u_1 r^2 + \ldots + u_1 r^{k-1}$$

Use this equation to compute $S - rS$, as shown on the next page.

Teaching Notes

Point out to students that the expression $u_1\left(\dfrac{1-r^k}{1-r}\right)$ given in the box for **Partial Sums of a Geometric Sequence** applies only when $r \neq 1$. When $r = 1$, the terms of the sequence are $u_1, u_1, u_1, \ldots$, so the expression for the kth partial sum is:

$$\underbrace{u_1 + u_1 + \ldots + u_1}_{k \text{ terms}} = k u_1.$$

In the proof, direct students' attention to the two lines at the top of page 62:

$$S = u_1 + u_1 r + u_1 r^2 + \ldots + u_1 r^{k-1}$$
$$rS = u_1 r + u_1 r^2 + \ldots + u_1 r^{k-1} + u_1 r^k$$

Emphasize that the right side of the second equation is obtained by multiplying *every term* on the right side of the first equation by r. Point out that all the terms in the second equation have been shifted one place to the right so that like terms are aligned.

Math Background

In the proof of the formula

$$\sum_{n=1}^{k} u_n = u_1\left(\frac{1-r^k}{1-r}\right),$$ the kth partial sum is denoted by S. Recall that in the proof of the formula for partial sums of an arithmetic sequence (page 27), the kth partial sum was denoted by S_k. Both notations are acceptable because they are clearly defined in each context.

Example Notes

In **Example 6,**

- To help students see that $r = -\frac{1}{2}$, write $\left(-\frac{3}{2}\right)\left(?\right) = \frac{3}{4}$.

- You may want to show students how the first step comes from the formula on page 61:

$$\sum_{n=1}^{k} u_n = u_1\left(\frac{1 - r^k}{1 - r}\right) \text{ (from box on}$$

page 61)

$$\sum_{n=1}^{9} \frac{-3}{2}\left(\frac{-1}{2}\right)^{n-1} = u_1\left(\frac{1 - r^9}{1 - r}\right)$$

- Caution students that

$$1 - \left(\frac{-1}{2}\right)^9 = 1 + \left(\frac{1}{2}\right)^9 \text{ only because}$$

9 is odd.

- Suggest that students use a calculator to find $-1 - \frac{1}{2^9}$ as an approximate decimal. Then use the calculator to express the decimal as a fraction.

```
-1-1/2^9
        -1.001953125
Ans▶Frac
            -513/512
```

$$S = u_1 + u_1r + u_1r^2 + \ldots + u_1r^{k-1}$$
$$rS = \qquad u_1r + u_1r^2 + \ldots + u_1r^{k-1} + u_1r^k$$
$$S - rS = u_1 \qquad\qquad\qquad\qquad\qquad - u_1r^k$$
$$(1 - r)S = u_1(1 - r^k)$$

Because $r \neq 1$, both sides of the last equation can be divided by $1 - r$ to complete the proof.

$$S = \frac{u_1(1 - r^k)}{1 - r} = u_1\left(\frac{1 - r^k}{1 - r}\right) \qquad \blacksquare$$

Example 6   **Partial Sum**

Find the sum

$$-\frac{3}{2} + \frac{3}{4} - \frac{3}{8} + \frac{3}{16} - \frac{3}{32} + \frac{3}{64} - \frac{3}{128} + \frac{3}{256} - \frac{3}{512}.$$

Solution

This is the ninth partial sum of the geometric sequence $\left\{\frac{-3}{2}\left(\frac{-1}{2}\right)^{n-1}\right\}$, where the common ratio is $r = -\frac{1}{2}$. The formula in the box shows that

$$\sum_{n=1}^{9} \frac{-3}{2}\left(\frac{-1}{2}\right)^{n-1} = u_1\left(\frac{1 - r^9}{1 - r}\right) = \left(\frac{-3}{2}\right)\left[\frac{1 - \left(\frac{-1}{2}\right)^9}{1 - \left(\frac{-1}{2}\right)}\right] = \left(\frac{-3}{2}\right)\left(\frac{1 + \left(\frac{1}{2}\right)^9}{\frac{3}{2}}\right)$$

$$= \left(\frac{-3}{2}\right)\left(\frac{2}{3}\right)\left(1 + \frac{1}{2^9}\right) = -1 - \frac{1}{2^9} = -1 - \frac{1}{512} = -\frac{513}{512} \qquad \blacksquare$$

Example 7 calculates the distance traveled by the ball discussed in Section 1.2 Example 4 when it hits the ground for the seventh time by using a partial sum of a geometric sequence.

Example 7   **Application of Partial Sum**

A ball is dropped from a height of 9 feet. It hits the ground and bounces to a height of 6 feet. It continues to bounce up and down. On each bounce it rises to $\frac{2}{3}$ of the height of the previous bounce. How far has the ball traveled (both up and down) when it hits the ground for the seventh time?

Solution

First consider how far the ball travels on each bounce. On the first bounce, it rises 6 feet and falls 6 feets for a total of 12 feet. On the second bounce it rises and falls $\frac{2}{3}$ of the previous height, i.e., it travels $\frac{2}{3}$ of 12 feet. The distance traveled is a geometric sequence with $u_1 = 12$ and $r = \frac{2}{3}$. If u_n denotes the distance traveled on the nth bounce, then

$$u_n = 12\left(\frac{2}{3}\right)^{n-1}$$

So $\{u_n\}$ is a geometric sequence with common ratio $r = \left(\frac{2}{3}\right)$. When the ball hits the ground for the seventh time, it has completed six bounces. Therefore, the total distance it has traveled is the distance it was originally dropped, 9 feet, plus the distance traveled in six bounces.

$$9 + u_1 + u_2 + u_3 + u_4 + u_5 + u_6 = 9 + \sum_{n=1}^{6} u_n$$

$$= 9 + u_1\left(\frac{1 - r^6}{1 - r}\right)$$

$$= 9 + 12\left(\frac{1 - \left(\frac{2}{3}\right)^6}{1 - \frac{2}{3}}\right) \approx 41.84 \text{ feet}$$

Exercises 1.6

In Exercises 1–8, determine whether the sequence is arithmetic, geometric, or neither.

1. $2, 7, 12, 17, 22, \ldots$
Arithmetic

2. $2, 6, 18, 54, 162, \ldots$
Geometric

3. $13, \frac{13}{2}, \frac{13}{4}, \frac{13}{8}, \ldots$
Geometric

4. $-1, -\frac{1}{2}, 0, \frac{1}{2}, \ldots$
Arithmetic

5. $50, 48, 46, 44, \ldots$
Arithmetic

6. $2, -3, \frac{9}{2}, -\frac{27}{4}, -\frac{81}{8}, \ldots$
Neither arithmetic nor geometric

7. $3, \frac{3}{2}, \frac{3}{4}, \frac{3}{8}, \frac{3}{16}, \cdots$
Geometric

8. $-6, -3.7, -1.4, 9, 3.2, \ldots$
Arithmetic

In Exercises 9–14, the first term, u_1, and the common ratio, r, of a geometric sequence are given. Find the sixth term and the recursive and explicit formulas for the nth term.

9. $u_1 = 5, r = 2$
$u_6 = 160$; $u_n = 2^{n-1} \cdot 5$

10. $u_1 = 1, r = -2$
$u_6 = -32$; $u_n = (-2)^{n-1}$

11. $u_1 = 4, r = \frac{1}{4}$
$u_6 = \frac{1}{256}$; $u_n = \frac{1}{4^{n-2}}$

12. $u_1 = -6, r = \frac{2}{3}$
$u_6 = -\frac{64}{81}$; $u_n = -\frac{2^n}{3^{n-2}}$

13. $u_1 = 10, r = -\frac{1}{2}$

14. $u_1 = \pi, r = \frac{1}{5}$

In Exercises 15–18, find the kth partial sum of the geometric sequence $\{u_n\}$ with common ratio r.

15. $k = 6, u_1 = 5, r = \frac{1}{2}$
$\frac{315}{32}$

16. $k = 8, u_1 = 9, r = \frac{1}{3}$
$\frac{3280}{243}$

19. $\frac{u_n}{u_{n-1}} = \frac{\left(-\frac{1}{2}\right)^n}{\left(-\frac{1}{2}\right)^{n-1}} = -\frac{1}{2}$; geometric

with $r = -\frac{1}{2}$

20. $\frac{u_{n+1}}{u_n} = \frac{2^{3(n+1)}}{2^{3n}} = 8$; geometric
with $r = 8$

21. $\frac{u_n}{u_{n-1}} = \frac{5^{n+2}}{5^{(n-1)+2}} = 5$; geometric
with $r = 5$

22. $\frac{u_{n+1}}{u_n} = \frac{3^{(n+1)/2}}{3^{n/2}} = \sqrt{3}$; geometric
with $r = \sqrt{3}$

23. $u_5 = 1$; $u_n = \frac{(-1)^{n-1}64}{4^{n-2}} = \frac{(-1)^{n-1}}{4^{n-5}}$

24. $u_5 = \frac{1}{486}$; $u_n = \frac{1}{6}\left(-\frac{1}{3}\right)^{n-1}$

$= \frac{(-1)^{n-1}}{2 \cdot 3^n}$

25. $u_5 = \frac{1}{16}$; $u_n = \frac{1}{4^{n-3}}$

27. $u_5 = -\frac{8}{25}$; $u_n = -\frac{2^{n-2}}{5^{n-3}}$

35. a. Since for all n, the ratio r is

$\frac{u_{n+1}}{u_n} = \frac{1.71(1.191^{n+1})}{1.71(1.191^n)}$

$= \frac{1.71(1.191^n)(1.191)}{1.71(1.191^n)}$

$= 1.191$,

the sequence is geometric.

b. $217.47

36. a. $\frac{b_{n+1}}{b_n} = 1.1999$; geometric with
$r = 1.1999$

b. approximately 3.05

43. $u_n = u_1 r^{n-1}$;
$\log u_n = \log (u_1 r^{n-1})$
$= \log u_1 + \log (r^{n-1})$
$= \log u_1 + (n-1) \log r$

44. $u_n = c + dn$, $\frac{C^{u_{n+1}}}{C^{u_n}} = C^d$

45. The sequence is $\{2^{n-1}\}$ and $r = 2$.
So for any k, the kth term is 2^{k-1},
and the sum of the preceding terms
is the $(k-1)$th partial sum of the
sequence,

$\sum_{n=1}^{k-1} 2^{n-1} = \frac{1 - 2^{k-1}}{1 - 2} = 2^{k-1} - 1$

---

17. $k = 7, u_2 = 6, r = 2$ **18.** $k = 9, u_2 = 6, r = \frac{1}{4}$
381   **approximately 31.99988**

In Exercises 19–22, show that the given sequence is geometric and find the common ratio.

19. $\left\{\left(-\frac{1}{2}\right)^n\right\}$ **20.** $\{2^{3n}\}$

21. $\{5^{n+2}\}$ **22.** $\{3^{\frac{n}{2}}\}$

In Exercises 23–28, use the given information about the geometric sequence $\{u_n\}$ to find u_5 and recursive and explicit formulas for u_n.

23. $u_1 = 256, u_2 = -64$ **24.** $u_1 = \frac{1}{6}, u_2 = -\frac{1}{18}$

25. $u_2 = 4, u_5 = \frac{1}{16}$ **26.** $u_3 = 4, u_6 = -32$
                                      $u_5 = 16$; $u_n = (-2)^{n-1}$

27. $u_4 = -\frac{4}{5}, r = \frac{2}{5}$ **28.** $u_2 = 6, u_7 = 192$
                                      $u_5 = 48$; $u_n = 3(2)^{n-1}$

In Exercises 29–34, find the sum.

29. $\sum_{n=1}^{7} 2^n$ **254**   **30.** $\sum_{k=1}^{6} 3\left(\frac{1}{2}\right)^k$ $\frac{189}{64}$

31. $\sum_{n=1}^{9} \left(-\frac{1}{3}\right)^n$ $-\frac{4921}{19,683}$ **32.** $\sum_{n=1}^{5} 5 \cdot 3^{n-1}$ **605**

33. $\sum_{j=1}^{6} 4\left(\frac{3}{2}\right)^{j-1}$ $\frac{665}{8}$ **34.** $\sum_{t=1}^{8} 6(0.9)^{t-1}$ ≈ 34.17197

35. For 1987–1998, the annual revenue per share in year n of a company's stock are approximated by $u_n = 1.71(1.191)^n$, where $n = 7$ represents 1987.
  a. Show that the sequence $\{u_n\}$ is a geometric sequence.
  b. Approximate the total revenues per share for the period 1987–1998.

36. The annual dividends per share of a company's stock from 1989 through 1998 are approximated by the sequence $\{b_n\}$, where $n = 9$ corresponds to 1989 and $b_n = 0.0228(1.1999)^n$.
  a. Show that the sequence $\{b_n\}$ is a geometric sequence.
  b. Approximate the total dividends per share for the period 1989–1998.

37. A ball is dropped from a height of 8 feet. On each bounce it rises to half its previous height. When the ball hits the ground for the seventh time, how far has it traveled? **23.75 ft**

38. A ball is dropped from a height of 10 feet. On each bounce it rises to 45% of its previous height. When it hits the ground for the tenth time, how far has it traveled? **26.35 ft**

39. If you are paid a salary of 1¢ on the first day of March, 2¢ on the second day, and your salary continues to double each day, how much will you earn in the month of March? **$21,474,836.47**

40. Starting with your parents, how many ancestors do you have for the preceding ten generations?
2046 ancestors

41. A car that sold for $8000 depreciates in value 25% each year. What is it worth after five years?
$1898.44

42. A vacuum pump removes 60% of the air in a container at each stroke. What percentage of the original amount of air remains after six strokes?
$u_6 \approx 0.41\%$

43. *Critical Thinking* Suppose $\{u_n\}$ is a geometric sequence with common ratio $r > 0$ and each $u_n > 0$. Show that the sequence $\{\log u_n\}$ is an arithmetic sequence with common difference $\log r$.

44. *Critical Thinking* Suppose $\{u_n\}$ is an arithmetic sequence with common difference d. Let C be any positive number. Show that the sequence $\{C^{u_n}\}$ is a geometric sequence with common ratio C^d.

45. *Critical Thinking* In the geometric sequence $1, 2, 4, 8, 16, \dots$ show that each term is 1 plus the sum of all preceding terms.

46. *Critical Thinking* In the geometric sequence $2, 6, 18, 54, \dots$ show that each term is twice the sum of 1 and all preceding terms.

47. *Critical Thinking* The minimum monthly payment for a certain bank credit card is the larger of $5 or $\frac{1}{25}$ of the outstanding balance. If the balance is less than $5, then the entire balance is due. If you make only the minimum payment each month, how long will it take to pay off a balance of $200 (excluding any interest that might accrue)?
37 payments

---

46. $u_n = 2(3)^{n-1}$;

$1 + \sum_{n=1}^{k} u_n = 1 + 2\left(\frac{1 - 3^k}{1 - 3}\right)$

$= 1 + 2\left(\frac{3^k - 1}{2}\right)$

$= 1 + 3^k - 1$

$= 3^k = \frac{u_{k+1}}{2}$

CHAPTER

1

REVIEW

Important Concepts

65

Important Facts and Formulas

A **sequence** is an ordered list of numbers.

A sequence is defined **recursively** if the first term is given and there is a method of determining the nth term by using the terms that precede it.

A sequence is defined **explicitly** if terms are determined by their position.

An **arithmetic sequence** is a sequence in which the difference between each term and the preceding term is a constant d.

Facts about an arithmetic sequence $\{u_n\}$ with common difference d:

- the recursive form of the sequence is
  $u_n = u_{n-1} + d$ for $n \geq 2$.
- the explicit form of the sequence is $u_n = u_1 + (n-1)d$.
- the kth partial sum is $\displaystyle\sum_{n=1}^{k} u_n = \frac{k}{2}(u_1 + u_k)$

The **slope** of a line that passes through (x_1, y_1) and (x_2, y_2) is given by

$$m = \frac{\Delta y}{\Delta x} = \frac{y_2 - y_1}{x_2 - x_1}.$$

The **slope-intercept form** of the equation of a line is $y = mx + b$, where m is the slope and b is the y-intercept.

The **point-slope form** of the equation of a line is $y - y_1 = m(x - x_1)$, where m is the slope and (x_1, y_1) is a given point on the line.

The **standard form** of the equation of a line is $Ax + By = C$, where A, B, and C are integers.

The equation of a **vertical line** has the form $x = h$.

The equation of a **horizontal line** has the form $y = k$.

Parallel lines have equal slopes.

The product of the slopes of **perpendicular lines** is -1.

The difference between an actual data value and a predicted data value is called a **residual.**

The **correlation coefficient** always has the same sign as the slope of the least squares regression line.

A **geometric sequence** is a sequence in which terms are found by multiplying a preceding term by a nonzero constant r.

Facts about the geometric sequence $\{u_n\}$ with common ratio $r \neq 0$:

- the recursive form is $u_n = ru_{n-1}$ for $n \geq 2$.
- the explicit form is $u_n = r^{n-1}u_1$ or $u_n = u_1 r^{n-1}$
- if $r \neq 1$, the kth partial sum is $\displaystyle\sum_{n=1}^{k} u_n = u_1\left(\frac{1 - r^k}{1 - r}\right)$

Review Exercises

In Exercises 1–10, identify the smallest subset of the real numbers—natural numbers, whole numbers, integers, rational numbers, or irrational numbers—that contains the given number.

Section 1.1

1. $\sqrt{3}$ **2.** 0.255 **3.** e **4.** 11 **5.** 0

6. -3 **7.** $\sqrt{121}$ **8.** $\dfrac{4}{9}$ **9.** 5 **10.** $0.2\overline{55}$

11. List two real numbers that are *not* rational numbers.

In Exercises 12–15, which sets of points represent a function? Why?

12. $\{(2, 3), (3, 4), (4, 5), (5, 6), (6, 7)\}$
This is a function; for each input there is exactly one output.
13. $\{(2, -3), (2, 4), (2, -5), (2, 6), (2, -7)\}$
This is not a function; the input 2 has more than one output.
14. $\{(2, 3), (3, 3), (4, 3), (5, 3), (6, 3)\}$
This is a function; for each input there is exactly one output.
15. $\{(-2, 3), (3, 4), (-4, 5), (5, 6), (-6, 7)\}$
This is a function; for each input there is exactly one output.
16. Let f be the function given by the rule $f(x) = 7 - 2x$. Complete the following table.

x	0	1	2	-4	t
$f(x)$	**7**	**5**	**3**	**15**	**$7 - 2t$**

17. What is the domain of the function g given by $g(t) = \dfrac{\sqrt{t-2}}{t-3}$?
all real numbers greater than or equal to 2 and not equal to 3
18. If $f(x) = |3 - x|\sqrt{x - 3} + 7$, then $f(7) - f(4) = $ **7** .

19. What is the domain of the function given by $g(r) = \sqrt{r - 4} + \sqrt{r} - 2$?
$r \geq 4$
20. What is the domain of the function $f(x) = \sqrt{-x + 2}$? **$x \leq 2$**

21. The radius of an oil spill (in meters) is 50 times the square root of the time t (in hours).
a. Write the rule of a function f that gives the radius of the spill at time t.
b. Write the rule of a function g that gives the area of the spill at time t.
c. What are the radius and area of the spill after 9 hours?
d. When will the spill have an area of 100,000 square meters?

22. The function whose graph is shown below gives the amount of money (in millions of dollars) spent on tickets for major concerts in selected years. (*Source:* Pollstar)

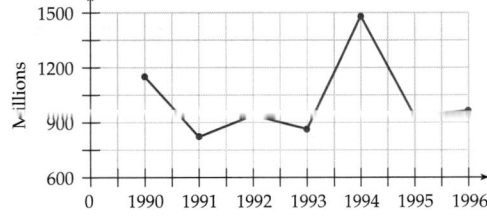

ANSWERS

1. $\sqrt{3}$ is an irrational number.

2. 0.255 is a rational number.

3. $e \approx 2.718$ is an irrational number.

4. 11 is a natural number.

5. 0 is a whole number.

6. -3 is an integer.

7. $\sqrt{121}$ is a natural number.

8. $\dfrac{4}{9}$ is a rational number.

9. 5 is a natural number.

10. $0.2\overline{55}$ is a rational number.

11. Answers may vary; for example, π and $\sqrt{2}$ are real numbers that are not rational.

21. a. $f(t) = 50\sqrt{t}$

b. $g(t) = 2500\pi t$

c. radius: 150 meters; area: 70,685.83 square meters

d. 12.73 hr

a. What is the domain of the function? **1990, 1991, 1992, 1993, 1994, 1995, 1996**

b. What is the approximate range of the function? **about 825 to about 1500**

c. Over what one-year interval is the rate of change the largest? **from 1993 to 1994**

Use the graph of the function f in the figure below to answer Exercises 23–26.

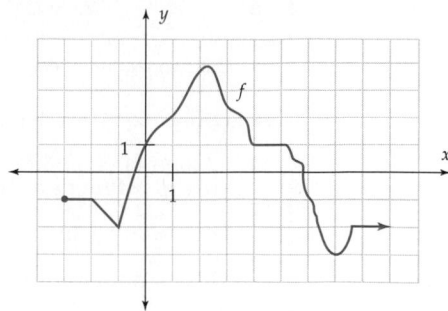

23. What is the domain of f? **$x \geq -3$**

24. What is the range of f? **$-3 \leq x \leq 4$**

25. Find all numbers x such that $f(x) = 1$. **$x = 0$ and $4 \leq x \leq 5$**

26. Find a number x such that $f(x + 1) < f(x)$. (Many correct answers are possible.) **Answers may vary. Possible answer: $x = 3$**

Use the graph of the function f in the figure to answer Exercises 27–33.

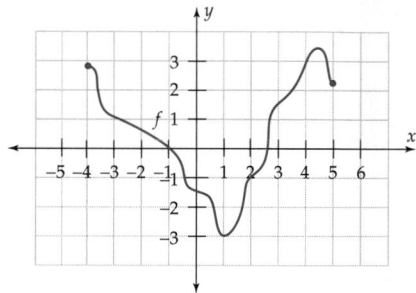

27. What is the domain of f? **$-4 \leq x \leq 5$**

28. $f(-3) = \underline{\text{ 1 }}$ 29. $f(2 + 2) = \underline{\text{ 3 }}$ 30. $f(-1) + f(1) = \underline{\text{ }-3}$

31. True or false: $2f(2) = f(4)$. **false**

32. True or false: $3f(2) = -f(4)$. **true**

33. True or false: $f(x) = 3$ for exactly one number x. **false**

Section 1.2

34. The population of Gallatin is growing at the rate of 2.75% per year. The present population is 20,000. Find a recursive sequence that represents **$u_1 = 20{,}000$ and $u_n = 1.0275u_{n-1}$ for $n \geq 2$; $u_n = (1.0275)^{n-1}(20{,}000)$;**

Gallatin's population each year. Represent the *n*th term of the sequence both explicitly and recursively. Find the first seven terms of the sequence. **20,000; 20,550; 21,115; 21,696; 22,292; 22,905; 23,535**

35. Roberta had $1525 in a savings account 2 years ago. What will be the value of her account 1 year from now, assuming that no deposits or withdrawals are made and the account earns 6.9% interest compounded annually? Find the solution using both a recursive and an explicit formula. **$1862.96**

36. Suppose that $3,000 is invested at 6.5% annual interest, compounded monthly.
   a. What is the balance after 6 years? **$4426.28**
   b. Suppose $150 is added to the account every month. What is the balance after 6 years? **$17,591.96**

37. The "biological" specimen *Geomeuricus sequencius* is 5 centimeters long when born. On the second day it grows 3 centimeters. The third day it grows 1.8 centimeters, and on each following day it grows 60% of the previous day's growth. What is its length after two weeks? What is the maximum length that it could grow? **12.49 cm; 12.5 cm**

In Exercises 38–39, let

$$u_n = \frac{\left(1 + \sqrt{5}\right)^n - \left(1 - \sqrt{5}\right)^n}{2^n\sqrt{5}}$$

38. a. Show that $u_1 = 1$ and $u_2 = 1$.
   b. Show that the first ten terms of $\{u_n\}$ are Fibonacci numbers. (See Exercises 30–32 Section 1.2)

39. a. For the ninth term, compute the ratio   **≈1.618**

$$\frac{u_n}{u_{n-1}}$$

   b. As *n* gets large, what number does the ratio approach? This number is also referred to as the "golden ratio." This ratio is believed to have been used in the construction of the Great Pyramid in Egypt, where the ratio equals the sum of the areas of the four face triangles divided by the total surface area. **1.618033989 . . .**

40. For the sequence $u_n = 3u_{n-1} + 1$ with $u_1 = 1.5$, write the first four terms. **1.5, 5.5, 17.5, 53.5**

41. For the sequence $u_n = 3u_{n-1} + 2$ with $u_1 = -4$, write the first five terms. **−4, −10, −28, −82, −244**

42. For the sequence $u_n = 3u_{n-1}$ with $u_1 = \frac{1}{9}$, write the first four terms. $\frac{1}{9}, \frac{1}{3}, 1, 3$

Section 1.3

In Exercises 43–46, find a formula for u_n; assume that the sequence is arithmetic.

43. $u_1 = 3$ and the common difference is –6. $u_n = 9 - 6n$

44. $u_2 = 4$ and the common difference is 3. $u_n = -2 + 3n$

45. $u_1 = -5$ and $u_6 = 7$.   **46.** $u_4 = 2$ and $u_9 = -1$.
   $u_n = 6n - 11$ $u_n = \frac{17}{4} - \frac{3}{4}n$

38. a.

$$u_1 = \frac{\left(1 + \sqrt{5}\right)^1 - \left(1 - \sqrt{5}\right)^1}{2^1\sqrt{5}}$$

$$= \frac{2\sqrt{5}}{2\sqrt{5}} = 1$$

$$u_2 = \frac{\left(1 + \sqrt{5}\right)^2 - \left(1 - \sqrt{5}\right)^2}{2^2\sqrt{5}}$$

$$= \frac{1 + 2\sqrt{5} + 5 - (1 - 2\sqrt{5} + 5)}{4\sqrt{5}}$$

$$= \frac{4\sqrt{5}}{4\sqrt{5}} = 1$$

b.

{1, 1, 2, 3, 5, 8, 13, 21, 34, 55}

49.

50.

56.

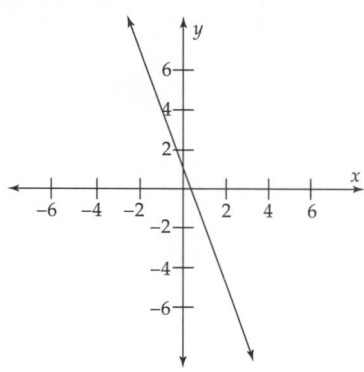

47. Find the 12th partial sum of the arithmetic sequence with $u_1 = -3$ and $u_{12} = 16$. **78**

48. Find numbers b, c, and d such that 8, b, c, d, 23 are the first five terms of an arithmetic sequence. **$b = 11.75$, $c = 15.50$, $d = 19.25$**

Section **1.4**

49. The national unemployment rates for 1990–1996 were as follows. (Source: U.S. Department of Labor, Bureau of Labor Statistics)

Year	1990	1991	1992	1993	1994	1995	1996
Rate (%)	5.6	6.8	7.5	6.9	6.1	5.6	5.4

Sketch a scatter plot and a line graph for the data, letting $x = 0$ correspond to 1990.

50. The table shows the average speed (mph) of the winning car in the Indianapolis 500 race in selected years.

Year	1980	1982	1984	1986	1988	1990	1992	1994	1996
Speed (mph)	143	162	164	171	145	186	134	161	148

Sketch a scatter plot and a line graph for these data, letting $x = 0$ correspond to 1980.

51. a. What is the y-intercept of the graph of the line defined by $y = x - \dfrac{x-2}{5} + \dfrac{3}{5}$? **1**
   b. What is the slope of the line? $\dfrac{4}{5}$

52. Find the equation of the line passing through (1, 3) and (2, 5). **$y = 2x + 1$**

53. Find the equation of the line passing through (2, −1) with slope 3. **$y = 3x - 7$**

54. Find the equation of the line that crosses the y-axis at $y = 1$ and is perpendicular to the line $2y - x = 5$. **$y = -2x + 1$**

55. a. Find the y-intercept of the line defined by $2x + 3y - 4 = 0$. $\left(0, \dfrac{4}{3}\right)$
   b. Find the equation of the line through (1, 3) that has the same y-intercept as the line in part **a.** $y = \dfrac{5}{3}x + \dfrac{4}{3}$

56. Sketch the graph of the line defined by $3x + y - 1 = 0$.

57. Find the equation of the line through (−4, 5) that is parallel to the line through (1, 3) and (−4, 2). $y = \dfrac{1}{5}x + \dfrac{29}{5}$

58. As a balloon is launched from the ground, the wind blows it due east. The conditions are such that the balloon is ascending along a straight line with slope $\dfrac{1}{5}$. After 1 hour the balloon is 5000 ft directly above the ground. How far east has the balloon blown? **25,000 feet**

59. The point (u, v) lies on the line $y = 5x - 10$. What is the slope of the line passing through (u, v) and the point $(0, -10)$? **$m = 5$**

In Exercises 60–66, determine whether the statement is true or false.

60. The graph of $x = 5y + 6$ has y-intercept 6.   **false**

61. The graph of $2y - 8 = 3x$ has y-intercept 4.   **true**

62. The lines $3x + 4y = 12$ and $4x + 3y = 12$ are perpendicular.   **false**

63. Slope is not defined for horizontal lines.   **false**

64. The line in the figure at right has positive slope.   **false**

65. The line in the figure does not pass through Quadrant III.   **true**

66. The y-intercept of the line in the figure is negative.   **false**

67. Which of the following lines rises most steeply from left to right?   **(d)**
   a. $y = -4x - 10$ **b.** $y = 3x + 4$
   c. $20x + 2y - 20 = 0$ **d.** $4x = y - 1$
   e. $4x = 1 - y$

68. Which of the following lines is not perpendicular to the line $y = x + 5$?   **(e)**
   a. $y = 4 - x$ **b.** $y + x = -5$
   c. $4 - 2x - 2y = 0$ **d.** $x = 1 - y$
   e. $y - x = \dfrac{1}{5}$

69. Which of the following lines does not pass through Quadrant III?   **(e)**
   a. $y = x$ **b.** $y = 4x - 7$
   c. $y = -2x - 5$ **d.** $y = 4x + 7$
   e. $y = -2x + 5$

70. Let a and b be fixed real numbers. Where do the lines $x = a$ and $y = b$ **(b)**
   intersect?
   a. Only at (b, a).   **b.** Only at (a, b).
   c. These lines are parallel, so they don't intersect.
   d. If $a = b$, then these are the same line, so they have infinitely many
      points of intersection.
   e. Since these equations are not of the form $y = mx + b$, the graphs are not
      lines.

71. What is the y-intercept of the line $2x - 3y + 5 = 0$? $\dfrac{5}{3}$

72. For what values of k will the graphs of $2y + x + 3 = 0$ and
   $3y + kx + 2 = 0$ be perpendicular lines?   **−6**

73. The average life expectancy increased linearly from 62.9 years for a person
   born in 1940 to 75.4 years for a person born in 1990.   **$y = 0.25x + 62.9$**
   a. Find an equation that gives the average life expectancy y of a person
      born in year x, with $x = 0$ corresponding to 1940.
   b. Use the equation in part **a** to estimate the average life expectancy of a
      person born in 1980.   **$x = 40$, $y = 72.9$ yr**

74. The population of San Diego grew in an approximately linear fashion from
   334,413 in 1950 to 1,151,977 in 1994.

79. a.

100

20   70

0

b. Nonlinear

c. $20.10 - 19.58 = 0.52$

$20.79 - 20.10 = 0.69$

$25.23 - 20.79 = 4.44$

$34.89 - 25.23 = 9.66$

$48.55 - 34.89 = 13.66$

$69.17 - 48.55 = 20.62$

$98.92 - 69.17 = 29.75$

The finite differences show that the data is not linear.

a. Find an equation that gives the population y of San Diego in year x, with $x = 0$ corresponding to 1950. **$y = 18{,}581x + 334{,}413$**

b. Use the equation in part **a** to estimate the population of San Diego in 1975 and 2000. **1975: 798,938; 2000: 1,263,463**

In Exercises 75–78, match the given information with the graph, and determine the slope of each line.

a.

b.

c.

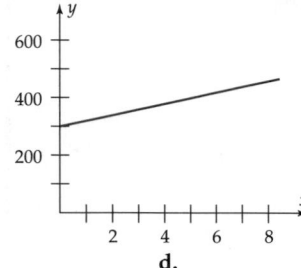

d.

75. A salesman is paid $300 per week plus $75 for each unit sold.
  c; $m = 75$

76. A person is paying $25 per week to repay a $300 loan.
  a; $m = -25$

77. A gold coin that was purchased for $300 appreciates $20 per year.
  d; $m = 20$

78. A CD player that was purchased for $300 depreciates $80 per year.
  b; $m = -80$

Section 1.5

79. The table shows the monthly premium (in dollars) for a term life insurance policy for women who smoke.

Age (years)	25	30	35	40	45	50	55	60
Premium	19.58	20.10	20.79	25.23	34.89	48.55	69.17	98.92

a. Make a scatter plot of the data, using x for age and y for amount of premium.

b. Does the data appear to be linear?

c. Calculate the finite differences. Do they confirm that the data is linear?

80. For which of the following scatter plots would a linear model be reasonable? Which sets of data show positive correlation, and which show negative correlation?

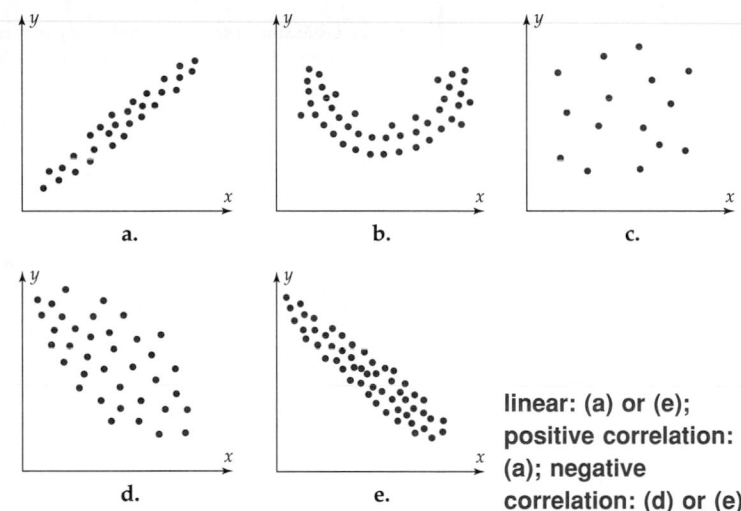

a.   b.   c.

d.   e.   **linear: (a) or (e); positive correlation: (a); negative correlation: (d) or (e)**

Exercises 81–82 refer to the following table, which shows the percentage of jobs that are classified as managerial and the percentage of male and female employees who are managers.

Year (since 1990)	Managerial jobs (%)	Female managers (%)	Male managers (%)
−8	12.32	6.28	16.81
−5	12.31	6.85	16.67
−2	12.00	7.21	16.09
0	11.83	7.45	15.64
1	11.79	7.53	15.52
3	11.43	7.65	14.79
5	11.09	7.73	14.10

81. a. Make scatter plots of each data set (managerial jobs, female managers, male managers).
  b. Match the following linear models with the correct data set. Explain your choices.

$$y_1 = 0.11x + 7.34 \quad y_2 = -0.09x + 11.74 \quad y_3 = -0.21x + 15.48$$

82. a. According to the models in Exercise 81, is the percentage of female or male managers increasing at the greater rate? **Female**

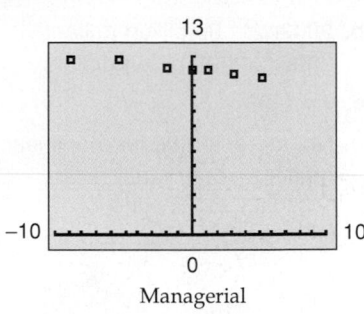

13

−10   10
0
Managerial

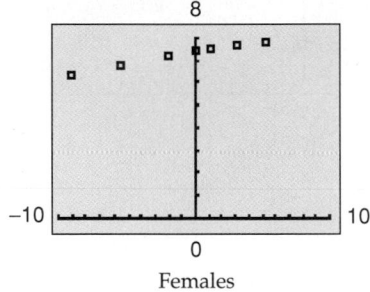

8

−10   10
0
Females

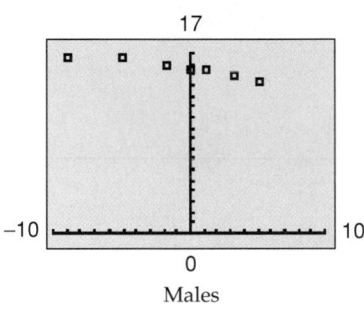

17

−10   10
0
Males

b. Managerial, y_2 (negative slope, y-intercept at 11.74); Female, y_1 (positive slope, y-intercept at 7.34); Male, y_3 (negative slope, y-intercept at 15.48)

84. a. $y - 10.2182x + 88.6818$

b. 2002: 211.30 billion dollars;
2005: 241.95 billion dollars

c. $r \approx 0.9579$

d. No, there is a better, nonlinear model for the data.

females: 8.44%; males: 13.38%

b. Use the models to predict the percentage of female managers and the percentage of male managers in the year 2000.

c. What year do the models indicate that the percentage of female managers will surpass the percentage of male managers? **2015**

83. The table shows the average hourly earnings of production workers in manufacturing. (Source: U.S. Bureau of Labor Statistics)

Year	1991	1993	1995	1997	1999	2001
Hourly earnings ($)	11.18	11.74	12.37	13.17	13.90	14.84

$$y = 0.3654x + 10.6741$$

a. Find a linear model for this data, with $x = 0$ corresponding to 1990.

b. Use the model to estimate the average hourly wage in 1993 and in 2000. The actual average in 1993 was $11.74 and in 2000 it was $14.38. How far off is the model? **$11.77; $14.33; The model is close**

c. Estimate the average hourly earnings in 2004. **$15.79**

84. The table shows the total amount of charitable giving (in billions of dollars) in the United States during recent years. (Source: Statistical Abstract of the U.S.: 2001)

Year	Total charitable giving
1990	101.4
1991	107.2
1992	110.4
1993	116.5
1994	119.2
1995	124.0
1996	138.6
1997	153.8
1998	172.1
1999	190.8
2000	203.5

a. Find a linear model for this data, with $x = 0$ corresponding to 1990.

b. Use your model to estimate the approximate total giving in 2002 and 2005.

c. Find the correlation coefficient for the model.

d. Make a residual plot of the model. Is a linear model appropriate for the data?

Section **1.6**

In Exercises 85–88, find a formula for u_n. Assume that the sequence is geometric.

85. $u_1 = 2$ and the common ratio is 3. $\quad u_n = 2 \cdot 3^{n-1}$

86. $u_1 = 5$ and the common ratio is $-\frac{1}{2}$. $\quad u_n = 5\left(-\frac{1}{2}\right)^{n-1}$

87. $u_2 = 192$ and $u_7 = 6$. $\quad u_n = 384\left(\frac{1}{2}\right)^{n-1}$

88. $u_3 = \frac{9}{2}$ and $u_6 = -\frac{243}{16}$. $\quad u_n = 2\left(-\frac{3}{2}\right)^{n-1}$

89. Find the 11th partial sum of the arithmetic sequence with $u_1 = 5$ and common difference -2. $\quad -55$

90. Find the fifth partial sum of the geometric sequence with $u_1 = \frac{1}{4}$ and common ratio 3. $\quad \frac{121}{4}$

91. Find the sixth partial sum of the geometric sequence with $u_1 = 5$ and common ratio $\frac{1}{2}$. $\quad \frac{315}{32}$

92. Find numbers c and d such that 8, c, d, 27 are the first four terms of a geometric sequence. $\quad c = 12, d = 18$

93. Is it better to be paid \$5 per day for 100 days or to be paid 5¢ the first day, 10¢ the second day, 20¢ the third day, and have your salary increase in this fashion every day for 100 days? **Second method is better.**

94. Tuition at a university is now \$3000 per year and will increase \$150 per year in subsequent years. If a student starts school now, spends four years as an undergraduate, three years in law school, and five years earning a Ph.D., how much tuition will she have paid? **\$45,900**

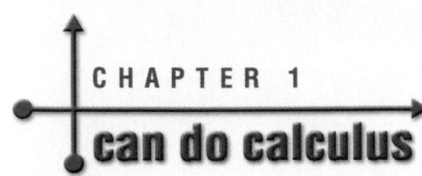

can do calculus

Infinite Geometric Series

The Can Do Calculus features introduce calculus topics that can be done using precalculus skills. In this feature, the concept of an infinite geometric series is developed, using two concepts that the students have just studied in Section 1.6 — an infinite geometric sequence and the partial sums of an infinite geometric sequence.

The concept of limits, introduced here, is formally presented in Chapter 14.

Teaching Notes

The section **Infinite Geometric Series** begins with the infinite geometric sequence defined by the rule $u_n = 2(0.6)^n$. First, have students find the first few terms of the sequence:
$u_1 = 2(0.6)^1 = 1.2, u_2 = 2(0.6)^2 = 0.72,$
$u_3 = 2(0.6)^3 = 0.432$

You may want to show in more detail how to get one of the partial sums of the sequence. For example,
$$S_3 = u_1 + u_2 + u_3$$
$$= 1.2 + 0.72 + 0.432 = 2.352$$

Emphasize that the partial sums themselves form a sequence:
1.2, 1.9, 2.352, 2.6112, ...

This sequence of partial sums is neither an arithmetic nor geometric sequence.

The expression $\sum_{n=1}^{\infty} a_n$ uses the infinity symbol ∞ instead of an upper limit, indicating an infinite series.

can do calculus

Infinite Geometric Series

NOTE Although TI, Sharp, and HP calculators use the letter "u" to denote terms of a sequence, the letter "a" is traditionally used.

Figure 1.C-1

NOTE If $a_1, a_2, a_3, \ldots$ is a geometric sequence, then an expression of the form $a_1 + a_2 + a_3 + \ldots$ (sometimes written as $\sum_{n=1}^{\infty} a_n$) is called a **geometric series.**

Calculus is a branch of mathematics that deals with changing quantities. It is based on the concept of quantities that can be approached more and more closely. There are two related branches of calculus: differential calculus and integral calculus. Differential calculus is used to calculate the change in one variable produced by change in a related variable, and integral calculus is used to calculate quantities like the total change of a quantity given its rate of change, area, and volume.

The Can Do Calculus features found here and at the end of each chapter are short adventures into the world of calculus. This first Can Do Calculus explores infinite series, which is closely related to infinite sequences. It is an example of the limit process, the fundamental building block of both differential and integral calculus.

Infinite Geometric Series

Consider the sequence $2(0.6)^n$ and let S_k denote its kth partial sum.

$$S_1 = 2(0.6) = 1.2$$
$$S_2 = 2(0.6) + 2(0.6)^2 = 1.92$$
$$S_3 = 2(0.6) + 2(0.6)^2 + 2(0.6)^3 = 2.352$$
$$S_4 = 2(0.6) + 2(0.6)^2 + 2(0.6)^3 + 2(0.6)^4 = 2.6112$$

The partial sums $S_1, S_2, S_3, S_4, \ldots$ themselves form a sequence. This sequence is a function whose domain is the set of natural numbers. The sequence can be described by the following function:

$$u_n = \begin{cases} 2(0.6) & n = 1 \\ 2(0.6)^n + u_{n-1} & n > 1 \end{cases}$$

By using the trace feature to find large values of n, the graph in Figure 1C-1 suggests that the terms of the sequence of partial sums are getting closer and closer to 3. Consequently,

$$2(0.6) + 2(0.6)^2 + 2(0.6)^3 + 2(0.6)^4 + \cdots = 3,$$

where 3 is said to be sum, or limit, of the *infinite series.*

In the general case, an **infinite series,** or simply **series,** is defined to be an expression of the form

$$a_1 + a_2 + a_3 + a_4 + a_5 + \cdots + a_n + \cdots$$

in which each a_n is a real number. This series is also denoted by the symbol $\sum_{n=1}^{\infty} a_n$.

76

The **partial sums** of the series $a_1 + a_2 + a_3 + a_4 + \cdots$ are

$$S_1 = a_1$$
$$S_2 = a_1 + a_2$$
$$S_3 = a_1 + a_2 + a_3$$
$$S_4 = a_1 + a_2 + a_3 + a_4$$

and in general, for any $k \geq 1$,

$$S_k = a_1 + a_2 + a_3 + a_4 + \cdots + a_k.$$

If it happens that the terms $S_1, S_2, S_3, S_4, \ldots$ of the *sequence* of partial sums get closer and closer to a particular real number S in such a way that the partial sum S_k is arbitrarily close to S when k is large enough, then the series **converges** and has a limit. Additionally, S is called the **sum of the convergent series.** The series $2(0.6) + 2(0.6)^2 + 2(0.6)^3 + 2(0.6)^4 + \cdots$ converges, and its sum is 3. This series is an infinite geometric series because it has a common ratio of 0.6.

Definition of Infinite Geometric Series

> If $\{a_n\}$ is a geometric sequence with common ratio r, then the corresponding infinite series
>
> $$a_1 + a_2 + a_3 + a_4 + \cdots$$
>
> is called an *infinite geometric series.*

By using the formula for the nth term of a geometric sequence, the corresponding geometric series can be expressed in the form

$$a_1 + ra_1 + r^2a_1 + r^3a_1 + \cdots$$

Under certain circumstances, an infinite geometric series is convergent and has a sum.

Sum of an Infinite Geometric Series

> If $|r| < 1$, then the infinite geometric series
>
> $$a_1 + ra_1 + r^2a_1 + r^3a_1 + \cdots$$
>
> converges, and its sum is
>
> $$\frac{a_1}{1 - r}.$$

NOTE A series that is not convergent is said to be **divergent.** If $|r| \geq 1$, the series is divergent. Therefore, a geometric series is only convergent when $|r| < 1$.

Example 1 Sum of an Infinite Geometric Series

Determine whether the infinite geometric series converges.

a. $\displaystyle\sum_{n=1}^{\infty} 6(2)^{n-1}$

b. $\displaystyle\sum_{n=1}^{\infty} \frac{8}{3^n}$

77

Teaching Notes

Point out that the phrase *partial sum of a series* and the phrase *partial sum of a sequence* have the same meaning. To help students see this, show that to write a series, you can simply write a sequence and replace the commas with + signs:

Infinite sequence: $a_1, a_2, a_3, a_4, \ldots$

Infinite series: $a_1 + a_2 + a_3 + a_4 + \ldots$

So, for example, the third partial sum of the sequence and the third partial sum of the series are the same: $a_1 + a_2 + a_3$.

A series **converges** if its sequence of partial sums converges. The graph of a convergent sequence forms a path that has a horizontal asymptote. In Figure 1.C-1, the asymptote is the line $y = 3$ because the series $2(0.6) + 2(0.6)^2 + 2(0.6)^3 + \ldots$ converges, and its sum is 3. If the series converges, it is said to have a **limit.** The limit is the sum of the infinite series. In Figure 1.C-1, the limit of the series is 3.

A series is an indicated sum, so a student might find the phrase *sum of the series* a bit awkward (strictly translated, we get *sum of the indicated sum*). However, *sum of the series* is traditional; it may be helpful to think of it as *value of the series.*

Math Background

There is more than one way to express any series in summation notation. For example,

$$\sum_{n=0}^{\infty} 2(0.4)^{n+1} = 2(0.4) + 2(0.4)^2 + \ldots$$

and

$$\sum_{n=1}^{\infty} 2(0.4)^n = 2(0.4) + 2(0.4)^2 + \ldots \text{ are}$$

the same series.

Example Notes

In **Example 1**, remind students of the formula for the kth partial sum of a geometric sequence (page 61).

1a. The graph of the sequence of partials sums increases exponentially without a limit.

1b. The graph of the sequence of partials sums approaches a limit of 2. Point out that $2 - \dfrac{2}{5^k}$, the kth partial sum of this series, gets close to 2 as k increases.

In **Example 2**, students may be better prepared to understand the example by seeing an easier one first.

$$0.444\cdots = 0.4 + 0.04 + 0.004 + \cdots$$
$$= 0.4 + (0.1)(0.4) + (0.1)^2(0.4) + \cdots$$

This is a geometric series with $a_1 = 0.4$ and $r = 0.1$, so its sum is

$$\frac{a_1}{1 - r} = \frac{0.4}{1 - 0.1} = \frac{0.4}{0.9} = \frac{4}{9}$$

Therefore,

$$0.444\cdots = 0.4 + 0.04 + 0.004 + \cdots$$
$$= \frac{4}{9}.$$

Teaching Notes

To understand why the value of $S_k = a_1\left(\dfrac{1 - r^k}{1 - r}\right)$ is close to the value of $\dfrac{a_1}{1 - r}$ for large values of k and $|r| < 1$, students need to understand why the value of $1 - r^k$ is close to the value of 1. Choose a value for r, say 0.7. Have students find some values of $1 - r^k$. For example, $1 - 0.7^{10} = 0.97175$, $1 - 0.7^{20} = 0.9992$, and so on.

The graph of $S_k = a_1\left(\dfrac{1 - r^k}{1 - r}\right)$ has a horizontal asymptote at $y = \dfrac{a_1}{1 - r}$ for $|r| < 1$. If $|r| > 1$, the graph of $S_k = a_1\left(\dfrac{1 - r^k}{1 - r}\right)$ has no maximum value.

Figure 1.C-2

Figure 1.C-3

Solution

a. The first term is 6 and the common ratio is 2. The sum of the first k terms is

$$S_k = a_1\left(\frac{1 - r^k}{1 - r}\right) = 6\left(\frac{1 - 2^k}{1 - 2}\right) = -6(1 - 2^k) = 6(2^k - 1)$$

The graph of $S_k = 6(2^k - 1)$, as shown in Figure 1.C-2, does not approach a single value. In fact, the sums get larger for each subsequent term. So this series with a common ratio of 2 does not converge. It diverges.

b. $\displaystyle\sum_{n=1}^{\infty} \frac{8}{5^n}$ is an infinite geometric series with $a_1 = \dfrac{8}{5}$ and $r = \dfrac{1}{5}$. The kth partial sum of this series is the same as the kth partial sum of the sequence $\left\{\dfrac{8}{5^n}\right\}$.

$$S_k = a_1\left(\frac{1 - r^k}{1 - r}\right) = \frac{8}{5}\left[\frac{1 - \left(\frac{1}{5}\right)^k}{1 - \frac{1}{5}}\right] = \frac{8}{5}\left(\frac{1 - \frac{1}{5^k}}{\frac{4}{5}}\right) = \frac{8}{5}\cdot\frac{5}{4}\left(1 - \frac{1}{5^k}\right) =$$

$$2\left(1 - \frac{1}{5^k}\right) = 2 - \frac{2}{5^k}$$

The graph of S_k is shown in Figure 1.C-3. If you use the trace feature and move beyond approximately $n = 10$, the calculator will probably tell you that every partial sum is 2. Actually, the partial sums are slightly smaller than 2 but are rounded to 2 by the calculator. The graph gets very close to 2 as x gets larger, but it never reaches 2. According to the formula, the sum of the infinite series is

$$S = \frac{a_1}{1 - r} = \frac{\frac{8}{5}}{1 - \frac{1}{5}} = \frac{\frac{8}{5}}{\frac{4}{5}} = \frac{8}{4} = 2.$$

Example **1b** is typical of the general case, as can be seen algebraically. Consider the geometric series $a_1 + a_2 + a_3 + \cdots$ with common ratio r such that $|r| < 1$. The kth partial sum S_k is the same as the kth partial sum of geometric sequence $\{a_n\}$, and hence

$$S_k = a_1\left(\frac{1 - r^k}{1 - r}\right).$$

As k gets very large, the number r^k gets very close to 0 because $|r| < 1$. Consequently, when k is very large, $1 - r^k$ is very close to $1 - 0$ so that

$$S_k = a_1\left(\frac{1 - r^k}{1 - r}\right) \quad \text{is very close to} \quad a_1\left(\frac{1 - 0}{1 - r}\right) = \frac{a_1}{1 - r}.$$

Infinite geometric series provide another way of writing an infinite repeating decimal as a rational number.

Example 2   **Repeating Decimal as a Rational Number**

Express $6.8573573573\cdots$ as a rational number.

Solution

First write the number as $6.8 + 0.0573573573\cdots$. Then consider $0.0573573573\cdots$ as an infinite series:

$$0.0573 + 0.0000573 + 0.0000000573 + 0.0000000000573 + \cdots,$$

which is the same as

$$0.0573 + (0.001)(0.0573) + (0.001)^2(0.0573) + (0.001)^3(0.0573) + \cdots$$

This is a convergent geometric series with $a_1 = 0.0573$ and $r = 0.001$. Its sum is

$$\frac{a_1}{1 - r} = \frac{0.0573}{1 - 0.001} = \frac{0.0573}{0.999} = \frac{573}{9990}.$$

Therefore,

$$6.8573573573\cdots = 6.8 + [0.0573 + 0.0000573 + \cdots]$$

$$= 6.8 + \frac{573}{9990}$$

$$= \frac{68}{10} + \frac{573}{9990}$$

$$= \frac{68505}{9990} = \frac{4567}{666}$$

$\blacksquare$

Exercises

In Exercises 1–9, find the sum, or limit, of the infinite series, if it converges.

1. $\displaystyle\sum_{n=1}^{\infty} \frac{1}{2^n}$ **1**   **2.** $\displaystyle\sum_{n=1}^{\infty} \frac{2^n}{3}$ **Diverges**   **3.** $\displaystyle\sum_{n=1}^{\infty} \left(-\frac{3}{4}\right)^n$ $-\dfrac{3}{7}$

4. $1 - 0.5 + 0.25 - 0.125 + 0.0625 - \cdots$ $\dfrac{2}{3}$

5. $500 + 200 + 80 + 32 + \cdots$ $\dfrac{500}{0.6} = 833\frac{1}{3}$

6. $9 - 3\sqrt{3} + 3 - \sqrt{3} + 1 - \dfrac{1}{\sqrt{3}} + \cdots$ ≈ 5.7058

7. $2 + \sqrt{2} + 1 + \dfrac{1}{\sqrt{2}} + \dfrac{1}{2} + \cdots$ $4 + 2\sqrt{2}$

8. $4 - 2\sqrt{6} + 6 - 3\sqrt{6} + 9 - \dfrac{9\sqrt{6}}{2} + \cdots$ **Diverges**

9. $\displaystyle\sum_{n=1}^{\infty} \left(\frac{1}{2^n} - \frac{1}{3^n}\right)$ $\dfrac{1}{2}$

In Exercises 10–15, express the repeating decimal as a rational number.

10. $0.22222\cdots$ $\dfrac{2}{9}$ **11.** $0.37373737\cdots$ $\dfrac{37}{99}$

12. $5.4272727\cdots$ $\dfrac{597}{110}$ **13.** $85.131313\cdots$ $\dfrac{8428}{99}$

14. $2.1425425425\cdots$ $\dfrac{10{,}702}{4995}$ **15.** $3.7165165165\cdots$ $\dfrac{18{,}564}{4995}$

16. If $\{a_n\}$ is an arithmetic sequence with common difference $d > 0$ and each $a_i > 0$ explain why the infinite series $a_1 + a_2 + a_3 + a_4 + \cdots$ is not convergent.

17. Use the graphical approach illustrated in Example 1 to find the sum of the series in $\displaystyle\sum_{n=1}^{\infty} \left(\frac{-1}{2}\right)^n$. Does the graph get very close to the horizontal line through $-\dfrac{1}{3}$? Describe the behavior of the series.

79

CHAPTER 2

Equations and Inequalities

In this chapter students will solve equations and inequalities. They will use algebraic, graphical, and geometric techniques. The equations and inequalities will involve expressions of the following types: polynomial (including quadratic), absolute-value, radical, and rational. One section is devoted to solving applications problems.

CHAPTER 2

Equations and Inequalities

And the rockets' red glare . . .

Many Fourth of July firework displays are timed to coincide with patriotic music. To accomplish correct timing, each rocket must be detonated at precisely the correct height at the right moment. The time needed for a rocket to reach a specific height is the solution of an equation representing the height of the rocket as a function of time. See Exercise 24 of Section 2.3.

80

Chapter Outline

Interdependence of Sections

2.1

2.2 ⟶ 2.3

2.4

2.5 ⟶ 2.5.A

Graphing technology is useful for solving equations, but don't be misled into thinking that technology is always the best tool. For example, graphing technology is useless if you do not know enough algebra to understand the information displayed on the screen. When exact answers are required, algebraic techniques are usually needed. This chapter and the next two chapters develop both algebraic and graphical techniques for solving equations in one variable.

2.1 Solving Equations Graphically

Objectives

- Solve equations using the intersect method
- Solve equations using the x-intercept method

A **solution** of an equation is a number that, when substituted for the variable, produces a true statement. For example, 5 is a solution of $3x + 2 = 17$ because $3(5) + 2 = 17$ is a true statement. To **solve** an equation means to find all of its solutions.

Two equations are said to be **equivalent** if they have the same solutions. For example, $3x + 2 = 17$ and $x - 2 = 3$ are equivalent because 5 is the only solution of each equation.

Algebraic techniques provide exact solutions to linear and quadratic equations; however, there are no formulas that provide solutions to many other types of equations. For such equations, graphical approximation methods are practical alternatives.

NOTE If necessary, review the material on graphing in the Technology Appendix. Knowledge of a graphing calculator is assumed throughout the remainder of this book.

81

Section 2.1 Solving Equations Graphically

Teaching Notes

Stress to students that in many cases, a graphing calculator will not find the *exact* solutions of an equation; rather, it will find approximations. Most examples in this section require only approximate solutions.

You may want to provide students with additional practice with the term **equivalent.** Ask students to answer and explain.

- Are the equations $6x - 3 = 21$ and $x + 7 = 11$ equivalent?   yes; both have 4 as a solution
- Are the equations $5x + 4 = 14$ and $2x - 9 = 1$ equivalent?   no; the solutions, 2 and 5, are different
- Are the equations $x^2 = 9$ and $x + 3 = 6$ equivalent?   no; $x^2 = 9$ has solutions 3 and -3, but $x + 3 = 6$ has only 3 as a solution.

Example Notes

As noted in the solution for **Example 1**, you can approximate the x-coordinate of the intersection of the graphs by zooming in and using the TRACE feature. Have students do this (the result is shown below).

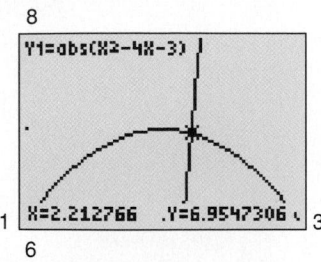

Point out that this method can be quite accurate by zooming in repeatedly, but the graphical intersection finder is more accurate and does not have to be repeated.

ADDITIONAL EXAMPLES

Example 1

Solve $|x^2 - 3x - 5| = x^3 - x - 2$.

Set $y_1 = |x^2 - 3x - 5|$ and $y_2 = x^3 - x - 2$ and graph both equations on the same screen, as shown, to find the x-coordinate of the intersection.

$x \approx -2.221$ is an approximate solution.

Teaching Notes

Solution to the **Graphing Exploration** (p. 83):

1.

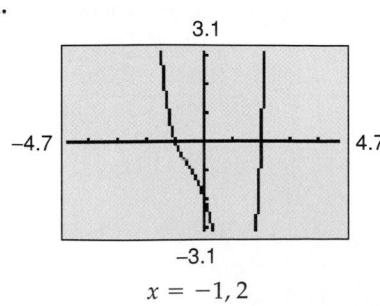

$x = -1, 2$

Technology Tip

Absolute value (ABS) is in the NUM submenu of the MATH menu of TI and in the NUM submenu of the OPTN menu of RUN mode of CASIO.

The graphical intersection finder is labeled INTERSECT, in the CALC menu of TI and ISCT in the G-SOLVE menu of Casio.

Figure 2.1-1

The Intersection Method

Complete Graphs

A viewing window is said to display a **complete graph** if it shows all the important features of the graph—including all peaks, valleys, and points where it touches an axis—and suggests the general shape of portions of the graph that are not in the window. Many different windows may show a complete graph, but it usually is best to use a window small enough to show as much detail as possible.

Later chapters develop algebraic facts that will enable you to know when graphs are complete. Until then try several different windows to see which, if any, appear to display a complete graph.

The Intersection Method

The following example illustrates a graphical method of approximating solutions of equations where both sides of an equation are algebraic expressions. Each side of the equation can be viewed as the output of a function, and the solutions of the equation represent inputs that produce equal outputs.

Example 1   Solving an Equation Using the Intersect Method

Solve $|x^2 - 4x - 3| = x^3 + x - 6$.

Solution

Set $y_1 = |x^2 - 4x - 3|$ and $y_2 = x^3 + x - 6$. Graph both equations on the same screen and find the x-coordinate of the point where the two graphs intersect. This coordinate can be approximated by zooming in and using the trace feature or by using a graphical intersection finder. As shown in Figure 2.1-1, $x \approx 2.207$ is an approximate solution.

$$|x^2 - 4x - 3| = x^3 + x - 6$$

Letting $x = 2.207$,

left side	*right side*
$|(2.207)^2 - 4(2.207) - 3|$	$(2.207)^3 + 2.207 - 6$
$|4.870849 - 8.828 - 3|$	$10.74996374 + 2.207 - 6$
6.957151	6.956963743

The difference between the value of the left side and the value of the right side is small. Therefore, the solution to the original equation is $x \approx 2.207$. ∎

To solve an equation of the form $f(x) = g(x)$ by using the *intersection method,* follow two steps.

1. Graph $y_1 = f(x)$ and $y_2 = g(x)$ on the same screen.
2. Find the x-coordinate of each point of intersection.

2. $f(x) = x^4 - 2x^2 - 3x - 2$
$f(-1) = (-1)^4 - 2(-1)^2 - 3(-1) - 2$
$\qquad = 1 - 2 + 3 - 2 = 0$
$f(2) = (2)^4 - 2(2)^2 - 3(2) - 2$
$\qquad = 16 - 8 - 6 - 2 = 0$

> **CAUTION**
>
> Check several viewing windows to ensure that a complete graph is shown for each side of the equation. If the graphs do not intersect, then they have no common output value. Therefore, there are no real solutions to the equation.

The *x*-Intercept Method

A **zero of a function** *f* is an input that produces an output of 0. For example, 2 is a zero of the function $f(x) = x^3 - 8$ because $f(2) = 2^3 - 8 = 0$. Note that 2 is also a solution of the equation $x^3 - 8 = 0$. In other words, the zeros of the function *f* are the **solutions,** or **roots,** of the equation $f(x) = 0$. The zeros of a function also have a graphical interpretation.

Technology Tip

A **decimal window** produces one-decimal-place values of the *x*-coordinates when using the trace feature.

For a decimal window select ZDECIMAL or ZOOMDEC in the TI ZOOM menu and INIT in the Casio V-WINDOW menu. If needed, review the material on decimal windows in the Technology Appendix.

> ### Graphing Exploration
>
> 1. Graph $y = x^4 - 2x^2 - 3x - 2$ using a decimal window. (See Technology Tip.) Find the points where the graph crosses the *x*-axis.
>
> 2. Verify that the *x*-coordinates found in Step 1 are zeros of the function *f*. That is, the *x*-coordinates are solutions of
> $$x^4 - 2x^2 - 3x - 2 = 0.$$

A point where the graph of $y = f(x)$ intersects the *x*-axis is of the form $(a, 0)$ because every point on the *x*-axis has *y*-coordinate 0. The number *a* is called an **x-intercept** of the graph of *f*. In the preceding Exploration, the *x*-intercepts of $f(x) = x^4 - 2x^2 - 3x - 2$ were found to be $x = -1$ and $x = 2$. The *x*-intercepts of the graph are the zeros of the function *f*.

Zeros, *x*-Intercepts, and Solutions

> Let *f* be a function. If *r* is a real number that satisfies any of the following statements, then *r* satisfies all the statements.
>
> - *r* is a **zero** of the function *f*
> - *r* is an **x-intercept** of the graph of *f*
> - $x = r$ is a **solution,** or **root,** of the equation $f(x) = 0$

Because the *x*-intercepts of the graph of $y = f(x)$ are the zeros of *f*, and the zeros of *f* are solutions of the related equation $f(x) = 0$, the *x*-intercepts can be used to solve $f(x) = 0$.

Teaching Notes

Emphasize the need to check several viewing windows as mentioned in the **CAUTION** note by showing the following example.

Consider the equation $|0.1x^4 - 5| = 0.1x^3 - 0.1x + 12$. Graphing $y_1 = |0.1x^4 - 5|$ and $y_2 = 0.1x^3 - 0.1x + 12$ on the same screen with a standard viewing window shows a point of intersection at $x \approx -3.4024$.

However, a viewing window with $-10 \le x \le 10$ and $-10 \le y \le 40$ shows a second point of intersection at $x \approx 3.8688$.

Illustrate the **Zeros, *x*-Intercepts, and Solutions** box with a particular function. For example, if $f(x) = \frac{1}{2}x - 3$, then

- 6 is a zero of *f* because
  $$f(6) = \frac{1}{2}(6) - 3 = 0$$

- 6 is an *x*-intercept of the graph of *f*

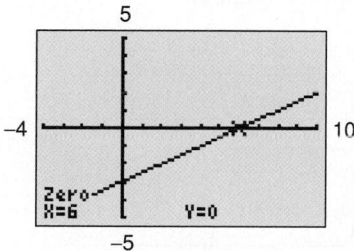

- $x = 6$ is a solution, or root, of $\frac{1}{2}x - 3 = 0$

Teaching Notes

After completing **Example 2**, point out that you can also get 0 on the left side: $0 = -x^5 + x^3 - x^2 + 5$

Now the associated function is $y = -x^5 + x^3 - x^2 + 5$. You can use it to solve the original equation:

ADDITIONAL EXAMPLES

Example 2

Solve the equation $-x^4 + 2x^2 = x^5 + 4$.

Rewrite the equation so that one side is zero.
$x^5 + x^4 - 2x^2 + 4 = 0$

$x \approx -1.277$ is an approximate solution.

Example 3

Solve $\sqrt{x^4 - 3x^3 + 2x^2 - 1} = 0$.

The graph of
$y = \sqrt{x^4 - 3x^3 + 2x^2 - 1}$ is shown. The trace feature and zero finder may not function properly.

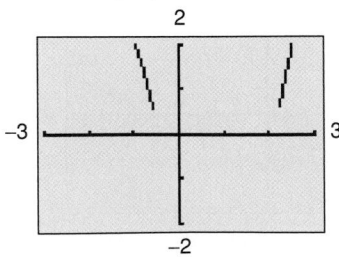

Instead, graph and find the solutions of $y = x^4 - 3x^3 + 2x^2 - 1$, since it will have the same zeros as the original equation.

The x-Intercept Method

Follow three steps to solve an equation by the *x*-intercept method.

1. Write the equation in the equivalent form $f(x) = 0$.
2. Graph $y = f(x)$.
3. Find the *x*-intercepts of the graph. The *x*-intercepts of the graph are the real solutions of the equation.

Figure 2.1-2

An advantage of using the *x*-intercept method is that solutions appear on the *x*-axis, and prior information about the range of the function is not needed.

Example 2   Solving an Equation by Using the *x*-Intercept Method

Solve the equation $x^5 + x^2 = x^3 + 5$.

Solution

Rewrite the equation so that one side is zero.
$$x^5 - x^3 + x^2 - 5 = 0$$

Graph $y = x^5 - x^3 + x^2 - 5$ in the **standard viewing window**.

Use the trace feature to find that the zero is between 1.3 and 1.5, then use zoom-in and trace features repeatedly, or use the **graphical zero finder**, to get a better approximation of 1.4242577. (See the Technology Tip for the location of the graphical zero finder.) Verify that 1.42 is an approximate solution by substituting $x = 1.42$ into the original equation. ∎

Technological Quirks

A graphical zero finder may fail to find some solutions of an equation, particularly when the graph of the equation touches, but does not cross, the *x*-axis. If the calculator does not show any *x*-intercepts on a graph or if its zero finder gives an error message, an alternative approach may be necessary, as illustrated in the next two examples.

Example 3   Solving $\sqrt{f(x)} = 0$ by Solving $f(x) = 0$

Solve $\sqrt{x^4 + x^2 - 2x - 1} = 0$.

Solution

Graph $y = \sqrt{x^4 + x^2 - 2x - 1}$. The trace feature may display no *y*-value for some points and the graphical zero finder may display an error message. See Figure 2.1-3 on the next page.

$x \approx -0.5128764$ and $x \approx 2.1787242$

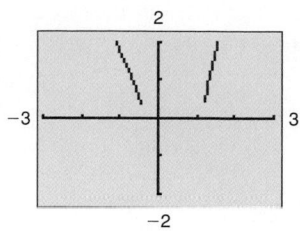

Figure 2.1-3

NOTE Solving radical and rational equations is presented in Section 2.4, and radical and rational functions are presented in Chapter 4.

Figure 2.1-5

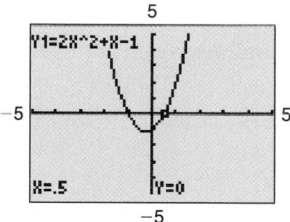

Figure 2.1-6

This difficulty can be eliminated by using the fact that the only number whose square root is zero is zero itself.

That is, the solutions of $\sqrt{x^4 + x^2 - 2x - 1} = 0$ are the same as the solutions of $x^4 + x^2 - 2x - 1 = 0$.

As the graphs below display, the solutions of $x^4 + x^2 - 2x - 1 = 0$ are

$$x \approx -0.4046978 \quad \text{and} \quad x \approx 1.1841347,$$

which are also approximate solutions of $\sqrt{x^4 + x^2 - 2x - 1} = 0$.

 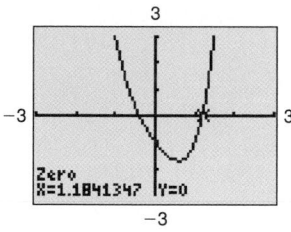

Figure 2.1-4a   **Figure 2.1-4b**

The solutions can be verified by substitution.

Example 4 Solving $\dfrac{f(x)}{g(x)} = 0$

Solve $\dfrac{2x^2 + x - 1}{9x^2 - 9x + 2} = 0$.

Solution

The graph of $y = \dfrac{2x^2 + x - 1}{9x^2 - 9x + 2}$ in Figure 2.1-5 is impossible to read. Using the zoom feature will display a better graph, but it may be easier to use the fact that a fraction is zero only when its numerator is zero and its denominator is nonzero.

The values that make the numerator zero can easily be found by finding the zeros of $y = 2x^2 + x - 1$. Discard any value that makes the denominator of the original equation zero because

an input that gives an undefined output is not in the domain.

Figure 2.1-6 shows that one x-intercept of $y = 2x^2 + x - 1$ is $x = 0.5$ and the other is $x = -1$ (not identified on the graph). Neither value makes the denominator zero, so they are the solutions to the given equation, which can be verified by substitution.

ADDITIONAL EXAMPLES

Example 4

Solve $\dfrac{2x^2 - x - 3}{8x^2 - 7x - 4} = 0$.

The graph of $y = \dfrac{2x^2 - x - 3}{8x^2 - 7x - 4}$ is shown and is difficult to read.

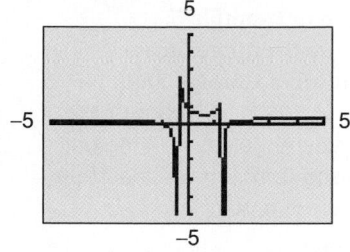

Instead, find the values that make the numerator zero and discard any such values that make the denominator zero. Find these values by graphing and finding the zeros of $y = 2x^2 - x - 3$.

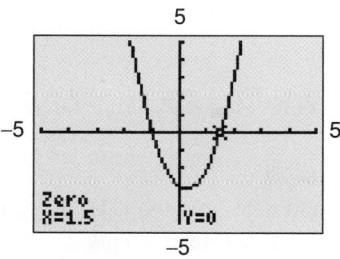

$x = -1$ and $x = 1.5$ are solutions of this equation. Neither of these values makes the denominator zero, so they are both solutions of the original equation.

Math Background

The equation $y = \dfrac{2x^2 + x - 1}{9x^2 - 9x + 2}$ in **Example 4** represents a rational function. In Section 4.4, students will encounter other rational functions in which *a zero of the numerator is also a zero of the denominator.*

For $\dfrac{x^2 - x - 2}{x^2 - 4x - 5} = \dfrac{(x + 1)(x - 2)}{(x + 1)(x - 5)}$, -1 is a zero of both the numerator *and* the denominator and therefore is *not* a solution of $\dfrac{x^2 - x - 2}{x^2 - 4x - 5} = 0$. Students will learn that the graph of the function $f(x) = \dfrac{(x + 1)(x - 2)}{(x + 1)(x - 5)}$ has discontinuities at $x = -1$ and $x = 5$.

Real-World Application

Deriving functions that model population data and then graphing the functions can help demographers analyze the data. The following questions can be answered by using the graph in **Example 5**:

What were the approximate populations of Chicago and Los Angeles in 1950?   Chicago: 3.62 million; Los Angeles: 1.97 million; substituting 0 for x gives the 1950 population of both cities

Which city's population is increasing and which is decreasing? How can you tell from the graph?   The point (0, 3.62) identifies the graph for Chicago, which falls from left to right for most of the period shown, corresponding to a decreasing population. The point (0, 1.97) identifies the graph for Los Angeles, which rises from left to right, corresponding to an increasing population.

If both trends continue as shown, what can be predicted about each city's population?   Los Angeles will increase; Chicago will remain fairly constant

ADDITIONAL EXAMPLES

Example 5

According to data from the U.S. Bureau of the Census, the approximate population y (in thousands) of Baltimore, Maryland and Austin, Texas between 1970 and 2003 are given by

Baltimore: $y = -0.0114x^3 + 0.6203x^2 - 16.573x + 905.04$

Austin: $y = -0.0076x^3 + 0.543x^2 + 3.4649x + 255.63$

where x represents the number of years past 1970. In what year did the two cities have the same population?

Graph both functions on the same screen and find the point of intersection.

Figure 2.1-7

The populations were the same when $x \approx 30.59$, which represents July of 2000.

Summary of Solving Equations Graphically

To solve $h(x) = g(x)$ use one of the following.

- *The Intersection Method*
  1. Graph $y_1 = h(x)$ and $y_2 = g(x)$.
  2. Find the x-coordinate of each point of intersection.

- *The x-Intercept Method*
  1. Rewrite the equation as $f(x) = 0$, where
     $$f(x) = h(x) - g(x).$$
  2. Graph $y = f(x)$.
  3. Find the x-intercepts of the graph of $f(x)$. The x-intercepts of the graph of $y = f(x)$ are the solutions of the equation.

The x-Intercept Method has the advantage of needing no information about the range of the functions.

Applications

Graphical solution methods can be helpful in dealing with applied problems because approximate solutions are adequate in most real-world contexts.

Example 5   Equal Populations

According to data from the U.S. Bureau of the Census, the approximate population y (in millions) of Chicago and Los Angeles between 1950 and 2000 are given by

Chicago	$y = 0.0000304x^3 - 0.0023x^2 + 0.02024x + 3.62$
Los Angeles	$y = 0.0000113x^3 - 0.000922x^2 + 0.0538x + 1.97$

where 0 corresponds to 1950. In what year did the two cities have the same population?

Solution

Graph both functions on the same screen, and find the x-value of their point(s) of intersection.

As shown in Figure 2.1-7, the populations were the same when $x \approx 28.75$, which represents September of 1978.   ∎

Exercises 2.1

In Exercises 1–6, determine graphically the number of solutions of the equation, but don't solve the equation. You may need a viewing window other than the standard one to find all of the x-intercepts.

1. $x^5 + 5 = 3x^4 + x$ **3**   **2.** $x^3 + 5 = 3x^2 + 24x$ **3**

3. $x^7 - 10x^5 + 15x + 10 = 0$ **3**

4. $x^5 + 36x + 25 = 13x^3$ **1**

5. $x^4 + 500x^2 - 8000x = 16x^3 - 32,000$ **2**

6. $6x^5 + 80x^3 + 45x^2 + 30 = 45x^4 + 86x$ **1**

In Exercises 7–34, use a graphical method to find all real solutions of the equation, approximating when necessary.

7. $x^3 + 4x^2 + 10x + 15 = 0$ $\ x \approx -2.426$

8. $x^3 + 9 = 3x^2 + 6x$ **9.** $x^4 + x - 3 = 0$
$x \approx -2.054, 1.111, 3.943$ $\quad x \approx -1.453, 1.164$

10. $x^5 + 5 = 3x^4 + x$ **11.** $\sqrt{x^4 + x^3} - x - 3 = 0$
$x \approx -1.104, 1.206, 2.974$ $\quad x \approx -1.475, 1.237$

12. $\sqrt{8x^4 - 14x^3 - 9x^2 + 11x - 1} = 0$
$x \approx -0.977, 0.100, 0.643, 1.984$

13. $\sqrt{\frac{2}{5}x^5 + x^2 - 2x} = 0$
$x = 0, \ x \approx -1.750, 1.192$

14. $\sqrt{x^4 + x^2 - 3x + 1} = 0$
$x = 1, \ x \approx 0.393$

15. $x^2 = \sqrt{x + 5}$
$x \approx -1.379, 1.603$

16. $\sqrt{x^2 - 1} - \sqrt{x + 9} = 0$
$x \approx -2.702, 3.702$

17. $\dfrac{2x^5 - 10x + 5}{x^3 + x^2 - 12x} = 0$
$x \approx -1.601, 0.507, 1.329$

18. $\dfrac{3x^5 - 15x + 5}{x^7 - 8x^5 + 2x^2 - 5} = 0$
$x \approx -1.569, 0.334, 1.397$

19. $\dfrac{x^3 - 4x + 1}{x^2 + x - 6} = 0$
$x \approx -2.115, 0.254, 1.861$

20. $\dfrac{4}{x + 2} - \dfrac{3}{x + 1} = 0$ [Use parentheses correctly.]
$x = 2$

21. $2x^3 - 4x^2 + x - 3 = 0$
$x \approx 2.102$

22. $6x^3 - 5x^2 + 3x - 2 = 0$
$x \approx 0.756$

23. $x^5 - 6x + 6 = 0$
$x \approx -1.752$

24. $x^3 - 3x^2 + x - 1 = 0$
$x \approx 2.769$

25. $10x^5 - 3x^2 + x - 6 = 0$
$x \approx 0.951$

26. $\frac{1}{4}x^4 - x - 4 = 0$ **27.** $2x - \frac{1}{2}x^2 - \frac{1}{12}x^4 = 0$
$x \approx -1.735, 2.235$ $\qquad x = 0, \ x \approx 2.207$

28. $\frac{1}{4}x^4 + \frac{1}{3}x^2 + 3x - 1 = 0$
$x \approx -2.214, 0.321$

29. $\dfrac{5x}{x^2 + 1} - 2x + 3 = 0$ **30.** $\dfrac{2x}{x + 5} = 1$
$x \approx 2.390$ $\qquad\qquad x = 5$

31. $|x^2 - 4| = 3x^2 - 2x + 1$
$x \approx -0.651, 1.151$

32. $|x^3 + 2| = 5 + x - x^2$
$x \approx -1.488, 1.359$

33. $\sqrt{x^2 + 3} = \sqrt{x - 2} + 5$
$x \approx 7.033$

34. $\sqrt{x^3 + 2} = \sqrt{x + 5} + 4$
$x \approx 3.583$

In Exercises 35–40, find an exact solution of the equation in the interval shown to the right of each equation. For example, if the graphical approximation of a solution begins .3333, check to see if $\frac{1}{3}$ is the exact solution. Similarly, if your approximation begins 1.414, check to see if $\sqrt{2}$ is a solution because $\sqrt{2} \approx 1.414$.

35. $3x^3 - 2x^2 + 3x - 2 = 0$ $\qquad 0 < x < 1$ $\ \boldsymbol{x = \dfrac{2}{3}}$

36. $4x^3 - 3x^2 - 3x - 7 = 0$ $\qquad 1 < x < 2$ $\ \boldsymbol{x = \dfrac{7}{4}}$

37. $12x^4 - x^3 - 12x^2 + 25x - 2 = 0$ $\ 0 < x < 1$ $\ \boldsymbol{x = \dfrac{1}{12}}$

38. $8x^5 + 7x^4 - x^3 + 16x - 2 = 0$ $\quad 0 < x < 1$ $\ \boldsymbol{x = \dfrac{1}{8}}$

39. $4x^4 - 13x^2 + 3 = 0$ $\qquad\qquad 1 < x < 2$
$\boldsymbol{x = \sqrt{3}}$

40. $x^3 + x^2 - 2x - 2 = 0$ $\qquad\quad 1 < x < 2$
$\boldsymbol{x = \sqrt{2}}$

41. According to data from the U.S. Department of Education, the average cost y of tuition and fees at public four-year institutions in year x is approximated by the equation

$$y = 0.024x^4 - 0.87x^3 + 9.6x^2 + 97.2x + 2196$$

where $x = 0$ corresponds to 1990. If this model continues to be accurate, during what year will tuition and fees reach $4000?
2004

42. Use the equation in Example 5 to determine the year in which the population of Los Angeles reached 2.6 million.
1964

43. According to data from the U.S. Department of Health and Human Services, the cumulative number y of AIDS cases (in thousands) as of year x is approximated by

$$y = 0.062x^4 - 1.54x^3 + 9.21x^2 + 57.54x + 199.36$$
$$(0 \leq x \leq 11)$$

where $x = 0$ corresponds to 1990. During what year did the cumulative number of cases reach 750,000? **1999**

44. **a.** How many real solutions does the equation

$$0.2x^5 - 2x^3 + 1.8x + k = 0$$

have when $k = 0$? **5**
   b. How many real solutions does it have when $k = 1$? **3**
   c. Is there a value of k for which the equation has just one real solution? **an integer of at least 8**
   d. Is there a value of k for which the equation has no real solution? **No**

Math Background

Applying a basic property of equality to an equation will result in an equivalent equation—that is, an equation with an identical solution set. For example, each equation below has the same solution, 6.

$$\begin{aligned} 2x - 3 &= 9 \\ +3 \quad &+3 \\ \hline 2x &= 12 \\ \frac{2x}{2} &= \frac{12}{2} \\ x &= 6 \end{aligned}$$

When we use one of the techniques listed at the bottom of the page to solve a quadratic equation that has two solutions, we get a *pair of equations* rather than *an equivalent equation*:

$$x^2 = 9$$
$$x = 3 \text{ or } x = -3$$

A quadratic equation of the form $ax^2 + bx + c = 0$ is sometimes said to be in **standard** or **general form.** Note that because a, b, and c are real numbers, they can be irrational as well as rational. For example, $\sqrt{3}x^2 - \sqrt{5}x + 1 = 0$ and $x^2 - \pi x = 0$ are quadratic equations.

2.2 **Solving Quadratic Equations Algebraically**

Objectives

- Solve equations by:
   - factoring
   - square root of both sides
   - completing the square
   - quadratic formula
- Solve equations in quadratic form

The basic strategy for solving equations is to use the basic properties of equality.

- **Add or subtract the same quantity from both *sides* of the equation.**
- **Multiply or divide both *sides* of the equation by the same *nonzero* quantity.**

The properties of equality apply to *all* equations. They, together with other techniques that are presented in this chapter, can be used to transform a given equation into one whose solutions are easily found. This section considers quadratic equations and techniques used to find their solutions.

Definition of a Quadratic Equation

A *quadratic*, or *second degree*, equation is one that can be written in the form

$$ax^2 + bx + c = 0$$

for real constants a, b, and c, with $a \neq 0$.

NOTE This chapter considers only **real solutions,** that is, solutions that are real numbers.

Techniques Used to Solve Quadratic Equations

There are four techniques normally used to algebraically find exact solutions of quadratic equations. Techniques that can be used to solve *some* quadratic equations include

- factoring
- taking the square root of both sides of an equation

Techniques that can be used to solve *all* quadratic equations include

- completing the square
- using the quadratic formula

As mentioned in the margin **NOTE,** we consider only real number solutions in this chapter. Complex solutions (solutions that contain the imaginary number i) are addressed in Section 4.5 (page 293).

Solving Quadratic Equations by Factoring

The factoring method of solving quadratic equations is based on the Zero Product Property of real numbers.

The Zero Product Property

> If a product of real numbers is zero, then at least one of the factors is zero. In other words,
>
> If $ab = 0$, then $a = 0$ or $b = 0$ (or both).

NOTE If needed, review factoring in the Algebra Appendix.

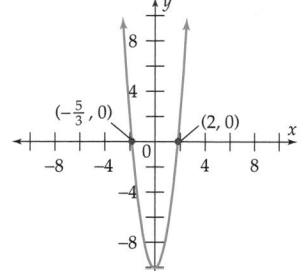

Figure 2.2-1

CAUTION

To guard against mistakes, always check solutions by substituting each solution into the *original* equation to make sure it really *is* a solution.

Example 1   Solving a Quadratic Equation by Factoring

Solve $3x^2 - x = 10$ by factoring.

Solution

Rearrange the terms so that one side is 0, and then factor.

$$3x^2 - x - 10 = 0 \qquad \textit{Subtract 10 from each side}$$
$$(3x + 5)(x - 2) = 0 \qquad \textit{Factor the left side}$$

Using the Zero Product Property, $3x + 5$ or $x - 2$ must be 0.

$$3x + 5 = 0 \qquad \text{or} \qquad x - 2 = 0$$
$$3x = -5 \qquad\qquad\qquad x = 2$$
$$x = -\frac{5}{3}$$

Therefore, the solutions are $-\dfrac{5}{3}$ and 2. See Figure 2.2-1. ∎

Solving $x^2 = k$

The equation $x^2 = -5$ has no real solutions because the square of a number is never negative. The equation $x^2 = 0$ has only one solution, $x = 0$. The equation $x^2 = 7$ has two solutions, $\sqrt{7}$ and $-\sqrt{7}$, because these are the only numbers whose square is 7. Similar facts are true for equations of the form $x^2 = k$, where k is a real number.

Solutions of $x^2 = k$

For a real number k,

	Number of Solutions	Solutions
$k < 0$	0	
$k = 0$	1	0
$k > 0$	2	$\sqrt{k}$ and $-\sqrt{k}$

Students may apply the **Zero Product Property** incorrectly. In **Example 1**, they may factor the expression on the left and try to solve as follows:

$$3x^2 - x = 10$$
$$x(3x - 1) = 10$$
$$x = 10 \text{ or } 3x - 1 = 10$$

Remind students to *isolate 0 on one side of the equation*, as shown in Example 1.

Example Notes

In the margin next to **Example 1**, Figure 2.2-1 shows the graph of the associated quadratic function $f(x) = 3x^2 - x - 10$ and its intercepts, $-\dfrac{5}{3}$ and 2. Remind students that x-intercepts of the graph of f are solutions of $f(x) = 0$. They learned the x-intercept method of solving an equation in Section 2.1; they can use that method as a way to check their solutions.

ADDITIONAL EXAMPLES

Example 1

Solve $2x^2 + 11x = 6$ by factoring.

$x = \dfrac{1}{2}$ and $x = -6$

Teaching Notes

Have students compare the form $x^2 = k$ with the form of a quadratic equation shown in the definition box, page 88. Ask them how to write $x^2 = k$ in the form $ax^2 + bx + c = 0$.

$1x^2 + 0x - k = 0$

Example Notes

For **Example 2**, remind students to first divide both sides of the equation by 3. (Point out that, when solving any equation of the form $ax^2 = k$, first divide both sides by a.) Make sure that students substitute both answers into the original equation to check:

$$\begin{array}{c|c} 3x^2 = 9 & 3x^2 = 9 \\ 3(\sqrt{3})^2 \mid 9 & 3(-\sqrt{3})^2 \mid 9 \\ 3(3) & 3(3) \\ 9 & 9 \end{array}$$

For **Example 3**, Figure 2.2-2 shows the *intersection method* from Section 2.1. To check solutions for this equation, have students substitute the decimal approximations into the original equation. They should get $5.9858 \approx 6$.

Before solving the equation in **Example 4**, it may be helpful for students to solve a simpler equation first. For example:

$$x^2 + 8x = 9$$
$$x^2 + 8x + 16 = 9 + 16$$
$$(x + 4)^2 = 25$$
$$x + 4 = 5 \text{ or } x + 4 = -5$$
$$x = 1 \text{ or } \qquad x = -9$$

> **CAUTION**
>
> When taking the square root of both sides of an equation, remember to write $\pm$ on one side of the equation.

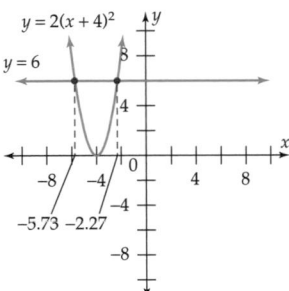

Figure 2.2-2

When k is positive, the two solutions of $x^2 = k$ are often written as $x = \pm\sqrt{k}$, which is read "x equals plus or minus the square root of k."

Taking the Square Root of Both Sides of an Equation

Example 2   Solving $ax^2 = b$

Solve $3x^2 = 9$.

Solution

$$\begin{aligned} 3x^2 &= 9 \\ x^2 &= 3 && \textit{Divide by 3} \\ x &= \pm\sqrt{3} \approx \pm 1.732 && \textit{Take the square root} \end{aligned}$$

Substitute both solutions into the original equation to check. ∎

The method of taking the square root of both sides of an equation can be used to solve equations of the form $a(x - h)^2 = k$.

Example 3   Solving $a(x - h)^2 = k$

Solve $2(x + 4)^2 = 6$.

Solution

The equation is in the form $au^2 = k$, where u represents $x + 4$. Therefore, the procedure outlined above can be applied.

$$\begin{aligned} 2(x + 4)^2 &= 6 \\ (x + 4)^2 &= 3 && \textit{Divide by 2} \\ x + 4 &= \pm\sqrt{3} && \textit{Take square roots} \\ x &= -4 \pm\sqrt{3} && \textit{Subtract 4} \\ x = -4 + \sqrt{3} \quad \text{or} \quad x &= -4 - \sqrt{3} && \textit{Exact solutions} \\ x \approx -2.27 \qquad\qquad x &\approx -5.73 && \textit{Approximate solutions} \end{aligned}$$
∎

Completing the Square

A variation of the method of taking the square root of both sides can be used to solve *any* quadratic equation. It is based on the fact that an expression of the form $x^2 + bx$ can be changed into a perfect square by adding a suitable constant. For example, adding 9 to the expression $x^2 + 6x$ changes it into a perfect square.

$$x^2 + 6x + 9 = (x + 3)^2$$

The number added is 9, which is 3^2, and 3 is one-half of 6, the coefficient of x in the original expression, $x^2 + 6x$. This technique, which is called **completing the square,** works in every case.

Completing the Square

NOTE The procedure of completing the square is used in other areas of mathematics, and knowledge of this procedure is important in later chapters.

To *complete the square* of the expression $x^2 + bx$, add the square of one-half the coefficient of x, namely $\left(\dfrac{b}{2}\right)^2$. The addition produces a perfect square trinomial.

$$x^2 + bx + \left(\frac{b}{2}\right)^2 = \left(x + \frac{b}{2}\right)^2$$

Solving a Quadratic Equation by Completing the Square

To solve a quadratic equation by completing the square, follow the procedure below.

1. Write the equation in the form $x^2 + bx = c$.

2. Add $\left(\dfrac{b}{2}\right)^2$ to both sides so that the left side is a perfect square and the right side is a constant.

3. Take the square root of both sides.

4. Simplify.

CAUTION

Completing the square only works when the coefficient of x^2 is 1. In an equation such as

$$2x^2 - 6x + 1 = 0$$

first divide both sides by 2 and *then* complete the square.

Example 4   Solving a Quadratic Equation by Completing the Square

Solve $2x^2 - 6x + 1 = 0$ by completing the square.

Solution

$$2x^2 - 6x + 1 = 0$$

$$2x^2 - 6x = -1 \qquad \textit{Subtract 1}$$

$$x^2 - 3x = -\frac{1}{2} \qquad \textit{Divide by 2}$$

$$x^2 - 3x + \frac{9}{4} = \frac{9}{4} - \frac{1}{2} \qquad \textit{Add } \left(\frac{3}{2}\right)^2 = \frac{9}{4}$$

$$\left(x - \frac{3}{2}\right)^2 = \frac{7}{4} \qquad \textit{Rewrite as perfect square and simplify}$$

$$x - \frac{3}{2} = \pm\sqrt{\frac{7}{4}} \qquad \textit{Take square root}$$

$$x = \frac{3}{2} \pm \sqrt{\frac{7}{4}} \qquad \textit{Add } \frac{3}{2}$$

$$x = \frac{3}{2} + \sqrt{\frac{7}{4}} \approx 2.823 \qquad \text{or} \qquad x = \frac{3}{2} - \sqrt{\frac{7}{4}} \approx 0.177$$

There are two real solutions. See Figure 2.2-3. ∎

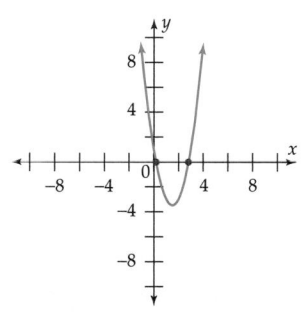

Figure 2.2-3

The technique of completing the square can be used to solve *any* quadratic equation.

Teaching Notes

You can model **Completing the Square** with geometry. The figure below on the left represents $x^2 + 6x$. To complete the square, add 9 unit-squares, as shown on the right. The now-completed square on the right represents $x^2 + 6x + 9$, or $(x + 3)^2$ in factored form.

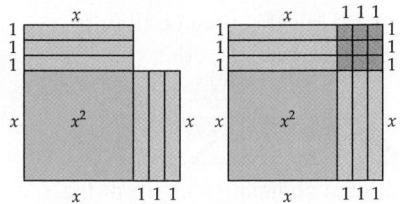

Emphasize to students that when they add $\left(\dfrac{b}{2}\right)^2$ to complete the square, they are changing the value of an expression, and therefore must *add* $\left(\dfrac{b}{2}\right)^2$ *to both sides of the equation.*

ADDITIONAL EXAMPLES

Example 2

Solve $4x^2 = 8$.

$x = \pm\sqrt{2} \approx \pm 1.414$

Example 3

Solve $5(x - 3)^2 = 15$.

$x = 3 + \sqrt{3}$ or $x = 3 - \sqrt{3}$

$x \approx 4.73 \qquad x \approx 1.27$

Example 4

Solve $8x^2 - 24x + 3 = 0$ by completing the square.

$x = \frac{3}{2} + \sqrt{\frac{15}{8}} \approx 2.869$ or

$x = \frac{3}{2} - \sqrt{\frac{15}{8}} \approx 0.131$

Math Background

The steps shown for solving $ax^2 + bx + c = 0$ by completing the square, together with the simplification that follows, constitute the derivation of the quadratic formula. Your students have probably used the formula in past math courses, but this may be their first opportunity to see it derived.

COMMON ERROR ALERT

Students sometimes interpret the ± symbol incorrectly. In **Example 5,** they may get the decimal approximation for the first solution, −0.4, and then think that the other solution is the opposite, 0.4. Stress that the ± symbol in the quadratic formula is a shorthand notation to save writing.

Remind them that $\dfrac{-b \pm \sqrt{b^2 - 4ac}}{2a}$ represents the two expressions

$$\dfrac{-b + \sqrt{b^2 - 4ac}}{2a} \text{ and } \dfrac{-b - \sqrt{b^2 - 4ac}}{2a}.$$

ADDITIONAL EXAMPLES

Example 5

Solve $x^2 - 13 = 10x$ by using the quadratic formula.

Rewrite the equation as $x^2 - 10x - 13 = 0$.

$$x = \dfrac{-(-10) \pm \sqrt{(-10)^2 - 4(1)(-13)}}{2(1)}$$

$$x = \dfrac{10 + \sqrt{152}}{2} \approx 11.2 \text{ or}$$

$$x = \dfrac{10 - \sqrt{152}}{2} \approx -1.2$$

Solving $ax^2 + bx + c = 0$ by Completing the Square

Solve $ax^2 + bx + c = 0$ by completing the square as follows:

1. Subtract c from both sides.
$$ax^2 + bx = -c$$

2. Divide both sides by a, the leading coefficient.
$$x^2 + \dfrac{b}{a}x = -\dfrac{c}{a}$$

3. Add the square of half of $\dfrac{b}{a}$, that is, $\left(\dfrac{b}{2a}\right)^2$, to both sides.
$$x^2 + \dfrac{b}{a}x + \left(\dfrac{b}{2a}\right)^2 = \left(\dfrac{b}{2a}\right)^2 - \dfrac{c}{a}$$

4. Write the left side of the equation as a perfect square.
$$\left(x + \dfrac{b}{2a}\right)^2 = \left(\dfrac{b}{2a}\right)^2 - \dfrac{c}{a}$$

5. Take the square root of both sides.
$$x + \dfrac{b}{2a} = \pm\sqrt{\left(\dfrac{b}{2a}\right)^2 - \dfrac{c}{a}}$$

6. Subtract $\dfrac{b}{2a}$ from both sides.
$$x = -\dfrac{b}{2a} \pm\sqrt{\left(\dfrac{b}{2a}\right)^2 - \dfrac{c}{a}}$$

The equation in step 6 can be simplified.

$$x = -\dfrac{b}{2a} \pm \sqrt{\dfrac{b^2}{4a^2} - \dfrac{c}{a}} \qquad \left(\dfrac{b}{2a}\right)^2 = \dfrac{b^2}{4a^2}$$

$$= \dfrac{-b}{2a} \pm \sqrt{\dfrac{b^2 - 4ac}{4a^2}} \qquad \dfrac{b^2}{4a^2} - \dfrac{c}{a} = \dfrac{b^2}{4a^2} - \dfrac{4ac}{4a^2}$$

$$= \dfrac{-b}{2a} \pm \dfrac{\sqrt{b^2 - 4ac}}{2a}$$

$$= \dfrac{-b \pm \sqrt{b^2 - 4ac}}{2a}$$

The final expression is known as the quadratic formula.

The Quadratic Formula

The solutions of the quadratic equation $ax^2 + bx + c = 0$ are

$$x = \dfrac{-b \pm \sqrt{b^2 - 4ac}}{2a}$$

Because the quadratic formula can be used to solve *any* quadratic equation, it should be memorized.

ADDITIONAL EXAMPLES

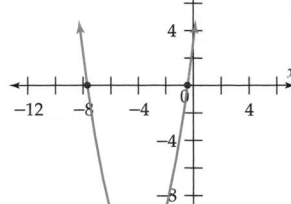

Figure 2.2-4

Example 5   Solving a Quadratic Equation by Using the Quadratic Formula

Solve $x^2 + 3 = -8x$ by using the quadratic formula.

Solution

Rewrite the equation as $x^2 + 8x + 3 = 0$, and apply the quadratic formula with $a = 1$, $b = 8$, and $c = 3$.

$$x = \frac{-8 \pm \sqrt{8^2 - 4(1)(3)}}{2(1)} = \frac{-8 \pm \sqrt{64 - 12}}{2} = \frac{-8 \pm \sqrt{52}}{2}$$

Therefore, $x = \dfrac{-8 + \sqrt{52}}{2} \approx -0.4$ or $x = \dfrac{-8 - \sqrt{52}}{2} \approx -7.6$.

The equation has two distinct real solutions, as confirmed in Figure 2.2-4. ∎

The Discriminant

The expression $b^2 - 4ac$ in the quadratic formula, called the **discriminant,** can be used to determine the *number* of real solutions of the equation $ax^2 + bx + c = 0$.

Real Solutions of a Quadratic Equation

Discriminant Value	Number of Real Solutions of $ax^2 + bx + c = 0$
$b^2 - 4ac > 0$	2 distinct real solutions
$b^2 - 4ac = 0$	1 distinct real solution
$b^2 - 4ac < 0$	0 real solutions

The discriminant can be used to determine if an equation has no real solutions without completing all computations.

Example 6   Determining the Number of Solutions by Using the Discriminant

Solve $2x^2 = -x - 3$.

Solution

First, write the equation in general form.

$$2x^2 + x + 3 = 0$$
$$b^2 - 4ac = 1 - 4(2)(3) = -23 < 0$$

Example 6

Solve $4x^2 = -x - 2$.

First, write the equation in general form.

$$4x^2 + x + 2 = 0$$
$$b^2 - 4ac = 1 - 4(4)(2) = -31 < 0$$

The discriminant is negative. Therefore, $4x^2 + x + 2 = 0$ (and $4x^2 = -x - 2$) has no real solutions.

Teaching Notes

For the **Real Solutions of a Quadratic Equation,** show these graphical representations:

$b^2 - 4ac > 0$
2 real solutions
2 x-intercepts of
$y = f(x)$

$b^2 - 4ac = 0$
1 real solution
1 x-intercept of
$y = f(x)$

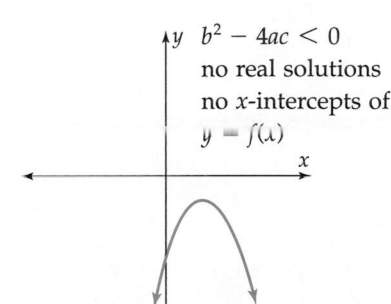

$b^2 - 4ac < 0$
no real solutions
no x-intercepts of
$y = f(x)$

Teaching Notes

Ask students to use the definition to determine whether these are **Polynomial Equations,** and to explain why or why not:

$5x^2 + x^4 + 2 = 3$

yes; it can be written
$1x^4 + 0x^3 + 5x^2 + 0x^1 - 1x^0 = 0$

$x^2 + \frac{1}{x} + 2 = 0$

no; it has a variable in a denominator

$-x^2 + \sqrt{x} + 5 = 0$

no; it has a variable under a radical sign

ADDITIONAL EXAMPLES

Example 7

Solve $3x^4 - 5x^2 + 2 = 0$.

Substitute u for x^2.

$3x^4 - 5x^2 + 2 = 0$

$3(x^2)^2 - 5x^2 + 2 = 0$

$3u^2 - 5u + 2 = 0$

$(3u - 2)(u - 1) = 0$

$3u - 2 = 0$ or $u - 1 = 0$

$u = \frac{2}{3}$ $\qquad u = 1$

Now solve for x.

$x^2 = \frac{2}{3}$ or $x^2 = 1$

The four solutions are: $x = \pm\sqrt{\dfrac{2}{3}}$ and $x = \pm 1$.

Figure 2.2-5

Definition of Polynomial Equation

NOTE Polynomials are discussed in Chapter 4.

The discriminant of $2x^2 + x + 3 = 0$ is negative. Therefore, $2x^2 + x + 3 = 0$ has no real solutions.

You can confirm this fact because the graph of $y = 2x^2 + x + 3$ does not touch the x-axis, as shown in Figure 2.2-5. Since the graph has no x-intercepts, the equation has no real solutions. ∎

NOTE A quadratic equation with no x-intercepts has no real solution.

Polynomial Equations

> **A polynomial equation of degree n is an equation that can be written in the form**
>
> $$a_n x^n + a_{n-1}x^{n-1} + \cdots + a_1 x + a_0 = 0,$$
>
> **where $a_n, \cdots, a_0$ are real numbers.**

For instance, $4x^6 - 3x^5 + x^4 + 7x^3 - 8x^2 + 4x + 9 = 0$ is a polynomial equation of degree 6. Similarly, $4x^3 - 3x^2 + 4x - 5$ is a polynomial expression of degree 3. Notice that polynomials have the following traits.

- no variables in denominators
- no variables under radical signs

As a general rule, polynomial equations of degree 3 and above are best solved by the graphical methods presented in Section 2.1. However, some equations are quadratic in form and can be solved algebraically.

Polynomial Equations in Quadratic Form

Example 7 Solving an Equation in Quadratic Form

Solve $4x^4 - 13x^2 + 3 = 0$.

Solution

To write $4x^4 - 13x^2 + 3 = 0$ in quadratic form, substitute u for x^2.

$$4x^4 - 13x^2 + 3 = 0$$
$$4(x^2)^2 - 13x^2 + 3 = 0 \qquad \textit{Write } x^4 \textit{ as } (x^2)^2$$
$$4u^2 - 13u + 3 = 0 \qquad \textit{Substitute } u \textit{ for } x^2$$

Then solve the resulting quadratic equation.

$$(u - 3)(4u - 1) = 0 \qquad \textit{Factor}$$

$$u - 3 = 0 \quad \text{or} \quad 4u - 1 = 0 \qquad \textit{Zero-Product Property}$$

$$u = 3 \qquad\qquad u = \frac{1}{4}$$

Figure 2.2-6

Because $u = x^2$,

$$x^2 = 3 \qquad \text{or} \qquad x^2 = \frac{1}{4}$$

$$x = \pm\sqrt{3} \qquad\qquad x = \pm\frac{1}{2}$$

Therefore, the original equation has four solutions, $x = \pm\sqrt{3}$ and $x = \pm\frac{1}{2}$, as shown in Figure 2.2-6. ■

Teaching Notes

Note that Figure 2.2-6 is not a parabola. Remind students that the equation $4x^4 - 13x^2 + 3 = 0$ is not a quadratic equation. It is a 4th-degree polynomial equation that can be written in quadratic form by making an appropriate substitution.

Exercises 2.2

ANSWERS

19. $s = \pm\sqrt{6} \approx \pm 2.449$

20. no real number solutions

21. $x = \pm\frac{2}{5}$

22. $x = \pm\sqrt{7} \approx \pm 2.646$

23. $w = \pm\sqrt{\dfrac{28}{3}} \approx \pm 3.055$

24. no real number solutions

53. no real number solutions

54. no real number solutions

Exercises 2.2

In Exercises 1–12, solve each equation by factoring.

1. $x^2 - 8x + 15 = 0$
  $x = 3$ or 5
2. $x^2 + 5x + 6 = 0$
  $x = -3$ or -2
3. $x^2 - 5x = 14$
  $x = -2$ or 7
4. $x^2 + x = 20$
  $x = -5$ or 4
5. $2y^2 + 5y - 3 = 0$
  $y = \frac{1}{2}$ or -3
6. $3t^2 - t - 2 = 0$
  $t = -\frac{2}{3}$ or 1
7. $4t^2 + 9t + 2 = 0$
  $t = -2$ or $-\frac{1}{4}$
8. $9t^2 + 2 = 11t$
  $t = \frac{2}{9}$ or 1
9. $3u^2 + u = 4$
  $u = 1$ or $-\frac{4}{3}$
10. $5x^2 + 26x = -5$
  $x = -\frac{1}{5}$ or -5
11. $12x^2 + 13x = 4$
  $x = \frac{1}{4}$ or $-\frac{4}{3}$
12. $18x^2 = 23x + 6$
  $x = -\frac{2}{9}$ or $\frac{3}{2}$

In Exercises 13–24, solve the equation by taking the square root of both sides. Give exact solutions and approximate solutions, if appropriate.

13. $x^2 = 9$
  $x = \pm 3$
14. $x^2 = 12$
  $x = \pm\sqrt{12} \approx \pm 3.464$
15. $x^2 = 40$
  $x = \pm\sqrt{40} \approx \pm 6.325$
16. $-x^2 = -10$
  $x = \pm\sqrt{10} \approx \pm 3.162$
17. $3x^2 = 12$
  $x = \pm 2$
18. $\frac{1}{2}v^2 = 10$
  $v = \pm\sqrt{20} \approx \pm 4.472$
19. $-5s^2 = -30$
20. $-3x^2 = 11$
21. $25x^2 - 4 = 0$
22. $4x^2 - 28 = 0$
23. $-3w^2 + 8 = -20$
24. $-2t^2 - 11 = 5$

In Exercises 25–28, solve the equation by completing the square.

25. $x^2 - 2x = 12$
  $x = 1 \pm \sqrt{13}$
26. $x^2 - 4x - 30 = 0$
  $x = 2 \pm \sqrt{34}$
27. $w^2 - w - 1 = 0$
  $w = \dfrac{1 \pm \sqrt{5}}{2}$
28. $t^2 + 3t - 2 = 0$
  $t = -\dfrac{3 \pm \sqrt{17}}{2}$

In Exercises 29–40, use the quadratic formula to solve the equation.

29. $x^2 - 4x + 1 = 0$
  $x = 2 \pm \sqrt{3}$
30. $x^2 - 2x - 1 = 0$
  $x = 1 \pm \sqrt{2}$
31. $x^2 + 6x + 7 = 0$
  $x = -3 \pm \sqrt{2}$
32. $x^2 + 4x - 3 = 0$
  $x = -2 \pm \sqrt{7}$
33. $x^2 + 6 = 2x$ no real number solutions
34. $x^2 + 11 = 6x$ no real number solutions
35. $4x^2 - 4x = 7$
  $x = \frac{1}{2} \pm \sqrt{2}$
36. $4x^2 - 4x = 11$
  $x = \frac{1}{2} \pm \sqrt{3}$
37. $4x^2 - 8x + 1 = 0$
  $x = \dfrac{2 \pm \sqrt{3}}{2}$
38. $2t^2 + 4t + 1 = 0$
  $t = -1 \pm \dfrac{\sqrt{2}}{2}$
39. $5u^2 + 8u = -2$
  $u = \dfrac{-4 \pm \sqrt{6}}{5}$
40. $4x^2 = 3x + 5$
  $x = \dfrac{3 \pm \sqrt{89}}{8}$

In Exercises 41–46, find the number of real solutions of the equation by computing the discriminant.

41. $x^2 + 4x + 1 = 0$
  2
42. $4x^2 - 4x - 3 = 0$
  2
43. $9x^2 = 12x + 1$
  2
44. $9t^2 + 15 = 30t$
  2
45. $25t^2 + 49 - 70t$
  1
46. $49t^2 + 5 = 42t$
  2

In Exercises 47–56, solve the equation by any method.

47. $x^2 + 9x + 18 = 0$
  $x = -3$ or -6
48. $3t^2 - 11t - 20 = 0$
  $t = -\frac{4}{3}$ or 5
49. $4x(x + 1) = 1$
  $x = \dfrac{-1 \pm \sqrt{2}}{2}$
50. $25y^2 = 20y + 1$
  $y = \dfrac{2 \pm \sqrt{5}}{5}$
51. $2x^2 = 7x + 15$
  $x = 5$ or $-\frac{3}{2}$
52. $2x^2 = 6x + 3$
  $x = \dfrac{3 \pm \sqrt{15}}{2}$
53. $t^2 + 4t + 13 = 0$
54. $5x^2 + 2x = -2$
55. $\dfrac{7x^2}{3} = \dfrac{2x}{3} - 1$
  no real number solutions
56. $25x + \dfrac{4}{x} = 20$
  $x = \frac{2}{5}$

In Exercises 57–60, use a calculator to find approximate solutions of the equation.

57. $4.42x^2 - 10.14x + 3.79 = 0$
  $x < 1.824$ or 0.470
58. $8.06x^2 + 25.8726x - 25.047256 = 0$
  $x < 0.779$ or -3.989
59. $3x^2 - 82.74x + 570.4923 = 0$
  $x = 13.79$
60. $7.63x^2 + 2.79x = 5.32$
  $x < 0.672$ or -1.038

In Exercises 61–68, find all exact real solutions of the equation.

61. $y^4 - 7y^2 + 6 = 0$ **$y = \pm 1$ or $\pm\sqrt{6}$**

62. $x^4 - 2x^2 + 1 = 0$ **$x = \pm 1$**

63. $x^4 - 2x^2 - 35 = 0$ **$x = \pm\sqrt{7}$**

64. $x^4 - 2x^2 - 24 = 0$ **$x = \pm\sqrt{6}$**

65. $2y^4 - 9y^2 + 4 = 0$ **$y = -2$ or $-\dfrac{1}{\sqrt{2}}$**

66. $6z^4 - 7z^2 + 2 = 0$ **$z = \pm\dfrac{1}{\sqrt{2}}$ or $\pm\sqrt{\dfrac{2}{3}}$**

67. $10x^4 + 3x^2 = 1$
  $x = \pm\dfrac{1}{\sqrt{5}}$

68. $6x^4 - 7x^2 = 3$
  $x = \pm\sqrt{\dfrac{3}{2}}$

In Exercises 69–72, find a number k such that the given equation has exactly one real solution.

69. $x^2 + kx + 25 = 0$ **$k = 10$ or -10**

70. $x^2 - kx + 49 = 0$ **$k = 14$ or -14**

71. $kx^2 + 8x + 1 = 0$ **$k = 16$**

72. $kx^2 + 24x + 16 = 0$ **$k = 9$**

73. Find a number k such that 4 and 1 are the solutions of $x^2 - 5x + k = 0$. **$k = 4$**

74. Suppose a, b, and c are fixed real numbers such that $b^2 - 4ac \geq 0$. Let r and s be the solutions of
$$ax^2 + bx + c = 0.$$

a. Use the quadratic formula to show that
  $r + s = -\dfrac{b}{a}$ and $rs = \dfrac{c}{a}$.

b. Use part **a** to verify that
  $ax^2 + bx + c = a(x - r)(x - s)$.

c. Use part **b** to factor $x^2 - 2x - 1$ and $5x^2 + 8x + 2$.

a. $r = \dfrac{-b + \sqrt{b^2 - 4ac}}{2a}$,

  $s = \dfrac{-b - \sqrt{b^2 - 4ac}}{2a}$,

  $r + s = \dfrac{-2b}{2a} = -\dfrac{b}{a}$

  $rs = \left(\dfrac{-b + \sqrt{b^2 - 4ac}}{2a}\right) \cdot$

  $\qquad\qquad \left(\dfrac{-b - \sqrt{b^2 - 4ac}}{2a}\right)$

  $= \dfrac{b^2 - (b^2 - 4ac)}{2a}$

  $= \dfrac{4ac}{4a^2} = \dfrac{c}{a}$

b. $a(x - r)(x - s)$

  $= a(x^2 - (r + s)x + rs)$

  $= a\left(x^2 - \left(-\dfrac{b}{a}\right)x + \dfrac{c}{a}\right)$

  $= ax^2 + bx + c$

c. $x^2 - 2x - 1$

  $= \left(x - (1 + \sqrt{2})\right) \cdot \left(x - (1 - \sqrt{2})\right)$

  $5x^2 + 8x + 2$

  $= 5\left(x - \left(\dfrac{-4 + \sqrt{6}}{5}\right)\right) \cdot$

  $\qquad\qquad \left(x - \left(\dfrac{-4 - \sqrt{6}}{5}\right)\right)$

2.3 **Applications of Equations**

Objectives

- Solve application problems

Real-life situations are usually described verbally, but they must be interpreted and expressed as equivalent mathematical statements. The following guideline may be helpful.

Applied Problems Guideline

1. *Read* the problem carefully, and determine what is asked for.
2. *Label* the unknown quantities with variables.
3. *Draw* a picture of the situation, if appropriate.
4. *Translate* the verbal statements in the problem and the relationships between the known and unknown quantities into mathematical language.
5. *Consolidate* the mathematical information into an equation in one variable that can be solved or an equation in two variables that can be graphed.
6. *Solve* for at least one of the unknown quantities.
7. *Find* all remaining unknown quantities by using the relationships given in the problem.
8. *Check and interpret* all quantities found in the original problem.

Example 1   **Number Relations**

The average of two real numbers is 41.125, and their product is 1683. Find the two numbers.

Solution

1. *Read:*   Two numbers are asked for.

2. *Label:*   Let the numbers be a and b.

3. *Draw:*   A diagram is not appropriate in this problem.

4. *Translate:*

English Language	Mathematical Language	
two numbers	a and b	
Their average is 41.125.	$\frac{a+b}{2} = 41.125$	[1]
Their product is 1683.	$ab = 1683$	[2]

5. *Consolidate:*   One technique to use when dealing with two unknowns is to express one in terms of the other, then substitute to obtain an equation in one variable. Solve equation [2] for b.

$$ab = 1683 \qquad\qquad [2]$$

$$b = \frac{1683}{a} \qquad \textit{Divide both sides by a}$$

Section 2.3 Applications of Equations

Example Notes

For **Example 1**, you can have students solve the equation algebraically, using the quadratic formula:

$$x + \frac{1683}{x} - 82.25 = 0$$

Multiply both sides by x:

$$x^2 - 82.25x + 1683 = 0$$

$$x = \frac{82.25 \pm \sqrt{(-82.25)^2 - 4(1)(1683)}}{2(1)}$$

$$x = \frac{82.25 \pm \sqrt{33.0625}}{2}$$

$$x = 44 \text{ or } 38.25$$

ADDITIONAL EXAMPLES

Example 1

The average of two real numbers is 39.625, and one number is 1500 times the reciprocal of the other. Find the two numbers.

Equations: $\frac{a+b}{2} = 39.625$

$$b = 1500 \cdot \frac{1}{a}$$

Solution:

$$\frac{a + \frac{1500}{a}}{2} = 39.625$$

$$a + \frac{1500}{a} = 79.25$$

Graph the related equation

$y_1 = x + \frac{1500}{x} - 79.25$ and find the x-intercepts.

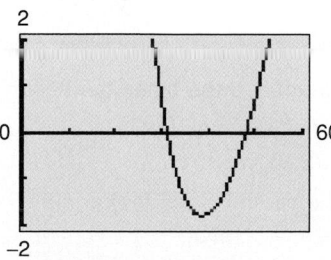

The solutions to the equation $a + \frac{1500}{a} = 79.25$ are $a = 48$ and $a = 31.25.$

Check:

Average: $\frac{48 + 31.25}{2} = 39.625$

Reciprocal relationship:

$1500 \cdot \frac{1}{48} = 31.25$

The two numbers are 48 and 31.25.

Nonlinear equations can yield multiple solutions. Remind students that the equation they solved in **Example 1** had two solutions. Point out that in an application problem, all *solutions of an equation* must be checked to see if they provide actual *solutions to the problem*. An application problem may have one or more solutions, or no solution at all. (In **Example 2**, one of the equation solutions is discarded because it does not provide a solution to the problem. In **Example 3**, two of three equation solutions provide solutions to the problem, each providing a different set of dimensions for a box.)

ADDITIONAL EXAMPLES

Example 2

The width of a rectangle is three times its height. If it has an area of 60.75 square feet, what are its dimensions?

$w = 3h$

Equations:
$$w = 3h$$
$$wh = 60.75$$

Solution: $(3h)h = 60.75$
$$3h^2 = 60.75$$
$$h = \pm 4.5$$

$h = 4.5$ feet
$w = 3h = 3 \cdot 4.5 = 13.5$

Check:

The width is three times the height and the area is correct.

$(4.5)(13.5) = 60.75$

So, the width is 13.5 feet and the height is 4.5 feet.

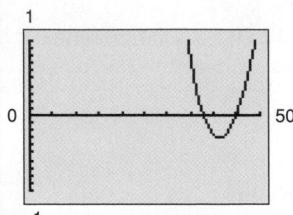

1

0   50

−1

Figure 2.3-1

Substitute the result into equation [1] and simplify.

$$\frac{a + b}{2} = 41.125 \qquad [1]$$

$$\frac{a + \frac{1683}{a}}{2} = 41.125 \qquad \textit{Substitute } \frac{1683}{a} \textit{ for } b$$

$$a + \frac{1683}{a} = 82.25 \qquad \textit{Multiply both sides by 2}$$

6. *Solve:*   Solve the equation by using the *x*-Intercept Method with the graph of $y_1 = x + \frac{1683}{x} - 82.25$, where *x* represents *a*. See Figure 2.3-1.

The solutions of $a + \frac{1683}{a} - 82.25$ are $a = 44$ and $a = 38.25$.

7. *Find:*   Find the other number, *b*, from the equation $ab = 1683$.

Let $a = 44$. $44b = 1683$
                          $b = 38.25$

Similarly, let $a = 38.25$ and use the same equation to find $b = 44$.

8. *Check:*   The average of 44 and 38.25 is $\frac{44 + 38.25}{2} = 41.125$.

The product of 44 and 38.25 is 1683.

The two numbers are 44 and 38.25.   ■

Solutions in Context

When solving an application problem, it is important to interpret answers in terms of the original problem. Each solution should

- make sense
- satisfy the given conditions
- answer the original question

In particular, an equation may have several solutions, some of which may not make sense in the context of the problem. For instance, distance cannot be negative, the number of people cannot be a fraction, etc.

Example 2   Dimensions of a Rectangle

A rectangle is twice as wide as it is high. If it has an area of 24.5 square inches, what are its dimensions?

Solution

1. *Read:*   The dimensions of the rectangle are asked for.

2. *Label:*   Let *w* denote the width and *h* denote the height.

3. *Draw:*   See Figure 2.3-2.

$w = 2h$

Figure 2.3-2

4. *Translate:* The area of a rectangle is width × height.

English Language	Mathematical Language	
Width is twice height.	$w = 2h$	[3]
The area is 24.5 in².	$wh = 24.5$	[4]

5. *Consolidate:* Substitute $2h$ for w in equation [4].

$$wh = 24.5$$
$$(2h)h = 24.5$$
$$2h^2 = 24.5$$

6. *Solve:* Solve by taking the square root of both sides.

$$h^2 = 12.25 \qquad \textit{Divide by 2}$$
$$h = \pm\sqrt{12.25} = \pm3.5 \qquad \textit{Take square root of both sides}$$

Because height is never negative, only the positive root applies to this situation. Therefore, $h = 3.5$ in.

7. *Find:* Find the width by using equation [3] and $h = 3.5$.

$$w = 2(3.5) = 7 \text{ in.}$$

8. *Check:* The width is twice the height and the area is correct.

$$3.5(7) = 24.5 \text{ in}^2$$

Thus, the width is 7 inches and the height is 3.5 inches. ∎

Example 3 Volume of a Rectangular Box

A rectangular box with a square base and no top is to have a volume of 30,000 cm³. If the surface area of the box is 6000 cm², what are the dimensions of the box?

Solution

1. *Read:* The quantities to be found are the length, width, and height of the box.

2. *Label:* Notice that the two sides of the base have the same length. Let s denote a side of the square base of the box. Let h denote the height of the box.

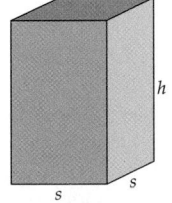

Figure 2.3-3

3. *Draw:* See Figure 2.3-3.

4. *Translate:* The volume of a box is given by length × width × height and the surface area is the sum of the area of the base and the area of the four sides of the box.

English Language	Mathematical Language	
length, width, height	s, s, and h	
surface area:		
base surface area	s^2	
each side surface area	sh	
total surface area	$s^2 + 4sh$	
Volume is 30,000 cm³	$s^2h = 30,000$	[5]
Surface area is 6000 cm²	$s^2 + 4sh = 6,000$	[6]

Determining the dimensions of a container to achieve a certain volume is a common problem to be solved in the business world because volume (capacity) is a measure of how much a container will hold. A reasonable approach might seem to be to design a container with the required volume and a minimum amount of construction materials (minimum surface area). However, there are often other considerations. Research has found that the dimensions of packages affect a customer's decision about which product to choose. For example, a customer may be more likely to choose one brand of cereal over another brand on the basis of the shape of the box.

ADDITIONAL EXAMPLES

Example 3

A storage locker in the shape of a rectangular prism with a square floor has a volume of 70,000 cubic inches. If the surface area of the four walls and the top is 10,000 square inches, what are the dimensions of the locker?

Volume: $s^2h = 70,000$
Surface area: $s^2 + 4sh = 10,000$

$$s^2 + 4s\left(\frac{70,000}{s^2}\right) = 10,000$$

$$s^2 + \frac{280,000}{s} = 10,000$$

Graph $y_1 = s^2 + \frac{280,000}{s}$ and $y_2 = 10,000$.

$s \approx 30.97$ or $s \approx 80.85$

$$h \approx \frac{70,000}{(30.97)^2} \approx 72.98$$

$$h = \frac{70,000}{(80.85)^2} \approx 10.71$$

Possible locker dimensions:
30.97 in. × 30.97 in. × 72.98 in.
80.85 in. × 80.85 in. × 10.71 in.
(not a good shape for a locker).

Example Notes

In **Example 3**, Figure 2.3-4, point out that there are three points of intersection of the graphs, but the solution generated by the point of intersection that lies in Quadrant II must be rejected because it represents a negative length.

It may help students to see how the formula $I = Prt$ is used in **Example 4**. Point out that in finance, a *return* is a profit, revenue, or yield on an investment. In this case, the return is an amount of interest earned on an investment. So, for the stock investment:

- I is called the return
- P is the principal, in this case the amount invested s
- r is the annual rate, 12% in this case
- t is the time, 1 year in this case

So, the return is
$I = Prt = (s)(0.12)(1) = 0.12s$. Have students use the formula $I = Prt$ to get the expression for the return on the savings account investment.

$I = Prt = (9000 - s)(0.06)(1)$
$= (0.06)(9000 - s) = 540 - 0.06s$

In **Example 5**, in order to solve the rational equation $\dfrac{420}{r-30} + \dfrac{420}{r+40} = 5$, both sides of the equation must be multiplied by the LCD $(r - 30)(r + 40)$. The solutions to the equation are $r = 170$ and $r = -12$, but -12 is not a reasonable rate.
Encourage students to check for $r = 170$:
$\dfrac{420}{170 - 30} + \dfrac{420}{170 + 40} = \dfrac{420}{140} + \dfrac{420}{210}$
$= 3 + 2 = 5 \checkmark$

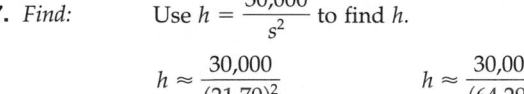

Figure 2.3-4

5. *Consolidate:* Solve equation [5] for h: $h = \dfrac{30{,}000}{s^2}$

Substitute the expression for h into equation [6].

$$s^2 + 4s\left(\dfrac{30{,}000}{s^2}\right) = 6000$$

$$s^2 + \dfrac{120{,}000}{s} = 6000$$

6. *Solve:* To solve by using the Intersection Method, graph $y_1 = s^2 + \dfrac{120{,}000}{s}$ and $y_2 = 6000$, as shown in Figure 2.3-4, and find the points of intersection. Therefore, $s \approx 21.70$ cm or $s \approx 64.29$ cm.

7. *Find:* Use $h = \dfrac{30{,}000}{s^2}$ to find h.

$h \approx \dfrac{30{,}000}{(21.70)^2}$ $\qquad$ $h \approx \dfrac{30{,}000}{(64.29)^2}$

$\approx \dfrac{30{,}000}{470.89} \approx 63.71$ cm $\qquad$ $\approx \dfrac{30{,}000}{4133.2041} \approx 7.26$ cm

8. *Check:* Volume
$\approx (21.7)^2(63.71)$ $\qquad$ $\approx (64.29)^2(7.26)$
$\approx 30{,}000.4019$ $\qquad$ $\approx 30{,}007.06177$

Surface Area
$\approx (21.7)^2 + 4(21.7)(63.71)$ $\qquad$ $\approx (64.29)^2 + 4(64.29)(7.26)$
≈ 6000.918 $\qquad$ ≈ 6000.1857

One base is approximately 21.7 cm × 21.7 cm with a height of approximately 63.71 cm. Another base is approximately 64.29 cm × 64.29 cm with a height of approximately 7.26 cm. ∎

Interest Applications

Calculating interest is common in real-world applications. When an amount, P, is deposited or borrowed, P is referred to as the **principal.** **Interest** is the fee paid for the use of the money and is calculated as a percentage of the principal each year. When the duration of a loan or a bank balance is less than 1 year, **simple interest** is generally used. The basic rule of **simple interest** is

$$I = Prt$$

P represents the principal, r represents the *annual* interest rate, and t represents time in years.

Example 4   Stock and Savings Returns

A high-risk stock pays dividends at a rate of 12% per year, and a savings account pays 6% interest per year. How much of a $9000 investment should be put in the stock and how much should be put in savings to obtain a return of 8% per year on the total investment?

ADDITIONAL EXAMPLES

NOTE In Precalculus, combining basic algebraic steps to promote clarity when simplifying is encouraged as long as it does not cause confusion.

Solution

Read and Label: Let s be the amount invested in stock. Then the rest of the $9000, namely $9000 - s$, will be the amount in the savings account.

Translate:

$$\left(\begin{array}{c}\text{Return on } s \text{ dollars}\\ \text{in stock at } 12\%\end{array}\right) + \left(\begin{array}{c}\text{Return on } 9000 - s\\ \text{dollars in savings at } 6\%\end{array}\right) = 8\% \text{ of } \$9000$$

$$12\% \text{ of } s \quad + \quad 6\% \text{ of } (9000 - s) \quad = \quad 0.08(9000)$$

$$0.12s + 0.06(9000 - s) = 720$$
$$0.12s + 540 - 0.06s = 720$$
$$0.12s - 0.06s = 720 - 540$$
$$0.06s = 180$$
$$s = \frac{180}{0.06} = 3000$$

Therefore, the investment should be as follows:

- $3000 in stock
- $(9000 - 3000) = \$6000$ in the savings account

If this is done, the total return will be 12% of $3000 plus 6% of $6000, making a total return of $360 + $360 = $720—which is 8% of $9000. ∎

Distance Applications

The basic formula for problems involving distance and a constant rate of velocity is

$$d = rt$$

where d represents the distance traveled at rate r for time t. The units for rate should be the distance units divided by the time units, such as miles per hour.

Example 5   Distance

A pilot wants to make an 840-mile round trip from Cleveland to Peoria and back in 5 hours flying time. There will be a headwind of 30 mph going to Peoria, and it is estimated that there will be a 40-mph tailwind returning to Cleveland. At what constant engine speed should the plane be flown?

Solution

Let r be the engine speed of the plane, and note that the headwind slows the velocity by 30 and the tailwind increases the velocity by 40.

Example 4

A real estate investment yields a return of 10% per year and a certificate of deposit (CD) pays 6% interest per year. How much of $7500 should be put in the real estate investment and how much should be put in the CD to obtain a return of 7% on the entire $7500?

$$\left(\begin{array}{c}\text{Return on}\\ s \text{ dollars}\\ \text{at } 10\%\end{array}\right) + \left(\begin{array}{c}\text{Return on}\\ 7500 - s \text{ dollars}\\ \text{at } 6\%\end{array}\right)$$
$$= 7\% \text{ of } \$7500$$
$$0.10s + 0.06(7500 - s) = 0.07(7500)$$
$$s = 1875$$

$1875 should be put in the real estate investment and $5625 in the certificate of deposit.

Check:

$$(0.10)(1875) + (0.06)(5625)$$
$$= 187.50 + 337.50 = 525;$$
$$(0.07)(7500) = 525$$

Example 5

A canoeist paddled a total of 11 hours on a 48-kilometer round trip to Bear Lake. The upstream trip to Bear Lake followed a period of heavy rain, and the current he paddled against was 3 kilometers per hour.

For the downstream return trip, he paddled with the current that had slowed to 2 kilometers per hour. At what speed could he paddle the canoe in still water?

$$\frac{24}{r - 3} + \frac{24}{r + 2} = 11$$
$$r = 6 \text{ or } r = -\frac{7}{11}$$

The speed of the canoe in still water was 6 kilometers per hour.

Check:

$$\frac{24}{6 - 3} + \frac{24}{6 + 2} = \frac{24}{3} + \frac{24}{8}$$
$$= 8 + 3$$
$$= 11$$

In **Example 6,** students may write the expressions $40 + x$ and $24 + x$ to describe the dimensions of the rectangle formed by the outer edges of the walkway. Remind them that the width of *two* walkways must be added to the garden's dimensions, one on each side.

Example Notes

For **Example 6,** remind students of the Quadratic Formula:

For $ax^2 + bx + c$, $a \neq 0$,

$$x = \frac{-b \pm \sqrt{b^2 - 4ac}}{2a}$$

In **Example 7,** to help students visualize the construction of the box, have them create a box by cutting 2-inch squares from the corners of an $8\frac{1}{2} \times 11$ piece of paper and taping up the flaps. Have students verify that the dimensions of the box are $4\frac{1}{2} \times 7 \times 2$.

ADDITIONAL EXAMPLES

Example 6

A walkway of uniform width is to be built around a square swimming pool with 18-foot edges. How wide should the walkway be to make the area of the walkway's surface 400 square feet?

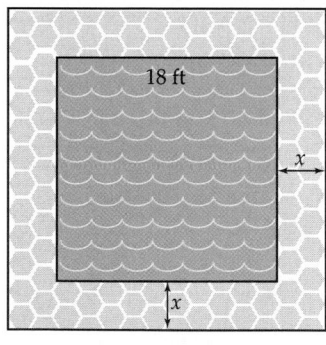

$$\binom{\text{area of}}{\text{outer square}} - \binom{\text{area of}}{\text{pool}} = \binom{\text{area of}}{\text{walkway}}$$

$(18 + 2x)(18 + 2x) - (18)^2 = 400$

$x^2 + 18x - 100 = 0$

$$x = \frac{-18 \pm \sqrt{18^2 - 4(1)(-100)}}{2(1)}$$

$x \approx 4.45$ or $x \approx -22.45$

The negative solution is unreasonable. The walkway should be about 4.45 feet wide.

	Distance	Actual Velocity	Time
Cleveland to Peoria	420	$r - 30$	$\frac{D}{r_P} = \frac{420}{r - 30}$
Peoria to Cleveland	420	$r + 40$	$\frac{D}{r_C} = \frac{420}{r + 40}$

The time traveling to Peoria plus the time traveling back to Cleveland is the total time traveled, or 5 hours.

$$(\text{Time to Peoria}) + (\text{Time to Cleveland}) = 5$$

$$\frac{420}{r - 30} + \frac{420}{r + 40} = 5$$

Multiply both sides by the common denominator $(r - 30)(r + 40)$, and simplify.

$$5(r - 30)(r + 40) = \frac{420}{r - 30}(r - 30)(r + 40) + \frac{420}{r + 40}(r - 30)(r + 40)$$

$$5(r - 30)(r + 40) = 420(r + 40) + 420(r - 30)$$

$$(r - 30)(r + 40) = 84(r + 40) + 84(r - 30)$$

$$r^2 + 10r - 1200 = 84r + 3360 + 84r - 2520$$

$$r^2 - 158r - 2040 = 0$$

$$(r - 170)(r + 12) = 0$$

$$r - 170 = 0 \quad \text{or} \quad r + 12 = 0$$

$$r = 170 \qquad\qquad r = -12$$

Obviously, the negative solution does not apply. Because both sides were multiplied by a quantity involving the variable, the positive solution, 170, should be checked in the original problem to make sure it *is* a solution.

Other Applications

Example 6   Width of a Garden Walk

A landscaper wants to put a cement walk of uniform width around a rectangular garden that measures 24 by 40 feet. She has enough cement to cover 660 square feet. How wide should the walk be in order to use all the cement?

Solution

Let x denote the width of the walk in feet and draw a picture of the situation, as shown in Figure 2.3-5.

The length of the outer rectangle is the garden length plus walks on each end, or $40 + 2x$, and its width is the garden width plus walks on each end, or $24 + 2x$. The area of the walk is found by subtracting the area of the garden from the area of the outer rectangle.

Figure 2.3-5

(Area of outer rectangle) − (Area of garden) = Area of the walk

$$(40 + 2x)(24 + 2x) \quad - \quad (40)(24) = 660$$
$$960 + 128x + 4x^2 - 960 = 660$$
$$4x^2 + 128x - 660 = 0$$
$$x^2 + 32x - 165 = 0$$
$$x = \frac{-32 \pm \sqrt{(32)^2 - 4(1)(-165)}}{2(1)} \quad \textit{Apply the quadratic formula}$$
$$x = \frac{-32 \pm \sqrt{1684}}{2}$$
$$x \approx 4.5 \text{ or } x \approx -36.5$$

Only the positive solution makes sense, so the walk should be approximately 4.5 feet wide. Check the solution in the original problem. ■

Example 7   Box Construction

A box with no top that has a volume of 1000 cubic inches is to be constructed from a 22×30-inch sheet of cardboard by cutting squares of equal size from each corner and folding up the flaps, as shown in Figure 2.3-6. What size square should be cut from each corner?

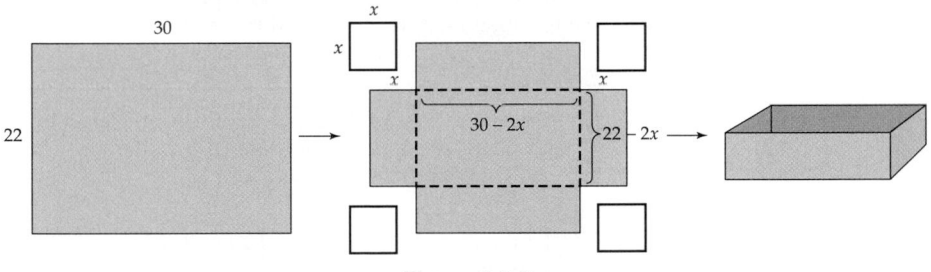

Figure 2.3-6

Solution

Let x represent the length of the side of the square to be cut from each corner. The dashed rectangle in Figure 2.3-6 is the bottom of the box. Its length is $30 - 2x$, as shown in the figure. Similarly, the width of the box will be $22 - 2x$, and its height will be x inches. Therefore,

$$\text{Length} \times \text{Width} \times \text{Height} = \text{Volume of the box}$$

$$(30 - 2x)(22 - 2x)x = 1000$$

Because the cardboard is 22 inches wide, x must be less than 11, and because x is a length, it must be positive. Therefore, the only meaningful solutions in this context are between 0 and 11.

ADDITIONAL EXAMPLES

Example 7

A container in the shape of a rectangular prism with no top that has a volume of 650 cubic inches is to be constructed from a 28×20-inch piece of sheet metal by cutting squares of equal size from each corner and folding up the flaps. What size square should be cut from each corner?

length × width × height = 650
$(28 - 2x)(20 - 2x)(x) = 650$
Graph $y_1 = (28 - 2x)(20 - 2x)(x)$ and $y_2 = 650$.

There are three points of intersection, with x-values: $x \approx 1.54$, $x \approx 6.68$, and $x \approx 15.78$. Because the piece of sheet metal is only 20 inches wide, x must be less than 10, so discard the solution $x \approx 15.78$. The other solutions are reasonable.

Two such containers can be made.

Case I:
Height: 1.54 in.
Length: $28 - 2(1.54) = 24.92$ in.
Width: $20 - 2(1.54) = 16.92$ in.

Case II
Height: 6.68 in.
Length: $28 - 2(6.68) = 14.64$ in.
Width: $20 - 2(6.68) = 6.64$ in.

One container has approximate dimensions 24.92 in. × 16.92 in. × 1.54 in.; the other has approximate dimensions 14.64 in. × 6.64 in. × 6.68 in.

Example Notes

For **Example 8**, emphasize the difference between *fluid* and *antifreeze*. Point out that, at the beginning, the radiator contains 12 quarts of fluid, 20% of which is antifreeze. So, it contains $0.20 \times 12 = 2.4$ quarts of antifreeze (the remaining 9.6 quarts, presumably, is water).

As you solve the problem, stop when you get to the equation $2.4 - 0.2x + x = 6$ and discuss it as follows:

In this equation,

- 2.4 is the number of quarts of antifreeze in the original tank (20% of 12).
- "$-0.2x$" represents the act of draining x quarts of fluid, 20% of which is antifreeze.
- "$+x$" represents the addition of x quarts of 100% antifreeze.
- 6 is the number of quarts of antifreeze in the final mixture.

ADDITIONAL EXAMPLES

Example 8

A chemist has 30 mL of a 40% acid solution in a test tube. How much of the solution should be poured off and replaced with pure acid so that the new mixture is 70% acid?

$$\begin{pmatrix} \text{Amount of} \\ \text{acid after} \\ \text{pouring} \\ \text{off } x \text{ mL} \end{pmatrix} + \begin{pmatrix} x \text{ mL} \\ \text{of} \\ \text{acid} \end{pmatrix} = \begin{pmatrix} \text{Amount} \\ \text{of acid} \\ \text{in final} \\ \text{mixture} \end{pmatrix}$$

$$40\% \text{ of } (30 - x) + x = 70\% \text{ of } 30$$
$$0.40(30 - x) + x = 0.70(30)$$
$$12 - 0.40x + x = 21$$
$$0.6x = 9$$
$$x = 15$$

The chemist should pour off 15 mL of the solution and replace it with pure acid.

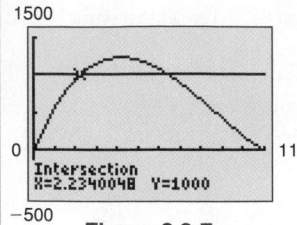

Figure 2.3-7

Graph $y_1 = (30 - 2x)(22 - 2x)x$ and $y_2 = 1000$. As shown in Figure 2.3-7, there are two points of intersection: one at approximately (2.23, 1000) and another at approximately (6.47, 1000), which is not identified on the graph. Because both are viable solutions, there are *two* boxes that meet the given conditions.

Find the dimensions of the box for each possible case.

	Case I	**Case II**
Height:	2.23 in.	6.47 in.
Length:	$30 - 2(2.23) = 25.54$ in.	$30 - 2(6.47) = 17.06$ in.
Width:	$22 - 2(2.23) = 17.54$ in.	$22 - 2(6.47) = 9.06$ in.

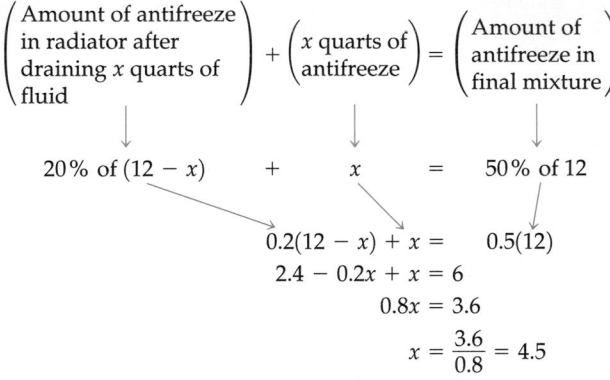

Figure 2.3-8

Example 8   Mixture Problem

A car radiator contains 12 quarts of fluid, 20% of which is antifreeze. How much fluid should be drained and replaced with pure antifreeze so that the resulting mixture is 50% antifreeze?

Solution

Let x be the number of quarts of fluid to be replaced by pure antifreeze. When x quarts are drained, there are $12 - x$ quarts of fluid left in the radiator, 20% of which is antifreeze.

$$\begin{pmatrix} \text{Amount of antifreeze} \\ \text{in radiator after} \\ \text{draining } x \text{ quarts of} \\ \text{fluid} \end{pmatrix} + \begin{pmatrix} x \text{ quarts of} \\ \text{antifreeze} \end{pmatrix} = \begin{pmatrix} \text{Amount of} \\ \text{antifreeze in} \\ \text{final mixture} \end{pmatrix}$$

$$20\% \text{ of } (12 - x) \quad + \quad x \quad = \quad 50\% \text{ of } 12$$

$$0.2(12 - x) + x = 0.5(12)$$
$$2.4 - 0.2x + x = 6$$
$$0.8x = 3.6$$
$$x = \frac{3.6}{0.8} = 4.5$$

Therefore, 4.5 quarts should be drained and replaced with pure antifreeze.

Exercises 2.3

In Exercises 1–4, a problem situation is given.

  a. **Decide what is being asked for, and label the unknown quantities.**

  b. **Translate the verbal statements in the problem and the relationships between the known and unknown quantities into mathematical language, using a table like those in Examples 1–3. The table is provided in Exercises 1–2. You need not find an equation to be solved.**

1. The sum of two numbers is 15 and the difference of their squares is 5. What are the numbers?

English Language	Mathematical Language
the two numbers	
Their sum is 15.	
The difference of their squares is 5.	

2. The sum of the squares of two consecutive integers is 4513. What are the integers?

English Language	Mathematical Language
the two integers	
The integers are consecutive.	
The sum of their squares is 4513.	

3. A rectangle has a perimeter of 45 centimeters and an area of 112.5 square centimeters. What are its dimensions?

4. A triangle has an area of 96 square inches, and its height is two-thirds of its base. What are the base and height of the triangle?

In Exercises 5–8, set up the problem by labeling the unknowns, translating the given information into mathematical language, and finding an equation that will produce the solution to the problem. You need not solve this equation.

5. A worker gets an 8% pay raise and now makes $1600 per month. What was the worker's old salary?

6. A merchant has 5 pounds of mixed nuts that cost $30. He wants to add peanuts that cost $1.50 per pound and cashews that cost $4.50 per pound to obtain 50 pounds of a mixture that costs $2.90 per pound. How many pounds of peanuts are needed?

7. The diameter of a circle is 16 cm. By what amount must the radius be decreased in order to decrease the area by 48π square centimeters?

8. A corner lot has dimensions 25 by 40 yards. The city plans to take a strip of uniform width along the two sides bordering the streets in order to widen these roads. How wide should the strip be if the remainder of the lot is to have an area of 844 square yards?

In Exercises 9–20, solve the problem.

9. You have already invested $550 in a stock with an annual return of 11%. How much of an additional $1100 should be invested at 12% and how much at 6% so that the total return on the entire $1650 is 9%? **$366.67 at 12% and $733.33 at 6%**

10. If you borrow $500 from a credit union at 12% annual interest and $250 from a bank at 18% annual interest, what is the effective annual interest rate (that is, what single rate of interest on $750 would result in the same total amount of interest)? **14%**

11. A radiator contains 8 quarts of fluid, 40% of which is antifreeze. How much fluid should be drained and replaced with pure antifreeze so that the new mixture is 60% antifreeze? $2\frac{2}{3}$ **qt**

12. A radiator contains 10 quarts of fluid, 30% of which is antifreeze. How much fluid should be drained and replaced with pure antifreeze so that the new mixture is 40% antifreeze? $1\frac{3}{7}$ **qt**

13. Two cars leave a gas station at the same time, one traveling north and the other south. The northbound car travels at 50 mph. After 3 hours the cars are 345 miles apart. How fast is the southbound car traveling? **65 mph**

14. An airplane flew with the wind for 2.5 hours and returned the same distance against the wind in 3.5 hours. If the cruising speed of the plane was a constant 360 mph in air, how fast was the wind blowing? *Hint:* If the wind speed is r miles per hour, then the plane travels at $(360 + r)$ mph with the wind and at $(360 - r)$ mph against the wind. **60 mph**

15. The average of two real numbers is 41.375 and their product is 1668. What are the numbers? **34.75 and 48**

Exercises 2.3

ANSWERS

1. The two numbers: x and y; their sum is 15: $x + y = 15$; the difference of their squares is 5: $x^2 - y^2 = 5$.

2. The two integers: x and y; the integers are consecutive: $y = x + 1$; the sum of their squares is 4513: $x^2 + y^2 = 4513$ or $x^2 + (x + 1)^2 = 4513$.

3.

English Language	Mathematical Language
Length of rectangle	x
Width of rectangle	y
Perimeter is 45	$x + y + x + y$ $= 45$ or $2x + 2y = 45$
Area is 112.5	$xy = 112.5$

4.

English Language	Mathematical Language
Base of triangle	b
Height of triangle	h
Area is 96	$\frac{1}{2}bh = 96$
Height is $\frac{2}{3}$ of base	$h = \frac{2}{3}b$

5. Let x be the old salary. Then the raise is 8% of x. Hence,
  old salary + raise = $1600
$$x + (8\% \text{ of } x) = 1600$$
$$x + 0.08x = 1600$$

6. Let p be the number of pounds of peanuts and c the number of pounds of cashews that are added to the mixed nuts. Then $p + c + 5 = 50$. Solve this equation for c to get $c = 45 - p$. Then $30 + 1.5p + 4.5c = 50(2.90)$, and $30 + 1.5p + 4.5(45 - p) = 50(290)$. This equation simplifies to $-3p + 232.50 = 145$.

7. The circle has radius $r = \frac{16}{2} = 8$, so its area is $\pi r^2 = \pi \cdot 8^2 = 64\pi$. Let x be the amount by which the radius is to be reduced. Then $r = 8 - x$ and the new area is $\pi(8 - x)^2$, which must be 48π less than the original area, that is, $\pi(8 - x)^2 = 64\pi - 48\pi$, or equivalently, $\pi(8 - x)^2 = 16\pi$.

8. Let w be the width of the strip. Then the new dimensions of the lot are $25 - w$ by $40 - w$. The equation $(25 - w)(40 - w) = 844$ will give the solution.

16. A rectangle is four times as long as it is wide. If it has an area of 36 square inches, what are its dimensions? **3 in. by 12 in.**

17. A 13-foot-long ladder leans on a wall. The bottom of the ladder is 5 feet from the wall. If the bottom is pulled out 3 feet farther from the wall, how far does the top of the ladder move down the wall? *Hint:* The ladder, ground, and wall form a right triangle. Draw pictures of this triangle before and after the ladder is moved. Use the Pythagorean Theorem to set up an equation. **≈1.75 ft**

18. A factory that makes can openers has fixed costs for building, fixtures, machinery, etc. of $26,000. The variable cost for material and labor for making one can opener is $2.75.
   a. What is the total cost of making 1000 can openers? 20,000? 40,000? **$28,750; $81,000; $136,000**
   b. What is the average cost per can opener in each case? **$28.75; $4.05; $3.40**

19. Red Riding Hood drives the 432 miles to Grandmother's house in 1 hour less than it takes the Wolf to drive the same route. Her average speed is 6 mph faster than the Wolf's average speed. How fast does each drive?
   Red Riding Hood, 54 mph; wolf, 48 mph

20. To get to work Sam jogs 3 kilometers to the train, then rides the remaining 5 kilometers. If the train goes 40 km per hour faster than Sam's constant rate of jogging and the entire trip takes 30 minutes, how fast does Sam jog?
   ≈7.6 km per hour

In Exercises 21–24, an object is thrown upward, dropped, or thrown downward and travels in a vertical line subject only to gravity with wind resistance ignored. The height h, in feet, of the object above the ground after t seconds is given by

$$h = -16t^2 + v_0 t + h_0$$

where h_0 is the initial height of the object at starting time $t = 0$, and v_0 is the initial velocity (speed) of the object at time $t = 0$. The value of v_0 is taken as positive if the object starts moving upward at time $t = 0$ and negative if the object starts moving downward at $t = 0$. An object that is dropped (rather than thrown downward) has initial velocity $v_0 = 0$.

21. How long does it take an object to reach the ground in each case?
   a. It is dropped from the top of a 640-foot-high building. **≈6.3 sec**

   b. It is thrown downward from the top of the same building, with an initial velocity of 52 feet per second. **≈4.9 sec**

22. You are standing on a cliff 200 feet high. How long will it take a rock to reach the ground at the bottom of the cliff in each case?
   a. You drop it. **≈3.5 sec**
   b. You throw it downward at an initial velocity of 40 feet per second. **2.5 sec**
   c. How far does the rock fall in 2 seconds if you throw it downward with an initial velocity of 40 feet per second. **144 ft**

23. A rocket is fired straight up from ground level with an initial velocity of 800 feet per second.
   a. How long does it take the rocket to rise 3200 feet? **≈4.4 sec**
   b. When will the rocket hit the ground? **after 50 sec**

24. A rocket loaded with fireworks is to be shot vertically upward from ground level with an initial velocity of 200 feet per second. When the rocket reaches a height of 400 feet on its upward trip, the fireworks will be detonated. How many seconds after lift-off will this take place? **2.5 sec**

25. The dimensions of a rectangular box are consecutive integers. If the box has volume of 13,800 cubic centimeters, what are its dimensions? **23 cm by 24 cm by 25 cm**

26. Find a real number that exceeds its cube by 2. **≈ −1.52138**

27. The lateral surface area S of the right circular cone at the left in the figure below is given by $S = \pi r \sqrt{r^2 + h^2}$. What radius should be used to produce a cone of height 5 inches and lateral surface area 100 square inches? **$r = 4.658$ in.**

28. The lateral surface area of the right square pyramid at the right in the figure above is given by $S = b\sqrt{b^2 + 4h^2}$. If the pyramid has height 10 feet and lateral surface area 100 square feet, what is the length of a side b of its base? **$b \approx 4.85868$ ft**

29. Suppose that the open-top box being made from a sheet of cardboard in Example 7 is required to have at least one of its dimensions *greater* than 18 inches. What size square should be cut from each corner? **x = 2.234 in.**

30. A homemade loaf of bread turns out to be a perfect cube. Five slices of bread, each 0.6 inch thick, are cut from one end of the loaf. The remainder of the loaf now has a volume of 235 cubic inches. What were the dimensions of the original loaf? **≈7.35 in. by 7.35 in. by 7.35 in.**

31. A rectangular bin with an open top and volume of 38.72 cubic feet is to be built. The length of its base must be twice the width and the bin must be at least 3 feet high. Material for the base of the bin costs $12 per square foot and material for the sides costs $8 per square foot. If it costs $538.56 to build the bin, what are its dimensions? **2.2 ft by 4.4 ft by 4 ft**

2.4 Other Types of Equations

Objectives

- Solve absolute-value equations
- Solve radical equations
- Solve fractional equations

Like linear and quadratic equations, other types of equations can be solved algebraically. This section outlines procedures for solving absolute-value, radical, and fractional equations.

Definition of Absolute Value

The **absolute value** of a number c is denoted $|c|$ and is defined as follows.

Algebraic Definition of Absolute Value

> If $c \geq 0$, then $|c| = c$.
>
> If $c < 0$, then $|c| = -c$.

For example, because 5 is positive, $|5| = 5$, and because -3 is negative, $|-3| = -(-3) = 3$. To determine $|\pi - 6|$, note that $\pi \approx 3.14$ and $\pi - 6 < 0$. Therefore, the second part of the definition applies.

$$|\pi - 6| = -(\pi - 6) = 6 - \pi$$

In all cases, the absolute value of a number is nonnegative.

Absolute value can also be interpreted geometrically as a distance. Observe that the distance between -5 and 3 on the number line is 8 units.

8 *units*

Figure 2.4-1

Notice that $|-5 - 3| = |-8| = 8$. This is an example of a key geometric property of absolute value.

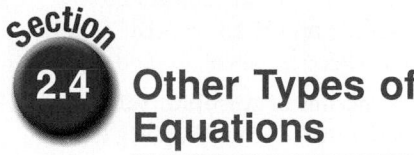

Teaching Notes

For **Absolute Value and Distance**, emphasize the fact that $|x - y|$ measures "how far apart" x and y are. For instance, $|3 - 5| = |5 - 3| = 2$ because 3 and 5 are 2 units apart. Note that order does not matter.

To present the **Geometric Definition of Absolute Value**, ask students how to apply the absolute value and distance concept to a real number c and 0. ($|c - d|$ is the distance between c and d, so $|c - 0|$, or $|c|$, is the distance between c and 0.)

In **Properties of Absolute Value**, consider introducing Property (3) *before* Property (2) and show the students how (2) follows from (3) as a special case:

$$|-c| = |(-1)\cdot c|$$
$$= |-1|\cdot|c|$$
$$= 1\cdot|c|$$
$$= |c|$$

To prepare for **The Triangle Inequality**, ask the students if they think that $|c + d| = |c| + |d|$, for all values of c and d.   no

Encourage them to try different combinations of positive and negative values for c and d. Elicit the following conclusions (sample values are shown to illustrate): $|c + d| = |c| + |d|$ if c and d have the same sign or one value is 0.

$$|2 + 3| = |2| + |3|$$
$$|-2 + (-3)| = |-2| + |-3|$$
$$|7 + 0| = |7| + |0|$$

$|c + d| < |c| + |d|$ if c and d have different signs.

$$|-2 + 3| < |-2| + |3|$$
$$|2 + (-3)| < |2| + |-3|$$

Absolute Value and Distance

> If c and d are real numbers, then
>
> $|c - d|$ is the distance between c and d on the number line.

For example, the number $|5 + \sqrt{2}|$ can be written as $|5 - (-\sqrt{2})|$ and thus represents the distance between 5 and $-\sqrt{2}$ on the number line. See Figure 2.4-2.

Figure 2.4-2

In the special case when $d = 0$, the distance formula shows that the distance from c to 0 is $|c - 0| = |c|$, which is an alternative definition of $|c|$.

Geometric Definition of Absolute Value

> If c is a real number, then
>
> $|c|$ is the distance from c to 0 on the number line.

For example, $|-3.5|$ denotes the distance from -3.5 to 0 on the number line, as shown below.

Figure 2.4-3

Properties of Absolute Value

The following properties are helpful in simplifying absolute value expressions.

> Let c and d represent real numbers.
>
> 1. $|c| \geq 0$ and $|c| > 0$ when $c \neq 0$
> 2. $|c| = |-c|$
> 3. $|cd| = |c| \cdot |d|$
> 4. $\left|\dfrac{c}{d}\right| = \dfrac{|c|}{|d|}$, where $d \neq 0$

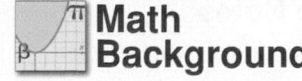

Math Background

CAUTION

When c and d have opposite signs, $|c + d|$ is *not equal* to $|c| + |d|$. For example, if $c = -3$ and $d = 5$, then

$$|c + d| = |-3 + 5|$$
$$= 2$$

But, $|c| + |d|$
$$= |-3| + |5|$$
$$= 3 + 5$$
$$= 8$$

Illustrations of Properties 2, 3, and 4 for absolute value are shown below.

Property 2: Let $c = 3$. Then $|c| = |3| = 3$ and $|-c| = |-3| = 3$.

Therefore, $|3| = |-3|$.

Property 3: Let $c = 6$ and $d = -2$.

$$|cd| = |6(-2)| = |-12| = 12$$
$$|c| \cdot |d| = |6| \cdot |-2| = 6 \cdot 2 = 12$$

Therefore, $|6(-2)| = |6| \cdot |-2|$.

Property 4: Let $c = -5$ and $d = 4$.

$$\left|\frac{c}{d}\right| = \left|\frac{-5}{4}\right| = \left|-\frac{5}{4}\right| = \frac{5}{4} \quad \text{and} \quad \frac{|c|}{|d|} = \frac{|-5|}{|4|} = \frac{5}{4}$$

Therefore, $\left|\frac{-5}{4}\right| = \frac{|-5|}{|4|}$.

The caution shows that $|c + d| < |c| + |d|$ when $c = -3$ and $d = 5$. The general case is called the Triangle Inequality.

The Triangle Inequality

> **For any real numbers c and d,**
>
> $$|c + d| \leq |c| + |d|.$$

Square Root of Squares

When c is a positive number, then $\sqrt{c^2} = c$. This is not true when c is negative. Consider the case when $c = -3$.

$$\sqrt{(-3)^2} = \sqrt{9} = 3, \text{ which is } not \ -3$$

But $\sqrt{c^2}$ is equal to the absolute value of c when c is any real number. That is, $\sqrt{(-3)^2} = \sqrt{9} = 3 = |-3|$.

Square Root of Squares

> **For every real number c,**
>
> $$\sqrt{c^2} = |c|.$$

Solving Absolute-Value Equations

Absolute-value equations can be solved by using the definitions. Some equations lend themselves to the geometric definition, while others are solved more easily using the algebraic definition. Graphing techniques can be used to check all solutions.

When discussing the difference quotient (Section 3.1), students are often tempted to say $f(x + h) = f(x) + f(h)$. The cases examined for the **Triangle Inequality** serve as counterexamples. If $f(x) = |x|$, then $f(x + h) = |x + h|$ and $f(x) + f(h) = |x| + |h|$. But as stated in the Triangle Inequality, $|x + h| \neq |x| + |h|$. When your students get to Section 3.1, you can remind them of the Triangle Inequality to illustrate why $f(x + h) \neq f(x) + f(h)$ in general.

Don't confuse the absolute value Triangle Inequality presented here with the Triangle Inequality that appears in geometry books. The absolute value Triangle Inequality involves only two real numbers. The Triangle Inequality property in geometry involves three real numbers; it states that the sum of the lengths of any two sides of a triangle is greater than the length of the third side.

Teaching Notes

To help students understand the concept presented in the **Square Root of Squares**, remind them that $\sqrt{}$ always represents a nonnegative number. Therefore, $\sqrt{(-3)^2} \neq -3$. And, because $|\ |$ also always represents a nonnegative number, $\sqrt{(-3)^2} = |-3| = 3$.

Example Notes

For **Example 1**, the following statements are equivalent:

- $|x - 4| = 8$
- The distance from x to 4 is 8 units.

This concept is not easy for all students to understand intuitively. Show them how to locate 4 on the number line and then count 8 units from 4 in both directions to get the solutions. *Require* students to check their solutions by substitution:

$$
\begin{array}{c|c}
|x - 4| = 8 & |x - 4| = 8 \\
|-4 - 4| \ \big|\ 8 & |12 - 4| \ \big|\ 8 \\
|-8| & |8| \\
8 \ \big|\ 8 & 8 \ \big|\ 8
\end{array}
$$

In **Example 2**, first point out to students that they cannot easily use a number line, since there is an x (rather than a constant) on the right side. Have students confirm by substitution that $\frac{3}{2}$ is a solution and $-\frac{1}{3}$ is not a solution. The check for $-\frac{1}{3}$ is shown below.

$$
\begin{array}{c|c}
|x + 4| & = & 5x - 2 \\
\left|-\dfrac{1}{3} + 4\right| & & 5\left(-\dfrac{1}{3}\right) - 2 \\
\left|\dfrac{11}{3}\right| & & -\dfrac{5}{3} - 2 \\
\dfrac{11}{3} & & -\dfrac{11}{3}
\end{array}
$$

Be sure students see the graphical confirmation of the solution $\frac{3}{2}$ (Figure 2.4-5).

In **Example 3**, point out that the graph only confirms the *existence* of four solutions, not their exact values. To be certain that the x-values are indeed solutions, challenge students to substitute them into the original equation.

The check for $-2 + \sqrt{5}$ is shown below.

$$
\begin{aligned}
|x^2 + 4x - 3| &= |(-2 + \sqrt{5})^2 + \\
&\qquad 4(-2 + \sqrt{5}) - 3| \\
&= |4 - 4\sqrt{5} + 5 - \\
&\qquad 8 + 4\sqrt{5} - 3| \\
&= |-2| \\
&= 2
\end{aligned}
$$

Technology Tip

To compute absolute values on a calculator, use the ABS feature. The ABS feature is in the NUM submenu of the MATH menu of TI and in the NUM submenu of the OPTN menu of Casio.

NOTE When dealing with long expressions inside absolute value bars, do the computations inside first, and then take the absolute value of the simplified expression.

Example 1   Using Absolute Value and Distance

Solve $|x - 4| = 8$ using absolute value and distance.

Solution

The equation $|x - 4| = 8$ can be interpreted as

> the distance from x to 4 is 8 units.

See Figure 2.4-4.

Figure 2.4-4

The two possible values of x that are solutions of the original equation are -4 and 12, as shown.

Extraneous Solutions

As shown in Example 2 below, some solutions do not make the original equation true when checked by substitution. Such "fake" solutions are called **extraneous solutions,** or **extraneous roots.** Because extraneous solutions may occur when solving absolute-value equations, all solutions *must* be checked by substituting into the original equation or by graphing.

Example 2   Using the Algebraic Definition of Absolute Value

Solve $|x + 4| = 5x - 2$ by using the algebraic definition of absolute value.

Solution

The absolute value of any quantity is either the quantity itself or the opposite of the quantity, depending on whether the quantity is positive or negative. So, $|x - 4|$ is either $x - 4$ or $-(x - 4)$. Therefore, the original equation can be rewritten as two equations that do not involve absolute value.

$$|x + 4| = 5x - 2$$

$$
\begin{array}{lcl}
x + 4 = 5x - 2 & \text{or} & -(x + 4) = 5x - 2 \\
-4x = -6 & & -x - 4 = 5x - 2 \\
x = \dfrac{6}{4} = \dfrac{3}{2} & & -6x = 2 \\
& & x = -\dfrac{2}{6} = -\dfrac{1}{3}
\end{array}
$$

Each solution must be checked in the original equation.

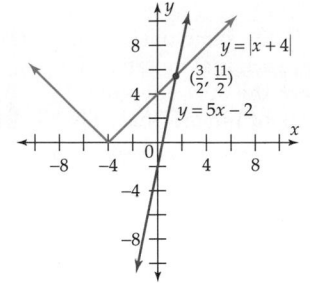

Figure 2.4-5

$x = \frac{3}{2}$ is a solution and checks in the original equation, as shown in Figure 2.4-5. However, $x = -\frac{1}{3}$ is an extraneous root because the graphs do not intersect when $x = -\frac{1}{3}$, which can be confirmed by substitution. Therefore, the only solution of $|x + 4| = 5x - 2$ is $x = \frac{3}{2}$.

Example 3 Solving an Absolute Value Equation

Solve $|x^2 + 4x - 3| = 2$.

Solution

Use the algebraic definition of absolute value to rewrite the original equation as two equations.

$$|x^2 + 4x - 3| = 2$$

$$\begin{array}{l|l}
x^2 + 4x - 3 = 2 & -(x^2 + 4x - 3) = 2 \\
x^2 + 4x - 5 = 0 & -x^2 - 4x + 3 = 2 \\
& -x^2 - 4x + 1 = 0
\end{array}$$

The equation on the left can be solved by factoring, and the equation on the right by using the quadratic formula.

$$\begin{array}{l|l}
x^2 + 4x - 5 = 0 & x^2 + 4x - 1 = 0 \\
(x + 5)(x - 1) = 0 & x = \dfrac{-4 \pm \sqrt{4^2 - 4(1)(-1)}}{2(1)} \\
x = -5 \text{ or } x = 1 & x = \dfrac{-4 \pm \sqrt{20}}{2} = \dfrac{-4 \pm 2\sqrt{5}}{2} \\
& x = -2 \pm \sqrt{5}
\end{array}$$

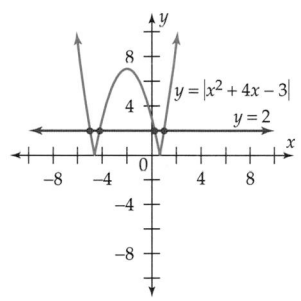

Figure 2.4-6

See Figure 2.4-6 to confirm that all four values are solutions.

Solving Radical Equations

Radical equations are equations that contain expressions with a variable under a radical symbol. Although the approximate solutions of a radical equation can be found graphically, exact solutions can be found algebraically in many cases.

The algebraic solution method depends on the following fact.

> **If A and B are algebraic expressions and $A = B$,**
> **then $A^n = B^n$ for every positive integer n.**

NOTE Squaring both sides of an equation may introduce extraneous roots.

For example, if $x - 2 = 3$, then $(x - 2)^2 = 3^2$. Therefore, every solution of $x - 2 = 3$ is also a solution of $(x - 2)^2 = 9$. However, -1 is a solution of $(x - 2)^2 = 9$, but -1 is *not* a solution of $x - 2 = 3$.

Teaching Notes

Illustrate the margin **NOTE** that squaring both sides of an equation may introduce extraneous roots. Use a simple example such as: $x = 2$ has 2 as its only solution, but $x^2 = 4$ has 2 and -2 as solutions. So, -2 is an extraneous root introduced by squaring both sides of $x = 2$.

In **Example 2**, students may forget to use parentheses in the second equation, and incorrectly write $-x + 4 = 5x - 2$ instead of $-(x + 4) = 5x - 2$. Remind them that $-x + 4 \neq -(x + 4)$.

ADDITIONAL EXAMPLES

Example 1

Solve $|x - 3| = 5$ using the geometric definition of absolute value.

The solutions are -2 and 8.

Example 2

Solve $|x + 3| = 4x - 1$ by using the algebraic definition of absolute value.

$-\frac{2}{5}$ is an extraneous solution. $\frac{4}{3}$ is the only solution. Verify graphically:

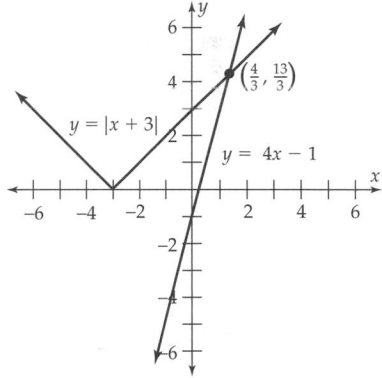

Example 3

Solve $|3x^2 + 6x - 1| = 1$.

The four solutions are: $\dfrac{-3 \pm \sqrt{15}}{3}$, 0, and -2. Verify graphically:

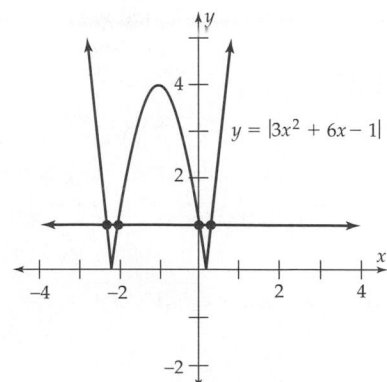

Teaching Notes

When applying the **Power Principle** multiple times to solve a single equation, the following general remarks may be helpful:

- Emphasize that you can only get rid of one radical term at a time. To do so, isolate one of them on one side by itself; then, square both sides. This gets rid of the stand-alone radical.
- If a radical term still exists, reapply the Power Principle to *this* equation by now isolating that radical term.

Emphasize the **CAUTION** note. For radical equations, solutions *must* be checked algebraically by substitution.

Example Notes

In **Example 4**, an alternative graphical method would be to find the intersection of $y_1 = \sqrt{3x - 11}$ and $y_2 = x - 5$.

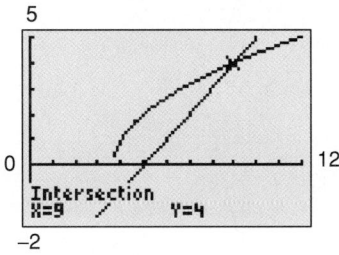

COMMON ERROR ALERT

A student may attempt to solve the equation in **Example 5** as follows:

$$\sqrt{2x - 3} - \sqrt{x + 7} = 2$$
$$\left(\sqrt{2x - 3} - \sqrt{x + 7}\right)^2 = 2^2$$
$$(2x - 3) - (x + 7) = 4$$

Emphasize that the left side was squared incorrectly above. Show that:

$$\left(\sqrt{2x - 3} - \sqrt{x + 7}\right)^2$$
$$= \left(\sqrt{2x - 3} - \sqrt{x + 7}\right)\left(\sqrt{2x - 3} - \sqrt{x + 7}\right)$$
$$= (2x - 3) - 2\sqrt{2x - 3}\sqrt{x + 7} + (x + 7)$$
$$= 3x + 4 - 2\sqrt{2x - 3}\sqrt{x + 7}$$

Power Principle

If both sides of an equation are raised to the same positive integer power, then every solution of the original equation is a solution of the new equation. However, the new equation may have solutions that are not solutions of the original one.

CAUTION

Although it is always a good idea to verify solutions, solutions to radical equations *must* be checked in the original equation.

Figure 2.4-7

Example 4   Solving a Radical Equation

Solve $5 + \sqrt{3x - 11} = x$

Solution

Rearrange terms to get the radical expression alone on one side.

$$\sqrt{3x - 11} = x - 5$$

Square both sides to remove the radical sign and solve the resulting equation.

$$\left(\sqrt{3x - 11}\right)^2 = (x - 5)^2$$
$$3x - 11 = x^2 - 10x + 25$$
$$0 = x^2 - 13x + 36$$
$$0 = (x - 4)(x - 9)$$
$$x - 4 = 0 \quad \text{or} \quad x - 9 = 0$$
$$x = 4 \qquad\qquad x = 9$$

If these values are solutions of the original equation, they should be x-intercepts of the graph of $y = \sqrt{3x - 11} - (x - 5)$. But Figure 2.4-7 shows that the graph does not have an x-intercept at $x = 4$. That is, $x = 4$ is an extraneous solution.

The graph suggests that $x = 9$ is a solution of the original equation, which can be confirmed by substitution. ∎

Sometimes the Power Principle must be applied more than once to eliminate all radicals.

Example 5   Using the Power Principle Twice

Solve $\sqrt{2x - 3} - \sqrt{x + 7} = 2$.

Solution

Rearrange terms so that one side contains only a single radical term.

$$\sqrt{2x - 3} = \sqrt{x + 7} + 2$$

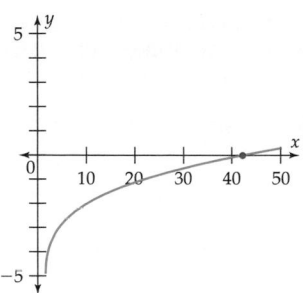

Figure 2.4-8

Square both sides and isolate the remaining radical.

$$\left(\sqrt{2x-3}\right)^2 = \left(\sqrt{x+7}+2\right)^2$$
$$2x-3 = \left(\sqrt{x+7}\right)^2 + 2\cdot 2\sqrt{x+7} + 2^2$$
$$2x-3 = x+7+4\sqrt{x+7}+4$$
$$x-14 = 4\sqrt{x+7}$$

Square both sides again, and solve the resulting equation.

$$(x-14)^2 = \left(4\sqrt{x+7}\right)^2$$
$$x^2 - 28x + 196 = 4^2\left(\sqrt{x+7}\right)^2$$
$$x^2 - 28x + 196 = 16(x+7)$$
$$x^2 - 28x + 196 = 16x + 112$$
$$x^2 - 44x + 84 = 0$$
$$(x-2)(x-42) = 0$$
$$x-2 = 0 \qquad \text{or} \qquad x-42 = 0$$
$$x = 2 \qquad\qquad\qquad x = 42$$

Verify by substitution that $x = 2$ is an extraneous root but that $x = 42$ is a solution. ∎

Technology Tip

Graphing calculators do not always show all solutions of a radical equation. See Example 3 in Section 2.1 for an illustration of a technological quirk.

Example 6   Distance

Stella is standing at point A on the bank of a river that is 2.5 kilometers wide. She wants to reach point B, which is 15 kilometers downstream on the opposite bank. She plans to row downstream to point C on the opposite shore and then run to B, as shown in Figure 2.4-9. She can row downstream at a rate of 4 kilometers per hour and can run at 8 kilometers per hour. If her trip is to take 3 hours, how far from B should she land?

Figure 2.4-9

Solution

Refer to Figure 2.4-9. The basic formula for distance can be written in different ways.

$$d = rt \qquad \text{or} \qquad t = \frac{d}{r}$$

Math Background

Applying the Power Principle can introduce extraneous solutions. This fact comes from the following property of logic:

A conditional statement "If P, then Q" may be true, while its converse "If Q, then P" is false.

For example:

"If a number is a solution of $2x = 6$, then that number is a solution of $4x^2 = 36$" is true, while its converse

"If a number is a solution of $4x^2 = 36$, then that number is a solution of $2x = 6$" is false (because -3 is a solution of $4x^2 = 36$, but not of $2x = 6$).

ADDITIONAL EXAMPLES

Example 4

Solve $1 + \sqrt{4x+33} = 2x$.

-2 is an extraneous solution. 4 is the only solution. Verify graphically by finding the x-intercept of

$y = 1 + \sqrt{4x+33} - 2x$:

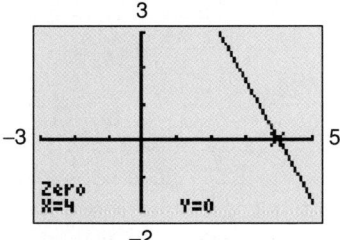

Example 5

Solve $\sqrt{x+2} - \sqrt{2x-3} = 1$.

14 is an extraneous solution. 2 is the only solution. Verify graphically by finding the x-intercept of

$y = \sqrt{x+2} - \sqrt{2x-3} - 1$:

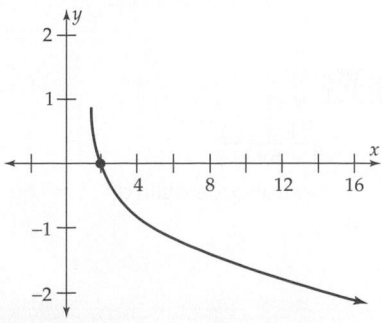

Example 6

An industrial engineer is designing a conveyor belt system for a factory. An item will move a distance of d meters along the belt from point P to point Q and then drop onto another belt and move x meters from point Q to point R. He needs to position Q so that an item will get from P to R in 4 minutes 24 seconds. The belt from P to Q will move at the rate of 4 meters per minute and the belt from Q to R will move at the rate of 10 meters per minute. Find the required distance x from Q to R.

$d^2 = (20 - x)^2 + 8^2$

$d = \sqrt{(20 - x)^2 + 8^2}$

$\text{time} = \dfrac{\text{distance}}{\text{rate}}$

$\text{total time} = \text{time}_{PQ} + \text{time}_{QR}$

$T(x) = \dfrac{d}{4} + \dfrac{x}{10}$

$4.4 = \dfrac{\sqrt{(20 - x)^2 + 64}}{4} + \dfrac{x}{10}$

$f(x) = \dfrac{\sqrt{(20 - x)^2 + 64}}{4} + \dfrac{x}{10} - 4.4$

The zeros of f are $x \approx 8.05$ and $x \approx 22.81$. $x \approx 22.81$ does not make sense for this application. Therefore, he should place point Q so that $x \approx 8.05$ meters.

Example 7

Solve $\dfrac{2x^2 + x - 3}{2x^2 + 5x + 3} = 0$.

$-\dfrac{3}{2}$ is an extraneous solution. 1 is the only solution.

NOTE To review the Pythagorean Theorem, see the Geometry Review Appendix.

Let x represent the distance between C and B, t represent the time required to run from C to B, and r represent the rate Stella can run (8 kilometers per hour).

Therefore, $t = \dfrac{x}{8}$ denotes the time needed to run from C to B.

Similarly, $t = \dfrac{d}{4}$ can express the time required to row distance d.

Since $15 - x$ is the distance from D to C, the Pythagorean Theorem can be applied to right triangle ADC.

$d^2 = (15 - x)^2 + 2.5^2$ or equivalently $d = \sqrt{(15 - x)^2 + 6.25}$

Therefore, the total time for the trip is given by a function of x.

$$T(x) = \text{rowing time} + \text{running time}$$
$$= \dfrac{d}{4} + \dfrac{x}{8}$$
$$= \dfrac{\sqrt{(x - 15)^2 + 6.25}}{4} + \dfrac{x}{8}$$

If the trip is to take 3 hours, then $T(x) = 3$.

$$\dfrac{\sqrt{(x - 15)^2 + 6.25}}{4} + \dfrac{x}{8} = 3$$

Using the viewing window with $0 \le x \le 20$ and $-2 \le y \le 2$, graph this function.

$$f(x) = \dfrac{\sqrt{(x - 15)^2 + 6.25}}{4} + \dfrac{x}{8} - 3$$

Find the zeros of f and interpret their values in the context of the problem.

The zeros of f are $x \approx 6.74$ and $x \approx 17.26$. These represent the distances that Stella should land from B. 6.74 represents a downstream destination from A and 17.26 represents an upstream destination from A. Therefore, Stella should land approximately 6.74 kilometers from B to make the downstream trip in 3 hours.

Fractional Equations

If $f(x)$ and $g(x)$ are algebraic expressions, the quotient $\dfrac{f(x)}{g(x)}$ is called a **fractional expression** with numerator $f(x)$ and denominator $g(x)$. As in all fractions, *the denominator, $g(x)$, cannot be zero.* That is, if $g(x) = 0$, the fraction $\dfrac{f(x)}{g(x)}$ is undefined. The following principle is used to solve fractional equations of the form $\dfrac{f(x)}{g(x)} = 0$.

Solving $\dfrac{f(x)}{g(x)} = 0$

Let $f(x)$ and $g(x)$ represent algebraic expressions. Then the solutions of the equation

$$\frac{f(x)}{g(x)} = 0$$

are all values of x such that $f(x) = 0$ and $g(x) \neq 0$.

Example 7   Solving a Fractional Equation

Solve $\dfrac{6x^2 - x - 1}{2x^2 + 9x - 5} = 0$.

Solution

Find all solutions to $6x^2 - x - 1 = 0$.

$$6x^2 - x - 1 = 0$$
$$(3x + 1)(2x - 1) = 0$$
$$3x + 1 = 0 \qquad \text{or} \qquad 2x - 1 = 0$$
$$x = -\frac{1}{3} \qquad\qquad x = \frac{1}{2}$$

Discard any solution that makes $2x^2 + 9x - 5 = 0$.

For $x = -\dfrac{1}{3}$: $2\left(-\dfrac{1}{3}\right)^2 + 9\left(-\dfrac{1}{3}\right) - 5 = -\dfrac{70}{9} \neq 0$

For $x = \dfrac{1}{2}$: $2\left(\dfrac{1}{2}\right)^2 + 9\left(\dfrac{1}{2}\right) - 5 = 0$

Therefore, $x = -\dfrac{1}{3}$ is the solution of $\dfrac{6x^2 - x - 1}{2x^2 + 9x - 5} = 0$, and $x = \dfrac{1}{2}$ is not a solution. Figure 2.4-10a confirms that $x = -\dfrac{1}{3}$ is a solution and that $x = \dfrac{1}{2}$ is extraneous. ∎

Figure 2.4-10a

Technology Tip

In Figure 2.4-10a, the vertical line shown at $x = -5$ is not part of the graph but is a result of the calculator evaluating the function just to the left of $x = -5$ and just to the right of $x = -5$, but not at $x = -5$. The calculator erroneously connects these points with a near vertical segment. By choosing a window such as $-7.7 \leq x \leq 1.7$ and $-2.2 \leq y \leq 10.2$, the near vertical line will not be drawn. Using the trace feature in Figure 2.4-10b identifies a hole at $x = \dfrac{1}{2}$, where the function is not defined.

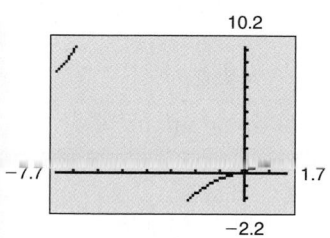

Figure 2.4-10b

Teaching Notes

It may be helpful for the student to say that a solution to an equation of the form $\dfrac{f(x)}{g(x)} = 0$ is an x-value that makes the numerator equal to 0 AND does not make the denominator equal to 0.

COMMON ERROR ALERT

Students tend to "cancel across addition and subtraction." Specifically, point out that

$$\frac{a + b}{a + d} \neq \frac{\cancel{a} + b}{\cancel{a} + d}.$$

For instance, $\dfrac{5 + 1}{5 + 2} \neq \dfrac{\cancel{5} + 1}{\cancel{5} + 2}$.

$$= \frac{6}{7} \qquad = \frac{1}{2}$$

Math Background

An alternate method for **Example 7** is to factor both numerator and denominator in the same step:

$$\frac{6x^2 - x - 1}{2x^2 + 9x - 5} = 0$$
$$\frac{(3x + 1)(2x - 1)}{(2x - 1)(x + 5)} = 0$$

The zeros of the numerator are $-\dfrac{1}{3}$ and $\dfrac{1}{2}$. $\dfrac{1}{2}$ is an extraneous solution because it is not in the domain of the function $f(x) = \dfrac{(3x + 1)(2x - 1)}{(2x - 1)(x + 5)}$. (See Section 4.4.)

It is tempting to say that $f(x) = \dfrac{(3x + 1)(2x - 1)}{(2x - 1)(x + 5)}$ and $g(x) = \dfrac{(3x + 1)}{(x + 5)}$ are the same function. This is not quite true because $\dfrac{1}{2}$ is in the domain of g, but not in the domain of f. If both f and g are graphed on a calculator, the graphs appear to be identical. However, there is actually a "hole" in the graph of f at $x = \dfrac{1}{2}$ that is not visible on the calculator graph.

Exercises 2.4

ANSWERS

1. $|y - 2| = 4$

$y = -2, 6$

2. $|x - 4| = 6$

$x = -2, 10$

3. $|3w - 2| = 8$

Since $3w = -6$ or 10,

$w = -2, 3\frac{1}{3}.$

4. $|4x - 3| = 6$

Since $4x = -3$ or 9,

$x = -\frac{3}{4}, \frac{9}{4}.$

5. $|-2x - 4| = 5$

Since $-2x = -1$ or 9,

$x = \frac{1}{2}, -\frac{9}{2}.$

6. $|-4z - 3| = 11$

Since $-4z = -8$ or 14,

$z = 2, -\frac{7}{2}.$

7. $|-3x - (-2)| = 5$ or

$|-3x + 2| = 5$

Since $-3x = -7$ or 3,

$x = \frac{7}{3}, -1.$

8. $|-4w - (-6)| = \frac{5}{2}$ or

$|-4w + 6| = \frac{5}{2}$

Since $-4w = -\frac{17}{2}$ or $-\frac{7}{2}$,

$w = \frac{17}{8}, \frac{7}{8}.$

17. $x = -5$ or 1 or -3 or -1

18. $x = -5$ or 3 or -3 or 1

19. $x = 1$ or 4 or $\dfrac{5 + \sqrt{33}}{2}$ or $\dfrac{5 - \sqrt{33}}{2}$

20. $x = \dfrac{-5 + \sqrt{553}}{24}$ or $\dfrac{-5 - \sqrt{553}}{24}$ or $-\dfrac{3}{4}$ or $\dfrac{1}{3}$

21. For any real number x, the distance between $2x^2$ and $-3x$ cannot be a negative number. Therefore, $|2x^2 + 3x| = -12$ has no real number solution.

Exercises 2.4

In Exercises 1–8, rewrite each statement using the geometric definition of absolute value. Represent each on a number line, and find the value(s) of the variable.

1. The distance between y and 2 is 4.

2. The distance between x and 4 is 6.

3. The distance between $3w$ and 2 is 8.

4. The distance between $4x$ and 3 is 6.

5. The distance between $-2x$ and 4 is 5.

6. The distance between $-4z$ and 3 is 11.

7. The distance between $-3x$ and -2 is 5.

8. The distance between $-4w$ and -6 is $\frac{5}{2}$.

In Exercises 9–20, find all real solutions of each equation.

9. $|2x + 3| = 9$
$x = -6$ or 3

10. $|3x - 5| = 7$
$x = 4$ or $-\frac{2}{3}$

11. $|6x - 9| = 0$ $x = \frac{3}{2}$

12. $|4x - 5| = -9$
no solution

13. $|2x + 3| = 4x - 1$
$x = 2$

14. $|3x - 2| = 5x + 4$
$x = -\frac{1}{4}$

15. $|x - 3| = x$ $x = \frac{3}{2}$

16. $|2x - 1| = 2x + 1$
$x = 0$

17. $|x^2 + 4x - 1| = 4$

18. $|x^2 + 2x - 9| = 6$

19. $|x^2 - 5x + 1| = 3$

20. $|12x^2 + 5x - 7| = 4$

21. Explain why there are no real numbers that satisfy the equation $|2x^2 + 3x| = -12$.

22. Describe in words the meaning of the inequality.

$$|a + b| \le |a| + |b|$$

Make sure to consider positive and negative values of a and b.

23. Joan weighs 120 pounds and her doctor told her that her weight is 5 percent from her ideal weight. What are the possible values, to the nearest pound, for Joan's ideal body weight?
114 lb or 126 lb

24. A tightrope walker is 8 feet from one end of the rope. If he takes 2 steps and each step is 10 inches long, how far is he from the same end of the rope? Give both possible answers.

9 ft 8 in. or 6 ft 4 in.

22. Case 1: If $a \ge 0$ and $b \ge 0$, then $|a + b| = |a| + |b|$. For example,

$|3 + 5| = |3| + |5|$

$|8| = 3 + 5$

$8 = 8$

The sum of the distances from 0 to a and 0 to b is the same as the distance from 0 to $a + b$.

---

25. An instrument measures a wind speed of 20 feet per second. The true wind speed is within 5 feet per second of the measured wind speed. What are the possible values for the true wind speed?
between 15 and 25 ft per sec

26. For two real numbers s and t, the notation $\min(s, t)$ represents the smaller of the two numbers. When $s = t$, $\min(s, t)$ represents the common value. It can be shown that $\min(s, t)$ can be expressed as shown.

$$\min(s, t) = \frac{s + t - |s - t|}{2}$$

For each of the following, verify the equation.
a. $s = 4$ and $t = 1$
b. $s = -2$ and $t = 3$
c. $s = t = -5$

27. In statistical quality control, one needs to find the proportion of the product that is not acceptable. The upper and lower control limits (CL) are found by solving the following equation in which p is the mean percent defective, and n is the sample size for CL. ≈ -0.0097 **and 0.0497**

$$|CL - p| = 3\sqrt{\frac{p(1 - p)}{n}}$$

In practice, CL is nonnegative,
Find CL when $p = 0.02$ and $n = 200$.
so CL would be 0 and 0.0497.

In Exercises 28–63, find all real solutions of each equation. Find exact solutions when possible, approximate solutions otherwise.

28. $\sqrt{x - 7} = 4$
$x = 23$

29. $\sqrt{4x + 9} = 5$
$x = 4$

30. $\sqrt{3x - 2} = 7$
$x = 17$

31. $\sqrt[3]{5 - 11x} = 3$
$x = -2$

32. $\sqrt[3]{6x - 10} = 2$
$x = 3$

33. $\sqrt[3]{x^2 - 1} = 2$
$x = \pm 3$

34. $\sqrt[3]{(x + 1)^2} = 4$
$x = 7$ **or** -9

35. $\sqrt{x^2 - x - 1} = 1$
$x = -1$ **or** 2

36. $\sqrt{x^2 - 5x + 4} = 2$
$x = 0$ **or** 5

37. $\sqrt{x + 7} = x - 5$
$x = 9$

38. $\sqrt{x + 5} = x - 1$
$x = 4$

39. $\sqrt{3x^2 + 7x - 2} = x + 1$ $x = \frac{1}{2}$

40. $\sqrt{4x^2 - 10x + 5} = x - 3$ **no solutions**

41. $\sqrt[3]{x^3 + x^2 - 4x + 5} = x + 1$ $x = \frac{1}{2}$ **or** -4

42. $\sqrt[3]{x^3 - 6x^2 + 2x + 3} = x - 1$ $x = -\frac{4}{3}$ **or** 1

43. $\sqrt[5]{9 - x^2} = x^2 + 1$
$x \approx \pm 0.73$

44. $\sqrt[4]{x^3 - x + 1} = x^2 - 1$
$x \approx -1.28$ or 1.52

45. $\sqrt[3]{x^5 - x^3 - x} = x + 2$
$x \approx -1.17$ or 2.59 or $x = -1$

46. $\sqrt{x^3 + 2x^2 - 1} = x^3 + 2x - 1$
no solutions

47. $\sqrt{x^2 + 3x - 6} = x^4 - 3x^2 + 2$
$x \approx 1.658$

48. $\sqrt[3]{x^4 + x^2 + 1} = x^2 - x - 5$
$x \approx -2.462$ or 3.893

49. $\sqrt{5x + 6} = 3 + \sqrt{x + 3}$
$x = 6$

50. $\sqrt{3y + 1} - 1 = \sqrt{y + 4}$
$y = 5$

51. $\sqrt{2x - 5} = 1 + \sqrt{x - 3}$
$x = 3$ or 7

52. $\sqrt{x - 3} + \sqrt{x + 5} = 4$
$x = 4$

53. $\sqrt{3x + 5} + \sqrt{2x + 3} + 1 = 0$
no solutions

54. $\sqrt{20 - x} = \sqrt{9 - x} + 3$ **$x = \dfrac{80}{9}$**

55. $\sqrt{6x^2 + x + 7} - \sqrt{3x + 2} = 2$
$x \approx -0.457$ or 1.400

56. $\sqrt{x^3 + x^2 - 3} = \sqrt{x^3 - x + 3} - 1$
$x \approx 1.311$

57. $\sqrt{x + 2} = 3$
$x = 7$

58. $\dfrac{x^2 - 2x + 1}{x - 2} = 0$
$x = 1$

59. $\dfrac{2x^2 - 3x - 4}{x - 4} = 0$
$x = \dfrac{3 \pm \sqrt{41}}{4}$

60. $\dfrac{x^2 - x - 2}{x^2 + 5x + 5} = 0$
$x = -1$ or 2

61. $\dfrac{x^2 - 3x + 2}{x^2 + x - 6} = 0$
$x = 1$

62. $\dfrac{2x^2 - 7x + 6}{3x^2 - 5x - 2} = 0$ **$x = \dfrac{3}{2}$**

63. $\dfrac{3x^2 + 4x + 1}{3x^2 - 5x - 2} = 0$
$x = -1$

In Exercises 64–67, assume that all letters represent positive numbers. Solve each equation for the required letter.

64. $T = 2\pi\sqrt{\dfrac{m}{g}}$ for g

65. $K = \sqrt{1 - \dfrac{x^2}{u^2}}$ for u

66. $R = \sqrt{d^2 + k^2}$ for d

67. $A = \sqrt{1 + \dfrac{a^2}{b^2}}$ for b

68. A rope is to be stretched at uniform height from a tree to a fence, 20 feet from the tree, and then to the side of a building, 35 ft from the tree, at a point 30 ft from the fence, as shown in the figure.
  a. If 63 ft of rope is to be used, how far from the building wall should the rope meet the fence?
  b. How far from the building wall should the rope meet the fence if as little rope as possible is to be used? *Hint:* What is the x value of the lowest point on the graph?

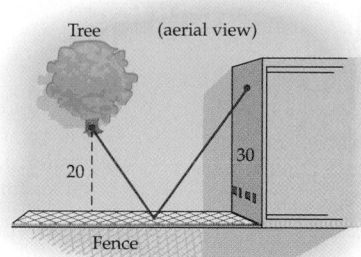

Tree   (aerial view)

20   30

Fence

69. A spotlight is to be placed on a building wall to illuminate a bench that is 32 feet from the base of the wall. The intensity of the light I at the bench is known to be $I = \dfrac{x}{d^3}$, where x is the spotlight's height above the ground and d is the distance from the bench to the spotlight.
  a. Express I as a function of x. It may help to draw a picture.
  b. How high should the spotlight be in order to provide maximum illumination at the bench? *Hint:* What is the x value of the highest point on the graph?

Helicopter

Field

1 mile

Road   Anne

70. Anne is standing on a straight road and wants to reach her helicopter, which is located 2 miles down the road from her and a mile off the road in a field. She can run 5 miles per hour on the road and 3 miles per hour in the field. She plans to run down the road, then cut diagonally across the field to reach the helicopter.
  a. Where should she leave the road in order to reach the helicopter in exactly 12 minutes, that is, 0.7 hour? **either 1.8 or 0.51 miles on the road**
  b. Where should she leave the road in order to reach the helicopter as soon as possible? (see Exercise 68b) **1.25 miles**

64. $g = \dfrac{4m\pi^2}{T^2}$

65. $u = \sqrt{\dfrac{x^2}{1 - K^2}}$

66. $d = \sqrt{R^2 - k^2}$

67. $b = \sqrt{\dfrac{a^2}{A^2 - 1}}$

68. **a.** approximately 11.47 ft or 29.91 ft
  b. 21 ft

69. **a.** $I = \dfrac{x}{(x^2 + 1024)^{\frac{3}{2}}}$
  b. approximately 22.63 ft

22. **Case 2:** If $a < 0$ and $b < 0$, then
$|a + b| = |a| + |b|$.

For example,

$|(-3) + (-5)| = |-3| + |-5|$

$|-8| = 3 + 5$

$8 = 8$

The sum of the distances from 0 to a and 0 to b is the same as the distance from 0 to $a + b$.

Case 3: If a and b are of opposite signs, $|a + b| < |a| + |b|$.

For example,

$|-8 + 3| < |-8| + |3|$

$|-5| < 8 + 3$

$5 < 11$

The sum of the distances from 0 to a and 0 to b is greater than the distance from 0 to $a + b$.

26. **a.** min(4, 1):
$\dfrac{4 + 1 - |4 - 1|}{2} = \dfrac{5 - 3}{2} = 1$

  b. min(−2, 3):
$\dfrac{-2 + 3 - |-2 - 3|}{2} = \dfrac{1 - 5}{2} = -2$

  c. min(−5, 5):
$\dfrac{-5 + (-5) - |-5 - (-5)|}{2}$
$= \dfrac{-10 - 0}{2} = -5$

Math Background

Previously, students solved inequalities and wrote the solutions as inequalities or as graphs. In this section, students are introduced to interval notation, which will be used throughout the rest of the book. For example, students will now see that the following all represent the same set of numbers:

$$[1, 5) \qquad 1 \leq x < 5$$

For a notation such as $(1, 5)$, it should always be clear from the context whether it represents an open interval or an ordered pair.

Teaching Notes

Students should easily understand that $c < d$ is equivalent to $d > c$. However, it may not be obvious that both inequalities mean $d - c$ is positive. Illustrate these relationships with examples such as:

$2 < 5; 5 > 2; 5 - 2$ is positive
$-6 < 3; 3 > -6; 3 - (-6)$ is positive

Show students the following graph to correspond to the third case in the **Interval Notation** box:

$$[c, d) \qquad c \leq x < d$$

Point out that the bracket corresponds to the closed circle, which means that c is included as a solution, and the parentheses corresponds to the open circle, which means that d is not included as a solution.

2.5 Inequalities

Objectives

- Use interval notation
- Solve linear inequalities and compound linear inequalities
- Find exact solutions of quadratic and factorable inequalities

The statement $c < d$, which is read "c is less than d," means that c is to the left of d on the real number line. Similarly, the statement $c > d$, which is read "c is greater than d," means that c is to the right of d on the real number line.

In the set of real numbers, any pair of numbers can be compared because the set of real numbers is **ordered.** That is, for any two real numbers a and b, exactly one of the following statements is true.

$$a < b \qquad a = b \qquad a > b$$

The two statements $c < d$ and $d > c$ are equivalent, and both mean that $d - c$ is positive. The statement $c \leq d$, read "c is less than or equal to d," means either c is less than d or c is equal to d. A similar statement applies to $c \geq d$.

The statement $b < c < d$, called a **compound inequality,** means

$$b < c \quad \text{and simultaneously} \quad c < d.$$

Interval Notation

An **interval** of numbers is the set of all numbers lying between two fixed numbers. Such sets appear frequently enough to merit special notation.

> ### Interval Notation
>
> Let c and d be real numbers with $c < d$.
>
> $[c, d]$ denotes the set of all real numbers x such that $c \leq x \leq d$.
>
> (c, d) denotes the set of all real numbers x such that $c < x < d$.
>
> $[c, d)$ denotes the set of all real numbers x such that $c \leq x < d$.
>
> $(c, d]$ denotes the set of all real numbers x such that $c < x \leq d$.

All four sets above are called intervals from c to d, where c and d are the **endpoints** of the interval. The interval $[c, d]$ is called the **closed interval** from c to d because both endpoints are included, as indicated by brackets, and (c, d) is called the **open interval** from c to d because neither endpoint is included, as indicated by parentheses. The last two intervals in the box above are called **half-open intervals,** where the bracket indicates which endpoint is included.

The half-line extending to the right or left of b is also called an interval.

* For the half-line to the right of b,
$[b, \infty)$ denotes the set of all real numbers x such that $x \geq b$.
(b, ∞) denotes the set of all real numbers x such that $x > b$.
* For the half-line to the left of b,
$(-\infty, b]$ denotes the set of all real numbers x such that $x \leq b$.
$(-\infty, b)$ denotes the set of all real numbers x such that $x < b$.

Similar notation is used for the entire number line.
$(-\infty, \infty)$ denotes the set of all real numbers.

NOTE The symbol ∞ is read "infinity" but does *not* denote a real number. It is simply part of the notation used to denote half-lines.

Solving Inequalities

Solutions of inequalities in one variable are all values of the variable that make the inequality true. Such solutions may be found by using algebraic, geometric, and graphical methods, each of which is discussed in this section. Whenever possible, algebra will be used to obtain exact solutions. When algebraic methods are tedious or when no algebraic method exists, approximate graphical solutions will be found.

Equivalent Inequalities

Like equations, two inequalities are **equivalent** if they have the same solutions. The basic tools for solving inequalities are as follows.

Basic Principles for Solving Inequalities

> **Performing any of the following operations on an inequality produces an equivalent inequality.**
>
> 1. **Add or subtract the same quantity on both sides of the inequality.**
> 2. **Multiply or divide both sides of the inequality by the same *positive* quantity.**
> 3. **Multiply or divide both sides of the inequality by the same *negative* quantity, and *reverse the direction of the inequality*.**

Note that Principles **1** and **2** are the same as the principles used in solving linear *equations*, but Principle **3** states that when an inequality is multiplied or divided by a negative number, the inequality sign must be reversed. For example,

$$2 < 5$$
$$(-1)(2) > (-1)(5) \qquad \textit{Multiply by } -1 \textit{ and reverse the inequality}$$
$$-2 > -5$$

Solving Linear Inequalities

Example 1   Solving a Compound Linear Inequality

Solve $2 \leq 3x + 5 < 2x + 11$.

Teaching Notes

Have students complete graphs for all four cases of Interval Notation.

$[c, d]$ $c \leq x \leq d$
(c, d) $c < x < d$
$[c, d)$ $c \leq x < d$
$(c, d]$ $c < x \leq d$

Show students the three equivalent representations for the interval $[b, \infty)$. Then, for each of the other cases, give one representation and have students provide the other two:

$[b, \infty)$ $x \geq b$
(b, ∞) $x > b$
$(-\infty, b]$ $x \leq b$
$(-\infty, b)$ $x < b$
$(-\infty, 0]$ $x \leq 0$
$(-2, \infty)$ $x > -2$
$(-\infty, \infty)$ x is any real number

Students should be familiar with principle 3 in the **Basic Principles** box, but it is important enough that it deserves emphasis.

Example Notes

Students probably have solved compound linear inequalities in past math courses. However, they may not have encountered the type in **Example 1**, and they may not realize the need to separate the compound inequality into two simple inequalities. They may attempt to solve Example 1 as follows:

$$
\begin{array}{ccccc}
2 & \leq & 3x + 5 & < & 2x + 11 \\
-5 & & -5 & & -5 \\
\hline
-3 & \leq & 3x & < & 2x + 6 \\
\dfrac{-3}{3} & \leq & \dfrac{3x}{3} & < & \dfrac{2x}{3} + \dfrac{6}{3} \\
-1 & \leq & x & < & \dfrac{2}{3}x + 2
\end{array}
$$

The steps above are valid, but there is no time or effort saved; note that the inequality $x < \frac{2}{3}x + 2$ still must be solved. Emphasize that the best way to solve Example 1 is to separate the compound inequality into two simple inequalities.

Example 2 *can be* solved by the "streamlined" method shown above, that is, performing the same operation on all three parts of the inequality in each step. Ask students why the streamlined method works in Example 2, but not in Example 1. The variable appears only in the middle in Example 2; that is not the case in Example 1.

COMMON ERROR ALERT

Students sometimes reverse an inequality symbol unnecessarily. In **Example 1**, a student may divide both sides of $-3 \leq 3x$ by 3 and get $-1 \geq x$, which is incorrect. Remind them to reverse the symbol only when they *multiply or divide by a negative number*.

Math Background

To solve **Example 3** by graphing, we need to be sure that we see the complete graph. This is an idea that is addressed later in the text (Section 4.3, pages 266–267). Figure 2.5-4 is the graph of a 4th-degree polynomial. A polynomial of degree 4 has at most 3 local extrema (high and low turning points). Therefore, Figure 2.5-4 does show the complete graph.

Solution

A solution of the inequality $2 \leq 3x + 5 < 2x + 11$ is any number that is a solution of *both* of the following inequalities.

$$2 \leq 3x + 5 \qquad \text{and} \qquad 3x + 5 < 2x + 11$$

Each of these inequalities can be solved by the principles listed above.

Subtract 5	*Subtract 2x and Subtract 5*
$2 - 5 \leq 3x$	$3x - 2x < 11 - 5$
Simplify	*Simplify*
$-3 \leq 3x$	$x < 6$
Divide by 3	
$-1 \leq x$	

The solutions are all real numbers that satisfy *both* $-1 \leq x$ *and* $x < 6$, that is, $-1 \leq x < 6$. Therefore, the solutions are the numbers in the interval $[-1, 6)$, as shown in Figure 2.5-1.

Figure 2.5-1

Example 2 Solving a Compound Linear Inequality

Solve $4 < 3 - 5x < 18$.

Solution

When a variable appears only in the middle of a compound inequality, the process can be streamlined by performing any operation on each part of the compound inequality.

$$
\begin{array}{lll}
4 < 3 - 5x < 18 & & \\
1 < -5x < 15 & & \textit{Subtract 3 from each part} \\
-\dfrac{1}{5} > x > -3 & & \textit{Divide each part by } -5 \\
& & \textit{and reverse direction of the} \\
& & \textit{inequalities}
\end{array}
$$

Intervals are usually written from the smaller to the larger, so the solution to the compound inequality is

$$-3 < x < -\frac{1}{5}.$$

Figure 2.5-2

The solution of the compound inequality is the interval $\left(-3, -\dfrac{1}{5}\right)$, as shown in Figure 2.5-2, where open circles indicate that the endpoints are not included in the interval.

Figure 2.5-3a

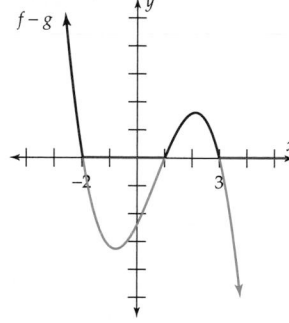

Figure 2.5-3b

Solving Other Inequalities

Although the basic principles play a role in the solution of nonlinear inequalities, geometrically the key to solving such inequalities is the following fact.

> The solutions of an inequality of the form $f(x) < g(x)$ consist of intervals on the *x*-axis where the graph of *f* is below the graph of *g*.

> The solutions of $f(x) > g(x)$ consist of intervals on the *x*-axis where the graph of *f* is above the graph of *g*.

In Figure 2.5-3a, the blue portion of the graph of *f* is below the graph of *g*. The solutions of $f(x) < g(x)$ correspond to the intervals on the *x*-axis denoted in red. In Figure 2.5-3a, $f(x) < g(x)$ when $-2 < x < 1$ and when $x > 3$.

Although the above procedure can always be used, solutions of an inequality expressed as $f(x) < g(x)$ are often easier to find by using an equivalent inequality in the form $f(x) - g(x) < 0$.

> The graph of $y = f(x) - g(x)$ lies above the *x*-axis when $f(x) - g(x) > 0$ and below the *x*-axis when $f(x) - g(x) < 0$.

Figure 2.5-3b shows the graph of $y = f(x) - g(x)$, the difference of the two functions shown in Figure 2.5-3a. This graph is below the *x*-axis in the same intervals where the graph of *f* is below the graph of *g*. Therefore, the solution of $f(x) < g(x)$ is the same as the solution of $f(x) - g(x) < 0$.

Any inequality of the form $f(x) < g(x)$ can be rewritten in the equivalent form $f(x) - g(x) < 0$ by subtracting $g(x)$ from both sides of the inequality. The procedure for solving $f(x) < g(x)$ is to graph $y = f(x) - g(x)$ and find the intervals on the *x*-axis where the graph is below the *x*-axis. A similar procedure applies when the inequality sign is reversed, except that the solution is determined by *x*-intervals where the graph is *above* the *x*-axis.

Example 3 Solving an Inequality

Solve $x^4 + 10x^3 + 21x^2 > 40x + 80$.

Solution

Rewrite the inequality as $(x^4 + 10x^3 + 21x^2) - (40x + 80) > 0$.

The graph of $f(x) = x^4 + 10x^3 + 21x^2 - 40x - 80$ is shown in Figure 2.5-4. The graph shows that $f(x)$ has two zeros, one between -2 and -1 and the other near 2. The portion of the graph above the *x*-axis is shown in red.

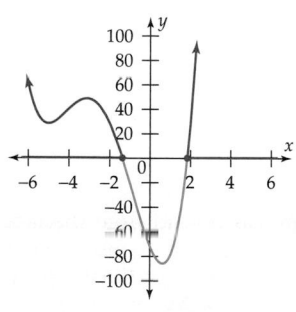

Figure 2.5-4

Teaching Notes

Begin by showing that the inequality $f(x) < g(x)$ is equivalent to $f(x) - g(x) < 0$ as follows:

$$\begin{aligned} f(x) &< g(x) \\ -g(x) \quad &-g(x) \\ \hline f(x) - g(x) &< 0 \end{aligned}$$

Figure 2.5-3a shows the solutions of $f(x) < g(x)$ as red intervals on the *x*-axis. Note that the red intervals correspond to the portions of $f(x)$ (shown in blue) that are below $g(x)$.

Figure 2.5-3b shows the same red intervals as those in Figure 2.5-3a. Note that the red intervals in this case correspond to the portions of $f(x) - g(x)$ (shown in blue) that are below the *x*-axis.

Students will probably agree that the solutions are easier to identify when the single graph of $f(x) - g(x)$ is used.

Note to students that a similar discussion with graphs can be applied to the equivalent inequalities $f(x) > g(x)$ and $f(x) - g(x) > 0$.

ADDITIONAL EXAMPLES

Example 1

Solve $-5 \le 2x - 1 \le x + 7$. $[-2, 8]$

Example 2

Solve $-2 < 4 - 3x < 6$. $\left(-\frac{2}{3}, 2\right)$

Example 3

Solve $x^4 - x^3 - 12x^2 > 4x + 10$.
Rewrite as
$(x^4 - x^3 - 12x^2) - (4x + 10) > 0$.
Graph $f(x) = x^4 - x^3 - 12x^2 - 4x - 10$.

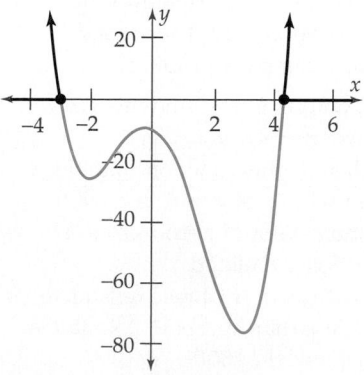

approximate solutions: all numbers *x* such that $x < -2.97$ or $x > 4.21$

Teaching Notes

Solution to the **Graphing Exploration:**

Example Notes

Students solved quadratic equations using the quadratic formula in Section 2.2 (pp 92-93). In **Example 4,** students use the quadratic formula to solve the *equation* $2x^2 + 3x - 4 = 0$. The solutions of the equation are the zeros of the function $f(x) = 2x^2 + 3x - 4$. The solutions of the original *inequality* $2x^2 + 3x - 4 \leq 0$ are shown by the red interval on the x-axis in Figure 2.5-5. Point out that we are able to find *exact solutions* in Example 4; in Example 3 we were able to find only *approximate solutions*. Remind students that $\frac{-3 - \sqrt{41}}{4}$ is exact and -2.35 is approximate.

For **Example 5,** point out the window change in Figures 2.5-6a and 2.5-6b. Both Figures have (different) advantages. The first shows the x-intercepts clearly. The second shows a complete graph.

For **Example 6,** ask students the following:

* Where is this function undefined and why? at $x = 0$; a denominator of zero makes a fraction undefined
* What word or phrase tells us to use the less than symbol? 'keep the cost below $1600'
* How is the phrase 'at most 450 printers' used in solving the problem? 450 represents the maximum value for x.

> **Graphing Exploration** ●
>
> Use the graphical root finder of a calculator to find approximate values of the x-intercepts.

The Exploration shows that the graph of f is above the x-axis approximately when $x < -1.53$ and when $x > 1.89$, so the approximate solutions of the original inequality are all numbers x such that $x < -1.53$ or $x > 1.89$. ∎

Quadratic and Factorable Inequalities

The preceding example shows that solving an inequality depends only on knowing the zeros of a function and the places where its graph is above or below the x-axis. In the case of quadratic inequalities or completely factored expressions, exact solutions can by found algebraically.

Example 4   Solving a Quadratic Inequality

Solve $2x^2 + 3x - 4 \leq 0$.

Solution

The solutions of $2x^2 + 3x - 4 \leq 0$ are the numbers x where the graph of $f(x) = 2x^2 + 3x - 4$ lies on or below the x-axis. The zeros of f can be found by using the quadratic formula.

$$x = \frac{-3 \pm \sqrt{3^2 - 4(2)(-4)}}{2(2)} = \frac{-3 \pm \sqrt{41}}{4}$$

As shown in Figure 2.5-5, the graph lies below the x-axis *between* the two zeros. Therefore, the solutions of the original inequality are all numbers x such that

$$\frac{-3 - \sqrt{41}}{4} \leq x \leq \frac{-3 + \sqrt{41}}{4} \qquad \textit{Exact solution}$$

$$-2.35 \leq x \leq 0.85 \qquad \textit{Approximate solution}$$
∎

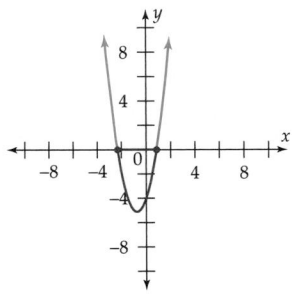

Figure 2.5-5

Example 5   Solving an Inequality

Solve $(x + 5)(x - 2)^6(x - 8) \leq 0$.

Solution

The zeros of $f(x) = (x + 5)(x - 2)^6(x - 8)$ are easily read from the factored form to be -5, 2, and 8. Therefore, you need only determine where the graph of f is on or below the x-axis. A partial graph of f that clearly shows all three x-intercepts is shown in Figure 2.5-6a. A complete graph, which does not clearly show the x-intercept at 2, is shown in Figure

2.5-6b. Using both graphs, or using the trace feature on either one, confirms that the graph is on or below the *x*-axis between $x = -5$ and $x = 8$. Therefore, the solutions of the inequality are all numbers *x* such that $-5 \le x \le 8$.

Figure 2.5-6a

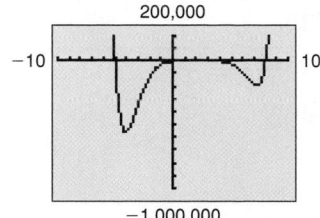

Figure 2.5-6b

The procedures used in the previous examples may be summarized as follows.

Solving Inequalities

1. **Write the inequality in one of the following forms.**

   $$f(x) > 0 \qquad f(x) \ge 0 \qquad f(x) < 0 \qquad f(x) \le 0$$

2. **Determine the zeros of f, exactly if possible, approximately otherwise.**

3. **Determine the interval, or intervals, on the *x*-axis where the graph of f is above (or below) the *x*-axis.**

Applications

Example 6   Solving a Cost Inequality

A computer store has determined the cost *C* of ordering and storing *x* laser printers.

$$C = 2x + \frac{300{,}000}{x}$$

If the delivery truck can bring at most 450 printers per order, how many printers should be ordered at a time to keep the cost below $1600?

Solution

To find the values of *x* that make *C* less than 1600, solve the inequality

$$2x + \frac{300{,}000}{x} < 1600 \quad \text{or equivalently,} \quad 2x + \frac{300{,}000}{x} - 1600 < 0.$$

Example 4

Solve $x^2 + 3x - 2 \le 0$.

$$\frac{-3 - \sqrt{17}}{2} \le x \le \frac{-3 + \sqrt{17}}{2}$$

Example 5

Solve $(x - 3)(x + 6)(x + 1)^4 \le 0$.

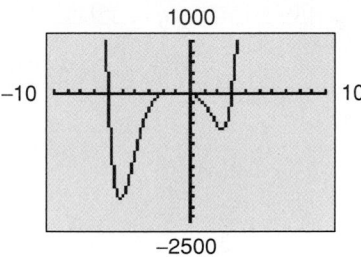

$-6 \le x \le 3$

Example 6

A projectile is fired straight upward from ground level with initial velocity 160 feet per second. Its height in feet after *x* seconds is modeled by $f(x) = -16x^2 + 160x$. During what time interval will the height of the projectile be greater than 336 feet?

To solve $-16x^2 + 160x > 336$, graph $y = -16x^2 + 160x - 336$.

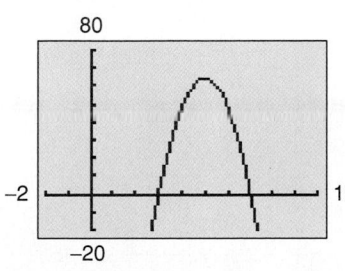

(3, 7)

The height will be greater than 336 feet between 3 and 7 seconds after the projectile is fired.

Exercises 2.5

ANSWERS

5. 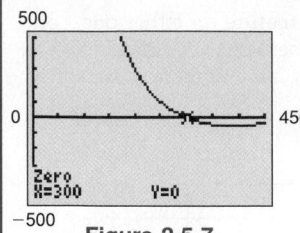 (number line: open circle at 0, closed at 8, labeled −2 0 2 4 6 8)

6. (number line: open circle at 0, ray to right, labeled −2 0 2 4)

7. (number line: closed at −2 and 1, labeled −3 −2 −1 0 1 2 3)

8. (number line: open circles at −1 and 1, labeled −2 −1 0 1 2)

9. (number line: ray to left, closed at 1, labeled −4 −2 0 1)

10. (number line: closed at −2, open at 7, labeled −2 0 2 4 6 8)

43. $x \le \dfrac{-9 - \sqrt{21}}{2}$ or $x \ge \dfrac{-9 + \sqrt{21}}{2}$

45. $x \le \dfrac{1 - \sqrt{33}}{2}$ or $x \ge \dfrac{1 + \sqrt{33}}{2}$

(graphing calculator figure: viewing window 0 to 450 horizontal, −500 to 500 vertical, Zero X=300 Y=0)

Figure 2.5-7

In this context, the only solutions that make sense are those between 0 and 450. Therefore, choose a viewing window, such as the one shown in Figure 2.5-7, and graph

$$f(x) = 2x + \frac{300{,}000}{x} - 1600.$$

The graph in Figure 2.5-7 shows that the zero of f is $x \approx 300$, and the graph of C is negative, i.e., below the x-axis, for values greater than 300. Therefore, to keep costs under \$1600, between 300 and 450 printers should be ordered per delivery. ■

Exercises 2.5

In Exercises 1–4, express the given statement in symbols.

1. x is nonnegative.
$x \ge 0$
2. t is positive.
$t > 0$
3. c is at most 3.
$c \le 3$
4. z is at least −17.
$z \ge -17$

In Exercises 5–10, represent the given interval on a number line.

5. $(0, 8]$ **6.** $(0, \infty)$ **7.** $[-2, 1]$

8. $(-1, 1)$ **9.** $(-\infty, 0]$ **10.** $[-2, 7)$

In Exercises 11–16, use interval notation to denote the set of all real numbers x that satisfy the given inequality.

11. $5 \le x \le 8$
$[5, 8]$
12. $-2 \le x \le 7$
$[-2, 7]$
13. $-3 < x < 14$
$(-3, 14)$
14. $7 < x < 135$
$(7, 135)$
15. $x \ge -8$
$[-8, \infty)$
16. $x \ge 12$
$[12, \infty)$

In Exercises 17–36, solve the inequality and express your answer in interval notation.

17. $2x + 4 \le 7$ $\left(-\infty, \frac{3}{2}\right]$
18. $3x - 5 > -6$ $\left(-\frac{1}{3}, \infty\right)$

19. $3 - 5x < 13$
$(-2, \infty)$
20. $2 - 3x < 11$
$(-3, \infty)$
21. $6x + 3 \le x$ $\left(-\infty, -\frac{5}{8}\right]$
22. $5x + 3 \le 2x + 7$ $\left(-\infty, \frac{4}{3}\right]$
23. $5 - 7x < 2x - 4$
$(1, \infty)$
24. $5 - 3x > 7x - 3$ $\left(-\infty, \frac{4}{5}\right)$
25. $2 < 3x - 4 < 8$
$(2, 4)$
26. $1 < 5x + 6 < 9$ $\left(-1, \frac{3}{5}\right)$
27. $0 < 5 - 2x \le 11$
$\left[-3, \frac{5}{2}\right)$
28. $-4 \le 7 - 3x < 0$
$\left(\frac{7}{3}, \frac{11}{3}\right]$

29. $2x + 7(3x - 2) < 2(x - 1)$ $\left(-\infty, \frac{4}{7}\right)$

30. $x + 3(x - 5) \ge 3x + 2(x + 1)$
$(-\infty, -17]$
31. $\frac{x+1}{2} - 3x \le \frac{x+5}{3}$ $\left[-\frac{7}{17}, \infty\right)$

32. $\frac{x-1}{4} + 2x \ge \frac{2x-1}{3} + 2$ $\left[\frac{23}{19}, \infty\right)$

33. $2x + 3 \le 5x + 6 < -3x + 7$ $\left[-1, \frac{1}{8}\right)$

34. $4x - 2 < x + 8 < 9x + 1$ $\left(\frac{7}{8}, \frac{10}{3}\right)$

35. $3 - x < 2x + 1 \le 3x - 4$
$[5, \infty)$
36. $2x + 5 \le 4 - 3x < 1 - 4x$
$(-\infty, -3)$

In Exercises 37–40, the constants a, b, c, and d are positive. Solve each inequality for x.

37. $ax - b < c$ $\quad x < \dfrac{b + c}{a}$
38. $d - cx > a$ $\quad x < \dfrac{d - a}{c}$
39. $0 < x - c < a$
$c < x < a + c$
40. $-d < x - c < d$
$c - d < x < c + d$

In Exercises 41–70, solve the inequality. Find exact solutions when possible, and approximate them otherwise.

41. $x^2 - 4x + 3 \le 0$
$1 \le x \le 3$
42. $x^2 - 7x + 10 \le 0$
$2 \le x \le 5$
43. $x^2 + 9x + 15 \ge 0$
44. $x^2 + 8x + 20 \ge 0$
all real numbers
45. $8 + x - x^2 \le 0$
46. $4 - 3x - x^2 \ge 0$
$-4 \le x \le 1$
47. $x^3 - x \ge 0$
$-1 \le x \le 0$ or $x \ge 1$
48. $x^3 + 2x^2 + x > 0$
$x > 0$
49. $x^3 - 2x^2 - 3x < 0$
$x < -1$ or $0 < x < 3$
50. $x^4 - 14x^3 + 48x^2 \ge 0$
$x \le 6$ or $x \ge 8$

51. $x^4 - 5x^2 + 4 < 0$
-2 < x < -1 or 1 < x < 2

52. $x^4 - 10x^2 + 9 \le 0$
-3 ≤ x ≤ -1 or 1 ≤ x ≤ 3

53. $x^3 - 2x^2 - 5x + 7 \ge 2x + 1$
-2.26 ≤ x ≤ 0.76 or x ≥ 3.51

54. $x^4 - 6x^3 + 2x^2 < 5x - 2$
0.39 < x < 5.79

55. $2x^4 + 3x^3 < 2x^2 + 4x - 2$
0.5 < x < 0.84

56. $x^5 + 5x^4 > 4x^3 - 3x^2 + 2$
-5.78 < x < -0.55 or x > 0.77

57. $\dfrac{3x + 1}{2x - 4} > 0$ **x < -$\frac{1}{3}$** **58.** $\dfrac{2x - 1}{5x + 3} \ge 0$ **x < -$\frac{3}{5}$ or x ≥ $\frac{1}{2}$**
or x > 2

59. $\dfrac{x^2 + x - 2}{x^2 - 2x - 3} < 0$ **60.** $\dfrac{2x^2 + x - 1}{x^2 - 4x + 4} \ge 0$

61. $\dfrac{x - 2}{x - 1} < 1$ **x > 1** **62.** $\dfrac{-x + 5}{2x + 3} \ge 2$ **-$\frac{3}{2}$ < x ≤ -$\frac{1}{5}$**

63. $\dfrac{x - 3}{x + 3} \le 5$ **x ≤ -$\frac{9}{2}$** **64.** $\dfrac{2x + 1}{x - 4} > 3$ **4 < x < 13**
or x > -3

65. $\dfrac{2}{x + 3} \ge \dfrac{1}{x - 1}$ **66.** $\dfrac{1}{x - 1} < \dfrac{-1}{x + 2}$ **x < -2 or -$\frac{1}{2}$ < x < 1**
-3 < x < 1 or x ≥ 5

67. $\dfrac{x^3 - 3x^2 + 5x - 29}{x^2 - 7} > 3$ **-$\sqrt{7}$ < x < $\sqrt{7}$ or x > 5.34**

68. $\dfrac{x^4 - 3x^3 + 2x^2 + 2}{x - 2} > 15$ **2 < x < 2.223 or x > 2.679**

69. $\dfrac{2x^2 + 6x - 8}{2x^2 + 5x - 3} < 1$ Be alert for hidden behavior.
x < -3 or $\frac{1}{2}$ < x < 5

70. $\dfrac{1}{x^2 + x - 6} + \dfrac{x - 2}{x + 3} > \dfrac{x + 3}{x - 2}$ **x < -3 or -$\frac{2}{5}$ < x < 2**

In Exercises 71–73, read the solution of the inequality from the given graph.

71. $3 - 2x < 0.8x + 7$
x > -1.43

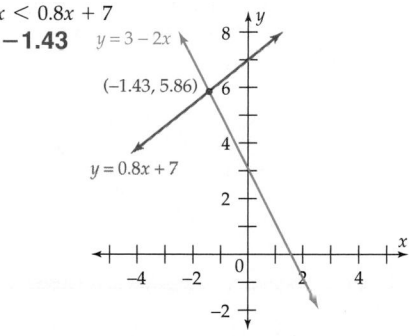

72. $8 - |7 - 5x| > 3$
0.4 < x < 2.4

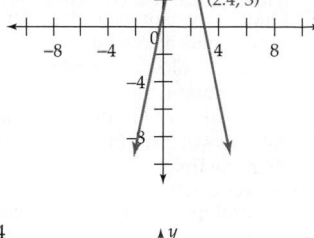

73. $x^2 + 3x + 1 \ge 4$

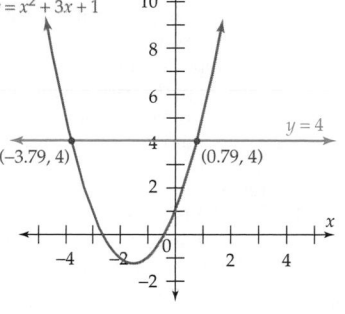

74. The graphs of the revenue and cost functions for a manufacturing firm are shown in the figure.
  a. What is the break-even point?
  b. Which region represents profit?

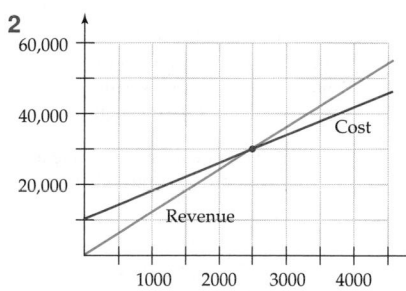

75. One freezer costs $623.95 and uses 90 kilowatt hours (kwh) of electricity each month. A second freezer costs $500 and uses 100 kwh of electricity each month. The expected life of each freezer is 12 years. What is the minimum electric rate in cents per kwh for which the 12-year total cost (purchase price + electricity costs) will be less for the first freezer?
approximately 8.608 cents per kwh

59. $-2 < x < -1$ or $1 < x < 3$

60. $x \le -1$ or $\frac{1}{2} \le x < 2$ or $x > 2$

73. $x \le -3.79$ or $x \ge 0.79$

74. a. about (2500, 30,000)

  b. the region between the red and blue lines to the right of the break-even point

76. A business executive leases a car for $300 per month. She decides to lease another brand for $250 per month, but has to pay a penalty of $1000 for breaking the first lease. How long must she keep the second car in order to come out ahead?
more than 20 months

77. One salesperson is paid a salary of $1000 per month plus a commission of 2% of her total sales. A second salesperson receives no salary, but is paid a commission of 10% of her total sales. What dollar amount of sales must the second salesperson have in order to earn more per month than the first?
more than $12,500

78. A developer subdivided 60 acres of a 100-acre tract, leaving 20% of the 60 acres as a park. Zoning laws require that at least 25% of the total tract be set aside for parks. For financial reasons the developer wants to have no more than 30% of the tract as parks. How many one-quarter-acre lots can the developer sell in the remaining 40 acres and still meet the requirements for the whole tract?
between 88 and 108 lots

79. If $5000 is invested at 8%, how much more should be invested at 10% in order to guarantee a total annual interest income between $800 and $940?
between $4000 and $5400

80. How many gallons of a 12% salt solution should be added to 10 gallons of an 18% salt solution in order to produce a solution whose salt content is between 14% and 16%?
between 5 and 20 gallons

81. Find all pairs of numbers that satisfy these two conditions: Their sum is 20 and the sum of their squares is less than 362.
$1 < x < 19$ and $y = 20 - x$

82. The length of a rectangle is 6 inches longer than its width. What are the possible widths if the area of the rectangle is at least 667 square inches?
$w \geq 23$

83. It costs a craftsman $5 in materials to make a medallion. He has found that if he sells the
$10 < x < 35$

medallions for $50 - x$ dollars each, where x is the number of medallions produced each week, then he can sell all that he makes. His fixed costs are $350 per week. If he wants to sell all he makes and show a profit each week, what are the possible numbers of medallions he should make?

84. A retailer sells file cabinets for $80 - x$ dollars each, where x is the number of cabinets she receives from the supplier each week. She pays $10 for each file cabinet and has fixed costs of $600 per week. How many file cabinets should she order from the supplier each week in order to guarantee that she makes a profit?
$10 < x < 60$

In Exercises 85–88, you will need the following formula for the height h of an object above the ground at time t seconds, where v_0 denotes initial velocity and h_0 denotes initial height. $h = -16t^2 + v_0t + h_0$

85. A toy rocket is fired straight up from ground level with an initial velocity of 80 feet per second. During what time interval will it be at least 64 feet above the ground?
$1 \leq t \leq 4$

86. A projectile is fired straight up from ground level with an initial velocity of 72 feet per second. During what time interval is it at least 37 feet above the ground?
$0.59168 < t < 3.9083$

87. A ball is dropped from the roof of a 120-foot-high building. During what time period will it be strictly between 56 feet and 39 feet above the ground?
$2 < t < 2.25$

88. A ball is thrown straight up from a 40-foot-high tower with an initial velocity of 56 feet per second.
  a. During what time interval is the ball at least 8 feet above the ground? **$0 \leq t < 4$**
  b. During what time interval is the ball between 53 feet and 80 feet above the ground?
  $0.25 < t < 1$ or $2.5 < t < 3.25$

Excursion: Absolute-Value Inequalities

2.5.A

Objectives

- Solve absolute-value inequalities by the Intersection Method
- Solve absolute-value inequalities by the *x*-Intercept Method

Polynomial and rational inequalities involving absolute value can be solved by either of two graphing methods.

Intersection Method

- Graph the expressions on each side of the inequality.
- Determine the intervals on the *x-axis* where the graph of the expression on one side of the inequality is above or below the graph of the expression on the other side of the inequality.

x-Intercept Method

- Rewrite the inequality in an equivalent form with 0 on one side of the inequality.
- Graph the function given by the nonzero side of the inequality.
- Determine the *x*-values where the graph is above or below the *x*-axis.

 Example 1   **Solving an Absolute-Value Inequality Using the Intersection Method**

Solve $|x^4 + 2x^2 - x + 2| < 11x$.

Solution

The solutions of $|x^4 + 2x^2 - x + 2| < 11x$ can be found be determining the *x*-intervals for which the graph of $f(x) = |x^4 + 2x^2 - x + 2|$ is below the graph of $g(x) = 11x$.

A graphical intersection finder shows that the points of intersection occur when $x \approx 0.17$ and $x \approx 1.92$, and the graph of f is below the graph of g between them, as shown in Figure 2.5.A-1. Therefore, approximate solutions of the original inequality are all x such that

$$0.17 < x < 1.92.$$

Figure 2.5.A-1

Example 2   **Solving an Absolute-Value Inequality Using the *x*-Intercept Method**

Solve $\left|\dfrac{x+4}{x-2}\right| > 3$.

Solution

Rewrite $\left|\dfrac{x+4}{x-2}\right| > 3$ as $\left|\dfrac{x+4}{x-2}\right| - 3 > 0$, graph $f(x) = \left|\dfrac{x+4}{x-2}\right| - 3$, and find the intervals on the *x*-axis where the graph is above the *x*-axis.

Section 2.5.A Excursion: Absolute-Value Inequalities

Teaching Notes

The **Intersection Method** and the **x-Intercept Method** as introduced in Section 2.1, are *graphing* methods that can be used to solve absolute-value inequalities. *Algebraic* methods will be discussed on page 128.

ADDITIONAL EXAMPLES

Example 1

Solve $|x^4 + x^2 - 2x + 3| < 5x$.

Determine the *x*-intervals for which the graph of $f(x) = |x^4 + x^2 - 2x + 3|$ is below the graph of $g(x) = 5x$.

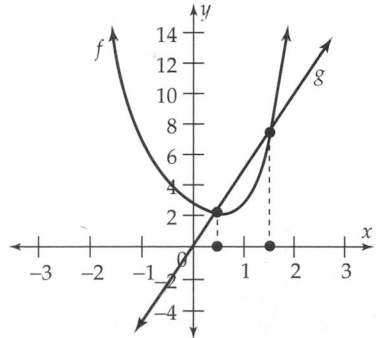

Points of intersection: $x \approx 0.47$ and $x \approx 1.52$

The approximate solutions of the original inequality are all x such that $0.47 < x < 1.52$.

ADDITIONAL EXAMPLES

Example 2

Solve $\left|\dfrac{x+3}{x-1}\right| > 2$.

Rewrite $\left|\dfrac{x+3}{x-1}\right| > 2$ as

$\left|\dfrac{x+3}{x-1}\right| - 2 > 0$.

Graph $f(x) = \left|\dfrac{x+3}{x-1}\right| - 2$ and find the intervals on the x-axis where the graph is above the x-axis.

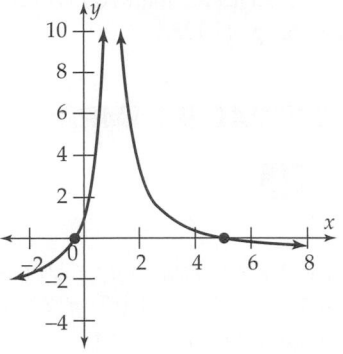

The zeros of the function are $-\dfrac{1}{3}$ and 5, and the function is not defined at $x = 1$.

The solutions of the original inequality are the x-intervals $\left(-\dfrac{1}{3}, 1\right)$ and $(1, 5)$.

Teaching Notes

Graphing methods are recommended for solving absolute-value inequalities involving rational expressions or polynomials with degree higher than 2, especially when an approximate answer is sufficient. Algebraic methods are effective for linear and quadratic inequalities and can be used to find exact answers.

The number line is a powerful tool for interpreting solutions to inequalities. Make sure that students understand the graphs shown in Figures 2.5.A-3a and 2.5.A-3b. If students have difficulty, use numerical examples.

Ask if the following values are solutions to $|r| \le 5$:
-2 yes   3 yes -6 no

Ask if the following values are solutions to $|r| \ge 5$:
-5 yes   4 no   6 yes

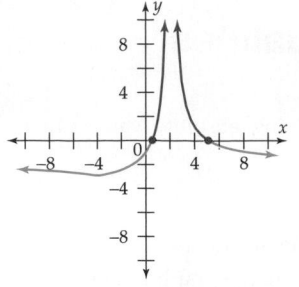

Figure 2.5.A-2

The graph of f is above the x-axis between the two zeros, which can be found algebraically or graphically to be $x = \dfrac{1}{2}$ and $x = 5$. Notice that the function is not defined at $x = 2$ because a fraction cannot have a zero denominator. Therefore, the solutions of

$$\left|\frac{x+4}{x-2}\right| - 3 > 0$$

are the x-intervals $\left(\dfrac{1}{2}, 2\right)$ and $(2, 5)$. The solution can also be written out.

$$\frac{1}{2} < x < 2 \quad \text{or} \quad 2 < x < 5$$

Algebraic Methods

Most linear and quadratic inequalities that contain absolute values can be solved exactly by using algebra. In fact, this is often the easiest way to solve such inequalities. The key to the algebraic method is to interpret the absolute value of a number as distance on the number line.

For example, the inequality $|r| \le 5$ states that

the distance from r to 0 is less than or equal to 5 units.

A glance at the number line in Figure 2.5.A-3a shows that these are the numbers r such that $-5 \le r \le 5$.

Figure 2.5.A-3a

Similarly, the inequality $|r| \ge 5$ states that

the distance from r to 0 is greater than or equal to 5 units.

These values are the numbers r such that $r \le -5$ or $r \ge 5$, as shown in Figure 2.5.A-3b.

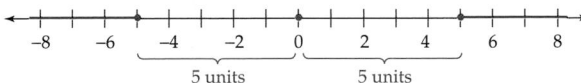

Figure 2.5.A-3b

Similar conclusions hold in the general cases, with 5 replaced by any number k.

Absolute-Value Inequalities

Let k be a positive real number and r any real number.

$|r| \leq k$ is equivalent to $-k \leq r \leq k$.

$|r| \geq k$ is equivalent to $r \leq -k$ or $r \geq k$.

Example 3   Solving an Absolute-Value Inequality

Solve $|3x - 7| \leq 11$.

Solution

Apply the first fact in the box above, with $3x - 7$ in place of r and 11 in place of k, and conclude that $|3x - 7| \leq 11$ is equivalent to

$$-11 \leq 3x - 7 \leq 11$$
$$-4 \leq \quad 3x \quad \leq 18 \qquad \textit{Add 7}$$
$$\frac{-4}{3} \leq \quad x \quad \leq 6 \qquad \textit{Divide by 3}$$

Therefore, the solution to $|3x - 7| \leq 11$ is all numbers in the interval $\left[-\frac{4}{3}, 6\right]$, that is, all x such that $-\frac{4}{3} \leq x \leq 6$.

Example 4   Solving an Absolute-Value Inequality

Solve $|5x + 2| > 3$.

Solution

Apply the second fact in the box with $5x + 2$ in place of r, 3 in place of k, and $>$ in place of $\geq$.

$$5x + 2 < -3 \qquad \text{or} \qquad 5x + 2 > 3$$
$$x < -1 \qquad\qquad\qquad x > \frac{1}{5}$$

Therefore, the solutions of the original inequality are the numbers in *either* of the intervals $(-\infty, -1)$ or $\left(\frac{1}{5}, \infty\right)$, that is, $x < -1$ or $x > \frac{1}{5}$.

Example 5   Solving an Absolute-Value Inequality

Solve $|x^2 - x - 4| \geq 2$.

Solution

Rewrite the absolute-value inequality as two quadratic inequalities using the algebraic definition.

Teaching Notes

Point out to students we can make similar statements to those in **Absolute-Value Inequalities** by omitting "*or equal to.*" That is, if k is a positive real number and r is any real number:
$|r| < k$ is equivalent to $-k < r < k$
and
$|r| > k$ is equivalent to $r < -k$
               or $r > k$.

Example Notes

In **Example 3**, to help students get from $|3x - 7| \leq 11$ to $-11 \leq 3x - 7 \leq 11$, you can use the inequality from the box at the left as shown below.

$|r| \quad\;\; \leq k \Leftrightarrow -k \leq \quad\; r \quad\; \leq k$
$|3x - 7| \leq 11 \Leftrightarrow -11 \leq 3x - 7 \leq 11$

Do a similar alignment for **Example 4**.

$|r| \quad\;\; > k \Leftrightarrow \quad\; r \quad\; < -k$ or
$\qquad\qquad\qquad\qquad\qquad\quad r \;\; > k$
$|5x + 2| > 3 \Leftrightarrow 5x + 2 < -3$ or
$\qquad\qquad\qquad\qquad\quad 5x + 2 > 3$

ADDITIONAL EXAMPLES

Example 3

Solve $|2x - 5| \leq 8$.

Rewrite as $-8 \leq 2x - 5 \leq 8$ and solve.

All numbers in the interval $\left[-\frac{3}{2}, \frac{13}{2}\right]$, that is, all x such that $-\frac{3}{2} \leq x \leq \frac{13}{2}$.

Example 4

Solve $|4x + 3| > 5$.

Rewrite as $4x + 3 < -5$ or $4x + 3 > 5$ and solve. Numbers in *either* of the intervals $(-\infty, -2)$ or $\left(\frac{1}{2}, \infty\right)$, that is, all x such that $x < -2$ or $x > \frac{1}{2}$.

Example Notes

Example 5 combines algebraic and graphing methods. Ask students to verify the x-intercepts by factoring $x^2 - x - 2$ and $x^2 - x - 6$.

$x^2 - x - 2 = (x - 2)(x + 1)$

$x^2 - x - 6 = (x - 3)(x + 2)$

In **Example 6**, if students are confused by the variables representing constants, give a numerical example, such as $|x - 2| < 5$, and relate it to the inequality in the example, $|x - a| < \delta$, as shown in the number line diagram below.

ADDITIONAL EXAMPLES

Example 5

Solve $|x^2 + x - 7| \geq 5$.

Rewrite as:

$x^2 + x - 7 \leq -5$ or $x^2 + x - 7 \geq 5$
$x^2 + x - 2 \leq 0$ $x^2 + x - 12 \geq 0$

Graph $f(x) = x^2 + x - 2$ and $g(x) = x^2 + x - 12$. Find intervals of x such that $f(x) \leq 0$ or $g(x) \geq 0$.

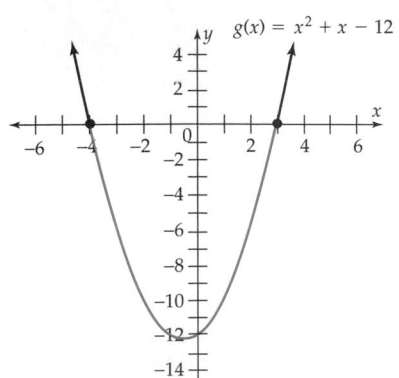

The inequality $|x^2 - x - 4| \geq 2$ is equivalent to two inequalities.

$$x^2 - x - 4 \leq -2 \quad \text{or} \quad x^2 - x - 4 \geq 2$$
$$x^2 - x - 2 \leq 0 \qquad\qquad x^2 - x - 6 \geq 0$$

The solutions are all numbers that are solutions of *either one* of the two inequalities shown above.

The solutions are the intervals on the x-axis that are determined by the following.

- $f(x) = x^2 - x - 2$ is on or below the x-axis
- $g(x) = x^2 - x - 6$ is on or above the x-axis

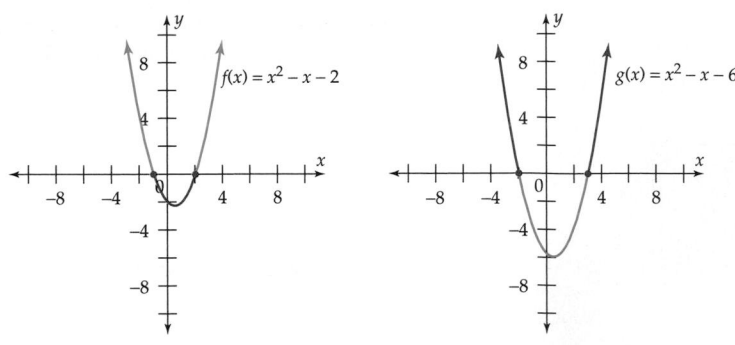

Figure 2.5.A-4a   **Figure 2.5.A-4b**

As shown in Figure 2.5.A-4a, the graph of $f(x) = x^2 - x - 2$ is on or below the x-axis when

$$-1 \leq x \leq 2.$$

As shown in Figure 2.5.A-4b, the graph of $g(x) = x^2 - x - 6$ is on or above the x-axis when

$$x \leq -2 \quad \text{or} \quad x \geq 3.$$

Therefore, the solutions of the original inequality are all numbers x such that $x \leq -2$ *or* $-1 \leq x \leq 2$ *or* $x \geq 3$, as shown in Figure 2.5.A-4c.

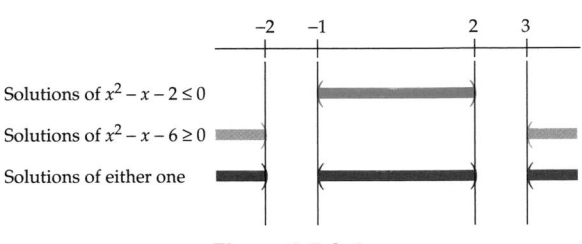

Figure 2.5.A-4c

The solutions of the original inequality are all numbers x such that $x \leq -4$ or $-2 \leq x \leq 1$ or $x \geq 3$.

Example 6 Interpreting an Absolute-Value Inequality

Let a and δ represent real numbers with δ positive.

a. Interpret $|x - a| < \delta$ geometrically.
b. Draw the interval represented.
c. Write the equivalent simplified extended inequality.
d. Interpret the last inequality.

Solution

a. Geometrically, $|x - a| < \delta$ means that

the distance from x to a is less than δ.

b.

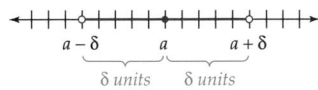

$$a - \delta \qquad a \qquad a + \delta$$
$$\underbrace{\qquad}_{\delta \text{ units}} \underbrace{\qquad}_{\delta \text{ units}}$$

Figure 2.5.A-5

c. $\qquad -\delta < x - a < \delta$
$\qquad a - \delta < x < a + \delta \qquad$ *Add a to each term*

d. The solutions of the inequality are all numbers strictly between $a - \delta$ and $a + \delta$.

Exercises 2.5.A

In Exercises 1–32, solve the inequality. Find exact solutions when possible, and approximate values otherwise.

1. $|3x + 2| \le 2$

2. $|5x - 1| < 3$

3. $|3 - 2x| < \dfrac{2}{3}$

4. $|4 - 5x| \le 4$

5. $|2x + 3| > 1$

6. $|3x - 1| \ge 2$

7. $|5x + 2| \ge \dfrac{3}{4}$

8. $|2 - 3x| > 4$

9. $\left|\dfrac{12}{5} + 2x\right| > \dfrac{1}{4}$

10. $\left|\dfrac{5}{6} + 3x\right| < \dfrac{7}{6}$

11. $\left|\dfrac{x - 1}{x + 2}\right| \le 3$

12. $\left|\dfrac{x + 1}{3x + 5}\right| < 2$

13. $\left|\dfrac{2x - 1}{x + 5}\right| > 1$

14. $\left|\dfrac{x + 1}{x + 2}\right| \ge 2$

15. $\left|\dfrac{1 - 4x}{2 + 3x}\right| < 1$

16. $\left|\dfrac{3x + 1}{1 - 2x}\right| \ge 2$

17. $|x^2 - 2| < 1$

18. $|x^2 - 4| \le 3$

19. $|x^2 - 2| > 4$

20. $\left|\dfrac{1}{x^2 - 1}\right| \le 2$

21. $|x^2 + x - 1| \ge 1$

22. $|x^2 + x - 4| \le 2$

23. $|3x^2 - 8x + 2| < 2$

24. $|x^2 + 3x - 4| < 6$

25. $|x^5 - x^3 + 1| < 2$

26. $|4x - x^3| > 1$

27. $|x^4 - x^3 + x^2 - x + 1| > 4$

28. $|x^3 - 6x^2 + 4x - 5| < 3$

29. $\dfrac{x + 2}{|x - 3|} \le 1$

30. $\dfrac{x^2 - 9}{|x^2 - 4|} \le -2$

31. $\left|\dfrac{2x^2 + 2x - 12}{x^3 - x^2 + x - 2}\right| > 2$

32. $\left|\dfrac{x^2 - x - 2}{x^2 + x - 2}\right| > 3$

19. $x < -\sqrt{6}$ or $x > \sqrt{6}$

20. $x \le -\sqrt{\dfrac{3}{2}}$ or $-\sqrt{\dfrac{1}{2}} \le x \le \sqrt{\dfrac{1}{2}}$ or $x \ge \sqrt{\dfrac{3}{2}}$

21. $x \le -2$ or $-1 \le x \le 0$ or $x \ge 1$

22. $-3 \le x \le -2$ or $1 \le x \le 2$

23. $0 < x < \dfrac{2}{3}$ or $2 < x < \dfrac{8}{3}$

24. $-5 < x < -2$ or $-1 < x < 2$

25. $-1.43 < x < 1.24$

26. $x < -2.115$ or $-1.861 < x < -0.254$
or $0.254 < x < 1.861$ or $x > 2.115$

27. $x < -0.89$ or $x > 1.56$

28. $5.319 < x < 5.539$

29. $x \le 2$ or $x \ge \dfrac{14}{3}$

30. $-2.38 < x < -2$ or
$-2 < x < 2$ or $2 < x < 2.38$

31. $-1.13 < x < 1.35$ or $1.35 < x < 1.67$

32. $-2.73 < x < -2$ or $-2 < x < -1.69$
or $0.73 < x < 1$ or $1 < x < 1.19$

Example 6

Let δ represent a positive real number.

a. Interpret $|x - 2| < \delta$ geometrically.

Geometrically, $|x - 2| < \delta$ means that the distance from x to 2 is less than δ.

b. Draw the intervals represented.

$$2 - \delta \qquad 2 \qquad 2 + \delta$$
$$\underbrace{\qquad}_{\delta \text{ units}} \underbrace{\qquad}_{\delta \text{ units}}$$

c. Write the equivalent simplified compound inequality.
$\qquad -\delta < x - 2 < \delta$
$\qquad 2 - \delta < x < 2 + \delta$

d. Interpret the last inequality.

The solutions of the inequality are all numbers between $2 - \delta$ and $2 + \delta$.

π β Math Background

Example 6 is preparing students for the ε-δ definition of limits (page 929).

Exercises 2.5A

ANSWERS

1. $-\dfrac{4}{3} \le x \le 0$

2. $-\dfrac{2}{5} < x < \dfrac{4}{5}$

3. $\dfrac{7}{6} < x < \dfrac{11}{6}$

4. $0 \le x \le \dfrac{8}{5}$

5. $x < -2$ or $x > -1$

6. $x \le -\dfrac{1}{3}$ or $x \ge 1$

7. $x \le -\dfrac{11}{20}$ or $x \ge -\dfrac{1}{4}$

8. $x < -\dfrac{2}{3}$ or $x > 2$

9. $x < -\dfrac{53}{40}$ or $x > -\dfrac{43}{40}$

10. $-\dfrac{2}{3} < x < \dfrac{1}{9}$

11. $x \le -\dfrac{7}{2}$ or $x \ge -\dfrac{5}{4}$

12. $x < -\dfrac{9}{5}$ or $x > -\dfrac{11}{7}$

13. $x < -5$ or $-5 < x < -\dfrac{4}{3}$
or $x > 6$

14. $-3 \le x < -2$ or $-2 < x \le -\dfrac{5}{3}$

15. $-\dfrac{1}{7} < x < 3$

16. $\dfrac{1}{7} \le x < \dfrac{1}{2}$ or $\dfrac{1}{2} < x \le 3$

17. $-\sqrt{3} < x < -1$ or $1 < x < \sqrt{3}$

18. $-\sqrt{7} \le x \le -1$ or $1 \le x \le \sqrt{7}$

33. *Critical Thinking* Let E be a fixed real number. Show that every solution of $|x - 3| < \frac{E}{5}$ is also a solution of $|(5x - 4) - 11| < E$.

If $|x - 3| < \frac{E}{5}$, then multiplying both sides by 5 shows that $5|x - 3| < E$.

But $5|x - 3| = |5| \cdot |x - 3|$

$$= |5(x - 3)|$$
$$= |5x - 15|$$
$$= |(5x - 4) - 11|.$$

Thus, $|(5x - 4) - 11| < E$.

34. *Critical Thinking* Let a and b be fixed real numbers with $a < b$. Show that the solutions of

$$\left| x - \frac{a + b}{2} \right| < \frac{b - a}{2}$$

are all x such that $a < x < b$.

$$\left| x - \frac{a + b}{2} \right| < \frac{b - a}{2};$$

$$-\left(\frac{b - a}{2} \right) < x - \frac{a + b}{2} < \frac{b - a}{2};$$

$$\frac{a - b}{2} < x - \frac{a + b}{2} < \frac{b - a}{2};$$

$$\frac{a + b}{2} + \frac{a - b}{2} < x < \frac{b - a}{2} + \frac{a + b}{2};$$

$$\frac{2a}{2} < x < \frac{2b}{b};$$

$$a < x < b$$

CHAPTER

2

REVIEW

Important Concepts

133

**Important Facts
and Formulas**

To solve an equation of the form $f(x) = g(x)$ with the **Intersection Method,** use two steps.

1. Graph $y_1 = f(x)$ and $y_2 = g(x)$

2. Find the x-coordinate of each point of intersection

When f is a function and a is a real number, the following are **equivalent statements:**

- a is a zero of the function $y = f(x)$
- a is an x-intercept of the graph of f
- a is a solution, or root, of the equation $f(x) = 0$

To solve an equation by the **x-Intercept Method,** use three steps.

1. Rewrite the equation in the form $f(x) = 0$

2. Graph f

3. Find the x-intercepts of the graph. The x-intercepts of the graph of f are the solutions of $f(x) = 0$.

The only number whose square root is zero is zero itself.

A fraction is zero only when its numerator is zero and its denominator is nonzero.

Quadratic Formula

If $a \neq 0$, then the solutions of $ax^2 + bx + c = 0$ are

$$x = \frac{-b \pm \sqrt{b^2 - 4ac}}{2a}$$

If $a \neq 0$, then the number of *real* solutions of $ax^2 + bx + c = 0$ is 0, 1, or 2, depending on whether the discriminant, $b^2 - 4ac$, is negative, zero, or positive, respectively.

Absolute Value

$$|x| = x \quad \text{if } x \geq 0$$
$$|x| = -x \text{ if } x < 0$$

$|c - d|$ represents the distance between c and d on the number line.

$|c|$ represents the distance between c and 0 on the number line.

Review Questions

In Questions 1–8, solve the equation graphically. You need only find solutions in the given interval.

Section 2.1

1. $x^3 + 2x^2 = 11x + 6$; $[0, \infty)$
   $x \approx 2.7644$

2. $x^3 + 2x^2 = 11x + 6$; $(-\infty, 0)$
   $x \approx -0.5102$ or -4.2517

3. $x^4 + x^3 - 10x^2 = 8x + 16$; $[0, \infty)$
   $x \approx 3.2678$

4. $2x^4 + x^3 - 2x^2 + 6x + 2 = 0$; $(-\infty, -1)$
   $x \approx -1.8049$

5. $\dfrac{x^3 + 2x^2 - 3x + 4}{x^2 + 2x - 15} = 0$; $(-10, \infty)$
   $x \approx -3.2843$

6. $\dfrac{3x^4 + x^3 - 6x^2 - 2x}{x^5 + x^3 + 2} = 0$; $[0, \infty)$
   $x = 0$ or $\sqrt{2}$

7. $\sqrt{x^3 + 2x^2 - 3x - 5} = 0$; $[0, \infty)$
   $x \approx 1.6511$

8. $\sqrt{1 + 2x - 3x^2 + 4x^3 - x^4} = 0$; $(-5, 5)$
   $x \approx -0.3028$ or 3.3028

Section 2.2

9. Solve for x: $3x^2 - 2x + 5 = 0$
   no real solutions

10. Solve for y: $3y^2 - 2y = 5$ **$y = \dfrac{5}{3}$ or -1**

11. Solve for z: $5z^2 + 6z = 7$ **$z = \dfrac{-3 \pm 2\sqrt{11}}{5}$**

12. Solve for x: $325x^2 + 17x - 127 = 0$ **$x = \dfrac{-17 \pm \sqrt{165{,}389}}{650}$**

13. Solve for x: $x^4 - 11x^2 + 18 = 0$
    $x = 3$ or -3 or $\sqrt{2}$ or $-\sqrt{2}$

14. Solve for x: $x^6 - 4x^3 + 4 = 0$
    $x = \sqrt[3]{2}$

15. Find the number of real solutions of the equation $20x^2 + 12 = 31x$.
    2

16. For what value of k does the equation $kt^2 + 5t + 2 = 0$ have exactly one real solution for t? **$k = \dfrac{25}{8}$**

Section 2.3

17. A jeweler wants to make a 1-ounce ring composed of gold and silver, using $200 worth of metal. If gold costs $600 per ounce and silver $50 per ounce, how much of each metal should she use? **gold, $\dfrac{3}{11}$ oz; silver, $\dfrac{8}{11}$ oz**

18. A calculator is on sale for 15% less than the list price. The sale price, plus a 5% shipping charge, totals $210. What is the list price?
    $\approx$ \$235.29

19. Karen can do a job in 5 hours and Claire can do the same job in 4 hours. How long will it take them to do the job together? **$2\dfrac{2}{9}$ hrs**

20. A car leaves the city traveling at 54 mph. A half hour later, a second car leaves from the same place and travels at 63 mph along the same road. How long will it take for the second car to catch up to the first?
    3.5 hrs

21. A 12-foot rectangular board is cut into two pieces so that one piece is four times as long as the other. How long is the bigger piece?
    9.6 ft

22. George owns 200 shares of stock, 40% of which are in the computer industry. How many more shares must he buy in order to have 50% of his total shares in computers?
    40 shares

23. A square region is changed into a rectangular one by making it 2 feet longer and twice as wide. If the area of the rectangular region is three times larger than the area of the original square region, what was the length of a side of the square before it was changed?
4 ft

24. The radius of a circle is 10 inches. By how many inches should the radius be increased so that the area increases by 5π square inches?
$\approx$**0.24695 in.**

25. If $c(x)$ is the cost of producing x units, then $\frac{c(x)}{x}$ is the *average cost* per unit.

The cost of manufacturing x caseloads of ballpoint pens is given by

$$c(x) = \frac{600x^2 + 600x}{x^2 + 1}$$

where $c(x)$ is in dollars. How many caseloads should be manufactured in order to have an average cost of $25? **25**

26. An open-top box with a rectangular base is to be constructed. The box is to be at least 2 inches wide, twice as long as it is wide, and must have a volume of 150 cubic inches. What should be the dimensions of the box if the surface area is 90 square inches?
A surface area of 90 square inches is not possible.

Section 2.4

27. Simplify: $|b^2 - 2b + 1|$
$(b - 1)^2$

In Exercises 28–40, find all real exact solutions.

28. $|x + 2| = 4$
$x = -6$ **or** 2

29. $|x + 3| = \dfrac{5}{2}$
$x = -\dfrac{1}{2}$ **or** $-\dfrac{11}{2}$

30. $|x - 5| = 3$
$x = 8$ **or** 2

31. $|3x - 1| = 4$ $x = \dfrac{5}{3}$ **or** -1

32. $|2x - 1| = x + 4$
$x = 5$ **or** -1

33. $\sqrt{x^2 - x - 2} = 0$ $x = 2$ **or** -1

34. $\sqrt{6x^2 - 7x - 5} = 0$ $x = \dfrac{5}{3}$ **or** $-\dfrac{1}{2}$

35. $\dfrac{x^2 - 6x + 8}{x - 1} = 0$
$x = 2$ **or** 4

36. $\dfrac{x^2 - x - 2}{x - 2} = 0$ $x = -1$

37. $\sqrt{x - 1} = 2 - x$ $x = \dfrac{5 - \sqrt{5}}{2}$

38. $\sqrt[3]{1 - t^2} = -2$
$t = \pm 3$

39. $\sqrt{x + 1} + \sqrt{x - 1} = 1$
no solutions

40. $\sqrt[3]{x^4 - 2x^3 + 6x - 7} = x + 3$
$x \approx -1.733$ **or** 5.521

Section 2.5

41. Express in interval notation:
  a. The set of all real numbers that are strictly greater than -8 $(-8, \infty)$
  b. The set of all real numbers that are less than or equal to 5. $(-\infty, 5]$

42. Express in interval notation:
  a. The set of all real numbers that are strictly between -6 and 9; $(-6, 9)$
  b. The set of all real numbers that are greater than or equal to 5, but strictly less than 14. $[5, 14)$

43. Solve for x: $-3(x - 4) \le 5 + x$. $\left[\dfrac{7}{4}, \infty\right)$

44. Solve for x: $-4 < 2x + 5 < 9$. $\left(-\dfrac{9}{2}, 2\right)$

45. On which intervals is $\dfrac{2x - 1}{3x + 1} < 1$?

$(-\infty, -2)$ **and** $\left(-\dfrac{1}{3}, \infty\right)$

46. On which intervals is $\dfrac{2}{x+1} < x$?
$(-2, -1)$ and $(1, \infty)$

47. Solve for x: $(x - 1)^2(x^2 - 1)x \le 0$.
$x \le -1$ or $0 \le x \le 1$

48. Solve for x: $x^2 + x > 12$.
$x < -4$ or $x > 3$

49. If $\dfrac{x + 3}{2x + 3} > 1$, then which of these statements is true? **e**

  a. $\dfrac{x - 3}{2x + 3} < -1$, **b.** $\dfrac{2x - 3}{x + 3} < -1$

  c. $\dfrac{3 - 2x}{x + 3} > 1$ **d.** $2x + 3 < x - 3$

  e. None of these

50. If $0 < r \le s - t$, then which of these statements is false? **c**
  a. $s \ge r + t$ **b.** $t - s \le -r$

  c. $-r \ge s - t$ **d.** $\dfrac{s - t}{r} > 0$

  e. $s - r \ge t$

51. Solve and express your answer in interval notation:

$$\left[-4, -\frac{5}{8}\right) \qquad 2x - 3 \le 5x + 9 < -3x + 4.$$

In Questions 52–61, solve the inequality.

52. $x^2 + x - 20 > 0$ **53.** $\dfrac{x - 2}{x + 4} \le 3$ **$x \le -7$ or $x > -4$**
$x < -5$ or $x > 4$

54. $(x + 1)^2(x - 3)^4(x + 2)^3(x - 7)^5 > 0$
$x < -2$ or $x > 7$

55. $\dfrac{x^2 + x - 9}{x + 3} < 1$ **56.** $\dfrac{x^2 - x - 6}{x - 3} > 1$
$x < -2\sqrt{3}$ or $-3 < x < 2\sqrt{3}$ **$-1 < x < 3$ or $x > 3$**

57. $\dfrac{x^2 - x - 5}{x^2 + 2} > -2$ **58.** $\dfrac{x^4 - 3x^2 + 2x - 3}{x^2 - 4} < -1$
$x < \dfrac{1 - \sqrt{13}}{6}$ or $x > \dfrac{1 + \sqrt{13}}{6}$ **$-2.12105 < x < -2$ or**

59. $\left|\dfrac{y + 2}{3}\right| \ge 5$ **60.** $\left|\dfrac{1}{1 - x^2}\right| \ge \dfrac{1}{2}$ **1.76475 < 2**

$y \le -17$ or $y \ge 13$

61. $|3x + 2| \ge 2$ **$-\sqrt{3} \le x < -1$**
$x \le -\dfrac{4}{3}$ or $x \ge 0$ **or $-1 < x < 1$ or $1 < x \le \sqrt{3}$**

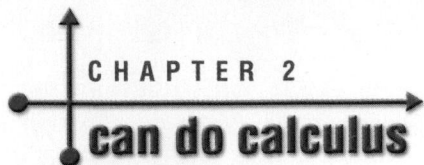
Maximum Area

Teaching Notes

Notice that the small shaded triangle in Figure 2.C-1 is enlarged to get Figure 2.C-3. The sum of the lengths of the hypotenuse and leg y must be 8.5, the width of the original paper before it is folded. This explains why the hypotenuse is labeled $8.5 - y$.

Example Notes

Students need an inch-ruler and an 8.5×11-inch piece of paper to complete **Example 1**. Encourage students to mark the bottom (long edge) of the paper with inch-marks up to 9 inches. These marks will give them the **Base** lengths for the table. Then they can fold the paper and measure to get each **Height**. Point out that the base is represented by x.

The answer to part **a.** can be written as $0 < x < 8.5$. Ask students to explain why x cannot be either 0 or 8.5. There would be no triangle.

The scatter plot for part **c.** is Base vs. Area

Math Background

The area function $A = \frac{1}{2}(x)\left(\dfrac{72.25 - x^2}{17}\right)$ is a cubic polynomial. Its complete graph is S-shaped (see Section 4.3).

CHAPTER 2

can do calculus

Maximum Area

There are two related branches of calculus: differential calculus and integral calculus. Differential calculus is a method of calculating the changes in one variable produced by changes in a related variable. It is often used to find maximum or minimum values of a function. Integral calculus is used to calculate quantities like distance, area, and volume. This Can Do Calculus finds the maximum area of the triangle formed by folding a piece of paper using different methods.

The Maximum Area of a Triangle Problem

One corner of an 8.5×11-inch piece of paper is folded over to the opposite side, as shown in Figure 2.C-1. A triangle is formed, and its area formula is $A = \frac{1}{2}$ (base)(height). The following Example will find the length of the base that will produce the maximum area of the triangle using numerical, graphical, and algebraic methods.

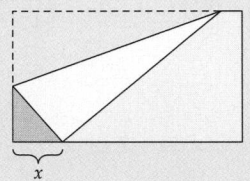

Figure 2.C-1

| Example 1 | Numerical Method |

One corner of an 8.5×11-inch piece of paper is folded over to the opposite side, as shown in Figure 2.C-1. The area of the darkly shaded triangle at the lower left is the focus of this problem.

a. Determine the shortest and the longest base that will produce a triangle by folding the paper.

b. Measure the height when x has the lengths given in the chart, and calculate the area in each case.

c. Create a scatter plot of the data.

d. Estimate the length of the base that produces the maximum area, and state the approximate maximum area.

Solution

a. The base must be greater than 0 and less than 8.5 inches, and *nt* in the chart indicates that no triangle can be formed with a base length of 9 inches.

b. The values shown in the chart may vary from your data.

Base	1″	2″	3″	4″	5″	6″	7″	8″	9″
Height	4.25	4.1	3.6	3.3	2.75	2	1.5	0.5	*nt*
Area	2.125	4.1	5.4	6.6	6.875	6	5.25	2	-

Figure 2.C-2

Figure 2.C-3

c. The graph of the data is shown in Figure 2.C-2.

d. A maximum area of 6.875 in² appears to occur when the base length is 5 in.

■

In Example 1, all calculations were accomplished with measurements. Notice that the hypotenuse is $8.5 - y$, where y is the height of the triangle. (Why?)

Because each triangle formed was a right triangle, the Pythagorean Theorem can be used to find an expression that gives the height as a function of the length of the base. That function can then be used to write a function that gives area in terms of the length of the base.

Example 2   Algebraic Method

Find a function of the base to represent the area of the triangle described in Example 1, graph the function along with the scatter plot of the data found in Example 1. Find the length of the base that produces maximum area. What is the maximum area?

Solution

The Pythagorean Theorem yields the following equation.

$$x^2 + y^2 = (8.5 - y)^2$$
$$x^2 + y^2 = 72.25 - 17y + y^2$$
$$x^2 = 72.25 - 17y$$
$$y = \frac{72.25 - x^2}{17} \quad \textit{Height as a function of the base}$$

Figure 2.C-4

Hence, the area is represented by $A = \frac{1}{2}(x)\left(\frac{72.25 - x^2}{17}\right)$. Using the maximum finder on a calculator indicates that the maximum area of 6.95 in² occurs at approximately $x = 4.9$ in.

■

To get exact values of x and the area, differential calculus is needed. However, graphing technology can provide very good approximations.

Exercises

In each problem, find the maximum by using a numerical method like the one shown in Example 1, and then by using an analytical and graphical method like the one shown in Example 2. Answer all questions given in the two examples.

1. Ten yards of wire is to be used to create a rectangle. What is the maximum possible area of the rectangle?

2. A rectangle is bounded by the x- and y-axes and the semicircle $y = \sqrt{36 - x^2}$. What are the dimensions of the rectangle with maximum area?

3. A rectangle is bounded by the x- and y-axes and the line $y = \frac{(4 - x)}{2}$. What are the dimensions of the rectangle with maximum area?

139

Exercises

ANSWERS

1–3. *See pp. 1054–1055.*

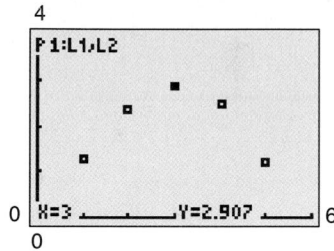

ADDITIONAL EXAMPLES

Example 1

One corner of a 5.5 × 8.5-inch piece of paper is folded over to the opposite side, as shown in Figure 2.C-1 (see SE). The area of the darkly shaded triangle at the lower left is the focus of this problem.

a. Determine the shortest and longest base that will produce a triangle by folding the paper.

The base must be greater than 0 and less than 5.5 inches.

b. Measure the height when x has the lengths given in the chart, and calculate the area in each case.

Base	1"	2"	3"	4"	5"	6"
Height	2.625	2.375	1.938	1.25	0.5	*nt*
Area	1.313	2.375	2.907	2.5	1.25	

c. Create a scatter plot of the data.

d. Estimate the length of the base that produces the maximum area, and state the approximate maximum area.

A maximum area of 2.907 in² appears to occur when the base length is 3 in.

Example 2

Find a function of the base to represent the area of the triangle described in Additional Example 1, and graph the function along with the scatter plot of the data found in Additional Example 1. Find the length of the base that produces the maximum area. What is the maximum area?

$$A = \frac{1}{2}(x)\left(\frac{30.25 - x^2}{11}\right)$$

The maximum area of 2.91 in² occurs at approximately $x = 3.175$ in.

Functions and Graphs

This chapter addresses functions and their graphs, transformations, operations on functions, inverse functions, and rates of change. There are two excursions that deal with symmetry and iterations of functions.

CHAPTER

3 Functions and Graphs

This *is* rocket science!

If a rocket is fired straight up from the ground, its height is a function of time. This function can be adapted to give the height of any object that is falling or thrown along a vertical path. The shape of the graph of the function, a *parabola*, appears in applications involving motion, revenue, communications, and many other topics. See Exercise 50 of Section 3.3.

140

Chapter Outline

Interdependence of Sections

The concept of a function and function notation are central to modern mathematics and its applications. In this chapter you will review functions, operations on functions, and how to use function notation. Then you will develop skill in constructing and interpreting graphs of functions.

 3.1 **Functions**

Objectives

- Determine whether a relation is a function

- Find the domain of functions

- Evaluate piecewise-defined and greatest integer functions

Figure 3.1-1

To understand the origin of the concept of a function it may help to consider some "real-life" situations in which one numerical quantity depends on, corresponds to, or determines another.

Example 1   Determining Inputs and Outputs of Functions

Describe the set of inputs, the set of outputs, and the rule for the following functions:

a. The amount of income tax you pay depends on your income.

b. Suppose a rock is dropped straight down from a high place. Physics tells us that the distance traveled by the rock in t seconds is $16t^2$ feet.

c. The weather bureau records the temperature over a 24-hour period in the form of a graph (Figure 3.1-1). The graph shows the temperature that corresponds to each given time.

141

Teaching Notes

Remind students of functions they studied in previous courses that show both numerical and graphical representations. Reviewing definitions of *independent* and *dependent* will help to illustrate the relationship between input and output values. Explain how the output values (dependent variables) *depend* on the input values (independent variables) as you discuss each example.

If students cannot decide which data item is input and which is output, it may help if they first decide which data could reasonably determine the other. In **Example 1c**, ask students if the outside temperature affects the time of day.

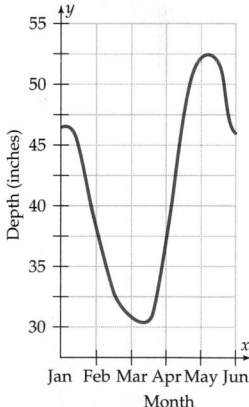

ADDITIONAL EXAMPLES

Example 1

Describe the set of inputs, set of outputs, and the rule for the following functions:

a. The cost of a tank of gasoline depends on the number of gallons purchased.   number of gallons; cost of tankful; price per gallon

b. The volume of a cube depends on the length of its edges.   edge length; volume; $V = s^3$, where s is edge length

c. A hydrologist records the depth at a certain place in a pond during a 6-month period in the form of a graph (right). The graph shows the depth recorded each month. month; depth; month/depth graph

Teaching Notes

Students may already be familiar with a different wording of the **Definition of a Function** as a set of ordered pairs (x, y) so that each value of x corresponds to one and only one value of y. The set of x-values, or inputs, is the domain of the function. The set of y-values, or outputs, is the range. Remind students that a relation is a set of ordered pairs.

A mapping can clarify the "one and only one" aspect of a function.

Example Notes

Mappings are shown for **Example 2:**

a.

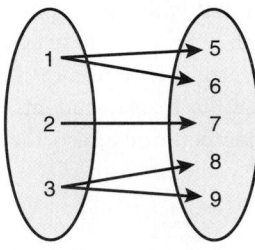

Because more than one arrow points from a domain value (see either 1 or 3), this relation is not a function.

b.

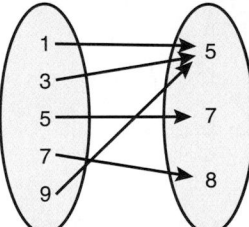

Because only one arrow points from each domain value, this relation is a function. Point out to students that more than one arrow can point to the same output value in a function.

Solution

The table below summarizes the features of each function.

	Set of inputs	Set of outputs	Function rule
a.	all incomes	all tax amounts	tax laws
b.	number of seconds, t, after dropping the rock	distance rock travels	Distance $= 16t^2$
c.	time	temperature	time/temperature graph

The formal definition of function incorporates the set of inputs, the function rule, and the set of outputs, with a slight change in terminology.

Definition of a Function

A *function* consists of

- a set of inputs, called the *domain*
- a rule by which each input determines one and only one output
- a set of outputs, called the *range*

The phrase "one and only one" means that for each input (element of the domain), the rule of a function determines exactly one output (element of the range). However, different inputs may produce the same output.

Example 2   Determining Whether a Relation is a Function

The tables below list the inputs and outputs for two relations. Determine whether each relation is a function.

a.

Inputs	1	1	2	3	3
Outputs	5	6	7	8	9

b.

Inputs	1	3	5	7	9
Outputs	5	5	7	8	5

Solution

In table **a**, the input 1 has two corresponding outputs, 5 and 6; and the input 3 has two corresponding outputs, 8 and 9. So the relation in table **a** is not a function.

In table **b**, each input determines exactly one output, so the relation in table **b** is a function. Notice that the inputs 1, 3, and 9 all produce the same output, 5, which is allowed in the definition of a function. ∎

The value of a function f that corresponds to a specific input value a, is found by substituting a into the function rule and simplifying the resulting expression. See Section 1.1 for a discussion of function notation.

Technology Tip

Function notation can be used directly. For example, if a function is entered as Y_1, evaluate the function at $x = 3$, press $Y_1(3)$, then ENTER.

```
Y₁(3)
        3.16227766
Y₁(-5)
        5.099019514
Y₁(0)
                  1
```

Figure 3.1-2

Example 3 Evaluating a Function

Find the indicated values of $f(x) = \sqrt{x^2 + 1}$.

a. $f(3)$ **b.** $f(-5)$ **c.** $f(0)$

Solution

a. To find the output of the function f for input 3, simply replace x with 3 in the function rule and simplify the result.

$$f(3) = \sqrt{3^2 + 1} = \sqrt{10} \approx 3.162$$

Similarly, replace x with -5 and 0 for **b** and **c**.

b. $f(-5) = \sqrt{(-5)^2 + 1} = \sqrt{26} \approx 5.099$

c. $f(0) = \sqrt{0^2 + 1} = 1$ ∎

Example 4 Finding a Difference Quotient

For $f(x) = x^2 - x + 2$ and $h \neq 0$, find each output.

a. $f(x + h)$ **b.** $f(x + h) - f(x)$ **c.** $\dfrac{f(x + h) - f(x)}{h}$

Solution

When function notation is used in expressions such as $f(x + h)$, the basic rule applies: Replace x in the function rule with the entire expression within parentheses and simplify the resulting expression.

a. Replace x with $x + h$ in the rule of the function.

$$f(x + h) = (x + h)^2 - (x + h) + 2$$
$$= x^2 + 2xh + h^2 - x - h + 2$$

ADDITIONAL EXAMPLES

Example 2

Determine whether each relation is a function.

a.

inputs	1	2	3	4
outputs	8	7	8	9

Yes

b.

inputs	10	12	11	10
outputs	8	7	8	9

No, the input 10 has two corresponding outputs.

Example 3

Find the indicated values of $g(x) = \sqrt{2x^2 + 7}$.

a. $g(1)$ 3
b. $g(-3)$ 5
c. $g(0)$ $\sqrt{7} \approx 2.646$

Example 4

For $s(x) = 3x^2 - 2x$ and $h \neq 0$, find each output.

a. $s(x + h)$
  $3x^2 + 6xh + 3h^2 - 2x - 2h$

b. $s(x + h) - s(x)$ $6xh + 3h^2 - 2h$

c. $\dfrac{s(x + h) - s(x)}{h}$ $6x + 3h - 2$

COMMON ERROR ALERT

In **Example 4a**, students may incorrectly expand the binomial $(x + h)^2$. They may think that $(x + h)^2 = x^2 + h^2$, *which is incorrect*. Remind them to expand the binomial by multiplying, as follows:

$$(x + h)^2 = (x + h)(x + h)$$
$$= x^2 + 2xh + h^2$$

Math Background

The *difference quotient* is also known as the average rate of change. In calculus, students will be taking the limit of an average rate of change to find an instantaneous rate of change.

Example Notes

To determine whether an equation in x and y represents a function, try to solve the equation for y.

In **Example 5a**, you can solve for y and get exactly one function in x, so the equation represents a function.

In **Example 5b**, when you solve for y you get two expressions in x, namely $y = \sqrt{x-1}$ and $y = -\sqrt{x-1}$. Therefore the equation does not represent a function.

ADDITIONAL EXAMPLES

Example 5

Determine whether each equation defines y as a function of x.

a. $2y^3 - 32x + 11 = 0$ Yes, y is a function of x with domain the set of all real numbers and rule
$$y = \sqrt[3]{16x - \frac{11}{2}}$$

b. $2x + y^2 - 3 = 0$ $y = \pm\sqrt{-2 + 3}$ No, y is not a function of x.

Example 6

Find the domain for each function given.

a. $f(x) = \dfrac{3}{x+4}$ all real numbers except -4

b. $f(w) = \sqrt{1 - 3w}$ $\left(-\infty, \dfrac{1}{3}\right]$

---

b. By part **a**,
$$f(x+h) - f(x) = [x^2 + 2xh + h^2 - x - h + 2] - [x^2 - x + 2]$$
$$= x^2 + 2xh + h^2 - x - h + 2 - x^2 + x - 2$$
$$= 2xh + h^2 - h$$

c. By part **b**,
$$\frac{f(x+h) - f(x)}{h} = \frac{2xh + h^2 - h}{h} = \frac{h(2x + h - 1)}{h} = 2x + h - 1 \blacksquare$$

If f is a function, then the quantity $\dfrac{f(x+h) - f(x)}{h}$, as in Example 4, is called the **difference quotient** of f. Difference quotients, whose significance is explained in Section 3.7, play an important role in calculus.

Functions Defined by Equations

Equations in two variables can be used to define functions. However, not every equation in two variables represents a function.

Example 5 **Determining if an Equation Defines a Function**

Determine whether each equation defines y as a function of x.

a. $4x - 2y^3 + 5 = 0$

b. $y^2 - x + 1 = 0$

Solution

a. The equation $4x - 2y^3 + 5 = 0$ can be solved uniquely for y.
$$2y^3 = 4x + 5$$
$$y^3 = 2x + \frac{5}{2}$$
$$y = \sqrt[3]{2x + \frac{5}{2}}$$

If a number is substituted for x in this equation, then exactly one value of y is produced. So the equation defines a function whose domain is the set of all real numbers and whose rule is stated below.
$$f(x) = \sqrt[3]{2x + \frac{5}{2}}$$

b. The equation $y^2 - x + 1 = 0$ can *not* be solved uniquely for y:
$$y^2 = x - 1$$
$$y = \pm\sqrt{x - 1}$$
$$y = \sqrt{x - 1} \quad \text{or} \quad y = -\sqrt{x - 1}$$

This equation does not define y as a function of x because, for example, the input $x = 5$ produces two outputs, 2 and -2. $\blacksquare$

Domains

When the rule of a function is given by a formula, as in Examples 3–6, its domain (set of inputs) is determined by the following convention.

Domain Convention

> Unless information to the contrary is given, the domain of a function f consists of every real number input for which the function rule produces a real number output.

Thus, the domain of a polynomial function such as $f(x) = x^3 - 4x + 1$ is the set of all real numbers, since $f(x)$ is defined for every value of x. However, in cases where applying the rule of a function leads to one of the following, the domain may not consist of all real numbers.

- division by zero
- the square root of a negative number (or nth root, where n is even)

Example 6 Finding Domains of Functions

Find the domain for each function given below.

a. $k(x) = \dfrac{x^2 - 6x}{x - 1}$ **b.** $f(u) = \sqrt{u + 2}$

Solution

a. When $x = 1$, the denominator of $\dfrac{x^2 - 6x}{x - 1}$ is 0 and the output is not defined. When $x \neq 1$, however, the denominator is nonzero and the fraction *is* defined. Therefore, the domain of k consists of all real numbers *except* 1, which is written as $x \neq 1$.

b. Since negative numbers do not have real square roots, $\sqrt{u + 2}$ is a real number only when $u + 2 \geq 0$, that is, when $u \geq -2$. Therefore, the domain of f consists of all real numbers greater than or equal to -2, that is, the interval $[-2, \infty)$. ∎

Applications and the Domain Convention

The domain convention does not always apply when dealing with applications. Consider the distance function for falling objects, $d(t) = 16t^2$. Since t represents time, only nonnegative values of t make sense here, even though the rule of the function is defined for all values of t. Analogous comments apply to other applications.

> A real-life situation may lead to a function whose domain does not include all the values for which the rule of the function is defined.

Teaching Notes

Explain that, as used here, a *convention* is an established practice, or generally accepted method. The **Domain Convention** describes the generally accepted method of getting the domain of a function when a domain is not specified.

In a sense, the domain convention says to use "the largest possible domain." For example, $f(x) = \dfrac{1}{x}$ is defined for every possible value of x except for $x = 0$. So, by the domain convention, the domain of $f(x) = \dfrac{1}{x}$ is the set of all real numbers except 0.

As explained in **Applications and the Domain Convention,** when a function is used in a real-life application,
- first, determine the domain using the domain convention, and then
- decide what values in that domain make sense for that application.

For example, if the function $f(x) = 0.45x + 2.50$ gives the cost in dollars of a taxicab ride, where x is distance expressed in fifths of a mile, then:
- by the domain convention, the domain of $f(x) = 0.45x + 2.50$ is the set of all real numbers, but
- in this application, the domain is $\{0, 0.2, 0.4, 0.6, \ldots\}$ because only fifths of a mile are used to compute fares.

Math Background

There are two cases cited in which applying the domain convention yields a domain other than the set of all real numbers. Two other cases are: $f(x) = \log x$, whose domain is the set of all positive numbers (page 359) $f(x) = \sin^{-1} x$, whose domain is the set of all x such that $-1 \leq x \leq 1$ (page 530).

Real-World Application

The "break-even point" in business is when revenue equals cost.

In **Example 7,** you can find the number of cups that need to be produced in one week in order for the factory to break even by solving the equation $R(x) = C(x)$ for x.

To accomplish this, graph $R(x) = 1.95x$ and $C(x) = 0.80x + 12,000$ on a calculator and use a graphical intersection finder to find the point of intersection (See **Section 2.1,** page 82).

40,000

Note that the break-even point is when $x \approx 10,434.783$. However, the domain for this application includes only whole numbers. So, to be very precise, if the company produces and sells 10,434 cups, it is still losing money. But if the company produces and sells 10,435 cups, it makes a profit. A business owner would say that 10,435 is the break-even point.

Example Notes

In **Example 8,** students will have more success evaluating a piecewise-defined function if they read it right to left.

Example 7   Finding the Domain of a Profit Function

A glassware factory has fixed expenses (mortgage, taxes, machinery, etc.) of $12,000 per week. In addition, it costs 80 cents to make one cup (labor, materials, shipping). A cup sells for $1.95. At most, 18,000 cups can be manufactured each week. Let x represent the number of cups made per week.
a. Express the weekly revenue R as a function of x.
b. Express the weekly cost C as a function of x.
c. Find the rule and the domain of the weekly profit function P.

Solution

a. $R(x) = $ (price per cup) $\cdot$ (number sold)
$R(x) = 1.95x$
b. $C(x) = $ (cost per cup) $\cdot$ (number sold) + (fixed expenses)
$C(x) = 0.80x + 12,000$
c. $P(x) = $ revenue $-$ cost $= R(x) - C(x)$
$P(x) = 1.95x - (0.80x + 12,000)$
$P(x) = 1.15x - 12,000$

Although this rule is defined for all real numbers x, the domain of the function P consists of the possible number of cups that can be made each week. Since only whole cups can be made and the maximum production is 18,000, the domain of P consists of all integers from 0 to 18,000. ∎

Piecewise-Defined and Greatest Integer Functions

A piecewise-defined function is one whose rule includes several formulas. The formula for each piece of the function is applied to certain values of the domain, as specified in the definition of the function.

Example 8   Evaluating a Piecewise-Defined Function

For the piecewise-defined function

$$f(x) = \begin{cases} 2x + 3 & \text{if } x < 4 \\ x^2 - 1 & \text{if } 4 \le x \le 10 \end{cases}$$

find each of the following.

a. $f(-5)$ **b.** $f(8)$ **c.** the domain of f.

Solution

a. Since -5 is less than 4, the first part of the rule applies.
$f(-5) = 2(-5) + 3 = -7$
b. Since 8 is between 4 and 10, the second part of the rule applies.
$f(8) = 8^2 - 1 = 63$
c. The rule of f gives directions when $x < 4$ and when $4 \le x \le 10$, so the domain of f consists of all real numbers x such that $x \le 10$, that is, $(-\infty, 10]$. ∎

The **greatest integer function** is a piecewise-defined function with infinitely many pieces.

$$f(x) = \begin{cases} \vdots \\ -3 & \text{if } -3 \leq x < -2 \\ -2 & \text{if } -2 \leq x < -1 \\ -1 & \text{if } -1 \leq x < 0 \\ 0 & \text{if } 0 \leq x < 1 \\ 1 & \text{if } 1 \leq x < 2 \\ 2 & \text{if } 2 \leq x < 3 \\ \vdots \end{cases}$$

The rule can be written in words as follows:

Greatest Integer Function

> **For any number x, round *down* to the nearest integer less than or equal to x.**

Technology Tip

The greatest integer function is denoted **INT** in the NUM submenu of the MATH menu of TI. It is denoted **INTG** in the NUM submenu of the Casio **OPTN** menu.

The domain of the greatest integer function is all real numbers, and the range is the set of integers. It is written as $f(x) = [x]$.

Example 9   **Evaluating the Greatest Integer Function**

Let $f(x) = [x]$. Evaluate the following:

a. $f(-4.7)$ **b.** $f(-3)$ **c.** $f(0)$ **d.** $f\left(\dfrac{5}{4}\right)$ **e.** $f(\pi)$

Solution

a. $f(-4.7) = [-4.7] = -5$ **b.** $f(-3) = [-3] = -3$

c. $f(0) = [0] = 0$ **d.** $f\left(\dfrac{5}{4}\right) = \left[\dfrac{5}{4}\right] = [1.25] = 1$

e. $f(\pi) = [\pi] = 3$

ADDITIONAL EXAMPLES

Example 7

Robin cleans small passenger airplane interiors at an airport. At most, she will clean 24 airplanes per month. Robin pays a license fee of \$150 per month to the airport. Her cost per plane (cleaning supplies, commute to the airport, and salary of a helper) is approximately \$82.50. She charges \$229 to clean each plane. Let x represent the number of planes she cleans in a month.

a. Express Robin's monthly revenue R as a function of x. $R(x) = 229x$

b. Express the monthly cost C as a function of x. $C(x) = 82.50x + 150$

c. Find the rule and the domain of the monthly profit function P. $P(x) = 146.50x - 150$ The domain of P consists of all integers from 0 to 24.

Example 8

Given:

$$h(x) = \begin{cases} 3x^2 - 5 & \text{if } x \geq 4 \\ 2x + 15 & \text{if } x < 3 \end{cases}$$

Find each of the following:

a. $h(0)$ 15

b. $h(3.5)$ undefined

c. $h(4)$ 43

Example 9

Let $f(x) = [x]$

Evaluate:

a. $f(-209.99)$ -210

b. $f(-51)$ -51

c. $f\left(-\dfrac{5}{4}\right)$ -2

d. $f(\sqrt{10})$ 3

Exercises 3.1

ANSWERS

1. The set of inputs is the number of hours you work in each pay period. The set of outputs is the amounts of your paychecks. The function rule is the amount of pay for each hour worked multiplied by the number of hours worked.

2. The set of inputs is the lengths of feet. The set of outputs is shoe sizes. The function rule is a chart assigning shoe sizes to foot lengths.

3. The set of inputs is temperatures of gas. The set of outputs is pressures of gas. The function rule is the formula $P = \frac{k}{T}$.

4. The set of inputs is the days of the year. The set of outputs is number of hours of daylight. The function rule is the graph shown.

22. $(\pi + 1)^2 + \frac{1}{\pi + 1} + 1 \approx 19.39$

23. $(a + k)^2 + \frac{1}{a + k} + 2$

24. $(-x)^2 + \frac{1}{(-x)} + 1 = x^2 - \frac{1}{x} + 1$

25. $(2 - x)^2 + \frac{1}{2 - x} + 2$
    $= 6 - 4x + x^2 + \frac{1}{2 - x}$

26. $(x - 3)^2 + \frac{1}{x - 3} + 1$

31. $(s + 1)^2 - 1 = s^2 + 2s$

32. $(1 - r)^2 - 1 = r^2 - 2r$

44. All real numbers except 0

46. All nonnegative real numbers

50. All real numbers greater than 1

52. All real numbers less than or equal to 0

54. $[-2, 2]$

Exercises 3.1

In Exercises 1–4, describe the set of inputs, the set of outputs, and the rule for each function.

1. The amount of your paycheck before taxes is a function of the number of hours worked.

2. Your shoe size is a function of the length of your foot.

3. In physics, the pressure P of a gas kept at a constant volume is a function of the temperature T, related by the formula $P \cdot T = k$ for some constant k.

4. The number of hours of daylight at a certain latitude is a function of the day of the year. The following graph shows the number of hours of daylight that corresponds to each day.

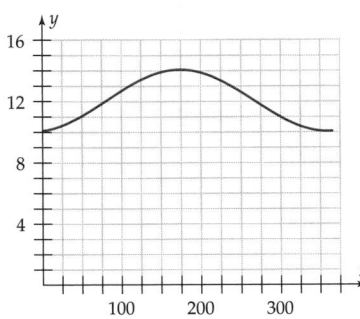

In Exercises 5–12, determine whether the equation defines y as a function of x.

5. $y = 3x^2 - 12$
   y is a function of x.
6. $y = 2x^4 + 3x^2 - 2$
   y is a function of x.
7. $y^2 = 4x + 1$
   y is not a function of x.
8. $5x - 4y^4 + 64 = 0$
   y is not a function of x.
9. $3x + 2y = 12$
   y is a function of x.
10. $y - 4x^3 - 14 = 0$
    y is a function of x.
11. $x^2 + y^2 = 9$
    y is not a function of x.
12. $y^2 - 3x^4 + 8 = 0$
    y is not a function of x.

Exercises 13–34 refer to the functions below. Find the indicated value of the function.

$$f(x) = \sqrt{x + 3} - x + 1$$
$$g(t) = t^2 - 1$$
$$h(x) = x^2 + \frac{1}{x} + 2$$

13. $f(0)$ $\sqrt{3} + 1 \approx 2.73$
14. $f(1)$ **2**
15. $f(\sqrt{2})$ $\sqrt{\sqrt{2} + 3} - \sqrt{2} + 1 \approx 1.69$
16. $f(\sqrt{2} - 1)$ $\sqrt{\sqrt{2} + 2} - \sqrt{2} + 2 \approx 2.43$

17. $f(-2)$ **4**
18. $f\left(-\frac{3}{2}\right)$ ≈ 3.72
19. $h(3)$ $\frac{34}{3}$
20. $h(-4)$ **17.75**
21. $h\left(\frac{3}{2}\right)$ $\frac{59}{12}$
22. $h(\pi + 1)$
23. $h(a + k)$
24. $h(-x)$
25. $h(2 - x)$
26. $h(x - 3)$
27. $g(3)$ **8**
28. $g(-2)$ **3**
29. $g(0)$ **−1**
30. $g(x)$ $x^2 - 1$
31. $g(s + 1)$
32. $g(1 - r)$
33. $g(-t)$ $t^2 - 1$
34. $g(t + h)$ $(t + h)^2 - 1$

In Exercises 35–42, compute and simplify the difference quotient (shown below). Assume $h \neq 0$.

$$\frac{f(x + h) - f(x)}{h}$$

35. $f(x) = x + 1$ **1**
36. $f(x) = -10x$ **−10**
37. $f(x) = 3x + 7$ **3**
38. $f(x) = x^2$ $2x + h$
39. $f(x) = x - x^2$ $-2x - h + 1$
40. $f(x) = x^3$ $3x^2 + 3xh + h^2$
41. $f(x) = \sqrt{x}$ $\frac{1}{\sqrt{x + h} + \sqrt{x}}$
42. $f(x) = \frac{1}{x}$ $-\frac{1}{x(x + h)}$

In Exercises 43–56, determine the domain of the function according to the domain convention.

43. $f(x) = x^2$
    All real numbers
44. $g(x) = \frac{1}{x^2} + 2$
45. $h(t) = |t| - 1$
    All real numbers
46. $k(u) = \sqrt{u}$
47. $k(x) = |x| + \sqrt{x - 1}$
    All nonnegative real numbers
48. $h(x) = \sqrt{(x + 1)^2}$
    All real numbers
49. $g(u) = \frac{|u|}{u}$
    All nonzero real numbers
50. $h(x) = \frac{\sqrt{x - 1}}{x^2 - 1}$
51. $g(y) = [-y]$
    All real numbers
52. $f(t) = \sqrt{-t}$
53. $g(u) = \frac{u^2 + 1}{u^2 - u - 6}$
    All real numbers except −2 and 3
54. $f(t) = \sqrt{4 - t^2}$
55. $f(x) = -\sqrt{9 - (x - 9)^2}$
    [6, 12]
56. $f(x) = \sqrt{-x} + \frac{2}{x + 1}$
    All real numbers less than or equal to 0 except for −1

In Exercises 57–62, find the following:

a. $f(0)$ **b.** $f(1.6)$
c. $f(-2.3)$ **d.** $f(5 - 2\pi)$
e. The domain of f

57. $f(x) = [x]$ **58.** $f(x) = \begin{cases} -x & \text{if } x < 0 \\ x & \text{if } x \geq 0 \end{cases}$

59. $f(x) = \begin{cases} x^2 + 2x & \text{if } x < 2 \\ 3x - 5 & \text{if } 2 \leq x \leq 20 \end{cases}$

60. $f(x) = \begin{cases} x + 5 & \text{if } -3 < x \leq 0 \\ 3x & \text{if } 0 < x \leq 5 \end{cases}$

61. $f(x) = \begin{cases} 2x - 3 & \text{if } x < -1 \\ |x| - 5 & \text{if } -1 \leq x \leq 2 \\ x^2 & \text{if } x > 2 \end{cases}$

62. $f(x) = \begin{cases} x^2 & \text{if } -4 \leq x < -2 \\ x - 3 & \text{if } -2 \leq x \leq 1 \\ 2x + 1 & \text{if } x > 1 \end{cases}$

63. Find an equation that expresses the area A of a circle as a function of its
a. radius r $A = \pi r^2$ **b.** diameter d $A = \frac{1}{4}\pi d^2$

64. Find an equation that expresses the area A of a square as a function of its
a. side s $A(s) = s^2$ **b.** diagonal d $A(d) = \dfrac{d^2}{2}$

65. A box with a square base of side x is four times higher than it is wide. Express the volume V of the box as a function of x. $V = 4x^3$

66. The surface area of a cylindrical can of radius r and height h is $2\pi r^2 + 2\pi rh$. If the can is twice as high as the diameter of its top, express its surface area S as a function of r. $S = 10\pi r^2$

67. A rectangular region of 6000 square feet is to be fenced in on three sides with fencing that costs $3.75 per foot and on the fourth side with fencing that costs $2.00 per foot.
a. Express the cost of the fence as a function of the length x of the fourth side.
b. Find the domain of the function.

68. A box with a square base measuring $t \times t$ ft is to be made of three kinds of wood. The cost of the wood for the base is $0.85 per square foot; the wood for the sides costs $0.50 per square foot, and the wood for the top $1.15 per square foot. The volume of the box must be 10 cubic feet.

a. Express the total cost of the box as a function of the length t.
b. Find the domain of the function.

69. A man walks for 45 minutes at a rate of 3 mph, then jogs for 75 minutes at a rate of 5 mph, then sits and rests for 30 minutes, and finally walks for 90 minutes at a rate of 3 mph.
a. Write a piecewise-defined function that expresses his distance traveled as a function of time.
b. Find the domain of the function.

70. Average tuition and fees in private four-year colleges in recent years were as follows. (Source: The College Board)

Year	Tuition & fees
1995	$12,432
1996	$12,823
1997	$13,664
1998	$14,709
1999	$15,380
2000	$16,332

a. Use linear regression to find the rule of a function f that gives the approximate average tuition in year x, where $x = 0$ corresponds to 1990.
b. Find $f(6), f(8),$ and $f(10)$. How do they compare with the actual data?
c. Use f to estimate tuition in 2003.

71. Suppose that a state income tax law reads as follows:

Annual income	Amount of tax
less than $2000	0
$2000–$6000	2% of income over $2000
more than $6000	$80 plus 5% of income over $6000

Write a piecewise-defined function that represents the income tax law. What is the domain of the function?

57. a. $f(0) = [0]$
   b. $f(1.6) = [1.6] = 1$
   c. $f(-2.3) = [-2.3] = -3$
   d. $f(5 - 2\pi) = [5 - 2\pi]$
        $\approx [-1.283] = -2$
   e. all real numbers

58. a. $f(0) = 0$
   b. $f(1.6) = 1.6$
   c. $f(-2.3) = 2.3$
   d. $f(5 - 2\pi) = 2\pi - 5$
   e. all real numbers

59. a. $f(0) = 0$
   b. $f(1.6) = 5.76$
   c. $f(-2.3) = 0.69$
   d. $f(5 - 2\pi) \approx -0.920$
   e. all real numbers ≤ 20

60. a. $f(0) = 5$
   b. $f(1.6) = 4.8$
   c. $f(-2.3) = 2.7$
   d. $f(5 - 2\pi) \approx 3.717$
   e. all real numbers x, such that $-3 < x \leq 5$

61. a. $f(0) = -5$
   b. $f(1.6) = -3.4$
   c. $f(-2.3) = -7.6$
   d. $f(5 - 2\pi) \approx -5.566$
   e. all real numbers

62. a. $f(0) = -3$
   b. $f(1.6) = 4.2$
   c. $f(-2.3) = 5.29$
   d. $f(5 - 2\pi) \approx -4.283$
   e. all real numbers x, such that $x \geq -4$

67. a. $C(x) = 5.75x + \dfrac{45,000}{x}$
   b. The domain is $x > 0$.

68. a. $C = 2t^2 + \dfrac{20}{t}$
   b. The domain is $t > 0$.

69. a. Let t be the number of hours since he started.
$$d(t) = \begin{cases} 3t & 0 \leq t \leq \frac{3}{4} \\ 2.25 + 5\left(t - \frac{3}{4}\right) & \frac{3}{4} < t \leq 2 \\ 8.5 & 2 < t \leq 2.5 \\ 8.5 + 3(t - 2.5) & 2.5 < t \leq 4 \end{cases}$$
   b. The domain is t such that $0 \leq t \leq 4$.

70. a. $f(x) = 806.1714x + 8177.0476$
   b. $f(6) \approx 13,014$;
      actual value: $12,823
      $f(8) \approx 14,626$;
      actual value: $14,709
      $f(10) \approx 16,239$;
      actual value: $16,332
   c. $f(13) \approx \$18,657$

71. Let x = amount of annual income and $f(x)$ = amount of tax.
$$f(x) = \begin{cases} 0 & x < 2000 \\ 0.02(x - 2000) & 2000 \leq x \leq 6000 \\ 80 + 0.05(x - 6000) & x > 6000 \end{cases}$$
The domain is $x \geq 0$.

72. The table below shows the 2002 federal income tax rates for a single person.

Taxable income	Tax
not over $6000	10% of income
over $6000, but not over $27,950	$600 + 15% of amount over $6000
over $27,950, but not over $67,700	$3892.50 + 27% of amount over $27,950
over $67,700, but not over $141,250	$14,625 + 30% of amount over $67,700
over $141,250, but not over $307,050	$36,690 + 35% of amount over $141,250
over $307,050	$94,720 + 38.6% of amount over $307,050

a. Write a piecewise-defined function T such that $T(x)$ is the tax due on a taxable income of x dollars. What is the domain of the function?

b. Find $T(24{,}000)$, $T(35{,}000)$, and $T(100{,}000)$.

Section
3.2 Graphs of Functions

Teaching Notes

Remind students that a graph is a picture of a relation. Functions are relations for which no two points have the same x-coordinate and different y-coordinates.

Review the **Definition of a Function** from Section 3.1. It may be helpful to graph the relation {(2, 3), (2, 6), (4, 1)}. Point out that this relation is not a function, and draw a vertical line through (2, 3) and (2, 6).

Example Notes

In **Example 2**, vertical lines other than $x = 4$ can be drawn to illustrate that the graph on the left is not a function (for example, $x = 1$). Also, demonstrate that while vertical lines can be drawn to intersect no points (ex. $x = -4$) or only one point (ex. $x = 0$), if there is *any* place on the graph where more than one point is intersected by a vertical line, then the graph does not represent a function.

For the graph on the right, suggest to students that they visualize all the possible vertical lines. You might demonstrate this by holding a yardstick vertically on the graph and moving it from left to right across the graph.

3.2   # Graphs of Functions

Objectives

- Determine whether a graph represents a function
- Analyze graphs to determine domain and range, local maxima and minima, inflection points, and intervals where they are increasing, decreasing, concave up, and concave down
- Graph parametric equations

NOTE An open circle on a graph indicates that the point is *not* a part of the graph, and a solid circle indicates that the point *is* a part of the graph.

Functions Defined by Graphs

A graph may be used to define a function or relation. Suppose that f is a function defined by a graph in the coordinate plane. If the point (x, y) is on the graph of f, then y is the output produced by the input x, or $y = f(x)$.

Example 1   **A Function Defined by a Graph**

The graph in Figure 3.2.1 defines the function f. Determine the following.

a. $f(0)$ **b.** $f(3)$ **c.** the domain of f **d.** the range of f

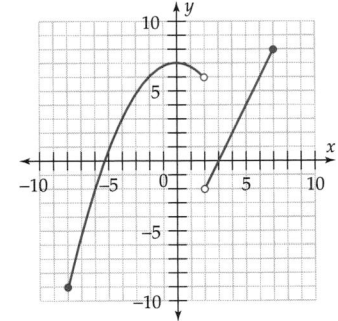

Figure 3.2-1

72. a.
$$T(x) = \begin{cases} 0.10x & 0 < x \le 6000 \\ 600 + 0.15(x - 6000) & 6000 < x \le 27{,}950 \\ 3892.50 + 0.27(x - 27{,}950) & 27{,}950 < x \le 67{,}700 \\ 14{,}625 + 0.30(x - 67{,}700) & 67{,}700 < x \le 141{,}250 \\ 36{,}690 + 0.35(x - 141{,}250) & 141{,}250 < x \le 307{,}050 \\ 94{,}720 + 0.386(x - 307{,}050) & x > 307{,}050 \end{cases}$$

The domain is $x \ge 0$.

b. $T(24{,}000) = 3300$; $T(35{,}000) = 5796$; $T(100{,}000) = 24{,}315$

Solution

a. To find $f(0)$, notice that the point $(0, 7)$ is on the graph. Thus, 7 is the output produced by the input 0, or $f(0) = 7$.

b. To find $f(3)$, notice that the point $(3, 0)$ is on the graph. Thus, 0 is the output produced by the input 3, or $f(3) = 0$.

c. To find the domain of the function, find the x-coordinates of the point farthest to the left and farthest to the right. Then, determine whether there are any gaps in the function between these values. $(-8, -9)$ is the point farthest to the left, and $(7, 8)$ is farthest to the right. The function does not have a point with an x-coordinate of 2, so the domain of f is $[-8, 2)$ and $(2, 7]$.

d. To find the range of the function, find the y-coordinates of the highest and lowest points, then determine if there are any gaps between these values. The highest point is $(7, 8)$ and the lowest point is $(-8, -9)$, and there are no y-values between -9 and 8 that do not correspond to at least one x-value. Thus, the range of f is $[-9, 8]$. ∎

The Vertical Line Test

If a graph represents a function, then each input determines one and only one output. Thus, no two points can have the same x-coordinate and different y-coordinates. Since any two such points would lie on the same vertical line, this fact provides a useful test for determining whether a graph represents a function.

Vertical Line Test

A graph in a coordinate plane represents a function if and only if no vertical line intersects the graph more than once.

Example 2   Determining Whether a Graph Defines a Function

Use the Vertical Line Test to determine whether the following graphs represent functions. If not, give an example of an input value that corresponds to more than one output value.

   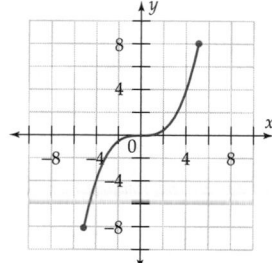

Figure 3.2-2

ADDITIONAL EXAMPLES

Example 1

The graph defines the function f.

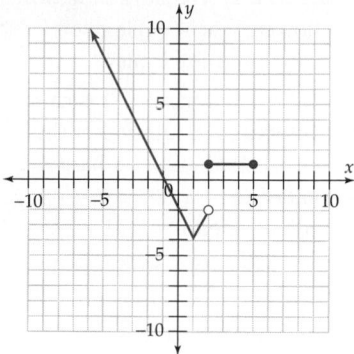

Determine the following:

a. $f(0)$ -2

b. $f(2)$ 1

c. the domain of f $(-\infty, 5]$

d. the range of f $(-4, \infty)$

Example 2

Use the Vertical Line Test to determine whether the following graphs represent functions. If not, give an example of an input value that corresponds to more than one output value.

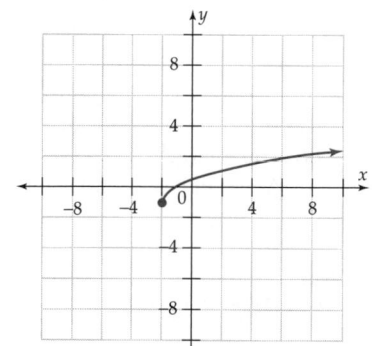

The graph represents a function.

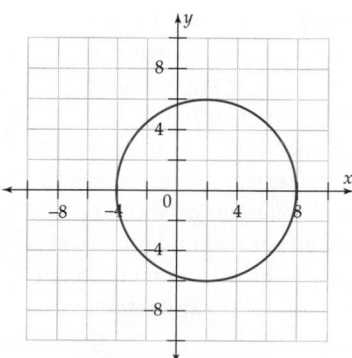

The graph does not represent a function.

The input 2 has two corresponding outputs, 6 and -6.

Solution

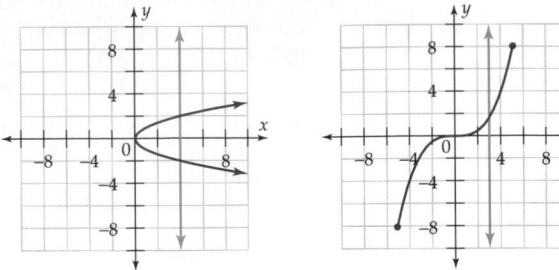

Figure 3.2-3

The vertical line $x = 4$ intersects the graph above at (4, 2) and (4, −2), so the graph is not a function. The input 4 has two corresponding outputs, 2 and −2.

There is no vertical line that intersects the graph above in more than one place, so this graph defines a function.

Analyzing Graphs

In order to discuss a graph or compare two graphs, it is important to be able to describe the features of different graphs. The most important features are the *x*- and *y*-intercepts, intervals where the graph is increasing or decreasing, local maxima and minima, intervals where the graph is concave up or concave down, and points of inflection.

Increasing and Decreasing Functions

A function is said to be **increasing** on an interval if its graph always rises as you move from left to right over the interval. It is **decreasing** on an interval if its graph always falls as you move from left to right over the interval. A function is said to be **constant** on an interval if its graph is a horizontal line over the interval.

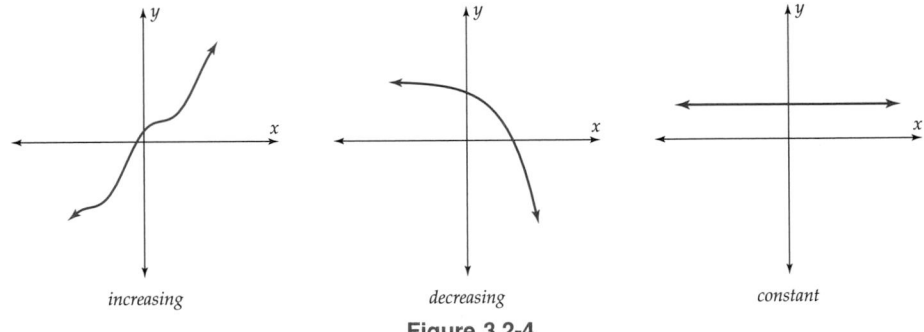

increasing   *decreasing*   *constant*

Figure 3.2-4

Figure 3.2-5

Figure 3.2-6

Figure 3.2-7

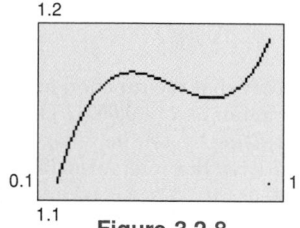

Figure 3.2-8

| Example 3 | Where a Function is Increasing/Decreasing |

On what interval is the function $f(x) = |x| + |x - 2|$ increasing? decreasing? constant?

Solution

The graph of the function, shown in Figure 3.2-5, suggests that f is decreasing on the interval $(-\infty, 0)$, increasing on $(2, \infty)$, and constant on $[0, 2]$. Using the trace feature on a graphing calculator, you can confirm the function is constant between 0 and 2. For an algebraic proof that f is constant on $[0, 2]$, see Exercise 55.

Local Maxima and Minima

The graph of a function may include some peaks and valleys, as in Figure 3.2-6. A peak may not be the highest point on the graph, but it is the highest point in its neighborhood. Similarly, a valley is the lowest point in its neighborhood.

A function f has a **local maximum** (plural: **local maxima**) at $x = c$ if the graph of f has a peak at the point $(c, f(c))$. This means that $f(x) \leq f(c)$ for all x near c. Similarly, a function has a **local minimum** (plural: **local minima**) at $x = d$ if the graph of f has a valley at $(d, f(d))$. This means $f(x) \geq f(d)$ for all x near d.

Calculus is usually needed to find exact local maxima and minima. However, they can be approximated with a calculator.

| Example 4 | Finding Local Maxima and Minima |

Graph $f(x) = x^3 - 1.8x^2 + x + 1$ and find all local maxima and minima.

Solution

In the decimal or standard window, the graph does not appear to have any local maxima or minima (see Figure 3.2-7). Select a viewing window such as the one in Figure 3.2-8 to see that the function actually has a local maximum and a local minimum (Figure 3.2-9). The calculator's minimum finder and maximum finder show that the local minimum occurs when $x \approx 0.763$ and the local maximum occurs when $x \approx 0.437$.

Figure 3.2-9

| Example 3 |

On what interval is the function $f(x) = |x + 3| - |x|$ increasing? decreasing? constant?

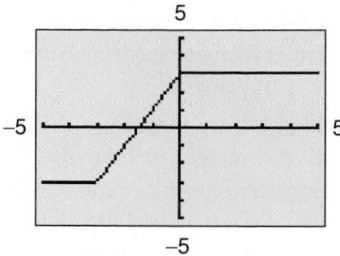

increasing on $(-3, 0)$

never decreasing

constant on $(-\infty, -3]$ and $[0, \infty)$

| Example 4 |

Graph $f(x) = x^3 - 2.1x^2 + x + 3$ and find all local maxima and minima.

(local maxima/minima not evident in standard window)

local maximum at $x \approx 0.304$

local minimum at $x \approx 1.096$

Math Background

The difference quotient introduced in Section 3.1 is used to find the derivative of a function. Students will use derivatives in calculus to quickly determine intervals on which a function is increasing/decreasing or concave up/down.

They will also learn in calculus that concavity is related to the rate of increase or decrease. For example, when a graph is concave up and increasing, its rate of increase is increasing.

Teaching Notes

Show several graphical examples that demonstrate combinations of increasing and decreasing with concave up and concave down. This will help the students to avoid making invalid conclusions about the links between these concepts. Some examples:

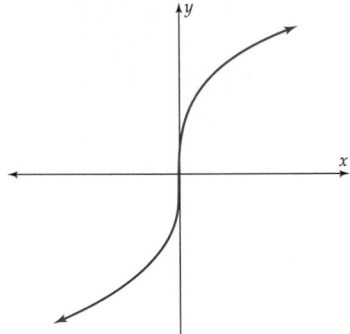

concave up, then concave down, increasing throughout

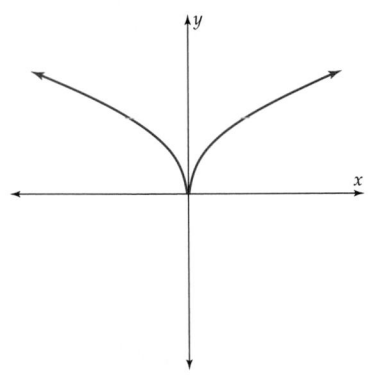

concave down throughout, decreasing, then increasing

When graphing **Piecewise-Defined Functions**, make sure that students use open and closed endpoints properly. For > and <, an open endpoint is used. For ≥ and ≤, a closed endpoint is used.

Concavity and Inflection Points

Concavity is used to describe the way that a curve bends. For any two points in a given interval that lie on a curve, if the segment that connects them is *above* the curve, then the curve is said to be **concave up** over the given interval. If the segment is *below* the curve, then the curve is said to be **concave down** over the interval (see Figure 3.2-10). A straight line is neither concave up nor concave down. A point where the curve changes concavity is called an **inflection point.**

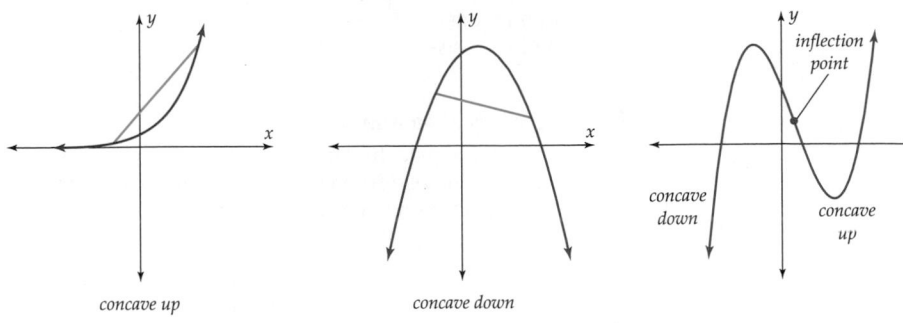

Figure 3.2-10

Example 5   Analyzing a Graph

Graph the function $f(x) = -2x^3 + 6x^2 - x + 3$ and estimate the following, using the graph and a maximum and minimum finder.

a. all local maxima and minima of the function

b. intervals where the function is increasing and where it is decreasing

c. all inflection points of the function

d. intervals where the function is concave up and where it is concave down

Solution

a.–b. The maximum and minimum finders show that the function has a local maximum at $x \approx 1.9129$ and a local minimum at $x \approx 0.0871$. Thus, the graph shows that the function is decreasing over the intervals $(-\infty, 0.0871)$ and $(1.9129, \infty)$, and increasing over the interval $(0.0871, 1.9129)$.

c.–d. The function is concave up on the left and concave down on the right, and the inflection point appears to be at about $x \approx 1$. Thus, the function is concave up over the interval $(-\infty, 1)$ and concave down over the interval $(1, \infty)$. ∎

Figure 3.2-11

Graphs of Piecewise-Defined and Greatest Integer Functions

The graphs of piecewise-defined functions are often discontinuous, that is, they commonly have jumps or holes. To graph a piecewise-defined function, graph each piece separately.

Example 6   Graphing a Piecewise-Defined Function

Graph the piecewise-defined function below.

$$f(x) = \begin{cases} x^2 & \text{if } x \le 1 \\ x + 2 & \text{if } 1 < x \le 4 \end{cases}$$

Solution

The graph is made up of parts of two different graphs, corresponding to the different parts of the function.

For $x \le 1$, the graph of f coincides with the graph of $y = x^2$.

For $1 < x \le 4$, the graph of f coincides with the graph of $y = x + 2$.

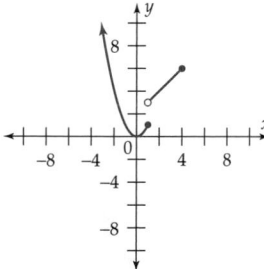

Combining these partial graphs produces the graph of f.

Figure 3.2-12

Piecewise-defined functions can be graphed on a calculator, provided that you use the correct syntax. However, the screen does not show which endpoints are included or excluded from the graph.

Example 5

Graph $f(x) = x^3 + 3x^2 - x$ and find the following, using a maximum and minimum finder.

a. all local maxima and minima of the function
local maximum at $x \approx -2.1547$
local minimum at $x \approx 0.1547$

b. intervals where the function is increasing and where it is decreasing
increasing on $(-\infty, -2.1547)$ and $(0.1547, \infty)$
decreasing on $(-2.1547, 0.1547)$

c. all inflection points of the function
inflection point appears to be at about $x \approx -1$

d. intervals where the function is concave up and where it is concave down
concave down on $(-\infty, -1)$
concave up on $(-1, \infty)$

Example 6

Graph the piecewise-defined function below:

$$f(x) = \begin{cases} 3 & \text{for } -2 \le x \le 2 \\ x^2 - 4x & \text{for } x > 2 \end{cases}$$

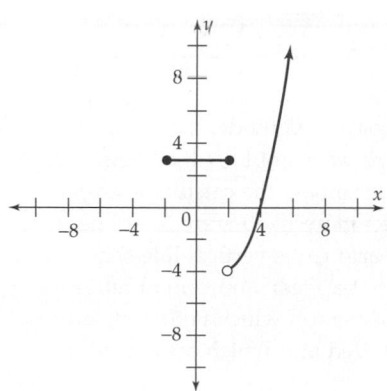

Teaching Notes

Solution to the **Graphing Exploration** on page 156:

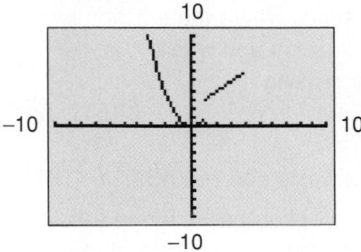

In the calculator graph, you cannot tell which endpoints are included or excluded.

Solution to the **Graphing Exploration** on page 157:

Connected mode:

Dot mode:

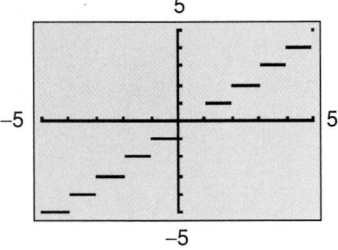

In connected mode, the calculator graph does not look like Figure 3.2-15. In dot mode, the calculator graph looks more like Figure 3.2-15 because the erroneous vertical line segments do not appear. You cannot tell from either graph which endpoints are included and which are excluded.

Technology Tip

Inequality symbols are in the TEST menu of TI-84/TI-83. TI-89 has the symbols <, >, and | on the keyboard, and other inequality symbols and logical symbols (such as "and") are in the TEST submenu of the MATH menu.

Graphing Exploration

Graph the function f from Example 6 on a calculator as follows: On TI-84/TI-83 calculators, graph these two equations on the same screen:

$$Y_1 = X^2/(X \le 1)$$
$$Y_2 = X + 2/((X > 1)(X \le 4))$$

On a TI-89/92, graph these equations on the same screen:

$$Y_1 = X^2 | X \le 1$$
$$Y_2 = X + 2 | X > 1 \quad \text{and} \quad X \le 4$$

To graph f on a Casio, graph these equations on the same screen (including commas and square brackets):

$$Y_1 = X^2, [-6, 1]$$
$$Y_2 = X + 2, [1, 4]$$

How does your graph compare with Figure 3.2-12?

Example 7 The Absolute-Value Function

Graph $f(x) = |x|$.

Solution

The absolute-value function $f(x) = |x|$ is also a piecewise-defined function, since by definition

$$|x| = \begin{cases} -x & \text{if } x < 0 \\ x & \text{if } x \ge 0 \end{cases}$$

Its graph can be obtained by drawing the part of the line $y = x$ to the right of the origin and the part of the line $y = -x$ to the left of the origin or by graphing $Y_1 = \text{ABS } X$ on a calculator.

Figure 3.2-13

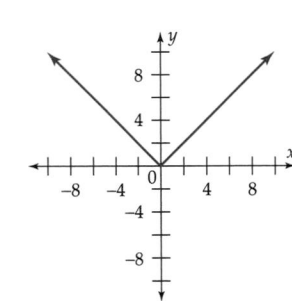

Figure 3.2-14

Example Notes

In **Example 8**, the Greatest Integer Function can also be defined as a piecewise function:

$$f(x) = \begin{cases} \vdots \\ -2 & \text{if } -2 \le x < -1 \\ -1 & \text{if } -1 \le x < 0 \\ 0 & \text{if } 0 \le x < 1 \\ 1 & \text{if } 1 \le x < 2 \\ 2 & \text{if } 2 \le x < 3 \\ \vdots \end{cases}$$

ADDITIONAL EXAMPLES

Example 8 The Greatest Integer Function

Graph the greatest integer function $f(x) = [x]$.

Solution

The greatest integer function can easily be graphed by hand, by considering the values of the function between each two consecutive integers. For instance, between $x = -2$ and $x = -1$ the value of $f(x) = [x]$ is always -2, so the graph there is a horizontal line segment, all of whose points have y-coordinate -2, with a solid circle on the left endpoint and an open circle on the right endpoint. The rest of the graph is obtained similarly.

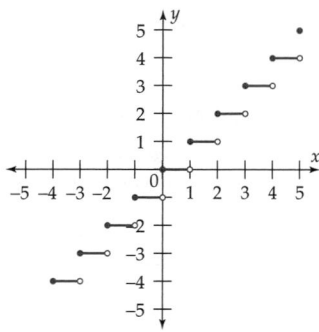

Figure 3.2-15

A function whose graph consists of horizontal line segments, such as Figure 3.2-15, is called a **step function.** Step functions can be graphed on a calculator, but some features of their graphs may not be shown.

Graphing Exploration

Graph the greatest integer function $f(x) = [x]$ on your calculator (see the Technology Tip on page 147). Does your graph look like Figure 3.2-15? Change your calculator to "dot" rather than "connected" mode (see the Technology Tip at left) and graph again. How does this graph compare with Figure 3.2-15? Can you tell from the graph which endpoints are included and which are excluded?

Parametric Graphing

In **parametric graphing,** the x-coordinate and the y-coordinate of each point on a graph are each given as a function of a third variable, t, called a **parameter.** The functions that give the rules for the coordinates are called **parametric equations.**

Example 7

Graph $f(x) = |x| + 1$.

Rewrite $f(x) = |x| + 1$ as a piecewise-defined function:

$$|x| + 1 = \begin{cases} -x + 1 & \text{if } x < 0 \\ x + 1 & \text{if } x \geq 0 \end{cases}$$

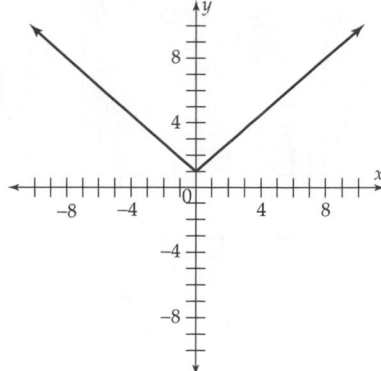

Example 8

Graph the function $f(x) = [x] - 2$.

Rewrite $f(x) = [x] - 2$ as a piecewise-defined function:

$$[x] - 2 = \begin{cases} \vdots \\ -4 & \text{if } -2 \leq x < -1 \\ -3 & \text{if } -1 \leq x < 0 \\ -2 & \text{if } \quad 0 \leq x < 1 \\ -1 & \text{if } \quad 1 \leq x < 2 \\ 0 & \text{if } \quad 2 \leq x < 3 \\ \vdots \end{cases}$$

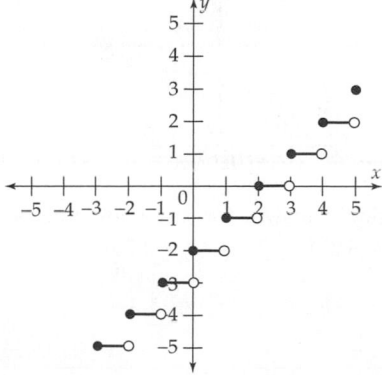

In **Parametric Graphing**, x is a function of t and y is a function of t, but y may or may not be a function of x. **Example 10** contains a case in which y is a function of x and a case in which y is not a function of x.

Solution to the **Graphing Exploration:**

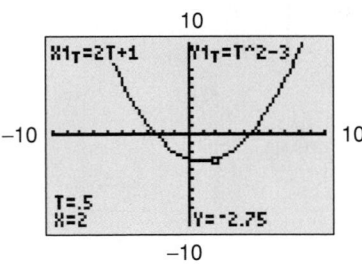

Possible answer for three new points:
$(-4, 3.25)$, $(-5, 6)$, $(2, -2.75)$

A parametric graph can be thought of as representing the function

$$f(t) = (x, y)$$

where

$$x = x(t) \quad \text{and} \quad y = y(t)$$

are the rules for the x- and y-coordinates. Note that the graph will not necessarily pass the Vertical Line Test.

Example 9 Graphing a Parametric Equation

Graph the curve given by

$$x = 2t + 1$$
$$y = t^2 - 3$$

Solution

Make a table of values for t, x, and y. Then plot the points from the table and complete the graph.

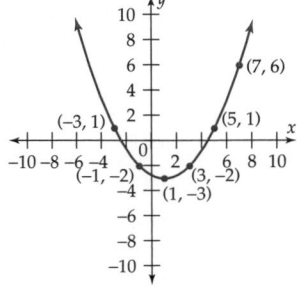

Figure 3.2-16

t	$x = 2t + 1$	$y = t^2 - 3$	(x, y)
-2	-3	1	$(-3, 1)$
-1	-1	-2	$(-1, -2)$
0	1	-3	$(1, -3)$
1	3	-2	$(3, -2)$
2	5	1	$(5, 1)$
3	7	6	$(7, 6)$

Technology Tip

- To change to parametric mode, choose **PAR** in the TI **MODE** menu or **PARM** in the **TYPE** submenu of the Casio **GRAPH** menu (on the main menu).

Graphing Exploration

Graph the equations from Example 9 on a calculator in parametric mode in the standard viewing window. Set the range so that $-10 \le t \le 10$, with t-step $= 0.1$. Use the trace feature to find at least three points on the graph that are not given in the table in Example 9.

Parametric mode can be used to graph equations of the form $y = f(x)$ or the form $x = f(y)$.

Graphing y = f(x) or x = f(y) in Parametric Mode

To graph $y = f(x)$ in parametric mode, let

$$x = t$$
$$y = f(t)$$

To graph $x = f(y)$ in parametric mode, let

$$x = f(t)$$
$$y = t$$

Example 10   Graphing in Parametric Mode

Graph the following equations in parametric mode on a calculator.

a. $y = \left(\dfrac{x-1}{2}\right)^2 - 3$ **b.** $x = y^2 - 3y + 1$

Solution

a. Let $x = t$ and $y = \left(\dfrac{t-1}{2}\right)^2 - 3$.   **b.** Let $x = t^2 - 3t + 1$ and $y = t$.

NOTE The graph in part **a** is the same as in Example 9. To obtain the equation in part **a** from the parametric equations in Example 9, solve the first equation for t and substitute the result into the second equation.

     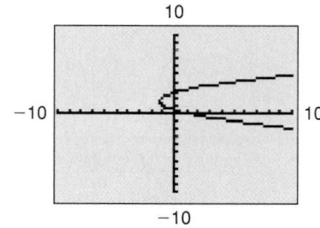

Figure 3.2-17

Notice that the graph in part **b** does not pass the Vertical Line Test. The equation does not represent y as a function of x.

Parametric equations will be studied more thoroughly in Chapter 11.

ADDITIONAL EXAMPLES

Example 9

Graph the curve given by
$x = t - 2$
$y = t^2 + 3t$

t	$x = t - 2$	$y = t^2 + 3t$	(x, y)
-3	-5	0	$(-5, 0)$
-2	-4	-2	$(-4, -2)$
-1	-3	-2	$(-3, -2)$
0	-2	0	$(-2, 0)$
1	-1	4	$(-1, 4)$
2	0	10	$(0, 10)$

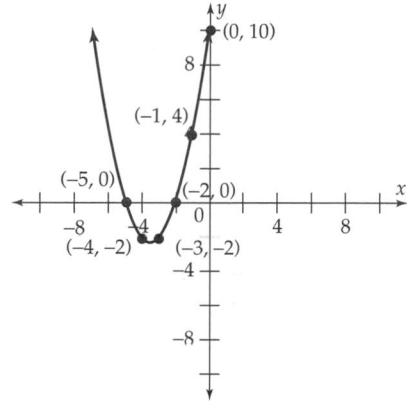

Example 10

Graph the following equations in parametric mode on a calculator.

a. $y = x^2 + x - 5$
Let $x = t$ and $y = t^2 + t - 5$.

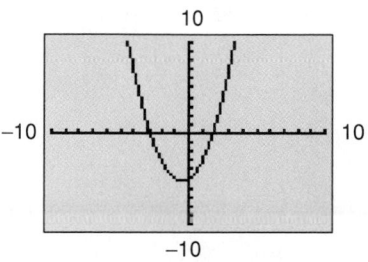

b. $x = 2(y + 3)^2 - 1$
Let $x = 2(t + 3)^2 - 1$ and $y = t$.

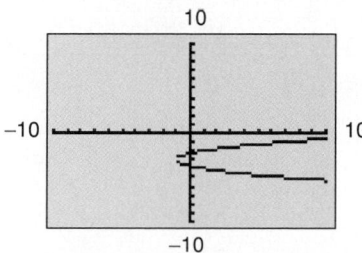

9. This is not a function; for example, there are three output values for an input value of 4.

11. This is not a function; for example, there are three output values for an input value of 2.

Exercises 3.2

In Exercises 1–4, the graph below defines a function, f. Determine the following:

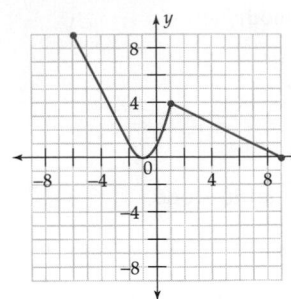

1. $f(-5)$ **7**

2. $f(1)$ **4**

3. the domain of f
   [−6, 9]

4. the range of f
   [0, 9]

In Exercises 5–8, the graph below defines a function, g. Determine the following:

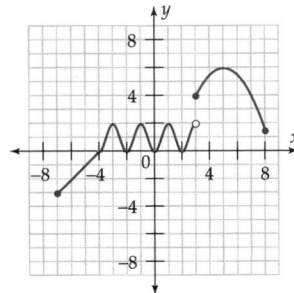

5. $g(1)$ **2**

6. $g(5)$ **6**

7. the domain of g
   [−7, 8]

8. the range of g
   [−3, 6]

In Exercises 9–14, use the Vertical Line Test to determine whether the graph defines a function. If not, give an example of an input value that corresponds to more than one output value.

9.

10.

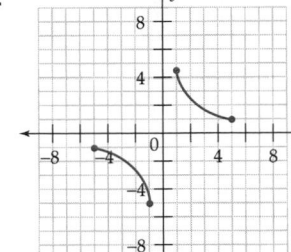

This is a function.

11.

12.

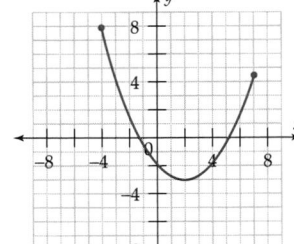

This is a function.

13.

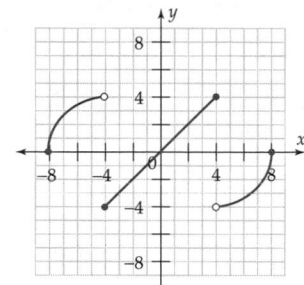

This is a function.

14.

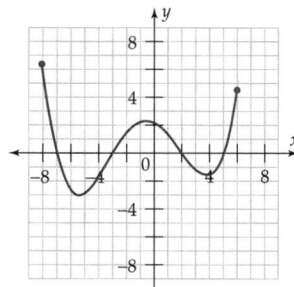

This is a function.

In Exercises 15 and 16, the graph of a function is shown. Find the approximate intervals on which the function is increasing and on which it is decreasing.

15.

16.

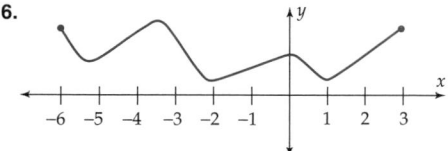

In Exercises 17–22, graph each function. Find the approximate intervals on which the function is increasing, decreasing, and constant.

17. $f(x) = |x - 1| - |x + 1|$

18. $g(x) = |x - 1| + |x + 2|$

19. $f(x) = -x^3 - 8x^2 + 8x + 5$

20. $f(x) = x^4 - 0.7x^3 - 0.6x^2 + 1$

21. $g(x) = 0.2x^4 - x^3 + x^2 - 2$

22. $g(x) = x^4 + x^3 - 4x^2 + x - 1$

In Exercises 23–28, graph each function. Estimate all local maxima and minima of the function.

23. $f(x) = x^3 - x$

24. $g(t) = -\sqrt{16 - t^2}$

25. $h(x) = \dfrac{x}{x^2 + 1}$

26. $k(x) = x^3 - 3x + 1$

27. $f(x) = x^3 - 1.8x^2 + x + 2$

28. $g(x) = 2x^3 + x^2 + 1$

29. a. A rectangle has a perimeter of 100 inches, and one side has length x. Express the area of the rectangle as a function of x.
b. Use the function in part **a** to find the dimensions of the rectangle with perimeter 100 inches and the largest possible area.

30. a. A rectangle has an area of 240 in^2, and one side has length x. Express the perimeter of the rectangle as a function of x.
b. Use the function in part **a** to find the dimensions of the rectangle with area 240 in^2 and the smallest possible perimeter.

31. a. A box with a square base has a volume of 867 in^3. Express the surface area of the box as a function of the length x of a side of the base. (Be sure to include the top of the box.)
b. Use the function in part **a** to find the dimensions of the box with volume 867 in^3 and the smallest possible surface area.

32. a. A cylindrical can has a surface area of 60 in^2. Express the volume of the can as a function of the radius r.
b. Use the function in part **a** to find the radius and height of the can with surface area 60 in^2 and the largest possible volume.

In Exercises 33–36, graph each function. Find the approximate intervals on which the function is concave up and concave down, and estimate all inflection points.

33. $f(x) = x^3$

34. $f(x) = x^3 - 2x$

35. $h(x) = x^4 - 2x^2$

36. $g(x) = x^3 - 3x^2 + 2x + 1$

15. Increasing on $(-2.5, 0)$ and $(1.7, 4)$; decreasing on $(-6, -2.5)$ and $(0, 1.7)$

16. Increasing on $(-5.2, -3.5)$, $(-2, -0)$, and $(1, 3)$; decreasing on $(-6, -5.2)$, $(-3.5, -2)$, and $(0, 1)$

17. Constant on $(-\infty, -1]$ and $[1, \infty)$; decreasing on $(-1, 1)$

18. Increasing on $(1, \infty)$; constant on $(-2, 1)$; decreasing on $(-\infty, -2)$

19. Increasing on $(-5.8, 0.5)$; decreasing on $(-\infty, -5.8)$ and $(0.5, \infty)$

20. Increasing on $(-0.34488, 0)$ and $(0.86988, \infty)$; decreasing on $(-\infty, -0.34488)$ and $(0, 0.86988)$

21. Increasing on $(0, 0.867)$ and $(2.883, \infty)$; decreasing on $(-\infty, 0)$ and $(0.867, 2.883)$

22. Increasing on $(-1.88278, 0.13278)$ and $(1, \infty)$; decreasing on $(-\infty, -1.88278)$ and $(0.13278, 1)$

23. Minimum at $x \approx 0.57735$; maximum at $x \approx -0.57735$

24. Minimum at $x = 0$; maxima at $x = \pm 4$

25. Minimum at $x = -1$; maximum at $x = 1$

26. Maximum at $x = -1$; minimum at $x = 1$

27. Minimum at $x \approx 0.7633$; maximum at $x \approx 0.4367$

28. Minimum at $x = 0$; maximum at $x = -\dfrac{1}{3}$

29. a. $A(x) = 50x - x^2$
b. To maximize area each side should be 25 in. long.

30. a. $P(x) = 2x + \dfrac{480}{x}$
b. To minimize perimeter each side should be approximately 15.49 in. long.

31. a. $SA(x) = 2x^2 + \dfrac{3468}{x}$
b. Base is approximately 9.5354 in. $\times$ 9.5354 in.; height is same (that is, 9.5354 in.).

32. a. $V(r) = 30r - \pi r^3$
b. Radius is approximately 1.7841 in.; height is approximately 3.5682 in.

33–36. For graphs see p. 1055.

33. This function is concave up over the interval $(0, \infty)$ and concave down over the interval $(-\infty, 0)$. Therefore, the point of inflection is at $(0, 0)$.

34. This function is concave up over the interval $(0, \infty)$ and concave down over the interval $(-\infty, 0)$. Therefore, the point of inflection is at $(0, 0)$.

35. The function is concave up over the approximate intervals $(-\infty, -0.6)$ and $(0.6, \infty)$ and concave down over the approximate interval $(-0.6, 0.6)$. Therefore, the points of inflection are approximately at $(-0.6, -0.6)$ and $(0.6, -0.6)$.

36. This function is concave up over the interval $(1, \infty)$ and concave down over the interval $(-\infty, 1)$. Therefore, the point of inflection is at $(1, 1)$.

37–40. *For graphs see p.* 1055.

37. b. This function is increasing over the interval $(1, \infty)$ and decreasing over the interval $(-\infty, 1)$.

  c. There is a local minimum at the point $(1, 0)$.

  d. This function is concave up over the interval $(-\infty, \infty)$.

  e. There is no point of inflection.

38. b. This function is increasing over the interval $(-\infty, -2)$ and decreasing over the interval $(-2, -\infty)$.

  c. There is a local maximum at the point $(-2, 1)$.

  d. This function is concave down over the interval $(-\infty, \infty)$.

  e. There is no point of inflection.

39. b. This function is increasing over the intervals $(-\infty, 0)$ and $(2, \infty)$ and decreasing over the interval $(0, 2)$.

  c. There is a local maximum at the point $(0, 2)$ and a local minimum at the point $(2, -2)$.

  d. This function is concave up over the interval $(1, \infty)$ and concave down over the interval $(-\infty, 1)$.

  e. There is a point of inflection at $(1, 0)$.

40. b. This function is increasing over the approximate interval $(-1.155, 1.155)$ and decreasing over the approximate intervals $(-\infty, -1.155)$ and $(-1.155, \infty)$.

  c. There is a local maximum at the point $(1.155, 1.079)$ and a local minimum at the point $(-1.115, -5.079)$.

  d. This function is concave up over the interval $(-\infty, 0)$ and concave down over the interval $(0, \infty)$.

  e. There is a point of inflection at $(0, -2)$.

41–44. *See p.* 1056.

45–49. *For graphs see p.* 1056.

45. a. $f(x) = \begin{cases} x + 2 & x \geq 0 \\ -x + 2 & x < 0 \end{cases}$

46. a. $g(x) = \begin{cases} x - 4 & \text{if } x \geq 0 \\ -x - 4 & \text{if } x < 0 \end{cases}$

47. a. $h(x) = \begin{cases} \dfrac{x}{2} - 2 & x \geq 0 \\ -\dfrac{x}{2} - 2 & x < 0 \end{cases}$

48. a. $g(x) = \begin{cases} x + 3 & \text{if } x \geq 0 \\ -x - 3 & \text{if } x < 0 \end{cases}$

49. a. $f(x) = \begin{cases} x - 5 & x \geq 5 \\ 5 - x & x < 5 \end{cases}$

50–53. *See p.* 1056.

In Exercises 37–40,

  a. Graph each function.

  b. Find the approximate intervals on which the function is increasing, decreasing, and constant.

  c. Estimate all local maxima and minima.

  d. Find the approximate intervals on which the function is concave up and concave down.

  e. Estimate the coordinates of any inflection points.

  37. $f(x) = x^2 - 2x + 1$ **38.** $f(x) = -x^2 - 4x - 3$

  39. $g(x) = x^3 - 3x^2 + 2$ **40.** $g(x) = -x^3 + 4x - 2$

In Exercises 41–44, sketch the graph of the function. Be sure to indicate which endpoints are included and which are excluded.

  41. $f(x) = \begin{cases} 2x + 3 & \text{if } x < -1 \\ x^2 & \text{if } x \geq -1 \end{cases}$

  42. $g(x) = \begin{cases} |x| & \text{if } x < 1 \\ -3x + 4 & \text{if } x \geq 1 \end{cases}$

  43. $k(u) = \begin{cases} -2u - 2 & \text{if } u < -3 \\ u - [u] & \text{if } -3 \leq u \leq 1 \\ 2u^2 & \text{if } u > 1 \end{cases}$

  44. $f(x) = \begin{cases} x^2 & \text{if } x < -2 \\ x & \text{if } -2 \leq x < 4 \\ \sqrt{x} & \text{if } x \geq 4 \end{cases}$

In Exercises 45–49,

  a. Use the fact that the absolute-value function is piecewise-defined (see Example 7) to write the rule of the given function as a piecewise-defined function whose rule does not include any absolute value bars.

  b. Graph the function.

  45. $f(x) = |x| + 2$ **46.** $g(x) = |x| - 4$

  47. $h(x) = \dfrac{|x|}{2} - 2$ **48.** $g(x) = |x + 3|$

  49. $f(x) = |x - 5|$

In Exercises 50–53, sketch the graph of the function. Be sure to indicate which endpoints are included and which are excluded.

  50. $f(x) = -[x]$

  51. $g(x) = [-x]$ (This is not the same function as in Exercise 50.)

  52. $h(x) = [x] + [-x]$ **53.** $f(x) = 2[x]$

54. A common mistake is to graph the function f in Example 6 by graphing both $y = x^2$ and $y = x + 2$ on the same screen, with no restrictions on x. Explain why this graph could not possibly be the graph of a function.

55. Show that the function $f(x) = |x| + |x - 2|$ is constant on the interval $[0, 2]$. *Hint:* Use the piecewise definition of absolute value in Example 7 to compute $f(x)$ when $0 \leq x \leq 2$.

In Exercises 56–59, use your calculator to estimate the domain and range of the function by tracing its graph.

  56. $g(x) = x^2 - 4$ **57.** $h(x) = \sqrt{x^2 - 4}$

  58. $k(x) = \sqrt{x^2 + 4}$ **59.** $f(x) = 3x - 2$

In Exercises 60 and 61, draw the graph of a function f that satisfies the given conditions. The function does not need to be given by an algebraic rule.

60. • $f(-1) = 2$

  • $f(x) \geq 2$ when x is in the interval $\left(-1, \dfrac{1}{2}\right)$

  • $f(x)$ starts decreasing when $x = 1$
  • $f(3) = 3 = f(0)$
  • $f(x)$ starts increasing when $x = 5$

61. • domain $f = [-2, 4]$
  • range $f = [-5, 6]$
  • $f(-1) = f(3)$
  • $f\left(\dfrac{1}{2}\right) = 0$

In Exercises 62–67, graph the curve determined by the parametric equations.

62. $x = 0.1t^3 - 0.2t^2 - 2t + 4$
    $y = 1 - t \quad (-5 \leq t \leq 6)$

63. $x = t^2 - 3t + 2$
    $y = 8 - t^3 \quad (-4 \leq t \leq 4)$

64. $x = t^2 - 6t$
    $y = \sqrt{t+7} \quad (-5 \leq t \leq 9)$

65. $x = 1 - t^2$
    $y = t^3 - t - 1 \quad (-4 \leq t \leq 4)$

66. $x = t^2 - t - 1$
    $y = 1 - t - t^2$

67. $x = 3t^2 - 5$
    $y = t^2 \quad (-4 \leq t \leq 4)$

54. The graph fails the vertical line test. For example, $x = 3$ is mapped to both 9 and 5.

55. When $0 \leq x \leq 2$, x is positive and $x - 2$ is negative, so $|x| = x$ and $|x - 2| = -(x - 2)$. Therefore,
$|x| + |x - 2| = x - (x - 2)$
$= x - x + 2 = 2$ when $0 \leq x \leq 2$.

56. Domain: all real numbers; range: all real numbers x such that $x \geq -4$

In Exercises 68–71, graph the equation in parametric mode. Give the rule for x and for y in terms of t.

68. $y = x^3 + x^2 - 6x$ $x = t, y = t^3 + t^2 - 6t$

69. $y = x^4 - 3x^3 + x^2$ $x = t, y = t^4 - 3t^3 + t^2$

70. $x = y^3 + 5y^2 - 4y - 5$
$x = t^3 + 5t^2 - 4t - 5, y = t$

71. $x = y^4 - 3y^2 - 5$
$x = t^4 - 3t^2 - 5, y = t$

68–71. *For graphs see p.* **1057.**

3.3 Quadratic Functions

Objectives

- Define three forms for quadratic functions
- Find the vertex and intercepts of a quadratic function and sketch its graph
- Convert one form of a quadratic function to another

Parabolas

The rule of a **quadratic function** is a polynomial of degree 2. The shape of the graph of a quadratic function is a **parabola.** Three parabolas are shown in Figure 3.3-1, with important points labeled.

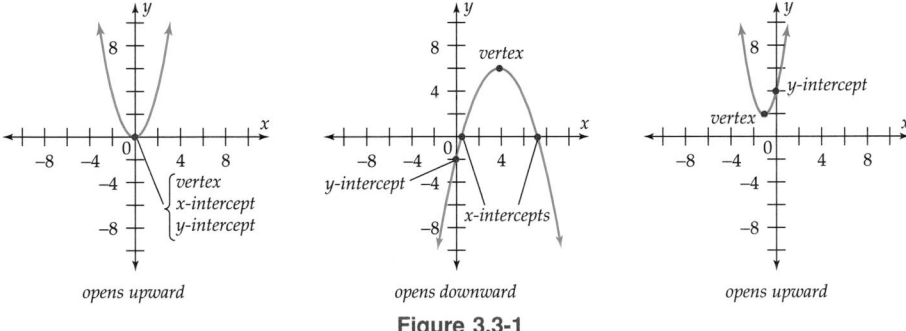

opens upward   opens downward   opens upward

Figure 3.3-1

Notice that the graph of a quadratic function

- can open either upward or downward
- always has a vertex which is either the maximum or minimum
- always has exactly 1 y-intercept
- can have 0, 1, or 2 x-intercepts

A parabola is symmetric about a line through the vertex called the **axis of symmetry.**

Quadratic Functions

Quadratic functions can be written in several forms.

3.3 Quadratic Functions

Teaching Notes

Discuss the important points (vertices and intercepts) in the graphs of the three parabolas in Figure 3.3-1. Note that we sometimes refer to intercepts as numbers and sometimes as points.

The y-value of a vertex is a maximum or minimum. For example, in the second graph in Figure 3.3-1, the vertex is the point (4, 6), and the maximum value is 6.

Ask students whether the vertex gives a maximum or a minimum when a parabola opens up (minimum) and when it opens down (maximum).

Ask students to try to draw a parabola with no y-intercept. (not possible) You may need to remind students that every parabola that opens up or down continues infinitely to the left and right to show that every parabola will intersect the y-axis eventually.

57. Domain: all real numbers x such that $x \le -2$ or $x \ge 2$; range: all nonnegative real numbers

58. Domain: all real numbers; range: all real numbers x such that $x \ge 2$

59. Domain: all real numbers; range: all real numbers

60–67. *See pp.* **1056–1057.**

Teaching Notes

You can use the **Transformation Form** of a quadratic function to find the vertex, the x-intercept, and the y-intercept. For intercepts, remind students that:

- The y-value associated with an x-intercept is 0.
- The x-value associated with the y-intercept is 0.

Students can refer back to Figure 3.3-1 on page 163 to verify these facts. For example, in the third graph, the y-intercept is 4; it occurs at $(0, 4)$.

Example Notes

In **Example 1**, help students identify the values of a, h, and k by writing the given function $f(x)$ under the transformation form as shown below.

$f(x) = a(x - h)^2 + k$
$f(x) = 2(x - 3)^2 - 4$
$f(x) = 2(x - 3)^2 + (-4)$
so, $a = 2$, $h = 3$, and $k = -4$.

ADDITIONAL EXAMPLES

Example 1

For the function $f(x) = -4(x - 2)^2 + 5$, find the vertex and the x- and y-intercepts. Then sketch the graph.
The vertex is $(2, 5)$.
The y-intercept is -11.
The x-intercepts are

$$2 + \sqrt{\frac{-5}{-4}} = 2 + \sqrt{\frac{5}{4}} \approx 3.1$$

$$2 - \sqrt{\frac{-5}{-4}} = 2 - \sqrt{\frac{5}{4}} \approx 0.9$$

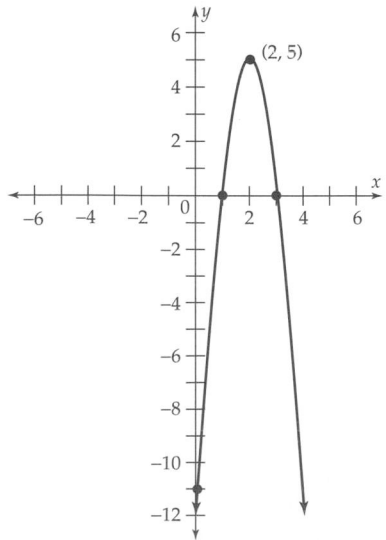

Three Forms of a Quadratic Function

> A quadratic function can be written in any of the following forms:
>
> Transformation form: $f(x) = a(x - h)^2 + k$
>
> Polynomial form: $f(x) = ax^2 + bx + c$
>
> x-Intercept form: $f(x) = a(x - s)(x - t)$
>
> where a, b, c, h, k, s, and t are real numbers and $a \neq 0$. If a is positive, the graph opens upward; and if a is negative, the graph opens downward.

Transformation Form

The transformation form is the most useful form for finding the vertex. For a quadratic function written in transformation form, $f(x) = a(x - h)^2 + k$, the vertex is the point with coordinates (h, k).

Since the y-intercept of a function is $f(0)$,

$$f(0) = a(0 - h)^2 + k = ah^2 + k$$

shows the y-intercept is $ah^2 + k$.

Since the x-intercepts occur when $y = 0$, the x-intercepts are the solutions of the quadratic equation $a(x - h)^2 + k = 0$.

$$a(x - h)^2 + k = 0$$
$$a(x - h)^2 = -k$$
$$(x - h)^2 = \frac{-k}{a}$$
$$x - h = \pm\sqrt{\frac{-k}{a}}$$
$$x = h \pm \sqrt{\frac{-k}{a}}$$

The x-intercepts are $h + \sqrt{\frac{-k}{a}}$ and $h - \sqrt{\frac{-k}{a}}$.

Example 1 Transformation Form

For the function $f(x) = 2(x - 3)^2 - 4$, find the vertex and the x- and y-intercepts. Then sketch the graph.

Solution

In $f(x) = 2(x - 3)^2 - 4 = 2(x - 3)^2 + (-4)$, $a = 2$, $h = 3$ and $k = -4$. The vertex is

$$(h, k) = (3, -4)$$

the y-intercept is

$$ah^2 + k = 2(3^2) + (-4) = 14$$

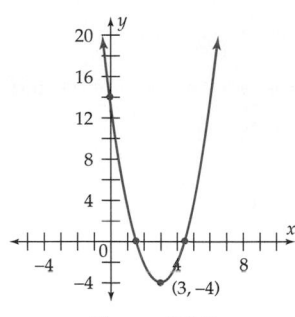

Figure 3.3-2

and the x-intercepts are

$$h + \sqrt{\frac{-k}{a}} = 3 + \sqrt{\frac{-(-4)}{2}} = 3 + \sqrt{2} \approx 4.4$$

$$h - \sqrt{\frac{-k}{a}} = 3 - \sqrt{\frac{-(-4)}{2}} = 3 - \sqrt{2} \approx 1.6$$

To graph the function, plot the vertex and intercepts, then draw the parabola. Since a is positive, the parabola opens upward. ∎

Polynomial Form

The polynomial form is the most useful form for finding the y-intercept. Since the y-intercept of a function is $f(0)$, the y-intercept is c.

$$f(0) = a(0)^2 + b(0) + c = 0 + 0 + c = c$$

The x-intercepts are the solutions of the quadratic equation $ax^2 + bx + c = 0$, which can be solved either by factoring or by the quadratic formula. In general, the x-intercepts are

$$\frac{-b + \sqrt{b^2 - 4ac}}{2a} \quad \text{and} \quad \frac{-b - \sqrt{b^2 - 4ac}}{2a}$$

for values which make $b^2 - 4ac$ positive. If $b^2 - 4ac = 0$, then there is only one x-intercept. If $b^2 - 4ac$ is negative, then there are no x-intercepts.

To find the vertex of the graph of a quadratic function in polynomial form, compare the transformation form to the polynomial form. First, multiply and distribute the terms in the transformation form, so the coefficients can be compared.

$$\begin{aligned} f(x) &= a(x - h)^2 + k && \textit{transformation form} \\ &= a(x^2 - 2hx + h^2) + k && \textit{multiply} \\ &= ax^2 - 2ahx + ah^2 + k && \textit{distribute the } a \\ &= ax^2 - 2ahx + (ah^2 + k) \end{aligned}$$

Match the second coefficient in each of the two equivalent forms.

$$b = -2ah$$

$$\frac{-b}{2a} = h$$

Since h is the x-coordinate of the vertex in the transformation form, $\dfrac{-b}{2a}$ is the x-coordinate of the vertex in the polynomial form. The y-coordinate of the vertex can be found by substituting $\dfrac{-b}{2a}$ into the function. Thus, the vertex of the graph of a quadratic function is

$$\left(\frac{-b}{2a}, \; f\!\left(\frac{-b}{2a} \right) \right)$$

Teaching Notes

When using the **Polynomial Form** to find x-intercepts, it is necessary to distinguish between a *quadratic function* and its associated *quadratic equation*. Point out that x-intercepts occur where $f(x) = 0$, so to find the x-intercepts for the *function* $f(x) = ax^2 + bx + c$, we solve the *equation* $0 = ax^2 + bx + c$.

Review how to interpret the discriminant $b^2 - 4ac$ to decide how many x-intercepts there are. Recall that the quadratic formula gives the solutions of $ax^2 + bx + c = 0$:

$$x = \frac{-b + \sqrt{b^2 - 4ac}}{2a} \text{ and }$$

$$x = \frac{-b - \sqrt{b^2 - 4ac}}{2a}.$$

So when the discriminant $b^2 - 4ac$ is positive, the equation $ax^2 + bx + c = 0$ has two solutions, and the graph of the function $f(x) = ax^2 + bx + c$ has two x-intercepts.

Similarly, when the discriminant is zero, there is only one solution and one x-intercept because $\dfrac{-b + \sqrt{0}}{2a}$ and $\dfrac{-b - \sqrt{0}}{2a}$ represent the same number. Finally, when the discriminant is negative, $\sqrt{b^2 - 4ac}$ is undefined, so the equation has no solutions, and the function has no x-intercepts.

Example Notes

In **Example 2,** another way to show that the vertex

$$\left(\frac{-b}{2a}, f\left(\frac{-b}{2a}\right)\right) = (-1, 2) \text{ is:}$$

$$x = \frac{-b}{2a}$$

$$= \frac{-2}{2(1)}$$

$$= -1$$

$$y = f(-1)$$

$$= (-1)^2 + 2(-1) + 3$$

$$= 1 + (-2) + 3$$

$$= 2$$

So, the vertex is $(-1, 2)$.

ADDITIONAL EXAMPLES

Example 2

For the function $f(x) = x^2 + 4x + 5$, find the vertex and the x- and y-intercepts. Then sketch the graph.
The y-intercept is 5.
The vertex is $(-2, 1)$.
There are no x-intercepts.

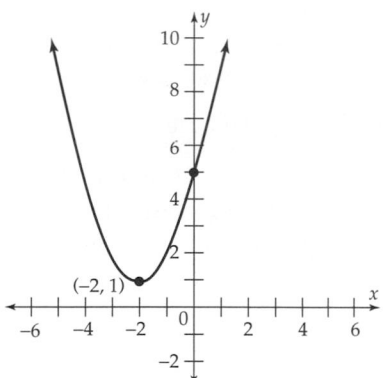

Example 3

For the graph of the function $f(x) = -2(x - 3)(x + 1)$, find the vertex and the x- and y-intercepts. Then sketch the graph.
The x-intercepts are $s = 3$ and $t = -1$.
The y-intercept is $ast = -2(3)(-1) = 6$.

The vertex is $\left(\frac{s+t}{2}, f\left(\frac{s+t}{2}\right)\right)$

$$= \left(\frac{3-1}{2}, f\left(\frac{3-1}{2}\right)\right)$$

$$= (1, f(1))$$

$$= (1, 8).$$

Example 2   Polynomial Form

For the function $f(x) = x^2 + 2x + 3$, find the vertex and the x- and y-intercepts. Then sketch the graph.

Solution

In $f(x) = x^2 + 2x + 3$, $a = 1$, $b = 2$, and $c = 3$. Thus, the y-intercept is

$$c = 3$$

and the vertex is

$$\left(\frac{-b}{2a}, f\left(\frac{-b}{2a}\right)\right) = \left(\frac{-2}{2(1)}, f\left(\frac{-2}{2(1)}\right)\right) = (-1, 2)$$

Since $b^2 - 4ac = -8$, the quadratic equation $x^2 + 2x + 3 = 0$ has no solutions, so there are no x-intercepts.

To graph the function, plot the vertex and y-intercept, then draw the parabola. Since a is positive, the parabola opens upward.

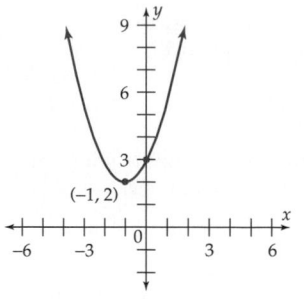

Figure 3.3-3

NOTE Not all quadratic functions can be written in x-intercept form. If the graph of a quadratic function has no x-intercepts, then there are no real values of s and t for which $f(x) = a(x - s)(x - t)$.

x-Intercept Form

The x-intercept form is the most useful form for finding the x-intercepts. For a quadratic function written in x-intercept form, $f(x) = a(x - s)(x - t)$, the x-intercepts of the graph are s and t. Notice that both of these values are solutions to the equation $f(x) = 0$.

$$f(s) = a(s - s)(s - t) = a(0)(s - t) = 0$$

and

$$f(t) = a(t - s)(t - t) = a(t - s)(0) = 0$$

Since the y-intercept of a function is $f(0)$,

$$f(0) = a(0 - s)(0 - t) = ast$$

so the y-intercept is ast.

To find the vertex of a graph of a quadratic function in x-intercept form, recall that a parabola is symmetric about a line through the vertex. Thus, the vertex is exactly halfway between the x-intercepts. The x-coordinate of the vertex is the average of the x-intercepts, or $\left(\frac{s+t}{2}\right)$. To find the y-coordinate of the vertex, substitute this value into the function. The vertex is

$$\left(\frac{s+t}{2}, f\left(\frac{s+t}{2}\right)\right)$$

Example 3 x-Intercept Form

For the graph of the function $f(x) = -\frac{1}{2}(x - 4)(x + 2)$, find the vertex and the x- and y-intercepts. Then sketch the graph.

continued from page 166

Solution

In $f(x) = -\frac{1}{2}(x - 4)(x + 2)$, $a = -\frac{1}{2}$, $s = 4$, and $t = -2$. The x-intercepts are

$$s = 4, \text{ and } t = -2$$

and the y-intercept is

$$ast = -\frac{1}{2}(4)(-2) = 4$$

and the vertex is

$$\left(\frac{s + t}{2}, f\left(\frac{s + t}{2}\right)\right) = \left(\frac{4 + (-2)}{2}, f\left(\frac{4 + (-2)}{2}\right)\right) = (1, 4.5)$$

To graph the function, plot the vertex and intercepts, then draw the parabola. Since a is negative, the parabola opens downward. ■

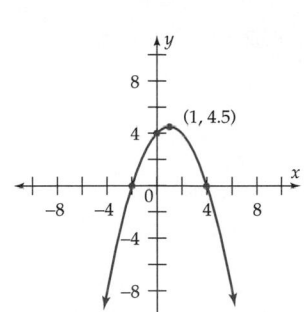

Figure 3.3-4

Changing from One Form to Another

It is sometimes necessary to change a quadratic function from one form to another. To change either transformation or x-intercept form to polynomial form, distribute and collect like terms. To change either polynomial or transformation form to x-intercept form, factor out the leading coefficient, then factor or use the quadratic formula to find the x-intercepts.

Example 4   Changing to Polynomial and x-Intercept Form

Write the following functions in polynomial and x-intercept form, if possible.

a. $f(x) = 0.4(x - 3)^2 + 2$
b. $g(x) = 3x^2 - 3.9x - 43.2$
c. $h(x) = -2(x - 4)(x + 2)$

Solution

a. To change the function f to polynomial form, distribute and collect like terms.

$$f(x) = 0.4(x - 3)^2 + 2$$
$$f(x) = 0.4(x^2 - 6x + 9) + 2$$
$$f(x) = 0.4x^2 - 2.4x + 5.6$$

Since $b^2 - 4ac = -3.2$ is negative, there are no x-intercepts. Thus, the function f cannot be written in x-intercept form.

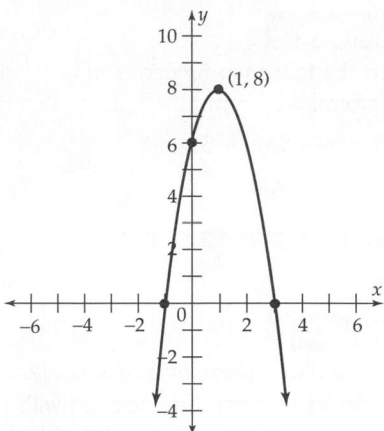

Example 4

Write the following functions in polynomial and x-intercept form, if possible.

a. $f(x) = 0.3(x - 2)^2 + 5$
To get polynomial form, distribute and collect like terms:
$f(x) = 0.3(x - 2)^2 + 5$
$f(x) = 0.3(x^2 - 4x + 4) + 5$
$f(x) = 0.3x^2 - 1.2x + 6.2$
Since $b^2 - 4ac = -6$ is negative, there are no intercepts, and the function cannot be written in x-intercept form.

b. $g(x) = 2x^2 - 5.8x - 27$
The function g is already given in polynomial form.
To get x-intercept form, factor out the 2 and find the x-intercepts:
$g(x) = 2x^2 + 5.8x - 27$
$g(x) = 2(x^2 + 2.9x - 13.5)$

x-intercepts:
$$\frac{-2.9 \pm \sqrt{(2.9)^2 - 4(1)(-13.5)}}{2(1)}$$
$$= \frac{-2.9 \pm 7.9}{2} = 2.5 \text{ and } -5.4$$
$g(x) = 2(x - 2.5)(x + 5.4)$

c. $h(x) = -3(x - 6)(x + 1)$
The function h is already given in x-intercept form.
To get polynomial form, distribute and collect like terms:
$h(x) = -3(x - 6)(x + 1)$
$h(x) = -3(x^2 - 5x - 6)$
$h(x) = -3x^2 + 15x + 18$

ADDITIONAL EXAMPLES

Example 5

Write the following functions in transformation form.

a. $f(x) = -5x^2 + 6x - 1$

$f(x) = -5\left(x - \dfrac{3}{5}\right)^2 + \dfrac{4}{5}$

b. $g(x) = 0.2(x - 3)(x + 2)$

$g(x) = 0.2(x - 0.5)^2 - 1.25$

Example 6

Find the dimensions of a rectangular parking lot that can be enclosed with 2400 feet of fence and that has the largest possible area.

600 ft by 600 ft

COMMON ERROR ALERT

Students often make sign errors when completing the square. In the Solution for **Example 5a,** students may forget to include $-\dfrac{4}{9}$ inside the parentheses, leading to the following error:

$-3\left(x^2 - \dfrac{4}{3}x + \dfrac{4}{9} - \dfrac{4}{9}\right) - 1$

$= -3\left(x - \dfrac{2}{3}\right)^2 - \dfrac{4}{9} - 1 \ [\textit{incorrect}]$

The correct steps are:

$-3\left(x^2 - \dfrac{4}{3}x + \dfrac{4}{9} - \dfrac{4}{9}\right) - 1$

$= -3\left(\left(x - \dfrac{2}{3}\right)^2 - \dfrac{4}{9}\right) - 1$

$= -3\left(x - \dfrac{2}{3}\right)^2 + \dfrac{4}{3} - 1 \ [\textit{correct}]$

---

b. The function g is already given in polynomial form. To find the x-intercept form, first factor out $a = 3$, then use the quadratic formula on the remaining expression.

$$g(x) = 3x^2 - 3.9x - 43.2$$
$$g(x) = 3(x^2 - 1.3x - 14.4)$$

x-intercepts:

$$\dfrac{1.3 \pm \sqrt{(-1.3)^2 - 4(1)(-14.4)}}{2} = \dfrac{1.3 \pm 7.7}{2} = 4.5 \text{ and } -3.2$$

So the x-intercept form is

$$g(x) = 3(x - 4.5)(x + 3.2)$$

c. The function h is already given in x-intercept form. To change the function to polynomial form, distribute and collect like terms.

$$h(x) = -2(x - 4)(x + 2)$$
$$h(x) = -2(x^2 - 2x - 8)$$
$$h(x) = -2x^2 + 4x + 16$$

To convert a quadratic function to transformation form, it may be necessary to complete the square.

Example 5 **Changing to Transformation Form**

Write the following functions in transformation form.

a. $f(x) = -3x^2 + 4x - 1$

b. $g(x) = 0.3(x - 2)(x + 1)$

Solution

a. Factor $a = -3$ out of the first two terms, then complete the square as shown below.

$f(x) = -3x^2 + 4x - 1$

$\quad = -3\left(x^2 - \dfrac{4}{3}x\right) - 1$ *Factor 3 out of first two terms*

$\quad = -3\left(x^2 - \dfrac{4}{3}x + \dfrac{4}{9} - \dfrac{4}{9}\right) - 1$ *Add and subtract* $\left(\dfrac{b}{2}\right)^2$

$\quad = -3\left(\left(x - \dfrac{2}{3}\right)^2 - \dfrac{4}{9}\right) - 1$ *Write* $x^2 - \dfrac{4}{3}x + \dfrac{4}{9}$ *as a perfect square*

$\quad = -3\left(x - \dfrac{2}{3}\right)^2 + \dfrac{4}{3} - 1$ *Distribute the -3 over the* $-\dfrac{4}{9}$

$f(x) = -3\left(x - \dfrac{2}{3}\right)^2 + \dfrac{1}{3}$ *Combine like terms*

b. Multiply the terms in parentheses, then complete the square as shown below.

$$
\begin{aligned}
g(x) &= 0.3(x - 2)(x + 1) \\
&= 0.3(x^2 - x - 2) && \textit{Multiply} \\
&= 0.3(x^2 - x + 0.25 - 0.25 - 2) && \textit{Add and subtract } \left(\tfrac{b}{2}\right)^2 \\
&= 0.3((x - 0.5)^2 - 0.25 - 2) && \textit{Write } x^2 - x + 0.25 \textit{ as a perfect square} \\
&= 0.3((x - 0.5)^2 - 2.25) && \textit{Combine like terms} \\
g(x) &= 0.3(x - 0.5)^2 - 0.675 && \textit{Distribute the 0.3 over the } -2.25
\end{aligned}
$$

Summary of Quadratic Forms

Summary of Quadratic Functions

Below is a summary of the basic forms and the important points of a quadratic function. You should memorize the highlighted items.

Name	Transformation	Polynomial	x-Intercept
Form	$f(x) = a(x - h)^2 + k$	$f(x) = ax^2 + bx + c$	$f(x) = a(x - s)(x - t)$
Vertex	(h, k)	$\left(\dfrac{-b}{2a}, f\left(\dfrac{-b}{2a}\right)\right)$	$\left(\dfrac{s + t}{2}, f\left(\dfrac{s + t}{2}\right)\right)$
x-Intercepts	$h + \sqrt{\dfrac{-k}{a}}$ and $h - \sqrt{\dfrac{-k}{a}}$	$\dfrac{-b + \sqrt{b^2 - 4ac}}{2a}$ and $\dfrac{-b - \sqrt{b^2 - 4ac}}{2a}$	s and t
y-Intercept	$ah^2 + k$	c	ast

Applications

In the graph of a quadratic function, the vertex of the parabola is either a maximum or a minimum of the function. Thus, the solution of many applications depends on finding the vertex of the parabola.

Example 6   Maximum Area for a Fixed Perimeter

Find the dimensions of a rectangular field that can be enclosed with 3000 feet of fence and that has the largest possible area.

Solution

Let x denote the length and y the width of the field, as shown in Figure 3.3-5.

$$
\begin{aligned}
\text{Perimeter} &= x + x + y + y = 2x + 2y \\
\text{Area} &= xy
\end{aligned}
$$

Figure 3.3-5

Real-World Application

Example 6 is about maximizing area when the perimeter is fixed. This is one of many types of problems encountered by landscape architects. They also need to know sun, soil, and water requirements for different plant species to help them determine what plants are suitable for certain locations. Another concern is how to obtain the desired functional utility from a design while causing the least possible disturbance to the environment.

Example Notes

In **Example 6**, you might want to ask the students to supply the missing steps for the derivation of $A(x)$ at the top of page 170. The additional steps are shown below in red.

$$
\begin{aligned}
2x + 2y &= 3000 \\
2(x + y) &= 3000 \\
x + y &= 1500 \\
y &= 1500 - x
\end{aligned}
$$

$$
\begin{aligned}
A(x) &= xy \\
&= x(1500 - x) \\
&= 1500x - x^2 \\
&= -x^2 + 1500x
\end{aligned}
$$

Math Background

Maximum Area for a Fixed Perimeter is a classic optimization problem in calculus. When applied to a rectangle, as in **Example 6**, the rectangle with the largest possible area is always a square. You can illustrate this concept by sketching rectangles with the following dimensions on the board: 1 by 5, 2 by 4, 3 by 3.

They all have perimeter 12, but the 3-by-3 rectangle has the largest area.

In **Example 7**, remind students that x represents the number of 10¢ price increases. The table below may help students understand how to get the profit function $P(x)$:

# sold	profit
275	275(0.50)
$275 - 25 \cdot 1$	$(275 - 25 \cdot 1)(0.50 + 0.10)$
$275 - 25 \cdot 2$	$(275 - 25 \cdot 2)(0.50 + 0.20)$
$\vdots$	$\vdots$
$275 - 25 \cdot x$	$(275 - 25 \cdot x)(0.50 + 0.10x)$

ADDITIONAL EXAMPLES

Example 7

The owner of a concession stand can sell 150 lunches per day at a price of $3 each. The cost to the owner is $2.25 per lunch. Each $0.25 price increase decreases sales by 30 lunches per day. What price should be charged to maximize profit?

$$P(x) = (0.25x + 0.75)(-30x + 150)$$
$$= -7.5(x + 3)(x + 5)$$

vertex of parabola: $x = \dfrac{-3 + 5}{2} = 1$

1 price increase

To maximize profit, charge $3.25 per lunch.

Exercises 3.3

ANSWERS

5. y-intercept $= 3$
The parabola opens upward.

6. y-intercept $= -1$
The parabola opens upward.

7. y-intercept $= 5$
The parabola opens downward.

8. y-intercept $= -1$
The parabola opens upward.

The perimeter is the length of the fence, or 3000.

$$2x + 2y = 3000$$
$$y = 1500 - x$$

The area of the field is

$$A(x) = xy = x(1500 - x) = -x^2 + 1500x$$

The graph of the function A is a parabola that opens downward, so the maximum occurs at the vertex. The function is in polynomial form, so the vertex occurs when $x = \dfrac{-b}{2a} = \dfrac{-1500}{2(-1)} = 750$.

The largest possible area is 562,500 ft², which occurs when $x = 750$ and $y = 1500 - 750 = 750$. The dimensions of the field are 750 by 750 ft.

Example 7   Maximizing Profit

A vendor can sell 275 souvenirs per day at a price of $2 each. The cost to the vendor is $1.50 per souvenir. Each 10¢ price increase decreases sales by 25 per day. What price should be charged to maximize profit?

Solution

Let x be the number of 10¢ price increases. Then the profit on each souvenir is $0.50 + $0.10x, and the number of souvenirs sold per day is $275 - 25x$. Thus, the profit per day is

$$P(x) = (0.1x + 0.5)(-25x + 275)$$

or, in x-intercept form,

$$P(x) = -2.5(x + 5)(x - 11)$$

The graph is a parabola that opens downward, so the maximum occurs at the vertex. The function is in x-intercept form, so the vertex occurs when

$$x = \dfrac{s + t}{2} = \dfrac{-5 + 11}{2} = 3.$$

The maximum profit of $160 per day occurs for 3 price increases, so the price should be $2 + 3($0.10) = $2.30 per souvenir.

Exercises 3.3

In Exercises 1–4, determine the vertex of the given quadratic function and state whether its graph opens upward or downward.

1. $f(x) = 3(x - 5)^2 + 2$
(5, 2), upward

2. $g(x) = -6(x - 2)^2 - 5$
(2, −5), downward

3. $f(x) = -(x - 1)^2 + 2$
(1, 2), downward

4. $h(x) = -x^2 + 1$
(0, 1), downward

In Exercises 5–8, determine the y-intercept of the given quadratic function and state whether its graph opens upward or downward.

5. $f(x) = x^2 - 6x + 3$

6. $g(x) = x^2 + 8x - 1$

7. $h(x) = -3x^2 + 4x + 5$

8. $g(x) = 2x^2 - x - 1$

In Exercises 9–12, determine the x-intercepts of the given quadratic function and state whether its graph opens upward or downward.

9. $f(x) = (x - 2)(x + 3)$
 $x = 2;\ x = -3;$ **upward**
10. $h(x) = -2(x + 3)(x + 1)$
 $x = -3;\ x = -1;$ **downward**
11. $g(x) = \frac{1}{3}\left(x - \frac{3}{4}\right)\left(x - \frac{1}{2}\right)$ $x = \frac{3}{4};\ x = \frac{1}{2};$ **upward**

12. $f(x) = -0.4(x + 2.1)(x - 0.7)$
 $x = -2.1;\ x = 0.7;$ **downward**

In Exercises 13–21, determine the vertex and x- and y-intercepts of the given quadratic function, and sketch a graph.

13. $f(x) = 2(x + 3)^2 - 4$ **14.** $g(x) = -\frac{1}{2}(x + 4)^2 + 2$

15. $h(x) = (x + 1)^2 + 4$ **16.** $f(x) = x^2 - 6x + 3$

17. $h(x) = -x^2 + 8x - 2$ **18.** $f(x) = 2x^2 - 4x + 2$

19. $g(x) = (x + 1)(x - 3)$ **20.** $h(x) = -(x + 2)(x + 6)$

21. $g(x) = 2(x - 3)(x + 4)$

Write the following functions in polynomial form.

22. $f(x) = 3(x - 2)(x + 1)$ $f(x) = 3x^2 - 3x - 6$

23. $g(x) = -2(x - 5)(x - 2)$ $g(x) = -2x^2 + 14x - 20$

24. $h(x) = 3(x - 4)^2 - 47$ $h(x) = 3x^2 - 24x + 1$

25. $f(x) = -\frac{1}{2}(x + 4)^2 - 5$ $f(x) = -\frac{1}{2}x^2 - 4x - 13$

Write the following functions in x-intercept form.

26. $f(x) = x^2 - 3x - 4$ **27.** $h(x) = -2x^2 + 13x + 7$
$f(x) = (x - 4)(x + 1)$ $h(x) = -(2x + 1)(x - 7)$
28. $g(x) = 3(x + 3)^2 - 3$ **29.** $f(x) = 6\left(x - \frac{2}{3}\right)^2 - \frac{2}{3}$

$g(x) = 3(x + 2)(x + 4)$ $f(x) = 2(3x - 1)(x - 1)$
Write the following functions in transformation form.

30. $g(x) = x^2 + 4x - 5$ **31.** $f(x) = -3x^2 + 6x - 1$
$g(x) = (x + 2)^2 - 9$ $f(x) = -3(x - 1)^2 + 2$
32. $h(x) = -(x - 4)(x + 2)$
$h(x) = -(x - 1)^2 + 9$
33. $g(x) = 2(x - 1)(x + 6)$ $g(x) = 2\left(x + \frac{5}{2}\right)^2 - \frac{49}{2}$

34. Write a rule in transformation form for the quadratic function whose graph is the parabola with vertex at the origin that passes through (2, 12).

$f(x) = 3x^2$

35. Write a rule in transformation form for the quadratic function whose graph is the parabola with vertex (0, 1) that passes through (2, −7).
 $f(x) = -2x^2 + 1$
36. Find the number c such that the vertex of $f(x) = x^2 + 8x + c$ lies on the x-axis. $c = 16$

37. If the vertex of $f(x) = x^2 + bx + c$ is at (2, 4), find b and c. $b = -4,\ c = 8$

38. If the vertex of $f(x) = -x^2 + bx + 8$ has y-coordinate 17 and is in the second quadrant, find b. $b = -6$

39. Find the number b such that the vertex of $f(x) = x^2 + bx + c$ lies on the y-axis. $b = 0$

40. If the vertex of $f(x) = a(x - s)(x - 4)$ has x-coordinate 7, find s. $s = 10$

41. If the y-intercept of $f(x) = a(x - 3)(x + 2)$ is 3, find a. $a = -\frac{1}{2}$

42. Find two numbers whose sum is −18 and whose product is the maximum.   **Maximum product is 81; numbers are both −9**
43. Find two numbers whose difference is 4 and whose product is the minimum.   **Minimum product is −4; numbers are 2 and −2**
44. The sum of the height h and the base b of a triangle is 30. What height and base will produce a triangle of maximum area?
Height is 15 and base is 15
45. A field bounded on one side by a river is to be fenced on three sides to form a rectangular enclosure. If the total length of fence is 200 feet, what dimensions will give an enclosure of maximum area?
Two 50-ft sides and one 100-ft side
46. A salesperson finds that her sales average 40 cases per store when she visits 20 stores per week. If she visits an additional store per week, her average sales per store decrease by one case. How many stores per week should she visit to maximize her sales?   **30 stores**

47. A potter can sell 120 bowls per week at $4 per bowl. For each 50¢ decrease in price, 20 more bowls are sold. What price should be charged in order to maximize revenue?   **$3.50**

48. When a basketball team charges $4 per ticket, average attendance is 400 people. For each 20¢ decrease in ticket price, average attendance increases by 40 people. What should the ticket price be to maximize revenue?   **$3.00**

13. Vertex is $(-3, -4)$.
 y-intercept = 14
 The x-intercepts are
 $x = -3 + \sqrt{2}$,
 $x = -3 - \sqrt{2}$ or $x \approx -1.586$, -4.414.

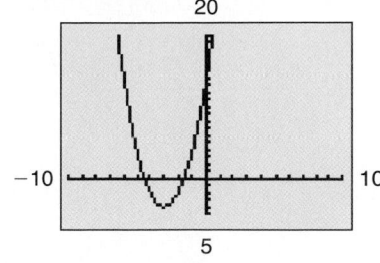

14. Vertex is $(-4, 2)$.
 y-intercept = -6
 The x-intercepts are -2 and -6.

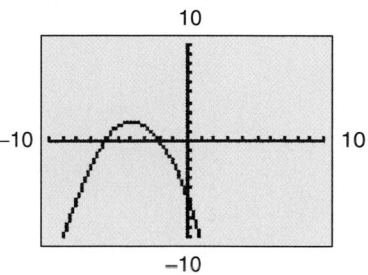

15. Vertex is $(-1, 4)$.
 y-intercept = 5
 There are no x-intercepts.

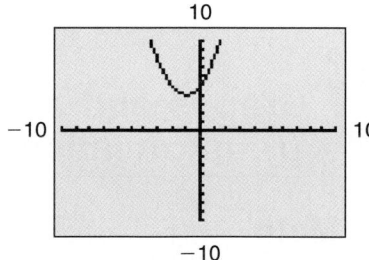

16. Vertex is $(3, -6)$.
 y-intercept = 3
 The x-intercepts are approximately 5.449 and 0.551.

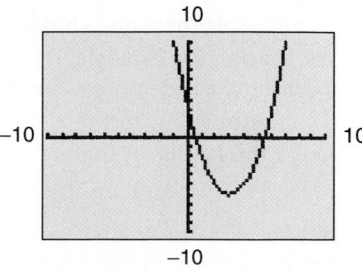

17–21. *For graphs see pp.* **1057–1058.**

17. Vertex is $(4, 14)$.
 y-intercept = -2
 The x-intercepts are approximately 0.258 and 7.742.

18. Vertex is $(1, 0)$.
 y-intercept = 2
 The only x-intercept is 1.

19. Vertex is $(1, -4)$.
 y-intercept = -3
 The x-intercepts are -1 and 3.

20. Vertex is $(-4, 4)$.
 y-intercept = -12
 The x-intercepts are -2 and -6.

21. Vertex is $(-0.5, -24.5)$.
 y-intercept = -24
 The x-intercepts are 3 and -4.

49. A ballpark concessions manager finds that each vendor sells an average of 40 boxes of popcorn per game when 20 vendors are working. For every additional vendor, each averages 1 fewer box sold per game. How many vendors should be hired to maximize sales? **30 vendors**

In Exercises 50–53, use the following equation for the height (in feet) of an object moving along a vertical line after t seconds:

$$s = -16t^2 + v_0 t + s_0$$

where s_0 is the initial height (in ft) and v_0 is the initial velocity (in ft/sec). The velocity is positive if it is traveling upward, and negative if it is traveling downward.

50. A rocket is fired upward from ground level with an initial velocity of 1600 ft/sec. When does the rocket reach its maximum height and how high is it at that time?
50 seconds; 40,000 feet

51. A ball is thrown upward from a height of 6 ft with an initial velocity of 32 ft/sec. When does the ball reach its maximum height and how high is it at that time?
1 second; 22 feet

52. A ball is thrown upward from the top of a 96-ft tower with an initial velocity of 80 ft/sec. When does the ball reach its maximum height and how high is it at that time?
2.5 seconds; 196 feet

53. A bullet is fired upward from ground level with an initial velocity of 1500 ft/sec. When does the bullet reach its maximum height and how high is it at that time?
46.875 seconds; 35,156.25 feet

54. *Critical Thinking* The *discriminant* of a quadratic function $f(x) = ax^2 + bx + c$ is the value $b^2 - 4ac$. For each value of the discriminant listed, state which graphs below could possibly be the graph of f. **(ii) or (iv)**
a. $b^2 - 4ac = 25$ **b.** $b^2 - 4ac = 0$ **(i)**
c. $b^2 - 4ac = -49$ **d.** $b^2 - 4ac = 72$
(iii)   **(ii) or (iv)**

(i)

(ii)

(iii)

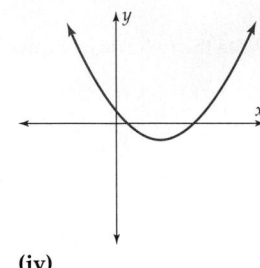
(iv)

Section
3.4 **Graphs and Transformations**

 Math Background

The rule of a **Parent Function** can be changed to produce a *family of functions*. A family of functions consists of functions that have a common algebraic form and similar geometric shapes. For example, the family of functions $f(x) = a(x - h)^2 + k$ has the parent function $f(x) = x^2$. Members of the family include $f(x) = -x^2$, $f(x) = \frac{1}{4}x^2$, and $f(x) = 2(x + 3)^2 - 1$. The graphs of all the members of the family are parabolas.

3.4 # Graphs and Transformations

Objectives
- Define parent functions
- Transform graphs of parent functions

When the rule of a function is algebraically changed in certain ways to produce a new function, then the graph of the new function can be obtained from the graph of the original function by a simple geometric transformation.

Parent Functions

The functions on the next page are often called **parent functions**. A parent function is a function with a certain shape that has the simplest algebraic rule for that shape. For example, $f(x) = x^2$ is the simplest rule for a parabola. You should memorize the basic shapes of the parent functions.

Teaching Notes

To help students memorize the **Parent Functions** and their shapes:
- Have students copy the equations and their graphs on paper to use for review.
- Make a transparency of the functions to use for reference.
- Make a bulletin board display of the functions and their graphs.

You may want to tell the students that there are many functions other than those shown here that can be considered to be parent functions.

Math Background

The terms *parent function* and *family of functions* do not have precise mathematical definitions, but their meanings are intuitive. By studying parent functions and their families, we see that:
- algebraic similarities result in graphs with common characteristics (for example, all quadratic functions have x^2 as the highest-degree term, and they all have U-shaped graphs called parabolas).
- algebraic differences result in geometric transformations of those graphs (for example, the graph of $f(x) = 2x^2$ is a vertical stretch of the graph of $f(x) = x^2$.

Parent functions and associated families occur under many different categories of functions — exponential, logarithmic, and trigonometric are some examples. A trigonometric function that is sometimes called a parent function is $f(x) = \sin x$ (or $h(t) = \sin t$, page 475). One of the "family members" is $g(t) = -\frac{1}{2}\sin t$ (page 481), whose graph is a reflection and vertical compression of $h(t) = \sin t$.

> **NOTE** The points $(0, 0)$ and $(1, 1)$ are labeled for reference in each case. The origin is not on the graph of the constant or reciprocal function.

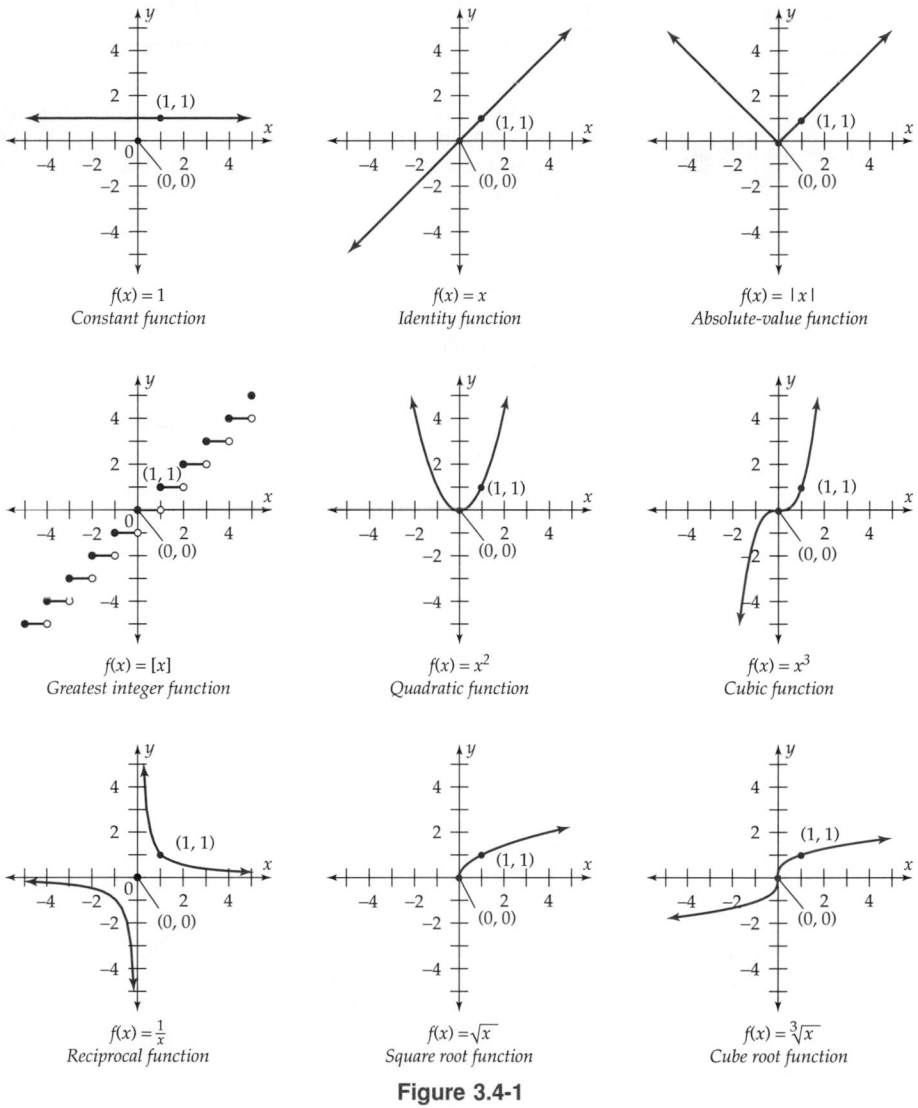

$f(x) = 1$
Constant function

$f(x) = x$
Identity function

$f(x) = |x|$
Absolute-value function

$f(x) = [x]$
Greatest integer function

$f(x) = x^2$
Quadratic function

$f(x) = x^3$
Cubic function

$f(x) = \frac{1}{x}$
Reciprocal function

$f(x) = \sqrt{x}$
Square root function

$f(x) = \sqrt[3]{x}$
Cube root function

Figure 3.4-1

The parent functions will be used to illustrate the rules for the basic transformations. Remember, however, that these transformation rules work for *all* functions.

Teaching Notes

Solution to the **Graphing Exploration**:

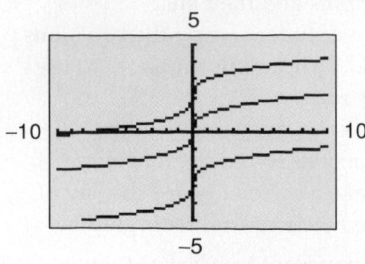

functions top to bottom: g, f, h
possible answer: The graph of g is the same as the graph of f moved up 2 units. The graph of h is the same as the graph of f moved down 3 units.

Ask the students to identify the parent function in the Graphing Exploration. $f(x) = \sqrt[3]{x}$

Note that the shifts of f upward and downward are vertical translations of f.

Point out to the students the benefits of the **Technology Tips** (page 174 and page 175). If they enter a function as Y_1, and then use Y_1 to define other functions, it will save them a lot of keystrokes and reduce the chance of errors.

ADDITIONAL EXAMPLES

Example 1

Graph $g(x) = x^2 - 4$ and $h(x) = x^2 + 3$ and state the parent function. The parent function is $f(x) = x^2$.

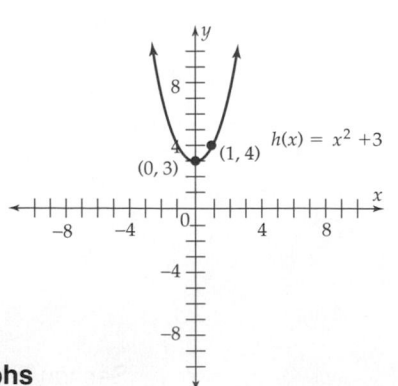

Technology Tip

If the function f is entered as Y_1, then the function

$$g(x) = f(x) + c$$

can be entered in Y_2 as $Y_1 + C$ and the function

$$g(x) = f(x) - c$$

can be entered in Y_3 as $Y_1 - C$.

Vertical Shifts

Vertical Shifts

Graphing Exploration

Graph these functions on the same screen and describe your results.

$$f(x) = \sqrt[3]{x} \qquad g(x) = \sqrt[3]{x} + 2 \qquad h(x) = \sqrt[3]{x} - 3$$

Notice that when a value is added to $f(x)$, the effect is to add the value to the y-coordinate of each point. The result is to shift every point on the graph by the same amount. A similar result is true for subtracting a value from $f(x)$.

> **Let c be a positive number.**
>
> **The graph of $g(x) = f(x) + c$ is the graph of f shifted upward c units.**
>
> **The graph of $g(x) = f(x) - c$ is the graph of f shifted downward c units.**

Example 1 Shifting a Graph Vertically

Graph $g(x) = |x| + 4$ and $h(x) = |x| - 3$.

Solution

The parent function is $f(x) = |x|$. The graph of $g(x)$ is the graph of $f(x) = |x|$ shifted upward 4 units, and the graph of $h(x)$ is the graph of $f(x) = |x|$ shifted downward 3 units.

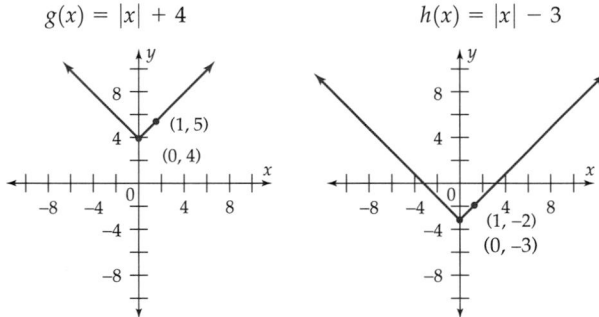

Figure 3.4-2

Technology Tip

If the function f is entered as Y_1, then the function

$$g(x) = f(x + c)$$

can be entered in Y_2 as $Y_1(X + C)$ and the function

$$g(x) = f(c - x)$$

can be entered in Y_3 as $Y_1(X - C)$.

Horizontal Shifts

> ### Graphing Exploration
>
> Graph these functions on the same screen and describe your results.
>
> $$f(x) = x^2 \qquad g(x) = (x - 1)^2 \qquad h(x) = (x + 3)^2$$

A table of values is helpful in visualizing the direction of a horizontal shift.

x	-3	-2	-1	0	1	2	3	4	5
$x - 1$	-4	-3	-2	-1	0	1	2	3	4
x^2	9	4	1	0	1	4	9	16	25
$(x - 1)^2$	16	9	4	1	0	1	4	9	16

When 1 is subtracted from the x-values, the result is that the entries in the table shift 1 position to the right. Thus, the entire graph is shifted 1 unit to the right. Construct a table for $h(x) = (x + 3)^2$ to see that the entries shift 3 positions to the left.

Horizontal Shifts

> Let c be a positive number.
>
> The graph of $g(x) = f(x + c)$ is the graph of f shifted c units to the left.
>
> The graph of $g(x) = f(x - c)$ is the graph of f shifted c units to the right.

Example 2   Shifting a Graph Horizontally

Graph $g(x) = \dfrac{1}{x - 3}$ and $h(x) = \dfrac{1}{x + 4}$.

Solution

The parent function is $f(x) = \dfrac{1}{x}$. The graph of $g(x)$ is the graph of $f(x) = \dfrac{1}{x}$ shifted 3 units to the right and the graph of $h(x)$ is the graph of $f(x) = \dfrac{1}{x}$ shifted 4 units to the left.

The paragraph just before the **Horizontal Shifts** box suggests that the reader construct a table for $h(x) = (x + 3)^2$. The table is shown below.

x	-3	-2	-1	0	1	2	3
$x + 3$	0	1	2	3	4	5	6
x^2	9	4	1	0	1	4	9
$(x + 3)^2$	0	1	4	9	16	25	36

COMMON ERROR ALERT

Some students may make horizontal shifts in the wrong direction. Stress that, if c is a positive number, $f(x + c)$ is a shift to the left and $f(x - c)$ is a shift to the right.

Example 2

Graph $g(x) = \sqrt{x - 3}$ and $h(x) = \sqrt{x + 2}$ and state the parent function.

The parent function is $f(x) = \sqrt{x}$.

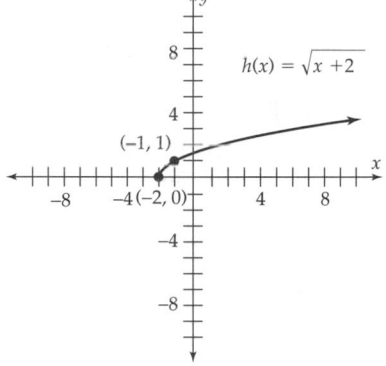

Teaching Notes

Solution to the **Graphing Exploration**:

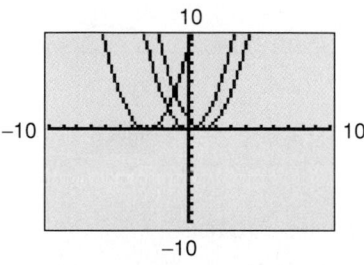

functions left to right: h, f, g
possible answer: The graph of g is the same as the graph of f moved right 1 unit. The graph of h is the same as the graph of f moved left 3 units.

Teaching Notes

Point out to students that although the graphs of g and h in Figure 3.4-3 appear to touch the x-axis, they do not. Show them that $\dfrac{1}{x-3}$ cannot equal 0.

Solution to the **Graphing Exploration:**

Example Notes

For **Example 3**, it would be very helpful to show f and g on the same coordinate system (see right); students will be able to see that g is the reflection of f over the x-axis. Point out that the black segment from $(0, 0)$ to $(1, 0)$ is the image of itself.

Likewise, showing f and h on the same coordinate system will help students see that h is the reflection of f over the y-axis.

$$g(x) = \frac{1}{x-3} \qquad\qquad h(x) = \frac{1}{x+4}$$

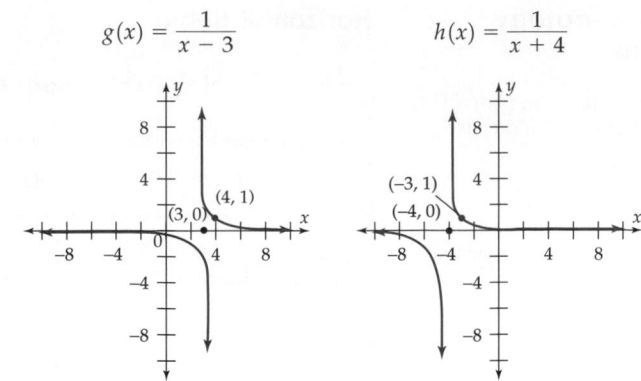

Figure 3.4-3

Reflections

Technology Tip

If the function f is entered as Y_1, then the function

$$g(x) = -f(x)$$

can be entered in Y_2 as $-Y_1$ and the function

$$g(x) = f(-x)$$

can be entered in Y_3 as $Y_1(-X)$.

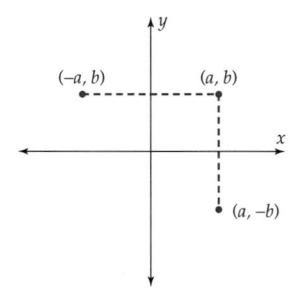

Figure 3.4-4

Graphing Exploration

Graph these functions on the same screen.

$$f(x) = \sqrt{x} \qquad g(x) = -\sqrt{x}$$

Use the TRACE feature to verify that for every point on the graph of f there is a point on the graph of g with the same x-coordinate and opposite y-coordinate.

Graph these functions on the same screen.

$$f(x) = \sqrt{x} \qquad h(x) = \sqrt{-x}$$

Use the TRACE feature to verify that for every point on the graph of f there is a point on the graph of h with the same y-coordinate and opposite x-coordinate.

The results of the first part of the Graphing Exploration show that in the functions $f(x) = \sqrt{x}$ and $g(x) = -\sqrt{x}$, if the point (a, b) is on the graph of f, then the point $(a, -b)$ is on the graph of g. These two points are reflections of each other across the x-axis, as shown in Figure 3.4-4.

In the second part of the Graphing Exploration, the results show that in the functions $f(x) = \sqrt{x}$ and $h(x) = \sqrt{-x}$, if the point (a, b) is on the graph of f, then the point $(-a, b)$ is on the graph of h. These two points are reflections of each other across the y-axis, as shown in Figure 3.4-4.

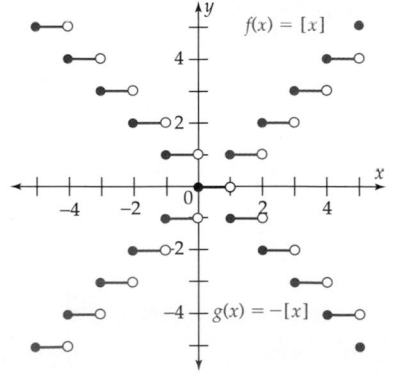

Reflections

The graph of $g(x) = -f(x)$ is the graph of f reflected across the x-axis.

The graph of $g(x) = f(-x)$ is the graph of f reflected across the y-axis.

Example 3

Example 3 Reflecting a Graph Across the x- or y-Axis

Graph $g(x) = -[x]$ and $h(x) = [-x]$.

Solution

The parent function is $f(x) = [x]$. The graph of $g(x)$ is the graph of $f(x) = [x]$ reflected across the x-axis, and the graph of $h(x)$ is the graph of $f(x) = [x]$ reflected across the y-axis. One difference in the reflections is whether the endpoint of each segment is included on the left or on the right. Study the functions closely, along with the parent function, to determine another difference in the two reflections.

Figure 3.4-5

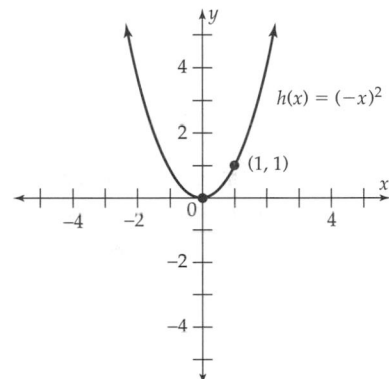

Technology Tip

If the function f is entered as Y_1, then the function

$$g(x) = c \cdot f(x)$$

can be entered in Y_2 as $C \cdot Y_1$ and the function

$$g(x) = f(c \cdot x)$$

can be entered in Y_3 as $Y_1(C \cdot X)$.

Stretches and Compressions

Graphing Exploration

Graph these functions on the same screen.

$$f(x) = \sqrt{x} \qquad g(x) = \sqrt{3x} \qquad h(x) = 3\sqrt{x}$$

Use the **TRACE** feature to locate the y-value on each graph when $x = 1$. Describe your results. Predict the graph of $j(x) = 4\sqrt{x}$.

Teaching Notes

Solution to the **Graphing Exploration**:

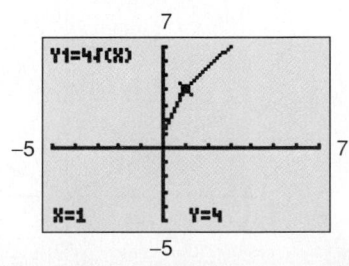

Possible answer: $f(1) < g(1) < h(1)$

Example Notes

In **Example 4**, show how the parent function $f(x) = x^3$ is stretched and compressed vertically (with respect to the *x*-axis) by graphing *f*, *g*, and *h* on the same set of axes as shown below. Show points on the graph with the same *x*-coordinate.

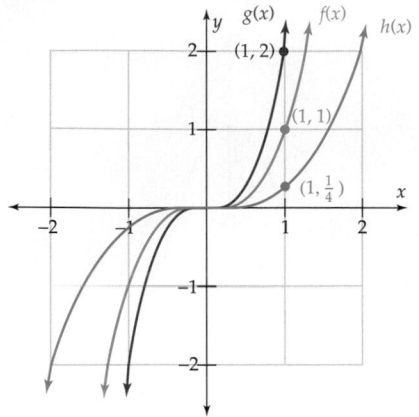

In **Example 5**, get students to recognize that:

- $g(x) = 2[x]$ is a vertical stretch of $f(x) = [x]$, away from the *x*-axis, by a factor of 2.
- $h(x) = [2x]$ is a horizontal compression of $f(x) = [x]$, toward the *y*-axis, by a factor of $\frac{1}{2}$.

Point out that if the point (1, 1) is on the graph of *f*, then the point $(1, 2 \cdot 1)$, or (1, 2), is on the graph of *g* and the point $\left(\frac{1}{2} \cdot 1, 1\right)$, or $\left(\frac{1}{2}, 1\right)$, is on the graph of *h*.

ADDITIONAL EXAMPLES

Example 4

Graph $g(x) = 2|x|$ and $h(x) = \frac{1}{2}|x|$ and state the parent function. The parent function is $f(x) = |x|$.

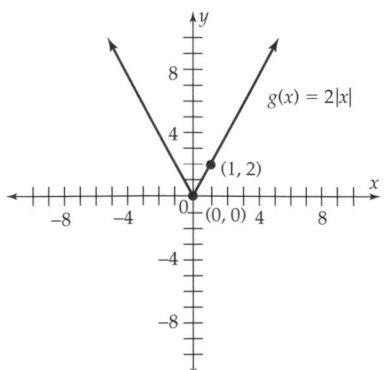

In addition to reflections and shifts, graphs of functions may be stretched or compressed, either vertically or horizontally. The following example illustrates the difference between a vertical stretch and compression.

Example 4   Vertically Stretching and Compressing a Graph

Graph $g(x) = 2x^3$ and $h(x) = \frac{1}{4}x^3$.

Solution

The parent function is $f(x) = x^3$. For the function $g(x) = 2x^3$, every *y*-coordinate of the parent function is multiplied by 2, stretching the graph of the function in the vertical direction, away from the *x*-axis. For the function $h(x) = \frac{1}{4}x^3$, every *y*-coordinate of the parent function is multiplied by $\frac{1}{4}$, compressing the graph of the function in the vertical direction, toward the *x*-axis.

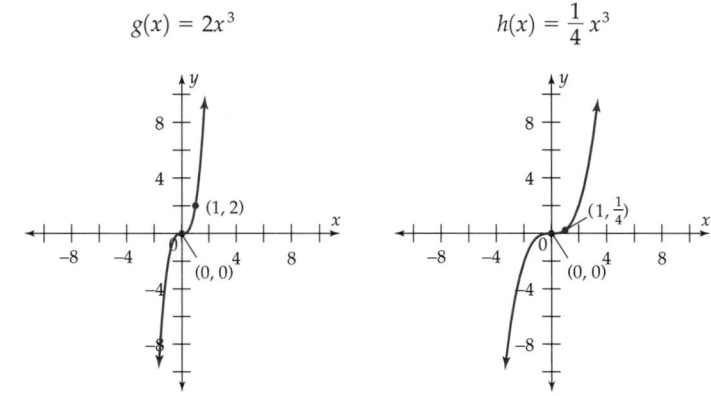

Figure 3.4-6

The following example illustrates the difference between a vertical and a horizontal stretch.

Example 5   Stretching a Function Vertically and Horizontally

Graph $g(x) = 2[x]$ and $h(x) = [2x]$.

Solution

The parent function is $f(x) = [x]$. In $g(x) = 2[x]$, the *y*-values are multiplied by 2, and in $h(x) = [2x]$, the *x*-values are multiplied by 2. The result is that in the graph of the first function, the "steps" get higher, and in the graph of the second function, they get narrower.

$g(x) = 2[x]$

$h(x) = [2x]$

Figure 3.4-7

Stretches and Compressions

> Let c be a positive number.
>
> **Vertical Stretches and Compressions**
>
> If (x, y) is a point on the graph of $f(x)$, then (x, cy) is a point on the graph of $g(x) = c \cdot f(x)$.
>
> If $c > 1$, the graph of $g(x) = c \cdot f(x)$ is the graph of f stretched vertically, away from the x-axis, by a factor of c.
>
> If $c < 1$, the graph of $g(x) = c \cdot f(x)$ is the graph of f compressed vertically, toward the x-axis, by a factor of c.
>
> **Horizontal Stretches and Compressions**
>
> If (x, y) is a point on the graph of $f(x)$, then $\left(\frac{1}{c}x, y\right)$ is a point on the graph of $g(x) = f(c \cdot x)$.
>
> If $c > 1$, the graph of $g(x) = f(c \cdot x)$ is the graph of f compressed horizontally, toward the y-axis, by a factor of $\frac{1}{c}$.
>
> If $c < 1$, the graph of $g(x) = f(c \cdot x)$ is the graph of f stretched horizontally, away from the y-axis, by a factor of $\frac{1}{c}$.

NOTE Some horizontal compressions can be expressed as vertical stretches, and vice versa. The graph of the function g below can be obtained from a horizontal compression of $f(x) = x^2$ by a factor of $\frac{1}{3}$ or from a vertical stretch by a factor of 9.

$$g(x) = (3x)^2 = 3^2x^2 = 9x^2$$

This is not possible for the greatest integer function (see Example 5) or trigonometric functions, which you will study in later chapters.

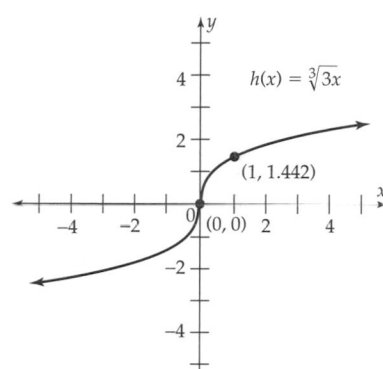

Example 6

Graph $g(x) = -(3x - 12)^2 + 2$.

Rewrite $g(x) = -(3x - 12)^2 + 2$ as $g(x) = -(3(x - 4))^2 + 2$. The parent function is $f(x) = x^2$.

Compress horizontally by factor of $\frac{1}{3}$.

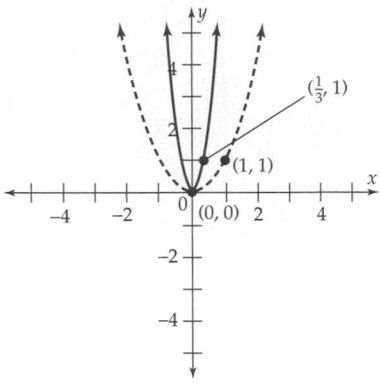

Shift 4 units to the right.

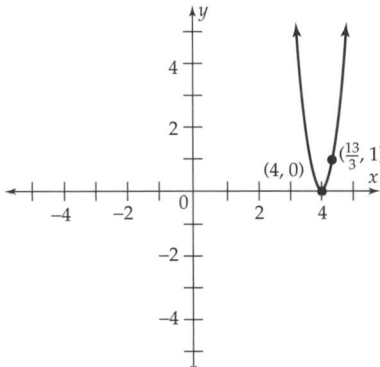

Reflect the graph across the x-axis.

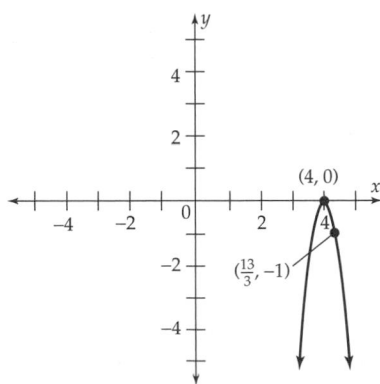

Transformations can be combined to produce many different functions. There is often more than one correct order in which to perform these transformations; however, *not every possible order is correct.* One method is shown below.

Combining Transformations

For a function of the form $g(x) = c \cdot f(a(x - b)) + d$, first graph $f(x)$.

1. If $a < 0$, reflect the graph across the y-axis.
2. Stretch or compress the graph horizontally by a factor of $\left|\dfrac{1}{a}\right|$.
3. Shift the graph horizontally by b units: right if $b > 0$, and left if $b < 0$.
4. If $c < 0$, reflect the graph across the x-axis.
5. Stretch or compress the graph vertically by a factor of $|c|$.
6. Shift the graph vertically by d units: up if $d > 0$, and down if $d < 0$.

Example 6 **Combining Transformations**

Graph the following function.

$$g(x) = -|2x - 1| + 4$$

Solution

Rewrite $g(x) = -|2x - 1| + 4$ as $g(x) = -\left|2\left(x - \dfrac{1}{2}\right)\right| + 4$. The parent function is $f(x) = |x|$.

Compress the graph horizontally by a factor of $\frac{1}{2}$.

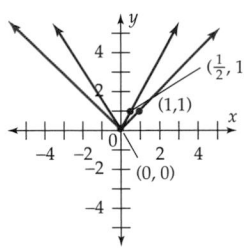

Shift the graph $\frac{1}{2}$ unit to the right.

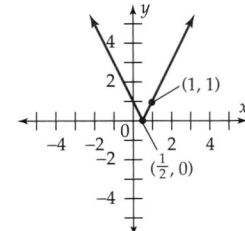

Reflect the graph across the x-axis.

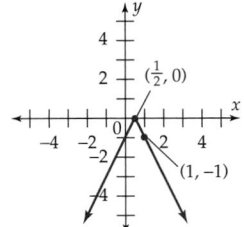

Shift the graph upward 4 units.

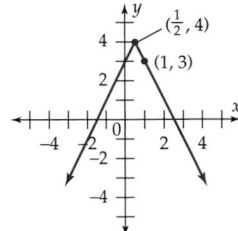

Figure 3.4-8

Shift upward 2 units.

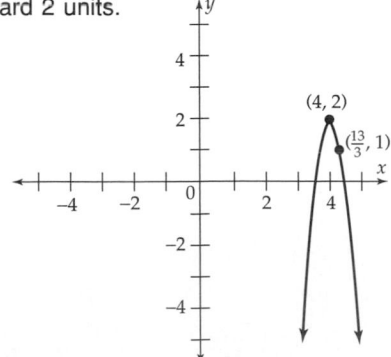

Graphing Exploration ●──────────

For the function $g(x) = -3\sqrt{-2x + 4} + 1$, list several different possible orders of the transformations performed on the graph of $f(x) = \sqrt{x}$ to produce the graph of $g(x)$. Then graph $g(x)$ on a calculator. Did any orders of transformations that you listed produce an incorrect graph? Try to determine some rules about the order in which the transformations may be performed. Compare your rules with those of your classmates.

Example 7 Package Delivery

An overnight delivery service charges $18 for a package weighing less than 1 pound, $21 for one weighing at least 1 pound, but less than 2 pounds, $24 for one weighing at least 2 pounds, but less than 3 pounds, and so on. The cost $c(x)$ of shipping a package weighing x pounds is given by $c(x) = 18 + 3[x]$. Graph $c(x)$ and interpret the result.

Solution

The parent function of $c(x)$ is $f(x) = [x]$. The parent function is stretched vertically by a factor of 3, then shifted upward 18 units. Note: although this rule is defined for all real numbers, the domain of this cost function is $x > 0$.

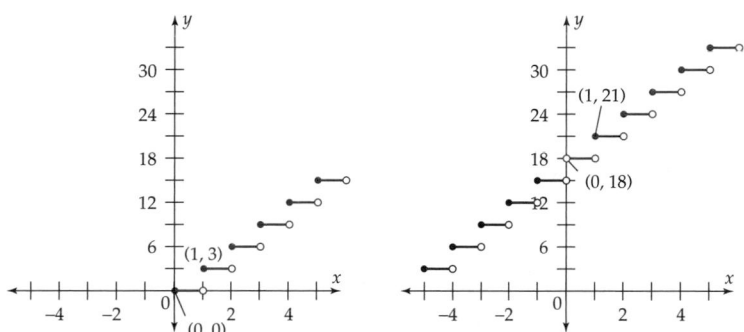

Figure 3.4-9

The function is stretched vertically by a factor of 3 because the increment from one step to the next is $3, and the function is shifted 18 units upward because the lowest rate for any package is $18.

The graph of $g(x)$ is:

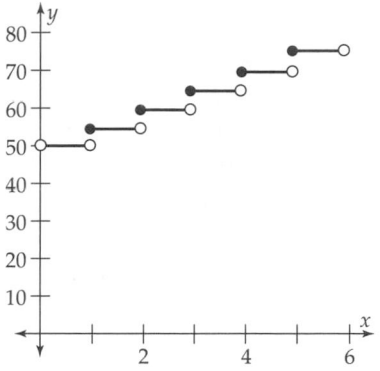

Exercises 3.4

ANSWERS

1. $f(x) = x^3$

2. $g(x) = |x|$

3. $f(x) = 1$

4. $h(x) = \sqrt{x}$

5. $g(x) = \frac{1}{x}$

6. $f(x) = x$

7. $h(x) = [x]$

8. $g(x) = \sqrt[3]{x}$

9. $h(x) = x^2$

10–21. *See p.* 1058.

28. Reflect the graph across the y-axis, stretch the graph horizontally by a factor of 2, shift the graph 6 units to the right, and then reflect the graph across the x-axis.

29. Shift the graph 4 units to the right and 1 unit upward; reflect the graph across the x-axis, and stretch it vertically by a factor of 3.

30. Stretch the graph horizontally by a factor of 3 and vertically by a factor of 2, and shift the graph 5 units upward.

31. Reflect the graph across the y-axis, shift it 2 units to the left, stretch vertically by a factor of 4, and shift 3 units downward.

32. Reflect the graph across the y-axis, compress horizontally by a factor of $\frac{1}{2}$, stretch vertically by a factor of 3, and shift 2 units to the right.

33. Compress the graph horizontally by a factor of $\frac{1}{1.3}$, shift it ≈ 3.23 units to the right, and shift 0.4 units upward.

34–41. *See pp.* 1058–1059.

Exercises 3.4

In Exercises 1–9, identify the parent function that can be used to graph each function. Do not graph the function.

1. $f(x) = -(x + 2)^3$

2. $g(x) = 4|x| - 3$

3. $f(x) = 7$

4. $h(x) = \sqrt{-2x + 4}$

5. $g(x) = \dfrac{2}{x - 1} + 4$

6. $f(x) = -3x + 2$

7. $h(x) = -6\left[\dfrac{1}{2}x + 3\right] + \dfrac{2}{3}$

8. $g(x) = 2\sqrt[3]{x} + 5$

9. $h(x) = 2(3 - x)^2 + 4$

In Exercises 10–21, graph each function and its parent function on the same set of axes.

10. $f(x) = -x^2$

11. $h(x) = -\dfrac{1}{x}$

12. $g(x) = |-x|$

13. $h(x) = \sqrt[3]{-x}$

14. $f(x) = x - 5$

15. $g(x) = [x] + 1$

16. $f(x) = \sqrt{x + 4}$

17. $h(x) = |x - 2|$

18. $g(x) = 3x$

19. $f(x) = \dfrac{1}{2}$

20. $g(x) = \left(\dfrac{1}{4}x\right)^3$

21. $h(x) = \dfrac{1}{3x}$

In Exercises 22–27, write a rule for the function whose graph can be obtained from the given parent function by performing the given transformations.

22. parent function: $f(x) = x^3$
    transformations: shift the graph 5 units to the left and upward 4 units $g(x) = (x + 5)^3 + 4$

23. parent function: $f(x) = \sqrt{x}$
    transformations: reflect the graph across the x-axis and shift it upward 3 units $g(x) = -\sqrt{x} + 3$

24. parent function: $f(x) = [x]$
    transformations: shift the graph 6 units to the right, stretch it vertically by a factor of 2, and shift it downward 3 units $g(x) = 2[x - 6] - 3$

25. parent function: $f(x) = |x|$
    transformations: shift the graph 3 units to the left, reflect it across the x-axis, and shrink it vertically by a factor of $\frac{1}{2}$ $g(x) = -\dfrac{1}{2}|x + 3|$

26. parent function: $f(x) = \dfrac{1}{x}$
    transformations: shift the graph 2 units to the right, stretch it horizontally by a factor of 2, and shift it upward 2 units $g(x) = \dfrac{1}{0.5(x - 2)} + 2$

27. parent function: $f(x) = x^2$
    transformations: shift the graph 3 units to the left, reflect it across the y-axis, and stretch it vertically by a factor of 1.5 $g(x) = 1.5(-x + 3)^2$

In Exercises 28–33, describe a sequence of transformations that transform the graph of the parent function f into the graph of the function g. Do not graph the functions.

28. $f(x) = \sqrt{x}$ $g(x) = -\sqrt{-\dfrac{1}{2}x + 3}$

29. $f(x) = x$ $g(x) = -3(x - 4) + 1$

30. $f(x) = [x]$ $g(x) = 2\left[\dfrac{1}{3}x\right] + 5$

31. $f(x) = x^3$ $g(x) = 4(2 - x)^3 - 3$

32. $f(x) = \dfrac{1}{x}$ $g(x) = \dfrac{3}{4 - 2x}$

33. $f(x) = \sqrt[3]{x}$ $g(x) = \sqrt[3]{1.3x - 4.2} + 0.4$

In Exercises 34–41, graph each function and its parent function on the same graph.

34. $f(x) = -2(x + 1)^2 + 3$

35. $g(x) = \dfrac{1}{4}\sqrt[3]{x + 3} - 1$

36. $f(x) = -\dfrac{3}{4}\left[-\dfrac{1}{3}x\right]$

37. $h(x) = 3(x - 1) + 5$

38. $g(x) = |-x + 5| - 3$

39. $f(x) = \dfrac{-3}{2 - x} + 4$

40. $h(x) = \sqrt{-4x + 3} - 1$

41. $g(x) = \dfrac{2}{5}(5 - x)^3 - \dfrac{3}{5}$

In Exercises 42–45, use the graph of the function *f* in the figure to sketch the graph of the function *g*.

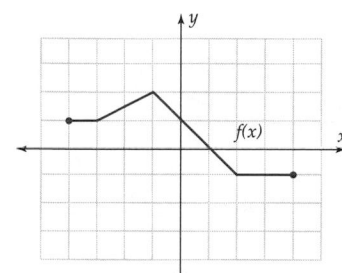

42. $g(x) = f(x) - 1$ **43.** $g(x) = 3f(x)$

44. $g(x) = 0.25f(x)$ **45.** $g(x) = f(x) + 3$

In Exercises 46–49, use the graph of the function *f* in the figure to sketch the graph of the function *h*.

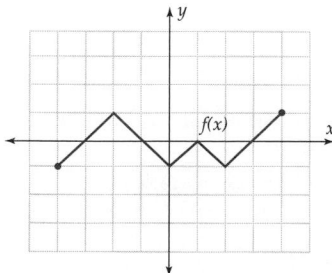

46. $h(x) = -4f(x)$ **47.** $h(x) = -f(x)$

48. $h(x) = f(-x)$ **49.** $h(x) = f(-2x)$

In Exercises 50–55, use the graph of the function *f* in the figure to sketch the graph of the function *g*.

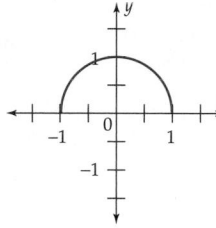

50. $g(x) = f(x - 2)$ **51.** $g(x) = f(x - 2) + 3$

52. $g(x) = f(x + 1) - 3$ **53.** $g(x) = 2 - f(x)$

54. $g(x) = f(-x) + 2$ **55.** $g(x) = f(x + 3)$

Exercises 56–61 refer to the parent function

$$f(x) = \sqrt{1 - x^2}$$

The graph of *f* is a semicircle with radius 1, as shown below.

Use the graph of *f* to sketch the graph of the function *g*.

56. $g(x) = -\sqrt{1 - x^2}$ **57.** $g(x) = \sqrt{1 - x^2} + 4$

58. $g(x) = \sqrt{1 - (x - 3)^2}$ **59.** $g(x) = 3\sqrt{1 - x^2}$

60. $g(x) = \sqrt{1 - (x + 2)^2} + 1$

61. $g(x) = 5\sqrt{1 - \left(\dfrac{1}{5}x\right)^2}$

62. In 2002, the cost of sending first-class mail was $0.37 for a letter weighing less than 1 ounce, $0.60 for a letter weighing at least one ounce, but less than 2 ounces, $0.83 for a letter weighing at least 2 ounces, but less than 3 ounces, and so on.
   a. Write a function $c(x)$ that gives the cost of mailing a letter weighing x ounces (see Example 7).
   b. Graph $c(x)$ and interpret the result.

63. A factory has a linear cost function $f(x) = ax + b$, where b represents fixed costs and a represents the labor and material costs of making one item, both in thousands of dollars.
   a. If property taxes (part of the fixed costs) are increased by $28,000 per year, what effect does this have on the graph of the cost function?
   b. If labor and material costs for making 100,000 items increase by $12,000, what effect does this have on the graph of the cost function?

42.

43.

44.

45.

46–63. *See pp.* 1059–1060.

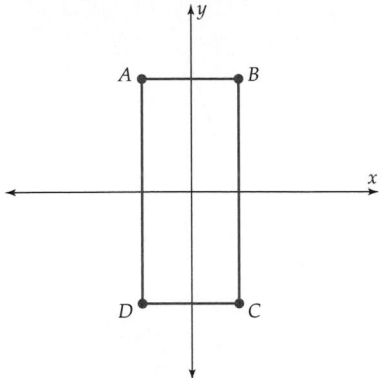

Section 3.4.A Excursion: Symmetry

Teaching Notes

You can illustrate all three types of symmetry addressed in this section with a figure like the one below:

Point out that:

A and B are symmetric with respect to the y-axis (a line).

A and D are symmetric with respect to the x-axis (a line).

A and C are symmetric with respect to the origin (a point).

It might be helpful to review *perpendicular bisector* of a line segment (see the third bullet on this page).

Math Background

Students studied reflections in Section 3.4. Every instance of symmetry in this Excursion is an instance of a reflection. For example, the right half of the ellipse in Figure 3.4.A-1 is the reflection image of the left half across the y-axis.

The concept of equivalent equations is used in the algebraic meaning of symmetry. Equivalent equations are equations with the same solution set. The equations $y = x^4 - 5x^2 + 3$ and $y = (-x)^4 - 5(-x)^2 + 3$ at the top of page 185 are equivalent because the same ordered pairs (x, y) satisfy both equations.

3.4.A Excursion: Symmetry

Objectives

- Determine whether a graph has y-axis, x-axis, or origin symmetry
- Determine whether a function is even, odd, or neither

This section presents three kinds of symmetry that a graph can have and ways to identify these symmetries both geometrically and algebraically.

y-Axis Symmetry

A graph of a function or relation is **symmetric with respect to the y-axis** if the part of the graph on the right side of the y-axis is the mirror image of the part on the left side of the y-axis, as shown in Figure 3.4.A-1.

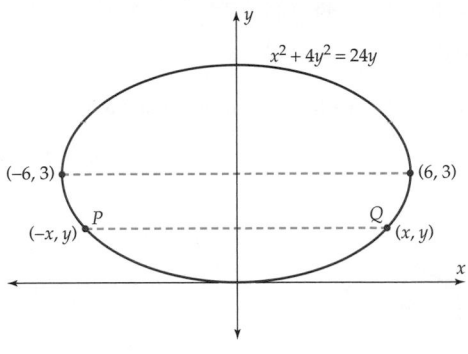

Figure 3.4.A-1

Each point P on the left side of the graph has a mirror image point Q on the right side of the graph, as indicated by the dashed lines. Note that

- their y-coordinates are the same
- their x-coordinates are opposites of each other
- the y-axis is the perpendicular bisector of $\overline{PQ}$

y-Axis Symmetry

A graph is symmetric with respect to the y-axis if whenever (x, y) is on the graph, then $(-x, y)$ is also on it.

In algebraic terms, this means that replacing x by $-x$ produces an equivalent equation.

Example 1 *y-Axis Symmetry*

Verify that $y = x^4 - 5x^2 + 3$ is symmetric with respect to the y-axis.

Solution

Replace x by $-x$ in the equation.

$$y = x^4 - 5x^2 + 3$$
$$y = (-x)^4 - 5(-x)^2 + 3$$

which is equivalent to the original equation because $(-x)^2 = x^2$ and $(-x)^4 = x^4$. Therefore, the graph is symmetric with respect to the y-axis. ∎

Graphing Exploration ●

Graph the equation $y = x^4 - 5x^2 + 3$ from Example 1. Use the TRACE feature to locate at least three points (x, y) on the graph and show that for each point, $(-x, y)$ is also on the graph.

---

x-Axis Symmetry

A graph of a relation is symmetric with respect to the x-axis if the part of the graph above the x-axis is the mirror image of the part below the x-axis, as shown in Figure 3.4.A-2.

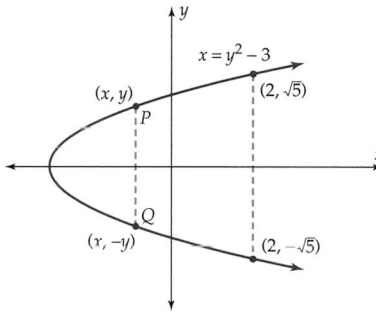

Figure 3.4.A-2

Each point P on the top of the graph has a mirror image point Q on the bottom of the graph, as indicated by the dashed lines. Note that

- their x-coordinates are the same
- their y-coordinates are opposites of each other
- the x-axis is the perpendicular bisector of $\overline{PQ}$

x-Axis Symmetry ○

A graph is symmetric with respect to the x-axis if whenever (x, y) is on the graph, then $(x, -y)$ is also on it.

In algebraic terms, this means that replacing y by $-y$ produces an equivalent equation.

ADDITIONAL EXAMPLES

Example 2

Verify that $y^2 = x + 2$ is symmetric with respect to the x-axis.

Replace y by $-y$ in the equation.

$$y^2 = x + 2$$
$$(-y)^2 = x + 2$$
$$y^2 = x + 2$$

The last equation is equivalent to the given equation, so the graph of the given equation is symmetric with respect to the x-axis.

Example 3

Verify that $y = -\dfrac{x^3}{2} + 5x$ is symmetric with respect to the origin.

Replace x by $-x$ and y by $-y$ in the equation. Then simplify.

$$y = -\frac{x^3}{2} + 5x$$
$$-y = -\frac{(-x)^3}{2} + 5(-x)$$
$$-y = \frac{x^3}{2} - 5x$$
$$-1(-y) = -1\left(\frac{x^3}{2} - 5x\right)$$
$$y = -\frac{x^3}{2} + 5x$$

The last equation is equivalent to the given equation, so the graph of the given equation is symmetric with respect to the origin.

Teaching Notes

Possible solution to the **Graphing Exploration:**

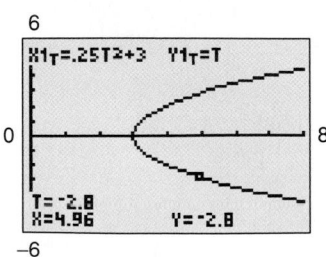

Students should get at least two more $(x, y)/(x, -y)$ pairs.

> **NOTE** Except for $f(x) = 0$, the graph of a function is never symmetric with respect to the x-axis. By the Vertical Line Test, a function's graph cannot contain points that lie on a vertical line, such as (x, y) and $(x, -y)$.

Example 2   *x-Axis Symmetry*

Verify that $y^2 = 4x - 12$ is symmetric with respect to the x-axis.

Solution

Replacing y by $-y$ in the equation gives

$$(-y)^2 = 4x - 12$$

which is equivalent to the original equation because $(-y)^2 = y^2$. Therefore, the graph is symmetric with respect to the x-axis. ■

Graphing Exploration ●

Graph the equation $y^2 = 4x - 12$ from Example 2 in parametric mode by entering the parametric equations below.

$$x_1 = \frac{1}{4}t^2 + 3$$
$$y_1 = t$$

Use the TRACE feature to locate at least three points (x, y) on the graph and show that for each point, $(x, -y)$ is also on the graph.

Origin Symmetry

A graph is **symmetric with respect to the origin** if a line through the origin and any point P on the graph also intersects the graph at a point Q such that the origin is the midpoint of $\overline{PQ}$, as shown in Figure 3.4.A-3.

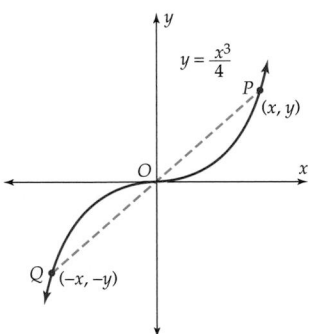

Figure 3.4.A-3

Using Figure 3.4.A-3, symmetry with respect to the origin can also be described in terms of coordinates and equations.

Origin Symmetry

> A graph is symmetric with respect to the origin if whenever (x, y) is on the graph, then $(-x, -y)$ is also on it.
>
> In algebraic terms, this means that replacing x by $-x$ and y by $-y$ produces an equivalent equation.

Example 3 **Origin Symmetry**

Verify that $y = \dfrac{x^3}{10} - x$ is symmetric with respect to the origin.

Solution

Replace x by $-x$ and y by $-y$ in the equation.

$$-y = \frac{(-x)^3}{10} - (-x)$$

$$-y = \frac{-x^3}{10} + x \qquad \textit{Simplify}$$

$$-1(-y) = -1\left(\frac{-x^3}{10} + x\right) \qquad \textit{Multiply both sides by } -1$$

$$y = \frac{x^3}{10} - x \qquad \textit{Simplify}$$

Therefore, the graph is symmetric with respect to the origin. ∎

— Graphing Exploration •——

Graph the equation $y = \dfrac{x^3}{10} - x$ from Example 3. Use the TRACE feature to locate at least three points (x, y) on the graph and show that for each point, $(-x, -y)$ is also on the graph.

Summary

There are a number of techniques used to understand the fundamental features of a graph. Symmetry, whether line or point, is beneficial when graphing a function. Knowing a graph's symmetry prior to graphing reduces the necessary number of coordinates needed to display a complete graph; thus, the graph can be sketched more quickly and easily.

Here is a summary of the various tests for line and point symmetry:

Example Notes

Note that in **Example 3**, you need to simplify and use a property of equality (multiplication property of equality). The purpose is to get an equation that is obviously equivalent to the given equation.

Math Background

A figure has rotational symmetry if it can be rotated less than 360° about some point so that the image coincides with the original figure. If the rotation is 180°, then the figure is said to have point symmetry.

If a figure is rotated 180° about the origin, it has origin symmetry. So, origin symmetry is a case of rotational symmetry.

Teaching Notes

If a graph has both x-axis and y-axis symmetry, then it also has origin symmetry. However, the converse is not true. That is, a graph can have origin symmetry without having x-axis or y-axis symmetry. You might ask what types of symmetry the following have:

$y = x^3$ origin symmetry only

$x^2 + y^2 = 25$ all three types

(Note that $x^2 + y^2 = 25$ is a circle with center $(0, 0)$ and radius 5.) any line through the origin origin symmetry only

Possible solution to the **Graphing Exploration:**

Students should get at least two more $(x, y)/(-x, -y)$ pairs.

Math Background

Prior to this section, students have learned the following graphing techniques: create tables of values, determine domains, find intercepts, and perform transformations of parent functions. Now they can use the **Symmetry Tests** shown here.

In Section 3.6, students will learn that inverse functions have the line $y = x$ as a line of symmetry.

Functions other than polynomials can also be even or odd: $f(x) = \sqrt{25 - x^2}$ is the semicircle above the x-axis with radius 5 and center $(0, 0)$; it is even. $f(x) = |x|$ is even. $f(x) = \sin x$ is odd (see page 483). $f(x) = \cos x$ is even.

Teaching Notes

Consider having students make up examples of **Even Functions**, with classmates determining if they are correct. Do a corresponding activity for **Odd Functions**.

You might want to ask students to use the margin **Notes** on pages 188 and 189 to identify the following polynomial functions as even, odd, or neither, and to explain:

$f(x) = x^4 + x^2 + 3$
even; $x^4 + x^2 + 3 = x^4 + x^2 + 3x^0$, i.e., all terms have even degree

$f(x) = x^5 + 7x^2$
neither; x^5 has odd degree and $7x^2$ has even degree

Symmetry Tests

Symmetry with respect to	Coordinate test	Algebraic test
y-Axis	If (x, y) is on the graph, then $(-x, y)$ is on the graph.	Replacing x by $-x$ produces an equivalent equation.
x-Axis	If (x, y) is on the graph, then $(x, -y)$ is on the graph.	Replacing y by $-y$ produces an equivalent equation.
Origin	If (x, y) is on the graph, then $(-x, -y)$ is on the graph.	Replacing x by $-x$ and y by $-y$ produces an equivalent equation.

Even and Odd Functions

For relations that are *functions*, the algebraic description of symmetry can take a different form.

Even Functions

A function f whose graph is symmetric with respect to the y-axis is called an **even function**.

Even Functions

> **A function f is even if**
>
> $$f(-x) = f(x) \text{ for every value } x \text{ in the domain of } f.$$
>
> **The graph of an even function is symmetric with respect to the y-axis.**

NOTE If the rule of a function is a polynomial in which all terms have even degree, then the function is even. (A constant term has degree 0, which is even.)

For example, $f(x) = x^4 + x^2$ is even because

$$f(-x) = (-x)^4 + (-x)^2 = x^4 + x^2 = f(x)$$

Thus, the graph of f is symmetric with respect to the y-axis, as you can verify with your calculator.

Odd Functions

A function f whose graph is symmetric with respect to the origin is called an **odd function**. If both (x, y) and $(-x, -y)$ are on the graph of such a function f, then

$$y = f(x) \quad \text{and} \quad -y = f(-x)$$
$$-y = -f(x)$$

so $f(-x) = -f(x)$.

Odd Functions

> A function f is odd if
>
> $f(-x) = -f(x)$ for every value x in the domain of f.
>
> The graph of an odd function is symmetric with respect to the origin.

NOTE If the rule of a function is a polynomial in which all terms have odd degree, then the function is odd.

For example, $f(x) = x^3 + 2x$ is an odd function because

$$f(-x) = (-x)^3 + 2(-x) = -x^3 - 2x$$
$$-f(x) = -(x^3 + 2x) = -x^3 - 2x$$

Hence, the graph of f is symmetric with respect to the origin, as you can verify with your calculator.

Exercises 3.4.A

In Exercises 1–6, graph the equation and state whether the graph has symmetry. If so, is it symmetric with respect to the x-axis, the y-axis, or the origin?

1. $y = x^2 + 2$ **2.** $x = (y - 3)^2$

3. $y = x^3 + 2$ **4.** $y = (x + 2)^3$

5. $y - \dfrac{\sqrt[3]{x}}{x^2}$ **6.** $|y| - x$

In Exercises 7–10, determine algebraically whether or not the graph of the given equation is symmetric with respect to the y-axis.

7. $x^2 + y^2 = 1$ **Yes**   **8.** $y = x^3 - x^2$ **No**

9. $4x^2 - 3y + y^2 = 7$ **Yes**   **10.** $x^4 + x^2 - x = y^3 + 1$ **No**

In Exercises 11–14, determine algebraically whether the graph of the given equation is symmetric with respect to the x-axis.

11. $x^2 - 6x + y^2 + 8 = 0$ **Yes**   **12.** $x^2 + 8x + y^2 = -15$ **Yes**

13. $x^2 - 2x + y^2 + 2y = 2$ **No**   **14.** $x^2 - x + y^2 - y = 0$ **No**

In Exercises 15–18, determine algebraically whether the graph of the given equation is symmetric with respect to the origin.

15. $4x^2 - 3y^2 + xy = 6$ **Yes** **16.** $x^3 + y^3 = x$ **Yes**

17. $|x| + |y| = x^2 + y^2$ **Yes** **18.** $3x^2 = 4y - 2x + 6$ **No**

In Exercises 19–24, determine whether the given graph is symmetric with respect to the y-axis, the x-axis, the origin, or any combination of the three.

19.   **Origin**

20.   **x-axis, y-axis, Origin**

21.   **Origin**

22. 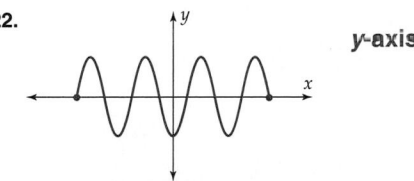   **y-axis**

Exercises 3.4.A
ANSWERS

1. The graph is symmetric with respect to the y-axis.

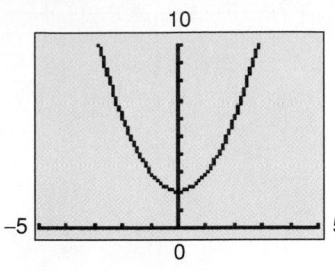

2. The graph does not have symmetry with respect to the x-axis, y-axis, or origin. However, it is symmetric with respect to the line $y = 3$.

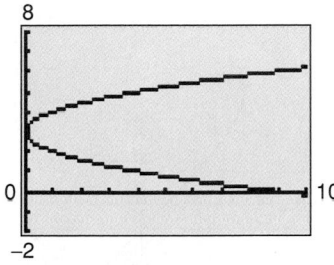

3. The graph does not have symmetry with respect to the x-axis, y-axis, or origin. However, it is symmetric with respect to the point $(0, 2)$.

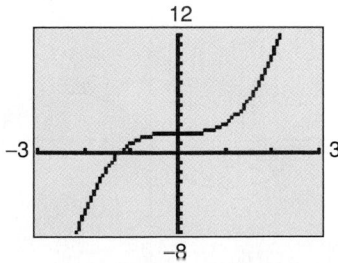

4. The graph does not have symmetry with respect to the x-axis, y-axis, or origin. However, it is symmetric with respect to the point $(-2, 0)$.

5. The graph is symmetric with respect to the origin.

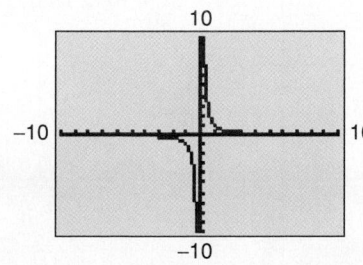

6. The graph is symmetric with respect to the x-axis.

35.

36.

37.

38.

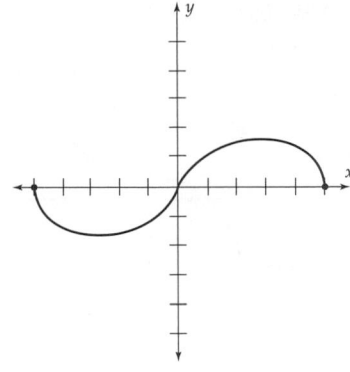

39. Many correct graphs, including the one shown here:

23.

    y-axis

24.

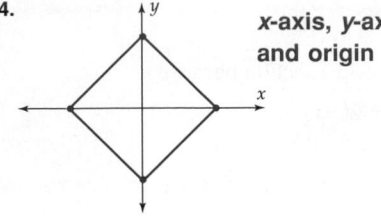   ***x*-axis, *y*-axis and origin**

In Exercises 25–34, determine whether the given function is even, odd, or neither.

25. $f(x) = 4x$ **Odd**   **26.** $k(t) = -5t$ **Odd**

27. $f(x) = x^2 - |x|$ **Even** **28.** $h(u) = |3u|$ **Even**

29. $k(t) = t^4 - 6t^2 + 5$ **30.** $f(x) = x(x^4 - x^2) + 4$ **Neither**
Even

31. $f(t) = \sqrt{t^2 - 5}$ **Even** **32.** $h(x) = \sqrt{7 - 2x^2}$ **Even**

33. $f(x) = \dfrac{x^2 + 2}{x - 7}$ **34.** $g(x) = \dfrac{x^2 + 1}{x^2 - 1}$ **Even**

   Neither

In Exercises 35–38, complete the graph of the given function, assuming that it satisfies the given symmetry condition.

35. Even

36. Even

37. Odd

38. Odd

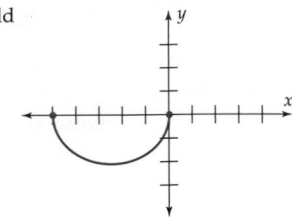

39. a. Plot the points $(0, 0)$, $(2, 3)$, $(3, 4)$, $(5, 0)$, $(7, -3)$, $(-1, -1)$, $(-4, -1)$, and $(-6, 1)$.
   b. Suppose the points in part **a** lie on the graph of an odd function f. Plot the points $(-2, f(-2))$, $(-3, f(-3))$, $(-5, f(-5))$, $(-7, f(-7))$, $(1, f(1))$, $(4, f(4))$, and $(6, f(6))$.

40. a. Plot the points $(1, -3)$, $(-5, 2)$, $(-3, 5)$, $(2, 3)$, and $(4, 1)$.
   b. Suppose the points in part **a** lie on the graph of an even function f. Plot the points $(-1, f(-1))$, $(5, f(5))$, $(3, f(3))$, $(-2, f(-2))$, and $(-4, f(-4))$.

41. Show that any graph that has two of the three types of symmetry (x-axis, y-axis, origin) always has the third type.

42. Use the midpoint formula (see the Algebra Review Appendix) to show that $(0, 0)$ is the midpoint of the segment joining (x, y) and $(-x, -y)$.

$$\left(\frac{-x + x}{2}, \frac{-y + y}{2}\right) = \left(\frac{0}{2}, \frac{0}{2}\right) = (0, 0)$$

40. a.

b.

3.5 **Operations on Functions**

Objectives
- Form sum, difference, product, and quotient functions and find their domains
- Form composite functions and find their domains

There are several ways in which two or more given functions can be used to create new functions.

Sums and Differences of Functions

If f and g are functions, their **sum** is the function h defined by this rule.

$$h(x) = f(x) + g(x)$$

For example, if $f(x) = 3x^2 + x$ and $g(x) = 4x - 2$, then

$$h(x) = f(x) + g(x) = (3x^2 + x) + (4x - 2) = 3x^2 + 5x - 2$$

Instead of using a different letter h for the sum function, we shall usually denote it by $f + g$. Thus, the sum $f + g$ is defined by the rule

$$(f + g)(x) = f(x) + g(x)$$

NOTE This rule is not just a formal manipulation of symbols. If x is a number, then so are $f(x)$ and $g(x)$. The plus sign in $f(x) + g(x)$ is addition of numbers, and the result is a number. But the plus sign in $f + g$ is addition of functions, and the result is a new function.

The **difference** function $f - g$ is the function defined by a similar rule.

$$(f - g)(x) = f(x) - g(x)$$

The domain of the sum and difference functions is the set of all real numbers that are in both the domain of f and the domain of g.

Technology Tip

If two functions are entered as Y_1 and Y_2, their sum function can be graphed by entering $Y_3 = Y_1 + Y_2$.

Difference, product, and quotient functions can be graphed similarly.

Example 1   Sum and Difference Functions

For $f(x) = \sqrt{9 - x^2}$ and $g(x) = \sqrt{x - 2}$.

a. write the rule for $f + g$ and $f - g$.

b. find the domain of $f + g$ and $f - g$.

Solution

a. $(f + g)(x) = \sqrt{9 - x^2} + \sqrt{x - 2}$
   $(f - g)(x) = \sqrt{9 - x^2} - \sqrt{x - 2}$

b. The domain of f consists of all x such that $9 - x^2 \geq 0$, that is, $-3 \leq x \leq 3$. Similarly, the domain of g consists of all x such that $x - 2 \geq 0$, that is, $x \geq 2$. The domain of $f + g$ and $f - g$ consists of all real numbers in both the domain of f and the domain of g, namely, all x such that $2 \leq x \leq 3$.

 Section 3.5 Operations on Functions

Teaching Notes

Remind students that only like terms may be combined when adding or subtracting polynomials.

To reduce sign errors, encourage students to use parentheses. Be sure students distribute negative signs correctly. To illustrate, write and simplify the difference function for $f(x) = 3x^2 + x$ and $g(x) = 4x - 2$ as follows:

$$(f - g)(x) = (3x^2 + x) - (4x - 2)$$
$$= 3x^2 + x - 4x + 2$$
$$= 3x^2 - 3x + 2$$

Example Notes

In **Example 1**, you may want to have students graph the domain of each function on a number line. Show students that the domain of a sum or difference function is the overlap, or the numbers in *common* to both domains.

The overlap is $2 \leq x \leq 3$.

ADDITIONAL EXAMPLES

Example 1

For $f(x) = \sqrt{1 - x}$ and $g(x) = \sqrt{x^2 - 1}$

a. write the rule for $f + g$ and $f - g$.
   $(f + g)(x) = \sqrt{1 - x} + \sqrt{x^2 - 1}$
   $(f - g)(x) = \sqrt{1 - x} - \sqrt{x^2 - 1}$

b. find the domain of $f + g$ and $f - g$.
   domain for $f + g$ and $f - g$:
   all x such that $x = 1$ or $x \leq -1$

---

41. Suppose the graph is symmetric to the x-axis and the y-axis. If (x, y) is on the graph, then $(x, -y)$ is on the graph by x-axis symmetry. Hence, $(-x, -y)$ is on the graph by y-axis symmetry. Therefore, (x, y) on the graph implies that $(-x, -y)$ is on the graph, so the graph is symmetric with respect to the origin. Next suppose that the graph is symmetric to the y-axis and the

origin. If (x, y) is on the graph, then $(-x, y)$ is on the graph by y-axis symmetry. Hence, $(-(-x), -y) = (x, -y)$ is on the graph by origin symmetry. Therefore, (x, y) on the graph implies that $(x, -y)$ is on the graph, so the graph is symmetric with respect to the x-axis. The proof of the third case is similar to that of the second case.

Teaching Notes

Graphing domains on number lines and using overlapping graphs to get domains of sum, difference, product, and quotient functions is a powerful tool that can be used in **Examples 1 and 2** and the corresponding Additional Examples. Remember to exclude values that would result in denominators equal to zero.

In **Example 2**, students may forget to exclude 1 from the domain of $\frac{f}{g}$. Remind them that if $x = 1$, $\frac{f}{g}$ is undefined, so 1 must be excluded.

Example Notes

In **Example 2**, a radical occurs in a denominator, so simplify by rationalizing the denominator.

$$\frac{\sqrt{3x}}{\sqrt{x^2-1}} \cdot \frac{\sqrt{x^2-1}}{\sqrt{x^2-1}} = \frac{\sqrt{3x^3-3x}}{x^2-1}$$

In **Example 3**, an alternate approach is to do parts c and d before doing parts a and b. For example, in part d, we find that

$$(f \circ g)(x) = f(g(x))$$

$$= \frac{4}{(x+2)^2} + 1$$

Use this expression to answer part b:

$$(f \circ g)(-1) = f(g(-1))$$

$$= \frac{4}{(-1+2)^2} + 1$$

$$= \frac{4}{(1)^2} + 1$$

$$= 5$$

Products and Quotients of Functions

The **product** and **quotient** of functions f and g are the functions defined by the following rules.

$$(fg)(x) = f(x) \cdot g(x) \qquad \text{and} \qquad \left(\frac{f}{g}\right)(x) = \frac{f(x)}{g(x)}$$

The domain of fg consists of all real numbers in both the domain of f and the domain of g. The domain of $\left(\frac{f}{g}\right)$ consists of all real numbers x in both the domain of f and the domain of g such that $g(x) \neq 0$.

Example 2   **Product and Quotient Functions**

For $f(x) = \sqrt{3x}$ and $g(x) = \sqrt{x^2 - 1}$

a. write the rule for fg and $\frac{f}{g}$.

b. find the domain of fg and $\frac{f}{g}$.

Solution

a. $(fg)(x) = \sqrt{3x} \cdot \sqrt{x^2 - 1} = \sqrt{3x^3 - 3x}$

$$\left(\frac{f}{g}\right)(x) = \frac{\sqrt{3x}}{\sqrt{x^2-1}} = \frac{\sqrt{3x^3-3x}}{x^2-1}$$

b. The domain of f consists of all x such that $3x \geq 0$, that is, $x \geq 0$. Similarly, the domain of g consists of all x such that $x^2 - 1 \geq 0$, that is, $x \leq -1$ or $x \geq 1$. The domain of fg consists of all real numbers in both the domain of f and the domain of g, that is, $x \geq 1$. The domain of $\left(\frac{f}{g}\right)$ consists of all these x for which $g(x) \neq 0$, so the value $x = 1$ must also be excluded. Thus, the domain of $\left(\frac{f}{g}\right)$ is $x > 1$. ∎

> **CAUTION**
>
> The function with the rule $\sqrt{3x^3 - 3x}$ is defined for values that are not in the domain of f and g. The domain of a sum, difference, product, or quotient function must be determined before the function is simplified.

Products with Constant Functions

If c is a real number and f is a function, then the product of f and the constant function $g(x) = c$ is

$$(cf)(x) = c \cdot f(x)$$

The domain of cf is the same as the domain of f. For example, if $f(x) = x^3 - x + 2$ and $c = 5$, then $5f$ is the function

$$(5f)(x) = 5 \cdot f(x) = 5(x^3 - x + 2) = 5x^3 - 5x + 10$$

and the domain of $5f$ is still all real numbers.

Composition of Functions

Another way of combining functions is to use the output of one function as the input of another. This operation is called **composition of functions**. The idea can be expressed in function notation as shown below.

input of f $\qquad$ output of $f =$ $\qquad$ output of g

$$f(x)$$
$$= \text{input of } g$$

$$x \;\to\; \boxed{f} \qquad \to \qquad \boxed{g} \;\to\; g(f(x))$$

Composite Functions

If f and g are functions, then the *composite function* of f and g is

$$(g \circ f)(x) = g(f(x))$$

The expression $g \circ f$ is read "g circle f" or "f followed by g."
Note the order carefully; the functions are applied right to left.

Technology Tip

To evaluate or graph composite functions, enter the equations as Y_1 and Y_2. Then enter $Y_1(Y_2(X))$ or $Y_2(Y_1(X))$.

Example 3 Composite Functions

If $f(x) = 4x^2 + 1$ and $g(x) = \dfrac{1}{x + 2}$, find the following.

a. $(g \circ f)(2)$ $\qquad\qquad$ **b.** $(f \circ g)(-1)$
c. $(g \circ f)(x)$ $\qquad\qquad$ **d.** $(f \circ g)(x)$

Solution

a. To find $(g \circ f)(2)$, first find $f(2)$.

$$f(2) = 4(2)^2 + 1 = 17$$

Next, use the result as an input in g.

$$g(17) = \frac{1}{17 + 2} = \frac{1}{19}$$

So $(g \circ f)(2) = \dfrac{1}{19}$.

b. To find $(f \circ g)(-1)$, first find $g(-1)$.

$$g(-1) = \frac{1}{-1 + 2} = 1$$

Next, use the result as an input in f.

$$f(1) = 4(1)^2 + 1 = 5$$

So $(f \circ g)(-1) = 5$.

ADDITIONAL EXAMPLES

Example 2

For $f(x) = \sqrt{2x}$ and $g(x) = \sqrt{x^2 - 4}$

a. write the rule for fg and $\dfrac{f}{g}$.

$$(fg)(x) = \sqrt{2x} \cdot \sqrt{x^2 - 4}$$
$$= \sqrt{2x^3 - 8x}$$

$$\left(\frac{f}{g}\right)(x) = \frac{\sqrt{2x}}{\sqrt{x^2 - 4}}$$

$$= \frac{\sqrt{2x^3 - 8x}}{x^2 - 4}$$

b. find the domain of fg and $\dfrac{f}{g}$.

domain of f: $x \geq 0$
domain of g: $x \leq -2$ or $x \geq 2$
domain of fg: $x \geq 2$
domain of $\dfrac{f}{g}$: $x > 2$

Example 3

If $f(x) = x^2 + 2x - 1$ and

$g(x) = \dfrac{1}{x - 3}$, find the following.

a. $(g \circ f)(-2)$

$-\dfrac{1}{4}$

b. $(f \circ g)(4)$

2

c. $(g \circ f)(x)$

$\dfrac{1}{x^2 + 2x - 4}$

d. $(f \circ g)(x)$

$\dfrac{1}{(x - 3)^2} + \dfrac{2}{x - 3} - 1$

Teaching Notes

After discussing the **Domain of** $g \circ f$, tell students that the domain of $f \circ g$ is defined in a similar manner. That is, the domain of $f \circ g$, or $f(g(x))$, is the set of real numbers x such that

• x is in the domain of g
• $g(x)$ is in the domain of f

Example Notes

In **Example 4**, it may appear to students that the domain for $g(f(x)) = x - 5$ is the set of all real numbers. Emphasize that this is not the case. The domain is restricted by the domain of the inner function, $f(x)$. The domain of $f(g(x)) = \sqrt{x^2 - 5}$ is not restricted by the domain of the inner function, $g(x)$, since the domain of $g(x)$ is the set of all real numbers. The domain is restricted, however, to only those values of x for which $x^2 - 5 \geq 0$, namely $x \leq -\sqrt{5}$ or $x \geq \sqrt{5}$.

ADDITIONAL EXAMPLES

Example 4

If $f(x) = \sqrt{x - 2}$ and $g(x) = x^2 - 1$,

a. find $g \circ f$ and $f \circ g$.

$(g \circ f)(x) = g(f(x)) = x - 3$
$(f \circ g)(x) = f(g(x)) = \sqrt{x^2 - 3}$

b. find the domain of each composite function.
domain of $g \circ f : x \geq 2$
domain of $f \circ g : x \leq -\sqrt{3}$
or $x \geq \sqrt{3}$

c. To find $(g \circ f)(x) = g(f(x))$, replace x with the rule for $f(x)$ in g.

$$(g \circ f)(x) = g(f(x)) = \frac{1}{f(x) + 2} = \frac{1}{(4x^2 + 1) + 2} = \frac{1}{4x^2 + 3}$$

d. To find $(f \circ g)(x) = f(g(x))$, replace x with the rule for $g(x)$ in f.

$$(f \circ g)(x) = f(g(x)) = 4(g(x))^2 + 1 = 4\left(\frac{1}{x + 2}\right)^2 + 1 = \frac{4}{(x + 2)^2} + 1$$

Notice that $(g \circ f)(x) \neq (f \circ g)(x)$. ∎

Domains of Composite Functions

The domain of $g \circ f$ is determined by the following convention.

Domain of
$g \circ f$

> Let f and g be functions. The domain of $g \circ f$ is the set of all real numbers x such that
>
> • x is in the domain of f
> • $f(x)$ is in the domain of g

Example 4 — Finding the Domain of a Composite Function

If $f(x) = \sqrt{x}$ and $g(x) = x^2 - 5$,

a. find $g \circ f$ and $f \circ g$.

b. find the domain of each composite function.

Solution

a. $(g \circ f)(x) = g(f(x)) = (f(x))^2 - 5 = \left(\sqrt{x}\right)^2 - 5 = x - 5$
$(f \circ g)(x) = f(g(x)) = \sqrt{g(x)} = \sqrt{x^2 - 5}$

b. Domain of $g \circ f$: even though the rule $x - 5$ is defined for every real number x, the domain of $g \circ f$ is *not* the set of all real numbers.

• The domain of f is $x \geq 0$
• The domain of g is all real numbers, so all values of $f(x)$ are in the domain of g.

Thus, the domain of $g \circ f$ is $x \geq 0$.

Domain of $f \circ g$:

• The domain of g is all real numbers.
• The values of $g(x)$ that are in the domain of f are

$$x^2 - 5 \geq 0$$
$$x \leq -\sqrt{5} \text{ or } x \geq \sqrt{5}$$

Thus, the domain of $f \circ g$ is $x \leq -\sqrt{5}$ or $x \geq \sqrt{5}$. ∎

Expressing Functions as Composites

In calculus, it is often necessary to write a function as the composition of two simpler functions. For a function with a complicated rule, this can usually be done in several ways.

Example 5   Writing a Function as a Composite

Let $h(x) = \sqrt{3x^2 + 1}$. Write h as a composition of functions in two different ways.

Solution

The function h can be written as the composite $g \circ f$, where $f(x) = 3x^2 + 1$ and $g(x) = \sqrt{x}$.

$$(g \circ f)(x) = g(f(x)) = g(3x^2 + 1) = \sqrt{3x^2 + 1}$$

Additionally, h can be written as the composite $j \circ k$, where $j(x) = \sqrt{x + 1}$ and $k(x) = 3x^2$.

$$(j \circ k)(x) = j(k(x)) = j(3x^2) = \sqrt{3x^2 + 1}$$ ∎

Graphs of Composite Functions

The graph of a composite function can sometimes be described in terms of transformations.

Example 6   Compositions with Absolute-Value Functions

Let $g(x) = |x|$ and $f(x) = \sqrt{x}$. Graph f and the composite function $f \circ g = f(|x|)$, and describe the relationship between the graphs of f and $f \circ g$ in terms of transformations.

Solution

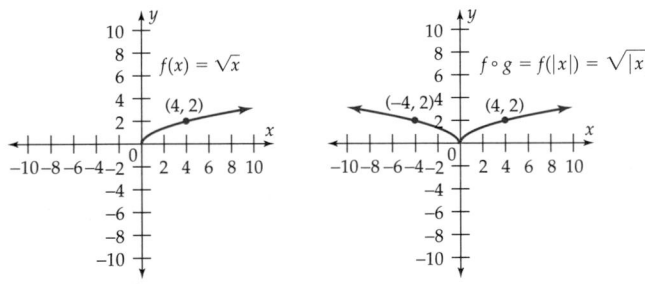

For $x \geq 0$, the graphs of f and $f \circ g$ are the same. For $x < 0$, the graph of $f \circ g$ is the graph of $f(-x)$, a reflection of the graph of f across the y-axis.

ADDITIONAL EXAMPLES

Example 5

Let $h(x) = \sqrt{x^3 - 5}$. Write h as a composition of functions in two different ways.

a. Let $f(x) = x^3 - 5$, $g(x) = \sqrt{x}$.

Then $h(x) = (g \circ f)(x)$
$= g(f(x))$
$= g(x^3 - 5)$
$= \sqrt{x^3 - 5}$.

b. Let $j(x) = \sqrt{x - 5}$, $k(x) = x^3$.

Then $h(x) = (j \circ k)(x)$
$= j(k(x))$
$= j(x^3)$
$= \sqrt{x^3 - 5}$.

Example 6

Let $g(x) = |x|$ and $f(x) = 1 - x$. Graph f and the composite function $g \circ f = |f(x)|$, and describe the relationship between the graphs of f and $g \circ f$ in terms of transformations.

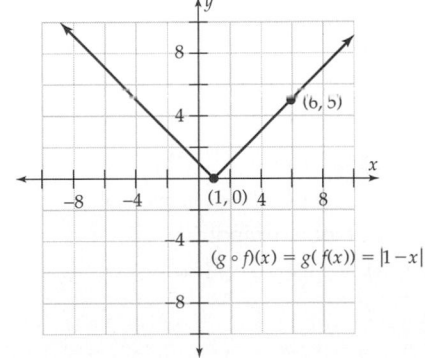

For $x \leq 1$, the graphs of f and $g \circ f$ are the same. For $x > 1$, the graph of $g \circ f$ is the graph of $-f(x)$, a reflection of the graph of f across the x-axis.

ADDITIONAL EXAMPLES

Example 7

A cylindrical container is being filled with water. After t minutes, the height of the water in the container is $h(t) = \frac{1}{2}t + 3$ inches. The volume V of the water in the container is given by $V(h) = \frac{\pi}{4}h^3$.

Express the volume as a function of time by finding $(V \circ h)(t) = V(h(t))$, and compute the volume at $t = 2$ minutes.

$$(V \circ h)(t) = V\left(\frac{1}{2}t + 3\right)$$

$$= \frac{\pi}{4}\left(\frac{1}{2}t + 3\right)^3$$

For $t = 2$,

$$(V \circ h)(2) = V\left(\frac{1}{2}(2) + 3\right)$$

$$= V(4)$$

$$= \frac{\pi}{4}(4)^3$$

$$= 16\pi$$

$$\approx 50.265 \text{ cu. in.}$$

Exercises 3.5

ANSWERS

1. $(f + g)(x) = x^3 - 3x + 2$;
   $(f - g)(x) = -x^3 - 3x + 2$;
   $(g - f)(x) = x^3 + 3x - 2$; domain for each is all real numbers

2. $(f + g)(x) = x^2 - 4x + 9$;
   $(f - g)(x) = x^2 + 4x - 5$;
   $(g - f)(x) = -x^2 - 4x + 5$;
   domain for each is all real numbers

3. $(f + g)(x) = \frac{1}{x} + x^2 + 2x - 5$;
   $(f - g)(x) = \frac{1}{x} - x^2 - 2x + 5$;
   $(g - f)(x) = x^2 + 2x - 5 - \frac{1}{x}$;
   domain for each is all real numbers except 0

4. $(f + g)(x) = \sqrt{x} + x^2 + 1$;
   $(f - g)(x) = \sqrt{x} - x^2 - 1$;
   $(g - f)(x) = x^2 + 1 - \sqrt{x}$;
   domain for each is $x \geq 0$

5. $(fg)(x) = -3x^4 + 2x^3$;
   $\left(\frac{f}{g}\right)(x) = \frac{-3x + 2}{x^3}$;
   $\left(\frac{g}{f}\right)(x) = \frac{x^3}{-3x + 2}$

6. $(fg)(x) = (4x^2 + x^4)\sqrt{x^2 + 4}$
   $\left(\frac{f}{g}\right)(x) = \frac{4x^2 + x^4}{\sqrt{x^2 + 4}}$
   $\left(\frac{g}{f}\right)(x) = \frac{\sqrt{x^2 + 4}}{4x^2 + x^4}$

7. $(fg)(x) = \sqrt{(x^2 - 1)(x - 1)}$
   $\left(\frac{f}{g}\right)(x) = \sqrt{x + 1}$
   $\left(\frac{g}{f}\right)(x) = \sqrt{\frac{1}{x + 1}}$

Applications

Composition of functions arises in applications involving several functional relationships. In such cases, one quantity may have to be expressed as a function of another.

Example 7   The Area of a Circular Puddle

A circular puddle of liquid is evaporating and slowly shrinking in size. After t minutes, the radius r of the surface of the puddle measures $r(t) = \dfrac{18}{2t + 3}$ inches. The area A of the surface of the puddle is given by $A(r) = \pi r^2$.

Express the area as a function of time by finding $(A \circ r)(t) = A(r(t))$, and compute the area of the surface of the puddle at $t = 12$ minutes.

Solution

Substitute $r(t) = \dfrac{18}{2t + 3}$ into the area function $A(r)$.

$$(A \circ r)(t) = A\left(\frac{18}{2t + 3}\right) = \pi\left(\frac{18}{2t + 3}\right)^2$$

At $t = 12$ minutes, the area of the surface of the puddle is

$$(A \circ r)(12) = \pi\left(\frac{18}{2 \cdot 12 + 3}\right)^2 = \frac{4\pi}{9} \approx 1.396 \text{ square inches.}$$

Exercises 3.5

In Exercises 1–4, find $(f + g)(x)$, $(f - g)(x)$, $(g - f)(x)$, and their domains.

1. $f(x) = -3x + 2$ $g(x) = x^3$

2. $f(x) = x^2 + 2$ $g(x) = -4x + 7$

3. $f(x) = \frac{1}{x}$ $g(x) = x^2 + 2x - 5$

4. $f(x) = \sqrt{x}$ $g(x) = x^2 + 1$

In Exercises 5–7, find $(fg)(x)$, $\left(\frac{f}{g}\right)(x)$, and $\left(\frac{g}{f}\right)(x)$.

5. $f(x) = -3x + 2$ $g(x) = x^3$

6. $f(x) = 4x^2 + x^4$ $g(x) = \sqrt{x^2 + 4}$

7. $f(x) = \sqrt{x^2 - 1}$ $g(x) = \sqrt{x - 1}$

In Exercises 8–11, find the domains of fg and $\frac{f}{g}$.

8. $f(x) = x^2 + 1$ $g(x) = \frac{1}{x}$

9. $f(x) = x + 2$ $g(x) = \frac{1}{x + 2}$

10. $f(x) = \sqrt{4 - x^2}$ $g(x) = \sqrt{3x + 4}$

11. $f(x) = 3x^2 + x^4 + 2$ $g(x) = 4x - 3$

In Exercises 12–14, find $(g \circ f)(3)$, $(f \circ g)(1)$, and $(f \circ f)(0)$.

12. $f(x) = 3x - 2$ $g(x) = x^2$ **49; 1; −8**

13. $f(x) = |x + 2|$ $g(x) = -x^2$ **−25; 1; 4**

14. $f(x) = x^2 - 1$ $g(x) = \sqrt{x}$ **8; 0; 0**

8. fg and $\frac{f}{g}$: all real numbers except 0

9. fg and $\frac{f}{g}$: all real numbers except −2

10. $\frac{f}{g}$: $\left[-\frac{4}{3}, 2\right]$;
    $\frac{f}{g}$: $\left(-\frac{4}{3}, 2\right]$

11. fg: all real numbers;
    $\frac{f}{g}$: all real numbers except $\frac{3}{4}$

In Exercises 15–18, find the indicated values, where

$$g(t) = t^2 - t \text{ and } f(x) = 1 + x.$$

15. $g(f(0)) + f(g(0))$ **1**   **16.** $(f \circ g)(3) - 2f(1)$ **3**

17. $g(f(2) + 3)$ **30**   **18.** $f(2g(1))$ **1**

In Exercises 19–22, find the rule of the function $g \circ f$ and its domain and the rule of $f \circ g$ and its domain.

19. $f(x) = x^2$ $g(x) = x + 3$

20. $f(x) = -3x + 2$ $g(x) = x^3$

21. $f(x) = \frac{1}{x}$ $g(x) = \sqrt{x}$

22. $f(x) = \frac{1}{2x + 1}$ $g(x) = x^2 - 1$

In Exercises 23–26, find the rules of the functions ff and $f \circ f$.

23. $f(x) = x^3$ **24.** $f(x) = (x - 1)^2$

25. $f(x) = \frac{1}{x}$ **26.** $f(x) = \frac{1}{x - 1}$

In Exercises 27–30, verify that $(f \circ g)(x) = x$ and $(g \circ f)(x) = x$ for the given functions f and g.

27. $f(x) = 9x + 2$ $g(x) = \frac{x - 2}{9}$

28. $f(x) = \sqrt[3]{x - 1}$ $g(x) = x^3 + 1$

29. $f(x) = \sqrt[3]{x} + 2$ $g(x) = (x - 2)^3$

30. $f(x) = 2x^3 - 5$ $g(x) = \sqrt[3]{\frac{x + 5}{2}}$

In Exercises 31–36, write the given function as the composite of two functions, neither of which is the identity function, $f(x) = x$. (There may be more than one possible answer.)

31. $f(x) = \sqrt[3]{x^2 + 2}$

32. $g(x) = \sqrt{x + 3} - \sqrt[3]{x + 3}$

33. $h(x) = (7x^3 - 10x + 17)^7$

34. $k(x) = \sqrt[3]{(7x - 3)^2}$

35. $f(x) = \frac{1}{3x^2 + 5x - 7}$ **36.** $g(t) = \frac{3}{\sqrt{t - 3}} + 7$

In Exercises 37 and 38, graph both $g \circ f$ and $f \circ g$ on the same screen. Use the graphs to show that $g \circ f \neq f \circ g$.

37. $f(x) = x^5 - x^3 - x$ $g(x) = x - 2$

38. $f(x) = x^3 + x$ $g(x) = \sqrt[3]{x - 1}$

For Exercises 39–42, complete the given tables by using the values of the functions f and g given below.

x	$f(x)$
1	3
2	5
3	1
4	2
5	3

x	$g(x)$
1	5
2	4
3	4
4	3
5	2

39.

x	$(g \circ f)(x)$
1	4
2	2
3	5
4	4
5	4

40.

x	$(f \circ g)(x)$
1	3
2	2
3	2
4	1
5	5

41.

x	$(f \circ f)(x)$
1	1
2	3
3	3
4	5
5	1

42.

x	$(g \circ g)(x)$
1	2
2	3
3	3
4	4
5	4

In Exercises 43–46, let $g(x) = |x|$. Graph the function f and the composite function $g \circ f = |f(x)|$ on the same graph.

43. $f(x) = 0.5x^2 - 5$

44. $f(x) = x^3 - 4x^2 + x + 3$

45. $f(x) = x + 3$ **46.** $f(x) = |x| - 2$

19. $(f \circ g)(x) = (x + 3)^2$;
$(g \circ f)(x) = x^2 + 3$; domain of
$f \circ g$ and $g \circ f$ is all real numbers.

20. $(f \circ g)(x) = -3x^3 + 2$;
$(g \circ f)(x) = (-3x + 2)^3$; domain
of $f \circ g$ and $g \circ f$ is all real
numbers.

21. $(f \circ g)(x) = \frac{1}{\sqrt{x}}$; $(g \circ f)(x) = \frac{1}{\sqrt{x}}$;
domain of $f \circ g$ and $g \circ f$ is $(0, \infty)$.

22. $(f \circ g)(x) = \frac{1}{2(x^2 - 1) + 1}$;
$(g \circ f)(x) = \left(\frac{1}{2x + 1}\right)^2 - 1$;
domain of $f \circ g$ is all real numbers
except $\pm\frac{1}{\sqrt{2}}$; domain of $g \circ f$ is
all real numbers except $-\frac{1}{2}$.

23. $(ff)(x) = x^6$; $(f \circ f)(x) = x^9$

24. $(ff)(x) = (x - 1)^4$;
$(f \circ f)(x) = \left((x - 1)^2 - 1\right)^2$

25. $(ff)(x) = \frac{1}{x^2}$; $(f \circ f)(x) = x$

26. $(ff)(x) = \left(\frac{1}{x - 1}\right)^2$;
$(f \circ f)(x) = \frac{x - 1}{2 - x}$

27. $(f \circ g)(x) = f\left(\frac{x - 2}{9}\right)$
$= 9\left(\frac{x - 2}{9}\right) + 2 = x$ and
$(g \circ f)(x) = g(9x + 2)$
$= \frac{(9x + 2) - 2}{9} = x$

28. $(f \circ g)(x) = f(x^3 + 1)$
$= \sqrt[3]{(x^3 + 1) - 1} = x$ and
$(g \circ f)(x) = g(\sqrt[3]{x - 1})$
$= \left(\sqrt[3]{x - 1}\right)^3 + 1 = x$

29. $(f \circ g)(x) = f(x - 2)^3$
$= \sqrt[3]{(x - 2)^3} + 2 = x$ and
$(g \circ f)(x) = g(\sqrt[3]{x} + 2)$
$= (\sqrt[3]{x} + 2 - 2)^3 = x$

30. $(f \circ g)(x) = f\left(\sqrt[3]{\frac{x + 5}{2}}\right)$
$= 2\left(\sqrt[3]{\frac{x + 5}{2}}\right)^3 - 5 = x$ and
$(g \circ f)(x) = g(2x^3 - 5)$
$= \sqrt[3]{\frac{(2x^3 - 5) + 5}{2}} = x$

31. $f(x) = (B \circ A)(x)$, where
$A(x) = x^2 + 2, B(x) = \sqrt[3]{x}$

32. $g(x) = (f \circ h)(x)$, where
$h(x) = x + 3, f(x) = \sqrt{x} - \sqrt[3]{x}$

33. $h(x) = (B \circ A)(x)$, where
$A(x) = 7x^3 - 10x + 17, B(x) = x^7$

34. $k(x) = (f \circ g)(x)$, where
$f(x) = \sqrt[3]{x}, g(x) = (7x - 3)^2$

35. $f(x) = (B \circ A)(x)$, where
$A(x) = 3x^2 + 5x - 7$,
$B(x) = \frac{1}{x}$

36. $g(t) = (f \circ h)(t)$, where
$f(t) = \frac{3}{t} + 7, h(t) = \sqrt{t - 3}$

37, 38. *See p.* 1060.

43–46. *See pp.* 1060–1061.

47. a. $(g \circ f)(x) = |f(x)|$; By the definition of absolute value,

$$|f(x)| = \begin{cases} f(x) & \text{if } f(x) \geq 0 \\ -f(x) & \text{if } f(x) < 0 \end{cases}$$

b. When $f(x) \geq 0$ the graph of $g \circ f$ is the same as the graph of f. When $f(x) < 0$, the graph of f is below the x-axis, but the graph of $-f$ is the reflection of f across the x-axis; therefore, the graph will be above the x-axis.

48.

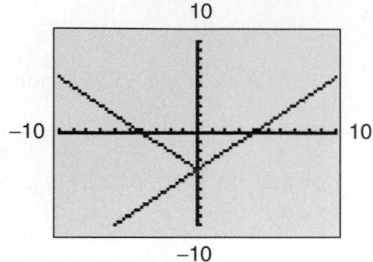

$y_1 = x - 4$,

$y_2 = f \circ g = f(|x|) = |x| - 4$

49.

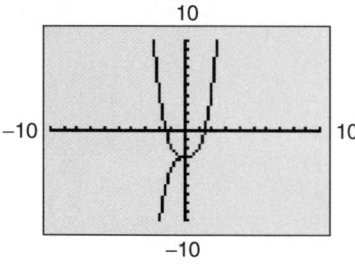

$y_1 = x^3 - 3$,

$y_2 = f \circ g = f(|x|) = |x|^3 - 3$

50.

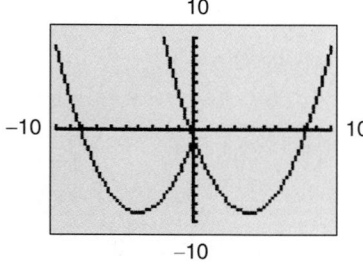

$y_1 = 0.5(x - 4)^2 - 9$,

$y_2 = f \circ g = f(|x|)$

$\quad = 0.5(|x| - 4)^2 - 9$

51.

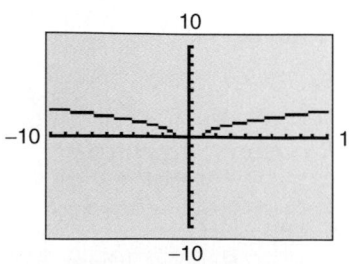

$y_1 = \sqrt{x - 1}$,

$y_2 = f \circ g = f(|x|) = \sqrt{|x| - 1}$

47. a. Use the piecewise definition of absolute value to explain why the following statement is true:

$$(g \circ f)(x) = \begin{cases} -f(x) & \text{if } f(x) < 0 \\ f(x) & \text{if } f(x) \geq 0 \end{cases}$$

b. Use part **a** and your knowledge of transformations to explain why the graph of $g \circ f$ consists of the parts of the graph of f that lie above the x-axis together with the reflection across the x-axis of those parts of the graph of f that lie below the x-axis.

In Exercises 48–52, let $g(x) = |x|$. **Graph the function f and the composite function $f \circ g = f(|x|)$ on the same graph.**

48. $f(x) = x - 4$ **49.** $f(x) = x^3 - 3$

50. $f(x) = 0.5(x - 4)^2 - 9$ **51.** $f(x) = \sqrt{x - 1}$

52. Write a piecewise definition for $f \circ g$.

53. If f is any function and I is the identity function $I(x) = x$, what are $f \circ I$ and $I \circ f$? $f \circ I = I \circ f = f$

54. In a laboratory culture, the number $N(d)$ of bacteria (in thousands) at temperature d degrees Celsius is given by the function

$$N(d) = \frac{-90}{d + 1} + 20 \quad (4 \leq d \leq 32)$$

and the temperature $D(t)$ at time t hours is given by the function $D(t) = 2t + 4$ $(0 \leq t \leq 14)$

a. What does the composite function $N \circ D$ represent?

b. How many bacteria are in the culture after 4 hours? after 10 hours?

55. Suppose that a manufacturer produces n telephones. The unit cost for producing each telephone is given by the function

$$U(n) = \frac{\text{total cost}}{\text{number of phones}} = \frac{12{,}000 + 15n}{n}$$

The price P of each telephone is the unit cost plus a 30% markup. Find $(P \circ U)(n)$, and interpret the result.

56. Find the unit price in Exercise 55 if 10,000 telephones are produced. **$21.06**

57. As a weather balloon is inflated, its radius increases at the rate of 4 cm per second. Express the volume of the balloon as a function of time, and determine the volume of the balloon after 4 seconds. *Hint:* the volume of a sphere of radius r is $\frac{4}{3}\pi r^3$. $V = \frac{256\pi t^3}{3}$; $\approx 17{,}157.28 \text{ cm}^3$

58. Express the surface area of the weather balloon in Exercise 57 as a function of time. *Hint:* the surface area of a sphere of radius r is $4\pi r^2$. $S(t) = 64\pi t^2$

59. Brandon, who is 6 ft tall, walks away from a streetlight that is 15 ft high at a rate of 5 ft per second, as shown in the figure. Express the length s of Brandon's shadow as a function of time. *Hint:* first use similar triangles to express s as a function of the distance d from the streetlight to Brandon.

$$s = \frac{10t}{3}$$

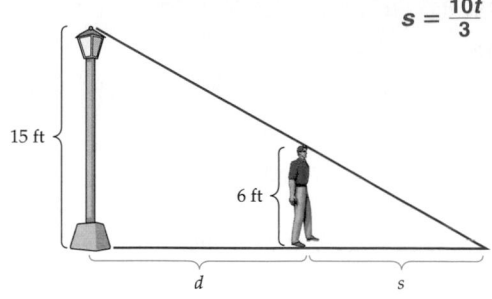

60. A water-filled balloon is dropped from a window 120 ft above the ground. Its height above the ground after t seconds is $120 - 16t^2$ ft. Laura is standing on the ground 40 ft from the point where the balloon will hit the ground, as shown in the figure.

a. Express the distance d between Laura and the balloon as a function of time.

b. When is the balloon exactly 90 ft from Laura?

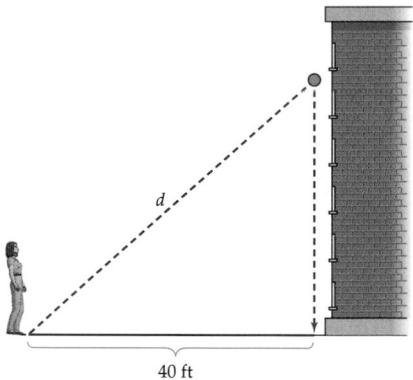

61. *Critical Thinking* Find a function f (other than the identity function) such that $(f \circ f \circ f)(x) = x$ for every value of x in the domain of f. (More than one correct answer is possible.)

One such function is $f(x) = \dfrac{x - 1}{x}$.

52. $f \circ g = \begin{cases} f(-x) & x < 0 \\ f(x) & x \geq 0 \end{cases}$

54. a. It gives the number of bacteria as a function of time.

b. about 13 thousand after 4 hours and 16.4 thousand after 10 hours

55. $(P \circ U)(n) = \dfrac{15{,}600 + 19.5n}{n}$ gives the unit price as a function of n, the number of telephones produced.

60. a. $d(t) = \sqrt{(120 - 16t^2)^2 + 40^2}$

b. approximately 1.56879 seconds

Excursion: Iterations and Dynamical Systems

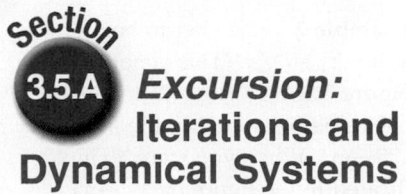

Excursion: Iterations and Dynamical Systems

Discrete dynamical systems, which deal with growth and change, occur in economics, biology, and a variety of other scientific fields. Compound interest provides a simple example of a discrete dynamical system. As discussed in Chapter 5, an investment of P dollars at 8% interest compounded annually for one year grows by a factor of 1.08 each year. For example, an investment of $1000 grows like this:

$1000.00   *Initial amount*

$1.08(1000) = \$1080.00$ *Amount after one year*

$1.08(1080) = \$1166.40$ *Amount after two years*

$1.08(1166.40) = \$1259.71$ *Amount after three years*

This process can be described in function notation as follows. Let $f(x) = 1.08x$.

$1000.00   *Initial amount*

$\$1080 = 1.08(1000) = f(1000)$ *After one year*

$\$1166.40 = 1.08(1080) = f(1080) = f(f(1000))$ *After two years*

$\$1259.71 = 1.08(1166.40) = f(1166.40) = f(f(f(1000)))$ *After three years*

In each step after the first one the output of the function f becomes the input for the next step, and the final result can be expressed in terms of a composite function.

Iteration

Iterations of a function are the repeated compositions of a function with itself.

1. Select a number k as the initial input.
2. Compute the output $f(k)$.
3. Using the output from Step 2 as input, compute the output $f(f(k))$.
4. Continue the process repeatedly, using the output from each step as the input for the next step.

Iterated Function Notation

Because function notation becomes cumbersome after several steps, the following abbreviated notation is used for iterations of functions:

x is the initial value

$f(x)$ denotes $f(x)$, the first iteration

$f^2(x)$ denotes $f(f(x))$, the second iteration

$f^3(x)$ denotes $f(f(f(x)))$, the third iteration

and in general

$f^n(x)$ denotes the nth iteration.

CAUTION

Do not confuse this notation with exponents. $f^2(x)$ does *not* represent the product of two output values, $f(x) \cdot f(x)$.

Teaching Notes

You may want to have students use a calculator to verify each of the calculations shown for computing the growth of an investment of $1,000.

Remind students that the factor 1.08 is the result of the compound interest formula, where $r = 0.08$ and $t = 1$.

$A = P(1 + r)^t$

$A = P(1 + 0.08)^1 = P(1.08)$

Remind students that $f(g(x))$ is the composition $(f \circ g)(x)$. Point out that $f(f(1000))$ is $(f \circ f)(1000)$.

Math Background

Iterated function notation is similar to higher order derivative notation that students will encounter in calculus. For example, $f^3(x)$ represents the third iteration $f(f(f(x)))$, while $f^{(3)}(x)$ is sometimes used to represent the third derivative of f with respect to x. Although the *notations* are similar, the operations they represent are entirely different.

Example Notes

In **Example 2**, remember to begin by entering $Y_1 = \sqrt{x}$. (This is not shown in Figure 3.5.A-1.) Store .25 in x as the initial value (indicated in the Figure by .25 → x). When you store Y_1 in x (indicated in the figure by $Y_1 \to x$), you are replacing the current value of x with its square root, $\sqrt{x}$. Then, every time you press ENTER, you replace the current value of x (the old square root) with its new square root.

In **Example 3**, Figure 3.5.A-2, remind students that 6.5536E-4 means 6.5536×10^{-4}, which is scientific notation for 0.00065536.

In finding the orbit for $x = 0.4$, if students repeatedly press the ENTER key, the display will eventually show 0. For $x = 2$, however, the display will continue to show larger numbers until an overflow error has occurred.

Teaching Notes

To help students understand **Converging Orbits,** after finding the solution for **Example 2**, have students continue to press ENTER until the display shows the value to which the orbit converges. When this happens, the calculator has reached a number so close that it rounds to that value.

Solution to the **Calculator Exploration** (at top of page 201):
For $x = 100$:
100
10
3.16227766
⋮
1.002251148
converges to 1

Possible Answers:
For $x = 1,000,000,000$:
1,000,000,000
31622.7766
177.827941
⋮
1.01017015
converges to 1

NOTE Throughout this section all numerical results are displayed rounded to four decimal places, but computations are done using the full decimal expansion given by a calculator.

Technology Tip

- If a function has been entered as Y_1 in the equation memory, it can be iterated as follows:
- Store the initial value as X.
- Key in Y_1 STO▸ X. Pressing ENTER repeatedly produces the iterated values of the function.

Example 1 **Iterated Function Notation**

Write the first four iterations of the function $f(x) = \sqrt{x}$ with $x = 0.25$ using iterated function notation.

Solution

$$f(0.25) = \sqrt{0.25} = 0.5$$
$$f^2(0.25) = \sqrt{\sqrt{0.25}} \approx 0.7071$$
$$f^3(0.25) = \sqrt{\sqrt{\sqrt{0.25}}} \approx 0.8409$$
$$f^4(0.25) = \sqrt{\sqrt{\sqrt{\sqrt{0.25}}}} \approx 0.9170$$

Orbits

For a given function, the **orbit** of a number, c, is the sequence of output values produced by starting with c and then iterating the function. That is, the orbit of a number c for a given function f is the sequence

$$c, f(c), f^2(c), f^3(c), f^4(c), f^5(c), \ldots$$

Example 2 **Orbits**

Find the orbit of $x = 0.25$ for $f(x) = \sqrt{x}$.

Solution

Enter $Y_1 = \sqrt{X}$ in the equation memory. Using the Technology Tip in the margin yields the orbit of $x = 0.25$.

Figure 3.5.A-1

Converging Orbits

Notice that the orbit of $x = 0.25$ in Example 2 has the property that as n gets larger, the terms of the orbit get closer and closer to 1. The orbit is said to **converge** to 1.

Calculator Exploration

Let $f(x) = \sqrt{x}$ and compute the first twelve terms of the orbit of $x = 100$. To what number does the orbit appear to converge?

Choose another positive number and compute its orbit. Does the orbit appear to converge? To what number?

Figure 3.5.A-2

Figure 3.5.A-3

Example 2 and the preceding Exploration suggest that the orbit of every positive number under the function $f(x) = \sqrt{x}$ converges to 1. The following notation is sometimes used to express this fact.

$$\text{For } f(x) = \sqrt{x} \text{ and } x > 0,$$
$$f^n(x) \to 1 \text{ as } n \to \infty$$

Example 3 Orbits

Find the orbits of $x = 0.4$ and $x = 2$ for the function $f(x) = x^2$.

Solution

Let $Y_1 = X^2$ and $x = 0.4$. Figure 3.5.A-2 shows that the orbit begins

$$0.4, 0.16, 0.0256, 0.0006554, 0.0000004295, \ldots$$

and that the orbit appears to converge to 0.

Now let $x = 2$. Figure 3.5.A-3 shows that the orbit begins

$$2, 4, 16, 256, 65536, 4294967296, \ldots$$

In this case, the orbit is not converging: its terms get larger and larger without bound as n increases. The fact is expressed by saying that the orbit diverges or that the orbit **approaches infinity.** ∎

Calculator Exploration

Choose a number strictly between -1 and 1 and find its orbit under the function $f(x) = x^2$. Does the orbit converge? To what number?

Choose another number with absolute value greater than 1 and find its orbit. How would you describe the behavior of the orbit?

Example 3 and the preceding Exploration suggest that the orbit of a number x converges to 0 when $-1 < x < 1$, but that the orbit of x approaches infinity when $|x| > 1$. This fact is expressed as follows.

$$\text{For } f(x) = x^2 \text{ and } |x| < 1, f^n(x) \to 0 \text{ as } n \to \infty$$
$$\text{For } f(x) = x^2 \text{ and } |x| > 1, f^n(x) \to \infty \text{ as } n \to \infty$$

Example 4

Describe the orbit of each of the following.

a. $x = 0$ under the function $f(x) = \sqrt{x}$
orbit: 0, 0, 0, ... Thus 0 is a fixed point.

b. $x = -1$ under $f(x) = |x|$
orbit: −1, 1, 1, 1, ... Thus −1 is an eventually fixed point.

c. $x = 3$ under $f(x) = \dfrac{1}{x}$
orbit: 3, $\dfrac{1}{3}$, 3, $\dfrac{1}{3}$, 3, ... The orbit is periodic and 3 is a periodic point.

d. $x = -1$ under $f(x) = |x - 3|$
orbit: −1, 4, 1, 2, 1, 2, ... The orbit is eventually periodic and −1 is an eventually periodic point.

Example 5

Analyze all the orbits of $f(x) = x^3$ and illustrate them graphically.

When $x > 1$, the orbit of x approaches ∞.

When $x < -1$, the orbit of x approaches $-\infty$.

When $-1 < x < 1$, the orbit of x converges to 0.

The orbit of 1 is 1, 1, 1, 1, ... so 1 is a fixed point.

The orbit of 0 is 0, 0, 0, 0, ... so 0 is a fixed point.

The orbit of −1 is −1, −1, −1, ... so −1 is a fixed point.

Red: Fixed points
Green: Orbits that converge to 0
Blue: Orbits that approach ∞ or $-\infty$

Fixed Points and Periodic Orbits

In addition to orbits that converge and orbits that approach infinity, there are several other possibilities, some of which are illustrated in the next example.

Example 4   Orbits

Describe the orbit of each of the following.

a. $x = 1$ under the function $f(x) = \sqrt{x}$
b. $x = -1$ under $f(x) = x^2$
c. $x = 4$ under $f(x) = \dfrac{1}{x}$
d. $x = \sqrt{2}$ under $f(x) = x^2 - 1$

Solution

a. Because $f(1) = \sqrt{1} = 1$, the orbit is 1, 1, 1, …. Consequently, 1 is said to be a **fixed point** of the function $f(x) = \sqrt{x}$.

b. The orbit is −1, 1, 1, 1, … because $f(-1) = (-1)^2 = 1$. Hence, −1 is said to be an **eventually fixed point** of the function $f(x) = x^2$.

c. Because $f(4) = \dfrac{1}{4}$ and $f\!\left(\dfrac{1}{4}\right) = \dfrac{1}{\frac{1}{4}} = 4$, the orbit is 4, $\dfrac{1}{4}$, 4, $\dfrac{1}{4}$, 4, ….

Since it repeats the same values, the orbit is said to be **periodic** and 4 is said to be a **periodic point.**

d. Direct computation shows that

$$f(\sqrt{2}) = (\sqrt{2})^2 - 1 = 1$$
$$f^2(\sqrt{2}) = 1^2 - 1 = 0$$
$$f^3(\sqrt{2}) = 0^2 - 1 = -1$$
$$f^4(\sqrt{2}) = (-1)^2 - 1 = 0.$$

Therefore, the orbit is $\sqrt{2}$, 1, 0, −1, 0 −1, 0, −1, …. Because the orbit begins to repeat its values after a few steps, it is said to be **eventually periodic** and $\sqrt{2}$ is said to be an **eventually periodic point.** ∎

Example 5   Orbit Analysis

Analyze all the orbits of $f(x) = x^2$ and illustrate them graphically.

Solution

Example 3 and the Calculator Exploration after it suggest two possibilities.
When $|x| < 1$, the orbit of x converges to 0.
When $|x| > 1$, the orbit of x approaches infinity.

Example Notes

In **Example 4c**, point out that $\dfrac{1}{4}$ is also a periodic point.

That is, the orbit of $x = \dfrac{1}{4}$ under $f(x) = \dfrac{1}{x}$ is $\dfrac{1}{4}$, 4, $\dfrac{1}{4}$, 4, $\dfrac{1}{4}$, ….

In **Example 5**, for Figure 3.5.A-4, point out that:
- the two green arcs represent all numbers in the intervals (−1, 0) and (0, 1), and
- the blue arcs represent all numbers in the intervals (−∞, −1) and (1, ∞) (not just integers).

The orbit of 1 is 1, 1, 1, ..., so 1 is a fixed point.
The orbit of 0 is 0, 0, 0, ..., so 0 is a fixed point.
The orbit of −1 is −1, 1, 1, ..., so −1 is an eventually fixed point.

Figure 3.5.A-4 illustrates the orbits of $f(x) = x^2$.

Red: Fixed points

Orange: Eventually fixed point

Green: Orbits that converge to 0

Figure 3.5.A-4   Blue: Orbits that approach ∞

For a function f, if $f(a) = a$, for some value a, then a is called a fixed point of the function.

Exercises 3.5.A

In Exercises 1–6, find the first eight terms of the orbit of the given number under the given function.

1. $x = 2$ and $f(x) = 1.08x$

2. $x = 0.8$ and $f(x) = -2.5x$

3. $x = 0.2$ and $f(x) = 4x(1 - x)$

4. $x = 1.2$ and $f(x) = 4x(1 - x)$

5. $x = 0.5$ and $f(x) = x^3 - x$

6. $x = 0.1$ and $f(x) = x^3 + x^2$

In Exercises 7–12, determine whether the orbit of the point under the function $f(x) = 4x(1 - x)$ converges or approaches infinity or neither.

7. $x = -1$ **8.** $x = -0.5$
   approaches infinity   approaches negative infinity
9. $x = 0$ **10.** $x = 0.5$
   converges to 0   converges to 0
11. $x = 1$ **12.** $x = 1.5$
   converges to 0   approaches negative
                         infinity

In Exercises 13–18, find the real number fixed points of the function (if any) by solving the equation $g(x) = x$.

13. $g(x) = x^2 - 6$ **14.** $g(x) = x^2 - 3x - 3$
   3 and −2 $\dfrac{4 + \sqrt{28}}{2}$ and $\dfrac{4 - \sqrt{28}}{2}$
15. $g(x) = x^3$ **16.** $g(x) = x^3 - 2x^2 + 2x$
   0, 1, and −1   **0 and 1**
17. $g(x) = x^2 - x - 1$ **18.** $g(x) = x^2 - x + 2$

19. Determine all the fixed points and all the eventually fixed points of the function $f(x) = |x|$.

20. Let $f(x) = |x - 2|$.
   a. Find the orbit of x for every integer value of x such that $-4 \le x \le 4$. Classify each point as fixed, eventually fixed, periodic, or eventually periodic.
   b. Describe a pattern in the classifications you made in part **a**.

21 Let $f(x) = |x - 1|$ and perform an orbit analysis as follows.
   a. Show that $x = 0.5$ is a fixed point and that $x = -0.5$ is an eventually fixed point.
   b. Show that $x = 0$ and $x = 1$ are periodic points.

Section 3.6 Inverse Functions

Teaching Notes

Remind students that a relation is a set of ordered pairs. The relation shown in the first table is {(1995, 5.69), (1996, 5.77), (1997, 5.85), (1998, 5.92), (1999, 6.00), (2000, 6.08)}. Its domain is {1995, 1996, 1997, 1998, 1999, 2000} and its range is {5.69, 5.77, 5.85, 5.92, 6.00, 6.08}.

By exchanging the numbers in each ordered pair, we get the inverse relation. So, the domain of the inverse relation is the range of the original relation and the range of the inverse relation is the domain of the original relation.

You may want to encourage students to observe that in this case both relations pass the vertical line test, i.e., that both relations are functions.

Real-World Application

Refer students to www.census.gov to have them collect similar population data about their state or community. Have them present their data set as a relation and an inverse relation.

Math Background

The inverse of a relation is always a relation (which may be a function). The inverse of a function is always a relation (which may be a function). Determining whether the inverse is, in fact, a function will be addressed on page 208.

3.6 Inverse Functions

Objectives

- Define inverse relations and functions
- Find inverse relations from tables, graphs, and equations
- Determine whether an inverse relation is a function
- Verify inverses using composition

Inverse Relations and Functions

Consider the following question:

What was the world population in 1997?

The answer to the question can be thought of as the output of a function. The input of the function is a year, 1997, and the output is a number of people. The function can be represented by a table of values or a scatter plot, as shown below. From the table, the output corresponding to the input of 1997 was a world population of 5.85 billion people.

Year	Population (in billions)
1995	5.69
1996	5.77
1997	5.85
1998	5.92
1999	6.00
2000	6.08

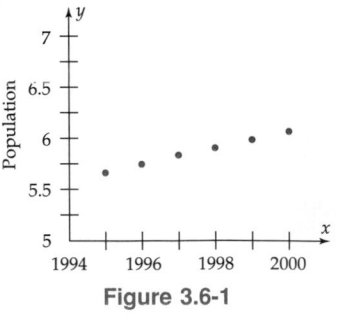

Figure 3.6-1

Now consider another question:

In what year was the world population 6 billion people?

In this question, the input and output are reversed. The input is a population, 6 billion, and the output is a year. To create a function to answer this question, exchange the columns in the table, or the axes of the scatter plot. From the table, the output corresponding to the input of 6 billion people was the year 1999.

Population (in billions)	Year
5.69	1995
5.77	1996
5.85	1997
5.92	1998
6.00	1999
6.08	2000

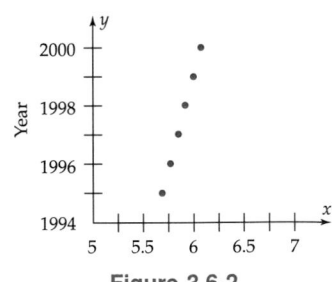

Figure 3.6-2

The result of exchanging the input and output values of a function or relation is called an **inverse relation.** If the inverse is a function, it is called the **inverse function.**

Graphs of Inverse Relations

Suppose that (x, y) is a point on the graph of a function. Then (y, x) is a point on its inverse function or relation. This fact can be used to graph the inverse of a function.

Example 1   Graphing an Inverse Relation

The graph of a function f is shown below. Graph the inverse, and describe the relationship between the function and its inverse.

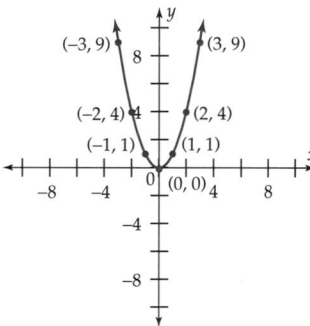

Figure 3.6-3

Solution

Start by reversing the coordinates of each labeled point. Plot these points, then sketch the relation.

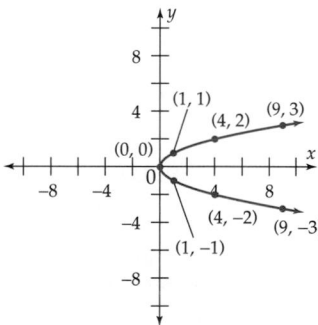

Figure 3.6-4

Example Notes

In **Example 1,** have students look at Figure 3.6-3. Ask what point should be plotted on the graph of the inverse to correspond to the point $(2, 4)$. $(4, 2)$
$(-3, 9)$? $(9, -3)$
$(1, 1)$? $(1, 1)$
Have students verify these corresponding points in Figure 3.6-4.

Students may or may not recognize that these relations are given by $y = x^2$ and $y = \pm\sqrt{x}$. Identifying the correct equations is not necessary in this example.

ADDITIONAL EXAMPLES

Example 1

The graph of a function f is shown. Graph the inverse, and describe the relationship between the function and its inverse.

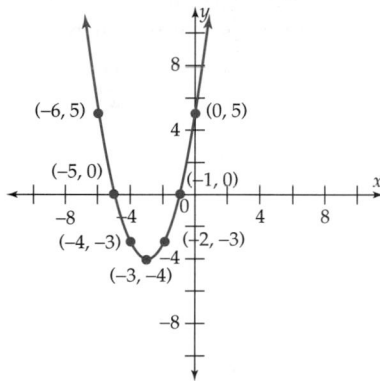

The graph of the inverse is the reflection of the graph of the original function across the line $y = x$.

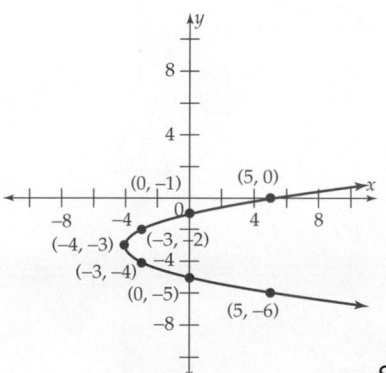

Teaching Notes

To help students visualize that the line $y = x$ is indeed the perpendicular bisector of a segment from (a, b) to (b, a), show a segment in Figure 3.6-5 from $(9, 3)$ to $(3, 9)$, as shown below.

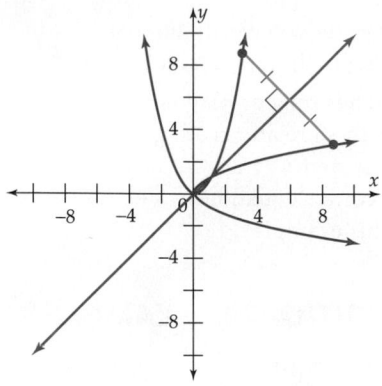

Example Notes

In **Example 2**, have students graph the line $y = x$ on the same graph as f and its inverse. Accomplish this by including a third set of parametric equations: $x_3 = t$ and $y_3 = t$.

Exercise 55 shows that the line $y = x$ is the perpendicular bisector of the segment from (a, b) to (b, a), which means that the two points are reflections of each other across the line $y = x$. Thus, the graph of the inverse of $f(x) = x^2$ in Example 1 is a reflection of the original graph across the line $y = x$.

> **CAUTION**
>
> When using a calculator to verify that an inverse is a reflection over the line $y = x$, it is important to use a square viewing window.

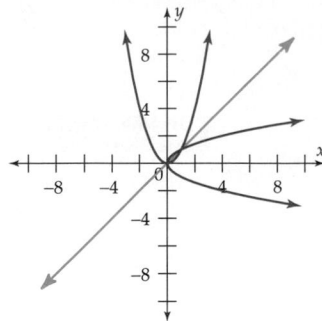

Figure 3.6-5

Graphs of Inverse Relations

> Let f be a function. If (a, b) is a point on the graph of f, then (b, a) is a point on the graph of its inverse.
>
> The graph of the inverse of f is a reflection of the graph of f across the line
> $$y = x$$

The definition of an inverse makes it very easy to graph an inverse by using parametric graphing mode. Recall that to graph the function $y = f(x)$ in parametric mode, let $x_1 = t$ and $y_1 = f(t)$. To graph the inverse, let $x_2 = f(t)$ and $y_2 = t$.

Example 2   Graphing an Inverse in Parametric Mode

Graph the function $f(x) = 0.7x^5 + 0.3x^4 - 0.2x^3 + 2x + 0.5$ and its inverse in parametric mode.

Solution

To graph f, let $x_1 = t$ and $y_1 = 0.7t^5 + 0.3t^4 - 0.2t^3 + 2t + 0.5$.

To graph the inverse of f, exchange x and y by letting $x_2 = 0.7t^5 + 0.3t^4 - 0.2t^3 + 2t + 0.5$ and $y_2 = t$.

Figure 3.6-6 shows the graph of f and its inverse on the same screen with the graph of $y = x$.

Figure 3.6-6

Algebraic Representations of Inverses

Suppose that a function is represented by an equation in x and y. Then the inverse of the function is found by exchanging the input and output values, that is, by exchanging x and y.

| **Example 3** | Finding an Inverse from an Equation |

Find $g(x)$, the inverse of $f(x) = 3x - 2$.

Solution

First, write the function in terms of x and y.

$$y = 3x - 2$$

Exchange the x and the y.

$$x = 3y - 2$$

Thus, the inverse relation is $x = 3y - 2$. It is common to solve for y, so that the relation can be represented in function notation.

$$y = \frac{x + 2}{3}$$

$$g(x) = \frac{x + 2}{3}$$

┌─── **Graphing Exploration** ●────────────────┐

Graph the functions f and g from Example 3 together on the same screen with the line $y = x$, and describe your results. Be sure to use a square viewing window.

└──┘

| **Example 4** | Finding an Inverse from an Equation |

Find the inverse of $f(x) = x^2 + 4x$.

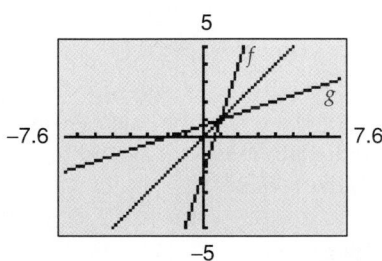

Example Notes

In **Example 4**, you may need to revisit the use of the quadratic formula. Show that for $ax^2 + bx + c = 0$,

$$x = \frac{-b \pm \sqrt{b^2 - 4ac}}{2a},$$

so for $(1)y^2 + (4)y + (-x) = 0$,

$$y = \frac{-4 \pm \sqrt{4^2 - (4)(1)(-x)}}{2(1)}.$$

COMMON ERROR ALERT

Students may incorrectly simplify expressions with radicals. Tell students to be sure that they factor out a common factor that is a square before simplifying. Show the following *correct steps* for **Example 4**:

$$\frac{-4 \pm \sqrt{16 + 4x}}{2} = \frac{-4 \pm \sqrt{4(4 + x)}}{2}$$

$$= \frac{-4 \pm \sqrt{4} \cdot \sqrt{4 + x}}{2}$$

$$= \frac{-4 \pm 2\sqrt{4 + x}}{2}$$

$$= -2 \pm \sqrt{4 + x}$$

Teaching Notes

After completing **Example 4**, explain that the inverse is not a function. Notice that for each value of x in the domain of the inverse (except $x = -4$), there are 2 corresponding y-values, namely $-2 + \sqrt{4 + x}$ and $-2 - \sqrt{4 + x}$. In order for the relation to be a function, each x-value in the domain must correspond to *exactly one y*-value.

Math Background

To determine whether a function is one-to-one, we use the horizontal line test on the graph. Another method is to apply the definition of one-to-one directly.

For example, consider $f(x) = x^3$.
If $f(a) = f(b)$, then $a^3 = b^3$, and $a = b$.
So, $f(x) = x^3$ is one-to-one.

Now consider $g(x) = x^2$.
If $g(a) = g(b)$, then $a^2 = b^2$, and $a = \pm b$.

So, $g(a) = g(b)$ does *not* imply that $a = b$.

Therefore, $g(x)$ is **not** one-to-one.

Solution

Write the function in terms of x and y.

$$y = x^2 + 4x$$

Exchange x and y.

$$x = y^2 + 4y$$

Thus, the inverse is $x = y^2 + 4y$. To solve for y, write the relation as a quadratic equation in y.

$$y^2 + 4y - x = 0$$

Then use the quadratic formula with $a = 1$, $b = 4$, and $c = -x$.

$$y = \frac{-4 \pm \sqrt{16 + 4x}}{2}$$

$$y = -2 \pm \sqrt{4 + x}$$

Notice that the inverse is not a function, so it cannot be written in function notation. ∎

Determining Whether an Inverse is a Function

The inverse of a function is also a function if every input of the inverse corresponds to exactly one output. This means that in the original function, every output corresponds to exactly one input. A function that has this property is called a **one-to-one** function.

One-to-One Functions

> **NOTE** By the definition of a function, $a = b$ implies that $f(a) = f(b)$.

> A function f is one-to-one if
> $$f(a) = f(b)$$
> implies that $a = b$.
>
> If a function is one-to-one, then its inverse is also a function.

Determining Whether a Graph is One-to-One

In Example 1, the points $(2, 4)$ and $(-2, 4)$ are both on the graph of f. These two points have different inputs and the same output, so f is not one-to-one. Also, the points $(2, 4)$ and $(-2, 4)$ lie on the same horizontal line, which suggests a graphical test for whether a function is one-to-one.

Horizontal Line Test

> A function f is one-to-one if and only if no horizontal line intersects the graph of f more than once.

Example 5   Using the Horizontal Line Test

Graph each function below and determine whether the function is one-to-one. If so, graph its inverse function.

a. $f(x) = 7x^5 + 3x^4 - 2x^3 + 2x + 1$

b. $g(x) = x^3 - 3x - 1$

c. $h(x) = 1 - 0.2x^3$

Solution

Complete graphs of each function are shown below.

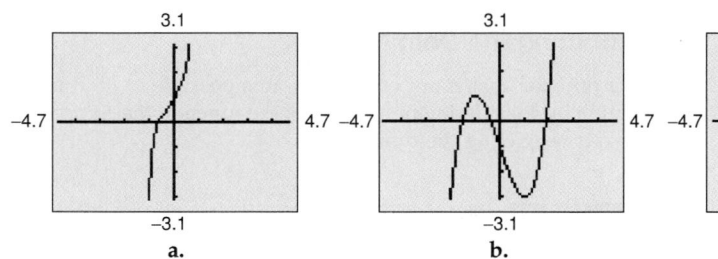

a.   **b.**   **c.**

Figure 3.6-7

Figure 3.6-8

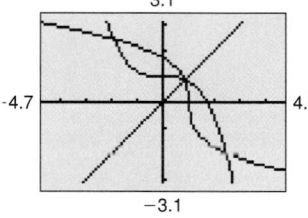

Figure 3.6-9

a. The graph of f passes the Horizontal Line Test, since no horizontal line intersects the graph more than once. Hence, f is one-to-one. The inverse function is the reflection of f across the line $y = x$, shown in Figure 3.6–8.

b. The graph of g fails the Horizontal Line Test because many horizontal lines, including the x-axis, intersect the graph more than once. Therefore, g is not one-to-one, and its inverse is not a function.

c. The graph of h appears to contain a horizontal line segment, so h appears to fail the Horizontal Line Test. In this case, it is helpful to use the trace feature to see that the points on the segment that appears horizontal do not have the same y-value. Thus, the graph of h passes the Horizontal Line Test, and so it is one-to-one. The function and its inverse are shown in Figure 3.6–9. ■

NOTE The function f in Example 5 is always increasing and the function h is always decreasing. Every increasing or decreasing function is one-to-one because its graph can never touch the same horizontal line twice—it would have to change from increasing to decreasing, or vice versa, to do so.

Example 4

Find the inverse of $f(x) = 4x^2 - 2x$.

$x = 4y^2 - 2y$

$0 = 4y^2 - 2y - x$

$a = 4, b = -2, c = -x$

$y = \dfrac{2 \pm \sqrt{4 + 16x}}{8}$

$y = \dfrac{2 \pm 2\sqrt{1 + 4x}}{8}$

$y = \dfrac{1 \pm \sqrt{1 + 4x}}{4}$

Example 5

Graph each function below and determine whether the function is one-to-one. If so, graph its inverse function.

a. $f(x) = 3x^5 - 2x^4 + 3x^3 + x - 2$

   f is one-to-one

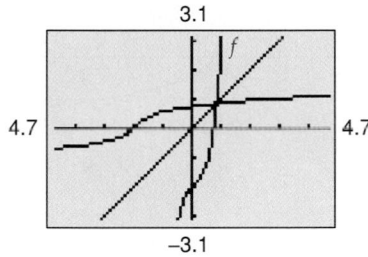

b. $g(x) = -0.5x^3 + x + 1$

   g is not one-to-one

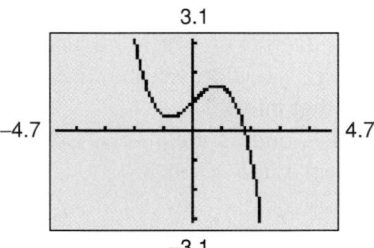

c. $h(x) = -2 - 0.8x^3$

   h is one-to-one

Restricting the domain is sometimes needed to ensure that an inverse is a function, as shown here in **Example 6**. Restricting the domain of the trigonometric functions (sine, cosine, and tangent) is also necessary to obtain inverse trigonometric functions, as discussed in Section 8.2.

In **Example 6**, the domain of $f(x) = x^2$ is restricted to $[0, \infty)$, yielding the inverse function $f^{-1}(x) = \sqrt{x}$. If the domain of $f(x) = x^2$ were restricted to $(-\infty, 0]$, then the associated inverse function would be $f^{-1}(x) = -\sqrt{x}$.

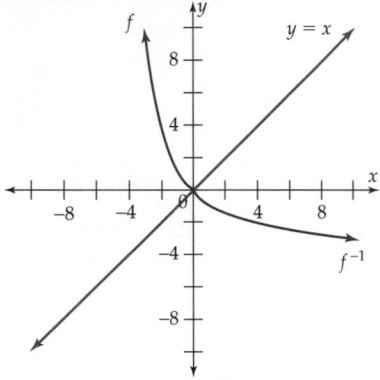

ADDITIONAL EXAMPLES

Example 6

Find an interval on which the function $f(x) = x^2 - 3$ is one-to-one, and find f^{-1} on that interval.

f is one-to-one on the interval $[0, \infty)$, as shown in the graph.

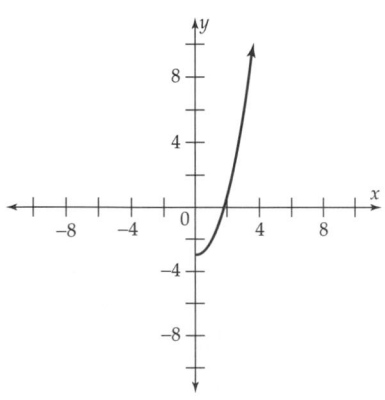

The inverse is found below:

$f(x) = x^2 - 3$
$y = x^2 - 3$
$x = y^2 - 3$
$x + 3 = y^2$
$y = \pm\sqrt{x + 3}$, so $f^{-1}(x) = \sqrt{x + 3}$

Inverse Functions

> Let f be a function. The following statements are equivalent.
> - **The inverse of f is a function.**
> - **f is one-to-one.**
> - **The graph of f passes the Horizontal Line Test.**
>
> The inverse function, if it exists, is written as f^{-1}, where
> $$\text{if } y = f(x), \text{ then } x = f^{-1}(y).$$
>
> The notation f^{-1} does not mean $\dfrac{1}{f}$.

Restricting the Domain

For a function that is not one-to-one, it is possible to produce an inverse function by considering only a part of the function that is one-to-one. This is called **restricting the domain**.

Example 6   Restricting the Domain

Find an interval on which the function $f(x) = x^2$ is one-to-one, and find f^{-1} on that interval.

Solution

The graph of f is one-to-one on the interval $[0, \infty)$, as shown in the graph. To find a rule for f^{-1}, first write the function in terms of x and y.

$$y = x^2$$

Exchange x and y in the equation, and solve for y.

$$x = y^2$$
$$y = \pm\sqrt{x}$$
$$y = \sqrt{x} \qquad \text{or} \qquad y = -\sqrt{x}$$

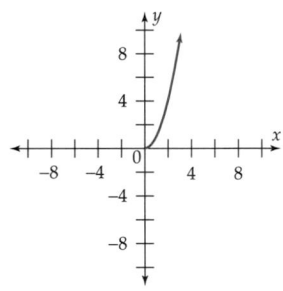

Figure 3.6-10

The values of x in $f(x)$ are restricted to nonnegative numbers. Therefore, the values of y in the inverse are restricted to nonnegative numbers.

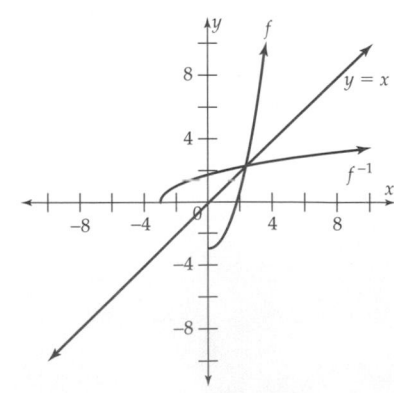

Because every point on the graph of the restricted function f has non-negative coordinates, the inverse function must be $y = \sqrt{x}$. Thus,

$$f^{-1}(x) = \sqrt{x}$$

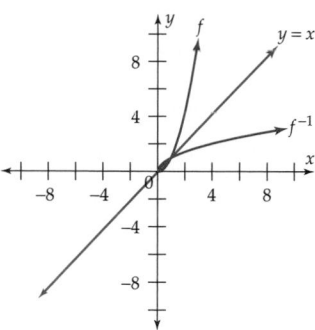

Figure 3.6-11

Composition of a Function and its Inverse

The inverse of a function f is designed to send each output of f back to the input it came from, that is,

$$f(a) = b \qquad \text{exactly when} \qquad f^{-1}(b) = a$$

Consequently, if you first apply f and then apply f^{-1} to the result, you obtain the number you started with.

$$f^{-1}(f(a)) = f^{-1}(b) = a$$

Similarly,

$$f(f^{-1}(b)) = f(a) = b$$

The results above can be generalized to all values in the domains of f and f^{-1}.

Composition of Inverse Functions

> A one-to-one function f and its inverse function f^{-1} have these properties.
>
> $(f^{-1} \circ f)(x) = x$ for every x in the domain of f
> $(f \circ f^{-1})(x) = x$ for every x in the domain of f^{-1}
>
> Also, any two functions having both properties are one-to-one and are inverses of each other.

Teaching Notes

Note to students that the information in the **Composition of Inverse Functions** box will be needed in **Example 7** on page 212, where g will be used in place of f^{-1}.

Math Background

The two concepts in the **Composition of Inverse Functions** are sometimes combined to form a definition of inverse functions. That definition is often stated as follows:

Functions f and g are inverse functions if and only if:
$(g \circ f)(x) = x$ for every x in the domain of f
and
$(f \circ g)(x) = x$ for every x in the domain of g.

In some cases, you must examine domains carefully to determine whether two functions are inverses. For example, $f(x) = x^2$ and $g(x) = \sqrt{x}$ are not inverses when the domain of f is not restricted, as shown below.

Let $f(x) = x^2$ (whose domain is the set of all real numbers) and $g(x) = \sqrt{x}$ (whose domain is the set of all real numbers greater than or equal to zero). Observe that:

$$f(g(x)) = f(\sqrt{x}) = \left(\sqrt{x}\right)^2 = x$$

for all x in the domain of g. ✓

$$g(f(x)) = g(x^2) = \sqrt{x^2} = |x|$$

for all x in the domain of f, and $|x| \neq x$ for all x in the domain of f. ✗

So, f and g are **not** inverse functions of each other.

Example 7

Let $f(x) = \dfrac{2x}{3-x}$ and $g(x) = \dfrac{3x}{x+2}$.

Use composition to verify that f and g are inverses of each other.

$$(g \circ f)(x) = \frac{3(f(x))}{f(x)+2} = \frac{3\left(\dfrac{2x}{3-x}\right)}{\left(\dfrac{2x}{3-x}\right)+2}$$

$$= \frac{\dfrac{6x}{3-x}}{\dfrac{2x+2(3-x)}{3-x}} = \frac{\dfrac{6x}{3-x}}{\dfrac{6}{3-x}}$$

$$= x$$

$$(f \circ g)(x) = \frac{2(g(x))}{3-g(x)} = \frac{2\left(\dfrac{3x}{x+2}\right)}{3-\left(\dfrac{3x}{x+2}\right)}$$

$$= \frac{\dfrac{6x}{x+2}}{\dfrac{3(x+2)-3x}{x+2}} = \frac{\dfrac{6x}{x+2}}{\dfrac{6}{x+2}}$$

$$= x$$

Thus, f and g are inverses of each other.

Exercises 3.6

ANSWERS

1.

y	f(y)
4	1
2	2
3	3
6	4
1	5

2.

y	f(y)
4	−1
3	0
4	1
1	2
5	3

3.

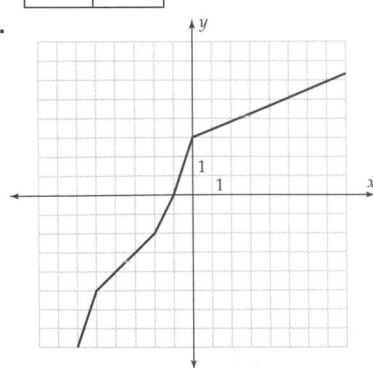

3 sample points on the inverse:
$(-2, -2)$, $(0, 3)$, $(8, 6)$

Example 7   Verifying the Inverse of a Function

Let

$$f(x) = \frac{5}{2x-4} \quad \text{and} \quad g(x) = \frac{4x+5}{2x}$$

Use composition to verify that f and g are inverses of each other.

Solution

$$(g \circ f)(x) = \frac{4(f(x))+5}{2(f(x))} = \frac{4\left(\dfrac{5}{2x-4}\right)+5}{2\left(\dfrac{5}{2x-4}\right)} = \frac{\dfrac{20+5(2x-4)}{2x-4}}{\dfrac{10}{2x-4}}$$

$$= \frac{20+5(2x-4)}{10} = \frac{20+10x-20}{10} = \frac{10x}{10} = x$$

$$(f \circ g)(x) = \frac{5}{2(g(x))-4} = \frac{5}{2\left(\dfrac{4x+5}{2x}\right)-4} = \frac{5}{\dfrac{4x+5}{x}-4}$$

$$= \frac{5}{\dfrac{4x+5-4x}{x}} = \frac{5}{\dfrac{5}{x}} = x$$

Thus, f and g are inverses of each other. ∎

Exercises 3.6

In Exercises 1 and 2, write a table that represents the inverse of the function given by the table.

1.

x	f(x)
1	4
2	2
3	3
4	6
5	1

2.

x	g(x)
−1	4
0	3
1	4
2	1
3	5

In Exercises 3 and 4, the graph of a function f is given. Sketch the graph of the inverse function of f and give the coordinates of three points on the inverse.

3.

4.

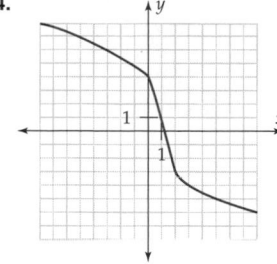

In Exercises 5–8, graph f and its inverse in parametric mode (see Example 2).

5. $f(x) = x^3 - 3x^2 + 2$ **6.** $f(x) = \sqrt[3]{x^2 - 1}$

7. $f(x) = x^4 - 3x^2$ **8.** $f(x) = \sqrt{x^2 + 1}$

In Exercises 9–22, find the rule for the inverse of the given function. Solve your answers for y and, if possible, write in function notation (see Examples 3 and 4).

9. $f(x) = -x$ **10.** $f(x) = -x + 1$

11. $f(x) = 5x^2 - 4$ **12.** $f(x) = -3x^2 + 5$

13. $f(x) = 5 - 2x^3$ **14.** $f(x) = (x^5 + 1)^3$

15. $f(x) = \sqrt{4x - 7}$ **16.** $f(x) = 5 + \sqrt{3x - 2}$

17. $f(x) = \dfrac{1}{x}$ **18.** $f(x) = \dfrac{1}{\sqrt{x}}$

19. $f(x) = \dfrac{1}{2x^2 + 1}$ **20.** $f(x) = \dfrac{x}{x^2 + 1}$

21. $f(x) = \dfrac{x^3 - 1}{x^3 + 5}$ **22.** $f(x) = \sqrt[5]{\dfrac{3x - 1}{x - 2}}$

In Exercises 23–30, use a calculator and the Horizontal Line Test to determine whether the function f is one-to-one.

23. $f(x) = x^4 - 4x^2 + 3$ **No**

24. $f(x) = x^4 - 4x + 3$ **No**

25. $f(x) = x^3 + x - 5$ **Yes**

26. $f(x) = \begin{cases} x - 3 & \text{for } x \le 3 \\ 2x - 6 & \text{for } x > 3 \end{cases}$ **Yes**

27. $f(x) = x^5 + 2x^4 - x^2 + 4x - 5$ **Yes**

28. $f(x) = x^3 - 4x^2 + x - 10$ **No**

29. $f(x) = 0.1x^3 - 0.1x^2 - 0.005x + 1$ **No**

30. $f(x) = 0.1x^3 + 0.005x + 1$ **Yes**

In Exercises 31–36, each given function has an inverse function. Sketch the graph of the inverse function.

31. $f(x) = \sqrt{x + 3}$

32. $f(x) = \sqrt{3x - 2}$

33. $f(x) = 0.3x^5 + 2$

34. $f(x) = \sqrt[3]{x + 3}$

35. $f(x) = \sqrt[5]{x^3 + x - 2}$

36. $f(x) = \begin{cases} x^2 - 1 & \text{for } x \le 0 \\ -0.5x - 1 & \text{for } x > 0 \end{cases}$

In Exercises 37–44, none of the functions is one-to-one. State at least one way of restricting the domain of the function so that the restricted function has an inverse that is a function. Then find the rule of the inverse function (see Example 6).

37. $f(x) = |x|$ **38.** $f(x) = |x - 3|$

39. $f(x) = -x^2$ **40.** $f(x) = x^2 + 4$

41. $f(x) = \dfrac{x^2 + 6}{2}$ **42.** $f(x) = \sqrt{4 - x^2}$

43. $f(x) = \dfrac{1}{x^2 + 1}$

44. $f(x) = 3(x + 5)^2 + 2$

In Exercises 45–50, use composition to show that f and g are inverses of each other (see Example 7).

45. $f(x) = x + 1$ $g(x) = x - 1$

46. $f(x) = 2x - 6$ $g(x) = \dfrac{x}{2} + 3$

47. $f(x) = \dfrac{1}{x + 1}$ $g(x) = \dfrac{1 - x}{x}$

48. $f(x) = \dfrac{-3}{2x + 5}$ $g(x) = \dfrac{-3 - 5x}{2x}$

49. $f(x) = x^5$ $g(x) = \sqrt[5]{x}$

50. $f(x) = x^3 - 1$ $g(x) = \sqrt[3]{x + 1}$

51. Show that the inverse function of the function f whose rule is $f(x) = \dfrac{2x + 1}{3x - 2}$ is f itself.

4.

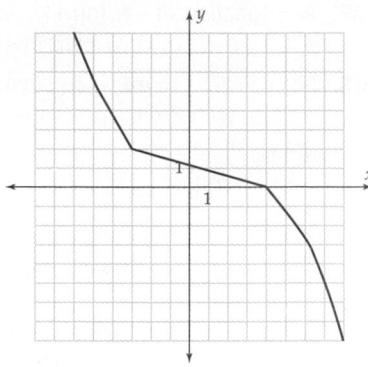

3 sample points on the inverse:
$(-3, 2), (4, 0), (8, -8)$

5.

6.

7.

8.

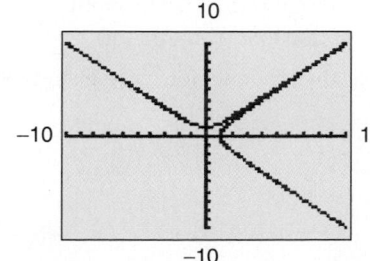

9. $g(x) = -x$

10. $g(x) = -x + 1$

11. $x = 5y^2 - 4, \ y = \pm\sqrt{\dfrac{x + 4}{5}}$

12. $g(x) = \pm\sqrt{\dfrac{-x + 5}{3}}$

13. $g(x) = \sqrt[3]{\dfrac{5 - x}{2}}$

14. $g(x) = \sqrt[5]{\sqrt[3]{x} - 1}$

15. $g(x) = \dfrac{x^2 + 7}{4}, \ (x \ge 0)$

16. $g(x) = \dfrac{(x - 5)^2 + 2}{3}, \ (x \ge 5)$

17. $g(x) = \dfrac{1}{x}$

18. $g(x) = \dfrac{1}{x^2}, \ (x \ge 0)$

19. $x = \dfrac{1}{2y^2 + 1}, \ y = \pm\sqrt{\dfrac{1 - x}{2x}}$

20. $g(x) = \dfrac{1 \pm \sqrt{1 - 4x^2}}{2x}$

21. $g(x) = \sqrt[3]{\dfrac{5x + 1}{1 - x}}$

22. $g(x) = \dfrac{2x^5 - 1}{x^5 - 3}$

31–51. *See p.* 1061.

52. Any function of the form
$f(x) = -x + c$ is its own inverse.

53. Let $y = f(x) = mx + b$. Since
$m \neq 0$, we can solve for x and
obtain
$x = \dfrac{y - b}{m}$. Hence, the rule of the
inverse function g is
$g(x) = \dfrac{x - b}{m}$, and we have:

$(f \circ g)(x) = f(g(x)) = f\left(\dfrac{x - b}{m}\right)$

$= m\left(\dfrac{x - b}{m}\right) + b = x$ and

$(g \circ f)(x) = g(f(x))$

$= g(mx + b) = \dfrac{(mx + b) - b}{m} = x.$

54. Suppose that $f(a) = f(b)$. Then
$1 - 0.2a^3 = 1 - 0.2b^3$. Then
$-0.2a^3 = -0.2b^3$ and $a^3 = b^3$
which means that $a = b$. Therefore,
it is impossible to have $f(a) = f(b)$
when $a \neq b$ and so the function is
one-to-one.

52. List three different functions (other than the one in Exercise 51), each of which is its own inverse. Many correct answers are possible.

53. *Critical Thinking* Let m and b be constants with $m \neq 0$. Show that the function $f(x) = mx + b$ is one-to-one, and find the rule of the inverse function f^{-1}.

54. *Critical Thinking* Prove that the function $h(x) = 1 - 0.2x^3$ of Example 5c is one-to-one by showing that it satisfies the definition: If $a \neq b$, then $f(a) \neq f(b)$.
Hint: Use the rule of f to show that when $f(a) = f(b)$ then $a = b$. If this is the case, then it is impossible to have $f(a) = f(b)$ when $a \neq b$.

55. *Critical Thinking* Show that the points $P = (a, b)$ and $Q = (b, a)$ are symmetric with respect to the line $y = x$ as follows:
  a. Find the slope of the line through P and Q.
  b. Use slopes to show that the line through P and Q is perpendicular to $y = x$.
  c. Let R be the point where the line $y = x$ intersects $\overline{PQ}$. Since R is on $y = x$, it has coordinates (c, c) for some number c, as shown in the figure. Use the distance formula to show that $\overline{PR}$ has the same length as $\overline{RQ}$. Conclude that the line $y = x$ is the perpendicular bisector of $\overline{PQ}$. Therefore, P and Q are symmetric with respect to the line $y = x$.

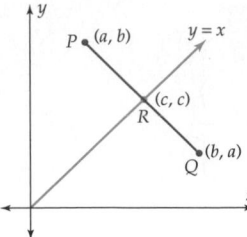

56. Let C be the temperature in degrees Celsius. Then the temperature in degrees Fahrenheit is given by

$$f(C) = \frac{9}{5}C + 32.$$

Let g be the function that converts degrees Fahrenheit to degrees Celsius. Find the rule of g and show that g is the inverse function of f.

$g(F) = \frac{5}{9}(F - 32);$

$(f \circ g)(F) = f\left(\frac{5}{9}(F - 32)\right)$

$= \frac{9}{5}\left(\frac{5}{9}(F - 32)\right) + 32 = F$ and

$g \circ f(C) = g\left(\frac{9}{5}C + 32\right)$

$= \frac{5}{9}\left(\frac{9}{5}C + 32 - 32\right) = C$

Section 3.7 Rates of Change

Teaching Notes

Students often ask, "When will I ever use this in real life?" The answers for rates of change are endless! Some possibilities are:
- average rate of speed (miles per hour)
- average rate of fuel consumption (miles per gallon)
- average rate of using paint (gallons per square foot)

Ask the students for more examples.

 3.7

Rates of Change

Objectives
- Find the average rate of change of a function over an interval
- Represent average rate of change geometrically as the slope of a secant line
- Use the difference quotient to find a formula for the average rate of change of a function

Rates of change play a central role in calculus. They also have an important connection with the difference quotient of a function, which was introduced in Section 3.1.

Average Rates of Change

When a rock is dropped from a high place, the distance the rock travels (ignoring wind resistance) is given by the function

$$d(t) = 16t^2$$

with distance $d(t)$ measured in feet and time t in seconds. The following table shows the distance the rock has fallen at various times.

Time t	0	1	2	3	3.5	4	4.5	5
Distance $d(t)$	0	16	64	144	196	256	324	400

---

55. a. Slope $= \dfrac{a - b}{b - a} = \dfrac{-(b - a)}{b - a} = -1$

  b. The line $y = x$ has slope 1 and by (a), line PQ has slope -1. Since the product of their slopes is -1, the lines are perpendicular.

  c. Length $PR = \sqrt{(a - c)^2 + (b - c)^2}$
  $= \sqrt{a^2 - 2ac + c^2 + b^2 - 2bc + c^2}$
  $= \sqrt{a^2 + b^2 + 2c^2 - 2ac - 2bc};$
  Length $RQ = \sqrt{(c - b)^2 + (c - a)^2}$
  $= \sqrt{c^2 - 2bc + b^2 + c^2 - 2ac + a^2}$
  $= \sqrt{a^2 + b^2 + 2c^2 - 2ac - 2bc}$

  Since the two lengths are the same, $y = x$ is the perpendicular bisector of segment PQ.

To find the distance the rock falls from time $t = 1$ to $t = 3$, note that at the end of three seconds, the rock has fallen $d(3) = 144$ feet, whereas it had only fallen $d(1) = 16$ feet at the end of one second.

$$d(3) - d(1) = 144 - 16 = 128 \text{ feet}$$

So during this time interval the rock traveled 128 feet. The distance traveled by the rock during other time intervals can be found the same way.

In general,

the distance traveled from time $t = a$ to time $t = b$ is $d(b) - d(a)$ feet.

From the chart, the length of each time interval can be computed by taking the difference between the two times. For example, from $t = 1$ to $t = 4$ is a time interval of length $4 - 1 = 3$ seconds. Similarly, the interval from $t = 2$ to $t = 3.5$ is of length $3.5 - 2 = 1.5$ seconds. In general,

the length of the time interval from $t = a$ to $t = b$ is $b - a$ seconds.

Since distance traveled = average speed $\cdot$ time interval,

$$\text{average speed} = \frac{\text{distance traveled}}{\text{time interval}}$$

so the average speed over the time interval from $t = a$ to $t = b$ is

$$\text{average speed} = \frac{\text{distance traveled}}{\text{time interval}} = \frac{d(b) - d(a)}{b - a}.$$

Example 1   Average Speed over a Given Interval

Find the average speed of the falling rock

a. from $t = 1$ to $t = 4$ and

b. from $t = 2$ to $t = 4.5$.

Solution

a. Apply the average speed formula with $a = 1$ and $b = 4$.

$$\text{average speed} = \frac{d(4) - d(1)}{4 - 1} = \frac{256 - 16}{4 - 1} = \frac{240}{3}$$

$$= 80 \text{ feet per second}$$

b. Similarly, from $t = 2$ to $t = 4.5$ the average speed is

$$\frac{d(4.5) - d(2)}{4.5 - 2} = \frac{324 - 64}{4.5 - 2} = \frac{260}{2.5} = 104 \text{ feet per second.}$$

The units in which average speed is measured in Example 1 (feet per second) indicate the rate of change of distance (feet) with respect to time (seconds). The average speed, or **average rate of change** of distance with respect to time, as time changes from $t = a$ to $t = b$ is given by

$$\text{average speed} = \text{average rate of change}$$

$$= \frac{\text{change in distance}}{\text{change in time}} = \frac{d(b) - d(a)}{b - a}.$$

Students may automatically express a rate of change as a rate of change with respect to time. In **Example 2**, they may write 3.18 gallons per second. Point out that the function V gives the volume of the balloon with respect to *radius*, not *time*. So, the units for the rate of change in volume are:

volume   with respect to   **radius**
↓   ↓   ↓
gallons   per   inch

ADDITIONAL EXAMPLES

A cone-shaped tank is being filled with water. The approximate volume of water in the tank in cubic meters is $V(x) = \frac{x^3}{4}$, where x is the height of the water in the tank.

Find the average rate of change of the volume of water as the height increases from 1 to 3 meters.

Rate of change of the volume
= 3.25 cubic meters per meter

Example 3

A manufacturing company makes toy cars. The cost (in dollars) of producing x cars is given by the function

$$c(x) = \sqrt[3]{4x^2} + 8$$

Find the average rate of change of the cost

a. from 0 to 10 cars
rising at an average rate of approximately $0.74 per car.

b. from 10 to 25 cars
rising at an average rate of approximately $0.41 per car.

c. from 25 to 50 cars
rising at an average rate of approximately $0.32 per car.

Although speed is the most familiar example, rates of change play a role in many other situations as well, as illustrated in Examples 2–4 below. The average rate of change of any function is defined below.

Average Rate of Change

Let f be a function. The *average rate of change* of $f(x)$ with respect to x as x changes from a to b is the value

$$\frac{\text{change in } f(x)}{\text{change in } x} = \frac{f(b) - f(a)}{b - a}$$

Example 2   Rate of Change of Volume

A balloon is being filled with water. Its approximate volume in gallons is

$$V(x) = \frac{x^3}{55}$$

where x is the radius of the balloon in inches. Find the average rate of change of the volume of the balloon as the radius increases from 5 to 10 inches.

Solution

$$\frac{\text{change in volume}}{\text{change in radius}} = \frac{V(10) - V(5)}{10 - 5} \approx \frac{18.18 - 2.27}{10 - 5} \approx \frac{15.91}{5}$$
$$\approx 3.18 \text{ gallons per inch}$$

NOTE Analyzing units is helpful in interpreting the meaning of a rate of change. In Example 2, the units of the answer are gallons per inch. This means that for every inch that the radius increases between 5 and 10 inches, the volume increases by an average of 3.18 gallons.

Example 3   Manufacturing Costs

A small manufacturing company makes specialty office desks. The cost (in thousands of dollars) of producing x desks is given by the function

$$c(x) = 0.0009x^3 - 0.06x^2 + 1.6x + 5$$

Find the average rate of change of the cost

a. from 0 to 10 desks

b. from 10 to 30 desks

c. from 30 to 50 desks.

Solution

a. As production increases from 0 to 10 desks, the average rate of change of cost is

$$\frac{\text{change in cost}}{\text{change in production}} = \frac{c(10) - c(0)}{10 - 0} = \frac{15.9 - 5}{10} = \frac{10.9}{10} = 1.09$$

This means that costs are rising at an average rate of 1.09 thousand dollars (that is, $1090) per desk.

b. As production goes from 10 to 30 desks, the average rate of change of cost is

$$\frac{c(30) - c(10)}{30 - 10} = \frac{23.3 - 15.9}{30 - 10} = \frac{7.4}{20} = 0.37$$

so costs are rising at an average rate of only $370 per desk.

c. As production goes from 30 to 50 desks

$$\frac{c(50) - c(30)}{50 - 30} = \frac{47.5 - 23.3}{50 - 30} = \frac{24.2}{20} = 1.21$$

so the rate increases to $1210 per desk. ∎

| **Example 4** | Rate of Change of Temperature |

The graph of the temperature function f during a particular day is given below. The temperature at x hours after midnight is $f(x)$. What is the average rate of change of the temperature

a. from 4 a.m. to noon?

b. from 3 p.m. to 8 p.m.?

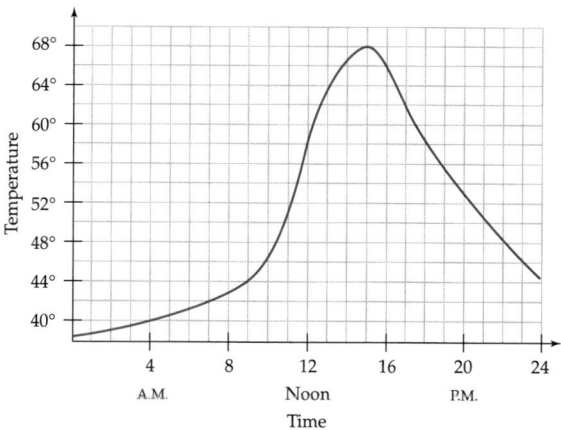

Figure 3.7-1

ADDITIONAL EXAMPLES

| **Example 4** |

The graph below shows the weekly sales (in hundreds of dollars) of magazine subscriptions made during a 12-week sales drive. The sales in any single week is $s(x)$, where x is the number of weeks since the sales drive began.

What is the average rate of change in sales

a. from week 2 to week 4?
The average rate of change in sales is −150 dollars per week (sales are decreasing).

b. from week 6 to week 11?
The average rate of change in sales is 160 dollars per week (sales are increasing).

Teaching Notes

After completing **Example 4**, you may want to ask students to find the average rate of change in temperature from noon to 5 p.m.

$\left(\frac{4°}{5} \text{ per hour}\right)$ Point out that the rate is positive, even though the temperature graph increases *and* decreases during that time interval. Explain that the average rate of change uses only the endpoints of the interval, and does not reflect any fluctuations within the interval.

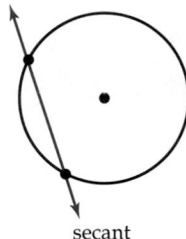 Math Background

$\dfrac{f(b) - f(a)}{b - a}$ is the slope of the secant line from $(a, f(a))$ to $(b, f(b))$.

$\dfrac{f(x + h) - f(x)}{(x + h) - x} = \dfrac{f(x + h) - f(x)}{h}$ is the slope of the secant line from $(x, f(x))$ to $(x + h, f(x + h))$. Students will learn in calculus that, along with appropriate limits, expressions like those above can be used to find the slope of a *tangent line*. They will learn that all of the following are equivalent:

- slope of the tangent line at the point $(x, f(x))$
- instantaneous rate of change of $f(x)$ with respect to x
- derivative of f with respect to x, denoted $f'(x)$

Teaching Notes

In geometry, a secant is a line that intersects a circle in two points, as shown below.

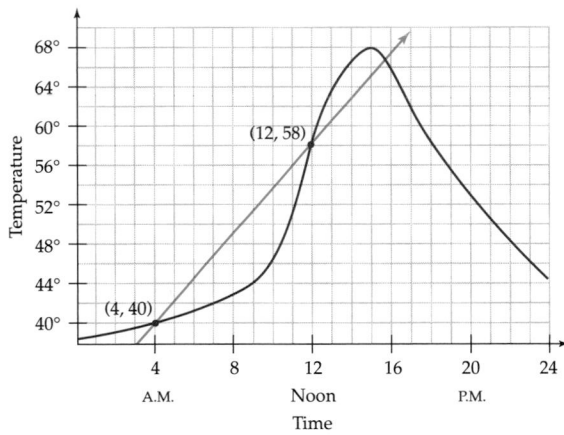

secant

A secant line for a curved graph intersects the graph in two or more points.

Solution

a. The graph shows that the temperature at 4 a.m. is $f(4) = 40°$ and the temperature at noon is $f(12) = 58°$. Thus, the average rate of change of temperature is

$$\frac{\text{change in temperature}}{\text{change in time}} = \frac{f(12) - f(4)}{12 - 4} = \frac{58 - 40}{12 - 4} = \frac{18}{8}$$
$$= 2.25° \text{ per hour}$$

Notice that the rate of change is positive. This is because the temperature is *increasing* at an average rate of 2.25° per hour.

b. The time 3 p.m. corresponds to $x = 15$ and 8 p.m. to $x = 20$. The graph shows that $f(15) = 68°$ and $f(20) = 53°$. Thus, the average rate of change of temperature is

$$\frac{\text{change in temperature}}{\text{change in time}} = \frac{f(20) - f(15)}{20 - 15} = \frac{53 - 68}{20 - 15} = \frac{-15}{5}$$
$$= -3° \text{ per hour}$$

The rate of change is negative because the temperature is *decreasing* at an average rate of 3° per hour.

Geometric Interpretation of Average Rate of Change

If P and Q are points on the graph of a function f, then the straight line determined by P and Q is called a **secant line.** Figure 3.7-2 shows the secant line joining the points (4, 40) and (12, 58) on the graph of the temperature function f of Example 3.

Figure 3.7-2

Using the points (4, 40) and (12, 58), the slope of this secant line is $\dfrac{58 - 40}{12 - 4} = \dfrac{18}{8} = 2.25$. To say that (4, 40) and (12, 58) are on the graph of f means that $f(4) = 40$ and $f(12) = 58$. Thus,

slope of secant line = 2.25

$$= \frac{58 - 40}{12 - 4}$$

$$= \frac{f(12) - f(4)}{12 - 4}$$

= average rate of change as x goes from 4 to 12.

The same thing happens in the general case.

**Secant Lines
and Average
Rates of Change**

Let f be a function.

$$\text{average rate of change} \atop \text{of } f \text{ from } x = a \text{ to } x = b = \frac{f(b) - f(a)}{b - a} = {\text{slope of secant line joining } (a, f(a)) \atop \text{and } (b, f(b)) \text{ on the graph of } f}$$

The Difference Quotient

Average rates of change are often computed for very small intervals, such as the rate from 4 to 4.01 or from 4 to 4.001. Since $4.01 = 4 + 0.01$ and $4.001 = 4 + 0.001$, both cases are essentially the same: computing the rate of change over the interval from 4 to $4 + h$ for some small quantity h. Furthermore, it is often possible to define a formula to determine the average rate for all possible values of h.

Example 5   Computing Average Speed by using a Formula

Find a formula for the average speed of a falling rock from time x to time $x + h$. Use the formula to find the average speed from 3 to 3.1 seconds.

Solution

Recall that the distance the rock travels is given by the function $d(t) = 16t^2$ with distance $d(t)$ measured in feet and time t in seconds.

$$\text{average speed} = \frac{d(x + h) - d(x)}{(x + h) - x} = \frac{16(x + h)^2 - 16x^2}{h}$$

$$= \frac{16(x^2 + 2xh + h^2) - 16x^2}{h} = \frac{16x^2 + 32xh + 16h^2 - 16x^2}{h}$$

$$= \frac{32xh + 16h^2}{h} = \frac{h(32x + 16h)}{h} = 32x + 16h$$

To find the average speed from 3 to 3.1 seconds, apply the formula above, with $x = 3$ and $h = 0.1$.

$$\text{average speed} = 32x + 16h$$
$$= 32(3) + 16(0.1) = 96 + 1.6 = 97.6 \text{ feet per second} \blacksquare$$

In general, the average rate of change of any function f over the interval from x to $x + h$ can be computed as in Example 5: Apply the definition of average rate of change with $a = x$ and $b = x + h$.

$$\text{average rate of change} = \frac{f(b) - f(a)}{b - a} = \frac{f(x + h) - f(x)}{(x + h) - x} = \frac{f(x + h) - f(x)}{h}$$

This last quantity is just the difference quotient of f (see page 144).

Teaching Notes

Point out that the formula for the **Average Rate of Change** from page 216 is repeated in **Secant Lines and Average Rates of Change** on this page. The new information is that *an average rate of change is the slope of a secant line.*

Example Notes

Before discussing **Example 5** (or after, as a way to check the answer), you may wish to compute the average speed of the falling rock from 3 to 3.1 seconds as it was done in previous examples:

$$\frac{d(3.1) - d(3)}{3.1 - 3} = \frac{16(3.1)^2 - 16(3)^2}{3.1 - 3}$$

$$= \frac{153.76 - 144}{3.1 - 3}$$

$$= \frac{9.76}{0.1}$$

$$= 97.6$$

Then you could discuss the advantage of the method used in Example 5 (i.e. finding the formula first) if you needed to calculate the average speed over several intervals.

ADDITIONAL EXAMPLES

Example 5

The distance traveled by a dropped object (ignoring wind resistance) is given by the function $d(t) = 4.9t^2$, with distance $d(t)$ measured in *meters* and time t in seconds. Find a formula for the average speed of a falling object from time x to time $x + h$. Use the formula to find the average speed from 2.8 to 3 seconds. $9.8x + 4.9h$

The average speed of the object is: $9.8(2.8) + 4.9(0.2) = 28.42$ meters per second.

Example Notes

The rate of change found in **Example 6** is a rate of change in volume (gallons) with respect to a change in x, which is in inches. Therefore, the answer, 3.495, is in gallons per inch.

ADDITIONAL EXAMPLES

Example 6

Find the difference quotient of
$$V(x) = \frac{x^3}{4}$$
and use it to find the average rate of change of V as h changes from 2 to 2.1 meters.

$$\frac{V(x+h) - V(x)}{h} = \frac{\frac{(x+h)^3}{4} - \frac{x^3}{4}}{h}$$

$$= \frac{3x^2 + 3xh + h^2}{4}$$

Let $x = 2$ and $h = 0.1$. Then the average rate of change is
$$\frac{3 \cdot 2^2 + 3 \cdot 2(0.1) + (0.1)^2}{4} = 3.1525$$
cubic meters per meter.

Exercises 3.7

1. **a.** 14 ft/sec
   b. 54 ft/sec
   c. 112 ft/sec
   d. $93\frac{1}{3}$ ft/sec
2. **a.** $550 per year
   b. $285.71 per year
   c. $-$100 per year
   d. $0 per year

Difference Quotients and Rates of Change

Let f be a function. The average rate of change of f over the interval from x to $x + h$ is given by the difference quotient.

$$\frac{f(x+h) - f(x)}{h}$$

Example 6 Using a Rate of Change Formula

Find the difference quotient of $V(x) = \frac{x^3}{55}$ and use it to find the average rate of change of V as x changes from 8 to 8.01.

Solution

Find the difference quotient of $V(x)$ and simplify.

$$\frac{V(x+h) - V(x)}{h} = \frac{\overbrace{\frac{(x+h)^3}{55}}^{V(x+h)} - \overbrace{\frac{x^3}{55}}^{V(x)}}{h} = \frac{\frac{1}{55}\left((x+h)^3 - x^3\right)}{h}$$

$$= \frac{1}{55} \cdot \frac{(x+h)^3 - x^3}{h} = \frac{1}{55} \cdot \frac{x^3 + 3x^2h + 3xh^2 + h^3 - x^3}{h}$$

$$= \frac{3x^2 + 3xh + h^2}{55}$$

To find the average rate of change as x changes from 8 to $8.01 = 8 + 0.01$, let $x = 8$ and $h = 0.01$. So the average rate of change is

$$\frac{3x^2 + 3xh + h^2}{55} = \frac{3 \cdot 8^2 + 3 \cdot 8(0.01) + (0.01)^2}{55} \approx 3.495$$

Exercises 3.7

1. A car moves along a straight test track. The distance traveled by the car at various times is shown in the table below. Find the average speed of the car over each interval.
   a. 0 to 10 seconds
   b. 10 to 20 seconds
   c. 20 to 30 seconds
   d. 15 to 30 seconds

Time (seconds)	0	5	10	15	20	25	30
Distance (feet)	0	20	140	400	680	1400	1800

2. The yearly profit of a small manufacturing firm is shown in the tables below. What is the average rate of change of profits over the given time span?
   a. 1996–2000 **b.** 1996–2003
   c. 1999–2002 **d.** 1998–2002

Year	1996	1997	1998	1999
Profit	$5000	$6000	$6500	$6800

Year	2000	2001	2002	2003
Profit	$7200	$6700	$6500	$7000

3. Find the average rate of change of the volume of the balloon in Example 2 as the radius increases
   a. from 2 to 5 inches.   **b.** from 4 to 8 inches.
   ≈0.709 gal/in.   **≈2.036 gal/in.**

4. Find the average rate of change of cost for the company in Example 3 when production increases from
   a. 5 to 25 desks.   **b.** 0 to 40 desks.
   $497.50 per desk   **$640 per desk**

5. The graph in the figure shows the monthly sales of floral pattern ties (in thousands of ties) made by a company over a 48-month period. Sales are very low when the ties are first introduced; then they increase significantly, hold steady for a while, and then drop off as the ties go out of fashion. Find the average rate of change of sales (in ties per month) over the given interval.
   a. 0 to 12   **b.** 8 to 24
   c. 12 to 24   **d.** 20 to 28
   e. 28 to 36   **f.** 32 to 44
   g. 36 to 40   **h.** 40 to 48

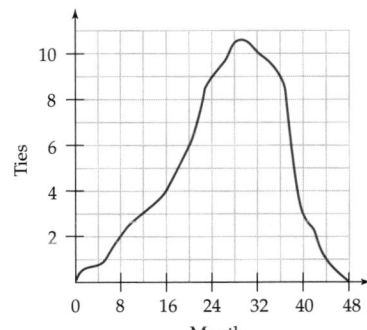

6. A certain company has found that its sales are related to the amount of advertising it does in trade magazines. The graph in the figure shows the sales (in thousands of dollars) as a function of the amount of advertising (in number of magazine ad pages). Find the average rate of change of sales when the number of ad pages increases from
   a. 10 to 20.   **b.** 20 to 60.
   c. 60 to 100.   **d.** 0 to 100.
   e. Is it worthwhile to buy more than 70 pages of ads if the cost of a one-page ad is $2000? if the cost is $5000? if the cost is $8000?

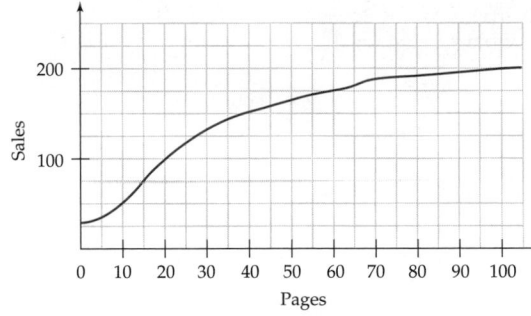

7. When blood flows through an artery (which can be thought of as a cylindrical tube) its velocity is greatest at the center of the artery. Because of friction along the walls of the tube, the blood's velocity decreases as the distance r from the center of the artery increases, finally becoming 0 at the wall of the artery. The velocity (in centimeters per second) is given by the function

$$v = 18{,}500(0.000065 - r^2)$$

where r is measured in centimeters. Find the average rate of change of the velocity as the distance from the center changes from
   a. $r = 0.001$ to $r = 0.002$. **−55.5**
   b. $r = 0.002$ to $r = 0.003$. **−92.5**
   c. $r = 0$ to $r = 0.025$.   **−462.5**

8. A car is stopped at a traffic light and begins to move forward along a straight road when the light turns green. The distance (in feet) traveled by the car in t seconds is given by $s(t) = 2t^2$ for $0 \le t \le 30$ What is the average speed of the car from
   a. $t = 0$ to $t = 5$?   **b.** $t = 5$ to $t = 10$?
   c. $t = 10$ to $t = 30$?   **d.** $t = 10$ to $t = 10.1$?

In Exercises 9–14, find the average rate of change of the function f over the given interval.

9. $f(x) = 2 - x^2$
   from $x = 0$ to $x = 2$
   −2

10. $f(x) = 0.25x^4 - x^2 - 2x + 4$
   from $x = -1$ to $x = 4$
   7.75

11. $f(x) = x^3 - 3x^2 - 2x + 6$
   from $x = -1$ to $x = 3$
   −1

12. $f(x) = -\sqrt{2x^2 - x + 4}$
   from $x = 0$ to $x = 3$
   −0.786

5. **a.** 250 ties/mo
   b. 438 ties/mo
   c. 500 ties/mo
   d. 563 ties/mo
   e. −188 ties/mo
   f. −750 ties/mo
   g. −1500 ties/mo
   h. −375 ties/mo

6. **a.** $5000 per page
   b. $1875 per page
   c. $625 per page
   d. $1750 per page
   e. More than 70 pages is not a good investment at these rates.

8. **a.** 10 ft/sec
   b. 30 ft/sec
   c. 80 ft/sec
   d. 40.2 ft/sec

23. a. Average rate of change is −7979.9, which means that water is leaving the tank at a rate of 7979.9 gal/min.

b. −7979.99 gal/min.

c. −7980 gal/min.

24. a. 49.21

b. 48.1201

c. 48.012001

d. 48

25. a. 6.5π

b. 6.2π

c. 6.1π

d. 6π

e. It's the same.

26. $-\dfrac{1}{500}$

27. a. C, 62.5 ft/sec; D, 75 ft/sec

b. Approximately $t = 4$ to $t = 9.8$ sec

c. The average speed of car D from $t = 4$ to $t = 10$ sec is the slope of the secant line joining the (approximate) points $(4, 100)$ and $(10, 600)$, namely, $\dfrac{600 - 100}{10 - 4} \approx$ 83.33 ft/sec. The average speed of car C is the slope of the secant line joining the (approximate) points $(4, 475)$ and $(10, 800)$, namely, $\dfrac{800 - 475}{10 - 4} \approx 54.17$ ft/sec.

28. a. The average rate of change depends only on the beginning point and the ending point, which are the same in all three years.

b. December of 1993

---

13. $f(x) = \sqrt{x^3 + 2x^2 - 6x + 5}$ **1.5858**
from $x = 1$ to $x = 2$

14. $f(x) = \dfrac{x^2 - 3}{2x - 4}$ **0.375**
from $x = 3$ to $x = 6$

In Exercises 15–22, compute the difference quotient of the function.

15. $f(x) = x + 5$ **1**

16. $f(x) = 7x + 2$ **7**

17. $f(x) = x^2 + 3$
2x + h

18. $f(x) = x^2 + 3x - 1$
2x + h + 3

19. $f(t) = 160{,}000 - 8000t + t^2$
2t + h − 8000

20. $V(x) = x^3$
3x² + 3xh + h²

21. $A(r) = \pi r^2$
2πr + πh

22. $V(p) = \dfrac{5}{p}$ $\dfrac{-5}{p(p + h)}$

23. Water is draining from a large tank. After t minutes there are $160{,}000 - 8000t + t^2$ gallons of water in the tank.
a. Use the results of Exercise 19 to find the average rate at which the water runs out in the interval from 10 to 10.1 minutes.
b. Do the same for the interval from 10 to 10.01 minutes.
c. Estimate the rate at which the water runs out after exactly 10 minutes.

24. Use the results of Exercise 20 to find the average rate of change of the volume of a cube whose side has length x as x changes from
a. 4 to 4.1.   **b.** 4 to 4.01.   **c.** 4 to 4.001.
d. Estimate the rate of change of the volume at the instant when $x = 4$.

25. Use the results of Exercise 21 to find the average rate of change of the area of a circle of radius r as r changes from
a. 3 to 3.5.   **b.** 3 to 3.2.   **c.** 3 to 3.1.
d. Estimate the rate of change at the instant when $r = 3$.
e. How is your answer in part **d** related to the circumference of a circle of radius 3?

26. Under certain conditions, the volume V of a quantity of air is related to the pressure p (which is measured in kilopascals) by the equation $V = \dfrac{5}{p}$. Use the results of Exercise 22 to estimate the rate at which the volume is changing at the instant when the pressure is 50 kilopascals.

---

27. Two cars race on a straight track, beginning from a dead stop. The distance (in feet) each car has covered at each time during the first 16 seconds is shown in the figure below.
a. What is the average speed of each car during this 16-second interval?
b. Find an interval beginning at $t = 4$ during which the average speed of car D was approximately the same as the average speed of car C from $t = 2$ to $t = 10$.
c. Use secant lines and slopes to justify the statement "car D traveled at a higher average speed than car C from $t = 4$ to $t = 10$."

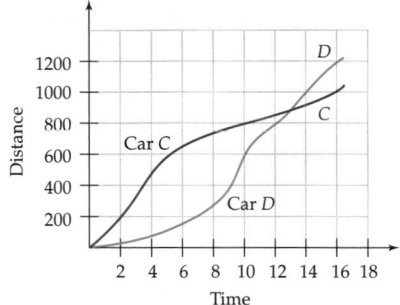

28. The figure below shows the profits earned by a certain company during the last quarter of three consecutive years.
a. Explain why the average rate of change of profits from October 1 to December 31 was the same in all three years.
b. During what month in what year was the average rate of change of profits the greatest?

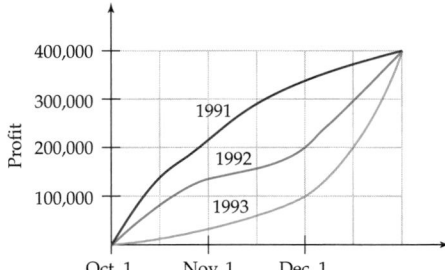

29. The graph in the figure shows the chipmunk population in a certain wilderness area. The population increases as the chipmunks reproduce, but then decreases sharply as predators move into the area.

---

a. During what approximate time period (beginning on day 0) is the average growth rate of the chipmunk population positive?

b. During what approximate time period, beginning on day 0, is the average growth rate of the chipmunk population 0?

c. What is the average growth rate of the chipmunk population from day 50 to day 100? What does this number mean?

d. What is the average growth rate from day 45 to day 50? from day 50 to day 55? What is the approximate average growth rate from day 49 to day 51?

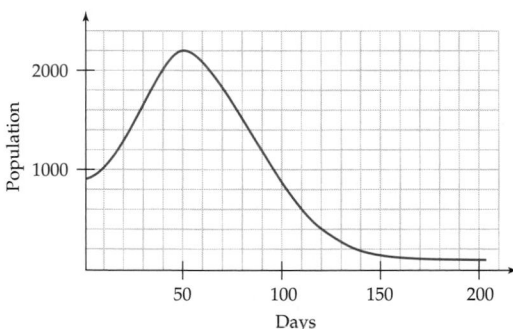

30. Lucy has a viral flu. How bad she feels depends primarily on how fast her temperature is rising at that time. The figure shows her temperature during the first day of the flu.

  a. At what average rate does her temperature rise during the entire day?

  b. During what 2-hour period during the day does she feel worst?

  c. Find two time intervals, one in the morning and one in the afternoon, during which she feels about the same (that is, during which her temperature is rising at the same average rate).

29. a. From day 0 until any day up to day 94, the average growth rate is positive.

  b. From day 0 to day 95

  c. −27, meaning that the population is decreasing at a rate of 27 chipmunks per day

  d. 20, −10, and 0 chipmunks per day

30. a. 0.1625 degrees per hour

  b. From hour 10 to hour 12

  c. For example, from hour 0 to hour 4 and from hour 20 until hour 24

CHAPTER 3

Review

CHAPTER 3 REVIEW

Important Concepts

224

Important Facts and Formulas

Vertical Line Test: A graph in a coordinate plane represents a function if and only if no vertical line intersects the graph more than once.

A quadratic function can be written in any of the following forms:
Transformation form: $f(x) = a(x - h)^2 + k$

- vertex (h, k)

- x-intercepts $h \pm \sqrt{\dfrac{-k}{a}}$

- y-intercept $ah^2 + k$

Polynomial form: $f(x) = ax^2 + bx + c$

- vertex $\left(\dfrac{-b}{2a}, f\left(\dfrac{-b}{2a}\right)\right)$

- x-intercepts $\dfrac{-b \pm \sqrt{b^2 - 4ac}}{2a}$

- y-intercept c

x-Intercept form: $f(x) = a(x - s)(x - t)$

- vertex $\left(\dfrac{s + t}{2}, f\left(\dfrac{s + t}{2}\right)\right)$

- x-intercepts s and t

- y-intercept ast

The graph of $g(x) = f(x) + c$ is the graph of f shifted upward c units.

The graph of $g(x) = f(x) - c$ is the graph of f shifted downward c units.

The graph of $g(x) = f(x + c)$ is the graph of f shifted c units to the left.

The graph of $g(x) = f(x - c)$ is the graph of f shifted c units to the right.

The graph of $g(x) = -f(x)$ is the graph of f reflected across the x-axis.

The graph of $g(x) = f(-x)$ is the graph of f reflected across the y-axis.

The graph of $g(x) = c \cdot f(x)$ is the graph of f stretched or compressed vertically by a factor of c.

The graph of $g(x) = f(c \cdot x)$ is the graph of f stretched or compressed horizontally by a factor of $\frac{1}{c}$.

Horizontal Line Test: A function is one-to-one if and only if no horizontal line intersects the graph more than once.

A one-to-one function f and its inverse f^{-1} have these properties.

- $(f^{-1} \circ f)(x) = x$
- $(f \circ f^{-1})(x) = x$

The average rate of change of a function f as x changes from a to b is the number

$$\frac{f(b) - f(a)}{b - a}$$

The average rate of change of a function f as x changes from x to $x + h$ is given by the difference quotient of the function,

$$\frac{f(x + h) - f(x)}{h}$$

Review Exercises

ANSWERS

Review Exercises

Section **3.1**

1. Let f be the function given by the rule $f(x) = 7 - 2x$. Complete the table below.

x	-2	-1	0	1	2	t	$b + 1$	$x + h$
$f(x)$	11	9	7	5	3	$7 - 2t$	$5 - 2b$	

$7 - 2x - 2h$

2. If $h(x) = x^2 - 3x$, then $h(t + 2) = \underline{}$
$(t + 2)^2 - 3(t + 2) = t^2 + t - 2$

3. If $f(x) = 2x^3 + x + 1$, then $f\left(\frac{x}{2}\right) = \underline{}$
$2\left(\frac{x}{2}\right)^3 + \left(\frac{x}{2}\right) + 1 = \frac{x^3}{4} + \frac{x}{2} + 1$

4. What is the domain of the function $f(x) = \sqrt{-x+2}$?

All real numbers ≤ 2

5. What is the domain of the function $g(t) = \dfrac{\sqrt{t-2}}{t-3}$?

All real numbers ≥ 2 except for 3

6. What is the domain of the function $h(r) = \sqrt{r-4} + \sqrt{r-2}$?

All real numbers ≥ 4

7. The cost of renting a limousine for 24 hours is given by

$$C(x) = \begin{cases} 150 & \text{if } 0 < x \leq 25 \\ 1.75x + 150 & \text{if } x > 25 \end{cases}$$

where x is the number of miles driven.

a. What is the cost if the limo is driven 20 miles? 30 miles? **\$150; \$202.50**

b. If the cost is \$218.25, how many miles were driven? **39 miles**

8. Let $[x]$ denote the greatest integer function and evaluate

a. $\left[\dfrac{-5}{2}\right] = $? **−3**   **b.** $[1755] = $? **1755**

c. $[18.7] + [-15.7] = $? **2**   **d.** $[-7] - [7] = $? **−14**

9. If $f(x) = x + |x| + [x]$, then find $f(0)$, $f(-1)$, $f\left(\dfrac{1}{2}\right)$, and $f\left(\dfrac{-3}{2}\right)$.

$f(0) = 0, f(-1) = -1, f\left(\dfrac{1}{2}\right) = 1, f\left(-\dfrac{3}{2}\right) = -2$

Section 3.2 | **Use the graph of the function f in the figure to answer Exercises 10–13.**

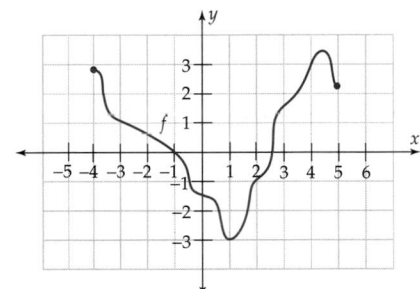

10. What is the domain of f? **$[-4, 5]$**

11. What is the range of f? **$[-3, 3.5]$**

12. $f(-3) = $? **1**

13. $f(-1) + f(1) = $? **−3**

14. a. 1990, 1991, 1992, 1993, 1994, 1995, 1996

b. about 800 to about 1475

c. from 1993 to 1994

15. No local maxima; minimum at $x = -0.5$; increasing on $(-0.5, \infty)$; decreasing on $(-\infty, -0.5)$. This function is concave up for all values of x; there are no points of inflection.

16. Maximum at $x = \frac{2}{3}$; minimum at $x = 1$; increasing on $\left(-\infty, \frac{2}{3}\right)$ and $(1, \infty)$; decreasing on $\left(\frac{2}{3}, 1\right)$. This function is concave up on the interval $\left(\frac{5}{6}, \infty\right)$ and concave down on the interval $\left(-\infty, \frac{5}{6}\right)$. There is a point of inflection at $x = \frac{5}{6}$.

17. Maximum at $x \approx -5.0704$; minimum at $x \approx -0.2630$; increasing on $(-\infty, -5.0704)$ and $(-0.2630, \infty)$; decreasing on $(-5.0704, -0.2630)$. This function is concave up on the interval $\left(-\frac{8}{3}, \infty\right)$ and concave down on the interval $\left(-\infty, -\frac{8}{3}\right)$. There is a point of inflection at $x = -\frac{8}{3}$.

18. Maximum at $x = -1$; minima at $x = -4$ and $x = 2$; increasing on $(-4, -1)$ and $(2, \infty)$, decreasing on $(-\infty, -4)$ and $(-1, 2)$. This function is concave up on the approximate intervals $(-\infty, -2.7)$ and $(0.7, \infty)$ and concave down on the approximate interval $(-2.7, 0.7)$. There are points of inflection at $x \approx -2.7$ and $x \approx 0.7$.

19. a. The graph does not pass the vertical line test; therefore, it does not represent a function of x.

b. The graph represents a function of x because it passes the vertical line test.

14. The function whose graph is shown gives the amount of money (in millions of dollars) spent on tickets for major concerts in selected years. [*Source: Pollstar*]

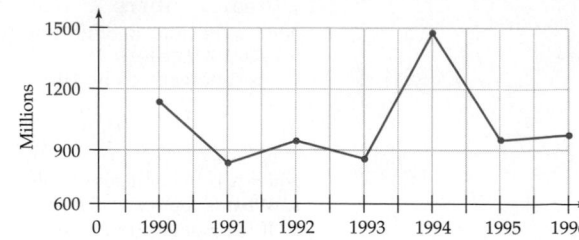

a. What is the domain of the function?
b. What is the approximate range of the function?
c. Over what one-year interval is the rate of change the largest?

In Exercises 15–18, determine the local maxima and minima of the function and the intervals on which the function is increasing and decreasing. Estimate the intervals on which it is concave up and concave down, and the inflection points.

15. $g(x) = \sqrt{x^2 + x + 1}$

16. $f(x) = 2x^3 - 5x^2 + 4x - 3$

17. $g(x) = x^3 + 8x^2 + 4x - 3$

18. $f(x) = 0.5x^4 + 2x^3 - 6x^2 - 16x + 2$

19. State whether the graphs below represent functions of x. Explain your reasoning.

a.   **b.**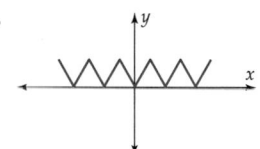

20. Draw the graph of a function f that satisfies the given conditions. The function does not need to be given by an algebraic rule.
- domain of $f = [-3, 4]$ • range of $f = [-2, 5]$
- $f(-2) = 0$ • $f(1) > 2$

21. Sketch the graph of the function $f(x) = \begin{cases} x^2 & \text{if } x \le 0 \\ x + 1 & \text{if } 0 < x < 4 \\ \sqrt{x} & \text{if } x \ge 4 \end{cases}$

In Exercises 22 and 23, sketch the graph of the curve given by the parametric equations.

22. $x = t^3 + 3t^2 - 1$
$y = t^2 + 1$ $(-3 \le t \le 2)$

23. $x = t^2 - 4$
$y = 2t + 1$ $(-3 \le t \le 3)$

20.

21.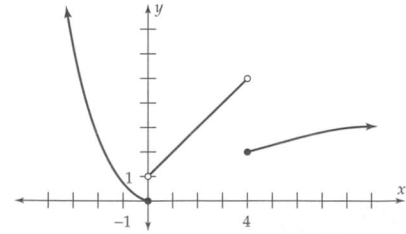

22, 23. *See p.* 1062.

Section 3.3

In Exercises 24–29, find the vertex, y-intercept, and x-intercepts (if any) of the quadratic function. Sketch the graph, with these points labeled.

24. $f(x) = 3(x + 4)^2 - 5$

25. $g(x) = (x - 4)^2 + 1$

26. $h(x) = 2x^2 - 4x - 3$

27. $f(x) = -x^2 - 2x - 7$

28. $g(x) = -2(x - 1)(x + 2)$

29. $h(x) = (x + 2.4)(x - 1.7)$

30. Write the function $f(x) = (x - 1)^2 - 1$ in polynomial and x-intercept form.

31. Write the function $f(x) = x^2 - 3x - 4$ in transformation and x-intercept form.

32. Write the function $f(x) = -2(x - 3)(x + 1)$ in transformation and polynomial form.

Section 3.4

In Exercises 33–38, graph each function with its parent function on the same graph.

33. $f(x) = -\sqrt{x}$

34. $h(x) = \dfrac{1}{x + 2}$

35. $g(x) = 1.5|x|$

36. $h(x) = [-x]$

37. $f(x) = x^2 - 3$

38. $g(x) = \sqrt[3]{2x}$

In Exercises 39–42, list the transformations, in the order they should be performed on the graph of $g(x) = x^2$, to produce a graph of the function f.

39. $f(x) = 0.25x^2 + 2$

40. $f(x) = -(x + 4)^2 - 5$

41. $f(x) = -3(x - 7)^2 + 2$

42. $f(x) = (x - 2)^2$

43. The figure shows the graph of a function f. If g is the function $g(x) = f(x + 2)$, then which of these statements is true?
  a. The graph of g touches, but does not cross, the x-axis.
  b. The graph of g touches, but does not cross, the y-axis.
  c. The graph of g crosses the y-axis at $y = 4$.
  d. The graph of g crosses the y-axis at the origin.
  e. The graph of g crosses the x-axis at $x = -3$.

28.

The vertex is $\left(-\dfrac{1}{2}, \dfrac{9}{2}\right)$.

The y-intercept is 4.

The x-intercepts are 1 and -2.

29–43. *See p.* 1062.

24.

Vertex is $(-4, -5)$.

The y-intercept is 43.

The x-intercepts are approximately -2.709 and -5.291.

25.

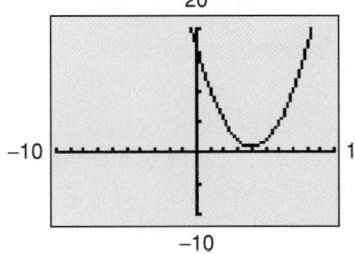

Vertex is $(4, 1)$.

The y-intercept is 17.

There are no x-intercepts.

26.

Vertex is $(1, -5)$.

The y-intercept is -3.

The x-intercepts are approximately 2.581 and -0.581.

27.

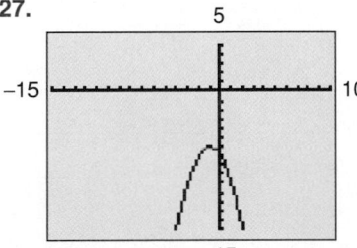

Vertex is $(-1, -6)$.

The y-intercept is -7.

There are no x-intercepts.

44.

$h(x) = 1 - f(x)$

$g(x) = -f(x)$

45.

Note: the right endpoint of each segment is a part of the graph; the left endpoint is *not* a part of the graph.

46. Not symmetric with respect to the *x*-axis, the *y*-axis or the origin.

52. a.

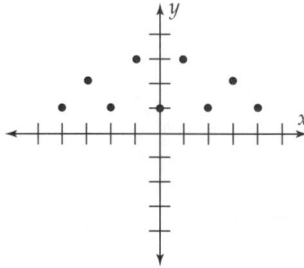

b.

44. The graph of a function *f* is shown in the figure. On the same coordinate plane, carefully draw the graphs of the functions *g* and *h* whose rules are:

$$g(x) = -f(x) \qquad \text{and} \qquad h(x) = 1 - f(x)$$

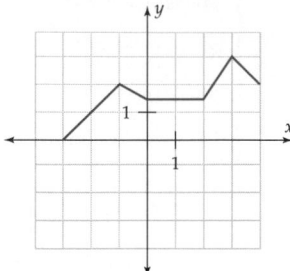

45. U.S. Express Mail rates in 2002 are shown in the following table. Sketch the graph of the function *e*, whose rule is *e*(*x*) = cost of sending a package weighing *x* pounds by Express Mail.

Express Mail

Letter Rate—Post Office to Addressee Service

Up to 8 ounces	$13.65
Over 8 ounces to 2 pounds	17.85
Up to 3 pounds	21.05
Up to 4 pounds	24.20
Up to 5 pounds	27.30
Up to 6 pounds	30.40
Up to 7 pounds	33.45

Section 3.4.A

In Exercises 46–48, determine algebraically whether the graph of the given equation is symmetric with respect to the *x*-axis, the *y*-axis, or the origin.

46. $5y = 7x^2 - 2x$ **47.** $x^2 = y^2 + 2$ **48.** $x^2 + y^2 + 6y = -5$
                          x-axis, y-axis, origin   **y-axis**

In Exercises 49–51, determine whether the given function is even, odd, or neither.

49. $g(x) = 9 - x^2$ **50.** $f(x) = |x| x + 1$ **51.** $h(x) = 3x^5 - x(x^4 - x^2)$
Even   **Neither**   **Odd**

52. Plot the points $(-2, 1), (-1, 3), (0, 1), (3, 2),$ and $(4, 1)$ on coordinate axes.
   a. Suppose the points lie on the graph of an even function *f*. Plot the points $(2, f(2)), (1, f(1)), (0, f(0)), (-3, f(-3)),$ and $(-4, f(-4))$.
   b. Suppose the points lie on the graph of an odd function *g*. Plot the points $(2, g(2)), (1, g(1)), (0, g(0)), (-3, g(-3)),$ and $(-4, g(-4))$.

Section 3.5

53. If $f(x) = 3x + 2$ and $g(x) = x^3 + 1$, find each value.
   a. $(f + g)(-1)$ **−1** **b.** $(f - g)(2)$ **−1** **c.** $(fg)(0)$ **2**

54. If $f(x) = \dfrac{1}{x - 1}$ and $g(x) = \sqrt{x^2 + 5}$, find the rule of each function and state its domain.

   a. $(f + g)(x)$ **b.** $(f - g)(x)$ **c.** $(fg)(x)$ **d.** $\left(\dfrac{f}{g}\right)(x)$

55. If $g(x) = x^2 - 1$ then $g(x - 1) - g(x + 1) = $? **−4x**

In Exercises 56–59, if $f(x) = \dfrac{1}{x + 1}$ and $g(x) = x^3 + 3$, find each value.

56. $(f \circ g)(1)$ $\dfrac{1}{5}$ **57.** $(g \circ f)(2)$ $\dfrac{82}{27}$ **58.** $g(f(-2))$ **2** **59.** $(g \circ f)(x - 1)$

In Exercises 60 and 61, let $f(x) = x^2 - x - 6$ and $g(x) = |x|$. **Describe the relationship between the graph of $f(x)$ and the composite function in terms of transformations.**

60. $f(g)$ **61.** $g(f)$

62. If $f(x) = \dfrac{1}{1 - x}$ and $g(x) = \sqrt{x}$, find the domain of the composite function $f \circ g$.

63. Find two functions f and g such that neither is the identity function and $(f \circ g)(x) = (2x + 1)^2$.

64. The radius of an oil spill (in meters) is 50 times the square root of the time t (in hours).
   a. Write the rule of a function f that gives the radius of the spill at time t.
   b. Write the rule of a function g that gives the area of the spill at time t.
   c. What are the radius and area of the spill after 9 hours?
   d. When will the spill have an area of 100,000 square meters?

Section 3.5.A

65. Find the first eight terms of the orbit of $x = 2$ under the function $f(x) = (1 - x)^2$.

66. Describe the set of fixed points of the function $f(x) = [x]$.

Section 3.6

67. The graph of a function f is shown in the figure. Sketch the graph of the inverse of f.

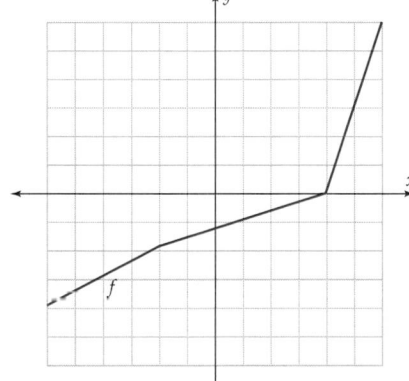

54. a. $(f + g)(x) = \dfrac{1}{x - 1} + \sqrt{x^2 + 5}$; domain: all real numbers except 1.

   b. $(f - g)(x) = \dfrac{1}{x - 1} - \sqrt{x^2 + 5}$; domain: all real numbers except 1.

   c. $(fg)(x) = \dfrac{\sqrt{x^2 + 5}}{x - 1}$; domain: all real numbers except 1.

   d. $\left(\dfrac{f}{g}\right)(x) = \dfrac{1}{x - 1} \div \sqrt{x^2 + 5}$
   $= \dfrac{1}{(x - 1)\sqrt{x^2 + 5}}$; domain: all real numbers except 1.

59. $\dfrac{1}{x^3} + 3$

60. For $x \geq 0$, the graphs of f and $f \circ g$ are the same. For $x < 0$, the graph of $f \circ g$ is the reflection of the graph of f, from $x > 0$, across the x-axis.

61. For $x \leq -2$ and $x \geq 3$, the graphs of f and $g \circ f$ are the same. For $-2 < x < 3$, the graph of $g \circ f$ is the graph of $-f$, a reflection of the graph of f across the x-axis.

62. $[0, 1)$ and $(1, \infty)$

63. $f(x) = x^2$, $g(x) = 2x + 1$

64. a. $f(t) = 50\sqrt{t}$
   b. $g(t) = 2500\pi t$
   c. The radius is 150 meters. The area is approximately 70,686 sq meters.
   d. after approximately 12.7 hours

65. 2, 1, 0, 1, 0, 1, 0, 1

66. The function $f(x) = [x]$ rounds every input value x down to the next integer less than or equal to x. The fixed points are the set of integers, because for any integer n, $[n] = n$.

67.

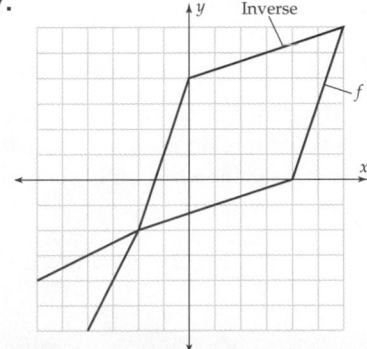

69. $x = 1 - y^2$, $f^{-1}(x) = \pm\sqrt{1 - x}$

71. $x = 2y + 1$, $f^{-1}(x) = \dfrac{x - 1}{2}$

72. $x = \sqrt{5 - y} + 7$

$\quad f^{-1}(x) = -x^2 + 14x - 44$ with $x \le 5$

73. $x = \sqrt[5]{y^3 + 1}$, $f^{-1}(x) = \sqrt[3]{x^5 - 1}$

74. This function is one-to-one and so has an inverse.

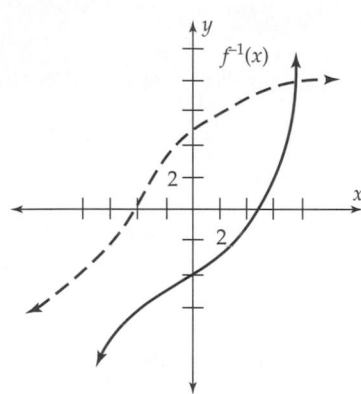

75. The graph of f passes the horizontal line test and hence has an inverse function. It is easy to verify either geometrically [by reflecting the graph of f across the line $y = x$] or algebraically [by calculating $f(f(x))$] that f is its own inverse function.

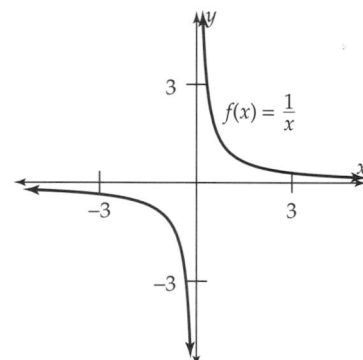

In Exercises 68–73, find the inverse relation of each function. If the inverse is a function, write its rule in function notation.

68. $f(x) = x^3$ $x = y^3$, $f^{-1}(x) = \sqrt[3]{x}$ **69.** $f(x) = 1 - x^2$

70. $f(x) = |x|$ $|y| = x$ **71.** $f(x) = 2x + 1$

72. $f(x) = \sqrt{5 - x} + 7$ **73.** $f(x) = \sqrt[5]{x^3 + 1}$

In Exercises 74–76, determine whether or not the given function is one-to-one. Give reasons for your answer. If so, graph the inverse function.

74. $f(x) = 0.02x^3 - 0.04x^2 + 0.6x - 4$ **75.** $f(x) = \dfrac{1}{x}$

76. $f(x) = 0.2x^3 - 4x^2 + 6x - 15$

In Exercises 77–80, use composition to verify that f and g are inverses.

77. $f(x) = 4x - 6$ $g(x) = 0.25x + 1.5$

78. $f(x) = x^3 - 1$ $g(x) = \sqrt[3]{x + 1}$

79. $f(x) = \dfrac{2x + 1}{x - 3}$ $g(x) = \dfrac{3x + 1}{x - 2}$

80. $f(x) = \dfrac{x + 1}{x - 1}$ $g(x) = \dfrac{x + 1}{x - 1}$

Section 3.7

81. Find the average rate of change of the function $g(x) = \dfrac{x^3 - x + 1}{x + 2}$ as x changes from
a. -1 to 1 $-\dfrac{1}{3}$ **b.** 0 to 2 $\dfrac{5}{8}$

82. Find the average rate of change of the function $f(x) = \sqrt{x^2 - x + 1}$ as x changes from
a. -3 to 0 **b.** -3 to 3.5 **c.** -3 to 5

83. If $f(x) = 2x + 1$ and $g(x) = 3x - 2$, find the average rate of change of the composite function $f \circ g$ as x changes from 3 to 5.   **6**

84. If $f(x) = x^2 + 1$ and $g(x) = x - 2$, find the average rate of change of the composite function $f \circ g$ as x changes from -1 to 1.   **−4**

In Exercises 85–88, find the difference quotient of the function and simplify.

85. $f(x) = 3x + 4$ **3**   **86.** $g(x) = 4x - 1$ **4**

87. $g(x) = x^2 - 1$ **$2x + h$**   **88.** $f(x) = x^2 + x$ **$2x + h + 1$**

---

76. This function is not one-to-one and so has no inverse. It fails the horizontal line test as is seen from the graph.

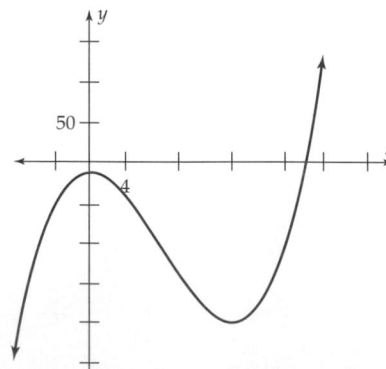

77. $(g \circ f)(x) = 0.25(4x - 6) + 1.5$
$\quad = x - 1.5 + 1.5 = x$
$\quad (f \circ g)(x) = 4(0.25x + 1.5) - 6$
$\quad = x + 6 - 6 = x$

78. $(g \circ f)(x) = \sqrt[3]{x^3 - 1 + 1} = \sqrt[3]{x^3} = x$

$\quad (f \circ g)(x) = \left(\sqrt[3]{x + 1}\right)^3 - 1$

$\quad = x + 1 - 1 = x$

79–80, 82. See p. 1062.

89. The graph of the function g in the figure consists of straight line segments. Find an interval over which the average rate of change of g is
   a. 0   **b.** -3 **c.** 0.5
   d. Explain why the average rate of change of g is the same from -3 to -1 as it is from -2.5 to 0.

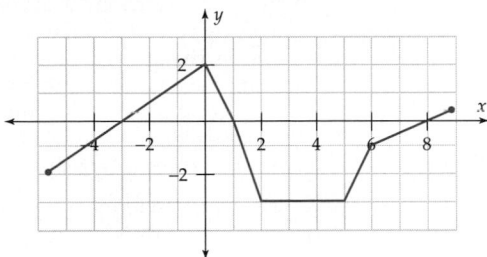

90. The graph in the figure below shows the population of fruit flies during a 50-day experiment in a controlled atmosphere.
   a. During what 5-day period is the average rate of population growth the slowest?
   b. During what 10-day period is the average rate of population growth the fastest?
   c. Find an interval beginning at the 30th day during which the average rate of population growth is the same as the average rate from day 10 to day 20.

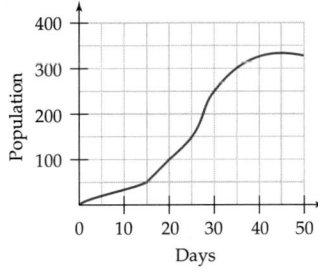

Days

91. The profit (in hundreds of dollars) from selling x tons of an industrial chemical is given by $P(x) = 0.2x^2 + 0.5x - 1$. What is the average rate of change in profit when the number of tons of the chemical sold increases from
   a. 4 to 8 tons?   **b.** 4 to 5 tons?   **c.** 4 to 4.1 tons?
    \$290/ton   **\$230/ton**   **\$212/ton**

92. On the planet Mars, the distance traveled by a falling rock (ignoring atmospheric resistance) in t seconds is $6.1t^2$ feet. How far must a rock fall in order to have an average speed of 25 feet per second over that time interval? **approximately 102.5 feet**

89. a. For example, from -3 to 1
   b. For example, from 1 to 2
   c. For example, from 6 to 8
   d. Both intervals are portions of the same line, so their slopes are the same.

90. a. From about day 45 to day 50
   b. For about any 10-day period starting at or after day 20 and ending at or before day 35
   c. From about day 30 to day 40

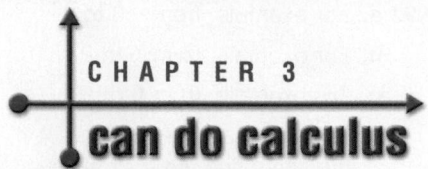

Instantaneous Rates of Change

Teaching Notes

Students may be familiar with the equation $s(t) = -4.9t^2 + v_0t + s_0$ from science classes. Point out that this is the position equation when the height is in meters.

Using the **Domain Convention,** the domain of $s(t) = -16t^2 + 48t + 160$ is the set of all real numbers. However, in this application, t represents the number of seconds after the ball is thrown. Figure 3.C-1 on page 236 shows that the domain in this application is the set of all real numbers from 0 to 5 inclusive (the interval [0, 5]).

Do not confuse the h in the difference quotient with the height of the object. The height is $s(t)$ and h is used here to represent a time interval.

Math Background

The equation $s(t) = -16t^2 + v_0t + s_0$ can also be applied to objects that are not in a strictly vertical motion, provided that v_0 is the *vertical component* of the initial velocity.

ADDITIONAL EXAMPLES

Example 1

A rock is thrown straight up from the edge of a cliff with an initial height of 250 feet and an initial velocity of 56 feet per second. The rock misses the edge of the cliff on its way down and falls to the bottom of the ravine below. Find the instantaneous velocity of the rock at $t = 3$ seconds.

At $t = 3$ seconds, the instantaneous velocity is -40 feet per second.

Rates of change are a major theme in differential calculus—not just the average rate of change discussed in Section 3.7, but the **instantaneous rate of change** of a function. Instantaneous rate of change is the rate of change at a particular instant, which is like a policeman finding the speed of a car at a particular moment by using radar. Even without calculus, however, quite accurate approximations of instantaneous rates of change can be obtained by using average rates appropriately.

The equation of the position (in feet) above the ground of a falling object after t seconds is given by the equation

$$s = -16t^2 + v_0t + s_0,$$

where s_0 is the initial height in feet and v_0 is the initial velocity in feet per second. The object must be moving straight upward or straight downward.

Example 1 **Instantaneous Velocity**

A ball is thrown straight up from a rooftop with an initial height of 160 feet and an initial velocity of 48 feet per second. The ball misses the rooftop on its way down and falls to the ground. Find the instantaneous velocity of the ball at $t = 2$ seconds.

Solution

The height of the ball is given by the equation

$$s(t) = -16t^2 + 48t + 160.$$

The exact speed of the ball at $t = 2$ can be approximated by finding the average speed over very small time intervals, say 2 to 2.01 or even shorter intervals. Over a very short time span, such as a hundredth of a second, the ball cannot change speed very much, so these average speeds should be a reasonable approximation of its speed at the instant $t = 2$.

The difference quotient of the function s, which represents the average velocity of the function s, is

$$\frac{\Delta s}{\Delta t} = \frac{s(t + h) - s(t)}{h}$$

$$= \frac{(-16(t + h)^2 + 48(t + h) + 160) - (-16t^2 + 48t + 160)}{h}$$

$$= \frac{(-16(t^2 + 2th + h^2) + 48(t + h) + 160) - (-16t^2 + 48t + 160)}{h}$$

$$= \frac{-16t^2 - 32th - 16h^2 + 48t + 48h + 160 + 16t^2 - 48t - 160}{h}$$

NOTE Δ is often used to denote change in the value of a quantity. $\dfrac{\Delta s}{\Delta t}$, which is read "change in s divided by change in t," represents the ratio of the change in position to the change in time, which is velocity.

234

$$= \frac{-32th - 16h^2 + 48h}{h}$$

$$= -32t - 16h + 48 \qquad \textit{General expression of average velocity}$$

When $t = 2$, the expression for average velocity is

$$-32(2) - 16h + 48 = -16 - 16h.$$

The values of the average velocity at times close to $t = 2$ are shown in the following table.

Change in Time 2 to 2 + h	h	Average Velocity at t = 2 −16 − 16h
2 to 2.1	0.1	−17.6
2 to 2.01	0.01	−16.16
2 to 2.001	0.001	−16.016
2 to 2.0001	0.0001	−16.0016
2 to 2.00001	0.00001	−16.00016

As the value of h gets very small, the values of the average velocity approach the value of the instantaneous velocity. Since these values approach -16, the instantaneous velocity at $t = 2$ is -16 feet per second. ∎

In the table in Example 1, notice that when h is small, the term $-16h$ contributes very little to the average rate of change. Therefore, the instantaneous velocity is the remaining term of the difference quotient at $t = 2$, namely -16. In a similar fashion, the general expression of the difference quotient, $-32t - 16h + 48$, becomes

$$-32t + 48 \qquad \textit{Instantaneous rate of change expression}$$

when h is very small. Instantaneous rate of change can be found by using $-32t + 48$ for different values of t.

Slope of the Tangent Line

In Example 1, the instantaneous rate of change was found by calculating the average rate of change over smaller and smaller intervals. This technique can also be represented on a graph. The average rate of change over an interval is the slope of the secant line that contains the points $(x, f(x))$ and $(x + h, f(x + h))$. If h is very small, the slope of the secant line approaches the slope of the **tangent line**, a line that touches the graph at only one point. The slope of the tangent line to a curve at a point is equal to the instantaneous rate of change of the function at that point.

235

Math Background

Point out that the long and tedious two-step process of simplifying the difference quotient $\frac{\Delta s}{\Delta t}$ to get the *general expression of average velocity*, followed by finding the *instantaneous rate of change expression* really only needs to be done once. In calculus, this two-step process is used to develop rules, and those rules are used to find the *instantaneous rate of change expression* very quickly and easily.

Example Notes

In **Example 1**, explain that velocity is a rate of change. Velocity is the rate of change in position along a straight line with respect to time.

For Example 1, you may want to develop the table below with students for average velocities over time intervals before 2 seconds:

2 + h to 2	h	−16 − 16h
1.9 to 2	−0.1	−14.4
1.99 to 2	−0.01	−15.84
1.999 to 2	−0.001	−15.984
1.9999 to 2	−0.0001	−15.9984

The table shows that the same value for the instantaneous velocity at $t = 2$ can be found by using average velocities "on the other side of $t = 2$."

Teaching Notes

Point out that in the discussion about **Slope of the Tangent Line**, the function notation has been changed from $s(t)$ to $f(x)$ for generality.

Teaching Notes

When h is used to represent a change in x, the secant line goes through $(x, f(x))$ and $(x + h, f(x + h))$. To help students see the connection between this fact and the secant lines in Figure 3.C-1, show this sketch of the secant line through $(2, f(2))$ and $(3, f(3))$:

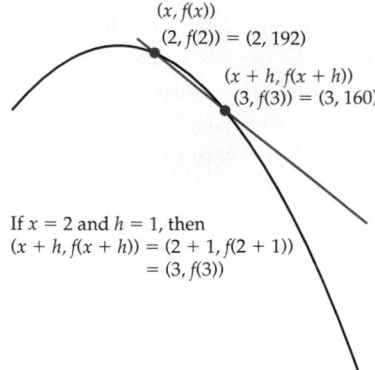

$(x, f(x))$
$(2, f(2)) = (2, 192)$

$(x + h, f(x + h))$
$(3, f(3)) = (3, 160)$

If $x = 2$ and $h = 1$, then
$(x + h, f(x + h)) = (2 + 1, f(2 + 1))$
$= (3, f(3))$

In Figure 3.C-1, the slope of the red tangent line is -16, as found in **Example 1**.

Example Notes

In **Example 2**, remind students that 196 is a local maximum, occurring at $t = 1.5$. Point out that a horizontal tangent line, indicating an instantaneous rate of change of zero, will always occur at a local maximum or minimum for a graph of a polynomial function (and for other "smooth" curves).

Figures 3.C-1 and 3.C-2 both show the same function, but use different scales.

Students can check the reasonableness of the maximum value 196 by observing 200 on the vertical axis in Figure 3.C-1.

In **Example 3**, to find the equation of the tangent line, y and x were used instead of s and t.

Point out that the y-intercept of the tangent line is 224. Have students use Figure 3.C-3 to verify that this is reasonable.

COMMON ERROR ALERT

The graph of $s(t) = -16t^2 + v_0t + s_0$ does not show the path of an object. Remember that the function gives the height of an object whose path is straight up and straight down.

236 can do calculus

Figure 3.C-1

Figure 3.C-2

236

The graph in Figure 3.C-1 shows secant lines that contain the fixed point $(2, f(2))$ and the points $(3, f(3))$, $(4, f(4))$, and $(5, f(5))$ for the function in Example 1. As the second point approaches the fixed point, the secant lines approach the tangent line, and the slopes of the secant lines approach the slope of the **tangent line.** The slope of the tangent line, shown in red, is the instantaneous rate of change of the function at the point $x = 2$. The tangent line can be used to determine when the instantaneous rate of change is 0, that is, when the object changes direction.

Example 2   Instantaneous Rate of Change Equal Zero

When is the instantaneous rate of change of the ball in Example 1 equal to zero? What is the maximum height reached by the ball?

Solution

The expression for instantaneous rate of change for $s(t) = -16t^2 + 48t + 160$ was found to be $-32t + 48$. Set this expression equal to zero and solve for t.

$$-32t + 48 = 0$$
$$t = \frac{48}{32} = 1.5 \text{ seconds}$$

Therefore, 1.5 seconds after the ball is thrown upward, its rate of change is zero. That is, the ball stops moving upward 1.5 seconds after being thrown, it will be at its highest at that time. Maximum height is given by $s(1.5)$.

$$s(1.5) = -16(1.5)^2 + 48(1.5) + 160$$
$$= -16(2.25) + 48(1.5) + 160$$
$$= -36 + 72 + 160$$
$$= 196 \text{ feet.}$$

The graph of s and the tangent line to the curve at $t = 1.5$ are shown in Figure 3.C-2. Notice that the tangent line is horizontal when $t = 1.5$. ∎

Writing the Equation of a Tangent Line

The equation of the tangent line to a curve at a point can be found by using the instantaneous rate of change at that point and the point-slope form of a line.

Example 3   Equation of a Tangent Line

Write the equation of the tangent line to the function given in Example 1 when $t = 2$.

Solution

When $t = 2$, the position of the ball is $s(2) = -16(2)^2 + 48(2) + 160 = 192$, therefore, the point on the graph is $(2, 192)$. From Example 1, the instantaneous rate of change when $t = 2$ is -16. So, the slope of the tangent line is -16.

300

`Y1=-16X^2+48X+160`

0 `X=2` `Y=192` 5

0

Figure 3.C-3

By using the point-slope form of a line with $m = -16$ and $(2, 192)$, the equation of the tangent line is

$$\begin{aligned}
y - y_1 &= m(x - x_1) && \text{\textit{Point-slope form}} \\
y - 192 &= -16(x - 2) \\
y - 192 &= -16x + 32 \\
y &= -16x + 224 && \text{\textit{Tangent line at} } (2, 192)
\end{aligned}$$

The graph of s and the tangent line at $t = 2$ is shown in figure 3.C-3.

Numerical Derivatives

Most graphing calculators will give you the value of the instantaneous rate of change of functions at particular input values. The instantaneous rate of change at a particular input value is usually called a **numerical derivative** and is denoted as nDeriv, nDer, d/dx, dY/dX, or ∂. On TI calculators, numerical derivatives are found in the MATH or CALC menu. On a Casio, numerical derivatives are displayed when using the TRACE, Graph-to-Table, and Table & Graph features if the Derivative item is On in the SET UP screen for graphs. Check your calculator's manual for the syntax.

Exercises

1. Write an equation for the height of a ball after t seconds that is thrown straight up from a bridge at an initial height of 75 ft with an initial velocity of 20 ft/sec. Find the instantaneous velocity of the ball at $t = 2$ seconds.

2. Find when the instantaneous velocity of the ball in Exercise 1 is 0 feet per second, and interpret the result.

3. Write an equation for the height of a ball after t seconds that is dropped from a tower at an initial height of 300 ft. Find the instantaneous velocity of the ball at $t = 3$ seconds. [*Hint:* When an object is dropped, and not thrown upward or downward, the initial velocity is 0.]

In Exercises 4–7, find the instantaneous rate of change of the function at the given value.

4. $f(t) = t^2 + 4t - 7$ at $t = 5$
   14

5. $f(t) = \dfrac{1}{t}$ at $t = 3$
   −0.111111

6. $f(x) = x^3 + 1$ at $x = 1$
   3

7. $f(u) = u^2$ at $u = a$
   2a

8. Find the instantaneous rate of change of $f(t) = -4t^2 + 16t + 12$ at $t = 4$ and use it to find the equation of the tangent line. Graph $f(t)$ and the tangent line on the same graph.

9. The surface area of a sphere of radius r is given by the formula $S(r) = 4\pi r^2$. Find the instantaneous rate of change of the surface area at $r = 1$ and interpret the result.

10. The profit, in dollars, of a manufacturer selling digital phones is given by the equation $P(x) = -0.05x^2 + 200x - 30{,}000$ where x is the number of phones sold. Find the instantaneous rate of change at $x = 1000$. What are the units of the rate of change? What does the instantaneous rate of change at $x = 1000$ tell you about the profit of the manufacturer?

    instantaneous rate of change = 100 dollars per phone; When $x = 1000$, for every additional phone sold, the profit increases by approximately $100.

237

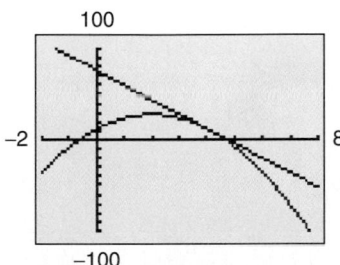

Polynomial and Rational Functions

In this chapter, students will learn about polynomial functions and their quotients, rational functions. They will study their graphs, zeros (real and complex), and applications. The chapter concludes with the Fundamental Theorem of Algebra, which shows that every polynomial has one or more zeros in the complex number system.

CHAPTER

4 | Polynomial and Rational Functions

Beauty between order and chaos!

Everyday life abounds in apparently random phenomena: changing weather, traffic clusters on the freeway, lightning paths, ocean turbulence, and many others. Chaos theory is an area of mathematics that analyzes such chaotic behavior. The Mandelbrot set, which is shown above, is a fascinating mathematical object derived from the complex numbers. Its beautiful boundary illustrates chaotic behavior. See *Excursion* 4.5.A.

238

Chapter Outline

Interdependence of Sections

$$4.1 \longrightarrow 4.2 \begin{array}{c} \nearrow 4.3 \\ \longrightarrow 4.4 \\ \searrow 4.5 \longrightarrow 4.6 \end{array}$$

Polynomial functions arise naturally in many applications. Many complicated functions can be approximated by polynomial functions or their quotients, rational functions.

Polynomial Functions

Objectives

- Define a polynomial
- Divide polynomials
- Apply the Remainder Theorem, the Factor Theorem, and the connections between remainders and factors
- Determine the maximum number of zeros of a polynomial

A **polynomial** is an algebraic expression that can be written in the form

$$a_n x^n + a_{n-1} x^{n-1} + \cdots + a_3 x^3 + a_2 x^2 + a_1 x + a_0$$

where n is a nonnegative integer, x is a variable, and each of $a_0, a_1, \ldots, a_n$ is a constant, called a **coefficient.** The coefficient a_0 is called the **constant term.** Note the characteristics of a polynomial.

- all exponents are whole numbers
- no variable is contained in a denominator
- no variable is under a radical

Any letter may be used as the variable in a polynomial. Examples of **polynomials** include the following.

$$x^3 - 6x^2 + \frac{1}{2} \qquad y^{15} + y^{10} + 7 \qquad w - 6.7 \qquad 12$$

239

Section 4.1 Polynomial Functions

Teaching Notes

Remind students that the set of whole numbers is the same as the set of nonnegative integers: $\{0, 1, 2, 3, \ldots\}$. Thus, the exponents in a polynomial cannot be negative numbers, fractions, or decimals.

Show students examples of algebraic expressions which are *not* polynomials:

$x^{-2} + 5$	exponent not whole number
$2y^{\frac{1}{3}} + 7y - 1$	exponent not whole number
$m + 2\sqrt{m}$	variable under radical
$p^2 - \frac{5}{p} + 3$	variable in denominator

Students may mistakenly identify the degree of a polynomial like $x + 3$ as 0, because the exponent is not shown. Remind them that $x = x^1$, so $x + 3$ is a first-degree polynomial.

Teaching Notes

Note that in the discussion of **Degree of a Polynomial,** the degree of 12 is 0. Remind students that $x^0 = 1$ if $x \neq 0$. Thus $12x^0 = 12 \cdot 1 = 12$.

Encourage students to write polynomials with the terms arranged in order of decreasing degree of the variable. For example, have them write the polynomial $x^2 + x^4 - 1$ as $x^4 + x^2 - 1$.

Connecting the **Definition of a Polynomial Function** to the characteristics of a polynomial listed on the previous page may aid in student understanding. Point out that all exponents are whole numbers, so if $f(x) = a_n x^n + a_{n-1} x^{n-1} + \cdots + a_1 x + a_0$ is a polynomial function, then:

- x cannot appear in a denominator (e.g., $\frac{1}{x^2} = x^{-2}$)
- x cannot appear under a radical (e.g., $\sqrt{x} = x^{\frac{1}{2}}$)

Example Notes

To prepare for polynomial division in **Example 1,** review numerical division with students. Use an example such as the one shown below to develop the steps *divide, multiply, subtract, bring down.*

$$
\begin{array}{r}
213 \\
12\overline{)2560} \\
\underline{24} \\
16 \\
\underline{12} \\
40 \\
\underline{36} \\
4
\end{array}
$$

The same set of steps will be used with polynomials.

Constant and Zero Polynomials

A polynomial that consists of only a constant term, such as the polynomial 12, is called a **constant polynomial.** The **zero polynomial** is the constant polynomial 0.

Degree of a Polynomial

The *exponent* of the highest power of x that appears with *nonzero* coefficient is the **degree** of the polynomial, and the nonzero coefficient of this highest power of the variable is the **leading coefficient.**

Polynomial	Degree	Leading coefficient	Constant term
$6x^7 + 4x^3 + 5x^2 - 7x + 10$	7	6	10
x^3	3	1	0
12	0	12	12
$0x^9 + 2x^6 + 3x^7 + x^8 - 2x - 4$	8	1	-4

The degree of the zero polynomial is *not defined* because in that case no power of x occurs with a *nonzero* coefficient.

Definition of a Polynomial Function

A *polynomial function* is a function whose rule is given by a polynomial

$$f(x) = a_n x^n + a_{n-1} x^{n-1} + \cdots + a_1 x + a_0$$

where $a_n, a_{n-1}, \ldots, a_1, a_0$ are real numbers with $a_n \neq 0$, and n is a nonnegative integer.

NOTE The term *polynomial* may refer to a polynomial expression or a polynomial function. The context should clarify the meaning.

Review addition, subtraction, and multiplication of polynomials in the Algebra Review Appendix, if needed.

Polynomial functions of degree less than 5 are often referred to by special names.

- First-degree polynomial functions are called **linear functions.**
- Second-degree polynomial functions are called **quadratic functions.**
- Third-degree polynomial functions are called **cubic functions.**
- Fourth-degree polynomial functions are called **quartic functions.**

Polynomial Division

Long division of polynomials is similar to long division of real numbers, as shown in Example 1.

Example 1 Polynomial Division

Divide $3x^4 - 8x^2 - 11x + 1$ by $x - 2$.

Solution

Expand the dividend to accommodate the missing term, $0x^3$, and write the problem as division.

$$Divisor \rightarrow \quad x - 2\overline{)3x^4 + 0x^3 - 8x^2 - 11x + 1} \quad \leftarrow Dividend$$

Divide the first term of the divisor, x, into the first term of the dividend, $3x^4$, and put the result, $\frac{3x^4}{x} = 3x^3$, on the top line. Then multiply $3x^3$ times the entire divisor, put the result on the third line, and subtract.

$$
\begin{array}{r}
3x^3 \\
x - 2\overline{)3x^4 + 0x^3 - 8x^2 - 11x + 1} \\
\underline{3x^4 - 6x^3 } \\
6x^3 - 8x^2 - 11x + 1
\end{array}
$$

Next, divide the first term of the divisor, x, into the leading term of the difference, $6x^3$, and put the result, $\frac{6x^3}{x} = 6x^2$, on the top line. Then multiply $6x^2$ times the entire divisor, put the result on the fifth line, and subtract.

Repeat the process until the remainder has a *smaller degree* than the divisor. Because the degree of the divisor in this case is 1, the process will stop when the subtraction results in a constant.

$$
\begin{array}{r}
3x^3 + 6x^2 + 4x - 3 \quad \leftarrow Quotient \\
Divisor \rightarrow \quad x - 2\overline{)3x^4 + 0x^3 - 8x^2 - 11x + 1} \quad \leftarrow Dividend \\
\underline{3x^4 - 6x^3 } \\
6x^3 - 8x^2 - 11x + 1 \\
\underline{6x^3 - 12x^2 } \\
4x^2 - 11x + 1 \\
\underline{4x^2 - 8x } \\
-3x + 1 \\
\underline{-3x + 6} \\
-5 \quad \leftarrow Remainder
\end{array}
$$

Synthetic Division

When the divisor is a first-degree polynomial such as $x - 2$ or $x + 5$, there is a convenient shorthand method of division called **synthetic division**. The problem from Example 1 is reconsidered below, where it is used to illustrate the procedure used in synthetic division.

$$Divisor \qquad\qquad Dividend$$

Step 1 In the first row, list the 2 from the divisor and the coefficients of the dividend in order of decreasing powers of x, inserting 0 for missing powers of x.

$$\underline{2|}\ \ 3 \quad 0 \quad -8 \quad -11 \quad 1$$

Step 2 Skip a line, draw a line, and draw a partial box under the line beneath the last coefficient in the first row. Bring the first coefficient of the dividend below the line.

$$\underline{2|}\ \ 3 \quad 0 \quad -8 \quad -11 \quad 1$$
$$3$$

Example 1

Divide $2x^4 - 25x^2 - 30x + 5$ by $x - 4$.

$$
\begin{array}{r}
2x^3 + 8x^2 + 7x - 2 \\
x - 4\overline{)2x^4 + 0x^3 - 25x^2 - 30x + 5} \\
\underline{2x^4 - 8x^3 } \\
8x^3 - 25x^2 - 30x + 5 \\
\underline{8x^3 - 32x^2 } \\
7x^2 - 30x + 5 \\
\underline{7x^2 - 28x } \\
-2x + 5 \\
\underline{-2x + 8} \\
-3
\end{array}
$$

The quotient is $2x^3 + 8x^2 + 7x - 2$ and the remainder is -3.

 Math Background

Dividing 13 by 6 is shown below.

$$
\begin{array}{r}
2 \\
6\overline{)13} \\
\underline{12} \\
1
\end{array}
$$

The result can be expressed as $2\frac{1}{6}$, or $2 + \frac{1}{6}$. The same concepts apply to polynomial division.

For example, $x^2 + 7x + 12$ divided by $x + 2$ is shown below.

$$
\begin{array}{r}
x + 5 \\
x + 2\overline{)x^2 + 7x + 12} \\
\underline{x^2 + 2x } \\
5x + 12 \\
\underline{5x + 10} \\
2
\end{array}
$$

This result can be expressed as $x + 5 + \frac{2}{x + 2}$.

Teaching Notes

Because synthetic division can only be used when the divisor is a first-degree polynomial, the degree of the quotient from synthetic division will always be one less than the degree of the dividend.

Example Notes

In **Example 2**, the divisor $x + 3$ is rewritten as $x - (-3)$ to get it in the required form $x - c$ (See **CAUTION** box on page 241). So, $c = -3$.

ADDITIONAL EXAMPLES

Example 2

Divide $x^4 + 5x^3 + 2x^2 + 6x - 17$ by $x + 5$ and check the result.

$$
\begin{array}{r|rrrrr}
-5 & 1 & 5 & 2 & 6 & -17 \\
 & & -5 & 0 & -10 & 20 \\
\hline
 & 1 & 0 & 2 & -4 & 3
\end{array}
$$

The quotient is $x^3 + 2x - 4$ and the remainder is 3.

Example 3

Determine if $3x^2 - 2$ is a factor of $3x^3 + 15x^2 - 2x - 10$.

$$
\begin{array}{r}
x + 5 \\
3x^2 - 2 \overline{\smash{)}3x^3 + 15x^2 - 2x - 10} \\
\underline{3x^3 \qquad\quad - 2x} \\
15x^2 \qquad\quad - 10 \\
\underline{15x^2 \qquad\quad - 10} \\
0
\end{array}
$$

Yes, $3x^2 - 2$ is a factor of $3x^3 + 15x^2 - 2x - 10$, and the other factor is the quotient, $x + 5$.

Step 3 Multiply the divisor constant, 2, and the number below the line, 3. Place the product, 6, under the dividend's next coefficient.

$$
\begin{array}{r|rrrrr}
2 & 3 & 0 & -8 & -11 & 1 \\
 & & 6 & & & \\
\hline
 & 3 & & & &
\end{array}
$$

Step 4 Add the numbers in that column and write the sum below the column under the line.

$$
\begin{array}{r|rrrrr}
2 & 3 & 0 & -8 & -11 & 1 \\
 & & 6 & & & \\
\hline
 & 3 & 6 & & &
\end{array}
$$

Step 5 Multiply the divisor and the last entry of the last row. Place the product under the dividend's next coefficient.

$$
\begin{array}{r|rrrrr}
2 & 3 & 0 & -8 & -11 & 1 \\
 & & 6 & 12 & & \\
\hline
 & 3 & 6 & & &
\end{array}
$$

Step 6 Add the numbers in that column and write the sum below the column under the line.

$$
\begin{array}{r|rrrrr}
2 & 3 & 0 & -8 & -11 & 1 \\
 & & 6 & 12 & & \\
\hline
 & 3 & 6 & 4 & &
\end{array}
$$

Step 7 Repeat steps **5** and **6** until a number appears in the box under the last column.

$$
\begin{array}{r|rrrrr}
2 & 3 & 0 & -8 & -11 & 1 \\
 & & 6 & 12 & 8 & -6 \\
\hline
 & 3 & 6 & 4 & -3 & -5
\end{array}
$$

The last number in the third row is the remainder. The other numbers in the third row are the coefficients of the quotient, arranged in order of decreasing powers of x. Because a *fourth*-degree polynomial was divided by a *first*-degree polynomial, the quotient is a *third*-degree polynomial. Therefore, the quotient is $3x^3 + 6x^2 + 4x - 3$ and the remainder is -5.

Example 2   Synthetic Division

Divide $x^5 + 5x^4 + 6x^3 - x^2 + 4x + 29$ by $x + 3$ and check the result.

Solution

To divide $x^5 + 5x^4 + 6x^3 - x^2 + 4x + 29$ by $x + 3$, write the divisor as $x - (-3)$ and perform synthetic division.

$$
\begin{array}{r|rrrrrr}
-3 & 1 & 5 & 6 & -1 & 4 & 29 \\
 & & -3 & -6 & 0 & 3 & -21 \\
\hline
 & 1 & 2 & 0 & -1 & 7 & 8
\end{array}
$$

The last row shows that the quotient is $x^4 + 2x^3 - x + 7$ and the remainder is 8. ∎

Checking Polynomial Division

Recall how to check a long division problem. When 4509 is divided by 31, the quotient is 145 and the remainder is 14. To check the division, multiply the quotient by the divisor and add the remainder,

$$4509 = 145 \cdot 31 + 14$$

Checking polynomial division uses the same process.

$$\text{Dividend} = \text{Divisor} \cdot \text{Quotient} + \text{Remainder}$$

Check the division in Example 2.

$$(x^4 + 2x^3 - x + 7)(x + 3) + 8 = (x^5 + 5x^4 + 6x^3 - x^2 + 4x + 21) + 8$$
$$= x^5 + 5x^4 + 6x^3 - x^2 + 4x + 29$$

The Division Algorithm

> If a polynomial $f(x)$ is divided by a nonzero polynomial $h(x)$, then there is a quotient polynomial $q(x)$ and a remainder polynomial $r(x)$ such that
>
> $$\text{Dividend} = \text{Divisor} \cdot \text{Quotient} + \text{Remainder}$$
>
> $$f(x) = h(x) \cdot q(x) + r(x)$$
>
> where either $r(x) = 0$ or $r(x)$ has degree less than the degree of the divisor, $h(x)$.

The Division Algorithm can be used to determine if one polynomial is a factor of another polynomial.

Remainders and Factors

> If the remainder is 0 when one polynomial is divided by another polynomial, the divisor and the quotient are factors of the dividend.

Example 3   Factors Determined by Division

Determine if $2x^2 + 1$ is a factor of $6x^3 - 4x^2 + 3x - 2$.

Solution

Divide $6x^3 - 4x^2 + 3x - 2$ by $2x^2 + 1$, and see if the remainder is 0.

$$
\begin{array}{r}
3x - 2 \\
2x^2 + 1 \overline{)6x^3 - 4x^2 + 3x - 2} \\
6x^3 \qquad + 3x \\
\hline
-4x^2 \qquad -2 \\
-4x^2 \qquad -2 \\
\hline
0
\end{array}
$$

The remainder is 0, and the Division Algorithm confirms the factorization.

$$\text{Dividend} = \text{Divisor} \cdot \text{Quotient} + \text{Remainder}$$
$$6x^3 - 4x^2 + 3x - 2 = (2x^2 + 1)(3x - 2) + 0$$
$$= (2x^2 + 1)(3x - 2)$$

Teaching Notes

Divide $x^2 + 5x + 7$ by $x - 2$ with the class. After completing the division, label $x - 2$ as $h(x)$, $x^2 + 5x + 7$ as $f(x)$, $x + 7$ as $q(x)$ and the remainder 21 as $r(x)$.

$$
\begin{array}{r}
x + 7 \qquad \leftarrow q(x) \\
h(x) \rightarrow x - 2 \overline{)x^2 + 5x + 7} \quad \leftarrow f(x) \\
x^2 - 2x \\
\hline
7x + 7 \\
7x - 14 \\
\hline
21 \quad \leftarrow r(x)
\end{array}
$$

Now illustrate **The Division Algorithm**, **Remainders and Factors**, the **Remainder Theorem** (page 244), and the **Factor Theorem** (page 245) as shown below:

Division Algorithm
$$f(x) = h(x) \cdot q(x) + r(x)$$
$$x^2 + 5x + 7 = (x - 2)(x + 7) + 21$$

Remainders and Factors (does not apply because the remainder is not 0)

Remainder Theorem
$f(x)$ was divided by $x - 2$.
$f(2) = (2 - 2)(2 + 7) + 21 = 21$, the remainder.

Factor Theorem (does not apply because $f(x)$ has no linear factors)

Now repeat the same process for this polynomial division:

$$
\begin{array}{r}
x - 1 \qquad \leftarrow q(x) \\
h(x) \rightarrow x - 5 \overline{)x^2 - 6x + 5} \quad \leftarrow f(x) \\
x^2 - 5x \\
\hline
-x + 5 \\
-x + 5 \\
\hline
0 \quad \leftarrow r(x)
\end{array}
$$

Division Algorithm
$$f(x) = h(x) \cdot q(x) + r(x)$$
$$x^2 - 6x + 5 = (x - 5)(x - 1) + 0$$

Remainders and Factors
$$x - 6x^2 + 5 = (x - 5)(x - 1)$$

Remainder Theorem
$f(x)$ was divided by $x - 5$.
$f(5) = (5 - 5)(5 - 1) = 0$, the remainder.

Factor Theorem
$f(x)$ has the linear factor $x - 5$ because $f(5) = 0$, and conversely.
$f(x)$ has the linear factor $x - 1$ because $f(1) = 0$, and conversely.

Teaching Notes

As stated under **Remainders**, the remainder is a constant when a polynomial $f(x)$ is divided by a first-degree polynomial. This is a direct result of the **Division Algorithm** on page 243, which states that the remainder is either zero or has degree less than the divisor.

Before discussing the **Remainder Theorem**, consider posing the problem in **Example 4** to the class (do not solve yet). They will quickly see that finding the remainder by actually dividing would be impossibly tedious. This exercise will provide motivation for the Remainder Theorem.

 Math Background

According to the **Division Algorithm**, $f(x) = h(x) \cdot q(x) + r(x)$, where h is the divisor, q is the quotient, and r is the remainder. If $h(x) = x - c$, as required in the **Remainder Theorem**, then $f(x) = (x - c) \cdot q(x) + r(x)$. For $x = c$, this simplifies to

$f(c) = (c - c) \cdot q(c) + r(c)$
$= 0 \cdot q(c) + r(c)$
$= r(c)$.

This proves the Remainder Theorem: If a polynomial $f(x)$ is divided by $x - c$, then the remainder is $f(c)$.

ADDITIONAL EXAMPLES

Example 4

Find the remainder when $x^{87} - 2x^{36} + 8$ is divided by $x + 1$. $x + 1 = x - (-1)$,

$f(-1) = (-1)^{87} - 2(-1)^{36} + 8$
$= -1 - 2(1) + 8 = 5$

The remainder is 5.

Therefore, $(2x^2 + 1)$ is a factor of $6x^3 - 4x^2 + 3x - 2$, and the other factor is the quotient, $(3x - 2)$.

Remainders

When a polynomial $f(x)$ is divided by a first-degree polynomial, such as $x - 3$ or $x + 5$, the remainder is a constant. For example, when

$$f(x) = x^3 - 2x^2 - 4x + 5 \text{ is divided by } x - 3,$$

the quotient is $x^2 + x - 1$ and the remainder is 2.

$$x^3 - 2x^2 - 4x + 5 = (x - 3)(x^2 + x - 1) + 2$$

Notice that $f(3) = (3 - 3)(3^2 + 3 - 1) + 2$
$= (0)(11) + 2 = 2.$

That is, the number $f(3)$ is the same as the remainder when $f(x)$ is divided by $x - 3$, as stated in the Remainder Theorem.

Remainder Theorem ——○

> If a polynomial $f(x)$ is divided by $x - c$, then the remainder is $f(c)$.

Example 4   The Remainder When Dividing by $x - c$

Find the remainder when $x^{79} + 3x^{24} + 5$ is divided by $x - 1$.

Solution

Let $f(x) = x^{79} + 3x^{24} + 5$ and apply the Remainder Theorem with $c = 1$.

$$f(1) = 1^{79} + 3(1)^{24} + 5 = 1 + 3 + 5 = 9$$

Therefore, the remainder when $x^{79} + 3x^{24} + 5$ is divided by $x - 1$ is 9. ■

Example 5   The Remainder When Dividing by $x + k$

Find the remainder when $3x^4 - 8x^2 + 11x + 1$ is divided by $x + 2$.

Solution

The divisor, $x + 2$, is not in the form $x - a$, so the Remainder Theorem must be applied *carefully*. Rewrite the divisor as $x - (-2)$, and find $f(-2)$.

$$f(-2) = 3(-2)^4 - 8(-2)^2 + 11(-2) + 1$$
$$= 3(16) - 8(4) + 11(-2) + 1$$
$$= 48 - 32 - 22 + 1$$
$$= -5$$

By the Remainder Theorem, when $3x^4 - 8x^2 + 11x + 1$ is divided by $x + 2$, the remainder is -5, which can be verified by division. ∎

Zeros and Factors

Recall that if $f(x)$ is a polynomial, then solutions of the equation $f(x) = 0$ are called **zeros** of the function. A zero that is a real number is called a **real zero.** The connection between zeros of a polynomial function and factors of the polynomial is given below.

Factor Theorem

> A polynomial function $f(x)$ has a linear factor $x - a$ if and only if
>
> $$f(a) = 0.$$

The Factor Theorem states

If a is a solution of $f(x) = 0$, then $x - a$ is a factor of $f(x)$.

and

If $x - a$ is a factor of $f(x)$, then a is a solution of $f(x) = 0$.

You can see why the Factor Theorem is true by noting that the remainder when $f(x)$ is divided by $x - a$ is $f(a)$ according to the Remainder Theorem. Therefore, by the Division Algorithm

$$f(x) = (x - a)q(x) + f(a).$$

Thus, when $f(a) = 0$, $f(x) = (x - a)q(x)$, so that $x - a$ is a factor. Conversely, when $x - a$ is a factor, the remainder $f(a)$ must be 0.

Example 6   The Factor Theorem

Show that $x - 3$ is a factor of $x^3 - 4x^2 + 2x + 3$ by using the Factor Theorem. Find $q(x)$ such that $(x - 3)q(x) = x^3 - 4x^2 + 2x + 3$.

Solution

Let $f(x) = x^3 - 4x^2 + 2x + 3$ and find $f(3)$.

$$\begin{aligned} f(3) &= 3^3 - 4(3^2) + 2(3) + 3 \\ &= 27 - 4(9) + 2(3) + 3 \\ &= 27 - 36 + 6 + 3 \\ &= 0 \end{aligned}$$

By the Factor Theorem, $x - 3$ is a factor of $x^3 - 4x^2 + 2x + 3$ because $f(3) = 0$.

Dividing $x^3 - 4x^2 + 2x + 3$ by $x - 3$ yields a quotient of $x^2 - x - 1$, and $f(x)$ can be written in factored form.

ADDITIONAL EXAMPLES

Example 5

Find the remainder when $2x^4 + 4x^3 + 5x - 6$ is divided by $x + 3$.

$$x + 3 = x - (-3),$$

$$f(-3) = 2(-3)^4 + 4(-3)^3 +$$
$$5(-3) - 6$$

$$= 2(81) + 4(-27) + 5(-3) - 6$$

$$= 162 - 108 - 15 - 6$$

$$= 33$$

The remainder is 33.

Example 6

Show that $x - 2$ is a factor of $x^3 + 5x^2 - 2x - 24$ by using the Factor Theorem. Find $q(x)$ such that $(x - 2)q(x) = x^3 + 5x^2 - 2x - 24$.

$$f(2) = 2^3 + 5(2)^2 - 2(2) - 24 = 0$$

By the Factor Theorem, $x - 2$ is a factor of $x^3 + 5x^2 - 2x - 24$ because $f(2) = 0$.

By the Division Algorithm,
$$x^3 + 5x^2 - 2x - 24$$
$$= (x - 2)(x^2 + 7x + 12),$$
so $q(x) = x^2 + 7x + 12$.

Math Background

The **Factor Theorem** is an *if and only if* (biconditional) statement. It is restated below the box as the two separate *if, then* statements that comprise it. Alternate versions of these two statements are:

If $f(a) = 0$, then $x - a$ is a factor of $f(x)$.

If $x - a$ is a factor of $f(x)$, then $f(a) = 0$.

The two *if, then* statements that comprise a biconditional are a conditional and its converse.

Teaching Notes

The **Zeros, x-intercepts, Solutions, and Factors of Polynomials** box is an extension of the **Zeros, x-Intercepts, and Solutions** box on page 83. Have students compare the boxes. Ask them what is new in the box on the current page.

$f(x)$ is a polynomial instead of just a function.

There is a fourth bullet that says "$x - r$ is a factor of the polynomial $f(x)$."

There is a statement that says "There is a one-to-one correspondence between the linear factors of $f(x)$ that have real coefficients and the x-intercepts of the graph of f."

Students have already studied quadratic functions. Before discussing **Example 7**, it may be beneficial to illustrate these polynomial connections with a quadratic function, as follows:

For $f(x) = x^2 - 2x - 3$
$= (x + 1)(x - 3),$

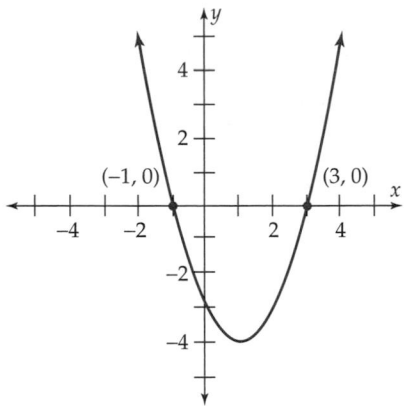

The x-intercepts of the graph are -1 and 3.

The zeros of f are -1 and 3.

The solutions of
$f(x) = x^2 - 2x - 3 = 0$
are -1 and 3.

The linear factors of
$f(x) = x^2 - 2x - 3$ are $x + 1$
and $x - 3$.

$$\text{\textit{Dividend} = \textit{Divisor} \cdot \textit{Quotient}}$$
$$x^3 - 4x^2 + 2x + 3 = (x - 3)(x^2 - x - 1)$$

The product can be verified by multiplication. ∎

Fundamental Polynomial Connections

Section 2.1 described the connection among the x-intercepts of the graph of $y = f(x)$, the zeros of the function f, and the solutions of $f(x) = 0$. This connection can be extended to include linear factors of $f(x)$, when $f(x)$ is a polynomial.

Zeros, x-Intercepts, Solutions, and Factors of Polynomials

> Let $f(x)$ be a polynomial. If r is a real number that satisfies any of the following statements, then r satisfies all the statements.
>
> - r is a zero of the function f
> - r is an x-intercept of the graph of the function f
> - $x = r$ is a solution, or root, of the equation $f(x) = 0$
> - $x - r$ is a factor of the polynomial $f(x)$
>
> There is a one-to-one correspondence between the linear factors of $f(x)$ that have real coefficients and the x-intercepts of the graph of f.

The box above states that a zero, an x-intercept, a solution, and the value of r in a linear factor of the form $x - r$ are all the same for a polynomial. Additionally, the x-intercepts correspond to the linear factors of $f(x)$ of the form $x - r$, where r is a real number.

Example 7 Fundamental Polynomial Connections

For $f(x) = 15x^3 - x^2 - 114x + 72$, find the following:

a. the x-intercepts of the graph of f

b. the zeros of f

c. the solutions to $15x^3 - x^2 - 114x + 72 = 0$

d. the linear factors with real coefficients of $15x^3 - x^2 - 114x + 72$

Solution

Graph $f(x) = 15x^3 - x^2 - 114x + 72$ in a standard viewing window, as shown in Figure 4.1-1.

a. Using the zero finder, find the x-intercepts.

$$-3, \frac{2}{3} \approx 0.6667, \text{ and } \frac{12}{5} = 2.4$$

Figure 4.1-1

b. The zeros of f are -3, $\frac{2}{3} \approx 0.6667$, and $\frac{12}{5} = 2.4$.

c. The solutions of $15x^3 - x^2 - 114x + 72 = 0$ are $x = -3$,
$x = \frac{2}{3} \approx 0.6667$, and $x = \frac{12}{5} = 2.4$, which can be verified by
substitution.

d. The linear factors of $15x^3 - x^2 - 114x + 72$ are $(x - (-3))$, $\left(x - \frac{2}{3}\right)$,
and $\left(x - \frac{12}{5}\right)$.

The product $(x + 3)\left(x - \frac{2}{3}\right)\left(x - \frac{12}{5}\right)$ is *not* the original polynomial.
There is a constant, a, such that

$$a(x + 3)\left(x - \frac{2}{3}\right)\left(x - \frac{12}{5}\right) = 15x^3 - x^2 - 114x + 72.$$

The leading coefficient of the original polynomial, 15, must be the leading coefficient of the product of the factors. So, $a = 15$.

$$15x^3 - x^2 - 114x + 72 = 15(x + 3)\left(x - \frac{2}{3}\right)\left(x - \frac{12}{5}\right)$$
$$= 3 \cdot 5(x + 3)\left(x - \frac{2}{3}\right)\left(x - \frac{12}{5}\right)$$
$$= (x + 3) \cdot 3\left(x - \frac{2}{3}\right) \cdot 5\left(x - \frac{12}{5}\right)$$
$$= (x + 3)(3x - 2)(5x - 12)$$

Example 8   A Polynomial with Specific Zeros

Find three polynomials of different degrees that have 1, 2, 3, and -5 as zeros.

Solution

A polynomial that has 1, 2, 3, and -5 as zeros must have $x - 1$, $x - 2$, $x - 3$, and $x - (-5) = x + 5$ as factors. Many polynomials satisfy these conditions, such as

$$g(x) = (x - 1)(x - 2)(x - 3)(x + 5)$$
$$h(x) = 8(x - 1)(x - 2)(x - 3)^2(x + 5)$$
$$k(x) = 2(x + 4)^2(x - 1)(x - 2)(x - 3)(x + 5)(x^2 + x + 1)$$

Notice that g has degree 4, h had degree 5, and k has degree 8.

The Number of Zeros of a Polynomial

If a polynomial $f(x)$ has four real zeros, say a, b, c, and d, then by the same argument used in Example 8, $f(x)$ must have

$$(x - a), (x - b), (x - c), \text{ and } (x - d)$$

ADDITIONAL EXAMPLES

Example 7

For $f(x) = 2x^3 - 7x^2 - 20x + 25$, find the following:

a. the x-intercepts of the graph of f

-2.5, 1, and 5

b. the zeros of f

-2.5, 1, and 5

c. the solutions to
$2x^3 - 7x^2 - 20x + 25 = 0$

$x = -2.5$, $x = 1$, and $x = 5$

d. the linear factors with real coefficients
of $2x^3 - 7x^2 - 20x + 25$

$2x + 5$, $x - 1$, and $x - 5$

Example 8

Find three polynomials of different degrees that have -2, 1, and 3 as zeros.

Many polynomials satisfy these conditions, provided they contain the factors $x + 2$, $x - 1$, and $x - 3$. Examples include

$$g(x) = (x + 2)(x - 1)(x - 3)$$
$$h(x) = (x + 2)^2(x - 1)(x - 3)$$
$$k(x) = 5(x + 2)(x - 1)(x - 3)(x^2 + 1)$$

which have degree 3, 4, and 5 respectively.

Math Background

A polynomial of degree n has exactly n zeros (see page 308). However, some zeros may not be distinct, and some may be complex numbers. Consider the fourth-degree polynomial $f(x) = (x - 5)(x - 5)(x + 3i)(x - 3i)$. It has four zeros, which are $x = 5$, $x = 5$, $x = -3i$, and $x = 3i$. 5 is a zero of multiplicity 2, and $3i$ and $-3i$ are complex zeros. This polynomial has only one distinct real zero, namely 5.

ADDITIONAL EXAMPLES

Example 9

State the maximum number of distinct real zeros of f.

$f(x) = 6x^5 + 2x^3 - x + 7$

The degree of f is 5. Thus, the maximum number of distinct real zeros of f is 5.

Exercises 4.1

ANSWERS

1. Polynomial of degree 3; leading coefficient 1; constant term 1

2. Polynomial of degree 0; leading coefficient -7; constant term -7

3. Polynomial of degree 3; leading coefficient 1; constant term -1

4. Not a polynomial

5. Polynomial of degree 2; leading coefficient 1; constant term -3

6. Not a polynomial

7. Not a polynomial

8. Polynomial of degree k; leading coefficient 1; constant term either 1 or -1, depending on whether the degree k is even or odd

as linear factors. Because its leading term is x^4, $(x - a)(x - b)(x - c)(x - d)$ has degree 4. Since $f(x)$ must have all four factors, its degree must be at least 4. In particular, this means that no polynomial of degree 3 can have four or more zeros. A similar argument holds in the general case.

Number of Zeros

A polynomial of degree n has at most n distinct real zeros.

Example 9   Maximum Number of Distinct Real Zeros

State the maximum number of distinct real zeros of f.

$$f(x) = 18x^4 - 51x^3 - 187x^2 - 56x + 80$$

Solution

The degree of f is 4. Therefore, the maximum number of distinct real zeros of f is 4. ∎

Exercises 4.1

In Exercises 1–8, determine whether the given algebraic expression is a polynomial. If it is, list its leading coefficient, constant term, and degree.

1. $1 + x^3$
2. -7
3. $(x - 1)(x^2 + 1)$
4. $7^x + 2x + 1$
5. $(x + \sqrt{3})(x - \sqrt{3})$
6. $4x^2 + 3\sqrt{x} + 5$
7. $\dfrac{7}{x^2} + \dfrac{5}{x} - 15$
8. $(x - 1)^k$ (where k is a fixed positive integer)

In Exercises 9–16, use synthetic division to find the quotient and remainder.

9. $(3x^4 - 8x^3 + 9x + 5) \div (x - 2)$
   $3x^3 - 2x^2 - 4x + 1; 7$
10. $(4x^3 - 3x^2 + x + 7) \div (x - 2)$
    $4x^2 + 5x + 11; 29$
11. $(2x^4 + 5x^3 - 2x - 8) \div (x + 3)$
    $2x^3 - x^2 + 3x - 11; 25$
12. $(3x^3 - 2x^2 - 8) \div (x + 5)$
    $3x^2 - 17x + 85; -433$
13. $(5x^4 - 3x^2 - 4x + 6) \div (x - 7)$
    $5x^3 + 35x^2 + 242x + 1690; 11,836$
14. $(3x^4 - 2x^3 + 7x - 4) \div (x - 3)$
    $3x^3 + 7x^2 + 21x + 70; 206$
15. $(x^4 - 6x^3 + 4x^2 + 2x - 7) \div (x - 2)$
    $x^3 - 4x^2 - 4x - 6; -19$
16. $(x^6 - x^5 + x^4 - x^3 + x^2 - x + 1) \div (x + 3)$
    $x^5 - 4x^4 + 13x^3 - 40x^2 + 121x - 364; 1093$

In Exercises 17–22, state the quotient and remainder when the first polynomial is divided by the second. Check your division by calculating (Divisor)(Quotient) + Remainder

17. $3x^4 + 2x^2 - 6x + 1; \quad x + 1$
    $3x^3 - 3x^2 + 5x - 11; 12$
18. $x^5 - x^3 + x - 5; \quad x - 2$
    $x^4 + 2x^3 + 3x^2 + 6x + 13; 21$
19. $x^5 + 2x^4 - 6x^3 + x^2 - 5x + 1; \quad x^3 + 1$
    $x^2 + 2x - 6; -7x + 7$
20. $3x^4 - 3x^3 - 11x^2 + 6x - 1; \quad x^3 + x^2 - 2$
    $3x - 6; -5x^2 + 12x - 13$
21. $5x^4 + 5x^2 + 5; \quad x^2 - x + 1$
    $5x^2 + 5x + 5; 0$
22. $x^5 - 1; \quad x - 1$
    $x^4 + x^3 + x^2 + x + 1; 0$

In Exercises 23–26, determine whether the first polynomial is a factor of the second.

23. $x^2 + 3x - 1; \quad x^3 + 2x^2 - 5x - 6$ **No**

24. $x^2 + 9; \quad x^5 + x^4 - 81x - 81$ **Yes**

25. $x^2 + 3x - 1$; $\quad x^4 + 3x^3 - 2x^2 - 3x + 1$
Yes

26. $x^2 - 5x + 7$; $\quad x^3 - 3x^2 - 3x + 9$
No

In Exercises 27–30, determine which of the given numbers are zeros of the given polynomial.

27. $2, 3, 0, -1$; $\quad g(x) = x^4 + 6x^3 - x^2 - 30x$
0, 2

28. $1, \frac{1}{2}, 2, -\frac{1}{2}, 3$; $\quad f(x) = 6x^2 + x - 1$ $\quad -\frac{1}{2}$

29. $2\sqrt{2}, \sqrt{2}, -\sqrt{2}, 1, -1$; $\quad h(x) = x^3 + x^2 - 8x - 8$
$2\sqrt{2}, -1$

30. $\sqrt{3}, -\sqrt{3}, 1, -1$; $\quad k(x) = 8x^3 - 12x^2 - 6x + 9$
None

In Exercises 31–40, find the remainder when $f(x)$ is divided by $g(x)$, without using division.

31. $f(x) = x^{10} + x^8$; $\quad g(x) = x - 1$
2

32. $f(x) = x^6 - 10$; $\quad g(x) = x - 2$
54

33. $f(x) = 3x^4 - 6x^3 + 2x - 1$; $\quad g(x) = x + 1$
6

34. $f(x) = x^5 - 3x^2 + 2x - 1$; $\quad g(x) = x - 2$
23

35. $f(x) = x^3 - 2x^2 + 5x - 4$; $\quad g(x) = x + 2$
−30

36. $f(x) = 10x^{75} - 8x^{65} + 6x^{45} + 4x^{32} - 2x^{15} + 5$;
15 $\quad g(x) = x - 1$

37. $f(x) = 2x^5 - 3x^4 + x^3 - 2x^2 + x - 8, g(x) = x - 10$
170,802

38. $f(x) = x^3 + 8x^2 - 29x + 44$; $\quad g(x) = x + 11$
0

39. $f(x) = 2x^5 - 3x^4 + 2x^3 - 8x - 8$; $\quad g(x) = x - 20$
5,935,832

40. $f(x) = x^5 - 10x^4 + 20x^3 - 5x - 95$; $g(x) = x + 10$
−220,045

In Exercises 41–46, use the Factor Theorem to determine whether $h(x)$ is a factor of $f(x)$.

41. $h(x) = x - 1$; $\quad f(x) = x^5 + 1$
No

42. $h(x) = x - \frac{1}{2}$; $\quad f(x) = 2x^4 + x^3 + x - \frac{3}{4}$
Yes

43. $h(x) = x + 2$; $\quad f(x) = x^3 - 3x^2 - 4x - 12$
No

44. $h(x) = x + 1$; $\quad f(x) = x^3 - 4x^2 + 3x + 8$
Yes

45. $h(x) = x - 1$; $\quad f(x) = 14x^{99} - 65x^{56} + 51$
Yes

46. $h(x) = x - 2$; $\quad f(x) = x^3 + x^2 - 4x + 4$
No

In Exercises 47–50, use the Factor Theorem and a calculator to factor the polynomial, as in Example 7.

47. $f(x) = 6x^3 - 7x^2 - 89x + 140$
$(x + 4)(2x - 7)(3x - 5)$

48. $g(x) = x^3 - 5x^2 - 5x - 6$
$(x - 6)(x^2 + x + 1)$

49. $h(x) = 4x^4 + 4x^3 - 35x^2 - 36x - 9$
$(x - 3)(x + 3)(2x + 1)^2$

50. $f(x) = x^5 - 5x^4 - 5x^3 + 25x^2 + 6x - 30$
$(x - 5)(x^2 - 3)(x^2 - 2)$

In Exercises 51–54, each graph is of a polynomial function $f(x)$ of degree 5 whose leading coefficient is 1, but the graph is not drawn to scale. Use the Factor Theorem to find the polynomial. *Hint:* What are the zeros of $f(x)$? What does the Factor Theorem tell you?

51.

52.

53.

54.

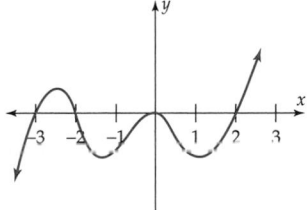

51. $f(x) = (x + 2)(x + 1) \cdot$
$(x - 1)(x - 2)(x - 3)$
$= x^5 - 3x^4 - 5x^3 +$
$15x^2 + 4x - 12$

52. $f(x) = x(x + 3)(x + 2)(x - 1) \cdot$
$(x - 2)$
$= x^5 + 2x^4 - 7x^3 - 8x^2 +$
$12x$

53. $f(x) = x(x + 1)(x - 1) \cdot$
$(x - 2)(x - 3)$
$= x^5 - 5x^4 + 5x^3 +$
$5x^2 - 6x$

54. $f(x) = x^2(x + 3)(x + 2)(x - 2)$
$= x^5 + 3x^4 - 4x^3 - 12x^2$

55. Possible answer:
$f(x) = (x - 1)(x - 7)(x + 4)$

56. Possible answer:
$f(x) = (x - 1)^2(x + 1)$

57. Possible answer:
$f(x) = (x - 1)(x - 2)^2(x - \pi)^3$

58. Possible answer: $f(x) = (x - 2)^5$

59. $f(x) = \frac{17}{100}(x - 5)(x - 8)x$

66. a. If $f(x) = x^n - c^n$, then
$f(c) = c^n - c^n = 0$ and
$x - c$ is a factor of f.

b. Let n be even, then
$f(-c) = (-c)^n - c^n$
$= c^n - c^n = 0$. Therefore,
$x - (-c) = x + c$ is a factor of
$f(x) = x^n - c^n$ if n is even.

67. a. If $n = 3$ and $c = 1$, then
$x + 1 = x - (-1)$ is not a
factor of $x^3 - 1$ since -1 is
not a solution of $x^3 - 1 = 0$.

b. Since n is odd $(-c)^n = -c^n$
and hence $-c$ is a solution of
$x^n + c^n = 0$. Thus,
$x - (-c) = x + c$ is a factor of
$x^n + c^n$ by the Factor Theorem.

In Exercises 55–58, find a polynomial with the given degree n, the given zeros, and no other zeros.

55. $n = 3$; zeros, 1, 7, -4 **56.** $n = 3$; zeros, 1, -1

57. $n = 6$; zeros 1, 2, π **58.** $n = 5$; zero 2

59. Find a polynomial function f of degree 3 such that $f(10) = 17$ and the zeros of $f(x)$ are 0, 5, and 8.

60. Find a polynomial function g of degree 4 such that the zeros of g are 0, -1, 2, -3, and $g(3) = 288$.
$g(x) = 4x(x + 1)(x - 2)(x + 3)$

In Exercises 61–64, find a number k satisfying the given condition.

61. $x + 2$ is a factor of $x^3 + 3x^2 + kx - 2$.
$k = 1$

62. $x - 3$ is a factor of $x^4 - 5x^3 - kx^2 + 18x + 18$.
$k = 2$

63. $x - 1$ is a factor of $k^2x^4 - 2kx^2 + 1$.
$k = 1$

64. $x + 2$ is a factor of $x^3 - kx^2 + 3x + 7k$. $k = \frac{14}{3}$

65. Use the Factor Theorem to show that for every real number c, $x - c$ is not a factor of $x^4 + x^2 + 1$.
If $x - c$ were a factor of $x^4 + x^2 + 1$, then c would be a solution of $x^4 + x^2 + 1 = 0$, that is, c would satisfy $c^4 + c^2 = -1$. But $c^4 \geq 0$ and $c^2 \geq 0$, so that is impossible. Hence, $x - c$ is not a factor.

66. Let c be a real number and n a positive integer.
a. Show that $x - c$ is a factor of $x^n - c^n$.
b. If n is even, show that $x + c$ is a factor of $x^n - c^n$. [Remember: $x + c = x - (-c)$.]

67. a. If c is a real number and n an odd positive integer, give an example to show that $x + c$ may not be a factor of $x^n - c^n$.
b. If c and n are as in part **a**, show that $x + c$ is a factor of $x^n + c^n$.

68. *Critical Thinking* For what value of k is the difference quotient of $g(x) = kx^2 + 2x + 1$ equal to $7x + 2 + 3.5h$?
$k = 3.5$

69. *Critical Thinking* For what value of k is the difference quotient of $f(x) = x^2 + kx$ equal to $2x + 5 + h$?
$k = 5$

70. *Critical Thinking* When $x^3 + cx + 4$ is divided by $x + 2$, the remainder is 4. Find c.
$c = -4$

71. *Critical Thinking* If $x - d$ is a factor of $2x^3 - dx^2 + (1 - d^2)x + 5$, what is d?
$d = -5$

 Math Background

It was shown by French mathematician Evariste Galois (1811–1832) that there are no formulas that can be used to solve general polynomial equations with degree greater than 4. The first proofs of this fact were by Niels Henrik Abel (1802–1829) of Norway and Paolo Ruffini (1765–1822) of Italy. Both proofs had some gaps and Ruffini's was not accepted at the time, but Abel's was. Galois determined which polynomials *could* be solved by a formula, which is a step beyond Abel and Ruffini.

 4.2   Real Zeros

Objectives

- Find all rational zeros of a polynomial function
- Use the Factor Theorem
- Factor a polynomial completely
- Find lower and upper bounds of zeros

Finding the real zeros of a polynomial $f(x)$ is the same as solving the related polynomial equation, $f(x) = 0$. The zero of a first-degree polynomial, such as $5x - 3$, can always be found by solving the equation $5x - 3 = 0$. Similarly, the zeros of any second-degree polynomial can be found by using the quadratic formula, as discussed in Section 2.2. Although the zeros of higher degree polynomials can always be approximated graphically as in Section 2.1, it is better to find exact values, if possible.

Rational Zeros

When a polynomial has *integer* coefficients, all of its **rational zeros** (zeros that are rational numbers) can be found exactly by using the following test.

Teaching Notes

In this section, and in subsequent sections, it is important to pay attention to restrictions placed on coefficients of polynomial functions. In the discussion of **Rational Zeros**, the coefficients of the polynomials are *integers*.

The Rational Zero Test

If a rational number $\frac{r}{s}$ (written in lowest terms) is a zero of the polynomial function

$$f(x) = a_nx^n + \dots + a_1x + a_0$$

where the coefficients $a_n, \dots, a_1$ are *integers* with $a_n \neq 0$ and $a_0 \neq 0$, then

- r is a factor of the constant term a_0 and
- s is a factor of the leading coefficient a_n.

The test states that every rational zero of a polynomial function with integer coefficients must meet the conditions that

- the numerator is a factor of the constant term, and
- the denominator is a factor of the leading coefficient.

By finding all the numbers that satisfy these conditions, a list of *possible* rational zeros is produced. The polynomial must be evaluated at each number in the list to see if the number actually is a zero. Using a calculator can considerably shorten this testing process, as shown in the next example.

Example 1   The Rational Zeros of a Polynomial

Find the rational zeros of $f(x) = 2x^4 + x^3 - 17x^2 - 4x + 6$.

Solution

If $f(x)$ has a rational zero $\frac{r}{s}$, then by the Rational Zero Test r must be a factor of the constant term, 6. Therefore, r must be one of the integers ±1, ±2, ±3, or ±6. Similarly, s must be a factor of the leading coefficient, 2. Therefore, s must be one of the integers ±1 or ±2. Consequently, the only *possibilities* for $\frac{r}{s}$, are $\frac{\pm1}{\pm1}, \frac{\pm2}{\pm1}, \frac{\pm3}{\pm1}, \frac{\pm6}{\pm1}, \frac{\pm1}{\pm2}, \frac{\pm2}{\pm2}, \frac{\pm3}{\pm2}, \frac{\pm6}{\pm2}$.

Eliminating duplications leaves a list of the only *possible* rational zeros.

$$1, -1, 2, -2, 3, -3, 6, -6, \frac{1}{2}, -\frac{1}{2}, \frac{3}{2}, -\frac{3}{2}$$

Graph $f(x)$ in a viewing window that includes all of these numbers on the x-axis, such as $-7 \leq x \leq 7$ and $-7 \leq y \leq 7$. A complete graph is not necessary because only the x-intercepts are of interest.

The graph in Figure 4.2-1a shows that the only numbers in the list that could possibly be zeros are -3, $-\frac{1}{2}$, and $\frac{1}{2}$, so these are the only ones that need to be tested. The table feature can be used to evaluate $f(x)$ at

Figure 4.2-1a

Example Notes

For **Example 1**, to show how **The Rational Zero Test** is used to find all possible rational zeros, write the following on the board:
factors of 6: ±1, ±2, ±3, ±6
factors of 2: ±1, ±2

Now tell students to form all possible fractions, using factors of 6 as numerators and factors of 2 as denominators.

ADDITIONAL EXAMPLES

Example 1

Find the rational zeros of
$f(x) = 2x^4 - 7x^3 - 19x^2 - 3x + 7$.

The only possible rational zeros are
$1, -1, 7, -7, \frac{1}{2}, -\frac{1}{2}, \frac{7}{2}, -\frac{7}{2}$.
With viewing window $-8 \leq x \leq 8$ and $-8 \leq y \leq 8$, graph the function.

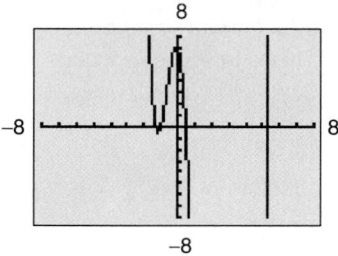

The graph shows that only the values -1 and $\frac{1}{2}$ could possibly be zeros of the function. Use the table feature:

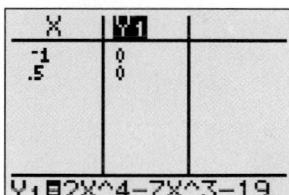

-1 and $\frac{1}{2}$ are the rational zeros of f. The two other zeros must be irrational.

Teaching Notes

Emphasize that to use **The Rational Zero Test,** the polynomial must have a *nonzero* constant term.

A polynomial with a *zero* constant term can be handled as follows:

$$f(x) = a_nx^n + \dots + a_1x + 0$$
$$f(x) = a_nx^n + \dots + a_1x$$
$$f(x) = x(a_nx^{n-1} + \dots + a_1)$$

Now apply the Rational Zero Test to $a_nx^{n-1} + \dots + a_1$ (See Exercise 5, page 258.)

Example Notes

For **Example 2**, remind students of the Factor Theorem (page 245): A polynomial function $f(x)$ has a linear factor $x - a$ if and only if $f(a) = 0$. You may also want to have students refer to the margin **NOTE** on page 253 showing $\dfrac{2 \pm \sqrt{12}}{2} = 1 \pm \sqrt{3}$. Have them verify that $x^2 - 2x - 2$

$= \left[x - \left(1 + \sqrt{3}\right)\right]\left[x - \left(1 - \sqrt{3}\right)\right]$.

Point out that

$f(x) = 2(x + 3)\left(x - \dfrac{1}{2}\right) \cdot$

$\left[x - \left(\dfrac{2 + \sqrt{12}}{2}\right)\right]\left[x - \left(\dfrac{2 - \sqrt{12}}{2}\right)\right]$.

ADDITIONAL EXAMPLES

Example 2

Find all the real zeros of the function given in Additional Example 1.

$f(x) = 2x^4 - 7x^3 - 19x^2 - 3x + 7$

There are four x-intercepts on the graph of f. Two have been found: $x = -1$ and $x = \dfrac{1}{2}$. By the factor theorem, $x - (-1) = x + 1$ and $x - \dfrac{1}{2}$ are factors of $f(x)$.

Factor out $x + 1$.

$$\begin{array}{r|rrrrr} -1 & 2 & -7 & -19 & -3 & 7 \\ & & -2 & 9 & 10 & -7 \\ \hline & 2 & -9 & -10 & 7 & \boxed{0} \end{array}$$

$f(x) = (x + 1)(2x^3 - 9x^2 - 10x + 7)$

Factor $x - \dfrac{1}{2}$ out of $2x^3 - 9x^2 - 10x + 7$.

$$\begin{array}{r|rrrr} \tfrac{1}{2} & 2 & -9 & -10 & 7 \\ & & 1 & -4 & -7 \\ \hline & 2 & -8 & -14 & \boxed{0} \end{array}$$

$f(x) = (x + 1)\left(x - \dfrac{1}{2}\right)(2x^2 - 8x - 14)$

$f(x) = 2(x + 1)\left(x - \dfrac{1}{2}\right)(x^2 - 4x - 7)$

The two remaining zeros of f are solutions of $x^2 - 4x - 7 = 0$.

$x = \dfrac{-(-4) \pm \sqrt{(-4)^2 - 4(1)(-7)}}{2(1)}$

$= \dfrac{4 \pm \sqrt{44}}{2} = \dfrac{4 \pm 2\sqrt{11}}{2} = 2 \pm \sqrt{11}$

$f(x)$ has two rational zeros, -1 and $\dfrac{1}{2}$, and two irrational zeros, $2 + \sqrt{11}$ and $2 - \sqrt{11}$.

Technology Tip

The table setup screen is labeled **TBLSET** on the TI and **RANG** in the Casio **TABLE** menu.

these three numbers, as shown in Figure 4.2-1b, where the function is entered in the $Y =$ editor and the independent variable is set to **Ask**.

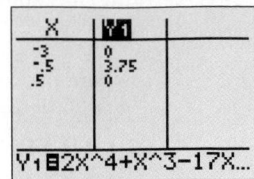

Figure 4.2-1b

The table shows that -3 and $\dfrac{1}{2}$ are the rational zeros of f and $-\dfrac{1}{2}$ is not a zero. Therefore, the two other zeros shown in Figure 4.2-1a cannot be rational numbers, that is, the two other zeros must be irrational.

Zeros and the Factor Theorem

Once some zeros of a polynomial have been found, the Factor Theorem can be used to factor the polynomial, which may lead to additional zeros.

Example 2   Finding All Real Zeros of a Polynomial

Find all the real zeros of the function given in Example 1.

$$f(x) = 2x^4 + x^3 - 17x^2 - 4x + 6$$

Solution

The graph of f, shown in Figure 4.2-1a, shows that there are four x-intercepts, and therefore, four real zeros. The rational zeros, -3 and $\dfrac{1}{2}$, were found in Example 1. By the Factor Theorem, $x - (-3) = x + 3$ and $x - \dfrac{1}{2}$ are factors of $f(x)$. The other factors can be found by using synthetic division twice. First, factor $x + 3$ out of $f(x)$.

$$\begin{array}{r|rrrrr} -3 & 2 & 1 & -17 & -4 & 6 \\ & & -6 & 15 & 6 & -6 \\ \hline & 2 & -5 & -2 & 2 & \boxed{0} \end{array}$$

$$f(x) = (x + 3)(2x^3 - 5x^2 - 2x + 2)$$

Then factor $x - \dfrac{1}{2}$ out of $2x^3 - 5x^2 - 2x + 2$.

$$\frac{1}{2} \begin{array}{|rrrr} 2 & -5 & -2 & 2 \\ & 1 & -2 & -2 \\ \hline 2 & -4 & -4 & \boxed{0} \end{array}$$

$$f(x) = (x + 3)\left(x - \frac{1}{2}\right)(2x^2 - 4x - 4)$$

Therefore, $2x^4 + x^3 - 17x^2 - 4x + 6 = (x + 3)\left(x - \frac{1}{2}\right)(2x^2 - 4x - 4)$

$$= 2(x + 3)\left(x - \frac{1}{2}\right)(x^2 - 2x - 2)$$

The two remaining zeros of f are the solutions of $x^2 - 2x - 2 = 0$, which can be found by using the quadratic formula.

$$x = \frac{-(-2) \pm \sqrt{(-2)^2 - 4(1)(-2)}}{2(1)} = \frac{2 \pm \sqrt{12}}{2}$$

Therefore, $f(x)$ has two rational zeros, -3 and $\frac{1}{2}$, and two irrational zeros, $\frac{2 + \sqrt{12}}{2}$ and $\frac{2 - \sqrt{12}}{2}$.

∎

NOTE Recall from algebra that $\frac{2 \pm \sqrt{12}}{2}$ can be simplified as follows:

$$\frac{2 \pm \sqrt{12}}{2} = \frac{2 \pm 2\sqrt{3}}{2}$$
$$= 1 \pm \sqrt{3}.$$

Irreducible and Completely Factored Polynomials

A polynomial that cannot be written as the product of polynomials of lesser degree is said to be **irreducible**. When a polynomial is written as the product of irreducible factors with real coefficients, it is said to be **completely factored over the set of real numbers**. All linear polynomials are irreducible, and some quadratic polynomials are irreducible over the set of real numbers.

Example 2 shows that $\frac{2 + \sqrt{12}}{2}$ and $\frac{2 - \sqrt{12}}{2}$ are zeros of $2x^2 - 4x - 4$.

By the Factor Theorem $x - \left(\frac{2 + \sqrt{12}}{2}\right)$ and $x - \left(\frac{2 - \sqrt{12}}{2}\right)$ are factors. You can verify that

$$2x^2 - 4x - 4 = 2\left[x - \left(\frac{2 + \sqrt{12}}{2}\right)\right]\left[x - \left(\frac{2 - \sqrt{12}}{2}\right)\right].$$

Therefore, the original polynomial can be written as

$$f(x) = 2x^4 + x^3 - 17x^2 - 4x + 6$$
$$= 2(x + 3)\left(x - \frac{1}{2}\right)\left[x - \left(\frac{2 + \sqrt{12}}{2}\right)\right]\left[x - \left(\frac{2 - \sqrt{12}}{2}\right)\right].$$

Notice that the Factor Theorem applies to irrational zeros as well as to rational zeros. That is, because $\frac{2 + \sqrt{12}}{2}$ is a zero, $x - \left(\frac{2 + \sqrt{12}}{2}\right)$ is a factor.

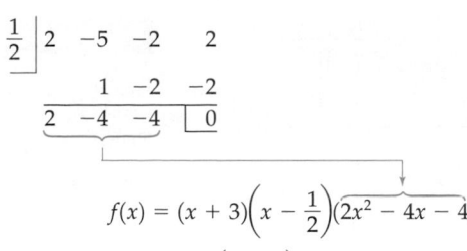

Math Background

Whether a polynomial is reducible (factorable) depends on what set of numbers is used.

Consider the following polynomials:

$$f(x) = x^2 + 9$$
$$g(x) = x^2 - 3$$
$$h(x) = x^2 - 9$$

As shown below, f is reducible over the set of complex numbers (see Section 4.5), g is reducible over the set of real numbers, and h is reducible over the set of rational numbers.

$$f(x) = (x + 3i)(x - 3i)$$
$$g(x) = \left(x + \sqrt{3}\right)\left(x - \sqrt{3}\right)$$
$$h(x) = (x + 3)(x - 3)$$

Furthermore, because all rational numbers are real numbers and all real numbers are complex numbers, we can restate these facts as follows:

f is reducible over the set of complex numbers.

g is reducible over the set of real and complex numbers.

h is reducible over the set of rational, real, and complex numbers.

Example Notes

In **Example 3**, $f(x) = (x + 1)(x - 3)(2x^3 - 6x^2 + x - 3)$. By letting $g(x) = (2x^3 - 6x^2 + x - 3)$, we can say every zero of g is a zero of f. By the Rational Zero Test, the possible rational zeros of $g(x) = 2x^3 - 6x^2 + x - 3$ are

$\pm\frac{1}{2}, \pm\frac{3}{2}, \pm 1,$ and ± 3.

However, since it is already established that the only rational zeros of f are -1 and 3, we only need to check -1 and 3 when finding the zeros of g.

Note that one of the zeros of g is 3, so it turns out that $x - 3$ is a repeated factor of f.

Math Background

From Figure 4.2-2, it appears that 3 is a zero of f (which would make $x - 3$ a factor of $f(x)$). We find in **Example 3** that $x - 3$ is a *repeated* factor of $f(x)$. Students will learn in Section 4.3 (page 265) that when a factor is repeated an even number of times, the graph of the function touches, but does not cross, the x-axis at the corresponding zero.

ADDITIONAL EXAMPLES

Example 3

Factor
$f(x) = x^5 - 5x^4 + 8x^3 - 8x^2 + 7x - 3$ completely.

Using the Rational Zero Test, the possible rational zeros for f are $\pm 1, \pm 3$. The graph of the function f shows that the only possible zeros are 1 and 3.

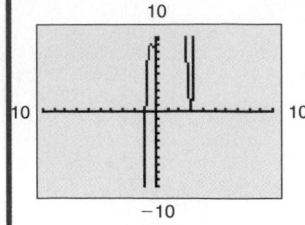

Figure 4.2-2

Example 3 — Factoring a Polynomial Completely

Factor $f(x) = 2x^5 - 10x^4 + 7x^3 + 13x^2 + 3x + 9$ completely.

Solution

Begin by finding as many rational zeros as possible. By the Rational Zero Test, every rational zero is of the form $\frac{r}{s}$, where $r = \pm 1, \pm 3,$ or ± 9 and $s = \pm 1$ or ± 2. Thus, the possible rational zeros are

$$\pm 1, \pm 3, \pm 9, \pm\frac{1}{2}, \pm\frac{3}{2}, \pm\frac{9}{2}$$

The graph of f shows that the only possible zeros are -1 and 3. It is easily verified that both numbers *are* zeros of $f(x)$. Consequently, $x - (-1) = x + 1$ and $x - 3$ are factors of $f(x)$ by the Factor Theorem. Division shows other factors.

$$2x^5 - 10x^4 + 7x^3 + 13x^2 + 3x + 9 = (x + 1)(2x^4 - 12x^3 + 19x^2 - 6x + 9)$$
$$= (x + 1)(x - 3)(2x^3 - 6x^2 + x - 3)$$

The other zeros of f are the zeros of $g(x) = 2x^3 - 6x^2 + x - 3$.

Because every zero of $g(x)$ is also a zero of $f(x)$, and the only rational zeros of f are -1 and 3, check if either is a zero of g by using substitution.

$$g(-1) = 2(-1)^3 - 6(-1)^2 + (-1) - 3 = -12$$
$$g(3) = 2(3)^3 - 6(3)^2 + (3) - 3 = 0$$

So 3 is a zero of g, but -1 is not. By the Factor Theorem, $x - 3$ is a factor of $g(x)$. Division shows that

$$f(x) = (x + 1)(x - 3)(2x^3 - 6x^2 + x - 3)$$
$$= (x + 1)(x - 3)(x - 3)(2x^2 + 1)$$

Because $2x^2 + 1$ has no real zeros, it cannot be factored further. So $f(x)$ is completely factored in the last statement above. ∎

Bounds

In some cases, special techniques may be needed to guarantee that all zeros of a polynomial are located.

Example 4 — Finding All Real Zeros of a Polynomial

Show that all the real zeros of $g(x) = x^5 - 2x^4 - x^3 + 3x + 1$ lie between -1 and 3, and find all the real zeros of $g(x)$.

Solution

First show that g has no zero larger than 3, as follows. Use synthetic division to divide $g(x)$ by $x - 3$.

Substitution shows that both 1 and 3 are zeros of $f(x)$, and division shows that $f(x) = (x - 1)(x - 3)(x^3 - x^2 + x - 1)$. The other zeros of f are zeros of $x^3 - x^2 + x - 1$. Checking 1 reveals that 1 is a zero again. The factored form of f is $f(x) = (x - 1)(x - 1)(x - 3)(x^2 + 1)$. The function cannot be factored further, since $x^2 + 1$ has no real zeros.

$$\begin{array}{r|rrrrrr} 3 & 1 & -2 & -1 & 0 & 3 & 1 \\ & & 3 & 3 & 6 & 18 & 63 \\ \hline & 1 & 1 & 2 & 6 & 21 & \boxed{64} \end{array}$$

Thus, the quotient is $x^4 + x^3 + 2x^2 + 6x + 21$ and the remainder is 64. Applying the Division Algorithm,

$$g(x) = x^5 - 2x^4 - x^3 + 3x + 1$$
$$= (x - 3)(x^4 + x^3 + 2x^2 + 6x + 21) + 64$$

When $x > 3$, the factor $x - 3$ is positive and $x^4 + x^3 + 2x^2 + 6x + 21$, the quotient, is also positive because all its coefficients are positive. The remainder, 64, is also positive. Therefore, $g(x)$ is positive whenever $x > 3$. In particular, $g(x)$ is never 0 when $x > 3$, and so there are no zeros of g greater than 3.

A similar procedure shows that g has no zero less than -1. Divide $g(x)$ by $x - (-1) = x + 1$ and rewrite $g(x)$ by applying the Division Algorithm.

$$g(x) = x^5 - 2x^4 - x^3 + 3x + 1$$
$$= (x + 1)(x^4 - 3x^3 + 2x^2 - 2x + 5) - 4$$

When $x < -1$, the factor $x + 1$ is negative. When x is negative, all odd powers of x are negative and all even powers are positive. Consequently, the quotient, $x^4 - 3x^3 + 2x^2 - 2x + 5$, is positive when $x < -1$ because all odd powers are multiplied by negative coefficients. The positive quotient multiplied by the negative factor $x + 1$ produces a negative product. The remainder, -4, is also negative. Hence, $g(x)$ is negative whenever $x < -1$, and there are no real zeros of g less than -1. Therefore, all the real zeros of $g(x)$ lie between -1 and 3.

Finally, find all the real zeros of $g(x) = x^5 - 2x^4 - x^3 + 3x + 1$. The only possible rational zeros are ± 1, and it is easy to verify that neither is actually a zero. The graph of g in Figure 4.2-3 shows that there are exactly three real zeros between -1 and 3. Because all real zeros of g lie between -1 and 3, g has only these three real zeros. They can be approximated by using a calculator's zero finder.

$$x \approx -0.3361 \qquad x \approx 1.4268 \qquad \text{and} \qquad x \approx 2.1012 \qquad \blacksquare$$

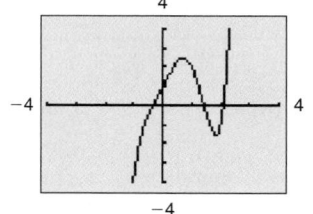

Figure 4.2-3

Upper Bound and Lower Bound

Suppose $f(x)$ is a polynomial and m and n are real numbers with $m < n$. If all the real zeros of $f(x)$ are between m and n, m is called a **lower bound** and n is called an **upper bound** for the real zeros of $f(x)$. Example 4 shows that -1 is a lower bound and 3 is an upper bound for the real zeros of $g(x) = x^5 - 2x^4 - x^3 + 3x + 1$.

If you know lower and upper bounds for the real zeros of a polynomial, you can usually determine the number of real zeros the polynomial has, as shown in Example 4. The technique used in Example 4 to test possible lower and upper bounds works in the general case.

Teaching Notes

Upper and lower bounds are not unique. For example, if 3 is an upper bound, any number greater than 3 is also an upper bound. If -1 is a lower bound, any number less than -1 is also a lower bound.

Example 4

Show that all the real zeros of $h(x) = 2x^5 + x^4 - 9x^2 + 4x + 1$ lie between -1 and 2, and find all the real zeros of $h(x)$.

Divide $h(x)$ by $x - 2$.

$$\begin{array}{r|rrrrrr} 2 & 2 & 1 & 0 & -9 & 4 & 1 \\ & & 4 & 10 & 20 & 22 & 52 \\ \hline & 2 & 5 & 10 & 11 & 26 & \boxed{53} \end{array}$$

So, $h(x) =$
$(x - 2)(2x^4 + 5x^3 + 10x^2 + 11x + 26) + 53.$

When $x > 2$, the factors $x - 2$ and $2x^4 + 5x^3 + 10x^2 + 11x + 26$ are positive. The remainder 53 is also positive. Therefore, $h(x)$ is positive whenever $x > 2$. So, there are no zeros greater than 2.

Divide $h(x)$ by $x + 1$.

$$\begin{array}{r|rrrrrr} -1 & 2 & 1 & 0 & -9 & 4 & 1 \\ & & -2 & 1 & -1 & 10 & -14 \\ \hline & 2 & -1 & 1 & -10 & 14 & \boxed{13} \end{array}$$

So, $h(x) =$
$(x + 1)(2x^4 - x^3 + x^2 - 10x + 14) - 13.$

When $x < -1$, the factor $x + 1$ is negative. When x is negative, all odd powers of x are negative and all even powers of x are positive. The factor $2x^4 - x^3 + x^2 - 10x + 14$ is positive when $x < -1$ because all odd powers are multiplied by negative coefficients. This positive factor multiplied by the negative factor $x + 1$ produces a negative product. The remainder -13 is also negative. So, $h(x)$ is negative if $x < -1$, and there are no real zeros of h less than -1. Therefore, all the real zeros of $h(x)$ lie between -1 and 2.

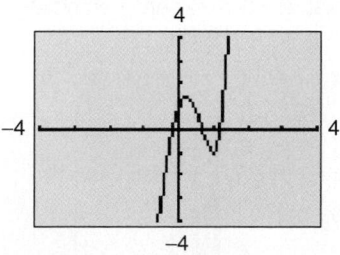

The graph shows there are exactly three real zeros between -1 and 2. The three real zeros are:

$x \approx -0.1785$, $x \approx 0.6930$, and $x \approx 1.2105$.

Math Background

Descartes' Rule of Signs states that for a polynomial $f(x)$ with real coefficients and a nonzero constant term:

- the number of positive real zeros of $f(x)$ is equal to the number of variations in sign (from $+$ to $-$ or from $-$ to $+$) in the polynomial, or equal to that number less a positive even whole number.
- the number of negative real zeros of $f(x)$ is equal to the number of sign variations in $f(-x)$, or equal to that number less a positive even whole number.

For example, in the polynomial $h(x) = 2x^5 + x^4 - 9x^2 + 4x + 1$ from Additional Example 4, there are two sign changes, so there are 2 or 0 positive real zeros. Replacing x with $-x$ in $h(x)$:

$$h(-x) = 2(-x)^5 + (-x)^4 - 9(-x)^2 + 4(-x) + 1$$
$$= -2x^5 + x^4 - 9x^2 - 4x + 1$$

There are 3 sign changes in $h(-x)$, so there are 3 or 1 negative real zeros of $h(x)$. In fact, it was found that there were 2 positive real zeros and 1 negative real zero for $h(x)$.

ADDITIONAL EXAMPLES

Example 5

Find all real zeros of $f(x) = x^6 + x^3 - 8x^2 - 4x + 1$.

By the Rational Zero Test, the only possible rational zeros are ± 1, but substitution shows that neither is a zero of f. The graph shows that there are 4 real zeros between -2 and 2.

Bounds Test

Let $f(x)$ be a polynomial with positive leading coefficient.

- If $d > 0$ and every number in the last row in the synthetic division of $f(x)$ by $x - d$ is nonnegative, then d is an upper bound for the real zeros of f.
- If $c < 0$ and the numbers in the last row of the synthetic division of $f(x)$ by $x - c$ are alternately positive and negative, with 0 considered as either, then c is a lower bound for the real zeros of f.

Example 5   Finding All Real Zeros of a Polynomial

Find all real zeros of $f(x) = x^6 + x^3 - 7x^2 - 3x + 1$.

Solution

By the Rational Zero Test, the only possible rational zeros are ± 1, but neither is a zero of f. Hence, the real zeros are irrational. Figure 4.2-4 shows four x-intercepts between -2 and 2, but because f has degree 6, there may be two more zeros that are not shown. Use the Bounds Test to see if all the zeros are between -2 and 2.

To see if 2 is an upper bound, divide $f(x)$ by $x - 2$.

```
2 | 1   0   0   1   -7   -3    1
  |     2   4   8   18   22   38
  ---------------------------------
    1   2   4   9   11   19 | 39
```
All nonnegative

Because the divisor and every term in the last row are positive, 2 is an upper bound for the real zeros of f.

Now divide $f(x)$ by $x - (-2)$ to see if -2 is a lower bound.

```
-2 | 1    0    0    1   -7    -3     1
   |     -2    4   -8   14   -14    34
   -----------------------------------------
     1   -2    4   -7    7   -17 |  35
```
Alternating signs

Because the divisor number is negative and the signs in the last row of the synthetic division alternate, -2 is a lower bound.

Therefore, all real zeros of f are between -2 and 2, and all zeros of f are shown in Figure 4.2-4. Using a zero finder, there are four zeros.

$$x \approx -1.5837 \qquad x \approx -0.6180 \qquad x \approx 0.2220 \qquad \text{and} \qquad x \approx 1.6180$$

The examples in this section illustrate the following guidelines for finding all the real zeros of a polynomial.

Use the Bounds Tests to show that all zeros are between -2 and 2.

```
-2 | 1    0    0    1   -8    -4     1
   |     -2    4   -8   14   -12    32
   -----------------------------------------
     1   -2    4   -7    6   -16 |  33
```

```
2 | 1    0    0    1   -8    -4     1
  |      2    4    8   18    20    32
  ---------------------------------------
    1    2    4    9   10    16 |  33
```

All real zeros are between -2 and 2. The four real zeros are $x \approx -1.6115$, $x \approx -0.6530$, $x \approx 0.1839$, and $x \approx 1.6979$.

Finding Real Zeros of Polynomials

1. Use the Rational Zero Test to find all the rational zeros of f. [*Examples 1, 3, and 6*]
2. Write $f(x)$ as the product of linear factors, one for each rational zero, and another factor $g(x)$. [*Examples 2 and 3*]
3. If $g(x)$ has degree 2, find its zeros by factoring or by using the quadratic formula. [*Example 2*]
4. If $g(x)$ has degree 3 or greater, use the Bounds Test, if possible, to find lower and upper bounds for the zeros of g. Approximate the remaining zeros graphically. [*Examples 4 and 5*]

Shortcuts and variations are always possible. For instance, if the graph of a cubic polynomial shows three x-intercepts, then it has three real zeros, which is the maximum number of zeros, and there is no point in finding bounds of the zeros. In order to find as many exact zeros as possible in Guideline 4 above, check to see if the rational zeros of f are also zeros of g. Factor $g(x)$ accordingly, as in Example 3.

Example 6 Finding All Real Zeros of a Polynomial

Find all real zeros of

$$f(x) = x^7 - 6x^6 + 9x^5 + 7x^4 - 28x^3 + 33x^2 - 36x + 20.$$

Solution

The graph of f shown in Figure 4.2-5 indicates 4 possible real zeros. By the Rational Zero Test, the only possible rational zeros are:

$$\pm 1, \pm 2, \pm 4, \pm 5, \pm 10, \text{ and } \pm 20.$$

It can be verified that both 1 and 2 are zeros of f. The graph also suggests that all the real zeros lie between -2 and 6. The Bounds Test shows that this is indeed the case.

Negative Divisor

-2	1	-6	9	7	-28	33	-36	20
		-2	16	-50	86	-116	166	-260
	1	-8	25	-43	58	-83	130	-240

Alternating signs

Positive Divisor

6	1	-6	9	7	-28	33	-36	20
		6	0	54	366	2028	12,366	73,980
	1	0	9	61	338	2061	12,330	74,000

All nonnegative

Therefore, all the real zeros of f are between -2 and 6, and the four x-intercepts shown in Figure 4.2-5 are the only real zeros of f: two are rational zeros, 1 and 2, and two are irrational, $x \approx -1.7913$ and $x \approx 2.7913$, as determined by using a zero finder. ∎

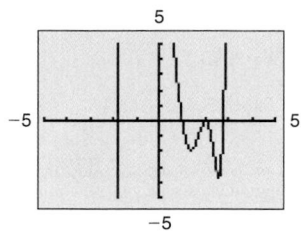

Figure 4.2-5

Example Notes

For **Example 6**, you cannot be sure from the graph (Figure 4.2-5) that 1 and 2 are zeros. To verify that they both are zeros, use the table feature of a graphing calculator.

ADDITIONAL EXAMPLES

Example 6

Find all real zeros of $f(x) = x^7 - 2x^6 - 5x^5 + 13x^4 - 10x^3 + 11x^2 - 4x - 4$.

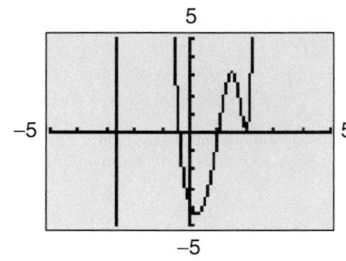

The graph of f indicates four possible real zeros. By the Rational Zero Test, the only possible rational zeros are $\pm 1, \pm 2, \pm 4$. It can be verified that both 1 and 2 are zeros of f. The Bounds Tests shows that all real zeros lie between -3 and 4.

-3	1	-2	-5	13	-10	11	-4	-4
		-3	15	-30	51	-123	336	-996
	1	-5	10	-17	41	-112	332	-1000

4	1	-2	-5	13	-10	11	-4	-4
		4	8	12	100	360	1484	5290
	1	2	3	25	90	371	1480	5916

Thus the four x-intercepts shown on the graph are the only real zeros of f: two are rational zeros, 1 and 2, and two are irrational, $x \approx -2.6180$ $x \approx -0.3820$.

ANSWERS

25. $x = 1, \frac{1}{2}$, or $\frac{1}{3}$

36. $x = -\frac{5}{3}$ or 2, $x \approx 1.19869$,
-0.286462, or -2.91223

37. a. The only possible rational
zeros of $f(x) = x^2 - 2$ are ± 1
or ± 2. But $\sqrt{2}$ is a zero of
$f(x)$ and $\sqrt{2} \neq \pm 1$ or ± 2.
Hence, $\sqrt{2}$ is irrational.

b. $\sqrt{3}$ is a zero of $x^2 - 3$ whose
only possible rational zeros
are ± 1 or ± 3. But $\sqrt{3} \neq \pm 1$
or ± 3.

38. a. We see two real zeros and so
there are two distinct linear
factors of f. If we divide these
out we will be left with another
linear factor which must
correspond to another real
zero.

b. $x = 5, -6$, or 200

39. a. 8.6378 people per 100,000

b. 1995

c. 1991

Exercises 4.2

When asked to find the zeros of a polynomial, find
exact zeros whenever possible and approximate the
other zeros.

In Exercises 1–12, find all the rational zeros of the
polynomial.

1. $x^3 + 3x^2 - x - 3$ **2.** $x^3 - x^2 - 3x + 3$
$x = \pm 1$ or -3   **$x = 1$**
3. $x^3 + 5x^2 - x - 5$ **4.** $3x^3 + 8x^2 - x - 20$ $\frac{4}{3}$
$x = \pm 1$ or -5   **$x = \frac{4}{3}$**

5. $2x^5 + 5x^4 - 11x^3 + 4x^2$ *Hint:* The Rational Zero
Test can only be used on polynomials with
nonzero constant terms. Factor $f(x)$ as a product
of a power of x and a polynomial $g(x)$ with
nonzero constant term. Then use the Rational
Zero Test on $g(x)$.
$x = -4, 0, 1$ or $\frac{1}{2}$

6. $2x^6 - 3x^5 - 7x^4 - 6x^3$
$x = 0$ or 3

7. $\frac{1}{12}x^3 - \frac{1}{12}x^2 - \frac{2}{3}x + 1$ *Hint:* The Rational Zero
Test can only be used on polynomials with integer
coefficients. Note that $f(x)$ and $12f(x)$ have the
same zeros. (Why?)
$x = -3$ or 2

8. $\frac{2}{3}x^4 + \frac{1}{2}x^3 - \frac{5}{4}x^2 - x - \frac{1}{6}$ **$x = -\frac{1}{4}$ or $-\frac{1}{2}$**

9. $\frac{1}{3}x^4 - x^3 - x^2 + \frac{13}{3}x - 2$ **$x = 2$**

10. $\frac{1}{3}x^7 - \frac{1}{2}x^6 - \frac{1}{6}x^5 + \frac{1}{6}x^4$ **$x = 0$ or $\frac{1}{2}$**

11. $0.1x^3 - 1.9x + 3$ **$x = -5, 2$, or 3**

12. $0.05x^3 + 0.45x^2 - 0.4x + 1$ **$x = -10$**

In Exercises 13–18, factor the polynomial as a product
of linear factors and a factor $g(x)$ such that $g(x)$ is either
a constant or a polynomial that has no rational zeros.

13. $2x^3 - 4x^2 + x - 2$ **14.** $6x^3 - 5x^2 + 3x - 1$
$(x - 2)(2x^2 + 1)$ **$(2x - 1)(3x^2 - x + 1)$**
15. $x^6 + 2x^5 + 3x^4 + 6x^3$
$x^3(x^2 + 3)(x + 2)$
16. $x^5 - 2x^4 + 2x^3 - 3x + 2$
$(x - 1)^2(x + 1)(x^2 - x + 2)$
17. $x^5 - 4x^4 + 8x^3 - 14x^2 + 15x - 6$
$(x - 2)(x - 1)^2(x^2 + 3)$
18. $x^5 + 4x^3 + x^2 + 6x$
$x(x^4 + 4x^2 + x + 6)$

In Exercises 19–22, use the Bounds Test to find lower
and upper bounds for the real zeros of the polynomial.

19. $x^3 + 2x^2 - 7x + 20$ **20.** $x^3 - 15x^2 - 16x + 12$
Lower -5; upper 2   **Lower -2; upper 16**
21. $-x^5 - 5x^4 + 9x^3 + 18x^2 - 68x + 176$ *Hint:* The
Bounds Test applies only to polynomials with a
positive leading coefficient. The polynomial $f(x)$
has the same zeros as $-f(x)$. Why?
Lower -7; upper 3
22. $-0.002x^3 - 5x^2 + 8x - 3$
Lower -2502; upper 2

In Exercises 23–36, find all real zeros of the polynomial.

23. $2x^3 - 5x^2 + x + 2$ **24.** $t^4 - t^3 + 2t^2 - 4t - 8$
$x = 1, 2$, or $-\frac{1}{2}$ **$x = 2$ or -1**
25. $6x^3 - 11x^2 + 6x - 1$ **26.** $z^3 + z^2 + 2z + 2$
                         $x = -1$
27. $x^4 + x^3 - 19x^2 + 32x - 12$ **$x = 2$ or $\frac{-5 \pm \sqrt{37}}{2}$**

28. $3x^5 + 2x^4 - 7x^3 + 2x^2$ **$x = -2, 0, \frac{1}{3}$, or 1**

29. $2x^5 - x^4 - 10x^3 + 5x^2 + 12x - 6$
            $x = \frac{1}{2}$ or $\pm\sqrt{2}$ or $\pm\sqrt{3}$
30. $x^5 - x^3 + x$
$x = 0$
31. $x^6 - 4x^5 - 5x^4 - 9x^2 + 36x + 45$
$x = -1, 5$, or $\pm\sqrt{3}$
32. $x^5 + 3x^4 - 4x^3 - 11x^2 - 3x + 2$
              $x = -1, 2$, or $\frac{-3 \pm \sqrt{13}}{2}$
33. $3x^4 + 2x^3 - 4x^2 + 4x - 1$
              $x = \frac{1}{3}$ or $x \approx -1.8393$
34. $x^5 + 8x^4 + 20x^3 + 9x^2 - 27x - 27$
$x = -3$ or $x \approx 1.1479$
35. $x^4 - 48x^3 - 101x^2 + 49x + 50$ **$x \approx -2.2470$ or
            -0.5550 or 0.8019 or $x = 50$**
36. $3x^7 + 8x^6 - 13x^5 - 36x^4 - 10x^3 + 21x^2 + 41x + 10$

37. a. Show that $\sqrt{2}$ is an irrational number. *Hint:*
$\sqrt{2}$ is a zero of $x^2 - 2$. Does this polynomial
have any rational zeros?
b. Show that $\sqrt{3}$ is irrational.

38. Graph $f(x) = 0.001x^3 - 0.199x^2 - 0.23x + 6$ in the
standard viewing window.
a. How many zeros does $f(x)$ appear to have?
Without changing the viewing window, explain
why $f(x)$ must have an additional zero. *Hint:*
Each zero corresponds to a factor of $f(x)$. What
does the rest of the factorization consist of?
b. Find all the zeros of $f(x)$.

39. According to the FBI, the number of people
murdered each year per 100,000 population can
be approximated by the polynomial function
$f(x) = 0.0011x^4 - 0.0233x^3 + 0.1144x^2 + 0.0126x +$
8.1104 $(0 \leq x \leq 10)$, where $x = 0$ corresponds to
1987.

a. What was the murder rate in 1990?
b. In what year was the rate 8 people per 100,000?
c. In what year was the rate the highest?

40. During the first 150 hours of an experiment, the growth rate of a bacteria population at time t hours is $g(t) = -0.0003t^3 + 0.04t^2 + 0.3t + 0.2$ bacteria per hour.
   a. What is the growth rate at 50 hours? at 100 hours?
   b. What is the growth rate at 145 hours? What does this mean?
   c. At what time is the growth rate 0?
   d. At what time is the growth rate -50 bacteria per hour?
   e. Approximately at what time does the highest growth rate occur?

41. An open-top reinforced box is to be made from a 12-by-36-inch piece of cardboard by cutting along the marked lines, discarding the shaded pieces, and folding as shown in the figure. If the box must be less than 2.5 inches high, what size squares should be cut from the corners in order for the box to have a volume of 448 cubic inches?

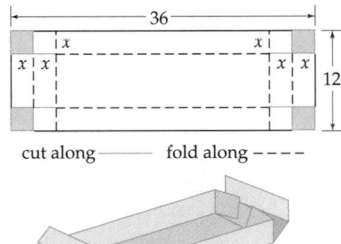

cut along ———— fold along ----

42. A box with a lid is to be made from a 48-by-24-inch piece of cardboard by cutting and folding, as shown in the figure. If the box must be at least 6 inches high, what size squares should be cut from the two corners in order for the box to have a volume of 1000 cubic inches?

43. In a sealed chamber where the temperature varies, the instantaneous rate of change of temperature with respect to time over an 11-day period is given by $F(t) = 0.0035t^4 - 0.4t^2 - 0.2t + 6$, where time is measured in days and temperature in degrees Fahrenheit (so that rate of change is in degrees per day).
   a. At what rate is the temperature changing at the beginning of the period ($t = 0$)? at the end of the period ($t = 11$)?
   b. When is the temperature increasing at a rate of 4°F per day?
   c. When is the temperature decreasing at a rate of 3°F per day?
   d. When is the temperature decreasing at the fastest rate?

44. *Critical Thinking*
   a. If c is a zero of
$$f(x) = 5x^4 - 4x^3 + 3x^2 - 4x + 5,$$
   show that $\dfrac{1}{c}$ is also a zero.
   b. Do part **a** with $f(x)$ replaced by $g(x)$.
$$g(x) = 2x^6 + 3x^5 + 4x^4 - 5x^3 + 4x^2 + 3x + 2$$
   c. Let
$$f(x) = a_{12}x^{12} + a_{11}x^{11} + \cdots + a_2x^2 + a_1x + a_0.$$
   If c is a zero of f, what conditions must the coefficients a_i satisfy so that $\dfrac{1}{c}$ is also a zero?

40. a. 77.7 bacteria per hour; 130.2 bacteria per hour
   b. -29.8875 bacteria per hour, so the population is shrinking
   c. approximately 140.485 hours
   d. approximately 147.765 hours
   e. approximately 92.493 hours

41. 2 by 2 in.

42. approximately 6.63564 in. by 6.63564 in.

43. a. 6° per day at the beginning; 6.6435° per day at the end
   b. Day 2.0330 and day 10.7069
   c. Day 5.0768 and day 9.6126
   d. Day 7.6813

44. a. $f\left(\dfrac{1}{c}\right) = 5\left(\dfrac{1}{c}\right)^4 - 4\left(\dfrac{1}{c}\right)^3 +$
$$3\left(\dfrac{1}{c}\right)^2 - 4\left(\dfrac{1}{c}\right) + 5$$
$$= \dfrac{5 - 4c + 3c^2 - 4c^3 + 5c^4}{c^4}$$
$$= \dfrac{0}{c^4} = 0$$

   b. $f\left(\dfrac{1}{c}\right) = 2\left(\dfrac{1}{c}\right)^6 + 3\left(\dfrac{1}{c}\right)^5 +$
$$4\left(\dfrac{1}{c}\right)^4 - 5\left(\dfrac{1}{c}\right)^3 + 4\left(\dfrac{1}{c}\right)^2 +$$
$$3\left(\dfrac{1}{c}\right) + 2$$
$$= \dfrac{2 + 3c + 4c^2 - 5c^3 + 4c^4 + 3c^5 + 2c^6}{c^6}$$
$$= \dfrac{0}{c^6} = 0$$

   c. $a_0 = a_{12}, a_1 = a_{11}, a_2 = a_{10},$ etc.

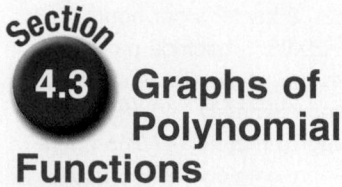

Section 4.3 Graphs of Polynomial Functions

Teaching Notes

The graphs of polynomial functions of the form $f(x) = ax^n$ depend on two parameters, a and n. To show how a affects a graph, have students graph the following functions on the same screen, making these observations:

$f(x) = x^3, g(x) = \frac{1}{4}x^3$, and $h(x) = 4x^3$

$|a| < 1$ causes a vertical compression, and $|a| > 1$ causes a vertical stretch (see page 179).

Repeat the activity to show how n affects a graph, using these functions:

$f(x) = x^3, g(x) = x^5$, and $h(x) = x^{15}$

For $|x| < 1$, a greater value of n causes a vertical compression.

For $|x| > 1$, a greater value of n causes a vertical stretch.

Solution to the **Graphing Exploration:**

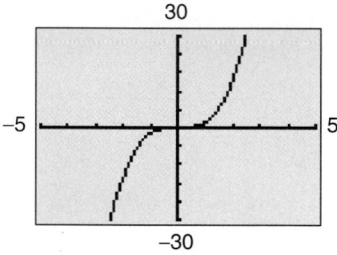

The graph of f is like the graph in Figure 4.3-1a.

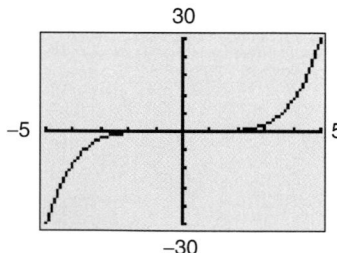

The graph of g is like the graph in Figure 4.3-1a.

4.3 Graphs of Polynomial Functions

Objectives

- Recognize the shape of basic polynomial functions
- Describe the graph of a polynomial function
- Identify properties of general polynomial functions: Continuity, End Behavior, Intercepts, Local Extrema, Points of Inflection
- Identify complete graphs of polynomial functions

The graph of a first-degree polynomial function is a straight line, as discussed in Section 1.4. The graph of a second-degree, or quadratic, polynomial function is a parabola, as discussed in Section 3.3. The emphasis in this section is on higher degree polynomial functions.

Basic Polynomial Shapes

The simplest polynomial functions are those of the form $f(x) = ax^n$, where a is a constant and n is a nonnegative integer. The graphs of polynomial functions of the form $f(x) = ax^n$, with $n \geq 2$, are of two basic types. The different types are determined by whether n is even or odd.

Polynomial Functions of Odd Degree

When the degree of a polynomial function in the form $f(x) = ax^n$, is *odd*, its graph has the basic form shown is Figures 4.3-1a and 4.3-1b. Notice that the graph shown in Figure 4.3-1b has the same shape as the graph shown in Figure 4.3-1a, but it is the reflection of the Figure 4.3-1a across either the x-axis or the y-axis.

$$f(x) = ax^n, \ n \text{ odd}$$

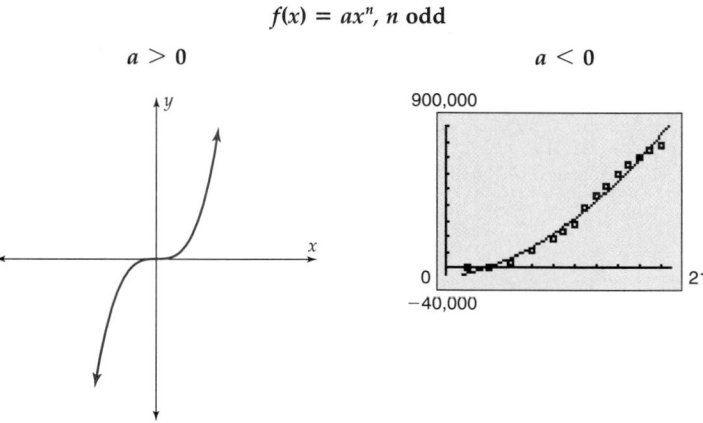

Figure 4.3-1a

Figure 4.3-1b

Graphing Exploration

Graph each of the following functions of odd degree in the window with $-5 \leq x \leq 5$ and $-30 \leq y \leq 30$, and compare each shape with those shown in Figure 4.3-1a and 4.3-1b.

- $f(x) = 2x^3$
- $h(x) = -x^3$
- $g(x) = 0.01x^5$
- $k(x) = -2x^7$

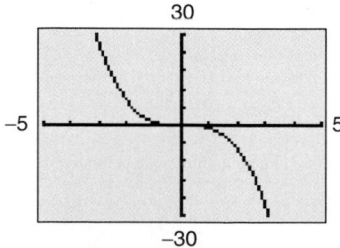

The graph of h is like the graph in Figure 4.3-1b.

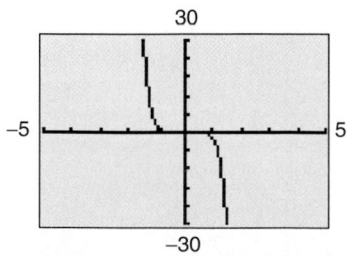

The graph of k is like the graph in Figure 4.3-1b.

Polynomial Functions of Even Degree

When the degree of a polynomial function in the form $f(x) = ax^n$ is even, its graph has the form shown in Figures 4.3-2a or 4.3-2b. Again, the graph of $f(x) = ax^n$, when a is negative, is the reflection of Figure 4.3-2a across the x-axis.

$$f(x) = ax^n, \; n \text{ even}$$

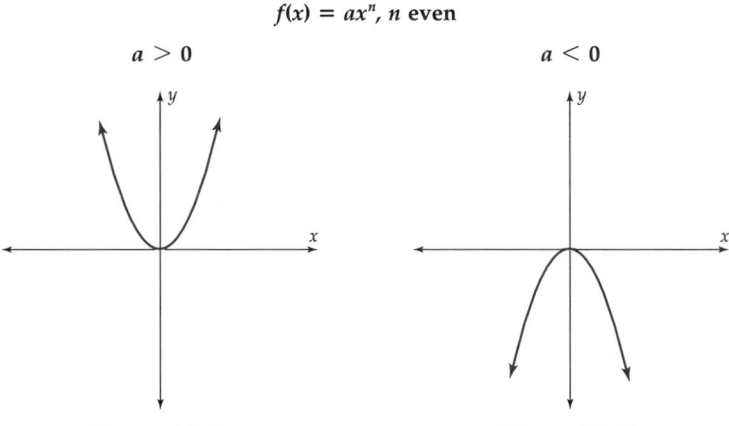

$a > 0$	$a < 0$

Figure 4.3-2a   **Figure 4.3-2b**

Graphing Exploration ●

Graph each of the following functions of even degree in the window with $-5 \le x \le 5$ and $-30 \le y \le 30$, and compare each shape with those shown in Figure 4.3-2a or 4.3-2b.

- $f(x) = 2x^4$
- $h(x) = -2x^2$
- $g(x) = 6x^6$
- $k(x) = -3x^4$

Properties of General Polynomial Functions

The graphs of other polynomial functions can vary considerably in shape. Understanding the properties that follow should assist you in interpreting graphs correctly and in determining when a graph of a polynomial function is complete.

Continuity

Every graph of a polynomial function is **continuous,** that is, it is an unbroken curve, with no jumps, gaps, or holes. Furthermore, graphs of polynomial functions have no sharp corners. Thus, *neither* of the graphs shown in Figure 4.3-3 represents a polynomial function. Note: some calculator graphs of polynomial functions may appear to have sharp corners; however, zooming in on the area in question will show a smooth curve.

Teaching Notes

Solution to the **Graphing Exploration:**

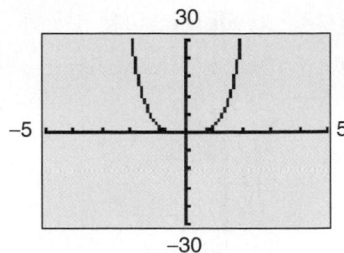

The graph of f is like the graph in Figure 4.3-2a.

The graph of g is like the graph in Figure 4.3-2a.

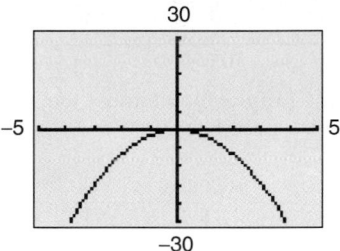

The graph of h is like the graph in Figure 4.3-2b.

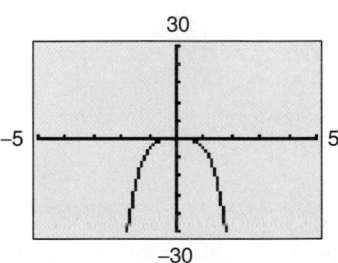

The graph of k is like the graph in Figure 4.3-2b.

When discussing **continuity** remind students of the parent functions they studied (page 173). $f(x) = \lfloor x \rfloor$ and $f(x) = \dfrac{1}{x}$ are examples of functions that are *not* continuous.

Teaching Notes

Solution to the **Graphing Exploration:**

-

  possible answer: In the standard viewing window, the graph of f has a local maximum and a local minimum; the graph of g does not. The graphs start to look the same as they increase out of the window and decrease out of the window.

-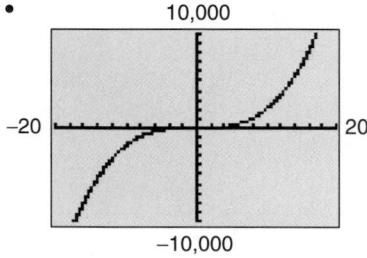

  yes; the graphs look almost the same

-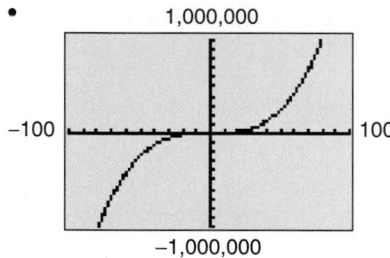

  yes; the graphs look virtually identical

After the Graphing Exploration, refer students to the table at the right. Ask them to describe the relationship among the entries in the last column, under the x-value 100. 2,009,400 is the sum of -600, 10,000, and 2,000,000. Emphasize that for values of x with large absolute values, the terms x^2 and $-6x$ in the polynomial $2x^3 + x^2 - 6x$ contribute relatively little to the function value.

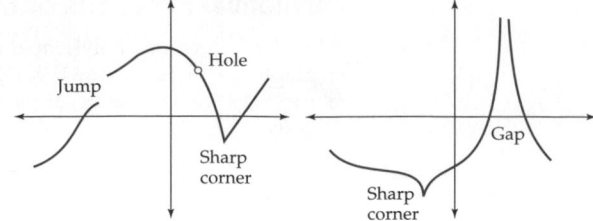

Figure 4.3-3

End Behavior

The shape of a polynomial graph at the far left and far right of the coordinate plane, that is, when $|x|$ is large, is called the **end behavior** of the graph. End behavior of graphs of functions of the form $f(x) = ax^n$ have common characteristics when n is odd and when n is even. The Graphing Exploration below asks you to find a generalization about the end behavior of polynomial functions of odd degree.

Graphing Exploration ●

Consider the function $f(x) = 2x^3 + x^2 - 6x$ and the function determined by its leading term $g(x) = 2x^3$.

- In a standard viewing window, graph f and g. Describe how the graphs look different and how they look the same.
- In the viewing window $-20 \le x \le 20$ and $-10{,}000 \le y \le 10{,}000$, graph f and g. Do the graphs look almost the same?
- In the viewing window

  $$-100 \le x \le 100 \text{ and } -1{,}000{,}000 \le y \le 1{,}000{,}000,$$

  graph f and g. Do the graphs look virtually identical?

The reason that the answer to the last question is "yes" can be understood by observing which term contributes the most to the output value $f(x)$ when x is large, as shown in the following chart.

Values of Specific Terms of $f(x) = 2x^3 + x^2 - 6x$

x	-100	-50	70	100
$-6x$	600	300	-420	-600
x^2	10,000	2,500	4,900	10,000
$g(x) = 2x^3$	$-2{,}000{,}000$	$-250{,}000$	686,000	2,000,000
$f(x) = 2x^3 + x^2 - 6x$	$-1{,}989{,}400$	$-247{,}200$	690,480	2,009,400

The chart shows that when $|x|$ is large, the terms x^2 and $-6x$ are insignificant compared with $2x^3$, and they play a very minor role in determining the end behavior of $f(x)$. Hence, the values of $f(x)$ and $g(x)$ are relatively close for large values of x.

End Behavior of Polynomial Functions

> When $|x|$ is large, the graph of a polynomial function closely resembles the graph of its highest degree term.
>
> When a polynomial function has *odd* degree, one end of its graph shoots upward and the other end downward.
>
> When a polynomial function has *even* degree, both ends of its graph shoot upward or both ends shoot downward.

Following are some illustrations of the facts listed in the preceding box. In Figures 4.3-4a–d, the graph of a polynomial function is shown on the left and the graph of its leading term is shown on the right. The end behavior of the graph of the polynomial is the same as the end behavior of the graph of the leading term. Note the degree of each set of graphs and whether the leading coefficient is positive or negative.

$$f(x) = 2x^4 - 5x^2 + 2 \qquad g(x) = 2x^4$$

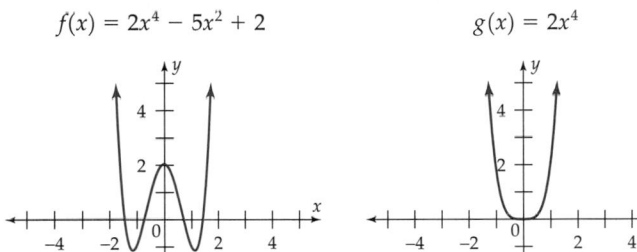

Figure 4.3-4a

$$f(x) = -3x^6 + 5x^2 + 2 \qquad g(x) = -3x^6$$

Figure 4.3-4b

Teaching Notes

When $|x|$ is large, the graph of the polynomial function resembles the graph of its highest term. Have students graph functions f and g together for each of Figures 4.3-4a through 4.3-4d in the viewing window $-100 \le x \le 100$, $-1{,}000{,}000 \le y \le 1{,}000{,}000$:

Figure 4.3-4a

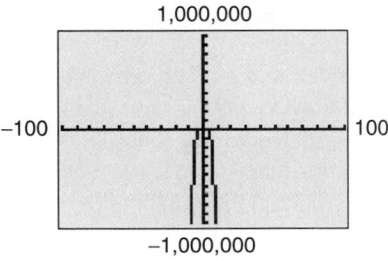

Figure 4.3-4b

continued from page 263

Figure 4.3-4c

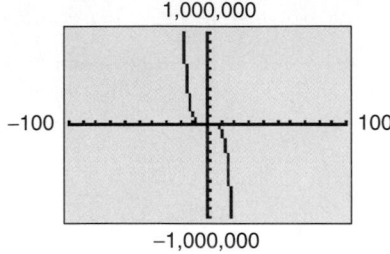

Figure 4.3-4d

Ask students to explain why the graph of every polynomial function has a y-intercept. The graph of every polynomial function extends infinitely left and right, so it must intersect the y-axis.

Ask students to explain why the graph of every polynomial function has *only one* y-intercept. The graph of every function must pass the vertical line test. That is, there cannot be more than one point of the graph on the y-axis.

Ask students to use the polynomial function form $f(x) = a_n x^n + a_{n-1}x^{n-1} + \cdots + a_1 x + a_0$ to explain why the y-intercept is a_0. The y-intercept is the value of the function at $x = 0$.

$$f(0) = a_n(0)^n + a_{n-1}(0)^{n-1} + \cdots + a_1(0) + a_0 = a_0$$

Ask students which of the following functions *do not* have an x-intercept, and why:

$f(x) = x^2 - 9$ x-intercepts at -3 and 3

$f(x) = x^2 + 9$ no x-intercept because f has no real zeros

$f(x) = x^4$ x-intercept at zero

$f(x) = -x^4 - 16$ no x-intercept because f has no real zeros

$f(x) = 0.4x^3 - x^2 - 2x + 3$ $g(x) = 0.4x^3$

Figure 4.3-4c

$f(x) = -0.6x^5 + 4x^2 + x - 4$ $g(x) = -0.6x^5$

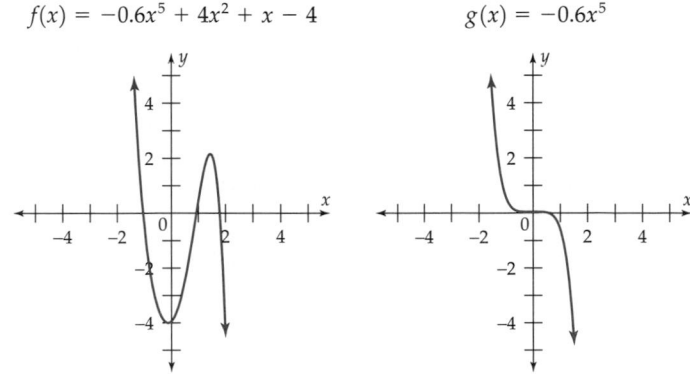

Figure 4.3-4d

Intercepts

Consider a polynomial function written in polynomial form.

$$f(x) = a_n x^n + a_{n-1}x^{n-1} + \ldots + a_1 x + a_0$$

- The y-intercept of the graph of f is the constant term, a_0.
- The x-intercepts of the graph of f are the real zeros of f.

The graph of every polynomial function has exactly one y-intercept, and because a polynomial of degree n has at most n distinct zeros, the number of x-intercepts is limited.

Intercepts

> **The graph of a polynomial function of degree n**
>
> - **has one y-intercept, which is equal to the constant term.**
> - **has at most n x-intercepts.**

That is, the number of x-intercepts can be no greater than the degree of the polynomial function.

Multiplicity

There is another connection between zeros and graphs. If $x - r$ is a factor that occurs m times in the complete factorization of a polynomial expression, then r is called a zero with **multiplicity** m of the related polynomial function.

For example, -3, -1 and 1 are zeros of $f(x) = (x + 3)^2(x + 1)(x - 1)^3$. The multiplicity of each zero is shown in the following chart.

Zero	-3	-1	1
Multiplicity	2	1	3

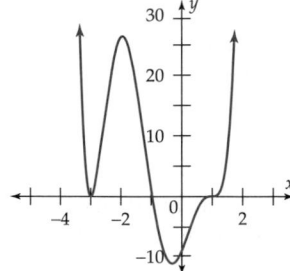

Figure 4.3-5

Observe in Figure 4.3-5 that the graph of f does not cross the x-axis at -3, a zero of *even* multiplicity, but does cross the x-axis at -1 and 1, zeros of *odd* multiplicity.

Multiplicity and Graphs

> Let c be a zero of multiplicity k of a polynomial f.
>
> - If k is odd, the graph of f crosses the x-axis at c.
> - If k is even, the graph of f touches, but does not cross, the x-axis at c.

Example 1 Multiplicity of Zeros

Find all zeros of $f(x) = (x + 1)^2(x - 2)(x - 3)^3$. State the multiplicity of each zero, and state whether the graph of f touches or crosses the x-axis at each corresponding x-intercept.

Solution

The following chart lists the zeros of f, the multiplicity of each, and whether the graph touches or crosses the x-axis at the corresponding x-intercept.

Zero	Multiplicity	x-axis
-1	2	touches
2	1	crosses
3	3	crosses

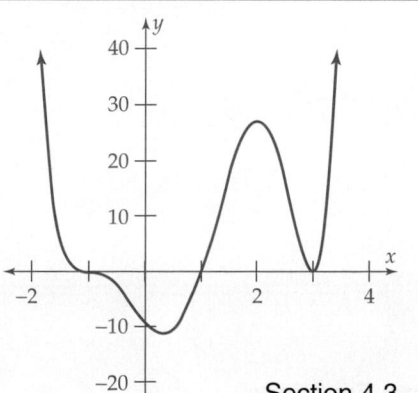

Figure 4.3-6

The graph of f, shown in Figure 4.3-6, verifies that the graph touches but does not cross the x-axis at -1 and crosses the x-axis at 2 and 3. ∎

Teaching Notes

To introduce the concept of multiplicity, you may want to use a function such as $f(x) = x^2 + 4x + 4$ which can be written $f(x) = (x + 2)(x + 2)$.

Find the zeros:

$(x + 2)(x + 2) = 0$

$x + 2 = 0$ or $x + 2 = 0$

$x = -2$ or $x = -2$

There are two solutions, but both are -2. Thus the zero of the function f is -2 with multiplicity 2. Point out that $f(x) = (x + 2)(x + 2)$ can also be written as $f(x) = (x + 2)^2$ and that the multiplicity of the zero is given by the exponent.

Then graph the function to show that it touches, but does not cross, the x-axis.

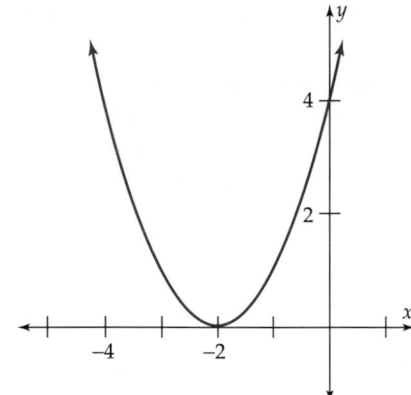

ADDITIONAL EXAMPLES

Example 1

Find all zeros of $f(x) = (x + 1)^3(x - 1)(x - 3)^2$. State the multiplicity of each zero, and state whether the graph of f touches or crosses the x-axis at each corresponding x-intercept.

Zero	Multiplicity	x-axis
-1	3	crosses
1	1	crosses
3	2	touches

Teaching Notes

Solution to the **Graphing Exploration:**

There are 4 local extrema. The degree of f is 5.

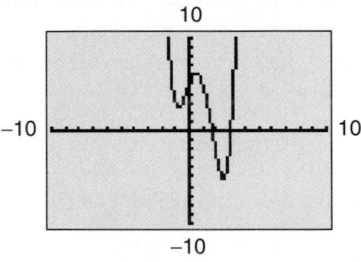

There are 3 local extrema. The degree of g is 4.

Each polynomial function of degree n in the Graphing Exploration has $n - 1$ local extrema. Point out that the **Number of Local Extrema** for a polynomial function of degree n is *at most* $n - 1$. Ask students to locate a function on page 263 that has *less than* $n - 1$ local extrema. $g(x) = 2x^4$ or $g(x) = -3x^6$ or $f(x) = -3x^6 + 5x^2 + 2$

Make sure students understand that if a graph touches, but does not cross the x-axis, there is a local maximum or minimum at that point.

Remind students (page 154) that a function is concave up in a given interval if for any two points in the given interval that lie on the curve, the segment that connects them is above the curve. A function is concave down in a given interval if for any two points in the given interval that lie on the curve, the segment that connects them is below the curve.

Note to students that the second statement in **Number of Points of Inflection** applies to any odd degree n, where $n > 2$, so linear functions are not included.

Local Extrema

The term **local extremum** (plural, extrema) refers to either a local maximum or a local minimum, that is, a point where the graph has a peak or a valley. Local extrema occur when the output values change from increasing to decreasing, or vice versa, as discussed in Section 3.2.

> **Graphing Exploration** •
>
> • Graph $f(x) = 0.5x^5 + 1.5x^4 - 2.5x^3 - 7.5x^2 + 2x + 5$ in the standard viewing window. What is the total number of local extrema on the graph? What is the degree of f?
>
> • Graph $g(x) = x^4 - 3x^3 - 2x^2 + 4x + 5$ in the standard viewing window. What is the total number of local extrema on the graph? What is the degree of $g(x)$?

The two polynomials graphed in the Exploration are illustrations of the following fact.

Number of Local Extrema

> A polynomial function of degree n has at most $n - 1$ local extrema.

That is, that total number of peaks and valleys on the graph is at most one less than the degree of the function.

Points of Inflection

Recall from Section 3.2 that an inflection point occurs where the concavity of a graph of a function changes. The number of inflection points on the graph of a polynomial is governed by the degree of the function.

Number of Points of Inflection

> • The graph of a polynomial function of degree n, with $n \geq 2$, has at most $n - 2$ points of inflection.
> • The graph of a polynomial function of odd degree, with $n > 2$, has at least one point of inflection.

Thus, the graph of a quadratic function, which has degree 2, has no points of inflection because it can have at most $n - 2 = 2 - 2 = 0$. The graph of a cubic has exactly one point of inflection because it has at least 1 and at most $3 - 2 = 1$.

Technology Tip

Points of inflection may be found by using INFLC in the TI-86/89 GRAPH MATH menu.

Figure 4.3-7

Complete Graphs of Polynomial Function

By using the facts discussed in this section, you can often determine whether or not the graph of a polynomial function is complete, that is, shows all the important features.

Example 2 A Complete Graph of a Polynomial

Find a complete graph of $f(x) = x^4 + 10x^3 + 21x^2 - 40x - 80$.

Solution

Because the y-intercept is -80, graph f in the window with $-10 \leq x \leq 10$ and $-100 \leq y \leq 100$, as shown in Figure 4.3-7.

The three peaks and valleys shown are the only local extrema because a fourth-degree polynomial graph has at most three local extrema.

There cannot be more x-intercepts than the two shown because if the graph turned toward the x-axis farther to the right or farther to the left, there would be an additional peak, which is impossible.

Finally, the end behavior of the graph resembles the graph of $y = x^4$, the highest degree term.

Figure 4.3-7 includes all the important features of the graph and is therefore complete. ∎

Example 3 A Complete Graph of a Polynomial

Find a complete graph of $f(x) = x^3 - 1.8x^2 + x + 2$.

Solution

The graph of f, shown in Figure 4.3-8a on the next page, is similar to the graph of its leading term $y = x^3$, but it does not appear to have any local extrema. However, if you use the trace feature on the flat portion of the graph to the right of the y-axis, you should see that the y-coordinates increase, then decrease, and then increase again.

Zoom in on the portion of the graph between 0 and 1, as shown in Figure 4.3-8b. Observe that the graph actually has two local extrema, one peak and one valley, which is the maximum possible number of local extrema for a cubic function. Figures 4.3-8a and 4.3-8b together provide a complete graph of f.

> **NOTE** No polynomial graph of a function of degree $n > 1$ contains horizontal line segments like those shown in Figure 4.3-8a. Always investigate such segments by using trace or zoom-in to determine any hidden behavior.

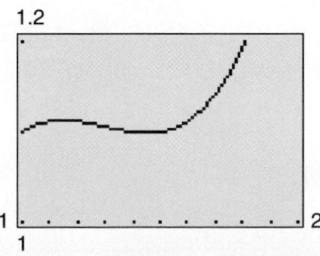

The two graphs provide a complete graph of f.

Example 2

Find a complete graph of
$f(x) = x^4 + 11x^3 + 25x^2 - 50x - 70$.

The y-intercept is -70.
The three peaks and valleys shown are the only local extrema because a fourth-degree polynomial graph has at most three local extrema.
There cannot be more x-intercepts than the two shown because if the graph turned toward the x-axis farther to the right or farther to the left, there would be an additional peak, which is impossible.
The end behavior of the graph resembles the graph of $y = x^4$, the highest degree term.
The graph is complete.

Example 3

Find a complete graph of
$f(x) = x^3 - 3.9x^2 + 5x - 1$.

The graph of f is similar to the graph of its leading term, $y = x^3$, but does not appear to have any local extrema. Use the trace feature on the flat portion of the graph to show that the y-coordinates increase, decrease, and increase again. Zoom in on the portion of the graph between 1 and 2 to show that the graph has two local extrema, one peak and one valley, which is the maximum number of local extrema for a cubic function.

Example Notes

For **Example 4**, to help students see why both graphs are needed, point out that Figure 4.3-9b shows an *x*-intercept that is not shown in Figure 4.3-9a.

ADDITIONAL EXAMPLES

Example 4

Determine if the graph shown below is a complete graph of
$$f(x) = 0.02x^5 + x^4 - x^3 - 5x^2 + 4x + 2.$$

This cannot be a complete graph because when $|x|$ is large, the graph must resemble the graph of $f(x) = 0.02x^5$, whose left end goes downward. The graph of *f* must turn downward and cross the *x*-axis somewhere to the left of the origin. So, the graph must have one more peak where the graph turns downward, and must have another *x*-intercept. The graph below displays the local maximum and *x*-intercept not included in the graph above.

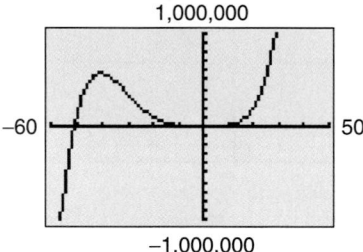

Both graphs are necessary to show all 5 *x*-intercepts and all 4 local extrema of the function.

Figure 4.3-8a

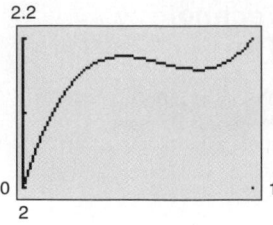

Figure 4.3-8b

Example 4   A Complete Graph of a Polynomial

Determine if the graph shown in Figure 4.3-9a is a complete graph of
$$f(x) = 0.01x^5 + x^4 - x^3 - 6x^2 + 5x + 4.$$

Solution

The graph shown in Figure 4.3-9a cannot be a complete graph because, when $|x|$ is large, the graph of *f* must resemble the graph of $g(x) = 0.01x^5$, whose left end goes downward.

So the graph of *f* must turn downward and cross the *x*-axis somewhere to the left of the origin. Therefore, the graph must have one more peak, where the graph turns downward, and must have another *x*-intercept.

One additional peak and the ones shown in Figure 4.3-9a make a total of four, the maximum possible for a polynomial of degree 5. Similarly, the additional *x*-intercept makes a total of 5 *x*-intercepts. Because *f* has degree 5, there are no other *x*-intercepts.

A viewing window that includes the local maximum and the *x*-intercept shown in Figure 4.3-9b will not display the local extrema and *x*-intercepts shown in Figure 4.3-9a. Consequently, a complete graph of *f* requires both Figure 4.3-9a and Figure 4.3-9b to illustrate the important features of the graph.

Figure 4.3-9a

Figure 4.3-9b

The graphs shown in Examples 2–4 were known to be complete because they included the maximum possible number of local extrema. Many graphs, however, may have fewer than the maximum number of possible peaks and valleys. In such cases, use any available information and try several viewing windows to obtain the most complete graph.

Exercises 4.3

In Exercises 1–6, decide whether the given graph could possibly be the graph of a polynomial function.

1.

Yes

2.

No

3.

Yes

4.

No

5.

No

6.

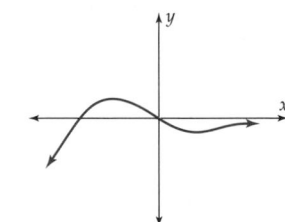

Yes

In Exercises 7–12, determine whether the given graph could possibly be the graph of a polynomial function of degree 3, degree 4, or degree 5.

7.

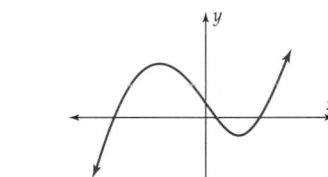

**Degree 3, yes;
degree 4, no;
degree 5, yes**

8.

**Degree 3, no;
degree 4, yes;
degree 5, no**

9.

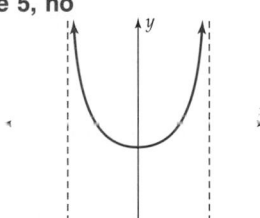

No

13. The graphs have the same *shape* in the window with $-40 \leq x \leq 40$ and $-1000 \leq y \leq 5000$ but don't look identical.

16. -2 and 0 are zeros of even multiplicity; 3 is a zero of odd multiplicity

17. -2 and -1 are zeros of odd multiplicity; 2 is a zero of even multiplicity

18. -2 and 2 are both zeros of even multiplicity

10.

Degree 3, no; degree 4, no; degree 5, yes

11.

Degree 3, no; degree 4, no; degree 5, yes

12.

No

In Exercises 13 and 14, find a viewing window in which the graph of the given polynomial function f appears to have the same general shape as the graph of its leading term.

13. $f(x) = x^4 - 6x^3 + 9x^2 - 3$

14. $f(x) = x^3 - 5x^2 + 4x - 2$
$-20 \leq x \leq 20, -1000 \leq y \leq 1000$

In Exercises 15–18, the graph of a polynomial function is shown. List each zero of the polynomial and state whether its multiplicity is even or odd.

15.

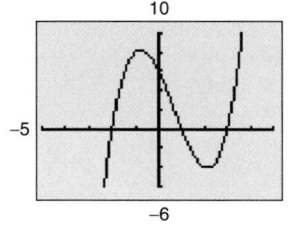

-2, 1, and 3 are zeros of odd multiplicity

16.

17.

18.

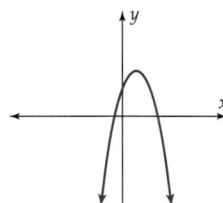

In Exercises 19–24, use your knowledge of polynomial graphs, *not* a calculator, to match the given function with one of graphs a–f.

a.

b.

c.

d.

e.

f.

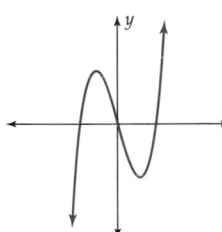

19. $f(x) = 2x - 3$ **e**   **20.** $g(x) = x^2 - 4x + 7$ **d**

21. $g(x) = x^3 - 4x$ **f**   **22.** $f(x) = x^4 - 5x^2 + 4$ **a**

23. $f(x) = -x^4 + 6x^3 - 9x^2 + 2$ **c**

24. $g(x) = -2x^2 + 3x + 1$ **b**

In Exercises 25–28, graph the function in the standard viewing window and explain why that graph cannot possibly be complete.

25. $f(x) = 0.01x^3 - 0.2x^2 - 0.4x + 7$

26. $g(x) = 0.01x^4 + 0.1x^3 - 0.8x^2 - 0.7x + 9$

27. $h(x) = 0.005x^4 - x^2 + 5$

---

28. $f(x) = 0.001x^5 - 0.01x^4 - 0.2x^3 + x^2 + x - 5$

In Exercises 29–34, find a single viewing window that shows a complete graph of the function.

29. $f(x) = x^3 + 8x^2 + 5x - 14$
$-9 \le x \le 3$ and $-20 \le y \le 40$
30. $g(x) = x^3 - 3x^2 - 4x - 5$
$-3 \le x \le 5$ and $-20 \le y \le 5$
31. $g(x) = -x^4 - 3x^3 + 24x^2 + 80x + 15$
$-6 \le x \le 6$ and $-60 \le y \le 320$
32. $f(x) = x^4 - 10x^3 + 35x^2 - 50x + 24$
$0 \le x \le 5$ and $-2 \le y \le 10$
33. $f(x) = 2x^5 - 3.5x^4 - 10x^3 + 5x^2 + 12x + 6$
$-3 \le x \le 4$ and $-35 \le y \le 20$
34. $g(x) = x^5 + 8x^4 + 20x^3 + 9x^2 - 27x - 7$
$-5 \le x \le 2$ and $-18 \le y \le 20$

In Exercises 35–40, find a complete graph of the function and list the viewing window(s) that show(s) this graph.

35. $f(x) = 0.1x^5 + 3x^4 - 4x^3 - 11x^2 + 3x + 2$

36. $g(x) = x^4 - 48x^3 - 101x^2 + 49x + 50$

37. $g(x) = 0.03x^3 - 1.5x^2 - 200x + 5$
$-90 \le x \le 120$ and $-15{,}000 \le y \le 5000$
38. $f(x) = 0.25x^6 + 0.25x^5 - 35x^4 - 7x^3 + 823x^2 + 25x - 2750$
$-12 \le x \le 12$ and $-45{,}000 \le y \le 5000$
39. $g(x) = 2x^3 - 0.33x^2 - 0.006x + 5$

40. $f(x) = 0.3x^5 + 2x^4 - 7x^3 + 2x^2$

41. a. Explain why the graph of a cubic polynomial function has either two local extrema or none at all. *Hint:* If it had only one, what would the graph look like when $|x|$ is very large?
b. Explain why the general shape of the graph of a cubic polynomial function must be one of the following.

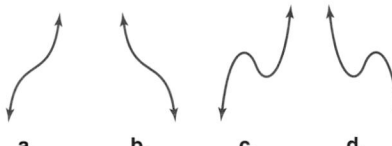

a.   **b.**   **c.**   **d.**

42. The figure shows an incomplete graph of an even polynomial function f of fourth degree. (Even functions were defined in *Excursion* 3.4.A.)
a. Find the zeros of f.
b. Explain why
$$f(x) = k(x - a)(x - b)(x - c)(x - d)$$
where a, b, c, d are the zeros of f.

---

25. The graph in the standard viewing window does not rise at the far right as does the graph of the highest degree term x^3, so it is not complete.

26. The graph in the standard viewing window does not rise at the far left as does the graph of the highest degree term x^4, so it is not complete.

27. The graph in the standard viewing window does not rise at the far left and far right as does the graph of the highest degree term $0.005x^4$, so it is not complete.

28. The graph in the standard viewing window does not rise at the far right and fall at the far left as does the graph of the highest degree term $0.001x^5$, so it is not complete.

35. Left half: $-33 \le x \le -2$ and $-50{,}000 \le y \le 250{,}000$;
right half: $-2 \le x \le 3$ and $-20 \le y \le 30$

36. Overall: $-20 \le x \le 60$ and $-700{,}000 \le y \le 100000$;
near y-axis: $-3 \le x \le 2$ and $-100 \le y \le 100$

39. Overall: $-3 \le x \le 3$ and $-20 \le y \le 20$;
near y-axis: $-0.1 \le x \le 0.2$ and $4.997 \le y \le 5.001$

40. Overall: $-10 \le x \le 10$ and $-500 \le y \le 2500$;
near x-axis: $0 \le x \le 3$ and $-10 \le y \le 5$;
near y-axis: $-0.5 \le x \le 0.5$ and $-0.1 \le y \le 0.1$

41. a. The graph of a cubic polynomial (degree 3) has at most $3 - 1 = 2$ local extrema. When $|x|$ is large, the graph resembles the graph of ax^3, that is, one end shoots upward and the other end downward. If the graph had only one local extremum, both ends of the graph would go in the same direction (both up or down). Thus, the graph of a cubic polynomial has either two local extrema or none.

b. These are the only possible shapes for a graph that has 0 or 2 local extrema, 1 point of inflection, and resembles the graph of ax^3 when $|x|$ is large.

---

42. a. $x = -4, -2, 2,$ or 4

b. We have four distinct zeros of a fourth degree polynomial. Each zero corresponds to a linear factor of f.

c. $k = 0.25$

d. $(0, 16)$ is a local maximum; $(\pm3.162, -9)$ are local minima

e. Increasing on $(-3.162, 0)$ and $(3.162, \infty)$ decreasing on $(-\infty, -3.162)$ and $(0, 3.162)$

47.

48.

49.

50.

51.

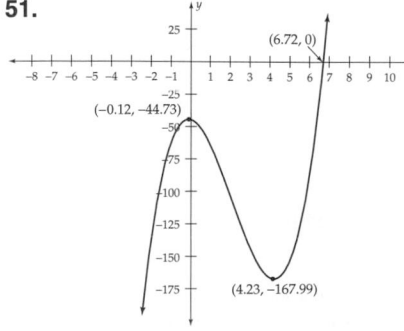

c. Experiment with your calculator to find the value of k that produces the graph in the figure.

d. Find all local extrema of f.

e. List the approximate intervals on which f is increasing and those on which it is decreasing.

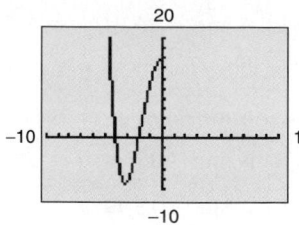

43. A complete graph of a polynomial function g is shown below.

a. Is the degree of $g(x)$ even or odd? **Odd**

b. Is the leading coefficient of $g(x)$ positive or negative? **Positive**

c. What are the real zeros of $g(x)$? **−2, 0, 4, and 6**

d. What is the smallest possible degree of $g(x)$?

5

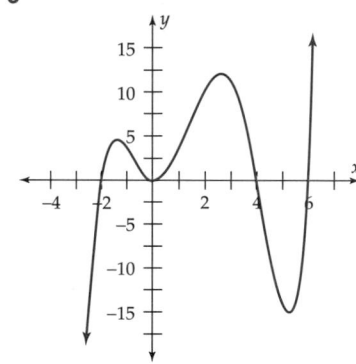

44. Do Exercise 43 for the polynomial function g whose complete graph is shown here.

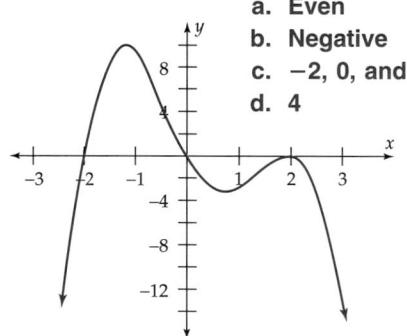

a. Even

b. Negative

c. −2, 0, and 2

d. 4

45. The figure below is a partial view of the graph of a cubic polynomial whose leading coefficient is negative. Which of the patterns shown in Exercise 41 does this graph have? **d**

46. The figure below is a partial view of the graph of a fourth-degree polynomial. Sketch the general shape of the graph and state whether the leading coefficient is positive or negative. **Negative**

In Exercises 47–56, sketch a complete graph of the function. Label each x-intercept and the coordinates of each local extremum; find intercepts and coordinates exactly when possible, otherwise approximate them.

47. $f(x) = x^3 - 3x^2 + 4$ **48.** $g(x) = 4x - \dfrac{4x^3}{3}$

49. $h(x) = 0.25x^4 - 2x^3 + 4x^2$

50. $f(x) = 0.25x^4 - \dfrac{2x^3}{3}$

51. $g(x) = 3x^3 - 18.5x^2 - 4.5x - 45$

52. $h(x) = 2x^3 + x^2 - 4x - 2$

53. $f(x) = x^5 - 3x^3 + x + 1$

54. $g(x) = 0.25x^4 - x^2 + 0.5$

55. $h(x) = 8x^4 + 22.8x^3 - 50.6x^2 - 94.8x + 138.6$

56. $f(x) = 32x^6 - 48x^4 + 18x^2 - 1$

57. *Critical Thinking*

a. Graph $g(x) = 0.01x^3 - 0.06x^2 + 0.12x + 3.92$ in the viewing window with $-3 \le x \le 3$ and $0 \le y \le 6$ and verify that the graph appears to coincide with the horizontal line $y = 4$ between

52–56. *See p.* 1063.

$x = 1$ and $x = 3$. In other words, it appears that every x with $1 \le x \le 3$ is a solution of the equation

$$0.01x^3 - 0.06x^2 + 0.12x + 3.92 = 4.$$

Explain why this is impossible. Conclude that the actual graph is not horizontal between $x = 1$ and $x = 3$.

b. Use the trace feature to verify that the graph is actually rising from left to right between $x = 1$ and $x = 3$. Find a viewing window that shows this.

c. Show that it is not possible for the graph of a polynomial $f(x)$ to contain a horizontal segment. *Hint:* A horizontal line segment is part of the horizontal line $y = k$ for some constant k. Adapt the argument in part **a**, which is the case $k = 4$.

58. *Critical Thinking*
  a. Let $f(x)$ be a polynomial of odd degree. Explain why $f(x)$ must have at least one real zero. *Hint:* Why must the graph of f cross the x-axis, and what does this mean?
  b. Let $g(x)$ be a polynomial of even degree, with a negative leading coefficient and a positive

constant term. Explain why $g(x)$ must have at least one positive and at least one negative zero.

59. *Critical Thinking* The graph of

$$f(x) = (x + 18)(x^2 - 20)(x - 2)^2(x - 10)$$

has x-intercepts at each of its zeros, that is, at $x = -18, \pm\sqrt{20} \approx \pm4.472, 2$, and 10. It is also true that $f(x)$ has a relative minimum at $x = 2$.
  a. Draw the x-axis and mark the zeros of $f(x)$. Then use the fact that $f(x)$ has degree 6 (Why?) to sketch the general shape of the graph, as was done for cubics in Exercise 41.
  b. Now graph $f(x)$ in the standard viewing window. Does the graph resemble your sketch? Does it even show all the x-intercepts between -10 and 10?
  c. Graph $f(x)$ in the viewing window with $-19 \le x \le 11$ and $-10 \le y \le 10$. Does this window include all the x-intercepts, as it should?
  d. List viewing windows that give a complete graph of $f(x)$.

57. a. The solutions are zeros of $g(x) - 4 = 0.01x^3 - 0.06x^2 + 0.12x - 0.08$. This polynomial has degree 3 and hence has at most 3 zeros.

  b. $1 \le x \le 3$ and $3.99 \le y \le 4.01$

  c. Suppose $f(x)$ has degree n. If the graph of $f(x)$ had a horizontal segment lying on the line $y = k$ for some constant k, then the equation $f(x) = k$ would have infinitely many solutions. But the polynomial $f(x) - k$ has degree n and thus has at most n roots. Hence the equation $f(x) = k$ has at most n solutions, which means the graph cannot have a horizontal segment.

58–59. *See p. 1063.*

 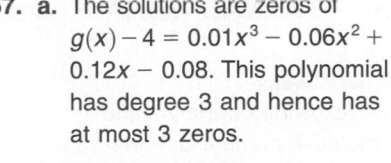

Excursion: Polynomial Models

4.3.A

Objectives

• Fit a polynomial model to data

Linear regression was used in Section 1.5 to construct a linear function that modeled a set of data points. When the scatter plot of the data points looks more like a higher degree polynomial graph than a straight line, similar least squares regression procedures are available on most calculators for constructing quadratic, cubic, and quartic polynomial functions to model the data.

Example 1   A Polynomial Model

The following data, which is based on statistics from the Department of Health and Human Services, gives the *cumulative* number of reported cases of AIDS in the United States from 1982 through 2000. Find a quadratic, a cubic, and a quartic regression equation and determine which equation best models the data.

 Math Background

Non-linear regression is sometimes called curvilinear regression. Polynomial regression is one type of curvilinear regression. Other types of curvilinear regression include exponential regression, power regression, and logarithmic regression.

ADDITIONAL EXAMPLES

Example 1

The following data gives the cumulative number of home runs hit by Rafael Palmeiro from 1986 through 2004. Find a quadratic, a cubic, and a quartic regression equation and determine which equation best models the data.

1986	13	1995	194	2000	400
1988	25	1996	233	2001	447
1990	47	1997	271	2002	490
1992	95	1998	314	2003	528
1994	155	1999	361	2004	551

Let $x = 0$ correspond to 1984 and plot the data points (2, 13), (4, 25), etc. to make a scatter plot of the data.

quadratic: $f(x) = 1.1x^2 + 8.3x - 25.9$

cubic: $g(x) = -0.10x^3 + 4.39x^2 - 22.94x + 46.58$

quartic:
$h(x) = -0.005x^4 + 0.135x^3 + 0.917x^2 - 3.427x + 15.285$

The quadratic model using full coefficients, shown below, is the best model, as the cubic and quartic models turn downward at higher values of x.

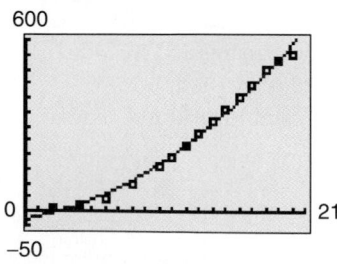

Teaching Notes

Solution to the **Graphing Exploration** (right):

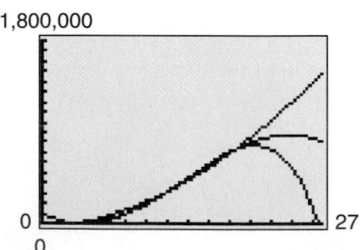

Technology Tip

Quadratic, cubic, and quartic regression are denoted by QuadReg, CubicReg, QuartReg in the CALC submenus of the TI STAT menu and by x^2, x^3, x^4 in the CALC REG submenu of the Casio STAT menu.

Year	Cases	Year	Cases	Year	Cases
1982	1563	1991	232,383	1996	595,559
1984	10,845	1992	278,189	1997	652,439
1986	41,662	1993	380,601	1998	698,527
1988	105,489	1994	457,789	1999	743,418
1990	188,872	1995	528,421	2000	784,518

Solution

Let $x = 0$ correspond to 1980 and plot the data points (2, 1563), (4, 10845), etc., to obtain the scatter plot shown in Figure 4.3.A-1a. The points are not in a straight line, but could be part of a polynomial graph of degree 2 or more.

Figure 4.3.A-1a

Using the same procedure as for linear regression, find a quadratic, a cubic, and a quartic regression equation for the data. See the Technology Tip in the margin on this page for the specific calculator procedure needed. The polynomial functions shown below have rounded coefficients, but the graph in Figure 4.3.A-1b shows the data points along with the quadratic regression equation and was produced using full coefficients.

$f(x) = 1758.0x^2 + 9893.3x - 59,024.3$ *Quadratic*
$g(x) = -219.18x^3 + 9111.66x^2 - 59,991.75x + 103,255.32$ *Cubic*
$h(x) = -20.29x^4 + 681.94x^3 - 4318.57x^2 + 15,550.81x - 17,877.25$ *Quartic*

The graphs of f, g, and h are virtually identical in the viewing window shown. Although any one of f, g, or h provides a reasonable model for the given data, knowledge of polynomial graphs suggests that the cubic and quartic models, should not be used for predicting future results. As x gets larger, the graphs of g and h will resemble respectively those of $y = -219.2x^3$ and $y = -20.3x^4$, which turn downward. However, the cumulative number of cases cannot decrease because even when there are no new cases, the cumulative total stays the same.

> #### Graphing Exploration
>
> Graph the functions f, g, and h in the window with $0 \le x \le 27$ and $0 \le y \le 1{,}800{,}000$. In this window, can you distinguish the graphs of f and g? Assuming no medical breakthroughs or changes in the current social situation, does the graph of f seem to be a plausible model for the next few years? What about the graph of g?

Yes, you can distinguish the graphs of f and g.

Possible answers: The graph of f is a plausible model for the next few years. The graph of g is not a plausible model as it begins to turn downward.

Example 2 Estimating Data Values

The population of San Francisco in selected years is given in the table.

Year	1950	1960	1970	1980	1990	2000
Population	775,357	740,316	715,674	678,974	723,959	776,733

[*Source: U.S. Census Bureau*]

Let $x = 0$ correspond to 1950. Find a polynomial regression model that is a reasonably good fit and estimate the population of San Francisco in 1995 and in 2004.

Solution

The scatter plot of the data shown in Figure 4.3.A-2a suggests a parabola. However, the data points do not climb quite so steeply in the later years, so a higher-degree polynomial graph might fit the data better. The quadratic, cubic, and quartic regression models are shown below.

Figure 4.3.A-2a

$f(x) \approx 128.14x^2 - 6632.39x + 783,517.18$ *Quadratic*

$g(x) \approx 2.48x^3 - 58.10x^2 - 3230.49x + 776,067.76$ *Cubic*

$h(x) \approx -0.11x^4 + 13.20x^3 - 387.24x^2 - 168.65x + 774,230.65$ *Quartic*

Quadratic   Cubic   Quartic

Figure 4.3.A-2b

The quartic appears to be the best fitting function. Use h to estimate the population in 1995 and 2004 by finding $h(45)$ and $h(54)$.

$$h(45) \approx 745,843.98 \quad \text{and} \quad h(54) \approx 803,155.18$$

That is, the estimated population of San Francisco in 1995 was approximately 745,844 and the estimated population of San Francisco in 2004 was approximately 803,155. ∎

In Example 2, a model may not be accurate when applied outside the range of points used to construct it. For instance, $f(-174) \approx 5,817,115$, suggesting that the population of San Francisco in 1776 was about 5,817,115.

Cubic (g)   Quartic (h)

ADDITIONAL EXAMPLES

Example 2

The total United States civilian labor force (in thousands) for ages 16 years and older in selected years is given in the table.

Year	1950	1960	1970
Labor Force	62,208	69,628	82,771

Year	1980	1990	2000
Labor Force	106,940	125,840	140,863

Let $x = 0$ correspond to 1950. Find a polynomial regression model that is a reasonably good fit and estimate the civilian labor force in 1995 and 2004.

scatter plot of the data:

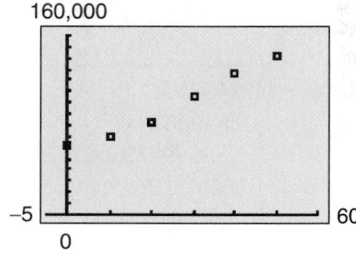

$f(x) \approx 10.90x^2 + 1129.49x + 59,812.32$

$g(x) \approx -0.90x^3 + 78.18x^2 - 99.52x + 62,503.57$

$h(x) \approx -0.008x^4 - 0.082x^3 + 53.156x^2 + 133.281x + 62,363.893$

Quadratic (f)

The cubic appears to be the best fit.

$g(45) = 134,327.2$ and
$g(54) = 143,384.8$

The estimated civilian labor force in 1995 was approximately 134,327,200 and the estimated civilian labor force in 2004 was approximately 143,384,800.

Real-World Application

In **Example 2,** page 275, the 1995 estimated population of San Francisco from the polynomial model is about 745,844. This is close to the actual population of San Francisco in 1995, 751,700.

Teaching Notes

To help students understand that the minimum number of data points required is the number of coefficients in the corresponding polynomial model, remind them that the cubic polynomial $ax^3 + bx^2 + cx + d$ has 4 coefficients: a, b, c, and d.

Exercises 4.3.A

ANSWERS

5. **a.** $y = -0.6343350111x^3 + 11.79490831x^2 - 51.88599279x + 4900.867065$

   b. 1987: 4898.0 per 100,000; 1995: 4635.6 per 100,000

   c. 3138.2

   d. Answers may vary

NOTE The following table lists the minimum number of data points required for polynomial regression. In each case, the minimum number of data points required is the number of coefficients in the polynomial function modeling the data. If you have exactly the required minimum number of data points, no two of them can have the same first coordinate.

Model	Minimum number of data points
Quadratic Regression	3
Cubic Regression	4
Quartic Regression	5

When using the minimum number of data points, the polynomial regression function will pass through all the data points and will fit exactly. When using more than the minimum number of data points required, the fit will generally be approximate rather than exact.

Exercises 4.3.A

In Exercises 1–4, a scatter plot of data is shown. State the type of polynomial model that seems most appropriate for the data (linear, quadratic, cubic, or quartic). If none of them is likely to provide a reasonable model, say so.

1.
   Cubic

2.
   Linear

3.
   Quadratic

4.
   Quartic

5. The table, which is based on the United States FBI Uniform Crime Report, shows the rate of property crimes per 100,000 population.

Year	Crimes	Year	Crimes
1982	5032.5	1994	4660.0
1984	4492.1	1996	4450.1
1986	4862.6	1997	4318.7
1988	5027.1	1998	4051.8
1990	5088.5	1999	3743.6
1992	4902.7	2000	3617.9

   a. Use cubic regression to find a polynomial function that models this data, with $x = 0$ corresponding to 1980.

   b. According to this model, what was the property crime rate in 1987 and 1995?

c. The actual crime rate was about 3698 in 2001. What does the model predict?

d. Is this model a reasonable one?

6. The table, which is based on the U.S. National Center for Educational Statistics, shows actual and projected enrollment (in millions) in public high schools in selected years.

Year	Enrollment	Year	Enrollment
1975	14.3	1995	12.5
1980	13.2	2000	13.5
1985	12.4	2005	14.4
1990	11.3	2010	14.1

a. Use quartic regression to find a polynomial function that models this data, with $x = 0$ corresponding to 1975.

b. According to this model, what was the enrollment in 1998 and 1999?

c. According to the model, in what year between 1975 and 2000 was enrollment at its lowest level?

d. Does this estimate appear to be accurate?

7. The table shows the air temperature at various times during a spring day in Gainesville, Florida.

Time	Temp (F°)	Time	Temp (F°)
6 a.m.	52	1 p.m.	82
7 a.m.	56	2 p.m.	86
8 a.m.	61	3 p.m.	85
9 a.m.	67	4 p.m.	83
10 a.m.	72	5 p.m.	78
11 a.m.	77	6 p.m.	72
noon	80		

a. Sketch a scatter plot of the data, with $x = 0$ corresponding to midnight.

b. Find a quadratic polynomial model for the data.

c. What is the predicted temperature for noon? for 9 a.m.? for 2 p.m.?

8. The table, which is based on data from the Association of Departments of Foreign Languages, shows the fall enrollment (in thousands) in college level Spanish classes.

Year	Enrollment	Year	Enrollment
1970	389.2	1986	411.3
1974	362.2	1990	533.9
1977	376.7	1995	606.3
1980	379.4	1998	656.6
1983	386.2		

a. Sketch a scatter plot of the data, with $x = 0$ corresponding to 1970.

b. Find a cubic polynomial model for this data.

Use the following table for Exercises 9–10. It shows the median income of U.S. households in 1999 dollars.

Year	Median Income	Year	Median Income
1985	$36,568	1993	$36,019
1987	38,220	1995	37,251
1989	38,836	1997	38,411
1991	36,850	1999	40,816

[*Source: U.S. Census Bureau*]

9. a. Sketch a scatter plot of the data from 1985 to 1999, with $x = 0$ corresponding to 1985.

b. Decide whether a quadratic or quartic model seems more appropriate.

c. Find an appropriate polynomial model.

6. a. $y = -0.0000356x^4 + 0.0021146x^3 - 0.02714x^2 - 0.12059x + 14.2996$

b. 1998: $\approx$12.9 million; 1999: $\approx$13.2 million

c. 1989

d. Yes, this estimate appears to be very close to the actual data.

7. a.

b. $y = -0.5179820180x^2 + 14.65684316x - 20.88711289$

c. Noon: 80°; 9 A.M.: 69°; 2 P.M.: 83°

8. a.

b. $y = -0.01456x^3 + 1.2034x^2 - 12.6646x + 394.28196$

9. a.

b. Quartic

c. $y = -1.595348011x^4 + 58.04379735x^3 - 630.033381x^2 + 2131.441153x + 36,466.9811$

d. $\approx$$42,545.95

e. According to this model, income will drop steeply after 2002.

11. a. 24,000

0   22

0

b. $y = -0.084189248x^4 -$
$0.528069153x^3 +$
$66.26642628x^2 +$
$397.2751554x +$
3965.686061

c. 1996: $19,606; The estimate is lower.

12. a. 300

-2   12

0

b. $y = 0.83804x^2 +$
$2.53493x + 127.77571$

c. 1995: $161.40; 2002: $278.87

d. during the year 2004

d. Use the model to predict the median income in 2002.

e. Does this model seem reasonable after 2002?

10. a. Sketch a scatter plot of the data from 1989 to 1999, with $x = 0$ corresponding to 1989.

b. Find both a cubic and a quartic model for this data.

c. Is there any significant difference between the models from 1989 to 1999? What about from 1999 to 2005?

d. According to these models, when will the median income reach $45,000?

11. The table shows the U.S. public debt per person, in dollars, in selected years.

Year	Debt	Year	Debt
1981	$4,338	1993	$17,105
1983	5,870	1995	18,930
1985	7,598	1997	20,026
1987	9,615	1999	20,746
1989	11,545	2001	20,353
1991	14,436		

[Source: U.S. Department of Treasury, Bureau of Public Debt]

a. Sketch a scatter plot of the data with $x = 0$ corresponding to 1980.

b. Find a quartic model for the data.

c. Use the model to estimate the public debt per person in 1996. How does your estimate compare with the actual figure of $19,805?

12. The table shows the total advertising expenditures, in billions of dollars, in selected years.

Year	Expenditures	Year	Expenditures
1990	$129.59	1996	$175.23
1992	132.65	1998	201.59
1994	151.68	2000	236.33

[Source: Statistical abstract of the United States 2001]

a. Sketch a scatter plot of the data with $x = 0$ corresponding to 1990.

b. Find a quadratic model for the data.

c. Use the model to estimate expenditures in 1995 and 2002.

d. If this model remains accurate, when will expenditures reach $350 billion?

Section

4.4 **Rational Functions**

Teaching Notes

For this lesson, students need to know how to factor and divide polynomials and how to find zeros and intercepts of polynomial functions.

Emphasize that the domains of most rational functions exclude one or more real numbers.

4.4 **Rational Functions**

Objectives

- Find the domain of a rational function
- Find intercepts, vertical asymptotes, and horizontal asymptotes
- Identify holes
- Describe end behavior
- Sketch complete graphs

Recall that a polynomial is an algebraic expression that can be written as

$$a_n x^n + a_{n-1} x^{n-1} + \cdots + a_2 x^2 + a_1 x + a_0$$

where n is a nonnegative integer.

A **rational function** is a function whose rule is the quotient of two polynomials, such as

$$f(x) = \frac{1}{x} \qquad t(x) = \frac{4x - 3}{2x + 1} \qquad k(x) = \frac{2x^3 + 5x + 2}{x^2 - 7x + 6}$$

10. a. 45,000

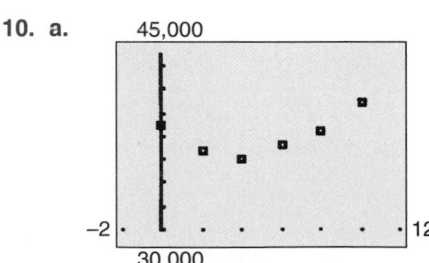

-2   12

30,000

b. Cubic: $y = -6.8924x^3 + 236.9524x^2 -$
$1487.44x + 38,847.167$

Quartic: $y = 0.5326x^4 - 17.543x^3 + 302.38x^2 -$
$1609.1687x + 38,861.77$

c. There is not a significant difference between the models from 1989 to 1999; between 1999 and 2005, the quartic model increases faster.

d. Cubic: in 2002; quartic: in 2001

Although a polynomial function is defined for every real number x, a rational function is defined only when its denominator is nonzero.

COMMON ERROR
/// ALERT \\\

Some students may exclude zeros of the numerator from the domain of a rational function. For example, they may exclude 3 from the domain of $t(x) = \dfrac{2x - 6}{2x + 1}$. Remind students that the domain of a rational function is the set of all real numbers that are not zeros of its *denominator*. The domain of t is the set of all real numbers except $x = -\dfrac{1}{2}$.

Domain of Rational Functions

> The domain of a rational function is the set of all real numbers that are *not* zeros of its denominator.

Example 1 The Domain of a Rational Function

Find the domain of each rational function.

a. $f(x) = \dfrac{1}{x^2}$ **b.** $g(x) = \dfrac{x^2 + 3x + 1}{x^2 - x - 6}$

Solution

a. The domain of $f(x) = \dfrac{1}{x^2}$ is the set of all real numbers except $x = 0$, because the denominator is 0 when $x = 0$, making the fraction undefined.

b. The domain of $g(x) = \dfrac{x^2 + 3x + 1}{x^2 - x - 6}$ is the set of all real numbers except the solutions of $x^2 - x - 6 = 0$. Because $x^2 - x - 6$ factors into $(x + 2)(x - 3)$, the solutions to $x^2 - x - 6 = 0$ are $x = -2$ and $x = 3$. Therefore, the domain of g is the set of all real numbers except $x = -2$ and $x = 3$.

■

Properties of Rational Graphs

Because calculators often do a poor job of graphing rational functions, the emphasis in this section is on the algebraic analysis of rational functions. Such analysis should enable you to interpret misleading screen images.

Intercepts

As with any function, the y-intercept of the graph of a rational function f occurs at $f(0)$, provided that f is defined at $x = 0$. The x-intercepts of the graph of a rational function occur when its numerator is 0 and its denominator is nonzero.

Intercepts of Rational Functions

> If f has a y-intercept, it occurs at $f(0)$.
>
> The x-intercepts of the graph of a rational function occur at the numbers that
>
> • are zeros of the numerator
> • are *not* zeros of the denominator

Math Background

In **Example 1a**, the domain is described as the set of all real numbers except $x = 0$. Other notations that describe this set include:

• $\{x \mid x \neq 0\}$ (set notation)
• $(-\infty, 0) \cup (0, \infty)$ (interval notation)

ADDITIONAL EXAMPLES

Example 1

Find the domain of each rational function.

a. $f(x) = \dfrac{1}{x^3}$ all real numbers except $x = 0$

b. $\dfrac{x^2 + 4}{x^2 - 2x - 8}$ all real numbers except $x = -2$ and $x = 4$

Teaching Notes

Have students use their calculators to graph the function in **Example 1b**, and then direct their attention to the paragraph under **Properties of Rational Graphs.** The calculator probably does a poor job with the graph of the function g. Point out that if their graph of g appears as shown to the left, the vertical segments are not really part of the graph. (Possible ways to avoid these "extra" line segments are given in the **Technology Tips** on pages 283 and 284.)

Teaching Notes

After doing **Example 2**, you may want to point out that not all rational functions have x- and/or y-intercepts. For example, the function $f(x) = \frac{1}{x}$ has neither an x-intercept nor a y-intercept.

The paragraph under **Continuity** mentions breaks in graphs of rational functions. There are two types of breaks. One type of break occurs at a point where a **vertical asymptote** may be drawn. Vertical asymptotes are defined at the bottom of page 281. The other type of break occurs at a point that is a hole in the function (see page 283).

After learning about vertical asymptotes, some students may ask about other types of asymptotes. For horizontal asymptotes; see page 284; for slant/oblique and parabolic asymptotes, see pages 285–286. You may want to mention that the restriction that the graph never crosses an asymptote applies only to vertical asymptotes.

Example Notes

In **Example 3**, Figure 4.4-2a, the values for X in the table must be entered manually into the calculator.

Math Background

Under **Continuity**, note that except for breaks where the function is not defined, a rational function graph is a continuous unbroken curve. Students may ask about the graph in Figure 4.4-4b, which is a line with a hole in it. The broad meaning of *curve* in mathematics is a one-dimensional figure obtained by transforming a line or line segment. Applying this broad meaning, a line or line segment itself is a special case of a curve.

The method used in **Example 3**— analyzing the behavior of a function very close to a given value, from both the left and the right of the value—is a method that will be used often in other mathematics courses.

Locating the intercepts can help you determine if you correctly entered the parentheses when graphing a rational function on a graphing calculator.

Example 2 — Intercepts of a Rational Graph

Find the intercepts of $f(x) = \frac{x^2 - x - 2}{x - 1}$.

Solution

The y-intercept is $f(0) = \frac{0^2 - 0 - 2}{0 - 1} = \frac{-2}{-1} = 2$.

The x-intercepts are solutions of $x^2 - x - 2 = 0$ that are not solutions of $x - 1 = 0$. Solutions of $x^2 - x - 2 = 0$ can be found by factoring.

$$x^2 - x - 2 = 0$$
$$(x + 1)(x - 2) = 0$$
$$x = -1 \quad \text{or} \quad x = 2.$$

Neither -1 nor 2 is a solution of $x - 1 = 0$, so both are x-intercepts of the graph of f, as shown in Figure 4.4-1. ∎

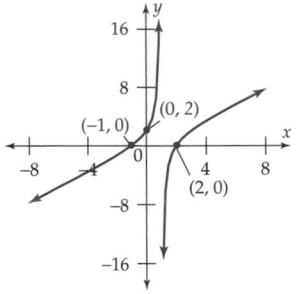

Figure 4.4-1

Continuity

There are breaks in the graph of a rational function wherever the function is not defined, that is, at the zeros of the denominator. Except for breaks, the graph is a continuous unbroken curve. Additionally, the graph has no sharp corners.

Vertical Asymptotes

Unlike polynomial functions, a rational function has breaks in its graph at all points where the function is not defined. Vertical asymptotes occur at every number that is a zero of the denominator but not of the numerator. The key to understanding the behavior of a rational function near these asymptotes is a fact from arithmetic.

The Big-Little Concept

If c is a number far from 0, then $\frac{1}{c}$ is a number close to 0.

If c is close to 0, then $\frac{1}{c}$ is far from 0.

In less precise, but more suggestive terms

$$\frac{1}{big} = little \quad \text{and} \quad \frac{1}{little} = big$$

For example, 5000 is big and $\frac{1}{5000}$ is little. Similarly, $\frac{-1}{1000}$ is little and $\frac{1}{\frac{-1}{1000}} = -1000$ is big. Note that even though -1000 is negative, it is far from zero and therefore is large in absolute value. The role played by the Big-Little Concept when graphing rational functions is illustrated in Example 3.

Example 3   A Rational Function Near a Vertical Asymptote

Without using a calculator, describe the graph of $f(x) = \frac{x + 1}{2x - 4}$ near $x = 2$. Then sketch the graph for values near $x = 2$.

Solution

The function is not defined at $x = 2$ because the denominator is 0 there. When x is greater than 2 but very close to 2,

- The numerator, $x + 1$, is very close to $2 + 1 = 3$.
- The denominator, $2x - 4$, is a positive number very close to $2(2) - 4 = 0$.

By the Big-Little Concept,

$$f(x) = \frac{x + 1}{2x - 4} = \frac{3}{little} = 3 \cdot \frac{1}{little} = 3(big) = very\ big$$

This fact can be confirmed by a table of values for $f(x)$ near $x = 2$ when $x = 2.01, 2.001, 2.0001$, etc., as shown in Figure 4.4-2a. In graphical terms, the points with x-coordinates slightly greater than 2 have very large y-coordinates, so the graph shoots upward just to the right of $x = 2$. That is,

> f increases without bound as x approaches 2 from the right.

A similar analysis when x is less than 2 but very close to 2 shows that the numerator, $x + 1$, is very close to 3 and the denominator is negative and very close to 0. Using the Big-Little Concept, the quotient is a negative number far from 0. As x approaches 2 from values less than 2, the quotient becomes a larger and larger negative number. Therefore, the graph of f shoots downward just to left of $x = 2$. That is,

> f decreases without bound as x approaches 2 from the left.

The portion of the graph of f near $x = 2$ is shown in Figure 4.4–2b. ∎

The dashed vertical line in Figure 4.4-2b is included for easier visualization, but it is *not* part of the graph. Such a line is called a **vertical asymptote** of the graph. The graph approaches a vertical asymptote very closely, but never touches or crosses it because the function is not defined at that value of x.

Figure 4.4-2a

Figure 4.4-2b

Example 2

Find the intercepts of $f(x) = \frac{x^2 - x - 6}{x - 2}$.

y-intercept: 3

x-intercepts: -2 and 3

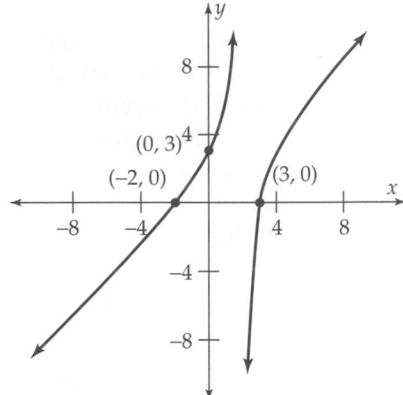

Example 3

Without using a calculator, describe the graph of $f(x) = \frac{x + 2}{3x - 9}$ near $x = 3$. Then sketch the graph for values near $x = 3$.

The function is not defined for $x = 3$ because the denominator is 0 there. f increases without bound as x approaches 3 from the right. f decreases without bound as x approaches 3 from the left.

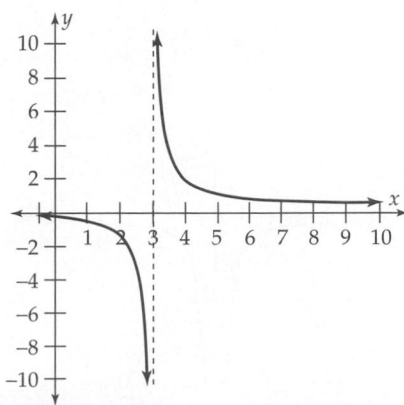

The first sentence on this page says, "All rational functions have vertical asymptotes at values that are zeros of their denominators but not zeros of their numerators." As with all other statements prior to this point, we are considering only the real number system. There *are* rational functions that have zeros of their denominators that are not zeros of their numerator and *do not have* vertical asymptotes at those values. However, such zeros are *imaginary* zeros, which will be addressed in Section 4.5 (Imaginary numbers are in the complex number system.). An example of such a function is $f(x) = \dfrac{1}{x^2 + 1}$, shown below. Its denominator has imaginary zeros $\pm i$. Note that the graph has no vertical asymptotes.

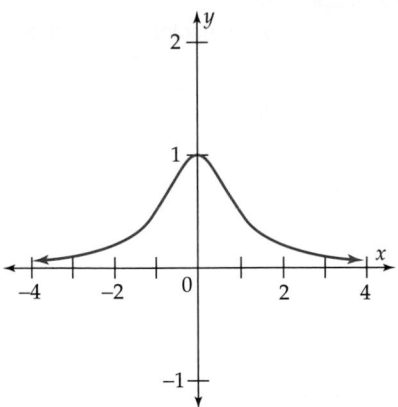

Teaching Notes

You may wish to show students examples of functions that produce the types of vertical asymptotes shown in Figure 4.4-3:

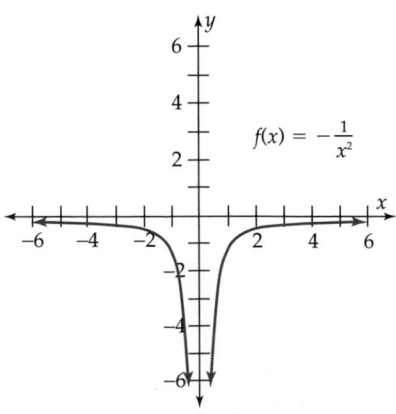

$f(x) = -\dfrac{1}{x^2}$

Vertical Asymptotes

All rational functions have vertical asymptotes at values that are zeros of their denominators but not zeros of their numerators.

> A rational function has a vertical asymptote at $x = c$, provided
> - c is a zero of the denominator
> - c is *not* a zero of the numerator

Near a vertical asymptote, the graph of a rational fraction may look like the graph in Figure 4.4-2b, or like one of the graphs in Figure 4.4-3.

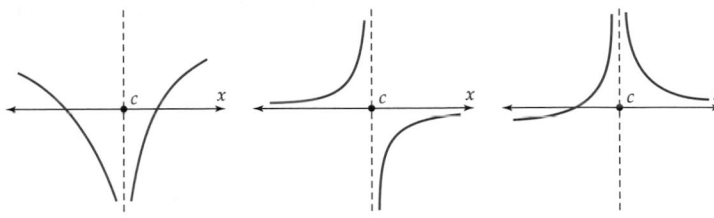

vertical asymptotes at x = c
Figure 4.4-3

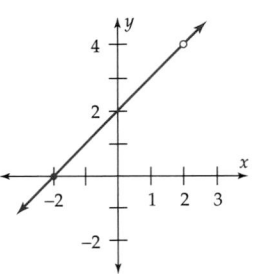

Figure 4.4-4a

Figure 4.4-4b

Holes

When a number c is a zero of both the numerator and denominator of a rational function, the function might have a vertical asymptote at $x = c$, or it might behave differently.

You have often cancelled factors to reduce fractions.

$$\frac{x^2 - 4}{x - 2} = \frac{(x + 2)(x - 2)}{x - 2} = x + 2$$

But the functions

$$p(x) = \frac{x^2 - 4}{x - 2} \quad \text{and} \quad q(x) = x + 2$$

are *not* the same, because when $x = 2$

$$p(2) = \frac{2^2 - 4}{2 - 2} = \frac{0}{0}, \text{ which is not defined, but}$$

$$q(x) = 2 + 2 = 4.$$

For any number other than 2, the two functions have the same values, and hence, the same graphs. The graph of $q(x) = x + 2$ is a straight line that includes the point $(2, 4)$, as shown in Figure 4.4-4a. The graph of $p(x)$ is the same straight line, but with the point $(2, 4)$ omitted. That is, there is a **hole** in the graph of p at $x = 2$ because p is not defined there. The graph of p is shown in Figure 4.4-4b.

$g(x) = -\dfrac{1}{x}$

$h(x) = \dfrac{1}{x^2}$

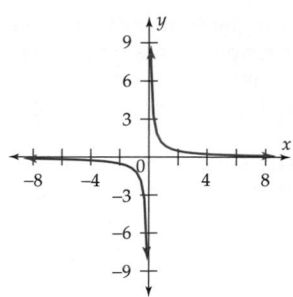

Figure 4.4-5

The graph of $g(x) = \dfrac{x^2}{x^3}$, shown in Figure 4.4-5, is the same as the graph of $f(x) = \dfrac{1}{x}$. At $x = 0$ neither function is defined. There is a vertical asymptote rather than a hole at $x = 0$. Note that the vertical asymptote occurs at $x = 0$, which is a zero of multiplicity 2 in the numerator, but of larger multiplicity 3 in the denominator.

Holes

Let $f(x) = \dfrac{g(x)}{h(x)}$ be a rational function and let d denote a zero of both g and h.

- If the multiplicity of d as a zero of g is greater than or equal to its multiplicity as a zero of h, then the graph of f has a hole at $x = d$.
- Otherwise, the graph has a vertical asymptote at $x = d$.

Accurate Rational Function Graphs

Getting an accurate graph of a rational function on a calculator often depends on choosing an appropriate viewing window. For example, the following are graphs of $f(x) = \dfrac{x+1}{2x-4}$ in different viewing windows.

Figure 4.4-6a

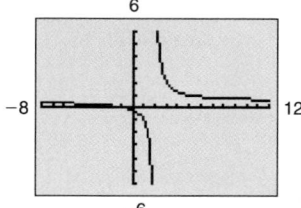

Figure 4.4-6b

The vertical segment shown in Figure 4.4-6a is *not* a vertical asymptote. It is a result of the calculator evaluating f just to the left of $x = 2$ and just to the right of $x = 2$, but not at $x = 2$, and then erroneously connecting these points with a near vertical segment that looks like an asymptote. In the accurate graph shown in Figure 4.4-6b, the calculator attempted to plot a point with $x = 2$ and when it found that $f(2)$ was not defined, skipped a pixel and did not join the points on either side of the one skipped.

Technology Tip

To avoid erroneous vertical lines, use a window with a vertical asymptote in the center of the screen. In Figure 4.4-6b, the asymptote at $x = 2$ is halfway between -8 and 12. See the Technology Appendix for further information.

In the **Technology Tip,** the asymptote $x = 2$ is halfway between -8 and 12 because $\dfrac{-8 + 12}{2} = 2$.

Teaching Notes

Review with students the definition of multiplicity: If $x - r$ is a factor that occurs m times in the complete factorization of a polynomial expression, then r is called a zero with multiplicity m of the related polynomial function (page 265).

You may want to provide students with examples of the different possibilities referred to in the **Holes** box:

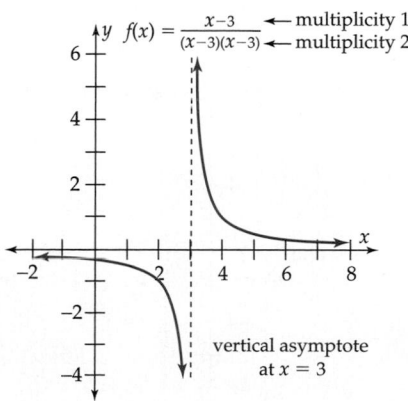

Example Notes

In **Example 4a**, point out to students that the function value is never exactly $-\frac{3}{2}$.

ADDITIONAL EXAMPLES

Example 4

List the vertical asymptotes and describe the end behavior of the following functions. Then sketch each graph.

a. $f(x) = \dfrac{-4x + 8}{2 - 3x}$

vertical asymptote: $x = \frac{2}{3}$; When $|x|$ gets large, the graph of f gets very close to the horizontal asymptote $y = \frac{4}{3}$.

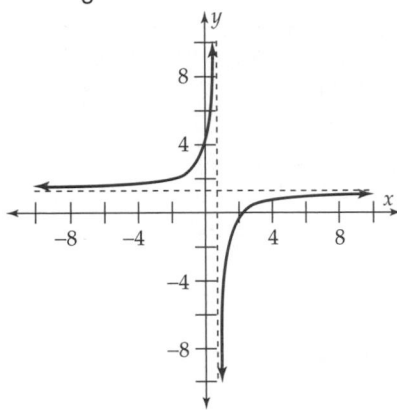

b. $g(x) = \dfrac{x}{x^2 - 9}$

vertical asymptotes: $x = 3$ and $x = -3$; When $|x|$ gets large, the graph of g gets very close to the horizontal asymptote $y = 0$.

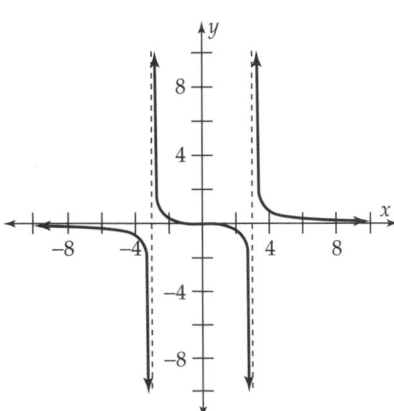

c. $h(x) = \dfrac{3x^3 - x}{x^3 - 1}$

vertical asymptote: $x = 1$; When $|x|$ gets large, the graph of h gets very close to the horizontal asymptote $y = 3$.

A calculator graph may also fail to show holes in graphs that should have them. Even if a window is chosen so that the graph skips a pixel where the hole should be, the hole may be difficult to see.

End Behavior

As with polynomials, the behavior of a rational function when $|x|$ is large is called its **end behavior.** Known facts about the end behavior of polynomial functions make it easy to determine the end behavior of rational functions in which the degree of the numerator is less than or equal to the degree of the denominator.

Example 4   End Behavior of Rational Functions

List the vertical asymptotes and describe the end behavior of the following functions. Then sketch each graph.

a. $f(x) = \dfrac{3x - 6}{5 - 2x}$ **b.** $g(x) = \dfrac{x}{x^2 - 4}$ **c.** $h(x) = \dfrac{2x^3 - x}{x^3 + 1}$

Solution

a. The zero of the denominator of $f(x) = \dfrac{3x - 6}{5 - 2x}$ is $\dfrac{5}{2}$ and it is not a zero of the numerator. So the vertical asymptote occurs at $x = \dfrac{5}{2}$.

When $|x|$ is large, a polynomial function behaves like its highest degree term, as shown in Section 4.3. The highest degree term of the numerator of f is $3x$ and the highest degree term of the denominator is $-2x$. Therefore, when $|x|$ is large, the function reduces to approximately $-\dfrac{3}{2}$.

$$f(x) = \frac{3x - 6}{5 - 2x} = \frac{3x - 6}{-2x + 5} \approx \frac{3x}{-2x} = -\frac{3}{2}$$

Thus, when $|x|$ is large, the graph of f gets very close to the horizontal line $y = -\dfrac{3}{2}$, which is called a **horizontal asymptote** of the graph. The dashed lines in Figure 4.4-7 indicate the vertical and horizontal asymptotes of the graph.

b. The zeros of the denominator of $g(x) = \dfrac{x}{x^2 - 4}$ are ± 2 and neither is a zero of the numerator. So the graph has vertical asymptotes at $x = -2$ and at $x = 2$.

When $|x|$ is large,

$$g(x) = \frac{x}{x^2 - 4} \approx \frac{x}{x^2} = \frac{1}{x}$$

and $\dfrac{1}{x}$ is very close to 0 by the Big-Little Concept. Therefore, the graph of g approaches the horizontal line $y = 0$ (the x-axis) when $|x|$ is large and this line is a horizontal asymptote of the graph, as shown in Figure 4.4-8.

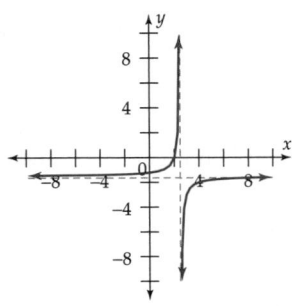

Figure 4.4-7

Technology Tip

When the vertical asymptotes of a rational function occur at numbers such as $-2.1, -2, -1.9, \ldots, 2.9, 3$, etc., a decimal window normally produces an accurate graph because the calculator actually evaluates the function at the asymptotes, finds that it is undefined, and skips a pixel.

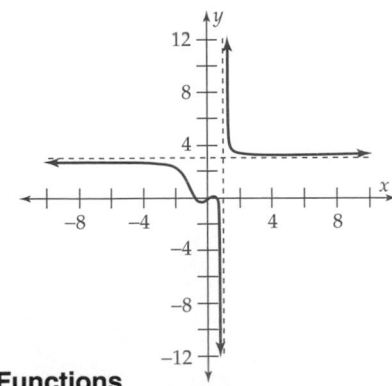

Teaching Notes

Tell students that the **Technology Tip** on page 284 may not apply if they use a built-in decimal window (or ZDecimal) feature for a function whose asymptote does not occur within the resulting window, such as $y = \dfrac{1}{x - 8}$. In such cases, the Technology Tip on page 283 would be better to use. For example, have them graph $y = \dfrac{1}{x - 8}$ using Xmin = 0 and Xmax = 16.

CAUTION

Unlike a vertical asymptote that is never crossed by a graph, a graph may cross a horizontal or oblique asymptote at some values of $|x|$.

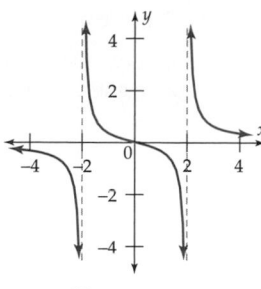

Figure 4.4-8

c. The only real zero of the denominator of $h(x) = \dfrac{2x^3 - x}{x^3 + 1}$ is $x = -1$, which is not a zero of the numerator. So, the graph has a vertical asymptote at $x = -1$.

When $|x|$ is large,

$$h(x) = \frac{2x^3 - x}{x^3 + 1} \approx \frac{2x^3}{x^3} = \frac{2}{1} = 2$$

Therefore, the graph of h has a horizontal asymptote at $y = 2$, as shown in Figure 4.4-9. ∎

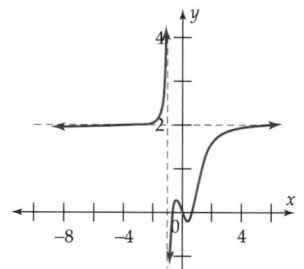

Figure 4.4-9

The function in Example 4b illustrates a useful fact. When the degree of the numerator is less than the degree of the denominator of a rational function, the x-axis is the horizontal asymptote of the graph.

When the numerator and denominator have the same degree, as in Examples 4a and 4c, the horizontal asymptote is determined by the leading coefficients of the numerator and denominator:

Function	Horizontal asymptote
$f(x) = \dfrac{3x - 6}{-2x + 5}$	$y = -\dfrac{3}{2}$
$h(x) = \dfrac{2x^3 - x}{x^3 + 1}$	$y = \dfrac{2}{1} = 2$

ALERT

Based on the way function f is written in **Example 4a,** some students may mistakenly identify the leading coefficients of the numerator and denominator as 3 and 5, respectively. They may say that a horizontal asymptote of $f(x) = \dfrac{3x - 6}{5 - 2x}$ is $y = \dfrac{3}{5}$. Remind students that the leading coefficient in a polynomial is the nonzero coefficient of the *highest power of the variable.* The correct horizontal asymptote is $y = -\dfrac{3}{2}$.

Some students may try to use the leading coefficients of the numerator and denominator to identify horizontal asymptotes when it is not an appropriate method. To illustrate, in **Example 4b,** some students may say that a horizontal asymptote of $g(x) = \dfrac{x}{x^2 - 4}$ is $y = \dfrac{1}{1} = 1$. Emphasize that when the degree of the numerator is less than the degree of the denominator, the x-axis, or $y = 0$, is the horizontal asymptote of the graph. (See **End Behavior of Rational Functions,** page 287.)

Other Asymptotes

When the degree of the numerator of a rational function is greater than the degree of its denominator, the graph will not have a horizontal asymptote. To determine the end behavior in this case, the Division Algorithm must be used.

Example 5 **A Slant Asymptote**

Describe the end behavior of the graph of $f(x) = \dfrac{x^2 - x - 2}{x - 5}$.

Example Notes

In **Example 6**, Figure 4.4-11, it appears that the function graph and the parabolic asymptotes coincide in some places. Students can try different window settings on a graphing calculator, as shown below, to see that the curves do not touch.

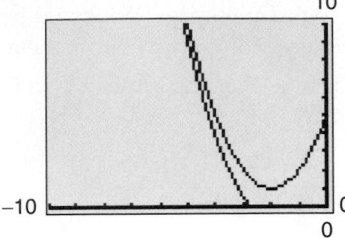

ADDITIONAL EXAMPLES

Example 5

Describe the end behavior of the graph of $f(x) = \dfrac{x^2 - x - 6}{x + 4}$.

$f(x) = \dfrac{x^2 - x - 6}{x + 4} = (x - 5) + \dfrac{14}{x + 4}$

As $|x|$ gets large, the graph of f approaches the slant asymptote $y = x - 5$.

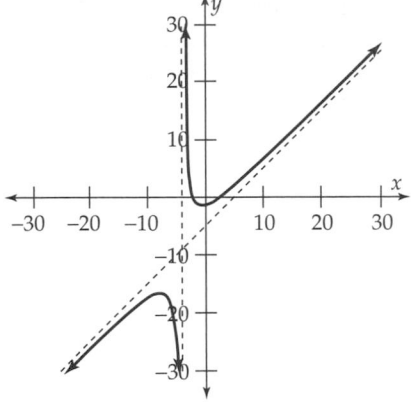

Example 6

Describe the end behavior of
$f(x) = \dfrac{x^3 + x^2 + 3x - 1}{x + 1}$.

$f(x) = \dfrac{x^3 + x^2 + 3x - 1}{x + 1}$

$= (x^2 + 3) - \dfrac{4}{x + 1}$

As $|x|$ gets large, the graph of f approaches the parabolic asymptote $y = x^2 + 3$.

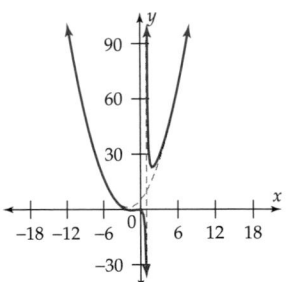

Solution

Use synthetic or long division to divide the denominator into the numerator, and rewrite the rational expression by using the Division Algorithm.

$$Dividend = Divisor \cdot Quotient + Remainder$$
$$x^2 - x - 2 = (x - 5)(x + 4) + 18$$

$$f(x) = \frac{x^2 - x - 2}{x - 5}$$

$$= \frac{(x - 5)(x + 4) + 18}{x - 5}$$

$$= \frac{(x - 5)(x + 4)}{x - 5} + \frac{18}{x - 5}$$

$$= (x + 4) + \frac{18}{x - 5}$$

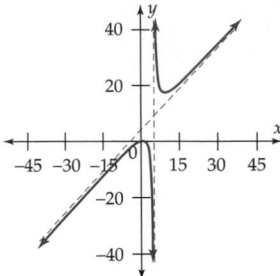

Figure 4.4-10

When $|x|$ is large, $x - 5$ is also large, and by the Big-Little Concept $\dfrac{18}{x - 5}$ is very close to 0. Therefore, $f(x) \approx x + 4$, and the graph of f approaches the line $y = x + 4$ as $|x|$ gets large (see Figure 4.4-10). The line $y = x + 4$ is called a **slant** or **oblique asymptote** of the graph. Note that $x + 4$ is the quotient without the remainder in the division of the numerator by the denominator.

Example 6   A Parabolic Asymptote

Describe the end behavior of the graph of $f(x) = \dfrac{x^3 + 3x^2 + x + 1}{x - 1}$.

Solution

Divide the denominator into the numerator and rewrite the function.

$$Quotient + \frac{Remainder}{Divisor}$$

$$f(x) = \frac{x^3 + 3x^2 + x + 1}{x - 1} = (x^2 + 4x + 5) + \frac{6}{x - 1}$$

When $|x|$ is large, so is $x - 1$ and by the Big-Little Concept $\dfrac{6}{x - 1}$ is very close to 0. Therefore, $f(x) \approx x^2 + 4x + 5$ for large values of $|x|$. The graph of f approaches the parabola $y = x^2 + 4x + 5$, as shown in Figure 4.4-11. The curve $y = x^2 + 4x + 5$ is called a **parabolic asymptote.** Note that $x^2 + 4x + 5$ is the quotient in the division.

Figure 4.4-11

End Behavior of Rational Functions

Let $f(x) = \dfrac{ax^n + \cdots}{cx^k + \cdots}$ be a rational function whose numerator has degree n and whose denominator has degree k.

• If $n < k$, then the x-axis is a horizontal asymptote.

• If $n = k$, then the line $y = \dfrac{a}{c}$ is a horizontal asymptote.

• If $n > k$, then the quotient polynomial when the numerator is divided by the denominator is the asymptote that describes the end behavior of the graph.

Notice that when the degree of the numerator and the denominator are the same, the horizontal asymptote is the horizontal line determined by the quotient of the leading coefficients of the numerator and denominator.

Graphs of Rational Functions

The facts presented in this section can be used in conjunction with a calculator to find accurate, complete graphs of rational functions.

Graphing Rational Functions

1. Analyze the function algebraically to determine its vertical asymptotes, holes, and intercepts.

2. Determine the end behavior of the graph.

   If the degree of the numerator is less than or equal to the degree of the denominator, find the horizontal asymptote by using the facts in the box above.

   Otherwise, divide the numerator by the denominator. The quotient is the nonvertical asymptote of the graph.

3. Use the preceding information to select an appropriate viewing window, or windows, to interpret the calculator's version of the graph, and display a complete graph of the function.

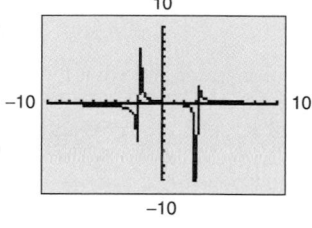

10

−10 ———————— 10

−10

Figure 4.4-12a

Example 7   A Complete Graph of a Rational Function

Find a complete graph of $f(x) = \dfrac{x - 1}{x^2 - x - 6}$.

Solution

The graph of f is shown in Figure 4.4-12a. It is hard to determine whether or not the graph is complete, so analyze the function algebraically.

Teaching Notes

The concepts in the **End Behavior of Rational Functions** box may seem intimidating, but they are really fairly simple. Write the following on the board:

$$f(x) = \frac{\Box x^\Box + \cdots}{\Box x^\Box + \cdots}$$

Now, fill in the boxes with numbers to illustrate each of the bulleted cases with examples such as:

• $f(x) = \dfrac{-7x^2 + \cdots}{2x^3 + \cdots}$

  (x-axis is a horizontal asymptote)

• $f(x) = \dfrac{3x^2 + \cdots}{2x^2 + \cdots}$

  ($y = \frac{3}{2}$ is a horizontal asymptote)

• $f(x) = \dfrac{x^2 - 21}{x + 5} = x - 5 + \dfrac{4}{x + 5}$

  ($y = x - 5$ is an asymptote)

You may want to review the following skills to prepare students for step 1 in the **Graphing Rational Functions** box:

• Factor the numerator and the denominator.

• After the numerator and denominator are factored, determine the domain of the function.

• Find the x- and y-intercepts.

• For excluded domain values, determine whether there are vertical asymptotes or holes.

• Find values of the function near any vertical asymptote, on both sides of the asymptote.

For step 2, determining end behavior, remind students of the 3 types of asymptotes:

• straight line horizontal

• straight line slant

• curved

ADDITIONAL EXAMPLES

Example 7

Find a complete graph of
$$f(x) = \frac{x+2}{x^2+x-12}.$$
calculator graph:

analyze the function algebraically:
$$f(x) = \frac{x+2}{x^2+x-12} = \frac{x+2}{(x+4)(x-3)}$$

Vertical Asymptotes: $x = -4$ and $x = 3$.

Intercepts:

   y-intercept: $f(0) = -\frac{1}{6}$

   x-intercept: $x = -2$

Horizontal Asymptote: $y = 0$

complete graph:

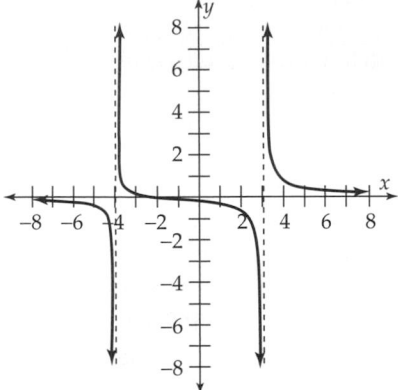

Begin by writing the function in factored form. Then read off the relevant information.

$$f(x) = \frac{x-1}{x^2-x-6} = \frac{x-1}{(x+2)(x-3)}$$

Vertical Asymptotes: $x = -2$ and $x = 3$ *zeros of the denominator but not the numerator*

Intercepts:

   y-intercept: $f(0) = \frac{0-1}{0^2-0-6} = \frac{1}{6}$

   x-intercept: $x = 1$ *zero of numerator but not of denominator*

Horizontal Asymptote: $y = 0$ *degree of numerator is less than degree of denominator*

Interpreting the above information suggests that a complete graph of f looks similar to Figure 4.4-12b.

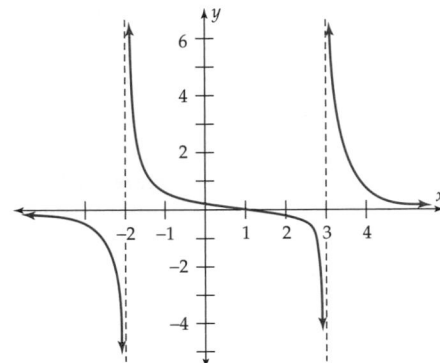

Figure 4.4-12b

Example 8   **A Complete Graph of a Rational Function**

Find a complete graph of $f(x) = \dfrac{x^3 - 2x^2 - 5x + 6}{x^2 + 3x + 2}$.

Solution

The denominator is easily factored. To factor the numerator, note that the only possible rational zeros of $x^3 - 2x^2 - 5x + 6$ are $\pm 1, \pm 2, \pm 3$, and ± 6 by the Rational Zeros Test. Verify that $-2, 1$ and 3 actually are zeros and use the Factor Theorem to write the numerator in factored form. Then reduce the fraction.

Holes:

$$f(x) = \frac{x^3 - 2x^2 - 5x + 6}{x^2 + 3x + 2} = \frac{(x + 2)(x - 1)(x - 3)}{(x + 2)(x + 1)}$$

$$= \frac{(x - 1)(x - 3)}{x + 1}, \text{ where } x \neq -2.$$

Therefore, the graph of f is the same as the graph of

$$g(x) = \frac{(x - 1)(x - 3)}{x + 1} = \frac{x^2 - 4x + 3}{x + 1}$$

except there is a hole when $x = -2$. Because

$$g(-2) = \frac{(-2 - 1)(-2 - 3)}{-2 + 1} = \frac{(-3)(-5)}{-1} = -15,$$

the hole occurs at $(-2, -15)$.

Intercepts:

  y-intercept: $g(0) = \dfrac{(0 - 1)(0 - 3)}{0 + 1} = \dfrac{(-1)(-3)}{1} = 3$

  x-intercepts: The *x*-intercepts of f are the same as the *x*-intercepts of g. Solving $(x - 1)(x - 3) = 0$ yields $x = 1$ or $x = 3$.

Vertical Asymptote: The vertical asymptote is $x = -1$.

End Behavior: Dividing the numerator by the denominator produces a quotient of $x - 5$. Therefore, the slant asymptote that describes the end behavior of the function is the line $y = x - 5$.

The graph of f is shown in Figure 4.4-13.

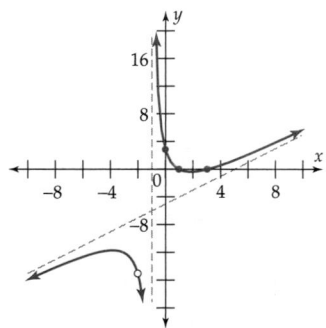

Figure 4.4-13

ADDITIONAL EXAMPLES

Example 8

Find a complete graph of

$$f(x) = \frac{x^3 - x^2 - 10x - 8}{x^2 - 7x + 12}.$$

Possible rational zeros of $x^3 - x^2 - 10x - 8$:

$\pm 1, \pm 2, \pm 4, \pm 8$

Verify that the actual zeros are $-1, -2$ and 4.

$$f(x) = \frac{x^3 - x^2 - 10x - 8}{x^2 - 7x + 12}$$

$$= \frac{(x - 4)(x + 1)(x + 2)}{(x - 4)(x - 3)}$$

$$= \frac{(x + 1)(x + 2)}{(x - 3)}$$

Holes: The graph of f is the same as the graph of $g(x) = \dfrac{(x + 1)(x + 2)}{(x - 3)}$ except there is a hole when $x = 4$. Because $g(4) = 30$, the hole occurs at $(4, 30)$.

Intercepts:

  y-intercept: $g(0) = -\dfrac{2}{3}$

  x-intercepts: $x = -1$ and $x = -2$

Vertical Asymptote: $x = 3$

End Behavior: Dividing the numerator by the denominator produces a quotient of $x + 6$. Therefore, the slant asymptote that describes the end behavior of the function is the line $y = x + 6$.

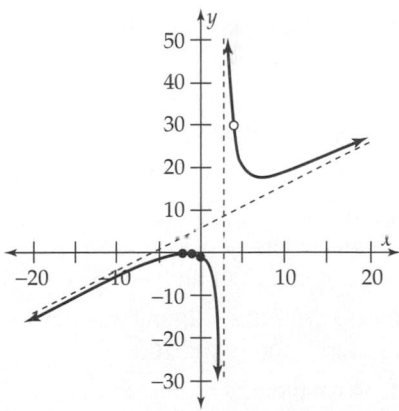

ANSWERS

1. All real numbers except $-\frac{5}{2}$

2. All real numbers except 3 and $-\frac{1}{2}$

3. All real numbers except $3 \pm \sqrt{5}$

4. All real numbers except 0 and $\pm\sqrt{6}$

5. All real numbers except $\pm\sqrt{2}$ and 1

6. All real numbers except $x \approx 1.00948$ and $x \approx -2.76232$

7. Vertical asymptotes $x = -1$ and $x = 6$

8. Vertical asymptotes $x = 0$ and $x = \frac{-7\pm\sqrt{41}}{2}$

9. Hole at $x = 0$; vertical asymptote $x = -1$

10. Hole at $x = 0$; no vertical asymptotes

11. Vertical asymptote at $x = -2$; hole at $x = 2$

12. Hole at $x = 3$; vertical asymptote at $x = -2$

13. $y = 3$; any window with $-115 \leq x \leq 110$

14. $y = \frac{3}{2}$; any window with $-20 \leq x \leq 20$

15. $y = -1$; any window with $-31 \leq x \leq 35$

16. $y = 0$; any window with $-20 \leq x \leq 20$

17. $y = \frac{5}{2}$; any window with $-40 \leq x \leq 42$

18. $y = 16$; window: $-500 \leq x \leq 500$ and $0 \leq y \leq 20$

19. Asymptote: $y = x$; window: $-14 \leq x \leq 14$ and $-15 \leq y \leq 15$

20. $y = x^2 - 2x + 2$; any window with $-100 \leq y \leq 100$

21. Asymptote: $y = x^2 - x$; window: $-15 \leq x \leq 6$ and $-40 \leq y \leq 240$

22. $y = x + 4$; standard viewing window

Exercises 4.4

In Exercises 1–6, find the domain of the function.

1. $f(x) = \dfrac{-3x}{2x + 5}$

2. $g(x) = \dfrac{x^3 + x + 1}{2x^2 - 5x - 3}$

3. $h(x) = \dfrac{6x - 5}{x^2 - 6x + 4}$

4. $g(x) = \dfrac{x^3 - x^2 - x - 1}{x^5 - 36x}$

5. $f(x) = \dfrac{x^5 - 2x^3 + 7}{x^3 - x^2 - 2x + 2}$

6. $h(x) = \dfrac{x^5 - 5}{x^4 + 12x^3 + 60x^2 + 50x - 125}$

In Exercises 7–12, use algebra to determine the location of the vertical asymptotes and holes in the graph of the function.

7. $f(x) = \dfrac{x^2 + 4}{x^2 - 5x - 6}$

8. $g(x) = \dfrac{x - 5}{x^3 + 7x^2 + 2x}$

9. $f(x) = \dfrac{x}{x^3 + 2x^2 + x}$

10. $g(x) = \dfrac{x}{x^3 + 5x}$

11. $f(x) = \dfrac{x^2 - 4x + 4}{(x + 2)(x - 2)^3}$

12. $h(x) = \dfrac{x - 3}{x^2 - x - 6}$

In Exercises 13–22, find the horizontal or other asymptote of the graph of the function when $|x|$ is large, and find a viewing window in which the ends of the graph are within 0.1 of this asymptote.

13. $f(x) = \dfrac{3x - 2}{x + 3}$

14. $g(x) = \dfrac{3x^2 + x}{2x^2 - 2x + 4}$

15. $h(x) = \dfrac{5 - x}{x - 2}$

16. $f(x) = \dfrac{4x^2 - 5}{2x^3 - 3x^2 + x}$

17. $g(x) = \dfrac{5x^3 - 8x^2 + 4}{2x^3 + 2x}$

18. $h(x) = \dfrac{8x^5 - 6x^3 + 2x - 1}{0.5x^5 + x^4 + 3x^2 + x}$

19. $f(x) = \dfrac{x^3 - 1}{x^2 - 4}$

20. $g(x) = \dfrac{x^3 - 4x^2 + 6x + 5}{x - 2}$

21. $h(x) = \dfrac{x^3 + 3x^2 - 4x + 1}{x + 4}$

22. $f(x) = \dfrac{x^3 + 3x^2 - 4x + 1}{x^2 - x}$

In Exercises 23–50, analyze the function algebraically: list its vertical asymptotes, holes, and horizontal asymptote. Then sketch a complete graph of the function.

23. $f(x) = \dfrac{1}{x + 5}$

24. $q(x) = \dfrac{-7}{x - 6}$

25. $k(x) = \dfrac{-3}{2x + 5}$

26. $g(x) = \dfrac{-4}{2 - x}$

27. $f(x) = \dfrac{3x}{x - 1}$

28. $p(x) = \dfrac{x - 2}{x}$

29. $f(x) = \dfrac{2 - x}{x - 3}$

30. $g(x) = \dfrac{3x - 2}{x + 3}$

31. $f(x) = \dfrac{1}{x(x + 1)^2}$

32. $g(x) = \dfrac{x}{2x^2 - 5x - 3}$

33. $f(x) = \dfrac{x - 3}{x^2 + x - 2}$

34. $g(x) = \dfrac{x + 2}{x^2 - 1}$

35. $h(x) = \dfrac{(x^2 + 6x + 5)(x + 5)}{(x + 5)^3(x - 1)}$

36. $f(x) = \dfrac{x^2 - 1}{x^3 - 2x^2 + x}$

37. $f(x) = \dfrac{-4x^2 + 1}{x^2}$

38. $k(x) = \dfrac{x^2 + 1}{x^2 - 1}$

39. $q(x) = \dfrac{x^2 + 2x}{x^2 - 4x - 5}$

40. $F(x) = \dfrac{x^2 + x}{x^2 - 2x + 4}$

41. $p(x) = \dfrac{(x + 3)(x - 3)}{(x - 5)(x + 4)(x + 3)}$

42. $p(x) = \dfrac{x^3 + 3x^2}{x^4 - 4x^2}$

43. $f(x) = \dfrac{x^2 - x - 6}{x - 2}$

44. $k(x) = \dfrac{x^2 + x - 2}{x}$

45. $Q(x) = \dfrac{4x^2 + 4x - 3}{2x - 5}$

46. $K(x) = \dfrac{3x^2 - 12x + 15}{3x + 6}$

47. $f(x) = \dfrac{x^3 - 2}{x - 1}$

48. $p(x) = \dfrac{x^3 + 8}{x + 1}$

49. $q(x) = \dfrac{x^3 - 1}{x - 2}$

50. $f(x) = \dfrac{x^4 - 1}{x^2}$

23.

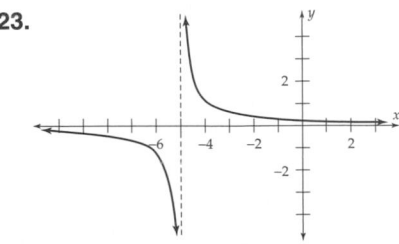

vertical asymptote $x = -5$

horizontal asymptote $y = 0$

24–50. *See* pp. 1063–1066.

In Exercises 51–60, find a viewing window or windows that show(s) a complete graph of the function using asymptotes, intercepts, end behavior, and holes. Be alert for hidden behavior.

51. $f(x) = \dfrac{x^3 + 4x^2 - 5x}{(x^2 - 4)(x^2 - 9)}$

52. $g(x) = \dfrac{x^2 + x - 6}{x^3 - 19x + 30}$ **53.** $h(x) = \dfrac{2x^2 - x - 6}{x^3 + x^2 - 6x}$

54. $f(x) = \dfrac{x^3 - x + 1}{x^4 - 2x^3 - 2x^2 + x - 1}$

55. $f(x) = \dfrac{2x^4 - 3x^2 + 1}{3x^4 - x^2 + x - 1}$ **56.** $g(x) = \dfrac{x^4 + 2x^3}{x^5 - 25x^3}$

57. $h(x) = \dfrac{3x^2 + x - 4}{2x^2 - 5x}$ **58.** $f(x) = \dfrac{2x^2 - 1}{3x^3 + 2x + 1}$

59. $g(x) = \dfrac{x - 4}{2x^3 - 5x^2 - 4x + 12}$

60. $h(x) = \dfrac{x^2 - 9}{x^3 + 2x^2 - 23x - 60}$

In Exercises 61–66, find a viewing window or windows that show(s) a complete graph of the function—if possible, with no erroneous vertical line segments. Be alert for hidden behavior.

61. $f(x) = \dfrac{2x^2 + 5x + 2}{2x + 7}$ **62.** $g(x) = \dfrac{2x^3 + 1}{x^2 - 1}$

63. $h(x) = \dfrac{x^3 - 2x^2 + x - 2}{x^2 - 1}$

64. $f(x) = \dfrac{3x^3 - 11x - 1}{x^2 - 4}$

65. $g(x) = \dfrac{2x^4 + 7x^3 + 7x^2 + 2x}{x^3 - x + 50}$

66. $h(x) = \dfrac{2x^3 + 7x^2 - 4}{x^2 + 2x - 3}$

67. a. Graph $f(x) = \dfrac{1}{x}$ in the viewing window with $-6 \le x \le 6$ and $-6 \le y \le 6$.
   b. Without using a calculator, describe how the graph of $g(x) = \dfrac{2}{x}$ can be obtained from the graph of $f(x)$. *Hint:* $g(x) = 2f(x)$
   c. Without using a calculator, describe how the graphs of each of the following functions can be obtained from the graph of $f(x)$.

$$h(x) = \frac{1}{x} + 4 \quad k(x) = \frac{1}{x - 3} \quad t(x) = \frac{1}{x + 2}$$

   d. Without using a calculator, describe how the graph of $p(x) = \dfrac{2}{x - 3} + 4$ can be obtained from the graph of $f(x) = \dfrac{1}{x}$.
   e. Show that the function $p(x)$ of part **d** is a rational function by rewriting its rule as the quotient of two first-degree polynomials.
   f. If r, s, and t are constants, describe how the graph of $q(x) = \dfrac{r}{x + s} + t$ can be obtained from the graph of $f(x) = \dfrac{1}{x}$.
   g. Show that the function $q(x)$ of part **f** is a rational function by rewriting its rule as the quotient of two first-degree polynomials.

68. The graph of $f(x) = \dfrac{2x^3 - 2x^2 - x + 1}{3x^3 - 3x^2 + 2x - 1}$ has a vertical asymptote. Find a viewing window that demonstrates this fact.

69. a. Find the difference quotient of $f(x) = \dfrac{1}{x}$ and express it as a single fraction in lowest terms.
   b. Use the difference quotient in part **a** to determine the average rate of change of $f(x)$ as x changes from 2 to 2.1, from 2 to 2.01, and from 2 to 2.001. Estimate the instantaneous rate of change of $f(x)$ at $x = 2$.
   c. Use the different quotient in part **a** to determine the average rate of change of $f(x)$ as x changes from 3 to 3.1, from 3 to 3.01, and from 3 to 3.001. Estimate the instantaneous rate of change of $f(x)$ at $x = 3$.
   d. How are the estimated instantaneous rates of change of $f(x)$ at $x = 2$ and $x = 3$ related to the values of $g(x) = \dfrac{-1}{x^2}$ at $x = 2$ and $x = 3$?

70. Do Exercise 69 for the functions $f(x) = \dfrac{1}{x^2}$ and $g(x) = \dfrac{-2}{x^3}$.

71. a. When $x \ge 0$, what rational function has the same graph as $f(x) = \dfrac{x - 1}{|x| - 2}$? *Hint:* Use the definition of absolute value.
   b. When $x < 0$, what rational function has the same graph as $f(x) = \dfrac{x - 1}{|x| - 2}$? See the hint for part **a**.

51. Overall: $-5 \le x \le 4.4$ and $-8 \le y \le 4$; hidden area near origin: $-2 \le x \le 2$ and $-0.5 \le y \le 0.5$; hidden area near $x = -5$: $-15 \le x \le -3$ and $-0.07 \le y \le 0.02$

52. $-8 \le x \le 8$ and $-5 \le y \le 5$

53. $-9.4 \le x < 9.4$ and $-4 \le y \le 4$; there is a hole at $x = 2$.

54. $-5 \le x \le 8$ and $-3 \le y \le 2$

55. Overall: $-4.7 \le x \le 4.7$ and $-2 \le y \le 2$; there is a hole at $x = -1$; to see the vertical asymptote, use $0.65 \le x \le 0.75$ and $-3 \le y \le 3$.

56. $-12 \le x \le 12$ and $-4 \le y \le 4$ there is a hole at $x = 0$

57. For vertical asymptotes and x-intercepts: $-4.7 \le x \le 4.7$ and $-8 \le y \le 8$; to see graph get close to the horizontal asymptote: $-40 \le x \le 35$ and $-2 \le y \le 3$

58. $-5 \le x \le 5$ and $-5 \le y \le 5$

59. Overall: $-4.7 \le x \le 4.7$ and $-2 \le y \le 2$; hidden area near $x = 4$: $3 \le x \le 15$ and $-0.02 \le y \le 0.01$

60. $-8 \le x \le 8$ and $-8 \le y \le 8$; there is a hole at $x = -3$

61. $-15.5 \le x \le 8.5$ and $-16 \le y \le 8$

62. $-5 \le x \le 5$ and $-7 \le y \le 7$

63. $-4.7 \le x \le 4.7$ and $-12 \le y \le 8$

64. $-4 \le x \le 4$ and $-12 \le y \le 12$

65. Overall: $-13 \le x \le 7$ and $-20 \le y \le 20$; hidden area near the origin: $-2.5 \le x \le 1$ and $-0.02 \le y \le 0.02$

66. $-6 \le x \le 6$ and $-12 \le y \le 12$

67–71. *See p.* **1066.**

Left column (answers)

72. a. about 26%

b.

c. The horizontal asymptote is $c = 0$. The amount of the drug in the bloodstream gets vanishingly small.

d. There is about 55.9% in the blood at time 1.12.

73. a. $C(x) = \frac{3}{100}(2x^2) + \frac{1.25}{100}\left(4x \cdot \frac{1000}{x^2}\right)$

$= 0.06x^2 + \frac{50}{x}$

b. $x \approx 16.85$ in.

74. a. $C(x) = \frac{2800 + 3.5x^2}{x}$

b. speeds of about 13.91 and 57.52 miles per hour

c. about 28.28 miles per hour

75. a. $c(x) = \frac{20 + x}{50 + x}$

b. between 25 gallons and 100 gallons

c. $x = 50$ gallons

76. a. $P(x) = \frac{500 + x^2}{x}$

b. between 10 and 50 meters

77. a. $a(x) = \frac{c(x)}{x} = \frac{40,000 + 2.60x}{x}$

b.

c. $y = 2.60$; the average cost can never be below \$2.60.

78. a. $h_1 = h - 2$

b. $h_1 = \frac{150}{\pi r^2} - 2$

c. $V = \pi(r - 1)^2\left(\frac{150}{\pi r^2} - 2\right)$

d. r must be more than 1 since the walls are 1 foot thick.

---

c. Use parts **a** and **b** to explain why the graph of $f(x) = \frac{x - 1}{|x| - 2}$ has two vertical asymptotes. What are they? Confirm your answer by graphing the function.

72. The percentage c of a drug in a person's bloodstream t hours after its injection is approximated by $c(t) = \frac{5t}{4t^2 + 5}$.

a. Approximately what percentage of the drug is in the person's bloodstream after four and a half hours?

b. Graph the function c in an appropriate window for this situation.

c. What is the horizontal asymptote of the graph? What does it tell you about the amount of the drug in the bloodstream?

d. At what time is the percentage the highest? What is the percentage at that time?

73. A box with a square base and a volume of 1000 cubic inches is to be constructed. The material for the top and bottom of the box costs \$3 per 100 square inches and the material for the sides costs \$1.25 per 100 square inches.

a. If x is the length of a side of the base, express the cost of constructing the box as a function of x.

b. If the side of the base must be at least 6 inches long, for what value of x will the cost of the box be \$20?

74. A truck traveling at a constant speed on a reasonably straight, level road burns fuel at the rate of $g(x)$ gallons per mile, where x is the speed of the truck in miles per hour and $g(x)$ is given by $g(x) = \frac{800 + x^2}{200x}$.

a. If fuel costs \$1.40 per gallon, find the rule of the cost function $c(x)$ that expresses the cost of fuel for a 500-mile trip as a function of the speed. *Hint:* $500 \cdot g(x)$ gallons of fuel are needed to go 500 miles. (Why?)

b. What driving speed will make the cost of fuel for the trip \$250?

c. What driving speed will minimize the cost of fuel for the trip?

75. Pure alcohol is being added to 50 gallons of a coolant mixture that is 40% alcohol.

a. Find the rule of the concentration function $c(x)$ that expresses the percentage of alcohol in the resulting mixture as a function of the number x of gallons of pure alcohol that are added. *Hint:* The final mixture contains $50 + x$ gallons.

(Why?) So $c(x)$ is the amount of alcohol in the final mixture divided by the total amount $50 + x$. How much alcohol is in the original 50-gallon mixture? How much is in the final mixture?

b. How many gallons of pure alcohol should be added to produce a mixture that is at least 60% alcohol and no more than 80% alcohol?

c. Determine algebraically the exact amount of pure alcohol that must be added to produce a mixture that is 70% alcohol.

76. A rectangular garden with an area of 250 square meters is to be located next to a building and fenced on three sides, with the building acting as a fence on the fourth side.

a. If the side of the garden parallel to the building has length x meters, express the amount of fencing needed as a function of x.

b. For what values of x will less than 60 meters of fencing be needed?

77. A certain company has fixed costs of \$40,000 and variable costs of \$2.60 per unit.

a. Let x be the number of units produced. Find the rule of the average cost function. (The average cost is the cost of the units divided by the number of units.)

b. Graph the average cost function in a window with $0 \le x \le 100,000$ and $0 \le y \le 20$.

c. Find the horizontal asymptote of the average cost function. Explain what the asymptote means in this situation, that is, how low can the average cost possibly be?

78. Radioactive waste is stored in a cylindrical tank, whose exterior has radius r and height h as shown in the figure. The sides, top, and bottom of the tank are one foot thick and the tank has a volume of 150 cubic feet including top, bottom, and walls.

a. Express the interior height h_1 (that is, the height of the storage area) as a function of h.

b. Express the interior height as a function of r.

c. Express the volume of the interior as a function of r.

d. Explain why r must be greater than 1.

---

79. The relationship between the fixed focal length F of a camera, the distance u from the object being photographed to the lens, and the distance v from the lens to the film is given by $\frac{1}{F} = \frac{1}{u} + \frac{1}{v}$.

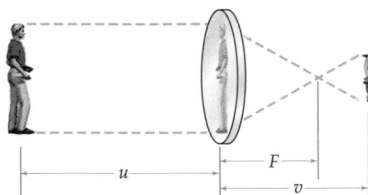

a. If the focal length is 50 mm, express v as a function of u.

b. What is the horizontal asymptote of the graph of the function in part **a**?

c. Graph the function in part **a** when 50 mm $< u <$ 35,000 mm.

80. a. ≈**9.801 meters per second per second**

d. When you focus the camera on an object, the distance between the lens and the film is changed. If the distance from the lens to the camera changes by less than 0.1 millimeter, the object will remain in focus. Explain why you have more latitude in focusing on distant objects than on very close ones.

80. The formula for the gravitational acceleration in units of meters per second squared of an object relative to the earth is

$$g(r) = \frac{3.987 \times 10^{14}}{(6.378 \times 10^6 + r)^2}$$

where r is the distance in meters above the earth's surface.

a. What is the gravitational acceleration at the earth's surface?

b. Graph the function $g(r)$ for $r \geq 0$.

c. Can you ever escape the pull of gravity? Does the graph have any r-intercepts?

b.

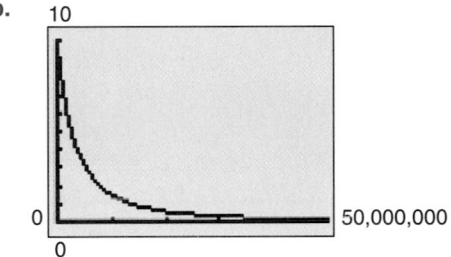

c. no; no

4.5 Complex Numbers

Objectives

* Write complex numbers in standard form

* Perform arithmetic operations on complex numbers

* Find the conjugate of a complex number

* Simplify square roots of negative numbers

* Find all solutions of polynomial equations

If restricted to nonnegative numbers, you cannot solve the equation $x + 5 = 0$. Enlarging the number system to include negative integers makes it possible to find the solution to this equation. By enlarging the number system to include rational numbers, it is possible to solve equations that have no integer solution, such as $3x = 7$. Similarly, the equation $x^2 = 2$ has no rational solution, but $x = \sqrt{2}$ and $x = -\sqrt{2}$ are real number solutions. The idea of enlarging a number system to include solutions to equations that cannot be solved in a particular number system is a natural one.

Complex Numbers

Equations such as $x^2 = -1$ and $x^2 = -4$ have no solutions in the real number system because $\sqrt{-1}$ and $\sqrt{-4}$ are not real numbers. In order to solve such equations, that is, to find the square roots of negative numbers, the number system must be enlarged again. There is a number system, called the **complex number system,** with the desired properties.

---

79. a. $v = \dfrac{50u}{u - 50}$

b. $v = 50$

c. 100

d. If the object is close, a small change in u leads to a large change in v. However, when u is large, a small change in u leads to nearly no change in v, so that u may change substantially while the object stays in focus.

Section

4.5 Complex Numbers

Teaching Notes

Point out that when you build a new number system from a smaller one, the new one should contain the smaller one. In particular, all natural numbers are integers, all integers are rational numbers, all rational numbers are real numbers, and, in the present setting, all real numbers are complex numbers.

You may want to review (from Section 2.2):

* The solutions of a quadratic equation $ax^2 + bx + c = 0$ are

$$x = \frac{-b \pm \sqrt{b^2 - 4ac}}{2a}.$$

* If $b^2 - 4ac < 0$, then $\sqrt{b^2 - 4ac}$ is not a real number, and the equation has no real solutions.

In this section, students will learn that when $b^2 - 4ac < 0$, there are solutions of $ax^2 + bx + c = 0$ that are complex numbers.

Teaching Notes

Make the following points about the **Properties of the Complex Number System:**

For property 1, every real number is a complex number because any real number a can be written $a + 0i$.

For property 2, review the following exponent laws:

$(ab)^m = a^m b^m$ [used in the Solution for **Example 3a:** $(2i)^2 = 2^2 i^2 = 4i^2$]

$a^m \cdot a^n = a^{m+n}$ [used in the margin **NOTE** on page 296: $i^{54} = i^{52+2} = i^{54} \cdot i^2$]

For property 3, the number i is *defined* to satisfy $i^2 = -1$. Students may ask *why* this is true. Point out that a motivation for developing the complex number system was to solve equations such as $x^2 = -1$. Defining this number allowed mathematicians to give a name to solutions of such equations.

For property 4, mention that a is often referred to as the *real part* and b is often referred to as the *imaginary part*.

Property 5 is used to solve **Example 1.**

Example Notes

In **Example 2b,** remind students to distribute the negative:
$-(8 - 6i) = -8 + 6i$. In **2c,** point out that $4i\left(\frac{1}{2}i\right) = 4 \cdot \frac{1}{2} \cdot i \cdot i = 2i^2$. In **2d,** review how to multiply binomials.

Example 3 contains two special cases of binomial multiplication. For **3a,** the special product $(a + b)(a - b) = a^2 - b^2$ is used:
$(3 + 2i)(3 - 2i) = 3^2 - (2i)^2 = 9 - 4i^2$.

For **3b,** the special product $(a + b)^2 = a^2 + 2ab + b^2$ is used:
$(4 + i)^2 = 4^2 + 2 \cdot 4 \cdot i + i^2$
$= 16 + 8i + i^2$.

Properties of the Complex Number System

1. The complex number system contains all real numbers.
2. Addition, subtraction, multiplication, and division of complex numbers obey the same rules of arithmetic that hold in the real number system, with one exception:

   the exponent laws hold for *integer* exponents, but not necessarily for fractional ones (see p. 297).

3. The complex number system contains a number, denoted i, such that

$$i^2 = -1.$$

4. Every complex number can be written in the *standard form*

$$a + bi,$$

   where a and b are real numbers.
5. $a + bi = c + di$ if and only if $a = c$ and $b = d$.

Numbers of the form bi, where b is a real number, are called **imaginary numbers.** Sums of real and imaginary numbers, numbers of the form $a + bi$, are called **complex numbers.** For example,

$$5 + 2i \qquad 7 - 4i \qquad 18 + \frac{3}{2}i \qquad 3 - 12i$$

are all complex numbers.

Just as every integer is a rational number because it can be written as a fraction with denominator of 1, every real number a is a complex number because it can be written as $a + 0i$. Similarly, every imaginary number bi is a complex number because it can be written as $0 + bi$.

NOTE The mathematicians who invented the complex numbers in the seventeenth century were very uneasy about a number i such that $i^2 = -1$. Consequently, they called numbers of the form bi, where b is a real number and $i = \sqrt{-1}$, imaginary numbers.

The existence of imaginary numbers is as *real* as any of the familiar numbers that are called real numbers, such as 3, $\frac{2}{3}$ or $-\sqrt{2}$.

Example 1   **Equating Two Complex Numbers**

Find x and y if $2x - 3i = -6 + 4yi$.

Solution

Property 5 of the Complex Number System states that two complex numbers $a + bi$ and $c + di$ are equal exactly when $a = c$ and $b = d$. So,

$$2x = -6 \qquad \text{and} \qquad -3 = 4y$$
$$x = -3 \qquad\qquad\qquad y = -\frac{3}{4}$$

Direct substitution verifies the solution.

$$2(-3) - 3i = -6 + 4\left(-\frac{3}{4}\right)i$$
$$-6 - 3i = -6 - 3i$$

NOTE Hereafter, in the complex numbers $a + bi$ and $c + di$, it is assumed that a, b, c, and d are real numbers.

Unless directed otherwise, express answers in the standard form $a + bi$.

Arithmetic of Complex Numbers

Because the usual laws of arithmetic hold, it is easy to add, subtract, and multiply complex numbers. As the following examples demonstrate,

all symbols can be treated as if they were real numbers,
provided that i^2 is replaced by -1.

Example 2   Adding, Subtracting, and Multiplying Complex Numbers

Perform the indicated operation and write the result in the form $a + bi$.

a. $(1 + i) + (3 - 7i)$

b. $(4 + 3i) - (8 - 6i)$

c. $4i\left(2 + \dfrac{1}{2}i\right)$

d. $(2 + i)(3 - 4i)$

Solution

a. $(1 + i) + (3 - 7i) = 1 + i + 3 - 7i = (1 + 3) + (1 - 7)i = 4 - 6i$

b. $(4 + 3i) - (8 - 6i) = 4 + 3i - 8 + 6i = (4 - 8) + (3 + 6)i = -4 + 9i$

c. $4i\left(2 + \dfrac{1}{2}i\right) = 4i(2) + 4i\left(\dfrac{1}{2}i\right) = 8i + 2i^2 = 8i + 2(-1) = -2 + 8i$

d. $(2 + i)(3 - 4i) = 2(3 - 4i) + i(3 - 4i) = 6 - 8i + 3i - 4i^2$
$= 6 - 5i - 4(-1) = 6 + 4 - 5i = 10 - 5i$ ∎

The familiar multiplication patterns and exponent laws for integer exponents hold in the complex number system.

Example 3   Products and Powers of Complex Numbers

Perform the indicated operation and write the result in the form $a + bi$.

a. $(3 + 2i)(3 - 2i)$

b. $(4 + i)^2$

Solution

a. $(3 + 2i)(3 - 2i) = 3^2 - (2i)^2 = 9 - 4i^2 = 9 - 4(-1) = 9 + 4 = 13$

b. $(4 + i)^2 = 4^2 + 2(4)(i) + i^2 = 16 + 8i + i^2 = 16 + 8i - 1 = 15 + 8i$ ∎

Powers of i

Observe that

$$i^1 = i$$
$$i^2 = -1 \qquad \textit{Definition of } i$$
$$i^3 = i^2 \cdot i = -1 \cdot i = -i$$
$$i^4 = i^2 \cdot i^2 = (-1)(-1) = 1$$
$$i^5 = i^4 \cdot i = 1 \cdot i = i$$

Example 1

Find x and y if $-4x + 5i = 8 - 6yi$.

$x = -2$ and $y = -\dfrac{5}{6}$

Example 2

Perform the indicated operation and write the result in the form $a + bi$.

a. $(2 - 3i) + (1 + i)$ $3 - 2i$

b. $(2 + 3i) - (4 - 2i)$ $-2 + 5i$

c. $10i\left(5 + \dfrac{1}{5}i\right)$ $-2 + 50i$

d. $(3 + i)(2 - 5i)$ $11 - 13i$

Example 3

Perform the indicated operation and write the result in the form $a + bi$.

a. $(4 + 5i)(4 - 5i)$ 41

b. $(3 + i)^2$ $8 + 6i$

COMMON ERROR ALERT

When asked to identify the values of a and b for a complex number in standard form $a + bi$, students often neglect variable parts or the signs of the values. In **Example 1** on page 294, some students might look at $2x - 3i$ and think $a = 2$ or $b = 3$. Rewriting $2x - 3i$ as $(2x) + (-3)i$ may help students clearly see that $a = 2x$ and $b = -3$.

In **Example 3b,** students may incorrectly distribute the exponent. Point out that $(4 + i)^2 \neq 4^2 + i^2$. Remind them that
$(4 + i)^2 = (4 + i)(4 + i)$.

Teaching Notes

When teaching the **Powers of i**, it may be helpful to continue the pattern started on page 296 to verify the cycle.

$i^5 = i^4 \cdot i = 1 \cdot i = i$

$i^6 = i^4 \cdot i^2 = 1 \cdot i^2 = i^2 = -1$

$i^7 = i^4 \cdot i^3 = 1 \cdot i^3 = i^3 = -i$

$i^8 = i^4 \cdot i^4 = 1 \cdot 1 = 1$

$i^9 = i^8 \cdot i = 1 \cdot i = i$

Emphasize the fact that the strategy involved in simplifying higher powers of i makes use of previously computed powers of i, particularly i, i^2, i^3, and i^4.

To introduce **Square Roots of Negative Numbers** remind students that $\sqrt{9} = 3$ because $(3)^2 = 9$. Extend this idea to complex numbers:
$\sqrt{-9} = i\sqrt{9}$ because $(i\sqrt{9})^2$
$= i^2(\sqrt{9})^2 = -1 \cdot 9 = -9$.
So, for any positive real number b, we make the definition: $\sqrt{-b} = i\sqrt{b}$ because $(i\sqrt{b})^2 = i^2(\sqrt{b})^2$
$$= -1 \cdot b = -b.$$

 Math Background

Writing any integer power of i as i, i^2, i^3, or i^4 makes use of the standard division algorithm. That is, when any positive integer is divided by 4, the remainder can only be 0, 1, 2, or 3. The margin **NOTE**, $i^{54} = i^{52} \cdot i^2 = i^{4 \cdot 13} \cdot i^2$, can be generalized as follows:
$i^m = i^{4n} \cdot i^p$, where m, n, and p are nonnegative integers, and p is the remainder when m is divided by 4.

Students will learn in Section 10.3 that a complex number $a + bi$ can be written in polar form as $r(\cos\theta + i\sin\theta)$.

The powers of i form a cycle. Any power of i must be one of four values: i, -1, $-i$, or 1. To find higher powers of i, such as i^n, divide n by 4 and match the *remainder* to one of the powers listed above.

Example 4   Powers of i

Find i^{54}.

Solution

The remainder when 54 is divided by 4 is 2, so $i^{54} = i^2 = -1$. ∎

NOTE The result of Example 4 can also be seen by rewriting i^{54} using exponent rules.

$i^{54} = i^{52} \cdot i^2$

$= i^{4 \cdot 13} i^2$

$= (i^4)^{13} i^2$

$= 1^{13}(-1)$

$= -1.$

Complex Conjugates

The **conjugate** of the complex number $a + bi$ is the number $a - bi$, and the conjugate of $a - bi$ is $a + bi$. For example, the conjugate of $3 + 4i$ is $3 - 4i$, and the conjugate of $-3i = 0 - 3i$ is $0 + 3i = 3i$. The numbers $3 + 4i$ and $3 - 4i$ are called **conjugate pairs**. Because $a + 0i = a - 0i$ for each real number a, *every real number is its own conjugate*.

The product of conjugate pairs is a real number, as shown below.

Let $a + bi$ be a complex number. Then the product of $a + bi$ and its conjugate $a - bi$ is

$$(a + bi)(a - bi) = a^2 - (bi)^2 = a^2 - b^2 i^2 = a^2 - b^2(-1) = a^2 + b^2$$

Because a^2 and b^2 are nonnegative real numbers, so is $a^2 + b^2$.

Quotients of Complex Numbers

The procedure used to find the quotient of two complex numbers uses the fact that the product of conjugate pairs is a real number.

Example 5   Quotients of Two Complex Numbers

Express the quotient $\dfrac{3 + 4i}{1 + 2i}$ in standard form.

Solution

To find the quotient $\dfrac{3 + 4i}{1 + 2i}$, multiply both the numerator and denominator by the *conjugate* of the denominator, $1 - 2i$.

$$\frac{3 + 4i}{1 + 2i} = \frac{3 + 4i}{1 + 2i} \cdot \frac{1 - 2i}{1 - 2i}$$

$$= \frac{(3 + 4i)(1 - 2i)}{(1 + 2i)(1 - 2i)} = \frac{3(1 - 2i) + 4i(1 - 2i)}{1^2 - (2i)^2} = \frac{3 - 6i + 4i - 8i^2}{1 - 4i^2}$$

$$= \frac{3 - 6i + 4i - 8(-1)}{1 - 4(-1)} = \frac{3 + 8 - 6i + 4i}{1 + 4} = \frac{11 - 2i}{5} = \frac{11}{5} - \frac{2}{5}i$$ ∎

Square Roots of Negative Numbers

Because $i^2 = -1$, $\sqrt{-1}$ is defined to be i. Similarly, because

$$(5i)^2 = 5^2 i^2 = 25(-1) = -25,$$

$\sqrt{-25}$ is defined to be $5i$. In general,

*Square Roots
of Negative
Numbers*

Let b be a positive real number.

$$\sqrt{-b} \text{ is defined to be } i\sqrt{b}$$

because $(i\sqrt{b})^2 = i^2(\sqrt{b})^2 = -1 \cdot b = -b$

Example 6   **Square Roots of Negative Numbers**

Write each of the following as a complex number.

a. $\sqrt{-3}$ **b.** $\dfrac{1 - \sqrt{-7}}{3}$ **c.** $(7 - \sqrt{-4})(5 + \sqrt{-9})$

Solution

a. $\sqrt{-3} = i\sqrt{3}$ by definition

b. $\dfrac{1 - \sqrt{-7}}{3} = \dfrac{1 - i\sqrt{7}}{3} = \dfrac{1}{3} - \dfrac{\sqrt{7}}{3}i$

c. $(7 - \sqrt{-4})(5 + \sqrt{-9}) = (7 - i\sqrt{4})(5 + i\sqrt{9})$

$$= (7 - 2i)(5 + 3i)$$

$$= 35 + 21i - 10i - 6i^2$$

$$= 35 + 11i - 6(-1)$$

$$= 41 + 11i$$

*Technology
Tip*

Most calculators that do complex number arithmetic will return a complex number when asked for the square root of a negative number. Make sure the MODE is set to "rectangular" or "$a + bi$."

CAUTION

The property $\sqrt{cd} = \sqrt{c} \cdot \sqrt{d}$—or equivalently in exponential notation $(cd)^{\frac{1}{2}} = c^{\frac{1}{2}} d^{\frac{1}{2}}$—which is valid for positive real numbers, *does not hold* when both c and d are negative. To avoid difficulty,

**always write square roots of negative numbers in terms of i
before doing any simplification.**

For example,

$$\sqrt{-20} \cdot \sqrt{-5} = i\sqrt{20} \cdot i\sqrt{5} = i^2\sqrt{20 \cdot 5} = -\sqrt{100} = -10.$$

Therefore, $\sqrt{-20} \cdot \sqrt{-5} = -\sqrt{20 \cdot 5}$.

NOTE When i is multiplied by a radical, it is customary to write $i\sqrt{b}$ instead of $\sqrt{b}\,i$ to make clear that i is *not* under the radical.

Teaching Notes

Make sure that students understand the statement, **Every quadratic equation with real coefficients has solutions in the complex number system.** It does *not* mean that every quadratic equation has imaginary solutions. Remind students that the set of real numbers is a subset of the set of complex numbers. If both solutions are real (of the form $a + 0i$), they are also complex.

Example Notes

In **Example 8**, review the formula for factoring the difference of two cubes: $a^3 - b^3 = (a - b)(a^2 + ab + b^2)$.

```
   COMMON ERROR
///   ALERT   \\\
```

In **Example 8**, students will be tempted to solve this equation by taking the cube root of both sides to get $x = 1$. However, this method overlooks two complex solutions. Emphasize that students *must* rewrite the equation to get zero on one side, and then solve it by factoring.

Teaching Notes

Students can check the solutions for **Example 7**. The check for $-\frac{1}{4} + \frac{\sqrt{23}}{4}i$ is shown:

$$2\left(-\frac{1}{4} + \frac{\sqrt{23}}{4}i\right)^2 + \left(-\frac{1}{4} + \frac{\sqrt{23}}{4}i\right) + 3$$

$$= 2\left[\frac{1}{16} - \frac{\sqrt{23}}{8}i - \frac{23}{16}\right] + \left(-\frac{1}{4} + \frac{\sqrt{23}}{4}i\right) + 3$$

$$= 2\left[-\frac{22}{16} - \frac{\sqrt{23}}{8}i\right] + \left(-\frac{1}{4} + \frac{\sqrt{23}}{4}i\right) + 3$$

$$= -\frac{11}{4} - \frac{\sqrt{23}}{4}i - \frac{1}{4} + \frac{\sqrt{23}}{4}i + 3 = 0$$

ADDITIONAL EXAMPLES

Example 7

Find all solutions to
$3x^2 - 5x + 13 = 0$.

$x = \frac{5}{6} \pm \frac{\sqrt{131}}{6}i$

Example 8

Find all solutions of $x^3 = 64$.

$x = 4$, $x = -2 + 2i\sqrt{3}$,
$x = -2 - 2i\sqrt{3}$

Because every negative real number has two square roots in the complex number system, complex solutions can be found for equations that have no real solutions. For example, the solutions of $x^2 = -25$ are

$$x = \pm\sqrt{-25} = \pm 5i$$

Every quadratic equation with real coefficients has solutions in the complex number system.

Example 7   Complex Solutions to a Quadratic Equation

Find all solutions to $2x^2 + x + 3 = 0$.

Solution

Apply the quadratic formula.

$$x = \frac{-1 \pm \sqrt{1^2 - 4 \cdot 2 \cdot 3}}{2 \cdot 2} = \frac{-1 \pm \sqrt{-23}}{4}$$

Because $\sqrt{-23}$ is not a real number, this equation has no real number solutions. However, $\sqrt{-23}$ *is* an imaginary number, namely, $\sqrt{-23} = i\sqrt{23}$. Thus, the equation has solutions in the complex number system.

$$x = \frac{-1 \pm \sqrt{-23}}{4} = \frac{-1 \pm i\sqrt{23}}{4} = -\frac{1}{4} \pm \frac{\sqrt{23}}{4}i$$

Note that the two solutions, $-\frac{1}{4} + \frac{\sqrt{23}}{4}i$ and $-\frac{1}{4} - \frac{\sqrt{23}}{4}i$, are complex conjugates. ■

Example 8   Zeros of Unity

Find all solutions of $x^3 = 1$.

NOTE See the Algebra Review Appendix to review factoring the difference of two cubes.

Solution

Rewrite the equation as $x^3 - 1 = 0$ and use the difference of cubes pattern to factor the left side.

$$x^3 = 1$$
$$x^3 - 1 = 0$$
$$(x - 1)(x^2 + x + 1) = 0$$
$$x - 1 = 0 \qquad \text{or} \qquad x^2 + x + 1 = 0$$

$$x = 1 \quad \text{or} \quad x = \frac{-1 \pm \sqrt{1^2 - 4 \cdot 1 \cdot 1}}{2 \cdot 1} \qquad \textit{Quadratic formula}$$

$$= \frac{-1 \pm \sqrt{-3}}{2}$$

$$= \frac{-1 \pm i\sqrt{3}}{2} = -\frac{1}{2} \pm \frac{\sqrt{3}}{2}i$$

Therefore, the equation $x^3 = 1$ has one real solution, $x = 1$, and two non-real complex solutions, $x = -\frac{1}{2} + \frac{\sqrt{3}}{2}i$ and $x = -\frac{1}{2} - \frac{\sqrt{3}}{2}i$. Each of the solutions is said to be a **cube root of one** or a **cube root of unity.** Observe that the two nonreal cube roots of unity are complex conjugates. ∎

Examples 7 and 8 illustrated the following useful fact.

Conjugate Solutions

> If $a + bi$ is a solution of a polynomial equation with *real* coefficients, then its conjugate, $a - bi$, is also a solution of the equation.

Calculator Exploration

The following exploration demonstrates how matrices can be used for complex number arithmetic.

1. The complex number $a + bi$ is expressed in matrix notation as the matrix $\begin{pmatrix} a & b \\ -b & a \end{pmatrix}$. For example, $-3 + 6i$ is written as $\begin{pmatrix} -3 & 6 \\ -6 & -3 \end{pmatrix}$.

   a. Write $3 + 4i$, $1 + 2i$, and $1 - i$ in matrix form and enter them in your calculator as $[A]$, $[B]$, $[C]$.

   b. We know that $(3 + 4i) + (1 + 2i) = 4 + 6i$. Verify that $[A] + [B]$ is $\begin{pmatrix} 4 & 6 \\ -6 & 4 \end{pmatrix}$, which represents the complex number $4 + 6i$.

   c. Use matrix addition, subtraction, and multiplication to find the following. Interpret the answers as complex numbers.
   $$[A] - [C],\ [B] + [C],\ [A][B],\ [B][C]$$

   d. In Example 5 we saw that $\frac{3 + 4i}{1 + 2i} = \frac{11}{5} - \frac{2}{5}i = 2.2 - 0.4i$. Do this problem in matrix form by computing $[A] \cdot [B]^{-1}$. Use the x^{-1} key for the exponent.

   e. Do each of the following calculations and interpret the answer in terms of complex numbers.
   $$[A] \cdot [C]^{-1},\ [B][A]^{-1},\ [B][C]^{-1}$$

Solution to the **Calculator Exploration:**

1a. for $[A]$:

```
MATRIX[A] 2 ×2
[ 3    4      ]
[ -4   3      ]
```

$[B]$ and $[C]$ are similar.

1b.
```
[A]+[B]
        [[4   6]
         [-6  4]]
```

1c.
```
[A]-[C]
        [[2   5]
         [-5  2]]
[B]+[C]
        [[2   1]
         [-1  2]]
```

$[A] - [C]: (3 + 4i) - (1 - i) = 2 + 5i$
$[B] + [C]: (1 + 2i) + (1 - i) = 2 + i$

```
[A] [B]
        [[-5   10]
         [-10  -5]]
[B] [C]
        [[3   1]
         [-1  3]]
```

$[A][B]: (3 + 4i)(1 + 2i) = -5 + 10i$
$[B][C]: (1 + 2i)(1 - i) = 3 + i$

1d.
```
[A] [B]-1
        [[2.2  -.4]
         [.4   2.2]]
```

1e.
```
[A] [C]-1
        [[-.5   3.5]
         [-3.5  -.5]]
[B] [A]-1
        [[.44   .08]
         [-.08  .44]]
```

```
[B] [C]-1
        [[-.5   1.5]
         [-1.5  -.5]]
```

$[A][C]^{-1}: \frac{3 + 4i}{1 - i} = -0.5 + 3.5i$

$[B][A]^{-1}: \frac{1 + 2i}{3 + 4i} = 0.44 + 0.08i$

$[B][C]^{-1}: \frac{1 + 2i}{1 - i} = -0.5 + 1.5i$

ANSWERS

23. $\frac{5}{29} + \frac{2}{29}i$

24. $-i$

25. $-\frac{1}{3}i$

26. $\frac{1}{5} + \frac{2}{5}i$

27. $\frac{12}{41} - \frac{15}{41}i$

28. $3 - 2i$

29. $-\frac{5}{41} - \frac{4}{41}i$

30. $\frac{1}{5}$

31. $\frac{10}{17} - \frac{11}{17}i$

32. $\frac{10}{221} - \frac{28}{221}i$

33. $\frac{7}{10} + \frac{11}{10}i$

34. $\frac{71}{65} - \frac{22}{65}i$

35. $-\frac{113}{170} + \frac{41}{170}i$

36. $\frac{31}{5} + \frac{3}{5}i$

50. $(-5 + 3\sqrt{3}) + (15 + \sqrt{3})i$

51. $(2 + 5\sqrt{2}) + (\sqrt{5} - 2\sqrt{10})i$

59. $x = \frac{1}{3} \pm \frac{\sqrt{14}}{3}i$

60. $x = -\frac{1}{5} \pm \frac{2}{5}i$

61. $x = -\frac{1}{2} \pm \frac{\sqrt{7}}{2}i$

62. $x = \frac{3}{5} \pm \frac{1}{5}i$

63. $x = \frac{1}{4} \pm \frac{\sqrt{31}}{4}i$

64. $x = 2 \pm \sqrt{3}$

65. $x = \frac{3 \pm \sqrt{3}}{2}$

66. $x = -\frac{5}{6} \pm \frac{\sqrt{23}}{6}i$

67. $x = 2, -1 \pm i\sqrt{3}$

68. $x = -5, \frac{5}{2} \pm \frac{5\sqrt{3}}{2}i$

73. If $z = a + bi$, with a, b real numbers, then
$z - \bar{z} = (a + bi) - (a - bi)$
$= 2bi$. If $z = a + bi$ is real, then $b = 0$ and hence, $z - \bar{z} = 2bi = 0$. Therefore, $z = \bar{z}$. Conversely, if $z = \bar{z}$, then $0 = z - \bar{z} = 2bi$, which implies that $b = 0$. Hence, $z = a$ is real.

74. **a.** $\dfrac{z + \bar{z}}{2} = \dfrac{(a + bi) + (a - bi)}{2}$
$= \dfrac{2a}{2} = a$

b. $\dfrac{z - \bar{z}}{2i} = \dfrac{(a + bi) - (a - bi)}{2i}$
$= \dfrac{2bi}{2i} = b$

75. $\dfrac{1}{z} = \left(\dfrac{a}{a^2 + b^2}\right) + \left(\dfrac{-b}{a^2 + b^2}\right)i$

Exercises 4.5

In Exercises 1–54, perform the indicated operation and write the result in the form $a + bi$.

1. $(2 + 3i) + (6 - i)$
$8 + 2i$

2. $(-5 + 7i) + (14 + 3i)$
$9 + 10i$

3. $(2 - 8i) - (4 + 2i)$
$-2 - 10i$

4. $(3 + 5i) - (3 - 7i)$
$12i$

5. $\frac{5}{4} - \left(\frac{7}{4} + 2i\right)$
$-\frac{1}{2} - 2i$

6. $(\sqrt{3} + i) + (\sqrt{5} - 2i)$
$(\sqrt{3} + \sqrt{5}) - i$

7. $\left(\frac{\sqrt{2}}{2} + i\right) - \left(\frac{\sqrt{3}}{2} - i\right)$
$\left(\frac{\sqrt{2} - \sqrt{3}}{2}\right) + 2i$

8. $\left(\frac{1}{2} + \frac{\sqrt{3}}{2}i\right) + \left(\frac{3}{4} - \frac{5\sqrt{3}}{2}i\right)$
$\frac{5}{4} - 2i\sqrt{3}$

9. $(2 + i)(3 + 5i)$
$1 + 13i$

10. $(2 - i)(5 + 2i)$
$12 - i$

11. $(-3 + 2i)(4 - i)$
$-10 + 11i$

12. $(4 + 3i)(4 - 3i)$
25

13. $(2 - 5i)^2$
$-21 - 20i$

14. $(1 + i)(2 - i)i$
$-1 + 3i$

15. $(\sqrt{3} + i)(\sqrt{3} - i)$
4

16. $\left(\frac{1}{2} - i\right)\left(\frac{1}{4} + 2i\right)$
$\frac{17}{8} + \frac{3}{4}i$

17. i^{15}
$-i$

18. i^{26}
-1

19. i^{33}
i

20. $(-i)^{53}$
$-i$

21. $(-i)^{107}$
i

22. $(-i)^{213}$
$-i$

23. $\frac{1}{5 - 2i}$

24. $\frac{1}{i}$

25. $\frac{1}{3i}$

26. $\frac{i}{2 + i}$

27. $\frac{3}{4 + 5i}$

28. $\frac{2 + 3i}{i}$

29. $\frac{1}{i(4 + 5i)}$

30. $\frac{1}{(2 - i)(2 + i)}$

31. $\frac{2 + 3i}{i(4 + i)}$

32. $\frac{2}{(2 + 3i)(4 + i)}$

33. $\frac{2 + i}{1 - i} + \frac{1}{1 + 2i}$

34. $\frac{1}{2 - i} + \frac{3 + i}{2 + 3i}$

35. $\frac{i}{3 + i} - \frac{3 + i}{4 + i}$

36. $6 + \frac{2i}{3 + i}$

37. $\sqrt{-36}$ **$6i$**

38. $\sqrt{-81}$ **$9i$**

39. $\sqrt{-14}$ **$i\sqrt{14}$**

40. $\sqrt{-50}$ **$5i\sqrt{2}$**

41. $-\sqrt{-16}$ **$-4i$**

42. $-\sqrt{-12}$ **$-2i\sqrt{3}$**

43. $\sqrt{-16} + \sqrt{-49}$ **$11i$**

44. $\sqrt{-25} - \sqrt{-9}$ **$2i$**

45. $\sqrt{-15} - \sqrt{-18}$
$(\sqrt{15} - 3\sqrt{2})i$

46. $\sqrt{-12}\sqrt{-3}$ **-6**

47. $\dfrac{\sqrt{-16}}{\sqrt{-36}}$ $\frac{2}{3}$

48. $\dfrac{-\sqrt{-64}}{\sqrt{-4}}$ **-4**

49. $(\sqrt{-25} + 2)(\sqrt{-49} - 3)$ **$-41 - i$**

50. $(5 - \sqrt{-3})(-1 + \sqrt{-9})$

51. $(2 + \sqrt{-5})(1 - \sqrt{-10})$

52. $\sqrt{-3}(3 - \sqrt{-27})$
$9 + 3i\sqrt{3}$

53. $\dfrac{1}{1 + \sqrt{-2}}$ $\frac{1}{3} - \frac{\sqrt{2}}{3}i$

54. $\dfrac{1 + \sqrt{-4}}{3 - \sqrt{-9}}$
$-\frac{1}{6} + \frac{1}{2}i$

In Exercises 55–58, find x and y.

55. $3x - 4i = 6 + 2yi$
$x = 2, y = -2$

56. $8 - 2yi = 4x + 12i$
$x = 2, y = -6$

57. $3 + 4xi = 2y - 3i$
$x = -\frac{3}{4}, y = \frac{3}{2}$

58. $8 - xi = \frac{1}{2}y + 2i$
$x = -2, y = 16$

In Exercises 59–70, solve the equation and express each solution in the form $a + bi$.

59. $3x^2 - 2x + 5 = 0$

60. $5x^2 + 2x + 1 = 0$

61. $x^2 + x + 2 = 0$

62. $5x^2 - 6x + 2 = 0$

63. $2x^2 - x = -4$

64. $x^2 + 1 = 4x$

65. $2x^2 + 3 = 6x$

66. $3x^2 + 4 = -5x$

67. $x^3 - 8 = 0$

68. $x^3 + 125 = 0$

69. $x^4 - 1 = 0$
$x = \pm i, \pm 1$

70. $x^4 - 81 = 0$
$x = \pm 3i, \pm 3$

71. Simplify: $i + i^2 + i^3 + \cdots + i^{15}$
-1

72. Simplify: $i - i^2 + i^3 - i^4 + i^5 - \cdots + i^{15}$
1

73. *Critical Thinking* If $z = a + bi$ is a complex number, then its conjugate is usually denoted $\bar{z}$, that is, $\bar{z} = a - bi$. Prove that for any complex number $z = a + bi$, z is a real number exactly when $\bar{z} = z$.

74. *Critical Thinking* The **real part** of the complex number $a + bi$ is defined to be the real number a. The **imaginary part** of $a + bi$ is defined to be the real number b (not bi). See Exercise 73 for notation.

a. Show that the real part of $z = a + bi$ is $\dfrac{z + \bar{z}}{2}$.

b. Show that the imaginary part of z is $\dfrac{z - \bar{z}}{2i}$.

75. *Critical Thinking* If $z = a + bi$ (with a and b real numbers, not both 0), express $\dfrac{1}{z}$ in standard form.

Excursion: The Mandelbrot Set

4.5.A

Chapter 1 introduced the recursive process of beginning with a value and adding a specific number repeatedly, and Section 3.5.A discussed iterating real-valued functions. This section will extend the iterative process to the set of complex numbers and complex-valued functions and will illustrate the Mandelbrot set, which is used to produce many fractal images. Before reading this section, review Section 3.5.A for terminology and processes, if needed.

The Complex Plane

Every complex number $a + bi$, where a and b are real numbers, corresponds to the point (a, b) in the coordinate plane. Therefore, complex numbers can be plotted in a coordinate plane, where the horizontal axis represents the real axis and the vertical axis represents the imaginary axis. For example, several complex numbers are plotted in Figure 4.5.A-1.

NOTE The complex plane is discussed in detail in Section 10.3.

When dealing with functions that have the complex numbers as their domains, the input variable is usually denoted as *z*, not *x*.

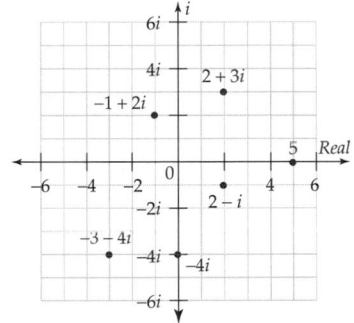

Figure 4.5.A-1

Orbits of Complex Numbers

The concepts and processes described in Section 3.5.A apply equally well to functions with complex number inputs. For instance, the process of finding the orbit of a complex number under a complex-valued function is the same as finding the orbit of a real number under a real-valued function. For example, the orbit of i under $f(z) = iz$ was illustrated in Section 4.5, where it was shown that the powers of i form an orbit of period 4.

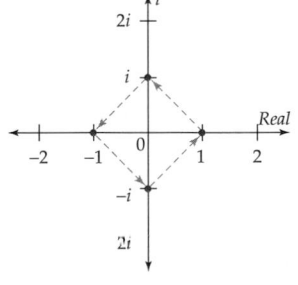

Figure 4.5.A-2

$$z = i$$
$$f(i) = i \cdot i = i^2 = -1$$
$$f^2(i) = i \cdot (-1) = -i$$
$$f^3(i) = i \cdot (-i) = -i^2 = -(-1) = 1$$ $f^2(i) = f[f(i)]$
$$f^4(i) = i \cdot 1 = i$$

The orbit of i under $f(z) = iz$ is shown graphically in Figure 4.5.A-2.

Math Background

In **The Complex Plane,** a real number $a = a + 0i$ corresponds to the point $(a, 0)$ on the real axis and an imaginary number $bi = 0 + bi$ corresponds to the point $(0, b)$ on the imaginary axis.

The absolute value of a complex number $a + bi$ is defined as $|a + bi| = \sqrt{a^2 + b^2}$. It is the distance from the complex number to the origin $(0, 0)$ (page 638).

The graph of the Mandelbrot set is a fractal image. A *fractal image* is an image that is *self-similar*. That is, it consists of parts that resemble the whole image.

Teaching Notes

In **Orbits of Complex Numbers,** the *period* of an orbit is equal to the number of terms of the orbit that form a cycle (i.e., the portion that repeats over and over again). For example, if an orbit has period 4, this means that the first 4 terms of the orbit form the cycle, and the fifth term coincides with the first term, the sixth with the second, and so on. This is precisely what occurs for the orbit of i under $f(z) = iz$.

Consider having your students find the orbits of $-1, 1,$ and $-i$ under $f(z) = iz$:

$z = -1$ $z = 1$
$f(-1) = i \cdot -1 = -i$ $f(1) = i \cdot 1 = i$
$f^2(-1) = i \cdot -i = -i^2 = 1$ $f^2(1) = i \cdot i = i^2 = -1$
$f^3(-1) = i \cdot 1 = i$ $f^3(1) = i \cdot -1 = -i$
$f^4(-1) = i \cdot i = i^2 = -1$ $f^4(1) = i \cdot -i = -i^2 = 1$

$z = -i$
$f(-i) = i \cdot -i = -i^2 = 1$
$f^2(-i) = i \cdot 1 = i$
$f^3(-i) = i \cdot i = i^2 = -1$
$f^4(-i) = i \cdot -1 = -1$

Example Notes

In **Example 2a**, you may want to have students find the 1st three iterations by hand, so they do not lose sight of the process:

$f(z) = z^2 + (1 + i) = z^2 + 1 + i$

$f^1(0) = 0^2 + 1 + i = 1 + i$

$$\begin{aligned} f^2(0) = f(1 + i) &= (1 + i)^2 + 1 + i \\ &= 1 + 2i + i^2 + 1 + i \\ &= 1 + 2i - 1 + 1 + i \\ &= 1 + 3i \end{aligned}$$

$$\begin{aligned} f^3(0) = f(1 + 3i) &= (1 + 3i)^2 + 1 + i \\ &= 1 + 6i + 9i^2 + 1 + i \\ &= 1 + 6i - 9 + 1 + i \\ &= -7 + 7i \end{aligned}$$

In **Example 2b**, emphasize that it requires many iterations to see that the orbit approaches infinity. (In **Additional Example 2b**, it will require about 30 iterations).

Teaching Notes

In **Examples 1** and **2**, you may alternatively use matrices (**Calculator Exploration**, page 299) to compute the various iterations in these orbits. For **Example 1a**, follow these steps:

1. Represent $-0.25 + 0.25i$ in matrix form:

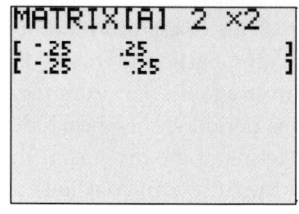

2. Compute $[A]^2 + [A]$. This is the second term of the orbit.

3. Next, compute $ANS^2 + [A]$. This is the third term of the orbit.

```
[A]²+[A]
    [[-.25   .125]
     [-.125  -.25]]
Ans²+[A]
    [[-.203125  .187...
     [-.1875    -.20...
```

4. Now, use the [2nd] [Entry] keys to obtain subsequent terms of the orbit.

NOTE All decimals are shown rounded to four decimal places, but calculations are done using the decimal capacity of the calculator.

Orbits of complex numbers of many functions are very interesting, but the discussion that follows will be limited to the orbit of 0 under $f(z) = z^2 + c$ for different values of c.

Example 1   The Orbit of 0 for $f(z) = z^2 + c$

Describe the orbit of 0 under $f(z) = z^2 + c$ for the given complex number c.

a. $c = -0.25 + 0.25i$ **b.** $c = -1.2 + 0.05i$

Solution

a. For $c = -0.25 + 0.25i$,
$f(z) = z^2 + (-0.25 + 0.25i) = z^2 - 0.25 + 0.25i.$

The orbit of 0 under $f(z) = z^2 - 0.25 + 0.25i$ is as follows.

$f^1(0) = 0^2 - 0.25 + 0.25i = -0.25 + 0.25i$

$f^2(0) = (-0.25 + 0.25i)^2 + (-0.25 + 0.25i) = -0.25 + 0.125i$

$f^3(0) = f(-0.25 + 0.125i) = -0.203125 + 0.187500i$

$f^4(0) = f(-0.203125 + 0.187500i) = -0.2439 + 0.1738i$

$f^5(0) = f(-0.243896 + 0.173828i) = -0.2207 + 0.1652i$

$f^6(0) = f(-0.220731 + 0.165208i) = -0.2286 + 0.1771i$

Use iteration on your calculator to find $f^{15}(0)$. It suggests that the orbit of 0 is approaching a number near $-0.2277 + 0.1718i$. In fact, it can be shown that for $c = -0.25 + 0.25i$,

$$f^n(0) \to -0.2276733451 + 0.1717803749i \text{ as } n \to \infty$$

b. For $c = -1.2 + 0.05i$, $f(z) = z^2 + (-1.2 + 0.05i) = z^2 - 1.2 + 0.05i.$

The orbit of 0 under $f(z) = z^2 - 1.2 + 0.05i$ is as follows.

$f^1(0) = -1.2 + 0.05i$ $f^2(0) = 0.2375 - 0.0700i$

$f^3(0) = -1.1485 + 0.0168i$ $f^4(0) = 0.1188 + 0.0115i$

$f^5(0) = -1.1860 + 0.0527i$ $f^6(0) = 0.2039 - 0.0751i$

$f^7(0) = -1.1641 + 0.0194i$ $f^8(0) = 0.1547 + 0.0049i$

$f^9(0) = -1.1761 + 0.0515i$ $f^{10}(0) = 0.1805 - 0.0712i$

$f^{11}(0) = -1.1725 + 0.0243i$ $f^{12}(0) = 0.1741 - 0.0070i$

$f^{13}(0) = -1.1697 + 0.0476i$ $f^{14}(0) = 0.1660 - 0.0613i$

$f^{15}(0) = -1.1762 + 0.0296i$ $f^{16}(0) = 0.1825 - 0.0197i$

Viewing additional iterations, the orbit of 0 when $c = -1.2 + 0.05i$ appears to oscillate between two values that are close to $-1.17 + 0.04i$ and $0.17 - 0.04i$ as illustrated in Figure 4.5.A-3.

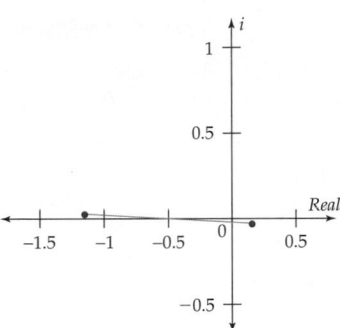

Figure 4.5.A-3

Example 2 **The Orbit of 0 for $f(z) = z^2 + c$**

Describe the orbit of 0 under $f(z) = z^2 + c$ for the given complex number c.

a. $c = 1 + i$ **b.** $c = 0.25 + 0.625i$

Solution

Figure 4.5.A-4

a. The first seven iterations of $f(z) = z^2 + (1 + i)$ are shown in Figure 4.5.A-4. If each of these numbers is plotted in the complex plane, successive iterations get farther and farther from the origin at a very fast rate. For instance,

$$f^5(0) = -9407 - 193i$$
$$f^6(0) = 88,454,401 + 3,631,103i$$
$$f^7(0) = (7.81 \times 10^{15}) + (6.42 \times 10^{14})i$$

The distance formula shows that after only five iterations, the distance to the origin is about 9509 and after seven iterations, it is *gigantic.* In this case, the orbit of 0 is said to **approach infinity,** which is sometimes expressed as follows.

If $f(z) = z^2 + (1 + i)$, then $f^n(0) \to \infty$ as $n \to \infty$.

Figure 4.5.A-5a

b. The iterations $f^1(0)$ through $f^7(0)$ are shown in Figure 4.5.A-5a and $f^{15}(0)$ through $f^{21}(0)$ are shown in Figure 4.5.A-5b. As you can see, successive iterations stay fairly close to the origin through the 16th iteration and then quickly move farther and farther away.

$$f^{20}(20) = -167.4 - 522.8i$$
$$f^{21}(0) = -254,270 + 175,058i$$
$$f^{22}(0) = (2.95 \times 10^{10}) - (8.59 \times 10^{10})i$$

Figure 4.5.A-5b

Therefore, the orbit of 0 approaches infinity. In other words,

if $f(z) = z^2 + (0.25 + 0.625i)$, then $f^n(0) \to \infty$ as $n \to \infty$.

iterations $f^1(0)$ through $f^7(0)$:

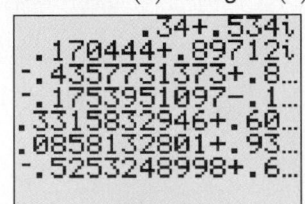

ADDITIONAL EXAMPLES

Example 1

Describe the orbit of 0 under $f(z) = z^2 + c$ for the given complex number c:

a. $c = -0.17 + 0.17i$
approaches a number near $-0.1607 + 0.1286i$

b. $c - -1.1 + 0.04i$
oscillates between two values that are close to -1.09 and $0.09 - 0.03i$

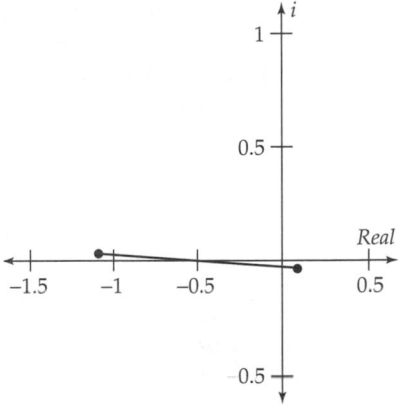

Example 2

Describe the orbit of 0 under $f(z) = z^2 + c$ for the given complex number c:

a. $c = 2 + i$
approaches infinity

b. $c = 0.34 + 0.534i$
approaches infinity

iterations $f^{26}(0)$ through $f^{32}(0)$:

Math Background

Benoit Mandelbrot (1924–) is known as the founder of fractal geometry. During a career that has included professorships at Harvard, Yale, and IBM, Mandelbrot developed computer programs to print computer graphics and discovered **The Mandelbrot Set.**

One of the leading experts in the study of sets such as the Mandelbrot set is Dr. Robert Devaney. He has created videotapes and activities appropriate for high school audiences. Such activities are available on his website at Boston University and can be used for additional exploration.

Challenge interested students to write a computer or calculator program to generate the Mandelbrot set.

Encourage students to use a freeware or shareware fractal generator program.

COMMON ERROR ALERT

Some students may think that a complex number such as $-1.1 + 0i$ is not in the Mandelbrot set. They may remember from Section 3.5.A (**Example 5,** Orbit Analysis) that an orbit approaches infinity when $|x| > 1$.

Remind them that Example 5 in Section 3.5.A involved real numbers and the function $f(x) = x^2$. The current function is $f(z) = z^2 + c$, and the numbers are complex numbers.

Have the students find the orbit of $-1.1 + 0i$ to show that the orbit oscillates between -1.09161 and 0.09161.

Teaching Notes

You may want to have the students trace Figure 4.5.A-6 and then plot the points in **Examples 1 and 2** ($-0.25 + 0.25i$, $-1.2 + 0.05i$, $1 + i$, and $0.25 + 0.625i$) on their diagram.

The Mandelbrot Set

The Mandelbrot set is defined by whether or not the orbit of 0 under the function $f(z) = z^2 + c$ approaches infinity for each complex number c.

The Mandelbrot Set

> The *Mandelbrot set* is the set of complex numbers c such that the orbit of 0 under the function $f(z) = z^2 + c$ does not approach infinity.

To avoid awkward repetition in the following discussion, the orbit of 0 under the function $f(z) = z^2 + c$ will be referred to as "the orbit of c."

Example 1 shows that the orbit of $c = -0.25 + 0.25i$ converges and the orbit of $c = -1.2 + 0.05i$ oscillates. Neither orbit approaches infinity, so both numbers are in the Mandelbrot set. Example 2 shows that the orbits of $c = 1 + i$ and $c = 0.25 + 0.625i$ approach infinity, so these numbers are not in the Mandelbrot set.

Diagram of the Mandelbrot Set

Although the Mandelbrot set is defined analytically, it is usually viewed geometrically by plotting the numbers in the Mandelbrot set as points in the complex plane. The Mandelbrot set is the white region in Figure 4.5.A-6, in which the tick marks on each axis are $\frac{1}{2}$ unit apart. Note that the Mandelbrot set is symmetric with respect to the real axis, but not with respect to the imaginary axis.

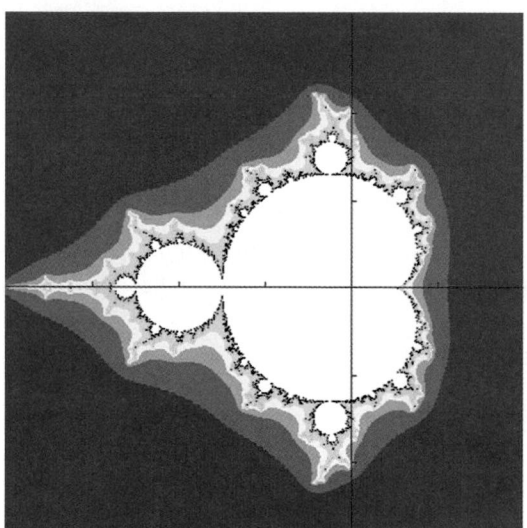

Figure 4.5.A-6

Figure 4.5.A-6 illustrates the following fact in which the complex numbers are considered as points in the complex plane.

> If c lies outside the circle of radius 2 with center at the origin, then c is not in the Mandelbrot set.

Furthermore, it can be proved that

> **If c lies inside the circle of radius 2 with center at the origin, but some number in its orbit lies outside the circle, then c is not in the Mandelbrot set.**

Determining whether a particular point c is in the Mandelbrot set can be quite difficult, particularly if the numbers in its orbit move away from the origin very slowly. Even after hundreds of iterations, it may not be clear whether or not the orbit approaches infinity. Because of round-off errors, a calculator is inadequate for such calculations, and even computers have their limitations.

Border of the Mandelbrot Set

The border of the Mandelbrot set, which consists of the points just outside of the set, is shown in various colors in Figure 4.5.A-6. The colors indicate how quickly the orbit of the point approaches infinity. The colors are determined by the number of iterations n needed for a number in the orbit of the point to be more than 3 units from the origin, as indicated in the following table.

Red	Medium Red	Light Red	Light Yellow	Yellow	Blue	Black
$n \leq 5$	$6 \leq n \leq 7$	$8 \leq n \leq 9$	$10 \leq n \leq 12$	$13 \leq n \leq 19$	$20 \leq n \leq 49$	$n \geq 50$

Example 2 shows that $1 + i$ is in the red region because the second iteration produces a point more than 3 units from the origin and that $0.25 + 0.625i$ is in the yellow region.

The border of the Mandelbrot set is very jagged and chaotic. The varying rates at which the orbits of these border points approach infinity produce some interesting patterns of great complexity. When specific areas are magnified, you can see shapes that resemble islands, seahorse tails, and elephant trunks. The most fascinating aspect of the set is that some of these islands have the same shape as the entire set. Consequently, the Mandelbrot set is said to be **self-similar under magnification.**

The following figures show the region near the point $-0.75 + 0.3i$ under increasing magnification.

The purple points in Figure 4.5.A-7a indicate the Mandelbrot set. Each subsequent image is the magnification of the region denoted by the white square in the previous image. The image shown in Figure 4.5.A-7d is a copy of the set that is contained within the set, and even though the graphs shown do not indicate that all of the purple regions are connected, they are.

Teaching Notes

A complex number c lies in the Mandelbrot set if the orbit of 0 under the function $f(z) = z^2 + c$ converges or oscillates between two points.

Examples of points in the Mandelbrot set:
- In **Example 1a,** $-0.25 + 0.25i$ (converges)
- In **Example 1b,** $-1.2 + 0.05i$ (oscillates between two values)

A complex number c is *not* in the Mandelbrot set if
- the distance from c to the origin is greater than 2, or
- the distance of any number in the orbit of c from the origin is greater than 2.

Examples of points not in the Mandelbrot set:
- $2 + i$ is not in the set. ($|2 + i| = \sqrt{2^2 + 1^2} = \sqrt{5} > 2$, so the distance from $2 + i$ to the origin is greater than 2.)
- In **Example 2a,** $1 + i$ is not in the set (The result of the second iteration, $1 + 3i$, is more than 2 units from the origin.)
- In **Example 2b,** $0.25 + 0.625i$ is not in the set. (The result of the eighteenth iteration, $2.12 + 4.3i$, is more than 2 units from the origin.)

Ask students to explain how **Example 2** shows that $0.25 + 0.625i$ is in the yellow region of Figure 4.5.A-6. possible answer: Referring to the calculator screen shot, Figure 4.5.A-5b, $f^{18}(0) \approx 2.12 + 4.3i$, which is a point more than 3 units from the origin. Because $13 \leq 18 \leq 19$, $0.25 + 0.625i$ is in the yellow region (see table on page 305).

Teaching Notes

Figures 4.5.A-7a–4.5.A-7d show the region near the point $-0.75 + 0.3i$ under increasing magnification. This point is not in the Mandelbrot set. Note that $f(11) \approx 2.58 - 0.97i$; the distance from $2.58 - 0.97i$ to the origin is greater than 2.

Exercises 4.5.A

ANSWERS

1. $f^1(0) = 0.3$;
   $f^2(0) = 0.39$; $f^3(0) = 0.4521$;
   $d = 0.4521$

2. $f^1(0) = 0.5i$;
   $f^2(0) = -0.25 + 0.5i$;
   $f^3(0) = -0.1875 + 0.25i$;
   $d = 0.3125$

3. $f^1(0) = 0.5 + 0.5i$;
   $f^2(0) = 0.5 + i$;
   $f^3(0) = -0.25 + 1.5i$;
   $d \approx 1.5207$

4. $f^1(0) = 1 + 0.5i$
   $f^2(0) = 1.75 + 1.5i$
   $f^3(0) = 1.8125 + 5.75i$
   $d \approx 6.0289$

5. $f^1(0) = -1.2 + 0.5i$;
   $f^2(0) = -0.01 - 0.7i$;
   $f^3(0) = -1.6899 + 0.514i$;
   $d \approx 1.7663$

6. $f^1(0) = -0.75 + 0.25i$;
   $f^2(0) = -0.25 - 0.125i$;
   $f^3(0) = -0.703125 + 0.3125i$;
   $d \approx 0.7694$

Figure 4.5.A-7a

Figure 4.5.A-7b

Figure 4.5.A-7c

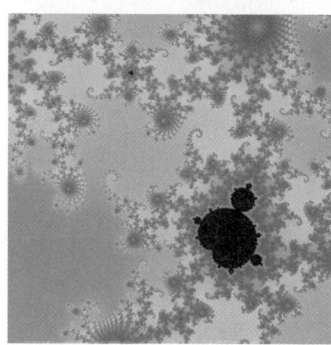

Figure 4.5.A-7d

Exercises 4.5.A

In Exercises 1–6, compute $f^1(0)$, $f^2(0)$, and $f^3(0)$ where $f(z) = z^2 + c$. Then determine the distance from $f^3(0)$ to the origin in the complex plane, where the distance from a point $a + bi$ to the origin is given by

$$\sqrt{a^2 + b^2}.$$

1. $c = 0.3$
2. $c = 0.5i$
3. $c = 0.5 + 0.5i$
4. $c = 1 + 0.5i$
5. $c = -1.2 + 0.5i$
6. $c = -0.75 + 0.25i$

In Exercises 7–12, show that c is *not* in the Mandelbrot set by finding a number in its orbit that is more than 2 units from the origin. How many iterations are needed to find the first such number?

7. $c = 0.4$ **seven**
8. $c = -1.1 + 0.4i$ **seven**
9. $c = 0.7i$ **thirteen**
10. $c = 0.2 + 0.8i$ **five**
11. $c = -0.5 - 0.7i$ **eight**
12. $c = 0.4 - 0.6i$ **fifteen**

In Exercises 13–18, determine whether or not c is in the Mandelbrot set.

13. $c = i$ **is**
14. $c = -i$ **is**
15. $c = 1$ **is not**
16. $c = 0.1 - 0.3i$ **is**
17. $c = -0.2 + 0.6i$ **is**
18. $-0.1 + 0.8i$ **is**

4.6   The Fundamental Theorem of Algebra

Objectives

- Use the Fundamental Theorem of Algebra
- Find complex conjugate zeros
- Find the number of zeros of a polynomial
- Give the complete factorization of polynomial expressions

The complex numbers were constructed in order to obtain a solution for the equation $x^2 = -1$, that is, a zero of the polynomial $f(x) = x^2 + 1$. *Every quadratic equation with real coefficients has solutions in the complex number system*, as discussed in Section 4.5. A natural question arises:

Does the complex number system need to be enlarged, perhaps many times, to find zeros of higher degree polynomial functions?

This section explains why the answer is no.

In order to give the full answer, the discussion will not be limited to polynomials with real coefficients but will consider polynomials with complex coefficients, such as

$$x^3 - ix^2 + (4 - 3i)x + 1 \quad \text{or} \quad (-3 + 2i)x^6 - 3x + (5 - 4i).$$

The discussion of polynomial division in Section 4.1 can easily be extended to include polynomials with complex coefficients. In fact,

All of the results in Section 4.1 are valid for polynomials with complex coefficients.

For example, for $f(x) = x^2 + (-1 + i)x + (2 + i)$, it is easy to verify that i is a zero of f and that $x - i$ is a factor of $f(x)$. Both statements can be checked using the same procedures as before.

$$f(i) = i^2 + (-1 + i)i + (2 + i) = i^2 - i + i^2 + 2 + i$$
$$= -1 - i - 1 + 2 + i = 0$$

Therefore, i is a zero of f.

$$
\begin{array}{r}
x + (-1 + 2i) \\
x - i \overline{\smash{\big)}\, x^2 + (-1 + i)x + 2 + i} \\
\underline{x^2 \qquad\quad - ix} \\
(-1 + 2i)x + 2 + i \\
\underline{(-1 + 2i)x + 2 + i} \\
0
\end{array}
$$

Therefore, $x - i$ is a factor of $f(x)$ and

$$f(x) = x^2 + (-1 + i)x + (2 + i) = (x - i)[x + (-1 + 2i)].$$

Because every real number is also a complex number, polynomials with real coefficients are just special cases of polynomials with complex coefficients. In the rest of this section, "polynomial" means "polynomial with complex, possibly real, coefficients" unless specified otherwise.

NOTE The graph of a polynomial with complex coefficients cannot be drawn on a coordinate plane.

Fundamental Theorem of Algebra

Every nonconstant polynomial has a zero in the complex number system.

Section 4.6   The Fundamental Theorem of Algebra

Teaching Notes

Students may need help with the polynomial division, specifically with the subtraction

$$
\begin{array}{r}
x^2 + (-1 + i)x \\
\underline{x^2 \qquad\quad - ix} \\
(-1 + 2i)x
\end{array}
$$

Have them show the steps:

$$x^2 + (-1 + i)x - (x^2 - ix)$$
$$= x^2 - x + ix - x^2 + ix$$
$$= -x + 2ix = (-1 + 2i)x$$

Synthetic division (Section 4.1, page 241) may also be used for the division:

$$
\begin{array}{r|rrr}
i & 1 & -1 + i & 2 + i \\
  &   & i & -2 - i \\
\hline
  & 1 & -1 + 2i & 0
\end{array}
$$

The **Fundamental Theorem of Algebra** requires a *nonconstant* polynomial. Ask students for examples of constant polynomials. possible answers: 5, $-\frac{1}{2}$, π, $\sqrt{7}$, $2 - 3i$

Emphasize that "polynomial" will now mean "polynomial with complex, possibly real, coefficients" unless otherwise stated (see bottom of page). Remind students that some complex numbers are real numbers and some are not. For example:

- 3 is complex and real ($3 = 3 + 0i$).
- $3 + 2i$ is complex, but not real.

An alternate version of the Fundamental Theorem is: Every polynomial of degree $n > 0$ has a zero in the complex number system. Ask students to explain why this version is equivalent. If the degree is greater than 0, then the polynomial must have a term with a variable, and is therefore nonconstant.

Teaching Notes

The **Fundamental Theorem of Algebra** on the preceding page is powerful because of the results that can be obtained by using it. All of the concepts on this page are results of recursively applying the Fundamental Theorem to a polynomial function.

The statements in the **Factorization over the Complex Numbers** box can be summarized as follows (in fact, this is a summary of the entire page): A polynomial of degree $n > 0$ has *exactly* (no more, no less) n complex zeros and corresponding linear factors. The zeros (and corresponding linear factors) are not necessarily distinct. This means that a zero (and corresponding linear factor) can be repeated.

In **Example 1**, the polynomial has degree 5. Its 5 linear factors are $(x - 1)$, $(x - 1)$, $(x - 1)$, $(x + 2)$, and $(x - 5)$.

Its 5 zeros are 1, 1, 1, -2, and 5.

In **Example 2**, the polynomial has degree 2. Its 2 linear factors are $[x - (3 + 2i)]$ and $[x - (3 - 2i)]$. Its 2 zeros are $3 + 2i$ and $3 - 2i$.

The explanation of Factorization over the Complex Numbers uses a recursive method, that is, it repeatedly applies the same concept. The Fundamental Theorem of Algebra says that a nonconstant polynomial has a complex zero. So, a polynomial of degree n can be rewritten as the product of a linear factor and a polynomial of degree $(n - 1)$. The Fundamental Theorem is then applied to the polynomial of degree $(n - 1)$, and so on.

Example Notes

In **Example 2**, there are two zeros of f, but no real zeros because the graph of f does not cross the x-axis.

Although this is a powerful result, neither the Fundamental Theorem nor its proof provides a practical method for *finding* a zero of a given polynomial. You may think it strange that you can prove a zero exists without actually finding one, but such "existence" proofs are quite common in mathematics.

Factorization over the Complex Numbers

Let $f(x)$ be a polynomial of degree $n > 0$ with leading coefficient a. Then there are n, not necessarily distinct, complex numbers $c_1, c_2, \ldots, c_n$ such that

$$f(x) = a(x - c_1)(x - c_2) \ldots (x - c_n)$$

Furthermore, $c_1, c_2 \ldots, c_n$ are the only zeros of f.

That is, every polynomial of degree $n > 0$ can be written as the product of n linear factors. The statement follows from the Fundamental Theorem and the Factor Theorem. By the Fundamental Theorem, $f(x)$ has a complex zero c_1, and by the Factor Theorem $x - c_1$ is a factor, so

$$f(x) = (x - c_1)g(x).$$

If $g(x)$ is nonconstant, then it has a complex zero c_2 by the Fundamental Theorem and a factor $x - c_2$ so that

$$f(x) = (x - c_1)(x - c_2)(h(x)).$$

This process can be continued until the final factor is a constant a, at which point you have the factorization shown in the preceding box.

Because the n zeros $c_1, c_2, \ldots, c_n$ of f may not all be distinct, the number of distinct zeros may be less than n.

Number of Zeros

Every polynomial of degree $n > 0$ has at most n different zeros in the complex number system.

Suppose f has repeated zeros, meaning that some of the $c_1, c_2, \ldots, c_n$ are the same in the factorization of $f(x)$. Recall that a zero c is said to have multiplicity k if $(x - c)^k$ is a factor of $f(x)$, but no higher power of $(x - c)$ is a factor. Consequently, *if every zero is counted as many times as its multiplicity*, then the statement in the preceding box implies that

A polynomial of degree n has exactly n complex zeros.

Example 1 Finding a Polynomial Given Its Zeros

Find a polynomial $f(x)$ of degree 5 such that 1, -2, and 5 are zeros, 1 is a zero of multiplicity 3, and $f(2) = -24$.

Solution

Because 1 is a zero of multiplicity 3, $(x - 1)^3$ must be a factor of $f(x)$. There are two other factors corresponding to the zeros -2 and 5.

$$x - (-2) = x + 2 \text{ and } x - 5$$

The product of these factors has degree 5, as does $f(x)$ so

$$f(x) = a(x - 1)^3(x + 2)(x - 5)$$

where a is the leading coefficient.

Because $f(2) = -24$,

$$a(2 - 1)^3(2 + 2)(2 - 5) = -24$$
$$-12a = -24$$
$$a = 2$$

Therefore, $f(x) = 2(x - 1)^3(x + 2)(x - 5)$

$$= 2x^5 - 12x^4 + 4x^3 + 40x^2 - 54x + 20$$

The graph of f is shown in Figure 4.6-1.

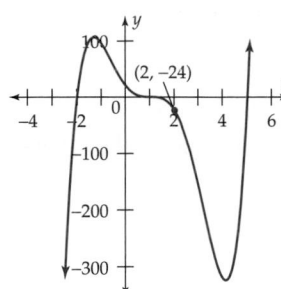

Figure 4.6-1

NOTE Complex zeros are not shown on the graph of a polynomial.

Polynomials with Real Coefficients

Recall that the **conjugate** of the complex number $a + bi$ is the number $a - bi$. We usually write a complex number as a single letter, say z, and indicate its conjugate by $\bar{z}$, sometimes read "z bar." For instance, if $z = 3 + 7i$, then $\bar{z} = 3 - 7i$. Conjugates play a role whenever a quadratic polynomial with real coefficients has complex zeros.

| **Example 2** | Conjugate Zeros |

Find the zeros of $f(x) = x^2 - 6x + 13$.

Solution

The quadratic formula shows that f has two complex zeros.

$$\frac{-(-6) \pm \sqrt{(-6)^2 - 4 \cdot 1 \cdot 13}}{2 \cdot 1} = \frac{6 \pm \sqrt{-16}}{2} = \frac{6 \pm 4i}{2} = 3 \pm 2i$$

The complex roots are $z = 3 + 2i$ and its conjugate $\bar{z} = 3 - 2i$. Notice that f has no real zeros, as shown in Figure 4.6-2.

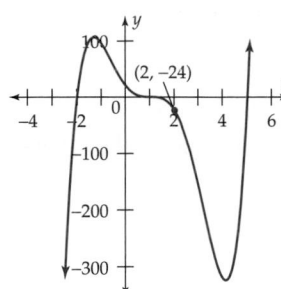

Figure 4.6-2

The preceding example is a special case of a more general theorem.

Conjugate Zero Theorem

> Let $f(x)$ be a polynomial with *real* coefficients. If the complex number z is a zero of f, then its conjugate $\bar{z}$ is also a zero of f.

| **Example 1** |

Find a polynomial $f(x)$ of degree 4 such that -3, -1, and 2 are zeros, 2 is of multiplicity 2, and $f(1) = 32$.

$$f(x) = a(x + 3)(x + 1)(x - 2)^2$$
$$a(1 + 3)(1 + 1)(1 - 2)^2 = 32$$
$$8a = 32$$
$$a = 4$$

$$f(x) = 4(x + 3)(x + 1)(x - 2)^2$$
$$= 4x^4 - 36x^2 + 16x + 48$$

The graph of f is shown below.

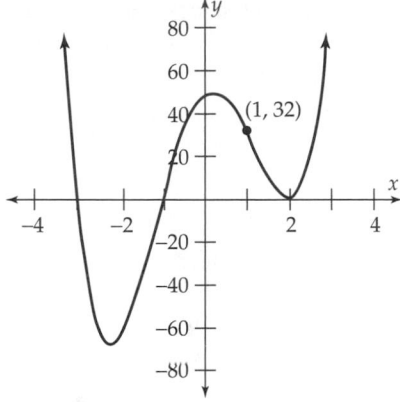

| **Example 2** |

Find the zeros of $f(x) = x^2 - 4x + 5$.
$2 \pm i$
The graph of f is shown below.

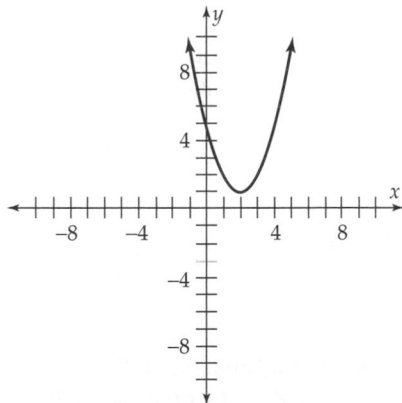

Teaching Notes

In the margin **NOTE**, the word *complex* should be interpreted as *complex and not real*. In **Example 2**, $3 + 2i$ and $3 - 2i$ are complex and not real.

The **Conjugate Zero Theorem** is sometimes stated as:

Complex zeros occur in conjugate pairs.

Teaching Notes

In **Factorization over the Real Numbers,** tell the students that an *irreducible quadratic polynomial* is one whose zeros are not real. Thus, it is one whose graph never intersects the *x*-axis. (The quadratic polynomial in **Example 2** on the previous page is irreducible.)

In **Example 3,** students may think that $(x - 2)[x - (3 + i)]$ will result in a polynomial with real coefficients whose zeros include 2 and $3 + i$. Explain that this is incorrect for two reasons:

- Multiplying the factors will result in coefficients that are not real.
  $(x - 2)[x - (3 + i)]$
  $= x^2 - (5 + i)x + (6 + 2i)$

- By the Conjugate Zero Theorem, if $3 + i$ is a zero, then $3 - i$ is also a zero.

Example Notes

In **Example 4,** tell students that "to completely factor a polynomial over the set of real numbers" means to express it as a product of linear and irreducible quadratic factors *with real coefficients*. Have students identify the linear factors and the quadratic factor.

linear: $(x + \sqrt{3})$ and $(x - \sqrt{3})$

irreducible quadratic: $(x^2 - 2x + 2)$

For **Example 5,** make the following points:

- To completely factor a polynomial of degree *n* over the set of complex numbers, we must get *n* linear factors, and some *coefficients may be complex.*

- Remind the students of the **Rational Zero Test** (Section 4.2, page 251); they will use the leading coefficient and the constant term to form possible rational zeros.

- Compare the titles in Examples 4 and 5. Note that one step in Example 5 is to factor over the real numbers, getting linear factors and an irreducible quadratic factor; the next step is to factor the quadratic into linear factors with complex coefficients.

Example 3 A Polynomial with Specific Zeros

Find a polynomial with real coefficients whose zeros include the numbers 2 and $3 + i$.

Solution

Because $3 + i$ is a zero, its conjugate, $3 - i$, must also be a zero. By the Factor Theorem, $x - (3 + i)$ and $x - (3 - i)$ are factors. Similarly, because 2 is a zero, $x - 2$ is a factor. So, consider the polynomial

$$f(x) = (x - 2)[x - (3 + i)][x - (3 - i)].$$

Obviously, $2, 3 + i$, and $3 - i$ are zeros of f. Multiplying out the factored form shows that $f(x)$ has real coefficients.

$$\begin{aligned} f(x) &= (x - 2)[x^2 - (3 - i)x - (3 + i)x + (3 + i)(3 - i)] \\ &= (x - 2)(x^2 - 3x + ix - 3x - ix + 9 - i^2) \\ &= (x - 2)(x^2 - 6x + 10) \\ &= x^3 - 8x^2 + 22x - 20 \end{aligned}$$

The next-to-last line of the calculation also shows that $f(x)$ can be factored as a product of a linear and a quadratic polynomial, each with *real* coefficients. The graph of f is shown in Figure 4.6-3. ∎

The technique used in Example 3 works because the product,

$$[x - (3 + i)][x - (3 - i)] = x^2 - 6x + 10,$$

has real coefficients. The proof of the following result shows why this must always be the case.

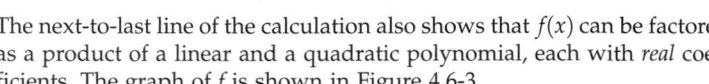

Factorization over the Real Numbers

> Every nonconstant polynomial with real coefficients can be factored as a product of linear and irreducible quadratic polynomials with real coefficients in such a way that the quadratic factors, if any, have no real zeros.

That is, every nonconstant polynomial with real coefficients can be written as the product of factors in the form $x - k$ or $ax^2 + bx + c$, where each quadratic factor is irreducible over the set of real numbers.

Proof The box on page 308 shows that for any polynomial $f(x)$,

$$f(x) = a(x - c_1)(x - c_2) \ldots (x - c_n)$$

where $c_1, c_2, \ldots, c_n$ are the zeros of f. If some c_r is a real number, then the factor $x - c_r$ is a linear polynomial with real coefficients. If some c_j is a nonreal complex zero, then its conjugate must also be a zero. Thus, some c_k is the conjugate of c_j, say, $c_j = a + bi$ and $c_k = a - bi$, with a and b real numbers. Thus,

(graph panel)

16

8

x

–8 –4   0   4   8

–8

–16

Figure 4.6-3

$$(x - c_j)(x - c_k) = [x - (a + bi)][x - (a - bi)]$$
$$= x^2 - (a - bi)x - (a + bi)x + (a + bi)(a - bi)$$
$$= x^2 - ax + bix - ax - bix + a^2 - (bi)^2$$
$$= x^2 - 2ax + (a^2 + b^2)$$

Therefore, the factor $(x - c_j)(x - c_k)$ is a quadratic expression with real coefficients because a and b are real numbers. Its zeros, c_j and c_k, are nonreal. By taking the real zeros of f one at a time and the nonreal ones in conjugate pairs in this fashion, the desired factorization of $f(x)$ is obtained.

Example 4   **Completely Factoring a Polynomial over the Real Numbers**

Completely factor $f(x) = x^4 - 2x^3 - x^2 + 6x - 6$ over the set of real numbers given that $1 + i$ is a zero of f.

Solution

Because $1 + i$ is a zero of f, its conjugate, $1 - i$, is also a zero of f, and $f(x)$ has the following quadratic factor.

$$[x - (1 + i)][x - (1 - i)] = x^2 - 2x + 2$$

Dividing $f(x)$ by $x^2 - 2x + 2$ shows that the other factor is $x^2 - 3$, which factors as $(x + \sqrt{3})(x - \sqrt{3})$. Therefore,

$$f(x) = (x + \sqrt{3})(x - \sqrt{3})(x^2 - 2x + 2)$$

is the complete factorization of $x^4 - 2x^3 - x^2 + 6x - 6$ over the real numbers. The graph of f is shown in Figure 4.6-4.

Figure 4.6-4

Complete Factorization of Polynomials

The techniques illustrated in this chapter can be used to completely factor some polynomials into linear factors.

Example 5   **Completely Factoring a Polynomial over the Complex Numbers**

Completely factor $f(x) = x^4 - 5x^3 + 4x^2 + 2x - 8$ over the set of real numbers and then over the set of complex numbers.

Solution

Because the degree of the polynomial is 4, there are exactly 4 complex zeros.

Find all rational zeros: The possible rational zeros are factors of 8.

$$\pm 1, \pm 2, \pm 4, \pm 8$$

Example 3

Find a polynomial with real coefficients whose zeros include the numbers -3 and $2 - i$.

$$f(x) = (x + 3)[x - (2 - i)][x - (2 + i)]$$
$$= (x + 3)(x^2 - 4x + 5)$$
$$= x^3 - x^2 - 7x + 15$$

The graph of f is shown below.

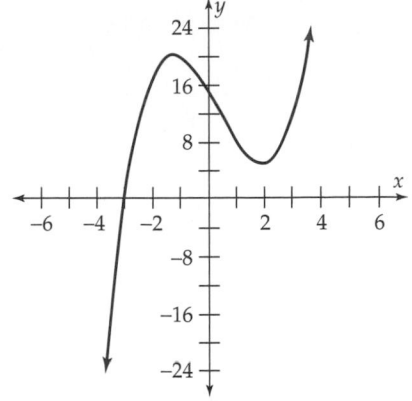

Example 4

Completely factor
$f(x) = x^4 - 4x^3 - 2x^2 + 28x - 35$
over the set of real numbers given that $2 - i$ is a zero of f.

$$[x - (2 - i)][x - (2 + i)] = x^2 - 4x + 5$$

Dividing by $x^2 - 4x + 5$ shows that

$$f(x) = (x^2 - 7)(x^2 - 4x + 5)$$
$$= (x + \sqrt{7})(x - \sqrt{7})(x^2 - 4x + 5).$$

The graph of f is shown below.

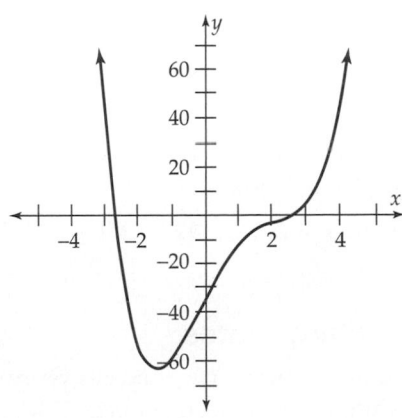

Example 5

Completely factor $f(x) = x^4 - 5x^3 + 2x^2 + 22x - 20$ over the set of real numbers, and then over the set of complex numbers.

The graph of f is shown below.

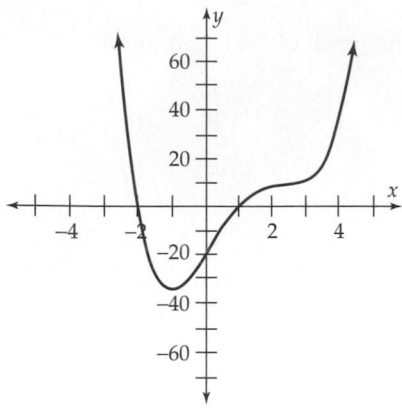

-2 and 1 are zeros.

Two linear factors of $f(x)$ are $x + 2$ and $x - 1$.

$$
\begin{array}{r|rrrrr}
-2 & 1 & -5 & 2 & 22 & -20 \\
   &   & -2 & 14 & -32 & 20 \\
\hline
   & 1 & -7 & 16 & -10 & \boxed{0}
\end{array}
$$

$f(x) = (x + 2)(x^3 - 7x + 16 - 10)$

$$
\begin{array}{r|rrrr}
1 & 1 & -7 & 16 & -10 \\
  &   & 1 & -6 & 10 \\
\hline
  & 1 & -6 & 10 & \boxed{0}
\end{array}
$$

$f(x) = (x + 2)(x - 1)(x^2 - 6x + 10)$

Find zeros of $g(x) = x^2 - 6x + 10$.

$$x = \dfrac{-(-6) \pm \sqrt{(-6)^2 - 4(1)(10)}}{2(1)}$$

$$= \dfrac{6 \pm \sqrt{-4}}{2} = \dfrac{6 \pm 2i}{2} = 3 \pm i$$

real factorization:

$f(x) = (x + 2)(x - 1)(x^2 - 6x + 10)$

complex factorization:

$f(x) = (x + 2)(x - 1)[x - (3 + i)] \cdot$
$\qquad\qquad\qquad\qquad [x - (3 - i)]$

Graph $f(x) = x^4 - 5x^3 + 4x^2 + 2x - 8$ and determine which of the possible zeros are the rational zeros.

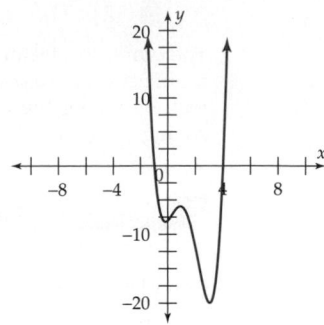

Figure 4.6-5

The graph suggests that -1 and 4 are zeros and you can easily verify that they are. The graph shows that there are no other real zeros.

Find all rational factors: Two linear factors of $f(x)$ are $x + 1$ and $x - 4$.

Find remaining factors: Use synthetic division twice to find another factor of $f(x)$.

$$
\begin{array}{r|rrrrr}
4 & 1 & -5 & 4 & 2 & -8 \\
  &   & 4 & -4 & 0 & 8 \\
\hline
  & 1 & -1 & 0 & 2 & \boxed{0}
\end{array}
$$

$f(x) = (x - 4)(x^3 - x^2 + 2)$

$$
\begin{array}{r|rrrr}
-1 & 1 & -1 & 0 & 2 \\
   &   & -1 & 2 & -2 \\
\hline
   & 1 & -2 & 2 & \boxed{0}
\end{array}
$$

$f(x) = (x - 4)(x + 1)(x^2 - 2x + 2)$

So, $x^4 - 5x^3 + 4x^2 + 2x - 8 = (x + 1)(x - 4)(x^2 - 2x + 2)$.

Use the quadratic formula to find the two zeros of $g(x) = x^2 - 2x + 2$.

$$x = \dfrac{2 \pm \sqrt{(-2)^2 - 4(1)(2)}}{2(1)}$$

$$= \dfrac{2 \pm \sqrt{-4}}{2} = \dfrac{2 \pm 2i}{2} = 1 \pm i$$

The complex factors are $x - (1 + i)$ and $x - (1 - i)$.

Teaching Notes

You may want to have students verify the products on the top of page 313:

$[x - (1 + i)][x - (1 - i)]$
$= x[x - (1 - i)] - (1 + i)[x - (1 - i)]$
$= x[x - 1 + i] - (1 + i)[x - 1 + i]$
$= [x^2 - x + ix] - 1[x - 1 + i] - i[x - 1 + i]$
$= x^2 - x + ix - x + 1 - i - ix + i - i^2$
$= x^2 - x + ix - x + 1 - i - ix + i + 1$
$= x^2 - 2x + 2$

$(x + 1)(x - 4)(x^2 - 2x + 2)$
$= (x^2 - 3x - 4)(x^2 - 2x + 2)$

$$
\begin{array}{r}
x^2 - 3x - 4 \\
x^2 - 2x + 2 \\
\hline
x^4 - 3x^3 - 4x^2 \\
-2x^3 + 6x^2 + 8x \\
2x^2 - 6x - 8 \\
\hline
x^4 - 5x^3 + 4x^2 + 2x - 8
\end{array}
$$

The complete factorizations of $f(x)$ over the set of real numbers and over the set of complex numbers are shown below.

$$x^4 - 5x^3 + 4x^2 + 2x - 8 = (x + 1)(x - 4)(x^2 - 2x + 2)$$
$$= (x + 1)(x - 4)[x - (1 + i)][x - (1 - i)]$$

Both products can be verified by multiplication. ∎

An expression that has *even* degree of 4 or greater may have only complex roots. Zeros and factors of such functions and expressions may be difficult to find, and the techniques illustrated in this chapter are of little use. However, functions of *odd* degree must have at least one real zero, and the corresponding expression must have at least one real linear factor. Therefore, a cubic expression can easily be approximately factored by estimating one zero, which yields the real linear factor, using synthetic division to determine the quadratic factor, and then using the quadratic formula to estimate the remaining two zeros.

Exercises 4.6

In Exercises 1–6, determine if $g(x)$ is a factor of $f(x)$ without using synthetic or long division.

1. $f(x) = x^{10} + x^8$ $g(x) = x - 1$
No

2. $f(x) = x^6 - 10$ $g(x) = x - 2$
No

3. $f(x) = 3x^4 - 6x^3 + 2x - 1$ $g(x) = x + 1$
No

4. $f(x) = x^5 - 3x^2 + 2x - 1$ $g(x) = x - 2$
No

5. $f(x) = x^3 - 2x^2 + 5x - 4$ $g(x) = x + 2$
No

6. $f(x) = 10x^{75} - 8x^{65} + 6x^{45} + 4x^{32} - 2x^{15} + 5$
$g(x) = x - 1$
No

In Exercises 7–10, list the zeros of the polynomial and state the multiplicity of each zero.

7. $f(x) = x^{54}\left(x + \dfrac{4}{5}\right)$

8. $g(x) = 3\left(x + \dfrac{1}{6}\right)\left(x - \dfrac{1}{5}\right)\left(x + \dfrac{1}{4}\right)$

9. $h(x) = 2x^{15}(x - \pi)^{14}[x - (\pi + 1)]^{13}$

10. $k(x) = (x - \sqrt{7})^7(x - \sqrt{5})^5(2x - 1)$

In Exercises 11–22, find all the zeros of f in the complex number system; then write $f(x)$ as a product of linear factors.

11. $f(x) = x^2 - 2x + 5$ **12.** $f(x) = x^2 - 4x + 13$

13. $f(x) = 3x^2 + 2x + 7$ **14.** $f(x) = 3x^2 - 5x + 2$

15. $f(x) = x^3 - 27$ *Hint:* Factor first.

16. $f(x) = x^3 + 125$ **17.** $f(x) = x^3 + 8$

18. $f(x) = x^6 - 64$
   Hint: Let $u = x^3$ and factor $u^2 - 64$ first.

19. $f(x) = x^4 - 1$ **20.** $f(x) = x^4 - x^2 - 6$

21. $f(x) = x^4 - 3x^2 - 10$ **22.** $f(x) = 2x^4 - 7x^2 - 4$

In Exercises 23–44, find a polynomial $f(x)$ with real coefficients that satisfies the given conditions. Some of the problems have many correct answers.

23. degree 3; only zeros are $1, 7, -4$
Possible answer: $f(x) = (x - 1)(x - 7)(x + 4)$
24. degree 3; only zeros are 1 and -1
Possible answer: $f(x) = (x - 1)^2(x + 1)$
25. degree 6; only zeros are $1, 2, \pi$
Possible answer: $f(x) = (x - 1)(x - 2)^2(x - \pi)^3$
26. degree 5; only zero is 2
Possible answer: $f(x) = (x - 2)^5$
27. degree 3; zeros $-3, 0, 4$; $f(5) = 80$
$f(x) = 2x(x - 4)(x + 3)$
28. degree 3; zeros $-1, \dfrac{1}{2}, 2$; $f(0) = 2$

29. zeros include $2 + i$ and $2 - i$
$f(x) = x^2 - 4x + 5$

17. $x = -2$ or $1 \pm i\sqrt{3}$
$f(x) = (x + 2)(x - 1 - i\sqrt{3})(x - 1 + i\sqrt{3})$

18. $x = -1 \pm i\sqrt{3}$ or $1 \pm i\sqrt{3}$ or ± 2;
$f(x) = (x - 2)(x + 2)(x - 1 - i\sqrt{3}) \cdot$
$(x - 1 + i\sqrt{3})(x + 1 - i\sqrt{3})(x + 1 + i\sqrt{3})$

19. $x = \pm 1$ or $\pm i$;
$f(x) = (x - 1)(x - i)(x + 1)(x + i)$

20. $x = \pm\sqrt{3}$ or $\pm i\sqrt{2}$;
$f(x) = (x - \sqrt{3})(x + \sqrt{3})(x - i\sqrt{2})(x + i\sqrt{2})$

21. $x = \pm\sqrt{5}$ or $\pm i\sqrt{2}$
$f(x) = (x - \sqrt{5})(x + \sqrt{5})(x - i\sqrt{2}) \cdot$
$(x + i\sqrt{2})$

22. $x = \pm 2$ or $\pm\dfrac{1}{\sqrt{2}}i$
$f(x) = 2\left(x - \dfrac{1}{\sqrt{2}}i\right)\left(x + \dfrac{1}{\sqrt{2}}i\right)(x - 2)(x + 2)$

28. $f(x) = 2(x + 1)\left(x - \dfrac{1}{2}\right)(x - 2)$

Teaching Notes

Challenge students to explain why a polynomial of odd degree must have at least one real zero.

By the Conjugate Zero Theorem, complex zeros must occur in conjugate pairs. So if there is a complex zero, there must be an even number of complex zeros. A polynomial of odd degree has an odd number of zeros, so at least one of the zeros must be real.

Exercises 4.6

ANSWERS

7. $x = 0$ (multiplicity 54);
$x = -\dfrac{4}{5}$ (multiplicity 1)

8. $x = -\dfrac{1}{6}$ (multiplicity 1);
$x = \dfrac{1}{5}$ (multiplicity 1);
$x = -\dfrac{1}{4}$ (multiplicity 1)

9. $x = 0$ (multiplicity 15);
$x = \pi$ (multiplicity 14);
$x = \pi + 1$ (multiplicity 13)

10. $x = \sqrt{7}$ (multiplicity 7);
$x = \sqrt{5}$ (multiplicity 5);
$x = -\dfrac{1}{2}$ (multiplicity 1)

11. $x = 1 \pm 2i$
$f(x) = (x - 1 - 2i)(x - 1 + 2i)$

12. $x = 2 \pm 3i$
$f(x) = (x - 2 + 3i)(x - 2 - 3i)$

13. $x = -\dfrac{1}{3} \pm \dfrac{2\sqrt{5}}{3}i$
$f(x) = \left(x + \dfrac{1}{3} - \dfrac{2\sqrt{5}}{3}i\right) \cdot$
$\left(x + \dfrac{1}{3} + \dfrac{2\sqrt{5}}{3}i\right)$

14. $x = 1$ or $\dfrac{2}{3}$; $f(x) = (3x - 2)(x - 1)$

15. $x = 3$ or $-\dfrac{3}{2} \pm \dfrac{3\sqrt{3}}{2}i$
$f(x) = (x - 3)\left(x + \dfrac{3}{2} - \dfrac{3\sqrt{3}}{2}i\right) \cdot$
$\left(x + \dfrac{3}{2} + \dfrac{3\sqrt{3}}{2}i\right)$

16. $x = -5$ or $\dfrac{5}{2} \pm \dfrac{5\sqrt{3}}{2}i$
$f(x) = (x + 5)\left(x - \dfrac{5}{2} - \dfrac{5\sqrt{3}}{2}i\right)^2 \cdot$
$\left(x - \dfrac{5}{2} + \dfrac{5\sqrt{3}}{2}i\right)$

44. $f(x) = -\frac{1}{12}x^3 + \frac{1}{6}x^2 - \frac{5}{12}x - \frac{13}{6}$

57. a. Since $z + w = (a + c) + (b + d)i$, $\overline{z + w} = (a + c) - (b + d)i$. Since $\bar{z} = a - bi$ and $\bar{w} = c - di$, $\bar{z} + \bar{w} = (a - bi) + (c - di) = (a + c) - (b + d)i$. Hence $\overline{z + w} = \bar{z} + \bar{w}$.

b. Since $zw = (ac - bd) + (ad + bc)i$, $\overline{zw} = (ac - bd) - (ad + bc)i$. Since $\bar{z} = a - bi$ and $\bar{w} = c - di$, $\bar{z} \cdot \bar{w} = (a - bi)(c - di) = (ac - bd) - (ad + bc)i$. Hence $\overline{zw} = \bar{z} \cdot \bar{w}$.

58. $f(x) = g(x) - h(x)$ is a polynomial at most of degree n. Therefore, unless it is a constant function, it can have at most n roots. But $f(c_i) = g(c_i) - h(c_i)$ is 0 for $n + 1$ different numbers c_i. Therefore, there are $n + 1$ different roots of the function and $f(x)$ must be a constant function with $f(x) = 0$ for all x. Therefore, $g(x) - h(x) = 0$, $g(x) = h(x)$ for all x.

59. a. $\overline{f(z)} = \overline{az^3 + bz^2 + cz + d}$ (definition of $f(z)$)

$= \overline{az^3} + \overline{bz^2} + \overline{cz} + \bar{d}$ (Exercise 57(a))

$= \bar{a}\,\overline{z^3} + \bar{b}\,\overline{z^2} + \bar{c}\,\bar{z} + \bar{d}$ (Exercise 57(b))

$= a\bar{z}^3 + b\bar{z}^2 + c\bar{z} + d$ ($r = \bar{r}$ for r real)

$= a\bar{z}^3 + b\bar{z}^2 + c\bar{z} + d$ (Exercise 57(b))

$= f(\bar{z})$ (definition of f)

b. Since $f(z) = 0$, we have $0 = \bar{0} = \overline{f(z)} = f(\bar{z})$.

Hence $\bar{z}$ is a zero of $f(x)$.

60. $f(\bar{z}) = a(\bar{z})^n + b(\bar{z})^{n-1} + \ldots + c(\bar{z}) + d = \overline{az^n} + \overline{bz^{n-1}} + \ldots + \overline{cz} + d = \overline{f(z)} = \bar{0} = 0$

61. If $f(z)$ is a polynomial with real coefficients, then $f(z)$ can be factored as $g_1(z)g_2(z)g_3(z)\cdots g_k(z)$, where each $g_i(z)$ is a polynomial with real coefficients and degree 1 or 2. The rules of polynomial multiplication show that the degree of $f(z)$ is the sum:

30. zeros include $1 + 3i$ and $1 - 3i$
$f(x) = x^2 - 2x + 10$
31. zeros include 2 and $2 + i$
$f(x) = (x - 2)(x^2 - 4x + 5)$
32. zeros include 3 and $4i - 1$
$f(x) = (x - 3)(x^2 + 2x + 17)$
33. zeros include -3, $1 - i$, $1 + 2i$
$f(x) = (x + 3)(x^2 - 2x + 2)(x^2 - 2x + 5)$
34. zeros include 1, $2 + i$, $3i - 1$
$f(x) = (x - 1)(x^2 - 4x + 5)(x^2 + 2x + 10)$
35. degree 2; zeros $1 + 2i$ and $1 - 2i$
$f(x) = x^2 - 2x + 5$
36. degree 4; zeros $3i$ and $-3i$, each of multiplicity 2
$f(x) = (x^2 + 9)^2$
37. degree 4; only zeros are 4, $3 + i$, and $3 - i$
$f(x) = (x - 4)^2(x^2 - 6x + 10)$
38. degree 5; zeros 2 of multiplicity 3, i, and $-i$
$f(x) = (x - 2)^3(x^2 + 1)$
39. degree 6; zeros 0 of multiplicity 3 and 3, $1 + i$, $1 - i$, each of multiplicity 1
$f(x) = x^3(x - 3)(x^2 - 2x + 2)$
40. degree 6; zeros include i of multiplicity 2 and 3
$f(x) = (x^2 + 1)^2(x - 3)^3$
41. degree 2; zeros include $1 + i$; $f(0) = 6$
$f(x) = 3(x^2 - 2x + 2)$
42. degree 2; zeros include $3 + i$; $f(2) = 3$
$f(x) = \frac{3}{2}x^2 - 9x + 15$
43. degree 3; zeros include i and 1; $f(-1) = 8$
$f(x) = -2x^3 + 2x^2 - 2x + 2$
44. degree 3; zeros include $2 + 3i$ and -2; $f(2) = -3$

In Exercises 45–48, find a polynomial with complex coefficients that satisfies the given conditions.
Possible answers:
45. degree 2; zeros i and $1 - 2i$
$f(x) = x^2 - (1 - i)x + (2 + i)$
46. degree 2; zeros $2i$ and $1 + i$
$f(x) = x^2 - (1 + 3i)x + (-2 + 2i)$
47. degree 3; zeros 3, i, and $2 - i$
$f(x) = x^3 - 5x^2 + (7 + 2i)x - (3 + 6i)$
48. degree 4; zeros $\sqrt{2}$, $-\sqrt{2}$, $1 + i$, and $1 - i$
$f(x) = x^4 - 2x^3 + 4x - 4$

In Exercises 49–56, one zero of the polynomial is given; find all the zeros.

49. $x^3 - 2x^2 - 2x - 3$; zero 3 $3, -\frac{1}{2} \pm \frac{\sqrt{3}}{2}i$

50. $x^3 + x^2 + x + 1$; zero i
$-1, \pm i$
51. $x^4 + 3x^3 + 3x^2 + 3x + 2$; zero i
$-1, -2, \pm i$
52. $x^4 - x^3 - 5x^2 - x - 6$; zero i
$3, -2, \pm i$
53. $x^4 - 2x^3 + 5x^2 - 8x + 4$; zero 1 of multiplicity 2
$1, \pm 2i$

54. $x^4 - 6x^3 + 29x^2 - 76x + 68$; zero 2 of multiplicity 2
$2, 1 \pm 4i$
55. $x^4 - 4x^3 + 6x^2 - 4x + 5$; zero $2 - i$
$\pm i, 2 \pm i$
56. $x^4 - 5x^3 + 10x^2 - 20x + 24$; zero $2i$
$3, 2, \pm 2i$
57. Let $z = a + bi$ and $w = c + di$ be complex numbers (a, b, c, d are real numbers). Prove the given equality by computing each side and comparing the results.
a. $\overline{z + w} = \bar{z} + \bar{w}$ (The left side says: "First find $z + w$ and then take the conjugate." The right side says: "First take the conjugates of z and w and then add.")
b. $\overline{z \cdot w} = \bar{z} \cdot \bar{w}$

58. Let $g(x)$ and $h(x)$ be polynomials of degree n and assume that there are $n + 1$ numbers $c_1, c_2, \ldots, c_n, c_{n+1}$ such that
$$g(c_i) = h(c_i) \quad \text{for every } i.$$
Prove that $g(x) = h(x)$. Hint: Show that each c_i is a zero of $f(x) = g(x) - h(x)$. If $f(x)$ is nonzero, what is its largest possible degree? To avoid a contradiction, conclude that $f(x) = 0$.

59. Suppose $f(x) = ax^3 + bx^2 + cx + d$ has real coefficients and z is a complex zero of f.
a. Use Exercise 57 and the fact that $\bar{r} = r$, when r is a real number, to show that
$\overline{f(z)} = \overline{az^3 + bz^2 + cz + d}$
$= a\bar{z}^3 + b\bar{z}^2 + c\bar{z} + d = f(\bar{z})$.
b. Conclude that $\bar{z}$ is also a zero of f. Note: $f(\bar{z}) = \overline{f(z)} = \bar{0} = 0$.

60. Let $f(x)$ be a polynomial with real coefficients and z a complex zero of f. Prove that the conjugate $\bar{z}$ is also a zero of f. Hint: Exercise 59 is the case when $f(x)$ has degree 3; the proof in the general case is similar.

61. Use the Factorization over the Real Numbers statement to show that every polynomial with real coefficients and odd degree must have at least one real zero.

62. Give an example of a polynomial $f(x)$ with complex, nonreal coefficients and a complex number z such that z is a zero of f but its conjugate is not. Therefore, the conclusion of the Conjugate Roots Theorem may be false if $f(x)$ doesn't have real coefficients.

degree $g_1(z)$ + degree $g_2(z)$ + degree $g_3(z)$ + $\cdots$ + degree $g_k(z)$. If all of the $g_i(z)$ have degree 2, then this last sum is an even number. But $f(z)$ has odd degree, so this can't occur. Therefore, at least one of the $g_i(z)$ is a first-degree polynomial and hence must have a real zero. This zero is also a zero of $f(z)$.

62. The linear polynomial $f(x) = x - i$ is one example. $z = i$ is a zero but $\bar{z} = -i$ is not.

CHAPTER 4 REVIEW

Important Concepts

315

Important Facts and Formulas

When f is a polynomial and r is a real number that satisfies any of the following statements, then r satisfies all the statements.

- r is a zero of the polynomial function $y = f(x)$
- r is an x-intercept of the graph of f
- r is a solution, or root, of the equation $f(x) = 0$
- $x - r$ is a factor of the polynomial expression $f(x)$
- There is a one-to-one correspondence between the linear factors of $f(x)$ that have real coefficients and the x-intercepts of the graph of f.

A polynomial of degree n has at most n distinct real zeros.

All rational zeros of a polynomial have the form $\frac{r}{s}$, where r is a factor of the constant term and s is a factor of the leading coefficient.

The end behavior of the graph of a polynomial function is similar to the end behavior of the graph of the highest degree term of the polynomial.

Zeros of even multiplicity touch but do not cross the x-axis. Zeros of odd multiplicity cross the x-axis.

The number of local extrema of the graph of a polynomial function is at most one less than the degree of a polynomial.

The number of points of inflection of the graph of a polynomial function is at most two less than the degree of the polynomial.

The graph of a rational function has a vertical asymptote at every number that is a zero of the denominator and not a zero of the numerator.

The x-intercepts of the graph of a rational function occur at the numbers that are zeros of the numerator but are not zeros of the denominator.

Every complex number can be written in the standard form $a + bi$.

$i^2 = -1$ and $i = \sqrt{-1}$

If $a + bi$ is a zero of a polynomial with real coefficients, then its conjugate $a - bi$ is also a zero.

A polynomial of degree n has exactly n complex zeros counting multiplicities.

Every polynomial expression with real coefficients can be factored into linear and irreducible quadratic factors with real coefficients.

Every polynomial expression can be factored into linear factors with complex coefficients.

Review Exercises

Review Exercises

ANSWERS

5. $\underline{2}$ | 1 -5 $\quad$ 8 $\quad$ 1 $\quad$ -17 $\quad$ 16 $\quad$ -4
$\qquad$ 2 $\quad$ -6 $\quad$ 4 $\quad$ 10 $\quad$ -14 $\quad$ 4
$\overline{\quad 1 \;\; -3 \quad 2 \quad 5 \quad -7 \quad 2 \;\;| \underline{0}}$
other factor: $x^5 - 3x^4 + 2x^3 + 5x^2 - 7x + 2$

Section 4.1

1. Which of the following are polynomials? **a, c, e, f**

  a. $2^3 + x^2$ $\qquad$ **b.** $x + \dfrac{1}{x}$ $\qquad$ **c.** $x^3 - \dfrac{1}{\sqrt{2}}$

  d. $\sqrt[3]{x^4}$ $\qquad$ **e.** $\pi^3 - x$ $\qquad$ **f.** $\sqrt{2} + 2x^2$

  g. $\sqrt{x} + 2x^2$ $\qquad$ **h.** $|x|$

2. What is the remainder when $x^4 + 3x^3 + 1$ is divided by $x^2 + 1$?
 $-3x + 2$

3. What is the remainder when $x^{112} - 2x^8 + 9x^5 - 4x^4 + x - 5$ is divided by $x - 1$?
 0

4. Is $x - 1$ a factor of $f(x) = 14x^{87} - 65x^{56} + 51$? Justify your answer.
 $f(1) = 14 - 65 + 51 = 0.$

5. Use synthetic division to show that $x - 2$ is a factor of $x^6 - 5x^5 + 8x^4 + x^3 - 17x^2 + 16x - 4$, and find the other factor.

6. Find a polynomial f of degree 3 such that $f(-1) = 0$, $f(1) = 0$, and $f(0) = 5$.
 $f(x) = 5(x - 1)^2(x + 1)$

Section 4.2

7. Find the zero(s) of $2\left(\dfrac{x}{5} + 7\right) - 3x - \dfrac{x + 2}{5} + 4$. $x = \dfrac{44}{7}$

8. Find the zeros of $3x^2 - 2x - 5$. $x = \dfrac{5}{3}, -1$

9. Factor the polynomial $x^3 - 8x^2 + 9x + 6$. *Hint:* 2 is a zero.
 $f(x) = (x - 2)\left(x - \left(3 + 2\sqrt{3}\right)\right)\left(x - \left(3 - 2\sqrt{3}\right)\right)$

10. Find all real zeros of $x^6 - 4x^3 + 4$.
 $x = \sqrt[3]{2}$

20. When $x^4 - 4x^3 + 16x - 16$ is divided by $x - 5$ synthetically, the last row, 1 1 5 41 189, is all positive. Therefore, 5 is an upper bound for the real zeros.

21. When $x^4 - 4x^3 + 15$ is divided by $x + 1$ synthetically, the last row, 1 −5 5 −5 20, has alternating signs. Therefore, −1 is a lower bound for the real zeros.

22. rational zeros: 1 and −1; irrational zeros: ≈ -0.86676 and 1.86676

23. rational zeros: −1 and 4; irrational zero: ≈ -1.328

24. 4: multiplicity 3;
2: multiplicity 2;
−17: multiplicity 3;
−2: multiplicity 1

25. −3: multiplicity 2;
4: multiplicity 1;
−3: multiplicity 1;
3: multiplicity 1

26. Answers may vary. Any graph that is not continuous is not the graph of a polynomial. Also, any graph that doesn't use all real numbers in its domain cannot be a polynomial. Another possibility is a graph with sharp corners like the one shown here. The graphs of polynomials are all smooth.

27. Answers may vary.

28. c

11. Find all real zeros of $9x^3 - 6x^2 - 35x + 26$. *Hint:* Try $x = -2$. **-2, $\dfrac{4 \pm \sqrt{3}}{3}$**

12. Find all real zeros of $3y^3(y^4 - y^2 - 5)$. **$0, \pm\sqrt{\dfrac{1 + \sqrt{21}}{2}}$**

13. Find the rational zeros of $x^4 - 2x^3 - 4x^2 + 1$.
-1

14. Consider the polynomial $2x^3 - 8x^2 + 5x + 3$.
a. List the only possible rational zeros. **± 3, ± 1, $\pm\dfrac{3}{2}$, $\pm\dfrac{1}{2}$**
b. Find one rational zero. **3**
c. Find all the zeros of the polynomial. **$\dfrac{1 \pm \sqrt{3}}{2}$**

15. a. Find all rational zeros of $x^3 + 2x^2 - 2x - 2$. **There are no rational**
b. Find two consecutive integers such that an irrational zero of **zeros**
$x^3 + 2x^2 - 2x - 2$ lies between them.
-3 and -2, -1 and 0, or 1 and 2

16. How many distinct real zeros does $x^3 + 4x$ have?
1

17. How many distinct real zeros does $x^3 - 6x^2 + 11x - 6$ have?
3

18. Find the zeros of $x^4 - 11x^2 + 18$.
$\pm 3, \pm\sqrt{2}$

19. The polynomial $x^3 - 2x + 1$ has **d**
a. no real zeros.
b. only one real zero.
c. three rational zeros.
d. only one rational zero.
e. none of the above.

20. Show that 5 is an upper bound for the real zeros of $x^4 - 4x^3 + 16x - 16$.

21. Show that −1 is a lower bound for the real zeros of $x^4 - 4x^3 + 15$.

In Exercises 22 and 23, find the real zeros of the polynomial.

22. $x^6 - 2x^5 - x^4 + 3x^3 - x^2 - x + 1$

23. $x^5 - 3x^4 - 2x^3 - x^2 - 23x - 20$

Section 4.3

24. List the zeros of the polynomial and the multiplicity of each zero.
$f(x) = 5(x - 4)^3(x - 2)(x + 17)^3(x^2 - 4)$

25. List the zeros of the polynomial and the multiplicity of each zero.
$f(x) = -2(x + 3)^2(x - 4)(x^2 - 9)$

26. Draw the graph of a function that could not possibly be the graph of a polynomial function, and explain why.

27. Draw a graph that could be the graph of a polynomial function of degree 5. You need not list a specific polynomial nor do any computation.

28. Which of the statements is not true about the polynomial function f whose graph is shown in the figure on the next page?

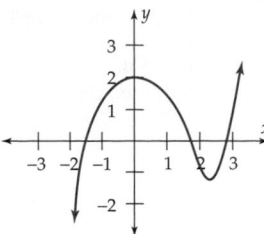

a. f has three zeros between -2 and 3
b. $f(x)$ could possibly be a fifth-degree polynomial
c. $(f \circ f)(0) > 0$
d. $f(2) - f(-1) < 3$
e. $f(x)$ is positive for all x in the interval $[-1, 0]$

29. Which of the statements **i–v** about the polynomial function f whose graph is shown in the figure below are false?

i, iv, and v are false.

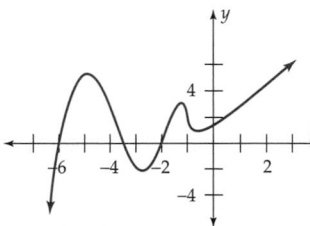

i f has 2 zeros in the interval $(-6, -3)$ **iv** $f(2) - 2 = 0$
ii $f(-3) - f(-6) < 0$ **v** f has degree ≤ 4
iii $f(0) < f(1)$

In Exercises 30–33, find a viewing window (or windows) that shows a complete graph of the function. Be alert for hidden behavior.

30. $f(x) = 0.5x^3 - 4x^2 + x + 1$

31. $g(x) = 0.3x^5 - 4x^4 + x^3 - 4x^2 + 5x + 1$

32. $h(x) = 4x^3 - 100x^2 + 600x$

33. $f(x) = 32x^3 - 99x^2 + 100x + 2$

In Exercises 34–37, sketch a complete graph of the function.

34. $f(x) = x^3 - 9x$ 35. $g(x) = x^3 - 2x^2 + 3$

36. $h(x) = x^4 - x^3 - 4x^2 + 4x + 2$ 37. $f(x) = x^4 - 3x - 2$

Section 4.3.A

38. HomeArt makes plastic replicas of famous statues. Their total cost to produce copies of a particular statue is shown in the table on the next page.
a. Sketch a scatter plot of the data.
b. Use cubic regression to find a function $C(x)$ that models the data—that

---

30. Use $-3 \leq x \leq 9$ and $-35 \leq y \leq 15$

31. Use $-10 \leq x \leq 20$ and $-10{,}000 \leq y \leq 500$ for the overall graph and $-2 \leq x \leq 2$ and $-10 \leq y \leq 5$ for behavior around the origin.

32. Use $-2 \leq x \leq 18$ and $-500 \leq y \leq 1100$

33. Use $0.2 \leq x \leq 2$ and $20 \leq y \leq 40$; $-1 \leq x \leq 0.2$, $-20 \leq y \leq 20$

34. Use $-4 \leq x \leq 4$ and $-12 \leq y \leq 12$. There are x-intercepts at $(-3, 0)$, $(0, 0)$ and $(3, 0)$, a local maximum at $(-1.732, 10.392)$ and a local minimum at $(1.732, -10.392)$.

35. Use $-2 \leq x \leq 3$ and $-5 \leq y \leq 5$. There is an x-intercept at $(-1, 0)$, a local maximum at $(0, 3)$, and a local minimum at $\left(\frac{4}{3}, \frac{49}{27}\right)$.

36. Use $-3 \leq x \leq 3$ and $-5 \leq y \leq 5$. There are x-intercepts at approximately $(-1.908, 0)$ and $(-0.376, 0)$, local minima at approximately $(-1.326, -4.914)$ and $(1.607, 0.617)$, and a local maximum at approximately $(0.469, 2.941)$.

37. Use $-3 \leq x \leq 3$ and $-5 \leq y \leq 5$. There are x-intercepts at $x \approx -0.618, 1.618$ and a local minimum at $x \approx 0.909$.

38. a. 4000

b. $c(x) = 0.008515x^3 - 1.10945x^2 + 56.25833x + 2017.25758$

38. c. $3466.47

d. 35 statues: $85.49;
75 statues: $47.82

39. a.   120,000

b. $y = 0.04x^4 + 0.19x^3 + 62.06x^2 + 1615.35x + 29{,}552.18$; $79,223 in 2007 and $127,317 in 2015

40. vertical asymptote: $x = -4$

horizontal asymptote: x-axis

41.

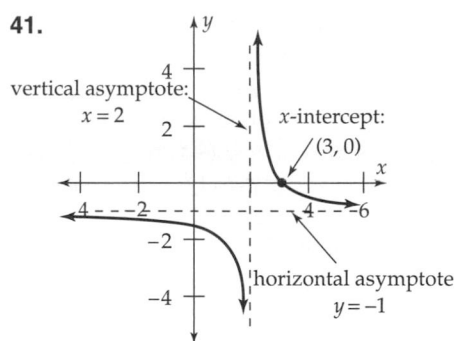

vertical asymptote: $x = 2$
x-intercept: $(3, 0)$
horizontal asymptote: $y = -1$

42.

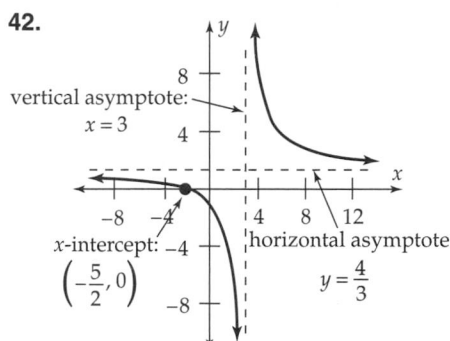

vertical asymptote: $x = 3$
x-intercept: $\left(-\frac{5}{2}, 0\right)$
horizontal asymptote: $y = \frac{4}{3}$

43.

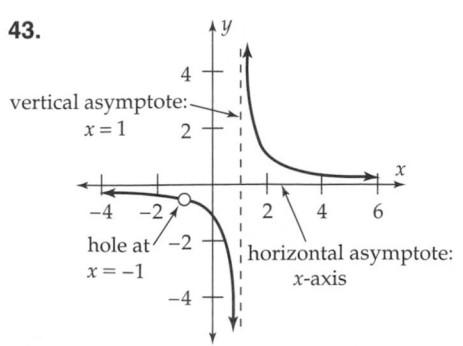

vertical asymptote: $x = 1$
hole at $x = -1$
horizontal asymptote: x-axis

is, the cost of making x statues. Assume C is reasonably accurate when $x \le 100$.

c. Use C to estimate the cost of making the seventy-first statue.

d. Use C to approximate the average cost per statue when 35 are made and when 75 are made. Recall that the average cost of x statues is $\frac{C(x)}{x}$.

Number of statues	Total cost
0	$2,000
10	2,519
20	2,745
30	2,938
40	3,021
50	3,117
60	3,269
70	3,425

39. The following table gives the estimated cost of a college education at a public institution. Costs include tuition, fees, books, and room and board for four years.

a. Sketch a scatter plot of the data (with $x = 0$ corresponding to 1990).

b. Use quartic regression to find a function C that models the data. Estimate the cost of a college education in 2007 and in 2015.

Enrollment Year	Costs	Enrollment Year	Costs
1998	$46,691	2008	$ 83,616
2000	52,462	2010	93,951
2002	58,946	2012	105,564
2004	66,232	2014	118,611
2006	74,418		

Source: Teachers Insurance and Annuity Association College Retirement Equities Fund

Section 4.4

In Exercises 40–43, sketch a complete graph of the function. Label the x-intercepts, all local extrema, holes, and asymptotes.

40. $g(x) = \dfrac{-2}{x + 4}$

41. $h(x) = \dfrac{3 - x}{x - 2}$

42. $k(x) = \dfrac{4x + 10}{3x - 9}$

43. $f(x) = \dfrac{x + 1}{x^2 - 1}$

In Exercises 44 and 45, list all asymptotes of the graph of the function.

44. $f(x) = \dfrac{x^2 - 1}{x^3 - 2x^2 - 5x + 6}$

45. $g(x) = \dfrac{x^4 - 6x^3 + 2x^2 - 6x + 2}{x^2 - 3}$

In Exercises 46–49, find a viewing window (or windows) that shows a complete graph of the function. Be alert for hidden behavior.

46. $f(x) = \dfrac{x - 3}{x^2 + x - 2}$

47. $g(x) = \dfrac{x^2 - x - 6}{x^3 - 3x^2 + 3x - 1}$

48. $h(x) = \dfrac{x^4 + 4}{x^4 - 99x^2 - 100}$

49. $k(x) = \dfrac{x^3 - 2x^2 - 4x + 8}{x - 10}$

50. Which of these statements is true about the graph of

$$f(x) = \frac{(x - 1)(x + 3)}{(x^2 + 1)(x^2 - 1)} ? \quad \textbf{d}$$

   a. The graph has two vertical asymptotes.
   b. The graph touches the x-axis at $x = 3$.
   c. The graph lies above the x-axis when $x < -1$.
   d. The graph has a hole at $x = 1$.
   e. The graph has no horizontal asymptotes.

Section 4.5

In Exercises 51–58, solve the equation in the complex number system.

51. $x^2 + 3x + 10 = 0$ $x = \dfrac{-3 \pm i\sqrt{31}}{2}$

52. $x^2 + 2x + 5 = 0$ $x = -1 \pm 2i$

53. $5x^2 + 2 = 3x$ $x = \dfrac{3 \pm i\sqrt{31}}{10}$

54. $-3x^2 + 4x - 5 = 0$ $x = \dfrac{2}{3} \pm \dfrac{\sqrt{11}}{3}i$

55. $3x^4 + x^2 - 2 = 0$

56. $8x^4 + 10x^2 + 3 = 0$

57. $x^3 + 8 = 0$

58. $x^3 - 27 = 0$

59. One zero of $x^4 - x^3 - x^2 - x - 2$ is i. Find all zeros.
   $\pm i, 2, -1$

60. One zero of $x^4 + x^3 - 5x^2 + x - 6$ is i. Find all zeros.
   $\pm i, -3, 2$

61. Give an example of a fourth-degree polynomial with real coefficients whose zeros include 0 and $1 + i$.
   Possible answer: $f(x) = x^4 - 2x^3 + 2x^2$

62. Find a fourth-degree polynomial f whose only zeros are $2 + i$ and $2 - i$ such that $f(-1) = 50$.
   $f(x) = \dfrac{1}{2}(x^4 - 8x^3 + 26x^2 - 40x + 25)$

Section 4.5.A

63. Find the orbit of 1 for $f(z) = \left(\dfrac{3}{5} + \dfrac{4}{5}i\right)z$.

64. Find the orbit of 0 for $f(z) = z^2 + c$ using the following values of c. State whether c is in the Mandelbrot set.

   a. $c = -1$
   b. $c = -0.5 + 0.6i$
   c. $c = 0.3 + 0.5i$

Section 4.6

Factor each of the following over the set of real numbers and over the set of complex numbers.

65. $x^3 - 6x^2 + 11x - 6$

66. $x^3 + 3x^2 + 3x + 2$

67. $x^4 - x^3 - x^2 - x - 2$

68. $2x^3 + 3x^2 + 9x + 4$

69. $x^4 + 2x^2 + 1$

70. $9x^5 + 30x^4 + 43x^3 + 114x^2 + 28x - 24$

---

44. vertical asymptotes: $x = 3$ and $x = -2$; horizontal asymptote: $y = 0$; hole at $\left(1, -\dfrac{1}{3}\right)$

45. vertical asymptotes: $x = \pm\sqrt{3}$; parabolic asymptote: $y = x^2 - 6x + 5$

46. Use $-4.7 \le x \le 4.7$ and $-5 \le y \le 5$. For hidden behavior use $2 \le x \le 30$ and $-0.2 \le y \le 0.1$.

47. Use $-4.7 \le x \le 4.7$ and $-10 \le y \le 10$. vertical asymptote $x = 1$; horizontal asymptote $y = 0$; x-intercepts at $x = -2$, $x = 3$; for hidden behavior use $-15 \le x \le 10$, $-0.5 \le y \le 0.5$

48. Use $-18.8 \le x \le 18.8$ and $-8 \le y \le 8$.

49. Use $-30 \le x \le 30$ and $-1000 \le y \le 1000$. For hidden behavior use $-7 \le x \le 7$, $-5 \le y \le 5$.

55. $x = \pm\sqrt{\dfrac{2}{3}}$ or $\pm i$

56. $x = \pm\dfrac{1}{\sqrt{2}}i$ or $\pm\dfrac{\sqrt{3}}{2}i$

57. $x = -2$ or $1 \pm i\sqrt{3}$

58. $x = 3$ or $-\dfrac{3}{2} \pm \dfrac{3\sqrt{3}}{2}i$

63. a fixed orbit of one point: $\left(\dfrac{3}{5}, \dfrac{4}{5}\right)$

64. a. $f^1(0) = -1$, $f^2(0) = 0$, $f^3(0) = -1$, $f^4(0) = 0$, ... The orbit has a period of 2; therefore, -1 is in the Mandelbrot set.

   b. The orbit has a period of 6 that is approximately $-0.5 + 0.6i$, -0.61, $-0.13 + 0.6i$, $-0.84 + 0.45i$, $0.01 - 0.15i$, $-0.52 + 0.60i$; therefore, $-0.5 + 0.6i$ is in the Mandelbrot set.

   c. The orbit has a period of 5 that is approximately $0.3 + 0.5i$, $0.14 + 0.8i$, $-0.32 + 0.72i$, $-0.12 + 0.36i$, $0.31 + 0.49i$; therefore, $0.3 + 0.5i$ is in the Mandelbrot set.

65. $(x - 1)(x - 2)(x - 3)$

---

66. $(x + 2)(x^2 + x + 1)$;
$(x + 2)\left(x - \left(\dfrac{-1 + i\sqrt{3}}{2}\right)\right) \cdot \left(x - \left(\dfrac{-1 - i\sqrt{3}}{2}\right)\right)$

67. $(x + 1)(x - 2)(x^2 + 1)$;
$(x + 1)(x - 2)(x + i)(x - i)$

68. $(2x + 1)(x^2 + x + 4)$;
$(2x + 1)\left(x - \left(\dfrac{-1 + i\sqrt{15}}{2}\right)\right) \cdot \left(x - \left(\dfrac{-1 - i\sqrt{15}}{2}\right)\right)$

69. $(x^2 + 1)(x^2 + 1)$;
$(x + i)(x - i)(x + i)(x - i)$

70. $(x + 3)(3x + 2)(3x - 1)(x^2 + 4)$;
$(x + 3)(3x + 2)(3x - 1)(x + 2i)(x - 2i)$

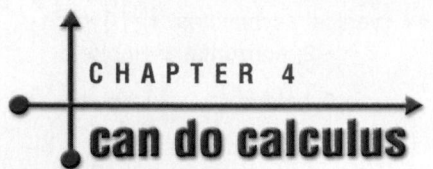

CHAPTER 4
can do calculus

Optimization Applications

Teaching Notes

Remind students of the **Applied Problems Guideline** (page 97): *Read, Label, Draw, Translate, Consolidate, Solve, Find, Check and interpret.*

Example Notes

In **Example 1,** point out to students that y is *not* one of the numbers the problem asks for. The two numbers are x and $\frac{50}{x}$.

For **Example 2,** try the following activity to enhance students' understanding:

Have every student begin with a sheet of paper (all sheets the same size). Assign various values for x, and tell each student to cut squares from the corners of his or her paper, using the assigned value of x, and then form a box as described in the problem. Then, have students compute and compare the volumes of the resulting boxes. This will illustrate the effect changing x has on the volume of the box.

ADDITIONAL EXAMPLES

Example 1

Find two negative numbers such that the product of one number and the square of the other is -100, and the sum of the numbers is as large as possible.

Let x and z be the numbers.

$x^2 z = -100$, $y = x + z$, $y = x + \left(\frac{-100}{x^2}\right)$

Graph $y = x + \left(\frac{-100}{x^2}\right)$:

CHAPTER 4
can do calculus

Optimization Applications

Many real-world situations require you to find the largest or smallest quantity satisfying certain conditions. For instance, automotive engineers want to design engines with maximum fuel efficiency. Similarly, a cereal manufacturer who needs a box of volume 300 cubic inches might want to know the dimensions of the box that requires the least amount of cardboard, which is the cheapest to make. The exact solutions of such minimum/maximum problems require calculus. However, graphing technology can provide very accurate approximate solutions.

Example 1   Maximum of a Rational Function

Find two negative numbers whose product is 50 and whose sum is as large as possible.

Solution

Let x and z be the two negative numbers, and let y be their sum. Then $xz = 50$ and $y = x + z$. Solving $xz = 50$ for z yields $z = \frac{50}{x}$ so that

$$y = x + z = x + \frac{50}{x}.$$

The desired quantity is the value of x that makes y as large as possible. Since x must be negative, graph $y = x + \frac{50}{x}$ in a window with $-20 \le x \le 0$.

Each point (x, y) on the graph represents the following:

- x represents one of the two negative number, and $\frac{50}{x}$ represents the other negative number
- y is the sum of the two negative numbers

The largest y possible is the point on the graph with largest y-coordinate, that is, the highest point on this part of the graph. Either zoom-in or use the maximum finder to approximate the highest point. As shown in Figure 4.C-1, the largest value of y is approximately -14.14214 which occurs when $x \approx -7.071067$. Therefore, the numbers are approximately -7.071067 and $\frac{50}{-7.071067} \approx -7.071069$. The exact solution, as found by using calculus, is $\sqrt{50}$—which is approximately -7.071068 and is very close to the graphical solution. ∎

Figure 4.C-1

The numbers are approximately -5.848038 and $\frac{-100}{(-5.848038)^2} \approx -2.924015$.

322

Example 2   Largest Volume of a Box

A box with no top is to be made from a 22 × 30 inch sheet of cardboard by cutting squares of equal size from each corner and bending up the flaps, as shown in Figure 4.C-2. To the nearest hundredth of an inch, what size square should be cut from each corner in order to obtain a box with the largest possible volume? What is the volume of this box?

Figure 4.C-2

Solution

Let x denote the length of the side of the square to be cut from each corner. Then,

$$\text{Volume of box} = \text{Length} \times \text{Width} \times \text{Height}$$
$$= (30 - 2x)(22 - 2x)x$$
$$= 4x^3 - 104x^2 + 660x$$

Thus, the equation $y = 4x^3 - 104x^2 + 660x$ gives the volume y of the box that results from cutting an $x \times x$ square from each corner. Because the shortest side of the cardboard is 22 inches, the length x of the side of the cut-out square must be less than 11. (Why?)

On the graph of $f(x) = 4x^3 - 104x^2 + 660x$,

Figure 4.C-3

- the x-coordinate of each point is the size of the square to be cut from each corner.
- the y-coordinate of each point is the volume of the resulting box.

The box with the largest volume corresponds to the point with the largest y-coordinate, that is, the highest point in the viewing window. A maximum find shows that the highest point is approximately (4.182, 1233.809), as shown in Figure 4.C-3. Therefore, a square measuring approximately 4.18 × 4.18 inches should be cut from each corner, producing a box of approximately 1233.81 cubic inches. ∎

323

ADDITIONAL EXAMPLES

Example 2

A container in the shape of a rectangular prism with no top is to be constructed from a 28 × 20-inch piece of sheet metal by cutting squares of equal size from each corner and folding up the flaps. What size square should be cut from each corner in order to obtain a container with the largest possible volume? What is the volume of this container?

$V = (28 - 2x)(20 - 2x)(x)$
$= 4x^3 - 96x^2 + 560x$
Graph $V = 4x^3 - 96x^2 + 560x$.

a square measuring approximately 3.84 × 3.84 inches; volume is approximately 961.32 cubic inches

Real-World Application

Example 2 is about maximizing the volume of a box, given certain dimensional limitations. Similar problems are encountered in many real-world applications. For domestic shipment by the United States Postal Service, the sum of the girth (distance around) and the length of a package can be at most 108 inches. Have students choose a length, and then challenge them to find the width and height of a package (in the shape of a rectangular prism) that will have the largest possible volume that can be shipped.

girth: distance around package

length

In **Example 3**, r must be 1 or greater, and cannot be more than 5. Point out that 1 is an exact lower bound and 5 is an overestimated upper bound. The purpose of finding the bounds is to get a window for the graph, so the overestimate is adequate.

ADDITIONAL EXAMPLES

Example 3

A cylindrical container with a volume of 1000 cubic inches is needed. It is to have no top. What dimensions will use the least amount of material?

$$V = \pi r^2 h$$

$$1000 = \pi r^2 h$$

$$\frac{1000}{\pi r^2} = h$$

$$S.A. = 2\pi rh + \pi r^2$$

$$= 2\pi r \frac{1000}{\pi r^2} + \pi r^2$$

$$= \frac{2000}{r} + \pi r^2$$

$$r \approx 6.828, \quad h \approx \frac{1000}{\pi \cdot (6.828)^2} \approx 6.828$$

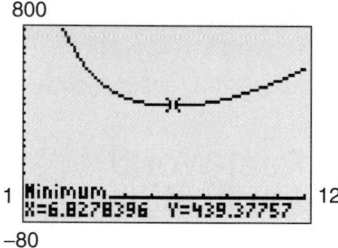

approximate dimensions:
radius $\approx$ 6.8 inches,
height $\approx$ 6.8 inches

 Math Background

Optimization problems are done in calculus using derivatives. A function has:

- a local maximum at a point if the first derivative equals zero and the second derivative is negative at that point.
- a local minimum at a point if the first derivative equals zero and the second derivative is positive at that point.

Figure 4.C-4

Figure 4.C-5

324

COMMON ERROR ALERT

In **Additional Example 3,** students may use $2\pi r^2$ in the formula for the surface area. Remind them that the container does not have a top.

Example 3   **Minimum Surface Area of a Cylinder**

A cylindrical can of volume 58 cubic inches (approximately 1 quart) is to be designed. For convenient handling, it must be at least 1 inch high and 2 inches in diameter. What dimensions will use the least amount of material?

Solution

The cylinder can be constructed by rolling a rectangular sheet of metal into a tube and then attaching the top and bottom, as shown in Figure 4.C-4. The surface area of the can, which determines the amount of material needed, has the following formula:

$$\text{Surface Area} = \text{Area of rectangular sheet} + \text{Area of top} + \text{Area of bottom}$$

$$= Ch + \pi r^2 + \pi r^2$$

$$= Ch + 2\pi r^2$$

When the sheet is rolled into a tube, the width c of the sheet is the circumference of the ends of the can, so $C = 2\pi r$.

$$\text{Surface Area} = Ch + 2\pi r^2$$

$$= 2\pi rh + 2\pi r^2$$

The volume of the cylinder of radius r and height h is $\pi r^2 h$. Since the can is to have volume 58 cubic inches,

$$\pi r^2 h = 58, \quad \text{or equivalently,} \quad h = \frac{58}{\pi r^2}.$$

Therefore,

$$\text{surface area} = 2\pi rh + 2\pi r^2 = 2\pi r \left(\frac{58}{\pi r^2}\right) + 2\pi r^2 = \frac{116}{r} + 2\pi r^2.$$

Note that r must be 1 or greater because the diameter $2r$ must be at least 2. Furthermore, r cannot be more than 5 because if $r > 5$ and $h \geq 1$, then the volume $\pi r^2 h$ would be at least $\pi(25)(1)$, which is greater than 58.

The situation can be represented by the graph of the equation $y = \frac{116}{x} + 2\pi x^2$. The x-coordinate of each point represents a possible radius, and the y-coordinate represents the surface area of the corresponding can. A graphical minimum finder shows that the coordinates of the lowest point are approximately (2.098, 82.947), as shown in Figure 4.C-5.

If the radius is 2.098, then the height is $\frac{58}{2.098^2 \cdot \pi} \approx 4.19$.

The dimensions of can that uses the least amount of materials are approximately a radius of 2.1 inches and a height of 4.2 inches. ∎

Exercises

1. Find the highest point on the part of the graph of $y = x^3 - 3x + 2$ that is shown in the given window. The answers are not all the same.
   a. $-2 \leq x \leq 0$
   b. $-2 \leq x \leq 2$
   c. $-2 \leq x \leq 3$

2. Find the lowest point on the part of the graph of $y = x^3 - 3x + 2$ that is shown in the given window.
   a. $0 \leq x \leq 2$
   b. $-2 \leq x \leq 2$
   c. $-3 \leq x \leq 2$

3. An open-top box with a square base is to be constructed from 120 square centimeters of material. What dimensions will produce a box
   a. of volume 100 cm³?
   b. with largest possible volume?

4. A 20-inch square piece of metal is to be used to make an open-top box by cutting equal-sized squares from each corner and folding up the sides (as in Example 2). The length, width, and height of the box are each to be less than 12 inches. What size squares should be cut out to produce a box with
   a. volume 550 in³?
   b. largest possible volume?

5. A cylindrical waste container with no top, a diameter of at least 2 feet, and a volume of 25 cubic feet is to be constructed. What should its radius be under the given conditions?
   a. 65 square feet of material will be used to construct it $r \approx 4.09977$ ft
   b. the smallest possible amount of material will be used to construct it (how much material is needed?) $r \approx 1.996$ in; ≈ 37.566 in²

6. If $c(x)$ is the cost of producing x units, then $\frac{c(x)}{x}$ is the average cost per unit. Suppose the cost of producing x units is given by $c(x) = 0.13x^3 - 70x^2 + 10{,}000x$ and that no more than 300 units can be produced per week.
   a. If the average cost is $1100 per unit, how many units are being produced?
   b. What production level should be used in order to minimize the average cost per unit? What is the minimum average cost?

7. If the cost of material to make the can in Example 3 is 5 cents per square inch for the top and bottom and 3 cents per square inch for the sides, what dimensions should be used to minimize the cost of making the can? [The answer is not the same as in Example 3.] $r \approx 1.769, h = \frac{58}{\pi r^2} \approx 5.8996$

8. A certain type of fencing comes in rigid 10-foot segments. Four uncut segments are used to fence in a garden on the side of a building, as shown in the figure. What value of x will result in a garden of the largest possible area? What is that area? **The maximum area of about 220.18 ft² occurs when x is about 9.31 ft.**

9. A rectangle is to be inscribed in a semicircle of radius 2, as shown in the figure. What is the largest possible area of such a rectangle? *Hint:* The width of the rectangle is the second coordinate of the point P (Why?), and P is on the top half of the circle $x^2 + y^2 = 4$. **4 units²**

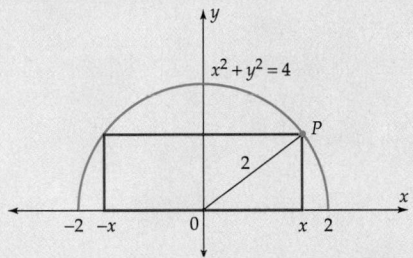

10. Find the point on the graph of $y = 5 - x^2$ that is closest to the point $(0, 1)$ and has positive coordinates. *Hint:* The distance from the point (x, y) on the graph to $(0, 1)$ is $\sqrt{(x - 0)^2 + (y - 1)^2}$; express y in terms of x.

$5 - x^2 \approx 1.5$. **The point that is closest to $(0, 1)$ has the exact value of $\left(\sqrt{\frac{7}{2}}, \frac{3}{2}\right)$, but approximations are okay.**

325

Exercises

1. a. $(-1, 4)$
   b. $(-1, 4)$ and $(2, 4)$
   c. $(3, 20)$

2. a. $(1, 0)$
   b. $(-2, 0)$ or $(1, 0)$
   c. $(-3, -16)$

3. a. approximately 3.785 cm $\times$ 6.980 cm or 8.560 cm $\times$ 1.365 cm
   b. $V \approx 126.49$ cm³ when side length is approximately 6.324 cm and height is approximately 3.163 cm

4. a. approximately 4.427 in. by 4.427 in.
   b. $x = \frac{10}{3}$ in.

6. a. approximately 206 units
   b. The minimum value of about 577 dollars per unit occurs when about 269 units are produced.

CHAPTER 5

Exponential and Logarithmic Functions

In this chapter, students will study radicals, rational exponents, and exponential functions. They will then study common and natural logarithms, including their properties and laws, as well as logarithmic functions to other bases. They will solve exponential and logarithmic equations and use exponential and logarithmic models to describe data.

CHAPTER 5

Exponential and Logarithmic Functions

Doorway to the past

The image above is of Pueblo Benito in Chaco Canyon, New Mexico. It was the home of the Anasazi people of the desert southwest for several centuries, and it includes timbers (shown above the doorway) that were used to date the buildings by using carbon-14 dating, which involves an exponential equation. See Exercise 55 Section 5.6.

326

Chapter Outline

Chapter Review

can do calculus Tangents to Exponential Functions

Interdependence of Sections

$$5.1 \longrightarrow 5.2 \longrightarrow 5.4 \longrightarrow 5.5 \nearrow^{5.3} \quad \nearrow^{5.6}$$
$$\searrow_{5.7}$$

Section 5.1 contains prerequisite review material for this chapter. If students are familiar enough with the objectives of this section, it may be skipped.

Exponential and logarithmic functions are essential for the mathematical description of a variety of phenomena in the physical sciences, engineering, and economics. Although a calculator is necessary to evaluate these functions for most values, you will not be able to use your calculator efficiently or interpret its answers unless you understand the properties of these functions. When calculations can readily be done by hand, you will be expected to do them without a calculator.

5.1 Radicals and Rational Exponents

Objectives

- Define and apply rational and irrational exponents
- Simplify expressions containing radicals or rational exponents

NOTE All constants, variables, and solutions in this chapter are real numbers.

nth Roots

Recall that when $c \geq 0$, the square root of c is the nonnegative solution of the equation $x^2 = c$. Cube roots, fourth roots, and higher roots are defined in a similar fashion as solutions of the equation $x^n = c$.

This equation can be solved graphically by finding the x-coordinate of the intersection points of the graphs of $y = x^n$ and $y = c$. (Review finding solutions graphically in Section 2.1 and the shape of the graph of $y = ax^n$ in Section 4.3, if needed.)

Depending on whether n is even or odd and whether c is positive or negative, $x^n = c$ may have two, one, or no solutions, as shown in the following figures.

327

Section

5.1 Radicals and Rational Exponents

Teaching Notes

Students have most recently studied the complex numbers. Tell them that now we are back on more familiar ground, the real numbers.

Tell students that **nth Roots** will be defined using the equation $x^n = c$. If $n = 3$ and $c = 10$, then $x^n = c$ becomes $x^3 = 10$. Students can solve $x^3 = 10$ graphically, as shown, using $Y_1 = x^3$ and $Y_2 = 10$.

Ask students how they can verify that the solution is reasonable.

$2^3 = 8$, so the solution of $x^3 = 10$ should be a little more than 2, and 2.1544347 is a little more than 2.

Encourage them to make a habit of verifying whether solutions are reasonable, using known powers of integers.

Teaching Notes

It may be worthwhile for students to solve some equations graphically with calculators to illustrate the first two figures at the right. For Figure 5.1-1, suggest $x^5 = 30$ (graph $y = x^5$ and $y = 30$) and $x^3 = -10$ (graph $y = x^3$ and $y = -10$). For Figure 5.1-2, they can solve $x^2 = 20$ (graph $y = x^2$ and $y = 20$) and $x^4 = 80$ (graph $y = x^4$ and $y = 80$). Again, have students verify that their solutions are reasonable.

Note that $y = x$ belongs to the group of functions represented by Figure 5.1-1, because $x = x^1$. Students should realize that, although the graph of $y = x$ is a line instead of S-shaped, there is exactly one solution of $x^1 = c$ for any c.

For the definition of *nth* Roots, show students the following equivalent expressions, which are probably familiar to them:

$\sqrt[3]{8}$ and $8^{\frac{1}{3}}$

$\sqrt{25}$ and $25^{\frac{1}{2}}$

Now generalize, saying that $\sqrt[n]{c}$ and $c^{\frac{1}{n}}$ are equivalent for any real number c and positive integer n.

By substituting $\sqrt[n]{c}$ for x in the equation $x^n = c$, we have the following facts:

For odd n, $\left(\sqrt[n]{c}\right)^n = c$.

For even n and $c \geq 0$, $\left(\sqrt[n]{c}\right)^n = c$.

The numerical examples below illustrate various cases of *nth* roots, addressing odd and even values of n and signs of c:

$\sqrt[3]{8} = 2$, $\sqrt[3]{-8} = -2$

$\sqrt[4]{16} = 2$, $\sqrt[4]{-16}$ is not defined.

$\sqrt[3]{0} = 0$, $\sqrt[4]{0} = 0$

COMMON ERROR ALERT

Students might try to apply the special product $(a + b)(a - b) = a^2 - b^2$ to an expression such as $\left(5 + \sqrt{c}\right)\left(2 - \sqrt{c}\right)$, getting $10 - c$ as the answer. Point out that in $\left(5 + \sqrt{c}\right)\left(2 - \sqrt{c}\right)$, $5 \neq 2$.

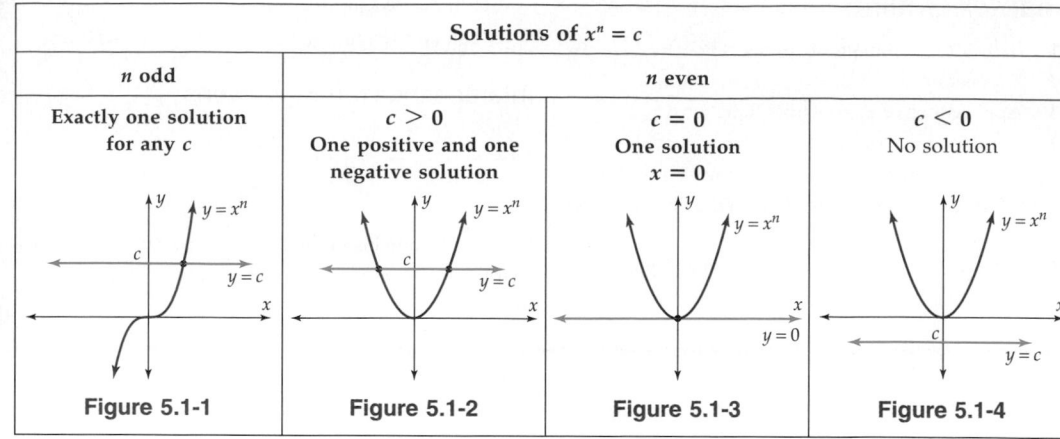

Solutions of $x^n = c$			
***n* odd**	***n* even**		
Exactly one solution for any c	$c > 0$ One positive and one negative solution	$c = 0$ One solution $x = 0$	$c < 0$ No solution
Figure 5.1-1	Figure 5.1-2	Figure 5.1-3	Figure 5.1-4

The figures illustrate the following definition of *nth* roots.

nth Roots

Let c be a real number and n a positive integer. The ***nth* root** of c is denoted by either of the symbols

$$\sqrt[n]{c} \qquad \text{or} \qquad c^{\frac{1}{n}}$$

and is defined to be

- the solution of $x^n = c$ when n is odd; or
- the nonnegative solution of $x^n = c$ when n is even and $c \geq 0$.

Examples of *nth* roots are shown below.

$$\sqrt[3]{-8} = (-8)^{\frac{1}{3}} = -2 \text{ because } -2 \text{ is the solution of } x^3 = -8.$$
$$\sqrt[4]{81} = (81)^{\frac{1}{4}} = 3 \text{ because } 3 \text{ is the nonnegative solution of } x^4 = 81.$$

Expressions involving *nth* roots can often be simplified or written in a variety of ways by using a basic fact of exponents.

$$\sqrt[n]{cd} = \sqrt[n]{c}\sqrt[n]{d} \qquad \text{or equivalently,} \qquad (cd)^{\frac{1}{n}} = c^{\frac{1}{n}}d^{\frac{1}{n}}$$

Example 1 Operations on *nth* Roots

Simplify each expression.

a. $\sqrt{8} \cdot \sqrt{12}$ **b.** $\sqrt{12} - \sqrt{75}$

c. $\sqrt[3]{8x^6y^4}$ **d.** $\left(5 + \sqrt{c}\right)\left(5 - \sqrt{c}\right)$, where $c > 0$

Solution

a. $\sqrt{8} \cdot \sqrt{12} = \sqrt{8 \cdot 12} = \sqrt{96} = \sqrt{16 \cdot 6} = \sqrt{16} \cdot \sqrt{6} = 4\sqrt{6}$

b. $\sqrt{12} - \sqrt{75} = \sqrt{4 \cdot 3} - \sqrt{25 \cdot 3} = \sqrt{4}\sqrt{3} - \sqrt{25}\sqrt{3}$
$$= 2\sqrt{3} - 5\sqrt{3} = -3\sqrt{3}$$

c. $\sqrt[3]{8x^6y^4} = \sqrt[3]{8} \cdot \sqrt[3]{x^3 \cdot x^3} \cdot \sqrt[3]{y^3 \cdot y} = 2x^2y\sqrt[3]{y}$

d. $\left(5 + \sqrt{c}\right)\left(5 - \sqrt{c}\right) = 5^2 - \left(\sqrt{c}\right)^2 = 25 - c$

When using a calculator, exponent notation for nth roots is usually preferred over radical notation. ∎

<table>
<tr><td>

CAUTION

When using exponent notation to evaluate nth roots with a calculator, be sure to use parentheses when raising to the fractional power. Example: To enter $\sqrt[3]{9}$, press 9^(1/3).

</td></tr>
</table>

Figure 5.1-6

Example 2 Evaluating nth Roots

Use a calculator to approximate each expression to the nearest ten-thousandth.

a. $40^{\frac{1}{5}}$ **b.** $225^{\frac{1}{11}}$

Solution

a. Because $\dfrac{1}{5} = 0.2$, the expressions $40^{\frac{1}{5}}$ and $40^{0.2}$ are equivalent, as shown at right.

$$40^{\frac{1}{5}} \approx 2.0913$$

b. The fraction $\dfrac{1}{11}$ is equivalent to the repeating decimal $0.090909 \cdots$. The fraction $\dfrac{1}{11}$ is not equivalent to this decimal if it is rounded off, as shown at left. Therefore, it is better to leave the exponent in fractional form.

$$225^{\frac{1}{11}} \approx 1.6362$$ ∎

```
40^(1/5)
         2.091279105
40^.2
         2.091279105
```

Figure 5.1-5

Rational Exponents

Rational exponents of the form $\dfrac{1}{n}$ are called nth roots. Rational exponents can also be of the form $\dfrac{m}{n}$, such as $4^{\frac{3}{2}}$. Rational exponents of the form $\dfrac{m}{n}$ can be defined in such a way that the laws of exponents, such as $c^{rs} = (c^r)^s$, are still valid. For example, because $\dfrac{3}{2} = (3)\dfrac{1}{2} = \left(\dfrac{1}{2}\right)3$, it is reasonable to say that $4^{\frac{3}{2}} = (4^3)^{\frac{1}{2}} = (4^{\frac{1}{2}})^3$. These expressions are equivalent.

$$4^{\frac{3}{2}} = (4^3)^{\frac{1}{2}} = (64)^{\frac{1}{2}} = \sqrt{64} = 8$$
$$4^{\frac{3}{2}} = (4^{\frac{1}{2}})^3 = \left(\sqrt{4}\right)^3 = (2)^3 = 8$$

This illustrates the definition of rational exponents.

Example Notes

An alternate method for **Example 1a** is:
$$\sqrt{8} \cdot \sqrt{12} = 2\sqrt{2} \cdot 2\sqrt{3} = 4\sqrt{6}$$

In **Example 2,** direct students' attention to the **CAUTION** box. Have them enter 40^1/5 into their calculator. Ask them to explain why they get 8. The calculator interprets this as 40^1 divided by 5.

COMMON ERROR ALERT

A common error is to only partially simplify a radical expression, using a perfect square factor in the radicand, but not using the *greatest* perfect square factor. For example,

$$\sqrt{48} = \sqrt{4 \cdot 12} = 2\sqrt{12}, \text{ but}$$

$2\sqrt{12}$ is not in simplest form because 12 contains a perfect square factor. If students use the factorization above, they must factor again to completely simplify the expression:

$$\sqrt{48} = \sqrt{4 \cdot 12} = 2\sqrt{12}$$
$$= 2\sqrt{4 \cdot 3} = 2 \cdot 2\sqrt{3} = 4\sqrt{3}$$

ADDITIONAL EXAMPLES

Example 1

Simplify each expression.

a. $\sqrt{6} \cdot \sqrt{8}$ $4\sqrt{3}$

b. $\sqrt{45} - \sqrt{125}$ $-2\sqrt{5}$

c. $\sqrt[3]{1000x^3y^7}$ $10xy^2\sqrt[3]{y}$

d. $\left(6 + \sqrt{b}\right)\left(6 - \sqrt{b}\right)$, where $b > 0$
   $36 - b$

Example 2

Use a calculator to approximate each expression to the nearest ten-thousandths.

a. $35^{\frac{1}{8}}$ ≈ 1.5596

b. $285^{\frac{1}{12}}$ ≈ 1.6017

Teaching Notes

Note that in the **Definition of Rational Exponents**, k must be positive. If k were allowed to be 0 or negative, then meaningless expressions of the forms $\sqrt[0]{c}$ and $\sqrt[-3]{c}$ would occur.

The expression $c^{\frac{t}{k}}$ is defined in both exponential notation and radical notation. Make sure that students understand which radical notation is equivalent to each exponential notation:

$$c^{\frac{t}{k}} = \left(c^t\right)^{\frac{1}{k}} = \sqrt[k]{c^t}$$

$$c^{\frac{t}{k}} = \left(c^{\frac{1}{k}}\right)^t = \left(\sqrt[k]{c}\right)^t$$

To demonstrate the value of being comfortable with both radical forms, ask students to evaluate $\sqrt[3]{125^2}$ without a calculator. Then show $\sqrt[3]{125^2} = \left(\sqrt[3]{125}\right)^2 = (5)^2 = 25$.

Emphasize that the **Laws of Exponents** are now stated for *rational* exponents. Use numerical examples such as these to illustrate some of the laws:

1. $8^{\frac{2}{3}} \cdot 8^{\frac{1}{3}} = 4 \cdot 2 = 8$

   $8^{\frac{2}{3}} \cdot 8^{\frac{1}{3}} = 8^{\frac{2}{3}+\frac{1}{3}} = 8^1 = 8$

2. $\dfrac{8^{\frac{2}{3}}}{8^{\frac{1}{3}}} = \dfrac{4}{2} = 2$

   $\dfrac{8^{\frac{2}{3}}}{8^{\frac{1}{3}}} = 8^{\frac{2}{3}-\frac{1}{3}} = 8^{\frac{1}{3}} = 2$

4. $(8 \cdot 27)^{\frac{2}{3}} = (216)^{\frac{2}{3}}$

   $= \left(\sqrt[3]{216}\right)^2$

   $= (6)^2$

   $= 36$

   $(8 \cdot 27)^{\frac{2}{3}} = 8^{\frac{2}{3}} \cdot 27^{\frac{2}{3}} = 4 \cdot 9 = 36$

5. $\left(\dfrac{8}{27}\right)^{\frac{2}{3}} = \left(\sqrt[3]{\dfrac{8}{27}}\right)^2 = \left(\dfrac{2}{3}\right)^2 = \dfrac{4}{9}$

   $\left(\dfrac{8}{27}\right)^{\frac{2}{3}} = \dfrac{8^{\frac{2}{3}}}{27^{\frac{2}{3}}} = \dfrac{4}{9}$

Definition of Rational Exponents

> Let c be a positive real number and let $\frac{t}{k}$ be a rational number with positive denominator.
>
> $c^{\frac{t}{k}}$ is defined to be the number $(c^t)^{\frac{1}{k}} = (c^{\frac{1}{k}})^t$
>
> In radical notation, $c^{\frac{t}{k}} = \sqrt[k]{c^t} = \left(\sqrt[k]{c}\right)^t$.

Every terminating decimal is a rational number; therefore, expressions such as $13^{3.78}$ can be expressed as $13^{\frac{378}{100}}$. Although the definition of rational exponents requires c to be positive, it remains valid when c is negative, *provided that* the exponent is in lowest terms with an odd denominator, such as $(-8)^{\frac{2}{3}}$. In Exercise 89, you will explore why these restrictions are necessary when c is negative.

> **CAUTION**
>
> Although $(-8)^{\frac{2}{3}} = \sqrt[3]{(-8)^2} = \sqrt[3]{64} = 4$, and 4 is a real number, entering $(-8)^{\frac{2}{3}}$ on some calculators may produce either an error message or a complex number. If this occurs, you can get the correct answer by entering one of the equivalent expressions below.
>
> $[(-8)^2]^{\frac{1}{3}}$ or $[(-8)^{\frac{1}{3}}]^2$

Laws of Exponents

You have seen that the law of exponents $c^{rs} = (c^r)^s$ is valid for rational exponents. In fact, all of the laws of exponents are valid for rational exponents.

Laws of Exponents

> Let c and d be nonnegative real numbers and let r and s be rational numbers. Then
>
> 1. $c^r c^s = c^{r+s}$
>
> 2. $\dfrac{c^r}{c^s} = c^{r-s}$ $(c \neq 0)$
>
> 3. $(c^r)^s = c^{rs}$
>
> 4. $(cd)^r = c^r d^r$
>
> 5. $\left(\dfrac{c}{d}\right)^r = \dfrac{c^r}{d^r}$ $(d \neq 0)$
>
> 6. $c^{-r} = \dfrac{1}{c^r}$ $(c \neq 0)$
>
> If $c \neq 1$ and $d \neq 1$,
>
> • $c^r = c^s$ if and only if $r = s$.
>
> • $c^r = d^r$ if and only if $c = d$.

Example 3 Simplifying Expressions with Rational Exponents

Write the expression $(8r^{\frac{3}{4}}s^{-3})^{\frac{2}{3}}$ using only positive exponents.

Solution

$$(8r^{\frac{3}{4}}s^{-3})^{\frac{2}{3}} = 8^{\frac{2}{3}}(r^{\frac{3}{4}})^{\frac{2}{3}}(s^{-3})^{\frac{2}{3}} \qquad (cd)^r = c^r d^r$$
$$= \sqrt[3]{8^2}(r^{\frac{6}{12}})(s^{-\frac{6}{3}}) \qquad \textit{definition and } (c^r)^s = c^{rs}$$
$$= \sqrt[3]{64}(r^{\frac{1}{2}})(s^{-2}) \qquad \textit{simplify}$$
$$= \frac{4r^{\frac{1}{2}}}{s^2} \qquad \textit{simplify and } c^{-r} = \frac{1}{c^r}$$

The expression $\dfrac{4r^{\frac{1}{2}}}{s^2}$ can also be written as $= \dfrac{4\sqrt{r}}{s^2}$ if it is more convenient. ∎

Example 4   **Simplifying Expressions with Rational Exponents**

Simplify the expression $x^{\frac{1}{2}}(x^{\frac{3}{4}} - x^{\frac{3}{2}})$.

Solution

$$x^{\frac{1}{2}}(x^{\frac{3}{4}} - x^{\frac{3}{2}}) = x^{\frac{1}{2}}x^{\frac{3}{4}} - x^{\frac{1}{2}}x^{\frac{3}{2}} \qquad a(b-c) = ab - ac$$
$$= x^{\frac{1}{2}+\frac{3}{4}} - x^{\frac{1}{2}+\frac{3}{2}} \qquad c^r c^s = c^{r+s}$$
$$= x^{\frac{5}{4}} - x^{\frac{4}{2}}$$
$$= x^{\frac{5}{4}} - x^2$$ ∎

Example 5   **Simplifying Expressions with Rational Exponents**

Simplify the expression $(x^{\frac{5}{2}}y^4)(xy^{\frac{7}{4}})^{-2}$.

Solution

$$(x^{\frac{5}{2}}y^4)(xy^{\frac{7}{4}})^{-2} = (x^{\frac{5}{2}}y^4)(x^{-2})(y^{\frac{7}{4}})^{-2} \qquad (cd)^r$$
$$= (x^{\frac{5}{2}}y^4)(x^{-2})(y^{-\frac{14}{4}}) \qquad (c^r)^s$$
$$= x^{\frac{5}{2}}x^{-2}y^4 y^{-\frac{7}{2}} \qquad \textit{commutative}$$
$$= x^{\frac{5}{2}-2}y^{4-\frac{7}{2}} \qquad c^r c^s = c^{r+s}$$
$$= x^{\frac{1}{2}}y^{\frac{1}{2}} \qquad \textit{simplify}$$ ∎

Example 6   **Simplifying Expressions with Rational Exponents**

Let k be a positive rational number. Write the expression $\sqrt[10]{c^{5k}}\sqrt{(c^{-k})^{\frac{1}{2}}}$ without radicals, using only positive exponents.

Solution

$$\sqrt[10]{c^{5k}}\sqrt{(c^{-k})^{\frac{1}{2}}} = (c^{5k})^{\frac{1}{10}}[(c^{-k})^{\frac{1}{2}}]^{\frac{1}{2}} \qquad \textit{definition}$$
$$= c^{\frac{5k}{10}}(c^{-\frac{k}{2}})^{\frac{1}{2}} \qquad (c^r)^s = c^{rs}$$
$$= c^{\frac{k}{2}}c^{-\frac{k}{4}} \qquad \textit{simplify and } (c^r)^s = c^{rs}$$
$$= c^{\frac{k}{2}-\frac{k}{4}} \qquad c^r c^s = c^{r+s}$$
$$= c^{\frac{k}{4}} \qquad \textit{simplify}$$ ∎

Example Notes

While discussing **Example 3** through **Example 6**, you may want to review operations with fractions. Remind students that a common denominator is needed to add or subtract, but not to multiply or divide. The following are from **Example 5**:

To find $\left(y^{\frac{7}{4}}\right)^{-2}$, multiply $\frac{7}{4} \cdot (-2)$.

$$\frac{7}{4} \cdot (-2) = \frac{7}{4} \cdot \frac{-2}{1} = \frac{-14}{4} = -\frac{7}{2}$$

To find $y^4 \cdot y^{-\frac{7}{2}}$, add $4 + \left(-\frac{7}{2}\right)$.

$$4 + \left(-\frac{7}{2}\right) = \frac{8}{2} + \left(-\frac{7}{2}\right) = \frac{1}{2}$$

ADDITIONAL EXAMPLES

Example 3

Write the expression $\left(16u^{\frac{2}{5}}v^{-4}\right)^{\frac{5}{4}}$ using only positive exponents. $\dfrac{32u^{\frac{1}{2}}}{v^5}$

Example 4

Simplify the expression $y^{\frac{1}{3}}\left(y^{\frac{1}{6}} - y^{\frac{5}{3}}\right)$. $y^{\frac{1}{2}} - y^2$

Example 5

Simplify the expression $\left(x^{\frac{7}{3}}y^3\right)\left(xy^{\frac{5}{6}}\right)^{-2}$. $x^{\frac{1}{3}}y^{\frac{4}{3}}$

Example 6

Let k be a positive rational number. Write the expression $\sqrt[12]{a^{4k}}\sqrt{(a^{-k})^{\frac{1}{3}}}$ without radicals, using only positive exponents. $a^{\frac{k}{6}}$

The product in **Example 7b** has the same form as the product in Example 1d, page 329:

$$\left(5 + \sqrt{c}\right)\left(5 - \sqrt{c}\right) = 25 - c$$

$$\left(3 + \sqrt{6}\right)\left(3 - \sqrt{6}\right) = 9 - 6$$

COMMON ERROR
//// **ALERT** \\\\

In **Example 7b,** students might attempt to mimic what was done in part **a.** That is, they might multiply the numerator and denominator by only $\sqrt{6}$. Remind students that $\left(3 + \sqrt{6}\right)\sqrt{6}$ requires distributing $\sqrt{6}$, so $\left(3 + \sqrt{6}\right)\sqrt{6} = 3\sqrt{6} + 6$. This does not eliminate the radical. Emphasize that they must use conjugates:

$$\left(3 + \sqrt{6}\right)\left(3 - \sqrt{6}\right) = 9 - 6 = 3$$

 Math Background

The expression in **Example 8** is an example of the difference quotient that students have encountered previously (pages 143, 220).

If $f(x) = \sqrt{x}$, then

$$\frac{f(x + h) - f(x)}{h} = \frac{\sqrt{x + h} - \sqrt{x}}{h}.$$

Students may have rationalized *denominators* in the past to transform fractions with radicals, but this is likely to be their first experience with rationalizing a *numerator*.

In calculus, students will learn the definition of the derivative of f at x:

$$f'(x) = \lim_{h \to 0} \frac{f(x + h) - f(x)}{h}$$

For $f(x) = \sqrt{x}$,

$$f'(x) = \lim_{h \to 0} \frac{\sqrt{x + h} - \sqrt{x}}{h}$$

To find $f'(x)$, they will rationalize the numerator as shown in Example 8, and then evaluate the limit:

$$f'(x) = \lim_{h \to 0} \frac{1}{\sqrt{x + h} + \sqrt{x}}$$

$$= \frac{1}{\sqrt{x} + \sqrt{x}}$$

$$= \frac{1}{2\sqrt{x}}$$

Rationalizing Denominators and Numerators

Transforming fractions with radicals in the denominator to equivalent fractions with no radicals in the denominator is called *rationalizing the denominator*. Before the common use of calculators, fractions with rational denominators were preferred because they were easier to calculate or estimate. With calculators today there is no computational advantage to rationalizing denominators. However, the skill of rationalizing numerators or denominators is useful in calculus.

Example 7   Rationalizing the Denominator

Rationalize the denominator of each fraction.

a. $\dfrac{7}{\sqrt{5}}$ **b.** $\dfrac{2}{3 + \sqrt{6}}$

Solution

a. Multiply the fraction by 1 using a suitable radical fraction.

$$\frac{7}{\sqrt{5}} = \frac{7}{\sqrt{5}} \cdot 1 = \frac{7}{\sqrt{5}} \cdot \frac{\sqrt{5}}{\sqrt{5}} = \frac{7\sqrt{5}}{5}$$

b. Use the multiplication pattern $(a + b)(a - b) = a^2 - b^2$ to determine a suitable radical fraction equivalent to 1.

$$\frac{2}{3 + \sqrt{6}} = \frac{2}{3 + \sqrt{6}} \cdot 1$$

$$= \frac{2}{3 + \sqrt{6}} \cdot \frac{3 - \sqrt{6}}{3 - \sqrt{6}}$$

$$= \frac{2\left(3 - \sqrt{6}\right)}{\left(3 + \sqrt{6}\right)\left(3 - \sqrt{6}\right)}$$

$$= \frac{6 - 2\sqrt{6}}{9 - 6}$$

$$= \frac{6 - 2\sqrt{6}}{3}$$

NOTE When rationalizing a denominator or numerator which contains a radical expression, use a suitable radical fraction, equal to one, that contains the conjugate of the expression.

Example 8   Rationalizing the Numerator

Assume $h \neq 0$. Rationalize the numerator of $\dfrac{\sqrt{x + h} - \sqrt{x}}{h}$.

Solution

Multiply the fraction by 1 using a suitable radical fraction.

$$\frac{\sqrt{x+h} - \sqrt{x}}{h} = \frac{\sqrt{x+h} - \sqrt{x}}{h} \cdot 1$$

$$= \frac{\sqrt{x+h} - \sqrt{x}}{h} \cdot \frac{\sqrt{x+h} + \sqrt{x}}{\sqrt{x+h} + \sqrt{x}}$$

$$= \frac{(\sqrt{x+h})^2 - (\sqrt{x})^2}{h(\sqrt{x+h} + \sqrt{x})}$$

$$= \frac{x+h-x}{h(\sqrt{x+h} + \sqrt{x})}$$

$$= \frac{h}{h(\sqrt{x+h} + \sqrt{x})}$$

$$= \frac{1}{\sqrt{x+h} + \sqrt{x}}$$

∎

Irrational Exponents

The example (not proof) below illustrates how a^t is defined when t is an irrational number.

To compute $10^{\sqrt{2}}$, the exponent could be replaced with the equivalent non-terminating decimal $1.414213562\ldots$. Each of the decimal approximations of $\sqrt{2}$ given below is a more accurate approximation than the preceding one.

$$1.4, 1.41, 1.414, 1.4142, 1.41421, \ldots.$$

We can raise 10 to each of these rational numbers.

$$10^{1.4} \approx 25.1189$$
$$10^{1.41} \approx 25.7040$$
$$10^{1.414} \approx 25.9418$$
$$10^{1.4142} \approx 25.9537$$
$$10^{1.41421} \approx 25.9543$$
$$10^{1.414213} \approx 25.9545$$

The pattern suggests that as the exponent r gets closer and closer to $\sqrt{2}$, 10^r gets closer and closer to a real number whose decimal expansion begins $25.954\ldots$. So $10^{\sqrt{2}}$ is defined to be this number.

Similarly, for any $a > 0$,

a^t **is a well-defined positive number for each real exponent** t.

The fact below shall be assumed.

The laws of exponents are valid for *all* **real exponents.**

Exercises 5.1

ANSWERS

46. $-(a+b)+(a+b)^{\frac{1}{3}}$

67. $x^{\frac{7}{6}} - x^{\frac{11}{6}}$

68. $3x^2 + 2$

69. $x - y$

70. $2x^{\frac{2}{3}} - x^{\frac{1}{3}}y^{\frac{3}{2}} + 2x^{\frac{1}{3}}y^{\frac{1}{2}} - y^2$

76. $\dfrac{5 + 5\sqrt{3} - \sqrt{10} - \sqrt{30}}{15}$

Exercises 5.1

Note: Unless directed otherwise, assume all letters represent positive real numbers.

In Exercises 1–15, evaluate each expression without using a calculator.

1. $\sqrt{144}$ **12**
2. $\sqrt[3]{64}$ **4**
3. $\sqrt[4]{16}$ **2**
4. $\sqrt[3]{-27}$ **−3**
5. $\sqrt{0.0081}$ **0.09**
6. $\sqrt{0.000169}$ **0.013**
7. $\sqrt[3]{0.008}$ **0.2**
8. $\sqrt[3]{-0.125}$ **−0.5**
9. $\sqrt{0.5^6}$ **0.125**
10. $\sqrt{(-3)^4}$ **9**
11. $27^{\frac{4}{3}}$ **81**
12. $81^{-\frac{1}{4}}$ **$\frac{1}{3}$**
13. $(-64)^{\frac{2}{3}}$ **16**
14. $\left(-\frac{1}{64}\right)^{-\frac{2}{3}}$ **16**
15. $16^{-\frac{3}{2}}$ **$\frac{1}{64}$**

In Exercises 16–40, simplify each expression without using a calculator.

16. $\sqrt{3^{15}}$ **$3^7\sqrt{3}$**
17. $\sqrt[3]{12^{16}}$ **$12^5(\sqrt[3]{12})$**
18. $\sqrt{0.08^{12}}$ **$(0.08)^6$**
19. $\sqrt{(-11)^{28}}$ **11^{14}**
20. $\sqrt[3]{(-0.05)^{24}}$ **$(-0.05)^8$**
21. $\sqrt[3]{0.4^{18}}$ **$(0.4)^6$**
22. $\sqrt{6}\cdot\sqrt{12}$ **$6\sqrt{2}$**
23. $\sqrt{8}\cdot\sqrt{96}$ **$16\sqrt{3}$**
24. $\sqrt[3]{18}\cdot\sqrt[3]{12}$ **6**
25. $\sqrt[3]{-32}\cdot\sqrt[3]{16}$ **−8**
26. $\dfrac{\sqrt{10}}{\sqrt{8}\cdot\sqrt{5}}$ **$\frac{1}{2}$**
27. $\dfrac{\sqrt{6}}{\sqrt{14}\cdot\sqrt{63}}$ **$\frac{\sqrt{3}}{21}$**
28. $\dfrac{\sqrt[3]{324}}{\sqrt[3]{6}\cdot\sqrt[3]{2}}$ **3**
29. $\dfrac{\sqrt[3]{54}}{\sqrt[3]{32}\cdot\sqrt[3]{-4}}$ **$-\frac{3}{4}$**
30. $\sqrt{27}+2\sqrt{3}$ **$5\sqrt{3}$**
31. $4\sqrt{5}-\sqrt{20}$ **$2\sqrt{5}$**
32. $(1+\sqrt{3})(2-\sqrt{3})$ **$-1+\sqrt{3}$**
33. $(3+\sqrt{2})(3-\sqrt{2})$ **7**
34. $(4-\sqrt{3})(5+2\sqrt{3})$ **$14+3\sqrt{3}$**
35. $(2\sqrt{5}-4)(3\sqrt{5}+2)$ **$22-8\sqrt{5}$**
36. $(3\sqrt{2}-4\sqrt{6})^2$ **$114-48\sqrt{3}$**
37. $5\sqrt{20}-\sqrt{45}+2\sqrt{80}$ **$15\sqrt{5}$**
38. $\sqrt[3]{40}+2\sqrt[3]{135}-5\sqrt[3]{320}$ **$-12\sqrt[3]{5}$**
39. $\dfrac{2^{\frac{11}{2}}\cdot 2^{-7}\cdot 2^{-5}}{2^3\cdot 2^{\frac{1}{2}}\cdot 2^{-10}}$ **1**
40. $\dfrac{(3^2)^{-\frac{1}{2}}(9^4)^{-1}}{27^{-3}}$ **1**

In Exercises 41–56, simplify each expression.

41. $\sqrt{16a^8b^{-2}}$ **$4\dfrac{a^4}{b}$**
42. $\sqrt{24x^6y^{-4}}$ **$\dfrac{2\sqrt{6x^3}}{y^2}$**
43. $\dfrac{\sqrt{c^2d^6}}{\sqrt{4c^3d^{-4}}}$ **$\dfrac{d^5}{2\sqrt{c}}$**
44. $\dfrac{\sqrt{a^{-10}b^{-12}}}{\sqrt{a^{14}d^{-4}}}$ **$\dfrac{d^2}{a^{12}b^6}$**
45. $\sqrt[9]{(4x+2y)^{18}}$ **$(4x+2y)^2$**
46. $\sqrt[3]{a+b}\cdot\sqrt[3]{-(a+b)^2}+\sqrt[3]{a+b}$
47. $\sqrt{x^7}\cdot x^{\frac{5}{2}}\cdot x^{-\frac{3}{2}}$ **$x^{\frac{9}{2}}$**
48. $(x^{\frac{1}{2}}y^3)(x^0y^7)^{-2}$ **$\dfrac{x^{\frac{1}{2}}}{y^{11}}$**
49. $(c^{\frac{2}{5}}d^{-\frac{2}{3}})(c^6d^3)^{\frac{4}{3}}$ **$c^{\frac{42}{5}}d^{\frac{10}{3}}$**
50. $\left(\dfrac{r^{\frac{2}{3}}}{s^{-\frac{1}{5}}}\right)^{\frac{15}{9}}$ **$\dfrac{r^{\frac{10}{9}}}{s^{\frac{1}{3}}}$**
51. $\dfrac{(7a)^2(5b)^{\frac{3}{2}}}{(5a)^{\frac{3}{2}}(7b)^4}$ **$\dfrac{a^{\frac{1}{2}}}{49b^{\frac{5}{2}}}$**
52. $\dfrac{(6a)^{\frac{1}{2}}\sqrt{ab}}{a^2b^{\frac{3}{2}}}$ **$\dfrac{6^{\frac{1}{2}}}{ab}$**
53. $\dfrac{(2a)^{\frac{1}{2}}(3b)^{-2}(4a)^{\frac{3}{5}}}{(4a)^{-\frac{3}{2}}(3b)^2(2a)^{\frac{1}{5}}}$ **$\dfrac{2^{\frac{9}{2}}a^{\frac{12}{5}}}{3^4b^4}$**
54. $\dfrac{(a^{\frac{3}{4}}b)^2(ab^{\frac{1}{4}})^3}{(ab)^{\frac{1}{2}}(bc)^{-\frac{1}{4}}}$ **$a^4b^2c^{\frac{5}{4}}$**
55. $(a^{x^2})^{\frac{1}{x}}$ **a^x**
56. $\dfrac{(b^x)^{x-1}}{b^{-x}}$ **b^{x^2}**

In Exercises 57–66, write each expression without radicals, using only positive exponents.

57. $\sqrt[3]{a^2+b^2}$ **$(a^2+b^2)^{\frac{1}{3}}$**
58. $\sqrt[4]{a^3-b^3}$ **$(a^3-b^3)^{\frac{1}{4}}$**
59. $\sqrt[4]{\sqrt[3]{a^3}}$ **$a^{\frac{3}{16}}$**
60. $\sqrt{\sqrt[3]{a^3b^4}}$ **$a^{\frac{1}{2}}b^{\frac{2}{3}}$**
61. $\sqrt[5]{t}\cdot\sqrt{16t^5}$ **$4t^{\frac{27}{10}}$**
62. $\sqrt{x}\cdot\sqrt[3]{x^2}\cdot\sqrt[4]{x^3}$ **$x^{\frac{23}{12}}$**
63. $\left(\sqrt[3]{xy^2}\right)^{-\frac{3}{5}}$ **$\dfrac{1}{x^{\frac{1}{5}}y^{\frac{2}{5}}}$**
64. $\left(\sqrt[4]{r^{14}s^{-\frac{21}{5}}}\right)^{-\frac{3}{7}}$ **$\dfrac{s^{\frac{9}{20}}}{r^{\frac{3}{2}}}$**
65. $\dfrac{c}{(c^{\frac{5}{6}})^{42}(c^{51})^{-\frac{2}{3}}}$ **1**
66. $(c^{\frac{5}{6}}-c^{-\frac{5}{6}})^2$ **$c^{\frac{5}{3}}-2+\dfrac{1}{c^{\frac{5}{3}}}$**

In Exercises 67–72, simplify each expression.

67. $x^{\frac{1}{2}}\left(x^{\frac{2}{3}}-x^{\frac{4}{3}}\right)$
68. $x^{\frac{1}{2}}\left(3x^{\frac{3}{2}}+2x^{-\frac{1}{2}}\right)$
69. $\left(x^{\frac{1}{2}}+y^{\frac{1}{2}}\right)\left(x^{\frac{1}{2}}-y^{\frac{1}{2}}\right)$
70. $\left(x^{\frac{1}{3}}+y^{\frac{1}{2}}\right)\left(2x^{\frac{1}{3}}-y^{\frac{3}{2}}\right)$
71. $(x+y)^{\frac{1}{2}}\left[(x+y)^{\frac{1}{2}}-(x+y)\right]$ **$x+y-(x+y)^{\frac{3}{2}}$**
72. $\left(x^{\frac{1}{3}}+y^{\frac{1}{3}}\right)\left(x^{\frac{2}{3}}-x^{\frac{1}{3}}y^{\frac{1}{3}}+y^{\frac{2}{3}}\right)$ **$x+y$**

In Exercises 73–78, rationalize the denominator and simplify your answer.

73. $\dfrac{3}{\sqrt{8}}$ **$\dfrac{3\sqrt{2}}{4}$**
74. $\dfrac{2}{\sqrt{6}}$ **$\dfrac{\sqrt{6}}{3}$**
75. $\dfrac{3\sqrt{3}-3}{2+\sqrt{12}}$ **$\dfrac{3}{4}$**
76. $\dfrac{1+\sqrt{3}}{5+\sqrt{10}}$
77. $\dfrac{2}{\sqrt{x}+2}$ **$\dfrac{2\sqrt{x}-4}{x-4}$**
78. $\dfrac{\sqrt{x}}{\sqrt{x}-\sqrt{c}}$ **$\dfrac{x+\sqrt{xc}}{x-c}$**

In Exercises 79–84, factor the given expression. For example, $x - x^{\frac{1}{2}} - 2 = (x^{\frac{1}{2}} - 2)(x^{\frac{1}{2}} + 1)$.

79. $x^{\frac{2}{3}} + x^{\frac{1}{3}} - 6$ **80.** $x^{\frac{2}{5}} + 11x^{\frac{1}{5}} + 30$

81. $x + 4x^{\frac{1}{2}} + 3$ **82.** $x^{\frac{1}{3}} + 7x^{\frac{1}{6}} + 10$

83. $x^{\frac{4}{5}} - 81$ **84.** $x^{\frac{2}{3}} - 6x^{\frac{1}{3}} + 9$

In Exercises 85–88, rationalize the numerator and simplify your answer. Assume $h \neq 0$.

85. $\dfrac{\sqrt{x + h + 1} - \sqrt{x + 1}}{h}$

86. $\dfrac{2\sqrt{x + h + 3} - 2\sqrt{x + 3}}{h}$

87. $\dfrac{\sqrt{(x + h)^2 + 1} - \sqrt{x^2 + 1}}{h}$

88. $\dfrac{\sqrt{(x + h)^2 - (x + h)} - \sqrt{x^2 - x}}{h}$

89. Some restrictions are necessary when defining fractional powers of a negative number.
   a. Explain why the equations $x^2 = -4$, $x^4 = -4$, $x^6 = -4$, etc., have no real solutions. Conclude that $c^{\frac{1}{2}}, c^{\frac{1}{4}}, c^{\frac{1}{6}}$ cannot be defined when $c = -4$.
   b. Since $\dfrac{1}{3}$ is the same as $\dfrac{2}{6}$, it should be true that $c^{\frac{1}{3}} = c^{\frac{2}{6}}$, that is, that $\sqrt[3]{c} = \sqrt[6]{c^2}$. Show that this is false when $c = -8$.

90. **a.** Suppose r is a solution of the equation $x^n = c$ and s is a solution of $x^n = d$. Verify that rs is a solution of $x^n = cd$.
   b. Explain why part **a** shows that $\sqrt[n]{cd} = \sqrt[n]{c} \cdot \sqrt[n]{d}$.

91. Write laws 3, 4, and 5 of exponents in radical notation in the case when $r = \dfrac{1}{m}$ and $s = \dfrac{1}{n}$.

92. **a.** Graph $f(x) = x^5$ and explain why this function has an inverse function.
   b. Show algebraically that the inverse function is $g(x) = x^{\frac{1}{5}}$.

93. If n is an odd positive integer, show that $f(x) = x^n$ has an inverse function and find the rule of the inverse function. *Hint:* Exercise 92 is the case when $n = 5$.

94. A long pendulum swings more slowly than a short pendulum. The time it takes for a pendulum to complete one full swing, or cycle,

is called its period. The relationship between the period T (in seconds) of the pendulum and its length x (in meters) is given by the function $T(x) = 2\text{p}\sqrt{\dfrac{x}{9.8}}$. Find the period for pendulums whose lengths are 0.5 m and 1.0 m.
   0.5 m: $\approx$1.4 sec; 1.0 m: $\approx$2.0 sec

95. In meteorology, the wind chill C can be calculated by using the formula $C = 0.0817(3.71\sqrt{V} + 5.81 - 0.25V)(t - 91.4) + 91.4$, where V is the wind speed in miles per hour and t is the air temperature in degrees Fahrenheit. Find the wind chill when the wind speed is 12 miles per hour and the temperature is 35°F.
   $\approx$19°F

96. The elevation E in meters above sea level and the boiling point of water, T, in degrees Celsius at that elevation are related by the equation $E \approx 1000(100 - T) + 580(100 - T)^2$. Find the approximate boiling point of water at an elevation of 1600 meters.
   $\approx$99°C

97. Accident investigators can usually estimate a motorist's speed s in miles per hour by examining the length d in feet of the skid marks on the road. The estimate of the speed also depends on the road surface and weather conditions. If f represents the coefficient of friction between rubber and the road surface, then $s = \sqrt{30fd}$ gives an estimate of the motorist's speed. The coefficient of friction f between rubber and concrete under wet conditions is 0.4. Estimate, to the nearest mile per hour, a motorist's speed under these conditions if the skid marks are 200 feet long.
   49 mph

98. Using a viewing window with $0 \leq x \leq 4$ and $0 \leq y \leq 2$, graph the following functions on the same screen.
$$f(x) = x^{\frac{1}{2}} \quad g(x) = x^{\frac{1}{4}} \quad h(x) = x^{\frac{1}{6}}$$
In each of the following cases, arrange $x^{\frac{1}{2}}, x^{\frac{1}{4}}$, and $x^{\frac{1}{6}}$ in order of increasing size and justify your answer by using the graphs.
   a. $0 < x < 1$ **b.** $x > 1$

99. Using a viewing window with $-3 \leq x \leq 3$ and $-1.5 \leq y \leq 1.5$, graph the following functions on the same screen.
$$f(x) = x^{\frac{1}{3}} \quad g(x) = x^{\frac{1}{5}} \quad h(x) = x^{\frac{1}{7}}$$
In each of the following cases, arrange $x^{\frac{1}{3}}, x^{\frac{1}{5}}$, and $x^{\frac{1}{7}}$ in order of increasing size and justify your answer by using the graphs.
   a. $x < -1$ **b.** $-1 < x < 0$
   c. $0 < x < 1$ **d.** $x > 1$

---

79. $\left(x^{\frac{1}{3}} + 3\right)\left(x^{\frac{1}{3}} - 2\right)$

80. $\left(x^{\frac{1}{5}} + 6\right)\left(x^{\frac{1}{5}} + 5\right)$

81. $\left(x^{\frac{1}{2}} + 3\right)\left(x^{\frac{1}{2}} + 1\right)$

82. $\left(x^{\frac{1}{6}} + 5\right)\left(x^{\frac{1}{6}} + 2\right)$

83. $\left(x^{\frac{2}{5}} + 9\right)\left(x^{\frac{1}{5}} + 3\right)\left(x^{\frac{1}{5}} - 3\right)$

84. $\left(x^{\frac{1}{3}} - 3\right)^2$

85. $\dfrac{1}{\sqrt{x + h + 1} + \sqrt{x + 1}}$

86. $\dfrac{2}{\sqrt{x + h + 3} + \sqrt{x + 3}}$

87. $\dfrac{2x + h}{\sqrt{(x + h)^2 + 1} + \sqrt{x^2 + 1}}$

88. $\dfrac{2x + h - 1}{\sqrt{(x + h)^2 - (x + h)} + \sqrt{x^2 - x}}$

89. **a.** The square (or any even power) of a real number is never negative. Graphically these equations lie strictly above or on the x-axis.
   b. $\sqrt[3]{-8} = -2$, whereas $\sqrt[6]{(-8)^2} = 2$

90. **a.** We know that $r^n = c$, $s^n = d$. Now $(rs)^n = r^n s^n = cd$
   b. Since $\sqrt[n]{a} = a^{\frac{1}{n}}$, if $\sqrt[n]{c} = x$, $\sqrt[n]{d} = y$, then $\sqrt[n]{cd} = xy$

91. $\sqrt[n]{\sqrt[m]{c}} = \sqrt[mn]{c}; \ \sqrt[m]{cd} = \sqrt[m]{c}\sqrt[m]{d};$
$$\sqrt[m]{\dfrac{c}{d}} = \dfrac{\sqrt[m]{c}}{\sqrt[m]{d}}$$

92. **a.**

The function has an inverse since it passes the horizontal line test and so is one-to-one.
   b. $y = x^5; \ y^{\frac{1}{5}} = (x^5)^{\frac{1}{5}}; \ y^{\frac{1}{5}} = x$
   Now switch variables and use function notation to have the inverse $g(x) = x^{\frac{1}{5}}$.

93. When n is an odd positive integer, if $a < b$, $a^n < b^n$. Therefore, $f(x) = x^n$ is an increasing function and thus is one-to-one. Therefore, $f(x) = x^n$ has an inverse if n is an odd positive integer. The inverse is $g(x) = \sqrt[n]{x}$.

98.

   a. $x^{\frac{1}{2}} < x^{\frac{1}{4}} < x^{\frac{1}{6}}$
   b. $x^{\frac{1}{6}} < x^{\frac{1}{4}} < x^{\frac{1}{2}}$

99.

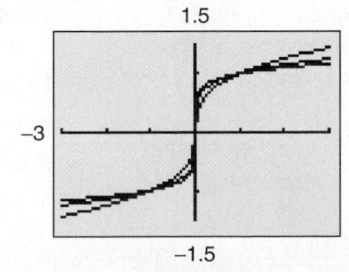

   a. $x^{\frac{1}{3}} < x^{\frac{1}{5}} < x^{\frac{1}{7}}$
   b. $x^{\frac{1}{7}} < x^{\frac{1}{5}} < x^{\frac{1}{3}}$
   c. $x^{\frac{1}{3}} < x^{\frac{1}{5}} < x^{\frac{1}{7}}$
   d. $x^{\frac{1}{7}} < x^{\frac{1}{5}} < x^{\frac{1}{3}}$

100. a. *g* is the graph of *f* moved 3 units left.

    b. *h* is the graph of *f* moved 2 units down.

    c. *k* is the graph of *f* moved 3 units left, then 2 units down.

100. Graph $f(x) = \sqrt{x}$ in the standard viewing window. Then, without doing any more graphing, describe the graphs of these functions.

    a. $g(x) = \sqrt{x + 3}$ *Hint:* $g(x) = f(x + 3)$; see Section 3.4.

    b. $h(x) = \sqrt{x} - 2$

    c. $k(x) = \sqrt{x + 3} - 2$

101. Do Exercise 100 with $\sqrt[3]{}$ in place of $\sqrt{}$.

    a. *g* is the graph of *f* moved 3 units left.

    b. *h* is the graph of *f* moved 2 units down.

    c. *k* is the graph of *f* moved 3 units left, then 2 units down.

Exponential Functions

Teaching Notes

Students will better understand properties of the **Graph of $f(x) = a^x$** by completing the following pencil-and-paper activity:

Copy and complete each table. Then plot the points to graph each function.

x	-3	-2	-1	0	1	2	3
$g(x) = 2^x$	$\frac{1}{8}$	$\frac{1}{4}$	$\frac{1}{2}$	1	2	4	8

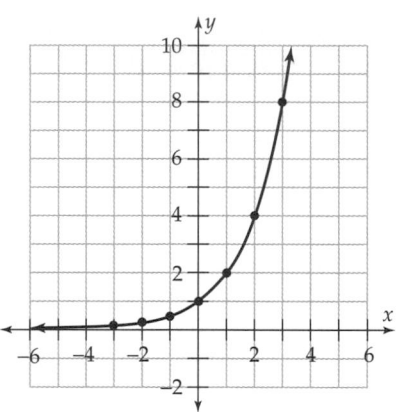

x	-3	-2	-1	0	1	2	3
$h(x) = \left(\frac{1}{2}\right)^x$	8	4	2	1	$\frac{1}{2}$	$\frac{1}{4}$	$\frac{1}{8}$

5.2 **Exponential Functions**

Objectives

- Graph and identify transformations of exponential functions
- Use exponential functions to solve application problems

Graph of
$f(x) = a^x$

Graphs of Exponential Functions

For each positive real number a, $a \ne 1$, there is an **exponential function with base a** whose domain is all real numbers and whose rule is $f(x) = a^x$. Some examples are shown below.

$$f(x) = 10^x \qquad g(x) = 2^x \qquad h(x) = \left(\frac{1}{2}\right)^x \qquad k(x) = \left(\frac{3}{2}\right)^x$$

The shape of the graph of an exponential function $f(x) = a^x$ depends only on the size of a, as shown in the following figures.

- **graph is above *x*-axis**
- **y-intercept is 1**
- **$f(x)$ is increasing**
- **$f(x)$ approaches the negative x-axis as x approaches $-\infty$**

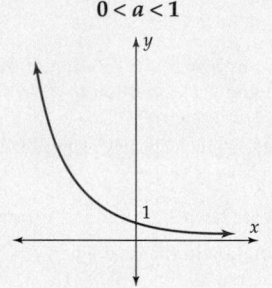

- **graph is above *x*-axis**
- **y-intercept is 1**
- **$f(x)$ is decreasing**
- **$f(x)$ approaches the positive x-axis as x approaches ∞**

For $a = 0$ or $a = 1$, the function $f(x) = a^x$ is a constant function, not exponential. Even roots of negative numbers are not defined in the set of real numbers, so when $a < 0$, a^x is not defined for any rational exponent that

---

What is the y-intercept for each graph? 1

Will either graph go below the x-axis? no

Are both functions in the form $f(x) = a^x$? yes

For $g(x)$, is $a > 1$ or is $a < 1$? $a > 1$

Is $g(x)$ increasing or decreasing? increasing

What happens to $g(x)$ as x approaches $-\infty$? It approaches the negative x-axis.

For $h(x)$, is $a > 1$ or is $a < 1$? $a < 1$

Is $h(x)$ increasing or decreasing? decreasing

What happens to $h(x)$ as x approaches ∞? It approaches the positive x-axis.

Explain why $a \ne 1$ and $a \ne 0$:

If $a = 1$, $f(x) = 1^x = 1$.

If $a = 0$, $f(x) = 0^x = 0$ (for $x \ne 0$).

In either case, the graph is a horizontal line.

has an even number as its denominator. Because within any interval there are infinitely many rational numbers that have an even denominator, $f(x) = a^x$ has an infinite number of holes in every interval when $a < 0$. Therefore, the function is not *well-behaved* for $a < 0$, so it is not defined for those values.

The following two Graphing Explorations illustrate the effect that the value of a has on the shape of the graph of an exponential function for $a > 1$ and for $0 < a < 1$.

Graphing Exploration ●──

a. Using a viewing window with $-3 \le x \le 7$ and $-2 \le y \le 18$, graph each function below on the same screen, and observe the behavior of each to the right of the y-axis.

$$f(x) = 1.3^x \quad g(x) = 2^x \quad h(x) = 10^x$$

As the graphs continue to the right, which graph rises least steeply? most steeply?

How does the steepness of the graph of $f(x) = a^x$ to the right of the y-axis seem to be related to the size of the base a?

b. Using the graphs of the same three functions in the viewing window with $-4 \le x \le 2$ and $-0.5 \le y \le 2$, observe the behavior to the *left* of the y-axis.

As the graph continues to the left, how does the size of the base a seem to be related to how quickly the graph of $f(x) = a^x$ falls toward the x-axis?

Graphing Exploration ●──

Using a viewing window with $-4 \le x \le 4$ and $-1 \le y \le 4$, graph each function below on the same screen, and observe the behavior of each.

$$f(x) = 0.2^x \quad g(x) = 0.4^x \quad h(x) = 0.6^x \quad k(x) = 0.8^x$$

Notice that the bases of the exponential functions are increasing in size: $0 < 0.2 < 0.4 < 0.6 < 0.8 < 1$

As the graphs continue to the right, which graph falls least steeply? most steeply?

How does the steepness of the graph of $f(x) = a^x$ seem to be related to the size of the base a?

The graphing explorations above show that the graph of $f(x) = a^x$ rises or falls less steeply as the base a gets closer to 1.

Solution to second **Graphing Exploration:**

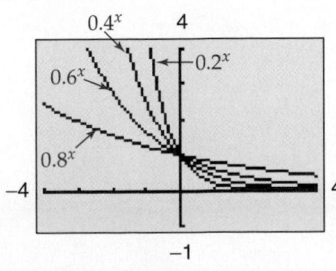

$k(x) = 0.8^x$ falls least steeply and $f(x) = 0.2^x$ falls most steeply. When $0 < a < 1$, steeper graphs correspond to smaller values of a.

Teaching Notes

The graph of $f(x) = a^x$ has an infinite number of holes within any interval when $a < 0$. *This is most likely a new and difficult concept for your students.* Try the following to help them understand.

Recall that even roots of negative numbers are not defined in the set of real numbers. For example, $(-16)^{\frac{3}{4}} = \left(\sqrt[4]{-16}\right)^3$ is not defined.

Now challenge students to choose any two rational numbers as x-values. Show that you can always find a number between the chosen numbers that has an even denominator (thereby making a^x undefined).

Example:

If $\frac{1}{5}$ and $\frac{1}{3}$ are chosen, show that $\frac{7}{30}$ is between them: $\frac{1}{5} = \frac{6}{30} < \frac{7}{30} < \frac{10}{30} = \frac{1}{3}$.

Solution to first **Graphing Exploration:**

a.

$f(x) = 1.3^x$ rises least steeply and $h(x) = 10^x$ rises most steeply. When $a > 1$, steeper graphs correspond to greater values of a.

b.

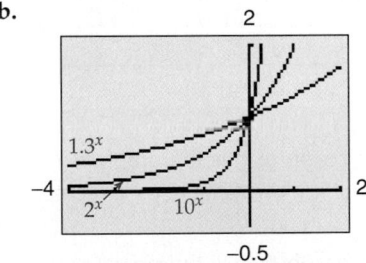

When $a > 1$, the graph falls toward the x-axis more quickly for greater values of a.

ADDITIONAL EXAMPLES

Example 1

The graph of $f(x) = 2^x$ is shown in Figure 5.2-1. Without graphing, describe the transformation from the graph of f to the graph of each function below. Verify by graphing.

a. $g(x) = 2^{x-4}$

The graph of g is the graph of f shifted horizontally 4 units to the right. See graph below.

b. $h(x) = 2^{x+2} + 3$

The graph of h is the graph of f shifted horizontally 2 units to the left and vertically 3 units up.

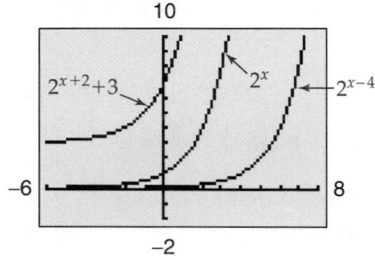

Example 2

The graph of $f(x) = 4^x$ is shown below. Without graphing, describe the transformation from the graph of f to the graph of each function below. Verify by graphing.

$g(x) = 4^{0.5x}$

The graph of g is the graph of f stretched horizontally by a factor of 2.

$h(x) = 4^{0.4x}$

The graph of h is the graph of f stretched horizontally by a factor of 2.5.

$k(x) = 4^{-x}$

The graph of k is the graph of f reflected across the y-axis.

$p(x) = 4^{-0.2x}$

The graph of p is the graph of f stretched horizontally by a factor of 5 and reflected across the y-axis.

Figure 5.2-1

Figure 5.2-2

Figure 5.2-3

Figure 5.2-4

Example 1   Translations

The graph of $f(x) = 2^x$ is shown in Figure 5.2-1. Without graphing, describe the transformation from the graph of f to the graph of each function below. Verify by graphing.

a. $g(x) = 2^{x+3}$ **b.** $h(x) = 2^{x-3} - 4$

Solution

a. If $f(x) = 2^x$, then $g(x) = 2^{x+3} = f(x + 3)$. So the graph of g is the graph of f shifted horizontally 3 units to the left, as shown in Figure 5.2-2.

b. If $f(x) = 2^x$, then $h(x) = 2^{x-3} - 4 = f(x - 3) - 4$. So the graph of $h(x)$ is the graph of $f(x) = 2^x$ shifted horizontally 3 units to the right and vertically 4 units downward, as shown in Figure 5.2-3. ∎

The graphs of exponential functions of the form $f(x) = a^x$ increase at an explosive rate. To see this, consider the graph of $f(x) = 2^x$ in Figure 5.2-3. If the x-axis were extended to the right, then $x = 50$ would be at the right edge of the page. At this point, the graph of $f(x) = 2^x$ is 2^{50} units high. The scale of the y-axis in Figure 5.2-3 is about 12 units per inch, or 144 units per foot, or 760,320 units per mile. Therefore, the height of the graph at $x = 50$ is

$$\frac{2^{50}}{760,320} = 1,480,823,741 \text{ miles,}$$

which would put that part of the graph well beyond the planet Saturn!

Since most quantities that grow exponentially do not change as dramatically as the graph of $f(x) = 2^x$, exponential functions that model real-life growth or decay are usually modified by the insertion of appropriate constants. These functions are generally of the form

$$f(x) = Pa^{kx},$$

such as the functions shown below.

$$f(x) = \frac{1}{2}(5.2^{0.45x}) \qquad g(x) = 3.5(10^{-0.03x}) \qquad h(x) = (-6)(1.076^{2x})$$

Their graphs have the same shape as the graph of $f(x) = a^x$, but may rise or fall more or less steeply, depending on the constants P, k, and a.

Example 2   Horizontal Stretches

The graph of $f(x) = 3^x$ is shown in Figure 5.2-4. Without graphing, describe the transformation from the graph of f to the graph of each function below. Verify by graphing.

$$g(x) = 3^{0.2x} \qquad h(x) = 3^{0.8x} \qquad k(x) = 3^{-x} \qquad p(x) = 3^{-0.4x}$$

Figure 5.2-5

Figure 5.2-6

Figure 5.2-7

Solution

The graphs of $g(x) = 3^{0.2x}$ and $h(x) = 3^{0.8x}$ are the graph of f stretched horizontally by a factor of $\frac{1}{0.2} = 5$ and $\frac{1}{0.8} = 1.25$, respectively. The graph of $k(x) = 3^{-x}$ is the graph of f reflected across the y-axis. The graph of $p(x) = 3^{-0.4x}$ is the graph of f stretched horizontally by a factor of $\frac{1}{0.4} = 2.5$ and reflected across the y-axis. The graphs are identified in Figure 5.2.5.

Example 3   Vertical Stretches

The graph of $p(x) = 3^{-0.4x}$ is shown in Figure 5.2-6. Without graphing, describe the transformation from the graph of p to the graph of each function below. Verify by graphing.

$$q(x) = 4 \cdot 3^{-0.4x} \qquad r(x) = (-2)3^{-0.4x}$$

Solution

The graph of $q(x) = 4 \cdot 3^{-0.4x}$ is the graph of $p(x) = 3^{-0.4x}$ stretched vertically by a factor of 4. The graph of $r(x) = (-2)3^{-0.4x}$ is the graph of $p(x) = 3^{-0.4x}$ stretched vertically by a factor of 2 and reflected across the x-axis. The graphs are identified in Figure 5.2-7.

Exponential Growth and Decay

In this section, you will see that exponential functions are useful for modeling situations in which a quantity increases or decreases by a fixed factor. In Section 5.3 you will learn how to construct these types of functions.

Example 4   Finance

If you invest \$5000 in a stock that is increasing in value at the rate of 3% per year, then the value of your stock is given by the function $f(x) = 5000(1.03)^x$, where x is measured in years.

a. Assuming that the value of your stock continues growing at this rate, how much will your investment be worth in 4 years?

b. When will your investment be worth \$8000?

Solution

a. Letting $x = 4$, $f(4) = 5000(1.03)^4 \approx 5627.54$.
In 4 years your stock is worth about \$5627.54.

b. Find the value of x for which $f(x) = 8000$. In other words, solve the equation $5000(1.03)^x = 8000$.

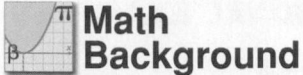

Math Background

The irrational number e has several different, equivalent definitions:

$$e = \lim_{n \to \infty}\left(1 + \frac{1}{n}\right)^n$$

e is the number such that

$$\ln e = 1 = \int_1^e \frac{1}{t}\, dt.$$

Students will learn in Section 5.4: When e is used as the base of a logarithmic function, that function is called the *natural* logarithmic function. The exponential function $f(x) = e^x$ and the natural logarithmic function $f(x) = \ln x$ are inverses.

Example Notes

Examples 4, 5, and **7** are examples of exponential growth. Each function is of the form $f(x) = ka^x$, where $a > 1$.

Example 6 is an example of exponential decay, with a function of the form $f(x) = ka^x$, where $0 < a < 1$. ($k = 1$ in this Example.) Note that exponential growth occurs when $a > 1$, and exponential decay occurs when $0 < a < 1$.

In **Example 5**, ask students to find the value of $g(0)$ without using a calculator, and to interpret the result. $g(0) = 2.5(1.0185)^0 = 2.5(1) = 2.5$

The world population in 1950 was 2.5 billion.

Real-World Application

The topic of **Example 6**, radioactive decay, should concern all citizens, not just scientists and government officials. As noted in the Example, plutonium decays so slowly that, for practical considerations, we can assume that it does not decay at all.

Suggest to students that they research the problem of nuclear waste disposal, focusing on what is being done in their state, in the country, and in the world.

Figure 5.2-8

Figure 5.2-9

Figure 5.2-10

The point of intersection of the graphs of $f(x) = 5000(1.03)^x$ and $y = 8000$ is approximately $(15.901, 8000)$.

Therefore, the stock will be worth \$8000 in about 16 years.

Example 5   Population Growth

Based on data from the past 50 years, the world population, in billions, can be approximated by the function $g(x) = 2.5(1.0185)^x$, where $x = 0$ corresponds to 1950.

a. Estimate the world population in 2015.

b. In what year will the population be double what it is in 2015?

Solution

a. Since $x = 0$ corresponds to 1950, $x = 1$ to 1951, and so on, the year 2015 corresponds to $x = 65$. Find $g(65)$.

$$g(65) = 2.5(1.0185)^{65} \approx 8.23$$

The world population in 2015 will be about 8.23 billion people.

b. Twice the population in 2015 is $2(8.23) = 16.46$ billion. Find the number x such that $g(x) = 16.46$; that is, solve $2.5(1.0185)^x = 16.46$.

A graphical intersection finder shows that the approximate coordinates of the point of intersection of the graphs of $g(x) = 2.5(1.0185)^x$ and $y = 16.46$ are $(102.81, 16.46)$. The x-coordinate 102.81, or 103 when rounded to the nearest year, corresponds to the year 2053. Notice that it takes only 38 years for the world population to double.

Example 6   Radioactive Decay

The amount from one kilogram of plutonium (^{239}Pu) that remains after x years can be approximated by the function $M(x) = 0.99997^x$. Estimate the amount of plutonium remaining after 10,000 years.

Solution

Because M is an exponential function with a base smaller than 1 but very close to 1, its graph falls very slowly from left to right. The fact that the graph falls so slowly as x gets large means that even after an extremely long time, a substantial amount of plutonium will remain.

When $x = 10,000$, $M(x) \approx 0.74$. Therefore, almost three-fourths of the original plutonium remains after 10,000 years! This is the reason that nuclear waste disposal is such a serious concern.

The Number *e* and the Natural Exponential Function

Figure 5.2-11

There is an irrational number, denoted *e*, that arises naturally in a variety of phenomena and plays a central role in the mathematical description of the physical universe. Its decimal expansion begins as shown below.

$$e = 2.718281828459045\ldots$$

Most calculators have an e^x key that can be used to evaluate the natural exponential function $f(x) = e^x$. When you evaluate e^1 using a calculator, the display will show the first part of the decimal expansion of *e*.

Figure 5.2-11 shows that the graph of $f(x) = e^x$ has the same shape as the graphs of $y = 2^x$ and $y = 3^x$, but it climbs more steeply than the graph of $y = 2^x$ and less steeply than the graph of $y = 3^x$.

Example 7   Population Growth

If the population of the United States continues to grow as it has since 1980, then the approximate population, in millions, of the United States in year *t*, where $t = 0$ corresponds to the year 1980, will be given by the function $P(t) = 227e^{0.0093t}$.

a. Estimate the population in 2015.

b. When will the population reach half a billion?

Solution

a. The year 2015 corresponds to $t = 35$. Find $P(35)$.

$$P(35) = 227e^{0.0093(35)} \approx 314.3$$

Therefore, the population in 2015 will be approximately 314.3 million people.

b. Half a billion is 500 million. Find the value of *t* for which $P(t) = 500$. A graphical intersection finder shows that the approximate coordinates of the point of intersection of the graphs of $P(t) = 227e^{0.0093t}$ and $y = 500$ are approximately (85, 500). A *t*-value of 85 corresponds to the year 2065. Therefore, the population will reach half a billion approximately by the year 2065. ∎

Figure 5.2-12

Other Exponential Functions

In most real-world applications, populations cannot grow infinitely large. The population growth models shown previously do not take into account factors that may limit population growth in the future. Example 8 illustrates a function, called a **logistic model,** which is designed to model situations that have limited future growth due to a fixed area, food supply, or other factors.

Example 5

The projected population of Tokyo, Japan, in millions, from 2000 to 2015 can be approximated by the function $g(x) = 26.4(1.0019)^x$, where $x = 0$ corresponds to the year 2000.

a. Estimate the population of Tokyo in 2015.   27.16 million

b. If the population continues to grow at this same rate after 2015, in what year will the population reach 30 million?   2067

Example 6

Geologists and archeologists use carbon-14 to determine the age of organic substances, such as bones or small plants and animals found embedded in rocks. The amount from one kilogram of carbon-14 that remains after *x* years can be approximated by the function $M(x) = 0.99988^x$. Estimate the amount of carbon-14 remaining after 2000 years.   about 0.79 kg

Example 7

The population of Los Angeles, California, since 1970, in millions, can be modeled by the function $P(t) = 2.7831e^{0.0096t}$, where *t* represents time in years. Assuming that this model continues to be appropriate, use it to answer the following:

a. Estimate the population in 2010.   4.1 million

b. When will the population reach 5 million?   in 2031

Example Notes

For **Example 8**, the following will help students understand that the function $p(t)$ approaches, but never quite reaches, 20,000:

Have students evaluate $24e^{-\frac{t}{4}}$ for $t = 0, 1, 10,$ and 40 (rounding the first three to the nearest whole number). **24, 19, 2, 0.001** This will help them see that, as t increases, the value of

$$p(t) = \frac{20,000}{1 + 24e^{-\frac{t}{4}}} \text{ approaches } \frac{20,000}{1 + 0}, \text{ or}$$

20,000.

Ask students for the equation of the horizontal asymptote in the graph, and ask them to explain it. $y = 20,000$; The function values approach, but never reach, 20,000 because the function rule is 20,000 divided by a positive number that approaches, but is always greater than, 1.

ADDITIONAL EXAMPLES

Teaching Notes

Solution to the **Graphing Exploration:** Greater x-coefficients correspond to steeper and narrower graphs.

Figure 5.2-13

Example 8   Logistic Model

The population of fish in a certain lake at time t months is given by the function $p(t) = \dfrac{20,000}{1 + 24e^{-\frac{t}{4}}}$, where $t \geq 0$. There is an upper limit on the fish population due to the oxygen supply, available food, etc. Graph the function, and find the upper limit on the fish population.

Solution

The graph of $p(t)$ at the left suggests that the horizontal line $y = 20,000$ is a horizontal asymptote of the graph. If so, the upper limit on the fish population is 20,000.

You can verify this by rewriting the rule of p as shown below.

$$p(t) = \frac{20,000}{1 + 24e^{-\frac{t}{4}}} = \frac{20,000}{1 + \dfrac{24}{e^{\frac{t}{4}}}}$$

As t increases, $\frac{t}{4}$ increases and $e^{\frac{t}{4}}$ grows very large. As $e^{\frac{t}{4}}$ grows very large, $\frac{24}{e^{\frac{t}{4}}}$ gets very close to 0. As $\frac{24}{e^{\frac{t}{4}}}$ gets closer and closer to 0, $p(t)$ gets closer and closer to $\frac{20,000}{1 + 0}$, or 20,000. Because $e^{\frac{t}{4}}$ is positive and $\frac{24}{e^{\frac{t}{4}}}$ never quite reaches 0, the denominator of $p(t)$ is always slightly larger than 1 and $p(t)$ is always less than 20,000. ∎

When a cable, such as a power line, is suspended between towers of equal height, it forms a curve called a catenary, which is the graph of a function of the form shown below for suitable constants A and k.

$$f(x) = A(e^{kx} + e^{-kx})$$

The Gateway Arch in St. Louis, shown in Figure 5.2-14, has the shape of an inverted catenary, which was chosen because it evenly distributes the internal structural forces.

Figure 5.2-14

Graphing Exploration ●

Using the viewing window with $-5 \leq x \leq 5$ and $-10 \leq y \leq 80$, graph each function below on the same screen, and observe their behavior.

$$Y_1 = 10(e^{0.4x} + e^{-0.4x}) \quad Y_2 = 10(e^{2x} + e^{-2x}) \quad Y_3 = 10(e^{3x} + e^{-3x})$$

How does the coefficient of x affect the shape of the graph?
Predict the shape of the graph of $y = -Y_1 + 80$. Confirm your answer by graphing.

The graph of $-Y_1 + 80$ will be the graph of Y_1 reflected across the x-axis and moved up 80 units.

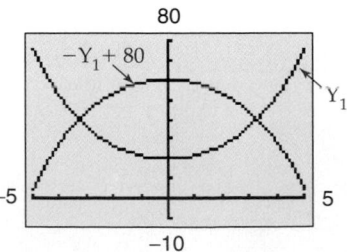

Exercises 5.2

In Exercises 1–6, list the transformations needed to transform the graph of $h(x) = 2^x$ into the graph of the given function. (Section 3.4 may be helpful.)

1. $f(x) = 2^x - 5$ **2.** $g(x) = -(2^x)$

3. $k(x) = 3(2^x)$ **4.** $g(x) = 2^{x-1}$

5. $f(x) = 2^{x+2} - 5$ **6.** $g(x) = -5(2^{x-1}) + 7$

In Exercises 7–13, list the transformations needed to transform the graph of $h(x) = 3^x$ into the graph of the given function. (Section 3.4 may be helpful.)

7. $f(x) = 3^x + 4$ **8.** $g(x) = 3^{-x}$

9. $k(x) = \frac{1}{4}(3^x)$ **10.** $g(x) = 3^{0.4x}$

11. $f(x) = 3^{2-x}$ **12.** $f(x) = 8 + 5(3^x)$

13. $g(x) = 4(3^{-0.15x})$

In Exercises 14–19, sketch a complete graph of the function.

14. $f(x) = 4^{-x}$ **15.** $f(x) = \left(\frac{5}{2}\right)^{-x}$

16. $f(x) = 2^{3x}$ **17.** $g(x) = 3^{\frac{x}{2}}$

18. $f(x) = 2^{5-x}$ **19.** $g(x) = 2^{x-5}$

In Exercises 20–21, match the functions to the graphs. Assume $a > 1$ and $c > 1$.

20. $f(x) = a^x$ **C**
$g(x) = a^x + 3$ **A**
$h(x) = a^{x+5}$ **B**

21. $f(x) = c^x$ **B**
$g(x) = -3c^x$ **C**
$h(x) = c^{x+5}$ **A**
$k(x) = -3c^x - 2$ **D**

In Exercises 22–29, find a viewing window (or windows) that shows a complete graph of the function.

22. $k(x) = e^{-x}$ **23.** $f(x) = e^{-x^2}$

24. $f(x) = \frac{e^x + e^{-x}}{2}$ **25.** $h(x) = \frac{e^x - e^{-x}}{2}$

26. $g(x) = 2^x - x$ **27.** $k(x) = \frac{2}{e^x + e^{-x}}$

28. $f(x) = \frac{5}{1 + e^{-x}}$ **29.** $g(x) = \frac{10}{1 + 9e^{-\frac{x}{2}}}$

In Exercises 30–34, determine whether the function is even, odd, or neither. (See *Excursion* 3.4A.)

30. $f(x) = 10^x$ **31.** $g(x) = 2^x - x$
    neither   **neither**

32. $f(x) = \frac{e^x + e^{-x}}{2}$ **33.** $f(x) = \frac{e^x - e^{-x}}{2}$
    even   **odd**

34. $f(x) = e^{-x^2}$
    even

35. Use the Big-Little concept (see Section 4.4) to explain why $e^x + e^{-x}$ is approximately equal to e^x when x is large.

In Exercises 36–39, find the average rate of change of the function. (See Section 3.7.)

36. $f(x) = x(2^x)$ as x goes from 1 to 3 **11**

37. $g(x) = 3^{x^2 - x}$ as x goes from -1 to 1 **−4**

38. $h(x) = 5^{-x^2}$ as x goes from -1 to 0 $\frac{4}{5}$

39. $f(x) = e^x - e^{-x}$ as x goes from -3 to -1 $\approx$**8.84**

In Exercises 40–43, find the difference quotient of the function. (See Section 3.7.)

40. $f(x) = 10^x$ **41.** $g(x) = 5^{x^2}$

42. $f(x) = 2^x + 2^{-x}$ **43.** $f(x) = e^x - e^{-x}$

In Exercises 44–49, list all asymptotes of the graph of the function and the approximate coordinates of each local extremum. (See Section 4.3.)

44. $f(x) = x(2^x)$ **45.** $g(x) = x(2^{-x})$

46. $h(x) = e^{\frac{x^2}{2}}$ **47.** $k(x) = 2^{x^2 - 6x + 2}$

48. $f(x) = e^{-x^2}$ **49.** $g(x) = -xe^{\frac{x^2}{20}}$
                                    No asymptotes;
                                    no extrema

41. $\dfrac{5^{(x+h)^2} - 5^{x^2}}{h}$

42. $\dfrac{(2^{x+h} + 2^{-(x+h)}) - (2^x + 2^{-x})}{h}$

43. $\dfrac{(e^{x+h} - e^{-x-h}) - (e^x - e^{-x})}{h}$

44. The x-axis is a horizontal asymptote; local minimum at $(-1.443, -0.531)$.

45. The x-axis is a horizontal asymptote; local maximum at $(1.44, 0.53)$.

46. No asymptotes; local minimum at $(0, 1)$.

47. No asymptotes; local minimum at $(3, 0.0078)$.

48. The x-axis is a horizontal asymptote; local maximum at $(0, 1)$.

Exercises 5.2
ANSWERS

1. Shift the graph of h vertically 5 units downward.

2. Reflect the graph of h across the x-axis.

3. Stretch the graph of h vertically by a factor of 3.

4. Shift the graph of h horizontally 1 unit to the right.

5. Shift the graph of h horizontally 2 units to the left, then vertically 5 units downward.

6. Shift the graph of h horizontally 1 unit to the right, then reflect it across the x-axis, then stretch it vertically by a factor of 5, then shift it vertically 7 units upward.

7. Shift the graph of h vertically 4 units upward.

8. Reflect the graph of h across the y-axis.

9. Compress the graph of h vertically by a factor of $\frac{1}{4}$.

10. Stretch the graph of h horizontally by a factor of 2.5.

11. Reflect the graph of h across the y-axis, then shift horizontally 2 units to the right.

12. Stretch the graph of h vertically by a factor of 5, then translate it vertically 8 units upward.

13. Reflect the graph of h across the y-axis, stretch horizontally by a factor of $\frac{1}{0.15} = 6\frac{2}{3}$, then stretch vertically by a factor of 4.

14–19. *See pp.* 1066–1067.

22. $-3 \le x \le 3$ and $0 \le y \le 12$

23. $-3 \le x \le 3$ and $0 \le y \le 1$

24. $-4 \le x \le 4$ and $0 \le y \le 10$

25. $-4 \le x \le 4$ and $-10 \le y \le 10$

26. $-10 \le x \le 10$ and $0 \le y \le 20$

27. $-4 \le x \le 4$ and $0 \le y \le 1$

28. $-10 \le x \le 10$ and $0 \le y \le 6$

29. $-5 \le x \le 20$ and $0 \le y \le 10$

35. When x is large, $e^{-x} \approx 0$, so $e^x + e^{-x} \approx e^x + 0 = e^x$.

40. $\dfrac{10^{x+h} - 10^x}{h}$

58. Any non-constant polynomial must either "blow up" or "blow down" as $|x|$ increases. Therefore, since any exponential of the form $f(x) = a^x$ where a is not 1 has the x-axis as a horizontal asymptote in either the positive or negative direction, no polynomial can be the same as an exponential of this form.

59. a. Not entirely

b. The graph of $f_8(x)$ appears to coincide with the graph of $g(x)$ on most calculator screens; when $-2.4 \leq x \leq 2.4$, the maximum error is at most 0.01.

c. Not at the right side of the viewing window; $f_{12}(x)$

50. If you deposit $750 at 2.2% interest, compounded annually and paid from the day of deposit to the day of withdrawal, your balance at time t is given by $B(t) = 750(1.022)^t$. How much will you have after 2 years? after 3 years and 9 months?
≈$783.36; ≈$813.77

51. The population of a colony of fruit flies t days from now is given by the function $p(t) = 100 \cdot 3^{\frac{t}{10}}$.
a. What will the population be in 15 days? in 25 days? **≈520; ≈1559**
b. When will the population reach 2500?
≈29.3 days

52. A certain type of bacteria grows according to the function $f(x) = 5000e^{0.4055x}$, where the time x is measured in hours. **≈128,180**
a. What will the population be in 8 hours?
b. When will the population reach 1 million?
≈13.07 hr

53. According to data from the National Center for Health Statistics, the life expectancy at birth for a person born in year x is approximated by the function below.

$$D(x) = \frac{79.257}{1 + 9.7135 \times 10^{24} \cdot e^{-0.0304x}}$$

$$(1900 \leq x \leq 2050)$$

a. What is the life expectancy of someone born in 1980? in 2000? **≈74.06 yr; ≈76.34 yr**
b. In what year was life expectancy at birth 60 years? **1930**

54. The number of subscribers, in millions, to basic cable TV can be approximated by the function

$$g(x) = \frac{76.7}{1 + 16 \cdot 0.8444^x}$$

where $x = 0$ corresponds to 1970. (Source: The Cable TV Financial Datebook and The Pay TV Newsletter)
a. Estimate the number of subscribers in 1995 and in 2005. **≈62.2 million; ≈73.5 million**
b. When does the number of subscribers reach 70 million? **2000**
c. According to this model, will the number of subscribers ever reach 90 million?
No; 76.7 million is the cap.

55. The estimated number of units that will be sold by a certain company t months from now is given by $N(t) = 100,000e^{-0.09t}$.
a. What are the current sales ($t = 0$)? What will sales be in 2 months? in 6 months?
a. 100,000; ≈83,527; ≈58,275

b. No. The graph continues to decrease toward zero.

b. From examining the graph, do you think that sales will ever start to increase again? Explain.

56. a. The function $g(t) = 1 - e^{-0.0479t}$ gives the percentage of the population (expressed as a decimal) that has seen a new TV show t weeks after it goes on the air. What percentage of people have seen the show after 24 weeks?
b. Approximately when will 90% of the people have seen it?
a. ≈68.3%.   b. ≈48 wk

57. a. The beaver population near a certain lake in year t is approximated by the function $p(t) = \dfrac{2000}{1 + 199e^{-0.5544t}}$. What is the population now (when $t = 0$) and what will it be in 5 years?
b. Approximately when will there be 1000 beavers?
a. 10; ≈149   b. ≈9.55 yr

58. *Critical Thinking* Look back at Section 4.3, where the basic properties of graphs of polynomial functions were discussed. Then review the basic properties of the graph of $f(x) = a^x$ discussed in this section. Using these various properties, give an argument to show that for any fixed positive number a, where $a \neq 1$, it is not possible to find a polynomial function $g(x) = c_nx^n + \cdots + c_1x + c_0$ such that $a^x = g(x)$ for all numbers x. In other words, *no exponential function is a polynomial function.*

59. *Critical Thinking* For each positive integer n, let f_n be the polynomial function below.

$$f_n(x) = 1 + x + \frac{x^2}{2!} + \frac{x^3}{3!} + \frac{x^4}{4!} + \cdots + \frac{x^n}{n!}$$

a. Using the viewing window with $-4 \leq x \leq 4$ and $-5 \leq y \leq 55$, graph $g(x) = e^x$ and $f_4(x)$ on the same screen. Do the graphs appear to coincide?
b. Replace the graph of $f_4(x)$ by that of $f_5(x)$, then by $f_6(x)$, $f_7(x)$, and so on until you find a polynomial $f_n(x)$ whose graph appears to coincide with the graph of $g(x) = e^x$ in this viewing window. Use the trace feature to move from graph to graph at the same value of x to see how accurate this approximation is.
c. Change the viewing window so that $-6 \leq x \leq 6$ and $-10 \leq y \leq 400$. Is the polynomial you found in part **b** a good approximation for $g(x)$ in this viewing window? If not, what polynomial is a good approximation?

5.3 Applications of Exponential Functions

Objective

- Create and use exponential models for a variety of exponential growth or decay application problems

In Section 5.2, you used several exponential functions that modeled exponential growth and decay. In this section you will learn how to construct such exponential models in a variety of real-life situations.

Compound Interest

When interest is paid on a balance that includes interest accumulated from the previous time periods it is called **compound interest.**

Example 1   Compounding Annually

If you invest $6000 at 8% interest, compounded annually, how much is in the account at the end of 10 years?

Solution

After one year the account balance is

Principal + Interest
$$6000 + 0.08(6000) = 6000(1 + 0.08) = 6000(1.08).$$

The account balance has changed by a factor of 1.08. If this amount is left in the account, the balance will again change by a factor of 1.08 after the second year.

$$[6000(1.08)](1.08), \text{ or } 6000(1.08)^2$$

Because the balance will change by a factor of 1.08 every year, the balance in the account at the end of year x is given by

$$B(x) = 6000 \cdot (1.08)^x.$$

Therefore, the balance (to the nearest penny) in the account after 10 years is

$$B(10) = 6000 \cdot (1.08)^{10} = \$12,953.55.$$ ∎

The pattern illustrated in Example 1 can be generalized as shown below.

Compound Interest

If P dollars is invested at interest rate r (expressed as a decimal) per time period t, then A is the amount after t periods.

$$A = P(1 + r)^t$$

Notice that in Example 1, $P = 6000$, $r = 0.08$, and the number of periods, or years, is $t = 10$.

5.3 Applications of Exponential Functions

Teaching Notes

Using the situation in **Example 1**, the following can help students understand that compound interest includes accumulated interest:

amount after 1 year:
$$6000 + 0.08(6000) = 6480$$
amount after 2 years:
$$6480 + 0.08(6480) = 6998.40$$
amount after 3 years:
$$6998.40 + 0.08(6998.40) \approx 7558.27$$

Using simple interest, the amounts would be:

amount after 1 year:
$$6000 + 0.08(6000) = 6480$$
amount after 2 years:
$$6480 + 0.08(6000) = 6960$$
amount after 3 years:
$$6960 + 0.08(6000) = 7440$$

Remind students that *interest* is money and an *interest rate* is a percent.

After completing Example 1, show how the formula in the **Compound Interest** box relates to the function found in Example 1:
$$B(x) = 6000 \ (1.08)^x$$
$$B(x) = 6000 \ (1 + 0.08)^x$$
$$A = \quad P \ (1 + r)^t$$

ADDITIONAL EXAMPLES

Example 1

If you invest $9000 at 4% interest, compounded annually, how much is in the account at the end of 5 years?
$$B(t) = 9000(1.04)^t$$
$$B(5) = 9000(1.04)^5 = \$10,949.88$$

Real-World Application

Examples 1–5 involve compound interest as an application of exponential growth. Point out to students that in business and consumer applications, interest is almost always compound interest (simple interest is rarely used). **Example 2** investigates how an amount is affected by different compounding periods. You might want to have your students investigate how an amount is affected by different times or interest rates.

Teaching Notes

After discussing **Example 2**, students will know that the more often interest is compounded, the larger the final amount will be. Ask them if an infinite number of compounding periods (continuous compounding) will result in an infinite final amount. no

Point out the table in **Example 4** (page 348) that establishes a maximum for a final amount ($2.72).

Have students compare interest earned by continuous compounding with interest earned by hourly or daily compounding. They should conclude that there is little difference.

Example Notes

In **Example 2d**, leap year is ignored for convenience.

The pattern in **Example 4** is extended to define **Continuous Compounding** as compounding with an infinite number of periods. The last entry in the table on page 348 is an approximation of the number e.

COMMON ERROR ALERT

Students sometimes use annual interest rate for r or number of years for t in the formula $A = P(1 + r)^t$. Remind them that r *is the interest rate for each period*, and t *is number of periods*. In **Example 2b**, they might use $r = 0.064$ or $t = 4$ instead of these correct expressions: $r = \frac{0.064}{4}$, $t = 4(3)$.

Example 2   Different Compounding Periods

Determine the amount that a $4000 investment over three years at an annual interest rate of 6.4% is worth for each compounding period.

a. annually   **b.** quarterly   **c.** monthly   **d.** daily

Solution

a. Use $P = 4000$, $r = 0.064$, and $t = 3$ in the compound interest formula.
$$A = 4000(1.064)^3 \approx \$4818.20$$

b. Quarterly compounding means that interest is compounded every one-fourth of a year or 4 times a year. Therefore,

- the interest rate per period is $r = \frac{0.064}{4}$, and
- the number of periods in 3 years is $t = 4(3)$.

$$A = 4000\left(1 + \frac{0.064}{4}\right)^{4(3)} \approx \$4839.32$$

c. Monthly compounding means that interest is compounded every $\frac{1}{12}$ of a year or 12 times a year. Therefore,

- the interest rate per period is $r = \frac{0.064}{12}$, and
- the number of periods in 3 years is $t = 12(3)$.

$$A = 4000\left(1 + \frac{0.064}{12}\right)^{12(3)} \approx \$4844.21$$

d. Daily compounding means that interest is compounded every $\frac{1}{365}$ of a year, or 365 times a year. Therefore,

- the interest rate per period is $r = \frac{0.064}{365}$, and
- the number of periods in 3 years is $t = 365(3)$.

$$A = 4000\left(1 + \frac{0.064}{365}\right)^{365(3)} \approx \$4846.60$$

Notice in Example 2 that the more often interest is compounded, the larger the final amount will be. Example 3 shows you how to write and solve an exponential equation to determine how long it will take for an investment to be worth a given amount.

Example 3 Solving for the Time Period

If \$5000 is invested at 7% annual interest, compounded daily, when will the investment be worth \$6800?

Solution

Use the compound interest formula with the final amount $A = 6800$ and $P = 5000$. Because the interest is compounded every $\frac{1}{365}$ of a year, the interest rate per period is $r = \frac{0.07}{365}$.

$$A = P(1 + r)^t$$
$$6800 = 5000\left(1 + \frac{0.07}{365}\right)^t$$

The point of intersection of the graphs of $y_1 = 5000\left(1 + \frac{0.07}{365}\right)^t$ and $y_2 = 6800$ is approximately (1603.5, 6800). Therefore, the investment will be worth \$6800 after about 1603 days, or about 4.4 years. ∎

Figure 5.3-1

Continuous Compounding and the Number *e*

As you have seen in previous examples, the more often interest is compounded, the larger the final amount will be. However, there is a limit that is reached, as you will see in Example 4.

Example 4 The Number *e*

Suppose you invest \$1 for one year at 100% annual interest, compounded n times per year. Find the maximum value of the investment in one year.

Solution

Use the compound interest formula. The annual interest rate is 1.00, so the interest rate per period is $\frac{1}{n}$, and the number of periods is n.

$$A = P(1 + r)^t$$
$$= 1\left(1 + \frac{1}{n}\right)^n$$
$$= \left(1 + \frac{1}{n}\right)^n$$

Observe what happens to the final amount as n grows larger and larger.

ADDITIONAL EXAMPLES

Example 2

Determine the amount that a \$5000 investment over ten years at an annual interest rate of 4.8% is worth for each compounding period.

a. annually

$A = 5000(1 + 0.048)^{10} = \$7990.66$

b. quarterly

$A = 5000\left(1 + \frac{0.048}{4}\right)^{4(10)} = \$8057.32$

c. monthly

$A = 5000\left(1 + \frac{0.048}{12}\right)^{12(10)} = \$8072.64$

d. daily

$A = 5000\left(1 + \frac{0.048}{365}\right)^{365(10)} = \$8080.12$

Example 3

If \$7000 is invested at 5% annual interest, compounded monthly, when will the investment be worth \$8500?

$$8500 = 7000\left(1 + \frac{0.05}{12}\right)^t$$

after about 47 months, or about 3.9 years

Example 4

If you invest \$100 at 100% annual interest, what is the maximum possible value of the investment after one year? Copy and complete the table to answer the question.

Compounding period	n	$100\left(1 + \frac{1}{n}\right)^n$
Annually	1	200
Quarterly	4	244.1406
Monthly	12	261.3035
Daily	365	271.45675
Hourly	8760	271.812669
Every second	31,536,000	271.8282473

The maximum possible value is about \$271.83.

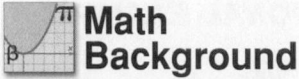
The pattern in the last column of the table suggests that

$$\lim_{n\to\infty}\left(1 + \frac{1}{n}\right)^n \approx 2.7182825.$$

In fact, 2.7182825 is an approximation for the number e,

because $\lim_{n\to\infty}\left(1 + \frac{1}{n}\right)^n = e$.

Teaching Notes

Emphasize that r and t represent *different quantities* in the continuous compounding formula on this page than in the compound interest formula on page 345.

For $A = P(1 + r)^t$,
- r is the interest rate per time period.
- t is the number of time periods.

For $A = Pe^{rt}$,
- r is the annual interest rate.
- t is the number of years.

To illustrate how r and t represent different quantities in these formulas, you can do several examples of the type shown below. (The more frequent the compounding in the formula $A = P(1 + r)^t$, the closer the results will be to the results of continuous compounding.)

Consider a $1000 investment at a 5% annual interest rate for 2 years.

Monthly compounding:

$$A = P(1 + r)^t = \$1000\left(1 + \frac{0.05}{12}\right)^{(12)(2)}$$

$$= \$1104.94$$

Daily compounding:

$$A = P(1 + r)^t = \$1000\left(1 + \frac{0.05}{365}\right)^{(365)(2)}$$

$$= \$1105.16$$

Continuous compounding:

$$A = Pe^{rt} = \$1000 \cdot e^{(0.05)(2)} = \$1105.17$$

Compounding period	n	$\left(1 + \frac{1}{n}\right)^n$
Annually	1	$\left(1 + \frac{1}{1}\right)^1 = 2$
Semiannually	2	$\left(1 + \frac{1}{2}\right)^2 = 2.25$
Quarterly	4	$\left(1 + \frac{1}{4}\right)^4 \approx 2.4414$
Monthly	12	$\left(1 + \frac{1}{12}\right)^{12} \approx 2.6130$
Daily	365	$\left(1 + \frac{1}{365}\right)^{365} \approx 2.71457$
Hourly	8760	$\left(1 + \frac{1}{8760}\right)^{8760} \approx 2.718127$
Every minute	525,600	$\left(1 + \frac{1}{525,600}\right)^{525,600} \approx 2.7182792$
Every second	31,536,000	$\left(1 + \frac{1}{31,536,000}\right)^{31,536,000} \approx 2.7182825$

The maximum amount of the $1 investment after one year is approximately $2.72, no matter how large n is. ∎

When the number of compounding periods increases without bound, the process is called **continuous compounding.** Note that the last entry in the preceding table is the same as the number e to five decimal places. Example 4 is the case when $P = 1$, $r = 100\%$, and $t = 1$. A similar result occurs in the general case and leads to the following formula.

Continuous Compounding

> If P dollars is invested at an annual interest rate of r, compounded continuously, then A is the amount after t years.
>
> $$A = Pe^{rt}$$

Example 5   Continuous Compounding

If you invest $4000 at 5% annual interest compounded continuously, how much is in the account at the end of 3 years?

Solution

Use the continuous compounding formula with $P = 4000$, $r = 0.05$, and $t = 3$.

$$A = Pe^{rt}$$
$$= 4000e^{0.05(3)}$$
$$\approx 4647.34$$

After 3 years the investment will be worth \$4647.34. ∎

Exponential Growth

Compound interest is one type of exponential growth; other exponential growth functions are very similar to the compound interest formula, as you will see in Example 6.

Example 6   Population Growth

The world population in 1950 was about 2.5 billion people and has been increasing at approximately 1.85% per year. Write the function that gives the world population in year x, where $x = 0$ corresponds to 1950.

Solution

If the population increases each year by 1.85%, then it increases each year by a factor of 1.0185. Notice that this pattern of population growth is the same as that of compound interest.

Year	1950	1951	1952	1953	...	1950 + x
Population (in billions)	2.5	2.5(1.0185)	2.5(1.0185)^2	2.5(1.0185)^3	...	2.5(1.0185)^x

So, the function that gives the world population, in billions, in year x, where $x = 0$ corresponds to 1950 is $f(x) = 2.5(1.0185)^x$. ∎

Exponential Growth ○——

> Exponential growth can be described by a function of the form
> $$f(x) = Pa^x,$$
> where $f(x)$ is the quantity at time x, P is the initial quantity when $x = 0$ and $a > 1$ is the factor by which the quantity changes when x increases by 1. If the quantity $f(x)$ is growing at rate r per time period, then $a = 1 + r$ and
> $$f(x) = Pa^x = P(1 + r)^x.$$

Teaching Notes

Example 7 is about exponential growth, so it uses the established function $f(x) = Pa^x$, $a > 1$. **Example 8** is about exponential decay, so a function is developed to solve the problem. The function developed has the same form, $f(x) = Pa^x$, but $0 < a < 1$.

Discuss the phrase *decreases by a fixed factor* (or *increases by a fixed factor* for growth). Explain that *fixed factor* describes a fixed rate, not a fixed amount, of growth or decay.

To illustrate:

If an initial quantity is 4, and the *amount increases by a fixed factor* of 1.5 per hour, then the hourly amounts are 4, 6, 9, 13.5, ... These amounts form a geometric sequence (page 58).

If an initial quantity is 4, and the *increase is by a fixed amount* of 1.5 per hour, then the hourly amounts are 4, 5.5, 6, 7.5, ...

These amounts form an arithmetic sequence (page 21).

Example Notes

In **Example 7,** have students use calculators to approximate the growth factor a: $a = \sqrt[5]{7.6} = (7.6)^{0.2} \approx 1.5$. Ask students to explain what this number means.
At any given time, there are about 1.5 times as many bacteria as there were an hour ago.

Ask students how they can determine whether 1.5 is reasonable for this problem.
Multiply 1000 by 1.5, then that result by 1.5, and so on. The result of 5 iterations is 7593.75, which is close to 7600, the given amount 5 hours later.

COMMON ERROR ALERT

In **Example 8,** students might use one of the following incorrect functions: $y = 0.3x$ or $y = 1.3x$. By careful reading, they will know that 30% is the percent of impurities *removed* by each layer. The next layer acts on the *remaining* impurities. Therefore, the correct function model must use 70%, so the correct model is $y = 0.7x$.

Example 7   Bacteria Growth

At the beginning of an experiment, a culture contains 1000 bacteria. Five hours later, there are 7600 bacteria. Assuming that the bacteria grow exponentially, how many bacteria will there be after 24 hours?

Solution

Use the exponential growth formula with $P = 1000$.

$$f(x) = 1000a^x$$

Because there are 7600 bacteria after 5 hours, $f(5) = 7600$ and $1000a^5 = 7600$. Solve for a to find the factor by which the bacteria population grows.

$$1000a^5 = 7600$$
$$a^5 = 7.6$$
$$a = \sqrt[5]{7.6}$$
$$a = 7.6^{\frac{1}{5}} = 7.6^{0.2}$$

Therefore, the function's growth factor is $7.6^{0.2}$.

$$f(x) = 1000 \cdot 7.6^{0.2x}$$

Find $f(24)$, the bacteria population after 24 hours.

$$f(24) = 1000 \cdot 7.6^{0.2(24)} \approx 16{,}900{,}721$$

After 24 hours, the bacteria population will be approximately 16,900,721. ∎

Exponential Decay

Sometimes a quantity decreases by a fixed factor as time goes on, as shown in Example 8.

Example 8   Filtering

When tap water is filtered through a layer of charcoal and other purifying agents, 30% of the chemical impurities in the water are removed. If the water is filtered through a second purifying layer, 30% of the remaining impurities in the water are removed. How many layers are needed to ensure that 95% of the impurities are removed from the water?

Solution

With the first layer, 30% of the impurities are removed and 70% of the impurities remain. With the second layer, 70% of the 70% of the impurities remain. The table below shows this pattern of exponential decay.

Layer	Impurities remaining
1	$0.7 = 70\%$
2	$0.7^2 = 0.49$, or 49%
3	$0.7^3 = 0.343$, or 34.3%
⋮	⋮
x	0.7^x

Therefore, the percentage of impurities remaining in the water after it passes through x layers of purifying material is given by the function

$$f(x) = 0.7^x.$$

When 95% of the impurities are removed, 5% remain. So, find the value of x for which $f(x) = 0.05$.

The point of intersection of the graphs of $y_1 = 0.7^x$ and $y_2 = 0.05$ is approximately $(8.4, 0.05)$. Because you cannot have a fractional part of a filter, 9 layers are needed to ensure that 95% of the impurities are removed from the water.

0.5

0 ┊ Intersection ┊ 12
X=8.3990544 Y=.05

−0.1

Figure 5.3-2

Example 8 illustrates **exponential decay.** Notice that the impurities were removed at a rate of $30\% = 0.3$ and that the amount of impurities remaining in the water was changing by a factor of $1 - 0.3 = 0.7$. This pattern is true in general for exponential decay.

Exponential Decay

> Exponential decay can be described by a function of the form
>
> $$f(x) = Pa^x,$$
>
> where $f(x)$ is the quantity at time x, P is the initial quantity when $x = 0$ and $0 < a < 1$ is the factor by which the quantity changes when x increases by 1. If the quantity $f(x)$ is decaying at rate r per time period then $a = 1 - r$ and
>
> $$f(x) = Pa^x = P(1 - r)^x.$$

The half-life of a radioactive substance is the time it takes a given quantity of the substance to decay to one-half of its original mass. The half-life depends only on the substance, not on the size of the sample. Because radioactive substances decay exponentially, their decay can be described by a function of the form $f(x) = Pa^x$, where x is measured in the same time units as the half-life. The constant a can be determined from the half-life of the substance.

Teaching Notes

The example at the top of the page shows how to find a, the rate of decay for a substance with a half-life of 25 years. Outline the method for students:

$f(x) = Pa^x$, so $f(25) = Pa^{25}$

$0.5P$ is the amount left after 25 years, so $f(25) = 0.5P$ also.

Now write $Pa^{25} = 0.5P$, and solve for a.

Ask students to supply the following missing step in solving for a:

$$a^{25} = 0.5$$
$$(a^{25})^{\frac{1}{25}} = (0.5)^{\frac{1}{25}}$$
$$a = 0.5^{\frac{1}{25}}$$

Summarize by noting that the function for this particular radioactive decay is $f(x) = P(0.5)^{\frac{x}{25}}$.

Show how the specific function above leads to the general formula for **Radioactive Decay,** in which h represents the half-life:

$$f(x) = P(0.5)^{\frac{x}{25}}$$
$$f(x) = P(0.5)^{\frac{x}{h}}$$

Example Notes

In **Example 9,** ask students how they can check the reasonableness of the answer. 50% of the carbon-14 is lost after 5730 years. Since the mastodon has lost 64% of its carbon-14, 8445.6 years is reasonable.

ADDITIONAL EXAMPLES

Example 9

The isotope iodine-131 is used to treat some types of thyroid disease. Iodine-131 decays exponentially with a half-life of 8.02 days. If a quantity of iodine-131 is administered to a patient, how long will it take for 99% of it to decay?

$0.01 = 0.5^{\frac{x}{8.02}}$

about 54 days

For example, suppose that the half-life of a substance is 25 years. Then after 25 years, the initial amount P decays to $0.5P$, or $f(25) = 0.5P$.

$$f(25) = 0.5P$$
$$Pa^{25} = 0.5P$$
$$a^{25} = 0.5$$
$$a = 0.5^{\frac{1}{25}}$$

The function for this radioactive decay is

$$f(x) = Pa^x = P(0.5^{\frac{1}{25}})^x = P(0.5)^{\frac{x}{25}}.$$

Radioactive Decay

> The amount of a radioactive substance that remains is given by the function
>
> $$f(x) = P(0.5)^{\frac{x}{h}},$$
>
> where P is the initial amount of the substance, $x = 0$ corresponds to the time when the radioactive decay began, and h is the half-life of the substance.

Example 9 Radioactive Decay

When a living organism dies, its carbon-14 decays exponentially. An archeologist determines that the skeleton of a mastodon has lost 64% of its carbon-14. The half-life of carbon-14 is 5730 years. Estimate how long ago the mastodon died.

Solution

Use the exponential decay formula for radioactive decay, with $h = 5730$.

$$f(x) = P(0.5^{\frac{x}{5730}})$$

Because the mastodon has lost 64% of its carbon-14, 36% of its carbon-14, or $0.36P$, remains. So, find the value of x for which $f(x) = 0.36P$.

$$0.36P = P(0.5^{\frac{x}{5730}})$$
$$0.36 = 0.5^{\frac{x}{5730}}$$

The point of intersection of the graphs of $y_1 = 0.5^{\frac{x}{5730}}$ and $y_2 = 0.36$ is approximately $(8445.6, 0.36)$ as shown in Figure 5.3-3. Therefore, the mastodon died about 8445.6 years ago.

Figure 5.3-3

Exercises 5.3

1. If $1,000 is invested at 8% interest, find the value of the investment after 5 years for each compounding period.
a. annually **$1469.33 b.** quarterly **$1485.95**
c. monthly **$1489.85 d.** weekly **$1491.37**

2. If $2500 is invested at 11.5% interest, what is the value of the investment after 10 years for each compounding period?
a. annually **b.** monthly **c.** daily
$7424.87 **$7852.37** **$7894.05**

In Exercises 3–12, determine how much money will be in a savings account with an initial deposit of $500 and the interest rate indicated below.

3. 2% compounded annually for 8 years
$585.83
4. 2% compounded annually for 10 years
$609.50
5. 2% compounded quarterly for 10 years
$610.40
6. 2.3% compounded monthly for 9 years
$614.87
7. 2.9% compounded daily for 8.5 years
$639.76
8. 3.5% compounded weekly for 7 years and 7 months
$651.93
9. 3% compounded continuously for 4 years
$563.75
10. 3.5% compounded continuously for 10 years
$709.53
11. 2.45% compounded continuously for 6.2 years
$582.02
12. 3.25% compounded continuously for 11.6 years
$728.95

A sum of money P that can be deposited today to yield some larger amount A in the future is called the *present value* of A. In Exercises 13–18, find the present value of the given amount A. *Hint:* Substitute the given amount A, the interest rate r per period, and the number of periods t into the compound interest formula, and solve for P.

13. A = $5000 at 6% compounded annually for 7 years
$\approx$**$3325.29**
14. A = $3500 at 5.5% compounded annually for 4 years
$\approx$**$2825.26**
15. A = $4800 at 7.2% compounded quarterly for 5 years
$\approx$**$3359.59**
16. A = $7400 at 5.9% compounded quarterly for 8 years
$\approx$**$4631.71**

17. A = $8900 at 11.3% compounded monthly for 3 years
$\approx$**$6351.16**
18. A = $9500 at 9.4% compounded monthly for 6 years
$\approx$**$5416.71**

In Exercises 19–26, use the compound interest formula. Given three of the quantities, A, P, r, and t, find the remaining one.

19. A typical credit card company charges 18% annual interest, compounded monthly, on the unpaid balance. If your current balance is $520 and you do not make any payments for 6 months, how much will you owe?
$\approx$**$568.59**
20. When his first child was born, a father put $3000 in a savings account that pays 4% annual interest, compounded quarterly. How much will be in the account on the child's 18th birthday?
$\approx$**$6141.30**
21. You have $10,000 to invest for 2 years. Fund A pays 13.2% interest, compounded annually. Fund B pays 12.7% interest, compounded quarterly, and Fund C pays 12.6% interest, compounded monthly. Which fund will return the most money?
Fund C
22. If you invest $7400 for 5 years, which will return more money: an interest rate of 5% compounded quarterly or an interest rate of 4.8% compounded continuously?
5% compounded quarterly
23. If you borrow $1200 at 14% interest, compounded monthly, and pay off the loan (principle and interest) at the end of 2 years, how much interest will you have paid?
$385.18
24. A developer borrows $150,000 at 6.5% interest, compounded quarterly, and agrees to pay off the loan in 4 years. How much interest will she owe?
$44,133.37
25. A manufacturer has settled a lawsuit out of court by agreeing to pay 1.5 million dollars 4 years from now. How much should the company put in an account paying 6.4% annual interest, compounded monthly, in order to have $1.5 million in 4 years? *Hint:* See Exercises 13–18.
$\approx$**$1,162,003.14**
26. Ellen wants to have $30,000 available in 5 years for a down payment on a house. She has inherited $25,000. How much of the inheritance should be invested at 5.7% interest, compounded quarterly, in order for the investment to reach a value of $30,000?
$\approx$**$22,605.85**

33. a. ≈9 years; ≈9 years; ≈9 years

b. Doubling time is not dependent on the amount invested, but on the rate at which it is invested.

27. Suppose you win a contest and have a choice of prizes. You can take $3000 now or you can receive $4000 in 4 years. If money can be invested at 6% interest, compounded annually, which prize is more valuable in the long run?
$4000

28. If money can be invested at 7% interest, compounded quarterly, which is worth more: $9000 now or $12,500 in 5 years?
$9000 now

29. If an investment of $1000 grows to $1407.10 in seven years with interest compounded annually, what is the interest rate?
≈5.00%

30. If an investment of $2000 grows to $2700 in $3\frac{1}{2}$ years, with an annual interest rate that is compounded quarterly, what is the annual interest rate?
≈8.67%

31. If you put $3000 in a savings account today, what interest rate (compounded annually) must you receive in order to have $4000 after 5 years?
≈5.92%

32. If interest is compounded continuously, what annual rate must you receive if your investment of $1500 is to grow to $2100 in 6 years?
≈5.6%

33. a. At an interest rate of 8%, compounded annually, how long will it take to double an investment of $100? of $500? of $1200?

b. What conclusion does part **a** suggest about doubling time?

34. At an interest rate of 6%, compounded annually, how long will it take to double an investment of P dollars?
≈11.9 years

35. How long will it take to double an investment of $500 at 7% interest, compounded continuously?
≈9.9 years

36. How long will it take to triple an investment of $5000 at 8% interest, compounded continuously?
≈13.7 years

37. a. Suppose P dollars is invested for 1 year at 12% interest, compounded quarterly. What interest rate r would yield the same amount in 1 year with annual compounding? r is called the **effective rate of interest.** *Hint:* Solve the equation $P\left(1 + \dfrac{0.12}{4}\right)^4 = P(1 + r)$ for r. The left side of the equation is the yield after 1 year at 12% interest, compounded quarterly, and the right side is the yield after 1 year at r% interest, compounded annually.   **≈12.6%**

b. Complete the following table:

12% interest compounding period	Effective rate
annually	12%
quarterly	**12.6%**
monthly	**≈12.7%**
daily	**≈12.7%**

38. This exercise investigates the continuous compounding formula, using a realistic interest rate. Consider the value of $4000 deposited for 3 years at 5% interest, compounded n times per year, for increasing values of n. In this case, the interest rate per period is $\dfrac{0.05}{n}$, and the number of periods in 3 years is $3n$. So, the value at the end of 3 years is given by:

$$A = 4000\left(1 + \frac{0.05}{n}\right)^{3n} = 4000\left[\left(1 + \frac{0.05}{n}\right)^n\right]^3$$

a. Complete the following table:

n	$\left(1 + \dfrac{0.05}{n}\right)^n$
1000	**1.0513**
10,000	**1.0513**
500,000	**1.0513**
1,000,000	**1.0513**
5,000,000	**1.0513**
10,000,000	**1.0513**

b. Compare the entries in the second column of the table in part **a** to the number $e^{0.05}$, and complete the following sentence:
As n gets larger and larger, the value of $\left(1 + \dfrac{0.05}{n}\right)^n$ gets closer and closer to the number_____?_____. **$e^{0.05}$**

c. Use your answer to part **b** to complete the following sentence:
As n gets larger and larger, the value of $A = 4000\left[\left(1 + \dfrac{0.05}{n}\right)^n\right]^3$ gets closer and closer to the number_____?_____. **4647.34**

d. Compare your answer to part **c** with the value given by the continuous compounding formula.

same

39. A weekly census of the tree-frog population in a state park is given below.

Week	1	2	3	4	5	6
Population	18	54	162	486	1458	4374

   a. Find a function of the form $f(x) = Pa^x$ that describes the frog population at time x weeks.

   b. What is the growth factor in this situation (that is, by what number must this week's population be multiplied to obtain next week's population)?

   c. Each tree frog requires 10 square feet of space and the park has an area of 6.2 square miles. Will the space required by the frog population exceed the size of the park in 12 weeks? in 14 weeks? (1 square mile = 5280^2 square feet)

40. The fruit fly population in a certain laboratory triples every day. Today there are 200 fruit flies.

   a. Make a table showing the number of fruit flies present for the first 4 days (today is day 0, tomorrow is day 1, etc.).

   b. Find a function of the form $f(x) = Pa^x$ that describes the fruit fly population at time x days.

   c. What is the growth factor here (that is, by what number must each day's population be multiplied to obtain the next day's population)?

   d. How many fruit flies will there be a week from now?

41. The population of Mexico was 100.4 million in 2000 and is expected to grow by approximately 1.4% each year.

   a. If $g(x)$ is the population, in millions, of Mexico in year x, where $x = 0$ corresponds to the year 2000, find the rule of the function g. (See Example 6.)

   b. Estimate the population of Mexico in the year 2010.

42. The number of dandelions in your lawn increases by 5% a week, and there are 75 dandelions now.

   a. If $f(x)$ is the number of dandelions in week x, find the rule of the function f.

   b. How many dandelions will there be in 16 weeks?

43. Average annual expenditure per pupil in elementary and secondary schools was $5550 in 1989–1990 and has been increasing at about 3.68% each year.

   a. Write the rule of a function that gives the expenditure per pupil in year x, where $x = 0$

corresponds to the 1989–1990 school year.

   b. According to this model, what are the expenditures per pupil in 1999–2000?

   c. In what year did expenditures first exceed $7000 per pupil?

44. There are now 3.2 million people who play bridge and the number increases by 3.5% a year.

   a. Write the rule of a function that gives the number of bridge players x years from now.

   b. How many people will be playing bridge 15 years from now?

   c. When will there be 10 million bridge players?

45. At the beginning of an experiment a culture contains 200 *h-pylori* bacteria. An hour later there are 205 bacteria. Assuming that the *h-pylori* bacteria grow exponentially, how many will there be after 10 hours? after 2 days? (See Example 7.)

46. The population of India was approximately 1030 million in 2001 and was 865 million a decade earlier. What will the population be in 2006 if it continues to grow exponentially at the same rate?

47. Use graphical methods to estimate the following values.

   a. $3^{\sqrt{3}}$ **b.** $4^{\sqrt{3}}$ **c.** $5^{\sqrt{3}}$

48. Kerosene is passed through a pipe filled with clay in order to remove various pollutants. Each foot of pipe removes 25% of the pollutants.

   a. Write the rule of a function that gives the percentage of pollutants remaining in the kerosene after it has passed through x feet of pipe. (See Example 8.)

   b. How many feet of pipe are needed to ensure that 90% of the pollutants have been removed from the kerosene?

49. If inflation runs at a steady 3% per year, then the amount that a dollar is worth today decreases by 3% each year.

   a. Write the function rule that gives the value of a dollar x years from today.

   b. How much will the dollar be worth in 5 years? in 10 years?

   c. How many years will it take before today's dollar is worth only a dime?

50. a. The half-life of radium is 1620 years. Find the rule of the function that gives the amount remaining from an initial quantity of 100 milligrams of radium after x years.

   b. How much radium is left after 800 years? after 1600 years? after 3200 years?

39. a. $f(x) = 6(3^x)$ or
     $f(x) = 18(3^{x-1})$

   b. 3

   c. no; yes

40. a.

Day	0	1	2	3
Flies	200	600	1800	5400

   b. $f(x) = 200 \cdot 3^x$

   c. 3

   d. 437,400 flies

41. a. $g(x) = 100.4(1.014)^x$

   b. 115.38 million

42. a. $f(x) = 75(1.05^x)$

   b. 164 dandelions

43. a. $E(x) = 5550(1.0368)^x$

   b. $7966

   c. in the sixth year

44. a. $f(x) = 3.2(1.035)^x$

   b. 5.36 million people

   c. in 33 years

45. ≈ 256; ≈ 654

46. ≈ 1124 million

47. a. 6.705

   b. 11.036

   c. 16.242

48. a. $f(x) = 100(0.75)^x$

   b. 8 feet

49. a. $f(x) = (0.97)^x$

   b. $0.86; $0.74

   c. ≈ 75 years

50. a. $f(x) = 100\left(0.5^{\frac{x}{1620}}\right)$

   b. ≈ 71.01 mg;
     ≈ 50.43 mg;
     ≈ 25.43 mg

51. a. The half-life of polonium-210 is 140 days. Find the rule of the function that gives the amount of polonium-210 remaining from an initial 20 milligrams after t days. $f(t) \approx 20(0.5^{\frac{t}{140}})$

b. How much polonium-210 is left after 15 weeks? after 52 weeks?
$\approx$**11.892 mg; $\approx$3.299 mg**

c. How long will it take for the 20 milligrams to decay to 4 milligrams?
$\approx$**325 days**

52. How old is a piece of ivory that has lost 58% of its carbon-14? (See Example 9.)
$\approx$**7171 years old**

53. How old is a mummy that has lost 49% of its carbon-14?
$\approx$**5566 years old**

Section 5.4 Common and Natural Logarithmic Functions

Teaching Notes

Remind students that if a function is one-to-one, its inverse is also a function.

To further illustrate the relationship between $f(x) = 10^x$ and $g(x) = \log x$, students can create a table of values for the function $f(x) = 10^x$ as shown.

x	-1	0	1	2
$f(x) = 10^x$	$\frac{1}{10}$	1	10	100

Students may then create another table of values for the inverse by switching values and renaming the function as shown.

x	$\frac{1}{10}$	1	10	100
$g(x) = \log x$	-1	0	1	2

Have students copy and complete the table below to reinforce the definition of the **common logarithmic function:**

$\log v = u$	is equivalent to	$10^u = v$
$\log 1000 = 3$		$10^3 = 1000$
$\log 100 = 2$		$10^2 = 100$
$\log 10 = 1$		$10^1 = 10$
$\log 1 = 0$		$10^0 = 1$
$\log \frac{1}{10} = -1$		$10^{-1} = \frac{1}{10}$
$\log \frac{1}{100} = -2$		$10^{-2} = \frac{1}{100}$
$\log \frac{1}{1000} = -3$		$10^{-3} = \frac{1}{1000}$

5.4 Common and Natural Logarithmic Functions

Objectives

- Evaluate common and natural logarithms with and without a calculator
- Solve common and natural exponential and logarithmic equations by using an equivalent equation
- Graph and identify transformations of common and natural logarithmic functions

Technology Tip

- The graph of $f(x) = 10^x$ can be obtained in parametric mode by letting

  $x = t$ and $y = 10^t$,

  where t is any real number.

  The graph of the inverse function g can then be obtained by letting

  $x = 10^t$ and $y = t$,

  where t is any real number.

From their invention in the seventeenth century until the development of computers and calculators, logarithms were the only effective tools for numerical computation in astronomy, chemistry, physics, and engineering. Although they are no longer needed for computation, logarithmic functions still play an important role in the sciences and engineering. In this section you will examine the two most important types of logarithms, those to base 10 and those to base e. Logarithms to other bases are considered in *Excursion 5.5A*.

Common Logarithms

The graph of the exponential function $f(x) = 10^x$ is shown in Figure 5.4-1. Because it is an increasing function, it is a one-to-one function, as explained in Section 3.6. Recall that the graphs of inverse functions are reflections of one another across the line $y = x$. The exponential function $f(x) = 10^x$ and its inverse function are graphed in Figure 5.4-2.

Figure 5.4-1   **Figure 5.4-2**

The inverse function of the exponential function $f(x) = 10^x$ is called the **common logarithmic function.** The value of this function at the number x is denoted as $\log x$ and called the common logarithm of the number x.

The functions $f(x) = 10^x$ and $g(x) = \log x$ are inverse functions.

$$\log v = u \qquad \text{if and only if} \qquad 10^u = v$$

Because logarithms are a special kind of exponent, every statement about logarithms is equivalent to a statement about exponents.

Logarithmic statement $\log v = u$	Equivalent exponential statement $10^u = v$
$\log 29 = 1.4624$	$10^{1.4624} = 29$
$\log 378 = 2.5775$	$10^{2.5775} = 378$

Example 1   Evaluating Common Logarithms

Without using a calculator, find each value.

a. $\log 1000$ **b.** $\log 1$ **c.** $\log \sqrt{10}$ **d.** $\log (-3)$

Solution

a. If $\log 1000 = x$, then $10^x = 1000$. Because $10^3 = 1000$, $\log 1000 = 3$.

b. If $\log 1 = x$, then $10^x = 1$. Because $10^0 = 1$, $\log 1 = 0$.

c. If $\log \sqrt{10} = x$, then $10^x = \sqrt{10}$. Because $10^{\frac{1}{2}} = \sqrt{10}$, $\log \sqrt{10} = \frac{1}{2}$.

d. If $\log (-3) = x$, then $10^x = -3$. Because there is no real number exponent of 10 that produces -3, $\log (-3)$ is not defined for real numbers. ∎

> **NOTE** Logarithms are rounded to four decimal places and an equal sign is used rather than the "approximately equal" sign. The word "common" will be omitted except when it is necessary to distinguish the common logarithm from another type of logarithm.

Every scientific and graphing calculator has a **LOG** key for evaluating logarithms. For example,

$$\log 0.6 = -0.2218 \quad \text{and} \quad \log 327 = 2.5145$$

A calculator is necessary to evaluate most logarithms, but you can get a rough estimate mentally. For example, because log 795 is greater than log 100 = 2 and less than log 1000 = 3, you can estimate that log 795 is between 2 and 3 and closer to 3.

Example 2   Using Equivalent Statements

Solve each equation by using an equivalent statement.

a. $\log x = 2$ **b.** $10^x = 29$

Solution

a. If $\log x = 2$, then $10^2 = x$. Therefore, $x = 100$.

b. If $10^x = 29$, then $\log 29 = x$. Therefore, $x = 1.4624$, as shown in Figure 5.4-3. ∎

log(29)
          1.462397998

Figure 5.4-3

Teaching Notes

Note to students that the graphs of the inverse pair $f(x) = e^x$ and $g(x) = \ln x$ on this page closely resemble the graphs of the inverse pair $f(x) = 10^x$ and $g(x) = \log x$ on page 356. Emphasize that they *are* similar in shape and properties, but they are not identical.

Have students graph these four functions on a graphing calculator using a viewing window with $-2 \leq x \leq 2$ and $-2 \leq y \leq 2$ to observe this.

Remind students of the examples they wrote to illustrate common logarithms:

$\log 1000 = 3$ is equivalent to $10^3 = 1000$
$\log 100 = 2$ is equivalent to $10^2 = 100$
etc.

Have them rewrite the logarithms as follows:

$\log 10^3 = 3$
$\log 10^2 = 2$
etc.

Now have them write these natural logarithms:

$\ln e^3 = 3$
$\ln e^2 = 2$
$\ln e^1 = 1$ $(\ln e = 1)$
$\ln e^0 = 0$ $(\ln 1 = 0)$
$\ln e^{-1} = -1$ $\left(\ln \dfrac{1}{e} = -1\right)$
$\ln e^{-2} = -2$ $\left(\ln \dfrac{1}{e^2} = -2\right)$

Students often have more trouble with natural logarithms than with common logarithms because of the bases; 10 is a whole number and e is irrational. Have them use their calculator to approximate e^3 and e^2 to the nearest whole number. **20, 7** Then have them copy and complete the following statements, using their calculators:

$3 = \ln e^3 \approx \ln 20$; $\ln 20 \approx 2.996$
$2 = \ln e^2 \approx \ln 7$; $\ln 7 \approx 1.950$

Natural Logarithms

The exponential function $f(x) = e^x$ is very useful in science and engineering. Consequently, another type of logarithm exists, based on the number e instead of 10.

The graph of the exponential function $f(x) = e^x$ is shown in Figure 5.4-4. Because it is an increasing function, it is one-to-one. The function $f(x) = e^x$ and its inverse function are graphed in Figure 5.4-5.

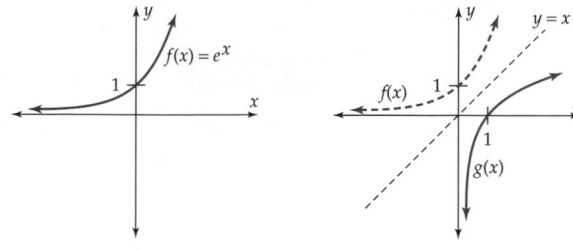

Figure 5.4-4　　　　　**Figure 5.4-5**

This inverse function of the exponential function $f(x) = e^x$ is called the **natural logarithmic function.** The value of this function at the number x is denoted as $\ln x$ and called the **natural logarithm** of the number x.

The functions $f(x) = e^x$ and $g(x) = \ln x$ are inverse functions.

$$\ln v = u \quad \textbf{if and only if} \quad e^u = v$$

Again, as with common logarithms, every statement about natural logarithms is equivalent to a statement about exponents.

Logarithmic statement $\ln v = u$	Equivalent exponential statement $e^u = v$
$\ln 14 = 2.6391$	$e^{2.6391} = 14$
$\ln 0.2 = -1.6094$	$e^{-1.6094} = 0.2$

Figure 5.4-6
```
ln(.15)
        -1.897119985
ln(186)
         5.225746674
```

Example 3   Evaluating Natural Logarithms

Use a calculator to find each value.

a. $\ln 0.15$ **b.** $\ln 186$ **c.** $\ln(-5)$

Solution

a. $\ln 0.15 = -1.8971$, which means that $e^{-1.8971} = 0.15$.

b. $\ln 186 = 5.2257$, which means that $e^{5.2257} = 186$.

c. $\ln(-5)$ is undefined for real numbers because there is no exponent of e that produces -5.

In a few cases you can evaluate ln x without a calculator.

$$\ln e = 1 \quad \text{because} \quad e^1 = e$$
$$\ln 1 = 0 \quad \text{because} \quad e^0 = 1$$

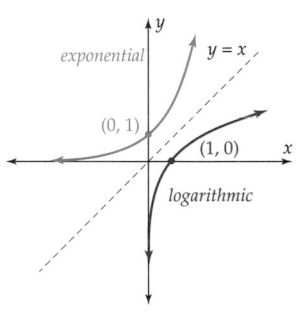

Figure 5.4-7

Example 4   **Solving by Using an Equivalent Statement**

Solve each equation by using an equivalent statement.

a. ln $x = 4$ **b.** $e^x = 5$

Solution

a. If ln $x = 4$, then $e^4 = x$. Therefore, $x = 54.5982$.

b. If $e^x = 5$, then ln $5 = x$. Therefore, $x = 1.6094$. ∎

Graphs of Logarithmic Functions

Because the graphs of exponential functions have the same basic shape and each logarithmic function is the inverse of an exponential function, the graphs of logarithmic functions have common characteristics.

The following table compares the graphs of exponential and logarithmic functions.

Figure 5.4-8

	Exponential functions	Logarithmic functions
Examples	$f(x) = 10^x; f(x) = e^x$	$g(x) = \log x; g(x) = \ln x$
Domain	all real numbers	all positive real numbers
Range	all positive real numbers	all real numbers
	$f(x)$ increases as x increases	$g(x)$ increases as x increases
	$f(x)$ approaches the x-axis as x decreases	$g(x)$ approaches the y-axis as x approaches 0
Reference points	$f(x) = 10^x$ $\left(-1, \frac{1}{10}\right), (0, 1), (1, 10)$	$g(x) = \log x$ $\left(\frac{1}{10}, -1\right), (1, 0), (10, 1)$
	$f(x) = e^x$ $\left(-1, \frac{1}{e}\right), (0, 1), (1, e)$	$g(x) = \ln x$ $\left(\frac{1}{e}, -1\right), (1, 0), (e, 1)$

Example 5   **Transforming Logarithmic Functions**

Describe the transformation from the graph of $g(x) = \log x$ to the graph of $h(x) = 2\log(x - 3)$. Give the domain and range of h.

Example Notes

For **Example 5**, review horizontal shifts (page 175) and vertical stretches (page 179).

For **Example 6**, review reflections (page 177) and vertical shifts (page 174).

In the graph for **Example 7b**, ask students why x-values greater than 1 probably would not be relevant. x represents the interest rate, and $1 = 100\%$. Interest rates greater than 100% are rare.

COMMON ERROR ALERT

When entering a function such as the one in **Example 7b** into a calculator, it is important that students include parentheses around the appropriate expression.

$\ln(2/\ln(1 + x)$ incorrect

$\ln(2)/\ln(1 + x)$ correct

ADDITIONAL EXAMPLES

Example 5

Describe the transformation from the graph of $g(x) = \log x$ to the graph of $h(x) = 3 \log(x + 4)$. Give the domain and range of h. The graph of h is the graph of g after a horizontal translation of 4 units left and a vertical stretch by a factor of 3.

Domain of h: all real numbers greater than -4

Range of h: all real numbers

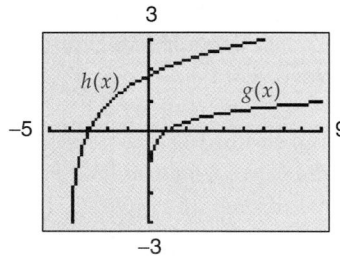

Solution

The graph of $h(x) = 2 \cdot g(x - 3)$ is the graph of $g(x) = \log x$ after a horizontal translation of 3 units right and a vertical stretch by a factor of 2.

Domain of h: The domain of $g(x) = \log x$ is all positive real numbers. The horizontal translation of 3 units to the right changes the domain to all real numbers greater than 3.

Range of h: The range of $g(x) = \log x$ is all real numbers, so the vertical stretch has no effect on the range.

The graphs of g and h are shown in Figure 5.4-9. The points $\left(\frac{1}{10}, -1\right)$, $(1, 0)$, and $(10, 1)$ on the graph of g are translated to the points $\left(3\frac{1}{10}, -2\right)$, $(4, 0)$, and $(13, 2)$ on the graph of h. Although the graph of $h(x) = 2 \log (x - 3)$ appears to stop abruptly at $x = 3$, you know that it continues to approach the asymptote at $x = 3$.

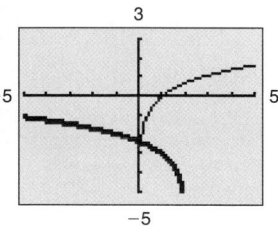

Figure 5.4-9

Example 6   Transforming Logarithmic Functions

Describe the transformation from $g(x) = \ln x$ to $h(x) = \ln(2 - x) - 3$. Give the domain and range of h.

Solution

Because $h(x) = g(-(x - 2)) - 3$, its graph is that of $g(x) = \ln x$ after a horizontal reflection across the y-axis followed by a horizontal translation of 2 units to the right and a vertical translation of 3 units downward.

Domain of h: The domain of $g(x) = \ln x$ is all positive real numbers. The reflection across the y-axis first changes the domain to all negative real numbers. Then the translation of 2 units to the right changes the domain from all negative real numbers to all real numbers less than 2.

Range of h: The range of $g(x) = \ln x$ is all real numbers, so the vertical translation does not affect the range.

The graphs of g and h are shown in Figure 5.4-10. The points $\left(\frac{1}{e}, -1\right)$, $(1, 0)$, and $(e, 1)$ on the graph of g are translated to points $\left(2 - \frac{1}{e}, -4\right)$, $(1, -3)$, and $(2 - e, -2)$ on the graph of h.

Figure 5.4-10

Example 7   Solving Logarithmic Equations Graphically

If you invest money at an interest rate r, compounded annually, then $D(r)$ gives the time in years that it would take to double.

$$D(r) = \frac{\ln 2}{\ln(1 + r)}$$

Example 6

Describe the transformation from the graph of $g(x) = \ln x$ to the graph of $h(x) = \ln(4 - x) + 2$. Give the domain and range of h.

$h(x) = g(-(x - 4)) + 2$

The graph of h is the graph of g after a horizontal reflection across the y-axis followed by a horizontal translation of 4 units right and a vertical translation of 2 units upward.

Domain of h: all real numbers less than 4

Range of h: all real numbers

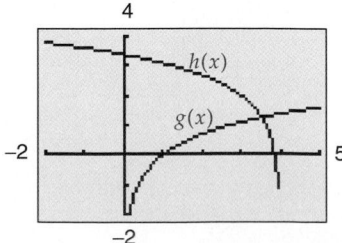

a. How long will it take to double an investment of $2500 at 6.5% annual interest?

b. What annual interest rate is needed in order for the investment in part **a** to double in 6 years?

Solution

a. The annual interest rate r is 0.065. Find $D(0.065)$.

$$D(0.065) = \frac{\ln 2}{\ln(1 + 0.065)} = 11.0067$$

Therefore, it will take approximately 11 years to double an investment of $2500 at 6.5% annual interest.

b. If the investment doubles in 6 years, then $D(r) = 6$. To find the annual interest rate r, solve $\frac{\ln 2}{\ln(1 + r)} = 6$ by graphing. The point of intersection of the graphs of $Y_1 = \frac{\ln 2}{\ln(1 + r)}$ and $Y_2 = 6$ is approximately $(0.1225, 6)$. Therefore, an annual interest rate of 12.25% is needed for the investment to double in 6 years. See Figure 5.4-11.

Figure 5.4-11

Exercises 5.4

Unless stated otherwise, all letters represent positive numbers.

In Exercises 1–4, find the value of each logarithm.

1. $\log 10,000$ **4**

2. $\log 0.001$ **−3**

3. $\log \frac{\sqrt{10}}{1000}$ **−2.5**

4. $\log \sqrt[3]{0.01}$ $-\frac{2}{3}$

In Exercises 5–14, translate the given logarithmic statement into an equivalent exponential statement.

5. $\log 1000 = 3$
$10^3 = 1000$

6. $\log 0.001 = -3$
$10^{-3} = 0.001$

7. $\log 750 = 2.8751$
$10^{2.8751} = 750$

8. $\log 0.8 = -0.0969$
$10^{-0.0969} = 0.8$

9. $\ln 3 = 1.0986$
$e^{1.0986} = 3$

10. $\ln 10 = 2.3026$
$e^{2.3026} = 10$

11. $\ln 0.01 = -4.6052$
$e^{-4.6052} = 0.01$

12. $\ln s = r$
$e^r = s$

13. $\ln(x^2 + 2y) = z + w$
$e^{z+w} = x^2 + 2y$

14. $\log(a + c) = d$
$10^d = a + c$

In Exercises 15–24, translate the given exponential statement into an equivalent logarithmic statement.

15. $10^{-2} = 0.01$
$\log 0.01 = -2$

16. $10^3 = 1000$
$\log 1000 = 3$

17. $10^{0.4771} = 3$
$\log 3 = 0.4771$

18. $10^{7k} = r$
$\log r = 7k$

19. $e^{3.25} = 25.79$
$\ln 25.79 = 3.25$

20. $e^{-4} = 0.0183$
$\ln 0.0183 = -4$

21. $e^{\frac{12}{7}} = 5.5527$
$\ln 5.5527 = \frac{12}{7}$

22. $e^k = t$
$\ln t = k$

23. $e^{\frac{2}{r}} = w$
$\ln w = \frac{2}{r}$

24. $e^{4uv} = m$
$\ln m = 4uv$

In Exercises 25–36, evaluate the given expression without using a calculator.

25. $\log 10^{\sqrt{43}}$
$\sqrt{43}$

26. $\log 10^{\sqrt{x^2+y^2}}$
$\sqrt{x^2 + y^2}$

27. $\ln e^{15}$
15

28. $\ln e^{3.78}$
3.78

29. $\ln \sqrt{e}$
$\frac{1}{2}$

30. $\ln \sqrt[5]{e}$
$\frac{1}{5}$

31. $e^{\ln 931}$
931

32. $e^{\ln 34.17}$
34.17

33. $\ln e^{x+y}$
$x + y$

34. $\ln e^{x^2+2y}$
$x^2 + 2y$

35. $e^{\ln x^2}$
x^2

36. $e^{\ln \sqrt{x+3}}$
$\sqrt{x + 3}$

In Exercises 37–40, find the domain of the given function.

37. $f(x) = \ln(x + 1)$
$(1, \infty)$

38. $g(x) = \ln(x + 2)$
$(2, \infty)$

39. $h(x) = \log(-x)$
$(-\infty, 0)$

40. $k(x) = \log(2 - x)$
$(-\infty, 2)$

ADDITIONAL EXAMPLES

Example 7

If you invest money at an interest rate r, compounded annually, then $T(r)$ gives the time in years that it would take to triple.

$$T(r) = \frac{\ln 3}{\ln(1 + r)}$$

a. How long would it take to triple an investment of $500 at 5% annual interest? approximately 22.5 years

b. What annual interest rate is needed in order for the investment in part **a** to triple in 15 years? 7.60%

Real-World Application

The function in **Example 7** is used to find the time in years it takes to double an investment at a certain interest rate. Accountants sometimes use an approximating technique called the *Rule of 72* for this task. The rule of 72 is: $f(R) = \frac{72}{R}$, where R is expressed as a percent. Have your students compare exact results with approximate results by entering $Y_1 = \frac{\ln 2}{\ln(1 + x)}$ and $Y_2 = \frac{72}{100x}$ into their calculators and using the TABLE feature, with increments of 0.01, to compare function values. (Note that the denominator of Y_2 is $100x$ because R is a percent, not a decimal.) The rule of 72 is also explored in exercise 65 (page 362).

X	Y1	Y2
.01	69.661	72
.02	35.003	36
.03	23.45	24
.04	17.673	18
.05	14.207	14.4
.06	11.896	12
.07	10.245	10.286

X=.07

Exercises 5.4

ANSWERS

43. Stretch the graph of g away from the x-axis by a factor of 2. domain: all positive reals; range: all reals

44. Shift the graph of g vertically 7 units downward. domain: all positive reals; range: all reals

45. Shift the graph of g horizontally 4 units to the right. domain: all reals > 4; range: all reals

46. Shift the graph of g horizontally 2 units to the left. domain: all reals > -2; range: all reals

47. Shift the graph of g horizontally 3 units to the left, then shift it vertically 4 units downward. domain: all reals > -3; range: all reals

48. Shift the graph of g horizontally 2 units to the right, then shift it 2 units upward. domain: all reals > 2; range: all reals

49–52. *See p.* 1067.

53. $0 \le x \le 9.4$ and $-6 \le y \le 6$ (vertical asymptote at $x = 1$)

54. $0 \le x \le 30$ and $-1 \le y \le 0.5$

55. $-10 \le x \le 10$ and $-3 \le y \le 3$

56. $1 \le x \le 10$ and $0 \le y \le 100$

57. $0 \le x \le 20$ and $-6 \le y \le 3$

58. $0 \le x \le 30$ and $-1 \le y \le 0.5$

64. a. ≈ 1.8484

  b. ≈ 1.8484

  c. The answers are the same. The function g is the same as the function f shifted horizontally 3 units to the right.

65. a. about: 17.67, 11.90, 9.01, 6.12, 4.19, 3.22, 2.25

  b. The rule of thumb is that the number of years it takes for your money to double at interest rate $r\%$ is 72 divided by r.

---

41. Compare the graphs of $f(x) = \log x^2$ and $g(x) = 2 \log x$. How are they alike? How are they different?
They are exactly the same.

42. Compare the graphs of $h(x) = \log x^3$ and $k(x) = 3 \log x$. How are they alike? How are they different?
They are exactly the same.

In Exercises 43–48, describe the transformation from $g(x) = \ln x$ to the given function. Give the domain and range of the given function.

43. $f(x) = 2 \ln x$

44. $f(x) = \ln x - 7$

45. $h(x) = \ln(x - 4)$

46. $k(x) = \ln(x + 2)$

47. $h(x) = \ln(x + 3) - 4$

48. $k(x) = \ln(x - 2) + 2$

In Exercises 49–52, sketch the graph of the function.

49. $f(x) = \log(x - 3)$

50. $g(x) = 2 \ln x + 3$

51. $h(x) = -2 \log x$

52. $f(x) = \ln(-x) - 3$

In Exercises 53–58, find a viewing window (or windows) that shows a complete graph of the function.

53. $f(x) = \dfrac{x}{\ln x}$

54. $g(x) = \dfrac{\ln x}{x}$

55. $h(x) = \dfrac{\ln x^2}{x}$

56. $k(x) = e^{\frac{2}{\ln x}}$

57. $f(x) = 10 \log x - x$

58. $f(x) = \dfrac{\log x}{x}$

In Exercises 59–62, find the average rate of change of the function. (See Section 3.7.)

59. $f(x) = \ln(x - 2)$, as x goes from 3 to 5
≈ 0.5493

60. $g(x) = x - \ln x$, as x goes from 0.5 to 1
≈ -0.3863

61. $g(x) = \log(x^2 + x + 1)$, as x goes from -5 to -3
≈ -0.2386

62. $f(x) = x \log |x|$, as x goes from 1 to 4
≈ 0.8027

63. a. What is the average rate of change of $f(x) = \ln x$, as x goes from 3 to $3 + h$? $\dfrac{\ln(3 + h) - \ln 3}{h}$

  b. What is the value of h when the average rate of change of $f(x) = \ln x$, as x goes from 3 to $3 + h$, is 0.25? $h \approx 2.2$

64. a. Find the average rate of change of $f(x) = \ln x^2$, as x goes from 0.5 to 2.

  b. Find the average rate of change of $g(x) = \ln(x - 3)^2$, as x goes from 3.5 to 5.

  c. What is the relationship between your answers in parts **a** and **b**? Explain why this is so.

---

65. a. Use the doubling function D from Example 7 to find the time it takes to double your money at each of these interest rates: 4%, 6%, 8%, 12%, 18%, 24%, and 36%.

  b. Round the answers in part **a** to the nearest year and compare them with these numbers: $\dfrac{72}{4}, \dfrac{72}{6}, \dfrac{72}{8}, \dfrac{72}{12}, \dfrac{72}{18}, \dfrac{72}{24},$ and $\dfrac{72}{36}$. Use this evidence to state a "rule of thumb" for determining approximate doubling time, without using the function D. This rule of thumb, which has long been used by bankers, is called the Rule of 72.

66. The height h above sea level (in meters) is related to air temperature t (in degrees Celsius), the atmospheric pressure p (in centimeters of mercury at height h), and the atmospheric pressure c at sea level by:

$$h = (30t + 8000) \ln\left(\dfrac{c}{p}\right)$$

If the pressure at the top of Mount Rainier is 44 centimeters on a day when sea level pressure is 75.126 centimeters and the temperature is 7°, what is the height of Mount Rainier? $\approx$**4392 m**

67. A class is tested at the end of the semester and weekly thereafter on the same material. The average score on the exam taken after t weeks is given by the following "forgetting function".

$$g(t) = 77 - 10 \ln(t + 1)$$

  a. What was the average score on the original exam? **77**

  b. What was the average score after 2 weeks? after 5 weeks? **66; 59**

68. Students in a precalculus class were given a final exam. Each month thereafter, they took an equivalent exam. The class average on the exam taken after t months is given by the following function.

$$F(t) = 82 - 8 \cdot \ln(t + 1)$$

  a. What was the average score on the original exam? **82**

  b. What was the average score after 6 months? after 10 months? **66; 63**

69. One person with a flu virus visited the campus. The number T of days it took for the virus to infect x people is given by T.

$$T = -0.93 \ln\left(\dfrac{7000 - x}{6999x}\right)$$

a. How many days did it take for 6000 people to become infected? **9.9 days**

b. After 2 weeks, how many people were infected? **≈6986**

70. *Critical Thinking* For each positive integer n, let f_n be the polynomial function whose rule is

$$f_n(x) = x - \frac{x^2}{2} + \frac{x^3}{3} - \frac{x^4}{4} + \frac{x^5}{5} - \cdots - \frac{x^n}{n}$$

where the sign of the last term is $+$ if n is odd and $-$ if n is even. In the viewing window with $-1 \le x \le 1$ and $-4 \le y \le 1$, graph $g(x) = \ln(1 + x)$ and $f_4(x)$ on the same screen. For what values of x does f_4 appear to be a good approximation of g?

$-0.5 \le x \le 0.5$

71. *Critical Thinking* Using the viewing window in Exercise 70, find a value of n for which the graph of the function f_n (as defined in Exercise 70)

$n = 30$ gives an approximation with a maximum error of 0.00001 when $-0.7 \le x \le 0.7$.

appears to coincide with the graph of $g(x) = \ln(1 + x)$. Use the trace feature to move from graph to graph to see how good this approximation actually is.

72. A bicycle store finds that N the number of bikes sold, is related to d, the number of dollars spent on advertising.

$$N = 51 + 100 \cdot \ln\left(\frac{d}{100} + 2\right)$$

a. How many bikes will be sold if nothing is spent on advertising? if $1000 is spent? if $10,000 is spent?

b. If the average profit is $25 per bike, is it worthwhile to spend $1000 on advertising? What about $10,000?

c. What are the answers in part **b** if the average profit per bike is $35?

72. a. ≈120 bikes; ≈299 bikes; ≈513 bikes

b. If $d = $1000, they make $7475 in profit. Less the advertising costs that's almost $6500 in profit. If $d = $10,000, that's $12,825 profit. Less the advertising costs that's only $2825 left over. Spending $1000 on ads is a better idea.

c. If profit is $35 per bike, then spending $1000 on advertising gives a profit of $10,465, or $9465 after the ads are paid for. Spending $10,000 on ads gives $17,955 in profits. Less ad costs, that's $7955. Better, but still spending $1000 pays off the most handsomely.

Section 5.5 Properties and Laws of Logarithms

5.5 Properties and Laws of Logarithms

Objectives

- Use properties and laws of logarithms to simplify and evaluate expressions

The definitions of common and natural logarithms differ only in their bases. Therefore, common and natural logarithms share the same basic properties and laws.

Basic Properties of Logarithms

Logarithms are only defined for positive real numbers. That is,

log v and ln v are defined only when $v > 0$.

NOTE Any number raised to the zero power, except zero, is 1.

$$x^0 = 1, \text{ where } x \ne 0$$

The graphs of $y = \log x$ and $y = \ln x$ both contain the point $(1, 0)$ because $10^0 = 1$ and $e^0 = 1$.

$$\log 1 = 0 \quad \text{and} \quad \ln 1 = 0$$

The values of $\log 10^4$ and $\ln e^9$ can be found by writing equivalent exponential statements.

If $\log 10^4 = x$, then $10^x = 10^4$. So $x = 4$.
If $\ln e^9 = x$, then $e^x = e^9$. So $x = 9$.

In general,

$$\log 10^k = k, \quad \text{for every real number } k.$$
$$\ln e^k = k, \quad \text{for every real number } k.$$

Section 5.5 Properties and Laws of Logarithms

Teaching Notes

Have students review Figure 5.4-8 on page 359. Remind them that it can represent either of the following function pairs:

- the exponential function $f(x) = 10^x$ and its inverse, the logarithmic function $f(x) = \log x$
- the exponential function $f(x) = e^x$ and its inverse, the logarithmic function $f(x) = \ln x$

Encourage them to remember this figure to serve as a "snapshot" summary of these basic properties of exponential and logarithmic functions:

- $10^0 = 1$ and $e^0 = 1$
- $\log 1 = 0$ and $\ln 1 = 0$
- both logarithmic functions are defined only for positive values of x

To help students understand the statements at the bottom of this page, stress that *a logarithm is an exponent.*

- The *log* of any number is the exponent that must be applied to the base 10 to produce that number. So, $\log 10^k = k$.
- The *ln* of any number is the exponent that must be applied to the base e to produce that number. So, $\ln e^k = k$.

Teaching Notes

To help students understand that $10^{\log 678} = 678$, again stress that *a logarithm is an exponent*. log 678 is the exponent that must be applied to the base 10 to produce 678, so of course, if that exponent is applied to the base 10, then 678 must be produced! That is, $10^{\log 678} = 678$. Ask students to use similar reasoning to explain why $e^{\ln 54} = 54$.

Point out that all the bold statements in the text on pages 363 and 364 are summarized in the table, **Basic Properties of Logarithms.**

Have students refer back to the **Composition of a Function and its Inverse** (page 211). Remind them that $(f \circ f^{-1})(x) = f(f^{-1}(x)) = x$ and $(f^{-1} \circ f)(x) = f^{-1}(f(x)) = x$.

Using g instead of f^{-1} establishes properties 3 and 4 in the table. Use the concept that inverse functions "undo each other" to reinforce this idea. Neglecting restrictions on x, properties 3 and 4 can be summarized as follows:
- $\log 10^x = 10^{\log x} = x$, and
- $\ln e^x = e^{\ln x} = x$

To explain that k can be any real number in property 3, write $10^{\square}$ and $e^{\square}$ on the board. Ask students if they can think of any number that would make either expression undefined if written in the box. no

To explain that v must be positive in property 4, remind them that both logarithmic functions are defined only for positive values (recall the logarithm graph in their "snapshot").

Illustrate the first **Product Law of Logarithms** as follows:
Let $v = 10^2, w = 10^3$. Then:
$\log(v \cdot w) = \log(10^2 \cdot 10^3)$
$\qquad = \log 10^5 = 5$
$\log v + \log w = \log 10^2 + \log 10^3$
$\qquad\qquad = 2 + 3 = 5$
Ask students to illustrate the second law.

Let $v = e^2, w = e^3$. Then:
$\ln(v \cdot w) = \ln(e^2 \cdot e^3) = \ln e^5 = 5$
$\ln v + \ln w = \ln e^2 + \ln e^3$
$\qquad\qquad = 2 + 3 = 5$

By definition, log 678 is the exponent to which 10 must be raised to produce 678.

$$10^{\log 678} = 678$$

Similarly, ln 54 is the exponent to which e must be raised to produce 54.

$$e^{\ln 54} = 54$$

In general,

$$10^{\log v} = v \quad \text{and} \quad e^{\ln v} = v, \qquad \text{for every } v > 0.$$

The facts presented above are summarized in the table below.

Basic Properties of Logarithms

Common logarithms	Natural logarithms
1. $\log v$ is defined only when $v > 0$	1. $\ln v$ is defined only when $v > 0$
2. $\log 1 = 0$ and $\log 10 = 1$	2. $\ln 1 = 0$ and $\ln e = 1$
3. $\log 10^k = k$ for every real number k	3. $\ln e^k = k$ for every real number k
4. $10^{\log v} = v$ for every $v > 0$	4. $e^{\ln v} = v$ for every $v > 0$

Properties 3 and 4 are restatements of the fact that the composition of inverse functions produces the identity function.

That is, if $f(x) = 10^x$ and $g(x) = \log x$, then

$$(f \circ g)(x) = f(\log x) = 10^{\log x} = x \text{ for all } x > 0$$
$$(g \circ f)(x) = g(10^x) = \log 10^x = x \text{ for all } x$$

Analogous statements are true for $f(x) = e^x$ and $g(x) = \ln x$.

The properties of logarithms can be used to simplify expressions and solve equations. For example, applying Property 3 with $k = 2x^2 + 7x + 9$ allows you to rewrite the expression $\ln e^{2x^2+7x+9}$ as $2x^2 + 7x + 9$.

Example 1 Solving Equations by Using Properties of Logarithms

Use the basic properties of logarithms to solve the equation $\ln(x + 1) = 2$.

Solution

Because $f(x) = e^x$ is a function, if $\ln(x + 1) = 2$, then $e^{\ln(x+1)} = e^2$.

$$\begin{aligned}
e^{\ln(x+1)} &= e^2 \\
x + 1 &= e^2 \qquad \textit{Apply Property 4 with } v = x + 1 \\
x &= e^2 - 1 \\
x &\approx 6.3891
\end{aligned}$$

The intersection of the graphs of $Y_1 = \ln(x + 1)$ and $Y_2 = 2$, shown in Figure 5.5-1, confirms the solution.

Intersection
X=6.3890561 Y=2

Figure 5.5-1

Laws of Logarithms

The Product Law of Exponents states that $b^m b^n = b^{m+n}$. Because logarithms are exponents, the following law holds.

Product Law of Logarithms

For all $v, w > 0$,

$$\log (vw) = \log v + \log w$$

$$\ln (vw) = \ln v + \ln w.$$

Proof According to Property 4 of logarithms, $10^{\log v} = v$ and $10^{\log w} = w$. Then, by the Product Law of Exponents:

$$vw = 10^{\log v} \cdot 10^{\log w} = 10^{\log v + \log w}$$

Again by Property 4 of logarithms:

$$10^{\log vw} = vw$$

Therefore, $10^{\log vw} = 10^{\log v + \log w}$; and because exponential functions are one-to-one, $\log vw = \log v + \log w$. A similar argument can be made for natural logarithms.

Example 2 Using the Product Law of Logarithms

Use the Product Law of Logarithms to evaluate each logarithm.

a. Given that $\log 3 = 0.4771$ and $\log 11 = 1.0414$, find $\log 33$.

b. Given that $\ln 7 = 1.9459$ and $\ln 9 = 2.1972$, find $\ln 63$.

Solution

a. $\log 33 = \log(3 \cdot 11) = \log 3 + \log 11 = 0.4771 + 1.0414 = 1.5185$

b. $\ln 63 = \ln(7 \cdot 9) = \ln 7 + \ln 9 = 1.9459 + 2.1972 = 4.1431$ ∎

CAUTION

A common error in applying the Product Law of Logarithms is to write the false statement

$$\ln 7 + \ln 9 = \ln(7 + 9) = \ln 16$$

instead of the correct statement

$$\ln 7 + \ln 9 = \ln (7 \cdot 9) = \ln 63.$$

Graphing Exploration ●

Using the viewing window with $-10 \le x \le 10$ and $-8 \le y \le 8$, graph both functions below on the same screen.

$$f(x) = \ln x + \ln 9 \qquad g(x) = \ln(x + 9)$$

Explain how the graph illustrates the caution in the margin.

The Quotient Law of Exponents states that $\dfrac{b^m}{b^n} = b^{m-n}$. When the exponents are logarithms, the Quotient Law is still valid.

Example 1

Use the basic properties of logarithms to solve the equation $\log (x - 3) = 1$. $x = 13$

The solution can be confirmed by graphing.

Example 2

Use the Product Law of Logarithms to evaluate each logarithm.

a. Given that $\log 3 = 0.4771$ and $\log 4 = 0.6021$, find $\log 12$. 1.0792

b. Given that $\ln 3 = 1.0986$ and $\ln 6 = 1.7918$, find $\ln 18$. 2.8904

Teaching Notes

Solution to the **Graphing Exploration:**

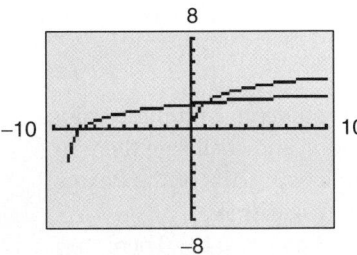

The graphs are different, so $\ln x + \ln 9 \ne \ln(x + 9)$ in general. In particular, $\ln 7 + \ln 9 \ne \ln(7 + 9)$.

Math Background

Notice the statement in the proof of the **Product Law of Logarithms:**

"Therefore, $10^{\log vw} = 10^{\log v + \log w}$; and because exponential functions are one-to-one, $\log vw = \log v + \log w$." Why is it necessary that exponential functions be one-to-one to justify this statement? In this case, the reason is found in the definition of a one-to-one function: If f is a one-to-one function, then $f(u) = f(v)$ implies $u = v$ (i.e. different inputs cannot have the same function value). So, because the exponential function $f(x) = 10^x$ is one-to-one, we have: $f(\log vw) = f(\log v + \log w)$ implies $\log vw = \log v + \log w$. That is, $10^{\log vw} = 10^{\log v + \log w}$ implies $\log vw = \log v + \log w$.

Teaching Notes

Illustrate the first **Quotient Law of Logarithms** with the following example:

Let $v = 10^5, w = 10^3$. Then:

$$\log\left(\frac{v}{w}\right) = \log\left(\frac{10^5}{10^3}\right) = \log 10^2 = 2$$

$$\log v - \log w = \log 10^5 - \log 10^3$$
$$= 5 - 3 = 2$$

Ask students to illustrate the second law.

Let $v = e^5, w = e^3$. Then:

$$\ln\left(\frac{v}{w}\right) = \ln\left(\frac{e^5}{e^3}\right) = \ln e^2 = 2$$

$$\ln v - \ln w = \ln e^5 - \ln e^3$$
$$= 5 - 3 = 2$$

Solution to the **Graphing Exploration:**

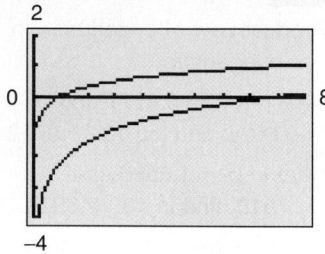

The graphs are different, so

$$\ln\left(\frac{x}{9}\right) \neq \frac{\ln x}{\ln 9}$$ in general. In particular,

$$\ln\left(\frac{7}{9}\right) \neq \frac{\ln 7}{\ln 9}.$$

Provide students with these values of k and v, and challenge them to illustrate both parts of the **Power Law of Logarithms:**

Let $k = 3$ and $v = 10^4$. Then:

$$\log v^k = \log(10^4)^3 = \log 10^{12} = 12$$
$$k \log v = 3 \log 10^4 = 3 \cdot 4 = 12$$

$$\ln v^k = \ln(e^4)^3 = \ln e^{12} = 12$$
$$k \ln v = 3 \ln e^4 = 3 \cdot 4 = 12$$

Quotient Law of Logarithms

For all $v, w > 0$,

$$\log\left(\frac{v}{w}\right) = \log v - \log w$$

$$\ln\left(\frac{v}{w}\right) = \ln v - \ln w.$$

The proof of the Quotient Law of Logarithms is similar to the proof of the Product Law of Logarithms.

Example 3   Using the Quotient Law of Logarithms

Use the Quotient Law of Logarithms to evaluate each logarithm.

a. Given that $\log 28 = 1.4472$ and $\log 7 = 0.8451$, find $\log 4$.

b. Given that $\ln 18 = 2.8904$ and $\ln 6 = 1.7918$, find $\ln 3$.

Solution

a. $\log 4 = \log\left(\frac{28}{7}\right) = \log 28 - \log 7 = 1.4472 - 0.8451 = 0.6021$

b. $\ln 3 = \ln\left(\frac{18}{6}\right) = \ln 18 - \ln 6 = 2.8904 - 1.7918 = 1.0986$

CAUTION

Do not confuse

$$\ln\left(\frac{7}{9}\right) = -0.2513$$ with the quotient

$$\frac{\ln 7}{\ln 9} = 0.8856.$$

They are *different* numbers.

Graphing Exploration

Using the viewing window with $0 \leq x \leq 8$ and $-4 \leq y \leq 2$, graph both functions below on the same screen.

$$f(x) = \ln\left(\frac{x}{9}\right) \qquad g(x) = \frac{\ln x}{\ln 9}$$

Explain how the graph illustrates the caution in the margin.

The Power Law of Exponents, which states that $(b^m)^k = b^{mk}$, can also be translated into a logarithmic statement.

Power Law of Logarithms

For all k and $v > 0$,

$$\log v^k = k \log v,$$

$$\ln v^k = k \ln v.$$

Proof

According to Property 4 of logarithms, $10^{\log v} = v$. Then, by the Power Law of Exponents:

$$v^k = (10^{\log v})^k = 10^{k \log v}$$

Again by Property 4 of logarithms:

$$10^{\log v^k} = v^k$$

So, $10^{\log v^k} = 10^{k \log v}$ and therefore, $\log v^k = k \log v$. A similar argument can be made for natural logarithms.

Example 4   **Using the Power Law of Logarithms**

Use the Power Law of Logarithms to evaluate each logarithm.

a. Given that $\log 6 = 0.7782$, find $\log \sqrt{6}$.
b. Given that $\ln 50 = 3.9120$, find $\ln \sqrt[3]{50}$.

Solution

a. $\log \sqrt{6} = \log 6^{\frac{1}{2}} = \dfrac{1}{2} \log 6 = \dfrac{1}{2}(0.7782) = 0.3891$

b. $\ln \sqrt[3]{50} = \ln 50^{\frac{1}{3}} = \dfrac{1}{3} \ln 50 = \dfrac{1}{3}(3.9120) = 1.3040$

The laws of logarithms can be used to simplify various expressions.

Example 5   **Simplifying Expressions**

Write $\ln 3x + 4 \ln x - \ln 3xy$ as a single logarithm.

Solution

$$\begin{aligned}
\ln 3x + 4 \ln x - \ln 3xy &= \ln 3x + \ln x^4 - \ln 3xy && \textit{Power Law}\\
&= \ln(3x \cdot x^4) - \ln 3xy && \textit{Product Law}\\
&= \ln\left(\frac{3x^5}{3xy}\right) && \textit{Quotient Law}\\
&= \ln\left(\frac{x^4}{y}\right)
\end{aligned}$$

Example 6   **Simplifying Expressions**

Simplify $\ln\left(\dfrac{\sqrt{x}}{x}\right) + \ln\left(\sqrt[4]{ex^2}\right)$.

The proof of the **Quotient Law of Logarithms** is similar to the proof of the **Product Law of Logarithms** that was given with respect to common logarithms on page 365. You may want to have your students prove the Quotient Law of Logarithms using natural logarithms:

According to Property 4 of logarithms, $e^{\ln v} = v$ and $e^{\ln w} = w$. By the Quotient Law of Exponents:

$$\frac{v}{w} = \frac{e^{\ln v}}{e^{\ln w}} = e^{\ln v - \ln w}$$

Again, by Property 4 of logarithms:

$$e^{\ln\left(\frac{v}{w}\right)} = \frac{v}{w}$$

Therefore, $e^{\ln\left(\frac{v}{w}\right)} = e^{\ln v - \ln w}$; and because exponential functions are one-to-one, $\ln\left(\frac{v}{w}\right) = \ln v - \ln w$.

ADDITIONAL EXAMPLES

Example 3

Use the Quotient Law of Logarithms to evaluate each logarithm.

a. Given that $\log 40 = 1.6021$ and $\log 8 = 0.9031$, find $\log 5$.   0.6990

b. Given that $\ln 32 = 3.4657$ and $\ln 8 = 2.0794$, find $\ln 4$.   1.3863

Example 4

Use the Power Law of Logarithms to evaluate each logarithm.

a. Given that $\log 25 = 1.3979$, find $\log \sqrt[4]{25}$.

$\log \sqrt[4]{25} = \dfrac{1}{4} \log 25 = 0.3495$

b. Given that $\ln 22 = 3.0910$, find $\ln \sqrt{22}$.

$\ln \sqrt{22} = \dfrac{1}{2} \ln 22 = 1.5455$

Example 5

Write $\log 8x + 3 \log x - \log 2x^2$ as a single logarithm. $\log 4x^2$

Example Notes

An alternate sequence of steps that can be used in **Example 6** is shown below:

$$\ln\left(\frac{\sqrt{x}}{x}\right) + \ln\left(\sqrt[4]{ex^2}\right)$$

$$= \ln\sqrt{x} - \ln x + \ln\left(\sqrt[4]{ex^2}\right)$$

$$= \ln x^{\frac{1}{2}} - \ln x + \ln(ex^2)^{\frac{1}{4}}$$

$$= \frac{1}{2}\ln x - \ln x + \frac{1}{4}\ln(ex^2)$$

$$= \frac{1}{2}\ln x - \ln x + \frac{1}{4}(\ln e + \ln x^2)$$

$$= \frac{1}{2}\ln x - \ln x + \frac{1}{4}(\ln e + 2\ln x)$$

$$= \frac{1}{2}\ln x - \ln x + \frac{1}{4}\ln e + \frac{1}{2}\ln x$$

$$= \frac{1}{4}\ln e$$

$$= \frac{1}{4}$$

ADDITIONAL EXAMPLES

Example 6

Simplify $2\log\left(\dfrac{\sqrt[4]{m}}{m}\right) + \log\left(\sqrt{100m^3}\right)$.

$$2\log\left(\frac{\sqrt[4]{m}}{m}\right) + \log\left(\sqrt{100m^3}\right)$$

$$= 2\log\left(\frac{m^{\frac{1}{4}}}{m}\right) + \log(100m^3)^{\frac{1}{2}}$$

$$= 2\log\left(m^{-\frac{3}{4}}\right) + \log(100m^3)^{\frac{1}{2}}$$

$$= -\frac{3}{4}(2)\log m + \frac{1}{2}\log 100m^3$$

$$= -\frac{3}{2}\log m + \frac{1}{2}(\log 100 + \log m^3)$$

$$= -\frac{3}{2}\log m + \frac{1}{2}(2 + 3\log m)$$

$$= -\frac{3}{2}\log m + 1 + \frac{3}{2}\log m$$

$$= 1$$

Example 7

An earthquake in Turkey in 1999 registered 7.6 on the Richter scale. Numerous aftershocks followed during the next few days, one of which had a magnitude of 5.0. How much more intense was the ground motion of the earthquake than that of this aftershock?
$10^{2.6} \approx 398$ times more intense

Solution

$$\ln\left(\frac{\sqrt{x}}{x}\right) + \ln(\sqrt[4]{ex^2}) = \ln\left(\frac{x^{\frac{1}{2}}}{x}\right) + \ln(ex^2)^{\frac{1}{4}}$$

$$= \ln(x^{-\frac{1}{2}}) + \ln(ex^2)^{\frac{1}{4}}$$

$$= -\frac{1}{2}\ln x + \frac{1}{4}\ln(ex^2) \qquad \textit{Power Law}$$

$$= -\frac{1}{2}\ln x + \frac{1}{4}(\ln e + \ln x^2) \qquad \textit{Product Law}$$

$$= -\frac{1}{2}\ln x + \frac{1}{4}(\ln e + 2\ln x) \qquad \textit{Power Law}$$

$$= -\frac{1}{2}\ln x + \frac{1}{4}\ln e + \frac{1}{2}\ln x$$

$$= \frac{1}{4}\ln e$$

$$= \frac{1}{4} \qquad\qquad \ln e = 1$$

NOTE The **zero earthquake** has ground motion amplitude of less than 1 micron on a standard seismograph 100 kilometers from the epicenter.

Applications

A logarithmic scale is a scale that is determined by a logarithmic function. Because logarithmic growth is slow, measurements on a logarithmic scale can sometimes be deceptive. The Richter scale is an illustration of this.

The magnitude $R(i)$ of an earthquake on the Richter scale is given by $R(i) = \log\left(\dfrac{i}{i_0}\right)$, where i is the amplitude of the ground motion of the earthquake and i_0 is the amplitude of the ground motion of the *zero earthquake*. A moderate earthquake might have 1000 times the ground motion of the zero earthquake, or $i = 1000i_0$. Its magnitude would be

$$\log\left(\frac{1000i_0}{i_0}\right) = \log 1000 = 3$$

An earthquake with 10 times this ground motion, or $i = 10{,}000i_0$, would have a magnitude of

$$\log\left(\frac{10{,}000i_0}{i_0}\right) = \log 10{,}000 = 4$$

So a tenfold increase in ground motion produces only a 1-point change on the Richter scale. In general,

> increasing the ground motion by a factor of 10^k increases the Richter magnitude by k units.

Example 7 Richter Scale

The 1989 World Series earthquake in San Francisco measured 7.0 on the Richter scale, and the great earthquake of 1906 measured 8.3. How much more intense was the ground motion of the 1906 earthquake than that of the 1989 earthquake?

Solution

The difference in Richter magnitude is $8.3 - 7.0 = 1.3$. Therefore, the 1906 earthquake was $10^{1.3} \approx 20$ times more intense than the 1989 earthquake in terms of ground motion. ∎

Exercises 5.5

In Exercises 1–4, solve each equation by using the basic properties of logarithms.

1. $\log(x - 3) = 2$
103

2. $\log(2x) = 3$
500

3. $\ln(x + 4) = -1$
≈−3.63

4. $5 + \ln(x - 1) = 8$
≈21.09

In Exercises 5–10, use laws of logarithms and the values given below to evaluate each logarithmic expression.

$$\log 7 = 0.8451 \quad \log 5 = 0.6990$$
$$\log 3 = 0.4771 \quad \log 2 = 0.3010$$

5. $\log 8$
≈0.9030

6. $\log 12$
≈1.0791

7. $\log\left(\dfrac{5}{7}\right)$
≈−0.1461

8. $\log\left(\dfrac{3}{14}\right)$
≈ −0.6690

9. $\log 0.6$
≈−0.2219

10. $\log 1.5$
≈0.1761

In Exercises 11–20, write the given expression as a single logarithm.

11. $\ln x^2 + 3 \ln y$
$\ln(x^2 y^3)$

12. $\ln 2x + 2 \ln x - \ln 3y$
$\ln\left(\dfrac{2x^3}{3y}\right)$

13. $\log(x^2 - 9) - \log(x + 3)$
$\log(x - 3)$

14. $\log 3x - 2[\log x - \log(2 + y)]$
$\log\left(\dfrac{3(2 + y)^2}{x}\right)$

15. $2 \ln x - 3(\ln x^2 + \ln x)$
$\ln(x^{-7})$

16. $\ln\left(\dfrac{e}{\sqrt{x}}\right) - \ln(\sqrt{ex})$
$\ln\left(\dfrac{\sqrt{e}}{x}\right)$

17. $3 \ln(e^2 - e) - 3$
$3 \ln(e - 1)$

18. $2 - 2 \log 20$
$\log \dfrac{1}{4}$

19. $\log 10x + \log 20y - 1$
$\log(20xy)$

20. $\ln(e^2 x) + \ln(ey) - 3$
$\ln xy$

In Exercises 21–26, let $u = \ln x$ and $v = \ln y$. Write the given expression in terms of u and v. For example,
$\ln x^3y = \ln x^3 + \ln y = 3 \ln x + \ln y = 3u + v$.

21. $\ln(x^2 y^5)$ **$2u + 5v$**

22. $\ln(x^3 y^2)$ **$3u + 2v$**

23. $\ln\left(\sqrt{x} \cdot y^2\right)$ **$\dfrac{1}{2}u + 2v$**

24. $\ln\left(\dfrac{\sqrt{x}}{y}\right)$ **$\dfrac{1}{2}u - v$**

25. $\ln\left(\sqrt[3]{x^2 \sqrt{y}}\right)$ **$\dfrac{2}{3}u + \dfrac{1}{6}v$**

26. $\ln\left(\dfrac{\sqrt{x^2 y}}{\sqrt[3]{y}}\right)$ **$u + \dfrac{1}{6}v$**

27. a. Graph $y = x$ and $y = e^{\ln x}$ in separate viewing windows. For what values of x are the graphs identical?
b. Use the properties of logarithms to explain your answer in part **a**.

28. a. Graph $y = x$ and $y = \ln e^x$ in separate viewing windows. For what values of x are the graphs identical?
b. Use the properties of logarithms to explain your answer in part **a**.

In Exercises 29–34, use graphical or algebraic means to determine whether the statement is true or false.

29. $\ln|x| = |\ln x|$

30. $\ln\left(\dfrac{1}{x}\right) = \dfrac{1}{\ln x}$

31. $\log x^5 = 5 \log x$

32. $e^{x \ln x} = x^x \; (x > 0)$

33. $\ln x^3 = (\ln x)^3$

34. $\log \sqrt{x} = \sqrt{\log x}$

In Exercises 35 and 36, find values of a and b for which the statement is false.

35. $\dfrac{\log a}{\log b} = \log\left(\dfrac{a}{b}\right)$

36. $\log(a + b) = \log a + \log b$

37. If $\ln b^7 = 7$, what is b?
$b = e$

38. Suppose $f(x) = A \ln x + B$, where A and B are constants. If $f(1) = 10$ and $f(e) = 1$, what are A and B?
$A = -9, B = 10$

39. If $f(x) = A \ln x + B$ and $f(e) = 5$ and $f(e^2) = 8$, find A and B.
$A = 3, B = 2$

40. Show that $g(x) = \ln\left(\dfrac{x}{1 - x}\right)$ is the inverse function of $f(x) = \dfrac{1}{1 + e^{-x}}$. (See Section 3.6.)

Real-World Application

The Richter scale, developed by Charles Richter (1900–1985), assigns a magnitude to each earthquake, based on the amplitude of measured seismic waves. Because the scale is logarithmic, an increase of 10 in seismic amplitude results in an increase of only 1 in the assigned magnitude. A logarithmic scale is well suited for this purpose because there is such a great range in magnitudes of earthquakes. For example, if one earthquake has 100 times the seismic amplitude as another earthquake, the Richter scale number assigned to it is only 2 greater.

Exercises 5.5

ANSWERS

27. a. For all $x > 0$
b. According to the fourth property of natural logarithms on page 364, $e^{\ln x} = x$ for every $x > 0$.

28. a. for all values of x
b. This is true because $f(x) = \ln x$ and $g(x) = e^x$ are inverse functions. $(f \circ g)(x) = \ln e^x = x$

29. False; the right side is not defined when $x < 0$, but the left side is.

30. False; Let $x = 1$ for example. The left side of the equation has the value 0 while the right side is undefined.

31. True by the Power Law

32. True; $e^{x \ln x} = e^{\ln x^x} = x^x$

33. False; the graph of the left side differs from the graph of the right side.

34. False; For example, let $x = e^{16}$. The left side of the equation has the value 8 while the right side has the value 4.

35. Answers may vary: $\dfrac{\log 3}{\log 2} \approx 1.585$ and $\log\left(\dfrac{3}{2}\right) = 0.1761$ thus $\dfrac{\log 3}{\log 2} \neq \log\left(\dfrac{3}{2}\right)$

36. Answers may vary; $\log(3 + 2) \approx 0.6990$ and $\log 3 + \log 2 \approx 0.7782$; thus $\log(3 + 2) \neq \log 3 + \log 2$

---

40. $(f \circ g)(x) = f\left(\ln\left(\dfrac{x}{1 - x}\right)\right)$

$= \dfrac{1}{1 + e^{-\left(\ln\left(\frac{x}{1-x}\right)\right)}}$

$= \dfrac{1}{1 + e^{\ln\left(\frac{1-x}{x}\right)}}$ and

$= \dfrac{1}{1 + \left(\dfrac{1 - x}{x}\right)}$

$= \dfrac{x}{x + (1 - x)} = x$

$(g \circ f)(x) = g\left(\dfrac{1}{1 + e^{-x}}\right)$

$= \ln\left(\dfrac{\frac{1}{1 + e^{-x}}}{1 + \frac{1}{1 + e^{-x}}}\right)$

$= \ln\left(\dfrac{1}{1 + e^{-x} - 1}\right)$

$= \ln\left(\dfrac{1}{e^{-x}}\right)$

$= \ln e^x = x$

51.
a. ≈ 1.2553

b. ≈ 3.9518

c. $\log x = \dfrac{\ln x}{\ln 10}$

52.
a. ≈ 0.9422

b. ≈ 1.9422

c. ≈ 2.9422

d. ≈ 3.9422

e. ≈ 4.9422

f. The sequence of numbers increases by a factor of 10. The logarithms increase by 1; on a logarithmic scale, each 1 unit increase corresponds to an increase by a factor of 10.

Section

5.5.A Excursion: Logarithmic Functions to Other Bases

 Math Background

The functions $f(x) = b^x$ and $g(x) = \log_b x$ are inverses. Recall the method of finding an inverse (page 207). To find the inverse of the function $f(x) = b^x$, rewrite the function using y, exchange the x and y variables, and then solve the equation for y:

$$f(x) = b^x$$
$$y = b^x$$
$$x = b^y$$
$$y = \log_b x$$
$$f^{-1}(x) = \log_b x$$

The equation $y = \log_b x$ above is where we "solve the equation for y." It might not seem like "solving" in the customary sense. We can think of it as giving a name to the inverse function. That is, we replace $x = b^y$ with its equivalent equation $y = \log_b x$.

In Exercises 41–44, state the magnitude on the Richter scale of an earthquake that satisfies the given condition.

41. 100 times stronger than the zero quake
2

42. $10^{4.7}$ times stronger than the zero quake
4.7

43. 350 times stronger than the zero quake
≈2.54

44. 2500 times stronger than the zero quake
≈3.4

Exercises 45–48 deal with the energy intensity i of a sound, which is related to the loudness of the sound by the function $L(i) = 10 \cdot \log\left(\dfrac{i}{i_0}\right)$, where i_0 is the minimum intensity detectable by the human ear and $L(i)$ is measured in decibels. Find the decibel measure of the sound.

45. ticking watch (intensity is 100 times i_0)
20 decibels

46. soft music (intensity is 10,000 times i_0)
40 decibels

47. loud conversation (intensity is 4 million times i_0)
≈66 decibels

48. Victoria Falls in Africa (intensity is 10 billion times i_0)
100 decibels

49. How much louder is the sound in Exercise 46 than the sound in Exercise 45?
100 times

50. The perceived loudness L of a sound of intensity I is given by $L = k \cdot \ln I$, where k is a certain constant. By how much must the intensity be increased to double the loudness? (That is, what must be done to I to produce $2L$?)
***I* must be squared to double *L*.**

51. Compute each of the following pairs of numbers:

a. $\log 18$ and $\dfrac{\ln 18}{\ln 10}$ b. $\log 8950$ and $\dfrac{\ln 8950}{\ln 10}$

c. What do the results in parts **a** and **b** suggest?

52. Find each of the following logarithms.

a. $\log 8.753$ b. $\log 87.53$ c. $\log 875.3$

d. $\log 8753$ e. $\log 87,530$

f. How are the numbers 8.753, 87.53, 875.3, 8753, and 87,530 related to one another? How are their logarithms related? State a general conclusion that this evidence suggests.

5.5.A Excursion: Logarithmic Functions to Other Bases

Objectives

- Evaluate logarithms to any base with and without a calculator

- Solve exponential and logarithmic equations to any base by using an equivalent equation

- Identify transformations of logarithmic functions to any base

- Use properties and laws of logarithms to simplify and evaluate logarithmic expressions to any base

Common and natural logarithms were defined by considering the inverse functions of the exponential functions $f(x) = 10^x$ and $f(x) = e^x$. In this section, you will see that a similar procedure can be carried out with any positive number b in place of 10 and e.

> **NOTE** In the discussion below, b is a fixed positive number with $b > 1$. The discussion on exponents and logarithms to base b is also valid for $0 < b < 1$, but in that case the graphs have a different shape.

Defining Logarithmic Functions to Other Bases

Because $f(x) = b^x$ is an increasing function, it is a one-to-one function and therefore has an inverse function. (See Section 3.6) Recall that the graphs of inverse functions are reflections of one another across the line $y = x$. An exponential function $f(x) = b^x$ and its inverse function are graphed in Figure 5.5.A-1.

y = x

f(x)

g(x)

Figure 5.5.A-1

This inverse function g is called the **logarithmic function to the base** b. The value of $g(x)$ at the number x is denoted $\log_b x$ and is called the **logarithm to the base** b of the number x.

Because the functions $f(x) = b^x$ and $g(x) = \log_b x$ are inverse functions,

$$\log_b v = u \quad \text{if and only if} \quad b^u = v.$$

Because all logarithms are exponents, every statement about logarithms is equivalent to a statement about exponents.

Logarithmic statement $\log_b v = u$	Equivalent exponential statement $b^u = v$
$\log_3 81 = 4$	$3^4 = 81$
$\log_4 64 = 3$	$4^3 = 64$
$\log_{125} 5 = \dfrac{1}{3}$	$125^{\frac{1}{3}} = 5$
$\log_8\left(\dfrac{1}{4}\right) = -\dfrac{2}{3}$	$8^{-\frac{2}{3}} = \dfrac{1}{4}$

Example 1 **Evaluating Logarithms to Other Bases**

Without using a calculator, find each value.

a. $\log_2 16$ **b.** $\log_{\frac{1}{3}} 9$ **c.** $\log_5(-25)$

Solution

a. If $\log_2 16 = x$, then $2^x = 16$. Because $2^4 = 16$, $\log_2 16 = 4$.

b. If $\log_{\frac{1}{3}} 9 = x$, then $\left(\dfrac{1}{3}\right)^x = 9$. Because $\left(\dfrac{1}{3}\right)^{-2} = 9$, $\log_{\frac{1}{3}} 9 = -2$

c. If $\log_5(-25) = x$, then $5^x = -25$. Because there is no real number exponent of 5 that produces a negative number, $\log_5(-25)$ is not defined. ∎

Example 2 **Solving Logarithmic Equations**

Solve each equation for x.

a. $\log_5 x = 3$ **b.** $\log_6 1 = x$ **c.** $\log_{\frac{1}{6}}(-3) = x$ **d.** $\log_6 6 = x$

Math Background

The **NOTE** mentions that graphs of logarithmic functions with bases between 0 and 1 have shapes that are different than those shown in the text. This is because graphs of exponential functions with bases between 0 and 1 have different shapes than graphs of exponential functions with bases greater than 1 (see page 336). The graphs of $y = \left(\dfrac{1}{2}\right)^x$ and its inverse, $y = \log_{\left(\frac{1}{2}\right)} x$ are shown below.

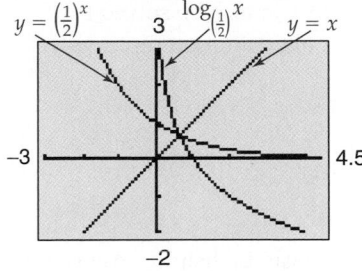

Teaching Notes

To prepare students for the definition of a **logarithm to the base** b, build on the two bases they are familiar with. Show the following alternate ways to write $\log x$ and $\ln x$: $\ln x = \log_e x$ and $\log x = \log_{10} x$. Then say that any positive number b other than 1 can be used as a base.

For the last row of the table, ask students to show why $8^{-\frac{2}{3}} = \dfrac{1}{4}$

$$8^{-\frac{2}{3}} = \dfrac{1}{8^{\frac{2}{3}}} = \dfrac{1}{\left(\sqrt[3]{8}\right)^2} = \dfrac{1}{2^2} = \dfrac{1}{4}$$

Example Notes

Remind students that a logarithm is an exponent.

In **Example 1a**, they can ask themselves, "What exponent must be applied to the base 2 to produce 16?"

In **Example 2a**, they can ask themselves, "What do I get when I apply the exponent 3 to the base 5?"

ADDITIONAL EXAMPLES

Example 1

Without using a calculator, find each value.

a. $\log_3 27$ 3
b. $\log_{\frac{1}{2}} 32$ −5
c. $\log_4(-64)$ undefined

Teaching Notes

For the **Basic Properties of Logarithms** box, have students review the corresponding box on page 364. They should see that the information is identical in both boxes. Ask them which Examples just completed illustrate property 1. Examples 1c and 2c

For the **Laws of Logarithms** box, have students review the corresponding boxes on pages 365–366.

Example Notes

Example 3 can also be solved by applying the definition directly:

$$\log_b v = u \quad \text{if and only if} \quad b^u = v$$

$$\log_3(x-1) = 4 \quad \text{if and only if} \quad \begin{aligned} 3^4 &= x - 1 \\ 81 &= x - 1 \\ 82 &= x \end{aligned}$$

Estimation can be helpful in checking the reasonableness of answers in **Example 4.** We know that $\log_7 1 = 0$, $\log_7 7 = 1$ and $\log_7 49 = 2$. So, *estimates* of the answers are:

4a slightly greater than 1
4b between 0 and 1
4c slightly less than 2

Encourage students to check actual answers as follows:
For **Example 4a,** $\log_7 10 = 1.1833$.
Therefore, $7^{1.1833}$ should equal 10.

$$7^{1.1833} \approx 10.0001 \checkmark$$

For **Example 4b,** $\log_7 2.5 = 0.4709$.
Therefore, $7^{0.4709}$ should equal 2.5.

$$7^{0.4709} \approx 2.5001 \checkmark$$

For **Example 4c,** $\log_7 48 = 1.9894$.
Therefore, $7^{1.9894}$ should equal 48.

$$7^{1.9894} \approx 47.9996 \checkmark$$

Solution

a. If $\log_5 x = 3$, then $5^3 = x$. Therefore, $x = 125$.

b. If $\log_6 1 = x$, then $6^x = 1$. Therefore, $x = 0$.

c. If $\log_{\frac{1}{6}}(-3) = x$, then $\left(\frac{1}{6}\right)^x = -3$. Because no real power of $\frac{1}{6}$ is a negative number, $\log_{\frac{1}{6}}(-3) = x$ has no real solution.

d. If $\log_6 6 = x$, then $6^x = 6$. Therefore, $x = 1$.

Basic Properties of Logarithms to Other Bases

Logarithms are only defined for positive real numbers. That is,

$$\log_b v \text{ is defined only when } v > 0.$$

The graph of $y = \log_b x$ contains the point $(1, 0)$ because $b^0 = 1$ for any $b > 0$. That is,

$$\log_b 1 = 0$$

The value of $\log_5 5^4$ can be found by writing an equivalent exponential statement.

$$\text{If } \log_5 5^4 = x, \text{ then } 5^x = 5^4. \text{ So } x = 4.$$

In general,

$$\log_b b^k = k \quad \text{for every real number } k.$$

By definition, $\log_3 104$ is the exponent to which 3 must be raised to produce 104. Therefore,

$$3^{\log_3 104} = 104.$$

In general,

$$b^{\log_b v} = v \text{ for every } v > 0.$$

The facts presented above are summarized in the table below.

Basic Properties of Logarithms

For $b > 0$ and $b \neq 1$,

1. $\log_b v$ is defined only when $v > 0$
2. $\log_b 1 = 0$ and $\log_b b = 1$
3. $\log_b b^k = k$ for every real number k
4. $b^{\log_b v} = v$ for every $v > 0$

Properties 3 and 4 are restatements of the fact that the composition of inverse functions produces the identity function.

If $f(x) = b^x$ and $g(x) = \log_b x$, then

$$(f \circ g)(x) = f(\log_b x) = b^{\log_b x} = x \text{ for all } x > 0$$
$$(g \circ f)(x) = g(b^x) = \log_b b^x = x \text{ for all } x$$

Equations that involve both logarithmic and constant terms may be solved by using basic properties of logarithms.

$$b^{\log_b v} = v \text{ for } b > 0 \text{ and } b \neq 1$$

Example 3 Solving Logarithmic Equations

Solve the equation $\log_3(x - 1) = 4$.

Solution

$$\log_3(x - 1) = 4$$
$$3^{\log_3 (x-1)} = 3^4 \qquad \textit{exponentiate both sides}$$
$$x - 1 = 3^4 \qquad b^{\log_b v} = v$$
$$x = 82$$

Laws of Logarithms to Other Bases

Because all logarithms are a form of exponents, the laws of exponents translate to the corresponding laws of logarithms to any base.

Laws of Logarithms

For all b, v, w, and k, with b, v, and w positive and $b \neq 1$:

Product Law: $\log_b(vw) = \log_b v + \log_b w$

Quotient Law: $\log_b\left(\dfrac{v}{w}\right) = \log_b v - \log_b w$

Power Law: $\log_b(v^k) = k \log_b v$

Example 4 Using the Laws of Logarithms

Use the Laws of Logarithms to evaluate each expression, given that $\log_7 2 = 0.3562$, $\log_7 3 = 0.5646$, and $\log_7 5 = 0.8271$.

a. $\log_7 10$ **b.** $\log_7 2.5$ **c.** $\log_7 48$

Solution

a. Use the Product Law.

$\log_7 10 = \log_7(2 \cdot 5) = \log_7 2 + \log_7 5 = 0.3562 + 0.8271 = 1.1833$

Example 2

Solve each equation for x.

a. $\log_6 x = 2$ $x = 36$

b. $\log_4 1 = x$ $x = 0$

c. $\log_{\frac{1}{5}}(-10) = x$ no real solution

d. $\log_7 7 = x$ $x = 1$

Example 3

Solve the equation $\log_5(x + 2) = 2$.

$$\log_5(x + 2) = 2$$
$$5^{\log_5 (x+2)} = 5^2$$
$$x + 2 = 25$$
$$x = 23$$

Example 4

Use the Laws of Logarithms to evaluate each expression, given that $\log_5 3 = 0.6826$, $\log_5 4 = 0.8614$, and $\log_5 6 = 1.1133$.

a. $\log_5 18$

$$\log_5 18 = \log_5(3 \cdot 6)$$
$$= \log_5 3 + \log_5 6$$
$$= 0.6826 + 1.1133$$
$$= 1.7959$$

b. $\log_5 0.75$

$$\log_5 0.75 = \log_5\left(\frac{3}{4}\right)$$
$$= \log_5 3 - \log_5 4$$
$$= 0.6826 - 0.8614$$
$$= -0.1788$$

c. $\log_5 54$

$$\log_5 54 = \log_5(6 \cdot 3^2)$$
$$= \log_5 6 + \log_5 3^2$$
$$= \log_5 6 + 2 \log_5 3$$
$$= 1.1133 + 2(0.6826)$$
$$= 2.4785$$

Teaching Notes

Since calculators only have common and natural logarithms, students need to use the **Change-of-Base Formula** to evaluate logarithms to other bases with the calculator.

 Math Background

The following alternate proof of the **Change-of-Base Formula** uses the same concept as the proof in the text, but slightly different notation:

Let $\log_b v = w$.

Then:
$$b^w = v$$
$$\log b^w = \log v$$
$$w \log b = \log v$$
$$w = \frac{\log v}{\log b}$$

Therefore, $\log_b v = \dfrac{\log v}{\log b}$.

ADDITIONAL EXAMPLES

Example 5

Simplify and write each expression as a single logarithm.

a. $\log_8(x + 5) + \log_8 z - \log_8(x^2 + 10x + 25)$

$\log_8 \dfrac{z}{x + 5}$

b. $2 + \log_3\left(\dfrac{x}{9}\right)$ $\log_3 x$

Example 6

Evaluate $\log_5 7$.   1.2091

COMMON ERROR ALERT

Students may mistakenly use the reciprocal in the **Change-of-Base Formula.** To help students remember the Change-of-Base Formula, note the locations of the variables. In both $\log_b v$ and $\dfrac{\log v}{\log b}$, b is the "lower" variable and v is the "upper" variable.

They can also check the reasonableness of their result. In **Example 6,** $\log_8 9$ must be greater than 1 because $8^1 = 8$. If a student mistakenly uses $\dfrac{\log 8}{\log 9}$, the result will be less than 1.

---

b. Use the Quotient Law.

$$\log_7 2.5 = \log_7\left(\frac{5}{2}\right) = \log_7 5 - \log_7 2 = 0.8271 - 0.3562 = 0.4709$$

c. Use the Product and Power Laws.

$$\log_7 48 = \log_7(3 \cdot 2^4)$$
$$= \log_7 3 + \log_7 2^4$$
$$= \log_7 3 + 4 \log_7 2$$
$$= 0.5646 + 4(0.3562)$$
$$= 1.9894$$

Example 5   **Using the Laws of Logarithms**

Simplify and write each expression as a single logarithm.

a. $\log_3(x + 2) + \log_3 y - \log_3(x^2 - 4)$

b. $3 - \log_5(125x)$

Solution

a. $\log_3(x + 2) + \log_3 y - \log_3(x^2 - 4) = \log_3[(x + 2)y] - \log_3(x^2 - 4)$

$$= \log_3\left[\frac{(x + 2)y}{x^2 - 4}\right]$$
$$= \log_3\left[\frac{(x + 2)y}{(x + 2)(x - 2)}\right]$$
$$= \log_3 \frac{y}{x - 2}$$

b. $3 - \log_5(125x) = 3 - (\log_5 125 + \log_5 x)$
$$= 3 - 3 - \log_5 x$$
$$= -\log_5 x$$

NOTE $-\log_5 x$ can also be expressed as $\log_5 x^{-1}$ or $\log_5\left(\dfrac{1}{x}\right)$.

Change-of-Base Formula

Scientific and graphing calculators have a **LOG** key and a **LN** key for calculating logarithms. No calculators have a key for logarithms to other bases. One way to evaluate logarithms to other bases is to use the formula below.

Change-of-Base Formula

For any positive number v,

$$\log_b v = \frac{\log v}{\log b} \quad \text{and} \quad \log_b v = \frac{\ln v}{\ln b}$$

Teaching Notes

Students will better understand **Graphing Logarithmic Functions to Other Bases** after some paper-and-pencil graphing. Although all logarithmic functions with base $b > 1$ have the basic shape shown in Figure 5.5A-3, they vary in "steepness." To help students understand this, have them graph $y = \log_2 x$ and $y = \log_3 x$ as follows:

Proof By Property 4 of the Basic Properties of Logarithms $b^{\log_b v} = v$.

$$b^{\log_b v} = v$$
$$\ln(b^{\log_b v}) = \ln v \qquad \text{\textit{take logarithms of both sides}}$$
$$\log_b v(\ln b) = \ln v \qquad \text{\textit{apply the Power Law}}$$
$$\log_b v = \frac{\ln v}{\ln b}$$

A similar argument can be made by taking common logarithms of both sides.

First, have them copy and complete the table below:

y	-2	-1	0	1
2^y	$\frac{1}{4}$	$\frac{1}{2}$	1	2
3^y	$\frac{1}{9}$	$\frac{1}{3}$	1	3

Example 6   Evaluating Logarithms to Other Bases

Evaluate $\log_8 9$.

Figure 5.5A-2

Solution

Use the change-of-base formula and a calculator.

$$\log_8 9 = \frac{\log 9}{\log 8} = 1.0566 \qquad \text{or} \qquad \log_8 9 = \frac{\ln 9}{\ln 8} = 1.0566$$

Next, have them use the values from above to copy and complete the following tables:

x	$\frac{1}{4}$	$\frac{1}{2}$	1	2
$y = \log_2 x$	-2	-1	0	1

x	$\frac{1}{9}$	$\frac{1}{3}$	1	3
$y = \log_3 x$	-2	-1	0	1

Graphing Logarithmic Functions to Other Bases

The graph of a logarithmic function to any base b shares characteristics with the graphs of natural logarithms and common logarithms. The following table compares the graphs of exponential and logarithmic functions for base b, where b is any real number, $b > 0$, and $b \neq 1$.

Finally, have them graph $y = \log_2 x$ and $y = \log_3 x$ on the same coordinate system:

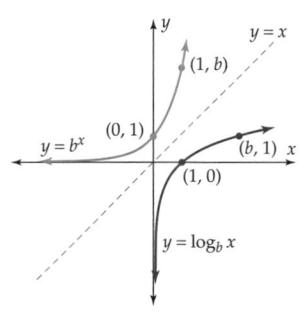

Figure 5.5A-3

	Exponential function $f(x) = b^x$	**Logarithmic function** $g(x) = \log_b x$
Domain	all real numbers	all positive real numbers
Range	all positive real numbers	all real numbers
	$f(x)$ increases as x increses	$g(x)$ increases as x increases
	$f(x)$ approaches the x-axis as x decreases	$g(x)$ approaches the y-axis as x approaches 0
Reference points	$\left(-1, \frac{1}{b}\right)$, $(0, 1)$, $(1, b)$	$\left(\frac{1}{b}, -1\right)$, $(1, 0)$, $(b, 1)$

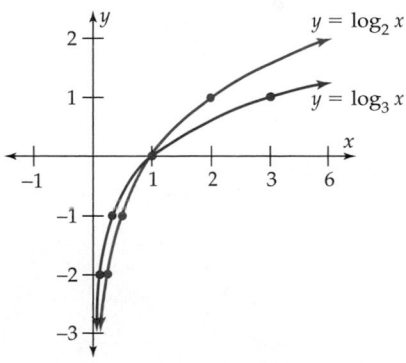

Example 7   Transforming Logarithmic Functions

Describe the transformation from $g(x) = \log_2 x$ to $h(x) = \log_2(x + 1) - 3$. Give the domain and range of h.

Notice that both graphs have the same basic shape, but the graph corresponding to the larger base stays closer to the x-axis everywhere except at $(1, 0)$.

ADDITIONAL EXAMPLES

Example 7

Describe the transformation from $g(x) = \log_3 x$ to $h(x) = \log_3 (x - 4) + 1$. Give the domain and range of h.

The graph of $h(x)$ is the graph of $g(x)$ after a horizontal translation of 4 units to the right and a vertical translation of 1 unit up.

Domain of h: all real numbers greater than 4

Range of h: all real numbers

Exercises 5.5.A

ANSWERS

1. $\log 0.01 = -2$

2. $\log 1000 = 3$

3. $\log \sqrt[3]{10} = \dfrac{1}{3}$

4. $\log 3 \approx 0.4771$

5. $\log r = 7k$

6. $\log c = a + b$

7. $\log_7 5{,}764{,}801 = 8$

8. $\log_2\left(\dfrac{1}{8}\right) = -3$

9. $\log_3\left(\dfrac{1}{9}\right) = -2$

10. $\log_b 3379 = 14$

Solution

Because $h(x) = g(x + 1) - 3$, its graph is the graph of $g(x) = \log_2 x$ after a horizontal translation of 1 unit to the left and a vertical translation of 3 units down.

Domain of h: The domain of $g(x) = \log_2 x$ is all positive real numbers. The horizontal translation of 1 unit to the left changes the domain to all real numbers greater than -1.

Range of h: The range of $g(x) = \log_2 x$ is all real numbers, so the vertical translation has no effect on the range.

The points $\left(\dfrac{1}{2}, -1\right)$, $(1, 0)$, and $(2, 1)$ on the graph of g are translated to the points $\left(-\dfrac{1}{2}, -4\right)$, $(0, -3)$, and $(1, -2)$ on the graph of h. To graph these functions with a calculator, graph $Y_1 = \dfrac{\ln x}{\ln 2}$ for $g(x) = \log_2 x$ and $Y_2 = \dfrac{\ln(x + 1)}{\ln 2} - 3$ for $h(x) = \log_2(x + 1) - 3$. The graphs of g and h are shown in Figure 5.5A-4. ∎

Figure 5.5A-4

Exercises 5.5.A

Note: Unless stated otherwise, all letters represent positive numbers and $b \neq 1$.

In Exercises 1–10, translate the given exponential statement into an equivalent logarithmic statement.

1. $10^{-2} = 0.01$ 2. $10^3 = 1000$ 3. $\sqrt[3]{10} = 10^{\frac{1}{3}}$

4. $10^{0.4771} \approx 3$ 5. $10^{7k} = r$ 6. $10^{(a+b)} = c$

7. $7^8 = 5{,}764{,}801$ 8. $2^{-3} = \dfrac{1}{8}$

9. $3^{-2} = \dfrac{1}{9}$ 10. $b^{14} = 3379$

In Exercises 11–20, translate the given logarithmic statement into an equivalent exponential statement.

11. $\log 10{,}000 = 4$
    $10^4 = 10{,}000$

12. $\log 0.001 = -3$
    $10^{-3} = 0.001$

13. $\log 750 = 2.8751$
    $10^{2.8751} \approx 750$

14. $\log 0.8 = -0.0969$
    $10^{-0.0969} \approx 0.8$

15. $\log_5 125 = 3$
    $5^3 = 125$

16. $\log_8\left(\dfrac{1}{4}\right) = -\dfrac{2}{3}$
    $8^{-\frac{2}{3}} = \dfrac{1}{4}$

17. $\log_2\left(\dfrac{1}{4}\right) = -2$
    $2^{-2} = \dfrac{1}{4}$

18. $\log_2 \sqrt{2} = \dfrac{1}{2}$
    $2^{\frac{1}{2}} = \sqrt{2}$

19. $\log(x^2 + 2y) = z + w$
    $10^{z+w} = x^2 + 2y$

20. $\log(a + c) = d$
    $10^d = a + c$

In Exercises 21–28, evaluate the given expression without using a calculator.

21. $\log 10^{\sqrt{43}}$
    $\sqrt{43}$

22. $\log_{17}(17^{17})$
    17

23. $\log 10^{\sqrt{x^2+y^2}}$
    $\sqrt{x^2 + y^2}$

24. $\log_{3.5}(3.5^{(x^2-1)})$
    $x^2 - 1$

25. $\log_{16} 4 \quad \dfrac{1}{2}$

26. $\log_2 64$
    6

27. $\log_{\sqrt{3}}(27)$
    6

28. $\log_{\sqrt{3}}\left(\dfrac{1}{9}\right)$
    -4

In Exercises 29–36, find the missing entries in each table.

29.

x	0	1	2	4
$f(x) = \log_4 x$	Not defined	0	0.5	1

30.

x	$\dfrac{1}{25}$	5	25	$\sqrt{5}$
$g(x) = \log_5 x$	**−2**	**1**	**2**	$\dfrac{1}{2}$

31.

x	?	$\dfrac{1}{6}$	1	216
$h(x) = \log_6 x$	**−2**	**−1**	**0**	**3**

32.

x	$\dfrac{10}{3}$	4	6	12
$k(x) = \log_3 (x - 3)$	**−1**	**0**	**1**	**2**

33.

x	0	$\dfrac{1}{7}$	$\sqrt{7}$	49
$f(x) = 2\log_7 x$	**Not defined**	**−2**	**1**	**4**

34.

x	?	?	100	1000
$g(x) = 3\log x$	**6**	**3**	**6**	**9**

35.

x	−2.75	−1	1	29
$h(x) = 3\log_2 (x + 3)$	**−6**	**3**	**6**	**15**

36.

x	$\dfrac{1}{e}$	1	e	e^2
$k(x) = 2\ln x$	**−2**	**0**	**2**	**4**

In Exercises 37–40, a graph or a table of values is given for the function $f(x) = \log_b x$. Find b.

37.

$b = 3$

38.

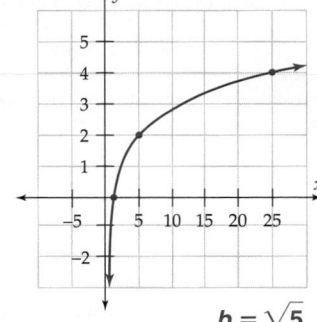

$b = \sqrt{5}$

39.

x	0.05	1	400	$2\sqrt{5}$
$f(x)$	−1	0	2	$\dfrac{1}{2}$

$b = 20$

40.

x	$\dfrac{1}{25}$	1	5	125
$f(x)$	−4	0	2	6

$b = \sqrt{5}$

In Exercises 41–46, solve each equation for x.

41. $\log_3 243 = x$ **5**

42. $\log_{81} 27 = x$ $\dfrac{3}{4}$

43. $\log_{27} x = \dfrac{1}{3}$ **3**

44. $\log_5 x = -4$ $\dfrac{1}{625}$

45. $\log_x 64 = 3$ **4**

46. $\log_x \left(\dfrac{1}{9}\right) = -\dfrac{2}{3}$ **27**

In Exercises 47–60, write the given expression as the logarithm of a single quantity. (See Example 5.)

47. $2\log x + 3\log y - 6\log z$ $\log\dfrac{x^2 y^3}{z^6}$

48. $5\log_8 x - 3\log_8 y + 2\log_8 z$

49. $\log x - \log(x + 3) + \log(x^2 - 9)$ $\log(x^2 - 3x)$

50. $\log_3 (y + 2) + \log_3 (y - 3) - \log_3 y$

51. $\dfrac{1}{2}\log_2 (25c^2)$ $\log_2 (5c)$

52. $\dfrac{1}{3}\log_2 (27b^6)$ $\log_2 (3b^2)$

53. $-2\log_4 (7c)$

54. $\dfrac{1}{3}\log_5 (x + 1)$

55. $2\ln(x + 1) - \ln(x + 2)$ $\ln\left(\dfrac{(x + 1)^2}{x + 2}\right)$

56. $\ln(z - 3) + 2\ln(z + 3)$ $\ln((z - 3)(z + 3)^2)$

48. $\log_8 \left(\dfrac{x^5 z^2}{y^3}\right)$

50. $\log_3 \left(\dfrac{(y + 2)(y - 3)}{y}\right)$

53. $\log_4 \left(\dfrac{1}{49c^2}\right)$

54. $\log_5 \sqrt[3]{x + 1}$

69. Horizontal shift of $\frac{4}{3}$ units to the right, then compress horizontally by a factor of $\frac{1}{3}$.
Domain: all real numbers $> \frac{4}{3}$
Range: all real numbers

70. Reflect across the x-axis, then a vertical stretch by a factor of 2, then a horizontal shift of 5 units to the left.
Domain: all real numbers > -5
Range: all real numbers

71. Compress the graph vertically by a factor of $\frac{1}{3}$, then a horizontal shift of 1 unit to the right, then a vertical shift of 7 units upward.
Domain: all real numbers > 1
Range: all real numbers

72. Stretch vertically by a factor of 3, then compress horizontally by a factor of $\frac{1}{2}$, then reflect across the y-axis.
Domain: all real numbers < 0
Range: all real numbers

82. $\log_b a = \dfrac{\ln a}{\ln b} = \dfrac{1}{\frac{\ln b}{\ln a}} = \dfrac{1}{\log_a b}$

84. Let $y = a^{\log b}$.
Then $\log y = \log\left(a^{\log b}\right)$
$= (\log b)(\log a)$
$= (\log a)(\log b)$
$= \log\left(b^{\log a}\right)$.
Therefore, $y = b^{\log a}$
and $a^{\log b} = b^{\log a}$.

85. $\log_b x = \frac{1}{2}\log_b v + 3$
$= \log_b \sqrt{v} + \log_b b^3$
$= \log_b\left(b^3 \cdot \sqrt{v}\right)$
hence $x = b^3\sqrt{v}$

86. $f(x) = g(x)$ only when $x = \frac{7}{6}$, so the statement is false.

87. $f(x) = g(x)$ only when $x \approx 0.123$, so the statement is false.

88. The y-axis is a vertical asymptote.

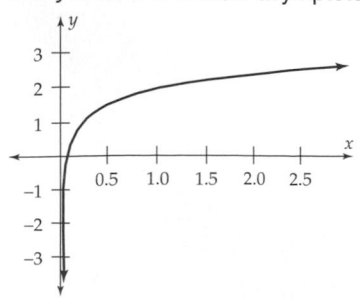

---

57. $\log_2(2x) - 1$ $\mathbf{\log_2(x)}$ **58.** $2 - \log_5(25z)$ $\mathbf{\log_5(z^{-1})}$

59. $2\ln(e^2 - e) - 2$ **60.** $4 - 4\log_5(20)$ $\mathbf{\log_5\left(\dfrac{1}{256}\right)}$
$\mathbf{\ln(e^2 - 2e + 1)}$

In Exercises 61–68, use a calculator and the change-of-base formula to evaluate the logarithm.

61. $\log_2 10$ **62.** $\log_2 22$ **63.** $\log_7 5$
≈ 3.3219 ≈ 4.4594 ≈ 0.8271
64. $\log_5 7$ **65.** $\log_{500} 1000$ **66.** $\log_{500} 250$
≈ 1.2091 ≈ 1.1115 ≈ 0.8885
67. $\log_{12} 56$ **68.** $\log_{12} 725$
≈ 1.6199 ≈ 2.6505

In Exercises 69–72, describe the transformation from f to g, and give the domain and range of g.

69. $f(x) = \log_5 x$ and $g(x) = \log_5(3x - 4)$

70. $f(x) = \log_7 x$ and $g(x) = -2 \cdot \log_7(x + 5)$

71. $f(x) = \log_2 x$ and $g(x) = \frac{1}{3} \cdot \log_2(x - 1) + 7$

72. $f(x) = \log_4 x$ and $g(x) = 3\log_4(-2x)$

In Exercises 73–78, answer true or false. Explain your answer.

73. $\log_b\left(\dfrac{r}{5}\right) = \log_b r - \log_b 5$ **True**

74. $\dfrac{\log_b a}{\log_b c} = \log_b\left(\dfrac{a}{c}\right)$ **False**

75. $\dfrac{\log_b r}{t} = \log_b\left(r^{\frac{1}{t}}\right)$ **True**

76. $\log_b(cd) = \log_b c + \log_b d$ **True**

77. $\log_5(5x) = 5(\log_5 x)$ **False**

78. $\log_b(ab)^t = t(\log_b a) + t$ **True**

79. Which is larger: 397^{398} or 398^{397}? *Hint:* $\log 397 \approx 2.5988$ and $\log 398 \approx 2.5999$ and $f(x) = 10^x$ is an increasing function.
$\mathbf{397^{398}}$

89.

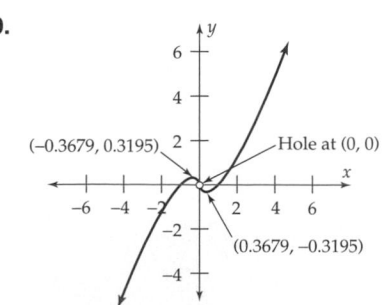

$(-0.3679, 0.3195)$ Hole at $(0, 0)$
$(0.3679, -0.3195)$

---

80. If $\log_b 9.21 = 7.4$ and $\log_b 359.62 = 19.61$, then what is $\dfrac{\log_b 359.62}{\log_b 9.21}$?
2.65

In Exercises 81–84, assume that a and b are positive, with $a \neq 1$ and $b \neq 1$.

81. Express $\log_b u$ in terms of logarithms to the base a.
$$\log_b u = \frac{\log_a u}{\log_a b}$$

82. Show that $\log_b a = \dfrac{1}{\log_a b}$.

83. How are $\log u$ and $\log_{100} u$ related?
$\mathbf{\log_{10} u = 2\log_{100} u}$

84. Show that $a^{\log b} = b^{\log a}$.

85. If $\log_b x = \frac{1}{2}\log_b v + 3$, show that $x = (b^3)\sqrt{v}$.

86. Graph the functions $f(x) = \log x + \log 7$ and $g(x) = \log(x + 7)$ on the same screen. For what values of x is it true that $f(x) = g(x)$? What do you conclude about the statement $\log 6 + \log 7 = \log(6 + 7)$?

87. Graph the functions $f(x) = \log\left(\dfrac{x}{4}\right)$ and $g(x) = \dfrac{\log x}{\log 4}$. Are they the same? What does this say about a statement such as $\log\left(\dfrac{48}{4}\right) = \dfrac{\log 48}{\log 4}$?

In Exercises 88–90, sketch a complete graph of the function, labeling any holes, asymptotes, or local extrema.

88. $f(x) = \log_5 x + 2$

89. $h(x) = x\log x^2$

90. $g(x) = \log_{20} x^2$

90. The y-axis is a vertical asymptote.

5.6 Solving Exponential and Logarithmic Equations

Objectives

• Solve exponential and logarithmic equations

• Solve a variety of application problems by using exponential and logarithmic equations

Exponential and logarithmic equations have been solved in this chapter so far by using the graphing method or by writing equivalent statements that can be easily solved. Most of them could also have been solved algebraically by using the techniques presented in this section, which depend primarily on the properties and laws of logarithms.

By definition of a function, if $u = v$ and f is a function, then $f(u) = f(v)$. This results in two statements.

> **If $u = v$, then $b^u = b^v$ for all real numbers $b > 0$.**
> **If $u = v$, then $\log_b u = \log_b v$ for all real numbers $b > 0$.**

Because exponential and logarithmic functions are one-to-one functions, the converse is also true.

> **If $b^u = b^v$, then $u = v$.**
> **If $\log_b u = \log_b v$, then $u = v$.**

Exponential Equations

The easiest exponential equations to solve are those in which both sides are powers of the same base.

> **Example 1**   Powers of the Same Base

Solve the equation $8^x = 2^{x+1}$. Confirm your solution with a graph.

Solution

Write the equation so that each side is a power of the same base.

$$8^x = 2^{x+1}$$
$$(2^3)^x = 2^{x+1}$$
$$2^{3x} = 2^{x+1}$$
$$3x = x + 1 \qquad \text{\small If } b^u = b^v, \text{ then } u = v.$$
$$2x = 1$$
$$x = \frac{1}{2}$$

Figure 5.6-1

To find a window for the graphs of $Y_1 = 8^x$ and $Y_2 = 2^{x+1}$, consider the basic shapes of the graphs and any transformations. Because both bases of these exponential functions are greater than 1, the graphs are increasing. Because there is no vertical shift on either function, both graphs are asymptotic to the x-axis. The intersection of the graphs of $Y_1 = 8^x$ and $Y_2 = 2^{x+1}$, shown at the left, confirms the solution. ∎

Example Notes

In **Example 2,** remind students that they can check their answer: $5^{0.4307} \approx 2.00008$

In **Example 4,** students must recognize that $e^{2x} = (e^x)^2$ so that they can identify the equation as a quadratic.

In **Example 5,** make sure students understand that if 58% is *lost,* 42% *remains.*

Students might evaluate $\frac{\ln 3 + \ln 2}{4 \ln 2 + \ln 3}$ incorrectly in **Example 3.**

- They might enter parentheses into their calculator incorrectly. Suggest that they evaluate the numerator and denominator separately before dividing.

- Other students might simplify the numerator, $\ln 3 + \ln 2$, as $\ln 5$. Remind them that $\ln 3 + \ln 2 = \ln 6$.

In **Example 4,** some students may incorrectly write $e^x e^x = e^{x^2}$. Remind them of the **Laws of Exponents** (page 330):

$e^x e^x = e^{x+x} = e^{2x}$, or $e^x e^x = (e^x)^2$

Teaching Notes

In **Example 5,** to help students understand why the function $M(t) = P(0.5)^{\frac{t}{5730}}$ gives the amount of carbon-14 remaining at time t, substitute 5730 for t: $M(5730) = P(0.5)^{\frac{5730}{5730}} = P(0.5)$. This function value confirms that if $t = 5730$ years, then half of the original amount, or $0.5P$, remains.

Math Background

In **Example 4,** an extraneous solution is introduced as a result of multiplying both sides of the equation by e^x. Multiplying both sides of an equation by a variable expression sometimes introduces extraneous solutions. In the example at right, the extraneous solution 0 is introduced:

> [!CAUTION]
> **CAUTION**
>
> $\dfrac{\ln 2}{\ln 5} \neq \ln\left(\dfrac{2}{5}\right)$ and
>
> $\dfrac{\ln 2}{\ln 5} \neq \ln 2 - \ln 5$

Figure 5.6-2

Figure 5.6-3

Example 2 **Powers of Different Bases**

Solve the equation $5^x = 2$. Confirm your solution with a graph.

Solution

$$5^x = 2$$
$$\ln 5^x = \ln 2 \qquad \textit{take logarithms on each side}$$
$$x \ln 5 = \ln 2 \qquad \textit{use the Power Law}$$
$$x = \frac{\ln 2}{\ln 5}$$
$$x = \frac{0.6931}{1.6094} = 0.4307$$

The intersection of the graphs of $Y_1 = 5^x$ and $Y_2 = 2$, shown at the left, confirms the solution.

Example 3 **Powers of Different Bases**

Solve the equation $2^{4x-1} = 3^{1-x}$. Confirm your solution with a graph.

Solution

$$2^{4x-1} = 3^{1-x}$$
$$\ln(2^{4x-1}) = \ln(3^{1-x}) \qquad \textit{Take logarithms on each side}$$
$$(4x - 1)\ln 2 = (1 - x)\ln 3 \qquad \textit{Power Law}$$
$$4x \ln 2 - \ln 2 = \ln 3 - x \ln 3 \qquad \textit{Distributive Property}$$
$$4x \ln 2 + x \ln 3 = \ln 3 + \ln 2 \qquad \textit{Rearrange terms and isolate } x$$
$$x(4 \ln 2 + \ln 3) = \ln 3 + \ln 2$$
$$x = \frac{\ln 3 + \ln 2}{4 \ln 2 + \ln 3}$$
$$x = 0.4628$$

The intersection of the graphs of $Y_1 = 2^{4x-1}$ and $Y_2 = 3^{1-x}$, shown at the left, confirms the solution.

When you multiply each side of an equation by the same expression, extraneous solutions may be introduced, as shown in Example 4.

Example 4 **Using Substitution**

Solve the equation $e^x - e^{-x} = 4$. Confirm your solution with a graph.

$$x = 3 \qquad \text{The only solution is 3.}$$
$$x \cdot x = 3 \cdot x \qquad \text{Multiply by } x.$$
$$x^2 = 3x$$
$$x^2 - 3x = 0 \qquad \text{The solutions are 3 and 0.}$$

Solution

First multiply each side by e^x to eliminate negative exponents.

$$e^x - e^{-x} = 4$$
$$e^x(e^x - e^{-x}) = e^x(4)$$
$$e^x e^x - e^x e^{-x} = 4e^x$$
$$e^{2x} - 1 = 4e^x \qquad \text{Product Law.}$$
$$e^{2x} - 4e^x - 1 = 0$$

Let $u = e^x$ and substitute.

$$u^2 - 4u - 1 = 0$$
$$u = \frac{-(-4) \pm \sqrt{(-4)^2 - 4(1)(-1)}}{2(1)}$$
$$u = \frac{4 \pm \sqrt{20}}{2}$$
$$u = \frac{4 \pm 2\sqrt{5}}{2}$$
$$u = 2 \pm \sqrt{5}$$

Replace u with e^x to get $e^x = 2 + \sqrt{5}$ or $e^x = 2 - \sqrt{5}$. Because e^x can only be positive and $2 - \sqrt{5}$ is negative, $e^x = 2 - \sqrt{5}$ has no solution.

$$e^x = 2 + \sqrt{5}$$
$$\ln e^x = \ln(2 + \sqrt{5})$$
$$x \cdot \ln e = \ln(2 + \sqrt{5})$$
$$x = 1.4436 \qquad \ln e = 1$$

The intersection of the graphs of $Y_1 = e^x - e^{-x}$ and $Y_2 = 4$, shown in Figure 5.6-4, confirms that there is exactly one solution ∎

Figure 5.6-4

Applications of Exponential Equations

When a living organism dies, its carbon-14 decays. The half-life of carbon-14 is 5730 years, so the amount of carbon-14 remaining at time t is given by $M(t) = P(0.5)^{\frac{t}{5730}}$, where P is the mass of carbon-14 that was present initially. The function M can be used to determine the age of fossils and some relics.

Example 5   Radiocarbon Dating

The skeleton of a mastodon has lost 58% of its original carbon-14. When did the mastodon die?

Solution

If the mastodon has lost 58% of its original carbon-14, then 42% of the initial amount, or $0.42P$, remains and $M(t) = 0.42P$. To determine when the mastodon died, solve $0.42P = P(0.5)^{\frac{t}{5730}}$ for t.

ADDITIONAL EXAMPLES

Example 2

Solve the equation $6^x = 3$. Confirm your solution with a graph.

$$6^x = 3$$
$$x \ln 6 = \ln 3$$
$$x = \frac{\ln 3}{\ln 6} = 0.6131$$

Example 3

Solve the equation $4^{2x-1} = 5^{1-x}$. Confirm your solution with a graph.

$$4^{2x-1} = 5^{1-x}$$
$$(2x - 1)\ln 4 = (1 - x)\ln 5$$
$$2x \ln 4 - \ln 4 = \ln 5 - x \ln 5$$
$$x(2\ln 4 + \ln 5) = \ln 4 + \ln 5$$
$$x = \frac{\ln 4 + \ln 5}{2\ln 4 + \ln 5}$$
$$= 0.6836$$

Example 4

Solve the equation $e^x - 5e^{-x} = -6$. Confirm your solution with a graph.

$$e^x - 5e^{-x} = -6$$
$$e^x(e^x - 5e^{-x}) = e^x(-6)$$
$$e^{2x} - 5 = -6e^x$$
$$(e^x)^2 + 6e^x - 5 = 0$$

Let $u = e^x$. $u^2 + 6u - 5 = 0$

$$u = \frac{-6 \pm \sqrt{(6)^2 - 4(1)(-5)}}{2(1)}$$
$$u = \frac{-6 \pm 2\sqrt{14}}{2}$$
$$u = -3 \pm \sqrt{14}$$

e^x must be positive, so $e^x = -3 + \sqrt{14}$.

$$x \ln e = \ln(-3 + \sqrt{14})$$
$$x = -0.2989$$

Real-World Application

A discussion of "inhibiting or stimulating factors" regarding population growth in **Example 7** can lay the foundation for the logistic model in **Example 8.** Some possible inhibiting factors in Example 7 are a limit on the food source or an introduction of an agent that kills some of the bacteria. A possible stimulating factor is an enrichment of the food source.

Example Notes

For **Example 6,** note that $\frac{10,680}{3000} = 3.56$ is exact, not rounded. Tell students that when they encounter a fraction that it is *not* exact, they should continue to use the fraction as they calculate, rounding only the final result. Rounding later increases accuracy.

Note that the function in **Example 7,** $S(t) = Pe^{rt}$, is a function of t, but also contains the variable r. So, to write the required function in **part a,** students must first find r. Point out that Figure 5.6-7 confirms the value of r, and Figure 5.6-8 confirms the value of t, which is the solution.

ADDITIONAL EXAMPLES

Example 5

It is determined that a mummy has lost 32% of its original carbon-14. When did the person die?

$$0.68 = (0.5)^{\frac{t}{5730}}$$

$$\ln 0.68 = \frac{t}{5730}(\ln 0.5)$$

$$t = \frac{5730(\ln 0.68)}{\ln 0.5} = 3188.1339$$

The person died approximately 3200 years ago.

Figure 5.6-5

1

0   **Intersection** X=7171.3171 Y=.42   10,000
0

Figure 5.6-5

14,000

0   **Intersection** X=64.120812 Y=10680   100
0

Figure 5.6-6

$$0.42P = P(0.5)^{\frac{t}{5730}}$$

$$0.42 = (0.5)^{\frac{t}{5730}}$$

$$\ln 0.42 = \ln(0.5)^{\frac{t}{5730}}$$

$$\ln 0.42 = \frac{t}{5730}(\ln 0.5)$$

$$t = \frac{5730(\ln 0.42)}{\ln 0.5}$$

$$t = 7171.3171$$

Therefore, the mastodon died approximately 7200 years ago. The intersection of the graphs of $Y_1 = 0.42$ and $Y_2 = (0.5)^{\frac{x}{5730}}$, shown in Figure 5.6-5, confirms the solution. ∎

Example 6   Compound Interest

If $3000 is to be invested at 8% per year, compounded quarterly, in how many years will the investment be worth $10,680?

Solution

The interest rate per quarter r is $\frac{0.08}{4}$, or 0.02. To find the time t that it will take the investment to be worth $10,680 use the compound interest formula $A = P(1 + r)^t$.

$$10,680 = 3000(1 + 0.02)^t$$

$$10,680 = 3000(1.02)^t$$

$$3.56 = (1.02)^t$$

$$\ln 3.56 = \ln(1.02)^t$$

$$\ln 3.56 = t(\ln 1.02)$$

$$t = \frac{\ln 3.56}{\ln 1.02} = 64.1208 \text{ quarters}$$

Therefore, it will take 64.12 quarters, or $\frac{64.12}{4} = 16.03$ years. The intersection of the graphs of $Y_1 = 10,680$ and $Y_2 = 3000(1 + 0.02)^x$, shown in Figure 5.6-6, confirms the solution. ∎

Example 7   Population Growth

A biologist knows that if there are no inhibiting or stimulating factors, the population of a certain type of bacteria will increase exponentially. The population at time t is given by the function

$$S(t) = Pe^{rt},$$

where P is the initial population and r is the continuous growth rate. The biologist has a culture that contains 1000 bacteria, and 7 hours later there are 5000 bacteria.

a. Write the function for this population.

b. When will the population reach 1 billion?

Solution

a. The initial population P is 1000. To find the growth rate r, use the fact that $S(7) = 5000$.

$$S(t) = 1000e^{rt}$$
$$5000 = 1000e^{r(7)}$$
$$5 = e^{7r}$$
$$\ln 5 = \ln e^{7r}$$
$$\ln 5 = 7r \ln e$$
$$\ln 5 = 7r \qquad \ln e = 1$$
$$r = \frac{\ln 5}{7} = 0.2299$$

Therefore, the function for this population is

$$S(t) = 1000e^{0.2299t}$$

The intersection of the graphs of $Y_1 = 5000$ and $Y_2 = 1000e^{7x}$, shown in Figure 5.6-7, confirms the value of r.

b. Find the value of t when $S(t)$ is 1 billion.

$$1000e^{0.2299t} = 1,000,000,000$$
$$e^{0.2299t} = 1,000,000$$
$$\ln e^{0.2299t} = \ln 1,000,000$$
$$0.2299t \ln e = \ln 1,000,000$$
$$0.2299t = \ln 1,000,000 \qquad \ln e = 1$$
$$t = \frac{\ln 1,000,000}{0.2299} = 60.0936 \text{ hours}$$

The bacteria population will reach 1 billion after about 60 hours. The intersection of the graphs of $Y_1 = 1000e^{0.2299x}$ and $Y_2 = 1,000,000,000$, shown in Figure 5.6-8, confirms the solution. ∎

6,000

Figure 5.6-7

1.5×10^9

Figure 5.6-8

Example 8   **Inhibited Population Growth**

A population of fish in a lake at time t months is given by the function F.

$$F(t) = \frac{20,000}{1 + 24e^{-\frac{t}{4}}}$$

How long will it take for the fish population to reach 15,000?

ADDITIONAL EXAMPLES

Example 6

If $8000 is to be invested at 6% per year, compounded monthly, in how many years will the investment be worth $22,520?

$$22{,}520 = 8000(1 + 0.005)^t$$
$$2.815 = 1.005^t$$
$$\ln 2.815 = t \ln 1.005$$
$$t = \frac{\ln 2.815}{\ln 1.005} = 207.5095 \text{ months}$$

17.29 years

Example 7

The population of a certain species of rabbit increases exponentially according to the function $S(t) = Pe^{rt}$, where P is the initial population and r is the continuous growth rate. At the beginning of a 12-month study, there were 50 rabbits, and at the end of the study there were 164 rabbits.

a. Write the function for this population.

$$164 = 50e^{r(12)}$$
$$3.28 = e^{12r}$$
$$\ln 3.28 = 12r \ln e$$
$$r = \frac{\ln 3.28}{12} = 0.990$$

So, $S(t) = 50e^{0.099t}$.

b. When will the population reach 1000?

$$1000 = 50e^{0.099t}$$
$$20 = e^{0.099t}$$
$$\ln 20 = 0.099t \ln e$$
$$t = \frac{\ln 20}{0.099} = 30.2599$$

about 30 months

Example Notes

Figure 5.6-9 shows that the function in **Example 8** is a logistic model. Rather than increasing exponentially, the growth levels off. Students might recall from Section 5.2 (pages 341–342) that a logistic model is designed for situations in which future growth is limited due to a fixed area, food supply, or other factors.

When discussing **Example 9**, remind students that the following property is true because logarithmic functions are one-to-one:

If $\log_b u = \log_b v$, then $u = v$.

This property justifies the following step:

If $\quad \ln(2x^2 - 5x - 3) = \ln x^2$

then $\quad 2x^2 - 5x - 3 = x^2$

Note that if students do not realize that $\ln(x - 3)$ is undefined for $x \le 3$, they *will* realize it by checking their solutions. By entering $\ln(-0.5414 - 3)$ on a calculator, they will get an ERROR message.

ADDITIONAL EXAMPLES

Example 8

The population of a certain bacteria culture at time t hours is given by the function F.

$$F(t) = \frac{20{,}000}{1 + 20e^{-\frac{t}{3}}}$$

How long will it take for the bacteria population to reach 8000?

$$8000 = \frac{20{,}000}{1 + 20e^{-\frac{t}{3}}}$$

$$1 + 20e^{-\frac{t}{3}} = \frac{20{,}000}{8000}$$

$$20e^{-\frac{t}{3}} = 2.5 - 1$$

$$e^{-\frac{t}{3}} = \frac{1.5}{20}$$

$$-\frac{t}{3} \ln e = \ln(0.075)$$

$$t = -3 \ln(0.075) = 7.7708$$

about 7.8 hours

25,000

0 ___ 30

−5,000   **Figure 5.6-9**

Solution

Find the value of t when $F(t)$ is 15,000.

$$15{,}000 = \frac{20{,}000}{1 + 24e^{-\frac{t}{4}}}$$

$$15{,}000(1 + 24e^{-\frac{t}{4}}) = 20{,}000$$

$$1 + 24e^{-\frac{t}{4}} = \frac{20{,}000}{15{,}000}$$

$$24e^{-\frac{t}{4}} = \frac{4}{3} - 1$$

$$e^{-\frac{t}{4}} = \frac{1}{3} \cdot \frac{1}{24}$$

$$\ln e^{-\frac{t}{4}} = \ln \frac{1}{72}$$

$$-\frac{t}{4} \ln e = \ln 1 - \ln 72$$

$$-\frac{t}{4} = 0 - \ln 72 \qquad \text{\small $\ln e = 1$ and $\ln 1 = 0$}$$

$$t = 4 \ln 72 = 17.1067$$

Therefore, it will take a little more than 17 months for the population to reach 15,000. The intersection of the graphs of $Y_1 = 15{,}000$ and $Y_2 = \dfrac{20{,}000}{1 + 24e^{-\frac{x}{4}}}$ shown in Figure 5.6-9 confirms the solution. ∎

Logarithmic Equations

Properties of one-to-one functions are useful when solving logarithmic equations, as shown in Example 9.

Example 9   Equations with Only Logarithmic Terms

Solve the equation $\ln(x - 3) + \ln(2x + 1) = 2(\ln x)$. Confirm your solution with a graph.

Solution

First use the Product and Power Laws to rewrite the equation.

$$\ln(x - 3) + \ln(2x + 1) = 2(\ln x)$$

$$\ln[(x - 3)(2x + 1)] = \ln x^2$$

$$\ln(2x^2 - 5x - 3) = \ln x^2$$

$$2x^2 - 5x - 3 = x^2 \qquad \text{\small $y = \ln x$ is a one-to-one function}$$

$$x^2 - 5x - 3 = 0$$

Use the Quadratic Formula to solve for x.

$$x = \frac{-(-5) \pm \sqrt{(-5)^2 - 4(1)(-3)}}{2(1)}$$

$$x = \frac{5 + \sqrt{37}}{2} \approx 5.5414 \quad \text{or} \quad x = \frac{5 - \sqrt{37}}{2} \approx -0.5414$$

Because $\ln(x - 3)$ is undefined for $x \le 3$, $x = \dfrac{5 - \sqrt{37}}{2} \approx -0.5414$ cannot be a solution. Therefore, the only solution of the original equation is $x = \dfrac{5 + \sqrt{37}}{2} \approx 5.5414$. The intersection of the graphs of $Y_1 = \ln(x - 3) + \ln(2x + 1)$ and $Y_2 = 2(\ln x)$, shown in Figure 5.6-10, confirms the solution. ∎

6

0 ———————— 10

Intersection
X=5.5413813   Y=3.4244876

−6

Figure 5.6-10

Equations that involve both logarithmic and constant terms may be solved by using the basic property of logarithms.

$$10^{\log v} = v \qquad \text{and} \qquad e^{\ln v} = v$$

Example 10   Equations with Logarithmic and Constant Terms

Solve the equation $\ln(x - 3) = 5 - \ln(x - 3)$. Confirm your solution with a graph.

Solution

First get all the logarithmic terms on one side of the equal sign and the constants on the other. Then rewrite the side that contains the logarithms as a single logarithm.

$$\ln(x - 3) = 5 - \ln(x - 3)$$
$$\ln(x - 3) + \ln(x - 3) = 5$$
$$2\ln(x - 3) = 5$$
$$\ln(x - 3) = \frac{5}{2}$$
$$e^{\ln(x-3)} = e^{\frac{5}{2}}$$
$$x - 3 = e^{\frac{5}{2}}$$
$$x = e^{\frac{5}{2}} + 3 \approx 15.1825$$

The intersection of the graphs of $Y_1 = \ln(x - 3)$ and $Y_2 = 5 - \ln(x - 3)$, shown in Figure 5.6-11, confirms the solution. ∎

6

0 ———————— 30

Intersection
X=15.182494   Y=2.5

−6

Figure 5.6-11

Example 11   Equations with Logarithmic and Constant Terms

Solve the equation $\log(x - 16) = 2 - \log(x - 1)$. Confirm your solution with a graph.

ADDITIONAL EXAMPLES

Example 9

Solve the equation
$\ln(4x - 1) + \ln(x + 2) = 2(\ln x)$.
Confirm your solution with a graph.

$$\ln(4x - 1) + \ln(x + 2) = 2(\ln x)$$
$$\ln[(4x - 1)(x + 2)] = 2(\ln x)$$
$$\ln(4x^2 + 7x - 2) = \ln x^2$$
$$4x^2 + 7x - 2 = x^2$$
$$3x^2 + 7x - 2 = 0$$
$$x = \frac{-7 \pm \sqrt{(7)^2 - 4(3)(-2)}}{2(3)}$$
$$= \frac{-7 \pm \sqrt{73}}{6}$$

Because $\ln(4x - 1)$ is undefined for $x \le \frac{1}{4}$, $x = \dfrac{-7 - \sqrt{73}}{6} \approx -2.5907$ cannot be a solution. Therefore, the only solution is

$$x = \frac{-7 + \sqrt{73}}{6} \approx 0.2573$$

0

0 ———————— 0.5

Intersection
X=.25733396   Y=-2.714761

−4

Example 10

Solve the equation
$\ln(2x + 1) = 8 - \ln(2x + 1)$.
Confirm your solution with a graph.

$$\ln(2x + 1) = 8 - \ln(2x + 1)$$
$$2\ln(2x + 1) = 8$$
$$\ln(2x + 1) = 4$$
$$e^{\ln(2x + 1)} = e^4$$
$$2x + 1 = e^4$$
$$2x = e^4 - 1$$
$$x = \frac{e^4 - 1}{2}$$
$$\approx 26.7991$$

10

0 ———————— 40
Intersection
X=26.799075   Y=4
0

Example 11

Solve the equation
$\log(x + 2) = 1 - \log(x - 1)$.
Confirm your solution with a graph.

$$\log(x + 2) = 1 -$$
$$\log(x - 1)$$
$$\log(x + 2) + \log(x - 1) = 1$$
$$\log[(x + 2)(x - 1)] = 1$$
$$\log(x^2 + x - 2) = 1$$
$$10^{\log(x^2 + x - 2)} = 10^1$$
$$x^2 + x - 2 = 10$$
$$x^2 + x - 12 = 0$$
$$(x + 4)(x - 3) = 0$$
$$x = -4; x = 3$$

Because $\log(x + 2)$ and $\log(x - 1)$ are not defined for $x = -4$, it cannot be a solution. Therefore, the only solution is $x = 3$.

Intersection
X=3   Y=.69897

Exercises 5.6

ANSWERS

9. $x = \dfrac{\ln 5}{\ln 3} \approx 1.465$

11. $x = \dfrac{\ln 3}{\ln 1.5} \approx 2.7095$

13. $x = \dfrac{\ln 3 - 5\ln 5}{\ln 5 + 2\ln 3} \approx -1.825$

14. $x = \dfrac{\ln 4 - 2\ln 3}{3\ln 4 - \ln 3} \approx -0.2650$

15. $x = \dfrac{\ln 2 - \ln 3}{3\ln 2 + \ln 3} \approx -0.1276$

16. $z = \dfrac{-3\ln 3}{\ln 3 - \ln 2} \approx -8.1285$

17. $x = \dfrac{(\ln 5)}{2} \approx 0.805$

19. $x = \dfrac{(-\ln 3.5)}{1.4} \approx -0.895$

20. $x = -3\ln\left(\dfrac{5.6}{3.4}\right) \approx -1.4970$

21. $x = \dfrac{2\ln\left(\dfrac{5}{2.1}\right)}{\ln 3} \approx 1.579$

22. $x = \dfrac{3\ln\left(\dfrac{14}{7.8}\right)}{\ln 5} \approx 1.0903$

Solution

$$\log(x - 16) = 2 - \log(x - 1)$$
$$\log(x - 16) + \log(x - 1) = 2$$
$$\log[(x - 16)(x - 1)] = 2$$
$$\log(x^2 - 17x + 16) = 2$$
$$10^{\log(x^2 - 17x + 16)} = 10^2$$
$$x^2 - 17x + 16 = 100$$
$$x^2 - 17x - 84 = 0$$
$$(x + 4)(x - 21) = 0$$
$$x + 4 = 0 \quad \text{or} \quad x - 21 = 0$$
$$x = -4 \qquad x = 21$$

Because $\log(x - 16)$ and $\log(x - 1)$ are not defined for $x = -4$, it cannot be a solution. Therefore, the only solution is $x = 21$. The intersection of the graphs of $Y_1 = \log(x - 16)$ and $Y_2 = 2 - \log(x - 1)$, shown in Figure 5.6-12, confirms the solution. ∎

3

0   30

Intersection
X=21   Y=.69897

−3

Figure 5.6-12

Exercises 5.6

In Exercises 1–8, solve the equation without using logarithms.

1. $3^x = 81$
$x = 4$

2. $3^x + 3 = 30$
$x = 3$

3. $3^{x+1} = 9^{5x}$
$x = \dfrac{1}{9}$

4. $4^{5x} = 16^{2x-1}$
$x = -2$

5. $3^{5x}9^{x^2} = 27$
$x = \dfrac{1}{2}$ or -3

6. $2^{x^2+5x} = \dfrac{1}{16}$
$x = -1$ or -4

7. $9^{x^2} = 3^{-5x-2}$
$x = -2$ or $-\dfrac{1}{2}$

8. $4^{x^2-1} = 8^x$
$x = -\dfrac{1}{2}$ or 2

In Exercises 9–29, solve the equation. Give exact answers (in terms of natural logarithms). Then use a calculator to find an approximate answer.

9. $3^x = 5$

10. $5^x = 4$ $x = \dfrac{\ln 4}{\ln 5} \approx 0.8614$

11. $2^x = 3^{x-1}$

12. $4^{x+2} = 2^{x-1}$ $x = \dfrac{-5\ln 2}{\ln 2} = -5$

13. $3^{1-2x} = 5^{x+5}$

14. $4^{3x-1} = 3^{x-2}$

15. $2^{1-3x} = 3^{x+1}$

16. $3^{z+3} = 2^z$

17. $e^{2x} = 5$

18. $e^{-3x} = 2$ $x = \dfrac{\ln 2}{-3} \approx -0.2310$

19. $6e^{-1.4x} = 21$

20. $3.4e^{-\frac{x}{3}} = 5.6$

21. $2.1e^{\frac{x}{2}\ln 3} = 5$

22. $7.8e^{\frac{x}{3}\ln 5} = 14$

23. $9^x - 4 \cdot 3^x + 3 = 0$ *Hint:* Note that $9^x = (3^x)^2$; let $u = 3^x$.
$x = 0$ or 1

24. $4^x - 6 \cdot 2^x = -8$ $x = 2$ or 1

25. $e^{2x} - 5e^x + 6 = 0$ *Hint:* Let $u = e^x$.

26. $2e^{2x} - 9e^x + 4 = 0$

27. $6e^{2x} - 16e^x = 6$

28. $8e^{2x} + 8e^x = 6$

29. $4^x + 6 \cdot 4^{-x} = 5$

In Exercises 30–32, solve the equation for x.

30. $\dfrac{e^x + e^{-x}}{e^x - e^{-x}} = t$ **31.** $\dfrac{e^x - e^{-x}}{2} = t$ **32.** $\dfrac{e^x - e^{-x}}{e^x + e^{-x}} = t$

33. Prove that if $\ln u = \ln v$, then $u = v$. *Hint:* Use the basic property of inverses $e^{\ln v} = v$.

34. a. Solve $7^x = 3$ using natural logarithms. Give an exact answer, not an approximation.

b. Solve $7^x = 3$ using common logarithms. Give an exact answer, not an approximation.

c. Use the change-of-base formula in *Excursion* 5.5.A to show that your answers in parts **a** and **b** are the same.

In Exercises 35–44, solve the equation. (See Example 9.)

35. $\ln(3x - 5) = \ln 11 + \ln 2$ $x = 9$

36. $\log(4x - 1) = \log(x + 1) + \log 2$ $x = \dfrac{3}{2}$

25. $x = \ln 2 \approx 0.693$ or $x = \ln 3 \approx 1.099$

26. $x = \ln\left(\dfrac{1}{2}\right) \approx -0.693$ or $x = \ln 4 \approx 1.386$

27. $x = \ln 3 \approx 1.099$

28. $x = \ln\left(\dfrac{1}{2}\right) \approx -0.693$

29. $x = \dfrac{\ln 2}{\ln 4} = \dfrac{1}{2}$ or $x = \dfrac{\ln 3}{\ln 4} \approx 0.792$

30. $x = \ln\sqrt{\dfrac{1 + t}{t - 1}}$

31. $x = \ln(t + \sqrt{t^2 + 1})$

32. $x = \ln\sqrt{\dfrac{t + 1}{1 - t}}$

33. If $\ln u = \ln v$, then $e^{\ln u} = e^{\ln v}$, so $u = v$.

34. a. $x = \dfrac{\ln 3}{\ln 7}$

b. $x = \dfrac{\log 3}{\log 7}$

c. $x = \dfrac{\ln 3}{\ln 7}$

37. $\log(3x - 1) + \log 2 = \log 4 + \log(x + 2)$
$\boldsymbol{x = 5}$

38. $\ln(x + 6) - \ln 10 = \ln(x - 1) - \ln 2$ $\boldsymbol{x = \dfrac{11}{4}}$

39. $2 \ln x = \ln 36$ **40.** $2 \log x = 3 \log 4$
$\boldsymbol{x = 6}$ $\boldsymbol{x = 8}$

41. $\ln x + \ln(x + 1) = \ln 3 + \ln 4$
$\boldsymbol{x = 3}$

42. $\ln(6x - 1) + \ln x = \dfrac{1}{2} \ln 4$ $\boldsymbol{x = \dfrac{2}{3}}$

43. $\ln x = \ln 3 - \ln(x + 5)$ $\boldsymbol{x = \dfrac{-5 + \sqrt{37}}{2}}$

44. $\ln(2x + 3) + \ln x = \ln e$ $\boldsymbol{x = \dfrac{-3 + \sqrt{9 + 8e}}{4}}$

In Exercises 45–52, solve the equation.

45. $\ln(x + 9) - \ln x = 1$ $\boldsymbol{x = \dfrac{9}{(e - 1)}}$

46. $\ln(2x + 1) - 1 = \ln(x - 2)$ $\boldsymbol{x = \dfrac{2e + 1}{e - 2}}$

47. $\log x + \log(x - 3) = 1$ $\boldsymbol{x = 5}$

48. $\log(x - 1) + \log(x + 2) = 1$ $\boldsymbol{x = 3}$

49. $\log \sqrt{x^2 - 1} = 2$ **50.** $\log \sqrt[3]{x^2 + 21x} = \dfrac{2}{3}$
$\boldsymbol{x = \pm\sqrt{10001}}$ $\boldsymbol{x = -25 \text{ or } 4}$

51. $\ln(x^2 + 1) - \ln(x - 1) = 1 + \ln(x + 1)$

52. $\dfrac{\ln(x + 1)}{\ln(x - 1)} = 2$ $\boldsymbol{x = \sqrt{\dfrac{e + 1}{e - 1}}}$
$\boldsymbol{x = 3}$

Exercises 53–62 deal with the half-life function $M(x) = c(0.5)^{\frac{x}{h}}$, **which was discussed in Section 5.3 and used in Example 5 of this section.**

53. How old is a piece of ivory that has lost 36% of its carbon-14?
≈3689 yr old

54. How old is a mummy that has lost 49% of its carbon-14?
≈5566 yr old

55. Find when part of the Pueblo Benito ruins was built if the doorway timbers have 89.14% of their original carbon-14. (See the image on the first page of this chapter.)
≈950.35 yr old

56. How old is a wooden statue that has only one-third of its original carbon-14?
≈9082 yr old

57. A quantity of uranium decays to two-thirds of its original mass in 0.26 billion years. Find the half-life of uranium.
≈444,000,000 yr

58. A certain radioactive substance loses one-third of its original mass in 5 days. Find its half-life.
≈8.55 days

59. Krypton-85 loses 6.44% of its mass each year. What is its half-life?
≈10.413 yr

60. Strontium-90 loses 2.5% of its mass each year. What is its half-life?
≈27.38 yr

61. The half-life of a certain substance is 3.6 days. How long will it take for 20 grams to decay to 3 grams?
≈9.853 days

62. The half-life of cobalt-60 is 4.945 years. How long will it take for 25 grams to decay to 15 grams?
≈3.64 yr

Exercises 63–68 deal with the compound interest formula $A = P(1 + r)^t$, **which was discussed in Section 5.3 and used in Example 6 of this section.**

63. At what annual rate of interest should $1000 be invested so that it will double in 10 years, if interest is compounded quarterly?
≈6.99%

64. Find how long it takes $500 to triple if it is invested at 6% in each compounding period.
a. annually   **b.** quarterly   **c.** daily
≈18.85 yr   **≈18.45 yr**   **≈18.31 yr**

65. a. How long will it take to triple your money if you invest $500 at a rate of 5% per year compounded annually? **≈22.5 yr**
    b. How long will it take at 5% compounded quarterly?
≈22.1 yr

66. At what rate of interest compounded annually should you invest $500 if you want to have $1500 in 12 years?
≈9.587%

67. How much money should be invested at 5% interest compounded quarterly so that 9 years later the investment will be worth $5000? This answer is called the present value of $5000 at 5% interest.
≈$3197.05

68. Find a formula that gives the time needed for an investment of P dollars to double, if the interest rate is r% compounded annually. *Hint:* Solve the compound interest formula for t, when $A = 2P$.

Exercises 69–76 deal with functions of the form $f(x) = Pe^{kx}$, **where k is the continuous exponential growth rate. See Example 7.**

69. The present concentration of carbon dioxide in the atmosphere is 364 parts per million (ppm) and is increasing exponentially at a continuous yearly rate of 0.4% (that is, $k = 0.004$). How many years will it take for the concentration to reach 500 ppm?
≈79.36 yr

70. The amount P of ozone in the atmosphere is currently decaying exponentially each year at a
≈277.26 yr

68. $t = \dfrac{\ln 2}{\ln\left(1 + \dfrac{r}{100}\right)}$

78. a. ≈ 9.55 years

b. No; $e^{-0.5544t}$ is always greater than 0, so $1 + 199e^{-0.5544t}$ is always greater than 1 for any value of t. Therefore, $\dfrac{2000}{1 + 199e^{-0.5544t}}$ is always less than 2000.

79. a. $k \approx 0.229$, $c \approx 83.3$

b. ≈ 12.43 weeks

80. a. in the 13th year; company A; company B

b. in the 31st year; company A; company B

---

continuous rate of $\frac{1}{4}\%$ (that is, $k = -0.0025$). How long will it take for half the ozone to disappear (that is, when will the amount be $\frac{P}{2}$)? Your answer is the half-life of ozone.

71. The population of Brazil increased exponentially from 151 million in 1990 to 173 million in 2000.
  a. At what continuous rate was the population growing during this period? $\approx$**1.3601%**
  b. Assuming that Brazil's population continues to increase at this rate, when will it reach 250 million? **in 2027**

72. Outstanding consumer debt increased exponentially from $781.5 billion in 1990 to $1765.5 billion in 2002. (Source: Federal Reserve Bulletin)
  a. At what continuous rate is consumer debt growing? $\approx$**6.79%**
  b. Assuming this rate continues, when will consumer debt reach $2500 billion? **in 2007**

73. The probability P percent of having an accident while driving a car is related to the alcohol level of the driver's blood by the formula $P = e^{kt}$, where k is a constant. Accident statistics show that the probability of an accident is 25% when the blood alcohol level is $t = 0.15$.
  a. Find k. Use $P = 25$, not 0.25. $k \approx$ **21.459**
  b. At what blood alcohol level is the probability of having an accident 50%? $t \approx$ **0.182**

74. Under normal conditions, the atmospheric pressure (in millibars) at height h feet above sea level is given by $P(h) = 1015e^{-kh}$, where k is a positive constant.
  a. If the pressure at 18,000 feet is half the pressure at sea level, find k. $k \approx$ **0.0000385**
  b. Using the information from part **a**, find the atmospheric pressure at 1000 feet, 5000 feet, and 15,000 feet. $\approx$**976.7**; $\approx$**837.3**; $\approx$**569.7**

75. One hour after an experiment begins, the number of bacteria in a culture is 100. An hour later there are 500.
  a. Find the number of bacteria at the beginning of the experiment and the number 3 hours later. **20; 2500**
  b. How long does it take the number of bacteria at any given time to double? $\dfrac{\ln 2}{\ln 5} \approx$ **0.43 hr**

76. If the population at time t is given by $S(t) = ce^{kt}$, find a formula that gives the time it takes for the population to double. $t = \dfrac{\ln 2}{k}$

77. The spread of a flu virus in a community of 45,000 people is given by the function

$$f(t) = \frac{45{,}000}{1 + 224e^{-0.889t}},$$

where $f(t)$ is the number of people infected in week t.
  a. How many people had the flu at the outbreak of the epidemic? after 3 weeks? **200;** $\approx$**2718**
  b. When will half the town be infected? $\approx$**6.09 weeks**

78. The beaver population near a certain lake in year t is approximately $p(t) = \dfrac{2000}{1 + 199e^{-0.5544t}}$.
  a. When will the beaver population reach 1000?
  b. Will the population ever reach 2000? Why?

79. *Critical Thinking* According to one theory of learning, the number of words per minute N that a person can type after t weeks of practice is given by $N = c(1 - e^{-kt})$, where c is an upper limit that N cannot exceed and k is a constant that must be determined experimentally for each person.
  a. If a person can type 50 wpm (words per minute) after 4 weeks of practice and 70 wpm after 8 weeks, find the values of k and c for this person. According to the theory, this person will never type faster than c wpm.
  b. Another person can type 50 wpm after 4 weeks of practice and 90 wpm after 8 weeks. How many weeks must this person practice to be able to type 125 wpm?

80. *Critical Thinking* Wendy has been offered two jobs, each with the same starting salary of $24,000 and identical benefits. Assuming satisfactory performance, she will receive a $1200 raise each year at the company A, whereas the company B will give her a 4% raise each year.
  a. In what year (after the first year) would her salary be the same at either company? Until then, which company pays better? After that, which company pays better?
  b. Answer the questions in part **a** assuming that the annual raise at company A is $1800.

5.7 Exponential, Logarithmic, and Other Models

Objectives

• Model real data sets with power, exponential, logarithmic, and logistic functions

Many data sets can be modeled by suitable exponential, logarithmic, and related functions. Most calculators have regression procedures for constructing the models described in the table below.

Model	Equation	Examples	
Power	$y = ax^r$	$y = 5x^{2.7}$	$y = 3.5x^{-0.45}$
Exponential	$y = ab^x$ or $y = ae^{kx}$	$y = 2(1.64)^x$	$y = 2e^{0.4947x}$
Logarithmic	$y = a + b \ln x$	$y = 5 + 4.2 \ln x$	$y = 2 - 3 \ln x$
Logistic	$y = \dfrac{a}{1 + be^{-kx}}$	$y = \dfrac{20,000}{1 + 24e^{-0.25x}}$	$y = \dfrac{650}{1 + 6e^{-0.3x}}$

Exponential Models

In the table of values for the exponential model $y = 3 \cdot 2^x$ that follows, examine the patterns in the ratios of successive y-values.

x	0	4	8	12	16
y	3	48	768	12,288	196,608

$$\frac{48}{3} = 16 \qquad \frac{768}{48} = 16 \qquad \frac{12,288}{768} = 16 \qquad \frac{196,608}{12,288} = 16$$

At each step, x changes from x to $x + 4$, y changes from $3 \cdot 2^x$ to $3 \cdot 2^{x+4}$, and the ratio of successive y-values is always the same.

$$\frac{3 \cdot 2^{x+4}}{3 \cdot 2^x} = \frac{3 \cdot 2^x \cdot 2^4}{3 \cdot 2^x} = 2^4 = 16$$

A similar argument applies to any exponential model $y = ab^x$ and shows that if x changes by a fixed amount k, then the ratio of the corresponding y-values is the constant b^k. In the exponential model $y = 3 \cdot 2^x$ above, b is 2 and k is 4. This fact identifies the model that would best represent the data.

> **When the ratio of successive entries in a table of data is approximately constant, an exponential model is appropriate.**

Example 1 U.S. Population Before the Civil War

In the years before the Civil War, the population of the United States grew rapidly, as shown in the following table. Find a model for this growth.

R^2 (or r^2) represents the coefficient of determination (see page 1033). Informally, r^2 is a number between 0 and 1 that gives the relative predictive power of a model. The closer r^2 is to 1, the better the model is. Note that for both the quadratic model and the exponential model, r^2 is very close to 1, but it is closer to 1 for the exponential model.

Example Notes

The first step in finding a model that fits the growth in each of Examples 1 and 2 is to construct a scatter plot of the data points.

In **Example 1,** the scatter plot suggests either a polynomial or an exponential model. Nearly equal ratios of successive populations indicate that an exponential model is a good model.

In **Example 2,** an exponential model is ruled out because ratios of successive populations are *not* nearly equal (i.e. the rate of growth is not nearly constant). Three models are compared at the top of page 392.

ADDITIONAL EXAMPLES

Example 1

The population of a group of 14 countries in south central Asia has been growing steadily over the last half of the 20th century as shown in the following table. Find a model for this growth.

Year	Population (in millions)
1950	514.3
1960	627.5
1970	788.3
1980	987.8
1990	1226.6
2000	1470.9

[*Source: U.S. Bureau of the Census*]

$\frac{627.5}{514.3} \approx 1.220$, $\frac{788.3}{627.5} \approx 1.256$,

$\frac{987.8}{788.3} \approx 1.253$, $\frac{1226.6}{987.8} \approx 1.242$,

$\frac{1470.9}{1226.6} \approx 1.199$

With $x = 0$ corresponding to 1950, an exponential regression produces this model:

$y = 513.3144(1.0216^x)$

Year	Population in millions	Year	Population in millions
1790	3.93	1830	12.86
1800	5.31	1840	17.07
1810	7.24	1850	23.19
1820	9.64	1860	31.44

[*Source: U.S. Bureau of the Census*]

Figure 5.7-1

> **NOTE** Throughout this section, coefficients are rounded for convenient reading, but the full expansion is used for calculations and graphs.

Solution

The data points, with $x = 0$ corresponding to 1790, are shown in Figure 5.7-1. Their shape suggests either a polynomial graph of even degree or an exponential graph. Since populations generally grow exponentially, an exponential model is likely to be a good choice. This can be confirmed by looking at the successive entries in the table.

Year	Population		Year	Population	
1790	3.93	$\frac{5.31}{3.93} \approx 1.351$	1830	12.86	$\frac{17.07}{12.86} \approx 1.327$
1800	5.31	$\frac{7.24}{5.31} \approx 1.363$	1840	17.07	$\frac{23.19}{17.07} \approx 1.359$
1810	7.24	$\frac{9.64}{7.24} \approx 1.331$	1850	23.19	$\frac{31.44}{23.19} \approx 1.356$
1820	9.64	$\frac{12.86}{9.64} \approx 1.334$	1860	31.44	
1830	12.86				

Because the ratios are almost constant, as they would be in an exponential model, use regression to find an exponential model. The procedure is the same as for linear and polynomial regression. An exponential regression produces this model.

$$y = 3.9572(1.0299^x)$$

The graph of the exponential model in Figure 5.7-2 appears to fit the data well. In fact, you can readily verify that the model has an error of less than 1% for each of the data points. Furthermore, as discussed before this example, when x changes by 10, the value of y changes by approximately $1.0299^{10} \approx 1.343$, which is very close to the successive ratios of the data. ∎

Figure 5.7-2

Logistic Models

A logistic model represents growth that has a limiting factor, such as food supplies, war, new diseases, etc. Logistic models are often used to model population growth, as shown in Example 2.

Example 2 U.S. Population After the Civil War

After the Civil War, the population of the United States continued to increase, as shown in the following table. Find a model for this growth.

Year	Population in millions	Year	Population in millions	Year	Population in millions
1870	38.56	1920	106.02	1960	179.32
1880	50.19	1930	123.20	1970	202.30
1890	62.98	1940	132.16	1980	226.54
1900	76.21	1950	151.33	1990	248.72
1910	92.23			2000	281.42

Solution

The model from Example 1 does not remain valid, as can be seen in Figure 5.7-3, which shows its graph together with all the data points from 1790 through 2000, where $x = 0$ corresponds to 1790.

Figure 5.7-3

The *rate* of growth has steadily decreased since the Civil War. For instance, the ratio of the first two entries is $\frac{50.19}{38.56} \approx 1.302$ and the ratio of the last two is $\frac{281.42}{248.72} \approx 1.131$. So an exponential model may not be the best choice.

Other possibilities are polynomial models, which grow at a slower rate, or logistic models, in which the growth rate decreases with time. Figure 5.7-4 on the next page shows these models compared to an exponential model.

Logistic Model
$$y = \frac{394,932.22}{1 + 208.675e^{-0.447x}}$$

ADDITIONAL EXAMPLES

Example 2

Many epidemics grow exponentially until they are contained or run through a large portion of the population. The table below shows the cumulative number of adult/adolescent deaths in the U.S. due to Acquired Immunodeficiency Syndrome (AIDS) by the end of certain years. Find a model for this growth.

End of Year	AIDS Deaths
1980	30
1982	596
1984	5513
1986	24,245
1988	61,012
1990	119,347
1992	195,364
1994	283,379

[*Source: U.S. Centers for Disease Control*]

The data points, with $x = 0$ corresponding to 1980, are shown in the graph below. The quartic and logistic models fit the data better than the exponential model. This is expected since the ratios of successive entries in the table are not nearly equal.

Exponential Model
$y = 180.2269 \cdot 1.84815^x$

Quartic Model
$y = -10.11x^4 + 315.53x^3 - 1083.42x^2 + 1318.66x + 2.288$

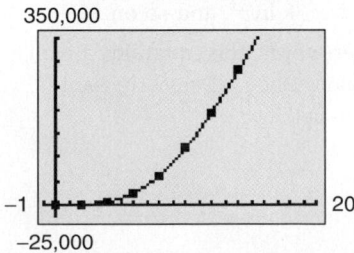

Students might need help understanding the purpose of the discussion about **Exponential versus Power Models.** The discussion begins with the exponential function $y = ab^x$. By taking natural logarithms and applying properties of logarithms, we get $\ln y = \ln a + x \ln b$. Rewrite this equation on the board as shown below, using color to show that the constants $\ln b$ and $\ln a$ are the slope and y-intercept, respectively, of a line:

$$\ln y = (\ln b)x + \ln a$$
$$y = mx + k$$

Then note that the line is the set of points $(x, \ln y)$ rather than the more familiar (x, y).

The discussion shows that:
If you have an exponential function $y = ab^x$, then the points (x, y) in the function satisfy the equation $\ln y = (\ln b)x + \ln a$; that is, they satisfy the linear function formed by the points $(x, \ln y)$.
By reversing the discussion, we can say that: If a set of points (x, y) satisfy the equation $\ln y = (\ln b)x + \ln a$, then they satisfy the exponential function $y = ab^x$.

This all establishes the guideline in bold near the bottom of the page:
If (x, y) are data points and if the points $(x, \ln y)$ are approximately linear, then an exponential model may be appropriate for the data.

Math Background

The discussion on page 392 is reversible because the chain of reasoning consists entirely of "if and only if" steps. That is, $y = ab^x$ if and only if $\ln y = \ln (ab^x)$, and $\ln y = \ln (ab^x)$ if and only if $\ln y = \ln a + \ln b^x$, and so on.

In other words, the equations are all equivalent (they all have the same solution set).

Exponential Model

$$y = 6.0662 \cdot 1.02039^x$$

Quartic Model

$$y = (7.94 \times 10^{-8})x^4 - (2.76 \times 10^{-5})x^3$$
$$+ 0.0093x^2 - 0.1621x + 5.462$$

Logistic Model

$$y = \frac{442.10}{1 + 56.329e^{-0.022x}}$$

Figure 5.7-4

The quartic and logistic models fit the data better than does the exponential model. The quartic model indicates unlimited future growth, but the logistic model has the population growing more slowly in the future. ∎

Exponential versus Power Models

In Example 1, the ratios of successive entries of the data table were used to determine that an exponential model was appropriate. Another way to determine if an exponential model might be appropriate is to consider the exponential function $y = ab^x$, as shown below.

$$y = ab^x$$
$\ln y = \ln (ab^x)$ *Take the natural logarithm of each side*
$\ln y = \ln a + \ln b^x$ *Product Law*
$\ln y = \ln a + x \ln b$ *Power Law*

Because $\ln a$ and $\ln b$ are constants, let $k = \ln a$ and $m = \ln b$.

$$\ln y = \ln a + x \ln b$$
$$\ln y = (\ln b)x + \ln a$$
$$\ln y = mx + k$$

The points $(x, \ln y)$ lie on a straight line with slope m and y-intercept k. Consequently, a guideline for determining if an exponential model is appropriate is as follows.

> **If (x, y) are data points and if the points $(x, \ln y)$ are approximately linear, then an exponential model may be appropriate for the data.**

Similarly, consider the power function $y = ax^r$

$$y = ax^r$$
$\ln y = \ln (ax^r)$ *Take the natural logarithm of each side*
$\ln y = \ln a + \ln x^r$ *Product Law*
$\ln y = \ln a + r \ln x$ *Power Law*

Because r and $\ln a$ are constants, let $k = \ln a$. Then:

$$\ln y = \ln a + r \ln x$$
$$\ln y = r \ln x + \ln a$$
$$\ln y = r \ln x + k$$

Thus, the points $(\ln x, \ln y)$ lie on the straight line with slope r and y-intercept k. Consequently, a guideline for determining if a power model is appropriate is as follows

If (x, y) are data points and if the points $(\ln x, \ln y)$ are approximately linear, then a power model may be appropriate for the data.

Example 3 Different Planet Years

The length of time that a planet takes to make one complete rotation around the sun is that planet's "year." The table below shows the length of each planet's year, relative to an Earth year, and the average distance of that planet from the Sun in millions of miles. Find a model for this data in which x is the length of the year and y is the distance from the Sun.

Planet	Year	Distance
Mercury	0.24	36.0
Venus	0.62	67.2
Earth	1.00	92.9
Mars	1.88	141.6
Jupiter	11.86	483.6

Planet	Year	Distance
Saturn	29.46	886.7
Uranus	84.01	1783.0
Neptune	164.79	2794.0
Pluto	247.69	3674.5

Technology Tip

Suppose the x- and y-coordinates of the data points are stored in lists L_1 and L_2, respectively. Keying in

LN L_2 STO $\rightarrow L_4$

produces the list L_4, whose entries are the natural logarithms of the numbers in list L_2, and stores it in the statistics editor. You can then use lists L_1 and L_4 to plot the points $(x, \ln y)$.

Solution

Figure 5.7-5 shows the data points for the five planets with the shortest years. Figure 5.7-6 shows all of the data points, but on this scale, the first four points look like a single large point near the origin.

Figure 5.7-5

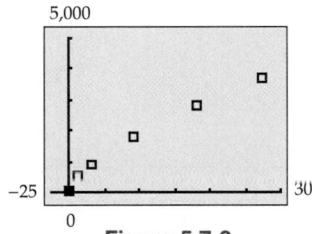

Figure 5.7-6

A power regression produces this model.

$$y = 0.3275x^{1.5016}$$

Its graph shown below shows that it fits the original data points well.

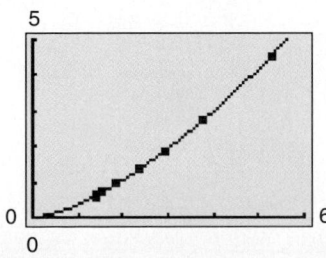

ADDITIONAL EXAMPLES

Example 3

The table below lists 11 of Saturn's 30 moons. There is a relationship between the radius of an orbit and the time of one orbit for these 11 moons. Find a model for this data in which x is the radius of an orbit and y is the time of one orbit.

Moon	Orbit Radius (100,000 km)	Orbit Time (d)
Atlas	1.3767	0.602
Prometheus	1.3935	0.613
Pandora	1.4170	0.629
Epimetheus	1.5142	0.694
Janus	1.5147	0.695
Mimas	1.8552	0.942
Enceladus	2.3802	1.370
Tethys	2.9466	1.888
Dione	3.7740	2.737
Helene	3.7740	2.737
Rhea	5.2704	4.518

Plotting the point $(x, \ln y)$ for each data point (x, y) produces the graph shown below. Its points do not show a linear pattern, so an exponential model is not appropriate.

Plotting the point $(\ln x, \ln y)$ for each data point (x, y) produces the graph shown below. Its points do show a linear pattern, so a power model should work.

Real-World Application

Example 4 involves modeling population growth with a logarithmic function. As shown in this section, population can be modeled with other types of functions, such as exponential, quartic, and logistic.

As an extension project, consider having students choose a time and geographic place (country, continent, etc.) and research to get data about population growth or decline, and then create several models for that population.

Teaching Notes

To decide whether or not a logarithmic model seems appropriate for a set of data from a scatter plot of the original data, students can keep the following features in mind. A logarithmic model:

(1) increases without bound to the right;

(2) has rapid growth early, followed by slower growth later

Students can also use a test similar to the ones for exponential and power models. If the points $(\ln x, y)$ fit a linear pattern, then the original points (x, y) may fit an logarithmic model.

Plotting the point $(x, \ln y)$ for each data point (x, y) produces the graph shown in Figure 5.7-7. Its points do not form a linear pattern, so an exponential model is not appropriate. The points $(\ln x, \ln y)$ shown in Figure 5.7-8 do form a linear pattern, which suggests that a power model will work.

Figure 5.7-7   **Figure 5.7-8**

A power regression produces this model:

$$y = 92.8932x^{0.6669}$$

Its graph in Figures 5.7-9 and 5.7-10 show that it fits the original data points well.

Figure 5.7-9   **Figure 5.7-10**   ∎

Logarithmic Models

Consider the logarithmic function $y = b \ln x + a$

Because a and b are constants, let $m = b$ and $k = a$. Then:

$$y = m(\ln x) + k$$

The points $(\ln x, y)$ lie on the straight line with slope m and y-intercept k. Consequently, a guideline for determining if a logarithmic model is appropriate is as follows.

> **If (x, y) are data points and if the points $(\ln x, y)$ are approximately linear, then a logarithmic model may be appropriate for the data.**

Example 4 Logarithmic Population Growth

Find a model for population growth in El Paso, Texas, given the information in the following table.

Year	1950	1970	1980	1990	2000
Population	130,485	322,261	425,259	515,342	563,662

[Source: U.S. Bureau of the Census.]

Solution

The scatter plot of the data, where $x = 50$ corresponds to 1950, shown in Figure 5.7-11, suggests a logarithmic curve with a very slight bend.

Figure 5.7-11

Figure 5.7-12

To determine whether a logarithmic model is appropriate for this data, plot points $(\ln x, y)$; that is $(\ln 50, 130{,}485) \ldots (\ln 100, 563{,}662)$. Because these points, shown in Figure 5.7-12, appear to be approximately linear, a logarithmic model seems appropriate.

Using logarithmic regression, the model is:

$$y = -2{,}382{,}368.345 + 640{,}666.815 \ln x$$

Figure 5.7-13

The graph of this model, shown in Figure 5.7-13, shows that it is a good fit for the data. ■

CAUTION

When using logarithmic models, you must have data points with positive first coordinates because logarithms of negative numbers and 0 are not defined.

ADDITIONAL EXAMPLES

Example 4

The table below gives the population of San Francisco, California, from 1860 to 1900. Find a model for the population growth in San Francisco during this time period. (Let $x = 10$ correspond to 1860.)

Year	Population
1860	56,802
1870	149,473
1880	233,959
1890	298,997
1900	342,782

[*Source: U.S. Bureau of the Census.*]

The scatter plot shown below suggests a logarithmic curve.

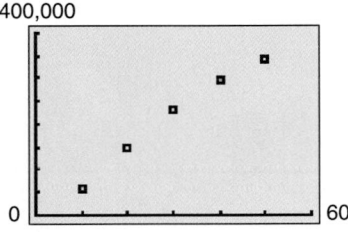

Plotting the points (ln x, y) produces the graph shown below. These points do show a linear pattern, so a logarithmic model seems appropriate.

Using logarithmic regression, the model is:

$y = -370{,}427.644 + 180{,}004.67 \ln x$

The graph of this model below shows that it is a good fit for the data.

Exercises 5.7

In Exercises 1–10, state which of the following models might be appropriate for the given scatter plot of data. More than one model may be appropriate.

Model	Corresponding function
A. Linear	$y = ax + b$
B. Quadratic	$y = ax^2 + bx + c$
C. Power	$y = ax^r$
D. Cubic	$y = ax^3 + bx^2 + cx + d$
E. Exponential	$y = ab^x$
F. Logarithmic	$y = a + b \ln x$
G. Logistic	$y = \dfrac{a}{1 + be^{-kx}}$

1.

Cubic, exponential, logistic

2.

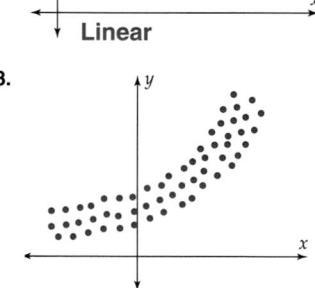

Linear

3.

Exponential, quadratic, cubic

4.

Logarithmic, quadratic

5.

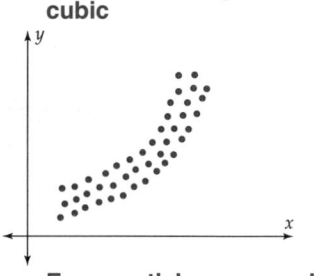

Exponential, logarithmic, quadratic, cubic

6.

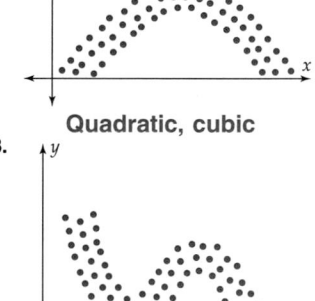

Exponential, power, cubic

7.

Quadratic, cubic

8.

Cubic

9.

Quadratic, cubic

10.

Exponential, power, cubic

In Exercises 11 and 12, compute the ratios of successive entries in the table to determine whether an exponential model is appropriate for the data.

11.

x	0	2	4	6	8	10
y	3	15.2	76.9	389.2	1975.5	9975.8

12.

x	1	3	5	7	9	11
y	3	21	55	105	171	253

13. a. Show algebraically that in the logistic model for the U.S. population in Example 2, the population can never exceed 442.10 million people.

 b. Confirm your answer in part **a** by graphing the logistic model in a window that includes the next three centuries.

14. According to estimates by the U.S. Bureau of the Census, the U.S. population was 287.7 million in 2002. Based on this information, which of the models in Example 2 appears to be the most accurate predictor?

15. Graph each of the following power functions in a window with $0 \le x \le 20$.
 a. $f(x) = x^{-1.5}$ **b.** $g(x) = x^{0.75}$ **c.** $h(x) = x^{2.4}$

16. Based on your graphs in Exercise 15, describe the general shape of the graph of $y = ax^r$, when $a > 0$ and r is as described below.
 a. $r < 0$ **b.** $0 < r < 1$ **c.** $r > 1$

In Exercises 17–20, determine whether an exponential, power, or logarithmic model (or none or several of these) is appropriate for the data by determining which (if any) of the following sets of points are approximately linear, where the given data set consists of the points $\{(x, y)\}$.

$$\{(x, \ln y)\} \qquad \{(\ln x, \ln y)\} \qquad \{(\ln x, y)\}$$

17.

x	1	3	5	7	9	11
y	2	25	81	175	310	497

18.

x	3	6	9	12	15	18
y	385	74	14	2.75	0.5	0.1

19.

x	5	10	15	20	25	30
y	17	27	35	40	43	48

20.

x	5	10	15	20	25	30
y	2	110	460	1200	2500	4525

21. The table shows the number of babies born as twins, triplets, quadruplets, etc., in recent years.

Year	Multiple births
1989	92,916
1990	96,893
1991	98,125
1992	99,255
1993	100,613
1994	101,658
1995	101,709

11. Ratios: 5.07, 5.06, 5.06, 5.08, 5.05; exponential is appropriate

12. Ratios: 7, 2.62, 1.91, 1.63, 1.48; exponential would not be appropriate

13. a. For large values of x the term $56.33e^{-0.0216x}$ is close to zero so the quantity $(1 + 56.33e^{-0.0216x})$ is slightly larger than 1, which means $\dfrac{442.1}{1 + 56.33e^{-0.0216x}}$ is always less than (but very close to) 442.1.

 b. 500

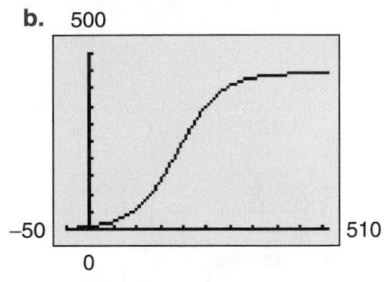

14. the quartic model

15. a. 2

 b. 10

 c. 1330

16. a. The graph is decreasing and is asymptotic to the x-axis as x gets large.

 b. The graph is increasing but is increasing less and less quickly as x gets large.

 c. The graph is increasing and is increasing more and more quickly as x gets large.

17. $\{(\ln x, \ln y)\}$ appears the most linear. Power model.

18. $\{(x, \ln y)\}$ appears the most linear. Exponential model.

19. $\{(\ln x, \ln y)\}$ and $\{(\ln x, y)\}$ are both nearly linear. Power or logarithmic model

20. $\{(\ln x, \ln y)\}$ appears the most linear. Power model

21. a.

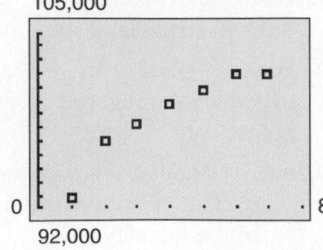

105,000

0 ⟶ 8

92,000

b.

105,000

$f(x)$

$g(x)$

0 ⟶ 8

92,000

c.

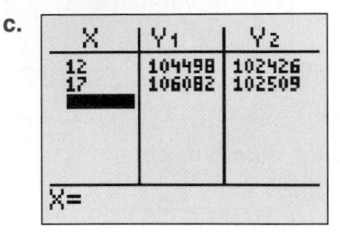

X	Y₁	Y₂
12	104498	102426
17	106082	102509

X=

d. The logarithmic model predicts continued but slowing growth while the logistic predicts a cap of about 102,520. Therefore, the logarithmic model seems the better one for the long run.

22. a. The logistic model understates the population projections by increasingly large amounts.

b. Letting $x = 0$ correspond with 1900 we get the logistic model

$$y = \frac{822.716}{1 + 9.479e^{-0.0159x}}$$

c. The estimates are much closer, but tend to overstate the projections by increasing amounts.

---

a. Sketch a scatter plot of the data, with $x = 1$ corresponding to 1989.

b. Plot both of the following models on the same screen with the scatter plot:

$$f(x) = 93{,}201.973 + 4{,}545.977 \ln x$$

and

$$g(x) = \frac{102{,}519.98}{1 + 0.1536e^{-0.4263x}}$$

c. Use the table feature to estimate the number of multiple births in 2000 and 2005.

d. Over the long run, which model do you think is the better predictor?

22. The graph shows the Census Bureau's estimates of future U.S. population.

U.S. Population Projections: 2000–2050

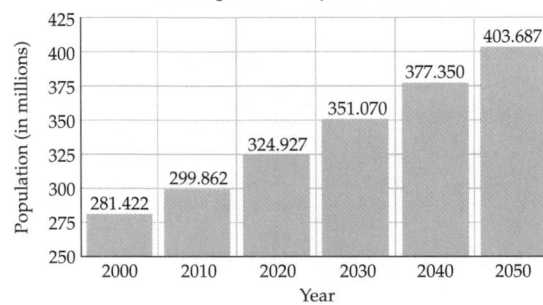

Population (in millions)

425
400
377.350
375
351.070
350
324.927
325
299.862
300
281.422
275
250

403.687

2000 2010 2020 2030 2040 2050

Year

a. How well do the projections in the graph compare with those given by the logistic model in Example 2?

b. Find a logistic model of the U.S. population, using the data given in Example 2 for the years from 1900 to 2000, with $x = 0$ corresponding to 1900.

c. How well do the projections in the graph compare with those given by the model in part **b**?

23. Infant mortality rates in the United States are shown in the following table.

Year	Infant mortality rate*	Year	Infant mortality rate*
1920	76.7	1980	12.6
1930	60.4	1985	10.6
1940	47.0	1990	9.2
1950	29.2	1995	7.6
1960	26.0	2000	6.9
1970	20.0		

*Rates are infant (under 1 year) deaths per 1000 live births.

a. Sketch a scatter plot of the data, with $x = 0$ corresponding to 1900.

b. Verify that the set of points $(x, \ln y)$, where (x, y) are the original data points, is approximately linear.

c. Based on part **b**, what type of model would be appropriate for this data? Find such a model.

24. The average number of students per computer in the U.S. public schools (elementary through high school) is shown in the table below.

Fall of school year	Students per computer
1987	32
1988	25
1989	22
1990	20
1991	18
1992	16
1993	14
1994	10.5
1995	10
1996	7.8
1997	6.1
1998	5.7
1999	5.4

---

23. a.

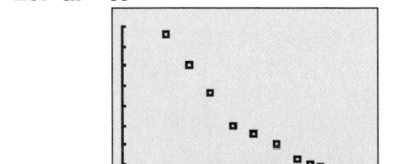

80

0   110
0

b.

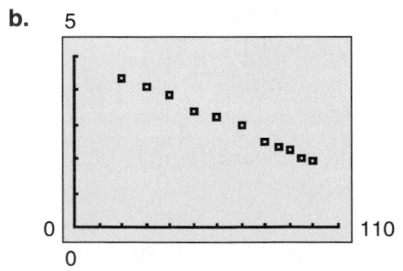

5

0   110
0

c. Exponential

$y = 152.22(0.97^x)$

175

0   110
0

---

a. Sketch a scatter plot of the data, with $x = 1$ corresponding to 1987.
b. Find an exponential model for the data.
c. Use the model to estimate the number of students per computer in 2003.
d. In what year, according to this model, will each student have his or her own computer in school?
e. What are the limitations of this model?

25. The number of children who were home-schooled in the United States in selected years is shown in the table below.

Fall of school year	Number of children (in 1000s)
1985	183
1988	225
1990	301
1992	470
1993	588
1994	735
1995	800
1996	920
1997	1100
1999	1400
2000	1700

[Source: National Home Education Research Institute]

a. Sketch a scatter plot of the data, with $x = 0$ corresponding to 1980.
b. Find a quadratic model for the data.
c. Find a logistic model for the data.
d. What is the number of home-schooled children predicted by each model for the year 2003?
e. What are the limitations of each model?

26. a. Find an exponential model for the federal debt, based on the data in the following table. Let $x = 0$ correspond to 1960.
$y = 199.183(1.089921)^x$

Accumulated gross federal debt	
Year	Amount (in billions of dollars)
1960	284.1
1965	313.8
1970	370.1
1975	533.2
1980	907.7
1985	1823.1
1990	3233.3
1995	4974.0
2000	5674.2

b. Use the model to estimate the federal debt in 2003.
≈8077 billion dollars

27. The table gives the life expectancy of a woman born in each given year.

Year	Life Expectancy (in years)	Year	Life Expectancy (in years)
1910	51.8	1960	73.1
1920	54.6	1970	74.7
1930	61.6	1980	77.5
1940	65.2	1990	78.8
1950	71.1	2000	79.4

[Source: National Center for Health Statistics]

a. Find a logarithmic model for the data, with $x = 10$ corresponding to 1910.
b. Use the model to find the life expectancy of a woman born in 1986. For comparison, the actual expectancy is 78.3 years.
c. Assume the model remains accurate. In what year will the life expectancy of a woman born in that year be at least 81 years?
a. $y = 17.5945 + 13.4239 \ln x$
b. 77.4 years
c. 2012

24. a.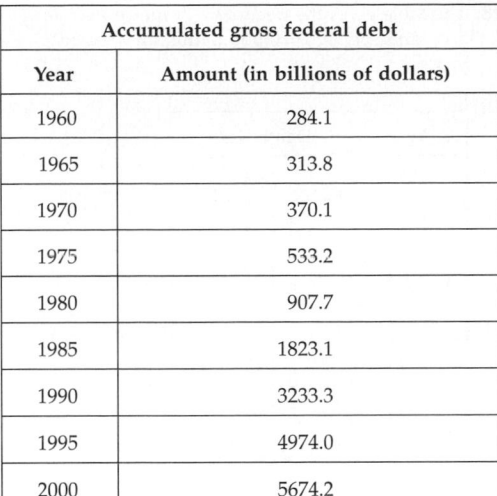

b. $y = 36.674(0.859193)^x$

c. ≈2.78

d. 2009

e. The model is not useful for fitting data before 1987.

25. a.

b. $y = 7.05x^2 - 78.34x + 398.73$

c. $y = \dfrac{6413.2}{1 + 107.2e^{-0.1815x}}$

d. 2325.01, 2419.97

e. The quadratic model will give an ever increasing number of children, and the rate of increase will continue to increase. Before too terribly long the number of children home-schooled by the quadratic model will exceed the number of children in the world. The logistic model, on the other hand, gives us a maximum that can never be exceeded.

28. The table gives the death rate in motor vehicle accidents, per 100,000 population, in selected years.

Year	Death Rate
1970	26.8
1980	23.4
1985	19.3
1990	18.8
1995	16.5
2000	15.6

$y = 26.97413(0.981341)^x$

a. Find an exponential model for the data, with $x = 0$ corresponding to 1970.

b. Use the model to predict the death rate in 1998 and in 2002. $\approx$**15.92;** $\approx$**14.76**

c. Assuming the model remains accurate, when will the death rate drop to 13 per 100,000? **2008**

29. Worldwide production of computers has grown dramatically, as shown in the first two columns of the following table.

a. Sketch a scatter plot of the data, with $x = 1$ corresponding to 1985. **see below**

b. Find an exponential model for the data. $y = 10.48(1.16^x)$

c. Use the model to complete column 3 of the table.

d. Fill in column 4 of the table by dividing each entry in column 2 by the preceding one.

e. What does column 4 tell you about the appropriateness of the model?

An exponential model may not be appropriate.

Year	Worldwide shipments (in thousands)	Predicted number of shipment (in thousands)	Ratio
1985	14.7	12.2	✕
1986	15.1	14.1	1.03
1987	16.7	16.4	1.11
1988	18.1	19	1.08
1989	21.3	22	1.18
1990	23.7	25.5	1.11
1991	27	29.6	1.14
1992	32.4	34.4	1.2
1993	38.9	39.9	1.20
1994	47.9	46.2	1.23
1995	60.2	53.6	1.26
1996	70.9	62.2	1.18
1997	84.3	72.2	1.19

[*Source: Dataquest*]

29a.

CHAPTER
5
REVIEW

401

Important Facts and Formulas

- *Rational Exponents:*

$$c^{\frac{1}{n}} = \sqrt[n]{c}$$

$$(c^t)^{\frac{1}{k}} = (c^{\frac{1}{k}})^t = c^{\frac{t}{k}}$$

- *Laws of Exponents:*

$$c^r c^s = c^{r+s} \qquad\qquad (cd)^r = c^r d^r$$

$$\frac{c^r}{c^s} = c^{r-s} \qquad\qquad \left(\frac{c}{d}\right)^r = \frac{c^r}{d^r}$$

$$(c^r)^s = c^{rs} \qquad\qquad c^{-r} = \frac{1}{c^r}$$

- $g(x) = \log x$ is the inverse function of $f(x) = 10^x$:

$$10^{\log v} = v \text{ for all } v > 0 \qquad \text{and} \qquad \log 10^u = u \text{ for all } u$$

- $g(x) = \ln x$ is the inverse function of $f(x) = e^x$:

$$e^{\ln v} = v \text{ for all } v > 0 \qquad \text{and} \qquad \ln e^u = u \text{ for all } u$$

- $h(x) = \log_b x$ is the inverse function of $k(x) = b^x$:

$$b^{\log_b v} = v \text{ for all } v > 0 \qquad \text{and} \qquad \log_b (b^u) = u \text{ for all } u$$

- *Logarithm Laws:* For all $v, w > 0$ and any k:

$$\ln(vw) = \ln v + \ln w \qquad\qquad \log_b (vw) = \log_b v + \log_b w$$

$$\ln\left(\frac{v}{w}\right) = \ln v - \ln w \qquad\qquad \log_b \left(\frac{v}{w}\right) = \log_b v - \log_b w$$

$$\ln(v^k) = k \ln v \qquad\qquad \log_b (v^k) = k \log_b v$$

- *Exponential Growth Functions:*

$$f(x) = P(1 + r)^x \quad (0 < r < 1)$$
$$f(x) = Pa^x \quad (a > 1)$$
$$f(x) = Pe^{kx} \quad (k > 0)$$

- *Exponential Decay Functions:*

$$f(x) = P(1 - r)^x \quad (0 < r < 1)$$
$$f(x) = Pa^x \quad (0 < a < 1)$$
$$f(x) = Pe^{kx} \quad (k < 0)$$

- *Logistic Function:* $f(x) = \dfrac{a}{1 + be^{-kx}}$

- *Compound Interest Formula:* $A = P(1 + r)^t$

- *Continuous Compounding:* $A = Pe^{rt}$

- *Radioactive Decay Function:* $f(x) = P(0.5)^{\frac{x}{h}}$

- *Change of Base Formula:* $\log_b v = \dfrac{\ln v}{\ln b}$

Review Exercises

Section 5.1

In Exercises 1–6, simplify the expression.

1. $\sqrt{\sqrt[3]{c^{12}}}$ c^2

2. $\left(\sqrt[3]{4c^3 d^2}\right)^3\left(c\sqrt{d}\right)^2$ $4c^{11}d^7$

3. $\left(a^{-\frac{2}{3}}b^{\frac{2}{5}}\right)\left(a^3 b^6\right)^{\frac{4}{3}}$ $a^{\frac{10}{3}}b^{\frac{42}{5}}$

4. $\dfrac{(3c)^{\frac{3}{5}}(2d)^{-2}(4c)^{\frac{1}{2}}}{(4c)^{\frac{1}{5}}(2d)^4(2c)^{-\frac{3}{2}}}$ $\dfrac{3^{\frac{3}{5}}c^{\frac{12}{5}}}{2^{\frac{39}{10}}d^6}$

5. $\left(u^{\frac{1}{4}}-v^{\frac{1}{4}}\right)\left(u^{\frac{1}{4}}+v^{\frac{1}{4}}\right)$ $u^{\frac{1}{2}}-v^{\frac{1}{2}}$

6. $c^{\frac{3}{2}}\left(2c^{\frac{1}{2}}+3c^{-\frac{3}{2}}\right)$ $2c^2+3$

In Exercises 7 and 8, simplify and write the expression without radicals or negative exponents.

7. $\dfrac{\sqrt[3]{6c^4 d^{14}}}{\sqrt[3]{48c^{-2}d^2}}$ $\dfrac{c^2 d^4}{2}$

8. $\dfrac{(8u^5)^{\frac{1}{4}}2^{-1}u^{-3}}{2u^8}$ $\dfrac{1}{2^{\frac{5}{4}}u^{\frac{39}{4}}}$

9. Rationalize the numerator and simplify: $\dfrac{\sqrt{2x+2h+1}-\sqrt{2x+1}}{h}$ $\dfrac{2}{\sqrt{2x+2h+1}+\sqrt{2x+1}}$

10. Rationalize the denominator: $\dfrac{5}{\sqrt{x}-3}$ $\dfrac{5\sqrt{x}+15}{x-9}$

Section 5.2

In Exercises 11–16, list the transformations needed to transform the graph of $f(x)=5^x$ into the graph of the given function.

11. $g(x)=-2\cdot 5^x$

12. $h(x)=5^{3x}$

13. $k(x)=5^{-\frac{1}{2}x}$

14. $g(x)=5^{2-x}$

15. $h(x)=5^x+4$

16. $h(x)=-5^{x+2}$

In Exercises 17 and 18, find a viewing window (or windows) that shows a complete graph of the function.

17. $f(x)=2^{x^3-x-2}$ $\begin{array}{l}-3\le x\le 3;\\ 0\le y\le 2\end{array}$

18. $g(x)=\dfrac{850}{1+5e^{-0.4r}}$ $-10\le x\le 30;\ -10\le y\le 1000$

19. Compunote offers a starting salary of $60,000 with $1000 yearly raises. Calcuplay offers a starting salary of $30,000 with a 6% raise each year.

   a. Complete the following table for each company.

Year	Compunote	Year	Calcuplay
1	$60,000	1	$30,000
2	$61,000	2	$31,800
3	**$62,000**	3	**$33,708**
4	**$63,000**	4	**$35,730**
5	**$64,000**	5	**$37,874**

   b. For each company write a function that gives your salary in terms of years employed. $S=60,000+1000(t-1);\ S=30,000(1.06)^{t-1}$

   c. If you plan on staying with the company for only five years, which job should you take to earn the most money? **Compunote**

   d. If you plan on staying with the company for 20 years, which is your best choice? **Calcuplay will be paying more this time, but your total earnings will be more from Compunote**

11. Reflection across the *x*-axis, stretch vertically by a factor of 2

12. Compress horizontally by a factor of $\dfrac{1}{3}$

13. Reflection across the *y*-axis, stretch horizontally by a factor of 2

14. Reflection across the *y*-axis, horizontal translation of 2 units to the right

15. Vertical translation of 4 units upward

16. Reflection across the *x*-axis, horizontal translation of 2 units left

20. A computer software company claims that the following function models the "learning curve" for their software.

$$P(t) = \frac{100}{1 + 48.2e^{-0.52t}}$$

where t is measured in months and $P(t)$ is the average percent of the software program's capabilities mastered after t months.

   a. Initially what percent of the program is mastered? **≈2.03%**
   b. After 6 months what percent of the program is mastered? **≈31.97%**
   c. Roughly, when can a person expect to "learn the most in the least amount of time"? **between about months 6 and 10**
   d. If the company's claim is true, how many months will it take to have completely mastered the program?
   never; $y = 100$ is a horizontal asymptote

Section 5.3

21. Phil borrows $800 at 9% annual interest, compounded annually.
   a. How much does he owe after 6 years? **≈$1341.68**
   b. If he pays off the loan at the end of 6 years, how much interest will he owe? **$541.68**

22. If you invest $5000 for 5 years at 9% annual interest, how much more will you make if interest is compounded continuously than if it is compounded quarterly?
   ≈$39.01

23. Mary Karen invests $2000 at 5.5% annual interest, compounded monthly.
   a. How much is her investment worth in 3 years? **≈$2357.90**
   b. When will her investment be worth $12,000?
   after ≈32.65 years

24. If a $2000 investment grows to $5000 in 14 years, with interest compounded annually, what is the interest rate?
   ≈6.8%

25. Company sales are increasing at 6.5% per year. If sales this year are $56,000, write the rule of a function that gives the sales in year x (where $x = 0$ corresponds to the present year). **$f(x) = 56,000(1.065)^x$**

26. The population of Potterville is decreasing at an annual rate of 1.5%. If the population is 38,500 now, what will be the population x years from now?
   $38,500(0.985)^x$

27. The half-life of carbon-14 is 5730 years. How much carbon-14 remains from an original 16 grams after 12,000 years?
   ≈3.75 grams

28. How long will it take for 4 grams of carbon-14 to decay to 1 gram?
   ≈11,460 years

Section 5.4

In Exercises 29–34, translate the given exponential statement into an equivalent logarithmic one.

29. $e^{6.628} = 756$
   ln 756 = 6.628

30. $e^{5.8972} = 364$
   ln 364 = 5.8972

31. $e^{r^2-1} = u + v$
   ln$(u + v) = r^2 - 1$

32. $e^{a-b} = c$
   ln $c = a - b$

33. $10^{2.8785} = 756$
   log 756 = 2.8785

34. $10^{c+d} = t$
   log $t = c + d$

In Exercises 35–38, translate the given logarithmic statement into an equivalent exponential one.

35. ln 1234 = 7.118
   $e^{7.118} = 1234$

36. ln$(ax + b) = y$
   $e^y = ax + b$

37. ln$(rs) = t$
   $e^t = rs$

38. log 1234 = 3.0913
   $10^{3.0913} = 1234$

39. Find log(-0.01).
   undefined

In Exercises 40–43, describe the transformation from $f(x) = \log x$ or $g(x) = \ln x$ to the given function. Give the domain and range of the given function.

40. $h(x) = -\dfrac{1}{2}\log(x + 3)$ **41.** $k(x) = \log(4 - x)$

42. $h(x) = \ln(3x)$ **43.** $k(x) = 3\ln x - 5$

44. You are conducting an experiment about memory. The people who participate agree to take a test at the end of your course and every month thereafter for a period of two years. The average score for the group is given by the model $M(t) = 91 - 14\ln(t + 1)$, $0 \le t \le 24$, where t is time in months after the first test.

    a. What is the average score on the initial exam? **91**

    b. What is the average score after three months? **≈71.6**

    c. When will the average drop below 50%? **after 18 months**

    d. Is the magnitude of the rate of memory loss greater in the first month after the course (from $t = 0$ to $t = 1$) or after the first year (from $t = 12$ to $t = 13$)? **The loss is greater in the first month.**

    e. Hypothetically, if the model could be extended past $t = 24$ months, would it be possible for the average score to be 0%?
    The model predicts 0% after about 664 months.

Section 5.5   In Exercises 45–48, evaluate the given expression without using a calculator.

45. $\ln e^3$ **3**   **46.** $\ln e$ **1**   **47.** $e^{\ln \frac{3}{4}}$ $\dfrac{3}{4}$ **48.** $e^{\ln(x + 2y)}$ $x + 2y$

49. Simplify: $3\ln\sqrt{x} + \dfrac{1}{2}\ln x$ **2 ln x**   **50.** Simplify: $\ln(e^{4e})^{-1} + 4e$ **0**

In Exercises 51 and 52, write the given expression as a single logarithm.

51. $\ln 3x - 3\ln x + \ln 3y$ $\ln\left(\dfrac{9y}{x^2}\right)$ **52.** $4\ln x - 2(\ln x^3 + 4\ln x)$ **−10 ln x**

53. Which of the following statements is *true*? **c**

    a. $\ln 10 = (\ln 2)(\ln 5)$ **b.** $\ln\left(\dfrac{e}{6}\right) = \ln e + \ln 6$

    c. $\ln\left(\dfrac{1}{7}\right) + \ln 7 = 0$ **d.** $\ln(-e) = -1$

    e. None of the above is true.

54. Which of the following statements is *false*? **a, d, and e**

    a. $10(\log 5) = \log 50$ **b.** $\log 100 + 3 = \log 10^5$

    c. $\log 1 = \ln 1$ **d.** $\dfrac{\log 6}{\log 3} = \log 2$

    e. All of the above are false.

55. What is the domain of the function $f(x) = \ln\left(\dfrac{x}{x - 1}\right)$?
    $(-\infty, 0)$ **and** $(1, \infty)$

Section 5.5.A   In Exercises 56 and 57, translate the given logarithmic statement into an equivalent exponential one.

56. $\log_5(cd - k) = u$ $5^u = cd - k$ **57.** $\log_d(uv) = w$ $d^w = uv$

58. Write $\log_7 7x + \log_7 y - 1$ as a single logarithm. $\log_7(xy)$

59. $\log_{20} 400 = ?$ **2**   **60.** If $\log_3 9^{x^2} = 4$, what is x? $x = \pm\sqrt{2}$

40. Reflection across the *x*-axis, vertical compression by a factor of $\dfrac{1}{2}$, horizontal translation of 3 units to the left; Domain: all real numbers > -3; Range: all real numbers

41. Reflection across the *y*-axis, horizontal translation of 4 units to the right; Domain: all real numbers < 4; Range: all real numbers

42. Horizontal compression of $\dfrac{1}{3}$; Domain: all positive real numbers; Range: all real numbers

43. Vertical stretch by a factor of 3, vertical translation of 5 units downward; Domain: all positive real numbers; Range: all real numbers

Use the following six graphs for Exercises 61 and 62.

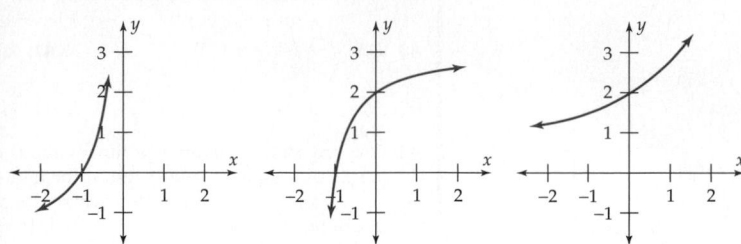

Figure I Figure II Figure III

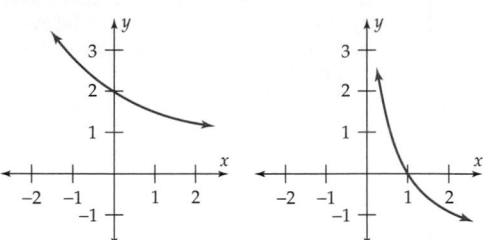

Figure IV Figure V Figure VI

61. If $b > 1$, then the graph of $f(x) = -\log_b x$ could possibly be **c**
  a. I   **c.** V   **e.** none of these
  b. IV   **d.** VI

62. If $0 < b < 1$ then the graph of $g(x) = b^x + 1$ could possibly be **c**
  a. II   **c.** IV   **e.** none of these
  b. III   **d.** VI

Section 5.6

In Exercises 63–71, solve the equation for x.

63. $8^x = 4^{x^2-3}$ $\dfrac{3 \pm \sqrt{57}}{4}$ **64.** $e^{3x} = 4$ $\approx$**0.4621**   **65.** $2 \cdot 4^x - 5 = -4$ $-\dfrac{1}{2}$

66. $725e^{-4x} = 1500$ $\approx$**0.1818**   **67.** $u = c + d \ln x$ $e^{\frac{(u-c)}{d}}$ **68.** $2^x = 3^{x+3}$ $\approx$**−8.1285**

69. $\ln x + \ln (3x - 5) = \ln 2$ **2**   **70.** $\ln (x + 8) - \ln x = 1$ $\dfrac{8}{e-1}$

71. $\log (x^2 - 1) = 2 + \log (x + 1)$ **101**

72. At a small community college the spread of a rumor through the population of 500 faculty and students can be modeled by

$$\ln n - \ln(1000 - 2n) = 0.65t - \ln 998,$$

where n is the number of people who have heard the rumor after t days.
  a. How many people know the rumor initially (at $t = 0$)? **1 person**
  b. How many people have heard the rumor after four days? **13 people**
  c. Roughly, in how many weeks will the entire population have heard the rumor? $\approx$**3 weeks**
  d. Use the properties of logarithms to write n as a function of t; in other words solve the model above for n in terms of t.
  $$n = \frac{1000e^{0.65t}}{998 + 2e^{0.65t}}$$

yes

e. Enter the function you found in part **d** into your calculator and use the table feature to check your answers to parts **a**, **b**, and **c**. Do they agree?

f. Graph the function. Over what time interval does the rumor seem to "spread" the fastest?

about day 7 to 14

73. The half-life of polonium (^{210}Po) is 140 days. If you start with 10 milligrams, how much will be left at the end of a year?

≈1.64 mg

74. An insect colony grows exponentially from 200 to 2000 in 3 months. How long will it take for the insect population to reach 50,000?

≈7.19 mo

75. Hydrogen-3 decays at a rate of 5.59% per year. Find its half-life.

≈12 yr

76. The half-life of radium-88 is 1590 years. How long will it take for 10 grams to decay to 1 gram?

≈5281.87 yr

77. How much money should be invested at 8% per year, compounded quarterly, in order to have $1000 in 10 years?

≈$452.89

78. At what annual interest rate should you invest your money if you want to double it in 6 years?

≈12.25%

79. One earthquake measures 4.6 on the Richter scale. A second earthquake is 1000 times more intense than the first. What does it measure on the Richter scale?

≈7.6

Section 5.7 **80.** The table below gives the population of Austin, Texas.

Year	1950	1970	1980	1990	2000
Population	132,459	253,539	345,890	465,622	656,562

a. Sketch a scatter plot of the data, with $x = 0$ corresponding to 1950.
b. Find an exponential model for the data.
c. Use the model to estimate the population of Austin in 1960 and 2005.

81. The wind-chill factor is the temperature that would produce the same cooling effect on a person's skin if there were no wind. The table shows the wind-chill factors for various wind speeds when the temperature is 25°F.

Wind speed (mph)	0	5	10	15	20	25	30	35	40	45
Wind chill temperature (°F)	25	19	15	13	11	9	8	7	6	5

[*Source: National Weather Service*]

a. What does a 20-mph wind make 25°F feel like?
b. Sketch a scatter plot of the data, with $x = 0$ corresponding to 0 mph.
c. Explain why an exponential model would be appropriate.
d. Find an exponential model for the data.
e. According to the model, what is the wind chill factor for a 23-mph wind?

80. a.

b. $y = 132,947.53(1.032285)^x$

c. ≈182,675; ≈763,254

81. a. 11°F

b.

c. The points $(x, \ln(y))$ are approximately linear.

d. $y = 22.42(0.967^x)$

e. ≈10.27°F

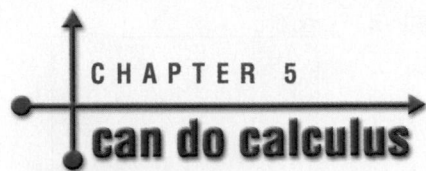

CHAPTER 5
can do calculus

Tangents to Exponential Functions

Math Background

In this section students will learn that:

- The slope of the tangent line to the exponential function $y = e^x$ at (x, y) is e^x.
- The slope of the tangent line to the exponential function $y = 2^x$ at (x, y) is $\ln 2(2^x)$.

Later, in calculus, they will learn to use these derivative rules to find the same tangent line slopes:

- For $f(x) = e^x$, $f'(x) = e^x$.
- For $f(x) = a^x$, $f'(x) = \ln a(a^x)$, where $a > 0$, $a \neq 1$.

Note that e^x is a special case of a^x: For $f(x) = e^x$, $f'(x) = \ln e(e^x) = 1(e^x) = e^x$. Also note that the function $f(x) = e^x$ is the derivative of itself!

Teaching Notes

Ask students to show why $\dfrac{f(b + h) - f(b)}{h}$ is the slope of the secant line through the points $(b, f(b))$ and $(b + h, f(b + h))$.

$$\frac{f(b + h) - f(b)}{(b + h) - b} = \frac{f(b + h) - f(b)}{h}$$

By drawing the graph of $f(x) = e^x$ on an overhead transparency, you can use a piece of dry spaghetti to dynamically illustrate how the secant lines approach the tangent line as h gets close to zero (see Figure 5.C-1).

Explain to students that $\dfrac{f(x) - f(b)}{x - b}$ is another expression for the slope of a secant line, equivalent to $\dfrac{f(b + h) - f(b)}{h}$. Note that in both expressions, $(b, f(b))$ is a fixed point. In $\dfrac{f(x) - f(b)}{x - b}$, $(x, f(x))$ is the "moving point." Show that if $b + h = x$, then $\dfrac{f(b + h) - f(b)}{h} = \dfrac{f(x) - f(b)}{x - b}$.

CHAPTER 5
can do calculus
Tangents to Exponential Functions

Tangent lines to a curve are important in calculus—where they are used to approximate function values close to a specific point and used for finding the zeros of general functions. The procedure developed in the Can Do Calculus for Chapter 3 will be used here to develop the equations of the tangent lines to exponential functions.

Slopes of Secant Lines and Tangent Lines

Recall that the difference quotient of f at the specific value $x = b$ is given by

$$\frac{f(b + h) - f(b)}{h},$$

where h is the amount of change in the x values from one point to another. The difference quotient can be interpreted as the slope of the secant line that passes through the points $(b, f(b))$ and $(b + h, f(b + h))$. As h gets very small, the value of $\dfrac{f(b + h) - f(b)}{h}$ approaches the value of the slope of the tangent line at $(b, f(b))$.

Also, if f is any function, then the slope of the secant line through $(b, f(b))$ and any other point $(x, f(x))$ on the graph of f is given by

$$\frac{f(x) - f(b)}{x - b}.$$

As the point $(x, f(x))$ approaches the point $(b, f(b))$, the value of $\dfrac{f(x) - f(b)}{x - b}$ approaches the value of the slope of the tangent line to the curve at $(b, f(b))$. Figure 5.C-1 shows four secant lines that pass through the point $(b, f(b))$. The tangent line to f at $(b, f(b))$ is shown in red.

Tangent Lines to the Exponential Function

Consider the function $f(x) = e^x$ and the values of the slopes of secant lines that pass through $(0, e^0)$, that is, $(0, 1)$. Find the values of

$$\frac{f(x) - f(0)}{x - 0} = \frac{e^x - e^0}{x} = \frac{e^x - 1}{x}$$

when x is near 0.

x	-0.01	-0.001	0.001	0.01
$\dfrac{e^x - 1}{x}$	0.99502	0.9995	1.0005	1.005

Figure 5.C-1

408

(Figure: graph showing secant lines through $(x, f(x))$ and $(b, f(b))$, labeled f, with axes x and y, and point b.)

Figure 5.C-2

The table suggests that the slope of the tangent line to $f(x) = e^x$ at $x = 0$ is 1. The tangent line to the curve at $x = 0$ contains the point $(0, 1)$ and has slope $m = 1$. Therefore, the equation of the tangent line to $f(x) = e^x$ at $x = 0$ can be found by using the point-slope form of a line.

$$y - y_0 = m(x - x_0) \qquad \text{\textit{Point-slope form of a line}}$$
$$y - 1 = 1(x - 0)$$
$$y - 1 = x$$
$$y = x + 1 \qquad \text{\textit{Equation of tangent line}}$$

The graph of $f(x) = e^x$ and the tangent line to the curve at $(0, 1)$ is shown in Figure 5.C-2.

Example 1 Tangent Line to the Exponential Function

Find the tangent line to $f(x) = e^x$ when $x = 1$. Graph f and the tangent line.

Solution

When $x = 1, f(1) = e^1 = e$, so the point $(1, e)$ is the point where the tangent line will touch the graph. To find the slope of the tangent line, look at values of the difference quotient near $x = 1$.

$$\frac{f(x) - f(1)}{x - 1} = \frac{e^x - e^1}{x - 1} = \frac{e^x - e}{x - 1}$$

Alternately, you may use the numerical derivative feature of your calculator to find an approximate value of the slope of the tangent line for $f(x) = e^x$ at $x = 1$. You should find that the value of the slope of the tangent line is approximately 2.718282282.

Recall that $e \approx 2.71828$. It appears that the slope of the tangent line to $f(x) = e^x$ at $(1, e)$ is e, which can be proved using calculus. Therefore, the tangent line's equation is

$$y - e = e(x - 1) \qquad \text{or equivalently} \qquad y = ex$$

and the graphs of f and the tangent line are in Figure 5.C-3b. ∎

Figure 5.C-3a

Figure 5.C-3b

> **Calculator Exploration** ●
>
> Find the slope of the tangent lines to $f(x) = e^x$ when $x = -3, -2,$ $-1, 2, 3, 4$. Plot the points (x, y), where y is the slope of the tangent line, along with the corresponding points for $x = 0, 1$. What function would represent the graph of these points?

409

Solution to the **Calculator Exploration:**

x	slope
-3	0.0498
-2	0.1353
-1	0.3679
2	7.3891
3	20.086
4	54.598

The plotted points are shown in Figure 5.C-4 on page 410. The function $f(x) = e^x$ would represent these points.

Figure 5.C-4 on page 410.

Example Notes

The slope-intercept form of an equation of a line is $y - y_1 = m(x - x_1)$. It is used in **Example 1** to find the equation of the tangent line through the point $(1, e)$ with slope e. Using $x_1 = 1, y_1 = e$, and $m = e$, the steps are:

$$y - y_1 = m(x - x_1)$$
$$y - e = e(x - 1)$$
$$y - e = ex - e$$
$$y = ex$$

Emphasize that $y = ex$ is *not* $y = e^x$.

ADDITIONAL EXAMPLES

Example 1

Find the tangent line to $f(x) = e^x$ when $x = 0.5$. Graph f and the tangent line.

values of the difference quotient $\frac{e^x - e^{0.5}}{x - 0.5}$ near $x = 0.5$:

equation of the tangent line at $(0.5, e^{0.5})$:

$$y = e^{0.5}x + e^{0.5}$$

Teaching Notes

For the **Calculator Exploration**, remind students that the tangent line to $f(x) = e^x$ has slope $= 1$ at $(0, 1)$ and slope $= e$ at $(1, e)$. In the Calculator Exploration, they will find the slopes for other points.

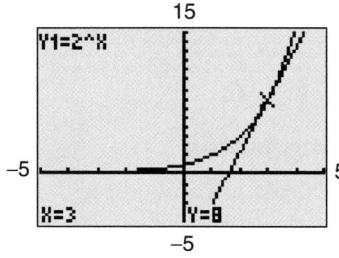
In the Calculator Exploration, you should have found the values and plotted the points shown in Figure 5.C-4. Also shown in Figure 5.C-4 are all the points on the graph of $f(x) = e^x$.

Figure 5.C-4

Slope of the Tangent line to $y = e^x$

> The slope of the tangent line at any point on $y = e^x$ has the same value as the y coordinate, e^x, at that point.

The exponential function is the only function with this characteristic.

Example 2 Slope of $y = e^x$

a. Find the x-value where the slope of $y = e^x$ is e^3.

b. Write the equation of the tangent line at $x = 3$.

c. Graph $y = e^x$ and the tangent line at $x = 3$ on the same screen.

Solution

a. The slope of $y = e^x$ is e^3 when $x = 3$.

b. Using the point-slope form of a line with $m = e^3$ and $(3, e^3)$, the equation of the tangent line to $y = e^x$ at $x = 3$ is

$$y - e^3 = e^3(x - 3)$$
$$y = e^3x - 2e^3 = e^3(x - 2)$$

c. The graphs of $y = e^x$ and $y = e^3(x - 2)$ are shown in Figure 5.C-5.

Figure 5.C-5

Exponential Functions with Bases Other Than *e*

The procedure for finding the equation of the tangent line at a specific value of x for exponential functions with bases other than e is the same as that for finding the equation of the tangent line at a specific value of x for any function.

1. Find the values of slopes of secant lines by using the difference quotient and several values of x near the point in question.

2. Find the slope of the tangent line by determining the value of the slope suggested by the values found in Step 1.

3. Write the equation of the tangent line using the point-slope form of a linear equation.

4. Confirm your finding by graphing the function and the tangent line.

Find the values of the slope of the tangent line for $y = 2^x$ at $x = -2, -1,$ $0, 1, 2, 3$. Graph the ordered pairs (x, slope of tangent) and find an equation to represent the graph by using exponential regression.

The points to be graphed in the Calculator Exploration are

$(-2, 0.17329)\ (-1, 0.34657)\ (0, 0.69315)\ (1, 1.3863)\ (2, 2.7726)\ (3, 5.5452)$

and the regression equation is

$$y = 0.6931471806(2^x).$$

Notice that $\ln 2 \approx 0.6931471806$. In fact, the slope of the tangent line at any point $(c, f(c))$ on the graph of $f(x) = 2^x$ is given by $\ln 2 \cdot f(c)$, or $\ln 2\ (2^c)$.

Example 3 Tangent Line of $y = 2^x$

Find the equation of the tangent line to the curve $y = 2^x$ at $x = 4$, and confirm your result by graphing.

Solution

The point on the curve at $x = 4$ is $(4, 2^4)$, or $(4, 16)$. The slope of the tangent line at that point is $(\ln 2)(16) \approx 11.09$, so the equation of the tangent line of $f(x) = 2^x$ at $(4, 16)$ is

$$y - 16 = 11.09(x - 4)$$
$$y = 11.09(x - 4) + 16$$

The graph of $f(x) = 2^x$ and $y = 11.09(x - 4) + 16$ are shown in Figure 5.C-6.

Figure 5.C-6

Teaching Notes

Solution to the **Calculator Exploration:**

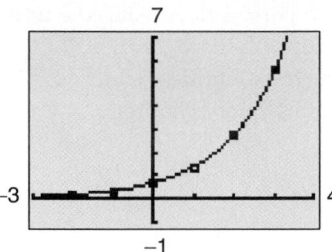

The regression equation is $y = 0.6931460951(2^x)$. Since $\ln 2$ is approximately equal to 0.6931460951, the exponential function of best fit for the points in the scatter plot above is $f(x) = \ln 2\ (2^x)$.

🌐 Real-World Application

The function $y = 3.9572(1.0299^x)$ is the exponential model of the U.S. population before the Civil War (page 390). Its graph is shown below with the tangent line at the point $(10, 5.31)$. The slope of the tangent line to the graph of a function at a point represents the instantaneous rate of change in the function values at that point. For this function model, $x = 10$ corresponds to the year 1800. The slope of the tangent line is approximately 0.16 at that point. So, in the year 1800, according to the model, the U.S. population was increasing at the rate of 0.16 million, or 160,000 per year.

Exercises

In Exercises 1–4, write the equation of the tangent line at the following values of x for the function $f(x) = e^{-x}$. Graph the function along with the tangent at each point.

1. $x = 0$
2. $x = 1$
3. $x = 2$
4. $x = -2$

In Exercises 5–8, write the equation of the tangent line at the following values of x for the function $f(x) = e^x + 2$. Graph the function along with the tangent at each point.

5. $x = 0$
6. $x = 1$
7. $x = 2$
8. $x = -2$

In Exercises 9–12, write the equation of the tangent line at the following values of x for the function $f(x) = 3^x$. Graph the function along with the tangent at each point.

9. $x = 0$
10. $x = 1$
11. $x = 2$
12. $x = -2$

411

Exercises

ANSWERS

1–12. *For graphs, see pp. 1067–1068.*

1. $y = -x + 1$
2. $y = -e^{-1}(x - 1) + e^{-1}$
3. $y = -e^{-2}(x - 2) + e^{-2}$
4. $y = -e^2(x + 2) + e^2$
5. $y = x + 3$
6. $y = e(x - 1) + e + 2$
7. $y = e^2(x - 2) + e^2 + 2$
8. $y = e^{-2}(x + 2) + e^{-2} + 2$
9. $y = (\ln 3)x + 1$
10. $y = (3 \ln 3)(x - 1) + 3$
11. $y = (9 \ln 3)(x - 2) + 9$
12. $y = \left(\dfrac{1}{9} \ln 3\right)(x + 2) + \dfrac{1}{9}$

Trigonometry

In this chapter, students will use right-triangle trigonometry and the six trigonometric ratios to explore many different applications. They will also study trigonometry from a functional perspective, using the unit circle. They will discover basic trigonometric identities, which will be used in subsequent chapters.

CHAPTER

6

Trigonometry

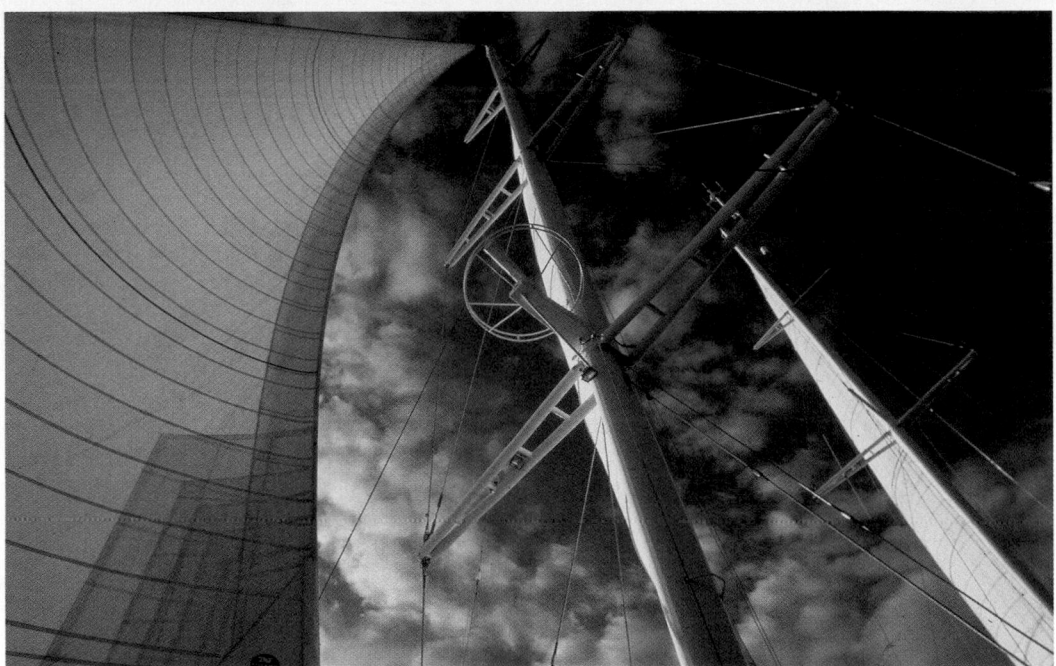

Where are we?

Navigators at sea must determine their location. Surveyors need to determine the height of a mountain or the width of a canyon when direct measurement is not feasible. A fighter plane's computer must set the course of a missile so that it will hit a moving target. Many phenomena such as the tides, seasonal change, and radio waves, have cycles that repeat. All of the situations can be described mathematically using trigonometry.

412

Chapter Outline

Interdependence of Sections

T**rigonometry,** which means "triangle measurement," was developed in ancient times for determining the angles and sides of triangles in order to solve problems in astronomy, navigation, and surveying. With the development of calculus and physics in the 17th century, a different viewpoint toward trigonometry arose, and trigonometry was used to model all kinds of periodic behavior, such as sound waves, vibrations, and planetary orbits. In this chapter, you will be introduced to both types of trigonometry, beginning with right-triangle trigonometry.

 # Right-Triangle Trigonometry

Objectives

- Define the six trigonometric ratios of an acute angle in terms of a right triangle
- Evaluate trigonometric ratios, using triangles and on a calculator

Angles and Degree Measure

Recall from geometry that an **angle** is a figure formed by two rays with a common endpoint, called the **vertex.** The rays are called the **sides** of the angle. An angle may be labeled by the angle symbol ($\angle$) and the vertex. The angle in Figure 6.1-1 may be labeled $\angle A$.

Figure 6.1-1

413

Teaching Notes

Point out to students that they have already solved problems involving triangle measurement and periodic behavior. Give familiar examples of these two types of problems. For the first type, remind students that they have used triangles to solve problems, for example, by finding lengths of sides using the Pythagorean Theorem or finding the measures of angles using similar triangles.

For the second type, show a specific example of something that exhibits periodic behavior, like the number of daylight hours in a year. Plot seasons of the year on the x-axis and hours of daylight on the y-axis. Explain that the number of daylight hours decreases to a minimum in the winter and reaches a maximum in the summer and that this behavior repeats itself for the following year.

Teaching Notes

Make the following chart to help summarize the first paragraph.

Part of Circle	Degree Measure
Whole	360
Half	$\left(\frac{1}{2}\right) \cdot 360 = 180$
Quarter	$\left(\frac{1}{4}\right) \cdot 360 = 90$

To help students understand the conversion of degrees, minutes, and seconds have students replace the word *degree* with *hours*:

One minute is $\frac{1}{60}$ of an *hour*.

One second is $\frac{1}{3600}$ of an *hour*.

Example Notes

In **Example 1a,** you may want to provide the following details for the first equation:

$$1' = \left(\frac{1}{60}\right)^\circ \quad \Big| \quad 1'' = \left(\frac{1}{3600}\right)^\circ$$

$$15 \cdot 1' = 15 \cdot \left(\frac{1}{60}\right)^\circ \quad \Big| \quad 27 \cdot 1'' = 27 \cdot \left(\frac{1}{3600}\right)^\circ$$

$$15' = \left(\frac{15}{60}\right)^\circ \quad \Big| \quad 27'' = \left(\frac{27}{3600}\right)^\circ$$

In **Example 1b,** to find the number of minutes in 0.3625° multiply by 60.
$0.3625° = (0.3625 \times 60)' = 21.75'$

To find the number of seconds in 0.75 minutes multiply by 60.
$0.75' = (0.75 \times 60)'' = 45''$

The solutions to Examples 1a and b may be verified on a calculator:

```
35°15'27"*1
          35.2575
48.3625°▸DMS
       48°21'45"
```

Some students may think that $10° 30' = 10.30°$. Remind them that

$$30' = 30\left(\frac{1}{60}\right)^\circ = \left(\frac{30}{60}\right)^\circ = 0.5°.$$

Angles may be measured in *degrees*, where 1 **degree** (°) is $\frac{1}{360}$ of a circle. (See Figure 6.1-2.) Thus, a 360° angle is an entire circle, a 180° angle is half of a circle, and a 90° angle is a quarter of a circle. A 90° angle is also called a **right angle.** A right angle is indicated on a diagram by a small square, as shown in Figure 6.1-3. An angle of less than 90° is called an **acute angle.** The measure of an angle is indicated by the letter m in front of the angle symbol, such as $m\angle A = 36°$.

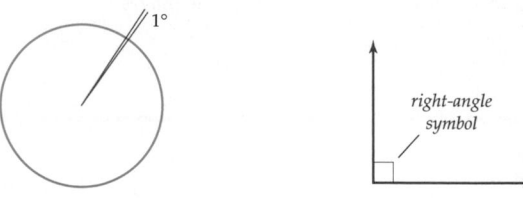

Figure 6.1-2   **Figure 6.1-3**

Minutes and Seconds

Fractional parts of a degree are usually expressed in decimal form or in *minutes* and *seconds*. A **minute** (') is $\frac{1}{60}$ of a degree, and a **second** (") is $\frac{1}{60}$ of a minute, or $\frac{1}{3600}$ of a degree. This form is often called **DMS form,** for degrees, minutes, seconds.

Example 1   Converting Between Decimal Form and DMS Form

a. Write 35° 15′ 27″ in decimal form.

b. Write 48.3625° in DMS form.

Solution

a. $35° \, 15' \, 27'' = 35° + \left(\frac{15}{60}\right)^\circ + \left(\frac{27}{3600}\right)^\circ$

$= 35° + 0.25° + 0.0075°$

$= 35.2575°$

b. First, convert the entire decimal part to minutes by writing it in terms of $\frac{1}{60}$ of a degree.

$$48.3625° = 48° + 0.3625° = 48° + \left(\frac{60}{60}\right)0.3625°$$

$$= 48° + \left(\frac{21.75}{60}\right)^\circ = 48° + 21.75'$$

Second, convert the decimal part of the minutes to seconds by writing it in terms of $\frac{1}{60}$ of a minute.

$$48° + 21.75' = 48° + 21' + \left(\frac{60}{60}\right)0.75'$$
$$= 48° + 21' + \left(\frac{45}{60}\right)'$$
$$= 48° \, 21' \, 45''$$

Similar Triangles and Trigonometric Ratios

Examine the following right triangles.

Figure 6.1-4

$$\frac{a}{c} = \frac{d}{f} \qquad\qquad \frac{b}{c} = \frac{e}{f} \qquad\qquad \frac{a}{b} = \frac{d}{e}$$

Since all right triangles that contain a 34° angle are similar, the corresponding ratios would be the same. Thus, the ratio is dependent only on the measure of the angle. These ratios, which can be determined for any angle between 0° and 90°, are the basis of trigonometry.

The **hypotenuse** (hyp) of a right triangle is the side across from the right angle. The hypotenuse is always the longest side of the triangle. The remaining sides are labeled by their relationship to the given angle, as shown in Figure 6.1-5. The **adjacent** (adj) side is the side of the given angle that is *not* the hypotenuse, and the **opposite** (opp) side is the side of the triangle that is across from the given angle.

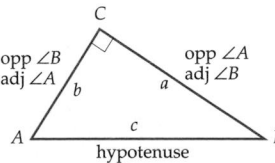

Figure 6.1-5

In the figure, if $\angle A$ is the given angle, the adjacent side is b and the opposite side is a. If $\angle B$ is the given angle, the adjacent side is a and the opposite side is b.

There are six possible ratios for the three sides of a triangle. These ratios are called **trigonometric ratios.**

ADDITIONAL EXAMPLES

Example 1

a. Write 42° 30′ 9″ in decimal form.
  42.5025°

b. Write 31.4125° in DMS form.
  31° 24′ 45″

 Math Background

The Babylonians used a base 60 number system and divided 1 hour into 60 minutes and 1 minute into 60 seconds. They also divided the circle into 360 degrees.

 Real-World Application

An example of an application that utilizes the DMS form of angle measure is the Global Positioning System (GPS). GPS uses satellites orbiting the Earth that give the coordinates (longitude and latitude) of a receiver on the Earth, by transmitting signals. For example, the coordinates of a location may be given as N 38° 51′ 0″ W 77° 2′ 14″.

Challenge students to convert this location to decimal form.
N 38.85° W 77.0372°

Each degree latitude is approximately equal to 70 miles. About how far north of the equator is this location? about 2,719.5 miles

Teaching Notes

In **Similar Triangles and Trigonometric Ratios,** ask students why the triangles in Figure 6.1-4 are similar, (Angle-Angle Similarity Postulate—two angles of one triangle are congruent to two angles of the other triangle, so the triangles are similar) and why the corresponding ratios are the same. (corresponding sides of similar triangles are proportional)

For Figure 6.1-5, have students draw another right triangle in a different orientation than the one shown and label the sides and angles. Then for each acute angle, have them identify the sides opposite and adjacent to that angle.

Teaching Notes

To help students remember the **Trigonometric Ratios**, suggest the following mnemonic:

SOH-CAH-TOA

- **SOH:** *Sine* is *Opposite* over *Hypotenuse*
- **CAH:** *Cosine* is *Adjacent* over *Hypotenuse*
- **TOA:** *Tangent* is *Opposite* over *Adjacent*

When **Evaluating Trigonometric Ratios Using a Calculator,** stress that the calculator needs to be set in the correct mode. For this section, make sure the mode is set to "degree." Radian measure will be introduced in Section 6.3.

Example Notes

In **Example 3,** the calculated values of the six trigonometric ratios are all approximate because the side lengths as given are approximate. For example, the solution has $\sin 62° \approx 0.8824$. Using a calculator, $\sin 62° \approx 0.8829475929$. Note that the calculator value is also an approximation.

ADDITIONAL EXAMPLES

Example 2

Evaluate the six trigonometric ratios of the angle θ, as shown below.

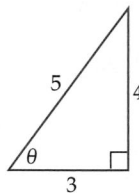

$\sin \theta = \dfrac{4}{5} = 0.8 \qquad \csc \theta = \dfrac{5}{4} = 1.25$

$\cos \theta = \dfrac{3}{5} = 0.6 \qquad \sec \theta = \dfrac{5}{3} \approx 1.6667$

$\tan \theta = \dfrac{4}{3} \approx 1.3333 \quad \cot \theta = \dfrac{3}{4} = 0.75$

Trigonometric Ratios

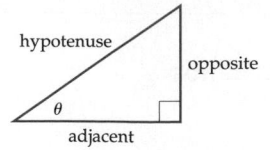

Figure 6.1-6

NOTE The Greek letter θ (theta) is commonly used to label the measure of an angle in trigonometry.

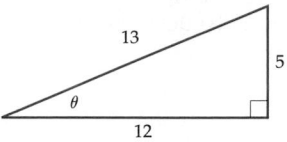

Figure 6.1-7

For a given acute angle θ in a right triangle:

The *sine* of θ, written as $\sin \theta$, is the ratio

$$\sin \theta = \frac{\text{opposite}}{\text{hypotenuse}}$$

The *cosine* of θ, written as $\cos \theta$, is the ratio

$$\cos \theta = \frac{\text{adjacent}}{\text{hypotenuse}}$$

The *tangent* of θ, written as $\tan \theta$, is the ratio

$$\tan \theta = \frac{\text{opposite}}{\text{adjacent}}$$

In addition, the reciprocal of each ratio above is also a trigonometric ratio.

cosecant of θ *secant* of θ *cotangent* of θ

$$\csc \theta = \frac{\text{hypotenuse}}{\text{opposite}} \qquad \sec \theta = \frac{\text{hypotenuse}}{\text{adjacent}} \qquad \cot \theta = \frac{\text{adjacent}}{\text{opposite}}$$

$$= \frac{1}{\sin \theta} \qquad\qquad = \frac{1}{\cos \theta} \qquad\qquad = \frac{1}{\tan \theta}$$

Example 2   Evaluating Trigonometric Ratios

Evaluate the six trigonometric ratios of the angle θ shown in Figure 6.1-7.

Solution

The opposite side has length 5, the adjacent side has length 12, and the hypotenuse has length 13.

$$\sin \theta = \frac{\text{opposite}}{\text{hypotenuse}} = \frac{5}{13} \approx 0.3846 \quad \csc \theta = \frac{\text{hypotenuse}}{\text{opposite}} = \frac{13}{5} = 2.6$$

$$\cos \theta = \frac{\text{adjacent}}{\text{hypotenuse}} = \frac{12}{13} \approx 0.9231 \quad \sec \theta = \frac{\text{hypotenuse}}{\text{adjacent}} = \frac{13}{12} \approx 1.0833$$

$$\tan \theta = \frac{\text{opposite}}{\text{adjacent}} = \frac{5}{12} \approx 0.4167 \qquad \cot \theta = \frac{\text{adjacent}}{\text{opposite}} = \frac{12}{5} = 2.4$$

Example 3   Evaluating Trigonometric Ratios

Evaluate the six trigonometric ratios of 62° by using the triangle in Figure 6.1-8. (Side lengths given are approximate.)

3

1.6

θ 62°

3.4

Figure 6.1-8

Solution

$$\sin 62° = \frac{\text{opposite}}{\text{hypotenuse}} \approx \frac{3}{3.4} \approx 0.8824 \quad \csc 62° = \frac{\text{hypotenuse}}{\text{opposite}} \approx \frac{3.4}{3} \approx 1.1333$$

$$\cos 62° = \frac{\text{adjacent}}{\text{hypotenuse}} \approx \frac{1.6}{3.4} \approx 0.4706 \quad \sec 62° = \frac{\text{hypotenuse}}{\text{adjacent}} \approx \frac{3.4}{1.6} \approx 2.1250$$

$$\tan 62° = \frac{\text{opposite}}{\text{adjacent}} \approx \frac{3}{1.6} \approx 1.8750 \quad \cot 62° = \frac{\text{adjacent}}{\text{opposite}} \approx \frac{1.6}{3} \approx 0.5333$$

Evaluating Trigonometric Ratios Using a Calculator

If the measure of an angle is given without a corresponding triangle, it may be difficult to accurately evaluate the trigonometric ratios of that angle. For example, to find sin 20°, it would be possible to draw a right triangle with an angle of 20° and measure its sides. However, there may be inaccuracies in drawing and measuring the triangle. Tables of trigonometric ratios are available, but it is usually most convenient to use a calculator.

Technology Tip

The following facts will be helpful in evaluating trigonometric ratios on a calculator.

- Scientific and graphing calculators have modes for different units of angle measurements. When using degrees, make sure that your calculator is set in degree mode.
- The functions $\sin^{-1}$, $\cos^{-1}$, and $\tan^{-1}$ on a calculator *do not* indicate the reciprocal functions. These functions will be discussed in Section 8.2.
- Some calculators automatically insert an opening parenthesis "(" after sin, cos, or tan. Be sure to place the closing parenthesis ")" in the appropriate place.

In trigonometry, many of the values used are approximate, and answers are usually rounded to 4 decimal places. However, in calculations involving trigonometric ratios, the values should not be rounded until the end of the problem.

Example 4 Evaluating Trigonometric Ratios on a Calculator

Evaluate the six trigonometric ratios of 20°.

Solution

Your calculator should have buttons for sine, cosine, and tangent. To find the cosecant, secant, and cotangent, take the reciprocal of each answer.

ADDITIONAL EXAMPLES

Example 3

Evaluate the six trigonometric ratios of 48° by using the triangle shown below. (Side lengths given are approximate.)

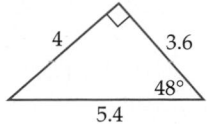

$$\sin 48° \approx \frac{4}{5.4} \approx 0.7470$$

$$\cos 48° \approx \frac{3.6}{5.4} \approx 0.6667$$

$$\tan 48° \approx \frac{4}{3.6} \approx 1.1111$$

$$\csc 48° \approx \frac{5.4}{4} \approx 1.35$$

$$\sec 48° \approx \frac{5.4}{3.6} \approx 1.5$$

$$\cot 48° \approx \frac{3.6}{4} \approx 0.9$$

Example 4

Evaluate the six trigonometric ratios of 15°.

```
sin(15)
        .2588190451
cos(15)
        .9659258263
tan(15)
        .2679491924
```

$$\sin 15° \approx 0.2588$$
$$\cos 15° \approx 0.9659$$
$$\tan 15° \approx 0.2679$$
$$\csc 15° \approx 3.8637$$
$$\sec 15° \approx 1.0353$$
$$\cot 15° \approx 3.7321$$

Example Notes

In **Example 5**, to help students memorize the sine and cosine values of 30°, 45°, and 60°, show them the following chart:

θ	$\sin\theta$	$\cos\theta$
30°	$\dfrac{\sqrt{1}}{2}$	$\dfrac{\sqrt{3}}{2}$
45°	$\dfrac{\sqrt{2}}{2}$	$\dfrac{\sqrt{2}}{2}$
60°	$\dfrac{\sqrt{3}}{2}$	$\dfrac{\sqrt{1}}{2}$

ADDITIONAL EXAMPLES

Example 5

Evaluate the six trigonometric ratios of 30°, 60°, and 45° in the triangles below.

θ	30°	45°	60°
$\sin\theta$	$\dfrac{1}{2}$	$\dfrac{\sqrt{2}}{2}$	$\dfrac{\sqrt{3}}{2}$
$\cos\theta$	$\dfrac{\sqrt{3}}{2}$	$\dfrac{\sqrt{2}}{2}$	$\dfrac{1}{2}$
$\tan\theta$	$\dfrac{\sqrt{3}}{3}$	1	$\sqrt{3}$
$\csc\theta$	2	$\sqrt{2}$	$\dfrac{2\sqrt{3}}{3}$
$\sec\theta$	$\dfrac{2\sqrt{3}}{3}$	$\sqrt{2}$	2
$\cot\theta$	$\sqrt{3}$	1	$\dfrac{\sqrt{3}}{3}$

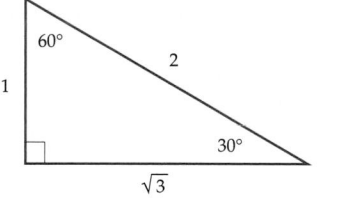

Figure 6.1-9

$\sin 20° \approx 0.3420$	$\csc 20° = \dfrac{1}{\sin 20°} \approx \dfrac{1}{0.3420} \approx 2.9238$
$\cos 20° \approx 0.9397$	$\sec 20° = \dfrac{1}{\cos 20°} \approx \dfrac{1}{0.9397} \approx 1.0642$
$\tan 20° \approx 0.3640$	$\cot 20° = \dfrac{1}{\tan 20°} \approx \dfrac{1}{0.3640} \approx 2.7475$

Special Angles

Properties of 30-60-90 and 45-45-90 triangles can be used to find exact values of the trigonometric ratios for 30°, 60°, and 45°. These angles are called **special angles**.

NOTE For a review of the properties of 30-60-90 and 45-45-90 triangles, see the Geometry Review in the Appendix.

Example 5 Evaluating Trigonometric Ratios of Special Angles

Evaluate the six trigonometric ratios of 30°, 60°, and 45°.

Solution

A 30-60-90 and a 45-45-90 triangle are shown below.

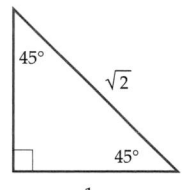

Figure 6.1-10

In the 30-60-90 triangle:

- the hypotenuse is 2
- for the 30° angle, 1 is opposite and $\sqrt{3}$ is adjacent
- for the 60° angle, $\sqrt{3}$ is opposite and 1 is adjacent

In the 45-45-90 triangle:

- the hypotenuse is $\sqrt{2}$
- for either 45° angle, 1 is both opposite and adjacent

The following table summarizes the values of the trigonometric ratios for the special angles.

NOTE The exact values of the trigonometric ratios of the special angles will be needed regularly. You should memorize the sine and cosine values for all three angles. The other ratios are easily derived from the sine and cosine.

θ		30°	45°	60°
$\sin \theta =$	$\dfrac{\text{opposite}}{\text{hypotenuse}}$	$\dfrac{1}{2}$	$\dfrac{1}{\sqrt{2}} = \dfrac{\sqrt{2}}{2}$	$\dfrac{\sqrt{3}}{2}$
$\cos \theta =$	$\dfrac{\text{adjacent}}{\text{hypotenuse}}$	$\dfrac{\sqrt{3}}{2}$	$\dfrac{1}{\sqrt{2}} = \dfrac{\sqrt{2}}{2}$	$\dfrac{1}{2}$
$\tan \theta =$	$\dfrac{\text{opposite}}{\text{adjacent}}$	$\dfrac{1}{\sqrt{3}} = \dfrac{\sqrt{3}}{3}$	$\dfrac{1}{1} = 1$	$\dfrac{\sqrt{3}}{1} = \sqrt{3}$
$\csc \theta =$	$\dfrac{\text{hypotenuse}}{\text{opposite}}$	$\dfrac{2}{1} = 2$	$\dfrac{\sqrt{2}}{1} = \sqrt{2}$	$\dfrac{2}{\sqrt{3}} = \dfrac{2\sqrt{3}}{3}$
$\sec \theta =$	$\dfrac{\text{hypotenuse}}{\text{adjacent}}$	$\dfrac{2}{\sqrt{3}} = \dfrac{2\sqrt{3}}{3}$	$\dfrac{\sqrt{2}}{1} = \sqrt{2}$	$\dfrac{2}{1} = 2$
$\cot \theta =$	$\dfrac{\text{adjacent}}{\text{opposite}}$	$\dfrac{\sqrt{3}}{1} = \sqrt{3}$	$\dfrac{1}{1} = 1$	$\dfrac{1}{\sqrt{3}} = \dfrac{\sqrt{3}}{3}$

Exercises 6.1

In Exercises 1–4, write the DMS degree measurement in decimal form.

1. 47° 15′ 36″
47.26°
2. 38° 33′ 9″
38.5525°
3. 15° 24′ 45″
15.4125°
4. 20° 51′ 54″
20.865°

In Exercises 5–8, write the decimal degree measurement in DMS form.

5. 23.16°
23°9′36″
6. 50.3625°
50°21′45″
7. 4.2075°
4°12′27″
8. 85.655°
85°39′18″

In Exercises 9–14, find the six trigonometric ratios for θ.

9.

10.

11.

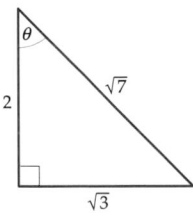

12.

Teaching Notes

If students struggle to remember the chart, encourage them to draw the triangles with the side and angle labels and use it as a reference. When drawing the triangles, if they remember the length of two sides but not the third, they can always use the Pythagorean Theorem.

For the 45-45-90 triangle, the sides opposite the 45-degree angles must be congruent (because the triangle is isosceles).

For the 30-60-90 degree triangle the smallest angle (30°) is opposite the smallest side (1) and the largest angle (90°) is opposite the largest side (2). Tell students that remembering a 30-60-90 triangle is "as easy as one, two, square root of three."

Exercises 6.1
ANSWERS

9. $\sin \theta = \sqrt{\dfrac{2}{11}}$, $\cos \theta = \dfrac{3}{\sqrt{11}}$,

$\tan \theta = \dfrac{\sqrt{2}}{3}$, $\cot \theta = \dfrac{3}{\sqrt{2}}$,

$\sec \theta = \dfrac{\sqrt{11}}{3}$, $\csc \theta = \sqrt{\dfrac{11}{2}}$

10. $\sin \theta = \dfrac{2\sqrt{5}}{5}$, $\cos \theta = \dfrac{\sqrt{5}}{5}$,

$\tan \theta = 2$, $\cot \theta = \dfrac{1}{2}$,

$\sec \theta = \dfrac{5}{\sqrt{5}}$, $\csc \theta = \dfrac{5}{2\sqrt{5}}$

11. $\sin \theta = \sqrt{\dfrac{3}{7}}$, $\cos \theta = \dfrac{2}{\sqrt{7}}$,

$\tan \theta = \dfrac{\sqrt{3}}{2}$, $\cot \theta = \dfrac{2}{\sqrt{3}}$,

$\sec \theta = \dfrac{\sqrt{7}}{2}$, $\csc \theta = \sqrt{\dfrac{7}{3}}$

12. $\sin \theta = \dfrac{15}{17}$, $\cos \theta = \dfrac{8}{17}$,

$\tan \theta = \dfrac{15}{8}$, $\cot \theta = \dfrac{8}{15}$,

$\sec \theta = \dfrac{17}{8}$, $\csc \theta = \dfrac{17}{15}$

13. $\sin \theta = \dfrac{h}{m}$, $\cos \theta = \dfrac{d}{m}$, $\tan \theta = \dfrac{h}{d}$,

$\cot \theta = \dfrac{d}{h}$, $\sec \theta = \dfrac{m}{d}$, $\csc \theta = \dfrac{m}{h}$

14. $\sin \theta = \dfrac{t}{\sqrt{1 + t^2}}$,

$\cos \theta = \dfrac{1}{\sqrt{1 + t^2}}$, $\tan \theta = t$,

$\cot \theta = \dfrac{1}{t}$, $\sec \theta = \sqrt{1 + t^2}$,

$\csc \theta = \dfrac{\sqrt{1 + t^2}}{t}$

33. False; $\sin 50° \approx 0.7660$
$\neq 2 \sin 25° \approx 0.8452$

34. True; $\sin 50° \approx 0.7660$
$= 2 \sin 25° \cos 25° \approx 0.7660$

35. True; $(\cos 28°)^2 \approx 0.7796$
$= 1 - (\sin 28°)^2 \approx 0.7796$

36. False; $(\cos 28°)^2 \approx 0.7796$
$\neq (1 - \sin 28°)^2 \approx 0.2815$

37. False; $\tan 75° \approx 3.7321$
$\neq \tan 30° + \tan 45° \approx 1.5774$

38. True; $\tan 75° \approx 3.7321$
$= \dfrac{\tan 30° + \tan 45°}{1 - \tan 30° \tan 45°} \approx 3.7321$

13.

14.

In Exercises 15–20, use a calculator in degree mode to find the following. Round your answers to four decimal places.

15. $\sin 32°$ **16.** $\cos 68°$ **17.** $\tan 6°$
≈ 0.5299 ≈ 0.3746 ≈ 0.1051
18. $\csc 25°$ **19.** $\sec 47°$ **20.** $\cot 39°$
≈ 2.3662 ≈ 1.4663 ≈ 1.2349

In Exercises 21–26, use the exact values of the trigonometric ratios for the special angles to find a value of θ that is a solution of the given equation. (See Example 5.)

21. $\sin \theta = \dfrac{1}{2}$ **22.** $\tan \theta = 1$ **23.** $\csc \theta = \sqrt{2}$
$\theta = 30°$ $\theta = 45°$ $\theta = 45°$
24. $\cot \theta = \sqrt{3}$ **25.** $\cos \theta = \dfrac{1}{2}$ **26.** $\sec \theta = 2$
$\theta = 30°$ $\theta = 60°$ $\theta = 60°$

In Exercises 27–32, refer to the figure below. Find the exact value of the trigonometric ratio for the given values of a, b, and c.

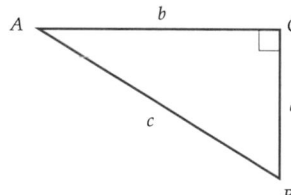

27. $a = 4, b = 2, \tan B =$ ___?___ $\dfrac{1}{2}$

28. $a = 5, c = 7, \sin A =$ ___?___ $\dfrac{5}{7}$

29. $b = 3, c = 8, \cos A =$ ___?___ $\dfrac{3}{8}$

30. $a = 12, b = 15, \cot A =$ ___?___ $\dfrac{5}{4}$

31. $a = 7, c = 16, \sec B =$ ___?___ $\dfrac{16}{7}$

32. $b = 2, c = 3, \csc B =$ ___?___ $\dfrac{3}{2}$

In Exercises 33–38, use a calculator in degree mode to determine whether the equation is true or false, and explain your answer.

33. $\sin 50° = 2 \sin 25°$

34. $\sin 50° = 2 \sin 25° \cos 25°$

35. $(\cos 28°)^2 = 1 - (\sin 28°)^2$

36. $(\cos 28°)^2 = (1 - \sin 28°)^2$

37. $\tan 75° = \tan 30° + \tan 45°$

38. $\tan 75° = \dfrac{\tan 30° + \tan 45°}{1 - \tan 30° \tan 45°}$

39. *Critical Thinking* Complete the table below.

θ	$\sin \theta$	$\cos \theta$
1°	?	?
0.1°	?	?
0.01°	?	?
0.001°	?	?

Based on the values in the table, what do you think would be a reasonable value for sin 0° and cos 0°? Verify your answers with a calculator. Why can't these values be found by using the definition on page 416?

40. *Critical Thinking* Complete the table below.

θ	$\sin \theta$	$\cos \theta$
89°	?	?
89.9°	?	?
89.99°	?	?
89.999°	?	?

Based on the values in the table, what do you think would be a reasonable value for sin 90° and cos 90°? Verify your answers with a calculator. Why can't these values be found by using the definition on page 416?

39.

θ	$\sin \theta$	$\cos \theta$
1°	0.0175	0.9998
0.1°	0.00175	0.999998
0.01°	0.000175	0.99999998
0.0001°	0.0000175	0.9999999998

sin 0° = 0; cos 0° = 1. Since no triangle has an angle of 0°, the right triangle definitions do not apply.

40.

θ	$\sin \theta$	$\cos \theta$
89°	0.9998	0.0175
89.9°	0.999998	0.00175
89.99°	0.99999998	0.000175
89.999°	0.9999999998	0.0000175

sin 90° = 1; cos 90° = 0. Since neither acute angle of a right triangle can measure 90°, these definitions do not apply.

41. *Critical Thinking* Use the diagram below to show that the area of a triangle with acute angle θ that has sides a and b is

$$A = \frac{1}{2} ab \sin \theta.$$

In Exercises 42–45, use the result of Exercise 41 to find the area of the given triangle.

42.

43.

44.

45.

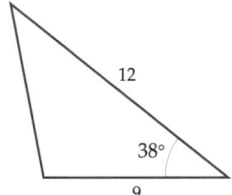

41. The area of the triangle is $\frac{1}{2} ah$.

The altitude h forms a right triangle with side b as the hypotenuse and side h opposite θ, so $\sin \theta = \frac{b}{h} \rightarrow h = b \sin \theta$.

Thus, the area of the triangle is $\frac{1}{2} ah = \frac{1}{2} a(b \sin \theta) = \frac{1}{2} ab \sin \theta$.

42. $A \approx 29.583$ units^2

43. $A \approx 4320.123$ units^2

44. $A = 220$ units^2

45. $A \approx 33.246$ units^2

 6.2 # Trigonometric Applications

Objectives

- Solve triangles using trigonometric ratios
- Solve applications using triangles

Solving Right Triangles

Many applications in trigonometry involve **solving a triangle.** This means finding the lengths of all three sides and the measures of all three angles when only some of these quantities are known. Solving right triangles by using trigonometric ratios involves two theorems from geometry:

> **Triangle Sum Theorem: The sum of the measures of the angles in a triangle is 180°.**
>
> **Pythagorean Theorem: In a right triangle with legs a and b and hypotenuse c, $a^2 + b^2 = c^2$.**

If the measures of two angles are known, the Triangle Sum Theorem can be used to find the measure of the third. If the lengths of two sides of a right triangle are known, the Pythagorean Theorem can be used to find the length of the third.

Trigonometric ratios are used to solve right triangles when the measure of an angle and the length of a side or when the lengths of two sides are given. The underlying idea is that the definition of each trigonometric ratio involves three quantities:

- the measure of an angle
- the lengths of two sides of the triangle

Section 6.2 ## Trigonometric Applications

Teaching Notes

To help students review the concepts discussed, show these two triangles on the board:

Point out to students that for the first triangle, you can find the measure of all the angles by using the Triangle Sum Theorem. For the second triangle, you can find the length of all the sides by using the Pythagorean Theorem.

Note that in the first triangle, the lengths of the sides are not known and for the second triangle, the measures of the angles are not known.

In this section, students will learn how to find missing sides and angles of right triangles given certain information, using trigonometric ratios as well as the two Theorems mentioned.

Example Notes

In **Example 1,** you may want to ask students to find the length of the side opposite the 65° angle using the sine ratio. ≈ 7.2505

Point out that they can check their work by using the Pythagorean Theorem.

In **Example 2,** some students may wonder why the table in Figure 6.2-3c starts with $x = 36.6$. Tell them that they obtain this table by scrolling down through the x values.

In **Example 2,** indicate that since all three sides of the triangle are given, the measure of angle θ could have been found by using $\cos \theta$ or $\tan \theta$. Have students find that $\cos \theta = 0.8$ and $\tan \theta = 0.75$. Then, use $\cos^{-1}\theta$ and $\tan^{-1}\theta$ to find θ.

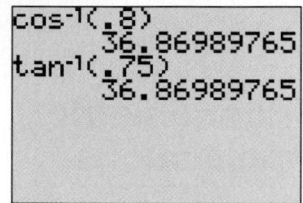

Teaching Notes

In **Example 2,** have the students find the third angle of the triangle using the trigonometric ratios sine, cosine, and tangent:

Name the third angle α (Greek letter alpha).

$$\sin \alpha = \frac{4}{5} \qquad \cos \alpha = \frac{3}{5} \qquad \tan \alpha = \frac{4}{3}$$

$\alpha \approx 53.1301°$

Some students may recognize that $\sin \alpha = \cos \theta$ and $\cos \alpha = \sin \theta$. Later the students will see this relationship as the cofunction identities (see page 586).

When two of the three quantities are known, the third can always be found, as illustrated in the next two examples.

Example 1   Finding a Side of a Triangle

Find side x of the right triangle in Figure 6.2-1.

Figure 6.2-1

Solution

The 65° angle and the hypotenuse are known. The adjacent side x must be found, so use the cosine ratio.

$$\cos 65° = \frac{\text{adjacent}}{\text{hypotenuse}} = \frac{x}{8}$$

Solve this equation for x and then use a calculator to evaluate $\cos 65°$.

$$\cos 65° = \frac{x}{8}$$

$$x = 8 \cos 65° \qquad \textit{Multiply both sides by 8}$$

$$\approx 3.3809 \qquad \textit{Use a calculator}$$

Example 2   Finding an Angle of a Triangle

Find the measure of angle θ in Figure 6.2-2.

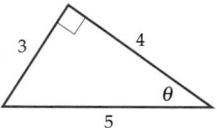

Figure 6.2-2

Solution

Note that

$$\sin \theta = \frac{\text{opposite}}{\text{hypotenuse}} = \frac{3}{5} = 0.6.$$

Before calculators were available, θ was found by using a table of sine values. You can do the same thing by having your calculator generate a table for $Y_1 = \sin(X)$ by using the settings shown in Figure 6.2-3a and Figure 6.2-3b.

View the table, shown in Figure 6.2-3c, and look through the column of sine values for the closest one to 0.6. Then look in the first column for the corresponding value of θ. The closest entry to 0.6 in the sine column is 0.60042, which corresponds to an angle of 36.9°. Hence, $\theta \approx 36.9°$.

Figure 6.2-3a

Figure 6.2-3b

| X | Y₁ |

Figure 6.2-3c

A faster and more accurate method of finding θ is to use the SIN^{-1} key on your calculator. (SIN^{-1} is labeled ASIN on some models.) When you key in $SIN^{-1}(0.6)$, as in Figure 6.2-3d, the calculator produces an acute angle whose sine is 0.6, namely, $\theta \approx 36.8699°$.

> **NOTE** Make sure your calculator is in degree mode.

Figure 6.2-3d

Thus, the SIN^{-1} key provides the electronic equivalent of searching the sine table, without actually having to construct the table. ∎

> **NOTE** In this chapter, the SIN^{-1} key and the analogous COS^{-1} and TAN^{-1} keys will be used as they were in Example 2 to find an angle θ. The other uses of these keys are discussed in Section 8.2, which deals with inverse trigonometric functions.

Here is a summary of how these techniques can be used to solve any right triangle.

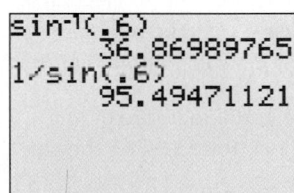

Teaching Notes

For **Solving Right Triangles, Case 1,** have students identify the given side's location in relation to the given angle:

- If the side given is opposite the angle, use sine to find the hypotenuse or tangent to find the adjacent side.
- If the side given is adjacent to the angle, use cosine to find the hypotenuse or tangent to find the opposite side.
- If the side given is the hypotenuse, use sine to find the opposite side or cosine to find the adjacent side.

Use the Pythagorean Theorem and the Triangle Sum Theorem to find the remaining sides and angles.

For **Case 2,** find the third side using the Pythagorean Theorem. You can then use any of the trigonometric ratios to find the two acute angles.

Example Notes

For **Example 3,** once the length of side a was found, the length of side b could have been found using the Pythagorean Theorem.

$a \approx 16.42$

$a^2 + b^2 = c^2$

$\qquad b^2 = c^2 - a^2$

$\qquad b^2 \approx (17)^2 - (16.42)^2 = 19.3836$

$\qquad b \approx 4.40$

Point out to students that this method uses the *calculated* (and approximate) value 16.42 whereas the solution in the text uses only given values. It is preferable to solve problems using given values as opposed to calculated values because a mistake may have been made in the calculation.

For **Example 4,** the measure of angle θ could have been found using the sine ratio: $\sin \theta = \dfrac{6}{12} = \dfrac{1}{2}, \theta = 30°$.

Solving Right Triangles

A right triangle can be solved if the following information is given.	
Case 1: an acute angle and a side	**Case 2:** two sides
Sketch the triangle and label the acute angle, the right angle, and the given side.	Sketch the triangle and label the right angle and the two given sides.
Find the remaining acute angle by subtracting the known angles from 180°.	Find the third side by using the Pythagorean Theorem.
Write a trigonometric equation that has an unknown side as the variable, and solve it with a calculator to evaluate the trigonometric ratio of the angle.	Write a trigonometric equation that has an unknown angle as the variable. If the angle is a special angle, you can solve it by recognizing the value of the trigonometric ratio.
Repeat the previous step or use the Pythagorean Theorem to find the third side.	If the angle is not one of the special angles, use the technique explained in Example 2.

Example 3   Solving a Right Triangle

Solve the right triangle in Figure 6.2-4.

Solution

One side and one angle are given, so use the first case above. To solve the triangle, it is necessary to find θ, a, and b.

To find θ, subtract the measures of the given angles from 180°.

$$\theta = 180° - 75° - 90° = 15°$$

Write a trigonometric equation that has a as the variable. Since a is opposite the given angle and the hypotenuse is given, the sine is used.

$$\sin 75° = \frac{a}{17} \qquad \frac{opposite}{hypotenuse}$$

$$a = 17 \sin 75°$$

$$a \approx 17(0.9659) \approx 16.42$$

Next, write a trigonometric equation that has b as the variable. Since b is adjacent to the given angle, cosine is used. Evaluate $\cos 75°$ by using a calculator, and solve.

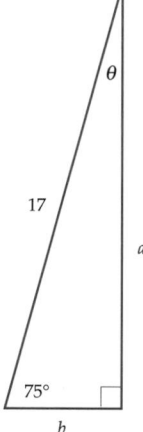

Figure 6.2-4

$$\cos 75° = \frac{b}{17} \qquad \frac{adjacent}{hypotenuse}$$

$$b = 17 \cos 75°$$

$$b \approx 4.40$$

Example 3

Solve the right triangle shown below.

$\theta = 70°$, $a \approx 34.54$, $b \approx 94.91$

Figure 6.2-5

Example 4   Solving a Right Triangle

Solve the right triangle in Figure 6.2-5.

Solution

Two sides are given, so use the second case above. To solve the triangle, it is necessary to find a, θ, and β.

To find a, use the Pythagorean Theorem.

$$a^2 + 6^2 = 12^2$$

$$a^2 = 108$$

$$a = \sqrt{108} = 6\sqrt{3}$$

To find β, use trigonometric ratios. The adjacent side and the hypotenuse are given, so cosine is used.

$$\cos \beta = \frac{6}{12} = \frac{1}{2} \qquad \frac{adjacent}{hypotenuse}$$

From the table of trigonometric ratios of special angles on page 419, $\cos 60° = \frac{1}{2}$. Since 60° is the only acute angle with a cosine of $\frac{1}{2}$,

$$\beta = 60° \qquad \text{and} \qquad \theta = 180° - 60° - 90° = 30°$$

Example 4

Solve the right triangle shown below.

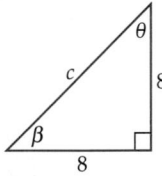

$c = 8\sqrt{2} \approx 11.31$, $\beta = 45°$, $\theta = 45°$

Example 5

A wheelchair ramp is 6 feet in length and makes a 4° angle with the ground. How many inches does the ramp rise off of the ground?

$\sin 4° = \dfrac{r}{72}$

$r = 72 \sin 4°$

$r \approx 5.02$ in.

The ramp rises about 5.02 inches off of the ground.

Applications

The following examples illustrate a variety of applications of the trigonometric ratios.

Example 5   Height Above Sea Level

A straight road leads from an ocean beach at a constant upward angle of 3°. How high above sea level is the road at a point 1 mile from the beach?

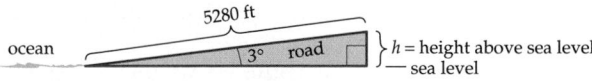

Figure 6.2-6

Teaching Notes

When introducing **Angles of Elevation and Depression,** it may be helpful to tell students to think of how their eyes move. If they are looking straight ahead, they have to raise, or *elevate,* their eyes to see the top of a tall building. If they are on the roof of a building looking straight ahead, they have to lower, or *depress,* their eyes to see a point on the ground.

In the figure below, the angle of elevation of the top of the lighthouse from the boat is equal to the angle of depression of the boat from the top of the lighthouse. The angle of depression and the corresponding angle of elevation are equal.

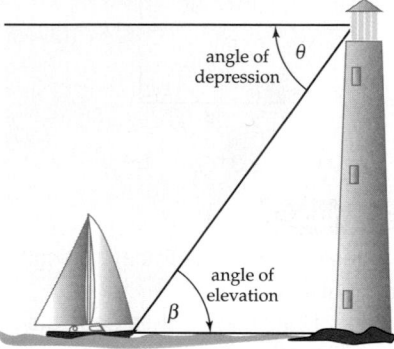

To give an example of the rounding error mentioned in the **Technology Tip,** have students do the calculations in **Example 5** (top of page 426) in two different ways as shown below.

To show how this rounding error can increase significantly, have students square the results of the previous calculations.

Technology Tip

When using a calculator to evaluate trigonometric ratios, do not round your answer until the end of the problem. The rounding error can be increased significantly as other operations are performed. It may help to store the value in the calculator's memory, or to use the entire trigonometric expression in each calculation.

Figure 6.2-7

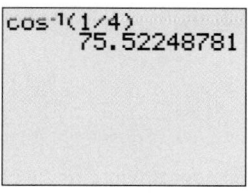

Figure 6.2-8

Solution

Figure 6.2-6 shows a right triangle with the road as the hypotenuse (1 mi = 5280 ft) and the opposite side *h* as the height above sea level. Write a trigonometric equation that uses sine.

$$\sin 3° = \frac{h}{5280} \qquad \frac{opposite}{hypotenuse}$$
$$h = 5280 \sin 3° \qquad \textit{Solve for h}$$
$$h \approx 5280(0.0523) \qquad \textit{Use a calculator to evaluate sin 3°}$$
$$h \approx 276.33 \text{ ft} \qquad \textit{Simplify}$$

At one mile, the road is about 276 feet above sea level.   ■

Example 6   Ladder Safety

According to the safety sticker on a 20-foot ladder, the distance from the bottom of the ladder to the base of the wall on which it leans should be one-fourth of the length of the ladder: 5 feet.

a. How high up the wall will the ladder reach?

b. If the ladder is in this position, what angle does it make with the ground?

Solution

Draw the right triangle formed by the ladder, the wall, and the ground. Label the sides and angles as shown in Figure 6.2-7.

a. Since the length of the ladder and the distance from the wall are known, find the third side by using the Pythagorean Theorem.

$$h^2 + 5^2 = 20^2$$
$$h^2 = 375$$
$$h \approx 19.36$$

The ladder will safely reach a height of a little more than 19 feet up the wall.

b. The hypotenuse and the side adjacent to angle θ are known, so use the cosine ratio.

$$\cos \theta = \frac{adjacent}{hypotenuse} = \frac{5}{20} = \frac{1}{4}$$

Use the COS^{-1} key to find that $\theta \approx 75.5°$, as shown in Figure 6.2-8.   ■

Angles of Elevation and Depression

In many applications the angle between a horizontal line and another line is used, such as the line of sight from an observer to a distant object. If the line is above the horizontal, the angle is called the **angle of elevation.**

Example Notes

In **Example 7,** the angle of elevation of the sun is formed by a horizontal line on the ground and the line of sight between the point at the end of the shadow farthest from the pole and the top of the pole.

If the line is below the horizontal, the angle is called the **angle of depression.**

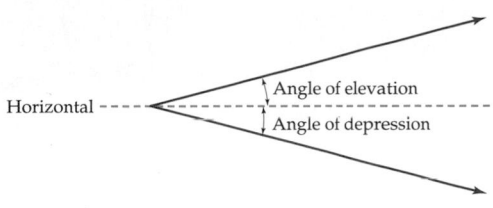

Figure 6.2-9

Example 7   **Indirect Measurement**

A flagpole casts a 60-foot shadow when the angle of elevation of the sun is 35°, as shown in Figure 6.2-10. Find the height of the flagpole.

Figure 6.2-10

Solution

A right triangle is formed by the flagpole and its shadow. The opposite side is unknown and the adjacent side is given, so the tangent is used.

$$\tan 35° = \frac{h}{60} \qquad \frac{opposite}{adjacent}$$
$$h = 60 \tan 35° \qquad \textit{Solve for } h$$
$$h \approx 42.012 \qquad \textit{Use a calculator}$$

Thus, the flagpole is about 42 feet high.

Example 8   **Indirect Measurement**

A wire needs to reach from the top of a building to a point on the ground. The building is 10 m tall, and the angle of depression from the top of the building to the point on the ground is 22°. How long should the wire be?

ADDITIONAL EXAMPLES

Example 6

A diagonal path through a rectangular park is 600 feet long. One side of the park measures 350 feet.

a. How long is the other side of the park?

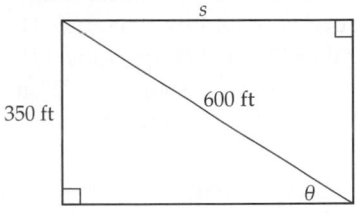

$$s^2 + 350^2 = 600^2$$
$$s^2 = 600^2 - 350^2$$
$$s \approx 487.34 \text{ feet}$$

b. What angle does the diagonal path make with the side whose length you found in part **a**?

$$\sin \theta = \frac{350}{600} = \frac{7}{12}$$

$$\theta \approx 35.7°$$

Example 7

The angle of elevation from a point on the street to the top of a building is 53°, as shown in the figure below. The building is 60 feet high. How far is the point on the street to the foot of the building?

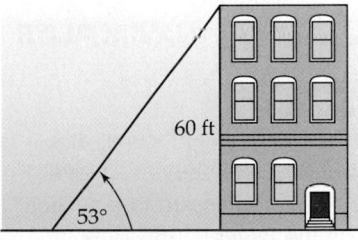

$$\tan 53° = \frac{60}{d}$$
$$d \cdot \tan 53° = 60$$
$$d = \frac{60}{\tan 53°} \approx \frac{60}{1.3270}$$
$$d \approx 45.21$$

The point is about 45 feet from the foot of the building.

Figure 6.2-11

Real-World Application

In **Example 6**, Ladder Safety (page 426), the one-fourth rule for placing ladders was given. According to the Occupational Safety and Health Administration (OSHA), the proper angle a non-supporting ladder should make with the ground is about 75°. If the angle is steeper than 75°, it may tip backward. Similarly, if the angle is less than 75°, it may slide out from the bottom.

Example Notes

In **Example 8**, the angle of depression is outside of the triangle used to solve the problem. The angle of depression is the complement of the angle α adjacent to it.

Another method of finding the angles in the triangle would have been to use the fact that the angle of depression and the corresponding angle of elevation are equal. Then use the Triangle Angle Sum Theorem to find α.

For **Example 9**, it would be helpful to discuss Figure 6.2-13 before any calculations are done. Point E represents the person's foot and point D represents the foot of the lamp post. $ACDE$ is a rectangle because all its angles are right angles.

Triangles ACB and ACD are right triangles. The width of the canal is AC (or ED). The height of the lamp post is $BC + CD$.

ADDITIONAL EXAMPLES

Example 8

From the top of a lighthouse, at a height of 100 feet above sea level, the angle of depression to a sailboat adrift on the water is 55°. How far from the foot of the lighthouse is the sailboat?

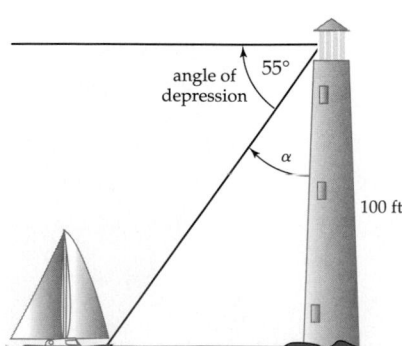

Solution

Figure 6.2-11 shows that the sum of the angle of depression and the angle α formed by the wall of the building and the wire is 90°.

$$\alpha = 90° - 22° = 68°$$

The wall, wire, and ground form a right triangle where the wall is the side adjacent to α and the wire is the hypotenuse. Thus,

$$\cos 68° = \frac{10}{w} \qquad \frac{adjacent}{hypotenuse}$$

$$w = \frac{10}{\cos 68°}$$

$$w \approx 26.7 \text{ m}$$

Thus, the wire should be about 27 m long. ∎

Example 9 Indirect Measurement

A person on the edge of a canal observes a lamp post on the other side with an angle of elevation of 12° to the top of the lamp post and an angle of depression of 7° to the bottom of the lamp post from eye level. The person's eye level is 152 cm (about 5 ft).

a. Find the width of the canal.

b. Find the height of the lamp post.

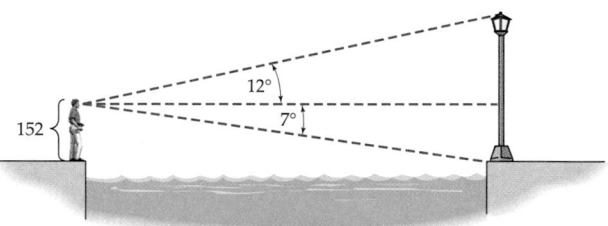

Figure 6.2-12

$\alpha = 35°$

$\tan 35° = \frac{x}{100}$

$\quad x = 100 \tan 35°$

$\quad x \approx 70.02$

The boat is about 70 feet from the lighthouse.

Solution

The essential information is shown in Figure 6.2-13 below. Note that $\overline{AC}$ is parallel to $\overline{DE}$, so CD is also 152 cm.

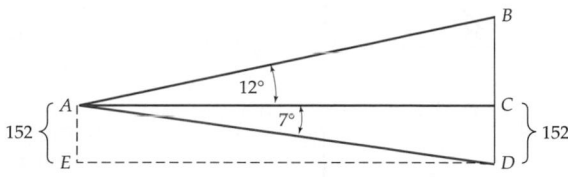

Figure 6.2-13

a. The width of the canal AC is adjacent to the $7°$ angle, and 152 is opposite the $7°$ angle.

$$\tan 7° = \frac{152}{AC} \quad \frac{opposite}{adjacent}$$

$$AC = \frac{152}{\tan 7°} \approx 1237.94 \text{ cm, or about 12.38 m wide}$$

b. The height BC can be represented in terms of the width of the canal found in part **a.**

$$\tan 12° = \frac{BC}{AC} \quad \frac{opposite}{adjacent}$$

$$BC = AC \tan 12° \approx (1237.94)(\tan 12°) \approx 263.13 \text{ cm}$$

The height of the lamp post is $BC + CD$.

$$BC + CD \approx 263.13 + 152 \approx 415.13 \text{ cm}$$

Exercises 6.2

In Exercises 1–6, find side c in the figure below by using the given conditions.

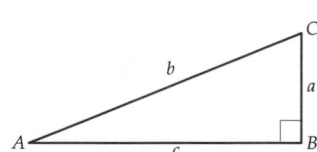

1. $\cos A = \dfrac{12}{13}$ $b = 39$

$c = 36$

2. $\sin C = \dfrac{3}{4}$ $b = 12$

$c = 9$

3. $\tan A = \dfrac{5}{12}$ $a = 15$

$c = 36$

4. $\sec A = 2$ $b = 8$

$c = 4$

5. $\cot A = 6$ $a = 1.4$

$c = 8.4$

6. $\csc C = 1.5$ $b = 4.5$

$c = 3$

In Exercises 7–12, find the exact value of h without using a calculator.

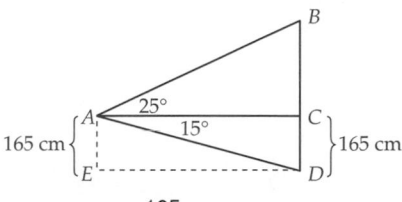

17. $m\angle A = 40°$, $a \approx 6.4$, $c \approx 7.7$

18. $m\angle A = 53°$, $a \approx 15.9$, $b \approx 19.9$

19. $m\angle C = 76°$, $b \approx 24.8$, $c \approx 24.1$

20. $m\angle C = 50°$, $b \approx 12.4$, $c \approx 9.5$

21. $m\angle C = 25°$, $a \approx 10.7$, $b \approx 11.8$

22. $m\angle A = 62°$, $a \approx 7.5$, $b \approx 8.5$

23. $m\angle C = 18°$, $a \approx 3.3$, $c \approx 1.1$

24. $m\angle A = 57°$, $b \approx 5.0$, $c \approx 2.7$

7. $h = \dfrac{25\sqrt{2}}{2}$

8. $h = 144$

9. $h = 300$

10. $h = 12\sqrt{2}$

11. $h = 50\sqrt{3}$

12. $h = 10\sqrt{3}$

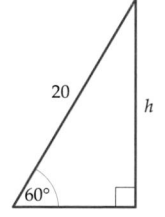

Use the figure below for Exercises 13–24.

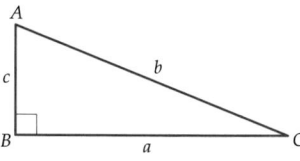

In Exercises 13–16, find the indicated value without using a calculator.

13. $a = 4$ $m\angle A = 60°$ $c = \dfrac{4\sqrt{3}}{3}$ Find c.

14. $c = 5$ $m\angle A = 60°$ $a = 5\sqrt{3}$ Find a.

15. $c = 10$ $m\angle A = 30°$ $a = \dfrac{10\sqrt{3}}{3}$ Find a.

16. $a = 12$ $m\angle A = 30°$ $c = 12\sqrt{3}$ Find c.

In Exercises 17–24, solve the triangle with the given conditions.

17. $b = 10$ $m\angle C = 50°$

18. $c = 12$ $m\angle C = 37°$

19. $a = 6$ $m\angle A = 14°$

20. $a = 8$ $m\angle A = 40°$

21. $c = 5$ $m\angle A = 65°$

22. $c = 4$ $m\angle C = 28°$

23. $b = 3.5$ $m\angle A = 72°$

24. $a = 4.2$ $m\angle C = 33°$

In Exercises 25–28, find angle θ.

25. $\approx 48.59°$

26. $\approx 33.56°$

27. $\approx 48.19°$

28.

$\approx 46.05°$

200

144

θ

In Exercises 29–36, use the figure for Exercises 13–24 to find angles A and C under the given conditions.

29. $a = 4$ and $c = 6$ **30.** $b = 14$ and $c = 5$

31. $a = 7$ and $b = 10$ **32.** $a = 5$ and $c = 3$

33. $b = 18$ and $c = 12$ **34.** $a = 4$ and $b = 9$

35. $a = 2.5$ and $c = 1.4$

36. $b = 3.7$ and $c = 2.2$

37. A 24-ft ladder positioned against a wall forms an angle of 75° with the ground. $\approx$**23.18 ft**
   a. How high up the wall does the ladder reach?
   b. How far is the base of the ladder from the wall? $\approx$**6.21 ft**

38. A guy wire stretches from the top of an antenna tower to a point on level ground 18 feet from the base of the tower. The angle between the wire and the ground is 63°. How high is the tower?
   $\approx$**35.3 ft**

39. A plane takes off at an angle of 5°. After traveling 1 mile along this flight path, how high (in feet) is the plane above the ground? (1 mi = 5280 ft)
   $\approx$**460.2 ft**

5°

40. A plane takes off at an angle of 6° traveling at the rate of 200 feet/second. If it continues on this flight path at the same speed, how many minutes will it take to reach an altitude of 8000 feet?
   $\approx$**6.4 min**

41. The Ohio Turnpike has a maximum uphill slope of 3°. How long must a straight uphill segment of the road be in order to allow a vertical rise of 450 feet?
   $\approx$**8598.3 ft**

42. Ruth is flying a kite. Her hand is 3 feet above ground level and is holding the end of a 300-ft

kite string, which makes an angle of 57° with the horizontal. How high is the kite above the ground? $\approx$**254.6 ft**

43. Suppose that a person with a reach of 27 inches and a shoulder height of 5 feet is standing upright on a mountainside that makes a 62° angle with the horizontal, as shown in the figure below. Can the person touch the mountain?

No

62°

44. A swimming pool is 3 feet deep in the shallow end. The bottom of the pool has a steady downward drop of 12° toward the deep end. If the pool is 50 feet long, how deep is the deep end?
   $\approx$**13.6 ft**

45. A wire from the top of a TV tower makes an angle of 49.5° with the ground and touches the ground 225 feet from the base of the tower. How high is the tower?
   $\approx$**263.44 ft**

46. A plane flies a straight course. On the ground directly below the flight path, observers 2 miles apart spot the plane at the same time. The plane's angle of elevation is 46° from one observation point and 71° from the other. How high is the plane?
   $\approx$**1.53 mi**

71°   46°

2 miles

29. $m\angle A \approx 33.7°$, $m\angle C \approx 56.3°$

30. $m\angle A \approx 69.1°$, $m\angle C \approx 20.9°$

31. $m\angle A \approx 44.4°$, $m\angle C \approx 45.6°$

32. $m\angle A \approx 59.0°$, $m\angle C \approx 31.0°$

33. $m\angle A \approx 48.2°$, $m\angle C \approx 41.8°$

34. $m\angle A \approx 26.4°$, $m\angle C \approx 63.6°$

35. $m\angle A \approx 60.8°$, $m\angle C \approx 29.2°$

36. $m\angle A \approx 53.5°$, $m\angle C \approx 36.5°$

47. A buoy in the ocean is observed from the top of a 40-meter-high radar tower on shore. The angle of depression from the top of the tower to the base of the buoy is 6.5°. How far is the buoy from the base of the radar tower?

≈**351.1 m**

48. A plane passes directly over your head at an altitude of 500 feet. Two seconds later you observe that its angle of elevation is 42°. How far did the plane travel during those 2 seconds?

≈**555.3 ft**

49. A man stands 12 feet from a statue. The angle of elevation from eye level to the top of the statue is 30°, and the angle of depression to the base of the statue is 15°. How tall is the statue?

≈**10.1 ft**

50. Two boats lie on a straight line with the base of a lighthouse. From the top of the lighthouse, 21 meters above water level, it is observed that the angle of depression of the nearest boat is 53° and the angle of depression of the farthest boat is 27°. How far apart are the boats?

≈**25.4 m**

51. A rocket shoots straight up from the launch pad. Five seconds after lift-off, an observer 2 miles away notes that the rocket's angle of elevation is 3.5°. Four seconds after that, the angle of elevation is 41°. How far did the rocket rise during those 4 seconds?

≈**1.6 mi**

52. From a window 35 meters high, the angle of depression to the top of a nearby streetlight is 55°. The angle of depression to the base of the streetlight is 57.8°. How tall is the streetlight?

≈**3.52 m**

53. A 60-foot drawbridge is 24 feet above water level when closed. When open, the bridge makes an angle of 33° with the horizontal.
  a. How high is the tip P of the open bridge above the water? ≈**56.7 ft**
  b. When the bridge is open, what is the distance from P to Q? ≈**9.7 ft**

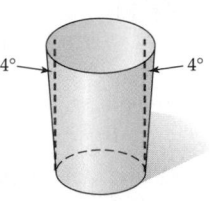

54. A drinking glass 5 inches tall has a 2.5-inch diameter base. Its sides slope outward at a 4° angle as shown. What is the diameter of the top of the glass?

≈**3.2 in.**

55. In aerial navigation, directions are given in degrees clockwise from north, called *headings*. Thus east is 90°, south is 180°, and so on, as shown below. A plane travels from an airport for 200 miles at a heading of 300°. How far west of the airport is the plane?

≈**173.2 mi**

56. A plane travels from an airport at a constant 300 mph at a heading of 65°. (See Exercise 55.)
  a. How far east of the airport is the plane after half an hour? ≈**135.9 mi**
  b. How far north of the airport is the plane after 2 hours and 24 minutes? ≈**304.3 mi**

57. A car on a straight road passes under a bridge. Two seconds later an observer on the bridge, 20 feet above the road, notes that the angle of depression to the car is 7.4°. How fast, in miles per hour, is the car traveling? (Note: 60 mph is equivalent to 88 feet/second.)

≈52.5 mph

58. A pedestrian overpass is shown in the figure below. If you walk on the overpass from one end to the other, how far have you walked?

≈205.7 ft

15°   18 ft   21°

200 ft

59. *Critical Thinking* A 50-ft flagpole stands on top of a building. From a point on the ground the angle of elevation to the top of the pole is 43° and the angle of elevation to the bottom of the pole is 40°. How high is the building?

≈449.1 ft

60. *Critical Thinking* Two points on level ground are 500 meters apart. The angles of elevation from these points to the top of a nearby hill are 52° and 67°, respectively. The two points and the ground-level point directly below the top of the hill lie on a straight line. How high is the hill?

≈1401.3 m

○ 6.3

Angles and Radian Measure

Objectives

- Use a rotating ray to extend the definition of angle measure to negative angles and angles greater than 180°

- Define radian measure and convert angle measures between degrees and radians

Extending Angle Measure

In geometry and triangle trigonometry, an angle is a static figure consisting of two rays that meet at a point. But in modern trigonometry, which will be introduced in the next section, an angle is thought of as being formed dynamically by *rotating* a ray around its endpoint, the **vertex.** The starting position of the ray is called the **initial side** and its final position after the rotation is called the **terminal side.**

The amount the ray is rotated is the measure of the angle. Counterclockwise rotations have positive measure and clockwise rotations have negative measure.

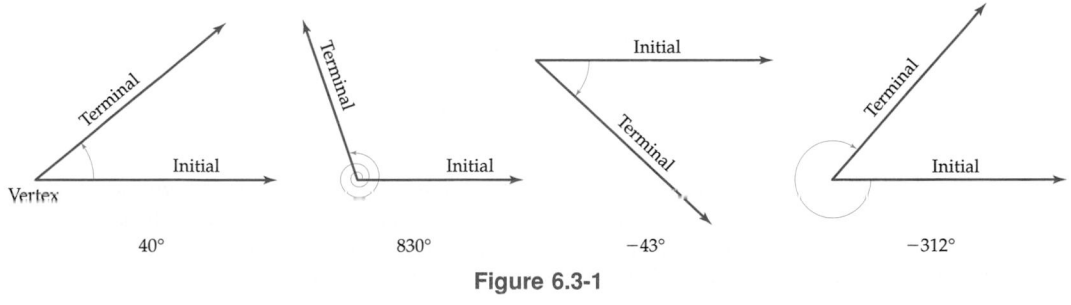

40°   830°   −43°   −312°

Figure 6.3-1

○ **6.3** **Angles and Radian Measure**

Teaching Notes

Emphasize that a dynamically formed angle consists of a *fixed* ray (the initial side) and a *rotating* ray (the terminal side).

To help students understand how the angles were formed in Figure 6.3-1, use a chalkboard compass or two rulers to form an angle. For each angle shown, demonstrate the rotation to show a counterclockwise turn for positive measure and a clockwise turn for negative measure. Show −312° by first rotating the terminal side 270° clockwise. Point out to students that another clockwise rotation of 42° would yield −312°. For 830°, show two complete counterclockwise turns of 360° for a sum of 720° and another counterclockwise turn of 110°.

Teaching Notes

To practice finding coterminal angles, ask students to find several coterminal angles for 180° and 90°.

180°: −900°, −540°, −180°, 540°, 900°
90°: −990°, −630°, −270°, 450°, 810°, 1170°

In the discussion of **Arc Length,** remind students that the measure of a central angle is equal to the measure of the intercepted arc. That is why the arc is $\frac{\theta}{360}$ of the circle.

There is no need for students to memorize the formula for arc length $l = \frac{\theta \pi r}{180}$ given at the top of page 435. The formula will be simplified to $l = r\theta$ after radians are introduced (see page 439).

ADDITIONAL EXAMPLES

Example 1

Find three angles coterminal with an angle of 30° in standard position.

Possible answer: 390°

Possible answer: −330°

Possible answer: 750°

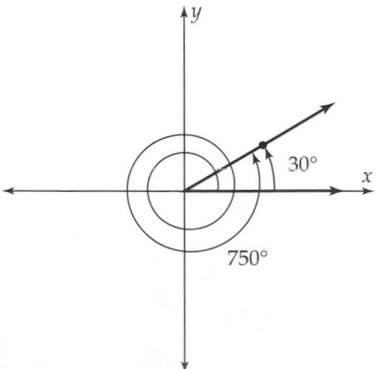

An angle in the coordinate plane is said to be in **standard position** if its vertex is at the origin and its initial side is on the positive x-axis.

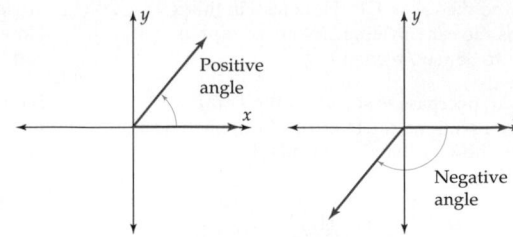

Figure 6.3-2

Angles formed by different rotations that have the same initial and terminal sides are called **coterminal.** (See Figure 6.3-3.) For example, 0° and 360° are coterminal angles.

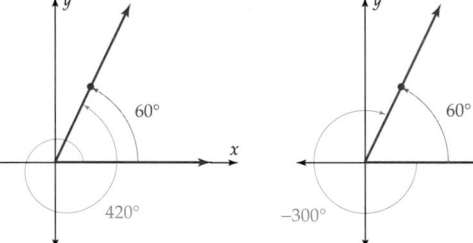

Figure 6.3-3

Example 1   Coterminal Angles

Find three angles coterminal with an angle of 60° in standard position.

Solution

To find an angle that is coterminal with a given angle, add or subtract a complete revolution, or 360°. To find additional angles, add or subtract any multiple of 360°. Three possible angles are shown below.

$$60° + 360° = 420° \qquad 60° − 360° = −300° \qquad 60° + 2(360°) = 780°$$

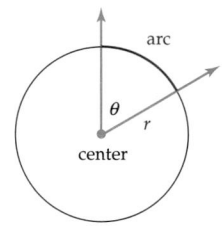

Figure 6.3-4

Arc Length

Recall from geometry that an **arc** is a part of a circle and that a **central angle** is an angle whose vertex is the center of the circle. The length of an arc depends on the radius of the circle and the measure of the central angle θ that it intercepts, as shown in Figure 6.3-5.

Figure 6.3-5

Arc length can be calculated by considering an arc as a fraction of the entire circle. Suppose an arc in a circle of radius r has a central angle measure of θ. Since there are 360° in a full circle, the arc is $\frac{\theta}{360}$ of the circle. The circumference of the circle is $2\pi r$, so, the length ℓ of the arc is

$$\ell = \frac{\theta}{360} \cdot 2\pi r = \frac{\theta \pi r}{180}$$

Example 2   **Finding an Angle Given an Arc Length**

An arc in a circle has an arc length ℓ which is equal to the radius r. Find the measure of the central angle that the arc intercepts.

Solution

$$r = \ell$$
$$r = \frac{\theta \pi r}{180}$$
$$180r = \theta \pi r$$
$$180 = \theta \pi$$
$$\frac{180}{\pi} = \theta$$

The central angle measure is $\left(\frac{180}{\pi}\right)^{\circ}$, or about 57.3°.

Radian Measure

The angle found in Example 2 leads to another unit used in finding angle measure called a *radian*. Because it simplifies many formulas in calculus and physics, radians are used as a unit of angle measurement in mathematical and scientific applications.

Angle measurement in radians can be described in terms of the **unit circle,** which is the circle of radius 1 centered at the origin, whose equation is $x^2 + y^2 = 1$. When an angle is in standard position, its initial side lies on the x-axis and passes through $(1, 0)$. Its terminal side intersects the unit circle at some point P, as shown in Figure 6.3-6.

Figure 6.3-6

Teaching Notes

To explain the **Definition of Radian Measure** and relate the idea that radians use arc length to describe angle measure show the following:

1 revolution of unit circle $= 2\pi$ radians

2π radians $= 360°$

π radians $= 180°$

$$1 \text{ radian} = \left(\frac{180}{\pi}\right)^\circ$$

For Figure 6.3-8, explain to students when finding radians, they are finding what fraction of the total circumference is shown. For example, for $\frac{3}{4}$ revolution, find $\frac{3}{4}$ of the total circumference 2π, which is $\frac{3\pi}{2}$. Go through each example if necessary to help students understand.

When discussing the examples in Figure 6.3-8, you may want to ask the students for the degree measurement of each angle:

2π radians $= 360°$,

$\frac{3\pi}{2}$ radians $= 270°$,

π radians $= 180°$, and

$\frac{\pi}{2}$ radians $= 90°$.

This will serve as a natural lead-in for the discussion of **Converting Between Degrees and Radians** on page 437.

From the examples in Figure 6.3-8, it can be deduced that an acute angle is between 0 and $\frac{\pi}{2}$ radians and an obtuse angle is between $\frac{\pi}{2}$ and π radians.

COMMON ERROR ALERT

Some students may get an answer of 3 degrees for the measure of an angle θ and write $\theta = 3$. Remind them of the **NOTE** on page 436 that says measurements in radians are not labeled with units. If the answer is in degrees, the degree sign must be used, $\theta = 3°$.

Definition of Radian Measure

NOTE Generally, measurements in radians are not labeled with units, although the word radian or the abbreviation rad may sometimes be used for clarity.

The radian measure of an angle is the distance traveled along the unit circle in a counterclockwise direction by the point P, as it moves from its starting position on the initial side to its final position on the terminal side of the angle.

$$1 \text{ radian} = \left(\frac{180}{\pi}\right)^\circ \approx 57.3°$$

If the vertex of an angle is the center of a circle of radius r, then an angle of 1 radian intercepts an arc of length r.

Movement along the unit circle is counterclockwise for positive measure and clockwise for negative measure.

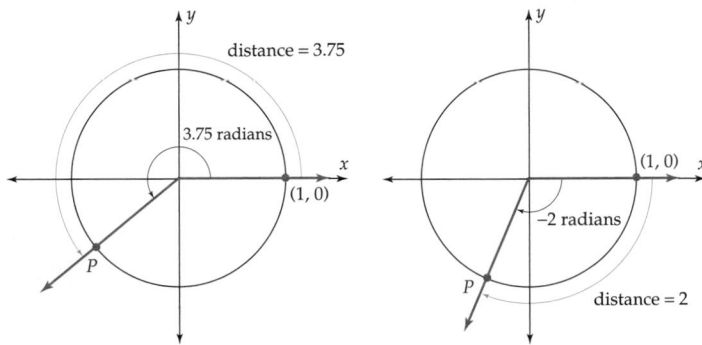

Figure 6.3-7

Consider an angle in standard position, with its terminal side rotating around the origin. In degree measure, one full revolution produces a 360° angle. The radian measure of this angle is the circumference of the unit circle, namely 2π. Other angles can be considered as a fraction of a full revolution, as shown in Figure 6.3-8.

1 revolution	3/4 revolution	1/2 revolution	1/4 revolution
2π radians	$\frac{3}{4} \cdot 2\pi = \frac{3\pi}{2}$ radians	$\frac{1}{2} \cdot 2\pi = \pi$ radians	$\frac{1}{4} \cdot 2\pi = \frac{\pi}{2}$ radians

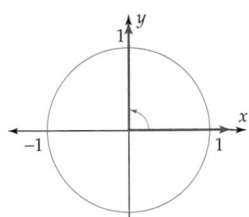

Figure 6.3-8

Radian Measure of Special Angles

The special angles of 30°, 60°, and 45° can also be considered as a fraction of a full revolution. Note that

- $\frac{360}{12} = 30$, so 30° is $\frac{1}{12}$ of a complete revolution: $30° = \frac{1}{12} \cdot 2\pi = \frac{\pi}{6}$ rad

- $\frac{360}{6} = 60$, so 60° is $\frac{1}{6}$ of a complete revolution: $60° = \frac{1}{6} \cdot 2\pi = \frac{\pi}{3}$ rad

- $\frac{360}{8} = 45$, so 45° is $\frac{1}{8}$ of a complete revolution: $45° = \frac{1}{8} \cdot 2\pi = \frac{\pi}{4}$ rad

Figure 6.3-9 shows a unit circle with radian and degree measures for important values. The radian measures for the angles shown in the first quadrant and on the x- and y-axes should be memorized.

NOTE Radian measurements are usually given in terms of π; however, it is useful to know the decimal equivalents for common measurements when using a calculator.

$\pi \approx 3.14$ $2\pi \approx 6.28$

$\frac{\pi}{2} \approx 1.57$ $\frac{\pi}{4} \approx 0.79$

$\frac{\pi}{6} \approx 0.52$ $\frac{\pi}{3} \approx 1.05$

Figure 6.3-9

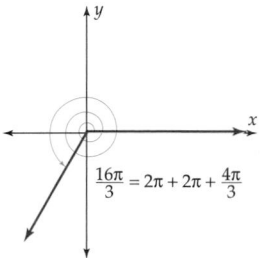

$\frac{16\pi}{3} = 2\pi + 2\pi + \frac{4\pi}{3}$

Figure 6.3-10

As shown in Figure 6.3-9, 2π radians corresponds to a full revolution of the terminal side of an angle in standard position. So an angle of radian measure t is coterminal with the angles whose radian measures are $t \pm 2\pi$, $t \pm 4\pi$, and so on, as shown in Figure 6.3-10.

Increasing or decreasing the radian measure of an angle by an integer multiple of 2π results in a coterminal angle.

Converting Between Degrees and Radians

As shown in Figure 6.3-9,

$$\pi \text{ radians} = 180°.$$

Teaching Notes

Another way to help students understand the **Radian Measure of Special Angles** is by having them find the fraction of the revolution the angle represents:

- 30 degrees is $\frac{30}{360}$ or $\frac{1}{12}$ of the full revolution. $\frac{1}{12}$ of 2π is $\frac{\pi}{6}$ radians.

- 60 degrees is $\frac{60}{360}$ or $\frac{1}{6}$ of the full revolution. $\frac{1}{6}$ of 2π is $\frac{\pi}{3}$ radians.

- 45 degrees is $\frac{45}{360}$ or $\frac{1}{8}$ of the full revolution. $\frac{1}{8}$ of 2π is $\frac{\pi}{4}$ radians.

Help students understand Figure 6.3-9 by having them find 90°, 180°, 270°, and 360° on the circle and have them explain why the corresponding radian measures are what they are. For example, 180 degrees corresponds to $\frac{1}{2}$ of the revolution. $\frac{1}{2}$ of 2π is π.

Use degrees to help students understand Figure 6.3-10. For any angle, you can find the coterminal angle by adding integer multiples of 360° to θ. For example, to find a coterminal angle for 30°, add 360° to it. Similarly, you can find coterminal angles represented in radians by adding an integer multiple of 2π.

Math Background

An alternate definition of radian measure is the following. The radian measure of the angle is the ratio of the length of the intercepted arc to the radius of the circle. For example, in a circle with radius 2, the circumference is 4π and the arc length of a quarter circle is $\frac{1}{4} \cdot 4\pi = \pi$. The radian measure of the angle that intercepts a quarter circle is $\frac{\text{arc length}}{\text{radius}} = \frac{\pi}{2}$.

Teaching Notes

Show students how canceling units can help remember which rule to use in the **Radian/Degree Conversion.** For example, if you know radians and want to find degrees, you want to cancel radians. Therefore, the radian measure π should be in the denominator, so you will use $\frac{180}{\pi}$.

For example, to change $\frac{\pi}{2}$ radians to degrees: $\frac{\pi}{2} \cdot \frac{180°}{\pi} = \frac{\cancel{\pi}^{1}}{{}_{1}\cancel{2}} \cdot \frac{\cancel{180°}^{90°}}{{}_{1}\cancel{\pi}} = 90°.$

On the other hand, if you know degrees and want to find radians, you will need degrees in the denominator, so you will use $\frac{\pi}{180}$.

For example, to change 45 degrees to radians multiply

$\frac{45°}{1} \cdot \frac{\pi}{180°} = \frac{\cancel{45°}^{1}}{1} \cdot \frac{\pi}{\cancel{180°}_{4}} = \frac{\pi}{4}$ radians.

An alternate way of performing radian/degree conversions is based on the fact that π radians $= 180°$. Students can use this equation to set up a proportion.

For example, to change 60° to radians:

$$\frac{\pi \text{ radians}}{180°} = \frac{x}{60°}$$
$$180° \cdot x = 60° \cdot \pi \text{ radians}$$
$$x = \frac{60° \cdot \pi \text{ radians}}{180°}$$
$$x = \frac{\pi}{3} \text{ radians}$$

And to change $\frac{2\pi}{3}$ radians to degrees:

$$\frac{\pi \text{ radians}}{180°} = \frac{\frac{2\pi}{3} \text{ radians}}{x}$$
$$x \cdot \pi \text{ radians} = 180° \cdot \frac{2\pi}{3} \text{ radians}$$
$$x = \frac{180° \cdot \frac{2\pi}{3} \text{ radians}}{\pi \text{ radians}}$$
$$= 180° \cdot \frac{2}{3}$$
$$x = 120°$$

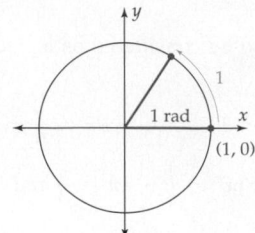

Figure 6.3-11

Radian/Degree Conversion

NOTE One radian, which is illustrated in Figure 6.3-11, is close to 60°. There are about 6 radians ($2\pi \approx 6.28$) in a complete circle.

NOTE To help you remember which conversion factor to use, it may be helpful to notice that radians are *usually* written in terms of π.

Degrees to radians: to get π in final answer, multiply by $\frac{\pi}{180}$

Radians to degrees: to cancel π in final answer, multiply by $\frac{180}{\pi}$

Dividing both sides by π shows that

$$1 \text{ radian} = \left(\frac{180}{\pi}\right)° \approx 57.3°,$$

which agrees with the definition of radian.

Similarly, both sides of the original equation can be divided by 180.

$$\frac{\pi}{180} \text{ radians} = 1°$$

These two equations give the conversion factors for radians to degrees and degrees to radians.

> To convert radians to degrees, multiply by $\frac{180}{\pi}$.
>
> To convert degrees to radians, multiply by $\frac{\pi}{180}$.

Example 3   Converting From Radians to Degrees

Convert the following radian measurements to degrees.

a. $\frac{\pi}{5}$ **b.** $\frac{4\pi}{9}$ **c.** 6π

Solution

a. $\frac{\pi}{5} \cdot \frac{180}{\pi} = 36°$ **b.** $\frac{4\pi}{9} \cdot \frac{180}{\pi} = 80°$ **c.** $6\pi \cdot \frac{180}{\pi} = 1080°$ ∎

Example 4   Converting From Degrees to Radians

Convert the following degree measurements to radians.

a. 75° **b.** 220° **c.** 400°

Solution

a. $75° \cdot \frac{\pi}{180} = \frac{5\pi}{12}$ **b.** $220° \cdot \frac{\pi}{180} = \frac{11\pi}{9}$ **c.** $400° \cdot \frac{\pi}{180} = \frac{20\pi}{9}$ ∎

Arc Length and Angular Speed

The formula for arc length can also be written in terms of radians.

Arc Length

> An arc with central angle measure θ radians has length
> $$\ell = r\theta$$
> In other words, the arc length is the radius times the radian measure of the central angle of the arc.

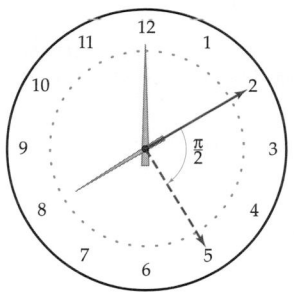

Figure 6.3-12

Example 5 Arc Length

The second hand on a clock is 6 inches long. How far does the tip of the second hand move in 15 seconds?

Solution

The second hand makes a full revolution every 60 seconds, that is, it moves through an angle of 2π radians. During a 15-second interval it will make $\frac{15}{60} = \frac{1}{4}$ of a revolution, moving through an angle of $\frac{1}{4}(2\pi) = \frac{\pi}{2}$ radians (Figure 6.3-12), so the tip of the second hand travels along an arc with a central angle measure of $\frac{\pi}{2}$. Therefore, the distance that the tip moves in 15 seconds is the arc length

$$\ell = r\theta = 6\left(\frac{\pi}{2}\right) = 3\pi \approx 9.4 \text{ inches.}$$

Example 6 Central Angle Measure

Find the central angle measure (in radians) of an arc of length 5 cm on a circle with a radius of 3 cm.

Solution

Solve the arc length formula $\ell = r\theta$ for θ.

$$\theta = \frac{\ell}{r} = \frac{5}{3} \text{ radians}$$

This is a little more than one-quarter of a complete revolution, as shown in Figure 6.3-13.

Figure 6.3-13

Linear and Angular Speed

Suppose that a wheel is rotating at a constant rate around its center, O, and P is a point on the outer edge of the wheel. There are two ways to measure the speed of point P, in terms of the distance traveled or in terms of the angle of rotation. The two measures of speed are called *linear speed* and *angular speed*.

Teaching Notes

Point out to students that the **Arc Length** formula is a simplified version of the formula for arc length found on page 435.

$l = \frac{\theta \pi r}{180}$ simplifies to $l = r\theta$ when r is measured in radians because

$1 \text{ radian} = \left(\frac{180}{\pi}\right)^{\circ}$.

ADDITIONAL EXAMPLES

Example 3

Convert the following radian measurements to degrees:

a. $\frac{\pi}{9}$ 20°   **b.** $\frac{3\pi}{5}$ 108°   **c.** 5π 900°

Example 4

Convert the following degree measurements to radians:

a. 150° $\frac{5\pi}{6}$ **b.** 330° $\frac{11\pi}{6}$ **c.** 540° 3π

Example 5

The second hand on a clock is 5 inches long. How far does the tip of the second hand move in 45 seconds?

$5\left(\frac{3\pi}{2}\right) \approx 23.6 \text{ inches}$

Example 6

Find the central angle measure (in radians) of an arc of length 11 cm on a circle with a radius of 4 cm.

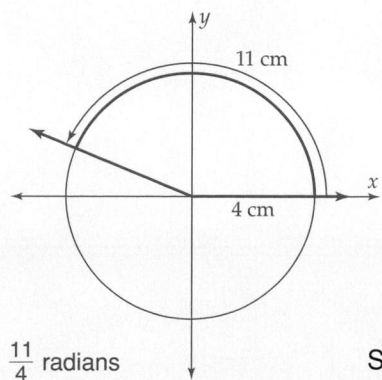

$\frac{11}{4}$ radians

Teaching Notes

An everyday reference to speed is miles per hour, or feet per second, which can be written as $\frac{miles}{hour}$ or $\frac{feet}{second}$. Note to students that the distance, or the amount traveled is the numerator, and time is in the denominator. With respect to discussing linear speed and angular speed, note that the amount traveled—whether it is arc length or angle of rotation—is the numerator, and speed is in the denominator.

ADDITIONAL EXAMPLES

Example 7

A circular mobile above a baby's crib makes 5 revolutions per minute.

a. What is the angular speed of the mobile in radians per minute?
10π radians per minute

b. How fast is a toy 9 inches from the center traveling in feet per minute?
$90\pi \approx 282.7$ inches per minute
≈ 23.6 feet per minute

c. How fast is a toy 6 inches from the center traveling in feet per minute?
$60\pi \approx 188.5$ inches per minute
≈ 15.7 feet per minute

 Real-World Application

Linear speed and angular speed are applied to merry-go-round horses in **Example 7.** The same concepts can be applied to *any object on the earth's equator,* because, from the center of the earth as a point of observation, any object on the equator travels in approximately a circular path. The radius of the earth at the equator is about 3960 miles. Challenge your students to find the linear speed of an object on the equator.

angular speed $= \frac{2\pi\,\text{radians}}{24\,\text{hours}}$
$= \frac{\pi}{12}$ radians per hour

linear speed $= 3960 \cdot \frac{\pi}{12}$
≈ 1037 miles per hour

So, when you are standing perfectly still on the equator, your speed relative to the center of the earth is 1037 miles per hour!

Figure 6.3-14

NOTE The angular speed of an object traveling in a circular path is the same, regardless of its distance from the center of the circle. When the angular speed of the object stays the same, the linear speed increases as the object moves farther from the center.

Recall that the speed of a moving object is $\frac{\text{distance}}{\text{time}}$. If the object is traveling in a circular path with radius r, the **linear speed** is given by

$$\text{linear speed} = \frac{\text{arc length}}{\text{time}} = \frac{r\theta}{t}$$

and the **angular speed** is given by

$$\text{angular speed} = \frac{\text{angle}}{\text{time}} = \frac{\theta}{t}$$

where θ is the radian measure of the angle through which the object travels in time t. Notice the relationship between linear speed and angular speed:

$$\text{linear speed} = r \cdot \text{angular speed}$$

Example 7 Linear and Angular Speed

A merry-go-round makes 8 revolutions per minute.

a. What is the angular speed of the merry-go-round in radians per minute?

b. How fast is a horse 12 feet from the center traveling?

c. How fast is a horse 4 feet from the center traveling?

Solution

a. Each revolution of the merry-go-round corresponds to a central angle of 2π radians, so the merry-go-round travels through an angle of $8 \cdot 2\pi = 16\pi$ radians in one minute.

$$\text{angular speed} = \frac{\theta}{t} = \frac{16\pi}{1} = 16\pi \text{ radians per minute}$$

b. The horse 12 feet from the center travels along a circle of radius 12. From part **a,**

$$\text{linear speed} = r \cdot \text{angular speed} = 12 \cdot 16\pi = 192\pi \text{ ft/min}$$

which is about 6.9 mph.

c. The horse 4 feet from the center travels along a circle of radius 4. From part **a,**

$$\text{linear speed} = r \cdot \text{angular speed} = 4 \cdot 16\pi = 64\pi \text{ ft/min}$$

which is about 2.3 mph.

NOTE The units ft/min in Example 7 can be converted to mph as follows:

$$\frac{192\pi \text{ ft}}{1 \text{ min}} \cdot \frac{60 \text{ min}}{1 \text{ hr}} \cdot \frac{1 \text{ mi}}{5280 \text{ ft}} \approx \frac{6.9 \text{ mi}}{1 \text{ hr}}$$

Exercises 6.3

In Exercises 1–10, find the degree and radian measure of the angle in standard position formed by rotating the terminal side by the given amount.

1. $\frac{1}{9}$ of a circle
   40°, $\frac{2\pi}{9}$ radians

2. $\frac{1}{24}$ of a circle
   15°, $\frac{\pi}{12}$ radians

3. $\frac{1}{18}$ of a circle
   20°, $\frac{\pi}{9}$ radians

4. $\frac{1}{72}$ of a circle
   5°, $\frac{\pi}{36}$ radians

5. $\frac{1}{36}$ of a circle
   10°, $\frac{\pi}{18}$ radians

6. $\frac{1}{5}$ of a circle
   72°, $\frac{2\pi}{5}$ radians

7. $\frac{2}{3}$ of a circle
   240°, $\frac{4\pi}{3}$ radians

8. $\frac{7}{12}$ of a circle
   210°, $\frac{7\pi}{6}$ radians

9. $\frac{4}{5}$ of a circle
   288°, $\frac{8\pi}{5}$ radians

10. $\frac{5}{36}$ of a circle
    50°, $\frac{5\pi}{18}$ radians

In Exercises 11–22, convert the given radian measure to degrees.

11. $\frac{\pi}{5}$
    36°

12. $-\frac{\pi}{6}$
    −30°

13. $-\frac{\pi}{10}$
    −18°

14. $\frac{2\pi}{5}$
    72°

15. $\frac{3\pi}{4}$
    135°

16. $-\frac{5\pi}{3}$
    −300°

17. $\frac{\pi}{45}$
    4°

18. $-\frac{\pi}{60}$
    −3°

19. $-\frac{5\pi}{12}$
    −75°

20. $\frac{7\pi}{15}$
    84°

21. $\frac{27\pi}{5}$
    972°

22. $-\frac{41\pi}{6}$
    −1230°

In Exercises 23–34, convert the given degree measure to radians. Write your answer in terms of π.

23. 6° $\frac{\pi}{30}$

24. −10° $\frac{\pi}{18}$

25. −12° $\frac{\pi}{15}$

26. 36° $\frac{\pi}{5}$

27. 75° $\frac{5\pi}{12}$

28. −105° $\frac{7\pi}{12}$

29. 135° $\frac{3\pi}{4}$

30. −165° $\frac{11\pi}{12}$

31. −225° $-\frac{5\pi}{4}$

32. 252° $\frac{7\pi}{5}$

33. 930° $\frac{31\pi}{6}$

34. −585° $-\frac{13\pi}{4}$

In Exercises 35–42, state the radian measure of an angle in standard position between 0 and 2π that is coterminal with the given angle in standard position.

35. $-\frac{\pi}{3}$ $\frac{5\pi}{3}$

36. $-\frac{3\pi}{4}$ $\frac{5\pi}{4}$

37. $\frac{19\pi}{4}$ $\frac{3\pi}{4}$

38. $\frac{16\pi}{3}$ $\frac{4\pi}{3}$

39. $-\frac{7\pi}{5}$ $\frac{3\pi}{5}$

40. $\frac{45\pi}{8}$ $\frac{13\pi}{8}$

41. 7 **$7 - 2\pi$**

42. 18.5 **$18.5 - 4\pi$**

In Exercises 43–46, find the radian measure of four angles in standard position that are coterminal with the given angle in standard position.

43. $\frac{\pi}{4}$

44. $\frac{7\pi}{5}$

45. $-\frac{\pi}{6}$

46. $-\frac{9\pi}{7}$

In Exercises 47–52, determine the positive radian measure of the angle that the second hand of a clock travels through in the given time.

47. 40 seconds

48. 50 seconds

49. 35 seconds

50. 2 minutes 15 seconds

51. 3 minutes 25 seconds

52. 1 minute 55 seconds

53. The second hand on a clock is 6 cm long. How far does its tip travel in 40 seconds?

54. The second hand on a clock is 5 cm long. How far does its tip travel in 2 minutes and 15 seconds?

55. If the radius of the circle in the figure is 20 cm and $\ell = 85$ cm, what is the radian measure of the angle θ? **$\frac{17}{4}$**

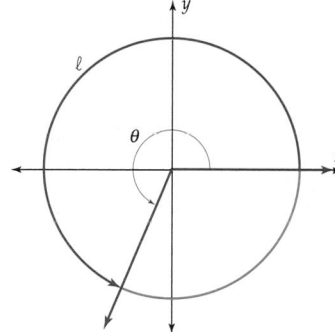

56. Find the radian measure of the angle θ in the preceding figure if the diameter of the circle is 150 cm and $\ell = 360$ cm. **$\frac{24}{5}$**

In Exercises 57–60, assume that a wheel on a car has radius 36 cm. Find the angle (in radians) that the wheel turns while the car travels the given distance.

57. 2 meters (200 cm) $\frac{50}{9}$

58. 5 meters $\frac{125}{9}$

59. 720 meters
    2000

60. 1 kilometer (1000 meters)
    $\frac{25,000}{9}$

In Exercises 61–64, find the length of the circular arc with the central angle whose radian measure is given. Assume that the circle has diameter 10.

61. 1 radian
    5

62. 2 radians
    10

63. 1.75 radians
    8.75

64. 2.2 radians
    11

ANSWERS

43. $\frac{9\pi}{4}, \frac{17\pi}{4}, -\frac{7\pi}{4}, -\frac{15\pi}{4}$

44. $\frac{17\pi}{5}, \frac{27\pi}{5}, -\frac{3\pi}{5}, -\frac{13\pi}{5}$

45. $\frac{11\pi}{6}, \frac{23\pi}{6}, -\frac{13\pi}{6}, -\frac{25\pi}{6}$

46. $\frac{5\pi}{7}, \frac{19\pi}{7}, -\frac{23\pi}{7}, -\frac{37\pi}{7}$

47. $\frac{4\pi}{3}$

48. $\frac{5\pi}{3}$

49. $\frac{7\pi}{6}$

50. $\frac{9\pi}{2}$

51. $\frac{41\pi}{6}$

52. $\frac{23\pi}{6}$

53. 8π cm

54. $\frac{45\pi}{2}$ cm

78. a. ≈2387.3 revolutions per min

　b. ≈2.51 min

79. a. 400π radians per min

　b. 800π in. per min;
　　$\frac{200\pi}{3}$ ft per min

80. a. 2400π radians per min

　b. 3360π ft per min;
　　≈119.95 mph

81. a. 5π radians per sec

　b. ≈6.69 mph

82. ≈18.95 radians per sec

83. ≈15.92 ft

The *latitude* of a point P on Earth is the degree measure of the angle θ between the point and the plane of the equator, with Earth's center as the vertex, as shown in the figure below.

In Exercises 65–68, the latitudes of a pair of cities are given. Assume that one city is directly south of the other and that the earth is a perfect sphere of radius 4000 miles. Use the arc length formula in terms of degrees to find the distance between the two cities.

65. The North Pole: latitude 90° north
Springfield, Illinois: latitude 40° north
≈3490.66 mi

66. San Antonio, Texas: latitude 29.5° north
Mexico City, Mexico: latitude 20° north
≈663.2 mi

67. Cleveland, Ohio: latitude 41.5° north
Tampa, Florida: latitude 28° north
≈942.48 mi

68. Rome, Italy: latitude 42° north
Copenhagen, Denmark: latitude 54.3° north
≈858.7 mi

In Exercises 69–76, a wheel is rotating around its axle. Find the angle (in radians) through which the wheel turns in the given time when it rotates at the given number of revolutions per minute (rpm). Assume $t > 0$ and $k > 0$.

69. 3.5 minutes, 1 rpm
7π

70. t minutes, 1 rpm
$2\pi t$

71. 1 minute, 2 rpm
4π

72. 3.5 minutes, 2 rpm
14π

73. 4.25 minutes, 5 rpm
42.5π

74. t minutes, 5 rpm
$10\pi t$

75. 1 minute, k rpm
$2\pi k$

76. t minutes, k rpm
$2tk\pi$

77. One end of a rope is attached to a circular drum of radius 2 feet and the other to a steel beam. When the drum is rotated, the rope wraps around it and pulls the object upward (see figure). Through what angle must the drum be rotated in order to raise the beam 6 feet?
3 radians (≈171.9°)

78. A circular saw blade has an angular speed of 15,000 radians per minute.
　a. How many revolutions per minute does the saw make?
　b. How long will it take the saw to make 6000 revolutions?

79. A circular gear rotates at the rate of 200 revolutions per minute (rpm).
　a. What is the angular speed of the gear in radians per minute?
　b. What is the linear speed of a point on the gear 2 inches from the center in inches per minute? in feet per minute?

80. A wheel in a large machine is 2.8 feet in diameter and rotates at 1200 rpm.
　a. What is the angular speed of the wheel?
　b. How fast is a point on the circumference of the wheel traveling in feet per minute? in miles per hour?

81. A riding lawn mower has wheels that are 15 inches in diameter, which are turning at 2.5 revolutions per second.
　a. What is the angular speed of a wheel?
　b. How fast is the lawn mower traveling in miles per hour?

82. A bicycle has wheels that are 26 inches in diameter. If the bike is traveling at 14 mph, what is the angular speed of each wheel?

83. A merry-go-round horse is traveling at 10 feet per second when the merry-go-round is making 6 revolutions per minute. How far is the horse from the center of the merry-go-round?

84. The pedal sprocket of a bicycle has radius 4.5 inches and the rear wheel sprocket has radius 1.5 inches (see figure). If the rear wheel has a radius of 13.5 inches and the cyclist is pedaling at the rate of 80 rpm, how fast is the bicycle traveling in feet per minute? in miles per hour?

≈1696.46 ft per min; ≈19.28 mph

85. A spy plane on a practice run over the Midwest takes a picture that shows Cleveland, Ohio, on the eastern horizon and St. Louis, Missouri, 520 miles away on the western horizon. (The figure is not to scale.) Assuming that the radius of the earth is 3950 miles, how high was the plane when the picture was taken? *Hint:* The sight lines from the plane to the horizons are tangent to the earth and a tangent line to a circle is perpendicular to the radius at that point. The arc of the earth between St. Louis and Cleveland is 520 miles long. Use this fact and the arc length formula to find angle θ. Your answers will be in radians. Note that

$\alpha = \dfrac{\theta}{2}$ (why?). **≈8.6 mi**

St. Louis θ α Cleveland

6.4

Trigonometric Functions

Objectives

- Define the trigonometric ratios in the coordinate plane
- Define the trigonometric functions in terms of the unit circle

---

NOTE P can be any point on the terminal side of the angle, except for the origin, since different choices for P generate similar right triangles. Thus, the value of a trigonometric ratio depends only on the angle.

Extending the Trigonometric Ratios

Trigonometric ratios were defined for acute angles in Section 6.1. The next step is to develop a definition of these ratios that applies to angles of any measure.

To do this, first consider an acute angle θ in standard position. Choose a point P, with coordinates (x, y), on the terminal side, and draw a right triangle, as shown in Figure 6.4-1. The side adjacent to θ has length x and the side opposite θ has length y. The length of the hypotenuse, r, is the distance from the origin, which may be found by using the Pythagorean Theorem.

$$x^2 + y^2 = r^2$$
$$r = \sqrt{x^2 + y^2}$$

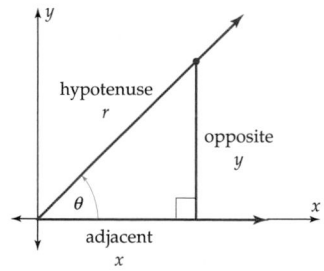

Figure 6.4-1

Section

6.4 **Trigonometric Functions**

Teaching Notes

In **Extending the Trigonometric Ratios**, the **NOTE** states that the value of a trigonometric ratio depends only on the angle and not the point P on the terminal side of the angle. The following illustrates this point.

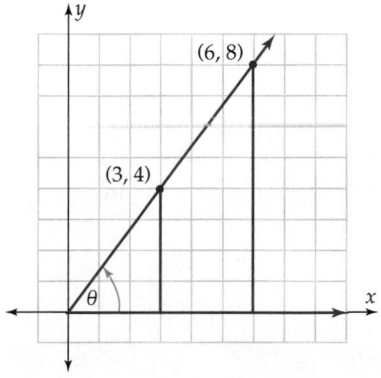

For $(3, 4)$:

$r = \sqrt{3^2 + 4^2}$

$ = \sqrt{25} = 5$

$\sin \theta = \dfrac{y}{r} = \dfrac{3}{5}$

$\cos \theta = \dfrac{x}{r} = \dfrac{4}{5}$

For $(6, 8)$:

$r = \sqrt{6^2 + 8^2}$

$ = \sqrt{100} = 10$

$\sin \theta = \dfrac{y}{r} = \dfrac{6}{10} = \dfrac{3}{5}$

$\cos \theta = \dfrac{x}{r} = \dfrac{8}{10} = \dfrac{4}{5}$

Teaching Notes

In Section 6.1, the trigonometric ratios were defined for acute angles θ, $0° < \theta < 90°$. The values of the trigonometric ratios of acute angles are all positive.

In **Trigonometric Ratios in the Coordinate Plane,** the trigonometric ratios are defined in terms of a point $P(x, y)$ on the terminal side of an angle θ and the distance r from P to the origin.

Based on this definition:

- The values of the trigonometric ratios can be positive, negative, or zero depending on which quadrant the point P is in.
- The angle can be measured in degrees or radians.
- The angle can be positive, negative, or zero.
- Because r is always positive, the sine and cosine are defined for all angle values.
- The tangent and secant are defined for all angle values except when $x = 0$.
- The cotangent and cosecant are defined for all angle values except when $y = 0$.
- Coterminal angles will have the same trigonometric ratios.

Example Notes

In **Example 1,** point out to students that they are no longer using a right triangle to get the trigonometric ratios.

The terminal point of the angle is in the third quadrant, so $180° < \theta < 270°$. Because both x- and y-coordinates are negative in the third quadrant, $\sin \theta < 0$, $\cos \theta < 0$, and $\tan \theta > 0$.

Trigonometric Ratios in the Coordinate Plane

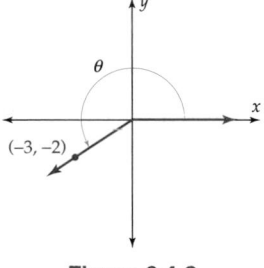

Figure 6.4-2

The trigonometric ratios can now be written in terms of x, y, and r. For example,

$$\sin \theta = \frac{\text{opposite}}{\text{hypotenuse}} = \frac{y}{r} \quad \text{and} \quad \cos \theta = \frac{\text{adjacent}}{\text{hypotenuse}} = \frac{x}{r}$$

Thus, the trigonometric ratios can be described without triangles by using a point on the terminal side of the angle. More importantly, this process can be carried out for *any* angle, not just acute angles. Therefore, the following definition applies to any angle and agrees with the previous definition when the angle is acute.

Let θ be an angle in standard position and let $P(x, y)$ be any point on the terminal side of θ. Let r be the distance from (x, y) to the origin:

$$r = \sqrt{x^2 + y^2}$$

Then the trigonometric ratios of θ are defined as follows:

$$\sin \theta = \frac{y}{r} \qquad \csc \theta = \frac{r}{y}$$

$$\cos \theta = \frac{x}{r} \qquad \sec \theta = \frac{r}{x}$$

$$\tan \theta = \frac{y}{x} \qquad \cot \theta = \frac{x}{y}$$

Example 1   Trigonometric Ratios in the Coordinate Plane

Find the sine, cosine, and tangent of the angle θ, whose terminal side passes through the point $(-3, -2)$.

Solution

Using the values $x = -3$, $y = -2$, and $r = \sqrt{(-3)^2 + (-2)^2} = \sqrt{13}$,

$$\sin \theta = \frac{-2}{\sqrt{13}} \qquad \cos \theta = \frac{-3}{\sqrt{13}} \qquad \tan \theta = \frac{-2}{-3} = \frac{2}{3}$$

Trigonometric Functions

Trigonometric ratios have been defined for all *angles*. But modern applications of trigonometry deal with *functions* whose domains consist of real numbers. The basic idea is quite simple: If t is a real number, then

$\sin t$ is defined to be the sine of an angle of t radians;

$\cos t$ is defined to be the cosine of an angle of t radians;

and so on. Instead of starting with angles, as was done up until now, this new approach starts with a number and only then moves to angles, as summarized below.

Trigonometric Functions of Real Numbers

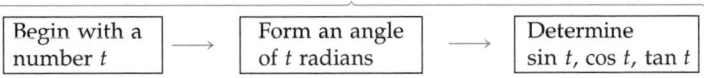

| Begin with a number t | $\longrightarrow$ | Form an angle of t radians | $\longrightarrow$ | Determine $\sin t$, $\cos t$, $\tan t$ |

Trigonometric Ratios of Angles

Adapting earlier definitions of ratios to this new viewpoint produces the following definition of trigonometric functions of real numbers. Use Figure 6.4-3 for reference.

Trigonometric Functions of a Real Variable

> **Let t be a real number. Choose any point (x, y) on the terminal side of an angle of t radians in standard position. Then**
>
> $$\sin t = \frac{y}{r} \qquad \cos t = \frac{x}{r} \qquad \tan t = \frac{y}{x}$$
>
> $$\csc t = \frac{r}{y} \qquad \sec t = \frac{r}{x} \qquad \cot t = \frac{x}{y}$$
>
> **where $r = \sqrt{x^2 + y^2}$ is the distance from (x, y) to the origin.**

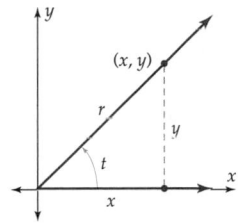

Figure 6.4-3

NOTE Unless stated otherwise, use radian mode when evaluating trigonometric functions of real numbers.

Although this definition is essential for developing various facts about the trigonometric functions, the values of these functions are usually approximated by a calculator in *radian mode*, as shown in Figure 6.4-4.

```
sin(2.5)
         .5984721441
cos(-6)
         .9601702867
tan(46/3)
        -.3931992341
```

Figure 6.4-4

Trigonometric Functions and the Unit Circle

Recall that the **unit circle** is the circle of radius 1 centered at the origin, whose equation is $x^2 + y^2 = 1$. The unit circle is the basis for the most useful description of trigonometric functions of real numbers.

Let t be any real number. Construct an angle of t radians in standard position. Let $P(x, y)$ be the point where the terminal side of this angle meets the unit circle, as shown in Figure 6.4-5.

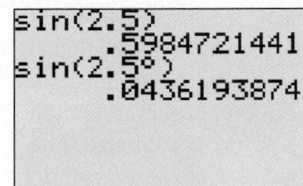

Teaching Notes

To illustrate the **NOTE** at the top of page 446, draw an arc outside the circle (as in Figure 6.3-13, page 439) and label it *t*.

In **Unit Circle Description of Trigonometric Functions**, point out that the definitions of tan *t* and sec *t* are valid for any real number *t* for which cos *t* ≠ 0, and similarly, cot *t* and csc *t* are defined for any real number *t* for which sin *t* ≠ 0,

You may want to review **Parametric Graphing** (pages 157–159) before assigning the Graphing Exploration.

Solution to the **Graphing Exploration:**

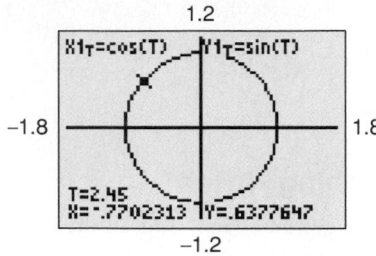

In **Domain and Range**, begin by having the students agree that both sin *t* and cos *t* are defined for any $0 \le t \le 2\pi$. Then, note that any angle whose radian measure is outside of this interval can be viewed as a coterminal angle of an angle whose radian measure *is* in this interval. Since the terminal side of an angle and any of its coterminal angles necessarily coincide (by definition), they both must intersect the unit circle in the same point and, consequently, must have the same sine and cosine values. This observation implies that the sine and cosine functions are, in fact, defined for all real numbers *t*.

For the range of the sine function, start with an angle *t* and label the intersection of its terminal side with the unit circle as *P*. Observe that if you track the *y*-coordinates of this point *P* as you rotate its terminal side 2π radians, the *y*-values attained all lie between −1 and 1, inclusive. The fact that *all* values between −1 and 1, inclusive, are attained for some angle in this process shows the *continuity* of the sine function. A similar argument can be made for the cosine function.

NOTE The length of the arc from (1, 0) to *P* is *t*.

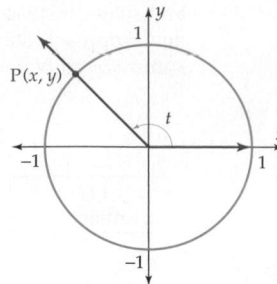

Figure 6.4-5

The distance from *P* to the origin is 1 because the unit circle has radius 1. Using the point *P*, $r = 1$, and the definition of trigonometric functions of real numbers shows the following:

$$\sin t = \frac{y}{r} = \frac{y}{1} = y \qquad \text{and} \qquad \cos t - \frac{x}{r} - \frac{x}{1} = x$$

Unit Circle Description of Trigonometric Functions

Let *t* be a real number and let *P* be the point where the terminal side of an angle of *t* radians in standard position meets the unit circle. Then

$$P \text{ has coordinates } (\cos t, \sin t)$$

and

$$\tan t = \frac{y}{x} = \frac{\sin t}{\cos t} \qquad \cot t = \frac{x}{y} = \frac{\cos t}{\sin t}$$

$$\sec t = \frac{1}{x} = \frac{1}{\cos t} \qquad \csc t = \frac{1}{y} = \frac{1}{\sin t}$$

Graphing Exploration

With your calculator in radian mode and parametric graphing mode, set the range values as follows:

$$0 \le t \le 2\pi \qquad -1.8 \le x \le 1.8 \qquad -1.2 \le y \le 1.2$$

Then, graph the curve given by these parametric equations:

$$x = \cos t \qquad y = \sin t$$

The graph is the unit circle. Use the trace to move around the circle. At each point, the screen will display three numbers: the values of *t*, *x*, and *y*. For each *t*, the cursor is on the point where the terminal side of an angle of *t* radians meets the unit circle, so the corresponding *x* is the number cos *t* and the corresponding *y* is the number sin *t*.

The coordinates of points on a circle of radius r that is centered at the origin can be written by using r and t with the definition of the trigonometric ratios in the coordinate plane. See Exercise 61.

Domain and Range

By the domain convention in Section 3.1, the domain of a function is all real numbers for which the function is defined. For any real number t, an appropriate angle of t radians and its intersection point with the unit circle are always defined, so

the domain of the sine function and of the cosine function is the set of all real numbers.

The range of a function is the set of all possible outputs. Because $\sin t$ and $\cos t$ are the coordinates of a point on the unit circle, they take on all values between -1 and 1 and no other values. Thus,

the range of the sine function and of the cosine function is the set of all real numbers between -1 and 1, that is, the interval $[-1, 1]$.

The tangent function is defined as $\tan t = \frac{y}{x}$, whenever $x \neq 0$, that is, for all points on the unit circle except $(0, 1)$ and $(0, -1)$. The point $(0, 1)$ is on the terminal side of an angle of $\frac{\pi}{2}$ radians or any angle obtained by adding integer multiples of 2π (a complete circle) to it, that is,

$$\ldots, -\frac{7\pi}{2}, -\frac{3\pi}{2}, \frac{\pi}{2}, \frac{5\pi}{2}, \frac{9\pi}{2}, \ldots$$

The point $(0, -1)$ is on the terminal side of an angle of $\frac{3\pi}{2}$ radians or any angle obtained by adding integer multiples of 2π to it, that is,

$$\ldots, -\frac{5\pi}{2}, -\frac{\pi}{2}, \frac{3\pi}{2}, \frac{7\pi}{2}, \frac{11\pi}{2}, \ldots$$

Combining these facts shows that

the domain of the tangent function consists of all real numbers except $\pm\frac{\pi}{2} + 2k\pi$, where $k = 0, \pm1, \pm2, \pm3, \ldots$.

In contrast to sine and cosine,

the range of the tangent function is the set of all real numbers.

A proof of this fact is found in Exercise 60. Figure 6.4-6 shows that values of the tangent can be very large positives, very large negatives, or in between.

Figure 6.4-6

Signs of the Trigonometric Functions

It is often important to know whether the value of a trigonometric function is positive or negative. For any real number t, the point $(\cos t, \sin t)$ is on the terminal side of an angle of t radians in standard position. The

Teaching Notes

It may be instructive to include questions of the following type as part of the discussion of the domains of the sine and cosine functions:

(i) For what real numbers in $[0, 2\pi]$ does $\sin t = 0$? $0, \pi, 2\pi$

(ii) What are *all* the real numbers for which $\sin t = 0$? $0 \pm k\pi$, where k is an integer

(iii) For what real numbers in $[0, 2\pi]$ does $\sin t = 1$? $\frac{\pi}{2}$

(iv) What are *all* the real numbers for which $\sin t = 1$? $\frac{\pi}{2} \pm 2k\pi$, where k is an integer

Similar questions involving the cosine function can also be asked. Such questions help to gather important information about the trigonometric functions (to be used later when developing their graphs in Chapter 7), and to reinforce the definitions of sine and cosine, as well as the relationship between an angle and its coterminal angles.

Remind students that since $\tan t = \frac{\sin t}{\cos t}$, it follows that the tangent function is undefined at any real number t such that $\cos t = 0$, namely $\frac{\pi}{2}, \frac{3\pi}{2}$, and their coterminal angles. This leads immediately to the domain of the tangent function.

Math Background

To prove that the range of the tangent function is the set of all real numbers, Exercise 60 (page 453) equates the slope of a line through the origin with the tangent of the angle t formed by the positive x-axis and the line. The tangent of t approaches infinity as t approaches $\frac{\pi}{2}$ from below because the slope of the line approaches infinity. The tangent of t approaches negative infinity as t approaches $\frac{\pi}{2}$ from above because the slope of the line approaches negative infinity. So, the range of the tangent function is the set of all real numbers.

Teaching Notes

The statement "**A**ll **S**tudents **T**ake **C**alculus" can be used to help students remember the **Signs of the Trigonometric Functions** given in Figure 6.4-7:

	All	**Students**	**Take**	**Calculus**
Quadrant	I	II	III	IV
Functions	All $+$	$\sin t$ $+$	$\tan t$ $+$	$\cos t$ $+$

For **Exact Values of Trigonometric Functions**, the unit circle may be used instead of the chart.

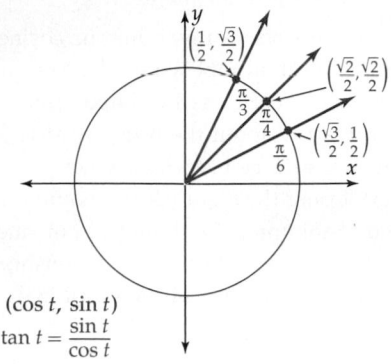

$(\cos t, \sin t)$
$\tan t = \dfrac{\sin t}{\cos t}$

Example Notes

In **Example 2**, the values of t are integer multiples of $\frac{\pi}{2}$.

ADDITIONAL EXAMPLES

Example 2

Find the exact value of the cosecant, secant, and cotangent functions when $t = 0, \frac{\pi}{2}, \pi, \frac{3\pi}{2}$, and 2π.

t	csc t	sec t	cot t
0	undefined	1	undefined
$\frac{\pi}{2}$	1	undefined	0
π	undefined	-1	undefined
$\frac{3\pi}{2}$	-1	undefined	0
2π	undefined	1	undefined

$\frac{\pi}{2} < t < \pi$
sin t +
cos t −
tan t −

$0 < t < \frac{\pi}{2}$
sin t +
cos t +
tan t +

$\pi < t < \frac{3\pi}{2}$
sin t −
cos t −
tan t +

$\frac{3\pi}{2} < t < 2\pi$
sin t −
cos t +
tan t −

Figure 6.4-7

quadrant in which this point lies determines the signs of sine and cosine, as well as those of the other trigonometric functions, as summarized in Figure 6.4-7.

Exact Values of Trigonometric Functions

Although a calculator is used to evaluate trigonometric functions approximately, there are a few special numbers for which exact values can be found. Recall that 30°, 45°, and 60° are the same as $\frac{\pi}{6}, \frac{\pi}{4}$, and $\frac{\pi}{3}$, respectively. Therefore, the chart on page 419 can be translated as follows.

t	$\dfrac{\pi}{6}$	$\dfrac{\pi}{4}$	$\dfrac{\pi}{3}$
$\sin t$	$\dfrac{1}{2}$	$\dfrac{1}{\sqrt{2}} = \dfrac{\sqrt{2}}{2}$	$\dfrac{\sqrt{3}}{2}$
$\cos t$	$\dfrac{\sqrt{3}}{2}$	$\dfrac{1}{\sqrt{2}} = \dfrac{\sqrt{2}}{2}$	$\dfrac{1}{2}$
$\tan t$	$\dfrac{1}{\sqrt{3}} = \dfrac{\sqrt{3}}{3}$	1	$\sqrt{3}$
$\csc t$	$\dfrac{2}{1} = 2$	$\dfrac{\sqrt{2}}{1} = \sqrt{2}$	$\dfrac{2}{\sqrt{3}} = \dfrac{2\sqrt{3}}{3}$
$\sec t$	$\dfrac{2}{\sqrt{3}} = \dfrac{2\sqrt{3}}{3}$	$\dfrac{\sqrt{2}}{1} = \sqrt{2}$	$\dfrac{2}{1} = 2$
$\cot t$	$\dfrac{\sqrt{3}}{1} = \sqrt{3}$	$\dfrac{1}{1} = 1$	$\dfrac{1}{\sqrt{3}} = \dfrac{\sqrt{3}}{3}$

The exact values of the trigonometric functions can also be found for any number that is an integer multiple of $\frac{\pi}{6}, \frac{\pi}{4}$, and $\frac{\pi}{3}$. The technique for doing this depends on the concept of a *reference angle*.

Example 2   Exact Values of Trigonometric Functions

Find the exact value of the sine, cosine, and tangent functions when $t = 0$, $\frac{\pi}{2}, \pi, \frac{3\pi}{2}$, and 2π.

Solution

If the measure of an angle is a multiple of $\frac{\pi}{2}$, then its terminal side lies on an axis. Thus, the only possible values of the sine and cosine functions

NOTE The diagram of the unit circle shown in Figure 6.4-8 will help you memorize the values of sin t and cos t for multiples of $\frac{\pi}{2}$.

of such angles are -1, 0 and 1. The following chart shows the value of the sine, cosine, and tangent functions for these angles between 0 and 2π.

t	sin t	cos t	tan t
0	0	1	0
$\frac{\pi}{2}$	1	0	undefined
π	0	-1	0
$\frac{3\pi}{2}$	-1	0	undefined
2π	0	1	0

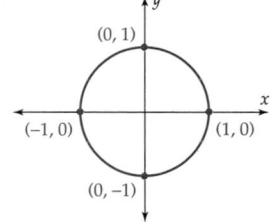

Figure 6.4-8

Reference Angles

Definition of Reference Angle

For an angle θ in standard position, the *reference angle* is the positive acute angle formed by the terminal side of θ and the x-axis.

In the following figure, the reference angle t' for an angle of t radians in standard position is shown in two ways.

Definition of Reference Angle

$t' = t$

$t' = \pi - t$

$t' = t - \pi$

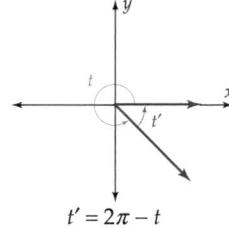
$t' = 2\pi - t$

Unit Circle with Reference Angle Placed in Quadrant I

Figure 6.4-9

Teaching Notes

In **Definition of Reference Angle**, you may want to mention that that reference angle of t is always formed in the quadrant containing its terminal side. The reason for this is that the reference angle is *acute*. Moreover, it is always formed between the terminal side and the positive or negative x-axis.

In Figure 6.4-9, it may be helpful to point out that the symmetry of the unit circle with respect to the x-axis and y-axis guarantees that the points (x, y), $(-x, y)$, $(-x, -y)$, and $(x, -y)$ are the vertices of a rectangle. Note that the diagonals of the rectangle connect angles that differ by π and they connect points whose coordinates have opposite signs. This observation is very useful when discussing the **Identities Involving** $\pi - t$ (see page 459).

🔢 Math Background

To help students remember exact values of the sine and cosine when $t = 0, \frac{\pi}{6}, \frac{\pi}{4}, \frac{\pi}{3}, \frac{\pi}{2}$, give them the chart below.

t	0	$\frac{\pi}{6}$	$\frac{\pi}{4}$	$\frac{\pi}{3}$	$\frac{\pi}{2}$
sin t	$\frac{\sqrt{0}}{2}$	$\frac{\sqrt{1}}{2}$	$\frac{\sqrt{2}}{2}$	$\frac{\sqrt{3}}{2}$	$\frac{\sqrt{4}}{2}$
cos t	$\frac{\sqrt{4}}{2}$	$\frac{\sqrt{3}}{2}$	$\frac{\sqrt{2}}{2}$	$\frac{\sqrt{1}}{2}$	$\frac{\sqrt{0}}{2}$

To find the tangent, just divide the sine value by the cosine value.

ADDITIONAL EXAMPLES

Example 3

Use reference angles to find the exact value of sin t, cos t, and tan t.

a. $t = \dfrac{5\pi}{4}$

reference angle: $\dfrac{5\pi}{4} - \pi = \dfrac{\pi}{4}$

$\sin \dfrac{5\pi}{4} = -\dfrac{\sqrt{2}}{2}$; $\cos \dfrac{5\pi}{4} = -\dfrac{\sqrt{2}}{2}$;

$\tan \dfrac{5\pi}{4} = 1$

b. $t = \dfrac{5\pi}{3}$

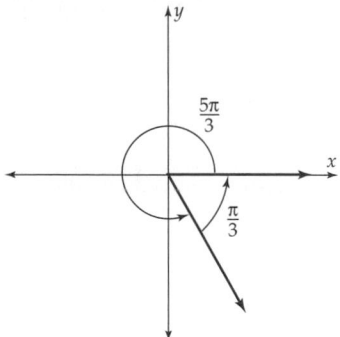

reference angle: $2\pi - \dfrac{5\pi}{3} = \dfrac{\pi}{3}$

$\sin \dfrac{5\pi}{3} = -\dfrac{\sqrt{3}}{2}$; $\cos \dfrac{5\pi}{3} = \dfrac{1}{2}$;

$\tan \dfrac{5\pi}{3} = -\sqrt{3}$

c. $t = \dfrac{5\pi}{6}$

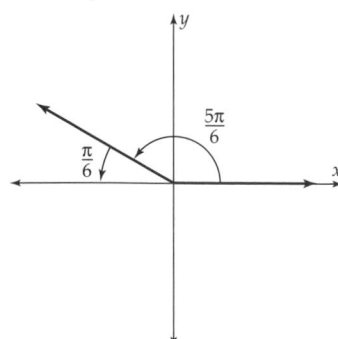

reference angle: $\pi - \dfrac{5\pi}{6} = \dfrac{\pi}{6}$

$\sin \dfrac{5\pi}{6} = \dfrac{1}{2}$; $\cos \dfrac{5\pi}{6} = -\dfrac{\sqrt{3}}{2}$;

$\tan \dfrac{5\pi}{6} = -\dfrac{\sqrt{3}}{3}$

In every case, the figure that references the unit circle illustrates the following fact that can be proved by using congruent triangles:

$$x\text{-coordinate of } Q = \pm(x\text{-coordinate of } P)$$
$$y\text{-coordinate of } Q = \pm(y\text{-coordinate of } P)$$

By definition, the values of the trigonometric functions for t are given by the coordinates of Q and the values of these functions for t' are given by the coordinates of P. So, these values will be the same, except for a plus or minus sign. The correct sign is determined by the quadrant in which the terminal side of an angle of t radians lies, as shown in Figure 6.4-7 on page 448.

Finding Trigonometric Function Values

> To find the sine, cosine, or tangent of t radians,
>
> - Sketch an angle of t radians in standard position and determine the quadrant in which the terminal side lies.
> - Find the reference angle, which has measure t' radians.
> - Find the sine, cosine, and tangent of t' and append the appropriate sign.

Example 3   Using Reference Angles

Use reference angles to find the exact value of sin t, cos t, and tan t.

a. $t = \dfrac{3\pi}{4}$ **b.** $t = \dfrac{4\pi}{3}$ **c.** $t = \dfrac{11\pi}{6}$

Solution

a. Sketch the angle, as shown in Figure 6.4-10. The terminal side is in the second quadrant, so the reference angle is $\pi - t$.

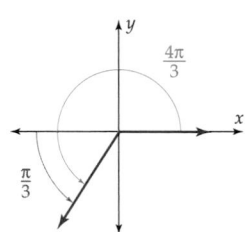

Figure 6.4-10

$$\pi - \dfrac{3\pi}{4} = \dfrac{\pi}{4}$$

Because the terminal side of the angle of $\dfrac{3\pi}{4}$ radians lies in the second quadrant, $\sin \dfrac{3\pi}{4}$ is positive, and $\cos \dfrac{3\pi}{4}$ and $\tan \dfrac{3\pi}{4}$ are negative.

$$\sin \dfrac{3\pi}{4} = \sin \dfrac{\pi}{4} = \dfrac{\sqrt{2}}{2} \qquad \cos \dfrac{3\pi}{4} = -\cos \dfrac{\pi}{4} = -\dfrac{\sqrt{2}}{2}$$

$$\tan \dfrac{4\pi}{3} = -\tan \dfrac{\pi}{4} = -1$$

b. Sketch the angle, as shown in Figure 6.4-11. The terminal side is in quadrant III, so the reference angle is $t - \pi$.

$$\dfrac{4\pi}{3} - \pi = \dfrac{\pi}{3}$$

Figure 6.4-11

Example 4

Find the sine, cosine, and tangent of $\dfrac{9\pi}{4}$.

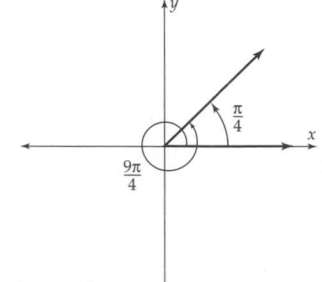

$\dfrac{9\pi}{4} = \dfrac{\pi}{4} + 2\pi$. So $\dfrac{9\pi}{4}$ is coterminal with $\dfrac{\pi}{4}$.

$$\sin \dfrac{9\pi}{4} = \sin \dfrac{\pi}{4} = \dfrac{\sqrt{2}}{2}$$

$$\cos \dfrac{9\pi}{4} = \cos \dfrac{\pi}{4} = \dfrac{\sqrt{2}}{2}$$

$$\tan \dfrac{9\pi}{4} = \tan \dfrac{\pi}{4} = 1$$

Thus, the sine, cosine, and tangent functions are

$$\sin\frac{4\pi}{3} = -\sin\frac{\pi}{3} = -\frac{\sqrt{3}}{2} \qquad \cos\frac{4\pi}{3} = -\cos\frac{\pi}{3} = -\frac{1}{2}$$

$$\tan\frac{3\pi}{4} = \tan\frac{\pi}{3} = \sqrt{3}$$

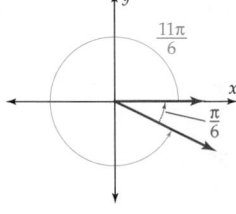

Figure 6.4-12

c. Sketch the angle, as shown in Figure 6.4-12. The terminal side is in quadrant IV, so the reference angle is $2\pi - t$.

$$2\pi - \frac{11\pi}{6} = \frac{\pi}{6}$$

Thus, the sine, cosine, and tangent functions are

$$\sin\frac{11\pi}{6} = -\sin\frac{\pi}{6} = -\frac{1}{2} \qquad \cos\frac{11\pi}{6} = \cos\frac{\pi}{6} = \frac{\sqrt{3}}{2}$$

$$\tan\frac{11\pi}{6} = -\tan\frac{\pi}{6} = -\frac{\sqrt{3}}{3}$$

If an angle is less than 0 or greater than 2π, it is possible to find a coterminal angle between 0 and 2π by adding or subtracting multiples of 2π. Thus, the trigonometric functions of a real variable have the following property.

Trigonometric Ratios of Coterminal Angles

> **Any trigonometric function of a real number t is equal to the same trigonometric function of all numbers $t \pm 2k\pi$, where k is an integer.**

Example 4   **Trigonometric Functions Where $t > 2\pi$**

Find the sine, cosine, and tangent of $\frac{7\pi}{3}$.

Solution

$\frac{7\pi}{3}$ can be written as $\frac{\pi}{3} + 2\pi$. Therefore, $\frac{7\pi}{3}$ is coterminal with $\frac{\pi}{3}$.

$$\sin\frac{7\pi}{3} = \sin\frac{\pi}{3} = \frac{\sqrt{3}}{2}$$

$$\cos\frac{7\pi}{3} = \cos\frac{\pi}{3} = \frac{1}{2}$$

$$\tan\frac{7\pi}{3} = \tan\frac{\pi}{3} = \sqrt{3}$$

Figure 6.4-13

Example Notes

In **Example 3a,** first draw the terminal side corresponding to $\frac{\pi}{4}$ in Quadrant I. Then, draw a horizontal line segment connecting the intercepts of the terminal sides of the angles $\frac{\pi}{4}$ and $\frac{3\pi}{4}$. Doing so mimics the second diagram in Figure 6.4-9 with $l' = \frac{\pi}{4}$, $l = \frac{3\pi}{4}$, $P(x, y) = \left(\frac{\sqrt{2}}{2}, \frac{\sqrt{2}}{2}\right)$, and $Q(-x, y)$ $= \left(-\frac{\sqrt{2}}{2}, \frac{\sqrt{2}}{2}\right)$.

Have students draw similar diagrams for parts **b** and **c.**

Teaching Notes

You may want to have students find the sine, cosine, and tangent of $-\frac{4\pi}{3}$ as an example of finding trigonometric functions of t where $t < 0$:

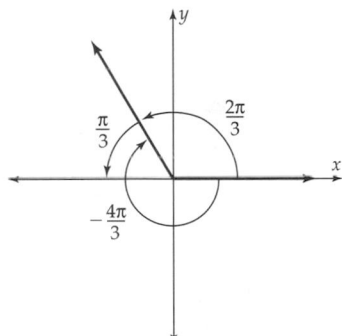

$-\frac{4\pi}{3}$ is coterminal with $\frac{2\pi}{3}$. $\frac{2\pi}{3}$ is in the second quadrant, so the reference angle is $\pi - \frac{2\pi}{3} = \frac{\pi}{3}$. In the second quadrant, sine is positive and cosine and tangent are negative.

$\sin\left(-\frac{4\pi}{3}\right) = \frac{\sqrt{3}}{2}$, $\cos\left(-\frac{4\pi}{3}\right) = -\frac{1}{2}$,

$\tan\left(-\frac{4\pi}{3}\right) = -\sqrt{3}$

The **Trigonometric Ratios of Coterminal Angles** can be written (in the case of sine and cosine) in the form of equalities, as follows:

$\sin t = \sin(t \pm 2k\pi)$

$\cos t = \cos(t \pm 2k\pi)$

COMMON ERROR ALERT

Students may mistakenly measure the angle between the terminal side and the *y-axis* instead of the *x-axis* to get the reference angle. For instance, in **Example 3b,** they might say that the reference angle is $\frac{\pi}{6}$ instead of $\frac{\pi}{3}$.

Remind them of the definition of reference angle.

Exercises 6.4

ANSWERS

1. $\dfrac{7}{\sqrt{53}}$; $\dfrac{2}{\sqrt{53}}$; $\dfrac{7}{2}$

2. $\dfrac{2}{\sqrt{13}}$; $-\dfrac{3}{\sqrt{13}}$; $-\dfrac{2}{3}$

3. $\dfrac{-6}{\sqrt{61}}$; $\dfrac{-5}{\sqrt{61}}$; $\dfrac{6}{5}$

4. $-\dfrac{3}{5}$; $\dfrac{4}{5}$; $-\dfrac{3}{4}$

5. $\dfrac{-10}{\sqrt{103}}$; $\dfrac{\sqrt{3}}{\sqrt{103}}$; $\dfrac{-10}{\sqrt{3}}$

6. $\dfrac{2}{\sqrt{\pi^2+4}}$; $-\dfrac{\pi}{\sqrt{\pi^2+4}}$; $-\dfrac{2}{\pi}$

7. $\dfrac{1}{\sqrt{5}}$; $-\dfrac{2}{\sqrt{5}}$; $-\dfrac{1}{2}$

8. $-\dfrac{3}{\sqrt{10}}$; $\dfrac{1}{\sqrt{10}}$; -3

9. $-\dfrac{4}{5}$; $-\dfrac{3}{5}$; $\dfrac{4}{3}$

10. -0.8; 0.6; $-\dfrac{4}{3}$

11. $\dfrac{\pi}{6}$; $\dfrac{1}{2}$; $\dfrac{\sqrt{3}}{2}$

12. $\dfrac{\pi}{2}$; 1; 0

13. 0; 0; 1

14. $\dfrac{\pi}{4}$; $\dfrac{\sqrt{2}}{2}$; $\dfrac{\sqrt{2}}{2}$

15. **a.** -0.9511; -0.3090; 3.0777

 b. Since the sine and cosine are both negative, the terminal side is in the third quadrant.

16. **a.** -1.0000; 0.0044; -225.9508

 b. Since the sine is negative and the cosine is positive, the terminal side is in the fourth quadrant.

17. **a.** 0.9848; 0.1736; 5.6713

 b. Since the sine and cosine are both positive, the terminal side is in the first quadrant.

18. **a.** 0; -1; 0

 b. Since the sine is 0 and the cosine is -1, the terminal side is on the negative x-axis.

19. **a.** -0.8660; -0.5; 1.7321

 b. Since the sine and cosine are both negative, the terminal side is in the third quadrant.

20. **a.** 0.9511; 0.3090; 3.0777

 b. Since the sine and cosine are both positive, the terminal side is in the first quadrant.

Exercises 6.4

Note: Unless stated otherwise, all angles are in standard position.

In Exercises 1–6, find sin t, cos t, and tan t when the terminal side of an angle of t radians passes through the given point.

1. $(2, 7)$ 2. $(-3, 2)$ 3. $(-5, -6)$

4. $(4, -3)$ 5. $(\sqrt{3}, -10)$ 6. $(-\pi, 2)$

In Exercises 7–10, find sin t, cos t, and tan t when the terminal side of an angle of t radians passes through the given point on the unit circle.

7. $\left(-\dfrac{2}{\sqrt{5}}, \dfrac{1}{\sqrt{5}}\right)$

8. $\left(\dfrac{1}{\sqrt{10}}, -\dfrac{3}{\sqrt{10}}\right)$

9. $\left(-\dfrac{3}{5}, -\dfrac{4}{5}\right)$

10. $(0.6, -0.8)$

In Exercises 11–14, identify an angle $0 \le t' \le \pi$ that is coterminal with the given angle, and find the sine and cosine of the given angle.

11. $\dfrac{13\pi}{6}$ 12. $\dfrac{9\pi}{2}$ 13. 16π 14. $-\dfrac{7\pi}{4}$

In Exercises 15–23,

a. Use a calculator in radian mode to find the sine, cosine, and tangent of each number. Round your answers to four decimal places.

b. Use the signs of the functions to identify the quadrant of the terminal side of an angle of t radians. If the terminal side lies on an axis, identify which axis and whether it is on the positive or negative side of the axis. Explain your reasoning.

15. $\dfrac{7\pi}{5}$ 16. 11 17. $-\dfrac{14\pi}{9}$

18. -23π 19. $\dfrac{10\pi}{3}$ 20. 6.4π

21. 9.5π 22. $\dfrac{\pi}{17}$ 23. -17

In Exercises 24–29, sketch each angle whose radian measure is given and find its reference angle.

24. $\dfrac{7\pi}{3}$ $\dfrac{\pi}{3}$ 25. $\dfrac{17\pi}{6}$ $\dfrac{\pi}{6}$ 26. $\dfrac{6\pi}{5}$ $\dfrac{\pi}{5}$

---

27. 1.75π $\dfrac{\pi}{4}$ 28. $-\dfrac{3\pi}{4}$ $\dfrac{\pi}{4}$ 29. $-\dfrac{\pi}{7}$ $\dfrac{\pi}{7}$

In Exercises 30–47, find the exact value of the sine, cosine, and tangent of the number without using a calculator.

30. $\dfrac{7\pi}{6}$ 31. $\dfrac{7\pi}{3}$ 32. $\dfrac{17\pi}{3}$ 33. $\dfrac{11\pi}{4}$

34. $\dfrac{5\pi}{4}$ 35. $-\dfrac{3\pi}{2}$ 36. 3π 37. $-\dfrac{23\pi}{6}$

38. $\dfrac{11\pi}{6}$ 39. $-\dfrac{19\pi}{3}$ 40. $-\dfrac{10\pi}{3}$ 41. $-\dfrac{15\pi}{4}$

42. $-\dfrac{25\pi}{4}$ 43. $\dfrac{5\pi}{6}$ 44. $-\dfrac{17\pi}{2}$ 45. $\dfrac{9\pi}{2}$

46. $-\pi$ 47. 4π

In Exercises 48–53, write the expression as a single real number. Do not use decimal approximations.

48. $\sin\left(\dfrac{\pi}{6}\right)\cos\left(\dfrac{\pi}{2}\right) - \cos\left(\dfrac{\pi}{6}\right)\sin\left(\dfrac{\pi}{2}\right)$

49. $\cos\left(\dfrac{\pi}{2}\right)\cos\left(\dfrac{\pi}{4}\right) - \sin\left(\dfrac{\pi}{2}\right)\sin\left(\dfrac{\pi}{4}\right)$

50. $\cos\left(\dfrac{2\pi}{3}\right)\cos\pi + \sin\left(\dfrac{2\pi}{3}\right)\sin\pi$

51. $\sin\left(\dfrac{3\pi}{4}\right)\cos\left(\dfrac{5\pi}{6}\right) - \cos\left(\dfrac{3\pi}{4}\right)\sin\left(\dfrac{5\pi}{6}\right)$

52. $\sin\left(\dfrac{-7\pi}{3}\right)\cos\left(\dfrac{5\pi}{4}\right) + \cos\left(\dfrac{-7\pi}{3}\right)\sin\left(\dfrac{5\pi}{4}\right)$

53. $\sin\left(\dfrac{\pi}{3}\right)\cos\pi + \sin\pi\cos\left(\dfrac{\pi}{3}\right)$

In Exercises 54–59, the terminal side of an angle of t radians lies in the given quadrant on the given line. Find sin t, cos t, and tan t. (*Hint:* Find a point on the terminal side of the angle.)

54. Quadrant III; line $2y - 4x = 0$

55. Quadrant IV; line through $(-3, 5)$ and $(-9, 15)$

56. Quadrant III; line through the origin parallel to $7x - 2y = -6$

---

21. **a.** -1; 0; undefined

 b. Since the sine is -1 and the cosine is 0, the terminal side is on the negative y-axis.

22. **a.** 0.1837; 0.9830; 0.1869

 b. Since the sine and cosine are both positive, the terminal side is in the first quadrant.

23. **a.** 0.9614; -0.2752; -3.4939

 b. Since the sine is positive and the cosine is negative, the terminal side is in the second quadrant.

24–29. *For graphs, see p. 1068.*

30–56. *See p. 1068.*

---

57. Quadrant II; line through the origin parallel to $2y + x = 6$

58. Quadrant I; line through the origin perpendicular to $3y + x = 6$

59. Quadrant IV; line $y = -3x$

60. The terminal side of an angle of t radians lies on a straight line through the origin, and therefore, has an equation of the form $y = mx$, where m is the slope of the line.

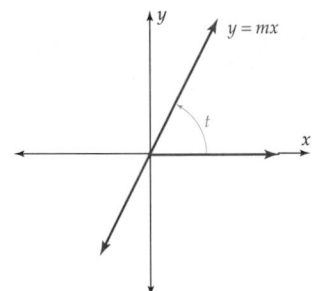

a. Prove that $m = \tan t$. *Hint:* a point on the terminal side of the angle has coordinates (x, mx)

b. Explain why $\tan t$ approaches infinity as t approaches $\frac{\pi}{2}$ from below. *Hint:* What happens to the slope of the terminal side when t is close to $\frac{\pi}{2}$?

c. Explain why $\tan t$ approaches negative infinity as t approaches $\frac{\pi}{2}$ from above. *Hint:* When t is a bit larger than $\frac{\pi}{2}$, is the slope of its terminal side positive or negative?

d. Use parts **b** and **c** to show that the range of the tangent function is the set of all real numbers.

61. The figure below shows an angle of t radians. Use trigonometric functions to write the coordinates of point P in terms of r and t.

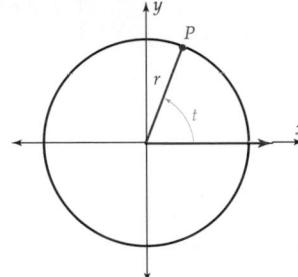

62. Complete the following table by writing each value as a fraction with denominator 2 and a radical in the numerator. You may find the resulting pattern an easy way to remember these function values.

t	0	$\dfrac{\pi}{6}$	$\dfrac{\pi}{4}$	$\dfrac{\pi}{3}$	$\dfrac{\pi}{2}$
$\sin t$	$\dfrac{\sqrt{?}}{2}$	$\dfrac{\sqrt{?}}{2}$	$\dfrac{\sqrt{?}}{2}$	$\dfrac{\sqrt{?}}{2}$	$\dfrac{\sqrt{?}}{2}$
$\cos t$	$\dfrac{\sqrt{?}}{2}$	$\dfrac{\sqrt{?}}{2}$	$\dfrac{\sqrt{?}}{2}$	$\dfrac{\sqrt{?}}{2}$	$\dfrac{\sqrt{?}}{2}$

63. Find the domain and range of the cosecant function.

64. Find the domain and range of the secant function.

65. Find the domain and range of the cotangent function.

66. *Critical Thinking* Using only the definition and no calculator, determine which number is larger: $\sin(\cos 0)$ or $\cos(\sin 0)$.

57. $\dfrac{1}{\sqrt{5}}; -\dfrac{2}{\sqrt{5}}; -\dfrac{1}{2}$

58. $\dfrac{3}{\sqrt{10}}; \dfrac{1}{\sqrt{10}}; 3$

59. $-\dfrac{3}{\sqrt{10}}; \dfrac{1}{\sqrt{10}}; -3$

60. a. Any point on the terminal side of θ has coordinates (x, mx).

Since $\tan\theta = \dfrac{y}{x} = \dfrac{mx}{x}$, $\tan\theta = m$.

b. As t approaches $\dfrac{\pi}{2}$ from below, the slope of the line through the terminal side increases without bound to approach positive infinity; therefore, $\tan t$ approaches positive infinity.

c. As t approaches $\dfrac{\pi}{2}$ from above, the slope of the line through the terminal side decreases without bound to approach negative infinity; therefore, $\tan t$ approaches negative infinity.

d. Parts (b) and (c) show that the range of the tangent function is from negative infinity to positive infinity, in other words, all real numbers.

61. $(r\cos t, r\sin t)$

62. $\sin 0 = \dfrac{\sqrt{0}}{2}$, $\sin\left(\dfrac{\pi}{6}\right) = \dfrac{\sqrt{1}}{2}$,

$\sin\left(\dfrac{\pi}{4}\right) = \dfrac{\sqrt{2}}{2}$, $\sin\left(\dfrac{\pi}{3}\right) = \dfrac{\sqrt{3}}{2}$,

$\sin\left(\dfrac{\pi}{2}\right) = \dfrac{\sqrt{4}}{2}$

$\cos 0 = \dfrac{\sqrt{4}}{2}$, $\cos\left(\dfrac{\pi}{6}\right) = \dfrac{\sqrt{3}}{2}$,

$\cos\left(\dfrac{\pi}{4}\right) = \dfrac{\sqrt{2}}{2}$, $\cos\left(\dfrac{\pi}{3}\right) = \dfrac{\sqrt{1}}{2}$

$\cos\left(\dfrac{\pi}{2}\right) = \dfrac{\sqrt{0}}{2}$

63. Domain: all real numbers with $\theta \neq$ a multiple of π
Range: $(-\infty, -1)$ and $(1, \infty)$

64. Domain: all real numbers with $\theta \neq \dfrac{\pi}{2}$ plus a multiple of π
Range: $(-\infty, -1)$ and $(1, \infty)$

65. Domain: all real numbers with $\theta \neq$ a multiple of π
Range: all real numbers

66. $\sin(\cos(0)) = \sin(1)$ and $\cos(\sin(0)) = \cos(0) = 1$.
The angle with measure 1 radian crosses the unit circle at a point whose y-coordinate is less than 1, so $\sin(1) < 1$ and $\sin(\cos(0)) < \cos(\sin(0))$.

Section 6.5 Basic Trigonometric Identities

Teaching Notes

Point out that while using $\sin t^3$ in place of $\sin(t^3)$ is common, the latter notation is less ambiguous. It is clear in the latter notation that one is taking the sine of the quantity t^3, while one might mistake $\sin t^3$ as meaning $(\sin t)^3$.

Encourage students to use grouping symbols with trigonometric functions as most calculators do, illustrated in the margin **NOTE.** By developing the habit of, for example, writing the cosine function as $\cos(\ )$ and then filling in the expression, mistakes such as writing $\cos t + 3$ instead of $\cos(t + 3)$ can always be avoided.

In Figure 6.5-2, point out that even though sin (4^3 and sin (4^3) produce the same value on some calculators, not closing the parentheses could lead to problems in more complicated calculations.

Remind students that the notation $\sin^{-1}\theta$ does not indicate the reciprocal function $\frac{1}{\sin\theta}$ (**Technology Tip** second bullet, page 417). To indicate the reciprocal function use $(\sin\theta)^{-1} = \frac{1}{\sin\theta}$.

6.5 Basic Trigonometric Identities

Objectives

- Develop basic trigonometric identities

NOTE Most calculators automatically insert an opening parenthesis when a trigonometric function key is pushed. The display $\cos(5 + 3$ is interpreted as $\cos(5 + 3)$. If you want cos $5 + 3$, you must insert a parenthesis after the 5: $\cos(5) + 3$.

Technology Tip

- Calculators do not use the convention of writing an exponent between the trigonometric function and its argument. In order to obtain $\sin^3 4$, you must enter sin (4)^3.

The algebra of trigonometric functions is just like that of other functions. They may be added, subtracted, composed, etc. However, two notational conventions are normally used with trigonometric functions.

Parentheses can be omitted whenever no confusion can result.

Figure 6.5-1 shows, however, that parentheses *are* needed to distinguish

$$\cos(t + 3) \qquad \text{and} \qquad \cos t + 3.$$

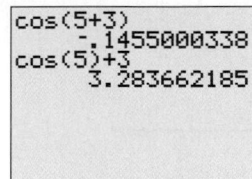

Figure 6.5-1

When dealing with powers of trigonometric functions,

exponents (other than −1) are written between the function symbol and the variable.

For example,

$$(\cos t)^3 \qquad \text{is written} \qquad \cos^3 t.$$

Furthermore,

$$\sin t^3 \qquad \text{means } \sin(t^3) \qquad not \ (\sin t)^3 \text{ or } \sin^3 t,$$

as illustrated in Figure 6.5-2.

Figure 6.5-2

Identities

Trigonometric functions have numerous relationships that can be expressed as *identities*. An **identity** is an equation that is true for all values of the variables for which every term of the equation is defined. For example,

$$(a + b)^2 = a^2 + 2ab + b^2$$

is an identity because it is true for all possible values of a and b.

The unit circle description of trigonometric functions (see the box on page 446) leads to the following **quotient identities**.

Quotient Identities

$$\tan t = \frac{\sin t}{\cos t} \qquad \cot t = \frac{\cos t}{\sin t}$$

Example 1   Quotient Identities

Simplify the expression below.

$$\tan t \cos t$$

Solution

By the quotient identity,

$$\tan t \cos t = \frac{\sin t}{\cos t} \cos t = \sin t$$

Reciprocal Identities

The **reciprocal identities** follow immediately from the definitions of the trigonometric functions.

Reciprocal Identities

$$\sin t = \frac{1}{\csc t} \qquad \cos t = \frac{1}{\sec t} \qquad \tan t = \frac{1}{\cot t}$$

$$\csc t = \frac{1}{\sin t} \qquad \sec t = \frac{1}{\cos t} \qquad \cot t = \frac{1}{\tan t}$$

> **CAUTION**
>
> An identity may not be true for a value of the variable that makes a term of the equation undefined. For example, if $t = 0$, then $\tan t = 0$ while $\cot t$ is undefined. Thus, $\tan t \neq \frac{1}{\cot t}$ for $t = 0$.

Example 2   Reciprocal Identities

Given that $\sin t = 0.28$ and $\cos t = 0.96$, find $\csc t$ and $\sec t$.

Solution

By the reciprocal identities,

$$\csc t = \frac{1}{\sin t} = \frac{1}{0.28} \approx 3.57 \qquad \sec t = \frac{1}{\cos t} = \frac{1}{0.96} \approx 1.04$$

ADDITIONAL EXAMPLES

Example 1

Simplify the expression $\cot t \sin t$.

$\cot t \sin t = \frac{\cos t}{\sin t} \sin t = \cos t$

Example 2

Given that $\cos t = 0.75$ and $\tan t = 0.88$, find $\sec t$ and $\cot t$.
$\sec t \approx 1.33$, $\cot t \approx 1.14$

Teaching Notes

The **Quotient Identities** were justified using the **Unit Circle Description of Trigonometric Functions** (page 446). An alternate way of justifying the quotient identities is to use the definition of **Trigonometric Functions of a Real Variable** (page 445):

$$\frac{\sin t}{\cos t} = \frac{\frac{y}{r}}{\frac{x}{r}} \qquad \qquad \frac{\cos t}{\sin t} = \frac{\frac{x}{r}}{\frac{y}{r}}$$

$$= \frac{y}{r} \cdot \frac{r}{x} \qquad \qquad = \frac{x}{r} \cdot \frac{r}{y}$$

$$= \frac{y}{r} \qquad \qquad = \frac{x}{y}$$

$$= \tan t \qquad \qquad = \cot t$$

The **Reciprocal Identities** can be proven in a similar fashion.

Math Background

There are two kinds of trigonometric equations: identities and conditional equations. A trigonometric identity is an equation that is valid for all values of the variable for which all terms of the equation are defined, such as $\tan t = \frac{\sin t}{\cos t}$. A conditional equation is valid only for certain values of the variable. For example, the solution of $\sin x = 0$ is $x = \pm k\pi$, where k is an integer.

The **Basic Trigonometric Identities** are discussed in this section and identities are further studied in Chapter 9 (**Trigonometric Identities and Proof**). Conditional equations are dealt with in Chapter 8 (**Solving Trigonometric Equations**).

In the **CAUTION** note, the values for which $\tan t = 0$ are $t = \pm k\pi$, where k is an integer. This is a direct result of the **Periodicity Identities** (page 458).

Teaching Notes

The **Pythagorean Identities** are based on the Pythagorean Theorem. They can be proven using the definition of **Trigonometric Functions of a Real Variable.**

- $\sin^2 t + \cos^2 t = \dfrac{y^2}{r^2} + \dfrac{x^2}{r^2} = \dfrac{y^2 + x^2}{r^2}$

$$= \dfrac{r^2}{r^2} = 1$$

- $\tan^2 t + 1 = \dfrac{y^2}{x^2} + \dfrac{x^2}{x^2} = \dfrac{y^2 + x^2}{x^2}$

$$= \dfrac{r^2}{x^2} = \sec^2 t$$

- $1 + \cot^2 t = \dfrac{y^2}{y^2} + \dfrac{x^2}{y^2} = \dfrac{y^2 + x^2}{y^2}$

$$= \dfrac{r^2}{y^2} = \csc^2 t$$

Example Notes

In **Example 3**, an alternate solution, by the Pythagorean and reciprocal identities, is given below.

$$\tan^2 t \cos^2 t + \cos^2 t = \cos^2 t(\tan^2 t + 1)$$
$$= \cos^2 t \sec^2 t$$
$$= \cos^2 t \left(\dfrac{1}{\cos^2 t}\right)$$
$$= 1$$

ADDITIONAL EXAMPLES

Example 3

Simplify the expression below.
$\cot^2 t \sin^2 t + \sin^2 t$

$\cot^2 t \sin^2 t + \sin^2 t$

$$= \dfrac{\cos^2 t}{\sin^2 t}\sin^2 t + \sin^2 t$$
$$= \cos^2 t + \sin^2 t$$
$$= 1$$

or

$\cot^2 t \sin^2 t + \sin^2 t = \sin^2 t(\cot^2 t + 1)$
$$= \sin^2 t \csc^2 t$$
$$= \sin^2 t \dfrac{1}{\sin^2 t}$$
$$= 1$$

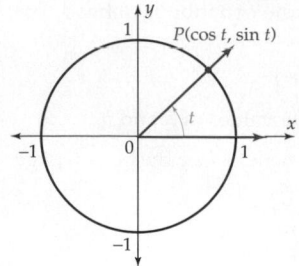

Figure 6.5-3

Pythagorean Identities

For any real number t, the coordinates of the point P where the terminal side of an angle of t radians meets the unit circle are $(\cos t, \sin t)$, as shown in Figure 6.5-3. Since P is on the unit circle, its coordinates must satisfy $x^2 + y^2 = 1$, which is the equation of the unit circle. That is,

$$\cos^2 t + \sin^2 t = 1$$

This identity, which is usually written $\sin^2 t + \cos^2 t = 1$, is called the **Pythagorean identity.** It can be used as follows to derive two other identities, which are also called **Pythagorean identities.**

$$\sin^2 t + \cos^2 t = 1$$
$$\dfrac{\sin^2 t}{\cos^2 t} + \dfrac{\cos^2 t}{\cos^2 t} = \dfrac{1}{\cos^2 t} \qquad \textit{Divide by } \cos^2 t$$
$$\tan^2 t + 1 = \sec^2 t \qquad \textit{Simplify}$$

Similarly, dividing both sides of $\sin^2 t + \cos^2 t = 1$ by $\sin^2 t$ shows that

$$1 + \cot^2 t = \csc^2 t$$

Pythagorean Identities ○

$$\sin^2 t + \cos^2 t = 1$$
$$\tan^2 t + 1 = \sec^2 t$$
$$1 + \cot^2 t = \csc^2 t$$

In addition to the version shown above, the following forms of the Pythagorean identity are also commonly used.

$$\sin^2 t = 1 - \cos^2 t$$
$$\cos^2 t = 1 - \sin^2 t$$

Example 3   Pythagorean Identities

Simplify the expression below.

$$\tan^2 t \cos^2 t + \cos^2 t$$

Solution

By the quotient and Pythagorean identities,

$$\tan^2 t \cos^2 t + \cos^2 t = \dfrac{\sin^2 t}{\cos^2 t}\cos^2 t + \cos^2 t = \sin^2 t + \cos^2 t = 1$$

■

Periodicity Identities

Let t be any real number. Construct two angles in standard position of measure t and $t + 2\pi$ radians, as shown in Figure 6.5-4. Since both of

---

these angles have the same terminal side, the point P where the terminal side intersects the unit circle is the same for both angles.

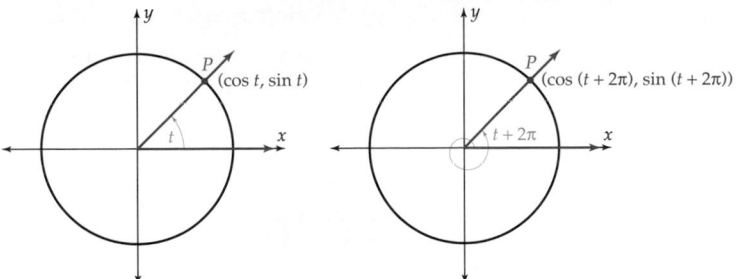

Figure 6.5-4

In both cases, the sine is the y-coordinate of P, so

$$\sin t = \sin(t + 2\pi).$$

In addition, the terminal side of the angle is the same for measures of t, $t \pm 2\pi, t \pm 4\pi, t \pm 6\pi$, and so on. Thus,

$$\sin t = \sin(t \pm 2\pi) = \sin(t \pm 4\pi) = \sin(t \pm 6\pi) = \ldots$$

Similarly in both cases, the cosine is the x-coordinate of P, so

$$\cos t = \cos(t \pm 2\pi) = \cos(t \pm 4\pi) = \cos(t \pm 6\pi) = \ldots$$

The identities above show that sine and cosine functions repeat their values at regular intervals. Such functions are called *periodic*. A function is said to be **periodic** if there exists some constant k such that

$$f(t) = f(t + k)$$

for every number t in the domain of f. The smallest value of k that has this property is called the **period** of the function f.

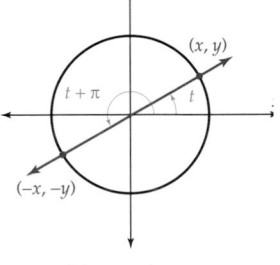

Figure 6.5-5

Since the tangent function is the quotient of the sine and cosine functions, it must also be true that $\tan t = \tan(t + 2\pi)$. However, there is a number smaller than 2π that has this property. Figure 6.5-5 shows the angles t and $t + \pi$. A rotation of π radians is the same as a rotation of 180°, so the image of the point (x, y) is $(-x, -y)$. Thus,

$$\tan(t + \pi) = \frac{-y}{-x} = \frac{y}{x} = \tan t$$

Calculator Exploration ●

Use your calculator to verify the following:

$$\sin 3 = \sin(3 + 2\pi) = \sin(3 - 4\pi)$$
$$\cos 4 = \cos(4 + 2\pi) = \cos(4 + 6\pi)$$
$$\tan 1 = \tan(1 + \pi) = \tan(1 - 5\pi)$$

Teaching Notes

The derivation, in the text, of the identity $\tan(t + \pi) = \tan t$ uses angles in Quadrant I and Quadrant III. A similar argument can be made for angles in Quadrant II and Quadrant IV. In particular, if t is in Quadrant II, then $t + \pi$ lands in Quadrant IV. In such case, if the intercept of the terminal side of t has coordinates $(-x, y)$, then

$$\tan t = \frac{y}{-x} \text{ and } \tan(t + \pi) = \frac{-y}{x}.$$

Since $\frac{y}{-x} = \frac{-y}{x}$, we can conclude that $\tan(t + \pi) = \tan t$.

Solution to the **Calculator Exploration:**

For $\sin 3 = \sin(3 + 2\pi)$,
$\qquad\qquad = \sin(3 - 4\pi)$,
enter the expressions below.

For $\cos 4 = \cos(4 + 2\pi)$
$\qquad\qquad = \cos(4 + 6\pi)$,
enter the expressions below.

For $\tan 1 = \tan(1 + \pi)$
$\qquad\qquad = \tan(1 - 5\pi)$,
enter the expressions below.

Teaching Notes

In **Negative Angle Identities,** emphasize the role that the symmetry of the circle plays in the proof.

Remind the students of the definition of *even* and *odd* functions:
- f is *even* if $f(t) = f(-t)$, for all t in the domain of f
- f is *odd* if $-f(t) = f(-t)$, for all t in the domain of f.

So, cosine is an even function and sine and tangent are odd functions. These identities are sometimes called the Even-Odd Identities.

To verify the Negative Angle Identities, you may want to have students use their calculators. For example, show that

$$\sin\left(\frac{\pi}{3}\right) = -\sin\left(-\frac{\pi}{3}\right).$$

```
sin(π/3)
        .8660254038
-sin(-π/3)
        .8660254038
```

Example Notes

In **Example 4,** remind the students of the earlier discussion in Section 6.4 concerning the computation of the sine and cosine of coterminal angles (page 451).

In **Example 6,** the exact value of $\sin\left(\frac{5\pi}{6}\right)$ could have just as easily been found using reference angles (pages 450–451). The solution presented in this example was made to illustrate how to use the identity $\sin t = \sin(\pi - t)$.

Periodicity Identities

> The sine and cosine functions are periodic with period 2π. For every real number t,
>
> $$\sin(t \pm 2\pi) = \sin t \quad \text{and} \quad \cos(t \pm 2\pi) = \cos t$$
>
> The tangent function is periodic with period π. For every number t in the domain of the tangent function,
>
> $$\tan(t \pm \pi) = \tan t$$

Example 4   **Periodicity Identities**

Find the exact value of $\sin \dfrac{13\pi}{6}$.

Solution

By the periodicity identity for sine,

$$\sin\frac{13\pi}{6} = \sin\left(\frac{\pi}{6} + \frac{12\pi}{6}\right) = \sin\left(\frac{\pi}{6} + 2\pi\right) = \sin\frac{\pi}{6} = \frac{1}{2} \qquad \blacksquare$$

Negative Angle Identities

Let t be any real number and construct two angles in standard position of measure t and $-t$ radians, as shown in Figure 6.5-6.

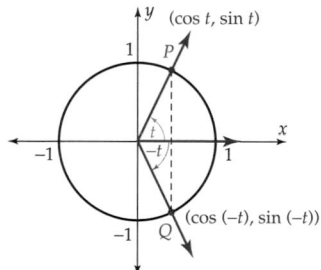

Figure 6.5-6

Since the point Q is the reflection of the point P across the x-axis, the x-coordinates of P and Q are the same, and the y-coordinates are opposites of each other. Thus,

$$\cos t = \cos(-t) \quad \text{and} \quad \sin t = -\sin(-t)$$

Also,

$$\tan(-t) = \frac{\sin(-t)}{\cos(-t)} = \frac{-\sin t}{\cos t} = -\frac{\sin t}{\cos t} = -\tan t$$

Negative Angle Identities

$$\sin(-t) = -\sin t$$
$$\cos(-t) = \cos t$$
$$\tan(-t) = -\tan t$$

Example 5   Negative Angle Identities

Find the exact value of $\sin\left(-\dfrac{\pi}{6}\right)$ and of $\cos\left(-\dfrac{\pi}{6}\right)$.

Solution

By the negative angle identities,

$$\sin\left(-\frac{\pi}{6}\right) = -\sin\frac{\pi}{6} = -\frac{1}{2} \quad \text{and} \quad \cos\left(-\frac{\pi}{6}\right) = \cos\frac{\pi}{6} = \frac{\sqrt{3}}{2}$$

Other Identities

Figure 6.5-7

Let t be any real number. Figure 6.5-7 shows the angles of t and $\pi - t$ radians in standard position. The terminal side of the angle of t radians meets the unit circle at P, and the terminal side of the angle of $\pi - t$ radians meets the unit circle at Q. Congruent triangles can be used to prove what the figure illustrates:

The y-coordinates of P and Q are the same, and their x-coordinates are opposites.

This leads to the following identities.

Identities Involving $\pi - t$

$$\sin t = \sin(\pi - t)$$
$$\cos t = -\cos(\pi - t)$$
$$\tan t = -\tan(\pi - t)$$

NOTE The identity $\sin t = \sin(\pi - t)$ is used in solving basic trigonometric equations. (See Section 8.3.)

Example 6   Identities Involving $\pi - t$

Find the exact value of $\sin\left(\dfrac{5\pi}{6}\right)$.

Solution

By the identity $\sin(\pi - t) = \sin t$,

$$\sin\left(\frac{5\pi}{6}\right) = \sin\left(\frac{6\pi}{6} - \frac{\pi}{6}\right) = \sin\left(\pi - \frac{\pi}{6}\right) = \sin\left(\frac{\pi}{6}\right) = \frac{1}{2}$$

Example 4

Find the exact value of $\cos\left(\dfrac{7\pi}{3}\right)$.

$$\cos\left(\frac{7\pi}{3}\right) = \cos\left(\frac{\pi}{3} + \frac{6\pi}{3}\right)$$
$$= \cos\left(\frac{\pi}{3} + 2\pi\right)$$
$$= \cos\left(\frac{\pi}{3}\right)$$
$$= \frac{1}{2}$$

Example 5

Find the exact value of $\sin\left(-\dfrac{\pi}{3}\right)$ and of $\cos\left(-\dfrac{\pi}{3}\right)$.

$$\sin\left(-\frac{\pi}{3}\right) = -\sin\left(\frac{\pi}{3}\right)$$
$$= -\frac{\sqrt{3}}{2}$$

and

$$\cos\left(-\frac{\pi}{3}\right) = \cos\left(\frac{\pi}{3}\right)$$
$$= \frac{1}{2}$$

Example 6

Find the exact value of $\cos\left(\dfrac{2\pi}{3}\right)$.

$$\cos\left(\frac{2\pi}{3}\right) = \cos\left(\frac{3\pi}{3} - \frac{\pi}{3}\right)$$
$$= \cos\left(\pi - \frac{\pi}{3}\right)$$
$$= -\cos\left(\frac{\pi}{3}\right)$$
$$= -\frac{1}{2}$$

Math Background

In Chapter 7, students will be introduced to graphs of trigonometric functions. In Section 7.4 (pages 506–507), students will use graphing techniques to determine if an equation involving trigonometric functions could possibly be an identity.

Teaching Notes

The **Summary of Identities** gives a handy reference of some basic trigonometric identities. You may want to make a bulletin board display of these identities. You may also want to have students write these identities on an index card for reference. These identities are used often in the study of trigonometry and calculus. These identities may also be found on the inside back cover of this book.

Real-World Application

There is a park in Washington, D.C. called the Ellipse. If the center of the Ellipse is the origin of a coordinate system, then its boundaries can be given by the equation

$\frac{x^2}{562,500} + \frac{y^2}{409,600} = 1$. By using the

Pythagorean Identity $\sin^2 t + \cos^2 t = 1$ and a technique of calculus called integration, you can find the area of the park (approximately 1.5 million square feet—see Section 11.1, Exercise 23).

Exercises 6.5

ANSWERS

9. $\cos t \approx 0.9457$, $\tan t \approx 0.3438$, $\cot t \approx 2.9089$, $\sec t \approx 1.0574$, $\csc t \approx 3.0760$

10. $\sin t \approx 0.9090$, $\tan t \approx 2.1815$, $\cot t \approx 0.4584$, $\sec t \approx 2.3998$, $\csc t \approx 1.1001$

11. $\sec t \approx 3.7646$, $\cos t \approx 0.2656$, $\sin t \approx 0.9641$, $\cot t \approx 0.2755$, $\csc t \approx 1.0372$

12. $\cos t \approx 0.3869$, $\sin t \approx 0.9221$, $\tan t \approx 2.3833$, $\cot t \approx 0.4196$, $\csc t \approx 1.0845$,

13. $\sin t \approx 0.1601$, $\cos t \approx 0.9871$, $\tan t \approx 0.1622$, $\cot t \approx 6.1668$, $\sec t \approx 1.0131$

14. $\tan t \approx 0.5412$, $\sec t \approx 1.1370$, $\cos t \approx 0.8795$, $\sin t \approx 0.4759$, $\csc t \approx 2.1011$

Summary of Identities

Quotient Identities:

$$\tan t = \frac{\sin t}{\cos t} \qquad \cot t = \frac{\cos t}{\sin t}$$

Reciprocal Identities:

$$\sin t = \frac{1}{\csc t} \qquad \cos t = \frac{1}{\sec t} \qquad \tan t = \frac{1}{\cot t}$$

$$\csc t = \frac{1}{\sin t} \qquad \sec t = \frac{1}{\cos t} \qquad \cot t = \frac{1}{\tan t}$$

Pythagorean Identities:

$$\sin^2 t + \cos^2 t = 1 \qquad \tan^2 t + 1 = \sec^2 t \qquad 1 + \cot^2 t = \csc^2 t$$

Periodicity Identities:

$$\sin(t \pm 2\pi) = \sin t \quad \cos(t \pm 2\pi) = \cos t \quad \tan(t \pm \pi) = \tan t$$

Negative Angle Identities:

$$\sin(-t) = -\sin t \qquad \cos(-t) = \cos t \qquad \tan(-t) = -\tan t$$

Identities Involving $\pi - t$:

$$\sin t = \sin(\pi - t) \quad \cos t = -\cos(\pi - t) \quad \tan t = -\tan(\pi - t)$$

Exercises 6.5

In Exercises 1–4, use the quotient and reciprocal identities to simplify the given expression.

1. $\cot t \sin t$
   $\cos t$

2. $\tan t \cot t$
   1

3. $\csc t \sin t$
   1

4. $\cot t \sec t$
   $\csc t$

In Exercises 5–8, use the Pythagorean identities to simplify the given expression.

5. $\sin^2 t + \cot^2 t \sin^2 t$
   1

6. $1 - \sec^2 t$
   $-\tan^2 t$

7. $\dfrac{\csc^2 t - \cot^2 t}{\sin^2 t}$
   $\csc^2 t$

8. $\dfrac{\sin^2 t - \cos^2 t \sin^2 t}{\sin^2 t}$
   $\sin^2 t$

In Exercises 9–14, the value of one trigonometric function is given for $0 < t < \frac{\pi}{2}$. Use quotient, reciprocal, and Pythagorean identities to find the values of the remaining five trigonometric functions. Round your answers to four decimal places.

9. $\sin t = 0.3251$

10. $\cos t = 0.4167$

11. $\tan t = 3.6294$

12. $\sec t = 2.5846$

13. $\csc t = 6.2474$

14. $\cot t = 1.8479$

In Exercises 15–25, use basic identities and algebra to simplify the expression. Assume all denominators are nonzero.

15. $(\sin t + \cos t)(\sin t - \cos t)$ **$\sin^2 t - \cos^2 t$**

16. $(\sin t - \cos t)^2$ **$1 - 2 \sin t \cos t$**

17. $\dfrac{\sin t}{\tan t}$ **$\cos t$**

18. $(\tan t + 2)(\tan t - 3) - (6 - \tan t) + 2 \tan t$
    $\tan^2 t + 2 \tan t - 12$

19. $\left(\dfrac{4 \cos^2 t}{\sin^2 t}\right)\left(\dfrac{\sin t}{4 \cos t}\right)^2$ **$\dfrac{1}{4}$**

---

20. $\dfrac{5\cos t}{\sin^2 t} \cdot \dfrac{\sin^2 t - \sin t \cos t}{\sin^2 t - \cos^2 t}$ $\dfrac{5\cos t}{\sin t(\sin t + \cos t)}$

21. $\dfrac{\cos^2 t + 4\cos t + 4}{\cos t + 2}$ **cos t + 2**

22. $\dfrac{\sin^2 t - 2\sin t + 1}{\sin t - 1}$ **sin t - 1**

23. $\dfrac{1}{\cos t} - \sin t \tan t$ **cos t**

24. $\dfrac{1 - \tan^2 t}{1 + \tan^2 t} + 2\sin^2 t$ **1**

25. $\sqrt{\sin^3 t \cos t} \cdot \sqrt{\cos t}$ **|sin t cos t|$\sqrt{\sin t}$**

Recall that a function is even if

$$f(x) = f(-x)$$

and a function is odd if

$$f(-x) = -f(x)$$

for every value of x in the domain of f. In Exercises 26–32, use the negative angle identities to determine whether the function is even, odd, or neither.

26. $f(t) = \sin t$
odd
27. $f(t) = \cos t$
even
28. $f(t) = \tan t$
odd
29. $f(t) = \sec t$
even
30. $f(t) = t \sin t$
even
31. $f(t) = t + \tan t$
odd
32. $f(t) = t + \cos t$
neither

In Exercises 33–36, use the Pythagorean identities to find $\sin t$ for the given value of $\cos t$. Make sure that the sign is correct for the given quadrant.

33. $\cos t = -0.5$ $-\dfrac{\sqrt{3}}{2}$ $\pi < t < \dfrac{3\pi}{2}$

34. $\cos t = -\dfrac{3}{\sqrt{10}}$ $\dfrac{1}{\sqrt{10}}$ $\dfrac{\pi}{2} < t < \pi$

35. $\cos t = \dfrac{1}{2}$ $\dfrac{\sqrt{3}}{2}$ $0 < t < \dfrac{\pi}{2}$

36. $\cos t = \dfrac{2}{\sqrt{5}}$ $-\dfrac{1}{\sqrt{5}}$ $\dfrac{3\pi}{2} < t < 2\pi$

In Exercises 37–44, $\sin t = \dfrac{3}{5}$ and $0 < t < \dfrac{\pi}{2}$. Use basic identities and the signs of the trigonometric functions in each quadrant to find each value.

37. $\sin(-t)$ $-\dfrac{3}{5}$
38. $\sin(t + 10\pi)$ $\dfrac{3}{5}$

39. $\sin(2\pi - t)$ $-\dfrac{3}{5}$
40. $\cos t$ $\dfrac{4}{5}$

41. $\tan t$ $\dfrac{3}{4}$
42. $\cos(-t)$ $\dfrac{4}{5}$

43. $\tan(2\pi - t)$ $-\dfrac{3}{4}$
44. $\sin(\pi - t)$ $\dfrac{3}{5}$

In Exercises 45–50, $\cos t = -\dfrac{2}{5}$ and $\pi < t < \dfrac{3\pi}{2}$. Use basic identities and the signs of the trigonometric functions in each quadrant to find each value.

45. $\sin t$ $-\dfrac{\sqrt{21}}{5}$
46. $\tan t$ $\dfrac{\sqrt{21}}{2}$

47. $\cos(2\pi - t)$ $-\dfrac{2}{5}$
48. $\cos(-t)$ $-\dfrac{2}{5}$

49. $\sin(4\pi + t)$ $-\dfrac{\sqrt{21}}{5}$
50. $\tan(4\pi - t)$ $-\dfrac{\sqrt{21}}{2}$

In Exercises 51–54, it is given that

$$\sin\dfrac{\pi}{8} = \dfrac{\sqrt{2 - \sqrt{2}}}{2}$$

Use basic identities to find each value.

51. $\cos\dfrac{\pi}{8}$ $\dfrac{\sqrt{2 + \sqrt{2}}}{2}$
52. $\tan\dfrac{\pi}{8}$ $\dfrac{\sqrt{2 - \sqrt{2}}}{\sqrt{2 + \sqrt{2}}}$

53. $\sin\dfrac{17\pi}{8}$ $\dfrac{\sqrt{2 - \sqrt{2}}}{2}$
54. $\tan\dfrac{-15\pi}{8}$ $\dfrac{\sqrt{2 - \sqrt{2}}}{\sqrt{2 + \sqrt{2}}}$

In Exercises 55–60, use the Pythagorean identities to determine if it is possible for a number t to satisfy the given conditions.

55. $\sin t = \dfrac{5}{13}$ and $\cos t = \dfrac{12}{13}$
possible

56. $\sin t = -2$ and $\cos t = 1$
not possible

57. $\sin t = -1$ and $\cos t = 1$
not possible

58. $\sin t = \dfrac{1}{\sqrt{2}}$ and $\cos t = \dfrac{1}{\sqrt{2}}$
possible

59. $\sin t = 1$ and $\tan t = 1$
not possible

60. $\cos t = \dfrac{8}{17}$ and $\tan t = \dfrac{15}{8}$
possible

61. Use the periodicity identities for sine, cosine, and tangent to write periodicity identities for cosecant, secant, and cotangent.

62. Use the negative angle identities for sine, cosine, and tangent to write negative angle identities for cosecant, secant, and cotangent.

61. $\csc t = \csc(t \pm 2\pi)$;
$\sec t = \sec(t \pm 2\pi)$;
$\cot t = \cot(t \pm \pi)$

62. $\csc t = -\csc(-t)$;
$\sec t = \sec(-t)$;
$\cot t = -\cot(-t)$

CHAPTER 6

Review

Important Concepts

Important Facts and Formulas

For a given acute angle θ:

$$\sin\theta = \frac{\text{opposite}}{\text{hypotenuse}} \qquad \cos\theta = \frac{\text{adjacent}}{\text{hypotenuse}} \qquad \tan\theta = \frac{\text{opposite}}{\text{adjacent}}$$

$$\csc\theta = \frac{\text{hypotenuse}}{\text{opposite}} \qquad \sec\theta = \frac{\text{hypotenuse}}{\text{adjacent}} \qquad \cot\theta = \frac{\text{adjacent}}{\text{opposite}}$$

θ	$\sin\theta$	$\cos\theta$	$\tan\theta$	$\csc\theta$	$\sec\theta$	$\cot\theta$
$30°$	$\frac{1}{2}$	$\frac{\sqrt{3}}{2}$	$\frac{\sqrt{3}}{3}$	2	$\frac{2\sqrt{3}}{3}$	$\sqrt{3}$
$60°$	$\frac{\sqrt{3}}{2}$	$\frac{1}{2}$	$\sqrt{3}$	$\frac{2\sqrt{3}}{3}$	2	$\frac{\sqrt{3}}{3}$
$45°$	$\frac{\sqrt{2}}{2}$	$\frac{\sqrt{2}}{2}$	1	$\sqrt{2}$	$\sqrt{2}$	1

To convert radians to degrees, multiply by $\frac{180}{\pi}$.

To convert degrees to radians, multiply by $\frac{\pi}{180}$.

Quotient Identities:

$$\tan t = \frac{\sin t}{\cos t} \qquad \cot t = \frac{\cos t}{\sin t}$$

Reciprocal Identities:

$$\sin t - \frac{1}{\csc t} \qquad \cos t - \frac{1}{\sec t} \qquad \tan t - \frac{1}{\cot t}$$

$$\csc t = \frac{1}{\sin t} \qquad \sec t = \frac{1}{\cos t} \qquad \cot t = \frac{1}{\tan t}$$

Pythagorean Identities:

$$\sin^2 t + \cos^2 t = 1 \qquad \tan^2 + 1 = \sec^2 t \qquad 1 + \cot^2 t = \sec^2 t$$

Important Facts and Formulas

Periodicity Identities:

$$\sin(t \pm 2\pi) = \sin t \qquad \cos(t \pm 2\pi) = \cos t \qquad \tan(t \pm \pi) = \tan t$$

Negative Angle Identities:

$$\sin(-t) = -\sin t \qquad \cos(-t) = \cos t \qquad \tan(-t) = -\tan(t)$$

Identities Involving $\pi - t$:

$$\sin t = \sin(\pi - t) \qquad \cos t = -\cos(\pi - t) \qquad \tan t = -\tan(\pi - t)$$

Review Exercises

ANSWERS

Review Exercises

Section **6.1**

1. Write $41°\ 6'\ 54''$ in decimal form.
41.115°

2. Write $10.5625°$ in DMS form.
10°33'45''

3. Which of the following statements about the angle θ is true? **d**

   a. $\sin \theta = \dfrac{3}{4}$ **b.** $\cos \theta = \dfrac{5}{4}$

   c. $\tan \theta = \dfrac{3}{5}$ **d.** $\sin \theta = \dfrac{4}{5}$

   e. $\sin \theta = \dfrac{4}{3}$

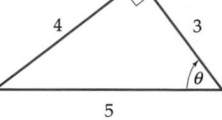

In Exercises 4–9, use the right triangle in the figure to find each ratio.

4. $\sin \theta$ $\dfrac{7}{\sqrt{65}}$ **5.** $\cos \theta$ $\dfrac{4}{\sqrt{65}}$ **6.** $\tan \theta$ $\dfrac{7}{4}$

7. $\csc \theta$ $\dfrac{\sqrt{65}}{7}$ **8.** $\sec \theta$ $\dfrac{\sqrt{65}}{4}$ **9.** $\cot \theta$ $\dfrac{4}{7}$

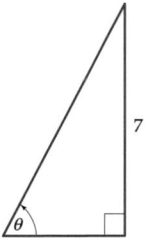

10. Find the length of side h in the triangle, given that angle A measures $40°$ and the distance from C to A is 25.

   $h \approx \mathbf{20.98}$

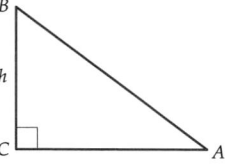

Section **6.2**

In Exercises 11–14, solve triangle *ABC*.

11. $A = 40°$ $b = 10$

12. $C = 35°$ $a = 12$

13. $A = 56°$ $a = 11$

14. $a = 3$ $c = 3$

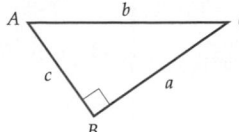

15. From a point on level ground 145 feet from the base of a tower, the angle of elevation to the top of the tower is 57.3°. How high is the tower?
≈ 225.9 ft

16. A pilot in a plane at an altitude of 22,000 feet observes that the angle of depression to a nearby airport is 26°. How many miles is the airport from the point on the ground directly below the plane?
≈ 8.5 mi

17. A lighthouse keeper 100 feet above the water sees a boat sailing in a straight line directly toward her. As she watches, the angle of depression to the boat changes from 25° to 40°. How far has the boat traveled during this time?
≈ 95.3 ft

Section **6.3**

18. $\dfrac{9\pi}{5}$ radians = __?__ degrees
324°

19. $\dfrac{17\pi}{12}$ radians = __?__ degrees
255°

20. $-\dfrac{11\pi}{4}$ radians = __?__ degrees
−495°

21. $36° =$ __?__ radians $\dfrac{\pi}{5}$

22. $220° =$ __?__ radians $\dfrac{11\pi}{9}$

23. $-135° =$ __?__ radians $-\dfrac{3\pi}{4}$

24. Find a number θ between 0 and 2π such that an angle of θ radians in standard position is coterminal with an angle of $-\dfrac{23\pi}{3}$ radians in standard position. $\dfrac{\pi}{3}$

25. Through how many radians does the second hand of a clock move in 2 minutes and 40 seconds? $\dfrac{16\pi}{3}$

26. 10 revolutions per minute – __?__ radians per minute **20π**

27. 4π radians per minute = __?__ revolutions per minute **2**

Section **6.4**

28. If the terminal side of an angle of t radians in standard position passes through the point $(-2, 3)$, then $\tan t =$ __?__ . $-\dfrac{3}{2}$

29. If the terminal side of an angle of t radians in standard position passes through the point $(6, -8)$, then $\cos t =$ __?__ . $\dfrac{3}{5}$

30. If the terminal side of an angle of t radians in standard position passes through the point $(1.2, 3.5)$, then $\sin t =$ __?__ . $\dfrac{35}{37}$

In Exercises 31–42, give the exact values.

31. $\cos\dfrac{47\pi}{2}$ **0**

32. $\sin(-13\pi)$ **0**

33. $\sin\dfrac{7\pi}{6}$ $-\dfrac{1}{2}$

34. $\cos\dfrac{3\pi}{4}$ $-\dfrac{\sqrt{2}}{2}$

35. $\tan\dfrac{8\pi}{3}$ $-\sqrt{3}$

36. $\sin\left(-\dfrac{7\pi}{4}\right)$ $\dfrac{\sqrt{2}}{2}$

11. $m\angle C = 50°$, $a \approx 6.4$, $c \approx 7.7$

12. $m\angle A = 55°$, $b \approx 14.6$, $c \approx 8.4$

13. $m\angle C = 34°$, $b \approx 13.3$, $c \approx 7.4$

14. $m\angle A = 45°$; $m\angle B = 45°$; $b = 3\sqrt{2}$

37. $\cot \dfrac{4\pi}{3}$ $\dfrac{\sqrt{3}}{3}$ **38.** $\cos\left(-\dfrac{\pi}{6}\right)$ $\dfrac{\sqrt{3}}{2}$ **39.** $\sec \dfrac{2\pi}{3}$ -2

40. $\sin\left(-\dfrac{11\pi}{6}\right)$ $\dfrac{1}{2}$ **41.** $\sin \dfrac{\pi}{3}$ $\dfrac{\sqrt{3}}{2}$ **42.** $\csc \dfrac{5\pi}{2}$ 1

43. The value of $\cos t$ is negative when the terminal side of an angle of t radians in standard position lies in which quadrants?

Quadrants II and III

In Exercises 44–46, express as a single real number (no decimal approximations allowed).

44. $\cos \dfrac{3\pi}{4} \sin \dfrac{5\pi}{6} - \sin \dfrac{3\pi}{4} \cos \dfrac{5\pi}{6}$ **45.** $\left(\sin \dfrac{\pi}{6} + 1\right)^2$ $\dfrac{9}{4}$

$\dfrac{-\sqrt{2} + \sqrt{6}}{4}$

46. $\sin\left(\dfrac{\pi}{2}\right) + \sin 0 + \cos 0$

2

Section 6.5

47. Write $\dfrac{\tan t}{\cot t}$ entirely in terms of $\sin t$ and $\cos t$, then simplify.

$\dfrac{\dfrac{\sin t}{\cos t}}{\dfrac{\cos t}{\sin t}} = \tan^2 t$

48. $\left[3 \sin\left(\dfrac{\pi}{5^{500}}\right)\right]^2 + \left[3 \cos\left(\dfrac{\pi}{5^{500}}\right)\right]^2 = ?$ **9**

49. Which of the following could possibly be a true statement about a real number t? **e**

   a. $\sin t = -2$ and $\cos t = 1$

   b. $\sin t = \dfrac{1}{2}$ and $\cos t = \dfrac{\sqrt{2}}{2}$

   c. $\sin t = -1$ and $\cos t = 1$

   d. $\sin t = \dfrac{\pi}{2}$ and $\cos t = 1 - \dfrac{\pi}{2}$

   e. $\sin t = \dfrac{3}{5}$ and $\cos t = \dfrac{4}{5}$

50. If $\dfrac{\pi}{2} < t < \pi$ and $\sin t = \dfrac{5}{13}$, then $\cos t = ?$ $-\dfrac{12}{13}$

51. If $\sin t = -\dfrac{4}{5}$ and the terminal side of an angle of t radians in standard position lies in the third quadrant, then $\cos t = \underline{\ ?\ }$. $-\dfrac{3}{5}$

52. Simplify $\dfrac{\tan (t + \pi)}{\sin (t + 2\pi)}$. **sec t**

53. If $\sin\left(-\dfrac{101\pi}{2}\right) = -1$, then $\sin\left(-\dfrac{105\pi}{2}\right) = ?$ -1

54. Which of the statements (i)–(iii) are true? **c**

   (i) $\sin (-x) = -\sin x$

   (ii) $\cos (-x) = -\cos x$

   (iii) $\tan (-x) = -\tan x$

   a. (i) and (ii) only

   b. (ii) only

   c. (i) and (iii) only

   d. all of them

   e. none of them

55. Suppose θ is a real number. Consider the right triangle with sides as shown in the figure. Then: **b**

   a. $x = 1$

   b. $x = 2$

   c. $x = 4$

   d. $x = 2(\cos\theta + \sin\theta)$

   e. none of the above

56. Determine the following segment lengths in terms of a single trigonometric function of t.

   a. OR **b.** PR **c.** SQ **d.** OQ

     cos t   **sin t**   **tan t**   **sec t**

Optimization with Trigonometry

Teaching Notes

Students have used calculator graphs and minimum/maximum finders to solve optimization problems. Stress the need to develop the ability to solve these problems by using tables. Students can use graphs and minimum/maximum finders to check solutions.

Example Notes

In **Example 1**, students will find a radian angle measure of 1.0472 (Figure 6.C-3, page 469). They might wonder how to determine that this angle measure is $\frac{4\pi}{12}$. Explain that the table interval was set to $\frac{\pi}{12}$, and 1.0472 is the 4th entry after 0 in the X column.

Alternatively, you can find the multiple of the interval by solving the following equation.

$$\frac{x\pi}{12} = 1.0472$$

$$x = 1.0472\left(\frac{12}{\pi}\right) = 4$$

In **Example 2**, the angle that has d_2 as a side is $\frac{\pi}{2} - t$. To explain, temporarily call it α:

$$t + 90° + \alpha = 180°$$

$$t + \frac{\pi}{2} + \alpha = \pi$$

$$\alpha = \pi - t - \frac{\pi}{2}$$

$$\alpha = \frac{\pi}{2} - t$$

COMMON ERROR ALERT

Students might enter a function in a calculator incorrectly by not using parentheses properly. In **Example 2**, they must enter the function *L*. If a calculator automatically inserts a left parenthesis after *sin*, they need to key in a right parenthesis.

$6/\sin(x + 8/\sin(\pi/2 - x)$ is *incorrect*.
$6/\sin(x) + 8/\sin(\pi/2 - x)$ is *correct*.

Optimization problems involve finding a solution that is either a maximum or a minimum value of a function. Calculus is needed to find exact solutions to most optimization problems, but tables or graphs can often be used to find approximate solutions.

Example 1   **Maximum Area**

A gutter is to be made from a strip of metal 24 inches wide by bending up the sides to form a trapezoid, as shown in Figure 6.C-1.

a. Express the area of the cross-section of the gutter as a function of the angle *t*.

b. For what value of *t* will this area be as large as possible?

Solution

a. The cross-section of the gutter is a trapezoid, shown in Figure 6.C-2.

Figure 6.C-1

The bases are parallel, so these alternate interior angles are equal.

Figure 6.C-2

The area of a trapezoid is $\dfrac{h(b_1 + b_2)}{2}$.

The top base $b_2 = 8 + 2x$, where   The height is *h*, where

$$\cos t = \frac{x}{8}.$$ $$\sin t = \frac{h}{8}.$$

So $x = 8 \cos t$.   So $h = 8 \sin t$.

Thus, the area of the cross-section is

$$A = \frac{8 \sin t(8 + 8 + 2(8 \cos t))}{2} = 4 \sin t(16 + 16 \cos t) = 64 \sin t(1 + \cos t).$$

b. To find the value of *t* that makes the area be as large as possible, first notice that *t* must be between 0 and $\frac{\pi}{2} \approx 1.57$. By examining a table of values, it is possible to estimate the maximum value of *A* over this interval.

🌍 Real-World Application

Example 2 is about finding the maximum length of a ladder that can fit around a corner in a corridor. If it is necessary for a certain length ladder to fit around the corner, an architect would need to solve this problem to know what widths to plan for the corridors.

A good starting interval for the table is $\frac{\pi}{12} \approx 0.26$. The table in Figure 6.C-3 shows the highest value at about 1.05, or $\frac{4\pi}{12} = \frac{\pi}{3}$.

NOTE Trigonometric functions often have maxima and minima at fractional multiples of π. It is a good idea to try these values as increments for a table.

Figure 6.C-3   **Figure 6.C-4**

It is possible to confirm this value or get a better estimate by using a table with a smaller step size, such as $\frac{\pi}{144} \approx 0.02$. Figure 6.C-4 confirms that $\frac{\pi}{3}$ appears to be the value of t that corresponds to the largest area, about 83.1 in².

Example 2   **Maximum Length**

Two corridors meet at a right angle. One corridor is 6 ft wide, and the other is 8 ft wide. A ladder is being carried horizontally along the corridor. What is the maximum length of a ladder that can fit around the corner?

Solution

Figure 6.C-5

The length of the longest ladder that fits around the corner is the same as the *shortest* length of the red segment in Figure 6.C-5 as it pivots about the corner. Let the part of the segment from the corner to the opposite wall of the 6-ft corridor be d_1, and the part to the wall of the 8-ft corridor be d_2. Then the desired length is $d_1 + d_2$.

For the angle t in Figure 6.C-5,

$$\sin t = \frac{6}{d_1} \qquad\qquad \sin\left(\frac{\pi}{2} - t\right) = \frac{8}{d_2}$$

$$d_1 = \frac{6}{\sin t} \qquad\qquad d_2 = \frac{8}{\sin\left(\frac{\pi}{2} - t\right)}$$

The function that describes the desired length is $L = \dfrac{6}{\sin t} + \dfrac{8}{\sin\left(\frac{\pi}{2} - t\right)}$.

469

b. For what value of θ will the window area be as large as possible?

θ must be between 0 and $\frac{\pi}{2} \approx 1.57$.

Using a table interval of $\frac{\pi}{144}$:

X	Y1
1.0254	259.68
1.0472	259.81
1.069	259.68
1.0908	259.32
1.1126	258.71
1.1345	257.87
1.1563	256.79

X=1.04719755119?

It appears that $\theta = \frac{\pi}{3} \approx 1.0472$ corresponds to the largest area, about 259.8 in².

Example 1

A window is needed for a circular opening with radius 10 inches. The window is to be hexagonal with 4 congruent sides, symmetric with respect to a diameter of the circle, as shown below.

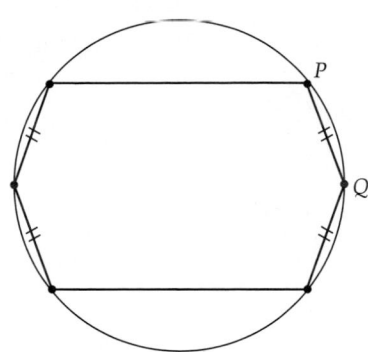

a. Express the area of the window as a function of a central angle θ. The sides of θ must pass through points P and Q. The top half of the hexagon is an isosceles trapezoid with height h and base lengths 20 and $20 - 2a$ as shown below.

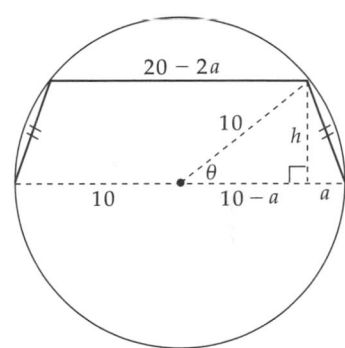

$$\sin\theta = \frac{h}{10} \qquad\Big|\qquad \cos\theta = \frac{10 - a}{10}$$
$$h = 10\sin\theta \quad\Big|\quad 10\cos\theta = 10 - a$$
$$\Big|\qquad a = 10 - 10\cos\theta$$

$$A_{trapezoid} = \frac{h(20 + 20 - 2a)}{2}$$
$$= \frac{h(40 - 2a)}{2}$$

Let A be the window area.

$$A = h(40 - 2a)$$
$$= 10\sin\theta(40 - 2(10 - 10\cos\theta))$$
$$= 10\sin\theta(40 - 20 + 20\cos\theta)$$
$$= 10\sin\theta(20 + 20\cos\theta)$$
$$= 200\sin\theta(1 + \cos\theta)$$

So area is $A = 200\sin\theta(1 + \cos\theta)$.

Example 2

A construction foreman needs a trash chute to extend from building A to the ground, resting on building B as shown below. Building B is 10 ft wide and 12 ft tall. Find the minimum length chute he can use.

Redraw the portion of the diagram needed, labeling as shown below. Let L represent the length of the chute, so $L = d_1 + d_2$.

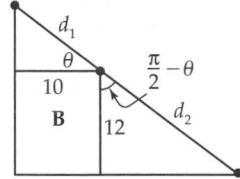

$$\cos \theta = \frac{10}{d_1} \qquad \cos\left(\frac{\pi}{2} - \theta\right) = \frac{12}{d_2}$$

$$d_1 = \frac{10}{\cos \theta} \qquad d_2 = \frac{12}{\cos\left(\frac{\pi}{2} - \theta\right)}$$

$$L = d_1 + d_2 = \frac{10}{\cos \theta} + \frac{12}{\cos\left(\frac{\pi}{2} - \theta\right)}$$

Using a table interval of $\frac{\pi}{144}$:

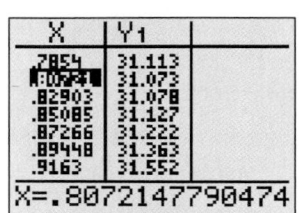

The minimum length chute he can use is about 31.1 ft; it makes an angle of about 0.807 radian, or about 46.2° with the top of building B.

To find the minimum of the function, note that t is between 0 and $\frac{\pi}{2}$. Construct a table with an increment of $\frac{\pi}{12}$, then use the minimum value to construct a table with an increment of $\frac{\pi}{144}$. The minimum appears to be at $t \approx 0.74$, which corresponds to a length of about 19.7 ft.

Figure 6.C-6

In Examples 1 and 2, an area and a length were represented in terms of an angle to find the optimal solution. In the following example, the angle is the quantity to be maximized.

Example 3 Maximum Viewing Angle

The best view of a statue is where the viewing angle is a maximum. In Figure 6.C-7, the height of the statue is 24 ft and the height of the pedestal is 8 ft. Find the distance from the statue where the viewing angle is optimal.

Figure 6.C-7

Solution

In Figure 6.C-8, the angle $t = t_1 - t_2$. The important quantities are opposite and adjacent to the angles, so the tangent function is used to describe the relationship.

$$\tan t_1 = \frac{27}{d} \qquad\qquad \tan t_2 = \frac{3}{d}$$

$$t_1 = \tan^{-1}\frac{27}{d} \qquad\qquad t_2 = \tan^{-1}\frac{3}{d}$$

$$t = \tan^{-1}\frac{27}{d} - \tan^{-1}\frac{3}{d}$$

statue 24 ft
pedestal 8 ft
t_1
t
t_2
eye level 5 ft
d

Figure 6.C-8

470

To create a table, first notice that $d > 0$. Start with a large increment, such as 5 ft, and narrow the increment to refine your estimate, as shown in Figure 6.C-9.

Figure 6.C-9

The best distance to view the statue is at about 9 ft away. The viewing angle at this distance is about 0.93 radians, which is about 53°.

Exercises

Estimate the maximum value of the given function between 0 and $\frac{\pi}{2}$ by using tables with increments of $\frac{\pi}{12}$ and $\frac{\pi}{144}$.

1. $f(t) = \sin t \cos t$ **2.** $f(t) = \sin t + 2 \cos t$

3. $f(t) = 3 \sin t + \sin\left(\frac{\pi}{2} - t\right)$

4. $f(t) = 2 \cos t - \dfrac{1}{1 + \sin t}$

5. The cross section of a tunnel is a semicircle with radius 10 meters. The interior walls of the tunnel form a rectangle.

a. Express the area of the rectangular cross-section of the tunnel opening as a function of angle t.
b. For what value of t is the cross-sectional area of the tunnel opening as large as possible? What are the dimensions of the tunnel opening in this case?

6. A 30-ft statue stands on a 10-ft pedestal. Find the best distance to view the statue, assuming eye level is 5 ft (see Example 3).

7. Two towns lie 10 miles apart on opposite sides of a mile-wide straight river, as shown. A road is to be built along one side of the river from town A to point X, then across the river to town B. The cost of building on land is \$10,000 per mile, and the cost of building over the water is \$20,000 per mile.
a. Express the cost of building the road as a function of the angle t.
b. Find the minimum cost of the road.

471

1. max of 0.5 when $x \approx 0.7854$
max of 0.5 when $x \approx 0.78538$

2. max of 2.2321 when $x \approx 0.5236$
max of 2.236 when $x \approx 0.45815$

3. max of 3.1566 when $x \approx 1.309$
max of 3.1622 when $x \approx 1.2435$

4. max of 1.1375 when $x \approx 0.2618$
max of 1.1387 when $x \approx 0.28362$

5. a. $200 \sin t \cos t$

b. $\dfrac{\pi}{4}$ radians; height $= 5\sqrt{2}$ meters and width $= 10\sqrt{2}$ meters

6. approximately 13.23 feet from the statue

7. a. road cost $= 10,000\left(10 - \dfrac{1}{\tan t}\right) + 20,000\left(\dfrac{1}{\sin t}\right)$

b. approximately \$117,321

ADDITIONAL EXAMPLES

Example 3

A motorist is driving on a straight road looking at a sign 50 ft wide. The sign is perpendicular to the road, and its nearest edge is 20 ft from the road. The motorist remains 10 feet from the edge of the road while driving. Find the distance x that makes the largest viewing angle θ.

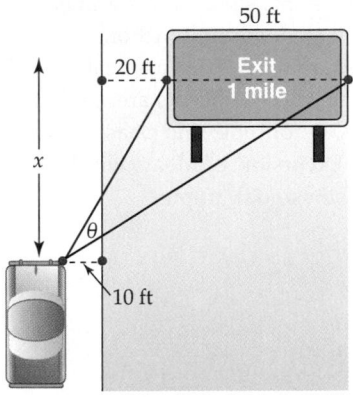

Redraw the diagram to get right triangles that involve x and θ.

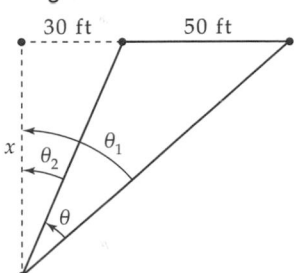

$\tan \theta_1 = \dfrac{80}{x}$ $\tan \theta_2 = \dfrac{30}{x}$

$\theta_1 = \tan^{-1}\left(\dfrac{80}{x}\right)$ $\theta_2 = \tan^{-1}\left(\dfrac{30}{x}\right)$

$\theta = \theta_1 - \theta_2 = \tan^{-1}\left(\dfrac{80}{x}\right) - \tan^{-1}\left(\dfrac{30}{x}\right)$

Using a table interval of 0.1 ft:

The distance that makes the largest viewing angle is about 49 ft, making the angle $\theta \approx 0.47$ radian, which is about 27°.

Exercises

ANSWERS

1–4. For tables, see pp. 1068–1069.

Trigonometric Graphs

In this chapter, students will study graphs of the six trigonometric functions. They will apply prior knowledge of reflections, stretches, compressions, shifts, and symmetry to the trigonometric functions. Some new vocabulary terms associated with applying these concepts are: periodic graphs, amplitude, and phase shifts. In the Excursion, students will learn about sinusoidal graphs.

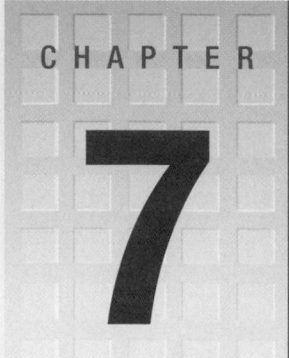

CHAPTER

7 Trigonometric Graphs

Stay tuned for more!

Radio stations transmit by sending out a signal in the form of an electromagnetic wave that can be described by a trigonometric function. The shape of this signal is modified by the sounds being transmitted. AM radio signals are modified by varying the "height," or amplitude, of the waves, whereas FM signals are modified by varying the frequency of the waves. The signal displayed in the photo is from an AM radio station found at 900 on the broadcast dial. See Exercise 65 of Section 7.3.

472

Chapter Outline

Interdepedence of Sections

7.1 ⟶ 7.3 ⟶ 7.4
　↘ 7.2

Graphs of trigonometric functions often make it very easy to see the essential properties of these functions, particularly the fact that they repeat their values at regular intervals. Because of the repeating, or periodic, nature of trigonometric functions, they are used to model a variety of phenomena that involve cyclic behavior, such as sound waves, electron orbitals, planetary orbits, radio transmissions, vibrating strings, pendulums, and many more.

7.1 Graphs of the Sine, Cosine, and Tangent Functions

Objectives

- Graph the sine, cosine, and tangent functions

- State all values in the domain of a basic trigonometric function that correspond to a given value of the range

- Graph transformations of the sine, cosine, and tangent graphs

Although a graphing calculator will quickly sketch the graphs of the sine, cosine, and tangent functions, it will not give you much insight into why these graphs have the shapes they do and why these shapes are important. So the emphasis in this section is the connection between the functions' definitions and their graphs.

Using radians and the unit circle, you learned in Chapter 6 that trigonometric functions can be defined as functions of real numbers. Using this definition, you will see that the graphs of trigonometric functions are directly related to angles in the unit circle.

Graph of the Sine Function

Consider an angle of t radians in standard position. Let P be the point where the terminal side of the angle meets the unit circle. Then the y-coordinate of P is the number $\sin t$. As t increases, the graph of $f(t) = \sin t$ can be sketched from the corresponding y-coordinates of P.

473

Section

7.1 Graphs of the Sine, Cosine, and Tangent Functions

Teaching Notes

Remind students that the trigonometric functions are defined using t, x, and y. Recall that two consequences of the definitions are:

- For each angle of t radians, the point $P(x, y)$ on the unit circle is $P(\cos t, \sin t)$.

- The tangent ratio is $\tan t = \dfrac{\sin t}{\cos t}$.

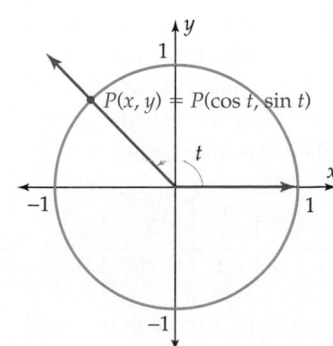

Teaching Notes

The full-page diagram illustrates how to use the y-coordinates on the unit circle to sketch one period of the sine function. To extend the sine graph to the right, beyond $t = 2\pi$, let P continue its counterclockwise path, retracing around the unit circle. To extend the graph left of the y-axis, let P move clockwise around the unit circle from 0 to $-\frac{\pi}{2}$, from $-\frac{\pi}{2}$ to $-\pi$, and so on. The result is the full **Graph of the Sine Function** on page 475.

Ask students to name the points on the sine graph that correspond to these points on the unit circle:

$(1, 0) \quad (0, 1) \quad (-1, 0) \quad (0, -1)$

$(0, 0) \quad \left(\frac{\pi}{2}, 1\right) \quad (\pi, 0) \quad \left(\frac{3\pi}{2}, -1\right)$

Ask students to name a local maximum point and a local minimum point of the sine function from the list above.

local maximum point: $\left(\frac{\pi}{2}, 1\right)$

local minimum point: $\left(\frac{3\pi}{2}, -1\right)$

From the same list, ask students to name the x-intercepts of the sine graph.

$(0, 0)$ and $(\pi, 0)$

Encourage students to remember the points discussed above as reference points.

The unit circle can be used to determine reference points such as those discussed above and intervals on which the sine curve is increasing and decreasing. However, it is not as useful in determining concavity. To get a more precise sketch, you can have students use calculators to complete the table below.

t	0	$\frac{\pi}{6}$	$\frac{\pi}{4}$	$\frac{\pi}{3}$	$\frac{\pi}{2}$
$\sin t$	0	0.5	0.707	0.866	1

Have them plot these points with paper and pencil to see that the sine curve is increasing and concave down on the interval $\left(0, \frac{\pi}{2}\right)$. This activity could be extended to verify the concavity on other intervals.

Change in t	Movement of point P	$\sin t$ (y-coordinate of P)	Corresponding graph
from 0 to $\frac{\pi}{2}$	from $(1, 0)$ to $(0, 1)$	increases from 0 to 1	
from $\frac{\pi}{2}$ to π	from $(0, 1)$ to $(-1, 0)$	decreases from 1 to 0	
from π to $\frac{3\pi}{2}$	from $(-1, 0)$ to $(0, -1)$	decreases from 0 to -1	
from $\frac{3\pi}{2}$ to 2π	from $(0, -1)$ to $(1, 0)$	increases from -1 to 0	

CAUTION

Throughout this chapter, the independent variable used for trigonometric functions will be t to avoid any confusion with the x and y that are part of the definition of these functions. However, using a graphing calculator in function mode, you must enter x as the independent variable.

Your graphing calculator can provide a dynamic view of the graph of the sine function and its relationship to points on the unit circle.

Graphing Exploration ●

With your graphing calculator in parametric mode, set the viewing window as shown below, with a *t*-step of 0.1.

$$0 \le t \le 2\pi \qquad -\frac{\pi}{3} \le x \le 2\pi \qquad -2.5 < y < 2.5$$

On the same screen, graph the two functions given below.

$$X_1 = \cos t, Y_1 = \sin t \qquad X_2 = t, Y_2 = \sin t$$

Use the trace feature to move the cursor along the first graph, which is the unit circle. Stop at a point, and note the values of *t* and *y*.

Use the up or down key to move the cursor to the second graph, which is the graph of the sine function. The value of *t* will remain the same. What are the *x*- and *y*-coordinates of this point?

How does the *y*-coordinate of the new point compare with the *y*-coordinate of the original point on the unit circle?

To complete the graph of the sine function, note that as *t* goes from 2π to 4π, the point *P* on the unit circle *retraces* the path it took from 0 to 2π, so *the same curve will repeat* on the graph. This repetition occurs each 2π units along the horizontal axis, therefore the sine function has a period of 2π. That is, for any real number *t*,

$$\sin(t \pm 2\pi) = \sin t.$$

Graph of the Sine Function

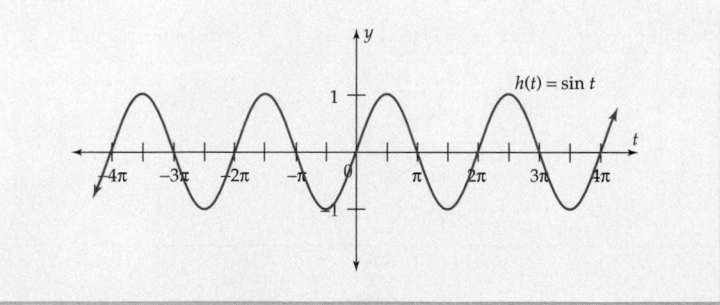

Graph of the Cosine Function

Let *P* be the point where the terminal side of an angle of *t* radians in standard position meets the unit circle. Then the *x*-coordinate of *P* is the number $\cos t$. To obtain the graph of $f(t) = \cos(t)$, the same process as

---

Teaching Notes

Direct students' attention to the **CAUTION** on page 474. Point out that to graph the sine function as shown at the bottom of this page, they would ordinarily use function mode and the independent variable *x*. However, in the Graphing Exploration at the left, they will be using parametric mode and the independent variable *t*. Remind students to use radian mode.

Solution to the **Graphing Exploration:**

When the cursor is on the unit circle at $t = 1$, $(x, y) = (0.5403, 0.8415)$.

When the cursor is moved to the sine function graph, $(x, y) = (1, 0.8415)$.

The *y*-coordinate is the same on the sine function graph and the unit circle.

To get a calculator graph of the sine function at the left, students can use $Y_1 = \sin(x)$ in function mode and set the window to $-4\pi \le x \le 4\pi$ and $-2 \le y \le 2$.

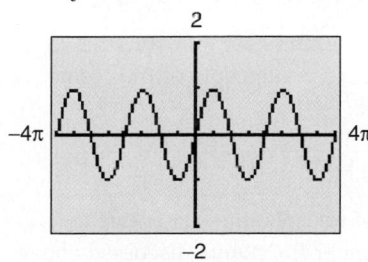

To see more or fewer periods, they can modify the *x*-values in the window.

Teaching Notes

The graph of the cosine function is sketched from the unit circle by a method similar to that used for the sine function. However, the cosine sketch could be more difficult for students. Emphasize the following:

- For the sine function, *y-values* from the unit circle become *y*-values on the sine curve.
- For the cosine function, *x-values* from the unit circle become *y*-values on the cosine curve.

Intuitively, it is easier to see the correspondence between the path of P on the unit circle and the graph of the sine function because they "rise and fall" together. But it is not as easy to see the correspondence in the case of the cosine function. For the cosine function, you need to be aware of the *x-values* as P travels on the unit circle, and plot points using these values as *y-values*. For example, when P is at $(1, 0)$ on the unit circle, the corresponding point on the cosine curve is $(0, 1)$.

Repeat the activity that was used for the sine graph. Ask students to name the points on the cosine graph that correspond to these points on the unit circle:

$(1, 0)$ $(0, 1)$ $(-1, 0)$ $(0, -1)$

$(0, 1)$ $\left(\dfrac{\pi}{2}, 0\right)$ $(\pi, -1)$ $\left(\dfrac{3\pi}{2}, 0\right)$

Ask students to name a local maximum point and a local minimum point of the cosine function from the list above.

local maximum point: $(0, 1)$

local minimum point: $(\pi, -1)$

From the same list, ask students to name the *x*-intercepts of the cosine graph.

$\left(\dfrac{\pi}{2}, 0\right)$ and $\left(\dfrac{3\pi}{2}, 0\right)$

As before, encourage students to remember the points discussed above as reference points.

You can have students make a table of values and plot points to verify concavity as done earlier with the sine function.

that used for the sine function is followed, except the *x*-coordinate is observed. The following chart illustrates the graph of the cosine function.

Change in t	Movement of point P	$\cos t$ (*x*-coordinate of P)	Corresponding graph
from 0 to $\dfrac{\pi}{2}$	from $(1, 0)$ to $(0, 1)$	decreases from 1 to 0	
from $\dfrac{\pi}{2}$ to π	from $(0, 1)$ to $(-1, 0)$	decreases from 0 to -1	
from π to $\dfrac{3\pi}{2}$	from $(-1, 0)$ to $(0, -1)$	increases from -1 to 0	
from $\dfrac{3\pi}{2}$ to 2π	from $(0, -1)$ to $(1, 0)$	increases from 0 to 1	

As the value of t increases, the point P on the unit circle *retraces* its path along the unit circle, so the graph of $f(t) = \cos(t)$ repeats the same curve at intervals of length 2π. Because the cosine function also has a period of 2π, for any number t,

$$\cos(t \pm 2\pi) = \cos t.$$

Graph of the Cosine Function

The graphs of the sine and cosine functions visually illustrate two basic facts about these functions. Because the graphs extend infinitely to the right and to the left,

the domain of the sine and cosine functions is the set of all real numbers.

Also, the y-coordinate of every point on these graphs lies between -1 and 1 (inclusive), so that

the range of the sine and cosine functions is the interval $[-1, 1]$.

You can use the period of the function to state all values of t for which $\sin t$ or $\cos t$ is a given number, as shown in Examples 1 and 2.

Example 1   **Finding All *t*-values**

State all values of t for which $\sin t$ is -1.

Solution

The sine function oscillates between -1 and 1 and has a period of 2π (i.e., it repeats the pattern every 2π units on the horizontal axis), so there are an *infinite* number of t-values for which $\sin t$ is -1. These points occur every 2π units on the horizontal axis, and a few are highlighted in red on the graph $y = \sin t$ shown in Figure 7.1.1.

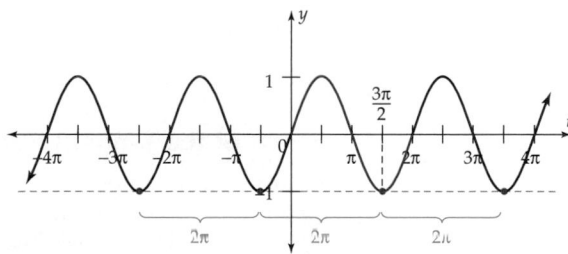

Figure 7.1-1

Teaching Notes

Students can easily see on pages 475 and 477 that the *sine and cosine graphs have identical shapes*. However, it is important for them to realize that the *graphs are not identical* (do not coincide). Have them graph both functions on the same screen using $Y_1 = \sin(x)$ and $Y_2 = \cos(x)$. The window used below is $-4\pi \le x \le 4\pi$ and $-2 \le y \le 2$.

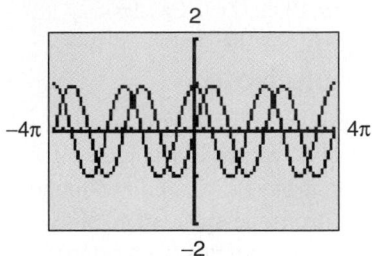

Ask what type of transformation could be applied to one of the graphs to get the other.   horizontal shift

Example Notes

Identifying the period of a function (page 457) is important throughout this section. On a graph, any pair of points that include one complete pattern, or cycle, between them can be used to find the period. The period is the horizontal distance between that pair of points. In **Example 1,** Figure 7.1-1, the period of the sine function is 2π, shown two different ways:

• the red portion of the curve on the interval $[0, 2\pi)$
• successive pairs of local minimum points shown as red dots

ADDITIONAL EXAMPLES

Example 1

State all values of t for which $\sin t$ is 1.

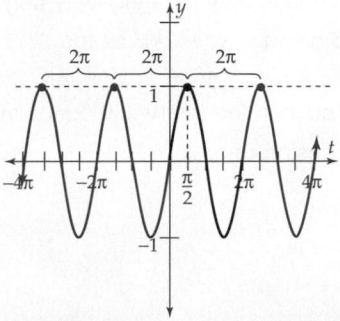

$t = \frac{\pi}{2} + 2k\pi$, where k is any integer

Teaching Notes

The interval $[0, 2\pi)$ is used to identify the period in Figure 7.1-1, page 477, and in Figure 7.1-2 on this page. Students might wonder why a half-open interval is used. Explain that successive half-open intervals can be "strung together" without overlap to represent the entire domain of the function. The domain consists of these intervals:

$$\dots, [-2\pi, 0), [0, 2\pi), [2\pi, 4\pi), \dots$$

Example Notes

In **Examples 1** and **2**, graphs are used to identify t-values in the interval $[0, 2\pi)$ that have a particular function value. Encourage students to show the t-values as angles in standard position.

For **Example 2**, $\frac{\pi}{3}$ and $\frac{5\pi}{3}$ are shown below in standard position. They both have the same cosine value, $\frac{1}{2}$. There are no other angles in the interval $[0, 2\pi)$ that have the cosine value $\frac{1}{2}$.

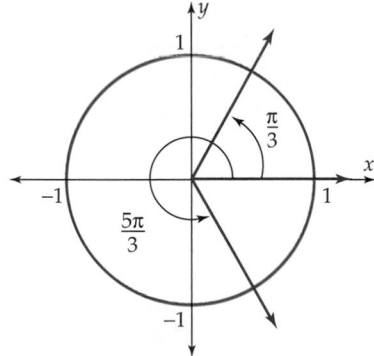

COMMON ERROR ALERT

In **Example 2**, students might identify only one t-value in the interval $[0, 2\pi)$, and then give an incomplete answer. For example, they might identify only $\frac{\pi}{3}$, and give $t = \frac{\pi}{3} + 2k\pi$ as the answer. Remind them to look for *every* point in the interval $[0, 2\pi)$ that has a cosine of $\frac{1}{2}$.

On the interval $[0, 2\pi)$, highlighted in red on the graph above, the graph of $y = \sin t$ has only one point, $\left(\frac{3\pi}{2}, -1\right)$, at which the y-coordinate is -1. Therefore, all values of t for which $\sin t$ is -1 can be expressed as $t = \frac{3\pi}{2} + 2k\pi$, where k is any integer. ∎

Example 2 Finding All t-values

State all values of t for which $\cos t$ is $\frac{1}{2}$.

Solution

The cosine function repeats its pattern of y-values at intervals of 2π, so there are an *infinite* number of t-values for which $\cos t$ is $\frac{1}{2}$. The graph of $y = \cos t$ shown in Figure 7.1-2 highlights a few points with a y-coordinate of $\frac{1}{2}$.

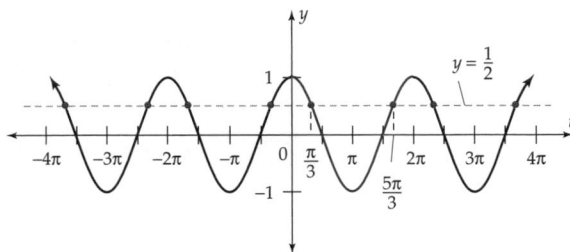

Figure 7.1-2

On the interval $[0, 2\pi)$, highlighted in red on the graph above, the graph of $y = \cos t$ has two points, $\left(\frac{\pi}{3}, \frac{1}{2}\right)$ and $\left(\frac{5\pi}{3}, \frac{1}{2}\right)$, at which the y-coordinate is $\frac{1}{2}$. Therefore, all values of t for which $\cos t$ is $\frac{1}{2}$ can be expressed as $t = \frac{\pi}{3} + 2k\pi$ or $\frac{5\pi}{3} + 2k\pi$, where k is any integer. ∎

Graph of the Tangent Function

To determine the shape of the graph of $f(t) = \tan t$, a connection between the tangent function and slope can be used. As shown in Figure 7.1-3, the point P where the terminal side of an angle of t radians in standard position meets the unit circle has coordinates $(\cos t, \sin t)$. This point and the point $(0, 0)$ can be used to compute the *slope* of the line containing the terminal side.

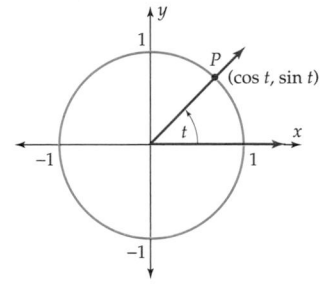

Figure 7.1-3

$$\text{slope} = \frac{\sin t - 0}{\cos t - 0} = \frac{\sin t}{\cos t} = \tan t$$

The graph of $f(t) = \tan t$ can be sketched by noting the slope of the terminal side of an angle of t radians, as t takes different values.

Change in t	Movement of terminal side	tan t (terminal side slope)	Corresponding graph
from 0 to $\frac{\pi}{2}$	from horizontal upward toward vertical	increases from 0 in the positive direction	
from 0 to $-\frac{\pi}{2}$	from horizontal downward toward vertical	decreases from 0 in the negative direction	

When $t = \pm\frac{\pi}{2}$, the terminal side of the angle is vertical, so its slope is not defined. The graph of the tangent function has vertical asymptotes at the values of t for which the function is undefined.

To complete the graph of the tangent function, note that as t goes from $\frac{\pi}{2}$ to $\frac{3\pi}{2}$, the terminal side goes from almost vertical with negative slope to almost vertical with positive slope, exactly as it does from $-\frac{\pi}{2}$ to $\frac{\pi}{2}$. So the graph repeats this pattern at intervals of length π.

Example 2

State all values of t for which $\cos t$ is $-\frac{1}{2}$.

$t = \frac{2\pi}{3} + 2k\pi$ or $t = \frac{4\pi}{3} + 2k\pi$, where k is any integer

Teaching Notes

For the **Graph of the Tangent Function,** review the slope formula and apply it to the points $(0, 0)$ and $(\cos t, \sin t)$ in Figure 7.1-3:

$$\frac{y_2 - y_1}{x_2 - x_1} = \frac{\sin t - 0}{\cos t - 0} = \frac{\sin t}{\cos t} = \tan t$$

Remind students that $\frac{0}{x} = 0$ (if $x \neq 0$) and $\frac{x}{0}$ is undefined. Ask what occurs in the graph at t-values for which the function is undefined. vertical asymptotes

Students can use calculators to complete the table below and then plot points on paper to verify concavity, as done earlier with the sine and cosine functions.

t	0	$\frac{\pi}{6}$	$\frac{\pi}{4}$	$\frac{\pi}{3}$	$\frac{\pi}{2}$
tan t	0	0.577	1	1.73	undefined

As t approaches $\frac{\pi}{2}$, tangent values increase without bound and the graph gets closer to the asymptote at $\frac{\pi}{2}$. To demonstrate this, note that $\frac{\pi}{2} \approx 1.5707963$. Have students use calculators to find the following tangent values:

tan 1.5 ≈ 14.1

tan 1.57 ≈ 1255.8

tan 1.5707 ≈ 10,381.3

Students might think the tangent function has the set of all real numbers as its domain, or 2π as its period, using the related facts from the sine and cosine functions. Encourage students to use the graph of the tangent function to help them remember the correct domain and period.

Teaching Notes

For **Basic Transformations of Sine, Cosine, and Tangent,** students will need to review graphical transformations in Section 3.4, pages 172–181. The Example Notes below specify the particular types of transformations needed in each case.

Example Notes

Example 4 is a vertical stretch. It uses the following concept from page 179:
For a positive number c,
- If $c > 1$, the graph of $g(x) = c \cdot f(x)$ is the graph of f stretched vertically, away from the x-axis, by a factor of c.
- If $c < 1$, the graph of $g(x) = c \cdot f(x)$ is the graph of f compressed vertically, toward the x-axis, by a factor of c.

Example 5 is a reflection across the x-axis and a vertical stretch. The reflection uses this concept from page 177:
- The graph of $g(x) = -f(x)$ is the graph of f reflected across the x-axis.
- The graph of $g(x) = f(-x)$ is the graph of f reflected across the y-axis.

Example 6 is a vertical shift. It uses this concept from page 174:
For a positive number c,
- The graph of $g(x) = f(x) + c$ is the graph of f shifted upward c units.
- The graph of $g(x) = f(x) - c$ is the graph of f shifted downward c units.

---

480 Chapter 7 **Trigonometric Graphs**

Graph of the Tangent Function

Notice that the **domain of the tangent function** is all real numbers except *odd* multiples of $\frac{\pi}{2}$. The **range of the tangent function** is all real numbers. Because the tangent function has a period of π, for any number t in its domain,

$$\tan(t \pm \pi) = \tan t.$$

 Example 3 Finding All *t*-values

State all values of t for which $\tan t$ is -1.

Solution

The tangent function repeats its pattern of y-values at intervals of π, so there are an *infinite* number t-values for which $\tan t$ is -1. The graph of $y = \tan t$ shown in Figure 7.1-4 highlights a few points with a y-coordinate of -1.

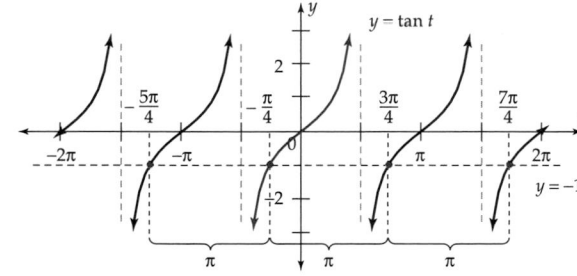

Figure 7.1-4

On the interval $\left[-\frac{\pi}{2}, \frac{\pi}{2} \right)$, highlighted in red on the graph above, the graph of $y = \tan t$ has only one point, $\left(-\frac{\pi}{4}, -1 \right)$, at which the y-coordinate is

-1. Therefore, all values of t for which $\tan t$ is -1 can be expressed as $t = -\frac{\pi}{4} + k\pi$, where k is any integer.

Basic Transformations of Sine, Cosine, and Tangent

The graphical transformations (such as shifting and stretching) that were considered in Section 3.4 also apply to trigonometric graphs.

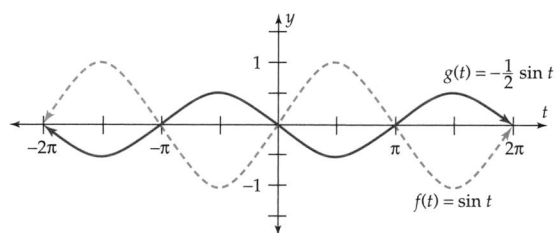

Figure 7.1-5

Example 4   Vertical Stretch

List the transformation needed to change the graph of $f(t) = \cos t$ into the graph of $h(t) = 4 \cos t$. Graph both equations on the same screen.

Solution

Because $h(t) = 4 \cdot f(t)$, the graph of h is the graph of f after a vertical stretch by a factor of 4. Both graphs are identified in Figure 7.1-5.

Example 5   Reflection and Vertical Stretch

Graph $g(t) = -\frac{1}{2} \sin t$ on the interval $[-2\pi, 2\pi]$.

Solution

The graph of g is the graph of $f(t) = \sin t$ reflected across the x-axis and compressed vertically by a factor of $\frac{1}{2}$, as shown in Figure 7.1-6.

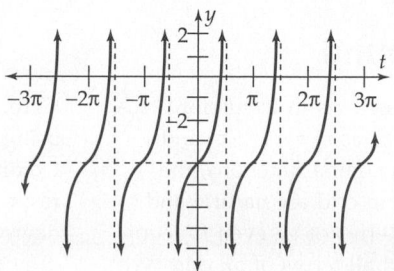

Figure 7.1-6

Example 6   Vertical Shift

Graph $h(t) = \tan t + 5$ on the interval $[-3\pi, 3\pi]$.

Solution

The graph of h is the graph of $f(t) = \tan t$ shifted up 5 units.

Example 6

Graph $h(t) = \tan t - 4$ on the interval $[-3\pi, 3\pi]$.
The graph of h is the graph of $f(t) = \tan t$ shifted down 4 units.

Example 3

State all values of t for which $\tan t$ is 1.

$t = \frac{\pi}{4} + k\pi$, where k is any integer

Example 4

List the transformation needed to change the graph of $f(t) = \cos t$ into the graph of $h(t) = 2 \cos t$. Graph both equations on the same screen. The graph of h is the graph of $f(t) = \cos t$ after a vertical stretch by a factor of 2.

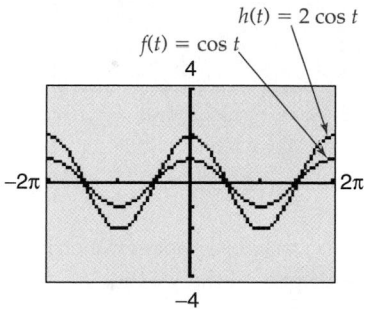

Example 5

Graph $g(t) = -\frac{1}{3} \sin t$ on the interval $[-2\pi, 2\pi]$.

The graph of g is the graph of f reflected across the x-axis and compressed vertically by a factor of $\frac{1}{3}$.

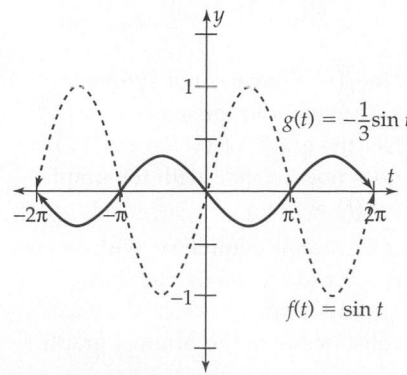

For the **Graphing Exploration,** students should use either a ZOOM TRIG feature or function mode, radian mode, and windows sufficient to show complete graphs. The windows used below are $-2\pi \le x \le 2\pi$ and $-3 \le y \le 3$.

Solution to the **Graphing Exploration:**

1.

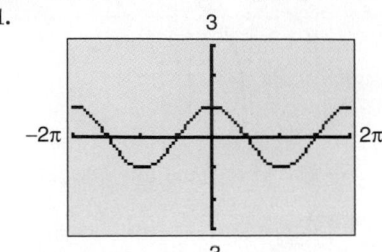

Yes, $f(t) = \cos t$ is symmetric with respect to the y-axis.
Yes, the graph of $g(t) = \cos(-t)$ appears to coincide with the graph of $f(t) = \cos t$.

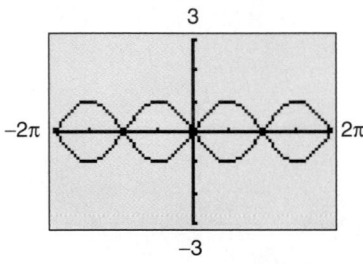

No, $f(t) = \sin t$ is not symmetric with respect to the y-axis.
No, the graph of $g(t) = \sin(-t)$ does not coincide with the graph of $f(t) = \sin t$.

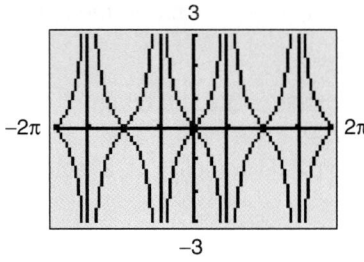

No, $f(t) = \tan t$ is not symmetric with respect to the y-axis.
No, the graph of $g(t) = \tan(-t)$ does not coincide with the graph of $f(t) = \tan t$.

2. If a graph is symmetric with respect to the y-axis, the image after reflecting it across the y-axis coincides with the original graph.

Figure 7.1-7

NOTE For a complete discussion of symmetry and odd and even functions, see *Excursion* 3.4.A.

Even and Odd Functions

Trigonometric functions can be classified as odd or even as determined by their symmetry.

Even Functions

A graph is *symmetric with respect to the y-axis* if the part of the graph on the right side of the y-axis is the mirror image of the part on the left side of the y-axis.

> **Graphing Exploration**
>
> **1.** For each pair of functions f and g below, answer the following questions.
>
> $$f(t) = \cos t \quad \text{and} \quad g(t) = \cos(-t)$$
> $$f(t) = \sin t \quad \text{and} \quad g(t) = \sin(-t)$$
> $$f(t) = \tan t \quad \text{and} \quad g(t) = \tan(-t)$$
>
> - Is f symmetric with respect to the y-axis?
> - Does the graph of g appear to coincide with the graph of f?
>
> **2.** If a graph is symmetric with respect to the y-axis, describe the graph after a reflection across the y-axis.

A function f whose graph is symmetric with respect to the y-axis is called an **even function.**

Even Function ○

> A function f is *even* if
>
> $f(-x) = f(x)$ **for every x in the domain of f.**
>
> **The graph of an even function is symmetric with respect to the y-axis.**

Math Background

The even and odd functions in Excursion 3.4.A were polynomials such as $y = x^4 + x^2$ and $y = x^3 + 2x$. For polynomial functions, the classifications even and odd are natural and intuitive because all terms of an even function have even degree and all terms of an odd function have odd degree.

Here, we classify sine, cosine, and tangent by using the same definitions stated in the Excursion. The definitions use symmetry with respect to an axis; they are not dependent on degree.

For example, $f(t) = \cos t$ is an even function because

$$\cos(-t) = \cos t \text{ for every } t \text{ in the domain of } f(t) = \cos t.$$

Odd Functions

If a graph is *symmetric with respect to the origin*, then whenever (x, y) is on the graph, $(-x, -y)$ is also on the graph. A function f whose graph is symmetric with respect to the origin is called an **odd function.**

Odd Function

> A function f is *odd* if
>
> $$f(-x) = -f(x) \text{ for every } x \text{ in the domain of } f.$$
>
> **The graph of an odd function is symmetric with respect to the origin.**

For example, $f(t) = \sin t$ and $g(t) = \tan t$ are odd functions because

$$\sin(-t) = -\sin t \text{ for every } t \text{ in the domain of } f(t) = \sin t$$
$$\tan(-t) = -\tan t \text{ for every } t \text{ in the domain of } g(t) = \tan t.$$

Summary of the Properties of Sine, Cosine, and Tangent Functions

Function	Symbol	Domain	Range	Period	Even/Odd
sine	$f(t) = \sin t$	all real numbers	all real numbers from -1 to 1, inclusive	2π	odd
cosine	$f(t) = \cos t$	all real numbers	all real numbers from -1 to 1, inclusive	2π	even
tangent	$f(t) = \tan t$	all real numbers except odd multiples of $\dfrac{\pi}{2}$	all real numbers	π	odd

Exercises 7.1

In Exercises 1–6, graph each function on the given interval.

1. $f(t) = \sin t; [2\pi, 6\pi]$

2. $g(t) = \cos t; [\pi, 3\pi]$

3. $h(t) = \tan t; [\pi, 2\pi]$

4. $f(t) = \sin t; [-5\pi, -3\pi]$

5. $g(t) = \cos t; \left[\dfrac{7\pi}{6}, \dfrac{7\pi}{2}\right]$

6. $h(t) = \tan t; \left[\dfrac{5\pi}{3}, 3\pi\right]$

7. For what values of t on the interval $[-2\pi, 2\pi]$ is $\sin t = 1$? $-\dfrac{3\pi}{2}, \dfrac{\pi}{2}$

8. For what values of t on the interval $[-2\pi, 2\pi]$ is $\cos t = 0$? $-\dfrac{3\pi}{2}, -\dfrac{\pi}{2}, \dfrac{\pi}{2}, \dfrac{3\pi}{2}$

9. What is the maximum value of $g(t) = \cos t$? **1**

10. What is the minimum value of $f(t) = \sin t$? **−1**

Real-World Application

Graphs of trigonometric functions and their transformations can be used to model natural and man-made phenomena. The graph in Figure 7.1-7 on page 482 is a transformation of the tangent function. A different transformation of the tangent function graph is used in Exercise 61 to model the position of a rotating beam of light. That graph is then used to estimate the position at various times as the beam rotates.

Exercises 7.1

ANSWERS

1.

2.

3.

4.

5.

6.

17. $-\frac{7\pi}{4} < t < -\frac{3\pi}{2}$, $-\frac{3\pi}{4} < t < -\frac{\pi}{2}$, $\frac{\pi}{4} < t < \frac{\pi}{2}$, and $\frac{5\pi}{4} < t < \frac{3\pi}{2}$

18. $-\frac{3\pi}{2} < t < \pi$, $-\frac{\pi}{2} < t < 0$, $\frac{\pi}{2} < t < \pi$, and $\frac{3\pi}{2} < t < 2\pi$

19. all values on the interval $[\pi, 2\pi]$ except $\frac{3\pi}{2}$

20. $t = 0 + n\pi$, where n is any integer

21. $t = \frac{\pi}{4} + 2n\pi$ or $t = \frac{3\pi}{4} + 2n\pi$, where n is any integer

22. $t = n\pi$, where n is any integer

23. $t = \frac{2\pi}{3} + 2n\pi$ or $t = \frac{4\pi}{3} + 2n\pi$, where n is any integer

24. $t = \frac{\pi}{4} + n\pi$, where n is any integer

25. $t = \frac{4\pi}{3} + 2n\pi$ or $t = \frac{5\pi}{3} + 2n\pi$, where n is any integer

26. $t = \frac{\pi}{2} + n\pi$, where n is any integer

27. $t = \frac{\pi}{6} + 2n\pi$ or $t = \frac{11\pi}{6} + 2n\pi$, where n is any integer

28. $t = \frac{\pi}{2} + 2n\pi$, where n is any integer

29. $t = \frac{\pi}{6} + 2n\pi$ or $t = \frac{5\pi}{6} + 2n\pi$, where n is any integer

30. $t = \frac{5\pi}{6} + n\pi$, where n is any integer

31. $t = \frac{3\pi}{4} + 2n\pi$ or $t = \frac{5\pi}{4} + 2n\pi$, where n is any integer

32. $t = \pi + 2n\pi$, where n is any integer

33. $t = \frac{\pi}{3} + n\pi$, where n is any integer

34. Shift the graph of f vertically 2 units downward. domain: all real numbers; range: $-3 \leq g(t) \leq -1$

35. Reflect the graph of f across the horizontal axis. domain: all real numbers; range: $-1 \leq g(t) \leq 1$

36. Reflect the graph of f across the horizontal axis, then stretch the resulting graph away from the horizontal axis by a factor of 3. domain: all real numbers; range $-3 \leq g(t) \leq 3$

37. Shift the graph of f vertically 5 units upward. domain: all real numbers except odd multiples of $\frac{\pi}{2}$; range: all real numbers

---

11. For what values of t on the interval $[-2\pi, 2\pi]$ does the graph of $h(t) = \tan t$ have vertical asymptotes? $-\frac{3\pi}{2}, -\frac{\pi}{2}, \frac{\pi}{2}, \frac{3\pi}{2}$

12. What is the y-intercept of the graph of $f(t) = \sin t$? **0**

13. What is the y-intercept of the graph of $g(t) = \cos t$? **1**

14. What is the y-intercept of the graph of $h(t) = \tan t$? **0**

15. For what values of t on the interval $[-\pi, \pi]$ is $f(t) = \sin t$ increasing? $-\frac{\pi}{2} \leq t \leq \frac{\pi}{2}$

16. For what values of t on the interval $[-3\pi, -\pi]$ is $g(t) = \cos t$ decreasing? $-2\pi \leq t \leq -\pi$

17. For what values of t on the interval $[-2\pi, 2\pi]$ is $\tan t$ greater than 1?

18. For what values of t on the interval $[-2\pi, 2\pi]$ is $\tan t$ less than 0?

19. For what values of t on the interval $[\pi, 2\pi]$ is $h(t) = \tan t$ increasing?

In Exercises 20–33, find all the exact t-values for which the given statement is true.

20. $\tan t = 0$

21. $\sin t = \frac{\sqrt{2}}{2}$

22. $\sin t = 0$

23. $\cos t = -\frac{1}{2}$

24. $\tan t = 1$

25. $\sin t = -\frac{\sqrt{3}}{2}$

26. $\cos t = 0$

27. $\cos t = \frac{\sqrt{3}}{2}$

28. $\sin t = 1$

29. $\sin t = \frac{1}{2}$

30. $\tan t = -\frac{\sqrt{3}}{3}$

31. $\cos t = -\frac{\sqrt{2}}{2}$

32. $\cos t = -1$

33. $\tan t = \sqrt{3}$

In Exercises 34–43, list the transformations that change the graph of f into the graph of g. State the domain and range of g.

34. $f(t) = \cos t$; $\quad g(t) = \cos t - 2$

35. $f(t) = \cos t$; $\quad g(t) = -\cos t$

---

36. $f(t) = \sin t$; $\quad g(t) = -3 \sin t$

37. $f(t) = \tan t$; $\quad g(t) = \tan t + 5$

38. $f(t) = \tan t$; $\quad g(t) = -\tan t$

39. $f(t) = \cos t$; $\quad g(t) = 3 \cos t$

40. $f(t) = \sin t$; $\quad g(t) = -2 \sin t$

41. $f(t) = \sin t$; $\quad g(t) = 3 \sin t + 2$

42. $f(t) = \cos t$; $\quad g(t) = 5 \cos t + 3$

43. $f(t) = \sin t$; $\quad g(t) = \sin t + 3$

In Exercises 44–48, sketch the graph of each function.

44. $f(t) = -2 \cos t$ $\qquad$ **45.** $f(t) = 5 \sin t + 1$

46. $f(t) = 4 \tan t$ $\qquad$ **47.** $f(t) = -\frac{1}{4} \cos t$

48. $f(t) = 3 \sin t - \frac{1}{2}$

In Exercises 49–54, match a graph to a function. Only one graph is possible for each function.

49. $h(t) = -2 \tan t$ **d** $\qquad$ **50.** $g(t) = 2.5 \cos t$ **c**

51. $h(t) = -\sin t + 1$ **e** $\qquad$ **52.** $f(t) = -2.5 \sin t$ **a**

53. $g(t) = 3 \tan t - 1$ **f** $\qquad$ **54.** $f(t) = -\cos t + 1$ **b**

a.

b.

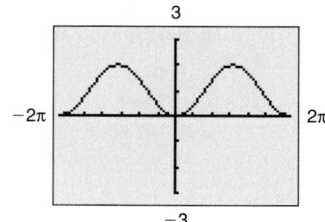

---

38. Reflect the graph of f across the horizontal axis. domain: all real numbers except odd multiples of $\frac{\pi}{2}$; range: all real numbers

39. Stretch the graph of f away from the horizontal axis by a factor of 3. domain: all real numbers; range: $-3 \leq g(t) \leq 3$

40. Reflect the graph of f across the horizontal axis, then stretch the resulting graph away from the horizontal axis by a factor of 2. domain: all real numbers; range: $-2 \leq g(t) \leq 2$

41. Stretch the graph of f away from the horizontal axis by a factor of 3, then shift the resulting graph vertically 2 units upward. domain: all real numbers; range: $-1 \leq g(t) \leq 5$

c.

d.

e.

f.

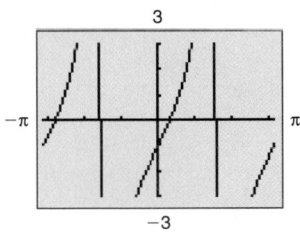

55. Fill the blanks with "even" or "odd" so that the resulting statement is true. Then prove the statement by using an appropriate identity. *Excursion* 3.4.A may be helpful.
a. $f(t) = \sin t$ is an ___ function. **odd; sin $(-t) = -\sin t$**
b. $g(t) = \cos t$ is an ___ function. **even; cos$(-t) = \cos t$**
c. $h(t) = \tan t$ is an ___ function. **odd; tan $(-t) = -\tan t$**
d. $f(t) = t \sin t$ is an ___ function. **even; sin $(-t) = -\sin t$**
e. $g(t) = t + \tan t$ is an ___ function. **odd; tan $(-t) = -\tan t$**

In Exercises 56–59, find tan t, where the terminal side of an angle of t radians lies on the given line.

56. $y = 1.5x$
1.5
58. $y = 0.32x$
0.32

57. $y = 1.4x$
1.4
59. $y = 11x$
11

60. Scientists theorize that the average temperature at a specific location fluctuates from cooler to warmer and then to cooler again over a long period of time. The graph shows a theoretical prediction of the average summer temperature for the last 150,000 years for a location in Alaska.

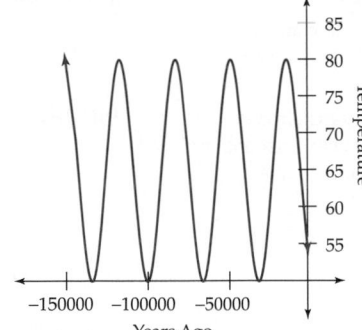

highest temperature = 80; lowest = 50
a. Find the highest and lowest temperature represented.
b. Over what time interval does the temperature repeat the cycle? **about 34,558 years**
c. What is the estimated average summer temperature at the present time? **about 55**

61. A rotating beacon is located at point P, 5 yards from a wall. The distance d, as measured along the wall, where the light shines is given by

$$d = 5 \tan 2\pi t$$

where t is time measured in seconds since the beacon began to rotate. When $t = 0$, the light is aimed at point A. When the beacon is aimed to the right of A, the distance d is positive, and when it is aimed to the left of A, the value of d is negative.

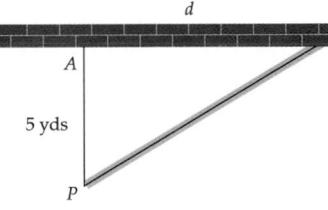

Graph the function and estimate the value of d for the following times.
a. $t = 0$ **b.** $t = 0.5$
c. $t = 0.7$ **d.** $t = 1.4$
e. Determine the position of the beacon when $t = 0.25$ and discuss the corresponding value of d for that value of t.

42. Stretch the graph of f away from the horizontal axis by a factor of 5, then shift the resulting graph vertically 3 units upward. domain: all real numbers; range: $-2 \le g(t) \le 8$

43. Shift the graph of f vertically 3 units upward. domain: all real numbers; range: $2 \le g(t) \le 4$

44.

45.

46.

47.

48.

61.

a. 0

b. 0

c. ≈15.4 yards

d. ≈−3.6 yards

e. When $t = 0.25$, d is undefined. The beam is parallel to the wall at this time.

Section

7.2 Graphs of the Cosecant, Secant, and Cotangent Functions

Teaching Notes

For the **Graphing Explorations**, remind students to use function mode; the variable on the calculator will be x.

Solution to the **Graphing Exploration**:

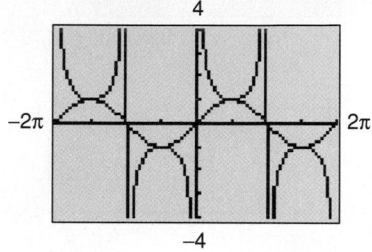

Possible answers to how the graphs are alike:

- They are positive over the same intervals and negative over the same intervals.
- They have the same period, 2π.

Possible answers to how the graphs are different:

- Every point where the graphs touch represents a local maximum for one graph and a local minimum for the other graph.
- f is increasing on intervals where g is decreasing, and vice versa.
- f is concave down on intervals where g is concave up, and vice versa.

You might want to have students use the TABLE feature on their calculators to verify that the **Graph of the Cosecant Function** has asymptotes at the zeros of the sine function. Have them enter $Y_1 = \sin x$, $Y_2 = 1/\sin x$, use $\Delta Tbl = .001$ as the TABLE increment, and set TblStart $= \pi$.

X	Y1	Y2
3.1416	0	ERROR
3.1426	-1E-3	-1000
3.1436	-.002	-500
3.1446	-.003	-333.3
3.1456	-.004	-250
3.1466	-.005	-200
3.1476	-.006	-166.7

X=3.14159265359

7.2 Graphs of the Cosecant, Secant, and Cotangent Functions

Objectives

- Graph the cosecant, secant, and cotangent functions
- Graph transformations of the cosecant, secant, and cotangent graphs

The graphs of $y = \sin t$, $y = \cos t$, and $y = \tan t$ that were developed in Section 7.1 are closely related to the graphs of the reciprocal functions $y = \csc t$, $y = \sec t$, and $y = \cot t$ that are studied in this section.

Graph of the Cosecant Function

The general shape of the graph of $f(t) = \csc t$ can be determined by using the graph of the sine function and the fact that $\csc t = \dfrac{1}{\sin t}$.

> **Graphing Exploration** •
>
> Graph the two functions below on the same screen in a viewing window with $-2\pi \le t \le 2\pi$ and $-4 \le y \le 4$
>
> $$f(t) = \sin t \qquad g(t) = \frac{1}{\sin t}$$
>
> How are the graphs alike and how are they different?

Because $\sin t$ and $\csc t$ are reciprocals, $\csc t$ is not defined when $\sin t = 0$; that is, when t is an integer multiple of π. Therefore, the **domain of $f(t) = \csc t$** is all real numbers except integer multiples of π, and the graph of $f(t) = \csc t$ has vertical asymptotes at integer multiples of π.

Graph of the Cosecant Function

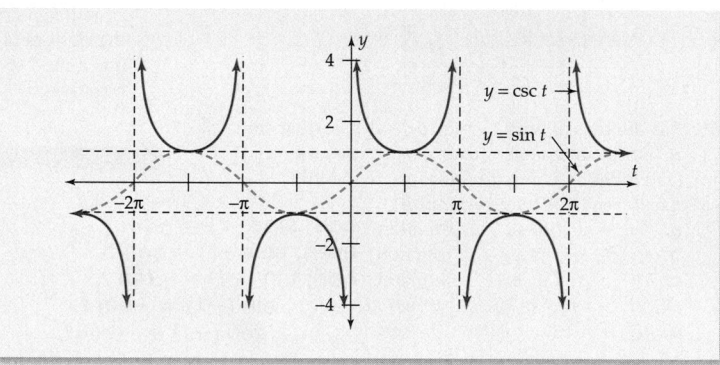

Notice that as the graph of $y = \sin t$ *increases* to a height of 1, the graph of $f(t) = \csc t$ *decreases* to a height of 1, and as the graph of $y = \sin t$ *decreases* to a height of -1, the graph of $f(t) = \csc t$ *increases* to a height of -1. The **range of** $f(t) = \csc t$ is all real numbers greater than or equal to 1 or less than or equal to -1. The period of the cosecant function is 2π.

COMMON ERROR
ALERT

Students might enter reciprocal functions incorrectly if they use calculators to verify their graphs. In **Example 1**, $Y_1 = 1/-3 \sin x$ is incorrect for $-3 \csc x$. The correct equivalent is $Y_1 = -3/\sin x$.

Example 1   Reflection and Vertical Stretch

Graph $h(t) = -3 \csc t$.

Solution

First consider the graph of $y = -3 \sin t$, which is the graph of $y = \sin t$ stretched vertically by a factor of 3 and reflected across the horizontal axis. The relationship between the graph of $y = -3 \sin t$ and that of $h(t) = -3 \csc t$ is similar to that between $y = \csc t$ and $y = \sin t$, as shown in Figure 7.2-1.

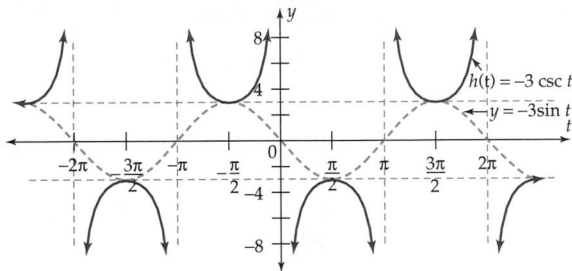

Figure 7.2-1

Graph of the Secant Function

The graph of $f(t) = \sec t$ is related to the cosine graph in the same way that the graph of $f(t) = \csc t$ is related to the sine graph.

Graphing Exploration

Graph the two functions below on the same screen in a viewing window with $-2\pi \le t \le 2\pi$ and $-4 \le y \le 4$.

$$f(t) = \cos t \qquad g(t) = \frac{1}{\cos t}$$

How are the graphs alike and how are they different?

Because $\cos t$ and $\sec t$ are reciprocals, $\sec t$ is not defined when $\cos t = 0$; that is, when t is an odd multiple of $\frac{\pi}{2}$. Therefore, the **domain of** $f(t) = \sec t$ is all real numbers except odd multiples of $\frac{\pi}{2}$, and the **range of** $f(t) = \sec t$ is all real numbers greater than or equal to 1 or less than or equal to -1. The period of the secant function is 2π.

ADDITIONAL EXAMPLES

Example 1

Graph $h(t) = -2 \csc t$.

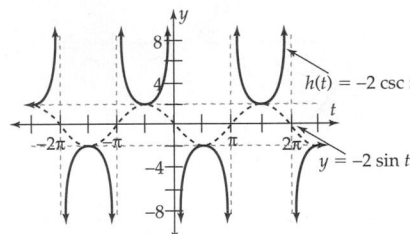

Teaching Notes

Solution to the **Graphing Exploration:**

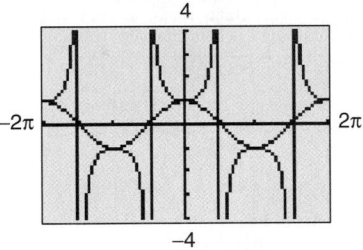

Possible answers to how the graphs are alike:

- They are positive over the same intervals and negative over the same intervals.
- They have the same period, 2π.

Possible answers to how the graphs are different:

- Every point where the graphs touch represents a local maximum for one graph and a local minimum for the other graph.
- f is increasing on intervals where g is decreasing, and vice versa.
- f is concave down on intervals where g is concave up, and vice versa.

Example Notes

To see the stretch and shift of the cosine function in **Example 2**, students can graph $Y_1 = \cos x$, $Y_2 = 2 \cos x$, and $Y_3 = 2 \cos x - 3$ on the same screen, using the window values $-2\pi \le x \le 2\pi$ and $-6 \le y \le 6$. They will see $y = \cos x$, then $y = 2 \cos x$, and then $y = 2 \cos x - 3$ graphed sequentially. The final result will be:

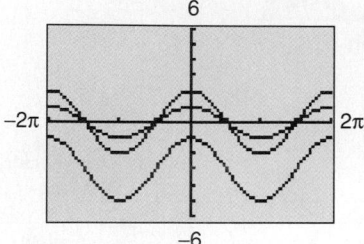

Students can verify the relationship between $y = 2 \cos t - 3$ and $y = 2 \sec t - 3$ by graphing $Y_3 = 2 \cos x - 3$ and $Y_4 = 2/\cos x - 3$. (For this, have them use $-10 \le y \le 6$.)

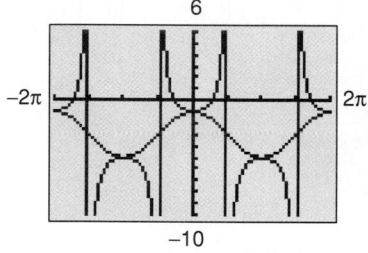

For **Example 3**, point out that cot t is the blue dotted graph in Figure 7.2-3 and the red solid graph at the top of page 489.

To see the reflection and vertical stretch of the cotangent function in Example 3, students can graph $Y_1 = \dfrac{\cos x}{\sin x}$ and $Y_2 = \dfrac{-3 \cos x}{\sin x}$.

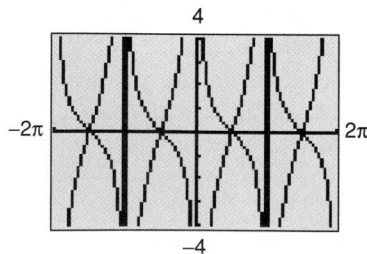

To see the horizontal shift, they can graph

$$Y_2 = \frac{-3 \cos x}{\sin x} \quad \text{and} \quad Y_3 = \frac{-3 \cos\left(x - \dfrac{\pi}{4}\right)}{\sin\left(x - \dfrac{\pi}{4}\right)}.$$

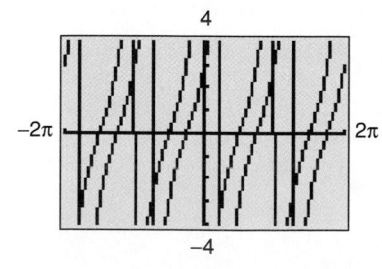

Graph of the Secant Function

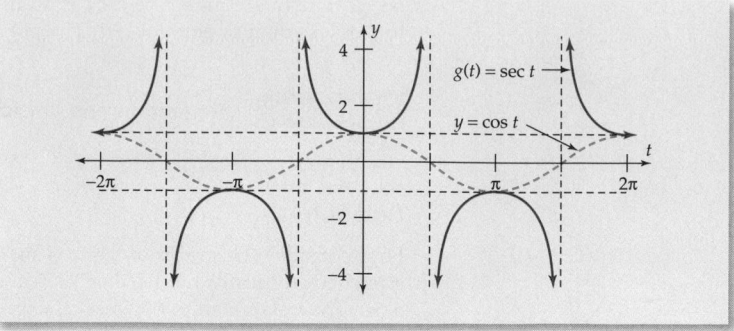

Example 2 Vertical Stretch and Vertical Shift

Graph $g(t) = 2 \sec t - 3$.

Solution

First graph $y = 2 \cos t - 3$, which is the graph of $y = \cos t$ stretched vertically by a factor of 2 and shifted down 3 units. The graphs of $g(t) = 2 \sec t - 3$ and $y = 2 \cos t - 3$ are related in the same way as the graphs of $y = \sec t$ and $y = \cos t$, as shown in Figure 7.2-2.

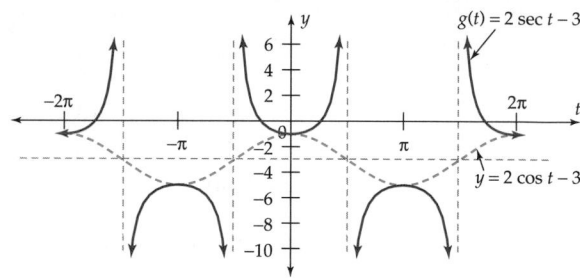

Figure 7.2-2

Graph of the Cotangent Function

Because $\cot t = \dfrac{\cos t}{\sin t}$, the graph of $f(t) = \cot t$ can be obtained by graphing the quotient

$$y = \frac{\cos t}{\sin t}.$$

The cotangent function is not defined when $\sin t = 0$, and this occurs whenever t is an integer multiple of π. Therefore the **domain of** $f(t) = \cot t$ consists of all real numbers except integer multiples of π, and the **range of** $f(t) = \cot t$ is the set of real numbers. The graph of $f(t) = \cot t$ has vertical asymptotes at integer multiples of π.

Graph of the Cotangent Function

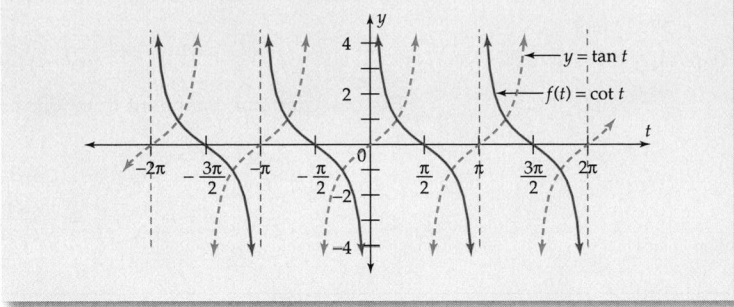

Notice that as the graph of $y = \tan t$ *increases*, the graph of $f(t) = \cot t$ *decreases*, and as the graph of $y = \tan t$ *decreases*, the graph of $f(t) = \cot t$ *increases*. The period of the cotangent function is π.

Example 3   Reflection, Vertical Stretch, and Horizontal Shift

Graph $k(t) = -3 \cot\left(t - \dfrac{\pi}{4}\right)$.

Solution

The graph of $k(t) = -3 \cot\left(t - \dfrac{\pi}{4}\right)$ is the graph of $y = \cot t$ after a horizontal shift of $\dfrac{\pi}{4}$ units to the right, a reflection across the horizontal axis, and a vertical stretch by a factor of 3. The graph of $k(t) = -3 \cot\left(t - \dfrac{\pi}{4}\right)$ is shown with the graph of $y = \cot t$ in Figure 7.2-3 below.

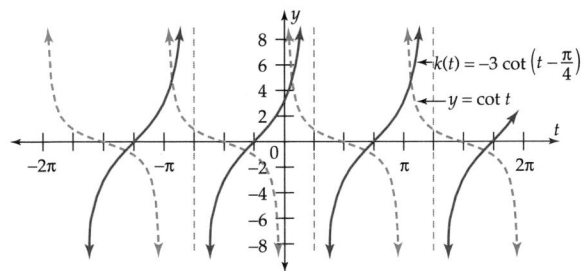

Figure 7.2-3

Even and Odd Functions

The fact that the cosecant, secant, and cotangent functions are reciprocals of the sine, cosine, and tangent functions, respectively, can be used to determine whether the functions are even or odd.

Real-World Application

The red graph in **Example 2**, Figure 7.2-2, is a transformation of the secant function. Exercise 40 contains a different transformation of the secant function. In Exercise 40 (a variation of Exercise 61 in Section 7.1), the graph of the transformed secant function is used to estimate distances at various times during the rotation of a light beam.

ADDITIONAL EXAMPLES

Example 2

Graph $g(t) = 3 \sec t + 2$.

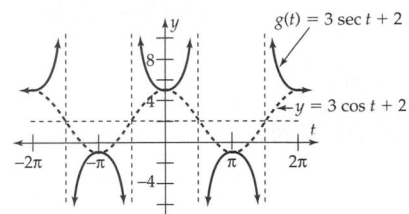

Example 3

Graph $k(t) = -4 \cot\left(t + \dfrac{\pi}{2}\right)$.

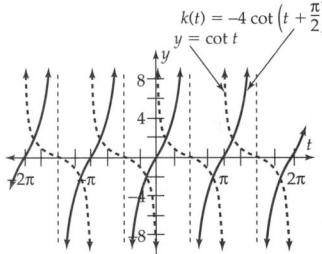

Teaching Notes

Ask students to complete the definitions of even and odd functions (pages 482–483):

A function f is even if $f(-x) =$ ___ for every x in the domain of f. The graph of an even function is symmetric with respect to the ____. $f(x)$, y-axis

A function f is odd if $f(-x) =$ ___ for every x in the domain of f. The graph of an odd function is symmetric with respect to the ____. $-f(x)$, origin

Show that the secant function is even because $f(-t) = \sec(-t) = \sec t = f(t)$.

Show that the cosecant and cotangent functions are odd because
$f(-t) = \csc(-t) = -\csc t = -f(t)$
and
$f(-t) = \cot(-t) = -\cot t = -f(t)$.

Exercises 7.2
ANSWERS

1. The graph of $s(t) = 3 \sec t - 2$ is the graph of $g(t) = \sec t$ stretched vertically by a factor of 3 and shifted down 2 units.

2. The graph of $q(t) = 5 \cot (t - 3)$ is the graph of $h(t) = \cot t$ stretched vertically by a factor of 5 and shifted 3 units to the right.

3. The graph of $m(t) = \csc(t) + 4$ is the graph of $f(t) = \csc t$ shifted 4 units up.

4. The graph of $r(t) = -2 \cot(t)$ is the graph of $h(t) = \cot t$ reflected across the horizontal and vertical axes and stretched vertically by a factor of 2.

5. The graph of $p(t) = \frac{1}{2} \sec t + 1$ is the graph of $g(t) = \sec t$ compressed vertically by a factor of $\frac{1}{2}$ and shifted up 1 unit.

6. The graph of $k(t) = -2 \csc t$ is the graph of $f(t) = \csc t$ reflected across the horizontal axis, and stretched vertically by a factor of 2.

7. The graph of $q(t) = \sec(-t) - 8$ is the graph of $g(t) = \sec t$ reflected across the vertical axis, and shifted 8 units down.

8. The graph of $s(t) = 5 + \cot (t + 2)$ is the graph of $h(t) = \cot t$ shifted 5 units up and 2 units to the left.

The secant function is an even function, as shown below.

$$\sec(-t) = \frac{1}{\cos(-t)} = \frac{1}{\cos t} = \sec t$$

The cosecant and cotangent functions are odd functions.

$$\csc(-t) = \frac{1}{\sin(-t)} = \frac{1}{-\sin t} = -\frac{1}{\sin t} = -\csc t$$

$$\cot(-t) = \frac{\cos(-t)}{\sin(-t)} = \frac{\cos t}{-\sin t} = -\frac{\cos t}{\sin t} = -\cot t$$

\multicolumn{7}{c}{**Summary of the Properties of Secant, Cosecant, and Cotangent Functions**}						
Function	**Symbol**	**Domain**	**Range**	**Period**	**Even/Odd**
secant	$f(t) = \sec t$	all real numbers except odd multiples of $\frac{\pi}{2}$	all real numbers less than or equal to -1 or greater than or equal to 1	2π	even
cosecant	$f(t) = \csc t$	all real numbers except multiples of π	all real numbers less than or equal to -1 or greater than or equal to 1	2π	odd
cotangent	$f(t) = \cot t$	all real numbers except multiples of π	all real numbers	π	odd

Exercises 7.2

In Exercises 1–10, describe the transformations that change the graph of $f(t) = \csc t, g(t) = \sec t,$ or $h(t) = \cot t$ into the graph of the given function.

1. $s(t) = 3 \sec t - 2$
2. $q(t) = 5 \cot(t - 3)$
3. $m(t) = \csc(t) + 4$
4. $r(t) = -2 \cot(t)$
5. $p(t) = \frac{1}{2} \sec t + 1$
6. $k(t) = -2 \csc t$
7. $q(t) = \sec(-t) - 8$
8. $s(t) = 5 + \cot(t + 2)$
9. $v(t) = \pi \csc t$
10. $j(t) = -\frac{1}{4} \sec(t)$

In Exercises 11–17, state the rule of a function g whose graph is the given transformation of the graph of f.

11. $f(t) = \sec t$ stretched vertically by a factor of 3 and shifted 1 unit to the left
 $g(t) = 3 \sec (t + 1)$

12. $f(t) = \csc t$ compressed vertically by a factor of 0.5 and shifted 1 unit up
 $g(t) = 0.5 \csc t + 1$

13. $f(t) = \sec t$ reflected across the horizontal axis and compressed vertically by a factor of $\frac{1}{4}$
 $g(t) = -\frac{1}{4} \sec t$

14. $f(t) = \cot t$ reflected across the vertical axis and shifted down 2 units
 $g(t) = \cot (-t) - 2$

15. $f(t) = \csc t$ shifted $\frac{\pi}{2}$ units to the right and 5 units down $g(t) = \csc \left(t - \frac{\pi}{2}\right) - 5$

16. $f(t) = \csc t$ compressed vertically by a factor of 0.75
 $g(t) = 0.75 \csc t$

9. The graph of $v(t) = \pi \csc t$ is the graph of $f(t) = \csc t$ reflected across the horizontal axis and stretched vertically by a factor of π.

10. The graph of $j(t) = -\frac{1}{4} \sec(t)$ is the graph of $g(t) = \sec t$ reflected across the horizontal axis and compressed vertically by a factor of $\frac{1}{4}$.

17. $f(t) = \cot t$ reflected across the vertical axis and across the horizontal axis $g(t) = -\cot(-t)$

In Exercises 18–21, match graph a, b, c, or d with each function.

18. $f(t) = \frac{1}{2}\cot t - 1$

a

19. $f(t) = \frac{1}{2}\cot t + 1$

d

20. $f(t) = 2\cot t + 1$

c

21. $f(t) = 2\cot t - 1$

b

In Exercises 22–25, match graph a or b with each function.

a.

b.

c.

d.

a.

b.

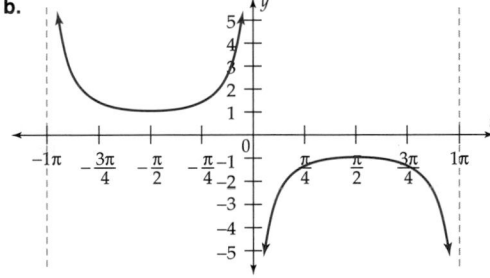

22. $f(t) = -\csc t$

b

23. $f(t) = \csc t$

a

24. $f(t) = \csc(-t)$

b

25. $f(t) = -\csc(-t)$

a

In Exercises 26–29, match graph a or b with each function.

a.

34.

35.

36.

37.

38.

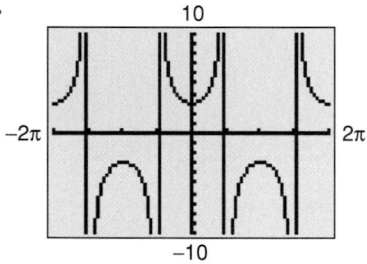

39. Look at the graph of $y = \sec t$ on page 488. If you draw in the line $y = t$, it will pass through $\left(-\frac{\pi}{2}, -\frac{\pi}{2}\right)$ and $\left(\frac{\pi}{2}, \frac{\pi}{2}\right)$, and obviously will not intersect the graph of $y = \sec t$ when $-\frac{\pi}{2} \le t \le \frac{\pi}{2}$. But it will intersect each part of the graph that lies above the horizontal axis, to the right of $t = \frac{\pi}{2}$; it will also intersect

b.

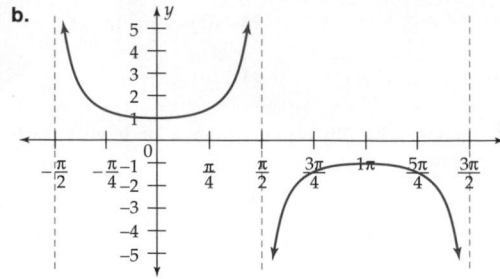

26. $f(t) = -\sec(-t)$
a
28. $f(t) = \sec(t)$
b

27. $f(t) = \sec(-t)$
b
29. $f(t) = -\sec(t)$
a

In Exercises 30–33, match graph a or b with each function.

a.

b.

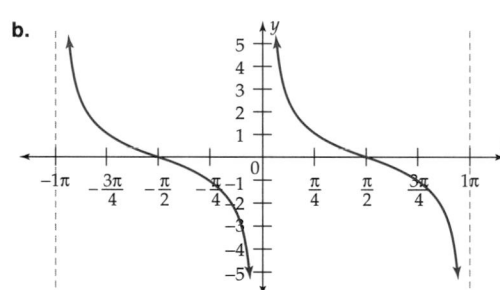

30. $f(t) = -\cot(-t)$
b
32. $f(t) = -\cot(t)$
a

31. $f(t) = \cot(-t)$
a
33. $f(t) = \cot(t)$
b

In Exercises 34–38, graph at least one cycle of the given function.

34. $f(t) = \sec 2t$

35. $f(t) = -\cot 3t + 4$

36. $f(t) = 5 \csc\left(t - \frac{\pi}{2}\right)$

37. $f(t) = \frac{3}{4} \csc \frac{t}{2}$

38. $f(t) = -3 \sec(t + \pi)$

39. *Critical Thinking* Show graphically that the equation $\sec t = t$ has infinitely many solutions, but none between $-\frac{\pi}{2}$ and $\frac{\pi}{2}$.

40. *Critical Thinking* A rotating beacon is positioned 5 yards from a wall at P. In the figure, the distance a is given by

$$a = 5 \left|\sec 2\pi t\right|,$$

where t is the number of seconds since the beacon began to rotate.

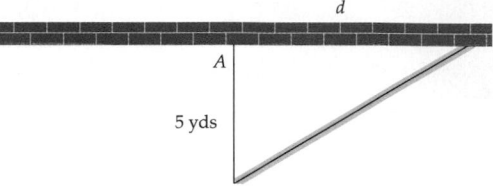

a. Use the graph of a as a function of t to find a for the following times.

$$t = 0 \qquad t = 0.75 \qquad t = 1$$

b. For what values of t is $a = 5$?
c. How fast is the beacon rotating?

those parts that lie below the horizontal axis, to the left of $-\frac{\pi}{2}$. The first coordinate of each of these infinitely many intersection points will be a solution of $\sec t = t$.

40. a. 5; undefined; 5

  b. all values of t that are multiples of 0.5

  c. 2 rotations per second

7.3 Periodic Graphs and Amplitude

Objectives

*   State the period and amplitude (if any) given the function rule or the graph of a sine, cosine, or tangent function

*   Use the period and amplitude (if any) to sketch the graph of a sine, cosine, or tangent function

A surprisingly large number of physical phenomena can be described by functions like the following:

$$f(t) = 5 \sin(3t + 4) \quad \text{and} \quad g(t) = -4 \cos(0.5t + 1) + 3$$

In this section and in the next, the graphs of such functions will be analyzed. All of these functions are periodic and their graphs consist of a series of identical *waves*. A single *wave* of the graph is called a **cycle**. The length of each cycle is the period of the function.

sine cycle

Figure 7.3-1

Every cycle for the sine function resembles the graph of $f(t) = \sin t$ from 0 to 2π, as shown in Figure 7.3-1.

*   beginning at a point midway between its maximum and minimum value
*   rising to its maximum value
*   falling to its minimum value
*   returning to the beginning point

Every cycle repeats the same pattern.

cosine cycle

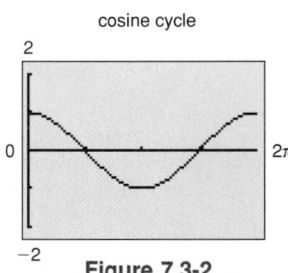

Figure 7.3-2

Similarly, every cycle for the cosine function resembles the graph of $g(t) = \cos t$ from 0 to 2π, as shown in Figure 7.3-2.

7.3 Periodic Graphs and Amplitude

Real-World Application

A phenomenon that can be described by a sine function occurs every time you turn on a radio. In radio vocabulary, AM indicates Amplitude Modulation and FM indicates Frequency Modulation.

The current generated by an AM radio transmitter is given by a function of the form $f(t) = A \sin 2000\pi mt$, where A represents amplitude, m is the location on the broadcast dial, and t is measured in seconds. By modulating (changing) the amplitude, the sound information in the radio signal can be controlled.

In Exercise 65, you are asked to find the period of $f(t) = A \sin 2000\pi mt$ for a radio station at 900 on the AM broadcast dial.

Teaching Notes

Discuss the meanings of *wave, cycle,* and *period:*

*   A wave is the same as a cycle. It is a portion of a graph that shows a complete pattern.
*   A period is a number; it is the horizontal distance required for one cycle.

Also make sure students understand that only one wave (not two) is shown in Figure 7.3-1.

Math Background

Students might use the term *wavelength* in science. Explain that the math term for wavelength is period. In Figure 7.3-1, we say the *period* is 2π, while a physicist might say the *wavelength* is 2π.

In calculus, students will learn how to use a definite integral to represent an *arc length*. In Figure 7.3-1, if you were able to use a piece of string to exactly fit on the curve, and then straighten the string and measure it, you would have the arc length of the curve.

Solution to the **Graphing Exploration:**

$$f(t) = \cos 4t$$
number of cycles: 4
period: $\dfrac{2\pi}{4} = \dfrac{\pi}{2}$

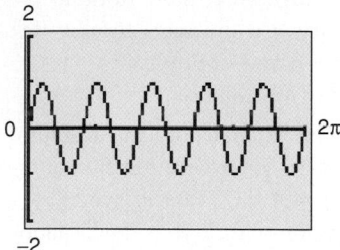

$$h(t) = \sin 5t$$
number of cycles: 5
period: $\dfrac{2\pi}{5}$

Ask students to explain how they found the period of each function in the Graphing Exploration.
For $f(t) = \cos 4t$, divide 2π by 4.
For $h(t) = \sin 5t$, divide 2π by 5.

The discussion at the bottom of the page uses the function $g(t) = \sin 3t$ to illustrate the **Period of sin bt.** If students need help in understanding why the period of $\sin 3t$ is $\dfrac{2\pi}{3}$, set up the following table:

t	$3t$	$\sin 3t$
?	0	0
⋮	⋮	⋮
?	2π	0

Explain that $3t$ is "what we are taking the sine of," so a cycle beginning at 0 is complete when $3t = 2\pi$. Then ask how we can find the corresponding values of t.   Divide each value of $3t$ by 3.
Show $0 \div 3 = 0$ and $2\pi \div 3 = \dfrac{2\pi}{3}$.
This shows that a complete cycle occurs as t increases from 0 to $\dfrac{2\pi}{3}$.

- beginning at its maximum value
- falling to its minimum value
- returning to the beginning point

Again, every cycle repeats the same pattern.

Period

Before proceeding to the discussion about functions that have different periods, it will be helpful to consider functions of the form

$$f(t) = \sin bt \qquad \text{and} \qquad g(t) = \cos bt$$

where b is a constant. The constant b changes the period of the sine or cosine function. Its effect on the graph is to increase or decrease the length of each cycle.

> **Graphing Exploration** ●
>
> Graph each function below, one at a time, in a viewing window with $0 \le t \le 2\pi$. Answer the questions that follow for each function.
>
> $$f(t) = \cos 4t \qquad h(t) = \sin 5t$$
>
> Determine the number of complete cycles between 0 and 2π.
>
> Find the period, or length of one complete cycle. *Hint:* Use division.

The exploration above suggests the following rule.

Period of sin bt and cos bt

> If $b > 0$, then the graph of either
>
> $$f(t) = \sin bt \qquad \text{or} \qquad g(t) = \cos bt$$
>
> makes b complete cycles between 0 and 2π, and each function has a period of $\dfrac{2\pi}{b}$.

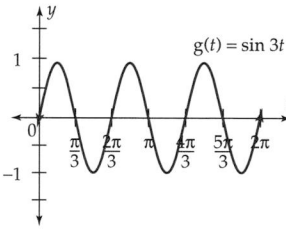

Figure 7.3-3

The graph of $h(t) = \sin t$ completes one cycle as t takes on values from 0 to 2π. Similarly, the graph of $g(t) = \sin 3t$ completes one cycle as $3t$ takes on values from 0 to 2π.

$$\text{When } 3t = 0, t \text{ must be } 0.$$

$$\text{When } 3t = 2\pi, t \text{ must be } \dfrac{2\pi}{3}.$$

Therefore, the graph of $g(t) = \sin 3t$ completes one cycle as t takes on values from 0 to $\dfrac{2\pi}{3}$, as shown in Figure 7.3-3.

Example 1 Determining Period

Determine the period of each function.

a. $k(t) = \cos 3t$

b. $f(t) = \sin \dfrac{t}{2}$

Solution

a. The function $k(t) = \cos 3t$ has a period of $\dfrac{2\pi}{b} = \dfrac{2\pi}{3}$, as shown in Figure 7.3-4.

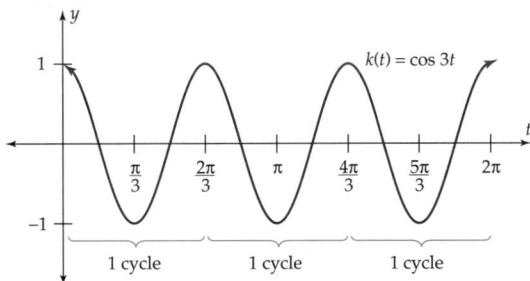

Figure 7.3-4

b. Rewrite $f(t) = \sin \dfrac{t}{2}$ as $f(t) = \sin\left(\dfrac{1}{2}t\right)$. The function $f(t) = \sin\left(\dfrac{1}{2}t\right)$ has a period of $\dfrac{2\pi}{b} = \dfrac{2\pi}{\frac{1}{2}} = 4\pi$, as shown in Figure 7.3-5.

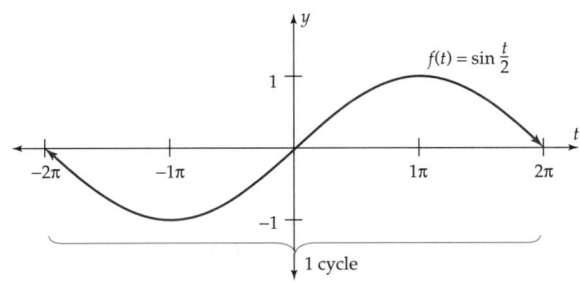

Figure 7.3-5

ADDITIONAL EXAMPLES

Example 1

Determine the period of each function.

a. $k(t) = \cos 5t$

period: $\dfrac{2\pi}{5}$

b. $f(t) = \sin \dfrac{t}{3}$

period: $\dfrac{2\pi}{\frac{1}{3}} = 6\pi$

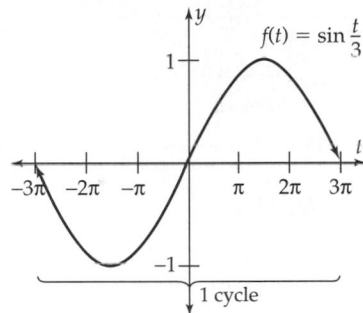

Teaching Notes

After completing **Example 1,** make sure students realize that, for $f(t) = \sin bt$ or $g(t) = \cos bt$:

• When $b > 1$, the function *repeats itself more frequently* than its parent function on any given interval (In **1a,** $k(t) = \cos 3t$ repeats itself more frequently than $y = \cos t$).

• When $b < 1$, the function *repeats itself less frequently* than its parent function on any given interval (In **1b,** $f(t) = \sin \dfrac{1}{2}t$ repeats itself less frequently than $y = \sin t$).

Note that changes in the period follow the rules for Horizontal Stretches and Compressions on page 179.

Teaching Notes

Solution to the **Graphing Exploration:**

$f(t) = \tan 3t$
number of cycles: 3
period: $\frac{\pi}{3}$

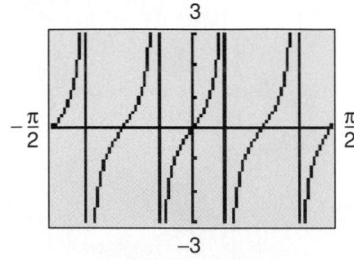

$g(t) = \tan 4t$
number of cycles: 4
period: $\frac{\pi}{4}$

Example Notes

For **Example 2,** refer students to the following phrase in the **Period of tan bt** box:

$f(t) = \tan bt$ makes b complete cycles between $-\frac{\pi}{2}$ and $\frac{\pi}{2}$.

For **2a,** $k(t) = \tan 2t$ makes 2 complete cycles between $-\frac{\pi}{2}$ and $\frac{\pi}{2}$. Therefore, as stated in the Solution, $k(t)$ makes 1 complete cycle between $-\frac{\pi}{4}$ and $\frac{\pi}{4}$.

COMMON ERROR ALERT

Students might use 2π instead of π to find the period of a tangent function (because 2π is used for sine and cosine functions). Remind them that:

- The period of sin bt and cos bt is $\frac{2\pi}{b}$.

- The period of tan bt is $\frac{\pi}{b}$.

CAUTION

A calculator may not produce an accurate graph of $f(t) = \sin bt$ or $g(t) = \cos bt$ for large values of b. For instance, the graph of

$$f(t) = \sin 50t$$

has 50 complete cycles between 0 and 2π, but that is not what your calculator will show. (try it!)

Graphing Exploration ●

Graph each function below, one at a time, in a viewing window with $-\frac{\pi}{2} \le t \le \frac{\pi}{2}$. Answer the questions that follow for each function.

$$f(t) = \tan 3t \qquad g(t) = \tan 4t$$

Determine the number of complete cycles between $-\frac{\pi}{2}$ and $\frac{\pi}{2}$.

Find the period, that is, the length of one complete cycle.

The exploration above suggests the following rule.

**Period of
tan bt**
○

If $b > 0$, then the graph of

$$f(t) = \tan bt$$

makes b complete cycles between $-\frac{\pi}{2}$ and $\frac{\pi}{2}$, and the function has a period of $\frac{\pi}{b}$.

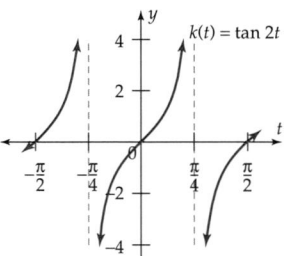

Figure 7.3-6

Example 2   Determining Period

Determine the period of each function.

a. $k(t) = \tan 2t$ **b.** $f(t) = \tan \frac{t}{3}$

Solution

a. The function $k(t) = \tan 2t$ has a period of $\frac{\pi}{b} = \frac{\pi}{2}$. It completes one cycle between $-\frac{\pi}{4}$ and $\frac{\pi}{4}$, as shown in Figure 7.3-6.

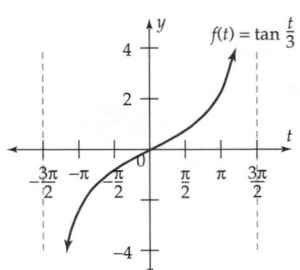

Figure 7.3-7

b. Rewrite as $f(t) = \tan \dfrac{t}{3}$ as $f(t) = \tan\left(\dfrac{1}{3}t\right)$. The function has a period of $\dfrac{\pi}{b} = \dfrac{\pi}{\frac{1}{3}} = 3\pi$, as shown in Figure 7.3-7. ∎

Amplitude

Recall from Section 3.4 that multiplying the rule of a function by a positive constant has the effect of stretching or compressing its graph vertically.

| **Example 3** | Vertical and Horizontal Stretches or Compressions |

Graph each function.

a. $g(t) = 7 \cos 3t$ **b.** $h(t) = \dfrac{1}{3} \sin \dfrac{t}{2}$

Solution

a. The function $g(t) = 7 \cos 3t$ is the function $k(t) = \cos 3t$ multiplied by 7. Consequently, the graph of g is the graph of k (see Example 1a) stretched vertically by a factor of 7.

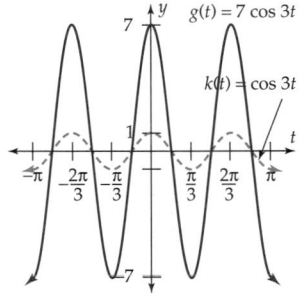

Figure 7.3-8

As Figure 7.3-8 shows, stretching the graph affects only the height of the waves in the graph, not the period of the function. So the period of g is the same as that of $k(t) = \cos 3t$, namely $\dfrac{2\pi}{b} = \dfrac{2\pi}{3}$.

b. The function $h(t) = \dfrac{1}{3} \sin \dfrac{t}{2}$ is the function $f(t) = \sin \dfrac{t}{2}$ multiplied by $\dfrac{1}{3}$. Consequently, the graph of h is the graph of f (see Example 1b) vertically compressed by a factor of $\dfrac{1}{3}$. The period of h is the same as the period of f, namely $\dfrac{2\pi}{b} = \dfrac{2\pi}{\frac{1}{2}} = 4\pi$. ∎

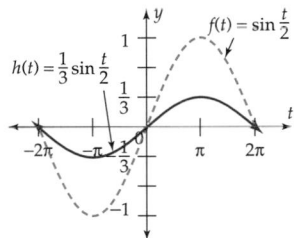

Figure 7.3-9

As the graphs in Example 3 illustrate, vertically stretching or compressing the graph affects only the height, not the period of the function.

The graph of $g(t) = 7 \cos 3t$ in Example 3 reaches a maximum value of 7 units above the horizontal axis and a minimum value of 7 units below the horizontal axis. In general, the graph of $f(t) = a \sin bt$ or $g(t) = a \cos bt$ reaches a distance of $|a|$ units above and below the horizontal axis, and is said to have an **amplitude** of $|a|$. The graph of $g(t) = 7 \cos 3t$ has an amplitude of 7.

b. $h(t) = \dfrac{1}{2} \sin \dfrac{t}{3}$

The graph of h is the graph of $f(t) = \sin \dfrac{t}{3}$ (see Additional Example 1b) vertically compressed by a factor of $\dfrac{1}{2}$.

Example 2

Determine the period of each function.

a. $k(t) = \tan 5t$ period: $\dfrac{\pi}{5}$

The function completes one cycle between $-\dfrac{\pi}{10}$ and $\dfrac{\pi}{10}$.

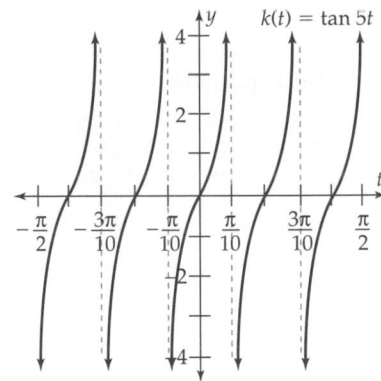

b. $f(t) = \tan \dfrac{t}{2}$ period: $\dfrac{\pi}{\frac{1}{2}} = 2\pi$

The function completes one cycle between $-\pi$ and π.

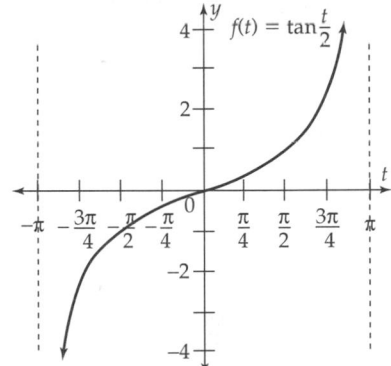

Example 3

Graph each function.

a. $g(t) = 4 \cos 5t$

The graph of g is the graph of $k(t) = \cos 5t$ (see Additional Example 1a) stretched vertically by a factor of 4.

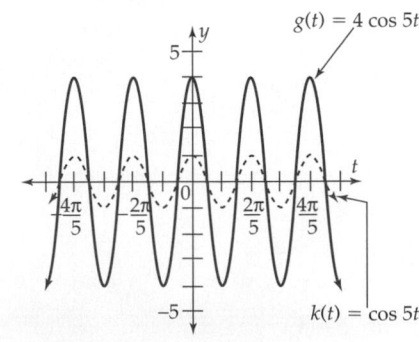

ADDITIONAL EXAMPLES

Example 4

Determine the amplitude and period of $f(t) = -3 \sin 2t$. Then graph f on the interval $[-\pi, \pi]$.

amplitude: $|-3| = 3$

period: $\dfrac{2\pi}{2} = \pi$

$f(t) = -3 \sin 2t$ is the graph of $h(t) = 3 \sin 2t$ reflected across the x-axis.

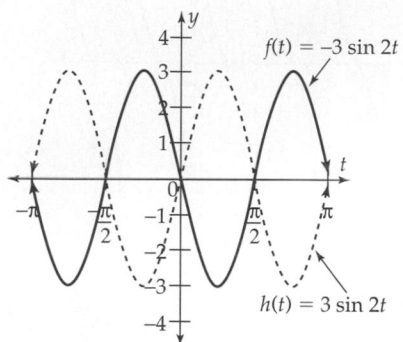

Exercises 7.3

ANSWERS

1. amplitude: 1; period: 2π

2. amplitude: 1; period: π

3. amplitude: 1; period: $\dfrac{2\pi}{3}$

4. amplitude: none; period: π

5. amplitude: 4; period: 2π

6. amplitude: 3; period: 2π

7. amplitude: none; period: $\dfrac{\pi}{2}$

8. amplitude: 1.2; period: 4π

9. amplitude: 0.3; period: 6π

10. amplitude: none; period: $\dfrac{5\pi}{2}$

11. amplitude: $\dfrac{1}{2}$; period: $\dfrac{2\pi}{3}$

12. amplitude: none; period: $\dfrac{\pi}{3}$

13. amplitude: 5; period: $\dfrac{20\pi}{17}$

14. amplitude: 2; period: 3

15. amplitude: none; period: 4

16. **a.** 1
    b. $t = 0, \dfrac{1}{2}$, or 1
    c. $t = \dfrac{1}{4}$
    d. $t = \dfrac{3}{4}$

17. **a.** 2
    b. $t = \dfrac{1}{2}$ or $\dfrac{3}{2}$
    c. $t = 0$ or 2
    d. $t = 1$

Amplitude and Period

> If $a \neq 0$ and $b > 0$, then each of the functions
>
> $$f(t) = a \sin bt \quad \text{or} \quad g(t) = a \cos bt$$
>
> has an amplitude of $|a|$ and a period of $\dfrac{2\pi}{b}$.

Example 4   Determining Amplitude and Period

Determine the amplitude and period of $f(t) = -2 \sin 4t$. Then graph f on the interval $\left[-\dfrac{\pi}{2}, \dfrac{\pi}{2}\right]$.

Solution

The amplitude of $f(t) = -2 \sin 4t$ is $|a| = |-2| = 2$, and the period of $f(t) = -2 \sin 4t$ is $\dfrac{2\pi}{b} = \dfrac{2\pi}{4} = \dfrac{\pi}{2}$. So the graph of f consists of cycles that are $\dfrac{\pi}{2}$ long and rise and fall between the heights of -2 and 2. To graph this function, be sure to notice that its graph is the reflection of $h(t) = 2 \sin 4t$ across the horizontal axis, as shown in Figure 7.3-10.

Figure 7.3-10

Although the graph of any function can be vertically stretched or compressed, amplitude only applies to bounded periodic functions.

Exercises 7.3

In Exercises 1–15, state the amplitude (if any) and period of each function.

1. $f(t) = -\cos t$
2. $f(t) = \sin 2t$
3. $f(t) = \cos 3t$
4. $f(t) = 2.5 \tan t$
5. $f(t) = 4 \cos t$
6. $f(t) = -3 \sin t$
7. $f(t) = 5 \tan 2t$
8. $f(t) = 1.2 \cos 0.5t$
9. $f(t) = -0.3 \sin \dfrac{t}{3}$
10. $f(t) = -\tan 0.4t$
11. $f(t) = \dfrac{1}{2} \sin 3t$
12. $f(t) = -\dfrac{1}{2} \tan 3t$
13. $f(t) = 5 \cos 1.7t$
14. $f(t) = 2 \sin \dfrac{2\pi t}{3}$
15. $f(t) = \dfrac{1}{3} \tan \dfrac{\pi t}{4}$

16. **a.** What is the period of $f(t) = \sin 2\pi t$?
    b. For what values of t (with $0 \le t \le 1$) is $f(t) = 0$?
    c. For what values of t (with $0 \le t \le 1$) is $f(t) = 1$?
    d. For what values of t (with $0 \le t \le 1$) is $f(t) = -1$?

17. **a.** What is the period of $f(t) = \cos \pi t$?
    b. For what values of t (with $0 \le t \le 2$) is $f(t) = 0$?
    c. For what values of t (with $0 \le t \le 2$) is $f(t) = 1$?
    d. For what values of t (with $0 \le t \le 2$) is $f(t) = -1$?

18. **a.** What is the period of $f(t) = \tan \pi t$?
    b. For what values of t $\left(\text{with } -\dfrac{1}{2} \le t \le \dfrac{1}{2}\right)$ is $f(t) = 0$?

18. **a.** 1
    b. $t = 0$
    c. $t = \dfrac{1}{4}$
    d. $t = -\dfrac{1}{4}$

19. g is the graph of f horizontally compressed by a factor of $\dfrac{1}{5}$; amplitude: 1; period: $\dfrac{2\pi}{5}$

20. g is the graph of f horizontally compressed by a factor of $\dfrac{1}{3}$; amplitude: none; period: $\dfrac{\pi}{3}$

21. g is the graph of f horizontally compressed by a factor of $\dfrac{1}{8}$; amplitude: 1; period: $\dfrac{\pi}{4}$

c. For what values of t $\left(\text{with } -\frac{1}{2} \le t \le \frac{1}{2}\right)$ is
$f(t) = 1$?

d. For what values of t $\left(\text{with } -\frac{1}{2} \le t \le \frac{1}{2}\right)$ is
$f(t) = -1$?

In Exercises 19–38, describe the transformations that change the graph of f into the graph of g. State the amplitude (if any) and the period of g.

19. $f(t) = \sin t; g(t) = \sin 5t$

20. $f(t) = \tan t; g(t) = \tan 3t$

21. $f(t) = \cos t; g(t) = \cos 8t$

22. $f(t) = \cos t; g(t) = \cos(-t)$

23. $f(t) = \tan t; g(t) = \tan(-t)$

24. $f(t) = \sin t; g(t) = \sin(-t)$

25. $f(t) = \sin t; g(t) = \sin 1.6t$

26. $f(t) = \cos t; g(t) = \cos 2.6t$

27. $f(t) = \sin t; g(t) = 3 \sin t$

28. $f(t) = \cos t; g(t) = \frac{1}{2} \cos t$

29. $f(t) = \tan t; g(t) = \frac{1}{3} \tan t$

30. $f(t) = \sin t; g(t) = 4 \sin \frac{t}{2}$

31. $f(t) = \sin t; g(t) = 5 \sin 2t$

32. $f(t) = \tan t; g(t) = -2 \tan \frac{t}{2}$

33. $f(t) = \tan t; g(t) = -2 \tan 0.2t$

34. $f(t) = \cos t; g(t) = 3 \cos 6t$

35. $f(t) = \cos t; g(t) = \frac{2}{5} \cos 8t$

36. $f(t) = \sin t; g(t) = -2 \sin \frac{3\pi t}{5}$

37. $f(t) = \tan t; g(t) = \frac{1}{3} \tan \pi t$

38. $f(t) = \cos t; g(t) = \frac{5}{3} \cos \frac{\pi t}{3}$

In Exercises 39–44, sketch at least one cycle of the graph of each function.

39. $f(t) = 4 \cos \frac{t}{2}$ **40.** $f(t) = \frac{2}{3} \sin 2t$

41. $f(t) = 2 \tan 3t$ **42.** $f(t) = -0.8 \cos \pi t$

43. $f(t) = 3.5 \sin 2\pi t$ **44.** $f(t) = \tan \frac{\pi t}{2}$

In Exercises 45–50, match a graph to a function. Only one graph is possible for each function.

a.

b.

c.

d.

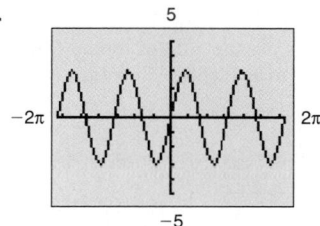

22. g is the graph of f reflected across the y-axis; amplitude: 1; period: 2π

23. g is the graph of f reflected across the y-axis; amplitude: none; period: π

24. g is the graph of f reflected across the y-axis; amplitude: 1; period: 2π

25. g is the graph of f horizontally compressed by a factor of $\frac{5}{8}$; amplitude: 1; period: $\frac{5\pi}{4}$

26. g is the graph of f horizontally compressed by a factor of $\frac{5}{13}$; amplitude: 1; period: $\frac{10\pi}{13}$

27. g is the graph of f vertically stretched by a factor of 3; amplitude: 3; period: 2π

28. g is the graph of f vertically compressed by a factor of $\frac{1}{2}$; amplitude: $\frac{1}{2}$; period: 2π

29. g is the graph of f vertically compressed by a factor of $\frac{1}{3}$; amplitude: none; period: π

30. g is the graph of f vertically stretched by a factor of 4 and horizontally stretched by a factor of 2; amplitude: 4; period: 4π

31. g is the graph of f vertically stretched by a factor of 5 and horizontally compressed by a factor of $\frac{1}{2}$; amplitude: 5; period: π

32. g is the graph of f reflected across the x-axis, vertically stretched by a factor of 2, and horizontally stretched by a factor of 2; amplitude: none; period: 2π

33. g is the graph of f reflected across the x-axis, vertically stretched by a factor of 2, and horizontally stretched by a factor of 5; amplitude: none; period: 5π

34. g is the graph of f vertically stretched by a factor of 3 and horizontally compressed by a factor of $\frac{1}{6}$; amplitude: 3; period: $\frac{\pi}{3}$

35. g is the graph of f vertically compressed by a factor of $\frac{2}{5}$ and horizontally compressed by a factor of $\frac{1}{8}$; amplitude: $\frac{2}{5}$; period: $\frac{\pi}{4}$

36. g is the graph of f reflected across the x-axis, vertically stretched by a factor of 2, and horizontally compressed by a factor of $\frac{5\pi}{3}$; amplitude: 2; period: $3\frac{1}{3}$

37. g is the graph of f vertically compressed by a factor of $\frac{1}{3}$ and horizontally compressed by a factor of $\frac{1}{\pi}$; amplitude: none; period: 1

38. g is the graph of f vertically stretched by a factor of $\frac{5}{3}$ and horizontally compressed by a factor of $\frac{3}{\pi}$; amplitude: $\frac{5}{3}$; period: 6

39.

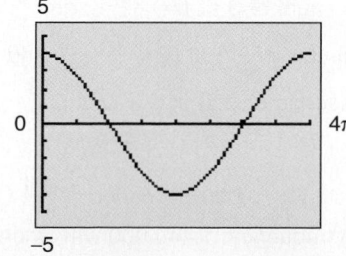

40–44. See p. 500.

40.

41.

42.

43.

44.

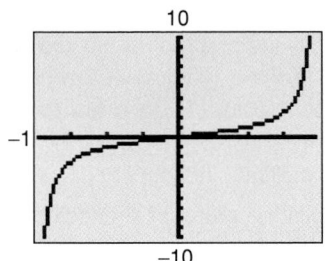

60. local maximum of 1 at $t = \frac{\pi}{4}$; local minimum of -1 at $t = \frac{3\pi}{4}$

61. local maximum of 1 at $t = 0$ and $t = \frac{2\pi}{3}$; local minimum of -1 at $t = \frac{\pi}{3}$

62. local maximum of 1 at $t = 0$; local minimum of -1 at $t = -2\pi$

63. local maximum of $\frac{\sqrt{3}}{2}$ at $t = \pi$; local minimum of -1 at $t = -\frac{3\pi}{2}$

e.

f.

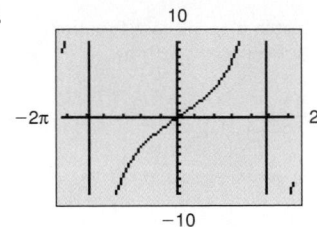

45. $f(t) = 3 \sin 2t$ **d**

46. $f(t) = -3 \cos 2t$ **a**

47. $f(t) = 3 \cos \frac{t}{2}$ **b**

48. $f(t) = -3 \sin \frac{t}{2}$ **e**

49. $f(t) = 5 \tan \frac{t}{3}$ **f**

50. $f(t) = 3 \tan 2t$ **c**

In Exercises 51–56, write an equation for a sine function with the given information.

51. amplitude $= 2$, period $= 4\pi$ $f(t) = 2 \sin \frac{t}{2}$

52. amplitude $= \frac{1}{2}$, period $= \frac{\pi}{2}$ $f(t) = \frac{1}{2} \sin 4t$

53. amplitude $= 1.8$, period $= \frac{3\pi}{2}$ $f(t) = 1.8 \sin \frac{4t}{3}$

54. amplitude $= 1$, period $= 2$ $f(t) = \sin \pi t$

55. amplitude $= \frac{3}{2}$, period $= 4$ $f(t) = \frac{3}{2} \sin \frac{\pi t}{2}$

56. amplitude $= 6$, period $= \frac{1}{2}$ $f(t) = 6 \sin 4\pi t$

In Exercises 57–59, state the rule of a sine function whose graph appears to be identical to the given graph.

57.

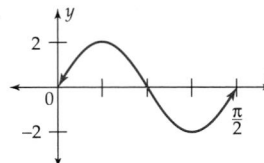

$f(t) = 2 \sin 4t$

64. local maximum of 3 at $t = -\frac{3}{4}, \frac{1}{4}$, and $\frac{5}{4}$; local minimum of -3 at $t = -\frac{5}{4}, -\frac{1}{4}$, and $\frac{3}{4}$

65. $\frac{1}{900,000}$ second or 900,000 waves per second

66. $f(t) = A \sin(2,880,000\pi t)$; period: $\frac{1}{1,440,000}$ seconds; frequency: 1,440,000 waves per second

58.

$f(t) = -3 \sin 3t$

59.

$f(t) = -5 \sin 5t$

In Exercises 60–64, state all local minima and maxima of the function on the given interval.

60. $f(t) = \sin 2t; \, 0 < t < \pi$

61. $f(t) = \cos 3t; \, 0 \le t \le \pi$

62. $f(t) = \cos \frac{t}{2}; \, -2\pi \le t \le \pi$

63. $f(t) = \sin \frac{t}{3}; \, -2\pi \le t \le \pi$

64. $f(t) = 3 \sin 2\pi t; \, -1.5 \le t \le 1.5$

65. The current generated by an AM radio transmitter is given by a function of the form $f(t) = A \sin 2000 \, \pi m t$, where $550 \le m \le 1600$ is the location on the broadcast dial and t is measured in seconds. For example, a station at 900 on the AM dial has a function of the form

$$f(t) = A \sin 2000\pi(900) \, t = A \sin 1,800,000\pi t$$

Sound information is added to this signal by modulating A, that is, by changing the amplitude of the waves being transmitted. AM means amplitude modulation. For a station at 900 on the dial, what is the period of function f?

66. Find the function f, its period, and its frequency for a radio station at 1440 on the dial. (See Exercise 65.)

7.4   Periodic Graphs and Phase Shifts

Objectives

- State the period, amplitude, vertical shift, and phase shift given the function rule or graph of a sine or cosine function
- Use graphs to determine whether an equation could possibly be an identity

In Section 7.3, you studied graphs of functions of the form

$$f(t) = a \sin bt \quad \text{and} \quad g(t) = a \cos bt$$

and learned how the constants a and b affect the amplitudes and periods of the functions. In this section, you will consider functions of the form

$$f(t) = a \sin(bt - c) + d \quad \text{and} \quad g(t) = a \cos(bt - c) + d$$

where a, b, c, and d are constants, and you will determine how these constants affect the graphs of the functions.

Vertical Shifts

Recall from Section 3.4 that adding a constant to the rule of a function shifts the graph vertically. Example 1 illustrates a vertical shift in combination with a reflection and a change in amplitude.

Example 1   Reflection, Vertical Stretch, and Vertical Shift

Describe the graph of $k(t) = -2 \cos t + 3$. Then graph k on the interval $[-2\pi, 2\pi]$.

Solution

The graph of $k(t) = -2 \cos t + 3$ is the graph of $g(t) = \cos t$ reflected across the horizontal axis, vertically stretched by a factor of 2, and shifted 3 units upward, as shown in Figure 7.4-1.

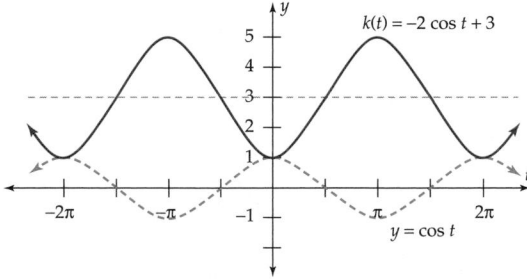

Figure 7.4-1

After the vertical shift, the graph of $k(t) = -2 \cos t + 3$ is vertically centered on the horizontal line $y = 3$.

Section
7.4   Periodic Graphs and Phase Shifts

Example Notes

For **Example 1**, ask students to identify the numbers or signs in the function $k(t) = -2 \cos t + 3$ that produce:

- a change in amplitude   2
- a reflection   the negative sign before the 2
- a vertical shift   3

This Example contains the first discussion about a function that has amplitude other than 1 and is not vertically centered on the horizontal axis. The function k has amplitude 2 and is vertically centered on the line $y = 3$. Point out that the graph reaches a maximum of 2 units above the line $y = 3$ and a minimum of 2 units below the line $y = 3$.

ADDITIONAL EXAMPLES

Example 1

Describe the graph of $k(t) = -3 \sin t - 4$. Then graph k on the interval $[-2\pi, 2\pi]$.

The graph of $k(t) = -3 \sin t - 4$ is the graph of $g(t) = \sin t$ reflected across the horizontal axis, vertically stretched by a factor of 3, and shifted 4 units downward.

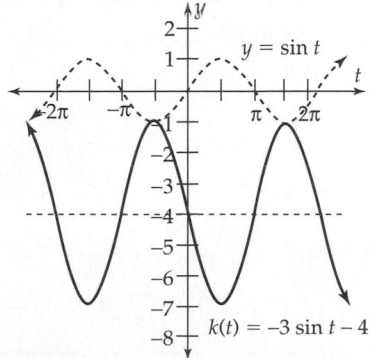

After the vertical shift, the graph of $k(t) = -3 \sin t - 4$ is vertically centered on the horizontal line $y = -4$.

Teaching Notes

Recall from Section 3.4 (page 175) that, if c is a positive number,
- The graph of $g(x) = f(x + c)$ is the graph of f shifted c units left.
- The graph of $g(x) = f(x - c)$ is the graph of f shifted c units right.

Point out that for periodic functions:
- A shift left is associated with a negative phase shift.
- A shift right is associated with a positive phase shift.

ADDITIONAL EXAMPLES

Example 2

Describe the graph of each function.

a. $g(t) = \sin\left(t - \dfrac{3\pi}{4}\right)$

The graph of $g(t) = \sin\left(t - \dfrac{3\pi}{4}\right)$ is the graph of $f(t) = \sin t$ shifted $\dfrac{3\pi}{4}$ units to the right.

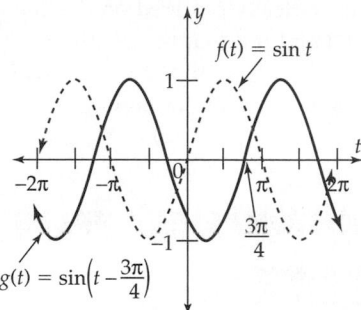

The cycle of f that begins at $t = 0$ becomes a cycle of g that begins at $t = \dfrac{3\pi}{4}$. Thus, g has a phase shift of $\dfrac{3\pi}{4}$.

b. $h(t) = \cos\left(t + \dfrac{\pi}{4}\right)$

The graph of $h(t) = \cos\left(t + \dfrac{\pi}{4}\right)$ is the graph of $f(t) = \cos t$ shifted $\dfrac{\pi}{4}$ units to the left.

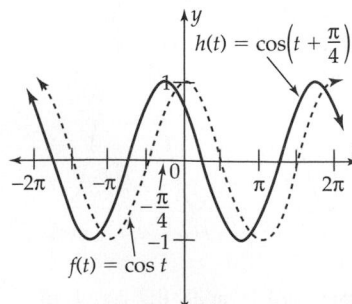

The cycle of f that begins at $t = 0$ becomes a cycle of h that begins at $t = -\dfrac{\pi}{4}$. Thus, h has a phase shift of $-\dfrac{\pi}{4}$.

Phase Shifts

Recall from Section 3.4 that when the independent variable t in the rule of a function is replaced by $t - c$, where c is a constant, the graph is shifted horizontally. For periodic functions, the number c is the **phase shift** associated with the graph.

Example 2   Phase Shift

Describe the graph of each function.

a. $g(t) = \sin\left(t + \dfrac{\pi}{2}\right)$ **b.** $h(t) = \cos\left(t - \dfrac{2\pi}{3}\right)$

Solution

a. The graph of $g(t) = \sin\left(t + \dfrac{\pi}{2}\right)$ is the graph of $f(t) = \sin t$ shifted to the left $\dfrac{\pi}{2}$ units, as shown in Figure 7.4-2.

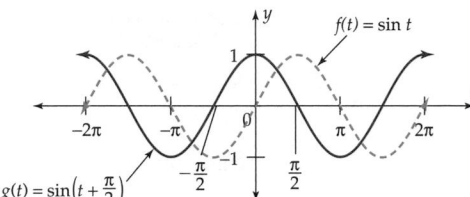

Figure 7.4-2

When the graph of $f(t) = \sin t$ is shifted to become the graph of $g(t) = \sin\left(t + \dfrac{\pi}{2}\right)$, the cycle of f that begins at $t = 0$ becomes a cycle of g that begins at $t = -\dfrac{\pi}{2}$. Thus, g has a phase shift of $-\dfrac{\pi}{2}$.

b. The graph of $h(t) = \cos\left(t - \dfrac{2\pi}{3}\right)$ is the graph of $f(t) = \cos t$ shifted to the right $\dfrac{2\pi}{3}$ units, as shown in Figure 7.4-3.

Figure 7.4-3

The cycle of $f(t) = \cos t$ that begins at $t = 0$ becomes a cycle of $h(t) = \cos\left(t - \frac{2\pi}{3}\right)$ that begins at $t = \frac{2\pi}{3}$. Thus, the function h has a phase shift of $\frac{2\pi}{3}$.

■

Combined Transformations

Now that you are familiar with the effects of various transformations on the sine and cosine functions, you are ready for some examples that simultaneously include changes in amplitude, period, and phase shift.

Example 3   Combined Transformations

State the amplitude, period, and phase shift of $f(t) = 3\sin(2t + 5)$.

Solution

Rewrite the function rule.

$$f(t) = 3\sin(2t + 5) = 3\sin\left[2\left(t + \frac{5}{2}\right)\right]$$

When the rule of f is written in this form, you can see that it is obtained from the rule of $k(t) = 3\sin 2t$ by replacing t with $t + \frac{5}{2}$. Therefore, the graph of f can be obtained by horizontally shifting the graph of k to the left $\frac{5}{2}$ units, as shown in Figure 7.4-4.

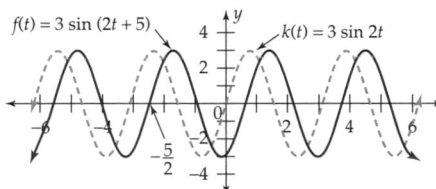

Figure 7.4-4

The cycle of k that begins at $t = 0$ becomes a cycle of f that begins at $t = -\frac{5}{2}$; so the function f has a phase shift of $-\frac{5}{2}$.

The amplitude of f is 3 and its period is $\frac{2\pi}{2} = \pi$.

■

Example Notes

For **Example 3**, students can review how the graph of $f(t) = 3\sin 2t$ is obtained by graphing the following functions on the same calculator screen:
$Y_1 = \sin x$, $Y_2 = \sin(2x)$, and
$Y_3 = 3\sin(2x)$

They will see the functions graphed in sequence, each function "building" on the previous function. The final result will be:

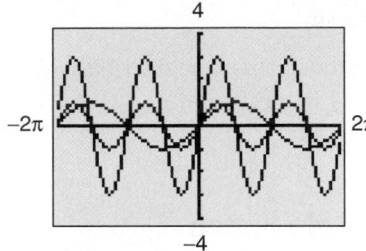

ADDITIONAL EXAMPLES

Example 3

State the amplitude, period, and phase shift of $f(t) = 2\cos(3t - 4)$.

Rewrite as $f(t) = 2\cos\left[3\left(t - \frac{4}{3}\right)\right]$.

The rule of f is obtained from the rule of $k(t) = 2\cos 3t$ by replacing t with $t - \frac{4}{3}$. So, the graph of f can be obtained by horizontally shifting the graph of k to the right $\frac{4}{3}$ units.

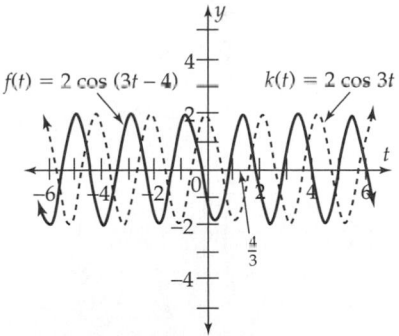

The cycle of k that begins at $t = 0$ becomes a cycle of f that begins at $t = \frac{4}{3}$, so the function f has a phase shift of $\frac{4}{3}$.

amplitude: 2

period: $\frac{2\pi}{3}$

phase shift: $\frac{4}{3}$

Teaching Notes

All the previous results that were developed in Examples 1–3 are generalized in the **Combined Transformations** box. The fact that might be the most difficult to understand is that the phase shift $= \frac{c}{b}$. Refer to the equation at the top of this page:

$$f(t) = a \sin(bt - c) + d$$

$$= a \sin\left[b\left(t - \frac{c}{b}\right)\right] + d$$

Have students use the distributive property to verify that

$$bt - c = b\left(t - \frac{c}{b}\right).$$

Example Notes

In **Example 4**, it is not necessary to rewrite the function in the form $f(t) = a \cos\left[b\left(t - \frac{c}{b}\right)\right] + d$ to find the phase shift. From the form $f(t) = a \cos(bt - c) + d$, the phase shift can be determined directly using $\frac{c}{b}$.

ADDITIONAL EXAMPLES

Example 4

Describe the graph of
$g(t) = 3 \cos(2t - 1) + 4.$

amplitude: $|a| = |3| = 3$

period: $\frac{2\pi}{b} = \frac{2\pi}{2} = \pi$

phase shift: $\frac{c}{b} = \frac{1}{2}$

vertical shift: $d = 4$

The graph is vertically centered on the horizontal line $y = 4$. The waves reach a maximum of 3 units above and a minimum of 3 units below that horizontal line. The graph begins a cosine wave at $t = \frac{1}{2}$ and completes one cycle in π units.

The procedure that is used in Examples 1–3 can be used to analyze any function whose rule is of the form

$$f(t) = a \sin(bt - c) + d.$$

First rewrite the function rule as follows.

$$f(t) = a \sin(bt - c) + d = a \sin\left[b\left(t - \frac{c}{b}\right)\right] + d$$

Thus, the graph of f is obtained from the graph of $k(t) = a \sin bt$ by shifting it d units vertically and $\frac{c}{b}$ units horizontally. The cycle of k that begins at $t = 0$ becomes the cycle of f that begins at $t = \frac{c}{b}$, so f has phase shift $\frac{c}{b}$. The amplitude of both f and k is $|a|$ and both have period $\frac{2\pi}{b}$. A similar analysis applies to the function $g(t) = a \cos(bt - c) + d$.

Combined Transformations

If $a \neq 0$ and $b > 0$, then each of the functions

$$f(t) = a \sin(bt - c) + d \qquad \text{and} \qquad g(t) = a \cos(bt - c) + d$$

has the following characteristics:

$$\text{amplitude} = |a| \qquad\qquad \text{period} = \frac{2\pi}{b}$$

$$\text{phase shift} = \frac{c}{b} \qquad \text{vertical shift} = d$$

Example 4 Combined Transformations

Describe the graph of $g(t) = 2 \cos(3t - 4) - 1$.

Solution

Identify the amplitude, period, vertical shift and phase shift.

$$g(t) = 2 \cos(3t - 4) - 1$$

$$\text{amplitude } |a| = 2 \qquad \text{period} = \frac{2\pi}{b} = \frac{2\pi}{3}$$

$$\text{phase shift} = \frac{c}{b} = \frac{4}{3} \qquad \text{vertical shift} = -1$$

Figure 7.4-5

The graph of $g(t) = 2 \cos(3t - 4) - 1$, shown in Figure 7.4-5, is vertically centered on the horizontal line $y = -1$. The waves reach a maximum of 2 units above that horizontal line and a minimum of 2 units below that horizontal line. The graph begins a cosine wave at $t = \frac{4}{3}$ and completes one cycle in $\frac{2\pi}{3}$ units.

■

Example 5 Combined Transformations

Identify the amplitude, period, vertical shift, and phase shift of $f(t) = -4 \sin\left(\frac{t}{2} + 1\right) + 3$. Then graph at least one complete cycle of f.

Solution

The function rule $f(t)$ is of the form $a \sin(bt - c) + d$, with $a = -4$, $b = \frac{1}{2}$, $c = -1$, and $d = 3$.

$$\text{amplitude } |a| = |-4| = 4 \qquad \text{period} = \frac{2\pi}{b} = \frac{2\pi}{\frac{1}{2}} = 4\pi$$

$$\text{phase shift} = \frac{c}{b} = \frac{-1}{\frac{1}{2}} = -2 \qquad \text{vertical shift} = 3$$

The waves of the graph are vertically centered on the horizontal line $y = 3$ reaching a maximum of 7 and a minimum of -1. The graph begins a sine wave at $t = -2$ and completes one cycle in $4\pi \approx 12.6$ units. The graph of f is the graph of $y = 4 \sin\left(\frac{t}{2} + 1\right) + 3$ reflected across the horizontal line $y = 3$, as shown in Figure 7.4-6.

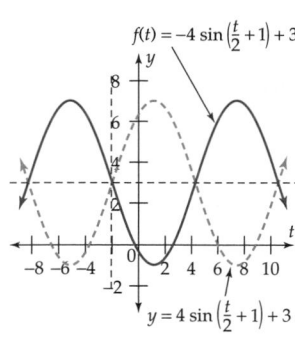

$f(t) = -4 \sin\left(\frac{t}{2} + 1\right) + 3$

$y = 4 \sin\left(\frac{t}{2} + 1\right) + 3$

Figure 7.4-6

Example 6 Identifying Graphs

Find a sine function and a cosine function whose graphs look like the graph shown in Figure 7.4-7.

Solution

Figure 7.4-7

This graph appears to have an amplitude of 2 and to be centered vertically on the horizontal axis. The period appears to be 2π, so $b = 1$. Therefore, the graph looks like the graph of $f(t) = 2 \sin t$ or $g(t) = 2 \cos t$ shifted horizontally.

The graph of $f(t) = 2 \sin t$ intercepts the x-axis at $t = 0$. The graph in Figure 7.4-7 intercepts the x-axis at $t = \frac{\pi}{4}$, so it looks like the graph of $f(t) = 2 \sin t$ shifted $\frac{\pi}{4}$ units to the right. Therefore, this graph closely resembles the graph of $h(t) = 2 \sin\left(t - \frac{\pi}{4}\right)$.

At $t = 0$, the graph of $g(t) = 2 \cos t$ reaches its maximum of 2. The graph in Figure 7.4-7 reaches its maximum of 2 at $t = \frac{3\pi}{4}$, so it looks like the graph of $g(t) = 2 \cos t$ shifted $\frac{3\pi}{4}$ units to the right. Therefore, this graph closely resembles the graph of $k(t) = 2 \cos\left(t - \frac{3\pi}{4}\right)$.

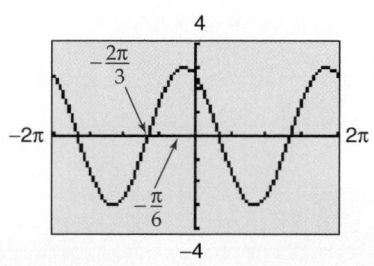

Example 5

Identify the amplitude, period, vertical shift, and phase shift of $f(t) = -2 \sin\left(\frac{t}{3} + 4\right) + 1$. Then graph at least one complete cycle of f.

The function rule is of the form $a \sin(bt - c) + d$, with $a = -2$, $b = \frac{1}{3}$, $c = -4$, and $d = 1$.

amplitude: $|a| = |-2| = 2$

period: $\frac{2\pi}{b} = \frac{2\pi}{\frac{1}{3}} = 6\pi$

phase shift: $\frac{c}{b} = \frac{-4}{\frac{1}{3}} = -12$

vertical shift: $d = 1$

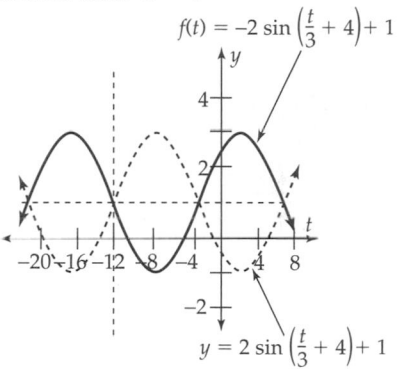

$f(t) = -2 \sin\left(\frac{t}{3} + 4\right) + 1$

$y = 2 \sin\left(\frac{t}{3} + 4\right) + 1$

The waves of the graph are vertically centered on the horizontal line $y = 1$, reaching a maximum of 3 and a minimum of -1. The graph begins a sine wave at $t = -12$ and completes one cycle in $6\pi \approx 18.8$ units. The graph of f is the graph of $y = 2 \sin\left(\frac{t}{3} + 4\right) + 1$ reflected across the horizontal line $y = 1$.

Example 6

Find a sine function and a cosine function whose graphs look like the graph shown.

It appears that the graph has an amplitude of 3, is centered vertically on the horizontal axis, and has a period of 2π.

It looks like the graph of $f(t) = 3 \sin t$ shifted $\frac{2\pi}{3}$ units to the left, so it could be the graph of $f(t) = 3 \sin\left(t + \frac{2\pi}{3}\right)$.

It looks like the graph of $f(t) = 3 \cos t$ shifted $\frac{\pi}{6}$ units to the left, so it could be the graph of $g(t) = 3 \cos\left(t + \frac{\pi}{6}\right)$.

ADDITIONAL EXAMPLES

Example 7

Which of the following equations could possibly be an identity?

a. $\sin\left(\dfrac{\pi}{2} - t\right) = \cos t$

The graphs of $f(t) = \sin\left(\dfrac{\pi}{2} - t\right)$ and $g(t) = \cos t$ appear to coincide, and the table values match, so $\sin\left(\dfrac{\pi}{2} - t\right) = \cos t$ is possibly an identity.

b. $\sin\left(-\dfrac{\pi}{2} - t\right) = \cos t$

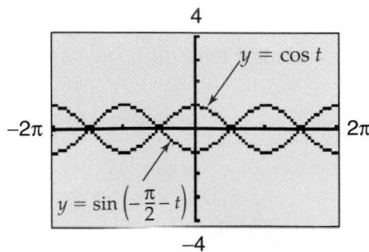

The graphs do not coincide, so $\sin\left(-\dfrac{\pi}{2} - t\right) = \cos t$ is not an identity.

NOTE Identities are proved algebraically in Chapter 9.

Figure 7.4-8

Graphs and Identities

Graphing calculators can be used to determine equations that could possibly be identities. A calculator cannot *prove* that such an equation is an identity, but it can provide evidence that it *might* be one. On the other hand, a calculator can prove that a particular equation is not an identity.

Example 7   **Possible Identities**

Which of the following equations could possibly be an identity?

a. $\cos\left(\dfrac{\pi}{2} + t\right) = \sin t$ **b.** $\cos\left(\dfrac{\pi}{2} - t\right) = \sin t$

Solution

a. If $\cos\left(\dfrac{\pi}{2} + t\right) = \sin t$ is an identity, then

$$f(t) = \cos\left(\frac{\pi}{2} + t\right) \text{ and } g(t) = \sin t$$

are equivalent functions and have the same graph. The graphs of f and g, shown in Figure 7.4-8 are obviously different. Therefore, $\cos\left(\dfrac{\pi}{2} + t\right) = \sin t$ is not an identity.

b. In Figure 7.4-9, the graphs of

$$f(t) = \cos\left(\frac{\pi}{2} - t\right) \text{ and } g(t) = \sin t$$

appear to coincide on the interval $[-2\pi, 2\pi]$. Comparing a table of values for f and g, shown in Figure 7.4-10, also supports the idea that $f(t) = \cos\left(\dfrac{\pi}{2} - t\right)$ and $g(t) = \sin t$ are equivalent functions.

Figure 7.4-9

Figure 7.4-10

This evidence strongly suggests that the equation $\cos\left(\dfrac{\pi}{2} - t\right) = \sin t$ is an identity, but does not prove it. Therefore, $\cos\left(\dfrac{\pi}{2} - t\right) = \sin t$ could possibly be an identity. ∎

Example 8 Possible Identities

Which of the following equations could possibly be an identity?

a. $\dfrac{\cot t}{\cos t} = \sin t$ **b.** $\dfrac{\sin t}{\tan t} = \cos t$

Solution

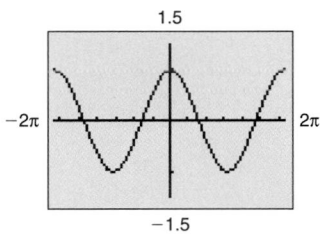

a. Rewrite f as $f(t) = \dfrac{\frac{1}{\tan t}}{\cos t}$ and compare its graph with the graph of $g(t) = \sin t$. The graphs of f and g, shown in Figure 7.4-11 are obviously different. Therefore, $\dfrac{\cot t}{\cos t} = \sin t$ is not an identity.

However, it does appear from the graph that $\dfrac{\cot t}{\cos t} = \csc t$ could possibly be an identity.

b. In Figure 7.4-12a, the graphs of $f(t) = \dfrac{\sin t}{\tan t}$ and $g(t) = \cos t$ appear to coincide. Comparing a table of values for f and g, shown in Figure 7.4-12b, also supports the idea that $f(t) = \dfrac{\sin t}{\tan t}$ and $g(t) = \cos t$ are equivalent functions for all values of t for which f is defined; that is, all values of t except those that make $\tan t = 0$.

Figure 7.4-12a   **Figure 7.4-12b**

Therefore, $\dfrac{\sin t}{\tan t} = \cos t$ could possibly be an identity for $\tan t \neq 0$.

CAUTION

Do not assume that two graphs that look the same on a calculator screen actually are the same. Depending on the viewing window, two graphs that are actually quite different may appear identical.

Figure 7.4-11

$f(t) = \dfrac{\cot t}{\cos t}$ $g(t) = \sin t$

ADDITIONAL EXAMPLES

Example 8

Which of the following equations could possibly be an identity?

a. $\dfrac{\cot t}{\csc t} = \sec t$

Rewrite the expressions:

$$\dfrac{\cot t}{\csc t} = \dfrac{\frac{1}{\tan t}}{\frac{1}{\sin t}}, \quad \sec t = \dfrac{1}{\cos t}.$$

Compare graphs:

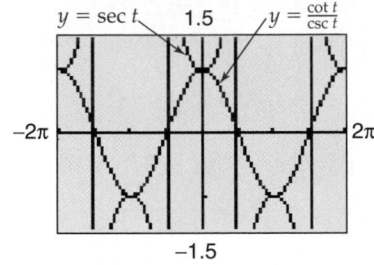

$y = \sec t$ $y = \dfrac{\cot t}{\csc t}$

$\dfrac{\cot t}{\csc t} = \sec t$ is not an identity because the graphs do not coincide.

b. $\dfrac{\tan t}{\sin t} = \sec t$

Rewrite $\sec t$ as $\dfrac{1}{\cos t}$. Compare graphs:

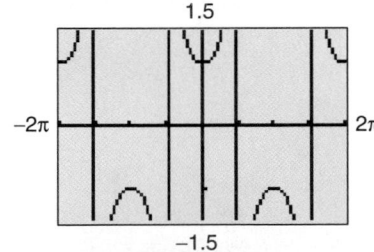

The graphs appear to coincide, and table values match for t-values that make both expressions defined, so $\dfrac{\tan t}{\sin t} = \sec t$ is possibly an identity for all values of t such that $\dfrac{\tan t}{\sin t}$ and $\sec t$ are both defined, (that is, all values of t such that $\sin t \neq 0$ and $\cos t \neq 0$).

Teaching Notes

In **Additional Example 8b**, both $\dfrac{\tan t}{\sin t}$ and $\sec t$ are undefined for certain values of t.

Exercises 7.4

ANSWERS

21. $f(t) = 3 \sin 8\left(t - \frac{\pi}{5}\right)$

22. $f(t) = \sin \pi(t - 3) + 4$

23. $f(t) = \frac{2}{3} \sin \frac{2}{3}\left(t + \frac{2\pi}{3}\right) - 2$

24. $f(t) = 8 \sin 4\pi\left(t - \frac{2}{3}\right) + 4$

25. $f(t) = 0.5 \sin 0.8\pi(t - 1.5) - 0.6$

26. $f(t) = \sin \frac{2\pi}{5}(t - 0) + 3$

27. $f(t) = 6 \sin \frac{6}{5}(t - 0) - 1$

28. $f(t) = 2 \sin \frac{1}{4}(t - 1) + 1$

29. $f(t) = \frac{5}{2} \sin \frac{10\pi}{9}(t - 0.2) + 0$

30. $f(t) = \sin 2\pi(t + 1) - 1$

31. a. $f(t) = 12 \sin\left(10t - \frac{\pi}{2}\right)$

    b. $g(t) = -12 \cos 10t$

32. a. $f(t) = 18 \sin (\pi t)$

    b. $g(t) = 18 \cos\left(\pi t - \frac{\pi}{2}\right)$

33. a. $f(t) = -\sin 2t$

    b. $g(t) = -\cos\left(2t - \frac{\pi}{2}\right)$

34. a. $f(t) = \sin\left(4t - \frac{\pi}{2}\right)$

    b. $g(t) = -\cos (4t\pi)$

35. a. $f(t) = \frac{1}{2} \sin 8t$

    b. $g(t) = \frac{1}{2} \cos\left(8t - \frac{\pi}{2}\right)$

36. a. $f(t) = -3.5 \sin\left(3t - \frac{\pi}{2}\right)$

    b. $g(t) = 3.5 \cos (3t)$

37. a. $f(t) = -4 \sin \frac{2}{3}t + 1$

    b. $f(t) = -4 \cos\left(\frac{2}{3}t - \frac{\pi}{2}\right) + 1$

38. a. $f(t) = 3 \sin\left(4t - \frac{\pi}{2}\right) - 5$

    b. $g(t) = -3 \cos 4t - 5$

39. a. $f(t) = -2 \sin\left(t - \frac{3\pi}{4}\right) + 6$

    b. $f(t) = 2 \cos\left(t - \frac{\pi}{4}\right) + 6$

40. a. $f(t) = -2 \sin\left(t + \frac{\pi}{4}\right) - 5$

    b. $g(t) = 2 \cos\left(t + \frac{3\pi}{4}\right) - 5$

Exercises 7.4

In Exercises 1–20, state the amplitude, period, phase shift, and vertical shift of the function.

1. $h(t) = \cos(t + 1)$
  1; 2π; −1; 0

2. $m(t) = 7 \cos(t + 3)$
  7; 2π; −3; 0

3. $f(t) = -5 \sin 2t$
  5; π; 0; 0

4. $k(t) = \cos\left(\frac{2\pi t}{3}\right)$
  1; 3; 0; 0

5. $k(t) = \sin(t - \pi) - 4$
  1; 2π; π; −4

6. $g(t) = 3 \sin(2t - \pi)$
  3; π; $\frac{\pi}{2}$; 0

7. $p(t) = 6 \cos(3\pi t + 1)$
  6; $\frac{2}{3}$; $-\frac{1}{3\pi}$; 0

8. $f(t) = 4.5 \sin(12t - 6) - 5$
  4.5; $\frac{\pi}{6}$; $\frac{1}{2}$; −5

9. $h(t) = -4 \cos\left(3t - \frac{\pi}{6}\right) + 1$ 4; $\frac{2\pi}{3}$; $\frac{\pi}{18}$; 1

10. $p(t) = -5 \sin\left(\frac{t}{4} + 3\right) - 1$ 5; 8π; −12; −1

11. $q(t) = -7 \sin\left(7t + \frac{1}{7}\right)$
  7; $\frac{2\pi}{7}$; $-\frac{1}{49}$; 0

12. $h(t) = 16 \sin\left(\frac{2t}{3} - 4\right)$ 16; 3π; 6; 0

13. $d(t) = -3 \sin\left(2t - \frac{5\pi}{4}\right)$ 3; π; $\frac{5\pi}{8}$; 0

14. $c(t) = -\cos\left(\frac{3t}{2} - \frac{\pi}{3}\right) - 5$ 1; $\frac{4\pi}{3}$; $\frac{2\pi}{9}$; −5

15. $g(t) = 97 \cos(14t + 5)$ 97; $\frac{\pi}{7}$; $-\frac{5}{14}$; 0
16. $f(t) = 3 - 2 \cos(4t + 1)$ 2; $\frac{\pi}{2}$; $-\frac{1}{4}$; 3

17. $s(t) = 7 - \cos 2\pi t$
  1; 1; 0; 7

18. $m(t) = 4 \cos(t - 5) + 2$
  4; 2π; 5; 2

19. $k(t) = 3 \cos\left(\frac{\pi t}{3} - 1\right) + 5$
  3; 6; $\frac{3}{\pi}$; 5

20. $h(t) = -4 - \sin\left(\frac{t}{3} + \frac{\pi}{4}\right)$
  1; 6π; $-\frac{3\pi}{4}$; −4

In Exercises 21–30, state the rule of a sine function with the given amplitude, period, phase shift, and vertical shift, respectively.

21. 3, $\frac{\pi}{4}$, $\frac{\pi}{5}$, 0   **22.** 1, 2, 3, 4

23. $\frac{2}{3}$, 3π, $-\frac{2\pi}{3}$, −2   **24.** 8, $\frac{1}{2}$, $\frac{2}{3}$, 4

25. 0.5, 2.5, 1.5, −0.6   **26.** 1, 5, 0, 3

27. 6, $\frac{5\pi}{3}$, 0, −1   **28.** 2, 8π, 1, 1

29. $\frac{5}{2}$, 1.8, 0.2, 0   **30.** 1, 1, −1, −1

In Exercises 31–40,

a. State the rule of a function of the form
$f(t) = a \sin(bt - c) + d$ whose graph appears to be identical to the given graph.

b. State the rule of a function of the form
$f(t) = a \cos(bt - c) + d$ whose graph appears to be identical to the given graph.

31.

32.

33.

34.

35.

36.

41.

42.

37.

38.

39.

40.

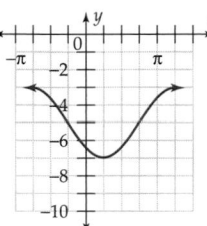

In Exercises 41–48, sketch the graph of at least one cycle of the function.

41. $k(t) = -3 \sin t$

42. $y(t) = -2 \cos 3t$

43. $p(t) = -\frac{1}{2} \sin 2t$

44. $q(t) = \frac{2}{3} \cos \frac{3}{2} t$

45. $h(t) = 3 \sin\left(2t + \frac{\pi}{2}\right)$

46. $p(t) = 3 \cos(3t - \pi)$

47. $f(t) = -\sin(2t - 3) + 1$

48. $g(t) = 5 \cos\left(t - \frac{\pi}{3}\right) + 2$

In Exercises 49–52, graph the function over the interval $(0, 2\pi)$, and determine the location of all local maxima and minima.

49. $f(t) = \frac{1}{2} \sin\left(t - \frac{\pi}{3}\right)$ **50.** $g(t) = 2 \sin\left(\frac{2t}{3} - \frac{\pi}{9}\right)$

51. $f(t) = -2 \sin(3t - \pi)$

52. $h(t) = \frac{1}{2} \cos\left(\frac{\pi}{2} t - \frac{\pi}{8}\right) + 1$

53. Describe the graph of $f(t) = \sin^2 t + \cos^2 t$.

In Exercises 54–57, use graphs to determine whether the equation could possibly be an identity or is definitely not an identity.

54. $\dfrac{\cos t}{\cos\left(t - \dfrac{\pi}{2}\right)} = \cot t$ **55.** $\dfrac{\sin t}{1 - \cos t} = \cot t$

possibly an identity   **not an identity**

56. $\dfrac{\sec t + \csc t}{1 + \tan t} = \csc t$ **57.** $\tan t = \cot\left(\dfrac{\pi}{2} - t\right)$

possibly an identity   **possibly an identity**

In Exercises 58–61, graph f in a viewing window with $-2\pi \le t \le 2\pi$. Use the trace feature to determine constants a, b, and c such that the graph of f appears to coincide with the graph of $g(t) = a \sin(bt - c)$.

58. $f(t) = -3 \sin t + 2 \cos t$
$A \approx -3.6056$, $b = 1$, $c \approx 0.588$
59. $f(t) = 3 \sin(4t + 2) + 2 \cos(4t - 1)$
$A \approx 3.8332$, $b = 4$, $c \approx -1.4572$
60. $f(t) = 2 \sin(3t - 5) - 3 \cos(3t + 2)$
$A \approx 4.5699$, $b = 3$, $c \approx -0.765$
61. $f(t) = 2 \sin t + 5 \cos t$
$A \approx 5.3852$, $b = 1$, $c \approx -1.1903$

In Exercises 62–63, explain why there could not possibly be constants a, b, and c such that the graph of $g(t) = a \sin(bt - c)$ coincides with the graph of f.

62. $f(t) = 2 \sin(3t - 1) + 3 \cos(4t + 1)$

63. $f(t) = \sin 2t + \cos 3t$

43.

44.

45.

46.

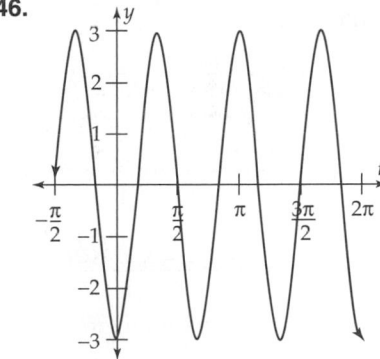

47–48. *See p. 1069.*

49–52. *For graphs, see p. 1069.*

49. Local maximum at
$t = \dfrac{5\pi}{6} \approx 2.6180$; local
minimum at $t = \dfrac{11\pi}{6} \approx 5.7596$

50. Local maximum at
$t = \dfrac{11\pi}{12} \approx 2.8798$; local
minimum at $t = \dfrac{29\pi}{12} \approx 7.5922$

51. Local maxima at $t = \dfrac{\pi}{6} \approx 0.5236$,
$t = \dfrac{5\pi}{6} \approx 2.6180$, $t = \dfrac{3\pi}{2} \approx 4.7124$;
local minima at $t = \dfrac{\pi}{2} \approx 1.5708$,
$t = \dfrac{7\pi}{6} \approx 3.6652$,
$t = \dfrac{11\pi}{6} \approx 5.7596$

52. local maxima at $x = \dfrac{1}{4}$, $x = \dfrac{17}{4}$;
local minima at $x = \dfrac{9}{4}$, $x = \dfrac{25}{4}$

53. The graph of $f(t) = \sin^2 t + \cos^2 t$
is the same as the graph of $f(x) = 1$,
a horizontal line intercepting the y-axis at 1.

58–61. *For graphs, see p. 1069.*

62. Although the graph is periodic, it is not a sine wave and cannot be constructed from a sine curve through translations, stretches, or contractions.

63. All waves in the graph of g are of equal height, which is not the case with the graph of f. It cannot be constructed from a sine curve through translations, stretches, or contractions.

Section 7.4.A Excursion: Other Trigonometric Graphs

Teaching Notes

Solution to the first **Graphing Exploration:**

The graphs appear to coincide.

Solution to the second **Graphing Exploration:**

1.

Yes, the function appears to be periodic.

2. maximum ≈ 4.950,
minimum ≈ −4.950,
amplitude a ≈ 4.950

3. period ≈ 2.598 − (−3.686) ≈
6.28 ≈ 2π, or period ≈ 5.739 −
(−0.544) ≈ 6.28 ≈ 2π

4. The smallest positive t-value that
begins a sine cycle is: t ≈ 2.598.

5. a = amplitude ≈ 4.950

period = $2\pi = \dfrac{2\pi}{b}$, so $b = 1$

phase shift ≈ 2.598

$$\approx -\frac{c}{b} = -\frac{c}{1}$$

so

$c \approx -2.598$

$f(t) = a \sin(bt + c)$

$f(t) \approx 4.950 \sin(t - 2.598)$

7.4.A Excursion: Other Trigonometric Graphs

Objectives

- Write a sine function whose graph looks like the graph of another given sinusoidal function

- Find viewing windows for the graphs of other trigonometric functions

A graphing calculator enables you to explore with ease a wide variety of trigonometric functions.

> ### Graphing Exploration
>
> Graph each function on the same screen in a viewing window with $0 \le t \le 2\pi$.
>
> $$g(t) = \cos t \qquad f(t) = \sin\left(t + \frac{\pi}{2}\right)$$
>
> How do the two graphs compare? Do they appear to coincide?

The exploration above suggests that the equation

$$\cos t = \sin\left(t + \frac{\pi}{2}\right)$$

is an identity and that the graph of the cosine function can be obtained by horizontally shifting the graph of the sine function. This is true, and it will be proved in Section 9.2. Consequently, every cosine function, such as $g(t) = 3\cos(4t + 5) + 6$, can be expressed as a sine function of the form $f(t) = a\sin(bt + c) + d$. The shape of the graph of such a function is called a **sinusoid**.

Other Sinusoidal Graphs

The exploration below suggests that other trigonometric functions can be expressed in the form $f(t) = a\sin(bt + c)$.

> ### Graphing Exploration
>
> 1. Graph $g(t) = -2\sin(t + 7) + 3\cos(t + 2)$ in a viewing window with $-2\pi \le t \le 2\pi$. Does the function appear to be periodic?
>
> 2. Using the calculator's minimum and maximum finders, determine the approximate amplitude of this function.
>
> 3. Using the calculator's zero finder, estimate the period of this function (find the length of a complete cycle).
>
> 4. What is the smallest positive t-value at which a sine cycle begins?
>
> 5. Use the information from Questions 2–4 to write a function of the form $f(t) = a\sin(bt + c)$ whose graph looks very much like the graph of $g(t) = -2\sin(t + 7) + 3\cos(t + 2)$. Graph the new function on the same screen with g. Do the graphs appear to coincide?

Yes, the graphs appear to coincide.

The results of the preceding graphing exploration suggest that the graph of $g(t) = -2 \sin(t + 7) + 3 \cos(t + 2)$ looks like the graph of $f(t) = 4.95 \sin(t - 2.60)$.

These results illustrate the following facts.

Sinusoidal Graphs

> If b, d, k, r, and s are constants, then the graph of the function
>
> $$g(t) = d \sin(bt + r) + k \cos(bt + s)$$
>
> is a sinusoid and there are constants a and c such that
>
> $$d \sin(bt + r) + k \cos(bt + s) = a \sin(bt + c).$$

Example 1 Sinusoidal Graphs

Find a sine function whose graph looks like the graph of

$$g(t) = 4 \sin(3t + 2) + 2 \cos(3t - 4).$$

Solution

The graph of $g(t) = 4 \sin(3t + 2) + 2 \cos(3t - 4)$ is shown in Figure 7.4.A-1.

By using a graphing calculator's minimum and maximum finders with the graph of $g(t) = 4 \sin(3t + 2) + 2 \cos(3t - 4)$, you see that g has an amplitude of approximately 3.94.

The function g has period $\dfrac{2\pi}{3}$ because this is the period of both $\sin(3t + 2)$ and $\cos(3t - 4)$. The function $f(t) = a \sin(bt + c)$ has period $\dfrac{2\pi}{b} = \dfrac{2\pi}{3}$. So $b = 3$.

By using a graphing calculator's zero finder, you can see that a sine cycle in the graph of g begins at approximately $t = -0.84$, so the phase shift $-\dfrac{c}{b}$ is approximately -0.84. Find c.

$$-\frac{c}{b} \approx -0.84$$

$$-\frac{c}{3} \approx -0.84 \qquad \textit{Substitute 3 for b}$$

$$-c \approx -2.52$$

$$c \approx 2.52$$

Therefore, $a \approx 3.94$, $b = 3$, $c \approx 2.52$, and the graph of

$$f(t) = 3.94 \sin(3t + 2.52)$$

looks like the graph of

$$g(t) = 4 \sin(3t + 2) + 2 \cos(3t - 4).$$

Figure 7.4.A-1

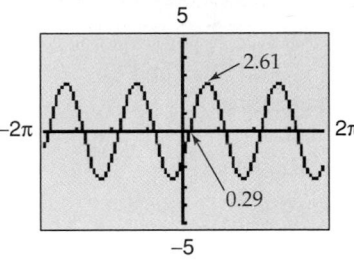

Example Notes

For **Example 2**, show how to find the least common multiple of 0.02 and 0.05:

.02 .04 .06 .08 **.10** .12 ...
.05 **.10** .15 ...

ADDITIONAL EXAMPLES

Example 2

Find a viewing window for one complete cycle of $f(t) = 3 \sin 50\pi t + 4 \cos 20\pi t$.
graph of f with viewing window of $-2\pi \le t \le 2\pi$:

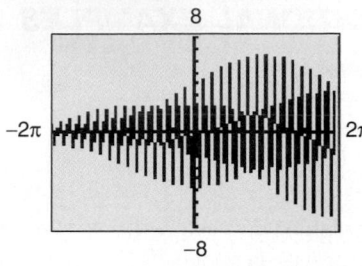

To find a suitable viewing window, find the period.

Let $h(t) = 3 \sin 50\pi t$ and $g(t) = 4 \cos 20\pi t$.

period for h: $\dfrac{2\pi}{50\pi} = \dfrac{1}{25} = 0.04$

period for g: $\dfrac{2\pi}{20\pi} = \dfrac{1}{10} = 0.1$

The least common multiple of 0.04 and 0.1 is 0.2. Therefore, use the viewing window $0 \le t \le 0.2$ to show one complete cycle:

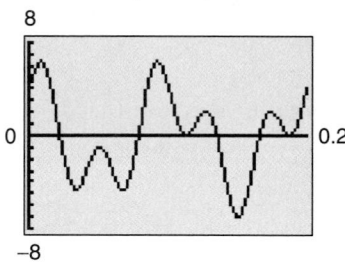

Other Trigonometric Graphs

In Example 1, the variable t has the same coefficient b in both the sine and cosine terms of the function's rule. When this is not the case, the graph will consist of waves of varying size and shape, as shown in Figure 7.4.A-2.

$f(t) = \sin 3t + \cos 2t$

$g(t) = -2 \sin(3t + 5) + 4 \cos(t + 2)$

$h(t) = 2 \sin 2t - 3 \cos 3t$

Figure 7.4.A-2

Figure 7.4.A-3

Figure 7.4.A-4

Example 2   Finding a Viewing Window

Find a viewing window for one complete cycle of

$$f(t) = 4 \sin 100\pi t + 2 \cos 40\pi t.$$

Solution

A graph of f in a viewing window with $-2\pi \le t \le 2\pi$ includes so many cycles that the calculator cannot display an accurate graph, as shown in Figure 7.4.A-3.

Instead, find the period of f by using the following method:

Let $h(t) = 4 \sin 100\pi t$ and $g(t) = 2 \cos 40\pi t$.

The period of h is $\dfrac{2\pi}{100\pi} = \dfrac{1}{50} = 0.02$. The period of g is $\dfrac{2\pi}{40\pi} = \dfrac{1}{20} = 0.05$. The period of f is the least common multiple of 0.02 and 0.05, which is 0.10.

Therefore, the viewing window with $0 \le t \le 0.10$ in Figure 7.4.A-4 shows one complete cycle of $f(t) = 4 \sin 100\pi t + 2 \cos 40\pi t$. ■

Damped and Compressed Trigonometric Graphs

Suppose a weight hanging from a spring is set in motion by an upward push. No spring is perfectly elastic, and friction acts to slow the motion of the weight as time goes on. Consequently, the graph showing the height of the weight above or below its equilibrium point at time t will consist of waves that get smaller and smaller as t gets larger. Many other physical situations can be described by functions whose graphs consist of waves of diminishing or increasing heights. Other situations, such as sound waves in FM radio transmission, are modeled by functions whose graphs consist of waves of uniform height and varying frequency.

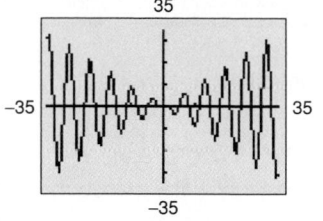

Figure 7.4.A-5

Example 3   Analyzing a Damped Graph

Analyze the graph of $f(t) = t \cos t$.

Solution

Graph f in a viewing window with $-35 \le t \le 35$ and $-35 \le y \le 35$, as shown in Figure 7.4.A-5.

Recall that $-1 \le \cos t \le 1$. Multiply each term of the inequality by t considering the cases $t \ge 0$ and $t < 0$. (Remember to reverse the inequality sign when $t < 0$.)

$$-t \le t \cos t \le t \quad \text{when } t \ge 0$$
$$-t \ge t \cos t \ge t \quad \text{when } t < 0$$

In graphical terms, this means that the graph of $f(t) = t \cos t$ lies between the straight lines $y = t$ and $y = -t$, with the waves growing larger or smaller to fit the space between the lines. The graph touches the lines $y = t$ and $y = -t$ exactly when $t \cos t = \pm t$, that is, when $\cos t = \pm 1$. This occurs when $t = 0 + k\pi$, where k is an integer.

Therefore, the graph of $f(t) = t \cos t$ consists of waves that diminish in amplitude as t approaches 0 from both negative and positive values, and the waves are bounded by the lines $y = \pm t$. ∎

> **Graphing Exploration** ●
>
> Illustrate the analysis of the graph $f(t) = t \cos t$ by graphing $f(t) = t \cos t$, $y = t$, and $y = -t$ on the same screen.

Example 4   Analyzing a Damped Graph

Analyze the graph of $g(t) = 0.5^t \sin t$.

Solution

No single viewing window gives a completely readable graph of g. To the left of the y-axis, the graph gets quite large; but to the right, it almost coincides with the t-axis. To get a better mental picture, note that $0.5^t > 0$ for every t. To find the bounds of $0.5^t \sin t$, multiply each term of the known inequality $-1 \le \sin t \le 1$ by 0.5^t.

$$-1 \le \sin t \qquad \le 1$$
$$-0.5^t \le 0.5^t \sin t \qquad \le 0.5^t \qquad \text{for every } t$$

Therefore, the graph of g lies between the graphs of the exponential functions $y = -0.5^t$ and $y = 0.5^t$. The graph of g will consist of sine waves

Figure 7.4.A-6

ADDITIONAL EXAMPLES

Example 3

Analyze the graph of $f(t) = t \sin t$. The graph of $f(t)$ with viewing window $-35 \le t \le 35$ and $-35 \le y \le 35$ is shown below.

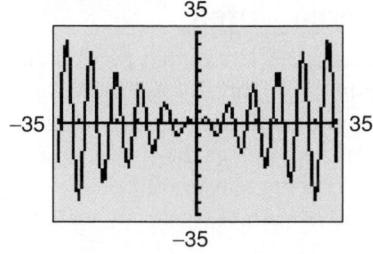

The graph lies between the lines $y = t$ and $y = -t$, touching the lines exactly when $t \sin t = \pm t$, that is, when $\sin t = \pm 1$. This occurs when $t = \frac{\pi}{2} + k\pi$, where k is an integer.

Example 4

Analyze the graph of $f(t) = 0.5^t \cos t$.

A picture of the graph of f is shown below, along with $y = 0.5^t$ and $y = -0.5^t$. The graph of f is not to scale, but is helpful for forming a mental picture of how the actual graph oscillates.

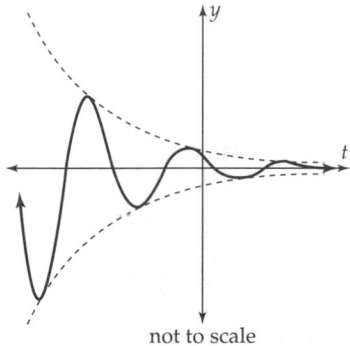

not to scale

The graph of f consists of cosine waves rising and falling between the graphs of $y = 0.5^t$ and $y = -0.5^t$.

Teaching Notes

Solution to the **Graphing Exploration:**

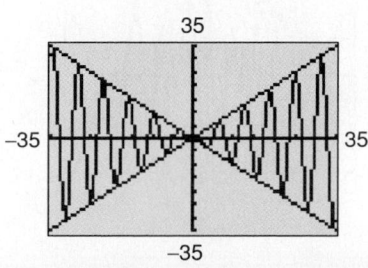

Possible solution to the Graphing Exploration:

For $-2\pi \le t \le 0$, use $-5 \le y \le 35$.

For $0 \le t \le 2\pi$, use $-0.1 \le y \le 0.5$.

For $2\pi \le t \le 4\pi$, use $-0.001 \le y \le 0.1$.

Example Notes

For **Example 5**, the dotted portion of the graph in Figure 7.4.A-8 indicates the infinite oscillating. The function is undefined only at the single value $t = 0$. Students may want to experiment with very narrow viewing windows. The graph of $f(t) = \sin\left(\dfrac{\pi}{t}\right)$ is shown below with a viewing window of $-1.0 \times 10^{-10.7} \le t \le 1.0 \times 10^{-10.7}$.

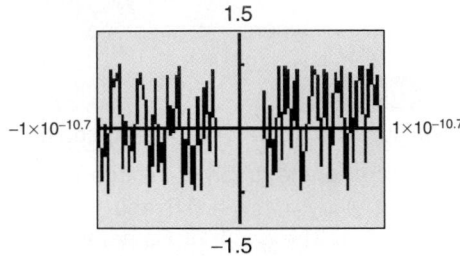

ADDITIONAL EXAMPLES

Example 5

Analyze the graph of $f(t) = \cos\left(\dfrac{\pi}{t}\right)$.

With a wide viewing window, the line $y = 1$ appears to be an asymptote.

Near the origin, the graph is not readable.

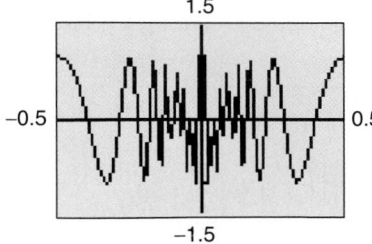

---

rising and falling between the graph of the exponential functions $y = -0.5^t$ and $y = 0.5^t$, as indicated in Figure 7.4.A-6 (which is not to scale). ∎

Graphing Exploration

Find viewing window ranges that clearly show the graph in Example 4 when t is in the following domains.

$$-2\pi \le t \le 0 \qquad 0 \le t \le 2\pi \qquad 2\pi \le t \le 4\pi$$

Example 5   Oscillating Behavior

Analyze the graph of $f(t) = \sin\left(\dfrac{\pi}{t}\right)$.

Solution

Using a wide viewing window, it is clear that the t-axis is an asymptote of the graph of $f(t) = \sin\left(\dfrac{\pi}{t}\right)$, as shown in Figure 7.4.A-7a. Near the origin, however, the graph is not readable, even in a very narrow viewing window like Figure 7.4.A-7b.

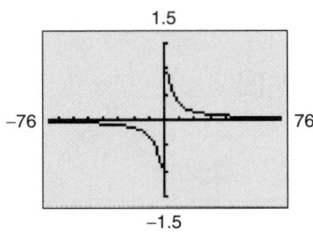

Figure 7.4.A-7a   **Figure 7.4.A-7b**

Consider what happens to the graph between $t = \dfrac{1}{2}$, and $t = 0$.

As t goes from $\dfrac{1}{2}$ to $\dfrac{1}{4}$, $\sin\left(\dfrac{\pi}{t}\right)$ goes from $\sin\left(\dfrac{\pi}{\frac{1}{2}}\right)$ to $\sin\left(\dfrac{\pi}{\frac{1}{4}}\right)$, that is from $\sin 2\pi$ to $\sin 4\pi$. Therefore, the graph of f makes one complete sine wave for $\dfrac{1}{4} \le t \le \dfrac{1}{2}$. Similarly, for $\dfrac{1}{6} \le t \le \dfrac{1}{4}$, the graph of f makes another complete sine wave. The same pattern continues so that the graph of f makes a complete wave for $\dfrac{1}{8} \le t \le \dfrac{1}{6}$, for $\dfrac{1}{10} \le t \le \dfrac{1}{8}$, and so on. A similar phenomenon occurs as t takes values between $-\dfrac{1}{2}$ and 0. Conse-

The graph near 0 oscillates infinitely often between -1 and 1, with the waves becoming more compressed as t gets closer to 0. The function is not defined at $t = 0$, so the left and right halves of the graph are not connected.

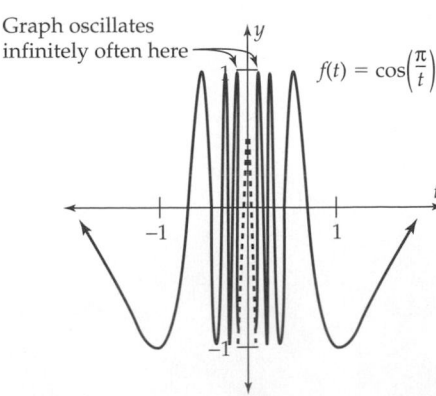

Graph oscillates infinitely often here

$f(t) = \cos\left(\dfrac{\pi}{t}\right)$

quently, the graph of f near 0 oscillates infinitely often between -1 and 1, with the waves becoming more and more compressed as t gets closer to 0, as indicated in Figure 7.4.A-8. Because the function is not defined at $t = 0$, the left and right halves of the graph are not connected.

Graph oscillates infinitely often here

$f(t) = \sin(\pi/t)$

Figure 7.4.A-8

Exercises 7.4.A

In Exercises 1–6, find a sine function whose graph looks like the graph of the given function f.

1. $f(t) = \sin t + 2 \cos t$
   $f(t) = 2.2361 \sin(t + 1.1071)$
2. $f(t) = 3 \sin t + 2 \cos t$
   $f(t) = 3.61 \sin(t + 0.588)$
3. $f(t) = 2 \sin 4t - 5 \cos 4t$
   $f(t) = 5.3852 \sin(4t - 1.1903)$
4. $f(t) = 3 \sin(2t - 1) + 4 \cos(2t + 3)$
   $f(t) = 6.570 \sin(2t - 1.410)$
5. $f(t) = -5 \sin(3t + 2) + 2 \cos(3t - 1)$
   $f(t) = 5.1164 \sin(3t - 0.7442)$
6. $f(t) = 0.3 \sin(2t + 4) - 0.4 \cos(2t - 3)$
   $f(t) = -0.304 \sin(2t - 0.59)$

In Exercises 7–16, find a viewing window that shows a complete graph of the function.

7. $g(t) = (5 \sin 2t)(\cos 5t)$ 8. $h(t) = e^{\sin t}$

9. $f(t) = \dfrac{t}{2} + \cos 2t$
   $-10 \le t \le 10$ and $-10 \le y \le 10$

10. $g(t) = \sin\left(\dfrac{t}{3} - 2\right) + 2\cos\left(\dfrac{t}{4} - 2\right)$
    $-24\pi \le t \le 24\pi$ and $-3 \le y \le 3$

11. $h(t) = \sin 300t + \cos 500t$
    $0 \le t \le \dfrac{\pi}{50}$ and $-2 \le y \le 2$

12. $f(t) = 3 \sin(200t + 1) - 2 \cos(300t + 2)$
    $0 \le t \le \pi/25$ and $-5 \le y \le 5$
13. $g(t) = -5 \sin(250\pi t + 5) + 2 \cos(400\pi t - 7)$
    $0 \le t \le 0.04$ and $-7 \le y \le 7$
14. $h(t) = 4 \sin(600\pi t + 3) - 6 \cos(500\pi t - 3)$
    $0 \le t \le 0.02$ and $-10 \le y \le 10$
15. $f(t) = 4 \sin 0.2\pi t - 5 \cos 0.4\pi t$
    $0 \le t \le 10$ and $-6 \le y \le 10$
16. $g(t) = 6 \sin 0.05\pi t + 2 \cos 0.04\pi t$
    $0 \le t \le 400$ and $-8 \le y \le 8$

In Exercises 17–24, describe the graph of the function verbally, including such features as asymptotes, undefined points, amplitude and number of waves between 0 and 2π. Find viewing windows that illustrate the main features of the graph.

17. $g(t) = \sin e^t$

18. $h(t) = \dfrac{\cos 2t}{1 + t^2}$

19. $f(t) = \sqrt{|t|} \cos t$

20. $g(t) = e^{-\frac{t^2}{8}} \sin 2\pi t$

21. $h(t) = \dfrac{1}{t} \sin t$

22. $f(t) = t \sin \dfrac{1}{t}$

23. $h(t) = \ln|\cos t|$

24. $h(t) = \ln|\sin t + 1|$

23. The function is periodic with period π. The graph lies on or below the t-axis because the logarithmic function is negative for numbers between 0 and 1 and $|\cos t|$ is always between 0 and 1. The graph has vertical asymptotes when
$t = \pm\dfrac{\pi}{2}, \pm\dfrac{3\pi}{2}, \pm\dfrac{5\pi}{2}, \pm\dfrac{7\pi}{2}, \ldots$ ($\cos t = 0$ at these points and $\ln 0$ is not defined).
Window: $-2\pi \le t \le 2\pi$ and $-3 \le y \le 1$ (four periods)

24. The graph is periodic with period 2π. The graph has a vertical asymptote wherever $\sin x = -1$.
Window: $-4\pi \le t \le 4\pi$ and $-5 \le y \le 2$

7. $0 \le t \le 2\pi$ and $-5 \le y \le 5$

8. $-10 \le t \le 10$ and $0 \le y \le 3$

17. To the left of the y-axis, the graph lies above the t-axis, which is a horizontal asymptote of the graph. To the right of the y-axis, the graph makes waves of amplitude 1, of shorter and shorter period.
Window: $-3 \le t \le 3.2$ and $-2 \le y \le 2$

18. The graph has the horizontal axis as an asymptote. There are 2 waves between 0 and 2π. There are waves of decreasing amplitude every π units as you move farther from the origin.
Window: $-2\pi \le t \le 2\pi$ and $-1 \le y \le 1$

19. The graph is symmetric with respect to the y-axis and consists of waves along the t-axis, whose amplitude slowly increases as you move farther from the origin in either direction.
Window: $-30 \le t \le 30$ and $-6 \le y \le 6$

20. The horizontal axis is an asymptote. There are 2π waves every 2π units.
Window: $-4 \le t \le 4$ and $-1 \le y \le 1$

21. There is a hole at point $(0, 1)$. The graph is symmetric with respect to the y-axis and consists of waves along the t-axis whose amplitude rapidly decreases as you move farther from the origin in either direction.
Window: $-30 \le t \le 30$ and $-0.3 \le y \le 1$

22. The horizontal line $y = 1$ is an asymptote. There is a hole at the origin. There are infinitely many waves in the interval $0 < x < 2\pi$.
Window: $-1 \le t \le 1$ and $-0.2 \le y \le 1$

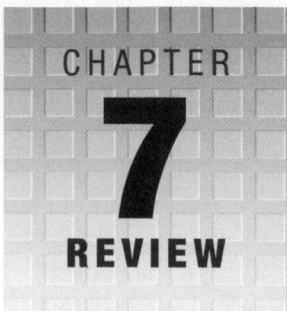

CHAPTER

7

REVIEW

Important Concepts

Important Facts and Formulas

If $a \neq 0$ and $b > 0$, then each of the functions $f(t) = a \sin(bt - c) + d$ and $g(t) = a \cos(bt - c) + d$ has:

$$\text{amplitude } |a|, \qquad \text{period } \frac{2\pi}{b},$$

$$\text{phase shift } \frac{c}{b} \qquad \text{vertical shift } d$$

If $b > 0$, then the function $h(t) = \tan bt$ has period $\frac{\pi}{b}$.

516

Review Exercises

Section 7.1

1. Which of the following is not true about the graph of $f(t) = \sin t$? **c**
  a. It has no sharp corners.
  b. It crosses the horizontal axis more than once.
  c. It rises higher and higher as t gets larger.
  d. It is periodic.
  e. It has no vertical asymptotes.

In Exercises 2–4, graph each function on the given interval.

2. $f(t) = \sin t \quad \left[\dfrac{7\pi}{2}, 7\pi\right]$ **3.** $g(t) = \cos t \quad \left[-5\pi, -\dfrac{7\pi}{2}\right]$

4. $h(t) = \tan t \quad [2\pi, 3\pi]$

In Exercises 5–7, find all the exact t-values for which the given statement is true.

5. $\cos t = 1$ $0 = n2\pi$, where n is an integer

6. $\sin t = -\dfrac{1}{2}$ $\dfrac{7\pi}{6} + n2\pi$ and $\dfrac{11\pi}{6} + n2\pi$, where n is an integer

7. $\tan t = -\sqrt{3}$ $-\dfrac{\pi}{3} + n\pi$, where n is an integer

In Exercises 8–10, list the transformations that change the graph of f into the graph of g. State the domain and range of g.

8. $f(t) = \sin t \quad g(t) = -\dfrac{1}{2}\sin t$ **9.** $f(t) = \tan t \quad g(t) = -\tan 2t$

10. $f(t) = \cos t \quad g(t) = \cos\left(-\dfrac{1}{2}t\right) - 1$

In Exercises 11–13, sketch the graph of each function.

11. $g(t) = -3\cos t$ **12.** $h(t) = \tan t - 4$

13. $k(t) = 2\sin t + 3$

14. Which of the following functions has the graph shown below between $-\pi$ and π? **c**
  a. $f(x) = \begin{cases} \sin x, & \text{if } x \ge 0 \\ \cos x, & \text{if } x < 0 \end{cases}$
  b. $g(x) = \cos x - 1$
  c. $h(x) = \begin{cases} \sin x, & \text{if } x \ge 0 \\ \sin(-x), & \text{if } x < 0 \end{cases}$
  d. $k(x) = |\cos x|$
  e. $p(x) = \sqrt{1 - \sin^2 x}$

15. Between (and including) 0 and 2π, the function $h(t) = \tan t$ has __?__ . **a**
  a. 3 zeros and is undefined at 2 places
  b. 2 zeros and is undefined at 3 places
  c. 2 zeros and is undefined at 2 places
  d. 3 zeros and is defined everywhere
  e. no zeros and is undefined at 3 places

2.

3.

4.

8. g is the graph of f reflected across the x-axis and compressed vertically by a factor of $\dfrac{1}{2}$.
domain: all real numbers; range: $-1 \le g(t) \le 1$

9. g is the graph of f reflected across the x-axis and compressed horizontally by a factor of $\dfrac{1}{2}$.
domain: all real numbers except $t = \dfrac{\pi}{4} + k\dfrac{\pi}{2}$, where k is an integer; range: all real numbers

10. g is the graph of f reflected across the y-axis, stretched horizontally by a factor of 2, and shifted 1 unit down. domain: all real numbers; range: $-2 \le g(t) < 0$

11.

12.

13.

16. c

17. c

18. d

19.

20.

21.

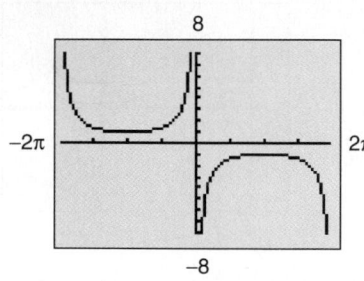

22. odd

23. even

24. a. $\frac{3}{2}$

   b. $\frac{\pi}{5} \approx 0.6283$

25.

26.

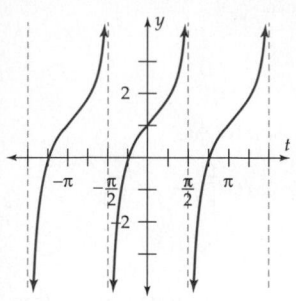

16. Which of the statements **i–iii** are true?
   i.   The sine function is an odd function.
   ii. The cosine function is an odd function.
   iii. The tangent function is an odd function.
   a. **i** and **ii** only
   b. **ii** only
   c. **i** and **iii** only
   d. all of them
   e. none of them

17. Which of the following functions has the graph shown at left?
   a. $f(t) = \tan t$
   b. $g(t) = \tan\left(t + \frac{\pi}{2}\right)$
   c. $h(t) = 1 + \tan t$
   d. $k(t) = 3 \tan t$
   e. $p(t) = -\tan t$

Section 7.2

18. Which of the following is true about $\sec t$?
   a. $\sec(0) = 0$
   b. $\sec t = \dfrac{1}{\sin t}$
   c. Its graph has no asymptotes.
   d. It is a periodic function.
   e. It is never negative.

In Exercises 19–21, sketch the graph of each function.

19 $g(t) = \cot t + 2$

20. $f(t) = 3 \sec t - 2$

21. $h(t) = -\csc\left(\frac{1}{2}t\right)$

In Exercises 22–23, complete the statement with "odd" or "even."

22. The cosecant function is an _____ function.

23. The secant function is an _____ function.

Section 7.3

24. Let $f(t) = \frac{3}{2} \sin 5t$.

   a. What is the largest possible value of $f(t)$?
   b. Find the smallest positive number t such that $f(t) = 0$.

25. Sketch the graph of $g(t) = -2 \cos t$.

26. Sketch the graph of $f(t) = -\frac{1}{2} \sin 2t$ on the interval $-2\pi \le t \le 2\pi$.

27. Sketch the graph of $f(t) = \sin 4t$ on the interval $0 \le t \le 2\pi$.

28. What is the period of the function $g(t) = \sin 4\pi t$?

29. If $g(t) = 20 \sin(200t)$, for how many values of t with $0 \le t \le 2\pi$ is it true that $g(t) = 1$?

27.

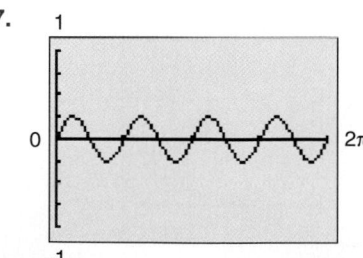

28. $\frac{1}{2}$

29. 400

30. What is the period of $f(t) = -\tan\left(\dfrac{t}{2}\right)$?

31. Which of the following statements is true?
 a. The amplitude of $f(t) = 3 \sin 2t + 1$ is 2.

 b. The period of $g(t) = -\dfrac{1}{2} \cos 2t$ is 4π.

 c. The period of $h(t) = 3 \tan 2t$ is $\dfrac{\pi}{2}$.

 d. The amplitude of $k(t) = -3 \tan t$ is 3.

Section 7.4

32. What are the amplitude, period, and phase shift of the function $h(t) = 13 \cos(14t + 15)$?

33. State the rule of a sine function with amplitude 8, period 5, and phase shift 14.

34. State the rule of a sine function with amplitude 3, period π, and phase shift $\dfrac{\pi}{3}$.

35. State the rule of a periodic function whose graph from $t = 0$ to $t = 2\pi$ closely resembles the graph at left.

In Exercises 36–38, sketch the graph of at least one cycle of each function.

36. $f(t) = \dfrac{1}{2} \cos(2t - \pi) + 3$ **37.** $g(t) = -\sin\left(\dfrac{1}{3}t + \pi\right)$

38. $g(t) = 4 \cos\left(\dfrac{2t}{3}\right) - 5$

In Exercises 39–42, determine graphically whether the given equation could possibly be an identity.

39. $\cos t = \sin\left(t - \dfrac{\pi}{2}\right)$ **40.** $\tan \dfrac{t}{2} = \dfrac{\sin t}{1 + \cos t}$

41. $\dfrac{\sin t - \sin 3t}{\cos t + \cos 3t} = -\tan t$ **42.** $\cos 2t = \dfrac{1}{1 - 2 \sin^2 t}$

Section 7.4.A

In Exercises 43 and 44, find a sine function whose graph looks like the graph of the given function.

43. $f(t) = 6 \sin(4t + 7) - 5 \cos(4t + 8)$

44. $f(t) = -5 \sin(5t - 3) + 2 \cos(5t + 2)$

In Exercises 45 and 46, find a viewing window that shows a complete graph of the function.

45. $f(t) = 3 \sin(300t + 5) - 2 \cos(500t + 8)$

46. $g(t) = 5 \sin(400\pi t + 1) + 2 \cos(150\pi t - 6)$

---

30. 2π

31. c

32. $13; \dfrac{\pi}{7}; -\dfrac{15}{14}$

33. $f(t) = 8 \sin\left(\dfrac{2\pi t - 28\pi}{5}\right)$

34. $f(t) = 3 \sin\left(2t - \dfrac{2\pi}{3}\right)$

35. $f(t) = 2 \cos\left(\dfrac{5t}{2}\right)$

36.

37.

38.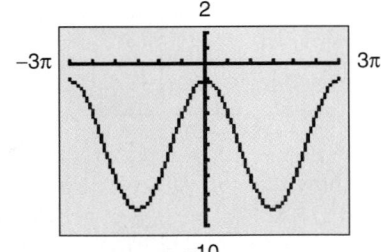

39. not an identity

40. possibly an identity

41. possibly an identity

42. not an identity

43. $f(t) = 10.5588 \sin(4t + 0.4580)$

44. $f(t) = 3.134 \sin(5t - 0.0404)$

45. $0 \le t \le \dfrac{\pi}{50}$ and $-5 \le y \le 5$ (one period)

46. $0 \le t \le 0.04$ and $-7 \le y \le 7$

Approximations with Infinite Series

Example Notes

For **Example 1**, note that $1 + x + x^2 + x^3 + x^4$ is a partial sum of the infinite series $1 + x + x^2 + x^3 + \cdots$. Every partial sum of this series has the form $1 + x + x^2 + \cdots + x^k$.

The graphs of functions of the form $f(x) = 1 + x + x^2 + \cdots + x^k$ can be very different outside of the interval $-1 < x < 1$.

Have students graph $y = \dfrac{1}{1 - x}$ and $y = 1 + x + x^2 + x^3 + x^4 + x^5$ (shown below) and compare the results to Figure 7.C-1.

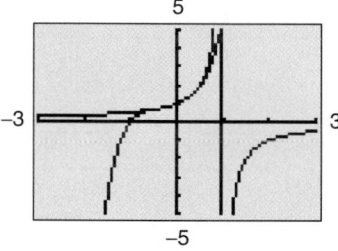

To show that the values of a partial sum $1 + x + x^2 + \cdots + x^k$ get closer to the values of $\dfrac{1}{1 - x}$ when more terms are used in the partial sum, have students graph these functions on the same screen with a viewing window of $-0.7 \le x \le -0.5, 0.5 \le y \le 0.7$:

$Y_1 = \dfrac{1}{1 - x}$, $Y_2 = 1 + x + x^2 + x^3 + x^4$, and
$Y_3 = 1 + x + x^2 + x^3 + x^4 + x^5$.

In the Chapter 1 Can Do Calculus, it was shown that the infinite geometric series $a + ar + ar^2 + ar^3 + \ldots = \dfrac{a}{1 - r}$ when $|r| < 1$. This section will investigate certain functions that can be represented by an infinite series, a topic considered in depth in calculus.

Example 1 Representing a Function as a Series

Write $f(x) = \dfrac{1}{1 - x}$ as an infinite series.

Solution

The expression $\dfrac{1}{1 - x}$ is in the form $\dfrac{a}{1 - r}$, where $a = 1$ and $r = x$. Because

$$\dfrac{a}{1 - r} = a + ar + ar^2 + ar^3 + \ldots \text{ when } |r| < 1,$$

$$\dfrac{1}{1 - x} = 1 + x + x^2 + x^3 + \ldots, \text{ when } |x| < 1.$$

■

To confirm that $\dfrac{1}{1 - x} = 1 + x + x^2 + x^3 + \ldots$ when $|x| < 1$, graph $y = \dfrac{1}{1 - x}$ and $y = 1 + x + x^2 + x^3 + x^4$ on the same screen, as shown in Figure 7.C-1 where $y = 1 + x + x^2 + x^3 + x^4$ is drawn with a heavy line. The graphs of the function and the series are very close when $|x| < 1$, but they diverge when $x < -1$ and when $x > 1$. When more terms are used in graphing the series, the series approximates the function more closely when $|x| < 1$. The set of all values of x for which the series converges to the function is called the **interval of convergence**. The function $\dfrac{1}{1 - x}$ has interval of convergence $-1 < x < 1$. It is not defined when $x = 1$, and when $x = -1$ the infinite series does not converge to a single value.

Other Types of Series

Many interesting functions that can be represented by a series include the product of all the integers from 1 to n. Such a product is written as $n!$, which is read **"n factorial."**

$$n! = 1 \cdot 2 \cdot 3 \cdot 4 \cdots (n - 2)(n - 1)n$$

0! is defined to be the number 1.

Figure 7.C-1

> **Technology Tip**
>
> The factorial feature is found in the **PROB** (or **PRB**) submenu of the **MATH** or **OPTN** menu on most calculators.

520

ADDITIONAL EXAMPLES

Example 1

Write $f(x) = \dfrac{2}{1 - x}$ as an infinite series.

$$\dfrac{2}{1 - x} = 2 + 2x + 2x^2 + 2x^3 + \ldots$$

when $|x| < 1$.

The graphs of $y = \dfrac{2}{1 - x}$ and

$y = 2 + 2x + 2x^2 + 2x^3 + 2x^4$ are shown below.

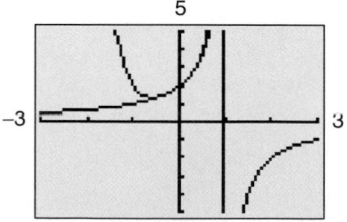

The interval of convergence is $-1 < x < 1$.

10

−10   10

−10

Figure 7.C-2a

10

−10   10

−10

Figure 7.C-2b

10

−10   10

−10

Figure 7.C-2c

Example 2   A Series that Approximates a Function

Find a function that is approximated by the following series in the interval $-\pi \le x \le \pi$.

$$x - \frac{x^3}{3!} + \frac{x^5}{5!} - \frac{x^7}{7!} + \frac{x^9}{9!} - \cdots + (-1)^{n-1}\frac{x^{2n-1}}{(2n-1)!}$$

Solution

Begin by graphing the function formed by the first five terms of the series, as shown in Figure 7.C-2a. Next graph the functions formed by first six terms of the series and then the first seven terms, as shown in Figures 7.C-2b and 7.C-2c.

The graph of the series is beginning to resemble the graph of the sine function. To test the hypothesis that the series converges to the sine function, graph both the sine function and the function formed by series on the same screen using several terms of the series. In Figure 7.C-2d, the series is displayed with the heavier line, and $y = \sin x$ is shown as the lighter line. In calculus it will be shown that the *infinite* series converges to the sine function, and the interval of convergence is the entire set of real numbers.

1

−15   15

−1

Figure 7.C-2d

Exercises

Find an infinite geometric series that represents the given function, and state the interval of convergence.

1. $y = \dfrac{2}{1 - 3x}$ **2.** $y = \dfrac{3}{1 - 2x}$

3. $y = \dfrac{-2}{1 + x}$ **4.** $y = \dfrac{-3}{1 + 2x}$

$-2 + 2x - 2x^2 +$ $-3 + 6x - 12x^2 +$

$2x^3 - 2x^4 + \ldots;$ $24x^3 - 48x^4 + \ldots;$

$-\dfrac{9}{16} \le x \le \dfrac{5}{8}$ $-\dfrac{1}{4} \le x \le \dfrac{11}{32}$

Find a function that is approximated by the following series. State the interval of convergence.

5. $1 - \dfrac{x^2}{2!} + \dfrac{x^4}{4!} - \dfrac{x^6}{6!} + \cdots$ **cos x**; $-\infty \le x \le \infty$

6. $1 - (x - 1) + (x - 1)^2 - (x - 1)^3 + (x - 1)^4 - \cdots$

   $\dfrac{1}{x}$; $0 \le x \le 2$

7. $1 + x + \dfrac{x^2}{2!} + \dfrac{x^3}{3!} + \dfrac{x^4}{4!} + \cdots$

   e^x; $-\infty \le x \le \infty$

521

Exercises

ANSWERS

1. $2 + 6x + 18x^2 + 54x^3 + 162x^4 + \ldots;$

   $-\dfrac{1}{6} \le x \le \dfrac{1}{6}$

2. $3 + 6x + 12x^2 + 24x^3 + 48x^4 + \ldots;$

   $-\dfrac{6}{16} \le x \le \dfrac{5}{16}$

ADDITIONAL EXAMPLES

Example 2

Find a function that is approximated by the following series in the interval $-\pi \le x \le \pi$.

$$5x - \frac{5x^3}{3!} + \frac{5x^5}{5!} - \frac{5x^7}{7!} + \frac{5x^9}{9!} + \cdots +$$
$$(-1)^{n-1}\frac{5x^{2n-1}}{(2n-1)!}$$

Graph of first 6 terms

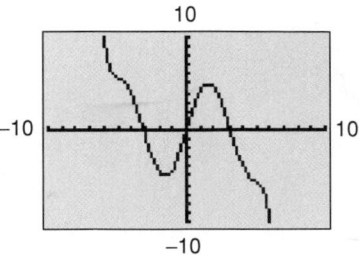

10

−10   10

−10

Graph of first 7 terms

10

−10   10

−10

The function is beginning to resemble a sine function with an amplitude of 5.

Graphs of the first 9 terms of the series and $f(x) = 5 \sin x$

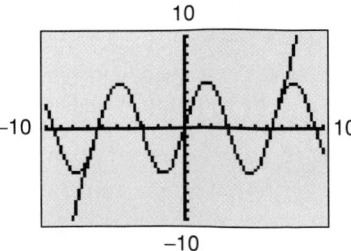

10

−10   10

−10

The function approximated by the series is $f(x) = 5 \sin x$, as shown in the last graph above.

Solving Trigonometric Equations

In this chapter, students will solve trigonometric equations by graphing and by algebraic methods. Most algebraic methods will require the use of inverse trigonometric functions and some algebraic methods will require the use of trigonometric identities. Students will also use modeling to solve harmonic motion problems.

CHAPTER

8 Solving Trigonometric Equations

Round and round we go!

Trigonometric functions are used to analyze periodic phenomena, because simple harmonic motion models circular motion or any phenomenon that is "back and forth." Some examples of simple harmonic motion include a vibrating prong of a tuning fork, a buoy bobbing up and down in water, seismic and ocean waves, spring-mass systems, a piston in a running engine, a particle of air during the passage of a simple sound wave, or a turning Ferris wheel. See Exercise 1 of Section 8.4.

522

Chapter Outline

Interdependence of Sections

8.1

8.2 $\longrightarrow$ 8.3 $\longrightarrow$ 8.4

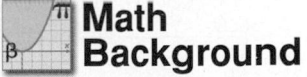

Math Background

Trigonometric identities are sometimes used to solve conditional equations. For example, in Section 8.3, **Example 9** (page 544), a Pythagorean identity is used in solving a conditional equation.

Teaching Notes

Students might need some explanation of the **NOTE** at the bottom of the page. Refer them to the first unit circle and its corresponding graph on page 474. Explain that they can now think of x instead of t as the radian measure of an angle in standard position. The horizontal axis on the corresponding graph can be labeled x, as is customary.

In this chapter, the trigonometric functions are functions of real numbers (which can be thought of as radian measures of angles unless otherwise noted). The independent variable will often be x, but not always.

There are two kinds of trigonometric equations. *Identities*, which will be studied more in Chapter 9, are equations that are valid for all values of the variable for which the equation is defined, such as

$$\sin^2 x + \cos^2 x = 1 \quad \text{and} \quad \cot x = \frac{1}{\tan x}.$$

In this chapter, *conditional equations* will be studied. Conditional equations are valid only for certain values of the variable, such as

$$\sin x = 0, \quad \cos x - \frac{1}{2}, \quad \text{and} \quad 3\sin^2 x - \sin x = 2.$$

If a trigonometric equation is conditional, solutions are found by using techniques similar to those used to solve algebraic equations. Graphs were used to solve some simple trigonometric equations in Chapter 7. This chapter will extend graphical solution techniques and introduce analytic solution methods.

Graphical solution methods are presented in 8.1. Inverse trigonometric functions are discussed in Section 8.2. Methods that use inverse functions, basic identities, and algebra to solve trigonometric equations are considered in Section 8.3. Skills from the Sections 8.1 through 8.3 are applied to problem-solving and real-world applications in Section 8.4.

NOTE In Chapter 7, the variable t was used for trigonometric functions to avoid confusion with the x's and y's that appear in their definitions. Now that you are comfortable with these functions, the letter x, or occasionally y, will be used for the variable. Unless otherwise stated, all trigonometric functions in this chapter are considered as functions of real numbers, rather than functions of angles in degree measure.

523

Section
8.1   Graphical Solutions to Trigonometric Equations

Teaching Notes

After completing **Example 2,** consider having students solve $\sin x = -0.75$ by the intersection method:
Let $Y_1 = \sin x$ and $Y_2 = -0.75$.

COMMON ERROR ALERT

When using the x-intercept method to solve an equation, sign errors are common. In **Example 2,** students might rewrite the equation as $\sin x - 0.75 = 0$. The graph of the incorrect function $f(x) = \sin x - 0.75$ might seem reasonable because it represents a *downward* shift of the graph of $y = \sin x$, and students see a *negative* number in the original equation. Caution students against such sign errors.

Real-World Application

The **Basic Trigonometric Equation** $\sin \alpha = \dfrac{1}{m}$ is used in Exercises 29–32 (page 529), where students will calculate the angle of elevation α of an airplane as a function of its Mach number m.

8.1   Graphical Solutions to Trigonometric Equations

Objectives

- Solve trigonometric equations graphically
- State the complete solution of a trigonometric equation

Any equation involving trigonometric functions can be solved graphically. To solve trigonometric equations graphically, the same methods of graphical solutions are used here as have been used previously to solve polynomial equations, except that trigonometric equations typically have an infinite number of solutions. These solutions are systematically determined by using the periodicity of the function.

Basic Trigonometric Equations

An equation that involves a single trigonometric function set equal to a number is called a **basic equation.** Some examples include the following:

$$\sin x = 0.39, \qquad \cos x = 0.5, \qquad \text{and} \qquad \tan x = -3$$

Examples 1 and 2 show how they can be solved graphically.

Example 1   The Intersection Method

Solve $\tan x = 2$.

Solution

The equation can be solved by graphing $Y_1 = \tan x$ and $Y_2 = 2$ on the same screen and finding intersection points. The x-coordinate of every such point is a number whose tangent is 2; or a solution of $\tan x = 2$. Figure 8.1-1 indicates that there are infinitely many intersection points, so the equation has an infinite number of solutions.

Figure 8.1-1

Figure 8.1-2

The function $f(x) = \tan x$ completes one cycle on the interval $\left(-\dfrac{\pi}{2}, \dfrac{\pi}{2}\right)$, and there is one solution of $\tan x = 2$ in this interval. Using the intersection finder on a graphing calculator gives the approximate solution in this interval.

$$x = 1.1071$$

Because the graph of $f(x) = \tan x$ repeats its pattern to the left and to the right, the other solutions will differ from this first solution by multiples of π, the period of the tangent function. The other solutions are

$$1.1071 \pm \pi, \qquad 1.1071 \pm 2\pi, \qquad \text{and} \qquad 1.1071 \pm 3\pi,$$

and so on. All solutions can be expressed as

$$1.1071 + k\pi,$$

where k is any integer.

NOTE Solutions in this chapter are often rounded, but the full decimal expansion given by the calculator is used in all computations. The symbol = is used rather than ≈ even though these calculator solutions are approximations of the actual solutions.

Example 2   **The x-Intercept Method**

Solve $\sin x = -0.75$.

Solution

Rewrite the equation $\sin x = -0.75$ as

$$\sin x + 0.75 = 0.$$

Recall from Section 2.1 that the solutions of this equation are the x-intercepts of the graph of

$$f(x) = \sin x + 0.75.$$

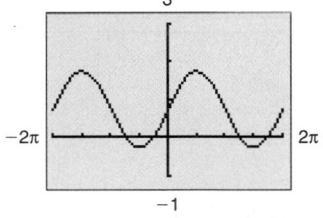

Figure 8.1-3

The graph of f is shown in Figure 8.1-3. The function has a period of 2π and the viewing window can be modified to show one period of $f(x) = \sin x + 0.75$. Figures 8.1-4a and 8.1-4b show that there are two zeros of f on the interval $[0, 2\pi]$, so the equation has two solutions on that interval.

The calculator's zero finder calculates the zeros:

$$x = 3.9897 \qquad\qquad\qquad x = 5.4351$$

Figure 8.1-4a   **Figure 8.1-4b**

All solutions can be expressed as $0.3363 + 2k\pi$ or $2.8053 + 2k\pi$, where k is any integer.

Example 1

Solve $\tan x = -1$.
The graphs of $Y_1 = \tan x$ and $Y_2 = -1$ intersect in an infinite number of points. The x-coordinates of the points of intersection are solutions of $\tan x = -1$.

All solutions can be expressed as $-0.7854 + k\pi$, where k is any integer.

Example 2

Solve $\sin x = 0.33$.
Rewrite the equation as $\sin x - 0.33 = 0$. Graph $f(x) = \sin x - 0.33$.

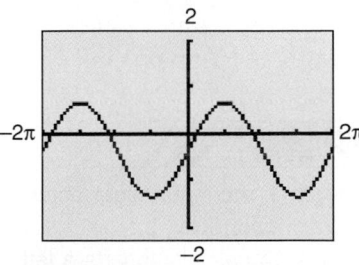

f has a period of 2π. Find the zeros of f on the interval $[0, 2\pi]$.

Teaching Notes

In the procedure **Solving Trigonometric Equations Graphically,** step 2 is to determine the period of f. To determine the period of f, it is a good practice to graph f over a large enough interval so that you can see a repeating pattern. In **Example 3,** f is graphed in a viewing window from -2π to 4π.

Point out that this procedure applies to trigonometric equations that involve one trigonometric function, as in **Examples 1** and **2,** or more than one trigonometric function, as in **Examples 3** and **4.**

The equation in **Example 3** can also be solved using the intersection method. Rewrite the equation as $3\sin^2 x - 2 = \cos x$. Graph the functions $Y_1 = 3\sin^2 x - 2$ and $Y_2 = \cos x$, and find x-coordinates of points of intersection. One of the solutions, 1.1216, is shown below.

You can ask students if they can think of another equation and pair of functions they could use to solve the equation by the intersection method.

possible answer: $3\sin^2 x = \cos x + 2$, $Y_1 = 3\sin^2 x$ and $Y_2 = \cos x + 2$

COMMON ERROR ALERT

In **Example 3,** students might enter the function incorrectly. If their calculator automatically inserts a left parenthesis after cos and sin, they *must* insert the matching right parenthesis.

$Y_1 = 3(\sin(x))^2 - \cos(x - 2$ *incorrect*
$Y_1 = 3(\sin(x))^2 - \cos(x) - 2$ *correct*

Because the graph repeats its pattern every 2π, the other solutions will differ from these two by multiples of 2π, the period of $f(x) = \sin x + 0.75$. Therefore, all solutions of $\sin x = -0.75$ are

$$x = 3.9897 + 2k\pi \quad \text{and} \quad x = 5.4351 + 2k\pi,$$

where k is any integer. ∎

Other Trigonometric Equations

The procedures in Examples 1 and 2 can be used to solve any trigonometric equation graphically.

Example 3   The *x*-intercept Method

Solve $3\sin^2 x - \cos x - 2 = 0$.

Solution

Both sine and cosine have period 2π, so the period of $f(x) = 3\sin^2 x - \cos x - 2$ is at most 2π. The graph of f, which is shown in two viewing windows in Figure 8.1-5, does not repeat its pattern over any interval of less than 2π, so you can conclude that f has a period of 2π.

Figure 8.1-5a

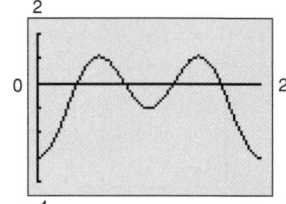

Figure 8.1-5b

The function f makes one complete period on the interval $[0, 2\pi)$, as shown in Figure 8.1-5b. The equation has four solutions between 0 and 2π, namely, the four x-intercepts of the graph in that interval. A graphical zero finder shows these four solutions.

$$x \approx 1.1216 \qquad x \approx 2.4459 \qquad x \approx 3.8373 \qquad x \approx 5.1616$$

Because the graph repeats its pattern every 2π, all solutions of the equation are given by

$$x \approx 1.1216 + 2k\pi, \qquad x \approx 2.4459 + 2k\pi,$$
$$x \approx 3.8373 + 2k\pi, \qquad x \approx 5.1616 + 2k\pi,$$

where k is any integer. ∎

Technology Tip

Enter $3\sin^2 x$ on a calculator as

$$3(\sin x)^2$$

or $3(\sin(x))^2$.

The solution methods in Examples 1 through 3 depend only on knowing the period of a function and all the solutions of the equation in one period. A similar procedure can be used to solve any trigonometric equation graphically.

Solving Trigonometric Equations Graphically

1. Write the equation in the form $f(x) = 0$.
2. Determine the period p of f.
3. Graph f over an interval of length p.
4. Use a calculator's zero finder to determine the x-intercepts of the graph in this interval.
5. For each x-intercept u, all of the numbers

$$u + kp \text{ where } k \text{ is any integer}$$

are solutions of the equation.

In Example 1, for example, p was π. In Examples 2 and 3, p was 2π.

Example 4   **Solving Any Trigonometric Equation**

Solve $\tan x = 3 \sin 2x$.

Solution

First rewrite the equation

$$\tan x - 3 \sin 2x = 0$$

Next, determine the period of $f(x) = \tan x - 3 \sin 2x$. Recall from Section 7.3 that $y = 3 \sin 2x$ has a period of $\frac{2\pi}{2} = \pi$, which is also the period of $y = \tan x$. Therefore, the period of f is π. Figure 8.1-6 shows the graph of f on the interval $\left(-\frac{\pi}{2}, \frac{\pi}{2}\right)$, an interval of length π.

Even without the graph, it can be easily verified that there is an x-intercept at 0.

$$f(0) = \tan 0 - 3 \sin(2 \cdot 0) = 0$$

Using the calculator's zero finder gives the other x-intercepts of the graph of f on this interval.

$$x = -1.1503 \quad \text{and} \quad x = 1.1503$$

Because f has a period of π, all solutions of the equation $\tan x = 3 \sin 2x$ are

$$x = -1.1503 + k\pi, \quad x = 0 + k\pi, \quad \text{and} \quad x = 1.1503 + k\pi,$$

where k is any integer. ∎

Figure 8.1-6

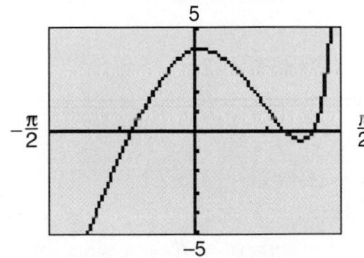

ADDITIONAL EXAMPLES

Example 5

Solve $3\cos^2\theta - 2\cos\theta - 3 = 0$.
The period of the function
$f(\theta) = 3\cos^2\theta - 2\cos\theta - 3$ is $360°$
and the graph is shown below.

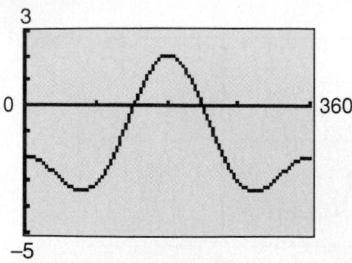

All solutions of the equation are given by $\theta \approx 136.12° + 360°k$ and $\theta \approx 223.88° + 360°k$, where k is any integer.

Exercises 8.1

ANSWERS

1–14. For graphs see pp. 1069–1070.

1. $x = 0.5275 + k\pi$ or $1.6868 + k\pi$

2. $x = 0.7124 + \dfrac{2\pi}{3}k$ or
   $1.8452 + \dfrac{2\pi}{3}k$

3. $x = 0.4959 + 2k\pi$ or
   $1.2538 + 2k\pi$ or $1.5708 + 2k\pi$ or
   $1.8877 + 2k\pi$ or $2.6457 + 2k\pi$
   or $4.7124 + 2k\pi$

4. $x = 0.3289 + k\pi$ or $2.8127 + k\pi$

5. $x = 0.1671 + 2k\pi$ or
   $1.8256 + 2k\pi$ or $2.8867 + 2k\pi$ or
   $4.5453 + 2k\pi$

6. $x = 4.7123 + 2k\pi$

7. $x = 1.2161 + 2k\pi$ or
   $5.0671 + 2k\pi$

8. $x = 1.0106 + 2k\pi$ or
   $2.1310 + 2k\pi$

9. $x = 2.4620 + 2k\pi$ or
   $3.8212 + 2k\pi$

10. $x = 0.9273 + 2k\pi$

11. $x = 0.5166 + 2k\pi$ or
    $5.6766 + 2k\pi$

12. $x = 2.4263 + 2k\pi$ or
    $3.8569 + 2k\pi$

13. **a.** The graph of $f(x) = \sin x$ on
    the interval from 0 to 2π
    shows that $\sin x = 1$ only
    when $x = \dfrac{\pi}{2}$. Since
    $\sin x$ has period 2π, all other
    solutions are obtained by

Trigonometric Equations in Degree Measure

Some real-world applications of trigonometric equations require solutions to be expressed as angles in degree measure. The graphical solution procedure is the same, except that you must set the mode of your calculator to "degree."

Example 5 Trigonometric Equations in Degree Measure

Solve $2\sin^2\theta - 3\sin\theta - 3 = 0$.

Solution

The period of the function $f(\theta) = 2\sin^2\theta - 3\sin\theta - 3$ is $360°$, and Figure 8.1-7 shows the graph of f on the interval $[0°, 360°)$.

A graphical zero finder determines the approximate x-intercepts.

$$\theta \approx 223.33° \qquad \text{and} \qquad \theta \approx 316.67°$$

Using the fact that the period of f is $360°$, all solutions of the equation are

$$\theta \approx 223.33° + 360°k \qquad \text{and} \qquad \theta \approx 316.67° + 360°k,$$

where k is any integer.

Figure 8.1-7

Exercises 8.1

In Exercises 1–12, solve the equation graphically.

1. $4\sin 2x - 3\cos 2x = 2$

2. $5\sin 3x + 6\cos 3x = 1$

3. $3\sin^3 2x = 2\cos x$

4. $\sin^2 2x - 3\cos 2x + 2 = 0$

5. $\tan x + 5\sin x = 1$

6. $2\cos^2 x + \sin x + 1 = 0$

7. $\cos^3 x - 3\cos x + 1 = 0$

8. $\tan x = 3\cos x$

9. $\cos^4 x - 3\cos^3 x + \cos x = 1$

10. $\sec x + \tan x = 3$

11. $\sin^3 x + 2\sin^2 x - 3\cos x + 2 = 0$

12. $\csc^2 x + \sec x = 1$

13. Use the graph of the sine function to show the following.

    a. The solutions of $\sin x = 1$ are
    $$x = \frac{\pi}{2}, \frac{5\pi}{2}, \frac{9\pi}{2}, \ldots \text{ and}$$
    $$x = \frac{-3\pi}{2}, \frac{-7\pi}{2}, \frac{-11\pi}{2}, \ldots.$$

    b. The solutions of $\sin x = -1$ are
    $$x = \frac{3\pi}{2}, \frac{7\pi}{2}, \frac{11\pi}{2}, \ldots \text{ and}$$
    $$x = \frac{-\pi}{2}, \frac{-5\pi}{2}, \frac{-9\pi}{2}, \ldots.$$

14. Use the graph of the cosine function to show the following.

    a. The solutions of $\cos x = 1$ are
    $x = 0, \pm 2\pi, \pm 4\pi, \pm 6\pi, \ldots.$

    b. The solutions of $\cos x = -1$ are
    $x = \pm\pi, \pm 3\pi, \pm 5\pi, \ldots.$

---

adding or subtracting integer multiples of 2π from $\dfrac{\pi}{2}$, that is,

$$\frac{\pi}{2} + 2\pi = \frac{5\pi}{2}, \frac{\pi}{2} + 2(2\pi) = \frac{9\pi}{2},$$

$$\frac{\pi}{2} + 3(2\pi) = \frac{13\pi}{2}, \text{ etc., and}$$

$$\frac{\pi}{2} - 2\pi = -\frac{3\pi}{2}, \frac{\pi}{2} - 2(2\pi) = -\frac{7\pi}{2},$$

$$\frac{\pi}{2} - 3(2\pi) = -\frac{11\pi}{2}, \text{ etc.}$$

b. Similarly, the graph shows that $\sin x = -1$ only when $x = \dfrac{3\pi}{2}$, so that all solutions are obtained by adding or subtracting integer multiples of 2π from $\dfrac{3\pi}{2}$:

$$\frac{3\pi}{2} + 2\pi = \frac{7\pi}{2}, \frac{3\pi}{2} + 2(2\pi) = \frac{11\pi}{2},$$

$$\frac{3\pi}{2} + 3(2\pi) = \frac{15\pi}{2}, \text{ etc.,}$$

and $\dfrac{3\pi}{2} - 2\pi = -\dfrac{\pi}{2}, \dfrac{3\pi}{2} - 2(2\pi) = -\dfrac{5\pi}{2},$

$$\frac{3\pi}{2} - 3(2\pi) = -\frac{9\pi}{2}, \text{ etc.}$$

In Exercises 15–18, approximate all solutions of the given equation in $(0, 2\pi)$.

15. $\sin x = 0.119$ **16.** $\cos x = 0.958$

17. $\tan x = 5$ **18.** $\tan x = 17.65$

In Exercises 19–28, find all angles θ with $0° \leq \theta < 360°$ that are solutions of the given equation.

19. $\tan \theta = 7.95$ **20.** $\tan \theta = 69.4$

21. $\cos \theta = -0.42$ **22.** $\cot \theta = -2.4$

23. $2 \sin^2 \theta + 3 \sin \theta + 1 = 0$

24. $4 \cos^2 \theta + 4 \cos \theta - 3 = 0$

25. $\tan^2 \theta - 3 = 0$ **26.** $2 \sin^2 \theta = 1$

27. $4 \cos^2 \theta + 4 \cos \theta + 1 = 0$
$\theta = 120°, 240°$
28. $\sin^2 \theta - 3 \sin \theta = 10$
no solution

At the instant you hear a sonic boom from an airplane overhead, your angle of elevation α to the plane is given by the equation

$$\sin \alpha = \frac{1}{m}$$

where m is the Mach number for the speed of the plane (Mach 1 is the speed of sound, Mach 2.5 is 2.5 times the speed of sound, etc.). In Exercises 29–32, find the angle of elevation (in degrees) for the given Mach number. Remember that an angle of elevation must be between 0° and 90°.

29. $m = 1.1$
$\alpha \approx$ **65.38°**
30. $m = 1.6$
$\alpha \approx$ **38.68°**
31. $m = 2$
$\alpha =$ **30°**
32. $m = 2.4$
$\alpha \approx$ **24.62°**

33. *Critical Thinking* Under what conditions (on the constant) does a basic equation involving the sine and cosine function have no solutions?

34. *Critical Thinking* Under what conditions (on the constant) does a basic equation involving the secant and cosecant function have no solutions?

15. $x \approx 0.1193$ or 3.0223
16. $x \approx 0.2909$ or $x = 5.9923$
17. $x \approx 1.3734$ or 4.5150
18. $x \approx 1.5142$ or $x = 4.6558$
19. $\theta \approx 82.83°, 262.83°$
20. $\theta \approx 89.17°, 269.17°$
21. $\theta \approx 114.83°, 245.17°$
22. $\theta \approx 337.38°, 157.38°$
23. $\theta = 210°, 270°, 330°$
24. $\theta = 60°, 300°$
25. $\theta = 60°, 120°, 240°, 300°$
26. $\theta = 45°, 135°, 225°, 315°$
33. $\sin x = k$ and $\cos x = k$ have no solutions when $k > 1$ or $k < -1$
34. $\sec x = k$ and $\csc x = k$ have no solutions when $-1 < k < 1$

8.2 Inverse Trigonometric Functions

Objectives

- Define the domain and range of the inverse trigonometric functions
- Use inverse trigonometric function notation

NOTE Other ways of restricting the domains of trigonometric functions are possible. Those presented here for sine, cosine, and tangent are the ones universally agreed upon by mathematicians.

Many trigonometric equations can be solved without graphing. Non-graphical solution methods make use of the *inverse trigonometric functions* that are introduced in this section.

Recall from Section 3.6 that a function cannot have an inverse function unless its graph has the following property.

No horizontal line intersects the graph more than once.

You have seen that the graphs of trigonometric functions do not have this property. However, restricting their domains can modify the trigonometric functions so that they do have inverse functions.

Inverse Sine Function

The *restricted sine function* is $f(x) = \sin x$, when its domain is restricted to the interval $\left[-\frac{\pi}{2}, \frac{\pi}{2}\right]$. Its graph in Figure 8.2-1 shows that for each number v in the interval $[-1, 1]$, there is exactly one number u in the interval $\left[-\frac{\pi}{2}, \frac{\pi}{2}\right]$ such that $\sin u = v$.

Section
8.2 Inverse Trigonometric Functions

Teaching Notes

Review these facts about inverse functions from page 210:
Let f be a function. The following statements are equivalent.
- The inverse of f is a function.
- f is one-to-one.
- The graph of f passes the Horizontal Line Test.
The inverse function, if it exists, is written as f^{-1}, where if $y = f(x)$, then $x = f^{-1}(y)$.

Point out that trigonometric functions are not one-to-one because different inputs can result in the same output. To illustrate this fact for the sine function, note that $\sin(\pi) = \sin(3\pi) = 0$.

You might want to recall the definition of a one-to-one function (page 208):

A function f is one-to-one if $f(a) = f(b)$ implies that $a = b$.

14. a. The graph of $f(x) = \cos x$ on the interval from 0 to 2π shows that $\cos x = 1$ only when $x = 2\pi$ and 0. Since $\cos x$ has period 2π, all other solutions are obtained by adding or subtracting integer multiples of 2π from 2π, that is,
$2\pi + 2\pi = 4\pi, 2\pi + 2(2\pi) = 6\pi$,
$2\pi + 3(2\pi) = 8\pi$, etc., and
$2\pi - 2\pi = 0, 2\pi - 2(2\pi) = -2\pi$,
$2\pi - 3(2\pi) = -4\pi$, etc.

b. Similarly, the graph shows that $\cos x = -1$ only when $x = \pi$, so that all solutions are obtained by adding or subtracting integer multiples of 2π from π: $\pi + 2\pi = 3\pi$,
$\pi + 2(2\pi) = 5\pi, \pi + 3(2\pi) = 7\pi$, etc., and $\pi - 2\pi = -\pi, \pi - 2(2\pi) = -3\pi$,
$\pi - 3(2\pi) = -5\pi$, etc.

Teaching Notes

Remind students that the notation $\left[-\frac{\pi}{2}, \frac{\pi}{2}\right]$ represents a closed interval, so it includes its endpoints $-\frac{\pi}{2}$ and $\frac{\pi}{2}$.

The range of the **Inverse Sine Function** is $\left[-\frac{\pi}{2}, \frac{\pi}{2}\right]$.

You might want to have students supply exact function values for the graph of $g(x) = \sin^{-1} x$ shown below. They can use page 448 for reference.

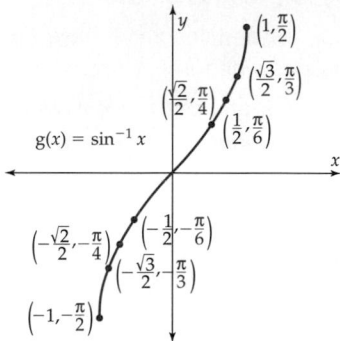

Use a diagram such as the one below to show the symmetric relationship of the restricted sine graph and the inverse sine graph.

Figure 8.2-1

Because the graph of the restricted sine function passes the Horizontal Line Test, it has an inverse function. This inverse function is called the **inverse sine** (or **arcsine**) **function** and is denoted by

$$g(x) = \sin^{-1} x \text{ or } g(x) = \arcsin x.$$

It is convenient to think of a value of an inverse trigonometric function as an angle; $\sin^{-1}\frac{\sqrt{3}}{2}$ represents an angle in the interval $\left[-\frac{\pi}{2}, \frac{\pi}{2}\right]$ whose sine is $\frac{\sqrt{3}}{2}$. Since $\sin\frac{\pi}{3} = \frac{\sqrt{3}}{2}$, then $\sin^{-1}\frac{\sqrt{3}}{2} = \frac{\pi}{3}$.

The graph of the inverse sine function, shown in Figure 8.2-2, is readily obtained from a calculator. Because $g(x) = \sin^{-1} x$ is the inverse of the restricted sine function, its graph is the reflection of the graph of the restricted sine function across the line $y = x$.

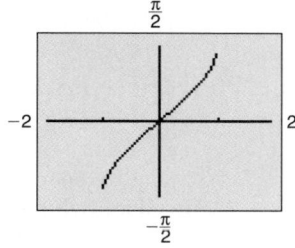

Figure 8.2-2

The domain of $g(x) = \sin^{-1} x$ is the interval $[-1, 1]$, and its range is the interval $\left[-\frac{\pi}{2}, \frac{\pi}{2}\right]$.

Inverse Sine Function

> For each v with $-1 \le v \le 1$,
>
> $\sin^{-1} v$ is the unique number u in the interval $\left[-\frac{\pi}{2}, \frac{\pi}{2}\right]$ whose sine is v; that is,
>
> $$\sin^{-1} v = u \quad \text{exactly when} \quad \sin u = v.$$

The inverse sine function can be evaluated by using the SIN^{-1} key (sometimes labeled ASIN) on a calculator. For example,

$$\sin^{-1}(-0.67) = -0.7342 \quad \text{and} \quad \sin^{-1} 0.42 = 0.4334.$$

For many special values, however, you can evaluate the inverse sine function without using a calculator.

Example 1 Special Values

Evaluate:

a. $\sin^{-1} \dfrac{1}{2}$ **b.** $\sin^{-1}\left(-\dfrac{\sqrt{2}}{2}\right)$

Solution

a. $\sin^{-1} \dfrac{1}{2}$ is the number in the interval $\left[-\dfrac{\pi}{2}, \dfrac{\pi}{2}\right]$ whose sine is $\dfrac{1}{2}$. From your study of special values, you know that $\sin \dfrac{\pi}{6} = \dfrac{1}{2}$. Because $\dfrac{\pi}{6}$ is in the interval $\left[-\dfrac{\pi}{2}, \dfrac{\pi}{2}\right]$, $\sin^{-1} \dfrac{1}{2} = \dfrac{\pi}{6}$.

b. $\sin^{-1}\left(-\dfrac{\sqrt{2}}{2}\right) = -\dfrac{\pi}{4}$ because $\sin\left(-\dfrac{\pi}{4}\right) = -\dfrac{\sqrt{2}}{2}$ and $-\dfrac{\pi}{4}$ is in the interval $\left[-\dfrac{\pi}{2}, \dfrac{\pi}{2}\right]$. ∎

CAUTION

The notation $\sin^{-1} x$ is *not* exponential notation. It does *not* mean $(\sin x)^{-1}$ or $\dfrac{1}{\sin x}$. For instance, Example 1 shows that

$$\sin^{-1} \frac{1}{2} = \frac{\pi}{6} \approx 0.5236,$$

but this is not equivalent to

$$\left(\sin \frac{1}{2}\right)^{-1} = \frac{1}{\sin \frac{1}{2}} \approx \frac{1}{0.4794} \approx 2.0858.$$

Suppose $-1 \le v \le 1$ and $\sin^{-1} v = u$. Then by definition of the inverse sine function, $-\dfrac{\pi}{2} \le u \le \dfrac{\pi}{2}$ and $\sin u = v$. Therefore,

$$\sin^{-1}(\sin u) = \sin^{-1}(v) = u \quad \text{and} \quad \sin(\sin^{-1} v) = \sin(u) = v.$$

This shows that the restricted sine function and the inverse sine function have the usual composition properties of other inverse functions.

Example Notes

Finding the inverse trigonometric function values in **Example 1** depends on knowing special trigonometric function values.

In **1a**, students can recall the appropriate angle in standard position whose sine is $\dfrac{1}{2}$. In **1b**, students can recall the appropriate angle in standard position whose sine is $-\dfrac{\sqrt{2}}{2}$, or $-\dfrac{1}{\sqrt{2}}$.

ADDITIONAL EXAMPLES

Example 1

a. Evaluate $\sin^{-1} \dfrac{\sqrt{3}}{2}$. $\dfrac{\pi}{3}$

b. Evaluate $\sin^{-1}(-1)$. $-\dfrac{\pi}{2}$

Teaching Notes

Discuss the second **Technology Tip** on page 531. Challenge students to find all values of x for which they will get an error message if they try to compute $\sin^{-1} x$. $x < -1$, $x > 1$

Math Background

The inverse sine function is also called the arcsine function because an inverse sine function value is an arc measure. For example, $\sin^{-1} \dfrac{\sqrt{3}}{2} = \dfrac{\pi}{3}$.

Note in the unit circle below, $\dfrac{\pi}{3}$ is the measure of arc PQ.

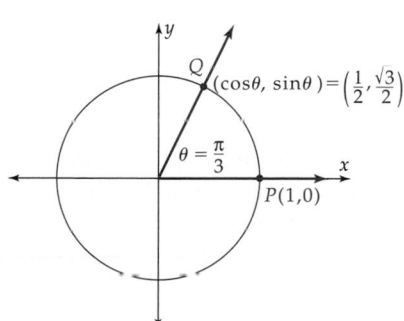

Teaching Notes

To illustrate the **Properties of Inverse Sine**, ask:

- What is the sine of $\frac{\pi}{2}$? 1
- What is the inverse sine of 1? $\frac{\pi}{2}$

Summarize these two facts by saying:

"The inverse sine of the sine of $\frac{\pi}{2}$ is $\frac{\pi}{2}$."
and
"The sine of the inverse sine of 1 is 1."

Example Notes

In **Example 2**, students can use decimal values to show that $\frac{\pi}{6}$ is in the interval $\left[-\frac{\pi}{2}, \frac{\pi}{2}\right]$, but $\frac{5\pi}{6}$ is not in that interval.

$\frac{\pi}{6} \approx 0.52$, $\frac{5\pi}{6} \approx 2.62$, $\frac{\pi}{2} \approx 1.57$

0.52 is in $[-1.57, 1.57]$, but 2.62 is not in $[-1.57, 1.57]$.

Teaching Notes

The range of the inverse cosine function is $[0, \pi]$.

You might want to have students supply exact function values for the graph of $g(x) = \cos^{-1} x$ shown below. They can use page 448 for reference.

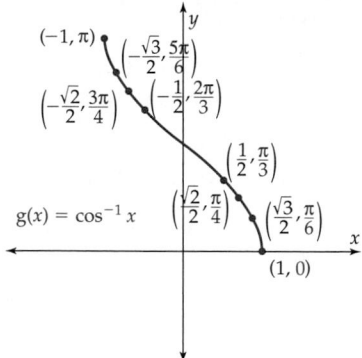

Use a diagram such as the one below to show the symmetric relationship of the restricted cosine graph and the inverse cosine graph.

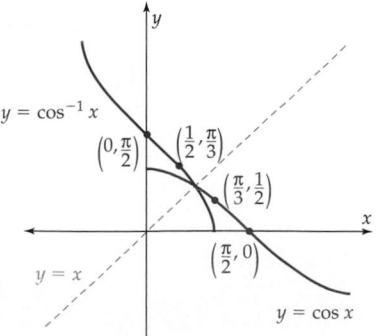

Properties of Inverse Sine

$$\sin^{-1}(\sin u) = u \quad \text{if} \quad -\frac{\pi}{2} \leq u \leq \frac{\pi}{2}$$

$$\sin(\sin^{-1} v) = v \quad \text{if} \quad -1 \leq v \leq 1$$

Example 2   **Composition of Inverse Functions**

Explain why $\sin^{-1}\left(\sin \frac{\pi}{6}\right) = \frac{\pi}{6}$ is true but $\sin^{-1}\left(\sin \frac{5\pi}{6}\right) = \frac{5\pi}{6}$ is *not* true.

Solution

You know that $\sin \frac{\pi}{6} = \frac{1}{2}$, so by substitution

$$\sin^{-1}\left(\sin \frac{\pi}{6}\right) = \sin^{-1}\left(\frac{1}{2}\right) = \frac{\pi}{6}$$

because $\frac{\pi}{6}$ is in the interval $\left[-\frac{\pi}{2}, \frac{\pi}{2}\right]$.

Although $\sin \frac{5\pi}{6}$ is also $\frac{1}{2}$, by substitution

$$\sin^{-1}\left(\sin \frac{5\pi}{6}\right) = \sin^{-1}\left(\frac{1}{2}\right) = \frac{\pi}{6},$$

not $\frac{5\pi}{6}$, because $\frac{5\pi}{6}$ is not in the interval $\left[-\frac{\pi}{2}, \frac{\pi}{2}\right]$. ∎

Inverse Cosine Function

The *restricted cosine function* is $f(x) = \cos x$, when its domain is restricted to the interval $[0, \pi]$. Its graph in Figure 8.2-3 shows that for each number v in the interval $[-1, 1]$, there is exactly one number u in the interval $[0, \pi]$ such that $\cos u = v$.

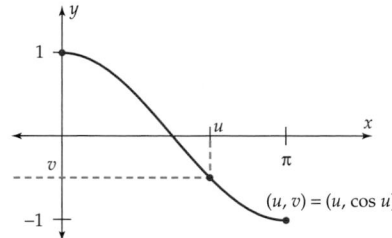

Figure 8.2-3

Because the graph of the restricted cosine function passes the horizontal line test, it has an inverse function. This inverse function is called the **inverse cosine** (or **arccosine**) **function** and is denoted by

$$g(x) = \cos^{-1} x \text{ or } g(x) = \arccos x.$$

The graph of the inverse cosine function, which is the reflection of the graph of the restricted cosine function (Figure 8.2-3) across the line $y = x$, is shown in Figure 8.2-4.

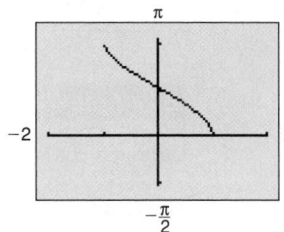

Figure 8.2-4

The domain of $g(x) = \cos^{-1} x$ is the interval $[-1, 1]$ and its range is $[0, \pi]$.

Inverse Cosine Function

For each v with $-1 \leq v \leq 1$,

$\cos^{-1} v$ is the unique number u in the interval $[0, \pi]$ whose cosine is v; that is,

$$\cos^{-1} v = u \qquad \text{exactly when} \qquad \cos u = v.$$

The properties of the inverse cosine function are similar to the properties of the inverse sine function.

Properties of Inverse Cosine

$$\cos^{-1}(\cos u) = u \quad \text{if} \quad 0 \leq u \leq \pi$$

$$\cos(\cos^{-1} v) = v \quad \text{if} \quad -1 \leq v \leq 1$$

Example 3   Evaluating Inverse Cosine Expressions

Evaluate the following.

a. $\cos^{-1} \dfrac{1}{2}$ **b.** $\cos^{-1} 0$ **c.** $\cos^{-1}(-0.63)$

Teaching Notes

Some students may wonder why the domain of the restricted cosine function is $[0, \pi]$ instead of $\left[-\dfrac{\pi}{2}, \dfrac{\pi}{2}\right]$.

Have students graph the cosine function with the viewing window $\left[-\dfrac{\pi}{2}, \dfrac{\pi}{2}\right]$ and explain why that interval is not the domain.

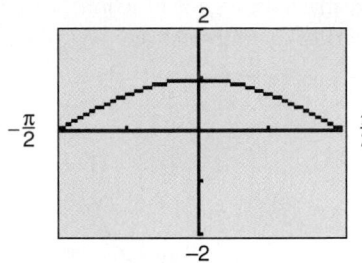

This graph does not pass the Horizontal Line Test.

ADDITIONAL EXAMPLES

Example 2

Explain why $\sin^{-1}\left(\sin \dfrac{\pi}{4}\right) = \dfrac{\pi}{4}$ is true,

but $\sin^{-1}\left(\sin \dfrac{7\pi}{4}\right) = \dfrac{7\pi}{4}$ is *not* true.

$$\sin^{-1}\left(\sin \dfrac{\pi}{4}\right) = \sin^{-1}\left(\dfrac{\sqrt{2}}{2}\right) = \dfrac{\pi}{4}$$

because $\dfrac{\pi}{4}$ is in the interval $\left[-\dfrac{\pi}{2}, \dfrac{\pi}{2}\right]$.

$$\sin^{-1}\left(\sin \dfrac{7\pi}{4}\right) = \sin^{-1}\left(-\dfrac{\sqrt{2}}{2}\right) = -\dfrac{\pi}{4},$$

not $\dfrac{7\pi}{4}$, because $\dfrac{7\pi}{4}$ is not in the interval $\left[-\dfrac{\pi}{2}, \dfrac{\pi}{2}\right]$.

Example 3

Evaluate the following.

a. $\cos^{-1} 1$ 0

b. $\cos^{-1}\left(-\dfrac{\sqrt{2}}{2}\right)$ $\dfrac{3\pi}{4}$

c. $\cos^{-1}(0.14)$ 1.4303

Teaching Notes

The tangent function is discontinuous at all values of x equal to $\frac{k\pi}{2}$, where k is any integer. Therefore, the domain of the restricted tangent function is the open interval $\left(-\frac{\pi}{2}, \frac{\pi}{2}\right)$, not the closed interval $\left[-\frac{\pi}{2}, \frac{\pi}{2}\right]$.

The restricted tangent function has vertical asymptotes at $x = -\frac{\pi}{2}$ and $x = \frac{\pi}{2}$.

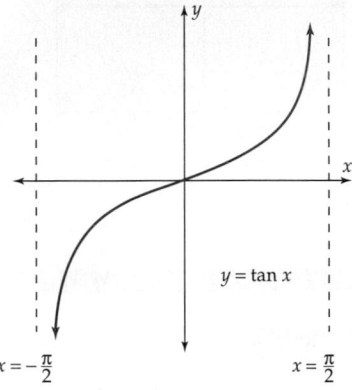

The inverse tangent function has horizontal asymptotes at $y = -\frac{\pi}{2}$ and $y = \frac{\pi}{2}$.

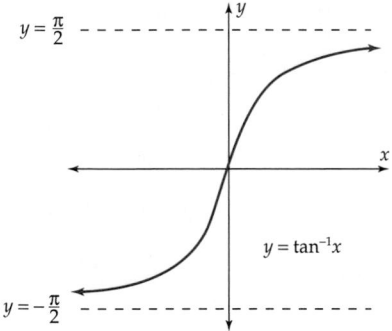

The range of the restricted tangent function is all real numbers. Therefore, the domain of the inverse tangent function is all real numbers.

The range of the inverse tangent function is $\left(-\frac{\pi}{2}, \frac{\pi}{2}\right)$.

> **CAUTION**
>
> $\cos^{-1}$ does *not* mean $(\cos x)^{-1}$ or $\frac{1}{\cos x}$.

Solution

a. $\cos^{-1} \frac{1}{2} = \frac{\pi}{3}$ because $\frac{\pi}{3}$ is the unique number in the interval $[0, \pi]$ whose cosine is $\frac{1}{2}$.

b. $\cos^{-1} 0 = \frac{\pi}{2}$ because $\cos \frac{\pi}{2} = 0$ and $0 \le \frac{\pi}{2} \le \pi$.

c. The $\cos^{-1}$ command on a calculator shows that $\cos^{-1}(-0.63) = 2.2523$. ∎

Example 4   Equivalent Algebraic Expressions

Write $\sin(\cos^{-1} v)$ as an algebraic expression in v.

Solution

Let $\cos^{-1} v = u$, where $0 \le u \le \pi$. Construct a right triangle containing an angle of u radians where $\cos u = \dfrac{\text{adjacent}}{\text{hypotenuse}} = v$, as shown in Figure 8.2-5. By the Pythagorean Theorem, the length of the side opposite u is $\sqrt{1 - v^2}$. By the definition of sine,

$$\sin u = \frac{\text{opposite}}{\text{hypotenuse}} = \frac{\sqrt{1 - v^2}}{1} = \sqrt{1 - v^2}$$

Therefore, $\sin(\cos^{-1} v) = \sqrt{1 - v^2}$. ∎

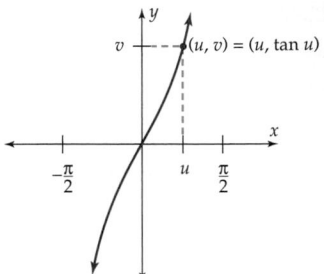

Figure 8.2-5

Inverse Tangent Function

The *restricted tangent function* is $f(x) = \tan x$, when its domain is restricted to the interval $\left(-\frac{\pi}{2}, \frac{\pi}{2}\right)$. Its graph in Figure 8.2-6 shows that for every real number v, there is exactly one number u between $-\frac{\pi}{2}$ and $\frac{\pi}{2}$ such that $\tan u = v$.

Figure 8.2-6

Because the graph of the restricted tangent function passes the horizontal line test, it has an inverse function. This inverse function is called the **inverse tangent** (or **arctangent**) **function** and is denoted

$$g(x) = \tan^{-1} x \text{ or } g(x) = \arctan x.$$

The graph of the inverse tangent function, which is the reflection of the graph of the restricted tangent function (Figure 8.2-6) across the line $y = x$, is shown in Figure 8.2-7.

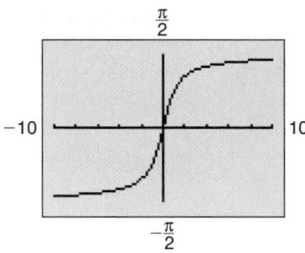

Figure 8.2-7

The domain of $g(x) = \tan^{-1} x$ is the set of all real numbers and its range is the interval $\left(-\dfrac{\pi}{2}, \dfrac{\pi}{2}\right)$.

Inverse Tangent Function

For each real number v,

$\tan^{-1} v$ is the unique number u in the interval $\left(-\dfrac{\pi}{2}, \dfrac{\pi}{2}\right)$ whose tangent is v; that is,

$$\tan^{-1} v = u \quad \text{exactly when} \quad \tan u = v.$$

The properties of the inverse tangent function are similar to the properties of the inverse sine and inverse cosine functions.

Properties of Inverse Tangent

$$\tan^{-1}(\tan u) = u \quad \text{if} \quad -\dfrac{\pi}{2} < u < \dfrac{\pi}{2}$$

$$\tan(\tan^{-1} v) = v \text{ for every real number } v.$$

CAUTION

$\tan^{-1}$ does *not* mean $(\tan x)^{-1}$ or $\dfrac{1}{\tan x}$.

Example 5 **Evaluating Inverse Tangent Expressions**

Evaluate:

a. $\tan^{-1} 1$ **b.** $\tan^{-1} 136$

Teaching Notes

You might want to have students supply exact function values for the graph of $g(x) = \tan^{-1} x$ shown below. They can use page 448 for reference.

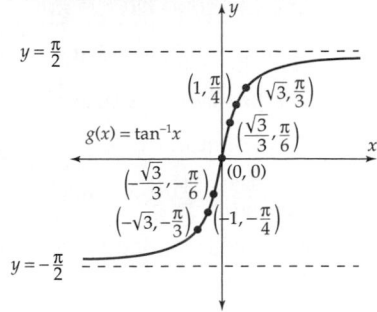

Use a diagram such as the one below to show the symmetric relationship of the restricted tangent graph and the inverse tangent graph.

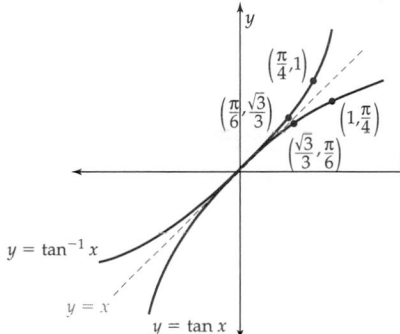

Example 4, in conjunction with **Additional Example 4**, proves the identity $\sin(\cos^{-1} v) = \cos(\sin^{-1} v)$.

ADDITIONAL EXAMPLES

Example 4

Write $\cos(\sin^{-1} v)$ as an algebraic expression in v.

Let $\sin^{-1} v = u$, where $-\dfrac{\pi}{2} \le u \le \dfrac{\pi}{2}$.

Sketch the triangle below showing

$$\sin u = \frac{\text{opposite}}{\text{hypotenuse}} = v.$$

$$\cos u = \frac{\text{adjacent}}{\text{hypotenuse}} = \frac{\sqrt{1 - v^2}}{1}$$

$$= \sqrt{1 - v^2}$$

Therefore, $\cos(\sin^{-1} v) = \sqrt{1 - v^2}$.

Example 5

Evaluate:

a. $\tan^{-1}(-1)$ $-\dfrac{\pi}{4}$

b. $\tan^{-1}(-14)$ -1.4995

Example 6

Find the exact value of $\sin\left(\tan^{-1}\frac{1}{2}\right)$.

Let $\tan^{-1}\frac{1}{2} = u$. Then $\tan u = \frac{1}{2}$,

where $-\frac{\pi}{2} < u < \frac{\pi}{2}$. Because

$\tan u = \frac{1}{2}$ is positive, u is between

0 and $\frac{\pi}{2}$. In a right triangle,

$\tan u = \dfrac{\text{opposite}}{\text{adjacent}} = \dfrac{1}{2}$. So by the

Pythagorean theorem, the hypotenuse
of the triangle has length

$\sqrt{1^2 + 2^2} = \sqrt{5}.$

Therefore, $\sin\left(\tan^{-1}\frac{1}{2}\right) = \dfrac{1}{\sqrt{5}} = \dfrac{\sqrt{5}}{5}.$

Real-World Application

Inverse trigonometric functions are
needed to solve many application
problems. An example is Exercise 51
(page 537), in which the goal is to
find an angle of elevation. For part b,
students will need to evaluate

$\sin^{-1}\left(\dfrac{40}{x}\right)$ when $x = 250$.

Exercises 8.2

ANSWERS

47.

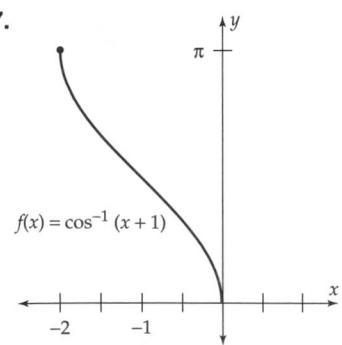

$f(x) = \cos^{-1}(x + 1)$

Solution

a. $\tan^{-1}1 = \dfrac{\pi}{4}$ because $\dfrac{\pi}{4}$ is the unique number in the interval $\left(-\dfrac{\pi}{2}, \dfrac{\pi}{2}\right)$
such that $\tan\dfrac{\pi}{4} = 1$.

b. The TAN^{-1} key on a calculator shows that $\tan^{-1}(136) = 1.5634$.

Example 6   Exact Values

Find the exact value of $\cos\left(\tan^{-1}\dfrac{\sqrt{5}}{2}\right)$.

Solution

Let $\tan^{-1}\dfrac{\sqrt{5}}{2} = u$. Then $\tan u = \dfrac{\sqrt{5}}{2}$ and $-\dfrac{\pi}{2} < u < \dfrac{\pi}{2}$.

Because $\tan u = \dfrac{\sqrt{5}}{2}$ is positive, u must be between 0 and $\dfrac{\pi}{2}$. Draw a right

triangle containing an angle of u radians whose tangent is $\dfrac{\sqrt{5}}{2}$.

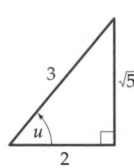
$\tan u = \dfrac{\text{opposite}}{\text{adjacent}} = \dfrac{\sqrt{5}}{2}$

Figure 8.2-8

The hypotenuse has length $\sqrt{2^2 + (\sqrt{5})^2} = \sqrt{4 + 5} = 3$. Therefore,

$$\cos\left(\tan^{-1}\dfrac{\sqrt{5}}{2}\right) = \cos u = \dfrac{\text{adjacent}}{\text{hypotenuse}} = \dfrac{2}{3}.$$

Exercises 8.2

In Exercises 1–14, find the exact value without using
a calculator.

1. $\sin^{-1}1$ $\dfrac{\pi}{2}$ **2.** $\cos^{-1}0$ $\dfrac{\pi}{2}$ **3.** $\tan^{-1}(-1)$ $-\dfrac{\pi}{4}$

4. $\sin^{-1}(-1)$ $-\dfrac{\pi}{2}$ **5.** $\cos^{-1}1$ **0**   **6.** $\tan^{-1}1$ $\dfrac{\pi}{4}$

7. $\tan^{-1}\dfrac{\sqrt{3}}{3}$ $\dfrac{\pi}{6}$ **8.** $\cos^{-1}\dfrac{\sqrt{3}}{2}$ $\dfrac{\pi}{6}$

9. $\sin^{-1}\left(-\dfrac{\sqrt{2}}{2}\right)$ $-\dfrac{\pi}{4}$ **10.** $\sin^{-1}\dfrac{\sqrt{3}}{2}$ $\dfrac{\pi}{3}$

11. $\tan^{-1}(-\sqrt{3})$ $-\dfrac{\pi}{3}$ **12.** $\cos^{-1}\left(-\dfrac{\sqrt{2}}{2}\right)$ $\dfrac{3\pi}{4}$

13. $\cos^{-1}\left(-\dfrac{1}{2}\right)$ $\dfrac{2\pi}{3}$ **14.** $\sin^{-1}\left(-\dfrac{1}{2}\right)$ $-\dfrac{\pi}{6}$

In Exercises 15–24, use a calculator in radian mode to
approximate the functional value.

15. $\sin^{-1}0.35$ **16.** $\cos^{-1}0.76$
    0.3576   **0.7075**
17. $\tan^{-1}(-3.256)$ **18.** $\sin^{-1}(-0.795)$
    −1.2728   **−0.9190**

48.

49.

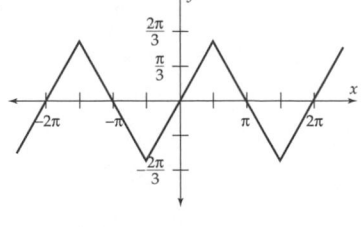

19. $\sin^{-1}(\sin 7)$ *Hint:* the answer is not 7.
0.7168
20. $\cos^{-1}(\cos 3.5)$ **21.** $\tan^{-1}[\tan(-4)]$
2.7832   **−0.8584**
22. $\sin^{-1}[\sin(-2)]$ **23.** $\cos^{-1}[\cos(-8.5)]$
−1.1416   **2.2168**
24. $\tan^{-1}(\tan 12.4)$
−0.1664

25. Given that $u = \sin^{-1}\left(-\dfrac{\sqrt{3}}{2}\right)$, find the exact value of $\cos u$ and $\tan u$. $\cos u = \dfrac{1}{2}; \tan u = -\sqrt{3}$

26. Given that $u = \tan^{-1}\left(\dfrac{4}{3}\right)$, find the exact value of $\sin u$ and $\sec u$. $\sin u = \dfrac{4}{5}, \sec u = \dfrac{5}{3}$

In Exercises 27–42, find the exact functional value without using a calculator.

27. $\sin^{-1}(\cos 0)$ **28.** $\cos^{-1}\left(\sin\dfrac{\pi}{6}\right)$
$\dfrac{\pi}{2}$ $\dfrac{\pi}{3}$
29. $\cos^{-1}\left(\sin\dfrac{4\pi}{3}\right)$ **30.** $\tan^{-1}(\cos \pi)$
$\dfrac{5\pi}{6}$ $-\dfrac{\pi}{4}$
31. $\sin^{-1}\left(\cos\dfrac{7\pi}{6}\right)$ **32.** $\cos^{-1}\left(\tan\dfrac{7\pi}{4}\right)$
$-\dfrac{\pi}{3}$ π

33. $\sin^{-1}\left(\sin\dfrac{2\pi}{3}\right)$ (See Exercise 19.) $\dfrac{\pi}{3}$

34. $\cos^{-1}\left(\cos\dfrac{5\pi}{4}\right)$ $\dfrac{3\pi}{4}$

35. $\cos^{-1}\left[\cos\left(-\dfrac{\pi}{6}\right)\right]$ $\dfrac{\pi}{6}$

36. $\tan^{-1}\left[\tan\left(-\dfrac{4\pi}{3}\right)\right]$ $-\dfrac{\pi}{3}$

37. $\sin\left[\cos^{-1}\left(\dfrac{3}{5}\right)\right]$ (See Example 6.) $\dfrac{4}{5}$

38. $\tan\left[\sin^{-1}\left(\dfrac{3}{5}\right)\right]$ $\dfrac{3}{4}$ **39.** $\cos\left[\tan^{-1}\left(-\dfrac{3}{4}\right)\right]$ $\dfrac{4}{5}$

40. $\cos\left[\sin^{-1}\left(\dfrac{\sqrt{3}}{5}\right)\right]$ $\dfrac{\sqrt{22}}{5}$ **41.** $\tan\left[\sin^{-1}\left(\dfrac{5}{13}\right)\right]$ $\dfrac{5}{12}$

42. $\sin\left[\cos^{-1}\left(\dfrac{\sqrt{3}}{13}\right)\right]$ $\dfrac{\sqrt{166}}{13}$

In Exercises 43–46, write the expression as an algebraic expression in v, as in Example 4.

43. $\cos(\sin^{-1}v)$ **44.** $\cot(\cos^{-1}v)$
$\sqrt{1 - v^2}$ $\dfrac{v}{\sqrt{1 - v^2}}$

45. $\tan(\sin^{-1}v)$ $\dfrac{v}{\sqrt{1 - v^2}}$ **46.** $\sin(2\sin^{-1}v)$ $2v\sqrt{1 - v^2}$

In Exercises 47–50, graph the function.

47. $f(x) = \cos^{-1}(x + 1)$

48. $g(x) = \tan^{-1}x + \pi$

49. $h(x) = \sin^{-1}(\sin x)$

50. $k(x) = \sin(\sin^{-1}x)$

51. A model plane 40 feet above the ground is flying away from an observer.

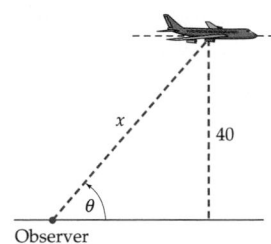

Observer

a. Express the angle of elevation θ of the plane as a function of the distance x from the observer to the plane. $\theta = \sin^{-1}\left(\dfrac{40}{x}\right)$
b. What is θ when the plane is 250 feet from the observer? $\approx 9.2°$

52. Show that the restricted secant function, whose domain consists of all numbers x such that
$0 \leq x \leq \pi$ and $x \neq \dfrac{\pi}{2}$, has an inverse function.
Sketch its graph.

53. Show that the restricted cosecant function, whose domain consists of all numbers x such that
$-\dfrac{\pi}{2} \leq x \leq \dfrac{\pi}{2}$ and $x \neq 0$, has an inverse function.
Sketch its graph.

54. Show that the restricted cotangent function, whose domain is the interval $(0, \pi)$, has an inverse function. Sketch its graph.

55. a. Show that the inverse cosine function actually has the two properties listed in the box on page 533.
b. Show that the inverse tangent function actually has the two properties listed in the box on page 535.

50.

52.
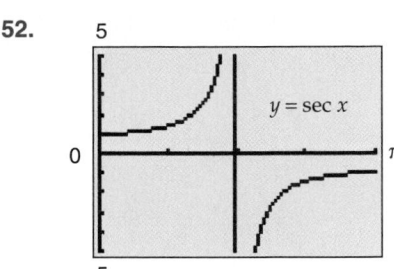

The graph of $y = \sec x$ is one-to-one and has an inverse.

53.
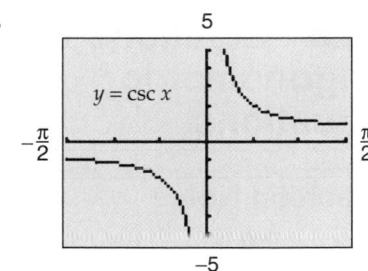

The graph of $y = \csc x$ is one-to-one and has an inverse.

54.
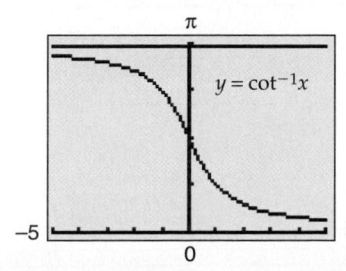

The graph of $y = \cot x$ is one-to-one and has an inverse.

55. *See p.* **538.**

55. a. Let $\cos u = w$ with $0 \le u \le \pi$.
Then $u = \cos^{-1} w$, and
$\cos^{-1}(\cos u) = \cos^{-1} w = u$.
Let $u = \cos^{-1} v$. Then
$\cos u = v$,
and $\cos(\cos^{-1} v) = \cos u = v$.

b. Let $\tan u = w$ with
$-\dfrac{\pi}{2} \le u \le \dfrac{\pi}{2}$.
Then $u = \tan^{-1} w$, and
$\tan^{-1}(\tan u) = \tan^{-1} w = u$.
Let $u = \tan^{-1} v$. Then
$\tan u = v$,
and $\tan(\tan^{-1} v) = \tan u = v$.

56. *Critical Thinking* A 15-foot-wide highway sign is placed 10 feet from a road, perpendicular to the road. A spotlight at the edge of the road is aimed at the sign, as shown in the figure below.

a. Express θ as a function of the distance x from point A to the spotlight.
b. How far from point A should the spotlight be placed so that the angle θ is as large as possible?

a. $\theta = \tan^{-1}\!\left(\dfrac{25}{x}\right) - \tan^{-1}\!\left(\dfrac{10}{x}\right)$

b. $x \approx 15.8$ feet

57. *Critical Thinking* A camera on a 5-foot-high tripod is placed in front of a 6-foot-high picture that is mounted 3 feet above the floor, as shown in figure below.

a. Express angle θ as a function of the distance x from the camera to the wall.
b. The photographer wants to use a particular lens, for which $\theta = 36°\left(\dfrac{\pi}{5}\text{ radians}\right)$. How far should she place the camera from the wall to be sure the entire picture will show in the photograph?

a. $\theta = \tan^{-1}\!\left(\dfrac{4}{x}\right) + \tan^{-1}\!\left(\dfrac{2}{x}\right)$

b. $x \approx 9.13$ feet

8.3 Algebraic Solutions of Trigonometric Equations

Teaching Notes

Point out that because trigonometric functions are periodic functions, there can be an infinite number of solutions to trigonometric equations. In fact, there are an infinite number of solutions to the **basic equations** shown here.

8.3

Algebraic Solutions of Trigonometric Equations

Objective

• Solve trigonometric equations algebraically

Trigonometric equations were solved graphically in Section 8.1. In this section you will learn how to use algebra with inverse trigonometric functions and identities to solve trigonometric equations.

Recall from Section 8.1 that equations such as

$$\sin x = -0.75, \quad \cos x = 0.6, \quad \text{and} \quad \tan x = 3$$

are called **basic equations.** Algebraic solution methods for basic equations are illustrated in Examples 1 through 3.

Example 1 Solving Basic Cosine Equations

Solve $\cos x = 0.6$.

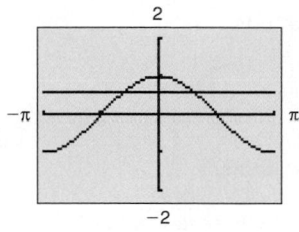

Figure 8.3-1

Solution

The graphs of $Y_1 = \cos x$ and $Y_2 = 0.6$ in Figure 8.3-1 show that there are just two solutions (intersection points) on the interval $[-\pi, \pi]$, which is one full period of the cosine function.

The definition of the inverse cosine function states that

$\cos^{-1} 0.6$ is the number in the interval $[0, \pi]$ whose cosine is 0.6.

Using the inverse cosine function, $x = \cos^{-1} 0.6 = 0.9273$ is one solution of $\cos x = 0.6$ on the interval $[-\pi, \pi]$. The second solution can be found by using the identity $\cos(-x) = \cos x$, with $x = 0.9273$.

$$\cos(-0.9273) = \cos 0.9273 = 0.6$$

Therefore, the solutions of $\cos x = 0.6$ on the interval $[-\pi, \pi]$ are

$$x = \cos^{-1} 0.6 = 0.9273 \qquad \text{and} \qquad x = -\cos^{-1} 0.6 = -0.9273$$

Because the interval $[-\pi, \pi]$ is one complete period of the cosine function, all solutions of $\cos x = 0.6$ are given by

$$x = 0.9273 + 2k\pi \qquad \text{and} \qquad x = -0.9273 + 2k\pi,$$

where k is any integer. ∎

Example 2   **Solving Basic Sine Equations**

Solve $\sin x = -0.75$.

Solution

The definition of the inverse sine function states that

$\sin^{-1}(-0.75)$ is the number in the interval $\left[-\dfrac{\pi}{2}, \dfrac{\pi}{2}\right]$ whose sine is -0.75.

Using the inverse sine function, $x = \sin^{-1}(-0.75) = -0.8481$ is the solution of $\sin x = -0.75$ on the interval $\left[-\dfrac{\pi}{2}, \dfrac{\pi}{2}\right]$. A second solution can be found by using the identity $\sin(\pi - x) = \sin x$, with $x = -0.8481$.

$$\sin[\pi - (-0.8481)] = \sin(3.9897) = -0.75$$

Therefore, $x = \pi - (-0.8481) = 3.9897$ is also a solution of $\sin x = -0.75$, and all solutions are given by

$$x = -0.8481 + 2k\pi \qquad \text{and} \qquad x = 3.9897 + 2k\pi,$$

where k is any integer.

Recall that there are an infinite number of solutions to many trigonometric equations. Figure 8.3-2 indicates that there are two solutions in the interval $[-\pi, \pi]$: $x = -2.2935$ and $x = -0.8481$. The solution $x = -2.2935$ can be found by letting $k = -1$ in the solution $x = 3.9897 + 2k\pi$. ∎

Figure 8.3-2

Example Notes

In **Example 1**, a solution in the interval $[0, \pi]$ is found using the definition of the inverse cosine function. Another solution is found using the identity $\cos(-x) = \cos x$. Both solutions are shown in Figure 8.3-1.

In **Example 2**, a solution in the interval $\left[-\dfrac{\pi}{2}, \dfrac{\pi}{2}\right]$ is found using the definition of the inverse sine function. Another solution is found using the identity $\sin(\pi - x) = \sin x$. Emphasize that the purpose of Figure 8.3-2 is *not* to show these two solutions. Figure 8.3-2 corresponds to the discussion at the bottom of the page. The solution shown in Figure 8.3-2, $x = -2.2935$, is found by letting $k = -1$ in the expression $3.9897 + 2k\pi$.

ADDITIONAL EXAMPLES

Example 1

Solve $\cos x = -0.2$.
The graphs of $Y_1 = \cos x$ and $Y_2 = -0.2$ show that there are 2 solutions in the interval $[-\pi, \pi]$.

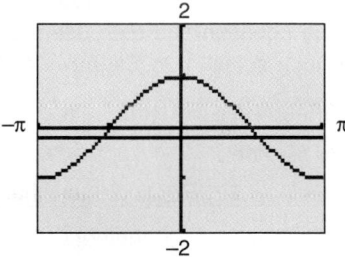

The two solutions indicated in the graph are $\cos^{-1}(-0.2) = 1.7722$ and $-\cos^{-1}(-0.2) = -1.7722$.

All solutions are given by
$x = 1.7722 + 2k\pi$ and
$x = -1.7722 + 2k\pi$, where k is any integer.

Example 2

Solve $\sin x = -0.33$.

Two solutions are

$\sin^{-1}(-0.33) = -0.3363$ and
$\pi - \sin^{-1}(-0.33)$
$\quad = \pi - (-0.3363) = 3.4779$.

All solutions are given by
$x = -0.3363 + 2k\pi$ and
$x = 3.4779 + 2k\pi$, where
k is any integer.

Teaching Notes

Refer students to the table **Solutions of Basic Trigonometric Equations.** Ask them for examples of the basic equations $\sin x = c$ and $\cos x = c$ that have no solution. Possible answers: $\sin x = 3$ and $\cos x = -1.2$

Remind students that:

- $\sin^{-1} c$ is a number in the interval $\left[-\dfrac{\pi}{2}, \dfrac{\pi}{2}\right]$ if it is defined.
- $\cos^{-1} c$ is a number in the interval $[0, \pi]$ if it is defined.
- $\tan^{-1} c$ is a number in the interval $\left(-\dfrac{\pi}{2}, \dfrac{\pi}{2}\right)$.

Example Notes

For **Example 4,** ask students to show that $x = 1.4455$ is in Quadrant I and $x = -1.4455$ is in Quadrant IV.

$0 < 1.4455 < 1.5708 \approx \dfrac{\pi}{2}$

$-\dfrac{\pi}{2} \approx -1.5708 < -1.4455 < 0$

COMMON ERROR ALERT

When solving trigonometric equations, students sometimes isolate a trigonometric function value on one side of the equation and then use that value in their solution. In **Example 4,** they might get $\cos x = \dfrac{1}{8}$ and then give their solutions as $x = \dfrac{1}{8} + 2k\pi$ and $x = -\dfrac{1}{8} + 2k\pi$. Remind them that if $\cos x = \dfrac{1}{8}$, then x is a number whose cosine is $\dfrac{1}{8}$; one such number is $x = \cos^{-1} \dfrac{1}{8} \approx 1.4455$.

Figure 8.3-3

Example 3   **Solving Basic Tangent Equations**

Solve $\tan x = 3$.

Solution

The definition of the inverse tangent function states that

$\tan^{-1} 3$ is the number in the interval $\left(-\dfrac{\pi}{2}, \dfrac{\pi}{2}\right)$ whose tangent is 3.

Using the inverse tangent function, $x = \tan^{-1} 3 = 1.2490$ is the solution of $\tan x = 3$ on the interval $\left(-\dfrac{\pi}{2}, \dfrac{\pi}{2}\right)$. Because $\left(-\dfrac{\pi}{2}, \dfrac{\pi}{2}\right)$ is one full period of the tangent function, all solutions are given by

$$x = 1.2490 + k\pi,$$

where k is any integer. ∎

The solution method used in Examples 1–3 is summarized in the following table, where k is any integer.

Solutions of Basic Trigonometric Equations		
Equation	**Possible values of c**	**Solutions**
$\sin x = c$	$-1 < c < 1$	$x = \sin^{-1} c + 2k\pi$ and $x = (\pi - \sin^{-1} c) + 2k\pi$
	$c = 1$	$x = \dfrac{\pi}{2} + 2k\pi$
	$c = -1$	$x = -\dfrac{\pi}{2} + 2k\pi$
	$c > 1$ or $c < -1$	no solution
$\cos x = c$	$-1 < c < 1$	$x = \cos^{-1} c + 2k\pi$ and $x = -\cos^{-1} c + 2k\pi$
	$c = 1$	$x = 0 + 2k\pi = 2k\pi$
	$c = -1$	$x = \pi + 2k\pi$
	$c > 1$ or $c < -1$	no solution
$\tan x = c$	all real numbers	$x = \tan^{-1} c + k\pi$

Example 4 Using the Solution Algorithm

Solve $8 \cos x - 1 = 0$.

Solution

First rewrite the equation as an equivalent basic equation.

$$8 \cos x - 1 = 0$$
$$\cos x = \frac{1}{8}$$

Then solve the basic equation using the inverse cosine function. One solution is in Quadrant I.

$$x = \cos^{-1}\frac{1}{8} = 1.4455$$

The other solution on the interval $[-\pi, \pi]$ is in Quadrant IV.

$$x = -\cos^{-1}\frac{1}{8} = -1.4455$$

All solutions are given by

$$x = 1.4455 + 2k\pi \quad \text{and} \quad x = -1.4455 + 2k\pi,$$

where k is any integer.

Example 5 Solving Basic Equations with Special Values

Solve $\sin u = \dfrac{\sqrt{2}}{2}$ exactly, without using a calculator.

Solution

Because $\sin\dfrac{\pi}{4} = \dfrac{\sqrt{2}}{2}$, $u = \dfrac{\pi}{4}$ is one solution of $\sin u = \dfrac{\sqrt{2}}{2}$ on the interval $[-\pi, \pi]$. Another solution is in Quadrant II.

$$u = \pi - \frac{\pi}{4} = \frac{3\pi}{4}$$

Therefore, the exact solution is given by

$$u = \frac{\pi}{4} + 2k\pi \quad \text{and} \quad u = \frac{3\pi}{4} + 2k\pi,$$

where k is any integer.

Sometimes trigonometric equations can be solved by using substitution to make them into basic equations.

Section 8.3 **Algebraic Solutions of Trigonometric Equations** **541**

ADDITIONAL EXAMPLES

Example 3

Solve $\tan x = -4$.

$\tan^{-1}(-4)$ is the number in the interval $\left(-\dfrac{\pi}{2}, \dfrac{\pi}{2}\right)$ whose tangent is -4.

$\tan^{-1}(-4) = -1.3258$

All solutions are given by $x = -1.3258 + k\pi$, where k is any integer.

Example 4

Solve $3 \cos x + 1 = 0$.

$$3 \cos x + 1 = 0$$
$$3 \cos x = -1$$
$$\cos x = -\frac{1}{3}$$

The solutions in the interval $[-\pi, \pi]$ are $x = \cos^{-1}\left(-\dfrac{1}{3}\right) = 1.9106$ and

$x = -\cos^{-1}\left(-\dfrac{1}{3}\right) = -1.9106$.

All solutions are given by $x = 1.9106 + 2k\pi$ and $x = -1.9106 + 2k\pi$, where k is any integer.

Example 5

Solve $\sin u = \dfrac{1}{2}$ exactly, without using a calculator.

$\sin\dfrac{\pi}{6} = \dfrac{1}{2}$, so $u = \dfrac{\pi}{6}$ is a solution. Another solution is in Quadrant II: $u = \pi - \dfrac{\pi}{6} = \dfrac{5\pi}{6}$. Therefore, the exact solutions are given by $u = \dfrac{\pi}{6} + 2k\pi$ and $u = \dfrac{5\pi}{6} + 2k\pi$, where k is any integer.

Real-World Application

The substitution technique shown in **Example 6** can be used in finding the angle of a rifle barrel needed to hit a desired target. See Exercise 56 on pages 546–547.

Example Notes

For **Example 8**, list values for each solution expression as shown below:

$0 + k\pi$: $\cdots, -3\pi, -2\pi, -\pi, 0, \pi, 2\pi, 3\pi, \cdots$
$0 + 2k\pi$: $\cdots, -4\pi, -2\pi, 0, 2\pi, 4\pi, \cdots$
$\pi + 2k\pi$: $\cdots, -5\pi, -3\pi, -\pi, \pi, 3\pi, 5\pi, \cdots$

This will help students understand that the single expression $0 + k\pi$ is sufficient to give all solutions.

ADDITIONAL EXAMPLES

Example 6

Solve $\sin 4x = \dfrac{\sqrt{3}}{2}$ exactly, without using a calculator.

Let $u = 4x$ and solve the basic equation $\sin u = \dfrac{\sqrt{3}}{2}$. The complete solutions of $\sin u = \dfrac{\sqrt{3}}{2}$ are given by $u = \frac{\pi}{3} + 2k\pi$ and $u = \frac{2\pi}{3} + 2k\pi$, where k is any integer.

Substitute $4x$ for u and solve for x.

$u = \frac{\pi}{3} + 2k\pi \qquad u = \frac{2\pi}{3} + 2k\pi$
$4x = \frac{\pi}{3} + 2k\pi \qquad 4x = \frac{2\pi}{3} + 2k\pi$
$x = \frac{\pi}{12} + \frac{k\pi}{2} \qquad x = \frac{\pi}{6} + \frac{k\pi}{2}$

All solutions are given by $x = \frac{\pi}{12} + \frac{k\pi}{2}$ and $x = \frac{\pi}{6} + \frac{k\pi}{2}$, where k is any integer.

Example 7

Find the solutions of
$4\sin^2 x + 5\sin x + 1 = 0$
in the interval $[-\pi, \pi]$.

Let $u = \sin x$. Rewrite the equation as $4u^2 + 5u + 1 = 0$ and solve for u.
$(4u + 1)(u + 1) = 0$
$u = -\frac{1}{4}$ or $u = -1$

Example 6 Using Substitution and Basic Equations

Solve $\sin 2x = \dfrac{\sqrt{2}}{2}$ exactly, without using a calculator.

Solution

First, let $u = 2x$, and solve the basic equation $\sin u = \dfrac{\sqrt{2}}{2}$. From Example 5, you know the complete exact solution of $\sin u = \dfrac{\sqrt{2}}{2}$ is given by

$$u = \frac{\pi}{4} + 2k\pi \qquad \text{and} \qquad u = \frac{3\pi}{4} + 2k\pi,$$

where k is any integer.

Because $u = 2x$, each of these solutions leads to a solution of the original equation. Substitute $2x$ for u, and solve for x.

$$u = \frac{\pi}{4} + 2k\pi \qquad\qquad u = \frac{3\pi}{4} + 2k\pi$$
$$2x = \frac{\pi}{4} + 2k\pi \qquad \text{and} \qquad 2x = \frac{3\pi}{4} + 2k\pi$$
$$x = \frac{\pi}{8} + k\pi \qquad\qquad x = \frac{3\pi}{8} + k\pi$$

Therefore, all solutions of $\sin 2x = \dfrac{\sqrt{2}}{2}$ are given by

$$x = \frac{\pi}{8} + k\pi \qquad \text{and} \qquad x = \frac{3\pi}{8} + k\pi,$$

where k is any integer.

Algebraic Techniques

Many trigonometric equations can be solved algebraically—by using factoring, the quadratic formula, and basic identities to write an equivalent equation that involves only basic equations, as shown in the following examples.

Example 7 Factoring Trigonometric Equations

Find the solutions of $3\sin^2 x - \sin x - 2 = 0$ in the interval $[-\pi, \pi]$.

Solution

Let $u = \sin x$.

$$3\sin^2 x - \sin x - 2 = 0$$
$$3u^2 - u - 2 = 0 \qquad \textit{Substitution}$$

continued from page 542

This quadratic equation can be solved by factoring.

$$3u^2 - u - 2 = 0$$
$$(3u + 2)(u - 1) = 0$$
$$u = -\frac{2}{3} \quad \text{or} \quad u = 1$$

Substituting sin x for u results in two basic equations.

$$\sin x = -\frac{2}{3} \quad \text{or} \quad \sin x = 1$$

If $\sin x = \left(-\frac{2}{3}\right)$, then

$$x = \sin^{-1}\left(-\frac{2}{3}\right) \qquad x = \pi - \sin^{-1}\left(-\frac{2}{3}\right)$$
$$\text{or}$$
$$= -0.7297 + 2k\pi \qquad = 3.8713 + 2k\pi$$

If $\sin x = 1$, then $x = \frac{\pi}{2} + 2k\pi$

Therefore, the solutions of $3\sin^2 x - \sin x - 2 = 0$ are

$$x = -0.7297 + 2k\pi, \quad x = \frac{\pi}{2} + 2k\pi, \quad \text{and} \quad x = 3.8713 + 2k\pi,$$

where k is any integer.

Figure 8.3-4 indicates that there are three solutions in the interval $[-\pi, \pi]$, which is marked with vertical lines. The solution $x = 3.8713$ is outside the interval, but the corresponding solution within the interval can be found by letting $k = -1$ in $x = 3.8713 + 2k\pi$. Within $[-\pi, \pi]$, the solutions are

$$x = 3.8713 - 2\pi = -2.4119, \quad x = -0.7297, \quad \text{and} \quad x = \frac{\pi}{2}. \quad \blacksquare$$

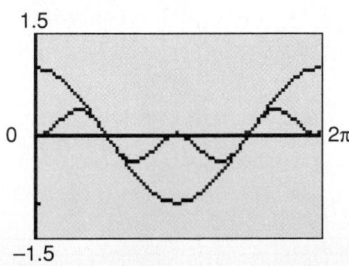

Example 8 Factoring Trigonometric Equations

Solve $\tan x \cos^2 x = \tan x$.

Solution

Write an equivalent equation as an expression equal to zero, and factor.

$$\tan x \cos^2 x - \tan x = 0$$
$$\tan x(\cos^2 x - 1) = 0$$
$$\tan x = 0 \quad \text{or} \quad \cos^2 x - 1 = 0$$
$$x = 0 + k\pi \qquad\qquad \cos^2 x = 1$$
$$\sqrt{\cos^2 x} = \sqrt{1}$$
$$\cos x = \pm 1$$
$$x = 0 + 2k\pi \quad \text{or} \quad x = \pi + 2k\pi$$

CAUTION

$$\cos^2 x - 1 \neq \sin^2 x$$

Substitute sin x for u and solve for x.

$$\sin x = -\frac{1}{4} \text{ or } \sin x = -1$$

Two solutions of $\sin x = -\frac{1}{4}$

are $x = \sin^{-1}\left(-\frac{1}{4}\right) = -0.2527$ and

$x = \pi - \sin^{-1}\left(-\frac{1}{4}\right) = 3.3943$.

So all solutions of $\sin x = -\frac{1}{4}$ are given by $x = -0.2527 + 2k\pi$ and $x = 3.3943 + 2k\pi$.

All solutions of $\sin x = -1$ are given by $x = -\frac{\pi}{2} + 2k\pi$.

The figure below indicates that there are three solutions in the interval $[-\pi, \pi]$.

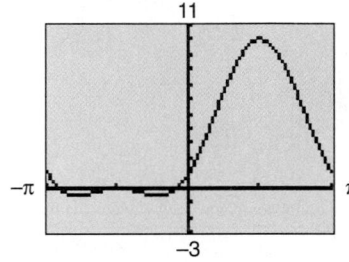

The solutions in the interval $[-\pi, \pi]$ are found by using appropriate values of k as shown below:

Let $k = 0$: $-0.2527 + 2(0)\pi = -0.2527$

Let $k = -1$: $3.3943 + 2(-1)\pi = -2.8889$

Let $k = 0$: $-\frac{\pi}{2} + 2(0)\pi = -\frac{\pi}{2}$

Example 8

Solve $\cos x \sin^2 x = \cos x$.

$$\cos x \sin^2 x - \cos x = 0$$
$$\cos x(\sin^2 x - 1) = 0$$
$$\cos x = 0 \text{ or } \sin^2 x - 1 = 0$$
$$\sin^2 x = 1$$
$$\sin x = \pm 1$$

All solutions of:

$\cos x = 0$ are given by $x = \frac{\pi}{2} + k\pi$,

$\sin x = 1$ are given by $x = \frac{\pi}{2} + 2k\pi$,

$\sin x = -1$ are given by $x = -\frac{\pi}{2} + 2k\pi$.

So, all solutions of $\cos x \sin^2 x = \cos x$ are given by $x = \frac{\pi}{2} + k\pi$, where k is any integer.

The graphs of $Y_1 = \cos x \sin^2 x$ and $Y_2 = \cos x$ are shown.

The Pythagorean Identities can be found on page 460 or on the inside of the back cover.

ADDITIONAL EXAMPLES

Example 9

Solve $-6 \sin^2 x + \cos x + 5 = 0$.

Substitute $1 - \cos^2 x$ for $\sin^2 x$, rewrite the equation in terms of the cosine function, and then solve.

$$-6 \sin^2 x + \cos x + 5 = 0$$
$$-6(1 - \cos^2 x) + \cos x + 5 = 0$$
$$-6 + 6 \cos^2 x + \cos x + 5 = 0$$
$$6 \cos^2 x + \cos x - 1 = 0$$
$$(2 \cos x + 1)(3 \cos x - 1) = 0$$
$$2 \cos x + 1 = 0 \qquad 3 \cos x - 1 = 0$$
$$\cos x = -\frac{1}{2} \text{ or } \qquad \cos x = \frac{1}{3}$$

The solutions of $\cos x = -\frac{1}{2}$ are

$$x = \cos^{-1}\left(-\frac{1}{2}\right) + 2k\pi$$

$$= \frac{2\pi}{3} + 2k\pi$$

and

$$x = -\cos^{-1}\left(-\frac{1}{2}\right) + 2k\pi$$

$$= -\frac{2\pi}{3} + 2k\pi \qquad .$$

The solutions of $\cos x = \frac{1}{3}$ are

$$x = \cos^{-1}\left(\frac{1}{3}\right) + 2k\pi = 1.2310 + 2k\pi$$

and

$$x = -\cos^{-1}\left(\frac{1}{3}\right) + 2k\pi$$

$$= -1.2310 + 2k\pi.$$

Therefore, all solutions are given by

$x = \frac{2\pi}{3} + 2k\pi$, $x = -\frac{2\pi}{3} + 2k\pi$,

$x = 1.2310 + 2k\pi$, and

$x = -1.2310 + 2k\pi$, where k is any integer.

The graph of $f(x) = -6 \sin^2 x + \cos x + 5$ below confirms that there are four solutions in the interval $[-\pi, \pi]$.

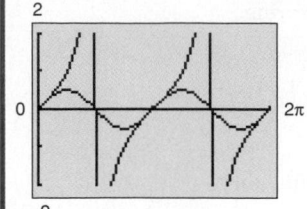

Figure 8.3-5

More simply stated, the solution of $\tan x \cos^2 x = \tan x$ is

$$x = 0 + k\pi = k\pi,$$

where k is any integer. The graphs of $Y_1 = \tan x \cos^2 x$ and $Y_2 = \tan x$ are shown in Figure 8.3-5.

∎

Many trigonometric equations can be solved if trigonometric identities are used to rewrite the original equation, as shown in Examples 9 and 10.

Example 9 Identities and Factoring

Solve $-10 \cos^2 x - 3 \sin x + 9 = 0$.

Solution

Use the Pythagorean identity to rewrite the equation in terms of the sine function.

$$-10 \cos^2 x - 3 \sin x + 9 = 0$$
$$-10(1 - \sin^2 x) - 3 \sin x + 9 = 0$$
$$-10 + 10 \sin^2 x - 3 \sin x + 9 = 0$$
$$10 \sin^2 x - 3 \sin x - 1 = 0$$

Factor the left side and solve.

$$(2 \sin x - 1)(5 \sin x + 1) = 0$$

$2 \sin x - 1 = 0 \qquad\qquad 5 \sin x + 1 = 0$

$\sin x = \frac{1}{2} \qquad\qquad \text{or} \qquad\qquad \sin x = -\frac{1}{5}$

$x = \sin^{-1}\left(\frac{1}{2}\right) \qquad\qquad x = \sin^{-1}\left(-\frac{1}{5}\right)$

$x = \frac{\pi}{6} + 2k\pi \quad \text{or} \qquad\qquad x = -0.2014 + 2k\pi \quad \text{or}$

$x = \pi - \frac{\pi}{6} + 2k\pi \qquad\qquad x = \pi - (-0.2014) + 2k\pi$

$\quad = \frac{5\pi}{6} + 2k\pi \qquad\qquad\qquad = 3.3430 + 2k\pi$

Therefore, all solutions of $-10 \cos^2 x - 3 \sin x + 9 = 0$ are

$$x = \frac{\pi}{6} + 2k\pi, \qquad x = \frac{5\pi}{6} + 2k\pi,$$

$$x = -0.2014 + 2k\pi, \qquad \text{and} \qquad x = 3.3430 + 2k\pi,$$

where k is any integer. The graph of $Y_1 = -10 \cos^2 x - 3 \sin x + 9$ shown in Figure 8.3-6 confirms the solution.

∎

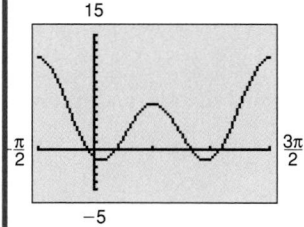

Figure 8.3-6

Example 10 Identities and Quadratic Formula

Solve $\sec^2 x + 5 \tan x = -2$.

ADDITIONAL EXAMPLES

Solution

Use a Pythagorean identity to rewrite the equation in terms of the tangent function.

$$\sec^2 x + 5 \tan x = -2$$
$$\sec^2 x + 5 \tan x + 2 = 0$$
$$(1 + \tan^2 x) + 5 \tan x + 2 = 0$$
$$\tan^2 x + 5 \tan x + 3 = 0$$

Use the quadratic formula to solve for $\tan x$.

$$\tan x = \frac{-5 \pm \sqrt{5^2 - 4(1)(3)}}{2(1)} = \frac{-5 \pm \sqrt{13}}{2}$$

$$\tan x = \frac{-5 + \sqrt{13}}{2} = -0.6972 \quad \text{or} \quad \tan x = \frac{-5 - \sqrt{13}}{2} = -4.3028$$

$$x = \tan^{-1}(-0.6972) \qquad\qquad x = \tan^{-1}(-4.3028)$$
$$= -0.6088 + k\pi \qquad\qquad = -1.3424 + k\pi$$

Therefore, the solution set of $\sec^2 x + 5 \tan x = -2$ is

$$x = -0.6089 + \pi k \quad \text{and} \quad x = -1.3424 + \pi k,$$

where k is any integer. The graphs of $Y_1 = \sec^2 x + 5 \tan x$ and $Y_2 = -2$ in Figure 8.3-7 confirm the solution. ■

Figure 8.3-7

Exercises 8.3

In Exercises 1–8, find the exact solutions.

1. $\sin x = \dfrac{\sqrt{3}}{2}$ **2.** $2 \cos x = \sqrt{2}$

3. $\tan x = -\sqrt{3}$ **4.** $\tan x = 1$

5. $2 \cos x = -\sqrt{3}$ **6.** $\sin x = 0$

7. $2 \sin x + 1 = 0$ **8.** $\csc x = \sqrt{2}$

In the following exercises, find exact solutions if possible and approximate solutions otherwise. When a calculator is used, round to four decimal places.

Use the following information in Exercises 9–12.

When a light beam passes from one medium to another (for instance, from air to water), it changes both its speed and direction. According to Snell's Law of Refraction,

$$\frac{\sin \theta_1}{\sin \theta_2} = \frac{v_1}{v_2},$$

where v_1 is the speed of light in the first medium, v_2 its speed in the second medium, θ_1 the angle of incidence, and θ_2 the angle of refraction, as shown in the figure. The number $\dfrac{v_1}{v_2}$ is called the index of refraction.

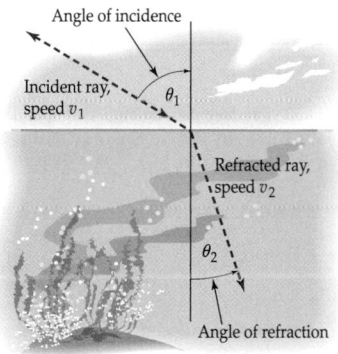

9. The index of refraction of light passing from air to water is 1.33. If the angle of incidence is 38°, find the angle of refraction.

Example 10

Solve $\sec^2 x - 2 \tan x = 3$.

Rewrite the equation in terms of the tangent function by substituting $1 + \tan^2 x$ for $\sec^2 x$ and then use the quadratic formula to solve for $\tan x$.

$$\sec^2 x - 2 \tan x = 3$$
$$\sec^2 x - 2 \tan x - 3 = 0$$
$$(1 + \tan^2 x) - 2 \tan x - 3 = 0$$
$$\tan^2 x - 2 \tan x - 2 = 0$$

$$\tan x = \frac{-(-2) \pm \sqrt{(-2)^2 - 4(1)(-2)}}{2(1)}$$

$$= \frac{2 \pm \sqrt{12}}{2} = 1 \pm \sqrt{3}$$

$$\tan x = 2.7321 \quad \text{or} \quad \tan x = -0.7321$$

All solutions are given by:

$$x = \tan^{-1} 2.7321 + k\pi = 1.2199 + k\pi$$
and $x = \tan^{-1}(-0.7321) + k\pi$
$$= -0.6319 + k\pi \quad,$$

where k is any integer. The graphs of $Y_1 = \sec^2 x - 2 \tan x$ and $Y_2 = 3$ below show that there are four solutions in the interval $\left[-\dfrac{\pi}{2}, \dfrac{3\pi}{2}\right]$.

Exercises 8.3

ANSWERS

1. $x = \dfrac{\pi}{3} + 2k\pi$ or $\dfrac{2\pi}{3} + 2k\pi$

2. $x = \pm\dfrac{\pi}{4} + 2k\pi$

3. $x = -\dfrac{\pi}{3} + k\pi$

4. $x = \dfrac{\pi}{4} + k\pi$

5. $x = \pm\dfrac{5\pi}{6} + 2k\pi$

6. $x = k\pi$

7. $x = -\dfrac{\pi}{6} + 2k\pi$ or $\dfrac{7\pi}{6} + 2k\pi$

8. $x = \dfrac{\pi}{4} + 2k\pi$ or $\dfrac{3\pi}{4} + 2k\pi$

9. 27.5746°

10. $11.0899°$

11. $14.1831°$

12. $31.6472°$

13. $x = -0.4836 + 2k\pi$ or $3.6252 + 2k\pi$

14. $x = -0.7505 + 2k\pi$ or $3.8921 + 2k\pi$

15. $x = \pm 2.1700 + 2k\pi$

16. $x = 1.9509 + 2k\pi$ or $4.3323 + 2k\pi$

17. $x = -0.2327 + k\pi$

18. $x = -1.4906 + k\pi$

19. $x = 0.4101 + k\pi$

20. $x = -0.2783 + k\pi$

21. $x = \pm 1.9577 + 2k\pi$

22. $x = 0.1909 + 2k\pi$ or $2.9507 + 2k\pi$

23. $x = -\dfrac{\pi}{6} + k\pi$ or $\dfrac{2\pi}{3} + k\pi$

24. $x = \dfrac{\pi}{8} + k\pi$ or $\dfrac{7\pi}{8} + k\pi$

25. $x = \pm\dfrac{\pi}{2} + 4k\pi$

26. $x = \dfrac{\pi}{2} + 6k\pi$ or $\dfrac{5\pi}{2} + 6k\pi$

27. $x = -\dfrac{\pi}{9} + \dfrac{k\pi}{3}$

28. $x = 0.2058 + k\pi$ or $1.3650 + k\pi$

29. $x = \pm 0.7381 + \dfrac{2k\pi}{3}$

30. $x = 0.3616 + \dfrac{k\pi}{4}$

31. $x = 2.2143 + 2k\pi$

32. $x = 3.7092 + 8k\pi$ or $8.8572 + 8k\pi$

33. $x = 3.4814, 5.9433$

34. $x = 0.6435, 5.6397$

35. $x = \dfrac{3\pi}{4}, \dfrac{7\pi}{4}, 2.1588, 5.3004$

36. $x = \dfrac{\pi}{2}$

37. $x = \dfrac{\pi}{4}, \dfrac{\pi}{2}, \dfrac{5\pi}{4}, \dfrac{3\pi}{2}$

38. $x = \dfrac{\pi}{4}, \dfrac{\pi}{2}, \dfrac{5\pi}{4}, \dfrac{3\pi}{2}$

39. $x = \dfrac{\pi}{6}, \dfrac{\pi}{2}, \dfrac{5\pi}{6}, \dfrac{3\pi}{2}$

40. $x = 0, \pi, 1.9106, 4.3726$

41. $x = 0.8481, 1.7682, 2.2935, 4.9098$

42. $x = 1.3694, 4.9137, 4.0689, 5.3559$

43. $x = 0.8213, 2.3203$

44. $x = 1.3770, 4.9062$

45. $x = 0.3649, 1.2059, 3.5065, 4.3475$

46. $x = 0.6283, 1.8850, 4.3982, 5.6549$

47. $x = 1.0591, 2.8679, 4.2007, 6.0095$

---

10. The index of refraction of light passing from air to ordinary glass is 1.52. If the angle of incidence is 17°, find the angle of refraction.

11. The index of refraction of light passing from air to dense glass is 1.66. If the angle of incidence is 24°, find the angle of refraction.

12. The index of refraction of light passing from air to quartz is 1.46. If the angle of incidence is 50°, find the angle of refraction.

In Exercises 13–32, find all the solutions of each equation.

13. $\sin x = -0.465$ **14.** $\sin x = -0.682$

15. $\cos x = -0.564$ **16.** $\cos x = -0.371$

17. $\tan x = -0.237$ **18.** $\tan x = -12.45$

19. $\cot x = 2.3$ $\left[\text{Hint: } \cot x = \dfrac{1}{\tan x}\right]$

20. $\cot x = -3.5$ **21.** $\sec x = -2.65$

22. $\csc x = 5.27$ **23.** $\sin 2x = -\dfrac{\sqrt{3}}{2}$

24. $\cos 2x = \dfrac{\sqrt{2}}{2}$ **25.** $2\cos\dfrac{x}{2} = \sqrt{2}$

26. $2\sin\dfrac{x}{3} = 1$ **27.** $\tan 3x = -\sqrt{3}$

28. $5\sin 2x = 2$ **29.** $5\cos 3x = -3$

30. $2\tan 4x = 16$ **31.** $4\tan\dfrac{x}{2} = 8$

32. $5\sin\dfrac{x}{4} = 4$

In Exercises 33–53, use factoring, the quadratic formula, or identities to solve the equation. Find all solutions in the interval $[0, 2\pi)$.

33. $3\sin^2 x - 8\sin x - 3 = 0$

34. $5\cos^2 x + 6\cos x = 8$

35. $2\tan^2 x + 5\tan x + 3 = 0$

36. $3\sin^2 x + 2\sin x = 5$

37. $\cot x \cos x = \cos x$

38. $\tan x \cos x = \cos x$ **39.** $\cos x \csc x = 2\cos x$

---

40. $\tan x \sec x + 3\tan x = 0$

41. $4\sin x \tan x - 3\tan x + 20\sin x - 15 = 0$
Hint: One factor is $\tan x + 5$.

42. $25\sin x \cos x - 5\sin x + 20\cos x = 4$

43. $\sin^2 x + 2\sin x - 2 = 0$

44. $\cos^2 x + 5\cos x = 1$ **45.** $\tan^2 x + 1 = 3\tan x$

46. $4\cos^2 x - 2\cos x = 1$ **47.** $2\tan^2 x - 1 = 3\tan x$

48. $6\sin^2 x + 4\sin x = 1$ **49.** $\sec^2 x - 2\tan^2 x = 0$

50. $9 - 12\sin x = 4\cos^2 x$

51. $\sec^2 x + \tan x = 3$

52. $\cos^2 x - \sin^2 x + \sin x = 0$

53. $2\tan^2 x + \tan x = 5 - \sec^2 x$

54. The number of hours of daylight in Detroit on day t of a non-leap year (with $t = 0$ being January 1) is given by the following function.

$$d(t) = 3\sin\left[\dfrac{2\pi}{365}(t - 80)\right] + 12$$

a. On what days of the year are there exactly 11 hours of daylight?
b. What day has the maximum amount of daylight?

55. A weight hanging from a spring is set into motion moving up and down. Its distance d (in centimeters) above or below the equilibrium point at time t seconds is given by

$$d = 5(\sin 6t - 4\cos 6t).$$

At what times during the first 2 seconds is the weight at the equilibrium position ($d = 0$)?

In Exercises 56–59, use the following information.

When a projectile (such as a ball or a bullet) leaves its starting point at angle of elevation θ with velocity v, the horizontal distance d it travels is given by the equation

$$d = \dfrac{v^2}{32}\sin 2\theta,$$

where d is measured in feet and v in feet per second. Note that the horizontal distance traveled may be the same for two different angles of elevation, so that some of these exercises may have more than one correct answer.

---

48. $x = 0.1949, 2.9466, 5.2472, 4.1776$

49. $x = \dfrac{\pi}{4}, \dfrac{3\pi}{4}, \dfrac{5\pi}{4}, \dfrac{7\pi}{4}$

50. $x = \dfrac{\pi}{6}, \dfrac{5\pi}{6}$

51. $x = \dfrac{\pi}{4}, \dfrac{5\pi}{4}$

52. $x = \dfrac{7\pi}{6}, \dfrac{11\pi}{6}, \dfrac{\pi}{2}$

53. $x = \dfrac{\pi}{4}, \dfrac{5\pi}{4}$

54. a. days 60 and 282

b. day 171

55. $t = \dfrac{\tan^{-1}4}{6} + \dfrac{k\pi}{6}$

$\approx 1.2682, 0.7446, 0.2210, 1.7918$

---

a

b

56. If muzzle velocity of a rifle is 300 feet per second, at what angle of elevation (in radians) should it be aimed in order for the bullet to hit a target 2500 feet away?

57. Is it possible for the rifle in Exercise 56 to hit a target that is 3000 feet away? At what angle of elevation would it have to be aimed?

58. A fly ball leaves the bat at a velocity of 98 miles per hour and is caught by an outfielder 288 feet away. At what angle of elevation (in degrees) did the ball leave the bat?

59. An outfielder throws the ball at a speed of 75 miles per hour to the catcher who is 200 feet away. At what angle of elevation was the ball thrown?

60. In an alternating current circuit, the voltage is given by the formula

$$V = V_{max} \cdot \sin(2\pi ft + \phi),$$

where V_{max} is the maximum voltage, f is the frequency (in cycles per second), t is the time in seconds, and ϕ is the phase angle.

a. If the phase angle is 0, solve the voltage equation for t.

b. If $\phi = 0$, $V_{max} = 20$, $V = 8.5$, and $f = 120$, find the smallest positive value of t.

61. *Critical Thinking* Find all solutions of $\sin^2 x + 3\cos^2 x = 0$ in the interval $[0, 2\pi)$.

62. *Critical Thinking* What is wrong with this "solution"?

$$\sin x \tan x = \sin x$$
$$\tan x = 1$$
$$x = \frac{\pi}{4} \quad \text{or} \quad \frac{5\pi}{4}$$

Hint: Solve the original equation by moving all terms to one side and factoring. Compare your answers with the ones above.

63. *Critical Thinking* Let n be a fixed positive integer. Describe all solutions of the equation $\sin nx = \frac{1}{2}$.

56. 0.5475 or 1.0233

57. not possible

58. 13.25° or 76.75°

59. 15.97° or 74.03°

60. a. $t = \dfrac{1}{2\pi f} \sin^{-1}\left(\dfrac{V}{V_{max}}\right) + \dfrac{k}{f}$

b. $t = 0.000582$ seconds

61. no solution

62. Since both sides are divided by $\sin x$ there are no solutions that correspond to $\sin x = 0$.

63. $x = \dfrac{\pi}{6n} + \dfrac{2k\pi}{n}, \dfrac{5\pi}{6n} + \dfrac{2k\pi}{n}$

Section 8.4   Simple Harmonic Motion and Modeling

Objective

- Write a sinusoidal function whose graph resembles a given graph

- Write a sinusoidal function to represent a given simple harmonic motion, and use the function to solve problems

- Find a sinusoidal model for a set of data, and use the model to make predictions

In Section 7.4, graphs of functions of the form

$$f(t) = a\sin(bt + c) + d \quad \text{and} \quad g(t) = a\cos(bt + c) + d,$$

were studied; and the constants a, b, c, and d were examined to see how they affect the graphs of the functions. In this section, trigonometric functions of this form are used to model real-world phenomena.

Recall that if $a \neq 0$ and $b > 0$, then each of the functions

$$f(t) = a\sin(bt + c) + d \quad \text{and} \quad g(t) = a\cos(bt + c) + d$$

has the following characteristics.

$$\text{amplitude} = |a| \qquad \text{period} = \frac{2\pi}{b}$$

$$\text{phase shift} = -\frac{c}{b} \qquad \text{vertical shift} = d$$

Section 8.4   Simple
Harmonic
Motion and Modeling

Math Background

Functions of the form $f(t) = a\sin(bt + c) + d$ and $g(t) = a\cos(bt + c) + d$ are sinusoidal functions. When two sinusoidal functions are added, the result is a sinusoidal function (see page 511).

Teaching Notes

After completing **Example 1,** have students graph both $g(t) = 3 \cos 2t + 1$ and

$$f(t) = 3 \sin \left(2t - \frac{3\pi}{2}\right) + 1 \text{ on}$$

the same screen to verify that they *both* resemble Figure 8.4-3. The graph is shown below.

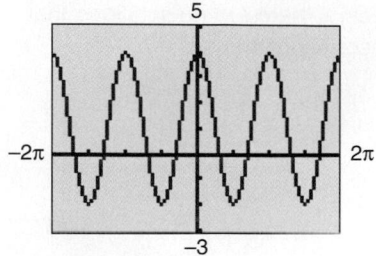

After graphing g and f, point out the margin **NOTE** on page 549. To illustrate this note, have students graph the three cosine functions and three sine functions listed below on the same screen. The graphs will all coincide with the graphs of functions g and f found in **Example 1.**

$y = 3 \cos \left(2(t + \pi)\right) + 1$

$y = 3 \cos \left(2(t + 2\pi)\right) + 1$

$y = 3 \cos \left(2(t + 3\pi)\right) + 1$

$y = 3 \sin \left(2\left(t - \frac{\pi}{4}\right)\right) + 1$

$y = 3 \sin \left(2\left(t - \frac{5\pi}{4}\right)\right) + 1$

$y = 3 \sin \left(2\left(t - \frac{9\pi}{4}\right)\right) + 1$

Example Notes

The graph in **Example 1** is vertically centered on the dotted horizontal line $y = 1$. Therefore, the vertical shift is $d = 1$. The graph rises at most 3 units above the dotted line, so the amplitude is $a = 3$.

Recall the shapes of sine and cosine waves.

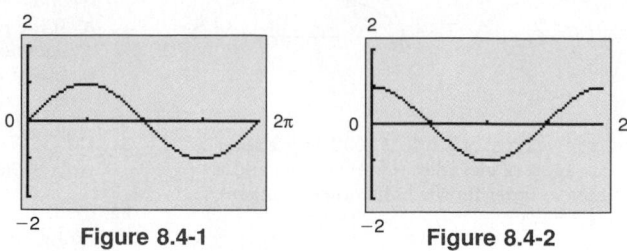

The wave shape of the graphs of these functions is called a **sinusoid** and the functions are called **sinusoidal functions.**

Recall that the amplitude of the function $f(t) = a \sin(bt)$ is the number $|a|$, and that its graph consists of waves that rise to $|a|$ units above the horizontal axis and fall to $-|a|$ units below the horizontal axis. In other words, the amplitude is half the distance from the maximum value to the minimum value of the function. This number remains the same when the graph is shifted vertically or horizontally. Thus the amplitude of the sinusoidal function $f(t) = a \sin(bt + c) + d$ or $g(t) = a \cos(bt + c) + d$ is the number

$$a = \frac{1}{2}(f_{max} - f_{min}),$$

where f_{max} and f_{min} denote the maximum and minimum values of f.

The vertical shift d of a sinusoidal function can be determined by averaging the maximum and minimum values as shown below.

$$\text{vertical shift} = d = \frac{f_{max} + f_{min}}{2}$$

Example 1   Constructing Sinusoidal Functions

Write a sine function and a cosine function whose graph resembles the sinusoidal graph below.

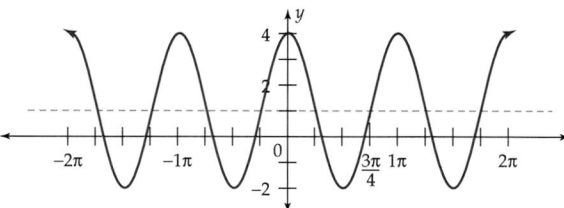

Figure 8.4-3

ADDITIONAL EXAMPLES

Solution

The graph shows that the function has a maximum of 4 and a minimum of -2. Therefore, the amplitude is

$$a = \frac{1}{2}(f_{max} - f_{min}) = \frac{1}{2}(4 - (-2)) = 3.$$

The graph shows one complete cosine cycle between 0 and π, so the period is π. Therefore,

$$\frac{2\pi}{b} = \pi$$
$$b = 2$$

The vertical shift d is one unit.

$$d = \frac{f_{max} + f_{min}}{2} = \frac{4 + (-2)}{2} = 1$$

The variable c depends on whether the function is described in terms of sine or cosine. If $g(t) = \cos t$ is used, there is no phase shift because a cosine wave's maximum occurs at $t = 0$. So the phase shift is 0, and a function for the sinusoidal graph in Figure 8.4-3 has a value of 0 for c.

$$g(t) = 3 \cos 2t + 1$$

The graph indicates that a sine wave begins at $t = \frac{3\pi}{4}$, so the phase shift for a function using $f(t) = \sin t$ is $\frac{3\pi}{4}$.

$$\frac{3\pi}{4} = -\frac{c}{b} \qquad \text{\textit{phase shift is} } -\frac{c}{b}$$
$$\frac{3\pi}{4} = -\frac{c}{2} \qquad \text{\textit{b} = 2}$$
$$c = -\frac{3\pi}{2} \qquad \text{\textit{Solve for c.}}$$

Therefore, a function for the sinusoidal graph in Figure 8.4-3 is

$$f(t) = 3 \sin\left(2t - \frac{3\pi}{2}\right) + 1.$$

■

Simple Harmonic Motion

Motion that can be described by a function of the form

$$f(t) = a \sin(bt + c) + d \qquad \text{or} \qquad g(t) = a \cos(bt + c) + d$$

is called **simple harmonic motion.** Many kinds of physical motion are simple harmonic motions.

NOTE The function that represents the graph, $g(t) = 3 \cos 2t + 1$, is not unique because infinitely many functions can name the graph, such as $h(t) = 3 \cos (2(t + \pi)) + 1$. They can be written using different phase shifts. The first function above is the representative answer because it uses the phase shift that is closest to zero.

Example 1

Write a sine function and a cosine function whose graph resembles the sinusoidal graph below.

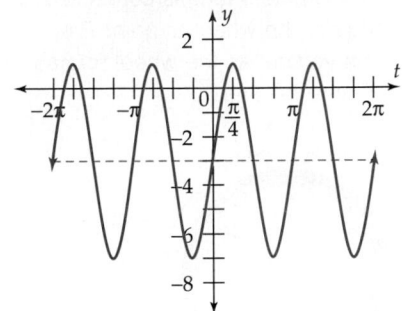

The maximum is 1 and the minimum is -7, so the amplitude is

$$a = \frac{1}{2}(f_{max} - f_{min}) = \frac{1}{2}(1 - (-7)) = 4.$$

The graph shows one complete sine cycle between 0 and π, so the period is π. Therefore, $\frac{2\pi}{b} = \pi$, and $b = 2$.

vertical shift:

$$d = \frac{f_{max} + f_{min}}{2} = \frac{1 + (-7)}{2} = -3$$

The graph shows a sine wave beginning at $t = 0$, so the phase shift is 0.

$$f(t) = a \sin (bt + c) + d$$
$$f(t) = 4 \sin (2t + 0) - 3$$
$$f(t) = 4 \sin 2t - 3$$

The graph indicates that a cosine wave begins at $\frac{\pi}{4}$, so the phase shift for a cosine function is $\frac{\pi}{4}$.

$$\frac{\pi}{4} = -\frac{c}{b}$$
$$\frac{\pi}{4} = -\frac{c}{2}$$
$$c = -\frac{\pi}{2}$$

$$g(t) = a \cos (bt + c) + d$$
$$g(t) = 4 \cos \left(2t - \frac{\pi}{2}\right) - 3$$

The graph of $f(t) = 4 \sin 2t - 3$ and the graph of

$$g(t) = 4 \cos \left(2t - \frac{\pi}{2}\right) - 3$$

resemble the graph above.

Example 2

A wheel with a radius of 3 centimeters is rotating counterclockwise at 2 radians per second. A free hanging rod 4 centimeters long is connected to the edge of the wheel at point P and remains vertical as the wheel rotates (see Figure below).

a. Assuming the center of the wheel is at the origin and that P is at $(3, 0)$ at time $t = 0$, find a function that describes the y-coordinate of point E at time t.
Point P moves through an angle of $2t$ radians in t seconds. Find the time t for one revolution by solving $2t = 2\pi$:

$t = \pi$ seconds for one revolution
Some t values and y values of point E that can be used to get a graph are:

t	0	$\dfrac{\pi}{4}$	$\dfrac{\pi}{2}$	$\dfrac{3\pi}{4}$	π
y	-4	-1	-4	-7	-4

Plot these ordered pairs to get the graph:

Figure 8.4-4

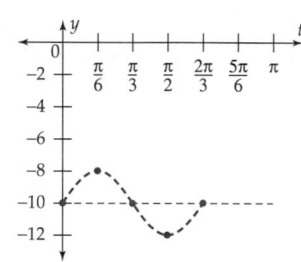

Figure 8.4-5

Find a sine function:

amplitude: $a = 3$

period $= \pi = \dfrac{2\pi}{b}$, so $b = 2$

phase shift $= 0$, so $c = 0$

vertical shift: $d = -4$

$f(t) = a \sin(bt + c) + d$

$f(t) = 3 \sin(2t + 0) - 4$

$f(t) = 3 \sin 2t - 4$

Example 2   **Rotating Wheel**

A wheel with a radius of 2 centimeters is rotating counterclockwise at 3 radians per second. A free-hanging rod 10 centimeters long is connected to the edge of the wheel at point P and remains vertical as the wheel rotates (Figure 8.4-4).

a. Assuming that the center of the wheel is at the origin and that P is at $(2, 0)$ at time $t = 0$, find a function that describes the y-coordinate of the tip E of the rod at time t.

b. What is the first time that the tip E of the rod will be at a height of -9 centimeters?

Solution

a. The wheel is rotating at 3 radians per second. After t seconds, the point P has moved through an angle of $3t$ radians and is 2 units from the origin.

To find the time t that it takes to complete one revolution (i.e., 2π), solve $3t = 2\pi$.

$$t = \frac{2\pi}{3}$$

After $\dfrac{1}{4}$ of a revolution, or $\dfrac{1}{4} \times \dfrac{2\pi}{3} = \dfrac{\pi}{6}$, the height of P reaches its maximum of 2 centimeters, so the y-coordinate of E is $2 - 10 = -8$. After $\dfrac{1}{2}$ of a revolution, or $\dfrac{1}{2} \times \dfrac{2\pi}{3} = \dfrac{\pi}{3}$, the height of P is at 0, so the y-coordinate of E is -10. Continuing this process, it can be found that at $\dfrac{\pi}{2}$ the y-coordinate of E is -12 and at $\dfrac{2\pi}{3}$ the y-coordinate of E is -10.

Plotting these key points shows the main features of the graph.

The amplitude is

$$a = \frac{1}{2}(f_{max} - f_{min}) = \frac{1}{2}(-8 - (-12)) = 2.$$

Use the period to find b.

$$\frac{2\pi}{3} = \frac{2\pi}{b}$$
$$b = 3$$

The sine wave begins at $t = 0$, so there is no phase shift and $c = 0$. The vertical shift, d, is -10 units.

$$d = \frac{f_{max} + f_{min}}{2} = \frac{-8 + (-12)}{2} = -10$$

Thus, the function giving the y-coordinate of E at time t is

$$f(t) = 2 \sin 3t - 10.$$

b. What is the first time that point E will be at a height of -3 centimeters?

$$3 \sin 2t - 4 = -3$$
$$3 \sin 2t = 1$$
$$\sin 2t = \frac{1}{3}$$

$$2t = \sin^{-1}\left(\frac{1}{3}\right) + 2k\pi \ (k \text{ is any integer})$$

$$t = \frac{1}{2} \sin^{-1}\left(\frac{1}{3}\right) + k\pi$$

$$t \approx 0.1699 + k\pi$$

0.1699 seconds

b. To find the first time that the tip E of the rod will be at a height of -9 centimeters, solve $2 \sin 3t - 10 = -9$ for t.

$$2 \sin 3t - 10 = -9$$
$$2 \sin 3t - 1$$
$$\sin 3t = \frac{1}{2}$$
$$3t = \sin^{-1}\left(\frac{1}{2}\right)$$
$$3t = \frac{\pi}{6} + 2k\pi \ (k \text{ is any integer})$$
$$t = \frac{\pi}{18} + \frac{2k\pi}{3} = 0.1745 + \frac{2k\pi}{3}$$

The first time that the tip E of the rod will be at a height of -9 cm is when $k = 0$, that is, $t = \frac{\pi}{18} \approx 0.1745$ seconds. ∎

Example 3 Bouncing Spring

Suppose that a weight hanging from a spring is set in motion by an upward push (Figure 8.4-6). It takes 5 seconds for it to complete one cycle of moving from its equilibrium position to 8 centimeters above, then dropping to 8 centimeters below, and finally returning to its equilibrium position. (This is an idealized situation in which the spring has perfect elasticity, and friction, air resistance, etc., are negligible.)

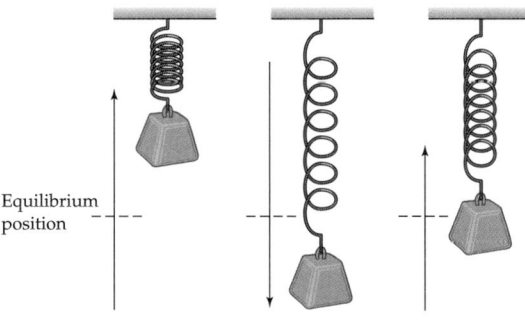

Equilibrium position

Figure 8.4-6

a. Find a sinusoidal function to represent the motion of the moving weight.

b. Sketch a graph of the function you wrote in part **a**.

c. Use the function from part **a** to predict the height of the weight after 3 seconds.

d. In the first 5 seconds, when will the height of the weight be 6 centimeters below the equilibrium position?

COMMON ERROR ALERT

In **Example 2b,** students might try to solve $\sin 3t = \frac{1}{2}$ by only finding $\sin^{-1}\left(\frac{1}{2}\right)$. That is, they might write $t = \frac{\pi}{6} + 2k\pi$.

Remind them that $\sin^{-1}\left(\frac{1}{2}\right) = \frac{\pi}{6}$ is a value for $3t$, so they must divide by 3 to get $t = \frac{\pi}{18} + \frac{2k\pi}{3}$.

Math Background

In **Example 3,** the equation

$$8 \sin\left(\frac{2\pi}{5} t\right) = -6$$ is solved graphically

by the intersection method (see top of page 553). Solving algebraically is more challenging, as shown below.

$$8 \sin\left(\frac{2\pi}{5} t\right) = -6$$
$$\sin\left(\frac{2\pi}{5} t\right) = -\frac{3}{4}$$

Consider $\frac{2\pi}{5}t$ as an angle in standard

position. $\frac{2\pi}{5}t = \sin^{-1}\left(-\frac{3}{4}\right) \approx -0.8481$

is in the interval $\left[-\frac{\pi}{2}, \frac{\pi}{2}\right]$. But, as

shown below, there are two terminating positions for angles whose sine is $-\frac{3}{4}$.

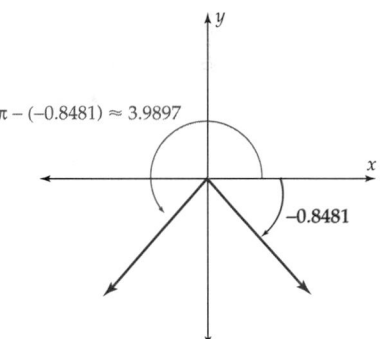

$\pi - (-0.8481) \approx 3.9897$

-0.8481

So, all solutions to the original equation are as follows, where k is any integer:

$$\frac{2\pi}{5}t \approx 3.9897 + 2k\pi$$
$$t \approx (3.9897 + 2k\pi)\left(\frac{5}{2\pi}\right)$$
$$t \approx 3.1749 + 5k$$
$$\frac{2\pi}{5}t \approx -0.8481 + 2k\pi$$
$$t \approx (-0.8481 + 2k\pi)\left(\frac{5}{2\pi}\right)$$
$$t \approx -0.6749 + 5k$$

To find the solutions on the required interval $0 \leq t \leq 5$, use $k = 0$ and $k = 1$ as shown:

$$t \approx 3.1749 + 5(0) = 3.1749$$
$$t \approx -0.6749 + 5(1) = 4.3251$$

Example 3

Suppose that the weight described in Figure 8.4-6 takes 8 seconds to complete one cycle and moves 6 cm below and 6 cm above the equilibrium position.

a. Find a sinusoidal function to represent the motion of the weight.

$$a = 6, \quad \frac{2\pi}{b} = 8, \quad -\frac{c}{b} = 0$$

$$a = 6, \quad b = \frac{\pi}{4}, \quad c = 0$$

$$h(t) = a \sin(bt + c)$$

$$h(t) = 6 \sin \frac{\pi}{4}t$$

b. Sketch a graph of the function you wrote in part **a.**

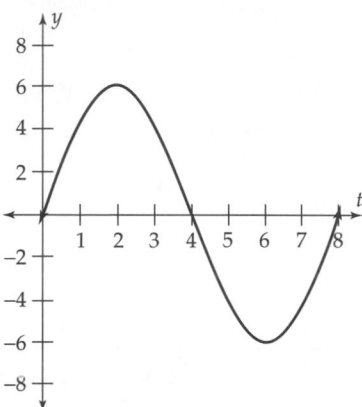

c. Use the function from part **a** to predict the height of the weight after 7 seconds.

$$h(7) = 6 \sin \frac{7\pi}{4} \approx -4.2$$

approximately 4.2 cm below the equilibrium position

d. In the first 8 seconds, when will the height of the weight be 2 centimeters above the equilibrium position?

Solve $6 \sin\left(\frac{\pi}{4}t\right) = 2 \quad (0 \le t \le 8)$.

Graph $Y_1 = 6 \sin\left(\frac{\pi}{4}t\right)$ and $Y_2 = 2$

and find the points of intersection:

$t \approx 0.4327$ seconds and
$t \approx 3.5673$ seconds

Solution

a. Let $h(t)$ denote the distance of the weight above (+) or below (−) its equilibrium position at time t. Then $h(t)$ is 0 when t is 0. As t increases from 0 to 5, $h(t)$ increases from 0 to 8, decreases to −8, and increases again to 0. In the next 5 seconds it repeats the same pattern, and so on. Therefore, the graph of h is periodic and has some kind of wave shape. Two possibilities are shown in Figures 8.4-7a and 8.4-7b.

or

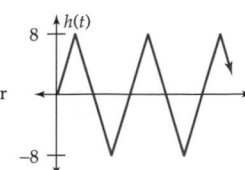

Figure 8.4-7a　　　　**Figure 8.4-7b**

Careful physical experiment suggests that the curve in Figure 8.4-7a, which resembles the sine graphs you have studied, is a reasonably accurate model of this process. Facts from physics and calculus show that the rule of the function h is the form $h(t) = a \sin(bt + c)$ for some constants a, b, and c.

The function h has an amplitude of 8, a period of 5, and a phase shift 0, so the constants a, b, and c must satisfy

$$|a| = 8, \quad \frac{2\pi}{b} = 5, \quad \text{and} \quad -\frac{c}{b} = 0,$$

or equivalently,

$$a = 8, \quad b = \frac{2\pi}{5}, \quad \text{and} \quad c = 0.$$

Therefore, the motion of the moving weight can be described by this function:

$$h(t) = 8 \sin \frac{2\pi}{5}t$$

b. The graph of $h(t) = 8 \sin \frac{2\pi}{5}t$ is shown in Figure 8.4-8.

c. The value of $h(3)$ gives the height of the weight after 3 seconds.

$$h(3) = 8 \sin\left(\frac{2\pi}{5} \cdot 3\right) = 8 \sin \frac{6\pi}{5} \approx -4.7$$

The height of the weight after 3 seconds is approximately 4.7 centimeters below the equilibrium point.

d. To find the times in the first 5 seconds when the weight is 6 centimeters below the equilibrium, you must solve the equation

Figure 8.4-8

Example 4

The average monthly temperature in Paris, France, for 1981–1990 is shown below.

Month	°F
Jan.	38.7
Feb.	38.7
Mar.	45.1
Apr.	49.5
May	56.7
June	61.7
July	66.2
Aug.	65.7
Sep.	61.0
Oct.	54.5
Nov.	45.1
Dec.	41.4

[*Source: worldclimate.com*]

Figure 8.4-9

Figure 8.4-10

$$8 \sin\left(\frac{2\pi}{5} t\right) = -6 \quad (0 \le t \le 5)$$

The graphs of $Y_1 = 8 \sin\left(\frac{2\pi}{5} t\right)$ and $Y_2 = -6$ in a window with $0 \le t \le 5$ are shown in Figure 8.4-9 and 8.4-10. The points of intersection show that the weight will be 6 centimeters below the equilibrium at two times between 0 and 5 seconds.

$$t \approx 3.1749 \quad \text{and} \quad t \approx 4.3251$$

∎

Modeling Trigonometric Data

Periodic data that appears to resemble a sinusoidal curve when plotted can often be modeled by a sine function, as shown in Example 4.

Example 4   Temperature Data

The following table shows the average monthly temperature in Cleveland, Ohio, based on data from 1971 to 2000. Since average temperatures are not likely to vary much from year to year, the data essentially repeats the same pattern in subsequent years. So, a periodic model is appropriate.

Month	Temperature (°F)
Jan.	25.7
Feb.	28.4
Mar.	37.5
Apr.	47.6
May	58.5
June	67.5

Month	Temperature (°F)
July	71.9
Aug.	70.2
Sep.	63.3
Oct.	52.2
Nov.	41.8
Dec.	31.1

[*Source: National Climatic Data Center*]

a. Make a scatter plot of the data.

a. Make a scatter plot of the data.

b. Find a sinusoidal function that models the temperature data.

c. Use the sine regression feature on a calculator to find another sinusoidal model for the data.

d. How do the models in parts **b** and **c** differ from one another?

e. Use one of the models to predict time(s) of year in which the average temperature is 45°F.

Solution

a. Let $t = 1$ represent January. Enter 1 through 12 in List 1 and the temperatures in List 2. The scatter plot is shown in Figure 8.4-11a.

b. Find a sinusoidal function that models the temperature data.

min: 38.7   max: 66.2

amplitude: $\frac{1}{2}(66.2 - 38.7) = 13.75$

The period is $\frac{2\pi}{b} = 12$, so $b = \frac{\pi}{6}$.

vertical shift: $d = \frac{66.2 + 38.7}{2} = 52.45$

A sine wave begins close to the point (4, 49.5) as seen in the graph below.

Figure 8.4-11a

The phase shift is approximately 4.

$$-\frac{c}{b} = 4$$

$$-\frac{c}{\frac{\pi}{6}} = 4, \text{ so } c = -\frac{2\pi}{3}$$

A sine function that models the data is

$$f(t) = 13.75 \sin\left(\frac{\pi}{6}t - \frac{2\pi}{3}\right) + 52.45.$$

Scatter plot and $f(t)$:

c. Use the sine regression feature on a calculator to find another sinusoidal model for the data.

$$f(t) = 13.7766 \sin(0.5339t - 2.3140) + \\ 52.2678$$

period $\approx \dfrac{2\pi}{0.5339} \approx 11.77$; not a very good approximation for a 12-month cycle.

Graph 2 cycles.

Use the sine regression feature to find a model for the 24 data points:

$$f(t) = 13.8381 \sin(0.5245t - 2.2525) + \\ 52.0475$$

period $\approx \dfrac{2\pi}{0.5245} \approx 11.98$, which is much closer to the expected 12-month period.

Graph of 2 cycles and model:

Figure 8.4-11b

b. To find a sinusoidal function to represent the temperature data, examine the properties of the scatter plot.

The minimum value is 25.7 and the maximum value is 71.9, so the amplitude is

$$a = \frac{1}{2}(f_{max} - f_{min}) = \frac{1}{2}(71.9 - 25.7) = 23.1.$$

One complete cycle is 12 months, so the period, $\dfrac{2\pi}{b}$, is 12.

$$\frac{2\pi}{b} = 12$$

$$b = \frac{\pi}{6}$$

The vertical shift is

$$d = \frac{f_{max} + f_{min}}{2} = \frac{71.9 + 25.7}{2} = 48.8.$$

A sine wave begins close to the data point (4, 47.6), as shown in Figure 8.4-11b, so the phase shift $-\dfrac{c}{b}$ is approximately 4. Find c.

$$-\frac{c}{b} = 4$$

$$-\frac{c}{\frac{\pi}{6}} = 4$$

$$c = -\frac{2\pi}{3}$$

Therefore, a sinusoidal function to represent the temperature data is approximately

$$f(t) = 23.1 \sin\left(\frac{\pi}{6}t - \frac{2\pi}{3}\right) + 48.8.$$

The graph of this function is shown with the scatter plot of the data in Figure 8.4-12.

c. Using the 12 given data points, the regression feature on a calculator produces the following model.

$$f(t) = 23.1202 \sin(0.5018t - 2.0490) + 48.6927$$

The period of this function is approximately

$$\frac{2\pi}{0.5018} = 12.52,$$

which is not a very good approximation for a 12-month cycle.

Because the data repeats the same pattern from year to year, a more accurate model can be obtained by using the same data repeated for

Figure 8.4-12

continued from page 553

Figure 8.4-13a

Figure 8.4-13b

the second year. The data for a two-year period is plotted in Figure 8.4-13a. The sine regression feature on a calculator produces this model from the 24 data points:

$$f(t) = 22.7000 \sin(0.5219t - 2.1842) + 49.5731$$

The period of this function is

$$\frac{2\pi}{0.5219} \approx 12.04,$$

which is slightly off from the expected 12-month period. However, its graph in Figure 8.4-13b appears to fit the data well.

d. Using the decimal approximation of π, the rule of the function found in part **b** becomes

$$f(t) \approx 23.1 \sin(0.5236t - 2.0944) + 48.8.$$

This model differs only slightly from the second model in part **c**.

$$f(t) = 22.7000 \sin(0.5219t - 2.1842) + 49.5731$$

Visually, however, the model shown in Figure 8.4-12 does not seem to fit the data points quite as well as the model shown in Figure 8.4-13b. Nevertheless, considering that the model found in part **b** can be obtained without technology, it is remarkably close.

e. The model from part **c** will be used to predict the times of year in which the average temperature is 45°F.

There are two points of intersection of the graphs of

$$y = 45 \text{ and } f(t) = 22.7000 \sin(0.5219t - 2.1842) + 49.5731,$$

as shown in Figure 8.4-14. Their approximate coordinates are (3.8, 45) and (10.6, 45). Therefore, according to this model, the temperature would be around 45°F in late March and late October. ■

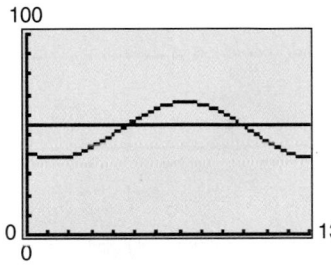

Figure 8.4-14

d. How do the models in parts **b** and **c** differ from one another? Using the decimal approximation of π, the model from part **b** becomes

$$f(t) \approx 13.75 \sin(0.5236t - 2.0944) + 52.45.$$

This model differs from the second model in part **c** (shown below), especially in the phase shift.

$$f(t) = 13.8381 \sin(0.5245t - 2.2525) + 52.0475$$

e. Use one of the models to predict time(s) of year in which the average temperature is 55 degrees. Use the second model from part **c**. Graph

$$f(t) = 13.8381 \sin(0.5245t - 2.2525) + 52.0475$$

and $y = 55$.

The approximate coordinates of the points of intersection are (4.7, 55) and (9.9, 55), so the average temperature would be 55 degrees in late April and late September.

Real-World Application

The original Ferris Wheel is described in Exercise 1. The vertical motion of one of its cars is an example of simple harmonic motion and can be modeled by a trigonometric function. Your students will find that the function $f(t) = 125 \sin\left(\frac{\pi t}{5}\right)$ gives the y-coordinate of car D, where t is time in minutes. Ask them to find $f(2.5)$, $f(5)$, and $f(7.5)$, and to interpret the results.

Exercises 8.4

1. The original Ferris wheel, built by George Ferris for the Columbian Exposition of 1893, was much larger and slower than its modern counterparts: It had a diameter of 250 feet and contained 36 cars, each of which held 40 people; it made one revolution every 10 minutes. Suppose that the Ferris wheel revolves counterclockwise in the x-y plane with its center at the origin. Car D in the figure had coordinates (125, 0) at time $t = 0$. Find the rule of a function that gives the y-coordinate of car D at time t.

$$f(t) = 125 \sin\left(\frac{\pi t}{5}\right)$$

$f(2.5) = 125$; the y-coordinate of car D when it is at the top, after $\frac{1}{4}$ revolution

$f(5) = 0$; the y-coordinate of car D when it is level with starting point (125, 0), after $\frac{1}{2}$ revolution

$f(7.5) = -125$; the y-coordinate of car D when it is at the bottom, after $\frac{3}{4}$ revolution

ANSWERS

2. $f(t) = -125 \cos(2t)$

3. $f(t) = \cos 20\pi t + \sqrt{16 - \sin^2(20\pi t)}$

4. $f(t) = 2\cos(100\pi t) + \sqrt{16 - 4\sin^2(100\pi t)}$

5. $h(t) = 6 \sin\left(\dfrac{\pi t}{2}\right)$

6. $h(t) = -6 \sin\left(\dfrac{\pi}{2}t\right)$

7. $h(t) = 6 \cos\left(\dfrac{\pi t}{2}\right)$

8. $h(t) = -6 \cos\left(\dfrac{\pi}{2}t\right)$

9. $d(t) = 10 \sin\left(\dfrac{\pi t}{2}\right)$

10. a. $4 \cos(4\pi t)$

b. $b(t) = 4 \cos\left(4\pi t + \dfrac{\pi}{2}\right)$,

$c(t) = 4 \cos\left(4\pi t + \dfrac{\pi}{4}\right)$,

$d(t) = 4 \cos\left(4\pi t - \dfrac{\pi}{4}\right)$,

$e(t) = 8 \cos(4\pi t)$,

$f(t) = 8 \cos\left(4\pi t + \dfrac{\pi}{4}\right)$,

$g(t) = 8 \cos\left(4\pi t + \dfrac{\pi}{2}\right)$

c.

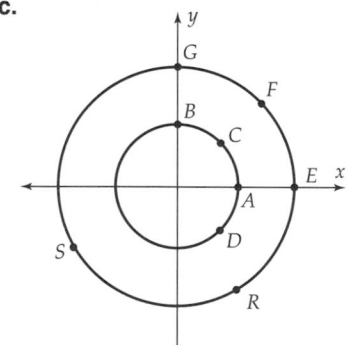

2. Do Exercise 1 if the wheel turns at 2 radians per minute and car D is at $(0, -125)$ at time $t = 0$.

3. A circular wheel with a radius of 1 foot rotates counterclockwise. A 4-foot rod has one end attached to the edge of this wheel and the other end to the base of a piston (see figure). It transfers the rotary motion of the wheel into a back-and-forth linear motion of the piston. If the wheel is rotating at 10 revolutions per second, point W is at $(1, 0)$ at time $t = 0$, and point P is always on x-axis, find the rule of a function that gives the x-coordinate of P at time t.

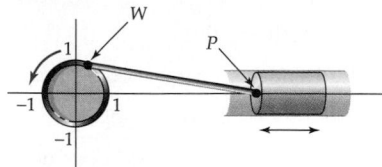

4. Do Exercise 3 if the wheel has a radius of 2 feet, rotates at 50 revolutions per second, and is at $(2, 0)$ when $t = 0$.

In Exercises 5–8, suppose a weight is hanging from a spring (under the same conditions as in Example 3). The weight is pushed to start it moving. At time t, let $h(t)$ be the distance of the weight above or below its equilibrium point. Assume the maximum distance the weight moves in either direction from the equilibrium point is 6 cm and that it moves through a complete cycle every 4 seconds. Express $h(t)$ in terms of the sine or cosine function under the given conditions.

5. There is an initial push upward from the equilibrium point.

6. There is an initial pull downward from the equilibrium point. *Hint:* What does the graph of $y = a \sin bt$ look like when $a < 0$?

7. The weight is pulled 6 cm above the equilibrium point, and the initial movement (at $t = 0$) is downward. *Hint:* Think of the cosine graph.

8. The weight is pulled 6 cm below its equilibrium point, and the initial movement is upward.

9. A pendulum swings uniformly back and forth, taking 2 seconds to move from the position directly above point A to the position directly above point B, as shown in the figure. The distance from A to B is 20 centimeters. Let $d(t)$ be the horizontal distance

from the pendulum to the (dashed) center line at time t seconds (with distances to the right of the line measured by positive numbers and distances to the left by negative ones). Assume that the pendulum is on the center line at time $t = 0$ and moving to the right. Assume the motion of the pendulum is simple harmonic motion. Find the rule of the function $d(t)$.

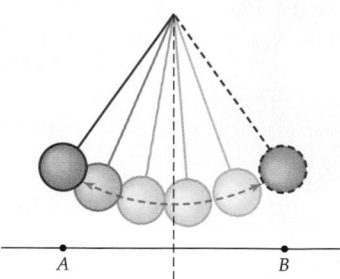

10. The following figure shows a diagram of a merry-go-round that is turning counterclockwise at a constant rate, making 2 revolutions in 1 minute. On the merry-go-round are horses A, B, C, and D 4 meters from the center and horses E, F, and G 8 meters from the center. There is a function $a(t)$ that gives the distance the horse A is from the y-axis (this is the x-coordinate of A's position) as a function of time t measured in minutes. Similarly, $b(t)$ gives the x-coordinate for B as a function of time, and so on. Assume the diagram shows the situation at time $t = 0$.

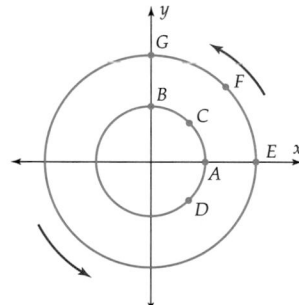

a. Which of the following function rules does $a(t)$ have?

$4 \cos t$, $4 \cos \pi t$, $4 \cos 2t$, $4 \cos 2\pi t$, $4 \cos\left(\dfrac{1}{2}t\right)$, $4 \cos\left(\dfrac{\pi}{2}t\right)$, $4 \cos 4\pi t$

b. Describe the function $b(t)$, $c(t)$, $d(t)$, $e(t)$, $f(t)$, and $g(t)$ using the cosine function.

c. Suppose the x-coordinate of a horse S is given by the function $s(t) = 4 \cos\left(4\pi t - \dfrac{5\pi}{6}\right)$ and the x-coordinate of another horse R is given by $r(t) = 8 \cos\left(4\pi t - \dfrac{\pi}{3}\right)$. Where are these horses located in relation to the rest of the horses? Copy the diagram and mark the positions of R and S at $t = 0$.

11. The following table shows the number, in millions, of unemployed people in the labor force for 1991–2002.

Year	Unemployed	Year	Unemployed
1991	8.628	1997	6.739
1992	9.613	1998	6.210
1993	8.940	1999	5.880
1994	7.996	2000	5.655
1995	7.404	2001	6.742
1996	7.236	2002	8.234

a. Sketch a scatter plot of the data, with $x = 0$ corresponding to 1990.
b. Does the data appear to be periodic? If so, find an appropriate model.
c. Do you think this model is likely to be accurate much beyond the year 2002? Why?

In Exercises 12 and 13, do the following:

a. Use 12 data points (with $x = 1$ corresponding to January) to find a periodic model of the data.
b. What is the period of the function found in part **a**? Is this reasonable?
c. Plot 24 data points (two years) and graph the function from part **a** on the same screen. Is the function a good model in the second year?
d. Use the 24 data points in part **c** to find another periodic model for the data.
e. What is the period of the function in part **d**? Does its graph fit the data well?

12. The table shows the average monthly temperature in Chicago, IL, based on data from 1971 to 2000.

Month	Temperature (°F)
Jan.	22.0
Feb.	27.0
Mar.	37.3
Apr.	47.8
May	58.7
June	68.2
July	73.3
Aug.	71.7
Sep.	63.8
Oct.	52.1
Nov.	39.3
Dec.	27.4

[Source: National Climatic Data Center]

13. The table shows the average monthly precipitation, in inches, in San Francisco, CA, based on data from 1971 to 2000.

Month	Precipitation
Jan.	4.45
Feb.	4.01
Mar.	3.26
Apr.	1.17
May	0.38
June	0.11
July	0.03
Aug.	0.07
Sep.	0.2
Oct.	1.04
Nov.	2.49
Dec.	2.89

[Source: National Climatic Data Center]

c.

The model is not a good fit in the second year.

d. $y = 2.1663 \sin(0.5113x + 1.0506) + 1.7144$

e. About 12.2. This model provides a much better fit.

11. a.

b. Roughly periodic; $y = 1.3582 \sin(0.4778x + 0.5691) + 7.6363$

c. No, the unemployment total will only be predicted in the range 6.2781 to 8.9944.

12. a. $y = 25.6296 \sin(0.4914x - 1.9451) + 47.4516$

b. About 12.8 which is pretty close to the expected 12 month period, but not ideal.

c.

The model is not a good fit in the second year.

d. $y = 24.8484 \sin(0.52135x - 2.1482) + 48.9479$

e. About 12.05. This model provides a much better fit.

13. a. $y = 2.9138 \sin(0.4002x + 1.8090) + 2.3764$

b. About 15.7, which is somewhat reasonable but may not be the best model to use.

14. *Critical Thinking* A grandfather clock has a pendulum length of k meters. Its swing is given (as in Exercise 9) by the function

$$f(t) = 0.25 \sin(\omega t), \text{ where } \omega = \sqrt{\frac{9.8}{k}}.$$

a. Find k such that the period of the pendulum is 2 seconds. **$k \approx 0.9929$**

b. The temperature in the summer months causes the pendulum to increase its length by 0.01%. How much time will the clock lose in June, July, and August? *Hint:* These three months have a total of 92 days (7,948,800 seconds). If k is increased by 0.01%, what is $f(2)$?

The clock loses about 0.000099998 seconds every 2 seconds or about 397.43 seconds in the 3 month span.

Section 8.4.A *Excursion:* Sound Waves

Teaching Notes

Before proceeding with the lesson, divide students into groups, making sure you have enough data collection devices, microphones, and tuning forks to accommodate each group.

The **Technology Tip** on page 559 discusses how data collections may vary. You should have each group perform the same experiment, and then compare their results.

Example Notes

For **Example 1,** to count the number of cycles on the graph, count the number of maximums *after* the first maximum. The first maximum is not included in the count.

8.4.A *Excursion:* Sound Waves

Objectives

- Find the frequency of a sound wave using a tuning fork and a data collection device

- Model sound wave data with sinusoidal functions and graphs

Sound travels through the air like small ripples traveling across a body of water. Throwing a rock into a calm body of water causes the water to begin to move up and down around the entry point. The movement of the water causes ripples to move outward. If a flower is floating in this body of water, the ripples will cause the flower to move up and down on the water.

Sound is produced by a vibrating object that disturbs the surrounding air molecules and causes them to vibrate. These vibrations cause a periodic change in air pressure that travels through the air much like the ripples in a body of water. When the air pressure waves reach the eardrum, they cause it to vibrate at the same frequency as the source. These air pressure waves are more commonly called **sound waves.** The voices and sounds heard each day are generally a combination of many different sound waves. The sound from a tuning fork is a single tone that can be described mathematically using a sinusoidal function, $f(t) = a \sin(bt + c) + d$ or $g(t) = a \cos(bt + c) + d$.

Recall from Sections 7.4 and 8.4 that if $a \neq 0$ and $b > 0$, then each of the functions

$$f(t) = a \sin(bt + c) + d \quad \text{and} \quad g(t) = a \cos(bt + c) + d$$

has the following characteristics:

$$\text{amplitude} = |a| \qquad \text{period} = \frac{2\pi}{b}$$

$$\text{phase shift} = -\frac{c}{b} \qquad \text{vertical shift} = d$$

The period of a sound wave determines the sound's *frequency.* The **frequency** f of a sound wave is the reciprocal of its period.

$$f = \frac{b}{2\pi}$$

Technology Tip

Data obtained may differ from one collection to another, and specific values produced by a calculator may vary.

NOTE A tuning program can be obtained by downloading or entering the DataMate application available from Texas Instruments.

Frequency gives the number of cycles (periods) that the sound wave completes in one second. Frequencies are measured in units called **Hertz** (Hz), where one Hertz is one cycle per second. Most tuning forks have their frequency and corresponding musical note listed on them.

A tuning fork, a microphone connected to a data collection device (such as a CBL2), and a calculator with a tuning program can be used to simulate the sounds heard through the eardrum.

Figure 8.4.A-1

Example 1   Frequency

Confirm with a sinusoid graph that the frequency of a sound wave formed by striking a C tuning fork is 262 Hz.

Solution

Connect the calculator to the data collection device, connect the microphone to the data collection device, and run the program needed to calculate the pressure for the sound waves. Follow the directions on the screen of your calculator to obtain a graph like the one shown in Figure 8.4.A-2.

Figure 8.4.A-2b

Figure 8.4.A-2c

Figure 8.4.A-2a

The period of the data can be found by dividing the differences between the x-value of the first maximum and the x-value for the last maximum by the number of complete cycles between the maximums. For the data

---

ADDITIONAL EXAMPLES

Example 1

Confirm with a sinusoid graph that the frequency of a sound wave formed by striking an A tuning fork is 426.7 Hz. Connect the calculator to the data collection device, connect the microphone to the data collection device, and run the program needed to calculate the pressure for sound waves.

For the data shown below, the first maximum occurs when $x = 0.0011$.

The last maximum occurs when $x = 0.0175$ as shown below.

There are 7 complete cycles between the first and last maximum.

$$\text{period}$$
$$= \frac{x\text{-value of last max.} - x\text{-value of 1st max.}}{\text{no. of complete cycles between max.'s}}$$
$$= \frac{0.0175 - 0.0011}{7} \approx 0.0023429 \qquad \textit{cycle length}$$
$$\text{frequency} = \frac{1}{\text{period}} \approx \frac{1}{0.0023429} \approx 426.829$$

So, the graph indicates a frequency of about 426.829, which is very close to the actual frequency of 426.7.

ADDITIONAL EXAMPLES

Example 2

Find a sinusoidal model to fit the sound waves produced by a tuning fork with the note D.

Use a data collection device, a D tuning fork, and a tuning program to obtain a graph of the data.

The amplitude is one half the difference between the maximum and minimum values.

amplitude:

$$a = \frac{0.107527 - (-0.068426)}{2}$$
$$= 0.0880$$

The first maximum occurs when $x = 0.0009$ and the last maximum occurs when $x = 0.0183$. There are 5 cycles between the first and last maximums.

period:

$$p = \frac{0.0183 - 0.0009}{5}$$
$$= 0.00348$$

Use the period to find b.

$$\frac{2\pi}{b} = 0.00348$$
$$b = \frac{2\pi}{0.00348}$$

The graph has a maximum at $x = 0.0009$, so the phase shift for the function using cosine is 0.0009.

Use the phase shift and b to find c.

$$-\frac{c}{b} = \text{phase shift}$$

$$c = -0.0009\left(\frac{2\pi}{0.00348}\right) = -0.517241\pi$$

Find the vertical shift d by finding the average of the maximum and minimum values.

$$d = \frac{0.107527 + (-0.068426)}{2} = 0.019551$$

So, the sinusoidal model to fit the sound waves produced with the note D is

$$y = 0.0880 \cos\left(\frac{2\pi}{0.00348}x - 0.517241\pi\right) + 0.019551$$

Note that the frequency, the reciprocal of the period, is 287.356, which is very close to the actual frequency of 288 Hz for the note D.

---

shown in Figure 8.4.A-2a, Figures 8.4.A-2b and 8.4.A-2c show that the first maximum occurs when $x = 0.0020768$, the last maximum occurs when $x = 0.0208608$, and there are five complete cycles between the first and last maximum. Therefore, the period of the data is given by the following.

$$\frac{0.0208608 - 0.0020768}{5} = 0.0037568 \quad \textit{cycle length}$$

The frequency is the reciprocal of the period.

$$\frac{1}{0.0037568} \approx 266.184$$

Therefore, the graph indicates a frequency of about 266.184, which is very close to the actual frequency of 262 Hz. ■

Example 2   Sinusoidal Model

Find a sinusoidal model to fit the sound waves produced by a tuning fork with the note G.

Solution

Use a data collection device, a G tuning fork, and a tuning program to obtain a graph similar to the one shown in Figure 8.4.A-3.

Figure 8.4.A-3

Find the amplitude a by finding half the difference between the maximum value and minimum value. The data graphed in Figure 8.4-3 has a maximum value of 0.043942 and a minimum value of -0.045618.

$$a = \frac{0.043942 - (-0.045618)}{2} = 0.04478 \quad \textit{amplitude}$$

To find the period, find the x-value of the first maximum of the graph, find the x-value of the last maximum of the graph, and divide the difference between the two x-values by 8 (the number of cycles between the first and last maximum). The first maximum shown on the graph occurs when $x = 0.0020768$, and the last maximum occurs when $x = 0.0221088$.

$$p = \frac{0.0221088 - 0.0020768}{8} = 0.002504 \quad \textit{period}$$

Use the period to find b.

$$\frac{2\pi}{b} = 0.002504$$

$$b = \frac{2\pi}{0.002504}$$

The graph has a maximum at $x = 0.0020768$, so the phase shift for a function using cosine is 0.0020768.

Use the phase shift and b to find c.

$$-\frac{c}{b} = \text{phase shift}$$

$$c = -0.0020768\left(\frac{2\pi}{0.002504}\right) = -1.658786\pi$$

Find the vertical shift d by finding the average of the maximum and minimum values. In this example, $d = 0$.

Therefore, the sinusoidal model to fit the sound waves produced by a tuning fork with the note G is

$$y = 0.04478 \cos\left(\frac{2\pi}{0.002504} x - 1.658786\pi\right).$$

Notice that the frequency, the reciprocal of the period, is 399.361, which is very close to the actual frequency of 392 Hz for the note G. ■

When two sounds of slightly different frequency are produced simultaneously, a *beat* is heard. A **beat** is a single sound that gets louder and softer at periodic intervals. By using more than one tuning fork, a beat can be displayed.

| **Example 3**   Chord Frequency |

Place tuning forks with notes of C and G close to a microphone.
a. Find a graphical representation for the sound waves produced by playing the two notes simultaneously.
b. Find the period of the function.
c. How does the frequency of this sound compare with the actual frequencies of C and G?

Solution

a. Using a data collection device, the graph in Figure 8.4.A-4 is obtained.

b. The graph appears to be periodic. By finding the length of one complete cycle, the period of this graph appears to be approximately 0.0077632.

c. The frequency of this sound is the reciprocal of the period of the function.

$$\frac{1}{0.0077632} = 128.8128607 \text{ Hz}$$

The frequency of this sound is very close to the difference between the actual frequency of C, 262 Hz, and the actual frequency of G, 392 Hz.

$$392 - 262 = 130$$

■

PRESSURE

TIME(S)

Figure 8.4.A-4

c. How does the frequency of this sound compare with the actual frequencies of A and D?
The frequency of this sound is the reciprocal of the period of the function.

$$\frac{1}{0.00723537} = 138.2099326 \text{ Hz}$$

The frequency of this sound is very close to the difference between the actual frequency of A, 426.7 Hz, and the actual frequency of D, 288 Hz.
$$426.7 - 288 = 138.7.$$

ADDITIONAL EXAMPLES

| **Example 3** |

Place tuning forks with notes of A and D close to a microphone.

a. Find a graphical representation for the sound waves produced by playing the same two notes simultaneously.
Using a data collection device, the graph is shown below.

b. Find the period of the function.
The graph appears to be periodic reaching a maximum at every third peak. To find the length of one cycle, find the x-value of the first maximum, find the x-value of the last maximum, and divide the difference by the number of cycles between the first and last maximum.

first maximum:

last maximum:

$$p = \frac{0.01511015 - 0.00063941}{2} = 0.00723537$$

By finding the length of one cycle, the period appears to be approximately 0.00723537.

Teaching Notes

Solution to the **Graphing Exploration:**
Using the data from Example 1, a sinusoidal function to model the graph produced by the C tuning fork is given by:

$$y = 0.042514 \cos\left(\frac{2\pi}{0.0037568}x - 1.105622\pi\right)$$

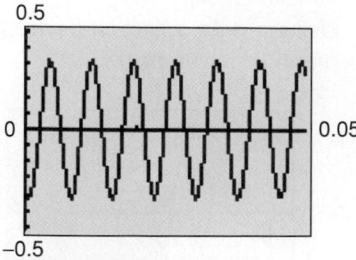

Graph of sum of sinusoidal models for C and G notes:

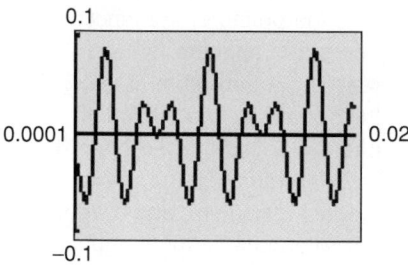

The frequency of the graph above is 133.0888048 Hz which is very close to the difference between the actual frequencies of C and G, 130 Hz.

Exercises 8.4.A

ANSWERS

1.

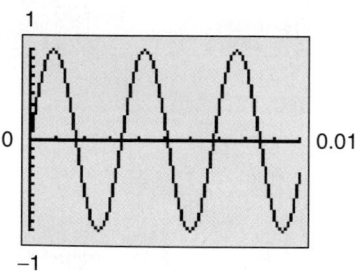

$y = \sin(294 \cdot 2\pi x)$

2.

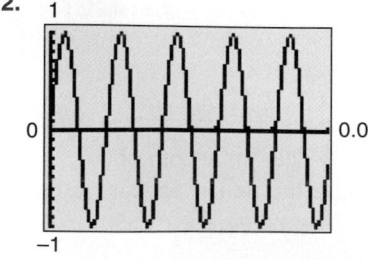

$y = \sin(494 \cdot 2\pi x)$

NOTE The intensity of the strike on the tuning fork determines the amplitude.

> ### Graphing Exploration ●
>
> Find a sinusoidal function to model the graph produced by the C tuning fork.
>
> Add the sinusoidal models for C and G notes. (Use the model from Example 2.) Graph this sum.
>
> What is the frequency of the graph? How does the frequency of this sound compare with the sum of the actual frequencies of C and G?

Most sounds are more complex than those produced by tuning forks. A tuning fork produces a graph of a single note. Most musical instruments produce a sound that is a combination of several different sounds.

A C-G chord was produced with the tuning forks in Example 3. The exploration above indicates that this sound can be modeled by the sum of the models for the C note and the G note.

Exercises 8.4.A

Bottles of water can be tuned using a microphone and data collection device. Place some water in the bottle and blow air over the top of the bottle to produce a sound. Use the frequency of the graph formed from the sound to approximate the frequency. If a higher note is needed, place more water in the bottle and calculate the frequency again. Display the graph of the following notes using the chart below.

Note	Frequency in Hz
C	262
C# or Db	277
D	294
D# or Eb	311
E	330
F	349
F# or Gb	370
G	392

Note	Frequency in Hz
G# or Ab	415
A	440
A# or Bb	466
B	494
C (next octave)	524

1. D   **2.** B   **3.** A   **4.** C#

5. Using only one tuning fork at a time and the sum of three functions, sketch a graph of the C-major chord (C + E + G).

6. Using three tuning forks for the notes C, E, and G at one time, find a graph of the C-major chord (C + E + G).

3.

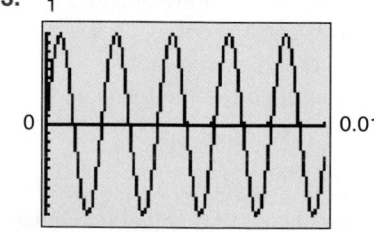

$y = \sin(440 \cdot 2\pi x)$

4.

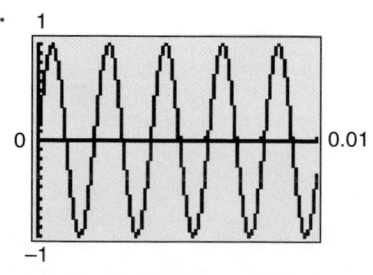

$y = \sin(277 \cdot 2\pi x)$

CHAPTER

8

REVIEW

Important Concepts

Important Facts and Formulas

$\sin^{-1} v = u$ exactly when $\sin u = v \left(-\dfrac{\pi}{2} \le u \le \dfrac{\pi}{2}, -1 \le v \le 1 \right)$

$\cos^{-1} v = u$ exactly when $\cos u = v \left(0 \le u \le \pi, -1 \le v \le 1 \right)$

$\tan^{-1} v = u$ exactly when $\tan u = v \left(-\dfrac{\pi}{2} < u < \dfrac{\pi}{2}, v \text{ a real number} \right)$

Let $a \ne 0$ and $b > 0$. The following functions have the given characteristics.

$$f(t) = a \sin(bt + c) + d \text{ and } g(t) = a \cos(bt + c) + d$$

$$\text{amplitude } |a| = \frac{1}{2}(f_{max} - f_{min})$$

$$\text{period } \frac{2\pi}{b}, \qquad \text{phase shift } -\frac{c}{b}$$

$$\text{vertical shift } d = \frac{1}{2}(f_{max} + f_{min})$$

563

5. (graph of C-major chord: C + E + G)

$y = \sin(262 \cdot 2\pi x) +$
$\sin(330 \cdot 2\pi x) + \sin(392 \cdot 2\pi x)$

6. Graph should match graph in Exercise 5.

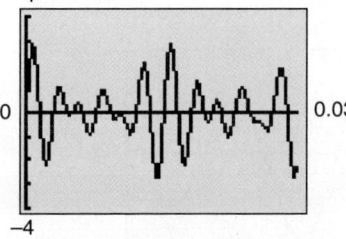

Review Exercises

1. $x = k\pi$

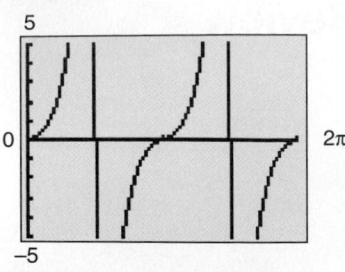

2. $x \approx 2.2907 + 2k\pi$ or
$5.0665 + 2k\pi$

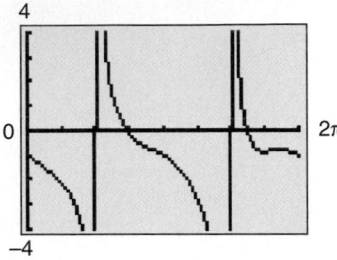

3. $x \approx 0.8419 + 2k\pi$ or
$2.2997 + 2k\pi$ or $4.1784 + 2k\pi$
or $5.2463 + 2k\pi$

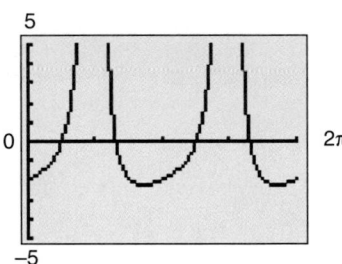

4. $x \approx 0.5225 + k\pi$ or $2.7947 + k\pi$

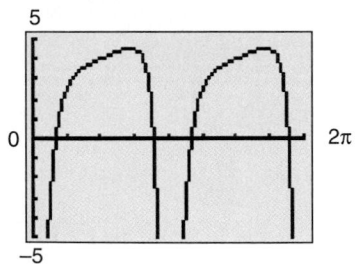

5. $x \approx 0.5236 + 2k\pi$ or
$2.6180 + 2k\pi$ or $4.7124 + 2k\pi$

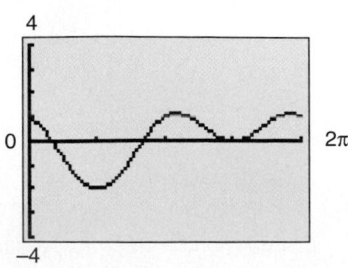

6. $x \approx 1.5708 + 2k\pi$ or $3.3090 + 2k\pi$ or
$4.7124 + 2k\pi$ or $6.1157 + 2k\pi$

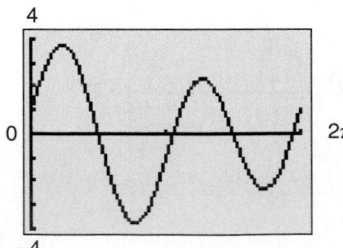

Review Exercises

In Exercises 1–6, solve each equation graphically.

Section 8.1

1. $5 \tan x = 2 \sin 2x$

2. $\sin^3 x + \cos^2 x - \tan x = 2$

3. $\sin x + \sec^2 x = 3$

4. $\cos^2 x - \csc^2 x + \tan\left(x - \dfrac{\pi}{2}\right) + 5 = 0$

5. $\cos 2x = \sin x$

6. $3 \sin 2x = -\cos x$

7. A weight hanging from a spring is set into motion, moving up and down. (See Figure 8.4-6 in Example 3 of Section 8.4.) Its distance in centimeters above or below the equilibrium point at time t seconds is given by $d = 5 \sin 3t - 3 \cos 3t$. At what times during the first two seconds is the weight at the equilibrium position ($d = 0$)? **0.1801 sec; 1.2273 sec**

In Exercises 8–17, find the exact value without using a calculator.

Section 8.2

8. $\cos^{-1}\left(\dfrac{\sqrt{2}}{2}\right) = ?$ $\dfrac{\pi}{4}$

9. $\sin^{-1}\left(\dfrac{\sqrt{3}}{2}\right) = ?$ $\dfrac{\pi}{3}$

10. $\tan^{-1}\sqrt{3} = ?$ $\dfrac{\pi}{3}$

11. $\sin^{-1}\left(\cos \dfrac{11\pi}{6}\right) = ?$ $\dfrac{\pi}{3}$

12. $\cos^{-1}\left(\sin \dfrac{5\pi}{3}\right) = ?$ $\dfrac{5\pi}{6}$

13. $\tan^{-1}\left(\cos \dfrac{7\pi}{2}\right) = ?$ **0**

14. $\sin^{-1}(\sin 0.75) = ?$ $\dfrac{3}{4}$

15. $\cos^{-1}(\cos 2) = ?$ **2**

16. $\sin^{-1}\left(\sin \dfrac{8\pi}{3}\right) = ?$ $\dfrac{\pi}{3}$

17. $\cos^{-1}\left(\cos \dfrac{13\pi}{4}\right) = ?$ $\dfrac{3\pi}{4}$

18. Sketch the graph of $f(x) = \tan^{-1} x - \pi$.

19. Sketch the graph of $g(x) = \sin^{-1}(x - 2)$.

20. Find the exact value of $\sin\left(\cos^{-1}\dfrac{1}{4}\right)$. $\dfrac{\sqrt{15}}{4}$

21. Find the exact value of $\sin\left(\tan^{-1}\dfrac{1}{2} - \cos^{-1}\dfrac{4}{5}\right)$. $-\dfrac{2}{5\sqrt{5}}$

Section 8.3

22. Find all angles θ with $0° \leq \theta \leq 360°$ such that $\sin \theta = -0.7133$.
≈314.5° or ≈225.5°

23. Find all angles θ with $0° \leq \theta \leq 360°$ such that $\tan \theta = 3.7321$.
≈75° or ≈255°

In Exercises 24–38, solve the equation by any means. Find exact solutions when possible and approximate solutions otherwise.

24. $2 \sin x = 1$

25. $\cos x = \dfrac{\sqrt{3}}{2}$

26. $\tan x = -1$

27. $\sin 3x = -\dfrac{\sqrt{3}}{2}$

28. $\sin x = 0.7$

29. $\cos x = -0.8$

30. $\tan x = 13$

31. $\cot x = 0.4$

32. $2 \sin^2 x + 5 \sin x = 3$

33. $4 \cos^2 x - 2 = 0$

34. $2 \sin^2 x - 3 \sin x = 2$

35. $\sec^2 x + 3 \tan^2 x = 13$

36. $\sec^2 x = 4 \tan x - 2$

37. $2 \sin^2 x + \sin x - 2 = 0$

38. $\cos^2 x - 3 \cos x - 2 = 0$

39. A cannon has a muzzle velocity of 600 feet per second. At what angle of elevation should it be fired in order to hit a target 3500 feet away? *Hint:* Use the projectile equation given for Exercises 56–59 of Section 8.3.

Section **8.4**

40. The following table gives the average population, in thousands, of a southern town for each month throughout the year. The population is greater in the winter and smaller in the summer, and it repeats this pattern from year to year.

Month	Population		Month	Population
Jan.	10.5		July	4.7
Feb.	9.3		Aug.	5.8
Mar.	7.8		Sep.	7.6
Apr.	6.0		Oct.	9.4
May	4.9		Nov.	10.6
June	4.5		Dec.	10.9

  a. Make a scatter plot of the data.
  b. Find a sinusoidal function to represent the population data.
  c. Use the sine regression feature on a calculator to find a periodic model for the data.
  d. Use the model from part **c** to predict time(s) of year in which the average population is 6200.

41. The paddle wheel of a steamboat is 22 feet in diameter and is turning at 3 revolutions per minute. The axle of the wheel is 8 feet above the surface of the water. Assume that the center of the wheel is at the origin and that a point P on the edge of the paddle wheel is at $(0, 19)$ at time $t = 0$ seconds.
  a. What maximum height above the water does point P reach?
  b. How far below the water does point P reach?
  c. In how many seconds does the wheel complete one revolution?
  d. Write a cosine function for the height of point P at time t.
  e. Write a sine function for the height of point P at time t.
  f. Use the function from part **d** or **e** to find the time(s) at which point P will be at a height of 10 feet.

Section **8.4.A**

42. Confirm with a sinusoid graph that the frequency of a sound wave formed by striking an F tuning fork is 349 Hz.

43. Find a sinusoidal model to fit the sound waves produced by striking an E tuning fork.

18.

19.

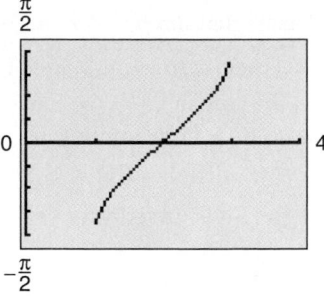

24. $x = \dfrac{\pi}{6} + 2k\pi$ or $x = \dfrac{5\pi}{6} + 2k\pi$

25. $x = \dfrac{\pi}{6} + 2k\pi$ or $x = \dfrac{11\pi}{6} + 2k\pi$

26. $x = -\dfrac{\pi}{4} + k\pi$

27. $x = \dfrac{4\pi}{9} + \dfrac{2k\pi}{3}$ or $x = \dfrac{5\pi}{9} + \dfrac{2k\pi}{3}$

28. $x \sim 0.7754 + 2k\pi$ or $x \approx 2.3662 + 2k\pi$

29. $x \approx 2.49809 + 2k\pi$ or $x \approx 3.78509 + 2k\pi$

30. $x \approx 1.4940 + k\pi$

31. $x \approx 1.19029 + k\pi$

32. $x = \dfrac{\pi}{6} + 2k\pi$ or $x = \dfrac{5\pi}{6} + 2k\pi$

33. $x = \dfrac{\pi}{4} + k\pi$ or $\dfrac{3\pi}{4} + k\pi$

34. $x = \dfrac{7\pi}{6} + 2k\pi$ or $-\dfrac{\pi}{6} + 2k\pi$

35. $x = \pm\dfrac{\pi}{3} + k\pi$

36. $x = \dfrac{\pi}{4} + k\pi$ or $x \approx 1.2490 + k\pi$

37. $x \approx 0.8959 + 2k\pi$ or $2.2457 + 2k\pi$

38. $x \approx 2.1671 + 2k\pi$ or $4.1161 + 2k\pi$

39. $\approx 9.06°$ or $\approx 80.94°$

40. a.

41. a. 19 ft

  b. 3 ft below water

  c. 20 sec

  d. possible answer: $g(t) = 11 \cos\left(\dfrac{\pi}{10} t\right) + 8$

  e. possible answer:

  $h(t) = 11 \sin\left(\dfrac{\pi}{10} t - \dfrac{\pi}{2}\right) + 8$

  f. $t \approx 4.418 + 20k$ and $t \approx 15.582 + 20k$ sec, where k is any integer.

42. The frequency should be close to the actual frequency of 349 Hz.

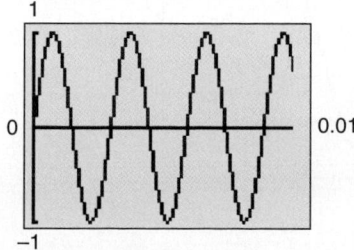

43. Using approximate values,
$y = 0.006 \cos(2094.768x - 8.379)$

b. $p(t) = 3.2 \sin\left(\dfrac{\pi}{6} x + \dfrac{3\pi}{2}\right) + 7.7$

c. $p(t) = 3.2929 \sin(0.5268x + 1.5341) + 7.6468$

d. late March and early August

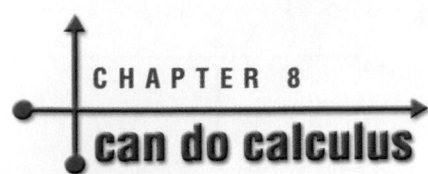

Teaching Notes

Emphasize that $\lim_{x \to n} f(x) = k$ can be true even when $f(n)$ is undefined. This is the case in all of the Examples in this section. In **Example 1**, if $f(x) = \frac{\sin x}{x}$, then $\lim_{x \to 0} f(x) = 1$, although $f(0)$ is undefined.

Example Notes

For **Example 1**, show students that the graph of $\frac{\sin x}{x}$ has a hole at (0, 1):

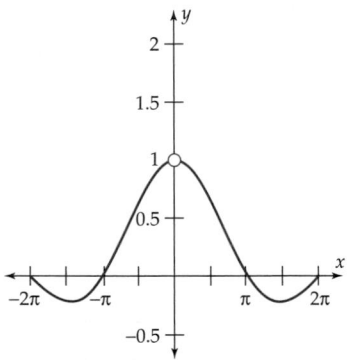

For **Example 3**, ask students for another name for the function $f(x) = \frac{1}{\cos x}$. $f(x) = \sec x$

ADDITIONAL EXAMPLES

Example 1

Find $\lim_{x \to 0} \frac{\sin 2x}{x}$, if it exists, by using a table and a graph.

The table shows that $\frac{\sin 2(0)}{0}$ is undefined.

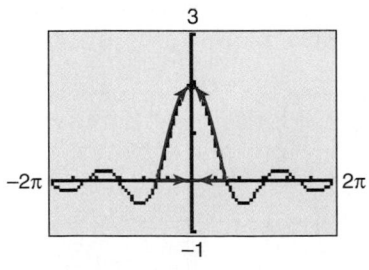

The graph confirms that the values of $\frac{\sin 2x}{x}$ are approaching 2 as x approaches 0 from either direction.

Figure 8.C-1

A main focus of calculus is the behavior of the output of a function as the input approaches a specific value. The value that the function approaches, if it exists, is called a **limit**. In this section an informal description of a limit is illustrated with some interesting trigonometric functions, but the discussion is not intended to be complete. See Chapter 14 for a detailed discussion of limits.

If the output of a function approaches a single real number k as the input approaches the real number n, then the function is said to have a *limit* of k as the input approaches n.

This is written as

$$\lim_{x \to n} f(x) = k,$$

and is read "the limit of $f(x)$ as x approaches n is k". See Figure 8.C-1.

If the outputs of the function do not approach a single real number as the inputs approach n, the limit does not exist.

Calculus is needed to find limits analytically, but a calculator's table feature and a graph can approximate a limit, if it exists. A table or a graph will also indicate when a limit does not exist. The following two limits are very important in calculus and are used in future can do calculus features.

Example 1   Limit of $\frac{\sin x}{x}$

Find $\lim_{x \to 0} \frac{\sin x}{x}$, if it exists, by using a table and a graph.

Solution

Enter $Y_1 = \frac{\sin x}{x}$ into the function editor of a calculator and produce the table shown in Figure 8.C-2a and the graph shown in Figure 8.C-2b.

Figure 8.C-2a

The table confirms that $\frac{\sin 0}{0} = \frac{0}{0}$ is undefined, but it also suggests that the values of $\frac{\sin x}{x}$ are approaching 1 for x-values near 0, both positive and negative.

Figure 8.C-2b

566

The graph confirms that the values of $\frac{\sin x}{x}$ are approaching 1 as x approaches 0 from the positive side and from the negative side. Therefore,

$$\lim_{x \to 0} \frac{\sin x}{x} = 1$$

Therefore, $\lim_{x \to 0} \frac{\sin 2x}{x} = 2.$

Figure 8.C-3a

Figure 8.C-3b

NOTE $\frac{\pi}{2} \approx 1.57$.

There is another trigonometric limit that is often used in calculus.

Example 2 Limit of $\frac{\cos x - 1}{x}$

Find $\lim\limits_{x \to 0} \frac{\cos x - 1}{x}$, if it exists, by using a table and a graph.

Solution

Figure 8.C-3a confirms that $\frac{\cos x - 1}{x} = \frac{0}{0}$ is undefined, but that the values of $\frac{\cos x - 1}{x}$ are approaching 0 when x is near 0. The graph shown in Figure 8.C-3b also illustrates this. Therefore,

$$\lim\limits_{x \to 0} \frac{\cos x - 1}{x} = 0.$$

There are two ways in which a limit may not exist, as shown in the next examples. The first example illustrates a function that does not have a limit as x approaches $\frac{\pi}{2}$ because function values on either side of $\frac{\pi}{2}$ do not approach a *single* real number. The second example illustrates a function that does not have a limit as x approaches 0 because the function values oscillate wildly.

Example 3 Determining the Behavior of a Function Near an x-Value

Discuss the behavior of $f(x) = \frac{1}{\cos x}$ as x approaches $\frac{\pi}{2}$. Find $\lim\limits_{x \to \frac{\pi}{2}} \frac{1}{\cos x}$, if it exists, by using a table and a graph.

Solution

As shown in Figure 8.C-4a, the values of $f(x) = \frac{1}{\cos x}$ when $x < \frac{\pi}{2}$ are large positive numbers, and the values are large negative numbers when $x > \frac{\pi}{2}$. Figure 8.C-4b shows that the graph of $f(x) = \frac{1}{\cos x}$ has a vertical asymptote at $\frac{\pi}{2}$. Because the values of $f(x)$ do not approach a single real number as x approaches $\frac{\pi}{2}$, $\lim\limits_{x \to \frac{\pi}{2}} \frac{1}{\cos x}$ does not exist.

567

Example 2

Find $\lim\limits_{x \to 0} \frac{\cos 2x - 1}{x}$, if it exists, by using a table and a graph.

The table shows that $\frac{\cos 2(0) - 1}{0}$ is undefined.

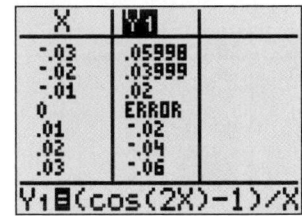

The graph confirms that $\frac{\cos 2x - 1}{x}$ is approaching 0 as x approaches 0.

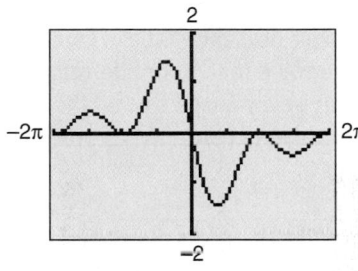

Therefore, $\lim\limits_{x \to 0} \frac{\cos 2x - 1}{x} = 0$

Example 3

Discuss the behavior of $f(x) = \frac{1}{\sin x}$ as x approaches π. Find $\lim\limits_{x \to \pi} \frac{1}{\sin x}$, if it exists, by using a table and a graph.

The values of $\frac{1}{\sin x}$ are large positive numbers when $x < \pi$ and large negative numbers when $x > \pi$.

$f(x) = \frac{1}{\sin x}$ has a vertical asymptote at π. Because the values of $f(x)$ do not approach a single real number, the limit does not exist.

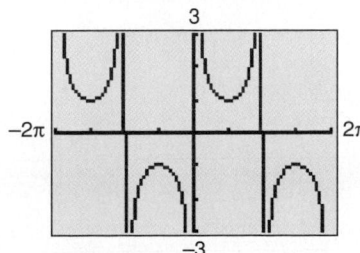

Example 4

Discuss the behavior of $f(x) = \cos\left(\dfrac{3}{x}\right)$

near $x = 0$ and find $\lim\limits_{x \to 0} \cos\left(\dfrac{3}{x}\right)$, if it
exists.

Table of values close to zero.

A table of values of $f(x) = \cos\left(\dfrac{3}{x}\right)$

suggests that function values near
$x = 0$ might be near -0.0221, but
using the trace feature on the graph
as shown below indicates that the
function value is near -0.901 when
x is near 0.

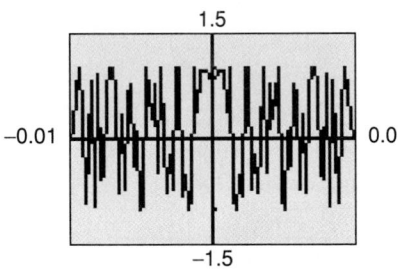

Using a window where
$-0.01 \le x \le 0.01$, you can see
that the graph oscillates wildly
around $x = 0$.

Because the values of $f(x) = \cos\left(\dfrac{3}{x}\right)$

oscillate as x approaches 0,

$\lim\limits_{x \to 0} \cos\left(\dfrac{3}{x}\right)$ does not exist.

Figure 8.C-4a

Figure 8.C-4b

Example 4 Oscillating Function Values

Discuss the behavior of $f(x) = \cos\left(\dfrac{1}{x}\right)$ near $x = 0$ and find $\lim\limits_{x \to 0} \cos\left(\dfrac{1}{x}\right)$,
if it exists.

Solution

A table of values of $f(x) = \cos\left(\dfrac{1}{x}\right)$ near $x = 0$ is shown in Figure 8.C-5a.

Figure 8.C-5a

The table suggests that the function values near $x = 0$ may be near 0.86232,
but using the trace feature on the graph shown in Figure 8.C-5b indicates
that the function value is near 0.365 when x is near 0.

Using a window where $-0.01 \le x \le 0.01$, you can see that the graph oscillates wildly around $x = 0$. See Figure 8.C-5c.

Figure 8.C-5c

Because the values of $f(x) = \cos\left(\dfrac{1}{x}\right)$ oscillate as x approaches 0,

$\lim\limits_{x \to 0} \cos\left(\dfrac{1}{x}\right)$ does not exist.

Figure 8.C-5b

568

Exercises

Discuss the behavior of the function around the given *x*-value by using a table and a graph. Find the limit of each function, if it exists.

1. $\lim\limits_{x \to 0} \dfrac{1}{\cos x}$ **1**

2. $\lim\limits_{x \to \frac{\pi}{2}} \dfrac{x}{\tan x}$ **0**

3. $\lim\limits_{x \to \frac{\pi}{2}} \dfrac{\tan x}{x}$
does not exist

4. $\lim\limits_{x \to 0} \dfrac{\tan x}{x}$ **1**

5. $\lim\limits_{x \to 0} \dfrac{\sin 3x}{3x}$ **1**

6. $\lim\limits_{x \to 0} \dfrac{\sin 2x}{2x}$ **1**

7. $\lim\limits_{x \to 0} \dfrac{x}{\tan^2 x}$
does not exist

8. $\lim\limits_{x \to 0} \dfrac{x}{\sin^2 x}$
does not exist

9. $\lim\limits_{x \to 0} \dfrac{3x}{\sin 3x}$ **1**

10. $\lim\limits_{x \to 0} \dfrac{x}{\sin x}$ **1**

11. $\lim\limits_{x \to 0} \dfrac{\sin 3x}{\sin 4x}$ **0.75**

12. $\lim\limits_{x \to 0} \dfrac{\sin 8x}{\sin 7x}$ $\dfrac{8}{7}$

13. $\lim\limits_{x \to 0} \sin\left(\dfrac{1}{x}\right)$
does not exist

14. $\lim\limits_{x \to 0} \dfrac{2x + \sin x}{x}$
3

15. $\lim\limits_{x \to \frac{\pi}{2}} \dfrac{x}{\cos x}$
does not exist

16. $\lim\limits_{x \to 0} \tan\left(\dfrac{1}{x}\right)$
does not exist

17. $\lim\limits_{x \to 2} 3x$
6

18. $\lim\limits_{x \to 2} -2x$
−4

19. $\lim\limits_{x \to 1} \dfrac{x}{1 - x}$
does not exist

20. $\lim\limits_{x \to -1} \dfrac{x}{1 - x}$
−0.5

21. $\lim\limits_{x \to 3} \dfrac{x^2 - x - 6}{x - 3}$
5

22. $\lim\limits_{x \to 1} \dfrac{x^2 - 2x - 3}{x - 1}$
does not exist

23. $\lim\limits_{x \to 1} \dfrac{x^3 - 1}{x - 1}$
3

24. $\lim\limits_{x \to -1} \dfrac{x^3 + x^2 + x + 1}{x - 1}$
0

25. Make a conjecture about the $\lim\limits_{x \to 0} \dfrac{\sin bx}{\sin cx}$, where *b* and *c* are real numbers.

$$\lim_{x \to 0} \frac{\sin bx}{\sin cx} = \frac{b}{c}$$

Trigonometric Identities and Proof

In this chapter, students will use basic trigonometric identities from Chapter 6 to prove new identities. They will then use identities to find exact values of trigonometric functions, solve equations, and simplify expressions. The Excursion relates the tangent function, the slope of a line, and the angle formed by two lines.

CHAPTER

9

Trigonometric Identities and Proof

Time.

To find the exact period of the oscillations of a simple pendulum, a trigonometric expression must be written in an alternate form, which is obtained by using trigonometric identities. See Exercise 75 in Section 9.3.

570

Interdependence of Sections

$9.1 \longrightarrow 9.2 \longrightarrow 9.3 \longrightarrow 9.4$

The basic trigonometric identities, which were discussed in Chapter 6 and used in Chapter 8, are not the only identities that are useful in rewriting trigonometric expressions and in solving trigonometric equations. This chapter presents many widely used trigonometric identities and specific methods for solving particular forms of trigonometric equations.

Identities and Proofs

Objectives

* Identify possible identities by using graphs

* Apply strategies to prove identities

Recall that an identity is an equation that is true for all values of the variable for which every term of the equation is defined. Several trigonometric identities have been discussed in previous sections. This section will introduce other identities and discuss techniques used to verify that an equation is an identity.

Trigonometric identities can be used for simplifying expressions, rewriting the rules of trigonometric functions, and performing numerical calculations. There are no hard and fast rules for dealing with identities, but some suggestions follow. The phrases "prove the identity" and "verify the identity" mean "prove that the given equation is an identity."

571

Identities and Proofs

Teaching Notes

In this chapter, students will be asked to prove (verify) identities. Point out how *proving* or *verifying* an identity is different from *solving* an equation.

To solve an equation, you *find the set of all numbers that make the equation true.* For example, students solved $\tan x \cos^2 x = \tan x$ in Section 8.3 (page 543). All solutions were given by $x = k\pi$, where k is any integer.

To prove an identity, you *show that an equation is true for all numbers* (for which all terms of the equation are defined). The equation $\tan x = \dfrac{\sin x}{\cos x}$ (from Section 6.4) is an identity because it is true for all values of x except values for which $\cos x = 0$.

In this chapter, students will be asked to prove new identities.

Teaching Notes

In Figures 9.1-1 and 9.1-2a, one graph is darker than another to emphasize that the graphs are different. Point out to students that when they do **Graphical Testing,** they should *not* make one graph darker than the other. Making one graph darker than the other might make it harder to detect whether the functions are different.

Solution to the **Graphing Exploration:**

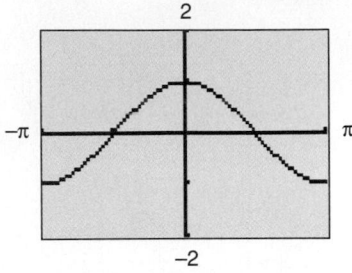

Yes, the graphs of the functions with $-\pi \leq x \leq \pi$ appear identical.

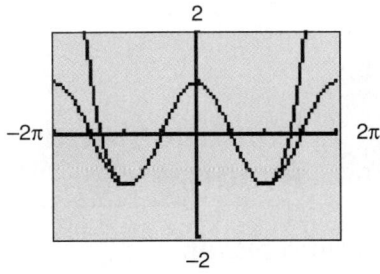

No, the equation is not an identity; the graphs are not identical, as seen in the viewing window $-2\pi \leq x \leq 2\pi$.

Math Background

In the **Graphing Exploration,** the graphs appear to be the same in the window with $-\pi \leq x \leq \pi$. Recall (page 521 Exercise 5) that the series

$$1 - \frac{x^2}{2!} + \frac{x^4}{4!} - \frac{x^6}{6!} + \cdots \quad \text{approximates}$$

$\cos x$.

Note that the series (page 521 Example 2)

$$x - \frac{x^3}{3!} + \frac{x^5}{5!} - \frac{x^7}{7!} + \frac{x^9}{9!} + \cdots +$$

$$(-1)^{n-1}\frac{x^{2n-1}}{(2n-1)!} \quad \text{approximates } \sin x.$$

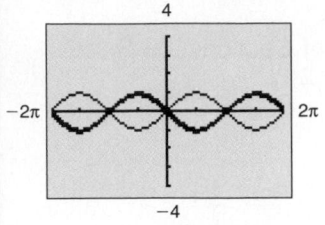

Figure 9.1-1

Graphical Testing

When presented with a trigonometric equation that *might* be an identity, it is a good idea to determine graphically whether or not this is possible. For instance, the equation $\cos\left(\frac{\pi}{2} + x\right) = \sin t$ can be tested to determine if it is possibly an identity by graphing $Y_1 = \cos\left(\frac{\pi}{2} + x\right)$ and $Y_2 = \sin x$ on the same screen, as shown in Figure 9.1-1 where the graph of Y_1 is darker than the graph of Y_2. Because the graphs are different, it can be concluded that the equation is not an identity.

Any equation can be tested by simultaneously graphing the two functions whose rules are given by the left and right sides of the equation. If the graphs are different, the equation is not an identity. If the graphs appear to be the same, then it is possible that the equation is an identity. However,

> **The fact that the graphs of both sides of an equation appear identical does not prove that the equation is an identity, as the following exploration demonstrates.**

Graphing Exploration ●

In the viewing window with $-\pi \leq x \leq \pi$ and $-2 \leq y \leq 2$, graph both sides of the equation

$$\cos x = 1 - \frac{x^2}{2} + \frac{x^4}{24} - \frac{x^6}{720} + \frac{x^8}{40,320}$$

Do the graphs appear identical? Now change the viewing window so that $-2\pi \leq x \leq 2\pi$. Is the equation an identity?

Example 1   **Graphical Identity Testing**

Is either of the following equations an identity?

a. $2\sin^2 x - \cos x = 2\cos^2 x + \sin x$

b. $\dfrac{1 + \sin x - \sin^2 x}{\cos x} = \cos x + \tan x$

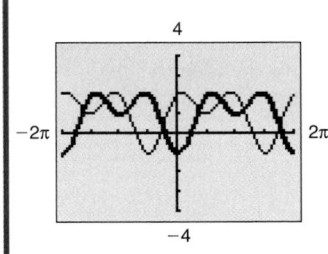

Figure 9.1-2a

Solution

Test each equation graphically to see if it might be an identity by graphing each side of the equation.

a. Graph $Y_1 = 2\sin^2 x - \cos x$ and $Y_2 = 2\cos^2 x + \sin x$ on the same screen, as shown in Figure 9.1-2a. The graph of Y_1 is shown darker than Y_2. Because the graphs are *not* the same, the equation $2\sin^2 x - \cos x = 2\cos^2 x + \sin x$ is not an identity.

b. The graph shown in Figure 9.1-2b suggests that

$$\frac{1 + \sin x - \sin^2 x}{\cos x} = \cos x + \tan x$$

may be an identity, but the proof that it actually is an identity must be done algebraically.

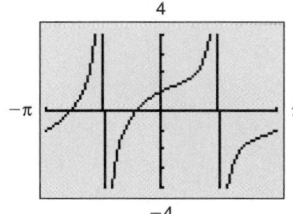

Figure 9.1-2b

Example 2   Finding an Identity

Find an equation involving 2 sin x cos x that could possibly be an identity.

Solution

Figure 9.1-3a

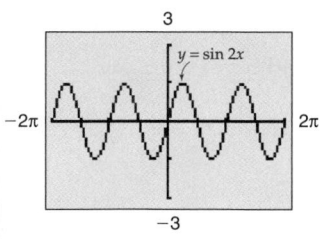

Figure 9.1-3b

The graph of $y = 2 \sin x \cos x$ is shown in Figure 9.1-3a. Does it look familiar? At first it looks like the graph of $y = \sin x$, but there is an important difference. The function graphed in Figure 9.1-3a has a period of π. As was shown in Section 7.3, the graph of $y = \sin 2x$ looks like the sine graph but has a period of π.

The graphs $Y_1 = 2 \sin x \cos x$ and $Y_2 = \sin 2x$ are shown in Figures 9.1-3a and 9.1-3b. Because the graphs appear identical, $2 \sin x \cos x = \sin 2x$ may be an identity.

Proving Identities

A useful feature of trigonometric functions is that they can be written in many ways. One form may be easier to use in one situation, and a different form of the same function may be more useful in another.

The elementary identities that were given in Section 6.5 are summarized for your reference on the following page. Memorizing these identities will benefit you greatly in the future.

NOTE   The definitions of the basic trigonometric ratios may help you remember the quotient and reciprocal identities. The shapes of the graphs of sine, cosine, and tangent may help you remember the periodicity and negative angle identities. Also, if you can remember the first of the Pythagorean identities, which is based on the Pythagorean Theorem, the other two can easily be derived from it.

Example 2

Find an equation involving $\cos^2 x - \sin^2 x$ that could possibly be an identity.
The graph of $\cos^2 x - \sin^2 x$ looks like the graph of cos x, except it has a period of π.

The graphs of $Y_1 = \cos^2 x - \sin^2 x$ and $Y_2 = \cos 2x$ appear to be identical. Therefore, $\cos^2 x - \sin^2 = \cos 2x$ may be an identity.

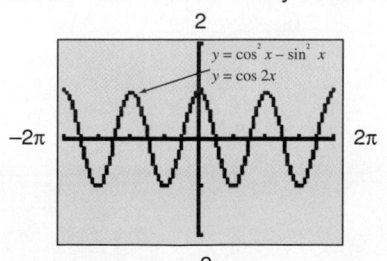

Example 1

Is either of the following equations an identity?

a. $3 \sin^2 x + 2 \cos x = 3 \cos^2 x - 2 \sin x$

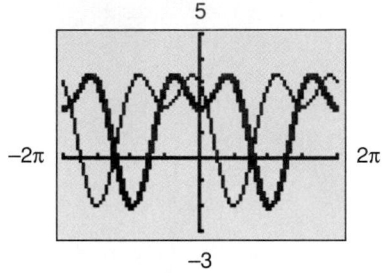

The graph of Y_1 is shown darker than Y_2. Because the graphs are not the same, the equation is not an identity.

b. $\dfrac{1 + \cos x - \cos^2 x}{\sin x} = \sin x + \cot x$

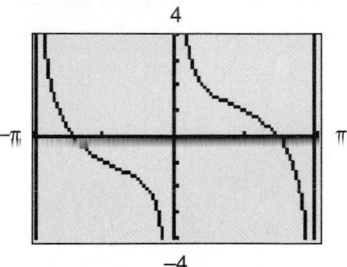

Because the graphs appear to be the same, the equation *may* be an identity.

Teaching Notes

Most of the **Basic Trigonometric Identities** on this page are from Section 6.5 (page 460). Emphasize the importance of memorizing them. They may also be found on the inside of the back cover.

If students can remember the first Pythagorean Identity, $\sin^2 x + \cos^2 x = 1$, they can derive the others from it, as shown below.

$$\sin^2 x + \cos^2 x = 1$$

$$\frac{\sin^2 x}{\cos^2 x} + \frac{\cos^2 x}{\cos^2 x} = \frac{1}{\cos^2 x}$$

$$\tan^2 x + 1 = \sec^2 x$$

$$\sin^2 x + \cos^2 x = 1$$

$$\frac{\sin^2 x}{\sin^2 x} + \frac{\cos^2 x}{\sin^2 x} = \frac{1}{\sin^2 x}$$

$$1 + \cot^2 x = \csc^2 x$$

If students remember the period of each trigonometric function, it will help them remember the Periodicity Identities. For example, since the period of $\sin x$ is 2π, $\sin(x \pm 2\pi) = \sin x$.

The **Strategies for Proving Trigonometric Identities** are used in the Examples in this section. **Examples 3** and **5** use the first strategy, **Example 4** uses the third strategy, **Example 6** uses the fourth strategy, and **Examples 7** and **8** use the fifth strategy.

Strategy 5 is based on the following property of proportions:

If $b \neq 0$ and $d \neq 0$, then $\frac{a}{b} = \frac{c}{d}$ if and only if $ad = bc$. Illustrate this property with numbers, such as:

$\frac{2}{3} = \frac{6}{9}$ because $2 \cdot 9 = 3 \cdot 6$, and

$2 \cdot 9 = 3 \cdot 6$ because $\frac{2}{3} = \frac{6}{9}$.

Basic Trigonometry Identities

Quotient Identities

$$\tan x = \frac{\sin x}{\cos x} \qquad \cot x = \frac{\cos x}{\sin x}$$

Reciprocal Identities

$$\sin x = \frac{1}{\csc x} \qquad \cos x = \frac{1}{\sec x}$$

$$\csc x = \frac{1}{\sin x} \qquad \sec x = \frac{1}{\cos x}$$

$$\cot x = \frac{1}{\tan x} \qquad \tan x = \frac{1}{\cot x}$$

Periodicity Identities

$$\sin(x \pm 2\pi) = \sin x \qquad \cos(x \pm 2\pi) = \cos x$$

$$\csc(x \pm 2\pi) = \csc x \qquad \sec(x \pm 2\pi) = \sec x$$

$$\tan(x \pm \pi) = \tan x \qquad \cot(x \pm \pi) = \cot x$$

Pythagorean Identities

$$\sin^2 x + \cos^2 x = 1 \qquad \tan^2 x + 1 = \sec^2 x \qquad 1 + \cot^2 x = \csc^2 x$$

Negative Angle Identities

$$\sin(-x) = -\sin x \qquad \cos(-x) = \cos x \qquad \tan(-x) = -\tan x$$

Just looking at the graphs of the two expressions that make up the equation is not enough to guarantee that it is an identity. Although there are no exact rules for simplifying trigonometric expressions or proving identities, there are some common strategies that are often helpful.

Strategies for Proving Trigonometric Identities

1. Use algebra and *previously* proven identities to transform one side of the equation into the other.
2. If possible, write the entire equation in terms of one trigonometric function.
3. Express everything in terms of sine and cosine.
4. Deal separately with each side of the equation $A = B$. First use identities and algebra to transform A into some expression C, then use (possibly different) identities and algebra to transform B into the *same* expression C. Conclude that $A = B$.
5. Prove that $AD = BC$, with $B \neq 0$ and $D \neq 0$. You can then conclude that $\frac{A}{B} = \frac{C}{D}$.

There are often a variety of ways to proceed, and it will take some practice before you can easily decide which strategies are likely to be the most efficient in a particular case. Keep these two purposes of working with trigonometric identities in mind:

- to learn the relationships among the trigonometric functions
- to simplify an expression by using an equivalent form

CAUTION

Proving identities is not the same as solving equations. Properties that apply to equations, such as adding the same value to both sides, are not valid when verifying identities because the beginning statement (to be verified) may not be true.

In the following example, the Pythagorean identity is used to replace $1 - \sin^2 x$ with $\cos^2 x$. Consider using one of the Pythagorean identities whenever a squared trigonometric function appears.

replace	with	replace	with
$\sin^2 x$	$1 - \cos^2 x$	$\csc^2 x$	$1 + \cot^2 x$
$\cos^2 x$	$1 - \sin^2 x$	$\sec^2 x$	$\tan^2 x + 1$
$\tan^2 x$	$\sec^2 x - 1$	$\cot^2 x$	$\csc^2 x - 1$

Example 3   Transform One Side into the Other Side

Verify that $\dfrac{1 + \sin x - \sin^2 x}{\cos x} = \cos x + \tan x$.

Solution

The graph of each side of the equation is shown in Figure 9.1-2b of Example 1, where it was noted that the equation *might* be an identity. Begin with the left side of the equation.

$$\frac{1 + \sin x - \sin^2 x}{\cos x} = \frac{(1 - \sin^2 x) + \sin x}{\cos x} \qquad \text{regrouping terms}$$

$$= \frac{\cos^2 x + \sin x}{\cos x} \qquad \text{Pythagorean identity}$$

$$= \frac{\cos^2 x}{\cos x} + \frac{\sin x}{\cos x} \qquad \frac{a + b}{c} = \frac{a}{c} + \frac{b}{c}$$

$$= \cos x + \frac{\sin x}{\cos x} \qquad \frac{a^2}{a} = a$$

$$= \cos x + \tan x \qquad \text{quotient identity}$$

Strategies for proving identities can also be used to simplify complex expressions.

Students sometimes forget to write exponents for the Pythagorean identities. For example, they might write $\sin x + \cos x = 1$, which is incorrect. To help them remember the exponents, remind them that the Pythagorean Theorem is about *squares* of sides of a right triangle.

Example Notes

The identity in **Example 3** was tested graphically in Example 1b. Now it will be proved (verified).

Example 3 uses a Pythagorean identity to replace $1 - \sin^2 x$ with $\cos^2 x$. Replacements to use in other expressions involving squared trigonometric functions are given above Example 3.

Remind students that an identity is true for all values of the variable for which all terms in the equation are defined. Ask them to describe values of x that would produce an undefined term in the identity in Example 3. all values of x for which $\cos x = 0$; that is, $x = \frac{\pi}{2} + k\pi$, where k is any integer

ADDITIONAL EXAMPLES

Example 3

Verify that
$\dfrac{1 + \cos x - \cos^2 x}{\sin x} = \sin x + \cot x$.

(It was noted in Additional Example 1h that this *might* be an identity.)

$$\frac{1 + \cos x - \cos^2 x}{\sin x}$$

$$= \frac{(1 - \cos^2 x) + \cos x}{\sin x} \qquad \text{regrouping terms}$$

$$= \frac{\sin^2 x + \cos x}{\sin x} \qquad \text{Pythagorean identity}$$

$$= \frac{\sin^2 x}{\sin x} + \frac{\cos x}{\sin x} \qquad \frac{a + b}{c} = \frac{a}{c} + \frac{b}{c}$$

$$= \sin x + \frac{\cos x}{\sin x} \qquad \frac{a^2}{a} = a$$

$$= \sin x + \cot x \qquad \text{quotient identity}$$

Example Notes

After students complete **Example 4**, point out that they have verified the identity

$$(\csc x + \cot x)(1 - \cos x) = \sin x.$$

The following is *not* a correct proof for **Example 5**:

$$\frac{\sin x}{1 + \cos x} = \frac{1 - \cos x}{\sin x}$$

$$\frac{\sin x}{1 + \cos x} \cdot \frac{1}{1 - \cos x} = \frac{1 - \cos x}{\sin x} \cdot \frac{1}{1 - \cos x}$$

$$\frac{\sin x}{1 - \cos^2 x} = \frac{1}{\sin x}$$

$$\frac{\sin x}{\sin^2 x} = \frac{1}{\sin x}$$

$$\frac{1}{\sin x} = \frac{1}{\sin x}$$

Therefore, the original equation is an identity.

The error made above was *assuming the first equation true*, and then multiplying both sides by $\frac{1}{1 - \cos x}$. In fact, the first equation *is the equation that is to be proved*. This type of error is addressed in the **CAUTION** on page 575.

Make sure students understand that $\frac{\sin x}{1 + \cos x} = \frac{1 - \cos x}{\sin x}$ *is an identity*, but the work shown above *does not prove it*.

ADDITIONAL EXAMPLES

Example 4

Simplify $(\sec x + \tan x)(1 - \sin x)$.

$(\sec x + \tan x)(1 - \sin x)$

$$= \left(\frac{1}{\cos x} + \frac{\sin x}{\cos x}\right)(1 - \sin x) \quad \textit{reciprocal and quotient identities}$$

$$= \left(\frac{1 + \sin x}{\cos x}\right)(1 - \sin x) \quad \frac{a}{c} + \frac{b}{c} = \frac{a + b}{c}$$

$$= \frac{(1 + \sin x)(1 - \sin x)}{\cos x} \quad \frac{a}{c} \cdot b = \frac{ab}{c}$$

$$= \frac{1 - \sin^2 x}{\cos x} \quad \begin{array}{l}(a + b)(a - b) \\ = a^2 - b^2\end{array}$$

$$= \frac{\cos^2 x}{\cos x} \quad \textit{Pythagorean identity}$$

$$= \cos x \quad \frac{x^2}{x} = x$$

NOTE If a denominator is of the form $1 + \cos x$, multiplying by $1 - \cos x$ gives $1 - \cos^2 x = \sin^2 x$. Similarly, if a denominator is of the form $1 + \sin x$, multiplying by $1 - \sin x$ gives $1 - \sin^2 x = \cos^2 x$. Compare this with earlier techniques used to rationalize denominators and simplify numbers with complex denominators.

Example 4 Write Everything in Terms of Sine and Cosine

Simplify $(\csc x + \cot x)(1 - \cos x)$.

Solution

$(\csc x + \cot x)(1 - \cos x)$

$$= \left(\frac{1}{\sin x} + \frac{\cos x}{\sin x}\right)(1 - \cos x) \quad \textit{reciprocal and quotient identities}$$

$$= \frac{(1 + \cos x)}{\sin x}(1 - \cos x) \quad \frac{a}{c} + \frac{b}{c} = \frac{a + b}{c}$$

$$= \frac{(1 + \cos x)(1 - \cos x)}{\sin x} \quad \frac{a}{c} \cdot b = \frac{ab}{c}$$

$$= \frac{1 - \cos^2 x}{\sin x} \quad (a + b)(a - b) = a^2 - b^2$$

$$= \frac{\sin^2 x}{\sin x} \quad \textit{Pythagorean identity}$$

$$= \sin x \quad \frac{x^2}{x} = x$$

The strategies presented above and those to be considered are "plans of attack." By themselves they are not much help unless you also have some techniques for carrying out these plans. In the previous examples, the techniques of basic algebra and the use of known identities were used to change trigonometric expressions into equivalent expressions. There is another technique that is often useful when dealing with fractions.

Rewrite a fraction in equivalent form by multiplying its numerator and denominator by the same quantity.

Example 5 Transform One Side into the Other Side

Prove that $\dfrac{\sin x}{1 + \cos x} = \dfrac{1 - \cos x}{\sin x}$.

Solution

Beginning with the left side, multiply the numerator and denominator by $1 - \cos x$.

$$\frac{\sin x}{1 + \cos x} = \frac{\sin x}{1 + \cos x} \cdot \frac{1 - \cos x}{1 - \cos x}$$

$$= \frac{\sin x(1 - \cos x)}{(1 + \cos x)(1 - \cos x)}$$

$$= \frac{\sin x(1 - \cos x)}{1 - \cos^2 x}$$

$$= \frac{\sin x(1 - \cos x)}{\sin^2 x} \quad \textit{Pythagorean identity}$$

$$= \frac{1 - \cos x}{\sin x}$$

Alternate Solution

The numerators of the given equation, $\sin x$ and $1 - \cos x$, look similar to the Pythagorean identity—except the squares are missing. So begin with the left side and introduce some squares by multiplying it by $\dfrac{\sin x}{\sin x} = 1$.

$$\frac{\sin x}{1 + \cos x} = \frac{\sin x}{\sin x} \cdot \frac{\sin x}{1 + \cos x}$$

$$= \frac{\sin^2 x}{\sin x(1 + \cos x)}$$

$$= \frac{1 - \cos^2 x}{\sin x(1 + \cos x)} \qquad \textit{Pythagorean identity}$$

$$= \frac{(1 - \cos x)(1 + \cos x)}{\sin x(1 + \cos x)} \qquad a^2 - b^2 = (a - b)(a + b)$$

$$= \frac{1 - \cos x}{\sin x}$$

■

Example 6   Dealing with Each Side Separately

Prove that $\csc x - \cot x = \dfrac{\sin x}{1 + \cos x}$.

Solution

Begin with the left side.

$$\csc x - \cot x = \frac{1}{\sin x} - \frac{\cos x}{\sin x}$$

$$= \frac{1 - \cos x}{\sin x} \qquad [1]$$

Example 5 shows that the right side of the identity to be proved can also be transformed into this same expression.

$$\frac{\sin x}{1 + \cos x} = \frac{1 - \cos x}{\sin x} \qquad [2]$$

Combining the equalities [1] and [2] proves the identity.

$$\csc x - \cot x = \frac{1 - \cos x}{\sin x} = \frac{\sin x}{1 + \cos x}$$

■

Proving identities involving fractions can sometimes be quite complicated. It often helps to approach a fractional identity indirectly, as in the following example.

ADDITIONAL EXAMPLES

Example 5

Prove that $\dfrac{\cos x}{1 - \sin x} = \dfrac{1 + \sin x}{\cos x}$.

$$\frac{\cos x}{1 - \sin x}$$

$$= \frac{\cos x}{1 - \sin x} \cdot \frac{1 + \sin x}{1 + \sin x}$$

$$= \frac{\cos x(1 + \sin x)}{(1 - \sin x)(1 + \sin x)}$$

$$= \frac{\cos x(1 + \sin x)}{1 - \sin^2 x}$$

$$= \frac{\cos x(1 + \sin x)}{\cos^2 x} \qquad \textit{Pythagorean identity}$$

$$= \frac{1 + \sin x}{\cos x}$$

Alternate Solution

$$\frac{\cos x}{1 - \sin x}$$

$$= \frac{\cos x}{\cos x} \cdot \frac{\cos x}{1 - \sin x}$$

$$= \frac{\cos^2 x}{\cos x(1 - \sin x)}$$

$$= \frac{1 - \sin^2 x}{\cos x(1 - \sin x)} \qquad \textit{Pythagorean identity}$$

$$= \frac{(1 + \sin x)(1 - \sin x)}{\cos x(1 - \sin x)} \qquad \begin{array}{l} a^2 - b^2 = \\ (a + b)(a - b) \end{array}$$

$$= \frac{1 + \sin x}{\cos x}$$

Example 6

Prove that $\sec x + \tan x = \dfrac{\cos x}{1 - \sin x}$.

Begin with the left side.

$$\sec x + \tan x = \frac{1}{\cos x} + \frac{\sin x}{\cos x}$$

$$= \frac{1 + \sin x}{\cos x}$$

Using Additional Example 5, transform the right side.

$$\frac{\cos x}{1 - \sin x} = \frac{1 + \sin x}{\cos x}$$

Thus,

$$\sec x + \tan x = \frac{1 + \sin x}{\cos x} = \frac{\cos x}{1 - \sin x}.$$

Therefore, $\sec x + \tan x = \dfrac{\cos x}{1 - \sin x}$.

Example Notes

For **Example 7**, point out that in part **b**, you can divide both sides of the equation $\sec x(\sec x - \cos x) = \tan^2 x$ by $\tan x(\sec x - \cos x)$ because the equation $\sec x(\sec x - \cos x) = \tan^2 x$ was *proved to be an identity* in part **a**.

Teaching Notes

After completing **Examples 7** and **8**, refer students to the paragraphs at the bottom of page 579. Challenge them to develop an alternate proof for Example 7b or 8.

An alternate proof for each is shown below.

Alternate proof for Example 7b:

$$\frac{\sec x}{\tan x}$$

$$= \frac{\sec x(\sec x - \cos x)}{\tan x(\sec x - \cos x)} \qquad \frac{a}{a} = 1$$

$$= \frac{\sec^2 x - \sec x \cos x}{\tan x(\sec x - \cos x)} \qquad \begin{array}{l}\textit{distributive}\\\textit{property}\end{array}$$

$$= \frac{\sec^2 x - \dfrac{1}{\cos x}\cos x}{\tan x(\sec x - \cos x)} \qquad \begin{array}{l}\textit{reciprocal}\\\textit{identity}\end{array}$$

$$= \frac{\sec^2 x - 1}{\tan x(\sec x - \cos x)} \qquad \frac{1}{a}\cdot a = 1$$

$$= \frac{\tan^2 x}{\tan x(\sec x - \cos x)} \qquad \begin{array}{l}\textit{Pythagorean}\\\textit{identity}\end{array}$$

$$= \frac{\tan x}{\sec x - \cos x} \qquad \frac{a^2}{a} = a$$

Alternate proof for Example 8:

$$\frac{\cot x - 1}{\cot x + 1}$$

$$= \frac{\tan x(\cot x - 1)}{\tan x(\cot x + 1)} \qquad \frac{a}{a} = 1$$

$$= \frac{\tan x \cot x - \tan x}{\tan x \cot x + \tan x} \qquad \begin{array}{l}\textit{distributive}\\\textit{property}\end{array}$$

$$= \frac{\tan x\dfrac{1}{\tan x} - \tan x}{\tan x\dfrac{1}{\tan x} + \tan x} \qquad \begin{array}{l}\textit{reciprocal}\\\textit{identity}\end{array}$$

$$= \frac{1 - \tan x}{1 + \tan x} \qquad a\cdot\frac{1}{a} = 1$$

Example 7 Proving Identities that Involve Fractions

Prove the first identity below, then use the first identity to prove the second identity.

a. $\sec x(\sec x - \cos x) = \tan^2 x$ **b.** $\dfrac{\sec x}{\tan x} = \dfrac{\tan x}{\sec x - \cos x}$

Solution

a. Begin by transforming the left side.

$$\sec x(\sec x - \cos x) = \sec^2 x - \sec x \cos x$$

$$= \sec^2 x - \frac{1}{\cos x}\cos x \qquad \textit{reciprocal identity}$$

$$= \sec^2 x - 1$$

$$= \tan^2 x \qquad \textit{Pythagorean identity}$$

Therefore, $\sec x(\sec x - \cos x) = \tan^2 x$.

b. By part **a**,

$$\sec x(\sec x - \cos x) = \tan^2 x$$

Divide both sides of this equation by $\tan x(\sec x - \cos x)$.

$$\frac{\sec x(\sec x - \cos x)}{\tan x(\sec x - \cos x)} = \frac{\tan^2 x}{\tan x(\sec x - \cos x)}$$

$$\frac{\sec x(\sec x - \cos x)}{\tan x(\sec x - \cos x)} = \frac{\tan x \tan x}{\tan x(\sec x - \cos x)}$$

$$\frac{\sec x}{\tan x} = \frac{\tan x}{\sec x - \cos x}$$

Look carefully at how identity **b** was proved in Example 7. First prove identity **a**, which is of the form $AD = BC$ (with $A = \sec x$, $B = \tan x$, $C = \tan x$, and $D = \sec x - \cos x$). Then divide both sides by BD, that is, by $\tan x(\sec x - \cos x)$, to conclude that $\dfrac{A}{B} = \dfrac{C}{D}$. This property provides a useful strategy for dealing with identities involving fractions.

Example 8 If $AD = BC$, with $B \neq 0$ and $D \neq 0$, then $\dfrac{A}{B} = \dfrac{C}{D}$.

Prove that $\dfrac{\cot x - 1}{\cot x + 1} = \dfrac{1 - \tan x}{1 + \tan x}$.

Solution

Use the same strategy used in Example 7. First prove $AD = BC$, with $A = \cot x - 1$, $B = \cot x + 1$, $C = 1 - \tan x$, and $D = 1 + \tan x$.

$$AD = BC$$

$$(\cot x - 1)(1 + \tan x) = (\cot x + 1)(1 - \tan x) \qquad [3]$$

Multiply out the left side of [3].

$$(\cot x - 1)(1 + \tan x) = \cot x + \cot x \tan x - 1 - \tan x$$
$$= \cot x + \frac{1}{\tan x} \tan x - 1 - \tan x$$
$$= \cot x + 1 - 1 - \tan x$$
$$= \cot x - \tan x.$$

Similarly, multiply the right side of [3].

$$(\cot x + 1)(1 - \tan x) = \cot x - \cot x \tan x + 1 - \tan x$$
$$= \cot x - 1 + 1 - \tan x$$
$$= \cot x - \tan x.$$

Because the left and right sides are equal to the same expression, [3] has been proven to be an identity. Therefore, conclude that

$$\frac{\cot x - 1}{\cot x + 1} = \frac{1 - \tan x}{1 + \tan x}$$

is also an identity. ∎

CAUTION

Strategy 5 does *not* say that you begin with a fractional equation $\frac{A}{B} = \frac{C}{D}$ and cross multiply to eliminate the fractions. If you did that, you would be assuming that the statement was true, which is what has to be proved. What the strategy says is that to prove an identity involving fractions, you need only prove a different identity that does not involve fractions. In other words, if you prove that $AD = BC$ whenever $B \neq 0$ and $D \neq 0$, then you can conclude that $\frac{A}{B} = \frac{C}{D}$. Note that you do not *assume* that $AD = BC$; you use some other strategy to *prove* this statement.

It takes a good deal of practice, as well as *much* trial and error, to become proficient at proving identities. The more practice you have, the easier it will become. Because there are many correct methods, your proofs may be quite different from those of your classmates, instructor, or text answers.

If you do not see what to do immediately, try something and see where it leads: multiply out, factor, or multiply numerator and denominator by the same nonzero quantity. Even if this does not lead anywhere, it may give you some ideas on other strategies to try. When you do obtain a proof, check to see if it can be done more efficiently. Do not include the "side trips" in your final proof—they may have given you some ideas, but they are not part of the proof.

Because $(\cos x - 1)(1 + \sec x) = \cos x - \sec x$ and $(\cos x + 1)(1 - \sec x) = \cos x - \sec x$, $(\cos x - 1)(1 + \sec x) = (\cos x + 1)(1 - \sec x)$ is an identity. Therefore, $\frac{\cos x - 1}{\cos x + 1} = \frac{1 - \sec x}{1 + \sec x}$ is also an identity.

ADDITIONAL EXAMPLES

Example 7

Prove the first identity below, then use the first identity to prove the second identity.

a. $\csc x(\csc x - \sin x) = \cot^2 x$

$$\csc x(\csc x - \sin x)$$
$$= \csc^2 x - \csc x \sin x$$
$$= \csc^2 x - \frac{1}{\sin x} \sin x \quad \text{\textit{reciprocal identity}}$$
$$= \csc^2 x - 1$$
$$= \cot^2 x \quad \text{\textit{Pythagorean identity}}$$

b. $\dfrac{\csc x}{\cot x} = \dfrac{\cot x}{\csc x - \sin x}$

By part **a,**
$$\csc x(\csc x - \sin x) = \cot^2 x.$$

Divide both sides by $\cot x(\csc x - \sin x)$.

$$\frac{\csc x(\csc x - \sin x)}{\cot x(\csc x - \sin x)}$$
$$= \frac{\cot^2 x}{\cot x(\csc x - \sin x)}$$

$$\frac{\csc x(\csc x - \sin x)}{\cot x(\csc x - \sin x)}$$
$$= \frac{\cot x \cot x}{\cot x(\csc x - \sin x)}$$

$$\frac{\csc x}{\cot x} = \frac{\cot x}{\csc x - \sin x}$$

Example 8

Prove that $\dfrac{\cos x - 1}{\cos x + 1} = \dfrac{1 - \sec x}{1 + \sec x}.$

First prove $(\cos x - 1)(1 + \sec x)$
$$= (\cos x + 1)(1 - \sec x).$$

Multiply out the left side.

$$(\cos x - 1)(1 + \sec x)$$
$$= \cos x + \cos x \sec x - 1 - \sec x$$
$$= \cos x + \cos x \frac{1}{\cos x} - 1 - \sec x$$
$$= \cos x + 1 - 1 - \sec x$$
$$= \cos x - \sec x$$

Multiply out the right side.

$$(\cos x + 1)(1 - \sec x)$$
$$= \cos x - \cos x \sec x + 1 - \sec x$$
$$= \cos x - \cos x \frac{1}{\cos x} + 1 - \sec x$$
$$= \cos x - 1 + 1 - \sec x$$
$$= \cos x - \sec x$$

Exercises 9.1

1. possibly an identity

2. not an identity

3. possibly an identity

4. possibly an identity

5. b

6. a

7. e

8. d

9. $\tan x \cos x = \left(\dfrac{\sin x}{\cos x}\right)\cos x$

   $= \sin x$

10. $\cot x \sin x = \left(\dfrac{\cos x}{\sin x}\right)\sin x = \cos x$

11. $\cos x \sec x = \cos x\left(\dfrac{1}{\cos x}\right) = 1$

Exercises 9.1

In Exercises 1–4, test the equation graphically to determine whether it might be an identity. You need not prove those equations that appear to be identities.

1. $\dfrac{\sec x - \cos x}{\sec x} = \sin^2 x$

2. $\tan x + \cot x = \sin x \cos x$

3. $\dfrac{1 - \cos 2x}{2} = \sin^2 x$

4. $\dfrac{\tan x + \cot x}{\csc x} = \sec x$

In Exercises 5–8, insert one of a–f on the right of the equal sign so that the resulting equation appears to be an identity when you test it graphically. You need not prove the identity.

a. $\cos x$ **b.** $\sec x$ **c.** $\sin^2 x$

d. $\sec^2 x$ **e.** $\sin x - \cos x$ **f.** $\dfrac{1}{\sin x \cos x}$

5. $\csc x \tan x = $ ____

6. $\dfrac{\sin x}{\tan x} = $ ____

7. $\dfrac{\sin^4 x - \cos^4 x}{\sin x + \cos x} = $ ____

8. $\tan^2(-x) - \dfrac{\sin(-x)}{\sin x} = $ ____

In Exercises 9–18, prove the identity.

9. $\tan x \cos x = \sin x$ 10. $\cot x \sin x = \cos x$

11. $\cos x \sec x = 1$ 12. $\sin x \csc x = 1$

13. $\tan x \csc x = \sec x$ 14. $\sec x \cot x = \csc x$

15. $\dfrac{\tan x}{\sec x} = \sin x$ 16. $\dfrac{\cot x}{\csc x} = \cos x$

17. $(1 + \cos x)(1 - \cos x) = \sin^2 x$

18. $(\csc x - 1)(\csc x + 1) = \cot^2 x$

In Exercises 19–48, state whether or not the equation is an identity. If it is an identity, prove it.

19. $\sin x = \sqrt{1 - \cos^2 x}$

---

20. $\cot x = \dfrac{\csc x}{\sec x}$

21. $\dfrac{\sin(-x)}{\cos(-x)} = -\tan x$

22. $\tan x = \sqrt{\sec^2 x - 1}$

23. $\cot(-x) = -\cot x$

24. $\sec(-x) = \sec x$

25. $1 + \sec^2 x = \tan^2 x$

26. $\sec^4 x - \tan^4 x = 1 + 2\tan^2 x$

27. $\sec^2 x - \csc^2 x = \tan^2 x - \cot^2 x$

28. $\sec^2 x + \csc^2 x = \sec^2 x \csc^2 x$

29. $\sin^2 x(\cot x + 1)^2 = \cos^2 x(\tan x + 1)^2$

30. $\cos^2 x(\sec x + 1)^2 = (1 + \cos x)^2$

31. $\sin^2 x - \tan^2 x = -\sin^2 x \tan^2 x$

32. $\cot^2 x - 1 = \csc^2 x$

33. $(\cos^2 x - 1)(\tan^2 x + 1) = -\tan^2 x$

34. $(1 - \cos^2 x)\csc x = \sin x$

35. $\tan x = \dfrac{\sec x}{\csc x}$

36. $\dfrac{\cos(-x)}{\sin(-x)} = -\cot x$

37. $\cos^4 x - \sin^4 x = \cos^2 x - \sin^2 x$

38. $\cot^2 x - \cos^2 x = \cos^2 x \cot^2 x$

39. $(\sin x + \cos x)^2 = \sin^2 x + \cos^2 x$

40. $(1 + \tan x)^2 = \sec^2 x$

41. $\dfrac{\sec x}{\csc x} + \dfrac{\sin x}{\cos x} = 2\tan x$

42. $\dfrac{1 + \cos x}{\sin x} + \dfrac{\sin x}{1 + \cos x} = 2\csc x$

43. $\dfrac{\sec x + \csc x}{1 + \tan x} = \csc x$

44. $\dfrac{\cot x - 1}{1 - \tan x} = \dfrac{\csc x}{\sec x}$

---

12. $\sin x \csc x = \sin x\left(\dfrac{1}{\sin x}\right) = 1$

13. $\tan x \csc x = \left(\dfrac{\sin x}{\cos x}\right)\left(\dfrac{1}{\sin x}\right) = \dfrac{1}{\cos x} = \sec x$

14. $\sec x \cot x - \left(\dfrac{1}{\cos x}\right)\left(\dfrac{\cos x}{\sin x}\right) = \dfrac{1}{\sin x} = \csc x$

15. $\dfrac{\tan x}{\sec x} = \dfrac{\frac{\sin x}{\cos x}}{\frac{1}{\cos x}} = \sin x$

16. $\dfrac{\cot x}{\csc x} = \dfrac{\frac{\cos x}{\sin x}}{\frac{1}{\sin x}} = \cos x$

17. $(1 + \cos x)(1 - \cos x) = 1 - \cos^2 x = \sin^2 x$

18. $(\csc x - 1)(\csc x + 1) = \csc^2 x - 1 = \cot^2 x$

19. not an identity

20. $\dfrac{\csc x}{\sec x} = \dfrac{\frac{1}{\sin x}}{\frac{1}{\cos x}} = \left(\dfrac{1}{\sin x}\right)\left(\dfrac{\cos x}{1}\right)$

    $= \dfrac{\cos x}{\sin x} = \cot x$

45. $\dfrac{1}{\csc x - \sin x} = \sec x \tan x$

46. $\dfrac{1 + \csc x}{\csc x} = \dfrac{\cos^2 x}{1 - \sin x}$

47. $\dfrac{\sin x - \cos x}{\tan x} = \dfrac{\tan x}{\sin x + \cos x}$

48. $\dfrac{\cot x}{\csc x - 1} = \dfrac{\csc x + 1}{\cot x}$

In Exercises 49–52, half of an identity is given. Graph this half in a viewing window with $-2\pi \le x \le 2\pi$ and write a conjecture as to what the right side of the identity is. Then prove your conjecture.

49. $1 - \dfrac{\sin^2 x}{1 + \cos x} = ?$ *Hint:* What familiar function has a graph that looks like this?

50. $\dfrac{1 + \cos x - \cos^2 x}{\sin x} - \cot x = ?$

51. $(\sin x + \cos x)(\sec x + \csc x) - \cot x - 2 = ?$

52. $\cos^3 x(1 - \tan^4 x + \sec^4 x) = ?$

In Exercises 53–66, prove the identity.

53. $\dfrac{1 - \sin x}{\sec x} = \dfrac{\cos^3 x}{1 + \sin x}$

54. $\dfrac{\sin x}{1 - \cot x} = \dfrac{\cos x}{1 - \tan x} = \cos x + \sin x$

55. $\dfrac{\cos x}{1 - \sin x} = \sec x + \tan x$

56. $\dfrac{1 + \sec x}{\tan x + \sin x} = \csc x$

57. $\dfrac{\cos x \cot x}{\cot x - \cos x} = \dfrac{\cot x + \cos x}{\cos x \cot x}$

58. $\dfrac{\cos^3 x - \sin^3 x}{\cos x - \sin x} = 1 + \sin x \cos x$

59. $\log_{10}(\cot x) = -\log_{10}(\tan x)$

60. $\log_{10}(\sec x) = -\log_{10}(\cos x)$

61. $\log_{10}(\csc x + \cot x) = -\log_{10}(\csc x - \cot x)$

62. $\log_{10}(\sec x + \tan x) = -\log_{10}(\sec x - \tan x)$

63. $\tan x - \tan y = -\tan x \tan y(\cot x - \cot y)$

64. $\dfrac{\tan x - \tan y}{\cot x - \cot y} = -\tan x \tan y$

65. $\dfrac{\cos x - \sin y}{\cos y - \sin x} = \dfrac{\cos y + \sin x}{\cos x + \sin y}$

66. $\dfrac{\tan x + \tan y}{\cot x + \cot y} = \dfrac{\tan x \tan y - 1}{1 - \cot x \cot y}$

21. $\dfrac{\sin(-x)}{\cos(-x)} = \dfrac{-\sin x}{\cos x} = -\tan x$

22. not an identity

23. $\cot(-x) = \dfrac{\cos(-x)}{\sin(-x)}$

$= \dfrac{\cos x}{-\sin x} = -\cot x$

24. $\sec(-x) = \dfrac{1}{\cos(-x)}$

$= \dfrac{1}{\cos x} = \sec x$

25. not an identity

26. $\sec^4 x - \tan^4 x$

$= (\sec^2 x - \tan^2 x)(\sec^2 x + \tan^2 x)$

$= 1(\sec^2 x + \tan^2 x)$

$= ((1 + \tan^2 x) + \tan^2 x)$

$= 1 + 2\tan^2 x$

27. $\sec^2 x - \csc^2 x$

$= (1 + \tan^2 x) - (1 + \cot^2 x)$

$= \tan^2 x - \cot^2 x$

28. $\sec^2 x + \csc^2 x = \dfrac{1}{\cos^2 x} + \dfrac{1}{\sin^2 x}$

$= \dfrac{\sin^2 x + \cos^2 x}{\cos^2 x \sin^2 x} = \dfrac{1}{\sin^2 x \cos^2 x}$

$= \left(\dfrac{1}{\sin^2 x}\right)\left(\dfrac{1}{\cos^2 x}\right) = \csc^2 x \sec^2 x$

29–66. *See p.* **1070–1072.**

9.2 **Addition and Subtraction Identities**

Objectives

- Use the addition and subtraction identities for sine, cosine, and tangent functions

- Use the cofunction identities

Many times, the input, or *argument*, of the sine or cosine function is the sum or difference of two angles, and you may need to simplify the expression. Be careful not to make this common student error.

$$\sin\left(x + \frac{\pi}{6}\right) \text{ is not } \sin x + \sin \frac{\pi}{6}$$

Graphing Exploration ●——

Verify graphically that the expressions above do NOT form an identity by graphing $Y_1 = \sin\left(x + \dfrac{\pi}{6}\right)$ and $Y_2 = \sin x + \sin \dfrac{\pi}{6}$.

Section **9.2** **Addition and Subtraction Identities**

Teaching Notes

Students may think $\sin(x + y) = \sin x + \sin y$. This is not true, as shown in the Graphing Exploration.

Solution to the **Graphing Exploration:**

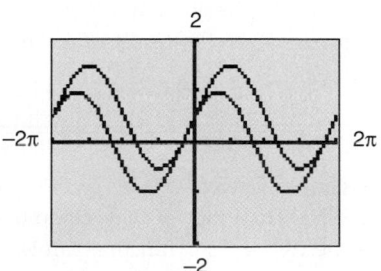

The graphs are different, so $\sin\left(x + \dfrac{\pi}{6}\right) = \sin x + \sin \dfrac{\pi}{6}$ is NOT an identity.

Teaching Notes

Solution to the first **Graphing Exploration:**

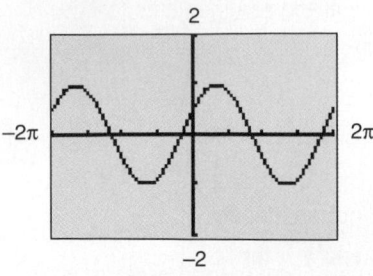

Yes, the graphs appear identical.

Solution to the second **Graphing Exploration:**

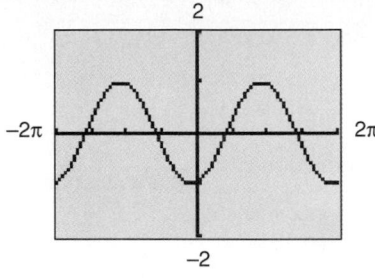

Yes, the graphs appear identical.

This suggests the identity
$\sin(x + 5) = \sin x \cos 5 + \cos x \sin 5$.
To repeat the process, students must use another number in place of 5. The graphs of $Y_1 = \sin(x + 8)$ and $Y_2 = \sin x \cos 8 + \cos x \sin 8$ are shown below (note that 8 is just one possible number that can be used).

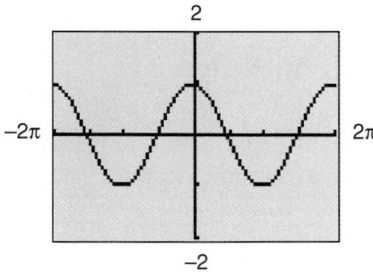

Again, the graphs of Y_1 and Y_2 appear to be identical, so the results are the same.

Example Notes

For **Example 1,** refer students to the margin **NOTE.** If they do not remember all the necessary exact function values, refer them to pages 448–449, or the inside of the back cover.

After completing **Example 2,** point out that the result is the identity $\sin(\pi - y) = \sin y$ that was introduced on page 459.

The exploration shows that $\sin(x + y) \neq \sin x + \sin y$ because it is false when $y = \frac{\pi}{6}$. So, is there an identity involving $\sin(x + y)$?

Graphing Exploration

Graph $Y_1 = \sin\left(x + \frac{\pi}{6}\right)$ and $Y_2 = \frac{\sqrt{3}}{2}\sin x + \frac{1}{2}\cos x$ on the same screen. Do the graphs appear identical?

The exploration suggests that $\sin\left(x + \frac{\pi}{6}\right) = \frac{\sqrt{3}}{2}\sin x + \frac{1}{2}\cos x$ may be an identity. Furthermore, note that the coefficients on the right side can be expressed in terms of $\frac{\pi}{6}$: $\cos\frac{\pi}{6} = \frac{\sqrt{3}}{2}$ and $\sin\frac{\pi}{6} = \frac{1}{2}$. In other words, the following equation appears to be an identity.

$$\sin\left(x + \frac{\pi}{6}\right) = \sin x \cos\frac{\pi}{6} + \cos x \sin\frac{\pi}{6}$$

Graphing Exploration

Graph $Y_1 = \sin(x + 5)$ and $Y_2 = \sin x \cos 5 + \cos x \sin 5$ on the same screen. Do the graphs appear identical? What identity does this suggest? Repeat the process with some other number in place of 5. Are the results the same?

The equations examined in the discussion and exploration above are examples of the first identity listed below. Each identity can be confirmed by assigning a constant value to y and then graphing each side of the equation, as in the Graphing Exploration above.

Addition and Subtraction Identities for Sine and Cosine

$$\sin(x + y) = \sin x \cos y + \cos x \sin y$$
$$\sin(x - y) = \sin x \cos y - \cos x \sin y$$
$$\cos(x + y) = \cos x \cos y - \sin x \sin y$$
$$\cos(x - y) = \cos x \cos y + \sin x \sin y$$

The addition and subtraction identities are important trigonometric identities. You should become familiar with the examples and special cases that follow.

Example 1 Addition Identities

Use the addition identities to find the *exact* values of $\sin\frac{5\pi}{12}$ and $\cos\frac{5\pi}{12}$.

Solution

Because $\frac{5\pi}{12}=\frac{2\pi}{12}+\frac{3\pi}{12}=\frac{\pi}{6}+\frac{\pi}{4}$, apply the addition identities with $x=\frac{\pi}{6}$ and $y=\frac{\pi}{4}$.

$$\sin\frac{5\pi}{12}=\sin\left(\frac{\pi}{6}+\frac{\pi}{4}\right)=\sin\frac{\pi}{6}\cos\frac{\pi}{4}+\cos\frac{\pi}{6}\sin\frac{\pi}{4}$$
$$=\frac{1}{2}\cdot\frac{\sqrt{2}}{2}+\frac{\sqrt{3}}{2}\cdot\frac{\sqrt{2}}{2}=\frac{\sqrt{2}(1+\sqrt{3})}{4}$$

$$\cos\frac{5\pi}{12}=\cos\left(\frac{\pi}{6}+\frac{\pi}{4}\right)=\cos\frac{\pi}{6}\cos\frac{\pi}{4}-\sin\frac{\pi}{6}\sin\frac{\pi}{4}$$
$$=\frac{\sqrt{3}}{2}\cdot\frac{\sqrt{2}}{2}-\frac{1}{2}\cdot\frac{\sqrt{2}}{2}=\frac{\sqrt{2}(\sqrt{3}-1)}{4}$$

Example 2 Subtraction Identity

Find $\sin(\pi-y)$.

Solution

Apply the subtraction identity for the sine function with $x=\pi$.

$$\sin(\pi-y)=\sin\pi\cos y-\cos\pi\sin y=0\cos y-(-1)\sin y=\sin y$$

Example 3 Addition Identity

Prove that $\cos x\cos y=\frac{1}{2}[\cos(x+y)+\cos(x-y)]$.

Solution

Begin with the more complicated right side and use the addition and subtraction identities for cosine to transform it into the left side.

$$\frac{1}{2}[\cos(x+y)+\cos(x-y)]$$
$$=\frac{1}{2}[(\cos x\cos y-\sin x\sin y)+(\cos x\cos y+\sin x\sin y)]$$
$$=\frac{1}{2}(\cos x\cos y+\cos x\cos y)=\frac{1}{2}(2\cos x\cos y)$$
$$=\cos x\cos y$$

In **Example 4,** some students might try to reduce the fraction $\frac{\sin h}{h}$ to sin. Remind them that sin h represents a function value and that sin by itself in an expression is meaningless.

Example Notes

The work for the last step in **Example 5** is shown below. **Additional Example 5** will require similar work for the last step.

$$\frac{3\sqrt{7} + 14\sqrt{2}}{7 - 6\sqrt{14}} \cdot \frac{7 + 6\sqrt{14}}{7 + 6\sqrt{14}}$$

$$= \frac{21\sqrt{7} + 18\sqrt{7}\sqrt{14} + 98\sqrt{2} + 84\sqrt{2}\sqrt{14}}{49 - 36 \cdot 14}$$

$$= \frac{21\sqrt{7} + 18 \cdot 7\sqrt{2} + 98\sqrt{2} + 84 \cdot 2\sqrt{7}}{-455}$$

$$= \frac{21\sqrt{7} + 126\sqrt{2} + 98\sqrt{2} + 168\sqrt{7}}{-455}$$

$$= \frac{189\sqrt{7} + 224\sqrt{2}}{-455}$$

$$= \frac{7(27\sqrt{7} + 32\sqrt{2})}{-7(65)}$$

$$= -\frac{27\sqrt{7} + 32\sqrt{2}}{65}$$

Additional Example 4 and Exercise 35 are identical.

ADDITIONAL EXAMPLES

Example 4

Show that for the function $f(x) = \cos x$ and any number $h \neq 0$,

$$\frac{f(x + h) - f(x)}{h}$$

$$= \cos x\left(\frac{\cos h - 1}{h}\right) - \sin x\left(\frac{\sin h}{h}\right).$$

$$\frac{f(x + h) - f(x)}{h} = \frac{\cos(x + h) - \cos x}{h}$$

$$= \frac{\cos x \cos h - \sin x \sin h - \cos x}{h}$$

$$= \frac{\cos x(\cos h - 1) - \sin x \sin h}{h}$$

$$= \cos x\left(\frac{\cos h - 1}{h}\right) - \sin x\left(\frac{\sin h}{h}\right)$$

NOTE Recall that the difference quotient of a function f is

$$\frac{f(x + h) - f(x)}{h}.$$

Addition and Subtraction Identities for Tangent

Simplifying the Difference Quotient of a Trigonometric Function

The difference quotient is very important in calculus, and the addition identities are needed to simplify difference quotients of trigonometric functions.

Example 4 The Difference Quotient of $f(x) = \sin x$

Show that for the function $f(x) = \sin x$ and any number $h \neq 0$,

$$\frac{f(x + h) - f(x)}{h} = \sin x\left(\frac{\cos h - 1}{h}\right) + \cos x\left(\frac{\sin h}{h}\right).$$

Solution

Use the addition identity for $\sin(x + y)$ with $y = h$.

$$\frac{f(x + h) - f(x)}{h} = \frac{\sin(x + h) - \sin x}{h}$$

$$= \frac{\sin x \cos h + \cos x \sin h - \sin x}{h}$$

$$= \frac{\sin x(\cos h - 1) + \cos x \sin h}{h}$$

$$= \sin x\left(\frac{\cos h - 1}{h}\right) + \cos x\left(\frac{\sin h}{h}\right)$$

Addition and Subtraction Identities for the Tangent Function

The addition and subtraction identities for sine and cosine can be used to obtain the addition and subtraction identities for the tangent function.

$$\tan(x + y) = \frac{\tan x + \tan y}{1 - \tan x \tan y}$$

$$\tan(x - y) = \frac{\tan x - \tan y}{1 + \tan x \tan y}$$

A proof of these identities is outlined in Exercise 36.

Example 5 Addition and Subtraction Identities for Tangent

Find the exact values of $\sin(x + y)$ and $\tan(x + y)$ if x and y are numbers such that $0 < x < \frac{\pi}{2}$, $\pi < y < \frac{3\pi}{2}$, $\sin x = \frac{3}{4}$, and $\cos y = -\frac{1}{3}$. Determine in which of the following intervals $x + y$ lies: $\left(0, \frac{\pi}{2}\right)$, $\left(\frac{\pi}{2}, \pi\right)$, $\left(\pi, \frac{3\pi}{2}\right)$, or $\left(\frac{3\pi}{2}, 2\pi\right)$.

NOTE See Figure 6.4-7 for the signs of the functions in each quadrant.

Figure 9.2-1a

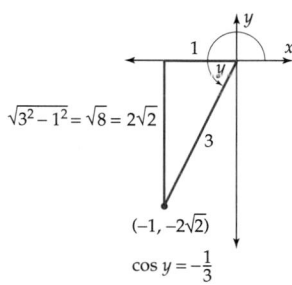

Figure 9.2-1b

Solution

Use the Pythagorean identity and the fact that $\cos x$ and $\tan x$ are positive in the first quadrant to obtain the following. See Figure 9.2-1a.

$$\cos x = \sqrt{1 - \sin^2 x} = \sqrt{1 - \left(\frac{3}{4}\right)^2} = \sqrt{1 - \frac{9}{16}} = \sqrt{\frac{7}{16}} = \frac{\sqrt{7}}{4}$$

$$\tan x = \frac{\sin x}{\cos x} = \frac{\frac{3}{4}}{\frac{\sqrt{7}}{4}} = \frac{3}{\sqrt{7}} = \frac{3\sqrt{7}}{7}$$

Because y lies between π and $\frac{3\pi}{2}$, its sine is negative. See Figure 9.2-1b.

$$\sin y = -\sqrt{1 - \cos^2 y} = -\sqrt{1 - \left(-\frac{1}{3}\right)^2} = -\sqrt{\frac{8}{9}} = -\frac{\sqrt{8}}{3} = -\frac{2\sqrt{2}}{3}$$

$$\tan y = \frac{\sin y}{\cos y} = \frac{-\frac{2\sqrt{2}}{3}}{-\frac{1}{3}} = \frac{-2\sqrt{2}}{3} \cdot \frac{3}{-1} = 2\sqrt{2}$$

The addition identities for sine and tangent show exact values.

$$\sin(x + y) = \sin x \cos y + \cos x \sin y$$
$$= \frac{3}{4} \cdot \frac{-1}{3} + \frac{\sqrt{7}}{4} \cdot \frac{-2\sqrt{2}}{3} = \frac{-3}{12} - \frac{2\sqrt{14}}{12} = \frac{-3 - 2\sqrt{14}}{12}$$

$$\tan(x + y) = \frac{\tan x + \tan y}{1 - \tan x \tan y}$$
$$= \frac{\frac{3\sqrt{7}}{7} + 2\sqrt{2}}{1 - \left(\frac{3\sqrt{7}}{7}\right)(2\sqrt{2})} = \frac{\frac{3\sqrt{7} + 14\sqrt{2}}{7}}{\frac{7 - 6\sqrt{14}}{7}}$$

$$= \frac{3\sqrt{7} + 14\sqrt{2}}{7 - 6\sqrt{14}} = -\frac{27\sqrt{7} + 32\sqrt{2}}{65}$$

Both the sine and tangent of $x + y$ are negative numbers. Therefore $x + y$ must be in the interval $\left(\frac{3\pi}{2}, 2\pi\right)$ because it is the only one of the four intervals in which both sine and tangent are negative. ∎

Cofunction Identities

Special cases of the addition and subtraction identities are the cofunction identities.

Example 5

Find the exact values of $\cos(x + y)$ and $\tan(x + y)$ if x and y are numbers such that $\frac{\pi}{2} < x < \pi, 0 < y < \frac{\pi}{2}$, $\cos x = -\frac{2}{3}$ and $\sin y = \frac{1}{4}$. Determine in which of the following intervals $x + y$ lies: $\left(0, \frac{\pi}{2}\right)$, $\left(\frac{\pi}{2}, \pi\right)$, $\left(\pi, \frac{3\pi}{2}\right)$, or $\left(\frac{3\pi}{2}, 2\pi\right)$.

$$\sin x = \sqrt{1 - \cos^2 x}$$
$$= \sqrt{1 - \left(-\frac{2}{3}\right)^2} = \sqrt{1 - \frac{4}{9}}$$
$$= \sqrt{\frac{5}{9}} = \frac{\sqrt{5}}{3}$$

$$\tan x = \frac{\sin x}{\cos x} = \frac{\frac{\sqrt{5}}{3}}{-\frac{2}{3}} = -\frac{\sqrt{5}}{2}$$

$$\cos y = \sqrt{1 - \sin^2 y}$$
$$= \sqrt{1 - \left(\frac{1}{4}\right)^2} = \sqrt{1 - \frac{1}{16}}$$
$$= \sqrt{\frac{15}{16}} = \frac{\sqrt{15}}{4}$$

$$\tan y = \frac{\sin y}{\cos y} = \frac{\frac{1}{4}}{\frac{\sqrt{15}}{4}}$$
$$= \frac{1}{\sqrt{15}} = \frac{\sqrt{15}}{15}$$

$$\cos(x + y) = \cos x \cos y - \sin x \sin y$$
$$= -\frac{2}{3} \cdot \frac{\sqrt{15}}{4} - \frac{\sqrt{5}}{3} \cdot \frac{1}{4}$$
$$= \frac{-2\sqrt{15} - \sqrt{5}}{12}$$

$$\tan(x + y) = \frac{\tan x + \tan y}{1 - \tan x \tan y}$$
$$= \frac{-\frac{\sqrt{5}}{2} + \frac{\sqrt{15}}{15}}{1 - \left(-\frac{\sqrt{5}}{2}\right)\left(\frac{\sqrt{15}}{15}\right)}$$

$$= \frac{\frac{-15\sqrt{5} + 2\sqrt{15}}{30}}{\frac{30 + \sqrt{75}}{30}} = \frac{-15\sqrt{5} + 2\sqrt{15}}{30 + \sqrt{75}}$$

$$= \frac{-15\sqrt{5} + 2\sqrt{15}}{30 + 5\sqrt{3}}$$

$$= \frac{-15\sqrt{5} + 2\sqrt{15}}{30 + 5\sqrt{3}} \cdot \frac{30 - 5\sqrt{3}}{30 - 5\sqrt{3}}$$

$$= \frac{9\sqrt{15} - 32\sqrt{5}}{55}$$

Both $\cos(x + y)$ and $\tan(x + y)$ are negative, so $x + y$ is in the interval $\left(\frac{\pi}{2}, \pi\right)$.

Teaching Notes

Point out that:
Sine and **co**sine are cofunctions.
Tangent and **co**tangent are cofunctions.
Secant and **co**secant are cofunctions.

The diagram below is a convenient way to remember the Reciprocal Identities (page 455) and the Cofunction Identities together:

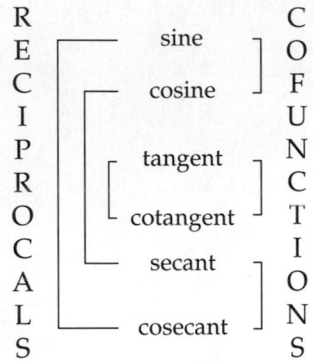

The following explanation of the **Cofunction Identity**

$\sin x = \cos\left(\dfrac{\pi}{2} - x\right)$ might be

helpful to some students:

Using the Negative Angle Identity,

$$\cos\left(\dfrac{\pi}{2} - x\right) = \cos\left[-\left(\dfrac{\pi}{2} - x\right)\right]$$

$$= \cos\left(x - \dfrac{\pi}{2}\right).$$

The graph of $y = \cos\left(x - \dfrac{\pi}{2}\right)$ is the

graph of $y = \cos x$, shifted to the right $\dfrac{\pi}{2}$ units. Therefore, the graph of

$y = \cos\left(\dfrac{\pi}{2} - x\right)$ is the graph of

$y = \cos x$, shifted to the right $\dfrac{\pi}{2}$ units. Furthermore, it is easily verified by a table of values that the graph of $y = \sin x$ is the graph of $y = \cos x$, shifted to the right $\dfrac{\pi}{2}$ units. Therefore, the graphs of $y = \sin x$ and

$y = \cos\left(\dfrac{\pi}{2} - x\right)$ are the same,

as shown.

Cofunction Identities

$$\sin x = \cos\left(\dfrac{\pi}{2} - x\right) \qquad\qquad \cos x = \sin\left(\dfrac{\pi}{2} - x\right)$$

$$\tan x = \cot\left(\dfrac{\pi}{2} - x\right) \qquad\qquad \cot x = \tan\left(\dfrac{\pi}{2} - x\right)$$

$$\sec x = \csc\left(\dfrac{\pi}{2} - x\right) \qquad\qquad \csc x = \sec\left(\dfrac{\pi}{2} - x\right)$$

The first cofunction identity is proved by using the identity for $\cos(x - y)$ with $\dfrac{\pi}{2}$ in place of x and x in place of y.

$$\cos\left(\dfrac{\pi}{2} - x\right) = \cos\dfrac{\pi}{2}\cos x + \sin\dfrac{\pi}{2}\sin x = 0 \cdot \cos x + 1 \cdot \sin x = \sin x$$

Because the first cofunction identity is valid for *every* number x, it is also valid with the number $\dfrac{\pi}{2} - x$ in place of x.

$$\sin\left(\dfrac{\pi}{2} - x\right) = \cos\left[\dfrac{\pi}{2} - \left(\dfrac{\pi}{2} - x\right)\right] = \cos x$$

Thus, the second cofunction identity is proved. The others now follow from these previous two. For instance,

$$\tan\left(\dfrac{\pi}{2} - x\right) = \dfrac{\sin\left(\dfrac{\pi}{2} - x\right)}{\cos\left(\dfrac{\pi}{2} - x\right)} = \dfrac{\cos x}{\sin x} = \cot x$$

Also,

$$\csc\left(\dfrac{\pi}{2} - x\right) = \dfrac{1}{\sin\left(\dfrac{\pi}{2} - x\right)} = \dfrac{1}{\cos x} = \sec x$$

Example 6　Cofunction Identities

Verify that $\dfrac{\cos\left(x - \dfrac{\pi}{2}\right)}{\cos x} = \tan x$.

Solution

Beginning with the left side, the term $\cos\left(x - \dfrac{\pi}{2}\right)$ looks almost, but not quite, like the term $\cos\left(\dfrac{\pi}{2} - x\right)$ in the cofunction identity. But note that $-\left(x - \dfrac{\pi}{2}\right) = \dfrac{\pi}{2} - x$. Therefore,

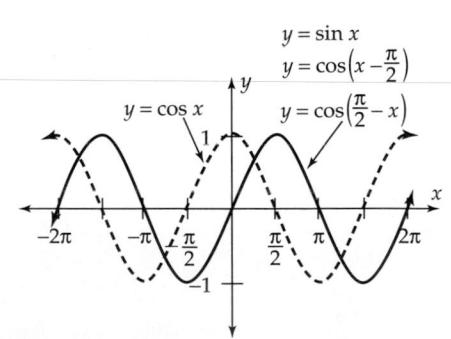

$$\frac{\cos\left(x - \frac{\pi}{2}\right)}{\cos x} = \frac{\cos\left[-\left(x - \frac{\pi}{2}\right)\right]}{\cos x} \qquad \textit{negative angle identity with } x - \frac{\pi}{2} \textit{ in place of } x$$

$$= \frac{\cos\left(\frac{\pi}{2} - x\right)}{\cos x}$$

$$= \frac{\sin x}{\cos x} \qquad \textit{cofunction identity}$$

$$= \tan x \qquad \textit{quotient identity}$$

Exercises 9.2

In Exercises 1–12, find the exact value.

1. $\sin\dfrac{\pi}{12}$ $\dfrac{\sqrt{6} - \sqrt{2}}{4}$ **2.** $\cos\dfrac{\pi}{12}$ $\dfrac{\sqrt{2} + \sqrt{6}}{4}$ **3.** $\tan\dfrac{\pi}{12}$ $2 - \sqrt{3}$

4. $\sin\dfrac{5\pi}{12}$ $\dfrac{\sqrt{6} + \sqrt{2}}{4}$ **5.** $\cot\dfrac{5\pi}{12}$ $2 - \sqrt{3}$ **6.** $\cos\dfrac{7\pi}{12}$ $\dfrac{\sqrt{2} - \sqrt{6}}{4}$

7. $\tan\dfrac{7\pi}{12}$ $-2 - \sqrt{3}$ **8.** $\cos\dfrac{11\pi}{12}$ $\dfrac{-\sqrt{2} - \sqrt{6}}{4}$ **9.** $\cot\dfrac{11\pi}{12}$ $-2 - \sqrt{3}$

10. $\sin 75°$ *Hint:* $75° = 45° + 30°$. $\dfrac{\sqrt{6} + \sqrt{2}}{4}$

11. $\sin 105°$ $\dfrac{\sqrt{6} + \sqrt{2}}{4}$ **12.** $\cos 165°$ $\dfrac{\sqrt{2} - \sqrt{6}}{4}$

In Exercises 13–18, rewrite the given expression in terms of $\sin x$ and $\cos x$.

13. $\sin\left(\dfrac{\pi}{2} + x\right)$ $\cos x$ **14.** $\cos\left(x + \dfrac{\pi}{2}\right)$ $-\sin x$

15. $\cos\left(x - \dfrac{3\pi}{2}\right)$ $-\sin x$ **16.** $\csc\left(x + \dfrac{\pi}{2}\right)$ $\dfrac{1}{\cos x}$

17. $\sec(x - \pi)$ $-\dfrac{1}{\cos x}$ **18.** $\cot(x + \pi)$ $\dfrac{\cos x}{\sin x}$

In Exercises 19–24, simplify the given expression.

19. $\sin 3 \cos 5 - \cos 3 \sin 5$ $-\sin 2$

20. $\sin 37° \sin 53° - \cos 37° \cos 53°$ 0

21. $\cos(x + y)\cos y + \sin(x + y)\sin y$ $\cos x$

22. $\sin(x - y)\cos y + \cos(x - y)\sin y$ $\sin x$

23. $\cos(x + y) - \cos(x - y)$ $-2\sin x \sin y$

24. $\sin(x + y) - \sin(x - y)$ $2\sin y \cos x$

25. If $\sin x = \dfrac{1}{3}$ and $0 < x < \dfrac{\pi}{2}$, then $\sin\left(\dfrac{\pi}{4} + x\right) = ?$ $\dfrac{4 + \sqrt{2}}{6}$

26. If $\cos x = -\dfrac{1}{4}$ and $\dfrac{\pi}{2} < x < \pi$, then $\cos\left(\dfrac{\pi}{6} - x\right) = ?$ $\dfrac{-\sqrt{3} + \sqrt{15}}{8}$

27. If $\cos x = -\dfrac{1}{5}$ and $\pi < x < \dfrac{3\pi}{2}$, then $\sin\left(\dfrac{\pi}{3} - x\right) = ?$ $\dfrac{2\sqrt{6} - \sqrt{3}}{10}$

28. If $\sin x = -\dfrac{3}{4}$ and $\dfrac{3\pi}{2} < x < 2\pi$, then $\cos\left(\dfrac{\pi}{4} + x\right) = ?$ $\dfrac{\sqrt{14} + 3\sqrt{2}}{8}$

In Exercises 29–34, assume that $\sin x = 0.8$ and $\sin y = \sqrt{0.75}$ and that x and y lie between 0 and $\dfrac{\pi}{2}$. Evaluate the given expressions.

29. $\cos(x + y)$ -0.393 **30.** $\sin(x + y)$ 0.9196

31. $\cos(x - y)$ 0.993 **32.** $\sin(x - y)$ -0.1196

33. $\tan(x + y)$ -2.34 **34.** $\tan(x - y)$ -0.1204

35. If $f(x) = \cos x$ and h is a fixed nonzero number, prove that the difference quotient is

$$\frac{f(x + h) - f(x)}{h} = \cos x\left(\frac{\cos h - 1}{h}\right) - \sin x\left(\frac{\sin h}{h}\right).$$

36. Prove the addition and subtraction identities for the tangent function. *Hint:*

$$\tan(x + y) = \frac{\sin(x + y)}{\cos(x + y)}$$

Use the addition identities on the numerator and denominator; then divide both numerator and denominator by $\cos x \cos y$, and simplify.

41. $\sin(u + v + w)$
$= \sin u \cos v \cos w + \cos u \sin v \cos w +$
$\quad \cos u \cos v \sin w - \sin u \sin v \sin w$

42. $\cos(x + y + z)$
$= \cos x \cos y \cos z - \sin x \sin y \cos z -$
$\quad \sin x \cos y \sin z - \cos x \sin y \sin z$

43. Since $y = \dfrac{\pi}{2} - x$,

$$\sin y = \sin\left(\frac{\pi}{2} - x\right) = \cos x.$$

Hence, $\sin^2 x + \sin^2 y = \sin^2 x + \cos^2 x = 1$

44. $\cot(x + y) = \dfrac{\cos(x + y)}{\sin(x + y)}$

$$= \frac{\cos x \cos y - \sin x \sin y}{\sin x \cos y + \sin y \cos x}$$

$$= \frac{\dfrac{\cos x \cos y - \sin x \sin y}{\sin x \sin y}}{\dfrac{\sin x \cos y + \sin y \cos x}{\sin x \sin y}}$$

$$= \frac{\cot x \cot y - 1}{\cot x + \cot y}$$

45. $\sin(x - \pi)$

$\quad = \sin x \cos \pi - \cos x \sin \pi$

$\quad = (\sin x)(-1) - (\cos x)(0)$

$\quad = -\sin x$

46. $\cos(x - \pi)$

$\quad = \cos x \cos \pi + \sin x \sin \pi$

$\quad = \cos x(-1) + \sin x(0) = -\cos x$

47. $\cos(\pi - x)$

$\quad = \cos \pi \cos x + \sin \pi \sin x$

$\quad = (-1)\cos x + (0)\sin x = -\cos x$

48. $\tan(\pi - x) = \dfrac{\sin(\pi - x)}{\cos(\pi - x)}$

$\quad = \dfrac{\sin \pi \cos x - \sin x \cos \pi}{\cos \pi \cos x + \sin \pi \sin x}$

$\quad = \dfrac{(0)\cos x - \sin x(-1)}{(-1)\cos x + (0)\sin x}$

$\quad = -\tan x$

49. $\sin(x + \pi)$

$\quad = \sin x \cos \pi + \cos x \sin \pi$

$\quad = (\sin x)(-1) + (\cos x)(0)$

$\quad = -\sin x$

50. $\cos(x + \pi)$

$\quad = \cos x \cos \pi - \sin x \sin \pi$

$\quad = \cos x(-1) - \sin x(0)$

$\quad = -\cos x$

51. By Exercises 49 and 50,

$\tan(x + \pi) = \dfrac{\sin(x + \pi)}{\cos(x + \pi)}$

$\quad = \dfrac{-\sin x}{-\cos x} = \tan x$

52. $\dfrac{1}{2}[\sin(x + y) + \sin(x - y)]$

$\quad = \dfrac{1}{2}[(\sin x \cos y + \sin y \cos x) +$

$\qquad (\sin x \cos y - \sin y \cos x)]$

$\quad = \dfrac{1}{2}(2 \sin x \cos y)$

$\quad = \sin x \cos y$

53. $\dfrac{1}{2}[\cos(x - y) - \cos(x + y)]$

$\quad = \dfrac{1}{2}[(\cos x \cos y + \sin x \sin y) -$

$\qquad (\cos x \cos y - \sin x \sin y)]$

$\quad = \dfrac{1}{2}(2 \sin x \sin y) = \sin x \sin y$

54. $\dfrac{1}{2}[\sin(x + y) - \sin(x - y)]$

$\quad = \dfrac{1}{2}[(\sin x \cos y + \sin y \cos x) -$

$\qquad (\sin x \cos y - \sin y \cos x)]$

$\quad = \dfrac{1}{2}(2 \sin y \cos x) = \cos x \sin y$

55. $\cos(x + y) \cos(x - y)$

$\quad = (\cos x \cos y - \sin x \sin y) \cdot$

$\qquad (\cos x \cos y + \sin x \sin y)$

$\quad = (\cos x \cos y)^2 - (\sin x \sin y)^2$

$\quad = \cos^2 x \cos^2 y - \sin^2 x \sin^2 y$

---

37. If x is in the first quadrant and y is in the second quadrant, $\sin x = \dfrac{24}{25}$, and $\sin y = \dfrac{4}{5}$, find the exact value of $\sin(x + y)$ and $\tan(x + y)$ and the quadrant in which $x + y$ lies.

38. If x and y are in the second quadrant, $\sin x = \dfrac{1}{3}$, and $\cos y = -\dfrac{3}{4}$, find the exact value of $\sin(x + y)$, $\cos(x + y)$, and $\tan(x + y)$ and the quadrant in which $x + y$ lies.

39. If x is in the first quadrant and y is in the second quadrant, $\sin x = \dfrac{4}{5}$, and $\cos y = -\dfrac{12}{13}$, find the exact value of $\cos(x + y)$ and $\tan(x + y)$ and the quadrant in which $x + y$ lies.

40. If x is in the fourth quadrant and y is in the first quadrant, $\cos x = \dfrac{1}{3}$, and $\cos y = \dfrac{2}{3}$, find the exact value of $\sin(x - y)$ and $\tan(x - y)$ and the quadrant in which $x - y$ lies.

41. Express $\sin(u + v + w)$ in terms of sines and cosines of u, v, and w. *Hint:* First apply the addition identity with $x = u + v$ and $y = w$.

42. Express $\cos(x + y + z)$ in terms of sines and cosines of x, y, and z.

43. If $x + y = \dfrac{\pi}{2}$, show that $\sin^2 x + \sin^2 y = 1$.

44. Prove that $\cot(x + y) = \dfrac{\cot x \cot y - 1}{\cot x + \cot y}$.

In Exercises 45–56, prove the identity.

45. $\sin(x - \pi) = -\sin x$

46. $\cos(x - \pi) = -\cos x$

47. $\cos(\pi - x) = -\cos x$

48. $\tan(\pi - x) = -\tan x$

49. $\sin(x + \pi) = -\sin x$

50. $\cos(x + \pi) = -\cos x$

51. $\tan(x + \pi) = \tan x$

52. $\sin x \cos y = \dfrac{1}{2}[\sin(x + y) + \sin(x - y)]$

53. $\sin x \sin y = \dfrac{1}{2}[\cos(x - y) - \cos(x + y)]$

54. $\cos x \sin y = \dfrac{1}{2}[\sin(x + y) - \sin(x - y)]$

55. $\cos(x + y) \cos(x - y) = \cos^2 x \cos^2 y - \sin^2 x \sin^2 y$

56. $\sin(x + y) \sin(x - y) = \sin^2 x \cos^2 y - \cos^2 x \sin^2 y$

In Exercises 57–66, determine graphically whether the equation could not possibly be an identity (by choosing a numerical value for y and graphing both sides), or write a proof that it is.

57. $\dfrac{\cos(x - y)}{\sin x \cos y} = \cot x + \tan y$

58. $\dfrac{\cos(x + y)}{\sin x \cos y} = \cot x - \tan y$

59. $\sin(x - y) = \sin x - \sin y$

60. $\cos(x + y) = \cos x + \cos y$

61. $\dfrac{\sin(x + y)}{\sin(x - y)} = \dfrac{\tan x + \tan y}{\tan x - \tan y}$

62. $\dfrac{\sin(x + y)}{\sin(x - y)} = \dfrac{\cot y + \cot x}{\cot y - \cot x}$

63. $\dfrac{\cos(x + y)}{\cos(x - y)} = \dfrac{\cot x + \tan y}{\cot x - \tan y}$

64. $\dfrac{\cos(x - y)}{\cos(x + y)} = \dfrac{\cot y + \tan x}{\cot y - \tan x}$

65. $\tan(x + y) = \tan x + \tan y$

66. $\cot(x - y) = \cot x - \cot y$

---

56. $\sin(x + y) \sin(x - y)$

$\quad = (\sin x \cos y + \sin y \cos x) \cdot$

$\qquad (\sin x \cos y - \sin y \cos x)$

$\quad = \sin^2 x \cos^2 y - \sin^2 y \cos^2 x$

57. $\dfrac{\cos(x - y)}{\sin x \cos y} = \dfrac{\cos x \cos y + \sin x \sin y}{\sin x \cos y}$

$\quad = \dfrac{\cos x}{\sin x} + \dfrac{\sin y}{\cos y}$

$\quad = \cot x + \tan y$

58. $\dfrac{\cos(x + y)}{\sin x \cos y} = \dfrac{\cos x \cos y - \sin x \sin y}{\sin x \cos y}$

$\quad = \dfrac{\cos x \cos y}{\sin x \cos y} - \dfrac{\sin x \sin y}{\sin x \cos y}$

$\quad = \cot x - \tan y$

59–66. *See p. 1072.*

Excursion: Lines and Angles

9.2.A

Objectives

- Find the angle of inclination of a line with a given slope

- Find the angle between two lines

Several interesting concepts dealing with lines are defined in terms of trigonometry. They lead to useful facts whose proofs are based on the addition and subtraction identities for sine, cosine, and tangent.

If L is a nonhorizontal straight line, the **angle of inclination** of L is the positive angle θ formed by the part of L above the x-axis and the x-axis, as shown in Figure 9.2.A-1.

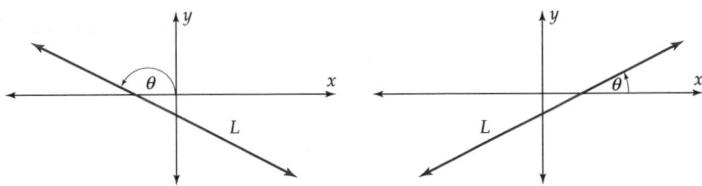

Figure 9.2.A-1

The angle of inclination of a horizontal line is defined to be $\theta = 0$. Thus, the radian measure of the angle of inclination of any line satisfies $0 \leq \theta < \pi$. Furthermore,

Angle of Inclination Theorem

> If L is a nonvertical line with angle of inclination θ, then $\tan \theta = $ slope of L.

Proof

If L is horizontal, then L has slope 0 and angle of inclination $\theta = 0$. Hence, $\tan \theta = \tan 0 = 0$, so $\tan \theta = $ slope of $L = 0$.

If L is not horizontal, then it intersects the x-axis at some point $(x_1, 0)$, as shown for two possible cases in Figure 9.2.A-2.

Figure 9.2.A-2a   **Figure 9.2.A-2b**

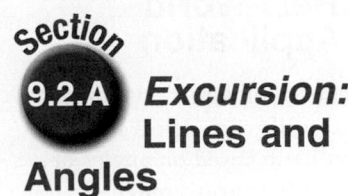

Section

9.2.A *Excursion: Lines and Angles*

Teaching Notes

Review the following facts about slope:

A line with a positive slope rises to the right.

A line with a negative slope falls to the right.

A horizontal line has a slope of zero.

A vertical line has an undefined slope.

Parallel lines have the same slope.

The slopes of perpendicular lines are negative reciprocals.

The **Angle of Inclination** of a line is positive, and therefore is *measured counterclockwise from the x-axis to the line*. Emphasize the angle shown below that is NOT an angle of inclination of line L.

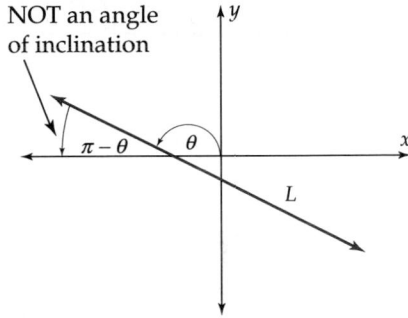

The **Angle of Inclination Theorem** specifies that L be a nonvertical line. The angle of inclination for a vertical line is $\frac{\pi}{2}$. The tangent of this angle as well as the slope of the vertical line are both undefined.

In Figure 9.2.A-2a and in the proof, $x_2 - x_1 > 0$ because $x_2 > x_1$.

In Figure 9.2.A-2b and in the proof, $x_1 - x_2 > 0$ because $x_1 > x_2$.

COMMON ERROR ALERT

In Figure 9.2.A-2b, some students might think that the angle of inclination is $\pi - \theta$. Remind them that the angle of inclination is the positive angle measured counterclockwise from the x-axis to the line.

Real-World Application

Some scientists think that hatchling loggerhead turtles can detect their latitude on Earth based on angles of inclination of the Earth's magnetic field lines. Of course, the turtles' behavior is instinctive, but scientists must understand angles of inclination to research this phenomenon.

Example Notes

In **Examples 1** and **2,** have students use the given slopes to draw the lines on graph paper. Then have them measure the angles of inclination to the nearest degree with a protractor.

Example 1:

Example 2:

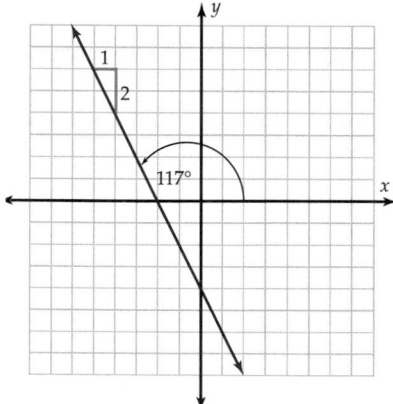

In **Example 2,** ask students why a calculator gives the approximate solution of $\tan\theta = -2$ as -1.1071 rather than 2.0344.

The calculator gives $\tan^{-1}(-2) = -1.1071$ because by definition, $-\frac{\pi}{2} < \tan^{-1} x < \frac{\pi}{2}$.

The right triangle in Figure 9.2.A-2a shows that

$$\text{slope of } L = \frac{y_2 - 0}{x_2 - x_1} = \frac{y_2}{x_2 - x_1} = \frac{opposite}{adjacent} = \tan\theta.$$

The right triangle in Figure 9.2.A-2b shows that

$$\text{slope of } L = \frac{0 - y_2}{x_1 - x_2} = -\frac{y_2}{x_1 - x_2} = -\frac{opposite}{adjacent} = -\tan(\pi - \theta). \quad [1]$$

Use the fact that the tangent function has period π and the negative angle identity for tangent to obtain

$$-\tan(\pi - \theta) = -\tan(-\theta) = -(-\tan\theta) = \tan\theta.$$

Combining this fact with [1] shows that slope of $L = \tan\theta$ in this case also.

Example 1   Angle of Inclination

Find the angle of inclination of a line of slope $\frac{5}{3}$.

Solution

By the Angle of Inclination Theorem, $\tan\theta = \frac{5}{3}$. The TAN^{-1} key on a calculator shows that $\theta \approx 1.0304$ radians, or $\theta \approx 59.04°$.

Example 2   Angle of Inclination

Find the angle of inclination of a line L with slope -2.

Solution

Because line L has slope -2, its angle of inclination is a solution of $\tan\theta = -2$ that lies between $\frac{\pi}{2}$ and π. A calculator gives the approximate solution -1.1071. Because an angle of inclination must be between 0 and π, another solution is needed.

Recall that $\tan t = \tan(t + \pi)$, for every t. So

$$\theta \approx -1.1071 + \pi \approx 2.0344$$

is the solution of $\tan\theta = -2$ in the interval from 0 to π. Therefore, the angle of inclination is approximately 2.03 radians, or about 116.57°.

Angles Between Two Lines

If two lines intersect, then they determine four angles with vertices at the point of intersection, as shown in Figure 9.2.A-3. If one of these angles

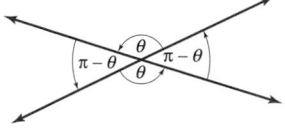

Figure 9.2.A-3

ADDITIONAL EXAMPLES

Example 1

Find the angle of inclination of a line of slope $\frac{4}{5}$.

0.6747 radians or 38.66°

Example 2

Find the angle of inclination of a line L with slope -4.

$\tan^{-1}(-4) \approx -1.3258$

$\theta \approx -1.3258 + \pi \approx 1.8158$ radians or 104.04°

measures θ radians, then each of the two angles adjacent to it measures $\pi - \theta$ radians. (Why?) The fourth angle also measures θ radians by the vertical angle theorem from plane geometry.

The angles formed by intersecting lines can be determined from the angles of inclination of the lines. Suppose L and M have angles of inclination α and β, respectively, such that $\beta \geq \alpha$. Basic facts about parallel lines, as illustrated in Figure 9.2.A-4, show that $\beta - \alpha$ is one angle between L and M, and $\pi - (\beta - \alpha)$ is the other.

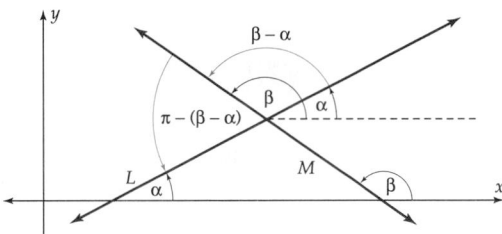

Figure 9.2.A-4

The angle between two lines can also be found from their slopes by using the following fact.

Angle Between Two Lines

> If two nonvertical, nonperpendicular lines have slopes m and k, then one angle θ between them satisfies
>
> $$\tan \theta = \left| \frac{m - k}{1 + mk} \right|.$$

Proof

Suppose L has slope k and angle of inclination α and that M has slope m and angle of inclination β. By the definition of absolute value

$$\left| \frac{m - k}{1 + mk} \right| = \frac{m - k}{1 + mk} \quad \text{or} \quad \left| \frac{m - k}{1 + mk} \right| = -\frac{m - k}{1 + mk}$$

whichever is positive. It will be shown that one angle between L and M has tangent $\dfrac{m - k}{1 + mk}$, and that the other has tangent $-\dfrac{m - k}{1 + mk}$. Thus, one of them necessarily has tangent $\left| \dfrac{m - k}{1 + mk} \right|$. If $\beta \geq \alpha$, then $\beta - \alpha$ is one angle between L and M. By the subtraction identity for tangent,

$$\tan(\beta - \alpha) = \frac{\tan \beta - \tan \alpha}{1 + \tan \beta \tan \alpha} = \frac{m - k}{1 + mk}$$

The other angle between L and M is $\pi - (\beta - \alpha)$ and by periodicity, the negative angle identity, and the addition identity

In Figure 9.2.A-4, note that a triangle is formed by the x-axis and the two lines. The angle measures in the triangle are α, $\pi - \beta$, and $\beta - \alpha$. If we add these angle measures, we find that $\alpha + (\pi - \beta) + (\beta - \alpha) = \pi$, which agrees with the fact that the sum of angle measures in any triangle equals 180°.

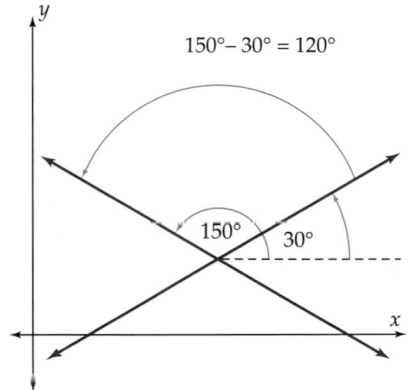

Example Notes

One angle between lines L and M in **Example 3** is found to be 0.4461 radians, or 25.56°. Ask students to find the other angle measure.

$\theta \approx \pi - 0.4461 \approx 2.6955$ radians, or
$\theta \approx 180° - 25.56° = 154.44°$

Have students draw lines L and M on graph paper and label all four angles.

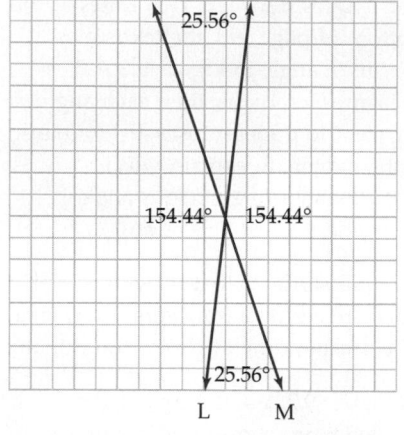

ADDITIONAL EXAMPLES

Example 3

If the slopes of lines L and M are 7 and -2, respectively, then find one angle between them.

$$\tan \theta = \left| \frac{7 - (-2)}{1 + 7(-2)} \right| = \left| \frac{9}{-13} \right| = \frac{9}{13}$$

$\theta \approx 0.6055$ radians, or 34.70°

Exercises 9.2.A

ANSWERS

$$\tan[\pi - (\beta - \alpha)] = \tan[-(\beta - \alpha)]$$
$$= -\tan(\beta - \alpha)$$
$$= -\frac{\tan \beta - \tan \alpha}{1 + \tan \beta \tan \alpha}$$
$$= -\frac{m - k}{1 + mk}.$$

This completes the proof when $\beta \geq \alpha$. The proof in the case $\alpha \geq \beta$ is similar. ∎

Example 3 The Angle Between Two Lines

If the slopes of lines L and M are 8 and -3, respectively, then find one angle between them.

Solution

Substitute 8 for m and -3 for k to find the tangent values.

$$\tan \theta = \left| \frac{8 - (-3)}{1 + 8(-3)} \right|$$
$$= \left| \frac{11}{-23} \right| = \frac{11}{23}$$

Solving the equation yields $\theta \approx 0.4461$ radians, or 25.56°. ∎

Exercises 9.2.A

In Exercises 1–6, find the angle of inclination of the straight line through the given points.

1. $(-1, 2), (3, 5)$
   0.64 radians

2. $(0, 4), (5, -1)$
   $-\frac{\pi}{4}$ **radians**

3. $(1, 4), (6, 0)$
   2.47 radians

4. $(4, 2), (-3, -2)$
   0.519 radians

5. $(3, -7), (3, 5)$
   $\frac{\pi}{2}$ **radians**

6. $(0, 0), (-4, -5)$
   0.896 radians

In Exercises 7–12, find one of the angles between the straight lines L and M.

7. L has slope $\frac{3}{2}$ and M has slope -1.
   1.37 radians or 1.77 radians

8. L has slope 1 and M has slope 3.
   0.4636 radians

9. L has slope -1 and M has slope 0.
   $\frac{\pi}{4}$ **radians or** $\frac{3\pi}{4}$ **radians**

10. L has slope -2 and M has slope -3.
   0.1419 radians

11. $(3, 2)$ and $(5, 6)$ are on L; $(0, 3)$ and $(4, 0)$ are on M.
   1.39 radians or 1.75 radians

12. $(-1, 2)$ and $(3, -3)$ are on L; $(3, -3)$ and $(6, 1)$ are on M.
   1.3182 radians

9.3 Other Identities

Objectives

- Use the following identities:
  - double-angle
  - power-reducing
  - half-angle
  - product-to-sum
  - sum-to-product

Double-Angle Identities

A variety of identities that are special cases of the addition and subtraction identities of Section 9.2 are presented in this section. These identities include double-angle identities, power-reducing identities, half-angle identities, product-to-sum identities, and sum-to-product identities.

Double-Angle Identities

Special cases of the addition identities occur when two angles have the same measure. These identities are called the **double-angle identities.**

$$\sin 2x = 2 \sin x \cos x$$

$$\cos 2x = \cos^2 x - \sin^2 x$$

$$\tan 2x = \frac{2 \tan x}{1 - \tan^2 x}$$

Proof Substitute x for y in the addition identities.

$$\sin 2x = \sin(x + x) = \sin x \cos x + \cos x \sin x = 2 \sin x \cos x$$

$$\cos 2x = \cos(x + x) = \cos x \cos x - \sin x \sin x = \cos^2 x - \sin^2 x$$

$$\tan 2x = \tan(x + x) = \frac{\tan x + \tan x}{1 - \tan x \tan x} = \frac{2 \tan x}{1 - \tan^2 x}$$

Example 1   Use Double-Angle Identities

If $\pi < x < \frac{3\pi}{2}$ and $\cos x = -\frac{8}{17}$, find $\sin 2x$ and $\cos 2x$, and show that $\frac{5\pi}{2} < 2x < 3\pi$.

Solution

In order to use the double-angle identities, first determine $\sin x$, which can be found by using the Pythagorean identity.

$$\sin^2 x = 1 - \cos^2 x = 1 - \left(-\frac{8}{17}\right)^2 = 1 - \frac{64}{289} = \frac{225}{289}$$

Thus, $\sin x = \pm\sqrt{\frac{225}{289}}$. Since $\pi < x < \frac{3\pi}{2}$, x must be in the third quadrant, and $\sin x$ is negative there.

$$\sin x = -\sqrt{\frac{225}{289}} = -\frac{15}{17}$$

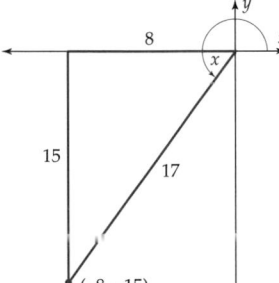

Figure 9.3-1

Multiply all the terms of $\pi < x < \frac{3\pi}{2}$ by 2 to find that $2\pi < 2x < 3\pi$. Both $\sin 2x$ and $\cos 2x$ are positive, so $2x$ is in Quadrant I, and $2\pi < 2x < \frac{5\pi}{2}$.

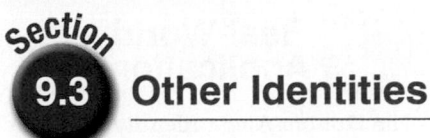

Section 9.3 Other Identities

Example Notes

In **Example 1**, it is given that $\pi < x < \frac{3\pi}{2}$ (that is, x terminates in Quadrant III). Based on this information alone, we know that $2\pi < 2x < 3\pi$ (that is, $2x$ terminates in either Quadrant I or Quadrant II). But we are asked to show that $\frac{5\pi}{2} < 2x < 3\pi$ (that is, show that $2x$ terminates in Quadrant II). The additional information needed to show this is obtained when we determine the signs of $\sin 2x$ and $\cos 2x$ (top of page 594).

ADDITIONAL EXAMPLES

Example 1

If $\pi < x < \frac{3\pi}{2}$ and $\cos x = -\frac{24}{25}$, find $\sin 2x$ and $\cos 2x$, and show that $2\pi < 2x < \frac{5\pi}{2}$.

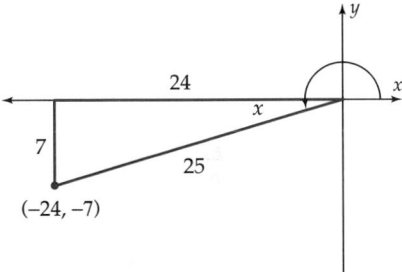

$$\sin^2 x = 1 - \cos^2 x = 1 - \left(-\frac{24}{25}\right)^2$$

$$= 1 - \frac{576}{625} = \frac{49}{625}$$

$\sin x = -\frac{7}{25}$ because x is in Quadrant III.

$$\sin 2x = 2 \sin x \cos x = 2\left(-\frac{7}{25}\right)\left(-\frac{24}{25}\right)$$

$$= \frac{336}{625} = 0.5376$$

$$\cos 2x = \cos^2 x - \sin^2 x$$

$$= \left(-\frac{24}{25}\right)^2 - \left(-\frac{7}{25}\right)^2$$

$$= \left(\frac{576}{625}\right) - \left(\frac{49}{625}\right)$$

$$= \left(\frac{527}{625}\right) = 0.8432$$

Real-World Application

The **Double-Angle Identity** for $\sin 2x$ can be used to calculate a distance. The approximate horizontal distance traveled by a batted baseball can be calculated using the formula $d = \dfrac{v^2 \sin \theta \cos \theta}{16}$ (see Exercise 76 page 602). By applying the identity $\sin 2x = 2 \sin x \cos x$, the formula can be shortened to $d = \dfrac{v^2 \sin 2\theta}{32}$. The latter formula only requires one trigonometric function value to calculate d, rather than two.

Teaching Notes

Ask your students to use the **Forms of cos 2x** to obtain the **Power-Reducing Identities.**

$$\cos 2x = 1 - 2 \sin^2 x$$
$$2 \sin^2 x = 1 - \cos 2x$$
$$\frac{2 \sin^2 x}{2} = \frac{1 - \cos 2x}{2}$$
$$\sin^2 x = \frac{1 - \cos 2x}{2}$$

$$\cos 2x = 2 \cos^2 x - 1$$
$$1 + \cos 2x = 2 \cos^2 x$$
$$\frac{1 + \cos 2x}{2} = \frac{2 \cos^2 x}{2}$$
$$\frac{1 + \cos 2x}{2} = \cos^2 x$$

ADDITIONAL EXAMPLES

Example 2

Express the rule of the function $f(x) = \cos 4x$ in terms of powers of $\cos\ x$ and constants.

$f(x) = \cos 4x = \cos(2x + 2x)$

$= \cos 2x \cos 2x - \sin 2x \sin 2x$

$= (\cos^2 x - \sin^2 x)(\cos^2 x - \sin^2 x) -$
$\qquad (2 \sin x \cos x)(2 \sin x \cos x)$

$= \cos^4 x - 2 \sin^2 x \cos^2 x + \sin^4 x -$
$\qquad\qquad 4 \sin^2 x \cos^2 x$

$= \cos^4 x - 2 \sin^2 x \cos^2 x +$
$\qquad \sin^2 x \sin^2 x - 4 \sin^2 x \cos^2 x$

$= \cos^4 x - 2(1 - \cos^2 x)\cos^2 x +$
$\qquad (1 - \cos^2 x)(1 - \cos^2 x) -$
$\qquad\qquad 4(1 - \cos^2 x)\cos^2 x$

$= \cos^4 x - 2(\cos^2 x - \cos^4 x) +$
$\qquad 1 - 2 \cos^2 x + \cos^4 x -$
$\qquad\qquad 4(\cos^2 x - \cos^4 x)$

$= \cos^4 x - 2 \cos^2 x + 2 \cos^4 x +$
$\qquad 1 - 2 \cos^2 x + \cos^4 x -$
$\qquad\qquad 4 \cos^2 x + 4 \cos^4 x$

$= 8 \cos^4 x - 8 \cos^2 x + 1$

Now substitute these values in the double-angle identities to find $\sin 2x$ and $\cos 2x$.

$$\sin 2x = 2 \sin x \cos x = 2\left(-\frac{15}{17}\right)\left(-\frac{8}{17}\right) = \frac{240}{289} \approx 0.8304$$

$$\cos 2x = \cos^2 x - \sin^2 x = \left(-\frac{8}{17}\right)^2 - \left(-\frac{15}{17}\right)^2 = \frac{64}{289} - \frac{225}{289} = -\frac{161}{289} \approx -0.5571$$

You know that x lies in the third quadrant. Multiply the inequality $\pi < x < \dfrac{3\pi}{2}$ by 2 to find that $2\pi < 2x < 3\pi$. That is, $2x$ is in either the first or second quadrant. The calculations above show that at $2x$, sine is positive and cosine is negative. This can occur only if $2x$ lies in the second quadrant, so $\dfrac{5\pi}{2} < 2x < 3\pi$. ∎

Example 2   Use Double-Angle Identities

Express the rule of the function $f(x) = \sin 3x$ in terms of powers of $\sin x$ and constants.

Solution

First use the addition identity for $\sin(x + y)$ with $y = 2x$.

$f(x) = \sin 3x = \sin(x + 2x) = \sin x \cos 2x + \cos x \sin 2x$

$\qquad = \sin x(\cos^2 x - \sin^2 x) + \cos x(2 \sin x \cos x)$
$\qquad\qquad\quad$ *identity for cos 2x* $\qquad$ *identity for sin 2x*

$\qquad = \sin x \cos^2 x - \sin^3 x + 2 \sin x \cos^2 x$

$\qquad = 3 \sin x \cos^2 x - \sin^3 x$

$\qquad = 3 \sin x(1 - \sin^2 x) - \sin^3 x$
$\qquad\qquad\quad$ *Pythagorean identity*

$\qquad = 3 \sin x - 3 \sin^3 x - \sin^3 x$

$\qquad = 3 \sin x - 4 \sin^3 x$ ∎

Forms of cos 2x

The double-angle identity for $\cos 2x$ can be rewritten in several useful ways. For instance, we can use the Pythagorean identity in the form of $\cos^2 x = 1 - \sin^2 x$ to obtain the following.

$$\cos 2x = \cos^2 x - \sin^2 x = (1 - \sin^2 x) - \sin^2 x = 1 - 2 \sin^2 x$$

Similarly, use the Pythagorean identity in the form $\sin^2 x = 1 - \cos^2 x$ to obtain the following.

$$\cos 2x = \cos^2 x - \sin^2 x = \cos^2 x - (1 - \cos^2 x) = 2 \cos^2 x - 1$$

Forms of cos 2x

$$\cos 2x = 1 - 2\sin^2 x$$
$$\cos 2x = 2\cos^2 x - 1$$

Example 3 Use Forms of cos 2x

Prove that $\dfrac{1 - \cos 2x}{\sin 2x} = \tan x$.

Solution

Use the first identity in the preceding box and the double-angle identity for sine.

$$\frac{1 - \cos 2x}{\sin 2x} = \frac{1-(1 - 2\sin^2 x)}{2\sin x \cos x} = \frac{2\sin^2 x}{2\sin x \cos x} = \frac{\sin x}{\cos x} = \tan x$$

Power-Reducing Identities

If the first equation in the preceding box is solved for $\sin^2 x$ and the second one for $\cos^2 x$, alternate forms for these identities are obtained. The new forms are called the **power-reducing identities.**

Power-Reducing Identities

$$\sin^2 x = \frac{1 - \cos 2x}{2}$$
$$\cos^2 x = \frac{1 + \cos 2x}{2}$$

Example 4 Use Power-Reducing Identities

Express the function $f(x) = \sin^4 x$ in terms of constants and first powers of cosine functions.

Solution

Begin by applying the power-reducing identity.

$$f(x) = \sin^4 x = \sin^2 x \cdot \sin^2 x$$
$$= \frac{1 - \cos 2x}{2} \cdot \frac{1 - \cos 2x}{2}$$
$$= \frac{1 - 2\cos 2x + \cos^2 2x}{1}$$

Teaching Notes

For each of the **Half-Angle Identities,** emphasize that the sign in front of the radical is determined by which quadrant $\frac{x}{2}$ is in, not which quadrant x is in.

After discussing the proof of the half-angle identity for sine, ask your students to prove the half-angle identities for cosine and tangent.

$$\cos^2\left(\frac{x}{2}\right) = \frac{1 + \cos 2\left(\frac{x}{2}\right)}{2} = \frac{1 + \cos x}{2}$$

$$\cos\left(\frac{x}{2}\right) = \pm\sqrt{\frac{1 + \cos x}{2}}$$

$$\tan\left(\frac{x}{2}\right) = \frac{\sin\left(\frac{x}{2}\right)}{\cos\left(\frac{x}{2}\right)} = \frac{\pm\sqrt{\frac{1 - \cos x}{2}}}{\pm\sqrt{\frac{1 + \cos x}{2}}}$$

$$= \pm\sqrt{\frac{\frac{1 - \cos x}{2}}{\frac{1 + \cos x}{2}}} = \pm\sqrt{\frac{1 - \cos x}{1 + \cos x}}$$

Example Notes

For **Example 5a,** students might need to review finding exact trigonometric function values of angles that terminate in quadrants other than Quadrant I (pages 450–451). Ask them to explain why $\cos\frac{5\pi}{4} = -\frac{\sqrt{2}}{2}$.

The reference angle for $\frac{5\pi}{4}$ is $\frac{5\pi}{4} - \pi = \frac{\pi}{4}$ because $\frac{5\pi}{4}$ is in Quadrant III.

$\cos\frac{\pi}{4} = \frac{\sqrt{2}}{2}$

Cosine values are negative in Quadrant III, so $\cos\frac{5\pi}{4} = -\frac{\sqrt{2}}{2}$.

In Example 5a, students can check their answer using a calculator.

```
cos(5π/8)
        -.3826834324
-(√(2-√(2)))/2
        -.3826834324
```

NOTE To write $\cos^2 2x$ in terms of first powers of cosine functions, use $2x$ in place of x in the power-reducing identity for cosine.

$$\cos^2 2x = \frac{1 + \cos 2(2x)}{2}$$
$$= \frac{1 + \cos 4x}{2}$$

Half-Angle Identities ○

Next apply the power-reducing identity for cosine to $\cos^2 2x$. (See Note.)

$$\frac{1 - 2\cos 2x + \cos^2 2x}{4} = \frac{1 - 2\cos 2x + \frac{1 + \cos 4x}{2}}{4}$$

$$= \frac{1}{4} - \frac{1}{2}\cos 2x + \frac{1}{8}(1 + \cos 4x)$$

$$= \frac{3}{8} - \frac{1}{2}\cos 2x + \frac{1}{8}\cos 4x \quad\blacksquare$$

Half-Angle Identities

The power-reducing identities with $\frac{x}{2}$ in place of x can be used to obtain the **half-angle identities.**

$$\sin^2\left(\frac{x}{2}\right) = \frac{1 - \cos 2\left(\frac{x}{2}\right)}{2} = \frac{1 - \cos x}{2}$$

$$\sin\left(\frac{x}{2}\right) = \pm\sqrt{\frac{1 - \cos x}{2}}$$

This proves the first of the half-angle identities.

> $$\sin\frac{x}{2} = \pm\sqrt{\frac{1 - \cos x}{2}} \qquad \cos\frac{x}{2} = \pm\sqrt{\frac{1 + \cos x}{2}}$$
>
> $$\tan\frac{x}{2} = \pm\sqrt{\frac{1 - \cos x}{1 + \cos x}}$$
>
> **The sign in front of the radical depends**
>
> **upon the quadrant in which $\frac{x}{2}$ lies.**

The half-angle identity for cosine is derived from a power-reducing identity, as was the half-angle identity for sine. The half-angle identity for tangent then follows immediately since $\tan\left(\frac{x}{2}\right) = \dfrac{\sin\left(\frac{x}{2}\right)}{\cos\left(\frac{x}{2}\right)}$.

Example 5 **Half-Angle Identities**

Find the exact value of

a. $\cos\frac{5\pi}{8}$

b. $\sin\frac{\pi}{12}$

Solution

a. Because $\dfrac{5\pi}{8} = \dfrac{1}{2}\left(\dfrac{5\pi}{4}\right)$, use the half-angle identity with $x = \dfrac{5\pi}{4}$ and

the fact that $\cos\dfrac{5\pi}{4} = -\dfrac{\sqrt{2}}{2}$. The sign chart given in Section 6.4

shows that $\cos\dfrac{5\pi}{8}$ is negative because $\dfrac{5\pi}{8}$ is in the second quadrant.

So, use the negative sign in front of the radical.

$$\cos\frac{5\pi}{8} = \cos\frac{\dfrac{5\pi}{4}}{2} = -\sqrt{\frac{1 + \cos\left(\dfrac{5\pi}{4}\right)}{2}}$$

$$= -\sqrt{\frac{1 + \left(-\dfrac{\sqrt{2}}{2}\right)}{2}}$$

$$= -\sqrt{\frac{\dfrac{(2 - \sqrt{2})}{2}}{2}}$$

$$= -\sqrt{\frac{2 - \sqrt{2}}{4}}$$

$$= -\frac{\sqrt{2 - \sqrt{2}}}{2}$$

b. Because $\dfrac{\pi}{12} = \dfrac{1}{2}\left(\dfrac{\pi}{6}\right)$ and $\dfrac{\pi}{12}$ is in the first quadrant, where sine is
positive,

$$\sin\frac{\pi}{12} = \sin\frac{\dfrac{\pi}{6}}{2} = \sqrt{\frac{1 - \cos\left(\dfrac{\pi}{6}\right)}{2}}$$

$$= \sqrt{\frac{1 - \dfrac{\sqrt{3}}{2}}{2}}$$

$$= \sqrt{\frac{\dfrac{2 - \sqrt{3}}{2}}{2}}$$

$$= \sqrt{\frac{2 - \sqrt{3}}{4}}$$

$$= \frac{\sqrt{2 - \sqrt{3}}}{2}$$

The problem of determining signs in the half-angle formulas can be eliminated for the tangent by using the following formulas.

Example 5

Find the exact value of

a. $\tan\dfrac{7\pi}{12}$

Since $\dfrac{7\pi}{12}$ is in the second quadrant,

$\tan\dfrac{7\pi}{12}$ is negative.

$$\tan\frac{7\pi}{12} = \tan\frac{\dfrac{7\pi}{6}}{2}$$

$$= -\sqrt{\frac{1 - \cos\dfrac{7\pi}{6}}{1 + \cos\dfrac{7\pi}{6}}}$$

$$= -\sqrt{\frac{1 - \left(-\dfrac{\sqrt{3}}{2}\right)}{1 + \left(-\dfrac{\sqrt{3}}{2}\right)}} = -\sqrt{\frac{1 + \dfrac{\sqrt{3}}{2}}{1 - \dfrac{\sqrt{3}}{2}}}$$

$$= -\sqrt{\frac{\dfrac{(2 + \sqrt{3})}{2}}{\dfrac{(2 - \sqrt{3})}{2}}} = -\sqrt{\frac{2 + \sqrt{3}}{2 - \sqrt{3}}}$$

$$= -\sqrt{\frac{2 + \sqrt{3}}{2 - \sqrt{3}} \cdot \frac{2 + \sqrt{3}}{2 + \sqrt{3}}}$$

$$= -\sqrt{\frac{4 + 4\sqrt{3} + 3}{4 - 3}}$$

$$= -\sqrt{7 + 4\sqrt{3}}$$

b. $\sin\dfrac{5\pi}{12}$

Since $\dfrac{5\pi}{12}$ is in the first quadrant, $\sin\dfrac{5\pi}{12}$
is positive.

$$\sin\frac{5\pi}{12} = \sin\frac{\dfrac{5\pi}{6}}{2} = \sqrt{\frac{1 - \cos\dfrac{5\pi}{6}}{2}}$$

$$= \sqrt{\frac{1 - \left(-\dfrac{\sqrt{3}}{2}\right)}{2}}$$

$$= \sqrt{\frac{\dfrac{2}{2} + \dfrac{\sqrt{3}}{2}}{2}}$$

$$= \sqrt{\frac{2 + \sqrt{3}}{4}}$$

$$= \frac{\sqrt{2 + \sqrt{3}}}{2}$$

ADDITIONAL EXAMPLES

Example 6

If $\tan x = -\dfrac{5}{8}$ and $\dfrac{3\pi}{2} < x < 2\pi$,

find $\tan \dfrac{x}{2}$.

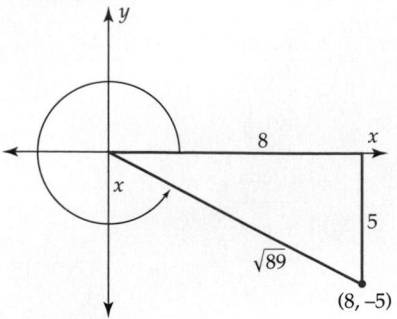

Since $\dfrac{3\pi}{2} < x < 2\pi$, angle x terminates in the fourth quadrant.

Since $\tan x = -\dfrac{5}{8}$, the terminal side of x passes through the point $(8, -5)$, and the distance from the origin to the point $(8, -5)$ is $\sqrt{89}$.

$\sin x = \dfrac{-5}{\sqrt{89}}$ and $\cos x = \dfrac{8}{\sqrt{89}}$.

$$\tan \frac{x}{2} = \frac{1 - \cos x}{\sin x}$$

$$= \frac{1 - \left(\dfrac{8}{\sqrt{89}}\right)}{\dfrac{-5}{\sqrt{89}}}$$

$$= \frac{\dfrac{\sqrt{89} - 8}{\sqrt{89}}}{\dfrac{-5}{\sqrt{89}}}$$

$$= -\frac{\sqrt{89} - 8}{5}$$

Teaching Notes

After completing **Example 6,** remind students that there are two **Half-Angle Identities for Tangent.** Consider challenging students to work Example 6 again, this time using the second identity.

$$\tan\left(\frac{x}{2}\right) = \frac{\sin x}{1 + \cos x}$$

$$= \frac{\dfrac{-3}{\sqrt{13}}}{1 + \left(\dfrac{-2}{\sqrt{13}}\right)} = \frac{\dfrac{-3}{\sqrt{13}}}{\dfrac{\sqrt{13} - 2}{\sqrt{13}}}$$

$$= \frac{-3}{\sqrt{13} - 2}$$

$$= \frac{-3\left(\sqrt{13} + 2\right)}{\left(\sqrt{13} - 2\right)\left(\sqrt{13} + 2\right)}$$

$$= \frac{-3\left(\sqrt{13} + 2\right)}{13 - 4} = \frac{-3\left(\sqrt{13} + 2\right)}{9}$$

$$= -\frac{\sqrt{13} + 2}{3}$$

Half-Angle Identities for Tangent

Proof

The proof of the first of these identities follows from the identity $\tan x = \dfrac{1 - \cos 2x}{\sin 2x}$, which was proved in Example 3. Replace x by $\dfrac{x}{2}$ in this identity.

$$\tan \frac{x}{2} = \frac{1 - \cos 2\left(\dfrac{x}{2}\right)}{\sin 2\left(\dfrac{x}{2}\right)} = \frac{1 - \cos x}{\sin x}$$

The second identity in the box is proved in Exercise 71.

Example 6   Use Half-Angle Identity for Tangent

If $\tan x = \dfrac{3}{2}$ and $\pi < x < \dfrac{3\pi}{2}$, find $\tan \dfrac{x}{2}$.

Solution

The terminal side of an angle of x radians in standard position lies in the third quadrant, as shown in Figure 9.3-2. The tangent of the angle in standard position whose terminal side passes through the point $(-2, -3)$ is $\dfrac{-3}{-2} = \dfrac{3}{2}$. Because there is only one angle in the third quadrant with tangent $\dfrac{3}{2}$, the point $(-2, -3)$ must lie on the terminal side of the angle of x radians.

The distance from $(-2, -3)$ to the origin is the hypotenuse of the triangle.

$$\sqrt{(-2 - 0)^2 + (-3 - 0)^2} = \sqrt{13}$$

Therefore,

$$\sin x = \frac{-3}{\sqrt{13}} \qquad \cos x = \frac{-2}{\sqrt{13}}$$

By the first of the half-angle identities for tangent,

$$\tan \frac{x}{2} = \frac{1 - \cos x}{\sin x} = \frac{1 - \left(\dfrac{-2}{\sqrt{13}}\right)}{\dfrac{-3}{\sqrt{13}}} = \frac{\dfrac{\sqrt{13} + 2}{\sqrt{13}}}{\dfrac{-3}{\sqrt{13}}} = -\frac{\sqrt{13} + 2}{3}$$

Figure 9.3-2

Product-to-Sum Identities

Use the addition and subtraction identities to rewrite $\sin(x+y) + \sin(x-y)$.

$$\sin(x+y) + \sin(x-y) = \sin x \cos y + \cos x \sin y + \sin x \cos y - \cos x \sin y$$
$$= 2 \sin x \cos y$$

Dividing both sides of the equation by 2 produces the first of the following identities.

Product-to-Sum Identities

$$\sin x \cos y = \frac{1}{2}\,[\sin(x+y) + \sin(x-y)]$$

$$\sin x \sin y = \frac{1}{2}\,[\cos(x-y) - \cos(x+y)]$$

$$\cos x \cos y = \frac{1}{2}\,[\cos(x+y) + \cos(x-y)]$$

$$\cos x \sin y = \frac{1}{2}\,[\sin(x+y) - \sin(x-y)]$$

The proofs of the second and fourth product-to-sum identities are similar to the proof of the first. The third product-to-sum identity was proved in Example 3 of Section 9.2.

Sum-to-Product Identities

Use the first product-to-sum identity with $\dfrac{x+y}{2}$ in place of x and $\dfrac{x-y}{2}$ in place of y to obtain the first sum-to-product identity.

$$\sin \frac{x+y}{2}\; \cos \frac{x-y}{2}$$
$$= \frac{1}{2}\left[\sin\!\left(\frac{x+y}{2} + \frac{x-y}{2}\right) + \sin\!\left(\frac{x+y}{2} - \frac{x-y}{2}\right)\right]$$
$$= \frac{1}{2}(\sin x + \sin y)$$

Multiplying both sides of the equation by 2 produces the identity.

Sum-to-Product Identities

$$\sin x + \sin y = 2 \sin \frac{x+y}{2}\, \cos \frac{x-y}{2}$$

$$\sin x - \sin y = 2 \cos \frac{x+y}{2}\, \sin \frac{x-y}{2}$$

$$\cos x + \cos y = 2 \cos \frac{x+y}{2}\, \cos \frac{x-y}{2}$$

$$\cos x - \cos y = -2 \sin \frac{x+y}{2}\, \sin \frac{x-y}{2}$$

Math Background

The proofs of several of the identities on this page are Exercises 52–54 in Section 9.2 (page 588). Proofs of several others are given below.

Product-to-Sum Identity for $\cos x \cos y$:

$$\cos(x+y) + \cos(x-y)$$
$$= \cos x \cos y - \sin x \sin y + \cos x \cos y + \sin x \sin y$$
$$= 2 \cos x \cos y$$

So, $2 \cos x \cos y$
$$= \cos(x+y) + \cos(x-y),$$

and $\frac{1}{2}[2 \cos x \cos y]$
$$= \frac{1}{2}[\cos(x+y) + \cos(x-y)].$$

Thus, $\cos x \cos y$
$$= \frac{1}{2}[\cos(x+y) + \cos(x-y)].$$

Sum-to-Product Identity for $\sin x - \sin y$:

$$\cos \frac{x+y}{2}\, \sin \frac{x-y}{2}$$
$$= \frac{1}{2}\left[\sin\!\left(\frac{x+y}{2} + \frac{x-y}{2}\right)\right.$$
$$\left. - \sin\!\left(\frac{x+y}{2} - \frac{x-y}{2}\right)\right]$$
$$= \frac{1}{2}\left[\sin \frac{2x}{2} - \sin \frac{2y}{2}\right]$$
$$= \frac{1}{2}(\sin x - \sin y)$$

So, $\frac{1}{2}(\sin x - \sin y)$
$$= \cos \frac{x+y}{2}\, \sin \frac{x-y}{2},$$

and $\sin x - \sin y = 2\cos \frac{x+y}{2}\, \sin \frac{x-y}{2}.$

Sum-to-Product Identity for $\cos x - \cos y$:

$$\sin \frac{x+y}{2}\, \sin \frac{x-y}{2}$$
$$= \frac{1}{2}\left[\cos\!\left(\frac{x+y}{2} - \frac{x-y}{2}\right) -\right.$$
$$\left. \cos\!\left(\frac{x+y}{2} + \frac{x-y}{2}\right)\right]$$
$$= \frac{1}{2}\left[\cos \frac{2y}{2} - \cos \frac{2x}{2}\right]$$
$$= \frac{1}{2}(\cos y - \cos x)$$
$$= -\frac{1}{2}(\cos x - \cos y)$$

So, $\frac{1}{2}(\cos x - \cos y)$
$$= \sin \frac{x+y}{2}\, \sin \frac{x-y}{2},$$

and $\cos x - \cos y$
$$= -2 \sin \frac{x+y}{2}\, \sin \frac{x-y}{2}.$$

Example 7

Prove the identity below.

$$\frac{\sin 3t - \sin t}{\cos 3t - \cos t} = -\cot 2t$$

$$\sin 3t - \sin t = 2 \cos\left(\frac{3t + t}{2}\right)\sin\left(\frac{3t - t}{2}\right)$$

$$= 2 \cos 2t \sin t$$

$$\cos 3t - \cos t$$

$$= -2 \sin\left(\frac{3t + t}{2}\right)\sin\left(\frac{3t - t}{2}\right)$$

$$= -2 \sin 2t \sin t$$

Therefore,

$$\frac{\sin 3t - \sin t}{\cos 3t - \cos t} = \frac{2 \cos 2t \sin t}{-2 \sin 2t \sin t}$$

$$= -\frac{\cos 2t}{\sin 2t}$$

$$= -\cot 2t$$

The other sum-to-product identities are proved the same way as the first.

Example 7   **Use Sum-to-Product Identities**

Prove the identity below.

$$\frac{\sin t + \sin 3t}{\cos t + \cos 3t} = \tan 2t$$

Solution

Use the first sum-to-product identity with $x = t$ and $y = 3t$.

$$\sin t + \sin 3t = 2 \sin\left(\frac{t + 3t}{2}\right)\cos\left(\frac{t - 3t}{2}\right) = 2 \sin 2t \cos(-t)$$

Similarly,

$$\cos t + \cos 3t = 2 \cos\left(\frac{t + 3t}{2}\right)\cos\left(\frac{t - 3t}{2}\right) = 2 \cos 2t \cos(-t).$$

Therefore,

$$\frac{\sin t + \sin 3t}{\cos t + \cos 3t} = \frac{2 \sin 2t \cos(-t)}{2 \cos 2t \cos(-t)} = \frac{\sin 2t}{\cos 2t} = \tan 2t.$$

Exercises 9.3

1. $\dfrac{\sqrt{2 + \sqrt{2}}}{2}$

2. $\sqrt{\dfrac{2 - \sqrt{2}}{2 + \sqrt{2}}}$

3. $\dfrac{\sqrt{2 + \sqrt{2}}}{2}$

4. $\dfrac{\sqrt{2 - \sqrt{2}}}{2}$

5. $2 - \sqrt{3}$

6. $\dfrac{\sqrt{2 + \sqrt{2}}}{2}$

7. $\dfrac{\sqrt{2 + \sqrt{3}}}{2}$

8. $-\sqrt{2} - 1$

9. $\dfrac{\sqrt{2 - \sqrt{2}}}{2}$

10. $-\dfrac{\sqrt{2 + \sqrt{2}}}{2}$

11. $-\sqrt{2} + 1$

12. $\sqrt{2} + 1$

13. $\frac{1}{2} \sin 10x - \frac{1}{2} \sin 2x$

14. $\frac{1}{2} \cos 2x - \frac{1}{2} \cos 12x$

15. $\frac{1}{2} \cos 6x + \frac{1}{2} \cos 2x$

16. $\frac{1}{2} \sin 8x - \frac{1}{2} \sin 2x$

17. $\frac{1}{2} \cos 20x - \frac{1}{2} \cos 14x$

18. $\frac{1}{2} \cos 8x + \frac{1}{2} \cos 18x$

19. $2 \sin 4x \cos x$

20. $2 \cos 4x \cos 2x$

21. $2 \sin 2x \cos 7x$

22. $2 \sin 6x \sin x$

Exercises 9.3

In Exercises 1–12, use the half-angle identities to evaluate the given expression exactly.

1. $\cos \dfrac{\pi}{8}$ 2. $\tan \dfrac{\pi}{8}$ 3. $\sin \dfrac{3\pi}{8}$ 4. $\cos \dfrac{3\pi}{8}$

5. $\tan \dfrac{\pi}{12}$ 6. $\sin \dfrac{5\pi}{8}$ 7. $\cos \dfrac{\pi}{12}$ 8. $\tan \dfrac{5\pi}{8}$

9. $\sin \dfrac{7\pi}{8}$ 10. $\cos \dfrac{7\pi}{8}$ 11. $\tan \dfrac{7\pi}{8}$ 12. $\cot \dfrac{\pi}{8}$

In Exercises 13–18, write each expression as a sum or difference.

13. $\sin 4x \cos 6x$ 14. $\sin 5x \sin 7x$

15. $\cos 2x \cos 4x$ 16. $\sin 3x \cos 5x$

17. $\sin 17x \sin(-3x)$ 18. $\cos 13x \cos(-5x)$

In Exercises 19–22, write each expression as a product.

19. $\sin 3x + \sin 5x$ 20. $\cos 2x + \cos 6x$

21. $\sin 9x - \sin 5x$ 22. $\cos 5x - \cos 7x$

In Exercises 23–30, find $\sin 2x$, $\cos 2x$, and $\tan 2x$ under the given conditions.

23. $\sin x = \dfrac{5}{13}$, for $0 < x < \dfrac{\pi}{2}$ $\dfrac{120}{169}$; $\dfrac{119}{169}$; $\dfrac{120}{119}$

24. $\sin x = -\dfrac{4}{5}$, for $\pi < x < \dfrac{3\pi}{2}$ $\dfrac{24}{25}$; $-\dfrac{7}{25}$; $-\dfrac{24}{7}$

25. $\cos x = -\dfrac{3}{5}$, for $\pi < x < \dfrac{3\pi}{2}$ $\dfrac{24}{25}$; $-\dfrac{7}{25}$; $-\dfrac{24}{7}$

26. $\cos x = -\dfrac{1}{3}$, for $\dfrac{\pi}{2} < x < \pi$ $-\dfrac{4\sqrt{2}}{9}$; $-\dfrac{7}{9}$; $\dfrac{4\sqrt{2}}{7}$

27. $\tan x = \dfrac{3}{4}$, for $\pi < x < \dfrac{3\pi}{2}$ $\dfrac{24}{25}$; $\dfrac{7}{25}$; $\dfrac{24}{7}$

28. $\tan x = -\dfrac{3}{2}$, for $\dfrac{\pi}{2} < x < \pi$ $-\dfrac{12}{13}$; $-\dfrac{5}{13}$; $\dfrac{12}{5}$

29. $\csc x = 4$, for $0 < x < \dfrac{\pi}{2}$ $\dfrac{\sqrt{15}}{8}$; $\dfrac{7}{8}$; $\dfrac{\sqrt{15}}{7}$

30. $\sec x = -5$, for $\pi < x < \dfrac{3\pi}{2}$ $\dfrac{4\sqrt{6}}{25}$; $-\dfrac{23}{25}$; $-\dfrac{4\sqrt{6}}{23}$

35. $\sqrt{\dfrac{\sqrt{5} + 2}{2\sqrt{5}}}$; $-\sqrt{\dfrac{\sqrt{5} - 2}{2\sqrt{5}}}$; $-\sqrt{5} - 2$

36. $\dfrac{\sqrt{2 + \sqrt{2}}}{2}$; $-\dfrac{\sqrt{2 - \sqrt{2}}}{2}$; $-\dfrac{\sqrt{2 + \sqrt{2}}}{\sqrt{2 - \sqrt{2}}}$

43. $\cos 3x = 4 \cos^3 x - 3 \cos x$

44. **a.** $\cos^3 x = \frac{1}{2} \cos x \cos 2x + \frac{1}{2} \cos x$

     b. $\cos^4 x = \frac{1}{8} \cos 4x + \frac{1}{2} \cos 2x + \frac{3}{8}$

51. $\sin 16x = \sin[2(8x)] = 2 \sin 8x \cos 8x$

52. $\cos 8x = \cos[2(4x)] = \cos^2 4x - \sin^2 4x$

53. $\cos^4 x - \sin^4 x = (\cos^2 x - \sin^2 x)(\cos^2 x + \sin^2 x)$

     $= \cos^2 x - \sin^2 x = \cos 2x$

54. $\sec 2x = \dfrac{1}{\cos 2x} = \dfrac{1}{1 - 2 \sin^2 x}$

In Exercises 31–36, find $\sin \frac{x}{2}$, $\cos \frac{x}{2}$, and $\tan \frac{x}{2}$ under the given conditions.

31. $\cos x = 0.4$, for $0 < x < \frac{\pi}{2}$
0.5477; 0.8367; 0.6547

32. $\sin x = 0.6$, for $\frac{\pi}{2} < x < \pi$ $\quad \frac{3}{\sqrt{10}}; \frac{1}{\sqrt{10}}; 3$

33. $\sin x = -\frac{3}{5}$, for $\frac{3\pi}{2} < x < 2\pi$ $\quad \frac{1}{\sqrt{10}}; -\frac{3}{\sqrt{10}}; -\frac{1}{3}$

34. $\cos x = 0.8$, for $\frac{3\pi}{2} < x < 2\pi$ $\quad \frac{1}{\sqrt{10}}; -\frac{3}{\sqrt{10}}; -\frac{1}{3}$

35. $\tan x = \frac{1}{2}$, for $\pi < x < \frac{3\pi}{2}$

36. $\cot x = 1$, for $-\pi < x < -\frac{\pi}{2}$

In Exercises 37–42, assume $\sin x = 0.6$ and $0 < x < \frac{\pi}{2}$ and evaluate the given expression.

37. $\sin 2x$ **38.** $\cos 4x$ **39.** $\cos 2x$
   0.96   **−0.8432**   **0.28**
40. $\sin 4x$ **41.** $\sin \frac{x}{2}$ **42.** $\cos \frac{x}{2}$
   0.5376   **0.3162**   **0.9487**

43. Express $\cos 3x$ in terms of $\cos x$.

44. **a.** Express the function $f(x) = \cos^3 x$ in terms of constants and first powers of the cosine function, as in Example 4.
     b. Do the same for $f(x) = \cos^4 x$.

In Exercises 45–50, simplify the given expression.

45. $\frac{\sin 2x}{2 \sin x}$ **cos x**   **46.** $1 - 2\sin^2\left(\frac{x}{2}\right)$ **cos x**

47. $2\cos 2y \sin 2y$ **sin 4y**

48. $\cos^2\left(\frac{x}{2}\right) - \sin^2\left(\frac{x}{2}\right)$ **cos x**

49. $(\sin x + \cos x)^2 - \sin 2x$ **1**

50. $2 \sin x \cos^3 x - 2 \sin^3 x \cos x$ **sin 2x cos 2x**

In Exercises 51–64, determine graphically whether the equation could not possibly be an identity, or write a proof showing that it is.

51. $\sin 16x = 2 \sin 8x \cos 8x$

52. $\cos 8x = \cos^2 4x - \sin^2 4x$

53. $\cos^4 x - \sin^4 x = \cos 2x$

54. $\sec 2x = \frac{1}{1 - 2\sin^2 x}$

55. $\cos 4x = 2\cos 2x - 1$

56. $\sin^2 x = \cos^2 x - 2\sin x$

57. $\frac{1 + \cos 2x}{\sin 2x} = \cot x$

58. $\sin 2x = \frac{2\cot x}{\csc^2 x}$

59. $\sin 3x = (\sin x)(3 - 4\sin^2 x)$

60. $\sin 4x = (4\cos x \sin x)(1 - 2\sin^2 x)$

61. $\cos 2x = \frac{2\tan x}{\sec^2 x}$

62. $\cos 3x = (\cos x)(3 - 4\cos^2 x)$

63. $\csc^2\left(\frac{x}{2}\right) = \frac{2}{1 - \cos x}$

64. $\sec^2\left(\frac{x}{2}\right) = \frac{2}{1 + \cos x}$

In Exercises 65–70, prove the identity.

65. $\frac{\sin x - \sin 3x}{\cos x + \cos 3x} = -\tan x$

66. $\frac{\sin x - \sin 3x}{\cos x - \cos 3x} = -\cot 2x$

67. $\frac{\sin 4x + \sin 6x}{\cos 4x - \cos 6x} = \cot x$

68. $\frac{\cos 8x + \cos 4x}{\cos 8x - \cos 4x} = -\cot 6x \cot 2x$

69. $\frac{\sin x + \sin y}{\cos x - \cos y} = -\cot\left(\frac{x - y}{2}\right)$

70. $\frac{\sin x - \sin y}{\cos x + \cos y} = \tan\left(\frac{x - y}{2}\right)$

71. **a.** Prove that $\frac{1 - \cos x}{\sin x} = \frac{\sin x}{1 + \cos x}$.
     b. Use part **a** and the half-angle identity proved in the text to prove that $\tan \frac{x}{2} = \frac{\sin x}{1 + \cos x}$.

72. If $x = \cos 2t$ and $y = \sin t$, find the relation between x and y by eliminating t.

---

55. not an identity

56. not an identity.

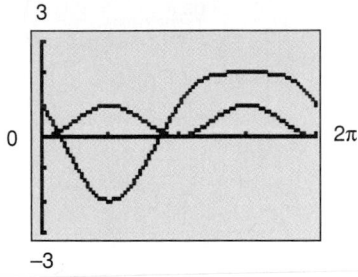

57. $\frac{1 + \cos 2x}{\sin 2x} = \frac{1 + (2\cos^2 x - 1)}{2\sin x \cos x}$
$= \frac{2\cos^2 x}{2\sin x \cos x}$
$= \frac{\cos x}{\sin x} = \cot x$

58. $\frac{2\cot x}{\csc^2 x} = \frac{\frac{2\cos x}{\sin x}}{\frac{1}{\sin^2 x}} = \frac{2\cos x}{\sin x} \cdot \frac{\sin^2 x}{1}$
$= 2\cos x \sin x = \sin 2x$

59. $\sin 3x = \sin(2x + x)$
$= \sin 2x \cos x + \cos 2x \sin x$
$= (2\sin x \cos x)\cos x +$
$\qquad\qquad (1 - 2\sin^2 x)\sin x$
$= 2\sin x \cos^2 x + \sin x - 2\sin^3 x$
$= 2\sin x(1 - \sin^2 x) +$
$\qquad\qquad \sin x - 2\sin^3 x$
$= \sin x(2 - 2\sin^2 x + 1 - 2\sin^2 x)$
$= \sin x(3 - 4\sin^2 x)$

60. $(4\cos x \sin x)(1 - 2\sin^2 x)$
$= 2\sin 2x \cos 2x = \sin 4x$

61. not an identity

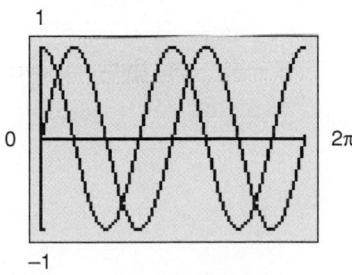

---

62. not an identity

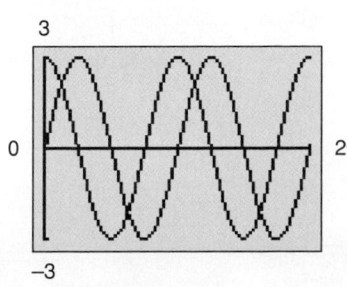

63. $\csc^2\left(\frac{x}{2}\right) = \frac{1}{\sin^2\left(\frac{x}{2}\right)} = \frac{1}{\frac{1 - \cos x}{2}} = \frac{2}{1 - \cos x}$

64. $\sec^2\left(\frac{x}{2}\right) = \frac{1}{\cos^2\left(\frac{x}{2}\right)} = \frac{1}{\left(\pm\sqrt{\frac{1 + \cos x}{2}}\right)^2}$
$= \frac{2}{1 + \cos x}$

65–72. *See p.* 1072–1073.

73. $R = vt \cos \alpha$

$R = v\left(\dfrac{2v \sin \alpha}{g}\right) \cos \alpha$

$R = \dfrac{2v^2 \sin \alpha \cos \alpha}{g}$

$R = \dfrac{v^2 \sin 2\alpha}{g}$

75. $2\left(\sin^2 \dfrac{1}{2}\alpha - \sin^2 \dfrac{1}{2}\theta\right)$

$= 2\left(\dfrac{1 - \cos 2\left(\frac{1}{2}\alpha\right)}{2} - \dfrac{1 - \cos 2\left(\frac{1}{2}\theta\right)}{2}\right)$

$= 2\left(\dfrac{1 - \cos \alpha - 1 + \cos \theta}{2}\right)$

$= \cos \theta - \cos \alpha$

73. The horizontal range of a projectile R is given by the equation

$$R = vt \cos \alpha,$$

where v is the initial velocity of the projectile, t is the time of flight, and α is the angle between the line of fire and the horizontal. If $t = \dfrac{2v \sin \alpha}{g}$, where g is acceleration due to gravity, show that $R = \dfrac{v^2 \sin 2\alpha}{g}$.

74. The expression $\sin\left(\dfrac{\pi}{2} - 2\theta\right)$ occurs in the theory of reflection of light waves. Show that this expression can be written as $1 - 2\sin^2\theta$.

$\sin\left(\dfrac{\pi}{2} - 2\theta\right)$

$= \sin\dfrac{\pi}{2}\cos 2\theta - \cos\dfrac{\pi}{2}\sin 2\theta$

$= 1 \cdot \cos 2\theta - 0 \cdot \sin 2\theta$

$= \cos 2\theta$

$= 1 - 2\sin^2\theta$

75. The expression $2\left(\sin^2 \dfrac{1}{2}\alpha - \sin^2 \dfrac{1}{2}\theta\right)$ is used in the theory of the motion of a pendulum. Show that this equation can be written as $\cos \theta - \cos \alpha$.

76. A batter hits a baseball that is caught by a fielder. If the ball leaves the bat at an angle of θ radians to the horizontal, with an initial velocity of v feet per second, then the approximate horizontal distance d traveled by the ball is given by

$$d = \dfrac{v^2 \sin \theta \cos \theta}{16}.$$

a. If the initial velocity is 90 ft/sec, find the horizontal distance traveled by the ball when $\theta = 0.5$ radian and when $\theta = 0.75$ radian.

b. Use an identity to show that $d = \dfrac{v^2 \sin 2\theta}{32}$.

a. **212.9973** ft; **252.4909** ft

b. $d = \dfrac{v^2 \sin \theta \cos \theta}{16} = \dfrac{2}{2}\left(\dfrac{v^2 \sin \theta \cos \theta}{16}\right)$

$= \dfrac{v^2 2 \sin \theta \cos \theta}{32}$

$= \dfrac{v^2 \sin 2\theta}{32}$

Section 9.4 Using Trigonometric Identities

Example Notes

For **Example 3**, an expression for $2x$ that is equivalent to $\dfrac{5\pi}{3} + 2\pi k$ is $-\dfrac{\pi}{3} + 2\pi k$.

The corresponding expression for x that is equivalent to $\dfrac{5\pi}{6} + \pi k$ is $-\dfrac{\pi}{6} + \pi k$.

These alternate expressions would be the result of applying the method shown in the table on page 540.

Take this opportunity to remind students that different expressions can represent the same set of numbers. $\dfrac{5\pi}{6} + \pi k$ represents

$\ldots, -\dfrac{7\pi}{6}, -\dfrac{\pi}{6}, \dfrac{5\pi}{6}, \dfrac{11\pi}{6}, \ldots$

$-\dfrac{\pi}{6} + \pi k$ represents the same set:

$\ldots, -\dfrac{7\pi}{6}, -\dfrac{\pi}{6}, \dfrac{5\pi}{6}, \dfrac{11\pi}{6}, \ldots$

9.4 Using Trigonometric Identities

Objectives

- Use identities to solve trigonometric equations

Recall that the basic identities are used to simplify expressions and to algebraically solve trigonometric equations. The trigonometric identities introduced in Section 9.3 can also be used with the techniques shown in Section 8.3, where equations were rewritten into a basic form and then solved.

Example 1 **Use Double-Angle Identities**

Solve $5 \cos x + 3 \cos 2x = 3$.

Solution

Use a double-angle identity to rewrite $\cos 2x$ in terms of $\cos^2 x$.

$5 \cos x + 3 \cos 2x = 3$

$5 \cos x + 3(2 \cos^2 x - 1) = 3$ *double-angle identity*

$5 \cos x + 6 \cos^2 x - 3 = 3$

$6 \cos^2 x + 5 \cos x - 6 = 0$

$(2 \cos x + 3)(3 \cos x - 2) = 0$ *factor the quadratic expression*

$2 \cos x + 3 = 0$ or $3 \cos x - 2 = 0$

$\cos x = -\dfrac{3}{2}$ $\cos x = \dfrac{2}{3}$

The equation $\cos x = -\frac{3}{2}$ has no solutions because $\cos x$ always lies between -1 and 1. A calculator shows that the solutions of $\cos x = \frac{2}{3}$ are

$$x \approx 0.8411 + 2k\pi \quad \text{and} \quad x \approx -0.8411 + 2k\pi$$

for any integer k.

◼

Example 2   Use Double-Angle Identities

Solve the equation $\sin x \cos x = 1$.

Solution

Use the double-angle identity to rewrite $\sin x \cos x$.

$$2 \sin x \cos x = \sin 2x$$
$$\sin x \cos x = \frac{1}{2} \sin 2x$$

Replace $\sin x \cos x$ with $\frac{1}{2} \sin 2x$ and multiply both sides by 2.

$$\frac{1}{2} \sin 2x = 1$$
$$\sin 2x = 2$$

Because the sine of any number must be between -1 and 1, there is no solution to the last equation. Therefore, there is no solution to the original equation.

◼

Example 3   Use Double-Angle Identities

Find exact solutions of $\cos^2 x - \sin^2 x = \frac{1}{2}$.

Solution

Because $\cos^2 x - \sin^2 x = \cos 2x$, the equation can be rewritten

$$\cos 2x = \frac{1}{2}$$
$$2x = \cos^{-1} \frac{1}{2}$$
$$2x = \frac{\pi}{3} + 2\pi k \quad \text{or} \quad 2x = \frac{5\pi}{3} + 2\pi k$$
$$x = \frac{\pi}{6} + \pi k \qquad\qquad x = \frac{5\pi}{6} + \pi k$$

for any integer k.

◼

Example Notes

In **Example 5,** make sure students understand how to find all the solutions after the statement $\cos x = -\frac{1}{2}$ or $\cos x = 1$.

If $\cos x = -\frac{1}{2}$, then (using the table on on page 540), $x = \frac{2\pi}{3} + 2\pi k$ or $x = -\frac{2\pi}{3} + 2\pi k$. Because $-\frac{2\pi}{3}$ and $\frac{4\pi}{3}$ are coterminal, these solutions can be written as $x = \frac{2\pi}{3} + 2\pi k$ or $x = \frac{4\pi}{3} + 2\pi k$.

If $\cos x = 1$, then $x = 0 + 2\pi k$.

Now find all solutions where $0 \le x \le 2\pi$:

Let $k = 0$ in $x = \frac{2\pi}{3} + 2\pi k$; $x = \frac{2\pi}{3}$

Let $k = 0$ in $x = \frac{4\pi}{3} + 2\pi k$; $x = \frac{4\pi}{3}$

Let $k = 0$ in $x = 0 + 2\pi k$; $x = 0$

Let $k = 1$ in $x = 0 + 2\pi k$; $x = 2\pi$

Have students check *all* solutions for Example 5 as instructed in the **CAUTION** on this page.

Students should find that 0, $\frac{2\pi}{3}$, and 2π are solutions, and that $\frac{4\pi}{3}$ is not. The checks for $\frac{2\pi}{3}$ and $\frac{4\pi}{3}$ are shown below.

Check $x = \frac{2\pi}{3}$: $\sin x = \sin \frac{x}{2}$

$\sin \dfrac{2\pi}{3}$	$\sin \dfrac{\frac{2\pi}{3}}{2}$
	$\sin \dfrac{\pi}{3}$
$\dfrac{\sqrt{3}}{2}$	$\dfrac{\sqrt{3}}{2}$ ✓

$\frac{2\pi}{3}$ is a solution.

Check $x = \frac{4\pi}{3}$: $\sin x = \sin \frac{x}{2}$

$\sin \dfrac{4\pi}{3}$	$\sin \dfrac{\frac{4\pi}{3}}{2}$
	$\sin \dfrac{2\pi}{3}$
$-\dfrac{\sqrt{3}}{2}$	$\dfrac{\sqrt{3}}{2}$ ✗

$\frac{4\pi}{3}$ is not a solution.

Example 4 Use Addition Identities

Find the exact solutions of $\sin 2x \cos x + \cos 2x \sin x = 1$.

Solution

The left side of the equation is similar to the right side of the addition identity for sine.

$$\sin(x + y) = \sin x \cos y + \cos x \sin y.$$

Substitute $2x$ for x and x for y.

$$\sin 2x \cos x + \cos 2x \sin x = \sin(2x + x) = 1$$
$$\sin 3x = 1$$
$$3x = \sin^{-1} 1$$

For any integer k,
$$3x = \frac{\pi}{2} + 2\pi k$$
$$x = \frac{\pi}{6} + \frac{2\pi k}{3}$$ ∎

Example 5 Use Half-Angle Identities

Find the solutions of $\sin x = \sin \frac{x}{2}$, where $0 \le x \le 2\pi$.

Solution

> **CAUTION**
>
> Squaring both sides of an equation may introduce extraneous solutions. Be sure to check all solutions in the original equation.

$$\sin x = \sin \frac{x}{2}$$
$$\sin x = \pm\sqrt{\frac{1 - \cos x}{2}} \qquad \textit{half-angle identity}$$
$$\sin^2 x = \frac{1 - \cos x}{2} \qquad \textit{square both sides}$$
$$1 - \cos^2 x = \frac{1 - \cos x}{2} \qquad \textit{Pythagorean identity}$$
$$2 - 2\cos^2 x = 1 - \cos x$$
$$2\cos^2 x - \cos x - 1 = 0$$
$$(2\cos x + 1)(\cos x - 1) = 0$$
$$2\cos x + 1 = 0 \qquad \text{or} \qquad \cos x - 1 = 0$$
$$\cos x = -\frac{1}{2} \qquad\qquad \cos x = 1$$

For any integer k,

$$x = \frac{2\pi}{3} + 2\pi k \qquad x = \frac{4\pi}{3} + 2\pi k \qquad x = 0 + 2\pi k$$

For $0 \le x \le 2\pi$, $x = 0, \frac{2\pi}{3}$, or 2π. ∎

Solving *a* sin *x* + *b* cos *x* = *c* (Optional)

Equations of the form $a \sin x + b \cos x = c$ occur often.

For the case when $c = 0$, the equations can be rewritten as

$$a \sin x = -b \cos x$$

$$\frac{\sin x}{\cos x} = -\frac{b}{a}$$

$$\tan x = -\frac{b}{a}$$

The last equation can be solved by methods discussed in Section 8.3.

For the case when $c \neq 0$, a very different approach is needed to find the solutions to

$$a \sin x + b \cos x = c$$

The procedure involves rewriting the equation as

$$\sin (x + \alpha) = k,$$

where α is the angle whose terminal side contains the point (a, b), and then using the addition identity for the sine function.

To find α, construct a right triangle in the coordinate plane with sides a and b, where a lies on the positive x-axis and α is the angle with its vertex at the origin.

Begin by writing the equation so that the coefficient of sin x, a, is positive. The position of the point (a, b) depends on whether b is positive or negative. If b is positive, the point is in the first quadrant; if b is negative, the point is in the fourth quadrant. Both possibilities are shown in Figures 9.4-1 and 9.4-2.

Figure 9.4-1

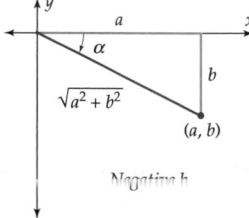

Figure 9.4-2

In both cases, $\sin \alpha = \dfrac{b}{\sqrt{a^2 + b^2}}$ and $\cos \alpha = \dfrac{a}{\sqrt{a^2 + b^2}}$. [1]

Divide each side of the original equation by $\sqrt{a^2 + b^2}$ to obtain

$$a \sin x \quad + \quad b \cos x \quad = \quad c$$

$$\frac{a}{\sqrt{a^2 + b^2}} \sin x + \frac{b}{\sqrt{a^2 + b^2}} \cos x = \frac{c}{\sqrt{a^2 + b^2}} \quad [2]$$

Substitute the equivalent expressions from [1] into equation [2].

$$\cos \alpha \sin x + \sin \alpha \cos x = \frac{c}{\sqrt{a^2 + b^2}}$$

Use the addition identity for sine to rewrite the left side of the equation.

$$\sin(x + \alpha) = \frac{c}{\sqrt{a^2 + b^2}}$$

The last equation can be solved by using the methods from Section 8.3. The steps of the procedure are summarized in the following box.

In **Example 4**, students might incorrectly solve $3x = \frac{\pi}{2} + 2\pi k$, getting $x = \frac{\pi}{6} + 2\pi k$. Remind them to divide *both* terms on the right side of the equation by 3 to get $x = \frac{\pi}{6} + \frac{2\pi k}{3}$.

ADDITIONAL EXAMPLES

Example 4

Find the exact solutions of $\cos 2x \cos x - \sin 2x \sin x = -1$.

$$\cos 2x \cos x - \sin 2x \sin x = -1$$

$$\cos(2x + x) = -1$$

$$\cos 3x = -1$$

$$3x = \pi + 2\pi k$$

$$x = \frac{\pi}{3} + \frac{2\pi k}{3}$$

for any integer k.

Example 5

Find the solutions of $\sin x = \cos \frac{x}{2}$, where $0 \leq x \leq 2\pi$.

$$\sin x = \cos \frac{x}{2}$$

$$\sin x = \pm\sqrt{\frac{1 + \cos x}{2}}$$

$$\sin^2 x = \frac{1 + \cos x}{2}$$

$$1 - \cos^2 x = \frac{1 + \cos x}{2}$$

$$2 - 2\cos^2 x = 1 + \cos x$$

$$2 \cos^2 x + \cos x - 1 = 0$$

$$(2 \cos x - 1)(\cos x + 1) = 0$$

$$2 \cos x - 1 = 0 \quad \text{or} \quad \cos x + 1 = 0$$

$$\cos x = \frac{1}{2} \quad \text{or} \quad \cos x = -1$$

For any integer k,

$$x = \frac{\pi}{3} + 2\pi k, \quad x = -\frac{\pi}{3} + 2\pi k,$$

$$x = \pi + 2\pi k$$

For $0 \leq x \leq 2\pi$, $x = \frac{\pi}{3}$, π, or $\frac{5\pi}{3}$.

Checking shows that all 3 solutions satisfy the original equation.

Example 6

Solve the equation
$-\sin x + \cos x = -1$.

1. Multiply both sides of the equation by -1.

$$-\sin x + \cos x = -1$$

$$\sin x - \cos x = 1$$

So, $a = 1$ and $b = -1$.

2. Sketch a diagram of the angle α that has $(1, -1)$ on its terminal side.

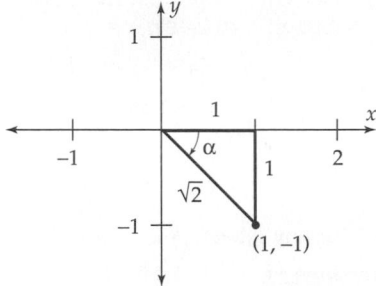

3. The length of the hypotenuse is $\sqrt{1^2 + (-1)^2} = \sqrt{2}$.

Find $\sin \alpha$ and $\cos \alpha$ from the figure.

$$\cos \alpha = \frac{1}{\sqrt{2}} = \frac{\sqrt{2}}{2}$$

$$\sin \alpha = -\frac{1}{\sqrt{2}} = -\frac{\sqrt{2}}{2}$$

Find α: $\alpha = -\frac{\pi}{4}$

4. Divide both sides of the equation in Step 1 by the hypotenuse, $\sqrt{2}$.

$$\sin x - \cos x = 1$$

$$\frac{\sin x}{\sqrt{2}} - \frac{\cos x}{\sqrt{2}} = \frac{1}{\sqrt{2}}$$

$$\frac{\sqrt{2}}{2}\sin x - \frac{\sqrt{2}}{2}\cos x = \frac{\sqrt{2}}{2}$$

5. Rewrite the equation by

substituting $\cos\left(-\frac{\pi}{4}\right)$ for $\frac{\sqrt{2}}{2}$ and

$\sin\left(-\frac{\pi}{4}\right)$ for $-\frac{\sqrt{2}}{2}$. Then, use the

addition identity for sine.

$$\frac{\sqrt{2}}{2}\sin x - \frac{\sqrt{2}}{2}\cos x = \frac{\sqrt{2}}{2}$$

$$\cos\left(-\frac{\pi}{4}\right)\sin x + $$

$$\sin\left(-\frac{\pi}{4}\right)\cos x = \frac{\sqrt{2}}{2}$$

$$\sin\left(x + \left(-\frac{\pi}{4}\right)\right) = \frac{\sqrt{2}}{2}$$

$$\sin\left(x - \frac{\pi}{4}\right) = \frac{\sqrt{2}}{2}$$

Solving
$a \sin x + b \cos x$
$= c,$
where $c \neq 0$

Let a, b, and c be nonzero real numbers. To solve

$$a \sin x + b \cos x = c$$

1. **Multiply by -1, if needed, to make a positive.**
2. **Plot the point (a, b) and let α be the angle in standard position that contains (a, b) on its terminal side.**
3. **Find**
   - **the length of the hypotenuse of the reference triangle**
   - **expressions that represent $\sin \alpha$ and $\cos \alpha$**
   - **the measure of α**
4. **Divide each side of the equation by $\sqrt{a^2 + b^2}$ yielding**

$$\frac{a}{\sqrt{a^2 + b^2}}\sin x + \frac{b}{\sqrt{a^2 + b^2}}\cos x = \frac{c}{\sqrt{a^2 + b^2}}$$

5. **Use the addition identity for sine to rewrite the equation.**

$$\sin(x + \alpha) = \frac{c}{\sqrt{a^2 + b^2}}$$

6. **Solve the equation using techniques previously discussed.**

Example 6   Solve $a \sin x + b \cos x = c$

Solve the equation $-\sqrt{3}\sin x + \cos x = -\sqrt{3}$.

Solution

Step 1   Make the coefficient of $\sin x$ positive by multiplying both sides of the equation by -1.

$$\sqrt{3}\sin x - \cos x = \sqrt{3} \quad \text{so } a = \sqrt{3} \text{ and } b = -1$$

Step 2   Sketch a diagram of the angle α that has $\left(\sqrt{3}, -1\right)$ on its terminal side. See Figure 9.4-3.

Step 3   The length of the hypotenuse is $\sqrt{(\sqrt{3})^2 + (-1)^2} = 2$.

Find $\sin \alpha$ and $\cos \alpha$ from the figure.

$$\cos \alpha = \frac{\sqrt{3}}{2} \text{ and } \sin \alpha = \frac{-1}{2}$$

Find α.

$$\alpha = -\frac{\pi}{6} \quad \text{or} \quad \alpha = \frac{11\pi}{6}$$

Step 4   Divide both sides of the equation in Step 1 by the hypotenuse, $\sqrt{(\sqrt{3})^2 + (-1)^2} = 2$.

$$\frac{\sqrt{3}}{2}\sin x - \frac{1}{2}\cos x = \frac{\sqrt{3}}{2}$$

Figure 9.4-3

---

continued from page 606

6. Solve the equation.

$$\sin\left(x - \frac{\pi}{4}\right) = \frac{\sqrt{2}}{2}$$

$$x - \frac{\pi}{4} = \frac{\pi}{4} + 2\pi k \quad \text{or} \quad x - \frac{\pi}{4} = \frac{3\pi}{4} + 2\pi k$$

$$x = \frac{\pi}{2} + 2\pi k \quad \text{or} \quad x = \pi + 2\pi k$$

for any integer k.

Example 7

Find the maximum and minimum of the function $f(x) = 5 \sin x + 12 \cos x$.

Note that $\sqrt{5^2 + 12^2} = \sqrt{169} = 13$.

Let $\alpha = \cos^{-1} \frac{5}{13} = \sin^{-1} \frac{12}{13}$.

$$f(x) = 13\left(\frac{5}{13} \sin x + \frac{12}{13} \cos x\right)$$

$$= 13(\cos \alpha \sin x + \sin \alpha \cos x)$$

$$= 13 \sin (x + \alpha)$$

The maximum is 13 and the minimum is -13.

Example Notes

For **Example 7**, a diagram of the angle α might be helpful, as shown below.

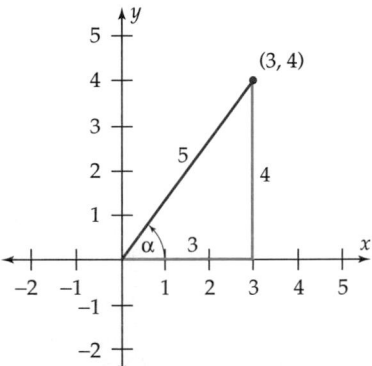

Step 5　Rewrite the equation by substituting

$$\cos \frac{11\pi}{6} \text{ for } \frac{\sqrt{3}}{2} \quad \text{and} \quad -\sin \frac{11\pi}{6} \text{ for } \frac{1}{2}$$

and then use the addition identity for sine.

$$\cos \frac{11\pi}{6} \sin x + \sin \frac{11\pi}{6} \cos x = \frac{\sqrt{3}}{2}$$

$$\sin\left(x + \frac{11\pi}{6}\right) = \frac{\sqrt{3}}{2}$$

Step 6　Solve the equation.

$$x + \frac{11\pi}{6} = \sin^{-1}\left(\frac{\sqrt{3}}{2}\right)$$

$$x + \frac{11\pi}{6} = \frac{\pi}{3} + 2\pi k \quad \text{or} \quad x + \frac{11\pi}{6} = \frac{2\pi}{3} + 2\pi k$$

$$x = \frac{\pi}{3} - \frac{11\pi}{6} + 2\pi k \qquad\qquad x = \frac{2\pi}{3} - \frac{11\pi}{6} + 2\pi k$$

$$x = -\frac{3\pi}{2} + 2\pi k \qquad\qquad\qquad x = -\frac{7\pi}{6} + 2\pi k$$

$$x = \frac{\pi}{2} + 2\pi k \qquad\qquad\qquad\quad x = \frac{5\pi}{6} + 2\pi k$$

for any integer k. ∎

Maxima and Minima of $f(x) = a \sin x + b \cos x$

For functions of the form $f(x) = a \sin x + b \cos x$, maximum and minimum values can be found by using a technique similar to that described in the algorithm to solve equations of the form $a \sin x + b \cos x = c$.

Example 7　Maximum and Minimum of $f(x) = a \sin x + b \cos x$

Find the maximum and minimum of the function

$$f(x) = 3 \sin x + 4 \cos x.$$

Solution

Note that $\sqrt{3^2 + 4^2} = \sqrt{25} = 5$. Let $\alpha = \cos^{-1} \frac{3}{5}$, or equivalently $\alpha = \sin^{-1} \frac{4}{5}$, and write the function in the form $f(x) = k \sin(x + \alpha)$.

$$f(x) = 5\left(\frac{3}{5} \sin x + \frac{4}{5} \cos x\right) = 5(\cos \alpha \sin x + \sin \alpha \cos x)$$

$$= 5 \sin(x + \alpha)$$

Because the sine function varies between -1 and 1, the maximum of $5 \sin(x + \alpha)$ is 5 and the minimum is -5. ∎

NOTE The value of α is not needed to find the maximum or minimum of the function.

Teaching Notes

Refer students to the margin **NOTE** at the bottom of page 607. As noted, the value of α is not needed to find the maximum or minimum of the function. However, the value of α is *needed to find the values of x that produce the maximum or minimum* of the function.

As shown at the right, the maximum value 5 for the function $f(x) = 3 \sin x + 4 \cos x$ occurs at $x \approx 0.6435$. So, $(0.6435, 5)$ is a local maximum point on the graph, as shown below.

To find the values of x that produce the maximum or minimum values of the function, solve the equation

$$a \sin x + b \cos x = c,$$

where c is the maximum or minimum value. In Example 7, the maximum value of 5 occurs when

$$3 \sin x + 4 \cos x = 5$$

$$\frac{3}{5} \sin x + \frac{4}{5} \cos x = 1$$

$$\sin(x + \alpha) = 1$$

$$x + \alpha = \sin^{-1} 1 = \frac{\pi}{2}$$

$$x = \frac{\pi}{2} - \alpha$$

$$\approx 1.5708 - 0.9273 \qquad \alpha = \cos^{-1} \frac{3}{5} \approx 0.9273$$

$$\approx 0.6435$$

In one revolution, the maximum occurs at approximately 0.6435.

Where the minimum value occurs is found in a similar manner.

Exercises 9.4

In Exercises 1–27, find all solutions of the equation in the interval $[0, 2\pi]$.

1. $\sin^2 x + 3 \cos^2 x = 0$

2. $\sin 2x + \cos x = 0$

3. $\cos 2x - \sin x = 1$

4. $\sin \frac{x}{2} = 1 - \cos x$

5. $4 \sin^2 \left(\frac{x}{2} \right) + \cos^2 x = 2$

6. $\sin 4x - \sin 2x = 0$

7. $\sin x \sin \frac{1}{2} x = 1 - \cos x$

8. $\sin 2t \cos t - \cos 2t \sin t = 0$

9. $\sin 2x \sin x + \cos x = 0$

10. $\cos x = \cos \frac{1}{2} x$ (Check for extraneous solutions.)

11. $\sin 2x + \cos 2x = 0$

12. $\cos 4x \cos x - \sin 4x \sin x = 0$

13. $\sin 4x = \cos 2x$

14. $\cos 2x + \sin^2 x = 0$

15. $2 \cos^2 x - 2 \cos 2x = 1$

16. $\cos \left(x + \frac{\pi}{2} \right) - \sin x = 1$

17. $\sin \left(x + \frac{\pi}{2} \right) + \cos x = 1$

18. $\sin x - \sqrt{3} \cos x = 0$

19. $\sin x + \cos x = 0$

20. $\sin 2x - \cos x = 0$

21. $\cos 2x + \cos x = 0$

22. $(\sin x - \cos x)^2 = 1$

Exercises 9.4

ANSWERS

1. no solution

2. $x = \dfrac{\pi}{2}, \dfrac{3\pi}{2}, \dfrac{7\pi}{6}, \dfrac{11\pi}{6}$

3. $x = 0, \pi, 2\pi, \dfrac{7\pi}{6}, \dfrac{11\pi}{6}$

4. $x = 0, 2\pi, \dfrac{\pi}{3}, \dfrac{5\pi}{3}$

5. $x = \dfrac{\pi}{2}, \dfrac{3\pi}{2}$

6. $x = 0, \dfrac{\pi}{2}, \pi, \dfrac{3\pi}{2}, 2\pi, \dfrac{\pi}{6}, \dfrac{5\pi}{6}, \dfrac{7\pi}{6}, \dfrac{11\pi}{6}$

7. $x = 0, 2\pi$

8. $t = 0, \pi, 2\pi$

9. $x = \dfrac{\pi}{2}, \dfrac{3\pi}{2}$

10. $x = 0, \dfrac{4\pi}{3}$

11. $x = \dfrac{3\pi}{8}, \dfrac{7\pi}{8}, \dfrac{11\pi}{8}, \dfrac{15\pi}{8}$

12. $x = \dfrac{\pi}{10}, \dfrac{3\pi}{10}, \dfrac{\pi}{2}, \dfrac{7\pi}{10}, \dfrac{9\pi}{10}, \dfrac{11\pi}{10}, \dfrac{13\pi}{10},$
$\dfrac{3\pi}{2}, \dfrac{17\pi}{10}, \dfrac{19\pi}{10}$

13. $x = \dfrac{\pi}{4}, \dfrac{3\pi}{4}, \dfrac{5\pi}{4}, \dfrac{7\pi}{4}, \dfrac{\pi}{12}, \dfrac{5\pi}{12},$
$\dfrac{13\pi}{12}, \dfrac{17\pi}{12}$

14. $x = \dfrac{\pi}{2}, \dfrac{3\pi}{2}$

15. $x = \dfrac{\pi}{4}, \dfrac{3\pi}{4}, \dfrac{5\pi}{4}, \dfrac{7\pi}{4}$

16. $x = \dfrac{7\pi}{6}, \dfrac{11\pi}{6}$

17. $x = \dfrac{\pi}{3}, \dfrac{5\pi}{3}$

18. $x = \dfrac{\pi}{3}, \dfrac{4\pi}{3}$

19. $x = \dfrac{3\pi}{4}, \dfrac{7\pi}{4}$

20. $x = \dfrac{\pi}{2}, \dfrac{3\pi}{2}, \dfrac{\pi}{6}, \dfrac{5\pi}{6}$

21. $x = \dfrac{\pi}{3}, \dfrac{5\pi}{3}, \pi$

22. $x = 0, \pi, 2\pi, \dfrac{\pi}{2}, \dfrac{3\pi}{2}$

23. $\sin x \cos x + \dfrac{1}{2} = 0$

24. $\sin^2\left(\dfrac{x}{2}\right) + \cos x = 0$

25. $\csc^2 \dfrac{x}{2} = 2 \sec x$

26. $-\sqrt{2} \sin x + \sqrt{2} \cos x = 1$

27. $2 \sin x - 2 \cos x = \sqrt{2}$

In Exercises 28–31, find the solution to each equation in the interval $[-\pi, \pi]$.

28. $\sin x + \cos x = 1$

29. $\sin^2 x + \cos 2x = 1$

30. $\sin 2x + \cos x = 0$

31. $-\cos x + \sqrt{3} \sin x = 1$

In Exercises 32–35, solve each equation in $[0, 2\pi)$.

32. $\sin 4x - \sin 2x = \sin x$

33. $\sin 2x = \sin \dfrac{1}{2} x$

34. $\cos 3x + \cos x = 0$

35. $\sin 3x - \sin x = 0$

In Exercises 36–40,

a. Express each function in the form
$f(x) = k \sin(x + \alpha)$.
b. Find the maximum value that $f(x)$ can assume.
c. Find all values of x in $[0, 2\pi]$ that give the maximum value of $f(x)$.

36. $f(x) = \sqrt{3} \sin x - \cos x$

37. $f(x) = \sin x + \sqrt{3} \cos x$

38. $f(x) = 2 \sin x + 2 \cos x$

39. $f(x) = \sin x - \cos x$

40. $f(x) = 4 \sin x - 3 \cos x$

23. $x = \dfrac{3\pi}{4}, \dfrac{7\pi}{4}$

24. $x = \pi$

25. $x = \dfrac{\pi}{3}, \dfrac{5\pi}{3}$

26. $x = \dfrac{\pi}{12}, \dfrac{17\pi}{12}$

27. $x = \dfrac{5\pi}{12}, \dfrac{13\pi}{12}$

28. $x = 0, \dfrac{\pi}{2}$

29. $x = -\pi, 0, \pi$

30. $x = -\dfrac{\pi}{2}, \dfrac{\pi}{2}, -\dfrac{\pi}{6}, -\dfrac{5\pi}{6}$

31. $x = \dfrac{\pi}{3}, -\pi, \pi$

32. $x = 0, \pi, 2\pi, \dfrac{\pi}{9}, \dfrac{5\pi}{9}, \dfrac{7\pi}{9},$
$\dfrac{11\pi}{9}, \dfrac{13\pi}{9}, \dfrac{17\pi}{9}$

33. $x = \dfrac{2\pi}{5}, \dfrac{6\pi}{5}, 2\pi, 0, \dfrac{4\pi}{3}$

34. $x = \dfrac{\pi}{2}, \dfrac{3\pi}{2}, \dfrac{\pi}{4}, \dfrac{3\pi}{4}, \dfrac{5\pi}{4}, \dfrac{7\pi}{4}$

35. $x = \dfrac{\pi}{4}, \dfrac{3\pi}{4}, \dfrac{5\pi}{4}, \dfrac{7\pi}{4}, 0, \pi, 2\pi$

36. a. $f(x) = 2 \sin\left(x + \dfrac{11\pi}{6}\right)$
   b. 2
   c. $x = \dfrac{2\pi}{3}$

37. a. $f(x) = 2 \sin\left(x + \dfrac{\pi}{3}\right)$
   b. 2
   c. $x = \dfrac{\pi}{6}$

38. a. $f(x) = 2\sqrt{2} \sin\left(x + \dfrac{\pi}{4}\right)$
   b. $2\sqrt{2}$
   c. $x = \dfrac{\pi}{4}$

39. a. $f(x) = \sqrt{2} \sin\left(x + \dfrac{7\pi}{4}\right)$
   b. $\sqrt{2}$
   c. $x = \dfrac{3\pi}{4}$

40. a. $f(x) = 5 \sin(x - 0.6435)$
   b. 5
   c. $x \approx 2.2143$

CHAPTER 9

Review

CHAPTER

9

REVIEW

Important Concepts

Important Facts and Formulas

Addition and Subtraction Identities

$$\sin(x + y) = \sin x \cos y + \cos x \sin y$$
$$\sin(x - y) = \sin x \cos y - \cos x \sin y$$
$$\cos(x + y) = \cos x \cos y - \sin x \sin y$$
$$\cos(x - y) = \cos x \cos y + \sin x \sin y$$
$$\tan(x + y) = \frac{\tan x + \tan y}{1 - \tan x \tan y}$$
$$\tan(x - y) = \frac{\tan x - \tan y}{1 + \tan x \tan y}$$

610

Cofunction Identities

$$\sin x = \cos\left(\frac{\pi}{2} - x\right) \qquad \cos x = \sin\left(\frac{\pi}{2} - x\right)$$

$$\tan x = \cot\left(\frac{\pi}{2} - x\right) \qquad \cot x = \tan\left(\frac{\pi}{2} - x\right)$$

$$\sec x = \csc\left(\frac{\pi}{2} - x\right) \qquad \csc x = \sec\left(\frac{\pi}{2} - x\right)$$

Double-Angle Identities

$$\sin 2x = 2 \sin x \cos x$$
$$\cos 2x = \cos^2 x - \sin^2 x = 2 \cos^2 x - 1 = 1 - 2 \sin^2 x$$
$$\tan 2x = \frac{2 \tan x}{1 - \tan^2 x}$$

Half-Angle Identities

$$\sin \frac{x}{2} = \pm\sqrt{\frac{1 - \cos x}{2}}$$

$$\cos \frac{x}{2} = \pm\sqrt{\frac{1 + \cos x}{2}}$$

$$\tan \frac{x}{2} = \frac{1 - \cos x}{\sin x} = \frac{\sin x}{1 + \cos x}$$

Review Exercises

Section 9.1

In Exercises 1–4, simplify the given expression.

1. $\dfrac{\sin^2 t + (\tan^2 t + 2 \tan t - 4) + \cos^2 t}{3 \tan^2 t - 3 \tan t}$

2. $\dfrac{\sec^2 t \csc t}{\csc^2 t \sec t}$

3. $\dfrac{\tan^2 x - \sin^2 x}{\sec^2 x}$

4. $\dfrac{(\sin x + \cos x)(\sin x - \cos x) + 1}{\sin^2 x}$

In Exercises 5–11, determine graphically whether the equation could not possibly be an identity, or write a proof showing that it is.

5. $\sin^4 t - \cos^4 t = 2 \sin^2 t - 1$

6. $1 + 2 \cos^2 t + \cos^4 t = \sin^4 t$

7. $\dfrac{\sin t}{1 - \cos t} = \dfrac{1 + \cos t}{\sin t}$

8. $\dfrac{\sin^2 t}{\cos^2 t} + 1 = \dfrac{1}{\cos^2 t}$

9. $\dfrac{\cos^2(\pi + t)}{\sin^2(\pi + t)} - 1 = \dfrac{1}{\sin^2 t}$

10. $\tan x + \cot x = \sec x \csc x$

11. $(\sin x + \cos x)^2 - \sin 2x = 1$

13. $\dfrac{\cos^4 x - \sin^4 x}{1 - \tan^4 x}$

$$= \frac{(\cos^2 x - \sin^2 x)(\cos^2 x + \sin^2 x)}{(1 - \tan^2 x)(1 + \tan^2 x)}$$

$$= \frac{\cos^2 x - \sin^2 x}{(1 - \tan^2 x)\sec^2 x}$$

$$= \frac{\cos^2 x - \sin^2 x}{\left(1 - \dfrac{\sin^2 x}{\cos^2 x}\right)\dfrac{1}{\cos^2 x}}$$

$$= \frac{(\cos^2 x - \sin^2 x) \cos^4 x}{\cos^2 x - \sin^2 x} = \cos^4 x$$

1. $\dfrac{1}{3} + \cot t$

2. $\tan t$

3. $\sin^4 x$

4. 2

5. $\sin^4 t - \cos^4 t$

$$= (\sin^2 t - \cos^2 t)(\sin^2 t + \cos^2 t)$$
$$= [\sin^2 t - (1 - \sin^2 t)](1)$$
$$= 2 \sin^2 t - 1$$

6. not an identity

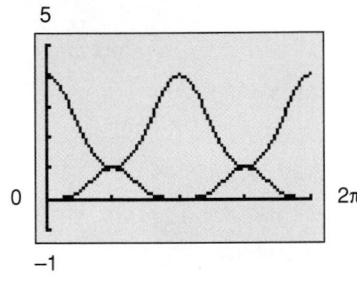

7. $\dfrac{\sin t}{1 - \cos t} = \dfrac{\sin t}{1 - \cos t} \cdot \dfrac{(1 + \cos t)}{(1 + \cos t)}$

$$= \frac{\sin t(1 + \cos t)}{1 - \cos^2 t}$$

$$= \frac{\sin t(1 + \cos t)}{\sin^2 t}$$

$$= \frac{1 + \cos t}{\sin t}$$

8. $\dfrac{\sin^2 t}{\cos^2 t} + 1 = \dfrac{\sin^2 t + \cos^2 t}{\cos^2 t} = \dfrac{1}{\cos^2 t}$

9. not an identity

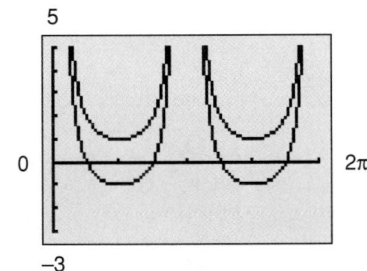

10. $\tan x + \cot x = \dfrac{\sin x}{\cos x} + \dfrac{\cos x}{\sin x}$

$$= \frac{\sin^2 x + \cos^2 x}{\cos x \sin x}$$

$$= \frac{1}{\cos x \sin x}$$

$$= \frac{1}{\cos x} \cdot \frac{1}{\sin x}$$

$$= \sec x \csc x$$

11. $(\sin x + \cos x)^2 - \sin 2x$

$$= \sin^2 x + 2 \sin x \cos x + \cos^2 x - 2 \sin x \cos x$$
$$= \sin^2 x + \cos^2 x = 1$$

12. $\dfrac{\sec x + 1}{\tan x} = \dfrac{(\sec x + 1)(\sec x - 1)}{\tan x(\sec x - 1)}$

$$= \frac{\sec^2 x - 1}{\tan x(\sec x - 1)}$$

$$= \frac{\tan^2 x}{\tan x(\sec x - 1)}$$

$$= \frac{\tan x}{\sec x - 1}$$

14. $\dfrac{1 + \tan^2 x}{\tan^2 x} = \dfrac{1}{\tan^2 x} + \dfrac{\tan^2 x}{\tan^2 x}$

$\qquad = \dfrac{1}{\tan^2 x} + 1$

$\qquad = \cot^2 x + 1$

$\qquad = \csc^2 x$

15. $\sec x - \cos x = \dfrac{1}{\cos x} - \cos x$

$\qquad = \dfrac{1 - \cos^2 x}{\cos x}$

$\qquad = \dfrac{\sin^2 x}{\cos x}$

$\qquad = \sin x \dfrac{\sin x}{\cos x}$

$\qquad = \sin x \tan x$

16. $\tan^2 x - \sec^2 x$

$\qquad = (\sec^2 x - 1) - \sec^2 x = -1$

Also, $\cot^2 x - \csc^2 x$

$\qquad = (\csc^2 x - 1) - \csc^2 x = -1.$

Therefore,

$\tan^2 x - \sec^2 x = \cot^2 x - \csc^2 x.$

17. a

18. b

19. $\cos(x + y)\cos(x - y)$

$\qquad = [\cos x \cos y - \sin x \sin y] \cdot$

$\qquad\qquad [\cos x \cos y + \sin x \sin y]$

$\qquad = \cos^2 x \cos^2 y - \sin^2 x \sin^2 y$

$\qquad = \cos^2 x(1 - \sin^2 y) -$

$\qquad\qquad (1 - \cos^2 x) \sin^2 y$

$\qquad = \cos^2 x - \cos^2 x \sin^2 y - \sin^2 y +$

$\qquad\qquad\qquad \cos^2 x \sin^2 y$

$\qquad = \cos^2 x - \sin^2 y$

20. $\dfrac{\cos(x - y)}{\cos x \cos y} = \dfrac{\cos x \cos y + \sin x \sin y}{\cos x \cos y}$

$\qquad = \dfrac{\cos x \cos y}{\cos x \cos y} + \dfrac{\sin x \sin y}{\cos x \cos y}$

$\qquad = 1 + \dfrac{\sin x \sin y}{\cos x \cos y}$

$\qquad = 1 + \tan x \tan y$

21. a. $-\dfrac{3}{5}$

b. $\dfrac{117}{44}$

c. $\dfrac{44}{125}$

22. $-\dfrac{56}{65}$

23. $-\dfrac{120}{169}$

24. $\dfrac{3\sqrt{5} + 1}{8}$

25. $\dfrac{\sqrt{42} + 2\sqrt{2}}{10}$

26. $\dfrac{\sqrt{2} + \sqrt{6}}{4}$

27. $-\dfrac{1}{\cos x}$

In Exercises 12–16, prove the given identity.

12. $\dfrac{\sec x + 1}{\tan x} = \dfrac{\tan x}{\sec x - 1}$

13. $\dfrac{\cos^4 x - \sin^4 x}{1 - \tan^4 x} = \cos^4 x$

14. $\dfrac{1 + \tan^2 x}{\tan^2 x} = \csc^2 x$

15. $\sec x - \cos x = \sin x \tan x$

16. $\tan^2 x - \sec^2 x = \cot^2 x - \csc^2 x$

17. $\sqrt{\dfrac{1 - \cos^2 x}{1 - \sin^2 x}} = ?$

  a. $|\tan x|$ **b.** $|\cot x|$

  c. $\sqrt{\dfrac{1 - \sin^2 x}{1 - \cos^2 x}}$ **d.** $\sec x$

  e. undefined

18. $\dfrac{1}{(\csc x)(\sec^2 x)} = ?$

  a. $\dfrac{1}{(\sin x)(\cos^2 x)}$ **b.** $\sin x - \sin^3 x$

  c. $\dfrac{1}{(\sin x)(1 + \tan^2 x)}$ **d.** $\sin x - \dfrac{1}{1 + \tan^2 x}$

  e. $1 + \tan^3 x$

Section 9.2   In Exercises 19–20, prove the given identity.

19. $\cos(x + y)\cos(x - y) = \cos^2 x - \sin^2 y$

20. $\dfrac{\cos(x - y)}{\cos x \cos y} = 1 + \tan x \tan y$

21. Evaluate the following in exact form, where the angles α and β satisfy the conditions:

$$\sin \alpha = \dfrac{4}{5} \text{ for } \dfrac{\pi}{2} < \alpha < \pi \qquad \tan \beta = \dfrac{7}{24} \text{ for } \pi < \beta < \dfrac{3\pi}{2},$$

  a. $\sin(\beta + \alpha)$ **b.** $\tan(\beta - \alpha)$ **c.** $\cos(\alpha - \beta)$

22. If $\tan x = \dfrac{4}{3}$ and $\pi < x < \dfrac{3\pi}{2}$, and $\cot y = -\dfrac{5}{12}$ with $\dfrac{3\pi}{2} < y < 2\pi$, find $\sin(x - y)$.

23. If $\sin x = -\dfrac{12}{13}$ with $\pi < x < \dfrac{3\pi}{2}$, and $\sec y = \dfrac{13}{12}$ with $\dfrac{3\pi}{2} < y < 2\pi$, find $\cos(x + y)$.

24. If $\sin x = \dfrac{1}{4}$ and $0 < x < \dfrac{\pi}{2}$, then $\sin\left(\dfrac{\pi}{3} + x\right) = ?$

25. If $\sin x = -\dfrac{2}{5}$ and $\dfrac{3\pi}{2} < x < 2\pi$, then $\cos\left(\dfrac{\pi}{4} + x\right) = ?$

26. Find the exact value of $\sin \dfrac{5\pi}{12}$.

---

28. $\dfrac{\pi}{4}$

29. ≈ 1.23 radians

30. a. $\dfrac{\sqrt{226}}{226}$

  b. $\dfrac{11{,}753}{15{,}625}$

  c. $\dfrac{-10{,}296}{11{,}753}$

  d. $\dfrac{-26{,}208}{14{,}125}$

31. $\dfrac{1 - \cos 2x}{\tan x} = \dfrac{1 - (1 - 2\sin^2 x)}{\tan x}$

$\qquad = \dfrac{2\sin^2 x}{\tan x}$

$\qquad = \dfrac{2\sin^2 x}{\dfrac{\sin x}{\cos x}}$

$\qquad = \dfrac{2\sin^2 x \cos x}{\sin x}$

$\qquad = 2\sin x \cos x$

$\qquad = \sin 2x$

27. Express $\sec(x - \pi)$ in terms of $\sin x$ and $\cos x$.

Section **9.2.A**   **28.** Find the angle of inclination of the straight line through the points $(2, 6)$ and $(-2, 2)$.

29. Find one of the angles between the line L through the points $(-3, 2)$ and $(5, 1)$ and the line M, which has slope 2.

Section **9.3**   **30.** Evaluate the following in exact form, where the angles α and β satisfy the conditions:

$$\sin \alpha = \frac{44}{125} \text{ for } \frac{\pi}{2} < \alpha < \pi \qquad \tan \beta = -\frac{15}{112} \text{ for } \frac{3\pi}{2} < \beta < 2\pi$$

a. $\sin \dfrac{\beta}{2}$ **b.** $\cos 2\alpha$

c. $\tan 2\alpha$ **d.** $\cos(\alpha - \beta) + \cos(\alpha + \beta)$

In Exercises 31–34, prove the given identity.

31. $\dfrac{1 - \cos 2x}{\tan x} = \sin 2x$ **32.** $\dfrac{\tan x - \sin x}{2 \tan x} = \sin^2 \dfrac{x}{2}$

33. $2 \cos x - 2 \cos^3 x = \sin x \sin 2x$

34. $\sin 2x = \dfrac{1}{\tan x + \cot 2x}$

35. If $\tan x = \dfrac{5}{12}$ and $\sin x > 0$, find $\sin 2x$.

36. If $\cos x = \dfrac{15}{17}$ and $0 < x < \dfrac{\pi}{2}$, find $\sin \dfrac{x}{2}$.

37. If $\sin x = 0$, is it true that $\sin 2x = 0$? Justify your answer.

38. If $\cos x = 0$, is it true that $\cos 2x = 0$? Justify your answer.

39. Show $\sqrt{2 + \sqrt{3}} = \dfrac{\sqrt{2} + \sqrt{6}}{2}$ by computing $\cos \dfrac{\pi}{12}$ in two ways, using the half-angle identity and the subtraction identity for cosine.

40. True or false: $2 \sin x = \sin 2x$. Justify your answer.

41. If $\sin x = 0.6$ and $0 < x < \dfrac{\pi}{2}$, find $\sin 2x$.

42. If $\sin x = 0.6$ and $0 < x < \dfrac{\pi}{2}$, find $\sin \dfrac{x}{2}$.

Section **9.4**   **Solve the equation. Find exact solutions when possible and approximate ones otherwise.**

43. $5 \tan x = 2 \sin 2x$ **44.** $\cos 2x = \cos x$

45. $2 \cos x + \sin x = 0$ **46.** $\sin 2x + \cos x = 0$

---

32. $\dfrac{\tan x - \sin x}{2 \tan x} = \dfrac{\tan x}{2 \tan x} - \dfrac{\sin x}{2 \tan x}$

$= \dfrac{1}{2} - \dfrac{\sin x}{\dfrac{2 \sin x}{\cos x}}$

$= \dfrac{1}{2} - \sin x \left(\dfrac{\cos x}{2 \sin x} \right)$

$= \dfrac{1}{2} - \dfrac{\cos x}{2}$

$= \dfrac{1 - \cos x}{2}$

$= \left(\pm \sqrt{\dfrac{1 - \cos x}{2}} \right)^2$

$= \left(\sin \left(\dfrac{x}{2} \right) \right)^2$

$= \sin^2 \left(\dfrac{x}{2} \right)$

33. $2 \cos x - 2 \cos^3 x$

$= 2 \cos x (1 - \cos^2 x)$

$= 2 \cos x (\sin^2 x)$

$= \sin x (2 \sin x \cos x)$

$= \sin x \sin 2x$

34. $\dfrac{1}{\tan x + \cot 2x}$

$= \dfrac{1}{\tan x + \dfrac{\cos 2x}{\sin 2x}}$

$= \dfrac{\sin 2x}{\sin 2x \tan x + \cos 2x}$

$= \dfrac{\sin 2x}{\left(\dfrac{\sin x}{\cos x} \right) 2 \sin x \cos x + \cos 2x}$

$= \dfrac{\sin 2x}{2 \sin^2 x + (1 - 2 \sin^2 x)}$

$= \dfrac{\sin 2x}{1} = \sin 2x$

35. $\dfrac{120}{169}$

36. $\dfrac{1}{\sqrt{17}}$

37. Yes. $\sin 2x = 2 \sin x \cos x$
$= 2(0) \cos x = 0$

38. No. $\cos 2x = 2 \cos^2 x - 1$
$= 2(0^2) - 1 = -1$

39. $\cos \left(\dfrac{\pi}{12} \right) = \cos \left[\dfrac{1}{2} \left(\dfrac{\pi}{6} \right) \right]$

$= \sqrt{\dfrac{1 + \cos \dfrac{\pi}{6}}{2}} = \sqrt{\dfrac{1 + \dfrac{\sqrt{3}}{2}}{2}}$

$= \sqrt{\dfrac{2 + \sqrt{3}}{4}} = \dfrac{\sqrt{2 + \sqrt{3}}}{2};$

$\cos \left(\dfrac{\pi}{12} \right) = \cos \left(\dfrac{\pi}{4} - \dfrac{\pi}{6} \right)$

$= \cos \dfrac{\pi}{4} \cos \dfrac{\pi}{6} + \sin \dfrac{\pi}{4} \sin \dfrac{\pi}{6}$

$= \dfrac{\sqrt{2}}{2} \left(\dfrac{\sqrt{3}}{2} \right) + \dfrac{\sqrt{2}}{2} \left(\dfrac{1}{2} \right) = \dfrac{\sqrt{6} + \sqrt{2}}{4}$

So, $\dfrac{\sqrt{2 + \sqrt{3}}}{2} = \dfrac{\sqrt{6} + \sqrt{2}}{4}$ or

$\sqrt{2 + \sqrt{3}} = \dfrac{\sqrt{2} + \sqrt{6}}{2}$

---

40. False. $\sin \left(2 \cdot \dfrac{\pi}{2} \right) = 0$,

but $2 \sin \dfrac{\pi}{2} = 2$

41. 0.96

42. $\dfrac{1}{\sqrt{10}}$

43. $x = k\pi$

44. $x = \dfrac{2\pi}{3} + 2k\pi, \dfrac{4\pi}{3} + 2k\pi, 2k\pi$

45. $x \approx 2.0344 + k\pi$

46. $x = \dfrac{\pi}{2} + 2k\pi, \dfrac{3\pi}{2} + 2k\pi,$

$\dfrac{7\pi}{6} + 2k\pi, \dfrac{11\pi}{6} + 2k\pi$

CHAPTER
9

can do calculus

Rates of Change in Trigonometry

Math Background

In **Example 1**, the derivation of the expression for the instantaneous rate of change of $f(x) = \sin x$ uses two limits found in the Chapter 8 can do calculus:

$$\lim_{x \to 0} \left(\frac{\sin x}{x} \right) = 1 \text{ and } \lim_{x \to 0} \left(\frac{\cos x - 1}{x} \right) = 0.$$

These limit statements are only true for x measured in radians. The table below shows values of $\frac{\sin x}{x}$ for x close to zero when x is measured in degrees. You can see that the values are not getting close to 1.

X	Y1
-.03	.01745
-.02	.01745
-.01	.01745
0	ERROR
.01	.01745
.02	.01745
.03	.01745

Y1■(sin(X))/(X)

COMMON ERROR ALERT

Some students might think that

$$\lim_{h \to 0} \left[\sin x \left(\frac{\cos h - 1}{h} \right) + \cos x \left(\frac{\sin h}{h} \right) \right]$$

$$= (0)(0) + (1)(1) = 1.$$

Point out to them that only h is approaching 0, not x.

Example Notes

In **Example 2**, we find that the instantaneous rate of change of $f(x) = \sin x$ at $x = \frac{\pi}{3}$ is $\cos \frac{\pi}{3} = \frac{1}{2}$.
Therefore, the slope of the line tangent to $f(x) = \sin x$ at $x = \frac{\pi}{3}$ is $\frac{1}{2}$.
These relationships are illustrated.

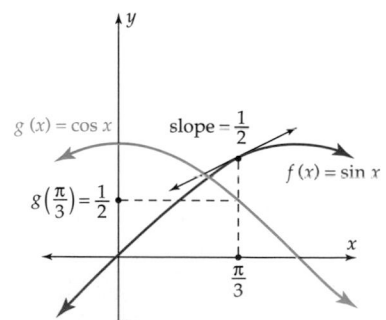

As discussed in Section 3.7, the difference quotient represents the average rate of change of a function over the interval from x to $x + h$.

$$\frac{f(x + h) - f(x)}{h} \qquad \textit{average rate of change}$$

As the value of h becomes smaller and smaller, the average rate of change approaches the instantaneous rate of change at x as discussed in the Chapter 3 Can Do Calculus.

Another way to represent the instantaneous rate of change is with limit notation, shown in the Can Do Calculus in Chapter 8. That is, instantaneous rate of change of a function f at x is the limit of the difference quotient.

$$\lim_{h \to 0} \frac{f(x + h) - f(x)}{h} \qquad \textit{instantaneous rate of change}$$

The instantaneous rate of change of a particular function is given by the expression in x that is the simplified form of the limit given above.

Example 1   Instantaneous Rate of Change of $f(x) = \sin x$

Find an expression for the instantaneous rate of change of $f(x) = \sin x$.

Solution

The difference quotient of $f(x) = \sin x$ can be simplified by using the addition identity for the sine function.

$$\sin(x + y) = \sin x \cos y + \cos x \sin y$$

Let $y = h$.

$$\sin(x + h) = \sin x \cos h + \cos x \sin h$$

Therefore, the difference quotient for the sine function can be simplified as follows. (See Example 4 of Section 9.2 for details of the simplification.)

$$\frac{\sin(x + h) - \sin x}{h} = \sin x \left(\frac{\cos h - 1}{h} \right) + \cos x \left(\frac{\sin h}{h} \right)$$

The expression that represents the instantaneous rate of change is found by finding the limit of $\sin x \left(\frac{\cos h - 1}{h} \right) + \cos x \left(\frac{\sin h}{h} \right)$ as h approaches 0.

$$\lim_{h \to 0} \left(\sin x \left(\frac{\cos h - 1}{h} \right) + \cos x \left(\frac{\sin h}{h} \right) \right) \qquad \textit{instantaneous rate of change}$$

614

The two fractional expressions in the limit above were evaluated in the Chapter 8 Can Do Calculus as follows:

NOTE See Chapter 14 for a complete discussion of limits.

$$\lim_{h \to 0} \frac{\sin h}{h} = 1 \qquad \text{and} \qquad \lim_{h \to 0} \frac{\cos h - 1}{h} = 0$$

Substitute the values above into the expression for instantaneous rate of change to find a simpler expression.

$$\lim_{h \to 0} \left(\sin x \left(\frac{\cos h - 1}{h} \right) + \cos x \left(\frac{\sin h}{h} \right) \right) = (\sin x)(0) + (\cos x)(1)$$

$$= \cos x \quad \textit{instantaneous rate of change}$$

The expression for the instantaneous rate of change for $f(x) = \sin x$ can be used to find the instantaneous rate of change at any particular value of x.

Example 2   Finding Instantaneous Rate of Change at $x = k$

Find the instantaneous rate of change of $f(x) = \sin x$ when $x = \frac{\pi}{3}$. Interpret the result.

Solution

Because the instantaneous rate of change of $f(x) = \sin x$ is given by $g(x) = \cos x$, the instantaneous rate of change at $x = \frac{\pi}{3}$ is $g\left(\frac{\pi}{3}\right) = \cos \frac{\pi}{3}$, or $\frac{1}{2}$. When $x = \frac{\pi}{3}$, $\sin x$ is changing $\frac{1}{2}$ unit per unit increase in x.

Exercises

1. What is the instantaneous rate of change of $f(x) = \sin x$ for the following values of x. Interpret each result.

  a. $x = 0$ **b.** $x = \frac{\pi}{4}$

  c. $x = \frac{\pi}{2}$ **d.** $x = \frac{\pi}{6}$

2. Find the expression for the instantaneous rate of change of $f(x) = \cos x$. **$-\sin x$**

3. What is the instantaneous rate of change of $f(x) = \cos x$ for the following values of x? Interpret each result.

  a. $x = 0$ **b.** $x = \frac{\pi}{4}$

  c. $x = \frac{\pi}{2}$ **d.** $x = \frac{\pi}{6}$

615

Review Exercises

ANSWERS

1. a. 1; $\sin x$ is changing at a rate of 1 unit per increase in x when $x = 0$.

  b. $\frac{\sqrt{2}}{2}$; $\sin x$ is increasing approximately 0.7071 per unit increase in x when $x = \frac{\pi}{4}$.

  c. 0; $\sin x$ is not changing per unit increase in x when $x = \frac{\pi}{2}$.

  d. $\frac{\sqrt{3}}{2}$; $\sin x$ is increasing approximately 0.8660 per unit increase in x when $x = \frac{\pi}{6}$.

3. a. 0; $\cos x$ is not changing per unit increase in x when $x = 0$.

  b. $-\frac{\sqrt{2}}{2}$; $\cos x$ is decreasing approximately 0.7071 units per unit increase in x when $x = \frac{\pi}{4}$.

  c. -1; $\cos x$ is decreasing 1 unit per unit increase in x when $x = \frac{\pi}{2}$.

  d. $-\frac{1}{2}$; $\cos x$ is decreasing $\frac{1}{2}$ unit per unit increase in x when $x = \frac{\pi}{6}$.

Trigonometric Applications

In this chapter, students will learn how to apply concepts of trigonometry to real-life situations. They will study the Laws of Cosines and Sines, polar form and *n*th roots of complex numbers, and vectors and their applications.

CHAPTER

10 | Trigonometric Applications

A Bridge over Troubled Waters

When planning a bridge or building, architects and engineers must determine the stress on cables and other parts of the structure to be sure that all parts are adequately supported. Problems like these can be modeled and solved by using vectors. See Exercise 50 in Section 10.6.

616

Chapter Outline

Interdependence of Sections

Trigonometry has a variety of useful applications in geometry, algebra, and the physical sciences. Several applications are discussed in this chapter.

10.1   The Law of Cosines

Objectives

- Solve oblique triangles by using the Law of Cosines.

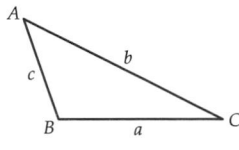

Figure 10.1-1

Sections 6.1 and 6.2 presented right triangle trigonometry and its applications. In this section, the solutions to **oblique triangles,** ones that do not contain a right angle, are considered.

Standard notation of triangles, which is used in this section and the next, is shown in Figure 10.1-1 and is described below.

Each vertex is labeled with a capital letter, and the length of the side opposite that vertex is denoted by the same letter in lower case. The letter A will also be used to label the angle at vertex A, and similarly for B and C. Thus, statements such as

$$A = 37° \qquad \text{or} \qquad \cos B = 0.326$$

will be made.

The first fact needed to solve oblique triangles is the Law of Cosines, whose proof is given at the end of this section.

Law of Cosines

> In any triangle ABC, with lengths a, b, c, as in Figure 10.1-1,
> $$a^2 = b^2 + c^2 - 2bc \cos A$$
> $$b^2 = a^2 + c^2 - 2ac \cos B$$
> $$c^2 = a^2 + b^2 - 2ab \cos C$$

617

Ask your students to state the Law of Cosines in *verbal* terms, that is, without using variables. The square of the length of any side of a triangle is equal to the sum of the squares of the lengths of the other two sides minus twice the product of the lengths of the other two sides and the cosine of the included angle.

Section 10.1   The Law of Cosines

COMMON ERROR ALERT

Students sometimes confuse *oblique* with *obtuse.* Remind them that an oblique triangle is either an acute triangle or an obtuse triangle.

Teaching Notes

Refer students to Figure 10.1-1 that illustrates **standard notation.** Show a triangle such as the one below, and ask the students how to finish labeling it.

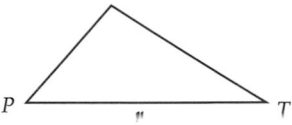

Label the third vertex R. Label the sides p and t, opposite vertices P and T, respectively.

Point out that the **Law of Cosines** applies to all triangles, including right triangles. Ask how the third equation in the box becomes simpler when C is a right angle.

$\cos 90° = 0$, so the third equation becomes $c^2 = a^2 + b^2 - 2ab \cos 90°$, or $c^2 = a^2 + b^2$.

(Now direct their attention to the first margin **NOTE** on page 618.)

Example Notes

In **Examples 1** and **2**, it is necessary to use answers to find other answers. In this situation, an incorrect answer can cause other incorrect answers. Encourage students to check their work by using different methods to find the same answer. In Example 1, have them find angle B by using the Law of Cosines. In Example 2, have them find angle C by using the Law of Cosines.

Refer students to the margin **NOTE** at the bottom of the page. Show them how to delay rounding as they evaluate an expression:

In **Example 1,** the value of c can be stored as shown below.

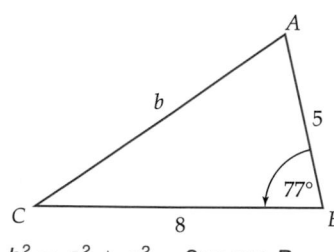

Then, when the students get to the step $\cos A \approx \dfrac{10^2 + 21.6^2 - 16^2}{2(10)(21.6)}$, they can use $\cos A \approx \dfrac{10^2 + c^2 - 16^2}{2(10)c}$ instead, and this more precise value of c will be used by the calculator.

ADDITIONAL EXAMPLES

Example 1

Solve triangle *ABC* shown below.

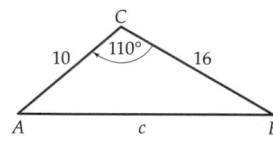

$b^2 = a^2 + c^2 - 2ac \cos B$

$b^2 = 8^2 + 5^2 - 2(8)(5) \cos 77°$

$b^2 = 89 - 80 \cos 77°$

$b = \sqrt{89 - 80 \cos 77°}$

$b \approx 8.4$

$\cos A = \dfrac{b^2 + c^2 - a^2}{2bc}$

$\cos A \approx \dfrac{8.4^2 + 5^2 - 8^2}{2(8.4)(5)}$

$A \approx \cos^{-1} 0.3798$

$A \approx 67.7°$

$C \approx 180° - (77° + 67.7°) = 35.3°$

You need only memorize one of these equations since each of them provides essentially the same information: the square of the length of one side of a triangle is given in terms of the angle opposite it and the other two sides.

Solving the first equation in the Law of Cosines for cos *A* results in the alternate form of the Law of Cosines, given below.

Alternate Form: Law of Cosines

> In any triangle *ABC*, with sides of lengths *a*, *b*, and *c*, as in Figure 10.1-1,
>
> $$\cos A = \frac{b^2 + c^2 - a^2}{2bc}.$$

NOTE When C is a right angle, then c is the hypotenuse and

$$\cos C = \cos 90° = 0,$$

so that the third equation in the Law of Cosines becomes the Pythagorean theorem.

$$c^2 = a^2 + b^2$$

The other two equations in the Law of Cosines can be similarly rewritten in an alternate form. In this form, the Law of Cosines provides a description of each angle of a triangle in terms of the three sides. Consequently, the Law of Cosines can be used to solve triangles in the following cases.

1. Two sides and the angle between them are known (SAS)

2. Three sides are known (SSS)

Example 1 Solve a Triangle with SAS Information

Solve triangle *ABC* shown in Figure 10.1-2.

Solution

Because *c* is the unknown quantity, use the third equation in the Law of Cosines.

$c^2 = a^2 + b^2 - 2ab \cos C$

$c^2 = 16^2 + 10^2 - 2(16)(10) \cos 110°$

$c^2 = 356 - 320 \cos 110°$

$c = \sqrt{356 - 320 \cos 110°}$ *Take the square root of each side.*

$c \approx 21.6$

Use the alternate form of the Law of Cosines to find the measure of angle *A*.

$\cos A = \dfrac{b^2 + c^2 - a^2}{2bc}$

$\cos A \approx \dfrac{10^2 + 21.6^2 - 16^2}{2(10)(21.6)}$

$\cos A \approx 0.7172$

$A \approx \cos^{-1} 0.7172$ *Use the COS⁻¹ key with the*

$A \approx 44.2°$ *calculator in degree mode.*

Figure 10.1-2

NOTE Throughout this chapter, no rounding is done in the actual computation until the final quantity is obtained.

Because the sum of the angle measures in a triangle is 180°,

$$B \approx 180° - (44.2° + 110°) = 25.8°.$$

Thus, $c \approx 21.6$, $A \approx 44.2°$, and $B \approx 25.8°$.

∎

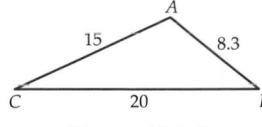

Figure 10.1-3

| Example 2 | Solve a Triangle with SSS Information |

Find the angles of triangle ABC shown in Figure 10.1-3.

Solution

The given information is $a = 20$, $b = 15$, and $c = 8.3$. To find angles, use the alternate form of the Law of Cosines.

$$\cos A = \frac{b^2 + c^2 - a^2}{2bc} \qquad \cos B = \frac{a^2 + c^2 - b^2}{2ac}$$

$$\cos A = \frac{15^2 + 8.3^2 - 20^2}{2(15)(8.3)} \qquad \cos B = \frac{20^2 + 8.3^2 - 15^2}{2(20)(8.3)}$$

$$\cos A \approx -0.4261 \qquad \cos B \approx 0.7346$$

$$A \approx 115.2° \qquad B \approx 42.7°$$

Use the sum of angle measures in a triangle to find the third angle.

$$C \approx 180° - (115.2° + 42.7°) = 22.1°$$

Thus, $A \approx 115.2°$, $B \approx 42.7°$, and $C \approx 22.1°$.

∎

| Example 3 | The Distance Between Two Vehicles |

Two trains leave a station on different tracks. The tracks make an angle of 125° with the station as the vertex. The first train travels at an average speed of 100 kilometers per hour, and the second train travels at an average speed of 65 kilometers per hour. How far apart are the trains after 2 hours?

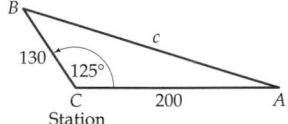

Figure 10.1-4

Solution

The first train, A, traveling at 100 kilometers per hour for 2 hours, goes a distance of $100 \times 2 = 200$ kilometers. The second train, B, travels a distance of $65 \times 2 = 130$ kilometers. The situation is shown in Figure 10.1-4.

By the Law of Cosines:

$$c^2 = a^2 + b^2 - 2ab \cos C$$
$$c^2 = 130^2 + 200^2 - 2(130)(200)\cos 125°$$
$$c^2 = 56{,}900 - 52{,}000 \cos 125°$$
$$c = \sqrt{56{,}900 - 52{,}000 \cos 125°}$$
$$c \approx 294.5$$

The trains are about 294.5 kilometers apart after 2 hours.

∎

By the Law of Cosines,

$$p^2 = q^2 + r^2 - 2qr \cos P$$
$$p^2 = 48^2 + 36^2 - 2(48)(36) \cos 55°$$
$$p^2 = 3600 - 3456 \cos 55°$$
$$p = \sqrt{3600 - 3456 \cos 55°}$$
$$p \approx 40.2$$

The ships are about 40.2 miles apart after 3 hours.

ADDITIONAL EXAMPLES

Example 2

Find the angles of triangle RST shown below.

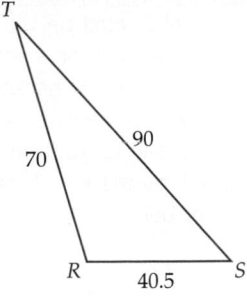

$$\cos R = \frac{s^2 + t^2 - r^2}{2st}$$

$$\cos R = \frac{70^2 + 40.5^2 - 90^2}{2(70)(40.5)}$$

$$\cos R \approx -0.2751$$

$$R \approx 106.0°$$

$$\cos T = \frac{r^2 + s^2 - t^2}{2rs}$$

$$\cos T = \frac{90^2 + 70^2 - (40.5)^2}{2(90)(70)}$$

$$\cos T \approx 0.9016$$

$$T \approx 25.6°$$

$$S \approx 180° - (106.0° + 25.6°) = 48.4°$$

So,
$R \approx 106.0°$, $S \approx 48.4°$, and $T \approx 25.6°$.

Example 3

A ship R leaves port P and travels at the rate of 16 miles per hour. Another ship Q leaves the same port at the same time and travels at 12 miles per hour. Both ships are traveling in straight paths. The directions taken by the two ships make an angle of 55°. How far apart are the ships after 3 hours?

After 3 hours, the first ship, R, has traveled $(16)(3) = 48$ miles and the second ship, Q, has traveled $(12)(3) = 36$ miles.

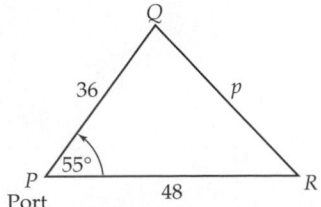

Example 4

A factory conveyor belt that makes an angle of 17° with the horizontal and rises from point Q on level 1 to point S on level 2 must be replaced. A design change calls for a vertical post RT and dimensions as shown in the diagram below. A new conveyor belt will be needed to go from Q to R to S. What will be the length of the new conveyor belt?

$m\angle PQT = 17°$, so

$m\angle QPT = 180° - (90° + 17°) = 73°$

$m\angle RPQ = 180° - 73° = 107°$

Using the Law of Cosines on triangle RPQ,

$p^2 = r^2 + q^2 - 2rq \cos P$

$p^2 = 72^2 + 40^2 - 2(72)(40) \cos 107°$

$p^2 = 6784 - 5760 \cos 107°$

$p = \sqrt{6784 - 5760 \cos 107°}$

$p \approx 92.02$

$m\angle RPS = 180° - m\angle RPQ$

$\quad\quad\quad = 180° - 107° = 73°$

Using the Law of Cosines on triangle RPS,

$u^2 = r^2 + s^2 - 2rs \cos P$

$u^2 = 64^2 + 40^2 - 2(64)(40) \cos 73°$

$u^2 = 5696 - 5120 \cos 73°$

$u = \sqrt{5696 - 5120 \cos 73°}$

$u \approx 64.80$

$p + u \approx 92.02 + 64.80 = 156.82$

The length of the new conveyor belt will be about 156.82 feet.

Example 4   **Find Angles with the Horizontal**

A 100-foot tall antenna tower is to be placed on a hillside that makes an angle of 12° with the horizontal. It is to be anchored by two cables from the top of the tower to points 85 feet uphill and 95 feet downhill from the base. How much cable is needed?

Solution

The situation is shown in Figure 10.1-5, where AB represents the tower and AC and AD represent the cables.

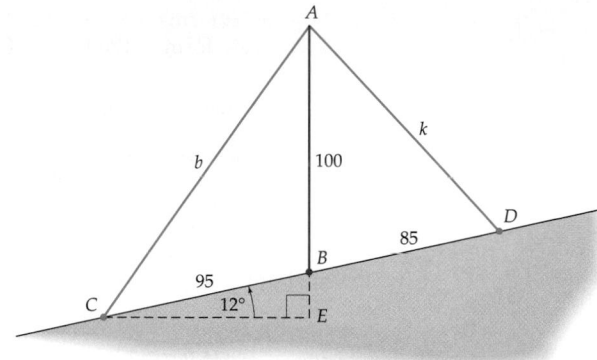

Figure 10.1-5

If the hillside makes an angle of 12° with the horizontal, then in triangle BEC, angle E is a right angle and angle C measures 12°. Use the sum of the angle measures in the triangle.

$$m\angle CBE = 180° - (90° + 12°) = 78°$$

As shown in Figure 10.1-5, adjacent angles ABC and CBE form a straight angle, which measures 180°.

$$m\angle ABC = 180° - 78° = 102°$$

Using the SAS information in triangle ABC, apply the Law of Cosines.

$$b^2 = a^2 + c^2 - 2ac \cos B$$
$$b^2 = 95^2 + 100^2 - 2(95)(100) \cos 102°$$
$$b^2 = 19{,}025 - 19{,}000 \cos 102°$$
$$b = \sqrt{19{,}025 - 19{,}000 \cos 102°}$$
$$b \approx 151.58$$

The length of the downhill cable is about 151.58 feet.

To find the length of the uphill cable, notice that adjacent angles ABC and ABD form a straight angle.

$$m\angle ABD = 180° - m\angle ABC = 180° - 102° = 78°$$

Real-World Application

Using the SAS information in triangle *ABD*, apply the Law of Cosines.

$$k^2 = 100^2 + 85^2 - 2(100)(85) \cos 78°$$
$$k^2 = 17{,}225 - 17{,}000 \cos 78°$$
$$k = \sqrt{17{,}225 - 17{,}000 \cos 78°}$$
$$k \approx 117.01$$

The length of the uphill cable is about 117.01 feet.

The amount of cable needed is the sum of the lengths of the uphill and downhill cables.

$$151.58 + 117.01 = 268.59$$

Therefore, the length of the cable needed is about 268.59 feet.   ∎

Proof of the Law of Cosines

Given triangle *ABC*, position it on a coordinate plane so that angle *A* is in standard position with initial side *c* and terminal side *b*. Depending on the size of angle *A*, there are two possibilities, as shown in Figure 10.1-6.

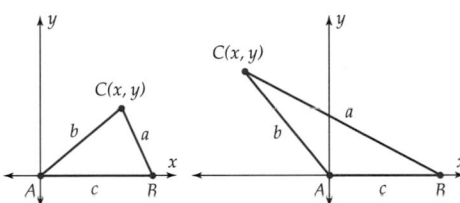

Figure 10.1-6

The coordinates of *B* are $(c, 0)$. Let (x, y) be the coordinates of *C*. Now *C* is a point on the terminal side of angle *A*, and the distance from *C* to the origin *A* is *b*. Therefore, according to the definitions of sine and cosine, the following statements are true.

$$\frac{x}{b} = \cos A, \quad \text{or equivalently,} \quad x = b \cos A$$

$$\frac{y}{b} = \sin A, \quad \text{or equivalently,} \quad y = b \sin A$$

Use the distance formula to find *a*, the distance from *C* to *B*.

$$a = \sqrt{(x - c)^2 + (y - 0)^2}$$
$$a = \sqrt{(b \cos A - c)^2 + (b \sin A - 0)^2} \qquad \textit{Substitute for x and y.}$$
$$a^2 = (b \cos A - c)^2 + (b \sin A)^2 \qquad \textit{Square each side.}$$
$$a^2 = b^2 \cos^2 A - 2bc \cos A + c^2 + b^2 \sin^2 A \qquad \textit{Simplify.}$$
$$a^2 = b^2 \cos^2 A + b^2 \sin^2 A + c^2 - 2bc \cos A \qquad \textit{Rearrange terms.}$$
$$a^2 = b^2(\cos^2 A + \sin^2 A) + c^2 - 2bc \cos A \qquad \textit{Factor out } b^2.$$
$$a^2 = b^2 + c^2 - 2bc \cos A \qquad \textit{Pythagorean identity}$$

Examples **3** and **4** are real world applications of the Law of Cosines. Note that they both involve triangles that do not contain right angles. Both Examples illustrate finding distances that might not be easily measured, using known measures and the Law of Cosines. Exercise 29 on page 623 asks for another distance that might not be easily measured. Many of the Exercises on pages 622–624 are real-world applications of the Law of Cosines.

Teaching Notes

To prepare for the **Proof of the Law of Cosines,** do the following:

Have students recall the definitions of sine and cosine of an angle in standard position (page 444).

Draw one of the triangles from Figure 10.1-6 on the board, labeling vertex *B* $(c, 0)$. Ask students to use the distance formula to express the distance *a*.

$$a = \sqrt{(x - c)^2 + (y - 0)^2}$$

Have students write out the expansion of $(b \cos A - c)^2$.

$$(b \cos A - c)(b \cos A - c)$$
$$= b^2 \cos^2 A - bc \cos A - bc \cos A + c^2$$
$$= b^2 \cos^2 A - 2bc \cos A + c^2$$

Have students recall the Pythagorean Identity that involves sin *A* and cos *A*.

$$\sin^2 A + \cos^2 A = 1$$

This proves the first equation in the Law of Cosines. Similar arguments beginning with angles B or C in standard position prove the other two equations.

Exercises 10.1

Standard notation for triangle ABC is used throughout. Use a calculator and round your answers to one decimal place at the end of each computation.

In Exercises 1–16, solve the triangle ABC under the given conditions.

1. $A = 20°, b = 10, c = 7$
   $a \approx 4.2, B \approx 125.0°, C \approx 35.0°$
2. $B = 40°, a = 12, c = 20$
   $b \approx 13.3, A \approx 35.5°, C \approx 104.5°$
3. $C = 118°, a = 6, b = 10$
   $c \approx 13.9, A \approx 22.5°, B \approx 39.5°$
4. $C = 52.5°, a = 6.5, b = 9$
   $c \approx 7.2, A \approx 45.6°, B \approx 81.9°$
5. $A = 140°, b = 12, c = 14$
   $a \approx 24.4, B \approx 18.4°, C \approx 21.6°$
6. $B = 25.4°, a = 6.8, c = 10.5$
   $b \approx 5.2, A \approx 33.8°, C \approx 120.8°$
7. $C = 78.6°, a = 12.1, b = 20.3$
   $c \approx 21.5, A \approx 33.5°, B \approx 67.9°$
8. $A = 118.2°, b = 16.5, c = 10.7$
   $a \approx 23.5, B \approx 38.2°, C \approx 23.6°$
9. $a = 7, b = 3, c = 5$
   $A \approx 120°, B \approx 21.8°, C \approx 38.2°$
10. $a = 8, b = 5, c = 10$
    $A \approx 52.4°, B \approx 29.7°, C \approx 97.9°$
11. $a = 16, b = 20, c = 32$
    $A \approx 24.1°, B \approx 30.8°, C \approx 125.1°$
12. $a = 5.3, b = 7.2, c = 10$
    $A \approx 30.8°, B \approx 44°, C \approx 105.2°$
13. $a = 7.2, b = 6.5, c = 11$
    $A \approx 38.8°, B \approx 34.5°, C \approx 106.7°$
14. $a = 6.8, b = 12.4, c = 15.1$
    $A \approx 26.4°, B \approx 54.1°, C \approx 99.6°$
15. $a = 12, b = 16.5, c = 21.3$
    $A \approx 34.1°, B \approx 50.5°, C \approx 95.4°$
16. $a = 5.7, b = 20.4, c = 16.8$
    $A \approx 13.7°, B \approx 122.0°, C \approx 44.3°$
17. Find the angles of the triangle whose vertices are $(0, 0), (5, -2)$, and $(1, -4)$. **54.2° at vertex (0, 0); 48.4° at vertex (5, −2); 77.5° at vertex (1, −4)**
18. Find the angles of the triangle whose vertices are $(-3, 4), (6, 1)$, and $(2, -1)$. **26.6° at vertex (−3, 4); 45° at vertex (6,1); 108.4° at vertex (2, −1)**
19. Two trains leave a station on different tracks. The tracks make a 112° angle with the station as

vertex. The first train travels at an average speed of 90 kilometers per hour and the second at an average speed of 55 kilometers per hour. How far apart are the trains after 2 hours and 45 minutes? **≈334.9 km**
20. One plane flies west from Cleveland at 350 miles per hour. A second plane leaves Cleveland at the same time and flies southeast at 200 miles per hour. How far apart are the planes after 1 hour and 36 minutes? **≈818.2 mi**
21. The pitcher's mound on a standard baseball diamond (which is actually a square) is 60.5 feet from home plate. How far is the pitcher's mound from first base? **≈63.7 ft**

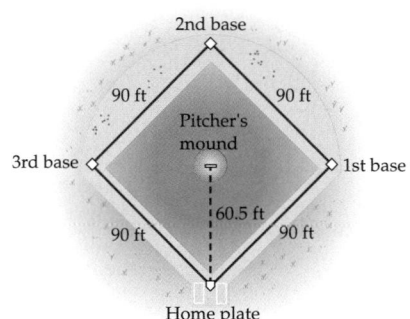

22. If the straight-line distance from home plate over second base to the center field wall in a baseball stadium is 400 feet, how far is it from first base to the same point in center field? Adapt the figure above. **≈342.3 ft**

23. A stake is located 10.8 feet from the end of a closed gate that is 8 feet long. The gate swings open, and its end hits the stake. Through what angle does the gate swing? **≈84.9°**

measurements shown in the figure below. How wide is the sinkhole?

≈154.5 ft

24. The distance from Chicago to St. Louis is 440 kilometers, from St. Louis to Atlanta 795 kilometers, and from Atlanta to Chicago 950 kilometers. What are the angles in the triangle with these three cities as vertices?

A ≈ 27.4°, B ≈ 96.3°, C ≈ 56.3°

25. A boat runs in a straight line for 3 kilometers, then makes a 45° turn and goes for another 6 kilometers. How far is the boat from its starting point?

≈8.4 km

26. A plane flies in a straight line at 400 miles per hour for 1 hour and 12 minutes. It makes a 15° turn and flies at 375 miles per hour for 2 hours and 27 minutes. How far is it from its starting point?

≈1388.0 mi

27. The side of a hill makes an angle of 12° with the horizontal. A wire is to be run from the top of a 175-foot tower on the top of the hill to a stake located 120 feet down the hillside from the base of the tower. What length of wire is needed?

≈231.9 ft

28. Two ships leave port, one traveling in a straight course at 22 miles per hour and the other traveling a straight course at 31 miles per hour. Their courses diverge by 38°. How far apart are they after 3 hours?

≈57.7 mi

29. An engineer wants to measure the width *CD* of a sinkhole. He places a stake *B* and determines the

30. A straight tunnel is to be dug through a hill. Two people stand on opposite sides of the hill where the tunnel entrances are to be located. Both can see a stake located 530 meters from the first person and 755 meters from the second. The angle determined by the two people and the stake (the vertex) is 77°. How long must the tunnel be?

≈819.1 m

31. One diagonal of a parallelogram is 6 centimeters long, and the other is 13 centimeters long. They form an angle of 42° with each other. How long are the sides of the parallelogram? *Hint:* The diagonals of a parallelogram bisect each other.

≈4.7 cm and 9.0 cm

32. A parallelogram has diagonals of lengths 12 and 15 inches that intersect at an angle of 63.7°. How long are the sides of the parallelogram?

≈7.2 in. and 11.5 in.

33. A ship is traveling at 18 miles per hour from Corsica to Barcelona, a distance of 350 miles. To avoid bad weather, the ship leaves Corsica on a route 22° south of the direct route (see the figure below). After 7 hours the bad weather has been bypassed. Through what angle should the ship now turn to head directly to Barcelona?

≈33.4°

34. In aerial navigation, directions are given in degrees clockwise from north. Thus east is 90°, south is 180°, and so on, as shown in the following figure. A plane leaves South Bend for Buffalo, 400 miles away, intending to fly a straight course in the

37. $AB = 24.27$, $AC = 21.23$,
$BC = 19.5$, $\angle A \approx 50.2°$,
$\angle B \approx 56.8°$, $\angle C \approx 73.0°$

38. $AB = 12.58$, $AC = 13.27$,
$BC = 15.39$, $\angle A \approx 73.0°$,
$\angle B \approx 55.6°$, $\angle C \approx 51.4°$

39. ≈ 17.0 m

40. Let α be the angle formed by the two diagonals of the parallelogram. Let c and d be the lengths of the diagonals and let s and t be the lengths of the adjacent sides of the parallelogram. Note that the diagonals of a parallelogram bisect each other and

$$\cos \alpha = \frac{\left(\dfrac{c}{2}\right)^2 + \left(\dfrac{d}{2}\right)^2 - s^2}{2\left(\dfrac{c}{2}\right)\left(\dfrac{d}{2}\right)}$$

$$\cos(180° - \alpha)$$
$$= \frac{\left(\dfrac{c}{2}\right)^2 + \left(\dfrac{d}{2}\right)^2 - t^2}{2\left(\dfrac{c}{2}\right)\left(\dfrac{d}{2}\right)}$$

Now $\cos \alpha + \cos(180° - \alpha) = 0$,

and so $\dfrac{\left(\dfrac{c}{2}\right)^2 + \left(\dfrac{d}{2}\right)^2 - s^2}{2\left(\dfrac{c}{2}\right)\left(\dfrac{d}{2}\right)} +$

$$\frac{\left(\dfrac{c}{2}\right)^2 + \left(\dfrac{d}{2}\right)^2 - t^2}{2\left(\dfrac{c}{2}\right)\left(\dfrac{d}{2}\right)} = 0$$

$$c^2 + d^2 = s^2 + s^2 + t^2 + t^2$$

direction 70°. After flying 180 miles, the pilot realizes that an error has been made and that he has actually been flying in the direction 55°.

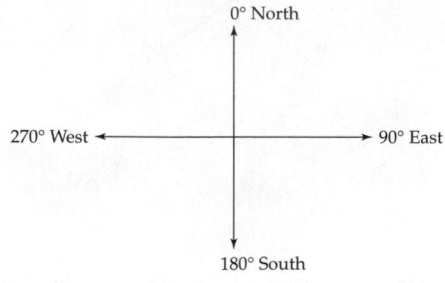

0° North

270° West ← → 90° East

180° South

≈ 230.9 mi

a. At that time, how far is the plane from Buffalo?
b. In what direction should the plane now go to reach Buffalo? $\approx 81.6°$

35. Assume that the earth is a sphere of radius 3980 miles. A satellite travels in a circular orbit around the earth, 900 miles above the equator, making one full orbit every 6 hours. If it passes directly over a tracking station at 2 P.M., what is the distance from the satellite to the tracking station at 2:05 P.M.? ≈ 978.7 mi

36. Two planes at the same altitude approach an airport. One plane is 16 miles from the control tower and the other is 22 miles from the tower. The angle determined by the planes and the tower, with the tower as the vertex, is 11°. How far apart are the planes? ≈ 7.0 mi

37. Assuming that the circles in the following figure are mutually tangent, find the lengths of the sides and the measures of the angles in triangle ABC.

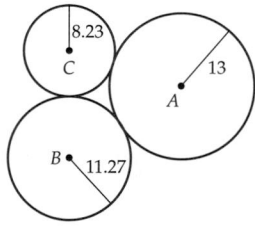

8.23
C
13
A
B • 11.27

38. Assuming that the circles in the following figure are mutually tangent, find the lengths of the sides and the measures of the angles in triangle ABC.

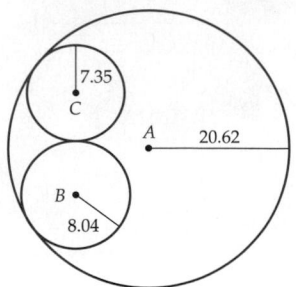

7.35
C
A 20.62
B •
8.04

39. *Critical Thinking* A rope is attached at points A and B and taut around a pulley whose center is at C, as shown in the following figure. The rope lies on the pulley from D to E and the radius of the pulley is 1 meter. How long is the rope?

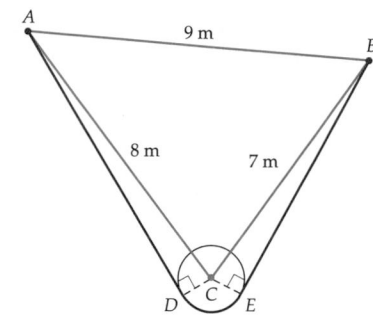

A
9 m
B
8 m
7 m
D C E

40. *Critical Thinking* Use the Law of Cosines to prove that the sum of the squares of the lengths of the two diagonals of a parallelogram equals the sum of the squares of the lengths of the four sides.

10.2 The Law of Sines

Objectives

- Solve oblique triangles by using the Law of Sines
- Use area formulas to find areas of triangles

In Section 10.1, the Law of Cosines was used to solve oblique triangles when SAS or SSS information was given. When different information is given about the triangle, the Law of Cosines may not be sufficient to solve them. In this case, the **Law of Sines** may be used.

Law of Sines

In any triangle ABC (in standard notation)

$$\frac{a}{\sin A} = \frac{b}{\sin B} = \frac{c}{\sin C}.$$

Proof Position triangle ABC on a coordinate plane so that angle C is in standard position, with initial side b and terminal side a, as shown in Figure 10.2-1.

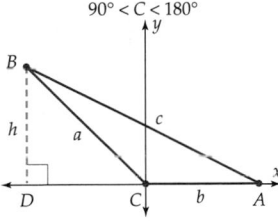

Figure 10.2-1

In each case, sin C can be computed by using the point B on the terminal side of angle C. The second coordinate of B is h, and the distance from B to the origin is a. Therefore, by the definition of sine,

$$\sin C = \frac{h}{a}, \qquad \text{or equivalently,} \qquad h = a \sin C.$$

In each case, right triangle ADB shows that

$$\sin A = \frac{\text{opposite}}{\text{hypotenuse}} = \frac{h}{c}, \qquad \text{or equivalently,} \qquad h = c \sin A.$$

Combine these two expressions for h.

$$a \sin C = c \sin A$$

Because angles in a triangle are nonzero, sin A ≠ 0 and sin C ≠ 0. Divide each side of the last equation by (sin A)(sin C).

$$\frac{a}{\sin A} = \frac{c}{\sin C}$$

Teaching Notes

Remind students of the labeling convention we are using for triangles: side a is opposite angle A, side b is opposite angle B, and so on.

The Law of Sines is a statement that three ratios are equal. It states that all of the following equations are true:

$$\frac{a}{\sin A} = \frac{b}{\sin B}$$

$$\frac{a}{\sin A} = \frac{c}{\sin C}$$

$$\frac{b}{\sin B} = \frac{c}{\sin C}$$

The Law of Sines can also be written using reciprocals:

$$\frac{\sin A}{a} = \frac{\sin B}{b} = \frac{\sin C}{c}$$

The equation $\frac{a}{\sin A} = \frac{c}{\sin C}$ is proved on this page. Use this equation to show students that the Law of Sines also applies to right triangles. If $C = 90°$, then sin C = sin 90° = 1, and we have:

$$\frac{a}{\sin A} = \frac{c}{\sin C}$$

$$\frac{a}{\sin A} = \frac{c}{1}$$

$$\sin A = \frac{a}{c}$$

This is consistent with the trigonometric ratio

$$\sin A = \frac{\text{opposite}}{\text{hypotenuse}} = \frac{a}{c},$$ as seen in the right triangle below.

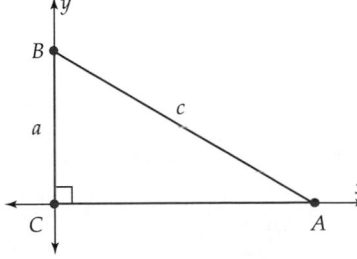

Teaching Notes

Remind students that the Law of Sines consists of three equations, only one of which is proved on the preceding page. Consider having your students write a proof for either

$$\frac{a}{\sin A} = \frac{b}{\sin B} \text{ or } \frac{b}{\sin B} = \frac{c}{\sin C}.$$

Example Notes

In **Example 1,** note that finding c is not dependent on knowing either A or a, so c could be found first.

Point out that the expression sin 129° is not calculated and rounded during the solving process (rounding before the last step introduces unnecessary inaccuracy).

If an incorrect answer is found for angle A, then side a will be incorrect. Students can trace Figure 10.2-2, label all sides and angles, and check to see if all angle measures and side lengths are reasonable.

ADDITIONAL EXAMPLES

Example 1

If $A = 115°$, $B = 27°$, and $a = 45$, find the other angle measure and side lengths. See the figure below.

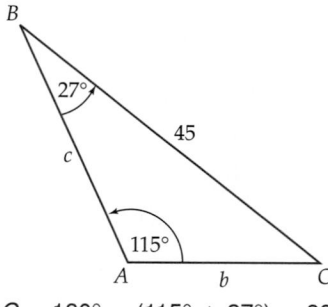

$C = 180° - (115° + 27°) = 38°.$

$$\frac{b}{\sin B} = \frac{a}{\sin A}$$

$$\frac{b}{\sin 27°} = \frac{45}{\sin 115°}$$

$$b = \frac{45 \sin 27°}{\sin 115°} \approx 22.5$$

$$\frac{c}{\sin C} = \frac{a}{\sin A}$$

$$\frac{c}{\sin 38°} = \frac{45}{\sin 115°}$$

$$c = \frac{45 \sin 38°}{\sin 115°} \approx 30.6$$

Therefore, $C = 38°$, $b \approx 22.5$, and $c \approx 30.6.$

This proves one proportion in the Law of Sines. Similar arguments beginning with angles A or B in standard position prove the other proportions.

The Law of Sines can be used to solve triangles in the following cases.

1. Two angles and one side are known (AAS)

2. Two sides and the angle opposite one of them are known (SSA)

Example 1   Solve a Triangle with AAS Information

If $B = 20°$, $C = 31°$, and $b = 210$, find the other angle measure and side lengths. See Figure 10.2-2.

Figure 10.2-2

Solution

Because the sum of the angle measures of a triangle is 180°,

$$A = 180° - (20° + 31°) = 129°.$$

In order to find a, notice that three of the four quantities in one of the Law of Sines proportions are known.

$$\frac{a}{\sin A} = \frac{b}{\sin B}$$

$$\frac{a}{\sin 129°} = \frac{210}{\sin 20°}$$

$$a = \frac{210 \sin 129°}{\sin 20°} \qquad \textit{Multiply each side by sin 129°.}$$

$$a \approx 477.2$$

c is found in a similar manner. Use a Law of Sines proportion involving c and the three known quantities.

$$\frac{c}{\sin C} = \frac{b}{\sin B}$$

$$\frac{c}{\sin 31°} = \frac{210}{\sin 20°}$$

$$c = \frac{210 \sin 31°}{\sin 20°} \qquad \textit{Multiply each side by sin 31°.}$$

$$c \approx 316.2$$

Therefore, $A = 129°$, $a \approx 477.2$, and $c \approx 316.2.$ ∎

The Ambiguous Case

Given AAS information, such as in Example 1, there is exactly one triangle satisfying the given data (see note). But when two sides of a triangle and the angle opposite one of them are known, as in the SSA case, there may be one, two, or no triangles that satisfy the given data. This is called the **ambiguous case.**

NOTE The four Triangle Congruence Theorems—AAS, SAS, SSS, and ASA—state that a unique triangle can be formed that is congruent to a given triangle. However, SSA is *not* a triangle congruence theorem because a unique triangle congruent to the given one is not guaranteed; zero, one, or two triangles can be formed from the side-side-angle information.

To see why the ambiguous case occurs, suppose sides a and b and angle A are given. Place angle A in standard position with terminal side b. If angle A is less than $90°$, then there are four possibilities for side a.

Ambiguous Case: SSA Information with $A < 90°$	
(i) $a < b$, and side a is too short to reach the third side: *no solution.*	(ii) $a < b$, and side a just reaches the third side and is perpendicular to it: *one solution.*
Figure 10.2-3	**Figure 10.2-4**
(iii) $a < b$, and an arc of radius a meets the third side at 2 points to the right of A: *two solutions.*	(iv) $a \geq b$, so that an arc of radius a meets the third side at just one point to the right of A: *one solution.*
Figure 10.2-5	**Figure 10.2-6**

Teaching Notes

In each figure illustrating **The Ambiguous Case,** angle A and side b are fixed. Therefore, the location of point C is fixed, and the perpendicular distance from C to the base of the figure is determined. That distance is the height of the triangle (if the triangle exists); call it h. Whether side a reaches the base of each figure and how many triangles are formed can be explained by comparing a, h, and b.

In Figure 10.2-3, side a is too short to reach the third side when $a < h$.

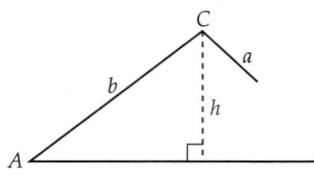

In Figure 10.2-4, side a just reaches the third side when $a = h$.

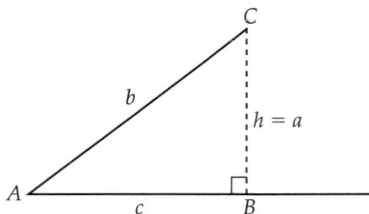

In Figure 10.2-5, an arc of radius a meets the third side at 2 points when $a > h$ and $a < b$.

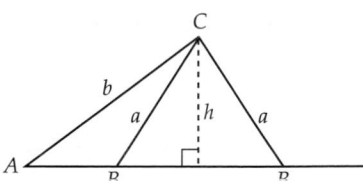

In Figure 10.2-6, an arc of radius a meets the third side at just one point to the right of A when $a > h$ and $a \geq b$.

Teaching Notes

The diagrams at the right clearly illustrate the two cases where $A > 90°$. However, you may want to review the following facts from geometry:

- A triangle can have at most one obtuse angle.
- The longest side of a triangle is opposite the largest angle.

Because of these facts, a must be the longest side when $A > 90°$.

Math Background

An alternate proof of the **Supplementary Angle Identity** uses the Subtraction Identity for Sines. Letting $\alpha = 180°$, we have:

$$\sin(\alpha - \theta) = \sin \alpha \cos \theta - \cos \alpha \sin \theta$$

$$\sin(180° - \theta) = \sin 180° \cos \theta - \cos 180° \sin \theta$$

$$= 0 \cdot \cos \theta - (-1) \cdot \sin \theta$$

$$= 0 + \sin \theta$$

$$= \sin \theta$$

In **Example 3**, assume that the surface of the water is a flat plane (for relatively short distances, assuming it is flat is sufficiently accurate). The following fact is interesting to note, but does not affect the Solution: The triangle in Figure 10.2-10 is not in the same plane as the surface of the water because the aircraft is above the water; however, the three noncollinear points do indeed form a triangle (and determine a plane).

ADDITIONAL EXAMPLES

Example 2

Given a possible triangle ABC with $b = 8$, $c = 5$, and $C = 54°$, find angle B.

$$\frac{b}{\sin B} = \frac{c}{\sin C}$$

$$\frac{8}{\sin B} = \frac{5}{\sin 54°}$$

$$\sin B = \frac{8 \sin 54°}{5} \approx 1.29$$

There is no angle B whose sine is greater than 1. Therefore, there is no triangle satisfying the given data.

If angle A is greater than 90°, then there are only two possibilities.

Ambiguous Case: SSA Information with $A > 90°$	
(i) $a \leq b$, so that side a is too short to reach the third side: *no solution*.	(ii) $a > b$, so that an arc of radius a meets the third side at just one point to the right of A: *one solution*.
Figure 10.2-7	Figure 10.2-8

Recall from Section 8.3 that when finding all solutions of a trigonometric equation involving the sine function, the identity $\sin x = \sin(\pi - x)$ is used. This same identity, stated in terms of degrees rather than radians, is used to deal with the ambiguous SSA case.

Supplementary Angle Identity

> If $0° \leq \theta \leq 90°$, then
>
> $$\sin \theta = \sin(180° - \theta).$$

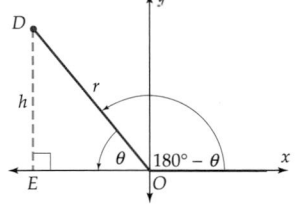

Figure 10.2-9

Proof Place the angle $180° - \theta$ in standard position and choose a point D on its terminal side. Let r be the distance from D to the origin. The situation is shown in Figure 10.2-9.

Because h is the second coordinate of D, then $\sin(180° - \theta) = \frac{h}{r}$. Right triangle OED shows that

$$\sin \theta = \frac{\text{opposite}}{\text{hypotenuse}} = \frac{h}{r} = \sin(180° - \theta).$$

Example 2 Solve a Triangle with SSA Information

Given a possible triangle ABC with $a = 6$, $b = 7$, and $A = 65°$, find angle B.

Solution

Use a proportion of the Law of Sines involving angle B and three known quantities.

$$\frac{b}{\sin B} = \frac{a}{\sin A}$$

$$\frac{7}{\sin B} = \frac{6}{\sin 65°}$$

$$\sin B = \frac{7 \sin 65°}{6}$$

$$\sin B \approx 1.06$$

There is no angle B whose sine is greater than 1. Therefore, there is no triangle satisfying the given data.

Example 3　**Solve a Triangle with SSA Information**

An airplane A takes off from carrier B and flies in a straight line for 12 kilometers. At that instant, an observer on destroyer C, located 5 kilometers from the carrier, notes that the angle determined by the carrier, the destroyer (the vertex), and the plane is 37°. How far is the plane from the destroyer?

Solution

The given information is organized in Figure 10.2-10.

Figure 10.2-10

Because there is no proportion of the Law of Sines using B that can be solved, use a proportion involving A to find a second angle of the triangle. This will provide you with enough information to find angle B and hence allowing you to use the Law of Sines to find b.

$$\frac{a}{\sin A} = \frac{c}{\sin C}$$

$$\frac{5}{\sin A} = \frac{12}{\sin 37°}$$

$$\sin A = \frac{5 \sin 37°}{12}$$

$$\sin A \approx 0.2508$$

$$A \approx 14.5° \quad \text{or} \quad A \approx 180° - 14.5° = 165.5°$$

Example 3

Lighthouse B is 3 miles east of lighthouse A. Boat C leaves lighthouse B and sails in a straight line. At the moment that the boat is 5 miles from lighthouse B, an observer at lighthouse A notes that the angle determined by the boat, lighthouse A (the vertex), and lighthouse B is 65°. Approximately how far is the boat from lighthouse A at that moment?

The given information is organized in the figure below.

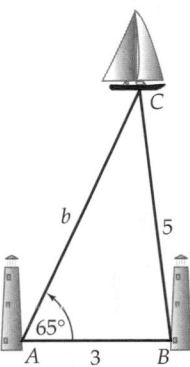

Information about angle B and side b is not available. Therefore, to find B, first use an equation involving A and C to find a second angle measure of the triangle.

$$\frac{a}{\sin A} = \frac{c}{\sin C}$$

$$\frac{5}{\sin 65°} = \frac{3}{\sin C}$$

$$\sin C = \frac{3 \sin 65°}{5} \approx 0.5438$$

$C \approx 32.9°$ or $C \approx 180° - 32.9° = 147.1$

If $C = 147.1°$ and $A = 65°$, then the sum of angles A, B, and C is greater than 180°. So, 32.9° is the only possible measure of angle C. Therefore,

$B \approx 180° - (65° + 32.9°) = 82.1°$.

All of the angles are known, so side b can be found using the Law of Sines.

$$\frac{b}{\sin B} = \frac{a}{\sin A}$$

$$\frac{b}{\sin 82.1°} = \frac{5}{\sin 65°}$$

$$b = \frac{5 \sin 82.1°}{\sin 65°} \approx 5.5$$

The boat is approximately 5.5 miles from lighthouse A.

ADDITIONAL EXAMPLES

Example 4

Solve triangle ABC when $a = 4.8$, $b = 6$, and $A = 28°$.

$$\frac{b}{\sin B} = \frac{a}{\sin A}$$

$$\frac{6}{\sin B} = \frac{4.8}{\sin 28°}$$

$$\sin B = \frac{6 \sin 28°}{4.8} \approx 0.5868$$

$B \approx 35.9°$ or $B \approx 180° - 35.9° = 144.1°$

Because the sum of angles A and B is less than 180° in each case, there are two possible cases, as shown in the figure below.

Case 1 $B = 35.9°$

$C = 180° - (35.9° + 28°) = 116.1°$

$$\frac{c}{\sin C} = \frac{a}{\sin A}$$

$$\frac{c}{\sin 116.1°} = \frac{4.8}{\sin 28°}$$

$$c = \frac{4.8 \sin 116.1°}{\sin 28°} \approx 9.2$$

Case 2 $B = 144.1°$

$C = 180° - (144.1° + 28°) = 7.9°$

$$\frac{c}{\sin C} = \frac{a}{\sin A}$$

$$\frac{c}{\sin 7.9°} = \frac{4.8}{\sin 28°}$$

$$c = \frac{4.8 \sin 7.9°}{\sin 28°} \approx 1.4$$

Thus, in Case 1, $B = 35.9°$, $C = 116.1°$, and $c = 9.2$; and in Case 2, $B = 144.1°$, $C = 7.9°$, and $c = 1.4$.

If $A = 165.5°$ and $C = 37°$, then the sum of angles A, B, and C would be greater than 180°. Because that is impossible, 14.5° is the only possible measure of angle A. Therefore,

$$B = 180° - (37° + 14.5°) = 128.5°.$$

All of the angles are known, and b can be found using either the Law of Cosines or the Law of Sines.

$$\frac{b}{\sin B} = \frac{c}{\sin C}$$

$$\frac{b}{\sin 128.5°} = \frac{12}{\sin 37°}$$

$$b = \frac{12 \sin 128.5°}{\sin 37°}$$

$$b \approx 15.6$$

The plane is approximately 15.6 kilometers from the destroyer.

Example 4   Solve a Triangle with SSA Information

Solve triangle ABC when $a = 7.5$, $b = 12$, and $A = 35°$.

Solution

Use a proportion of the Law of Sines involving the known quantities.

$$\frac{b}{\sin B} = \frac{a}{\sin A}$$

$$\frac{12}{\sin B} = \frac{7.5}{\sin 35°}$$

$$\sin B = \frac{12 \sin 35°}{7.5}$$

$$\sin B \approx 0.9177$$

$$B \approx 66.6° \quad \text{or} \quad B \approx 180° - 66.6° = 113.4°$$

Because the sum of angles A and B is less than 180° in each case, there are two possible cases, as shown in Figure 10.2-11.

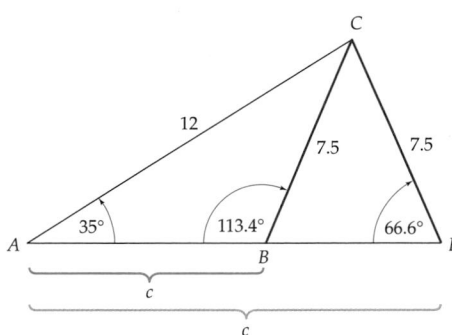

Figure 10.2-11

Case 1 $B = 66.6°$

$C = 180° - (35° + 66.6°) = 78.4°$

Use the Law of Sines.

$$\frac{c}{\sin C} = \frac{a}{\sin A}$$

$$\frac{c}{\sin 78.4°} = \frac{7.5}{\sin 35°}$$

$$c = \frac{7.5 \sin 78.4°}{\sin 35°}$$

$$c \approx 12.8$$

Case 2 $B = 113.4°$

$C = 180° - (35° + 113.4°) = 31.6°$

Use the Law of Sines.

$$\frac{c}{\sin C} = \frac{a}{\sin A}$$

$$\frac{c}{\sin 31.6°} = \frac{7.5}{\sin 35°}$$

$$c = \frac{7.5 \sin 31.6°}{\sin 35°}$$

$$c \approx 6.9$$

Thus, in Case 1, $B \approx 66.6°$, $C \approx 78.4°$, and $c \approx 12.8$; and in Case 2, $B \approx 113.4°$, $C \approx 31.6°$, and $c \approx 6.9$. ∎

Example 5   **Solve a Triangle with ASA Information**

A plane flying in a straight line parallel to the ground passes directly over point A and later directly over point B, which is 3 miles from A. A few minutes after the plane passes over B, the angle of elevation from A to the plane is $43°$ and the angle of elevation from B to the plane is $67°$. How high is the plane at that moment?

Solution

If C represents the plane, then the situation is represented in Figure 10.2-12. The height of the plane is h.

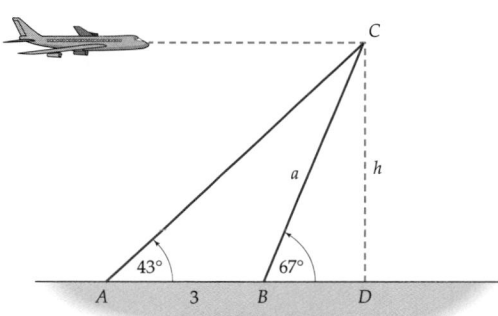

Figure 10.2-12

Angle ABC measures $180° - 67° = 113°$. So

$$m\angle BCA = 180° - (43° + 113°) = 24°.$$

ADDITIONAL EXAMPLES

Example 5

Two surveyors, standing at points A and B, are measuring a building. The surveyor at point A is 20 feet further away from the building than the surveyor at point B. The angle of elevation of the top of the building from point A is $58°$, and the angle of elevation of the top of the building from point B is $72°$. How tall is the building?

If C represents the top of the building, then this situation is represented in the figure below.

Angle ABC measures $180° - 72° = 108°$.

So,

$m\angle BCA = 180° - (108° + 58°) = 14°.$

Use the Law of Sines to find side a of triangle ABC.

$$\frac{a}{\sin 58°} = \frac{20}{\sin 14°}$$

$$a = \frac{20 \sin 58°}{\sin 14°} \approx 70.11$$

Now use $\sin 72° = \dfrac{h}{a}$ in right triangle CBD to find h.

$$\sin 72° = \frac{h}{70.11}$$

$$h = 70.11 \sin 72° \approx 66.68$$

The building is about 66.68 feet tall.

Teaching Notes

The variables a, b, and C in the expression for the **Area of a Triangle** represent side-angle-side. That is, the area of a triangle is equal to one-half the product of any two sides and the sine of their included angle. For triangle ABC, alternate forms of the area expression are $\frac{1}{2}bc\sin A$ and $\frac{1}{2}ac\sin B$.

Show that in a right triangle ABC with right angle C, the expression $\frac{1}{2}ab\sin C$ is equivalent to $\frac{1}{2} \cdot$ base $\cdot$ height:

$\frac{1}{2}ab\sin C = \frac{1}{2}ab\sin 90° = \frac{1}{2}ab(1) = \frac{1}{2}ab$,

where legs a and b are the base and height.

Figure 10.2-13 shows the case $C > 90°$. Have students draw a figure for the case $C < 90°$ and read the proof again. They will see that the proof applies to that case as well.

Real-World Application

Most area formulas for polygons require at least one accurate angle measure. For $A = \frac{1}{2}ab\sin C$, you would need angle C. For each formula below, you would need an accurate 90° angle to determine the height (h) or altitude (a).

$A = \frac{1}{2}bh$ (for triangles)

$A = bh$ (for rectangles and parallelograms)

$A = \frac{1}{2}h(h_1 + h_2)$ (for trapezoids)

$A = \frac{1}{2}aP$ (for regular polygons)

Use the Law of Sines to find side a of triangle ABC.

$$\frac{a}{\sin 43°} = \frac{3}{\sin 24°}$$

$$a = \frac{3\sin 43°}{\sin 24°}$$

$$a \approx 5.03$$

Now use $\sin 67° = \frac{h}{a}$ to find h in right triangle CBD.

$$\sin 67° = \frac{h}{5.03}$$

$$h = 5.03\sin 67°$$

$$h \approx 4.63$$

The plane is about 4.63 miles high. ∎

The Area of a Triangle

The proof of the Law of Sines leads to the following formula for the area of a triangle.

Area of a Triangle ○—

> The area of a triangle containing an angle C with adjacent sides of lengths a and b is
>
> $$\frac{1}{2}ab\sin C.$$

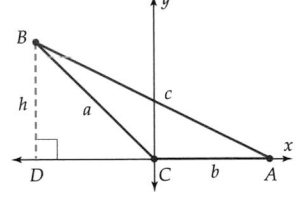

Figure 10.2-13

Proof Place the vertex of angle C at the origin, with side b on the positive x-axis, as in Figure 10.2-13. Then b is the base and h is the height of the triangle.

$$\text{area of triangle } ABC = \frac{1}{2} \cdot \text{base} \cdot \text{height} = \frac{1}{2}bh.$$

The proof of the Law of Sines shows that $h = a\sin C$. Therefore,

$$\text{area of triangle } ABC = \frac{1}{2}bh = \frac{1}{2}ab\sin C.$$

Figure 10.2-13 is the case when C is greater than 90°; the argument when C is less than 90° is similar.

Example 6 | **Find Area with SAS Information**

Find the area of the triangle shown in Figure 10.2-14.

Heron's Formula is powerful because it requires only side lengths, which are much easier to measure than angles in an actual application. In Exercise 57, page 637, students are asked to find how much paint is needed to cover a triangular deck using only side lengths.

Note that Heron's Formula *can be used to find the area of any polygon* because any polygon can be subdivided into triangles.

Figure 10.2-14

Solution

Use the new formula for the area of a triangle.

$$\frac{1}{2}\,ab\sin C = \frac{1}{2}(8)(13)\sin 130° \approx 39.83$$

Thus, the area is about 39.83 square centimeters. ∎

An alternate formula for the area of a triangle, **Heron's formula,** gives the area in terms of its sides.

Heron's Formula

> **The area of a triangle with sides *a*, *b*, and *c* is**
> $$\sqrt{s(s-a)(s-b)(s-c)},$$
> **where** $s = \frac{1}{2}(a + b + c).$

This formula is proved in Exercise 62.

Example 7   **Find Area with SSS Information**

Find the area of the triangle whose sides have lengths 7, 9, and 12.

Solution

Let $a = 7, b = 9$, and $c = 12$. To use the Heron's formula, first find s.

$$s = \frac{1}{2}(a + b + c) = \frac{1}{2}(7 + 9 + 12) = 14$$

Now, use Heron's formula.

$$\sqrt{s(s-a)(s-b)(s-c)} = \sqrt{14(14 - 7)(14 - 9)(14 - 12)}$$
$$= \sqrt{980} \approx 31.3$$

The area is about 31.3 square units. ∎

ADDITIONAL EXAMPLES

Example 6

Find the area of the triangle shown in the figure below.

$$\frac{1}{2}\,ab\sin C = \frac{1}{2}(5)(6)\sin 153°$$
$$\approx 6.81$$

The area of the triangle is about 6.81 square centimeters.

Example 7

Find the area of the triangle whose sides have lengths of 8, 10, and 14. Let $a = 8, b = 10$, and $c = 14$, and find s, to use Heron's Formula:

$$s = \frac{1}{2}(a + b + c)$$
$$= \frac{1}{2}(8 + 10 + 14)$$
$$= 16$$

Now, use Heron's Formula:
$$\sqrt{s(s-a)(s-b)(s-c)}$$
$$= \sqrt{16(16 - 8)(16 - 10)(16 - 14)}$$
$$= \sqrt{1536}$$
$$\approx 39.2$$

The area of the triangle is about 39.2 square units.

ANSWERS

23. $B_1 \approx 65.8°$, $A_1 \approx 58.2°$, $a_1 \approx 10.3$; $B_2 \approx 114.2°$, $A_2 \approx 9.8°$, $a_2 \approx 2.1$

24. $B \approx 79.6°$, $C \approx 28.4°$, $b \approx 12.8$

25. $C \approx 72°$, $b \approx 14.7$, $c \approx 15.2$

26. $B_1 \approx 41.8°$, $C_1 \approx 108.2°$, $c_1 \approx 57.0°$, $B_2 \approx 138.2°$, $C_2 \approx 11.8°$, $c_2 \approx 12.3$

Exercises 10.2

Standard notation for triangle ABC is used throughout. Use a calculator and round off your answers to one decimal place at the end of each computation.

In Exercises 1–8, solve triangle ABC under the given conditions.

1. $A = 48°$, $B = 22°$, $a = 5$
 $C = 110°$, $b \approx 2.5$, $c \approx 6.3$
2. $B = 33°$, $C = 46°$, $b = 4$
 $A = 101°$, $a \approx 7.2$, $c \approx 5.3$
3. $A = 116°$, $C = 50°$, $a = 8$
 $B = 14°$, $b \approx 2.2$, $c \approx 6.8$
4. $A = 105°$, $B = 27°$, $b = 10$
 $a \approx 21.3$, $c \approx 16.4$, $C = 48°$
5. $B = 44°$, $C = 48°$, $b = 12$
 $A = 88°$, $a \approx 17.3$, $c \approx 12.8$
6. $A = 67°$, $C = 28°$, $a = 9$
 $b \approx 9.7$, $c \approx 4.6$, $B = 85°$
7. $A = 102.3°$, $B = 36.2°$, $a = 16$
 $C = 41.5°$, $b \approx 9.7$, $c \approx 10.9$
8. $B = 97.5°$, $C = 42.5°$, $b = 7$
 $a \approx 4.5$, $c \approx 4.8$, $A = 40°$

In Exercises 9–16, find the area of triangle ABC under the given conditions.

9. $a = 4$, $b = 8$, $C = 27°$
 $\approx$**7.3 sq units**
10. $b = 10$, $c = 14$, $A = 36°$
 $\approx$**41.1 sq units**
11. $c = 7$, $a = 10$, $B = 68°$
 $\approx$**32.5 sq units**
12. $a = 9$, $b = 13$, $C = 75°$
 $\approx$**56.5 sq units**
13. $a = 11$, $b = 15$, $c = 18$
 $\approx$**82.3 sq units**
14. $a = 4$, $b = 12$, $c = 14$
 $\approx$**22.2 sq units**
15. $a = 7$, $b = 9$, $c = 11$
 $\approx$**31.4 sq units**
16. $a = 17$, $b = 27$, $c = 40$
 $\approx$**177.5 sq units**

In Exercises 17–36, solve the triangle. The Law of Cosines may be needed in Exercises 27–36.

17. $b = 15$, $c = 25$, $B = 47°$
 no solution
18. $b = 30$, $c = 50$, $C = 60°$
 $A \approx 88.7°$, $B \approx 31.3°$, $a \approx 57.7$
19. $a = 12$, $b = 5$, $B = 20°$
 $A_1 \approx 55.2°$, $C_1 \approx 104.8°$, $c_1 \approx 14.1$; $A_2 \approx 124.8°$,
 $C_2 \approx 35.2°$, $c_2 \approx 8.4$
20. $b = 12.5$, $c = 20.1$, $B = 37.3°$
 $A_1 \approx 65.7°$, $C_1 \approx 77.0°$, $a_1 \approx 18.8°$, $A_2 \approx 39.7°$,
 $C_2 \approx 103.0°$, $a_2 \approx 13.2$
21. $a = 5$, $c = 12$, $A = 102°$
 no solution
22. $a = 9$, $b = 14$, $B = 95°$
 $A \approx 39.8°$, $C \approx 45.2°$, $c \approx 10.0$

23. $b = 11$, $c = 10$, $C = 56°$

24. $a = 12.4$, $c = 6.2$, $A = 72°$

25. $A = 41°$, $B = 67°$, $a = 10.5$

26. $a = 30$, $b = 40$, $A = 30°$

27. $b = 4$, $c = 10$, $A = 75°$
 $a \approx 9.8$, $B \approx 23.3°$, $C \approx 81.7°$
28. $a = 50$, $c = 80$, $C = 45°$
 $A \approx 26.2°$, $B \approx 108.8°$, $b \approx 107.1$
29. $a = 6$, $b = 12$, $c = 16$
 $A \approx 18.6°$, $B \approx 39.6°$, $C \approx 121.9°$
30. $B = 20.67°$, $C = 34°$, $b = 185$
 $A \approx 125.33°$, $a \approx 427.6$, $c \approx 293.1$
31. $a = 16.5$, $b = 18.2$, $C = 47°$
 $c \approx 13.9$, $A \approx 60.1°$, $B \approx 72.9°$
32. $a = 21$, $c = 15.8$, $B = 71°$
 $b \approx 21.8$, $A \approx 65.7°$, $C \approx 43.3°$
33. $b = 17.2$, $c = 12.4$, $B = 62.5°$
 $C \approx 39.8°$, $A \approx 77.7°$, $a \approx 18.9$
34. $b = 24.1$, $c = 10.5$, $C = 26.3°$
 no solution
35. $a = 10.1$, $b = 18.2$, $A = 50.7°$
 no solution
36. $b = 14.6$, $c = 7.8$, $B = 40.4°$
 $A \approx 119.3°$, $C \approx 20.3°$, $a \approx 19.6$

In Exercises 37 and 38, find the area of the triangle with the given vertices.

37. $(0, 0)$, $(2, -5)$, $(-3, 1)$ $\approx$**6.5 sq units**

38. $(-4, 2)$, $(5, 7)$, $(3, 0)$ $\approx \frac{53}{2}$ **sq units**

In Exercises 39 and 40, find the area of the polygonal region. *Hint:* Divide the region into triangles.

39. $\approx$**7691 sq units**

40. $\approx$**1222.1 sq units**

41. A surveyor marks points A and B 200 meters apart on one bank of a river. She sights a point C on the opposite bank and determines the angles shown in the figure below. What is the distance from A to C? ≈**135.5 m**

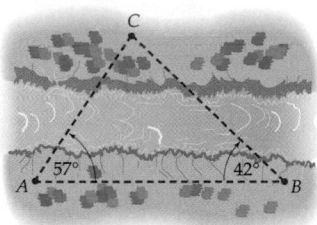

42. A forest fire is spotted from two fire towers. The triangle determined by the two towers and the fire has angles of 28° and 37° at the tower vertices. If the towers are 3000 meters apart, which one is closer to the fire?
the tower with the larger angle

43. A visitor to the Leaning Tower of Pisa observed that the tower's shadow was 40 meters long and that the angle of elevation from the tip of the shadow to the top of the tower was 57°. The tower is now 54 meters tall, measured from the ground to the top along the center line of the tower (see the figure). Approximate the angle α that the center line of the tower makes with the vertical. ≈**5.4°**

44. A pole tilts at an angle 9° from the vertical, away from the sun, and casts a shadow 24 feet long. The angle of elevation from the end of the pole's shadow to the top of the pole is 53°. How long is the pole? ≈**26.6 ft**

45. A side view of a bus shelter is shown in the following figure. The brace d makes an angle of 37.25° with the back and an angle of 34.85° with the top of the shelter. How long is the brace?
≈**5.0 ft**

46. A straight path makes an angle of 6° with the horizontal. A statue at the higher end of the path casts a 6.5-meter shadow straight down the path. The angle of elevation from the end of the shadow to the top of the statue is 32°. How tall is the statue? ≈**3.4 m**

47. A vertical statue 6.3 meters high stands on top of a hill. At a point on the side of the hill 35 meters from the statue's base, the angle between the hillside and a line from the top of the statue is 10°. What angle does the side of the hill make with the horizontal? ≈**5.3°**

48. A fence post is located 36 feet from one corner of a building and 40 feet from the adjacent corner. Fences are put up between the post and the building corners to form a triangular garden area. The 40-foot fence makes a 58° angle with the building. What is the area of the garden?
≈**564.3 sq ft**

49. Two straight roads meet at an angle of 40° in Harville, one leading to Eastview and the other to Wellston (see the figure on the next page). Eastview is 18 kilometers from Harville and 20 kilometers from Wellston. What is the distance from Harville to Wellston?
≈**30.1 km**

53. a. Use the Law of Cosines in triangle ABD to find $\angle ABD$; then $\angle EBA$ is $180° - \angle ABD$. Use the Law of Cosines in triangle ABC to find $\angle CAB$; then $\angle EAB$ is $180° - \angle CAB$. You now have two of the angles in triangle EAB and can easily find the third. Use these angles, side AB, and the Law of Sines to find AE.

b. ≈ 94.23 ft

60. The area of the triangle is $\frac{1}{2}ab \sin C$. From the Law of Sines we know $b = \frac{a \sin B}{\sin a}$. Substitute this expression for b in the area formula to get

$$\frac{1}{2}a\left(\frac{a \sin B}{\sin A}\right)\sin C = \frac{a^2 \sin B \sin C}{2 \sin A}$$

61. No such triangle exists because the sum of the lengths of any two sides of a triangle must be greater than the length of the third side, which is not the case here.

62. Area: $\frac{1}{2}ab \sin C = \sqrt{\left(\frac{1}{2}ab \sin C\right)^2}$

$$= \sqrt{\frac{1}{4}a^2b^2\left(1 - \cos^2 C\right)},$$

since $\sin^2 C - 1 - \cos^2 C$

$$= \sqrt{\frac{1}{2}ab(1 + \cos C)\frac{1}{2}ab(1 - \cos C)}$$

Law of Cosines:

$$\cos C = \frac{a^2 + b^2 - c^2}{2ab}$$

$\frac{1}{2}ab(1 + \cos C)$

$$= \frac{1}{2}ab\left(1 + \frac{a^2 + b^2 - c^2}{2ab}\right)$$

$$= \frac{a^2 + 2ab + b^2 - c^2}{4}$$

$$= \frac{(a + b)^2 - c^2}{4}$$

$$= \left(\frac{(a + b) + c}{2}\right)\left(\frac{(a + b) - c}{2}\right)$$

$$= s(s - c),$$

where s

$$= \frac{1}{2}(a + b + c)$$

50. Each of two observers 400 feet apart measures the angle of elevation to the top of a tree that sits on the straight line between them. These angles are 51° and 65° respectively. How tall is the tree? How far is the base of its trunk from each observer? $\approx$**313.5 ft; 253.8 and 146.2 ft**

51. From the top of the 800-foot-tall Cartalk Tower, Tom sees a plane; the angle of elevation is 67°. At the same instant, Ray, who is on the ground 1 mile from the building, notes that his angle of elevation to the plane is 81° and that his angle of elevation to the top of Cartalk Tower is 8.6°. Assume that Tom, Ray, and the airplane are in a plane perpendicular to the ground. (See the following figure.) How high is the airplane? $\approx$**9642.2 ft**

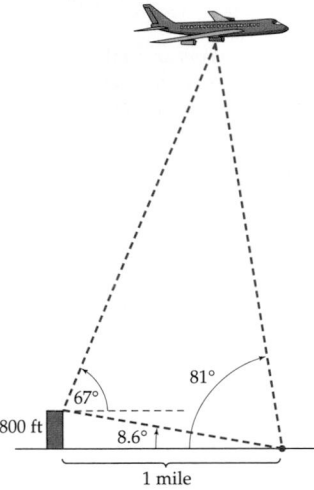

52. A plane flies in a direction of 105° from airport A. [Note: Aerial navigation directions are explained in Exercise 34 of Section 10.1.] After a time, it turns and proceeds in a direction of 267°. Finally, it lands at airport B, 120 miles directly south of airport A. How far has the plane traveled? $\approx$**762.9 mi**

53. Charlie is afraid of water; he can't swim and refuses to get in a boat. However, he must measure the width of a river for his geography

class. He has a long tape measure, but no way to measure angles. While pondering what to do, he paces along the side of the river using the five paths joining points A, B, C, and D (see the following figure). If he does not determine the width of the river, he will not pass the course.

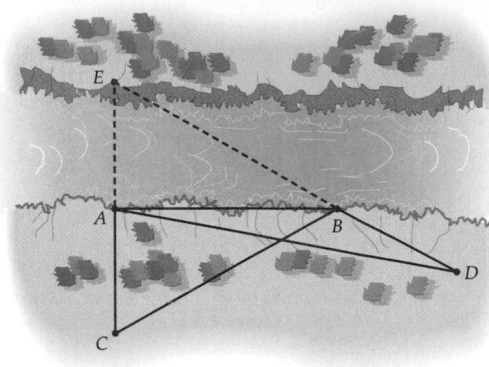

a. Save Charlie from disaster by explaining how he can determine the width AE simply by measuring the lengths AB, AC, AD, BC, and BD and using trigonometry.

b. Charlie determines that $AB = 75$ feet, $AC = 25$ feet, $AD = 90$ feet, $BC = 80$ feet, and $BD = 22$ feet. How wide is the river between A and E?

54. A plane flies in a direction of 85° from Chicago. [Note: Aerial navigation directions are explained in Exercise 34 of Section 10.1.] It then turns and flies in the direction of 200° for 150 miles. It is then 195 miles from its starting point. How far did the plane fly in the direction of 85°? $\approx$**203.1 mi**

55. A hinged crane makes an angle of 50° with the ground. A malfunction causes the lock on the hinge to fail and the top part of the crane swings down (see the figure). How far from the base of the crane does the top hit the ground? $\approx$**13.4 m**

Bottom (spanning)

$\frac{1}{2}ab(1 - \cos C) = \frac{1}{2}ab - \frac{a^2 + b^2 - c^2}{4}$

$$= \frac{-a^2 + 2ab - b^2 + c^2}{4}$$

$$= \frac{c^2 - (a - b)^2}{4}$$

$$= \left(\frac{c - (a - b)}{2}\right)\left(\frac{c + (a - b)}{2}\right)$$

$$= (s - a)(s - b)$$

Therefore, $\sqrt{\frac{1}{2}ab(1 + \cos C)\frac{1}{2}ab(1 - \cos C)}$

$$= \sqrt{s(s - a)(s - b)(s - c)}.$$

56. A triangular lot has sides of 120 feet and 160 feet. The angle between these sides is 42°. Adjacent to this lot is a rectangular lot whose longest side is 200 feet and whose shortest side is the same length as the shortest side of the triangular lot. What is the total area of both lots? **≈27,837.0 sq ft**

57. If a gallon of paint covers 400 square feet, how many gallons are needed to paint a triangular deck with sides of 65 feet, 72 feet, and 88 feet? **≈5.8 gal**

58. *Critical Thinking* Find the volume of the pyramid in the figure below. The volume is given by the formula $V = \frac{1}{3} Bh$, where B is the area of the base and h is the height. **≈270.2 cu units**

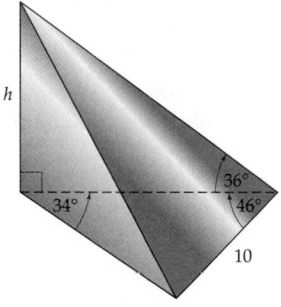

59. *Critical Thinking* A rigid plastic triangle ABC rests on three vertical rods, as shown in the figure. What is its area? **≈11.2 sq units**

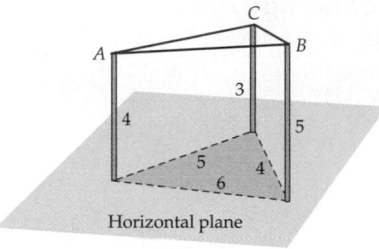

Horizontal plane

60. *Critical Thinking* Prove that the area of triangle ABC, in standard notation is given by $\frac{a^2 \sin B \sin C}{2 \sin A}$.

61. *Critical Thinking* What is the area of a triangle whose sides have lengths 12, 20, and 36? *Hint:* Drawing a diagram may be helpful.

62. *Critical Thinking* Use the area formula $\frac{1}{2} ab \sin C$ and the Pythagorean identity $\sin^2 C = 1 - \cos^2 C$ to show that
$$\frac{1}{2} ab \sin C = \sqrt{\frac{1}{2} ab(1 + \cos C)\frac{1}{2} ab(1 - \cos C)}.$$
Then use the Law of Cosines to show that $\frac{1}{2} ab(1 + \cos C) = s(s - c)$, where $s = \frac{1}{2}(a + b + c)$ and $\frac{1}{2} ab(1 - \cos C) = (s - a)(s - b)$. Combine the facts to prove Heron's Formula.

10.3 The Complex Plane and Polar Form for Complex Numbers*

Objectives

- Graph a complex number in the complex plane
- Find the absolute value of a complex number
- Express a complex number in polar form
- Perform polar multiplication and division

The real number system is represented geometrically by the number line. The complex number system can be represented geometrically by the coordinate plane:

The complex number $a + bi$ corresponds to the point (a, b) in the plane.

For example, the point (2, 3) shown in Figure 10.3-1 is labeled by $2 + 3i$. The other points shown are labeled similarly.

*Section 4.5 is a prerequisite for this section.

Section 10.3 The Complex Plane and Polar Form for Complex Numbers

Teaching Notes

In Section 4.5, students learned how to multiply and divide complex numbers in the standard form $a + bi$. In this section, students will learn how to write a complex number in polar form. Then they will multiply and divide complex numbers in polar form.

Real-World Application

The Mandelbrot set (pages 304–306) is the set of complex numbers c such that the orbit of 0 under the function $f(z) = z^2 + c$ does not approach infinity. The graph of the Mandelbrot set in the complex plane is shown on page 304. The graph of the Mandelbrot set is used to produce many fractal images.

One of the first people to be recognized for using a coordinate plane to represent a complex number was Swiss bookkeeper Jean Robert Argand in 1806. This is why the complex plane is sometimes known as the Argand plane.

Note that for each real number $a = a + 0i$,

$|a + 0i| = \sqrt{a^2 + 0^2} = \sqrt{a^2} = |a|$.

So, the definition of absolute value of a real number is consistent with the definition of absolute value of a complex number.

There are infinitely many ways to represent any complex number in polar form because there are infinitely many angles coterminal with any angle θ. Two other answers for

Example 2 are $2\left(\cos\dfrac{17\pi}{6} + i \sin\dfrac{17\pi}{6}\right)$

and $2\left(\cos\left(-\dfrac{7\pi}{6}\right) + i \sin\left(-\dfrac{7\pi}{6}\right)\right)$.

Generally, θ is chosen so that $0 \le \theta < 2\pi$.

Example Notes

For **Example 1b**, have students use a calculator (see the **Technology Tip** at the bottom of the page) to check their work.

```
abs(4-5i)
         6.403124237
√(41)
         6.403124237
```

For **Example 2**, have students identify the modulus and the argument for

$2\left(\cos\dfrac{5\pi}{6} + i \sin\dfrac{5\pi}{6}\right)$.

modulus = 2, argument = $\dfrac{5\pi}{6}$

Technology Tip

● Recall that complex numbers are entered by using the special i key on the TI keyboard or in the CPLX submenu of the Casio OPTN menu.

Figure 10.3-1

When the coordinate plane is used to graph complex numbers in this way, it is called the **complex plane.** Each real number $a = a + 0i$ corresponds to the point $(a, 0)$ on the horizontal axis; so this axis is called the **real axis.** The vertical axis is called the **imaginary axis** because every imaginary number $bi = 0 + bi$ corresponds to the point $(0, b)$ on the vertical axis.

The absolute value of a real number c is the distance from c to 0 on the number line. So the **absolute value** (or **modulus**) of the complex number $a + bi$ is defined to be the distance from $a + bi$ to the origin in the complex plane.

$|a + bi|$ represents the distance from (a, b) to $(0, 0)$, which is given by $\sqrt{(a - 0)^2 + (b - 0)^2} = \sqrt{a^2 + b^2}$.

Absolute Value of a Complex Number

The *absolute value* (or *modulus*) of the complex number $a + bi$ is

$$|a + bi| = \sqrt{a^2 + b^2}.$$

Technology Tip

● Use the ABS key to find the absolute value of a complex number. It is in the NUM submenu of TI and in the CPLX submenu of the Casio OPTN menu.

Example 1   Find Absolute Value of a Complex Number

Find the absolute value of each complex number.

a. $3 + 2i$ **b.** $4 - 5i$

Solution

a. $|3 + 2i| = \sqrt{3^2 + 2^2} = \sqrt{13}$ **b.** $|4 - 5i| = \sqrt{4^2 + (-5)^2} = \sqrt{41}$ ∎

Absolute values and trigonometry lead to a useful way of representing complex numbers. Let $a + bi$ be a nonzero complex number and denote $|a + bi|$ by r. Then r is the length of the line segment joining (a, b) and $(0, 0)$ in the plane. Let θ be the angle in standard position with this line segment as terminal side, as shown in Figure 10.3-2.

ADDITIONAL EXAMPLES

Example 1

Find the absolute value of each complex number.

a. $-6 + 3i$

$\begin{aligned} |-6 + 3i| &= \sqrt{(-6)^2 + (3)^2} \\ &= \sqrt{45} = 3\sqrt{5} \end{aligned}$

b. $1 - 5i$

$|1 - 5i| = \sqrt{(1)^2 + (-5)^2} = \sqrt{26}$

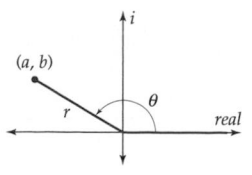

Figure 10.3-2

NOTE It is customary to place i in front of $\sin \theta$ rather than after it. Some books abbreviate $r(\cos \theta + i \sin \theta)$ as r cis θ.

Polar Form of a Complex Number

Using the definitions of sine and cosine, the coordinates a and b can be expressed in terms of r and θ.

$$\cos \theta = \frac{a}{r} \qquad \text{and} \qquad \sin \theta = \frac{b}{r}$$
$$a = r \cos \theta \qquad \qquad b = r \sin \theta$$

Consequently,

$$a + bi = r \cos \theta + (r \sin \theta)i = r(\cos \theta + i \sin \theta).$$

When a complex number $a + bi$ is written in this way, it is said to be in **polar form** or **trigonometric form**. The angle θ is called the **argument** and is usually expressed in radian measure. The number $r = |a + bi|$ is called the **modulus** (plural, moduli). The number 0 can also be written in polar notation by letting $r = 0$ and θ be any angle.

> **Every complex number $a + bi$ can be written in polar form**
>
> $$r(\cos \theta + i \sin \theta)$$
>
> **where $r = |a + bi| = \sqrt{a^2 + b^2}$, $a = r \cos \theta$, and $b = r \sin \theta$.**

When a complex number is written in polar form, the argument θ is not uniquely determined because $\theta, \theta \pm 2\pi, \theta \pm 4\pi$, and so on, all satisfy the conditions in the box.

Example 2   **Find Polar Form**

Express $-\sqrt{3} + i$ in polar form.

Solution

In this case, $a = -\sqrt{3}$ and $b = 1$. Therefore,

$$r = \sqrt{a^2 + b^2} = \sqrt{(-\sqrt{3})^2 + 1^2} = \sqrt{3 + 1} = 2.$$

The angle θ must satisfy the following two conditions.

$$\cos \theta = \frac{a}{r} = \frac{-\sqrt{3}}{2} \qquad \text{and} \qquad \sin \theta = \frac{b}{r} = \frac{1}{2}$$

Because $-\sqrt{3} + i$ is represented by the point $(-\sqrt{3}, 1)$ in the complex plane, it lies in the second quadrant, as shown in Figure 10.3-3. Therefore, θ must be a second-quadrant angle. So, $\theta = \frac{5\pi}{6}$ satisfies these conditions.

Thus, $-\sqrt{3} + i = 2\left(\cos \frac{5\pi}{6} + i \sin \frac{5\pi}{6}\right).$

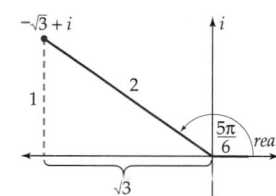

Figure 10.3-3

Example 2

Express $1 - i$ in polar form.

$a = 1, b = -1$

$r = \sqrt{a^2 + b^2} = \sqrt{(1)^2 + (-1)^2}$
$\quad = \sqrt{2}$

$\cos \theta = \frac{a}{r} = \frac{1}{\sqrt{2}}$ and $\sin \theta = \frac{b}{r} = \frac{-1}{\sqrt{2}}$

$1 - i$ is represented by $(1, -1)$, which lies in Quadrant IV in the complex plane.

$\theta = \frac{7\pi}{4}$ satisfies all conditions.

$1 - i = \sqrt{2}\left(\cos \frac{7\pi}{4} + i \sin \frac{7\pi}{4}\right)$

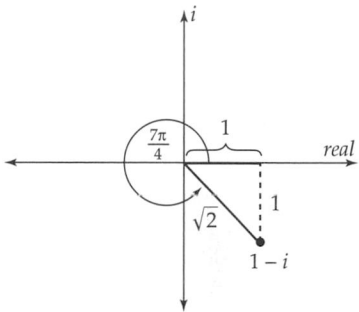

COMMON ERROR ALERT

When converting a complex number from standard form to polar form, students might make a sign error as shown below.

For $0 - i$, $\theta = \frac{3\pi}{2}$ and $\sin \theta = -1$, students might write

$0 - i = 1\left(\cos \frac{3\pi}{2} - i \sin \frac{3\pi}{2}\right)$, which is incorrect. The correct statement is

$0 - i = 1\left(\cos \frac{3\pi}{2} + i \sin \frac{3\pi}{2}\right)$. Remind students that the $+$ symbol will *always* appear between $\cos \theta$ and $i \sin \theta$ in the polar form $r(\cos \theta + i \sin \theta)$.

Math Background

Euler's formula (see page 688), shown below, is an identity that relates the exponential function e^x to the trigonometric functions $\sin x$ and $\cos x$ and the imaginary number i.

$$e^{ix} = \cos x + i \sin x$$

Using Euler's Formula, the polar form of a complex number can be written as follows:

$$r(\cos \theta + i \sin \theta) = re^{i\theta}$$

Example Notes

For **Example 3**, show these alternate ways to find θ:

$$\theta = \cos^{-1}\theta = \frac{-2}{\sqrt{29}} = 1.9513$$

$$\sin^{-1}\frac{5}{\sqrt{29}} = 1.1903; \theta = \pi - 1.1903$$

$$= 1.9513$$

In **Example 5**, have students use the **NOTE** (page 641) to write z_1, z_2 and $\frac{z_1}{z_2}$ in rectangular form.

$$z_1 = 10\left(\cos\frac{\pi}{3} + i\sin\frac{\pi}{3}\right)$$

$$= 10\left(\frac{1}{2} + \frac{\sqrt{3}}{2}i\right) = 5 + \left(5\sqrt{3}\right)i$$

$$z_2 = 2\left(\cos\frac{\pi}{4} + i\sin\frac{\pi}{4}\right)$$

$$= 2\left(\frac{\sqrt{2}}{2} + \frac{\sqrt{2}}{2}i\right) = \sqrt{2} + i\sqrt{2}$$

$$\frac{z_1}{z_2} = 5\left(\cos\frac{\pi}{12} + i\sin\frac{\pi}{12}\right)$$

$$\approx 5(0.9659 + 0.2588\,i)$$

$$\approx 4.8296 + 1.2941i$$

Math Background

You can use rectangular form to find $\frac{z_1}{z_2}$ in **Example 5**.

$$\frac{z_1}{z_2} = \frac{5 + \left(5\sqrt{3}\right)i}{\sqrt{2} + i\sqrt{2}}$$

$$= \frac{5 + \left(5\sqrt{3}\right)i}{\sqrt{2} + i\sqrt{2}} \cdot \frac{\sqrt{2} - i\sqrt{2}}{\sqrt{2} - i\sqrt{2}}$$

$$= \frac{5\sqrt{2} - \left(5\sqrt{2}\right)i + \left(5\sqrt{6}\right)i - \left(5\sqrt{6}\right)i^2}{2 - 2i^2}$$

$$= \frac{5\sqrt{2} + \left(-5\sqrt{2} + 5\sqrt{6}\right)i + 5\sqrt{6}}{4}$$

$$= \frac{\left(5\sqrt{2} + 5\sqrt{6}\right)}{4} + \frac{\left(-5\sqrt{2} + 5\sqrt{6}\right)i}{4}$$

$$\approx 4.8296 + 1.2941i$$

Example 3 Find Polar Form

Express $-2 + 5i$ in polar form.

Solution

In this case, $a = -2$ and $b = 5$. Therefore,

$$r = \sqrt{a^2 + b^2} = \sqrt{(-2)^2 + 5^2} = \sqrt{29}.$$

The angle θ must satisfy

$$\cos\theta = \frac{a}{r} = \frac{-2}{\sqrt{29}} \quad \text{and} \quad \sin\theta = \frac{b}{r} = \frac{5}{\sqrt{29}},$$

so that

$$\tan\theta = \frac{\sin\theta}{\cos\theta} = \frac{\frac{5}{\sqrt{29}}}{\frac{-2}{\sqrt{29}}} = -\frac{5}{2} = -2.5.$$

Because $-2 + 5i$ lies in the second quadrant (see Figure 10.3-4), θ lies between $\frac{\pi}{2}$ and π. Using the TAN^{-1} key, the calculator indicates that a solution to $\tan\theta = -2.5$ is $\theta = -1.1903$. Because that angle is in the fourth quadrant, the only solution between $\frac{\pi}{2}$ and π is

$$\theta = -1.1903 + \pi = 1.9513.$$

Thus, $-2 + 5i = \sqrt{29}(\cos 1.9513 + i\sin 1.9513)$.

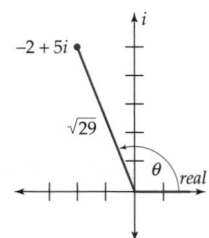

Figure 10.3-4

Multiplication and Division of Complex Numbers

Polar Multiplication and Division

If $z_1 = r_1(\cos\theta_1 + i\sin\theta_1)$ and $z_2 = r_2(\cos\theta_2 + i\sin\theta_2)$ are any two complex numbers, then

$$z_1z_2 = r_1r_2[\cos(\theta_1 + \theta_2) + i\sin(\theta_1 + \theta_2)]$$

and

$$\frac{z_1}{z_2} = \frac{r_1}{r_2}[\cos(\theta_1 - \theta_2) + i\sin(\theta_1 - \theta_2)], z_2 \neq 0.$$

That is, given two complex numbers written in polar form,

- to multiply the two numbers
  multiply the moduli and add the arguments.
- to divide the two numbers
  divide the moduli and subtract the arguments.

The proof of the multiplication statement, which is given at the end of this section, uses the addition identities for sine and cosine.

Example 4   Multiplication of Numbers in Polar Form

Find $z_1 z_2$ when $z_1 = 2\left(\cos\dfrac{5\pi}{6} + i\sin\dfrac{5\pi}{6}\right)$ and $z_2 = 3\left(\cos\dfrac{7\pi}{4} + i\sin\dfrac{7\pi}{4}\right)$.

Solution

In this case, $r_1 = 2$, $\theta_1 = \dfrac{5\pi}{6}$, $r_2 = 3$, and $\theta_2 = \dfrac{7\pi}{4}$. Therefore,

$$z_1 z_2 = r_1 r_2 [\cos(\theta_1 + \theta_2) + i\sin(\theta_1 + \theta_2)]$$
$$= (2)(3)\left[\cos\left(\frac{5\pi}{6} + \frac{7\pi}{4}\right) + i\sin\left(\frac{5\pi}{6} + \frac{7\pi}{4}\right)\right]$$
$$= 6\left[\cos\left(\frac{10\pi}{12} + \frac{21\pi}{12}\right) + i\sin\left(\frac{10\pi}{12} + \frac{21\pi}{12}\right)\right]$$
$$= 6\left(\cos\frac{31\pi}{12} + i\sin\frac{31\pi}{12}\right)$$

> **NOTE** A complex number written in polar form can be written in rectangular form by evaluating each term and simplifying. For example,
>
> $$2\left(\cos\frac{5\pi}{6} + i\sin\frac{5\pi}{6}\right)$$
> $$= 2\left(\frac{-\sqrt{3}}{2} + \frac{1}{2}i\right)$$
> $$= -\sqrt{3} + i$$

Example 5   Division of Numbers in Polar Form

Find $\dfrac{z_1}{z_2}$ when $z_1 = 10\left(\cos\dfrac{\pi}{3} + i\sin\dfrac{\pi}{3}\right)$ and $z_2 = 2\left(\cos\dfrac{\pi}{4} + i\sin\dfrac{\pi}{4}\right)$.

Solution

In this case, $r_1 = 10$, $\theta_1 = \dfrac{\pi}{3}$, $r_2 = 2$, and $\theta_2 = \dfrac{\pi}{4}$. Therefore,

$$\frac{z_1}{z_2} = \frac{10}{2}\left[\cos\left(\frac{\pi}{3} - \frac{\pi}{4}\right) + i\sin\left(\frac{\pi}{3} - \frac{\pi}{4}\right)\right]$$
$$= 5\left(\cos\frac{\pi}{12} + i\sin\frac{\pi}{12}\right)$$

Proof of the Polar Multiplication Rule

Let $z_1 = r_1(\cos\theta_1 + i\sin\theta_1)$ and $z_2 = r_2(\cos\theta_2 + i\sin\theta_2)$.

$$z_1 z_2 = [r_1(\cos\theta_1 + i\sin\theta_1)][r_2(\cos\theta_2 + i\sin\theta_2)]$$
$$= r_1 r_2(\cos\theta_1 + i\sin\theta_1)(\cos\theta_2 + i\sin\theta_2)$$
$$= r_1 r_2(\cos\theta_1\cos\theta_2 + i\sin\theta_1\cos\theta_2 + i\sin\theta_2\cos\theta_1 + i^2\sin\theta_1\sin\theta_2)$$
$$= r_1 r_2[(\cos\theta_1\cos\theta_2 - \sin\theta_1\sin\theta_2) + i(\sin\theta_1\cos\theta_2 + \sin\theta_2\cos\theta_1)]$$

Recall from Section 9.2 that

$$\cos(\theta_1 + \theta_2) = \cos\theta_1\cos\theta_2 - \sin\theta_1\sin\theta_2$$

ADDITIONAL EXAMPLES

Example 3

Express $-1 - 4i$ in polar form.

$a = -1$, $b = -4$

$r = \sqrt{a^2 + b^2} = \sqrt{(-1)^2 + (-4)^2}$
$\quad = \sqrt{17}$

$\cos\theta = \dfrac{a}{r} = \dfrac{-1}{\sqrt{17}}$, $\sin\theta = \dfrac{b}{r} = \dfrac{-4}{\sqrt{17}}$

$\tan\theta = \dfrac{\sin\theta}{\cos\theta} = \dfrac{\frac{-4}{\sqrt{17}}}{\frac{-1}{\sqrt{17}}} = 4$

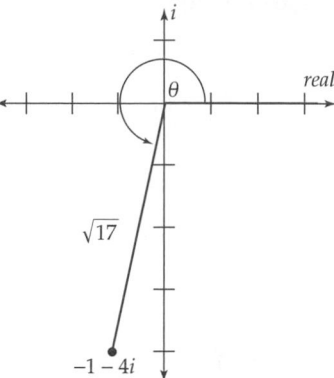

$-1 - 4i$ is in the third quadrant.

$\tan^{-1} 4 = 1.3258$

$\theta = 1.3258 + \pi = 4.4674$

Thus, $-1 - 4i = \sqrt{17}(\cos 4.4674 + i\sin 4.4674)$

Example 4

Find $z_1 z_2$ when $z_1 = 5\left(\cos\dfrac{\pi}{4} + i\sin\dfrac{\pi}{4}\right)$

and $z_2 = 4\left(\cos\dfrac{2\pi}{3} + i\sin\dfrac{2\pi}{3}\right)$.

$r_1 = 5$, $\theta_1 = \dfrac{\pi}{4}$, $r_2 = 4$, and $\theta_2 = \dfrac{2\pi}{3}$.

$z_1 z_2 = (5)(4)\left[\cos\left(\dfrac{\pi}{4} + \dfrac{2\pi}{3}\right) + i\sin\left(\dfrac{\pi}{4} + \dfrac{2\pi}{3}\right)\right]$

$\quad = 20\left[\cos\left(\dfrac{3\pi}{12} + \dfrac{8\pi}{12}\right) + i\sin\left(\dfrac{3\pi}{12} + \dfrac{8\pi}{12}\right)\right]$

$\quad = 20\left(\cos\dfrac{11\pi}{12} + i\sin\dfrac{11\pi}{12}\right)$

Example 5

Find $\dfrac{z_1}{z_2}$ when

$z_1 = 12\left(\cos\dfrac{4\pi}{3} + i\sin\dfrac{4\pi}{3}\right)$ and

$z_2 = 6\left(\cos\dfrac{3\pi}{4} + i\sin\dfrac{3\pi}{4}\right)$.

$r_1 = 12$, $\theta_1 = \dfrac{4\pi}{3}$, $r_2 = 6$, and $\theta_2 = \dfrac{3\pi}{4}$.

$\dfrac{z_1}{z_2} = \dfrac{12}{6}\cos\left[\left(\dfrac{4\pi}{3} - \dfrac{3\pi}{4}\right) + i\sin\left(\dfrac{4\pi}{3} - \dfrac{3\pi}{4}\right)\right]$

$\quad = 2\left(\cos\dfrac{7\pi}{12} + i\sin\dfrac{7\pi}{12}\right)$

ANSWERS

1–8. See p. 1073.

17–24. See pp. 1073–1074.

25. $5(\cos 0.9273 + i \sin 0.9273)$

26. $5(\cos 2.4981 + i \sin 2.4981)$

27. $13(\cos 5.1072 + i \sin 5.1072)$

28. $4(\cos 3.9897 + i \sin 3.9897)$

29. $\sqrt{5}(\cos 1.1071 + i \sin 1.1071)$

30. $\sqrt{34}(\cos 5.2528 + i \sin 5.2528)$

31. $\dfrac{\sqrt{74}}{2}(\cos 2.1910 + i \sin 2.1910)$

32. $4(\cos 0.9776 + i \sin 0.9776)$

33. $6\left(\cos\dfrac{2\pi}{3} + i \sin\dfrac{2\pi}{3}\right) = -3 + 3\sqrt{3}i$

34. $36\left(\cos\dfrac{\pi}{2} + i \sin\dfrac{\pi}{2}\right) = 36i$

35. $42\left(\cos\dfrac{7\pi}{6} + i \sin\dfrac{7\pi}{6}\right)$
$= -21\sqrt{3} - 21i$

36. $2\left(\cos\dfrac{\pi}{6} + i \sin\dfrac{\pi}{6}\right) = \sqrt{3} + i$

37. $\dfrac{3}{2}\left(\cos\dfrac{\pi}{4} + i \sin\dfrac{\pi}{4}\right)$
$= \left(\dfrac{3\sqrt{2}}{4}\right) + \left(\dfrac{3\sqrt{2}}{4}\right)i$

38. $3\left(\cos\dfrac{5\pi}{3} + i \sin\dfrac{5\pi}{3}\right)$
$= \dfrac{3}{2} - \dfrac{3\sqrt{3}}{2}i$

39. $2\sqrt{2}\left(\cos\dfrac{7\pi}{12} + i \sin\dfrac{7\pi}{12}\right)$

40. $6\left(\cos\dfrac{7\pi}{2} + i \sin\dfrac{7\pi}{2}\right)$

41. $\cos\dfrac{\pi}{2} + i \sin\dfrac{\pi}{2}$

42. $2\left(\cos\dfrac{\pi}{2} + i \sin\dfrac{\pi}{2}\right)$

43. $12\left(\cos\dfrac{2\pi}{3} + i \sin\dfrac{2\pi}{3}\right)$

44. $2\left(\cos\dfrac{4\pi}{3} + i \sin\dfrac{4\pi}{3}\right)$

45. $2\sqrt{2}\left(\cos\dfrac{19\pi}{12} + i \sin\dfrac{19\pi}{12}\right)$

46. $32\sqrt{2}\left(\cos\dfrac{59\pi}{12} + i \sin\dfrac{59\pi}{12}\right)$

and
$$\sin(\theta_1 + \theta_2) = \sin\theta_1 \cos\theta_2 + \cos\theta_1 \sin\theta_2.$$
Therefore,
$$z_1 z_2 = r_1 r_2[(\cos\theta_1 \cos\theta_2 - \sin\theta_1 \sin\theta_2) + i(\sin\theta_1 \cos\theta_2 + \sin\theta_2 \cos\theta_1)]$$
$$= r_1 r_2[\cos(\theta_1 + \theta_2) + i \sin(\theta_1 + \theta_2)]$$

This completes the proof of the multiplication rule. The division rule is proved similarly. See Exercise 51.

Exercises 10.3

In Exercises 1–8, plot the point in the complex plane that corresponds to each number.

1. $3 + 2i$ **2.** $-7 + 6i$ **3.** $-\dfrac{8}{3} - \dfrac{5}{3}i$

4. $\sqrt{2} - 7i$ **5.** $(1 + i)(1 - i)$ **6.** $(2 + i)(1 - 2i)$

7. $2i\left(3 - \dfrac{5}{2}i\right)$ **8.** $\dfrac{4}{3}i(-6 - 3i)$

In Exercises 9–14, find each absolute value.

9. $|5 - 12i|$ **13** **10.** $|2i|$ **2**   **11.** $|1 + i\sqrt{2}|$ $\sqrt{3}$

12. $|2 - 3i|$ $\sqrt{13}$ **13.** $|-12i|$ **12**   **14.** $|i^7|$ **1**

15. Give an example of complex numbers z and w such that $|z + w| = |z| + |w|$.
possible answer: $z = 2i$, $w = i$

16. If $z = 3 - 4i$, find $|z|^2$ and $z\bar{z}$ where $\bar{z}$ is the conjugate of z. See Section 4.5 for the definition of a complex conjugate. **25; 25**

In Exercises 17–24, sketch the graph of the equation in the complex plane (z denotes a complex number of the form $a + bi$).

17. $|z| = 4$ *Hint:* The graph consists of all points that lie 4 units from the origin.

18. $|z| = 1$

19. $|z - 1| = 10$ *Hint:* 1 corresponds to (1, 0) in the complex plane. What does the equation say about the distance from z to 1?

20. $|z + 3| = 1$ **21.** $|z - 2i| = 4$

22. $|z - 3i + 2| = 3$ *Hint:* Rewrite it as $|z - (-2 + 3i)| = 3$.

23. $\text{Re}(z) = 2$ [The **real part** of the complex number $z = a + bi$ is defined to be the number a and is denoted $\text{Re}(z)$.]

24. $\text{Im}(z) = -\dfrac{5}{2}$ [The **imaginary part** of $z = a + bi$ is defined to be the number b (not bi) and is denoted $\text{Im}(z)$.]

In Exercises 25–32, express each number in polar form.

25. $3 + 4i$ **26.** $-4 + 3i$ **27.** $5 - 12i$

28. $-\sqrt{7} - 3i$ **29.** $1 + 2i$ **30.** $3 - 5i$

31. $-\dfrac{5}{2} + \dfrac{7}{2}i$ **32.** $\sqrt{5} + i\sqrt{11}$

In Exercises 33–38, perform the indicated multiplication or division. Express your answer in both rectangular form $a + bi$ and polar form $r(\cos\theta + i \sin\theta)$.

33. $3\left(\cos\dfrac{\pi}{12} + i \sin\dfrac{\pi}{12}\right) \cdot 2\left(\cos\dfrac{7\pi}{12} + i \sin\dfrac{7\pi}{12}\right)$

34. $3\left(\cos\dfrac{\pi}{8} + i \sin\dfrac{\pi}{8}\right) \cdot 12\left(\cos\dfrac{3\pi}{8} + i \sin\dfrac{3\pi}{8}\right)$

35. $12\left(\cos\dfrac{11\pi}{12} + i \sin\dfrac{11\pi}{12}\right) \cdot \dfrac{7}{2}\left(\cos\dfrac{\pi}{4} + i \sin\dfrac{\pi}{4}\right)$

36. $\dfrac{8\left(\cos\dfrac{5\pi}{18} + i \sin\dfrac{5\pi}{18}\right)}{4\left(\cos\dfrac{\pi}{9} + i \sin\dfrac{\pi}{9}\right)}$

37. $\dfrac{6\left(\cos\dfrac{7\pi}{20} + i \sin\dfrac{7\pi}{20}\right)}{4\left(\cos\dfrac{\pi}{10} + i \sin\dfrac{\pi}{10}\right)}$

47. The polar form of i is $1(\cos 90° + i \sin 90°)$. Hence, by the Polar Multiplication Rule
$zi = r \cdot 1(\cos(\theta + 90°) + i \sin(\theta + 90°))$.
You can think of z as lying on a circle with center at the origin and radius r. Then zi lies on the same circle (since it too is r units from the origin), but 90° farther around the circle (in a counterclockwise direction).

38.
$$\frac{\sqrt{54}\left(\cos\frac{9\pi}{4} + i\sin\frac{9\pi}{4}\right)}{\sqrt{6}\left(\cos\frac{7\pi}{12} + i\sin\frac{7\pi}{12}\right)}$$

In Exercises 39–46, convert to polar form and then multiply or divide. Express your answer in polar form.

39. $(1 + i)(1 + i\sqrt{3})$ **40.** $(1 - i)(3 - 3i)$

41. $\dfrac{1 + i}{1 - i}$ **42.** $\dfrac{2 - 2i}{-1 - i}$

43. $3i(2\sqrt{3} + 2i)$ **44.** $\dfrac{-4i}{\sqrt{3} + i}$

45. $i(i + 1)(-\sqrt{3} + i)$

46. $(1 - i)(2\sqrt{3} - 2i)(-4 - 4i\sqrt{3})$

47. Explain what is meant by saying that multiplying a complex number $z = r(\cos\theta + i\sin\theta)$ by i amounts to rotating z 90° counterclockwise around the origin. *Hint:* Express i and iz in polar form; what are their relative positions in the complex plane?

48. Describe what happens geometrically when you multiply a complex number by 2.

49. *Critical Thinking* The sum of two distinct complex numbers, $a + bi$ and $c + di$, can be found geometrically by means of the so-called **parallelogram rule:** Plot the points $a + bi$ and $c + di$ in the complex plane and form the parallelogram, three of whose vertices are 0, $a + bi$ and $c + di$ as in the figure below. Then the fourth vertex of the parallelogram is the point whose coordinate is the sum

$$(a + bi) + (c + di) = (a + c) + (b + d)i.$$

Complete the following *proof* of the parallelogram rule when $a \neq 0$ and $c \neq 0$.
a. Find the slope of the line K from 0 to $a + bi$. *Hint:* K contains the points $(0, 0)$ and (a, b).
b. Find the slope of the line N from 0 to $c + di$.
c. Find the equation of the line L, through $a + bi$ and parallel to line N of part **b**. *Hint:* The point (a, b) is on L; find the slope of L by using part **b** and facts about the slope of parallel lines.
d. Find the equation of the line M, through $c + di$ and parallel to line K of part **a**.
e. Label the lines K, L, M, and N in each figure.
f. Show by using substitution that the point $(a + c, b + d)$ satisfies both the equation of line L and the equation of line M. Therefore, $(a + c, b + d)$ lies on both L and M. Because the only point on both L and M is the fourth vertex of the parallelogram, this vertex must be $(a + c, b + d)$. Hence, this vertex has coordinate
$$(a + c) + (b + d)i = (a + bi) + (c + di).$$

50. *Critical Thinking* Let $z = a + bi$ be a complex number and denote its conjugate $a - bi$ by $\bar{z}$. Prove that $|z|^2 = z\bar{z}$.

51. *Critical Thinking* Proof of the polar division rule. Let $z_1 = r_1(\cos\theta_1 + i\sin\theta_1)$ and $z_2 = r_2(\cos\theta_2 + i\sin\theta_2)$.

$$\frac{z_1}{z_2} = \frac{r_1(\cos\theta_1 + i\sin\theta_1)}{r_2(\cos\theta_2 + i\sin\theta_2)}$$

$$= \frac{r_1(\cos\theta_1 + i\sin\theta_1)}{r_2(\cos\theta_2 + i\sin\theta_2)} \cdot \frac{\cos\theta_2 - i\sin\theta_2}{\cos\theta_2 - i\sin\theta_2}$$

a. Multiply the denominators and use the Pythagorean identity to show that it is the number r_2.
b. Multiply the numerators; use the subtraction identities for sine and cosine (Section 9.2) to show that it is
$$r_1[\cos(\theta_1 - \theta_2) + i\sin(\theta_1 - \theta_2)].$$

Therefore,

$$\frac{z_1}{z_2} = \left(\frac{r_1}{r_2}\right)[\cos(\theta_1 - \theta_2) + i\sin(\theta_1 - \theta_2)].$$

52. *Critical Thinking*
a. If $s(\cos\beta + i\sin\beta) = r(\cos\theta + i\sin\theta)$, explain why $s = r$ must be true. *Hint:* Think distance.
b. If $r(\cos\beta + i\sin\beta) = r(\cos\theta + i\sin\theta)$, explain why $\cos\beta = \cos\theta$ and $\sin\beta = \sin\theta$. *Hint:* See Property 5 of the complex numbers in Section 4.5.

48. The distance from the origin, r, is doubled, but the direction angle is unchanged.

49. a. $\dfrac{b}{a}$

b. $\dfrac{d}{c}$

c. $y - b = \left(\dfrac{d}{c}\right)(x - a)$

d. $y - d = \dfrac{b}{a}(x - c)$

e. See figure at lower left

f. $(a + c, b + d)$ lies on L since
$$(b + d) - b = \frac{d}{c}[(a + c) - a]$$
and $(a + c, b + d)$ lies on M since
$$(b + d) - d = \frac{b}{a}[(a + c) - c].$$

50. $|z|^2 = \left(\sqrt{a^2 + b^2}\right)^2 = a^2 + b^2$;
$z\bar{z} = (a + bi)(a - bi) = a^2 + b^2$

51. a. $r_2(\cos\theta_2 + i\sin\theta_2) \cdot$
$\qquad\qquad (\cos\theta_2 - i\sin\theta_2)$
$= r_2(\cos^2\theta_2 + \sin^2\theta_2) = r_2$
b. $r_1(\cos\theta_1 + i\sin\theta_1) \cdot$
$\qquad\qquad (\cos\theta_2 - i\sin\theta_2)$
$= r_1[(\cos\theta_1 \cos\theta_2 +$
$\sin\theta_1 \sin\theta_2) + i(\sin\theta_1 \cos\theta_2 -$
$\qquad\qquad\qquad \cos\theta_1 \sin\theta_2)]$
$= r_1[\cos(\theta_1 - \theta_2) +$
$\qquad\qquad i\sin(\theta_1 - \theta_2)]$

52. a. $|s(\cos\beta + i\sin\beta)|$
$= |r(\cos\theta + i\sin\theta)|$
$\sqrt{s^2(\cos^2\beta + \sin^2\beta)}$
$= \sqrt{r^2(\cos^2\theta + \sin^2\theta)}$;
$\sqrt{s^2} = \sqrt{r^2}$; $s = r$

b. Since $r(\cos\beta + i\sin\beta)$
$= r(\cos\theta + i\sin\theta)$,
$\cos\beta + i\sin\beta$
$= \cos\theta + i\sin\theta$. Since the
two complex numbers are
equal, $\cos\beta = \cos\theta$,
$\sin\beta = \sin\theta$.

c. The point $(\cos\beta, \sin\beta)$ is the
point where the terminal side
of the angle of measure β hits
the unit circle. Similarly,
$(\cos\theta, \sin\theta)$ is the point where
the terminal side of the angle
of measure θ hits the unit
circle. Since these points are
the same, the terminal sides
must be the same.

d. From part **a**, $s = r$. Since β
and θ are coterminal, they
differ by only a multiple of 2π.
That is, $\beta = \theta + 2k\pi$.

c. If $\cos \beta = \cos \theta$ and $\sin \beta = \sin \theta$, show that angles β and θ in standard position have the same terminal side. *Hint:* $(\cos \beta, \sin \beta)$ and $(\cos \theta, \sin \theta)$ are points on the unit circle.

d. Use parts **a–c** to prove this equality rule for polar form:

$$s(\cos \beta + i \sin \beta) = r(\cos \theta + i \sin \theta)$$

exactly when $s = r$ and $\beta = \theta + 2k\pi$ for some integer k. *Hint:* Angles with the same terminal side must differ by an integer multiple of 2π.

Section

10.4 DeMoivre's Theorem and *n*th Roots of Complex Numbers

📐 Math Background

Abraham DeMoivre (1667–1754) was born in France but spent much of his life in England where he and Sir Isaac Newton were friends. In addition to the theorem named after him, DeMoivre made important contributions to the development of analytic geometry and probability theory. He is also famous for correctly predicting the day of his own death! He noted that he slept for 15 minutes longer each night, and calculating the sum of the arithmetic sequence, predicted that he would die on the day that he slept for 24 hours.

Example Notes

In both **Examples 1** and **2**, we convert from standard form $a + bi$ to polar form $r(\cos \theta + i \sin \theta)$ and then back to standard form.

Remind students that there are infinitely many ways to represent a complex number in polar form $r(\cos \theta + i \sin \theta)$. In **Example 1**, $\frac{\pi}{6}$ is coterminal with $\frac{25\pi}{6}$. We use $\frac{\pi}{6}$ for θ instead of $\frac{25\pi}{6}$, but the final answer, $16\sqrt{3} + 16i$, would be the same if we used $\frac{25\pi}{6}$ for θ. In **Example 2**, we could have used $\frac{\pi}{2}$ in place of $\frac{5\pi}{2}$ to get the final answer.

10.4 DeMoivre's Theorem and *n*th Roots of Complex Numbers

Objectives

- Calculate powers and roots of complex numbers
- Find and graph roots of unity

Polar form provides a convenient way to calculate both powers and roots of complex numbers. If $z = r(\cos \theta + i \sin \theta)$, then the multiplication formula from Section 10.3 shows the following:

$$z^2 = z \cdot z = r \cdot r[\cos(\theta + \theta) + i \sin(\theta + \theta)]$$
$$= r^2(\cos 2\theta + i \sin 2\theta)$$

and

$$z^3 = z^2 \cdot z = r^2 \cdot r[\cos(2\theta + \theta) + i \sin(2\theta + \theta)]$$
$$= r^3(\cos 3\theta + i \sin 3\theta)$$

and so on. Repeated application of the multiplication formula proves **DeMoivre's Theorem.**

DeMoivre's Theorem

> For any complex number $z = r(\cos \theta + i \sin \theta)$ and any positive integer n,
>
> $$z^n = r^n(\cos n\theta + i \sin n\theta).$$

NOTE

$$\tan^{-1} \frac{1}{-\sqrt{3}} = \frac{5\pi}{6}$$

Example 1 **Find Powers of Complex Numbers**

Evaluate $\left(-\sqrt{3} + i\right)^5$.

Solution

First express the complex number $-\sqrt{3} + i$ in polar form. (See Example 2 of Section 10.3.)

$$-\sqrt{3} + i = 2\left(\cos \frac{5\pi}{6} + i \sin \frac{5\pi}{6}\right)$$

ADDITIONAL EXAMPLES

Apply DeMoivre's Theorem.

$$\left(-\sqrt{3} + i\right)^5 = 2^5\left[\cos\left(5 \cdot \frac{5\pi}{6}\right) + i\sin\left(5 \cdot \frac{5\pi}{6}\right)\right]$$

$$= 32\left(\cos\frac{25\pi}{6} + i\sin\frac{25\pi}{6}\right)$$

Because $\frac{25\pi}{6} = \frac{\pi}{6} + \frac{24\pi}{6} = \frac{\pi}{6} + 4\pi$, $\frac{\pi}{6}$ can be substituted for $\frac{25\pi}{6}$.

$$\left(-\sqrt{3} + i\right)^5 = 32\left(\cos\frac{25\pi}{6} + i\sin\frac{25\pi}{6}\right)$$

$$= 32\left(\cos\frac{\pi}{6} + i\sin\frac{\pi}{6}\right) \qquad polar~form$$

$$= 32\left(\frac{\sqrt{3}}{2} + \frac{1}{2}i\right)$$

$$= 16\sqrt{3} + 16i \qquad rectangular~form \blacksquare$$

Example 2   **Find Powers of Complex Numbers**

Evaluate $(1 + i)^{10}$.

Solution

Express the complex number $1 + i$ in polar form.

$$1 + i = \sqrt{2}\left(\cos\frac{\pi}{4} + i\sin\frac{\pi}{4}\right)$$

Apply DeMoivre's Theorem.

$$(1 + i)^{10} = \left(\sqrt{2}\right)^{10}\left(\cos\frac{10\pi}{4} + i\sin\frac{10\pi}{4}\right)$$

$$= 32\left(\cos\frac{5\pi}{2} + i\sin\frac{5\pi}{2}\right) \qquad polar~form$$

$$= 32(0 + i)$$

$$= 32i \qquad rectangular~form \blacksquare$$

NOTE   With complex numbers, it is not possible to choose the positive root as the *n*th root of $a + bi$, as is done with real numbers, because "positive" and "negative" are not meaningful terms in the complex numbers. For instance, should $3 - 2i$ be called positive or negative?

Nth Roots

If $a + bi$ is a complex number and n is a positive integer, the equation $z^n = a + bi$ may have n different solutions in the complex numbers. Furthermore, there is no obvious way to designate one of these solutions as *the* *n*th root of $a + bi$ (see note). Consequently, *any* solution of the equation $z^n = a + bi$ is called an **nth root** of $a + bi$.

Every real number is a complex number. When the definition of *n*th root of a complex number is applied to a real number, the terminology for real numbers no longer applies. For instance, in the complex numbers, 16 has *four* fourth roots because each of 2, -2, $2i$, and $-2i$ is a solution of $z^4 = 16$, whereas in the real numbers, 2 is the fourth root of 16.

Example 1

Evaluate $\left(1 + i\sqrt{3}\right)^8$.

Express $\left(1 + i\sqrt{3}\right)$ in polar form:

$$1 + i\sqrt{3} = 2\left(\cos\frac{\pi}{3} + i\sin\frac{\pi}{3}\right)$$

Apply DeMoivre's Theorem:

$$\left(1 + i\sqrt{3}\right)^8$$

$$= 2^8\left[\cos\left(8 \cdot \frac{\pi}{3}\right) + i\sin\left(8 \cdot \frac{\pi}{3}\right)\right]$$

$$= 256\left(\cos\frac{8\pi}{3} + i\sin\frac{8\pi}{3}\right)$$

$\frac{8\pi}{3} = \frac{2\pi}{3} + \frac{6\pi}{3} = \frac{2\pi}{3} + 2\pi$, so $\frac{2\pi}{3}$ can be substituted for $\frac{8\pi}{3}$.

$$\left(1 - i\sqrt{3}\right)^8 = 256\left(\cos\frac{2\pi}{3} + i\sin\frac{2\pi}{3}\right)$$

$$= 256\left(-\frac{1}{2} + \frac{\sqrt{3}}{2}i\right)$$

$$= -128 + 128i\sqrt{3}$$

Example 2

Evaluate $(1 - i)^6$.

Express $(1 - i)$ in polar form.

$$1 - i = \sqrt{2}\left(\cos\frac{7\pi}{4} + i\sin\frac{7\pi}{4}\right)$$

Apply DeMoivre's Theorem:

$$(1 - i)^6 = \sqrt{2}^6\left(\cos\frac{42\pi}{4} + i\sin\frac{42\pi}{4}\right)$$

$$= 8\left(\cos\frac{21\pi}{2} + i\sin\frac{21\pi}{2}\right)$$

$\frac{21\pi}{2} = \frac{\pi}{2} + \frac{20\pi}{2} = \frac{\pi}{2} + 5(2\pi)$, so $\frac{\pi}{2}$ can be substituted for $\frac{21\pi}{2}$.

$$(1 - i)^6 = 8\left(\cos\frac{\pi}{2} + i\sin\frac{\pi}{2}\right)$$

$$= 8(0 + i)$$

$$= 8i$$

Example Notes

After completing **Example 3**, have students graph the fourth roots of $-8 + 8i\sqrt{3}$, labeling each point in both polar form and standard form. Have them connect the points to form a polygon.

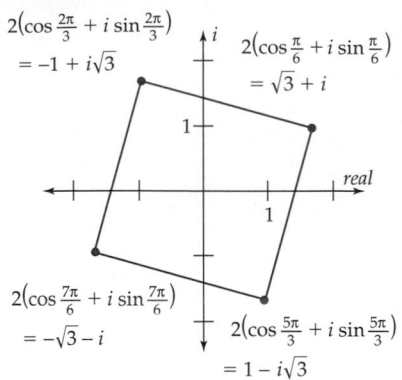

$$2\left(\cos\frac{2\pi}{3} + i\sin\frac{2\pi}{3}\right)$$
$$= -1 + i\sqrt{3}$$

$$2\left(\cos\frac{\pi}{6} + i\sin\frac{\pi}{6}\right)$$
$$= \sqrt{3} + i$$

$$2\left(\cos\frac{7\pi}{6} + i\sin\frac{7\pi}{6}\right)$$
$$= -\sqrt{3} - i$$

$$2\left(\cos\frac{5\pi}{3} + i\sin\frac{5\pi}{3}\right)$$
$$= 1 - i\sqrt{3}$$

Ask students to describe the polygon. square

Ask them to predict what kind of polygon would be formed by graphing:
• the fifth roots of a nonzero complex number
• the nth roots of a nonzero complex number

predictions might vary; actual answers are: regular pentagon and regular n-sided polygon

In **Example 4,** the five distinct roots shown on page 648 are in polar form. Consider having your students convert the first answer to standard form and then check it by raising it to the 5th power. See below.

```
√(2)(cos(π/20)+i
sin(π/20))
        1.397+.221i
Ans^5
      4.000+4.000i
```

Although nth roots are not unique in the complex numbers, the radical symbol will be used only for nonnegative real numbers and will have the same meaning as before. That is, if r is a nonnegative real number, then $\sqrt[n]{r}$ denotes the unique nonnegative real number whose nth power is r.

NOTE $\tan^{-1}\dfrac{8\sqrt{3}}{-8} = \dfrac{\pi}{3}$

Because $-8 + 8i\sqrt{3}$ is in Quadrant II of the complex plane, the angle is

$$-\frac{\pi}{3} + \pi = \frac{2\pi}{3}.$$

Example 3   Find Roots of Complex Numbers

Find the fourth roots of $-8 + 8i\sqrt{3}$.

Solution

Express the complex number $-8 + 8i\sqrt{3}$ in polar form.

$$-8 + 8i\sqrt{3} = 16\left(\cos\frac{2\pi}{3} + i\sin\frac{2\pi}{3}\right)$$

To solve $z^4 = 16\left(\cos\dfrac{2\pi}{3} + i\sin\dfrac{2\pi}{3}\right)$, find s and β such that $z = s(\cos\beta + i\sin\beta)$ is a solution. In other words, find s and β such that

$$[s(\cos\beta + i\sin\beta)]^4 = 16\left(\cos\frac{2\pi}{3} + i\sin\frac{2\pi}{3}\right).$$

Use DeMoivre's Theorem to rewrite the left side.

$$s^4(\cos 4\beta + i\sin 4\beta) = 16\left(\cos\frac{2\pi}{3} + i\sin\frac{2\pi}{3}\right)$$

The equality rules for complex numbers (proved in Exercise 52 of Section 10.3) show that the above equation is true if

$$s^4 = 16 \qquad \text{and} \qquad 4\beta = \frac{2\pi}{3} + 2k\pi$$

$$s = \sqrt[4]{16} = 2 \qquad\qquad \beta = \frac{\pi}{6} + \frac{k\pi}{2}$$

Therefore, the solutions of $z^4 = 16\left(\cos\dfrac{2\pi}{3} + i\sin\dfrac{2\pi}{3}\right)$ are

$$z = 2\left[\cos\left(\frac{\pi}{6} + \frac{k\pi}{2}\right) + i\sin\left(\frac{\pi}{6} + \frac{k\pi}{2}\right)\right],$$

where k is any integer. Letting $k = 0, 1, 2,$ and 3 produces four distinct solutions.

$$k = 0: \quad z = 2\left(\cos\frac{\pi}{6} + i\sin\frac{\pi}{6}\right) = \sqrt{3} + i$$

$$k = 1: \quad z = 2\left[\cos\left(\frac{\pi}{6} + \frac{\pi}{2}\right) + i\sin\left(\frac{\pi}{6} + \frac{\pi}{2}\right)\right]$$
$$= 2\left(\cos\frac{2\pi}{3} + i\sin\frac{2\pi}{3}\right) = -1 + i\sqrt{3}$$

$$k = 2: \quad z = 2\left[\cos\left(\frac{\pi}{6} + \pi\right) + i\sin\left(\frac{\pi}{6} + \pi\right)\right]$$
$$= 2\left(\cos\frac{7\pi}{6} + i\sin\frac{7\pi}{6}\right) = -\sqrt{3} - i$$

$$k = 3: \quad z = 2\left[\cos\left(\frac{\pi}{6} + \frac{3\pi}{2}\right) + i\sin\left(\frac{\pi}{6} + \frac{3\pi}{2}\right)\right]$$

$$= 2\left(\cos\frac{5\pi}{3} + i\sin\frac{5\pi}{3}\right) = 1 - i\sqrt{3}$$

Any other value of k produces an angle β with the same terminal side as one of the four angles already used and is the same solution. For instance, when $k = 4$, then $\beta = \frac{\pi}{6} + \frac{4\pi}{2} = \frac{\pi}{6} + 2\pi$, so β has the same terminal side as $\frac{\pi}{6}$. Therefore, all fourth roots of $-8 + 8i\sqrt{3}$ have been found. ∎

The general equation $z^n = r(\cos\theta + i\sin\theta)$ can be solved exactly by the same method used in Example 3: substitute n for 4, r for 16, and θ for $\frac{2\pi}{3}$, as follows. A solution is a number $s(\cos\beta + i\sin\beta)$ such that:

$$[s(\cos\beta + i\sin\beta)]^n = r(\cos\theta + i\sin\theta)$$
$$s^n(\cos n\beta + i\sin n\beta) = r(\cos\theta + i\sin\theta)$$

Therefore,

$$s^n = r \qquad n\beta = \theta + 2k\pi$$
$$\text{and}$$
$$s = \sqrt[n]{r} \qquad \beta = \frac{\theta + 2k\pi}{n}$$

where k is any integer. Letting $k = 0, 1, 2, \ldots, n - 1$ produces n distinct angles β. This is stated in the following **formula for *n*th roots.**

Formula for *n*th Roots

For each positive integer n, the nonzero complex number

$$r(\cos\theta + i\sin\theta)$$

has exactly n distinct nth roots. They are given by

$$\sqrt[n]{r}\left[\cos\left(\frac{\theta + 2k\pi}{n}\right) + i\sin\left(\frac{\theta + 2k\pi}{n}\right)\right],$$

where $k = 0, 1, 2, 3, \ldots, n - 1$.

Example 4   Find Roots of Complex Numbers

Find the fifth roots of $4 + 4i$.

Solution

Express the complex number $4 + 4i$ in polar form.

$$4 + 4i = 4\sqrt{2}\left(\cos\frac{\pi}{4} + i\sin\frac{\pi}{4}\right)$$

Example 3

Find the fourth roots of $-\frac{81}{2} - \frac{81\sqrt{3}}{2}i$.

Express $-\frac{81}{2} - \frac{81\sqrt{3}}{2}i$ in polar form:

$$-\frac{81}{2} - \frac{81\sqrt{3}}{2}i = 81\left(\cos\frac{4\pi}{3} + i\sin\frac{4\pi}{3}\right)$$

To solve $z^4 = 81\left(\cos\frac{4\pi}{3} + i\sin\frac{4\pi}{3}\right)$, find s and β such that

$$[s(\cos\beta + i\sin\beta)]^4$$
$$= 81\left(\cos\frac{4\pi}{3} + i\sin\frac{4\pi}{3}\right).$$

Use DeMoivre's Theorem to rewrite the left side:

$$s^4(\cos 4\beta + i\sin 4\beta)$$
$$= 81\left(\cos\frac{4\pi}{3} + i\sin\frac{4\pi}{3}\right)$$

$$s^4 = 81 \qquad 4\beta = \frac{4\pi}{3} + 2k\pi$$
$$\text{and}$$
$$s = \sqrt[4]{81} = 3 \qquad \beta = \frac{\pi}{3} + \frac{k\pi}{2}$$

So,

$$z = 3\left[\cos\left(\frac{\pi}{3} + \frac{k\pi}{2}\right) + i\sin\left(\frac{\pi}{3} + \frac{k\pi}{2}\right)\right],$$

where k is any integer.

Letting $k = 0, 1, 2,$ and 3 produces four distinct solutions:

$$k = 0: z = 3\left(\cos\frac{\pi}{3} + i\sin\frac{\pi}{3}\right) = \frac{3}{2} + \frac{3\sqrt{3}}{2}i$$

$$k = 1: z = 3\left[\cos\left(\frac{\pi}{3} + \frac{\pi}{2}\right) + i\sin\left(\frac{\pi}{3} + \frac{\pi}{2}\right)\right]$$
$$= 3\left(\cos\frac{5\pi}{6} + i\sin\frac{5\pi}{6}\right) = -\frac{3\sqrt{3}}{2} + \frac{3}{2}i$$

$$k = 2: z = 3\left[\cos\left(\frac{\pi}{3} + \pi\right) + i\sin\left(\frac{\pi}{3} + \pi\right)\right]$$
$$= 3\left(\cos\frac{4\pi}{3} + i\sin\frac{4\pi}{3}\right) = -\frac{3}{2} - \frac{3\sqrt{3}}{2}i$$

$$k = 3: z = 3\left[\cos\left(\frac{\pi}{3} + \frac{3\pi}{2}\right) + i\sin\left(\frac{\pi}{3} + \frac{3\pi}{2}\right)\right]$$
$$= 3\left(\cos\frac{11\pi}{6} + i\sin\frac{11\pi}{6}\right) = \frac{3\sqrt{3}}{2} - \frac{3}{2}i$$

For any other value of k, angle β has the same terminal side as one of the four angles used above, so, all fourth roots of $-\frac{81}{2} - \frac{81\sqrt{3}}{2}i$ have been found.

Teaching Notes

Have students apply the Formula for nth Roots from page 647 with $r = 1$ and $\theta = 0$ to get the **Formula for Roots of Unity.**

$$\sqrt[n]{r}\left[\cos\left(\frac{\theta + 2k\pi}{n}\right) + i \sin\left(\frac{\theta + 2k\pi}{n}\right)\right]$$

$$= \sqrt[n]{1}\left[\cos\left(\frac{0 + 2k\pi}{n}\right) + i \sin\left(\frac{0 + 2k\pi}{n}\right)\right]$$

$$= \cos\left(\frac{2k\pi}{n}\right) + i \sin\left(\frac{2k\pi}{n}\right)$$

for $k = 0, 1, 2, ..., n - 1$.

Refer students to the bottom of page 649. Ask them why

$$\sqrt{\cos^2\frac{2k\pi}{h} + \sin^2\frac{2k\pi}{h}} = \sqrt{1}.$$

$\cos^2 x + \sin^2 x = 1$ for all values of x.

ADDITIONAL EXAMPLES

Example 4

Find the fifth roots of $-16\sqrt{2} - \left(16\sqrt{2}\right)i$.

Express $-16\sqrt{2} - \left(16\sqrt{2}\right)i$ in polar form:

$$-16\sqrt{2} - \left(16\sqrt{2}\right)i$$
$$= 32\left(\cos\frac{5\pi}{4} + i \sin\frac{5\pi}{4}\right)$$

Apply the root formula with $n = 5$, $r = 32$, $\theta = \frac{5\pi}{4}$, and $k = 0, 1, 2, 3$, and 4.

$$\sqrt[5]{r} = \sqrt[5]{32} = 2$$

The fifth roots have the following form:

$$2\left[\cos\left(\frac{\frac{5\pi}{4} + 2k\pi}{5}\right) + i \sin\left(\frac{\frac{5\pi}{4} + 2k\pi}{5}\right)\right],$$

for $k = 0, 1, 2, 3$, and 4.

Apply the root formula with $n = 5$, $r = 4\sqrt{2}$, $\theta = \frac{\pi}{4}$, and $k = 0, 1, 2, 3$, and 4.

$$\sqrt[n]{r} = \sqrt[5]{4\sqrt{2}} = \left(4\sqrt{2}\right)^{\frac{1}{5}} = \left(2^2 2^{\frac{1}{2}}\right)^{\frac{1}{5}} = \left(2^{\frac{5}{2}}\right)^{\frac{1}{5}} = 2^{\frac{5}{10}} = 2^{\frac{1}{2}} = \sqrt{2}$$

The fifth roots have the following form.

$$\sqrt{2}\left[\cos\left(\frac{\frac{\pi}{4} + 2k\pi}{5}\right) + i \sin\left(\frac{\frac{\pi}{4} + 2k\pi}{5}\right)\right], \text{ for } k = 0, 1, 2, 3, \text{ and } 4$$

Therefore, the five distinct roots are as follows.

$$k = 0: \quad \sqrt{2}\left[\cos\left(\frac{\frac{\pi}{4}}{5}\right) + i \sin\left(\frac{\frac{\pi}{4}}{5}\right)\right] = \sqrt{2}\left[\cos\left(\frac{\pi}{20}\right) + i \sin\left(\frac{\pi}{20}\right)\right]$$

$$k = 1: \quad \sqrt{2}\left[\cos\left(\frac{\frac{\pi}{4} + 2\pi}{5}\right) + i \sin\left(\frac{\frac{\pi}{4} + 2\pi}{5}\right)\right]$$
$$= \sqrt{2}\left[\cos\left(\frac{9\pi}{20}\right) + i \sin\left(\frac{9\pi}{20}\right)\right]$$

$$k = 2: \quad \sqrt{2}\left[\cos\left(\frac{\frac{\pi}{4} + 4\pi}{5}\right) + i \sin\left(\frac{\frac{\pi}{4} + 4\pi}{5}\right)\right]$$
$$= \sqrt{2}\left[\cos\left(\frac{17\pi}{20}\right) + i \sin\left(\frac{17\pi}{20}\right)\right]$$

$$k = 3: \quad \sqrt{2}\left[\cos\left(\frac{\frac{\pi}{4} + 6\pi}{5}\right) + i \sin\left(\frac{\frac{\pi}{4} + 6\pi}{5}\right)\right]$$
$$= \sqrt{2}\left[\cos\left(\frac{5\pi}{4}\right) + i \sin\left(\frac{5\pi}{4}\right)\right]$$

$$k = 4: \quad \sqrt{2}\left[\cos\left(\frac{\frac{\pi}{4} + 8\pi}{5}\right) + i \sin\left(\frac{\frac{\pi}{4} + 8\pi}{5}\right)\right]$$
$$= \sqrt{2}\left[\cos\left(\frac{33\pi}{20}\right) + i \sin\left(\frac{33\pi}{20}\right)\right]$$ ∎

Roots of Unity

The n distinct nth roots of 1 (the solutions of $z^n = 1$) are called the nth **roots of unity.** Because $\cos 0 = 1$ and $\sin 0 = 0$, the polar form of the number 1 is $\cos 0 + i \sin 0$. Applying the root formula with $r = 1$ and $\theta = 0$ produces a formula for roots of unity.

Formula for Roots of Unity

For each positive integer n, there are n distinct nth roots of unity, which have the following form.

$$\cos\frac{2k\pi}{n} + i \sin\frac{2k\pi}{n}, \text{ for } k = 0, 1, 2, \ldots, n - 1.$$

continued from page 648

Therefore, the five distinct roots are as follows:

Example 5   Find Roots of Unity

Find the cube roots of unity.

Solution

Apply the formula for roots of unity with $n = 3$ and $k = 0, 1,$ and 2.

$$k = 0: \quad \cos 0 + i \sin 0 = 1$$

$$k = 1: \quad \cos \frac{2\pi}{3} + i \sin \frac{2\pi}{3} = -\frac{1}{2} + \frac{\sqrt{3}}{2}i$$

$$k = 2: \quad \cos \frac{4\pi}{3} + i \sin \frac{4\pi}{3} = -\frac{1}{2} - \frac{\sqrt{3}}{2}i$$

■

All roots of unity can be found from the first nonreal root. Let the first nonreal cube root of unity obtained in Example 5 be denoted by ω.

$$\omega = \cos \frac{2\pi}{3} + i \sin \frac{2\pi}{3}$$

Using DeMoivre's Theorem to find ω^2 and ω^3 produces the other two cube roots of unity.

$$\omega^2 = \left(\cos \frac{2\pi}{3} + i \sin \frac{2\pi}{3} \right)^2 = \cos \frac{4\pi}{3} + i \sin \frac{4\pi}{3}$$

$$\omega^3 = \left(\cos \frac{2\pi}{3} + i \sin \frac{2\pi}{3} \right)^3 = \cos \frac{6\pi}{3} + i \sin \frac{6\pi}{3} = \cos 2\pi + i \sin 2\pi = 1$$

In other words, all the cube roots of unity are powers of ω. The same is true in the general case, as stated below.

All Roots of Unity

Let n be a positive integer with $n > 1$. Then the number
$$z = \cos \frac{2\pi}{n} + i \sin \frac{2\pi}{n}$$
is an nth root of unity and all the nth roots of unity are
$$z, z^2, z^3, z^4, \ldots, z^{n-1}, z^n = 1.$$

The nth roots of unity have an interesting geometric interpretation. Every nth root of unity has absolute value of 1:

$$\left| \cos \frac{2k\pi}{n} + i \sin \frac{2k\pi}{n} \right| = \sqrt{ \left(\cos \frac{2k\pi}{n} \right)^2 + \left(\sin \frac{2k\pi}{n} \right)^2 }$$

$$= \sqrt{ \cos^2 \frac{2k\pi}{n} + \sin^2 \frac{2k\pi}{n} }$$

$$= \sqrt{1}$$

$$= 1$$

$$k = 0: \quad 2 \left[\cos \left(\frac{\frac{5\pi}{4}}{5} \right) + i \sin \left(\frac{\frac{5\pi}{4}}{5} \right) \right]$$

$$= 2 \left(\cos \frac{\pi}{4} + i \sin \frac{\pi}{4} \right)$$

$$k = 1: \quad 2 \left[\cos \left(\frac{\frac{5\pi}{4} + 2\pi}{5} \right) + i \sin \left(\frac{\frac{5\pi}{4} + 2\pi}{5} \right) \right]$$

$$= 2 \left(\cos \frac{13\pi}{20} + i \sin \frac{13\pi}{20} \right)$$

$$k = 2: \quad 2 \left[\cos \left(\frac{\frac{5\pi}{4} + 4\pi}{5} \right) + i \sin \left(\frac{\frac{5\pi}{4} + 4\pi}{5} \right) \right]$$

$$= 2 \left(\cos \frac{21\pi}{20} + i \sin \frac{21\pi}{20} \right)$$

$$k = 3: \quad 2 \left[\cos \left(\frac{\frac{5\pi}{4} + 6\pi}{5} \right) + i \sin \left(\frac{\frac{5\pi}{4} + 6\pi}{5} \right) \right]$$

$$= 2 \left(\cos \frac{29\pi}{20} + i \sin \frac{29\pi}{20} \right)$$

$$k = 4: \quad 2 \left[\cos \left(\frac{\frac{5\pi}{4} + 8\pi}{5} \right) + i \sin \left(\frac{\frac{5\pi}{4} + 8\pi}{5} \right) \right]$$

$$= 2 \left(\cos \frac{37\pi}{20} + i \sin \frac{37\pi}{20} \right)$$

Example 5

Find the eighth roots of unity.

Apply the formula for roots of unity with $n = 8$ and $k = 0, 1, 2, 3, 4, 5, 6,$ and 7.

$$k = 0: \quad \cos 0 + i \sin 0 = 1$$

$$k = 1: \quad \cos \frac{\pi}{4} + i \sin \frac{\pi}{4} = \frac{1}{\sqrt{2}} + \frac{1}{\sqrt{2}}i$$

$$k = 2: \quad \cos \frac{\pi}{2} + i \sin \frac{\pi}{2} = i$$

$$k = 3: \quad \cos \frac{3\pi}{4} + i \sin \frac{3\pi}{4} = \frac{-1}{\sqrt{2}} + \frac{1}{\sqrt{2}}i$$

$$k = 4: \quad \cos \pi + i \sin \pi = -1$$

$$k = 5: \quad \cos \frac{5\pi}{4} + i \sin \frac{5\pi}{4} = \frac{-1}{\sqrt{2}} - \frac{1}{\sqrt{2}}i$$

$$k = 6: \quad \cos \frac{3\pi}{2} + i \sin \frac{3\pi}{2} = -i$$

$$k = 7: \quad \cos \frac{7\pi}{4} + i \sin \frac{7\pi}{4} = \frac{1}{\sqrt{2}} - \frac{1}{\sqrt{2}}i$$

Teaching Notes

Graphing the *n*th roots of unity and connecting them in order will form a regular *n*-sided polygon. Note that $\cos 0 + i \sin 0 = 1$ is a root of unity for every integer $n > 1$, so the point $(1, 0)$ will be a vertex of any such regular polygon.

Solution to the **Graphing Exploration** on page 651:

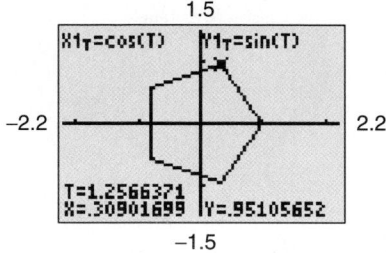

ADDITIONAL EXAMPLES

Example 6

Find the ninth roots of unity.

The ninth roots of unity have the following form.

$\cos \dfrac{2k\pi}{9} + i \sin \dfrac{2k\pi}{9}$ for $k = 0, 1, 2, 3, ..., 8.$

Therefore, the nine roots of unity are

$k = 0$: $\cos 0 + i \sin 0 = 1$

$k = 1$: $\cos \dfrac{2\pi}{9} + i \sin \dfrac{2\pi}{9}$

$k = 2$: $\cos \dfrac{4\pi}{9} + i \sin \dfrac{4\pi}{9}$

$k = 3$: $\cos \dfrac{2\pi}{3} + i \sin \dfrac{2\pi}{3}$

$k = 4$: $\cos \dfrac{8\pi}{9} + i \sin \dfrac{8\pi}{9}$

$k = 5$: $\cos \dfrac{10\pi}{9} + i \sin \dfrac{10\pi}{9}$

$k = 6$: $\cos \dfrac{4\pi}{3} + i \sin \dfrac{4\pi}{3}$

$k = 7$: $\cos \dfrac{14\pi}{9} + i \sin \dfrac{14\pi}{9}$

$k = 8$: $\cos \dfrac{16\pi}{9} + i \sin \dfrac{16\pi}{9}$

Therefore, in the complex plane, every *n*th root of unity is exactly 1 unit from the origin. That is, the *n*th roots of unity all lie on the unit circle in the complex plane.

Example 6 Find *n*th Roots of Unity

Find the fifth roots of unity.

Solution

The fifth roots of unity have the following form.

$$\cos \frac{2k\pi}{5} + i \sin \frac{2k\pi}{5}, \text{ for } k = 0, 1, 2, 3, \text{ and } 4$$

Therefore, the five roots of unity are

$k = 0$: $\cos 0 + i \sin 0 = 1$

$k = 1$: $\cos \dfrac{2\pi}{5} + i \sin \dfrac{2\pi}{5}$

$k = 2$: $\cos \dfrac{4\pi}{5} + i \sin \dfrac{4\pi}{5}$

$k = 3$: $\cos \dfrac{6\pi}{5} + i \sin \dfrac{6\pi}{5}$

$k = 4$: $\cos \dfrac{8\pi}{5} + i \sin \dfrac{8\pi}{5}$

These five roots can be plotted in the complex plane by starting at $1 = 1 + 0i$, and moving counterclockwise around the unit circle, moving through an angle of $\dfrac{2\pi}{5}$ at each step, as shown in Figure 10.4-1. If you connect these five roots, they form the vertices of a regular pentagon, as shown in Figure 10.4-2.

Figure 10.4-1

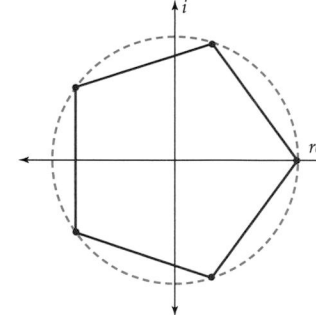

Figure 10.4-2

continued from page 650

The nine roots can be plotted in the complex plane starting at $1 = 1 + 0i$ and moving counterclockwise through an angle of $\frac{2\pi}{9}$ at each step. Connecting the nine roots results in a regular nonagon shown below with radius equal to 1.

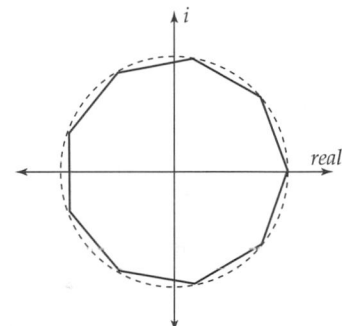

NOTE On wide screen calculators, you may choose to use $-2 \le x \le 2$ or $-1.7 \le x \le 1.7$ so that the unit circle looks like a circle.

Graphing Exploration ●

With your calculator in parametric graphing mode, use the following window settings.

$$0 \le t \le 2\pi \quad t\text{-step} \approx 0.067 \quad -2.2 \le x \le 2.2 \quad -1.5 \le y \le 1.5$$

Graph the unit circle, whose parametric equations are

$$x = \cos t \quad \text{and} \quad y = \sin t$$

Reset the *t*-step to be $\frac{2\pi}{5}$, and graph again. Your screen should now look exactly like the solid lines in Figure 10.4-2 because the calculator plotted only the five points corresponding to $t = 0, \frac{2\pi}{5}, \frac{4\pi}{5}, \frac{6\pi}{5},$ and $\frac{8\pi}{5}$, and connected them with the shortest possible segments.

Use the trace feature to move along the graph. The cursor will jump from vertex to vertex, that is, from one fifth root of unity to the next.

Example 7   Graph Roots of Unity

Graph the tenth roots of unity, and estimate the two tenth roots of unity in the first quadrant.

Solution

With a graphing calculator in parametric mode, set the range values as in the graphing exploration above.

Because $n = 10$, reset the *t*-step to $\frac{2\pi}{10} = \frac{\pi}{5}$ and graph. The result is a regular decagon whose vertices are the tenth roots of unity. By using the trace feature, you can approximate each tenth root of unity.

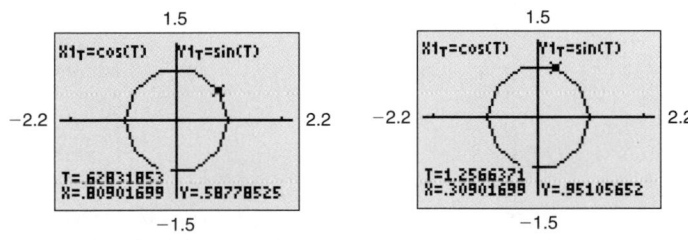

Figure 10.4-3   **Figure 10.4-4**

Figures 10.4-3 and 10.4-4 show the two approximate tenth roots of unity in the first quadrant.

$$0.8090 + 0.5878i \quad \text{and} \quad 0.3090 + 0.9511i.$$

Example 7

Graph the twelfth roots of unity and estimate the two twelfth roots of unity in the first quadrant.

Set up a graphing calculator as described in the Graphing Exploration.

Because $n = 12$, reset the *t*-step to $\frac{2\pi}{12} = \frac{\pi}{6}$. The result is a regular dodecagon whose vertices are the twelfth roots of unity.

The figures show the two approximate twelfth roots of unity in the first quadrant.

$0.8660 + 0.5i$ and $0.5 + 0.8660i$

ANSWERS

12. $-1, 1, -\dfrac{1}{2} - \dfrac{\sqrt{3}}{2}i,$

$-\dfrac{1}{2} + \dfrac{\sqrt{3}}{2}i, \dfrac{1}{2} - \dfrac{\sqrt{3}}{2}i,$

$\dfrac{1}{2} + \dfrac{\sqrt{3}}{2}i$

13. $4\left(\cos\dfrac{\pi}{15} + i\sin\dfrac{\pi}{15}\right),$

$4\left(\cos\dfrac{11\pi}{15} + i\sin\dfrac{11\pi}{15}\right),$

$4\left(\cos\dfrac{7\pi}{5} + i\sin\dfrac{7\pi}{5}\right)$

14. $2\left(\cos\dfrac{\pi}{30} + i\sin\dfrac{\pi}{30}\right),$

$2\left(\cos\dfrac{21\pi}{30} + i\sin\dfrac{21\pi}{30}\right),$

$2\left(\cos\dfrac{41\pi}{30} + i\sin\dfrac{41\pi}{30}\right)$

15. $3\left(\cos\dfrac{\pi}{48} + i\sin\dfrac{\pi}{48}\right),$

$3\left(\cos\dfrac{25\pi}{48} + i\sin\dfrac{25\pi}{48}\right),$

$3\left(\cos\dfrac{49\pi}{48} + i\sin\dfrac{49\pi}{48}\right),$

$3\left(\cos\dfrac{73\pi}{48} + i\sin\dfrac{73\pi}{48}\right)$

16. $\sqrt[5]{16}\left(\cos\dfrac{\pi}{35} + i\sin\dfrac{\pi}{35}\right),$

$\sqrt[5]{16}\left(\cos\dfrac{15\pi}{35} + i\sin\dfrac{15\pi}{35}\right),$

$\sqrt[5]{16}\left(\cos\dfrac{29\pi}{35} + i\sin\dfrac{29\pi}{35}\right),$

$\sqrt[5]{16}\left(\cos\dfrac{43\pi}{35} + i\sin\dfrac{43\pi}{35}\right),$

$\sqrt[5]{16}\left(\cos\dfrac{57\pi}{35} + i\sin\dfrac{57\pi}{35}\right)$

17. $\cos\dfrac{\pi}{5} + i\sin\dfrac{\pi}{5}, \cos\dfrac{3\pi}{5} + i\sin\dfrac{3\pi}{5},$

$\cos\pi + i\sin\pi, \cos\dfrac{7\pi}{5} + i\sin\dfrac{7\pi}{5},$

$\cos\dfrac{9\pi}{5} + i\sin\dfrac{9\pi}{5}$

18. $1, \cos\dfrac{2\pi}{7} + i\sin\dfrac{2\pi}{7},$

$\cos\dfrac{4\pi}{7} + i\sin\dfrac{4\pi}{7},$

$\cos\dfrac{6\pi}{7} + i\sin\dfrac{6\pi}{7},$

$\cos\dfrac{8\pi}{7} + i\sin\dfrac{8\pi}{7},$

$\cos\dfrac{10\pi}{7} + i\sin\dfrac{10\pi}{7},$

$\cos\dfrac{12\pi}{7} + i\sin\dfrac{12\pi}{7}$

Exercises 10.4

In Exercises 1–10, calculate each given product and express your answer in the form $a + bi$.

1. $\left(\cos\dfrac{\pi}{12} + i\sin\dfrac{\pi}{12}\right)^6$ i **2.** $\left(\cos\dfrac{\pi}{5} + i\sin\dfrac{\pi}{5}\right)^{20}$ 1

3. $\left[3\left(\cos\dfrac{7\pi}{30} + i\sin\dfrac{7\pi}{30}\right)\right]^5$ $\dfrac{-243\sqrt{3}}{2} - \dfrac{243}{2}i$

4. $\left[\sqrt[3]{4}\left(\cos\dfrac{7\pi}{36} + i\sin\dfrac{7\pi}{36}\right)\right]^{12}$ $128 + 128i\sqrt{3}$

5. $(1 - i)^{12}$ *Hint: Use polar form and DeMoivre's theorem.* -64

6. $(2 + 2i)^8$ 4096 **7.** $\left(\dfrac{\sqrt{3}}{2} + \dfrac{1}{2}i\right)^{10}$ $\dfrac{1}{2} - \dfrac{\sqrt{3}}{2}i$

8. $\left(-\dfrac{1}{2} + \dfrac{\sqrt{3}}{2}i\right)^{20}$ **9.** $\left(\dfrac{-1}{\sqrt{2}} + \dfrac{i}{\sqrt{2}}\right)^{14}$ i

$-\dfrac{1}{2} - \dfrac{\sqrt{3}}{2}i$

10. $(-1 + \sqrt{3}i)^8$ $-128 - 128i\sqrt{3}$

In Exercises 11 and 12, find all indicated roots of unity and express your answers in the form $a + bi$.

11. fourth roots of unity
$1, -1, i, -i$

12. sixth roots of unity

In Exercises 13–22, find the nth roots of each given number in polar form.

13. $64\left(\cos\dfrac{\pi}{5} + i\sin\dfrac{\pi}{5}\right); n = 3$

14. $8\left(\cos\dfrac{\pi}{10} + i\sin\dfrac{\pi}{10}\right); n = 3$

15. $81\left(\cos\dfrac{\pi}{12} + i\sin\dfrac{\pi}{12}\right); n = 4$

16. $16\left(\cos\dfrac{\pi}{7} + i\sin\dfrac{\pi}{7}\right); n = 5$

17. $-1; n = 5$ **18.** $1; n = 7$ **19.** $i; n = 5$

20. $-i; n = 6$ **21.** $1 + i; n = 2$ **22.** $1 - i\sqrt{3}; n = 3$

In Exercises 23–30, solve the given equation in the complex number system.

23. $x^6 = -1$ **24.** $x^6 + 64 = 0$ **25.** $x^3 = i$

26. $x^4 = i$ **27.** $x^3 + 27i = 0$ **28.** $x^6 + 729 = 0$

---

29. $x^4 = -1 + i\sqrt{3}$ **30.** $x^4 = -8 - 8i\sqrt{3}$

In Exercises 31–35, represent the roots of unity graphically. Then use the trace feature to obtain approximations of the form $a + bi$ for each root (round to four places).

31. seventh roots of unity

32. fifth roots of unity **33.** eighth roots of unity

34. twelfth roots of unity **35.** ninth roots of unity

36. Solve the equation $x^3 + x^2 + x + 1 = 0$. *Hint:* First find the quotient when $x^4 - 1$ is divided by $x - 1$, then consider solutions of $x^4 - 1 = 0$.

37. Solve $x^5 + x^4 + x^3 + x^2 + x + 1 = 0$ *Hint:* Consider $x^6 - 1$ and $x - 1$ and see Exercise 36.

38. What are the solutions of
$x^{n-1} + x^{n-2} + \cdots + x^3 + x^2 + x + 1 = 0$? (See Exercises 36 and 37.)

39. *Critical Thinking* In the complex plane, the unit circle consists of all numbers (points) z such that $|z| = 1$. Suppose v and w are two points (numbers) that move around the unit circle in such a way that $v = w^{12}$ at all times. When w has made one complete trip around the circle, how many trips has v made? *Hint:* Think polar and DeMoivre.

40. *Critical Thinking* Suppose u is an nth root of unity. Show that $\dfrac{1}{u}$ is also an nth root of unity. *Hint:* Use the definition, not polar form.

41. *Critical Thinking* Let $u_1, u_2, \cdots, u_n$ be the distinct nth roots of unity and suppose v is a nonzero solution of the equation $z^n = r(\cos\theta + i\sin\theta)$. Show that $vu_1, vu_2, \cdots, vu_n$ are n distinct solutions of the equation. *Hint:* Each u_i is a solution of $x^n = 1$.

42. *Critical Thinking* Use the formula for nth roots and the identities

$$\cos(x + \pi) = -\cos x \qquad \sin(x + \pi) = -\sin x$$

to show that the nonzero complex number $r(\cos\theta + i\sin\theta)$ has two square roots and that these square roots are negatives of each other.

---

19. $\cos\dfrac{\pi}{10} + i\sin\dfrac{\pi}{10}, \cos\dfrac{\pi}{2} + i\sin\dfrac{\pi}{2},$

$\cos\dfrac{9\pi}{10} + i\sin\dfrac{9\pi}{10}, \cos\dfrac{13\pi}{10} + i\sin\dfrac{13\pi}{10},$

$\cos\dfrac{17\pi}{10} + i\sin\dfrac{17\pi}{10}$

20. $\cos\dfrac{\pi}{4} + i\sin\dfrac{\pi}{4}, \cos\dfrac{7\pi}{12} + i\sin\dfrac{7\pi}{12},$

$\cos\dfrac{11\pi}{12} + i\sin\dfrac{11\pi}{12}, \cos\dfrac{5\pi}{4} + i\sin\dfrac{5\pi}{4},$

$\cos\dfrac{19\pi}{12} + i\sin\dfrac{19\pi}{12}, \cos\dfrac{23\pi}{12} + i\sin\dfrac{23\pi}{12}$

21. $\sqrt[4]{2}\left(\cos\dfrac{\pi}{8} + i\sin\dfrac{\pi}{8}\right),$

$\sqrt[4]{2}\left(\cos\dfrac{9\pi}{8} + i\sin\dfrac{9\pi}{8}\right),$

22. $\sqrt[3]{2}\left(\cos\dfrac{5\pi}{9} + i\sin\dfrac{5\pi}{9}\right),$

$\sqrt[3]{2}\left(\cos\dfrac{11\pi}{9} + i\sin\dfrac{11\pi}{9}\right),$

$\sqrt[3]{2}\left(\cos\dfrac{17\pi}{9} + i\sin\dfrac{17\pi}{9}\right)$

23–42. See p. 1074.

10.5   Vectors in the Plane

Objectives

- Find the components and magnitude of a vector
- Perform scalar multiplication of vectors, vector addition, and vector subtraction

Once a unit of measure has been agreed upon, quantities such as area, length, time, and temperature can be described by a single number. Other quantities, such as an east wind of 10 miles per hour, require two numbers to describe them because they involve both *magnitude* and *direction*. Quantities that have magnitude and direction are called **vectors** and are represented geometrically by a directed line segment or arrow, as shown in Figures 10.5-1 and 10.5-2.

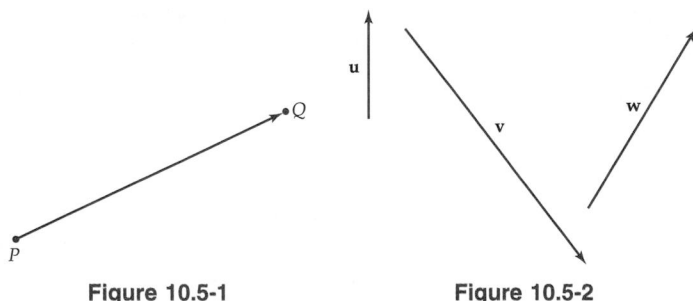

Figure 10.5-1   **Figure 10.5-2**

When a vector extends from a point P to a point Q, as in Figure 10.5-1, P is called the **initial point** of the vector, and Q is called the **terminal point,** and the vector is written $\overrightarrow{PQ}$. Its **length** is denoted by $\|\overrightarrow{PQ}\|$.

When the endpoints are not specified, as in Figure 10.5-2, vectors are denoted by boldface letters such as **u**, **v**, and **w**. The length of a vector **u** is denoted by $\|\mathbf{u}\|$ and is called the **magnitude of u**.

If **u** and **v** are vectors with the same magnitude and direction, the vectors **u** and **v** are said to be **equivalent,** written **u** = **v**. Some examples and nonexamples are shown in Figure 10.5-3.

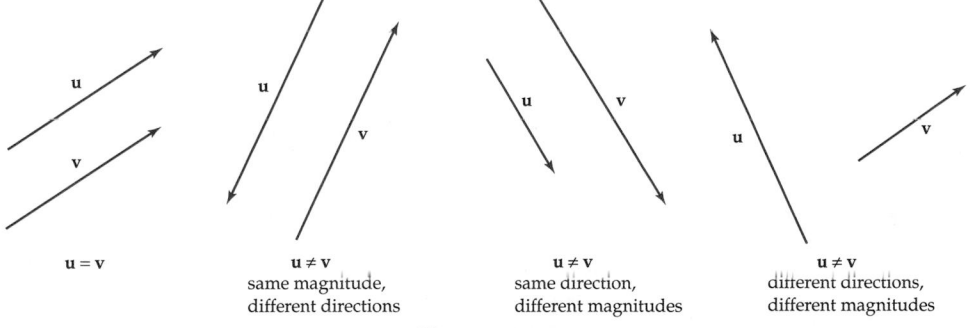

| **u = v** | **u ≠ v**
same magnitude,
different directions | **u ≠ v**
same direction,
different magnitudes | **u ≠ v**
different directions,
different magnitudes |

Figure 10.5-3

Math Background

A quantity that has only magnitude is called a *scalar*. Examples of scalars are:
- a force of 10 pounds
- a speed of 50 miles per hour

A quantity that has both magnitude and direction is called a *vector*. Examples of vectors are:
- a force of 10 pounds exerted horizontally
- a speed of 50 miles per hour in the direction 20° east of north

The directed line segments labeled $\overrightarrow{PQ}$, **u**, **v**, and **w** shown on this page are geometric representations of vectors. The first pair of vectors **u** and **v** shown in Figure 10.5-3 are called equivalent vectors; some texts would describe them as the same vector with different directed line segment representations. Although vocabulary varies slightly from text to text, this does not affect the properties, operations, and applications of vectors.

Teaching Notes

Students are accustomed to using directed line segments to represent rays in geometry. Emphasize that now we are using directed line segments to represent vectors. In geometry, a ray indicates a specific direction, but has infinite length in that direction. A vector also has a specific direction, but has a finite length in that direction.

The magnitude of a vector is the length of its directed line segment. The magnitude of vector **u** is denoted $\|\mathbf{u}\|$; the magnitude of vector $\overrightarrow{PQ}$ is denoted $\|\overrightarrow{PQ}\|$. Magnitude is defined on page 655.

Point out that for vectors **u** and **v**, the = symbol is used to mean equivalent; the statement **u** = **v** means vectors **u** and **v** are equivalent (same magnitude and same direction). Note that we use bold type to distinguish a variable from a vector.

Teaching Notes

Have students recall the formulas for distance and slope.

- distance between two points:

  $d = \sqrt{(x_2 - x_1)^2 + (y_2 - y_1)^2}$

- slope of a line: $m = \dfrac{(y_2 - y_1)}{(x_2 - x_1)}$

Explain that the concept in the **Equivalent Vectors** box allows us to "reposition" any vector so that it starts at the origin. This repositioning is convenient because the components of a vector that starts at the origin are just the coordinates of its endpoint. For example, the components of vector $\overrightarrow{OR}$ in Figure 10.5-4 are 4 and 2. Point out the $\langle \ , \ \rangle$ notation for a vector described at the top of page 655; the vector $\overrightarrow{OR}$ in Figure 10.5-4 is $\langle 4, 2 \rangle$.

Note that **Scalar Multiplication** is *not multiplication of scalars*; it is multiplication of a vector by a scalar.

Example Notes

Using the notation given in the **CAUTION** box, the components of vector $\overrightarrow{PQ}$ in **Example 2** can be found directly as follows:

$$\overrightarrow{PQ} = \langle x_2 - x_1, y_2 - y_1 \rangle$$

$$= \langle 4 - (-2), -3 - 6 \rangle = \langle 6, -9 \rangle$$

After completing Example 2, show the following sketch of $\overrightarrow{PQ}$ and $\overrightarrow{OR}$ to emphasize that they have the same magnitude, same direction, and same components.

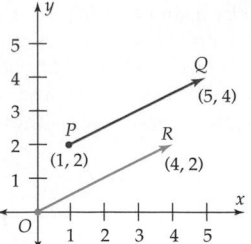

Figure 10.5-4

Example 1 Confirm Equivalent Vectors

Let $P = (1, 2)$, $Q = (5, 4)$, $O = (0, 0)$, and $R = (4, 2)$, as in Figure 10.5-4. Show that $\overrightarrow{PQ} = \overrightarrow{OR}$.

Solution

The distance formula shows that $\overrightarrow{PQ}$ and $\overrightarrow{OR}$ have the same length.

$$\|\overrightarrow{PQ}\| = \sqrt{(5 - 1)^2 + (4 - 2)^2} = \sqrt{4^2 + 2^2} = \sqrt{20}$$
$$\|\overrightarrow{OR}\| = \sqrt{(4 - 0)^2 + (2 - 0)^2} = \sqrt{4^2 + 2^2} = \sqrt{20}$$

The lines containing $\overrightarrow{PQ}$ and $\overrightarrow{OR}$ have the same slope:

$$\text{slope } \overleftrightarrow{PQ} = \frac{4 - 2}{5 - 1} = \frac{2}{4} = \frac{1}{2} \qquad \text{slope } \overleftrightarrow{OR} = \frac{2 - 0}{4 - 0} = \frac{2}{4} = \frac{1}{2}$$

Because $\overrightarrow{PQ}$ and $\overrightarrow{OR}$ both point to the upper right on lines of the same slope, $\overrightarrow{PQ}$ and $\overrightarrow{OR}$ have the same direction. Therefore, $\overrightarrow{PQ} = \overrightarrow{OR}$. ∎

According to the definition of equivalence, if two vectors are equivalent, then one of the vectors may be moved from one location to another, provided that its magnitude and direction are not changed, and the two vectors will remain equivalent.

Equivalent Vectors

> Every vector $\overrightarrow{PQ}$ is equivalent to a vector $\overrightarrow{OR}$ with initial point at the origin. If $P = (x_1, y_1)$ and $Q = (x_2, y_2)$, then
> $$\overrightarrow{PQ} = \overrightarrow{OR}, \qquad \text{where } R = (x_2 - x_1, y_2 - y_1).$$

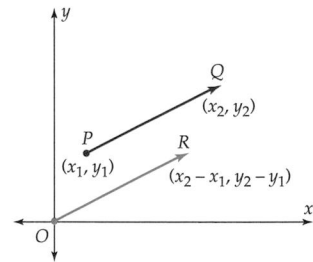

Figure 10.5-5

Proof The proof is similar to the one used in Example 1. It follows from the fact that $\overrightarrow{PQ}$ and $\overrightarrow{OR}$ have the same length:

$$\|\overrightarrow{OR}\| = \sqrt{[(x_2 - x_1) - 0]^2 + [(y_2 - y_1) - 0]^2}$$
$$= \sqrt{(x_2 - x_1)^2 + (y_2 - y_1)^2}$$
$$= \|\overrightarrow{PQ}\|$$

and either the lines containing $\overrightarrow{PQ}$ and $\overrightarrow{OR}$ are both vertical or they have the same slope:

$$\text{slope } \overleftrightarrow{OR} = \frac{(y_2 - y_1) - 0}{(x_2 - x_1) - 0}$$
$$= \frac{y_2 - y_1}{x_2 - x_1}$$
$$= \text{slope } \overleftrightarrow{PQ},$$

as shown in Figure 10.5-5.

Every vector can be written as a vector with the origin as its initial point. The magnitude and direction of a vector with the origin as its initial point are completely determined by the coordinates of its terminal point. Consequently, the vector with initial point $(0, 0)$ and terminal point (a, b) is denoted by $\langle a, b \rangle$. The numbers a and b are called the **components** of the vector $\langle a, b \rangle$.

Because the length of the vector $\langle a, b \rangle$ is the distance from $(0, 0)$ to (a, b), the distance formula gives its **magnitude,** which is also called its **norm.**

Magnitude

> The *magnitude* (or *norm*) of the vector $\mathbf{v} = \langle a, b \rangle$ is
> $$\|\mathbf{v}\| = \sqrt{a^2 + b^2}.$$

Example 2　Find Components and Magnitude of a Vector

Find the components and the magnitude of the vector with initial point $P = (-2, 6)$ and terminal point $Q = (4, -3)$.

Solution

According to the properties of equivalent vectors, where $x_1 = -2$, $y_1 = 6$, $x_2 = 4$, and $y_2 = -3$:

$$\overrightarrow{PQ} = \overrightarrow{OR}, \qquad \text{where } R = (4 - (-2), -3 - 6) = (6, -9).$$

In other words,

$$\overrightarrow{PQ} = \overrightarrow{OR} = \langle 6, -9 \rangle.$$

Therefore, the magnitude is

$$\|\overrightarrow{PQ}\| = \|\overrightarrow{OR}\| = \sqrt{6^2 + (-9)^2} = \sqrt{36 + 81} = \sqrt{117} \qquad ■$$

Vector Arithmetic

Vectors can be added, can be subtracted, and can be multiplied in three different ways. Addition, subtraction, and one type of multiplication are discussed in this section. Another type of multiplication is presented in the *Excursion* 10.6.A.

Scalar Multiplication

When dealing with vectors, it is customary to refer to ordinary real numbers as **scalars.** **Scalar multiplication** is an operation in which a scalar k is "multiplied" by a vector $\mathbf{v}$ to produce another vector denoted by $k\mathbf{v}$.

Scalar Multiplication

> If k is a real number and $\mathbf{v} = \langle a, b \rangle$ is a vector, then
> $$k\mathbf{v} \text{ is the vector } \langle ka, kb \rangle.$$
> The vector $k\mathbf{v}$ is called a *scalar multiple* of $\mathbf{v}$.

CAUTION

The order in which the coordinates of the initial point and terminal point are subtracted to obtain $\langle a, b \rangle$ is significant. For the points $P(x_1, y_1)$ and $Q(x_2, y_2)$:

$$\overrightarrow{PQ} = \langle x_2 - x_1, y_2 - y_1 \rangle$$
$$\overrightarrow{QP} = \langle x_1 - x_2, y_1 - y_2 \rangle$$

COMMON ERROR ALERT

Sign errors are common when working with vectors. Some students might do **Example 2** incorrectly as follows:

components of $\overrightarrow{PQ}$: $\langle 4 - 2, -3 - 6 \rangle = \langle 2, -9 \rangle$

magnitude of $\overrightarrow{PQ}$:

$$\sqrt{(4 - 2)^2 + (-3 - 6)^2} = \sqrt{4 + 81} = \sqrt{85}$$

Tell them to draw a sketch to check whether their answers are reasonable.

ADDITIONAL EXAMPLES

Example 1

Let $P = (3, 3)$, $Q = (6, 4)$, $O = (0, 0)$, and $R = (3, 1)$, as shown in the figure below. Show that $\overrightarrow{PQ} = \overrightarrow{OR}$.

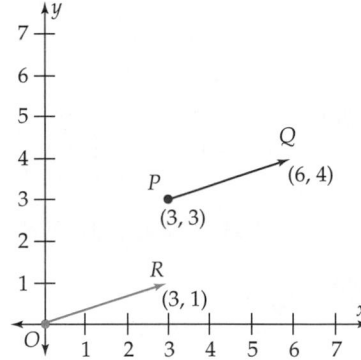

$$\|\overrightarrow{PQ}\| = \sqrt{(6 - 3)^2 + (4 - 3)^2}$$
$$= \sqrt{3^2 + 1^2} = \sqrt{10}$$
$$\|\overrightarrow{OR}\| = \sqrt{(3 - 0)^2 + (1 - 0)^2}$$
$$= \sqrt{3^2 + 1^2} = \sqrt{10}$$

$\overrightarrow{PQ}$ and $\overrightarrow{OR}$ have the same length.

slope $\overleftrightarrow{PQ} = \dfrac{4 - 3}{6 - 3} = \dfrac{1}{3}$ and

slope $\overleftrightarrow{OR} = \dfrac{1 - 0}{3 - 0} = \dfrac{1}{3}$

Because $\overrightarrow{PQ}$ and $\overrightarrow{OR}$ both point to the upper right on lines with the same slope, $\overrightarrow{PQ}$ and $\overrightarrow{OR}$ have the same direction. Therefore, $\overrightarrow{PQ} = \overrightarrow{OR}$.

Example 2

Find the components and the magnitude of the vector with initial point $P = (3, -5)$ and terminal point $Q = (-6, 9)$.

$\overrightarrow{PQ} = \overrightarrow{OR}$, where

$R = (-6 - 3, 9 - (-5)) = (-9, 14)$.

components: $\overrightarrow{PQ} = \overrightarrow{OR} = \langle -9, 14 \rangle$

The magnitude is

$$\|\overrightarrow{PQ}\| = \|\overrightarrow{OR}\| = \sqrt{(-9)^2 + 14^2}$$
$$= \sqrt{81 + 196}$$
$$= \sqrt{277}$$

Teaching Notes

After completing **Example 3,** have students verify that
$\|3\mathbf{v}\| = |3| \cdot \|\mathbf{v}\| = 3\|\mathbf{v}\|$ as the corresponding statement for $\|-2\mathbf{v}\|$ was verified.

$\|\mathbf{v}\| = \sqrt{10}$

$\|3\mathbf{v}\| = \|\langle 9, 3 \rangle\| = \sqrt{9^2 + 3}$
$\qquad = \sqrt{90} = 3\sqrt{10}$

Therefore,
$\|3\mathbf{v}\| = 3\sqrt{10} = 3\|\mathbf{v}\| = |3| \cdot \|\mathbf{v}\|.$

ADDITIONAL EXAMPLES

Example 3

Let $\mathbf{v} - \langle 4, -2 \rangle$. Find the components of $2\mathbf{v}$ and $-3\mathbf{v}$.

$2\mathbf{v} = 2\langle 4, -2 \rangle = \langle 2 \cdot 4, 2 \cdot -2 \rangle$
$\qquad = \langle 8, -4 \rangle$

$-3\mathbf{v} = -3\langle 4, -2 \rangle$
$\qquad = \langle -3 \cdot 4, -3 \cdot -2 \rangle = \langle -12, 6 \rangle$

Example 4

Let $\mathbf{u} = \langle -6, 3 \rangle$ and $\mathbf{v} = \langle -3, -4 \rangle$. Find the components of $\mathbf{u} + \mathbf{v}$.

$\mathbf{u} + \mathbf{v} = \langle -6, 3 \rangle + \langle -3, -4 \rangle$
$\qquad = \langle -6 + (-3), 3 + (-4) \rangle$
$\qquad - \langle -9, -1 \rangle$

Math Background

The Irish mathematician William Hamilton (1805–1865) realized that complex numbers could be represented as ordered pairs of the form (a, b), and then tried to extend these "two-dimensional" numbers to three dimensions. He was not successful, but did invent a system of four-dimensional numbers that he called quaternions. He wrote quaternions in the form $q = w + \mathbf{i}x + \mathbf{j}y + \mathbf{k}z$, where $w, x, y,$ and z were real numbers. He called w a scalar and $\mathbf{i}x + \mathbf{j}y + \mathbf{k}z$ a vector. Hamilton's work on quaternions was the basis of the modern study of vectors.

Example 3   Perform Scalar Multiplication

Let $\mathbf{v} = \langle 3, 1 \rangle$. Find the components of $3\mathbf{v}$ and $-2\mathbf{v}$.

Solution

$$3\mathbf{v} = 3\langle 3, 1 \rangle \qquad\qquad -2\mathbf{v} = -2\langle 3, 1 \rangle$$
$$\quad = \langle 3 \cdot 3, 3 \cdot 1 \rangle \qquad\qquad = \langle -2 \cdot 3, -2 \cdot 1 \rangle$$
$$\quad = \langle 9, 3 \rangle \qquad\qquad\qquad = \langle -6, -2 \rangle$$

The graphs of $\mathbf{v}$, $3\mathbf{v}$, and $-2\mathbf{v}$ from Example 3, shown in Figure 10.5-6, illustrates that $3\mathbf{v}$ has the same direction as $\mathbf{v}$ and $-2\mathbf{v}$ has the opposite direction.

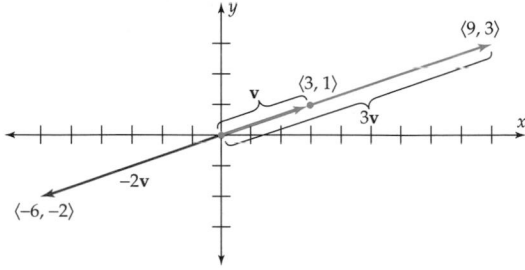

Figure 10.5-6

Also note that

$$\|\mathbf{v}\| = \|\langle 3, 1 \rangle\| = \sqrt{3^2 + 1^2} = \sqrt{10}$$
$$\|-2\mathbf{v}\| = \|\langle -6, 2 \rangle\| = \sqrt{(-6)^2 + 2^2} = \sqrt{40} = 2\sqrt{10}$$

Therefore,

$$\|-2\mathbf{v}\| = 2\sqrt{10} = 2\|\mathbf{v}\| = |-2| \cdot \|\mathbf{v}\|$$

Similarly, it can be verified that $\|3\mathbf{v}\| = |3| \cdot \|\mathbf{v}\| = 3\|\mathbf{v}\|$. Figure 10.5-6 is an illustration of the following facts.

Geometric Interpretation of Scalar Multiplication

The *magnitude* of the vector $k\mathbf{v}$ is $|k|$ times the length of $\mathbf{v}$, that is,

$$\|k\mathbf{v}\| = |k| \cdot \|\mathbf{v}\|.$$

The *direction of* $k\mathbf{v}$ is the same as that of $\mathbf{v}$ when k is positive and opposite that of $\mathbf{v}$ when k is negative.

Vector Addition

Vector addition is an operation in which two vectors **u** and **v** are added, resulting in a new vector denoted **u** + **v**.

Vector Addition

> If **u** = $\langle a, b \rangle$ and **v** = $\langle c, d \rangle$, then
>
> $$\mathbf{u} + \mathbf{v} = \langle a + c, b + d \rangle.$$

Example 4   **Perform Vector Addition**

Let **u** = $\langle -5, 2 \rangle$ and **v** = $\langle 3, 1 \rangle$. Find the components of **u** + **v**.

Solution

$$\mathbf{u} + \mathbf{v} = \langle -5, 2 \rangle + \langle 3, 1 \rangle$$
$$= \langle -5 + 3, 2 + 1 \rangle$$
$$= \langle -2, 3 \rangle$$ ∎

Geometric Interpretation of u + v

The graph of **u** + **v** from Example 4 is shown in Figure 10.5-7.

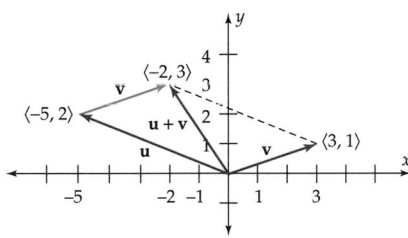

Figure 10.5-7

Figure 10.5-7 illustrates the following geometric interpretation of vector addition.

*Geometric
Interpretation
of Vector
Addition*

> 1. If u and v are vectors with the same initial point P, then u + v is the vector $\overrightarrow{PQ}$, where $\overrightarrow{PQ}$ is the diagonal of the parallelogram with adjacent sides u and v.
> 2. If the vector v is moved without changing its magnitude or direction so that its initial point lies on the endpoint of the vector u, then u + v is the vector with the same initial point P as u and the same terminal point Q as v.

Teaching Notes

After discussing the **Geometric Interpretation of Vector Addition**, have students draw two figures for **Additional Example 4**—one figure that shows **u** + **v** as the diagonal of a parallelogram and another figure that shows **u** + **v** as the third side of a triangle. In each figure, have them use the origin as the initial point of vector **u**.

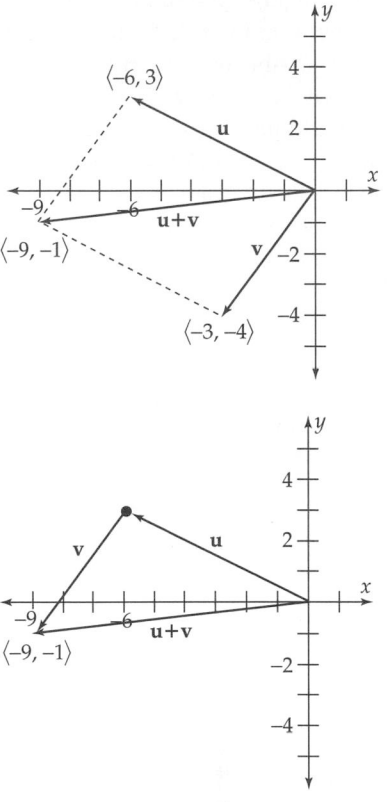

Math Background

The sum of two vectors is often called the *resultant vector* or *resultant*. In Section 10.6, vectors will be used to model systems of forces. The term *resultant force* will be used to describe the sum of all forces acting on an object.

Teaching Notes

Refer students to the margin **NOTE**. Have them use $\mathbf{v} = \langle 6, 1 \rangle$ from **Example 5** and its opposite to illustrate that $\mathbf{v}$ and $-\mathbf{v}$ have the same magnitude.

$\mathbf{v} = \langle 6, 1 \rangle$

$\|\mathbf{v}\| = \sqrt{6^2 + 1^2} = \sqrt{36 + 1} = \sqrt{37}$

$-\mathbf{v} = \langle -6, -1 \rangle$

$\|-\mathbf{v}\| = \sqrt{(-6)^2 + (-1)^2}$
$\qquad = \sqrt{36 + 1} = \sqrt{37}$

Point out that the rule for subtracting a vector is similar to the rule for subtracting a number: To subtract a vector, add its opposite. Again, using $\mathbf{v} = \langle 6, 1 \rangle$ from Example 5, ask students to draw the geometric interpretation of $\mathbf{v} - \mathbf{v}$ and discuss the magnitude and direction of the result.

$\mathbf{v} - \mathbf{v} = \langle 0, 0 \rangle = \mathbf{0}$; The result is the zero vector; it has magnitude zero and no direction.

Point out that the **Geometric Interpretation of $\mathbf{u} - \mathbf{v}$** is the geometric interpretation of $\mathbf{u} + (-\mathbf{v})$; it comes from the geometric interpretation of vector addition (page 657).

Have students draw the geometric interpretation of $\mathbf{u} - \mathbf{v}$ for **Additional Example 5**.

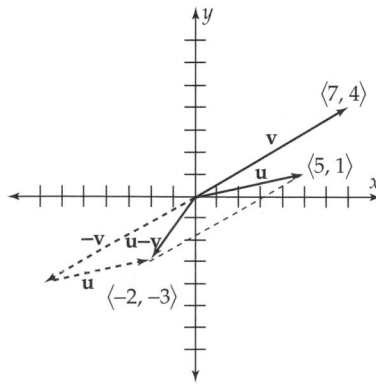

Exercise 33 asks for the proof of the geometric interpretation of vector addition stated above.

Vector Subtraction

The **negative** (or **opposite**) of a vector $\mathbf{v} = \langle c, d \rangle$ is defined to be the vector $(-1)\mathbf{v} = (-1)\langle c, d \rangle = \langle -c, -d \rangle$, and is denoted $-\mathbf{v}$. **Vector subtraction** is defined using the negative of a vector as follows.

Vector Subtraction

> If $\mathbf{u} = \langle a, b \rangle$ and $\mathbf{v} = \langle c, d \rangle$, then $\mathbf{u} - \mathbf{v}$ is the vector
> $$\mathbf{u} + (-\mathbf{v}) = \langle a, b \rangle + \langle -c, -d \rangle$$
> $$= \langle a - c, b - d \rangle$$

Example 5   Perform Vector Subtraction

Let $\mathbf{u} = \langle 2, 5 \rangle$ and $\mathbf{v} = \langle 6, 1 \rangle$. Find the components of $\mathbf{u} - \mathbf{v}$.

Solution

$$\mathbf{u} - \mathbf{v} = \langle 2, 5 \rangle - \langle 6, 1 \rangle$$
$$= \langle 2 - 6, 5 - 1 \rangle$$
$$= \langle -4, 4 \rangle$$

NOTE The vectors $\mathbf{v}$ and $-\mathbf{v}$ have the same magnitude, and lines that contain them have the same slope, but $\mathbf{v}$ and $-\mathbf{v}$ have opposite directions.

Geometric Interpretation of $\mathbf{u} - \mathbf{v}$

The graph of $\mathbf{u} - \mathbf{v}$ from Example 5 is shown in Figure 10.5-8.

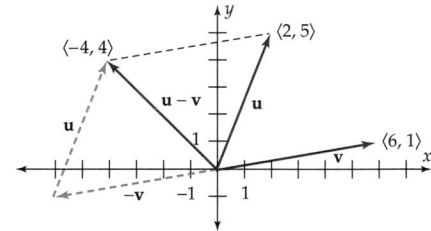

Figure 10.5-8

The Zero Vector

The vector $\langle 0, 0 \rangle$ is called the **zero vector** and is denoted $\mathbf{0}$.

Example 6   Perform Combined Vector Operations

Let $\mathbf{u} = \langle -1, 6 \rangle$, $\mathbf{v} = \left\langle \frac{2}{3}, -4 \right\rangle$, and $\mathbf{w} = \left\langle 2, \frac{5}{2} \right\rangle$. Find the components of each vector.

a. $2\mathbf{u} + 3\mathbf{v}$ **b.** $4\mathbf{w} - 2\mathbf{u}$

Solution

a. $2\mathbf{u} + 3\mathbf{v} = 2\langle -1, 6 \rangle + 3\left\langle \dfrac{2}{3}, -4 \right\rangle$ **b.** $4\mathbf{w} - 2\mathbf{u} = 4\left\langle 2, \dfrac{5}{2} \right\rangle - 2\langle -1, 6 \rangle$

$\qquad\qquad = \langle -2, 12 \rangle + \langle 2, -12 \rangle \qquad\qquad\qquad\qquad = \langle 8, 10 \rangle + \langle 2, -12 \rangle$

$\qquad\qquad = \langle -2 + 2, 12 - 12 \rangle \qquad\qquad\qquad\qquad\;\; = \langle 8 + 2, 10 - 12 \rangle$

$\qquad\qquad = \langle 0, 0 \rangle \qquad\qquad\qquad\qquad\qquad\qquad\quad = \langle 10, -2 \rangle$

$\qquad\qquad = \mathbf{0}$

Vector Properties

Operations on vectors share many of the same properties as arithmetical operations on numbers.

Properties of Vector Addition and Scalar Multiplication

> For any vectors **u**, **v**, and **w** and any scalars r and s,
>
> 1. $\mathbf{u} + (\mathbf{v} + \mathbf{w}) = (\mathbf{u} + \mathbf{v}) + \mathbf{w}$ *associative for addition*
> 2. $\mathbf{u} + \mathbf{v} = \mathbf{v} + \mathbf{u}$ *commutative*
> 3. $\mathbf{v} + \mathbf{0} = \mathbf{v} = \mathbf{0} + \mathbf{v}$ *additive identity*
> 4. $\mathbf{v} + (-\mathbf{v}) = \mathbf{0}$ *additive inverse*
> 5. $r(\mathbf{u} + \mathbf{v}) = r\mathbf{u} + r\mathbf{v}$ *distributive*
> 6. $(r + s)\mathbf{v} = r\mathbf{v} + s\mathbf{v}$ *distributive*
> 7. $(rs)\mathbf{v} = r(s\mathbf{v}) = s(r\mathbf{v})$ *associative for multiplication*
> 8. $1\mathbf{v} = \mathbf{v}$ *multiplicative identity*
> 9. $0\mathbf{v} = \mathbf{0}$ and $r\mathbf{0} = \mathbf{0}$ *multiplication by 0*

Proof of $\mathbf{u} + \mathbf{v} = \mathbf{v} + \mathbf{u}$

Let $\mathbf{u} = \langle a, b \rangle$ and $\mathbf{v} = \langle c, d \rangle$. Addition of real numbers is commutative; therefore,

$$\mathbf{u} + \mathbf{v} = \langle a, b \rangle + \langle c, d \rangle$$
$$= \langle a + c, b + d \rangle$$
$$= \langle c + a, d + b \rangle$$
$$= \langle c, d \rangle + \langle a, b \rangle$$
$$= \mathbf{v} + \mathbf{u}$$

The other properties are proved similarly. See Exercises 26–31.

ANSWERS

13. $\langle 3 + 4\sqrt{2}, 1 + 3\sqrt{2}\rangle$;
$\langle 3 - 4\sqrt{2}, -1 + 3\sqrt{2}\rangle$;
$\langle 9 - 8\sqrt{2}, -2 + 9\sqrt{2}\rangle$

14. $\left\langle -\frac{19}{3}, \frac{31}{3}\right\rangle$; $\left\langle \frac{23}{3}, -\frac{7}{3}\right\rangle$; $\left\langle 16, -\frac{2}{3},\right\rangle$

15. $\left\langle -\frac{23}{4}, 13\right\rangle$; $\left\langle -\frac{9}{4}, 7\right\rangle$; $\left\langle -\frac{17}{2}, 24\right\rangle$

26. $\mathbf{v} + \mathbf{0} = \langle c, d\rangle + \langle 0, 0\rangle = \langle c, d\rangle = \mathbf{v}$

27. $\mathbf{v} + (-\mathbf{v}) = \langle c, d\rangle + \langle -c, -d\rangle$
$= \langle 0, 0\rangle = \mathbf{0}$

28. $r(\mathbf{u} + \mathbf{v}) = r(\langle a, b\rangle + \langle c, d\rangle)$
$= r\langle a + c, b + d\rangle$
$= \langle r(a + c), r(b + d)\rangle$
$= \langle ra + rc, rb + rd\rangle$
$= \langle ra, rb\rangle + \langle rc, rd\rangle$
$= r\langle a, b\rangle + r\langle c, d\rangle$
$= r\mathbf{u} + r\mathbf{v}$

29. $(r + s)\mathbf{v} = (r + s)\langle c, d\rangle$
$= \langle (r + s)c, (r + s)d\rangle$
$= \langle rc, rd\rangle + \langle sc, sd\rangle$
$= r\mathbf{v} + s\mathbf{v}$

30. $(rs)\mathbf{v} = (rs)\langle c, d\rangle$
$= \langle rsc, rsd\rangle$
$= r\langle sc, sd\rangle = r(s\mathbf{v})$
$= r\langle sc, sd\rangle$
$= r\langle rsc, srd\rangle = s\langle rc, rd\rangle$
$= s(r\mathbf{v})$

31. $1\mathbf{v} = 1\langle c, d\rangle = \langle c, d\rangle = \mathbf{v}$,
$0\mathbf{v} = 0\langle c, d\rangle = \langle 0, 0\rangle = \mathbf{0}$

32. a. $\mathbf{v} = \langle x_2 - x_1, y_2 - y_1\rangle$
$k\mathbf{v} = \langle kx_2 - kx_1, ky_2 - ky_1\rangle$
b. $\|\mathbf{v}\| = \sqrt{(x_2 - x_1)^2 + (y_2 + y_1)^2}$;
$\|k\mathbf{v}\| = \sqrt{(kx_2 - kx_1)^2 + (ky_2 - ky_1)^2}$
c. $\|k\mathbf{v}\| = \sqrt{k^2(x_2 - x_1)^2 + k^2(y_2 - y_1)^2}$
$= \sqrt{k^2} \sqrt{(x_2 - x_1)^2 + (y_2 - y_1)^2}$
$= |k| \sqrt{(x_2 - x_1)^2 + (y_2 - y_1)^2}$
$= |k|\|\mathbf{v}\|$

33. a. $\sqrt{(a + c - a)^2 + (b + d - b)^2}$
$= \sqrt{c^2 + d^2} = \|\mathbf{v}\|$
b. $\sqrt{(a + c - c)^2 + (b + d - d)^2}$
$= \sqrt{a^2 + b^2} = \|\mathbf{u}\|$
c. The slope is $\frac{d}{c}$, which is the same as the slope of the vector $\mathbf{v}$.
d. The slope of the line is $\frac{b}{a}$, which is the same as the slope of the vector $\mathbf{u}$.

Exercises 10.5

In Exercises 1–4, find the magnitude of the vector $\overrightarrow{PQ}$.

1. $P = (2, 3), Q = (5, 9)$ $\mathbf{3\sqrt{5}}$

2. $P = (-3, 5), Q = (7, -11)$ $\mathbf{2\sqrt{89}}$

3. $P = (-7, 0), Q = (-4, -5)$ $\mathbf{\sqrt{34}}$

4. $P = (30, 12), Q = (25, 5)$ $\mathbf{\sqrt{74}}$

In Exercises 5–10, find a vector equivalent to the vector $\overrightarrow{PQ}$ with its initial point at the origin.

5. $P = (1, 5), Q = (7, 11)$ $\mathbf{\langle 6, 6\rangle}$

6. $P = (2, 7), Q = (-2, 9)$ $\mathbf{\langle -4, 2\rangle}$

7. $P = (-4, -8), Q = (-10, 2)$ $\mathbf{\langle -6, 10\rangle}$

8. $P = (-5, 6), Q = (-7, -9)$ $\mathbf{\langle -2, -15\rangle}$

9. $P = \left(\frac{4}{5}, -2\right), Q = \left(\frac{17}{5}, -\frac{12}{5}\right)$ $\mathbf{\left\langle \frac{13}{5}, -\frac{2}{5}\right\rangle}$

10. $P = (\sqrt{2}, 4), Q = (\sqrt{3}, -1)$ $\mathbf{\langle \sqrt{3} - \sqrt{2}, -5\rangle}$

In Exercises 11–15, find $\mathbf{u} + \mathbf{v}$, $\mathbf{u} - \mathbf{v}$, and $3\mathbf{u} - 2\mathbf{v}$.

11. $\mathbf{u} = \langle -2, 4\rangle, \mathbf{v} = \langle 6, 1\rangle$ $\mathbf{\langle 4, 5\rangle; \langle -8, 3\rangle; \langle -18, 10\rangle}$

12. $\mathbf{u} = \langle 4, 0\rangle, \mathbf{v} = \langle 1, -3\rangle$ $\mathbf{\langle 5, -3\rangle; \langle 3, 3\rangle; \langle 10, 6\rangle}$

13. $\mathbf{u} = \langle 3, 3\sqrt{2}\rangle, \mathbf{v} = \langle 4\sqrt{2}, 1\rangle$

14. $\mathbf{u} = \left\langle \frac{2}{3}, 4\right\rangle, \mathbf{v} = \left\langle -7, \frac{19}{3}\right\rangle$

15. $\mathbf{u} = 2\langle -2, 5\rangle, \mathbf{v} = \frac{1}{4}\langle -7, 12\rangle$

In Exercises 16–23, let $\mathbf{u} = \langle 3, 1\rangle, \mathbf{v} = \langle -8, 4\rangle$, and $\mathbf{w} = \langle -6, -2\rangle$. Find the magnitude of each vector.

16. $\mathbf{u} + \mathbf{v}$
$5\sqrt{2}$
18. $3\mathbf{u} + \mathbf{v}$
$5\sqrt{2}$
20. $2(\mathbf{v} - \mathbf{w})$
$4\sqrt{10}$
22. $\mathbf{u} + \frac{1}{2}\mathbf{w}$
0

17. $\mathbf{u} - \mathbf{v}$
$\sqrt{130}$
19. $\mathbf{v} + \mathbf{w}$
$10\sqrt{2}$
21. $-2(\mathbf{w} + 2\mathbf{u})$
0
23. $\frac{7}{6}\mathbf{v} - \frac{2}{3}\mathbf{v}$
$2\sqrt{5}$

If forces $\mathbf{u}_1, \mathbf{u}_2, \ldots, \mathbf{u}_k$ act on an object at the origin, the resultant force is the sum $\mathbf{u}_1 + \mathbf{u}_2 + \cdots + \mathbf{u}_k$. The forces are said to be in equilibrium if their resultant force is 0. In Exercises 24 and 25, find the resultant force and find an additional force $\mathbf{v}$, which, if added to the system, produces equilibrium.

24. $\mathbf{u}_1 = \langle 2, 5\rangle, \mathbf{u}_2 = \langle -6, 1\rangle, \mathbf{u}_3 = \langle -4, -8\rangle$
$\mathbf{\langle -8, -2\rangle; \langle 8, 2\rangle}$
25. $\mathbf{u}_1 = \langle 3, 7\rangle, \mathbf{u}_2 = \langle 8, -2\rangle, \mathbf{u}_3 = \langle -9, 0\rangle, \mathbf{u}_4 = \langle -5, 4\rangle$
$\mathbf{\langle -3, 9\rangle; \langle 3, -9\rangle}$

In Exercises 26–31, let $\mathbf{u} = \langle a, b\rangle, \mathbf{v} = \langle c, d\rangle$ and $\mathbf{w} = \langle e, f\rangle$, and let r and s be scalars. Prove that the stated property holds.

26. $\mathbf{v} + \mathbf{0} = \mathbf{v} = \mathbf{0} + \mathbf{v}$ **27.** $\mathbf{v} + (-\mathbf{v}) = \mathbf{0}$

28. $r(\mathbf{u} + \mathbf{v}) = r\mathbf{u} + r\mathbf{v}$ **29.** $(r + s)\mathbf{v} = r\mathbf{v} + s\mathbf{v}$

30. $(rs)\mathbf{v} = r(s\mathbf{v}) = s(r\mathbf{v})$ **31.** $1\mathbf{v} = \mathbf{v}$ and $0\mathbf{v} = \mathbf{0}$

32. Let $\mathbf{v}$ be the vector with initial point (x_1, y_1) and terminal point (x_2, y_2) and let k be any real number.
a. Find the component form of $\mathbf{v}$ and $k\mathbf{v}$.
b. Calculate $\|\mathbf{v}\|$ and $\|k\mathbf{v}\|$.
c. Use the fact that $\sqrt{k^2} = |k|$ to verify the following equation: $\|k\mathbf{v}\| = |k| \cdot \|\mathbf{v}\|$

33. Let $\mathbf{u} = \langle a, b\rangle$ and $\mathbf{v} = \langle c, d\rangle$. Verify the accuracy of the two geometric interpretations of vector addition given on page 657 as follows:
a. Show that the distance from (a, b) to $(a + c, b + d)$ is the same as $\|\mathbf{v}\|$.
b. Show that the distance from (c, d) to $(a + c, b + d)$ is the same as $\|\mathbf{u}\|$.
c. Show that the line through (a, b) and $(a + c, b + d)$ is parallel to $\mathbf{v}$ by showing that they have the same slope.
d. Show that the line through (c, d) and $(a + c, b + d)$ is parallel to $\mathbf{u}$.

34. Let $\mathbf{u} = \langle a, b\rangle$ and $\mathbf{v} = \langle c, d\rangle$. Show that $\|\mathbf{u} - \mathbf{v}\| = \|\mathbf{w}\|$.

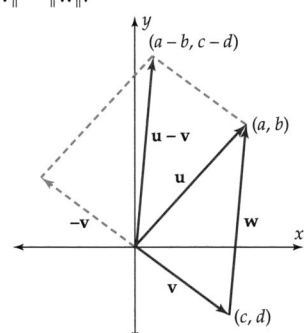

34. Since $\mathbf{u} - \mathbf{v} = \langle a - c, b - d\rangle$,
$\|\mathbf{u} - \mathbf{v}\| = \sqrt{(a - c)^2 + (b - d)^2}$.
The magnitude of $\mathbf{w}$ is given by
$\|\mathbf{w}\| = \sqrt{(a - c)^2 + (b - d)^2} = \|\mathbf{u} - \mathbf{v}\|$

10.6 Applications of Vectors in the Plane

Objectives

- Perform operations with linear combinations of vectors
- Determine the direction angle of a vector
- Determine resultant forces in physical applications

In the previous section, vectors were introduced and vector arithmetic was defined. In this section, vectors are applied to real-world situations.

Unit Vectors

A vector with length 1 is called a **unit vector.** For instance, $\left\langle \frac{3}{5}, \frac{4}{5} \right\rangle$ is a unit vector because

$$\left\| \left\langle \frac{3}{5}, \frac{4}{5} \right\rangle \right\| = \sqrt{\left(\frac{3}{5}\right)^2 + \left(\frac{4}{5}\right)^2} = \sqrt{\frac{9}{25} + \frac{16}{25}} = \sqrt{\frac{25}{25}} = 1.$$

Example 1   Unit Vectors

Find a unit vector $\mathbf{u}$ with the same direction as the vector $\mathbf{v} = \langle 5, 12 \rangle$.

Solution

Multiplying vector $\mathbf{v}$ by a scalar that is the reciprocal of its length produces a unit vector. The length of $\mathbf{v}$ is

$$\|\mathbf{v}\| = \|\langle 5, 12 \rangle\| = \sqrt{5^2 + 12^2} = \sqrt{169} = 13.$$

Let

$$\mathbf{u} = \frac{1}{13} \mathbf{v} = \frac{1}{13} \langle 5, 12 \rangle = \left\langle \frac{5}{13}, \frac{12}{13} \right\rangle.$$

The vector $\mathbf{u} = \left\langle \frac{5}{13}, \frac{12}{13} \right\rangle$ is a unit vector because

$$\|\mathbf{u}\| = \left\| \frac{1}{13} \mathbf{v} \right\| = \left| \frac{1}{13} \right| \cdot \|\mathbf{v}\| = \frac{1}{13} \cdot 13 = 1$$ ∎

Multiplying a vector by a positive scalar produces a vector with the same direction. Thus, $\mathbf{u} = \left\langle \frac{5}{13}, \frac{12}{13} \right\rangle$ is a unit vector with the same direction as the vector $\mathbf{v} = \langle 5, 12 \rangle$.

Multiplying a vector by the reciprocal of its length to produce a unit vector, as in Example 1, works in the general case, as stated below.

Unit Vectors

If $\mathbf{v}$ is a nonzero vector, then $\dfrac{1}{\|\mathbf{v}\|} \cdot \mathbf{v}$ is a unit vector with the same direction as $\mathbf{v}$.

Section 10.6 Applications of Vectors in the Plane

Teaching Notes

Illustrate $\langle 3, 4 \rangle$ and the unit vector $\left\langle \frac{3}{5}, \frac{4}{5} \right\rangle$. Point out that they have different magnitudes, but the same direction.

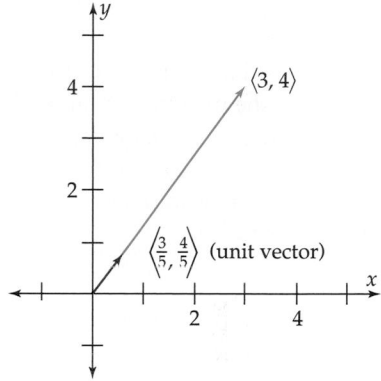

π Math Background

If $\|\mathbf{v}\| < 1$, then its associated unit vector $\mathbf{u}$ has a magnitude greater than $\|\mathbf{v}\|$. The vector $\mathbf{v} = \left\langle -\frac{12}{26}, \frac{5}{26} \right\rangle$ is shown below with its associated unit vector $\mathbf{u} = \left\langle -\frac{24}{26}, \frac{10}{26} \right\rangle$. You can verify the magnitudes:

$$\|\mathbf{v}\| = \sqrt{\left(-\frac{12}{26}\right)^2 + \left(\frac{5}{26}\right)^2} = \sqrt{\frac{169}{676}} < 1$$

$$\|\mathbf{u}\| = \sqrt{\left(-\frac{24}{26}\right)^2 + \left(\frac{10}{26}\right)^2} = \sqrt{\frac{676}{676}} = 1$$

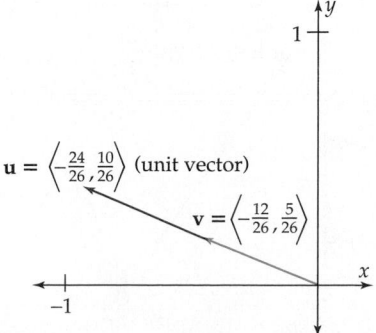

ADDITIONAL EXAMPLES

Example 1

Find a unit vector $\mathbf{u}$ with the same direction as the vector $\mathbf{v} = \langle 20, 21 \rangle$.

$$\|\mathbf{v}\| = \|\langle 20, 21 \rangle\| = \sqrt{20^2 + 21^2}$$
$$= \sqrt{841} = 29$$

Let $\mathbf{u} = \frac{1}{29} \mathbf{v} = \frac{1}{29} \langle 20, 21 \rangle = \left\langle \frac{20}{29}, \frac{21}{29} \right\rangle$

The vector $\mathbf{u} = \left\langle \frac{20}{29}, \frac{21}{29} \right\rangle$ is a unit vector because

$$\|\mathbf{u}\| = \left\| \frac{1}{29} \mathbf{v} \right\| = \left| \frac{1}{29} \right| \cdot \|\mathbf{v}\|$$
$$= \frac{1}{29} \cdot 29 = 1.$$

Teaching Notes

Show that the vector **i** lies on the x-axis and the vector **j** lies on the y-axis.

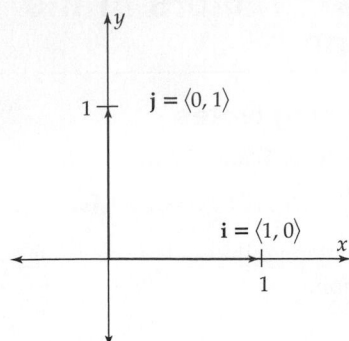

Students sometimes confuse the unit vector **i** with the imaginary number i. Show the graph of the imaginary number i below and compare it to the graph of the unit vector **i** shown above.

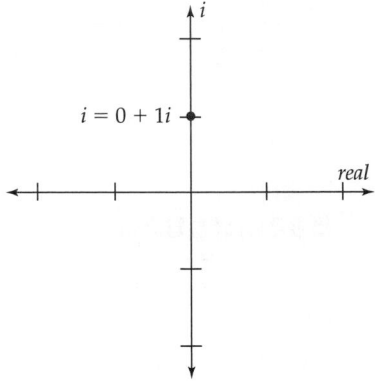

The sum $a\mathbf{i} + b\mathbf{j}$ is a vector that is the diagonal of a rectangle whose sides are $a\mathbf{i}$ and $b\mathbf{j}$. For example, $\mathbf{u} = 5\mathbf{i} - 7\mathbf{j}$ is the diagonal of the rectangle with sides $5\mathbf{i} = \langle 5, 0 \rangle$ and $-7\mathbf{j} = \langle 0, -7 \rangle$, as shown below.

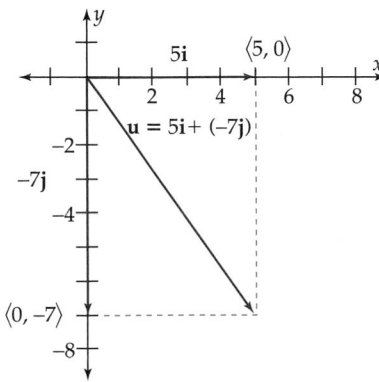

Alternate Vector Notation

It can be verified that the vectors $\mathbf{i} = \langle 1, 0 \rangle$ and $\mathbf{j} = \langle 0, 1 \rangle$ are unit vectors. The vectors **i** and **j** play a special role because they lead to a useful alternate notation for vectors. For example, if $\mathbf{u} = \langle 5, -7 \rangle$, then

$$\mathbf{u} = \langle 5, 0 \rangle + \langle 0, -7 \rangle = 5\langle 1, 0 \rangle - 7\langle 0, 1 \rangle = 5\mathbf{i} - 7\mathbf{j}.$$

Similarly, if $\mathbf{v} = \langle a, b \rangle$ is any vector, then

$$\mathbf{v} = \langle a, b \rangle = \langle a, 0 \rangle + \langle 0, b \rangle = a\langle 1, 0 \rangle + b\langle 0, 1 \rangle = a\mathbf{i} + b\mathbf{j}.$$

The vector $\mathbf{v} = a\mathbf{i} + b\mathbf{j}$ is said to be a **linear combination** of **i** and **j**. When vectors are written as linear combinations of **i** and **j**, then the properties of vector addition and scalar multiplication, given in Section 10.5, can be used to write the rules for vector addition and scalar multiplication in terms of **i** and **j**.

$$(a\mathbf{i} + b\mathbf{j}) + (c\mathbf{i} + d\mathbf{j}) = (a + c)\mathbf{i} + (b + d)\mathbf{j}$$

and

$$c(a\mathbf{i} + b\mathbf{j}) = ca\mathbf{i} + cb\mathbf{j}$$

Example 2 Perform Operations with Linear Combinations

If $\mathbf{u} = 2\mathbf{i} - 6\mathbf{j}$ and $\mathbf{v} = -5\mathbf{i} + 2\mathbf{j}$, find $3\mathbf{u} - 2\mathbf{v}$.

Solution

$$\begin{aligned}3\mathbf{u} - 2\mathbf{v} &= 3(2\mathbf{i} - 6\mathbf{j}) - 2(-5\mathbf{i} + 2\mathbf{j}) \\ &= 6\mathbf{i} - 18\mathbf{j} + 10\mathbf{i} - 4\mathbf{j} \\ &= 16\mathbf{i} - 22\mathbf{j}\end{aligned}$$

Direction Angles

If $\mathbf{v} = \langle a, b \rangle = a\mathbf{i} + b\mathbf{j}$ is a vector, then the direction of **v** is completely determined by the standard position angle θ between $0°$ and $360°$, whose terminal side is **v**, as shown in Figure 10.6-1.

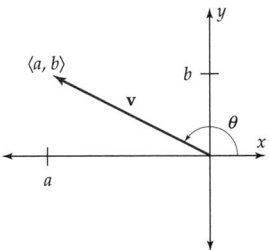

Figure 10.6-1

To explain **Components of the Direction Angle**, have students look at Figure 10.6-1 as you point out:
- **v** and $\langle a, b \rangle$ are different notations for the same vector.
- a, b, $\|\mathbf{v}\|$, $\cos \theta$, and $\sin \theta$ are all scalars.
- The components of the direction angle θ, $a = \|\mathbf{v}\| \cos \theta$ and $b = \|\mathbf{v}\| \sin \theta$, are also scalars.

Math Background

Force and *velocity* are types of vectors and have both a magnitude and direction. The magnitude of the velocity of an object is the *speed* of the object, which is a scalar quantity.

The angle θ is called the **direction angle** of the vector **v**. According to the definitions of the trigonometric functions,

$$\cos \theta = \frac{a}{\|\mathbf{v}\|} \quad \text{and} \quad \sin \theta = \frac{b}{\|\mathbf{v}\|}.$$

Rewriting each of these equations gives the following fact.

Components of the Direction Angle

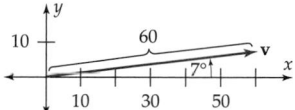

> If $\mathbf{v} = \langle a, b \rangle = a\mathbf{i} + b\mathbf{j}$, then
>
> $$a = \|\mathbf{v}\| \cos \theta \quad \text{and} \quad b = \|\mathbf{v}\| \sin \theta$$
>
> where θ is the direction angle of **v**.

Example 3   **Find Velocity Vectors**

Find the component form of the vector that represents the velocity of an airplane at the instant its wheels leave the ground, if the plane is going 60 miles per hour and the body of the plane makes a 7° angle with the horizontal.

Solution

The velocity vector $\mathbf{v} = a\mathbf{i} + b\mathbf{j}$ has magnitude 60 and direction angle $\theta = 7°$, as shown in Figure 10.6-2. Therefore,

$$\begin{aligned}
\mathbf{v} &= (\|\mathbf{v}\| \cos \theta)\mathbf{i} + (\|\mathbf{v}\| \sin \theta)\mathbf{j} \\
&= (60 \cos 7°)\mathbf{i} + (60 \sin 7°)\mathbf{j} \\
&\approx 59.55\mathbf{i} + 7.31\mathbf{j} \\
&\approx \langle 59.55, 7.31 \rangle
\end{aligned}$$

Figure 10.6-2

If $\mathbf{v} = a\mathbf{i} + b\mathbf{j}$ is a nonzero vector with direction angle θ, then

$$\tan \theta = \frac{\sin \theta}{\cos \theta} = \frac{\frac{b}{\|\mathbf{v}\|}}{\frac{a}{\|\mathbf{v}\|}} = \frac{b}{a}.$$

This fact provides a convenient way to find the direction angle of a vector.

Example 4   **Find Direction Angles**

Find the direction angle of each vector.
a. $\mathbf{u} = 5\mathbf{i} + 13\mathbf{j}$ b. $\mathbf{v} = -10\mathbf{i} + 7\mathbf{j}$

Solution

a. The direction angle θ of **u** satisfies

$$\tan \theta = \frac{b}{a} = \frac{13}{5} = 2.6.$$

Figure 10.6-3

Teaching Notes

Recall Figure 10.3-2, page 639, that was used for the polar form of a complex number:

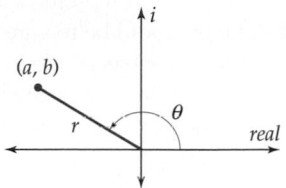

Compare and contrast Figure 10.3-2 (above) and Figure 10.6-1 (page 662) as follows:

10.3-2	10.6-1
complex plane	rectangular coordinate plane for real numbers
real axis and imaginary axis	x-axis and y-axis
(a, b) is the graph of a complex number $a + bi$	$\langle a, b \rangle$ is a vector
$r = |a + bi|$ is the modulus of $a + bi$; it is the distance from $a + bi$ to the origin	$\|\mathbf{v}\|$ is the magnitude of $\langle a, b \rangle$; it is the length of vector $\langle a, b \rangle$

ADDITIONAL EXAMPLES

Example 2

If $\mathbf{u} = 5\mathbf{i} - 4\mathbf{j}$ and $\mathbf{v} = 8\mathbf{i} + 2\mathbf{j}$, find $4\mathbf{u} - 5\mathbf{v}$.

$$\begin{aligned}
4\mathbf{u} - 5\mathbf{v} &= 4(5\mathbf{i} - 4\mathbf{j}) - 5(8\mathbf{i} + 2\mathbf{j}) \\
&= 20\mathbf{i} - 16\mathbf{j} - 40\mathbf{i} - 10\mathbf{j} \\
&= -20\mathbf{i} - 26\mathbf{j}
\end{aligned}$$

Example 3

Find the component form of the vector that represents the initial velocity of a baseball thrown at a speed of 80 feet per second, at an angle of 32° with the horizontal.

$$\begin{aligned}
\mathbf{v} &= (80 \cos 32°)\mathbf{i} + (80 \sin 32°)\mathbf{j} \\
&\approx 67.84\mathbf{i} + 42.39\mathbf{j} \\
&\approx \langle 67.84, 42.39 \rangle
\end{aligned}$$

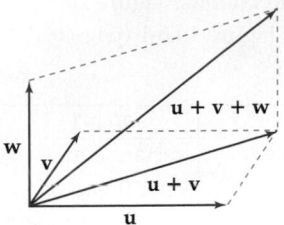

Math Background

A **resultant force** is the net effect of two or more forces. It represents a *single* force that would be required to cause the same effect as all the forces it is the resultant of. In each of **Examples 5–7**, we find the resultant of two forces.

The diagram below shows that $\mathbf{u} + \mathbf{v} + \mathbf{w}$ is a resultant of 3 vectors.

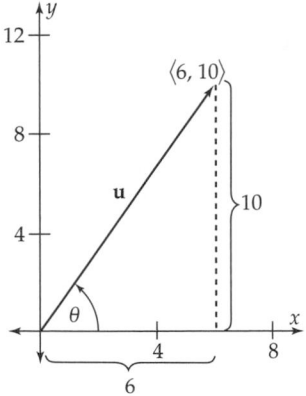

ADDITIONAL EXAMPLES

Example 4

Find the direction angle of each vector.

a. $\mathbf{u} = 6\mathbf{i} + 10\mathbf{j}$

The vector $\mathbf{u}$ lies in the first quadrant and the direction angle θ of $\mathbf{u}$ satisfies $\tan \theta = \dfrac{b}{a} = \dfrac{10}{6}$, so

$$\theta = \tan^{-1}\left(\frac{10}{6}\right) \approx 59.04°.$$

b. $\mathbf{v} = -9\mathbf{i} - 5\mathbf{j}$

The direction angle θ of $\mathbf{v}$ satisfies

$$\tan \theta = \frac{b}{a} = \frac{-5}{-9}$$

Because $\mathbf{v}$ lies in the third quadrant, angle θ must be between 180° and 270°.

Using a calculator:

$$\tan^{-1}\left(\frac{-5}{-9}\right) \approx 29.05°$$

So $\theta \approx 29.05° + 180° \approx 209.05°$.

Using the TAN^{-1} key on a calculator indicates that $\theta \approx 68.96°$. The vector $\mathbf{u}$ is shown in Figure 10.6-3.

b. The direction angle θ of $\mathbf{v}$ satisfies

$$\tan \theta = \frac{b}{a} = \frac{7}{-10} = -0.7.$$

Because $\mathbf{v}$ lies in the second quadrant, θ must be between 90° and 180°. A calculator shows that $t \approx -34.99°$ has a tangent that is approximately equal to -0.7. The period of tangent is 180°, so

$$\tan t = \tan(t + 180°)$$

for every t. Therefore,

$$\theta \approx -34.99° + 180° = 145.01°$$

is the angle between 90° and 180° such that $\tan \theta \approx -0.7$. The vector $\mathbf{v}$ is shown in Figure 10.6-4.

Figure 10.6-4

Vector Applications

A common application of vectors is in modeling a system of forces acting on an object. Every force has direction and magnitude, therefore, each can be represented by a vector. The sum of all the forces acting on an object is called the **resultant force.**

Example 5 Resultant Force

An object at the origin is acted upon by two forces. A 150-pound force makes an angle of 20° with the positive x-axis, and the other force of 100 pounds makes an angle of 70° with the positive x-axis, as shown in Figure 10.6-5. Find the direction and magnitude of the resultant force.

Figure 10.6-5

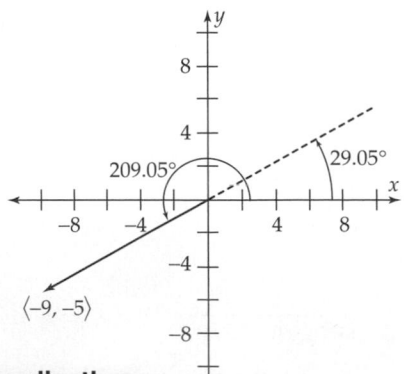

Solution

The forces acting upon the object are:

$$\overrightarrow{OP} = (150 \cos 20°)\mathbf{i} + (150 \sin 20°)\mathbf{j}$$
$$\overrightarrow{OQ} = (100 \cos 70°)\mathbf{i} + (100 \sin 70°)\mathbf{j}$$

The resultant force $\overrightarrow{OR}$ is the sum of $\overrightarrow{OP}$ and $\overrightarrow{OQ}$.

$$\overrightarrow{OR} = (150 \cos 20°)\mathbf{i} + (150 \sin 20°)\mathbf{j} + (100 \cos 70°)\mathbf{i} + (100 \sin 70°)\mathbf{j}$$
$$\overrightarrow{OR} \approx 175.16\mathbf{i} + 145.27\mathbf{j}$$

The magnitude of the resultant force $\overrightarrow{OR}$ is

$$\|\overrightarrow{OR}\| \approx \sqrt{175.16^2 + 145.27^2} \approx 227.56.$$

The direction angle θ of the resultant force satisfies

$$\tan \theta \approx \frac{145.27}{175.16} \approx 0.8294$$

A calculator in degree mode shows that $\theta \approx 39.67°$. ∎

Example 6   Resultant Force

A 200-pound box lies on a ramp that makes an angle of 24° with the horizontal. A rope is tied to the box from a post at the top of the ramp to keep it in position (see Figure 10.6-6). Ignoring friction, how much force is being exerted on the rope by the box?

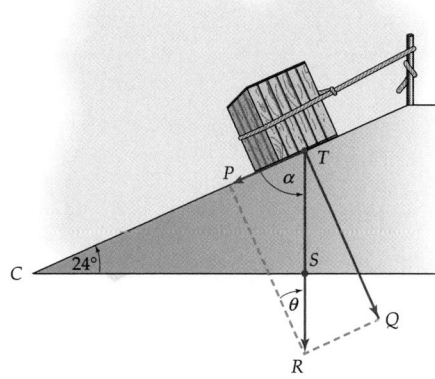

Figure 10.6-6

Solution

Because of gravity, the box exerts a 200-pound weight straight down (vector $\overrightarrow{TR}$). As Figure 10.6-6 shows, $\overrightarrow{TR}$ is the sum of $\overrightarrow{TP}$ and $\overrightarrow{TQ}$. The force on the rope is represented by $\overrightarrow{TP}$, the vector of the force pulling the box

---

Example 5

An object at the origin is acted upon by two forces. A 300-pound force makes an angle of 35° with the positive x-axis, and the other force of 125 pounds makes an angle of 85° with the positive x-axis. Find the direction and magnitude of the resultant force.

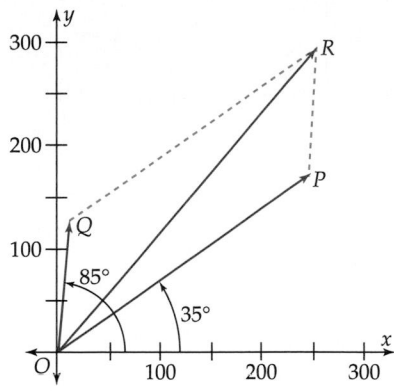

The forces acting upon the object are:

$\overrightarrow{OP} = (300 \cos 35°)\mathbf{i} + (300 \sin 35°)\mathbf{j}$

$\overrightarrow{OR} = (125 \cos 85°)\mathbf{i} + (125 \sin 85°)\mathbf{j}$

The resultant $\overrightarrow{OR}$ is the sum of $\overrightarrow{OP}$ and $\overrightarrow{OQ}$.

$\overrightarrow{OR} = (300 \cos 35°)\mathbf{i} + (300 \sin 35°)\mathbf{j}$
$\qquad + (125 \cos 85°)\mathbf{i} + (125 \sin 85°)\mathbf{j}$

$\overrightarrow{OR} \approx 256.64\mathbf{i} + 296.60\mathbf{j}$

The magnitude of the resultant $\overrightarrow{OR}$ is
$\|\overrightarrow{OR}\| = \sqrt{256.64^2 + 296.60^2}$

$\qquad \approx 392.22.$

The direction angle θ of the resultant force satisfies $\tan \theta \approx \frac{296.60}{256.64} \approx 1.1557$.

$\theta \approx 49.13°$

The resultant force has direction angle $\theta \approx 49.13°$ and magnitude ≈ 392.22 pounds.

Example 6

A 10-pound sled is held by a rope on an incline that makes a 15° angle with the horizontal. Ignoring friction, find the force exerted on the rope by the sled in the direction parallel to the incline.

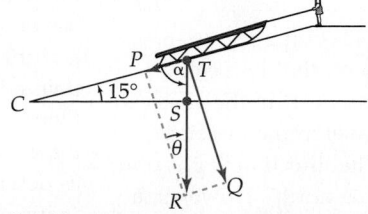

$\|\overrightarrow{TP}\|$ represents the magnitude of the force pulling the sled down the incline.

$\alpha + 15° = 90°$ and $\alpha + \theta = 90°$.

Therefore, $\theta = 15°$. $\|\overrightarrow{TR}\| = 10$

$$\sin \theta = \frac{\|\overrightarrow{TP}\|}{\|\overrightarrow{TR}\|}$$

$$\sin 15° = \frac{\|\overrightarrow{TP}\|}{10}$$

$$\|\overrightarrow{TP}\| = 10 \sin 15° \approx 2.59$$

The sled exerts about 2.59 pounds of force on the rope parallel to the incline.

ADDITIONAL EXAMPLES

Example 7

An airplane with an air speed of 210 mph is flying in the direction 75°, shown by vector **p**. A wind of 50 mph is blowing from the direction of 150°, shown by vector **w.** Find the course and ground speed of the plane.

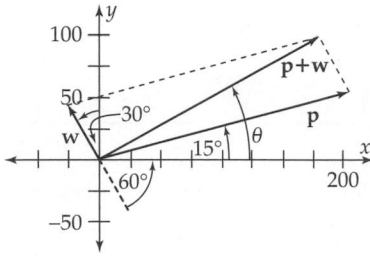

The direction angle of **p** is 15°. The angle that **w** makes with the positive y-axis is 30°, so the direction angle of **w** as measured from the positive x-axis is 30° + 90° = 120°.

$$\mathbf{p} = (210 \cos 15°)\mathbf{i} + (210 \sin 15°)\mathbf{j}$$

$$\mathbf{w} = (50 \cos 120°)\mathbf{i} + (50 \sin 120°)\mathbf{j}$$

$$\mathbf{p} + \mathbf{w} = [(210 \cos 15°)\mathbf{i} + (210 \sin 15°)\mathbf{j}]$$
$$+ [(50 \cos 120°)\mathbf{i} + (50 \sin 120°)\mathbf{j}]$$
$$= (210 \cos 15° + 50 \cos 120°)\mathbf{i}$$
$$+ (210 \sin 15° + 50 \sin 120°)\mathbf{j}$$
$$\approx 177.84\mathbf{i} + 97.65\mathbf{j}$$

Find the direction angle of **p** + **w**:

$$\tan \theta \approx \frac{97.65}{177.84} \approx 0.5491$$

$$\theta \approx 28.8°$$

The course of the plane is the angle between **p** + **w** and true north.

90° − 28.8° = 61.2°

The ground speed of the plane is ‖**p** + **w**‖.

$$\|\mathbf{p} + \mathbf{w}\| = \sqrt{(177.84)^2 + (97.65)^2}$$
$$\approx 202.89$$

So, the plane's course is about 61.2° and its ground speed is about 202.89 miles per hour.

---

down the ramp, and ‖$\overrightarrow{TP}$‖ represents the magnitude of the force.

In right triangle $TSC, \alpha + 24° = 90°$, and in right triangle $TRP, \alpha + \theta = 90°$. Therefore,

$$\alpha + \theta = \alpha + 24°$$
$$\theta = 24°$$

The box weighs 200 pounds, so ‖$\overrightarrow{TR}$‖ = 200. Use $\sin \theta$ to find ‖$\overrightarrow{TP}$‖.

$$\sin \theta = \frac{\|\overrightarrow{TP}\|}{\|\overrightarrow{TR}\|}$$

$$\sin 24° = \frac{\|\overrightarrow{TP}\|}{200}$$

$$\|\overrightarrow{TP}\| = 200 \sin 24° \approx 81.35$$

The force on the rope is about 81.35 pounds. ∎

Example 7   Resultant Force

An airplane is flying in the direction 50° with an air speed of 300 miles per hour. If there was no wind, the course of the airplane would be 50°. However, there is a 35-mile-per-hour wind from the direction 120°, as represented by the vectors **p** and **w** in Figures 10.6-7, which shows the angles using aerial navigation orientation. Find the *course* and *ground speed* of the plane (that is, its direction and speed relative to the ground taking the effect of the wind into consideration).

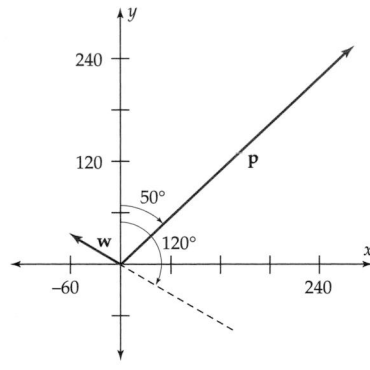

Figure 10.6-7

Solution

Figure 10.6-8 shows **p**, **w**, and **p** + **w**. The course of the plane is the direction angle of the vector **p** + **w**, and its ground speed is the magnitude of **p** + **w**.

The direction angle of **p** (the angle it makes with the positive x-axis) is 90° − 50° = 40°. The angle that **w** makes with the positive y-axis is

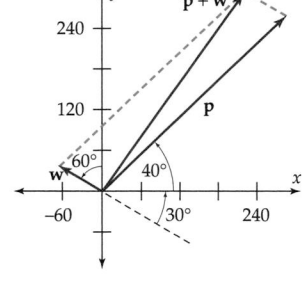

Figure 10.6-8

Example Notes

Example 7 and Exercises 42–47 (pages 668–669) concern the effect of wind on the course of an airplane. Explain to students that in the absence of wind, the plane will travel in the direction that it is pointed (where the direction is given in degrees clockwise from due north). However, a wind that is not in exactly the same or opposite direction of the airplane will push it off course. Therefore, the pilot will have to "point" the

plane at an angle to the desired direction of travel to compensate for the wind. In Example 7 and the Exercises, the direction the plane is pointed is described as the direction the plane is flying, or is the direction given in conjunction with the air speed. This is also called the "heading" as described in Exercise 55 on page 432. The "course" is the direction that the plane actually travels, taking the wind into consideration.

$180° - 120° = 60°$, so the direction angle of **w**, as measured from the positive x-axis, is $60° + 90° = 150°$. Therefore,

$$\mathbf{p} = (300 \cos 40°)\mathbf{i} + (300 \sin 40°)\mathbf{j}$$
$$\mathbf{w} = (35 \cos 150°)\mathbf{i} + (35 \sin 150°)\mathbf{j}$$
$$\mathbf{p} + \mathbf{w} = [(300 \cos 40°)\mathbf{i} + (300 \sin 40°)\mathbf{j}] + [(35 \cos 150°)\mathbf{i}$$
$$+ (35 \sin 150°)\mathbf{j}]$$
$$= (300 \cos 40° + 35 \cos 150°)\mathbf{i} + (300 \sin 40° + 35 \sin 150°)\mathbf{j}$$
$$\approx 199.50\mathbf{i} + 210.34\mathbf{j}$$

The direction angle of **p** + **w** is

$$\tan \theta = \frac{210.34}{199.50}$$
$$\tan \theta \approx 1.0543$$
$$\theta \approx 46.5°$$

The course of the plane is the angle between **p** + **w** and true north.

$$90° - 46.5° = 43.5°$$

The ground speed of the plane is $\|\mathbf{p} + \mathbf{w}\|$.

$$\|\mathbf{p} + \mathbf{w}\| = \sqrt{199.50^2 + 210.34^2} \approx 289.9$$

Thus, the plane's course is about 43.5° and its ground speed is about 289.9 miles per hour. ∎

Exercises 10.6

In Exercises 1–5, find **u** + **v**, **u** − **v**, and 3**u** − 2**v**.

1. $\mathbf{u} = \mathbf{i} - \mathbf{j}, \mathbf{v} = 2\mathbf{i} + \mathbf{j}$

2. $\mathbf{u} = 8\mathbf{i}, \mathbf{v} = 2(3\mathbf{i} - 2\mathbf{j})$

3. $\mathbf{u} = -4(-\mathbf{i} + \mathbf{j}), \mathbf{v} = -3\mathbf{i}$

4. $\mathbf{u} = -\left(2\mathbf{i} + \frac{3}{2}\mathbf{j}\right), \mathbf{v} = \frac{3}{4}\mathbf{i}$

5. $\mathbf{u} = \sqrt{2}\mathbf{j}, \mathbf{v} = \sqrt{3}\mathbf{i}$

In Exercises 6–11, find the components of the given vector, where $\mathbf{u} = \mathbf{i} - 2\mathbf{j}$, $\mathbf{v} = 3\mathbf{i} + \mathbf{j}$, and $\mathbf{w} = -4\mathbf{i} + \mathbf{j}$.

6. $\mathbf{u} + 2\mathbf{w}$ $-7\mathbf{i}$

7. $\frac{1}{2}(3\mathbf{v} + \mathbf{w})$ $\frac{5}{2}\mathbf{i} + 2\mathbf{j}$

8. $\frac{1}{2}\mathbf{w}$ $-2\mathbf{i} + \frac{1}{2}\mathbf{j}$

9. $-2\mathbf{u} + 3\mathbf{v}$ $7\mathbf{i} + 7\mathbf{j}$

10. $\frac{1}{4}(8\mathbf{u} + 4\mathbf{v} - \mathbf{w})$ $6\mathbf{i} - \frac{13}{4}\mathbf{j}$

11. $3(\mathbf{u} - 2\mathbf{v}) - 6\mathbf{w}$ $9\mathbf{i} - 18\mathbf{j}$

In Exercises 12–19, find the component form of the vector **v** whose magnitude and direction angle θ are given.

12. $\|\mathbf{v}\| = 4, \theta = 0°$ $\mathbf{v} = \langle 4, 0 \rangle$

13. $\|\mathbf{v}\| = 5, \theta = 30°$ $\mathbf{v} = \left\langle \frac{5\sqrt{3}}{2}, \frac{5}{2} \right\rangle$

14. $\|\mathbf{v}\| = 10, \theta = 225°$ $\mathbf{v} = \langle -5\sqrt{2}, -5\sqrt{2} \rangle$

15. $\|\mathbf{v}\| = 20, \theta = 120°$ $\mathbf{v} = \langle -10, 10\sqrt{3} \rangle$

16. $\|\mathbf{v}\| = 6, \theta = 40°$ $\mathbf{v} \approx \langle 4.5963, 3.8567 \rangle$

17. $\|\mathbf{v}\| = 8, \theta = 160°$ $\mathbf{v} \approx \langle -7.5175, 2.7362 \rangle$

18. $\|\mathbf{v}\| = \frac{1}{2}, \theta = 250°$ $\mathbf{v} \approx \langle -0.1710, -0.4698 \rangle$

19. $\|\mathbf{v}\| = 3, \theta = 310°$ $\mathbf{v} \approx \langle 1.9284, -2.2981 \rangle$

In Exercises 20–27, find the magnitude and direction angle of the vector **v**.

20. $\mathbf{v} = \langle 4, 4 \rangle$ $\|\mathbf{v}\| = 4\sqrt{2}, \theta = 45°$

21. $\mathbf{v} = \langle 5, 5\sqrt{3} \rangle$ $\|\mathbf{v}\| = 10, \theta = 60°$

22. $\mathbf{v} = \langle -8, 0 \rangle$ $\|\mathbf{v}\| = 8, \theta = 180°$

23. $\mathbf{v} = \langle 4, 5 \rangle$

24. $\mathbf{v} = 6\mathbf{j}$ $\|\mathbf{v}\| = 6, \theta = 90°$

25. $\mathbf{v} = 4\mathbf{i} - 8\mathbf{j}$ $\|\mathbf{v}\| = 4\sqrt{5}, \theta \approx 296.6°$

26. $\mathbf{v} = -2\mathbf{i} + 8\mathbf{j}$ $\|\mathbf{v}\| = 2\sqrt{17}, \theta \approx 104.04°$

27. $\mathbf{v} = -15\mathbf{i} - 10\mathbf{j}$

continued from page 666

Similarly, in Exercises 48 and 49 (page 669) a swimmer has to swim in a direction different than the direction she wants to travel in order to compensate for the current in the water. That is, her body will be pointed in a direction that is different from the direction that she wants to go.

Real-World Application

Example 7 is an application of the concept of a resultant force to aviation. Notice that the angle between the vectors **p** and **w** is obtuse, and the ground speed of the plane is found to be less than the air speed of the plane. Suppose that all quantities in Example 7 remain the same except for the direction of the wind. Suppose the wind is from the direction 160° instead of 120°, so that the angle between the vectors **p** and **w** is 70°, which is acute. Find the ground speed of the plane using this new wind direction.
about 313.7 mph
Make a conjecture about:
• ground speed vs air speed
• acute angle vs obtuse angle between the vectors
possible conjecture:
If the angle between the wind vector and the heading of the plane is acute, the air speed is greater than the ground speed (that is, the wind makes the plane go faster).

If the angle between the wind vector and the heading of the plane is obtuse, the air speed is less than the ground speed (that is, the wind makes the plane go slower).

Exercises 10.6

ANSWERS

1. $3\mathbf{i}; -\mathbf{i} - 2\mathbf{j}; -\mathbf{i} - 5\mathbf{j}$

2. $14\mathbf{i} - 4\mathbf{j}; 2\mathbf{i} + 4\mathbf{j}; 12\mathbf{i} + 8\mathbf{j}$

3. $\mathbf{i} - 4\mathbf{j}; 7\mathbf{i} - 4\mathbf{j}; 18\mathbf{i} - 12\mathbf{j}$

4. $-\frac{5}{4}\mathbf{i} - \frac{3}{2}\mathbf{j}; -\frac{11}{4}\mathbf{i} - \frac{3}{2}\mathbf{j}; -\frac{15}{2}\mathbf{i} - \frac{9}{2}\mathbf{j}$

5. $\sqrt{3}\mathbf{i} + \sqrt{2}\mathbf{j}; -\sqrt{3}\mathbf{i} + \sqrt{2}\mathbf{j}; -2\sqrt{3}\mathbf{i} + 3\sqrt{2}\mathbf{j}$

23. $\|\mathbf{v}\| = \sqrt{41} \approx 6.4031, \theta \approx 51.34°$

27. $\|\mathbf{v}\| = 5\sqrt{13}, \theta \approx 213.7°$

28. $\dfrac{4}{\sqrt{41}}\mathbf{i} - \dfrac{5}{\sqrt{41}}\mathbf{j}$

29. $-\dfrac{7}{\sqrt{113}}\mathbf{i} + \dfrac{8}{\sqrt{113}}\mathbf{j}$

30. $\dfrac{1}{\sqrt{5}}\mathbf{i} + \dfrac{2}{\sqrt{5}}\mathbf{j}$

31. $-\dfrac{1}{\sqrt{10}}\mathbf{i} - \dfrac{3}{\sqrt{10}}\mathbf{j}$

32. direction: 46.1°;
magnitude: 108.2 lb

33. direction: 82.5°;
magnitude: 9.52 lb

34. direction: 213.4°;
magnitude: 17.4 kg

35. direction: 18.4°;
magnitude: 80.4 kg

36. 48.58 lb

37. $\theta = \sin^{-1}\left(\dfrac{-894.8}{1500}\right) \approx -36.6°$

38. $\|\overrightarrow{TP}\| = 32.1$ lb
$\|\overrightarrow{TQ}\| = 38.3$ lb

39. parallel to plane: 68.4 lb;
perpendicular to plane: 187.9 lb

40. 66.4°

41. 1931.85 lb

42. ground speed: 253.2 mph;
course: 69.1°

43. ground speed: 401.1 mph;
course: 154.3°

44. ground speed: 304.1 mph;
course: 309.5°

In Exercises 28–31, find a unit vector that has the same direction as the given vector.

28. $\langle 4, -5 \rangle$

29. $-7\mathbf{i} + 8\mathbf{j}$

30. $5\mathbf{i} + 10\mathbf{j}$

31. $-3\mathbf{i} - 9\mathbf{j}$

In Exercises 32–35, an object at the origin is acted upon by two forces **u** and **v**, with direction angle $\theta_\mathbf{u}$ and $\theta_\mathbf{v}$, respectively. Find the direction and magnitude of the resultant force.

32. $\mathbf{u} = 30$ pounds, $\theta_\mathbf{u} = 0°$; $\mathbf{v} = 90$ pounds, $\theta_\mathbf{v} = 60°$

33. $\mathbf{u} = 6$ pounds, $\theta_\mathbf{u} = 45°$; $\mathbf{v} = 6$ pounds, $\theta_\mathbf{v} = 120°$

34. $\mathbf{u} = 12$ kilograms, $\theta_\mathbf{u} = 130°$; $\mathbf{v} = 20$ kilograms, $\theta_\mathbf{v} = 250°$

35. $\mathbf{u} = 30$ kilograms, $\theta_\mathbf{u} = 300°$; $\mathbf{v} = 80$ kilograms, $\theta_\mathbf{v} = 40°$

36. Two ropes are tied to a wagon. A child pulls one with a force of 20 pounds, while another child pulls the other with a force of 30 pounds. See the figure. If the angle between the two ropes is 28°, how much force must be exerted by a third child, standing behind the wagon, to keep the wagon from moving? *Hint:* Assume the wagon is at the origin and one rope runs along the positive *x*-axis. Proceed as in Example 5 to find the resultant force on the wagon from the ropes. The third child must use the same amount in the opposite direction.

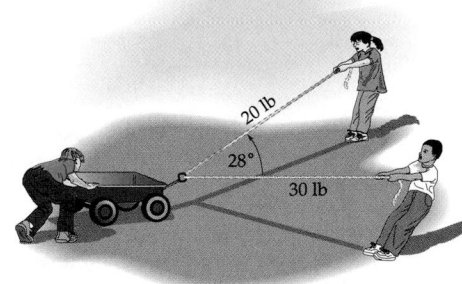

37. Two circus elephants, Bessie and Maybelle, are dragging a large wagon, as shown in the figure. If Bessie pulls with a force of 2200 pounds and Maybelle with a force of 1500 pounds and the wagon moves along the dashed line, what is angle θ?

Exercises 38–41 deal with an object on an inclined plane. The situation is similar to that in Figure 10.6-6 of Example 6, where $\|\overrightarrow{TP}\|$ is the component of the weight of the object parallel to the plane and $\|\overrightarrow{TQ}\|$ is the component of the weight perpendicular to the plane.

38. An object weighing 50 pounds lies on an inclined plane that makes a 40° angle with the horizontal. Find the components of the weight parallel and perpendicular to the plane. *Hint:* Solve an appropriate triangle.

39. Do Exercise 38 when the object weighs 200 pounds and the inclined plane makes a 20° angle with the horizontal.

40. If an object on an inclined plane weighs 150 pounds and the component of the weight perpendicular to the plane is 60 pounds, what angle does the plane make with the horizontal?

41. A force of 500 pounds is needed to pull a cart up a ramp that makes a 15° angle with the ground. Assuming that no friction is involved, find the weight of the cart. *Hint:* Draw a picture similar to Figure 10.6-6; the 500-pound force is parallel to the ramp.

In Exercises 42–47, find the course and ground speed of the plane under the given conditions. See Example 7. All angle measurements are given as aerial navigation directions. See Exercise 55 of Section 6.2.

42. air speed 250 miles per hour in the direction 60°; wind speed 40 miles per hour from the direction 330°

43. air speed 400 miles per hour in the direction 150°; wind speed 30 miles per hour from the direction 60°

44. air speed 300 miles per hour in the direction 300°; wind speed 50 miles per hour in (not from) the direction 30°

45. air speed 500 miles per hour in the direction 180°; wind speed 70 miles per hour in the direction 40°

46. The course and ground speed of a plane are 70° and 400 miles per hour respectively. There is a 60-mile-per-hour wind blowing from the south. Find the approximate direction and air speed of the plane.

47. A plane is flying in the direction 200° with an air speed of 500 miles per hour. Its course and ground speed are 210° and 450 miles per hour, respectively. What is the direction and speed of the wind?

48. A river flows from east to west. A swimmer on the south bank wants to swim to a point on the opposite shore directly north of her starting point. She can swim at 2.8 miles per hour, and there is a 1-mile-per-hour current in the river. In what direction should she swim in order to travel directly north (that is, what angle should the swimmer make with the south bank of the river)?

49. A river flows from west to east. A swimmer on the north bank swims at 3.1 miles per hour along a line that makes a 75° angle with the north bank of the river and reaches the south bank at a point directly south of his starting point. How fast is the current in the river?

50. A 400-pound weight is suspended by two cables (see the following figure). What is the force (tension) on each cable? *Hint:* Imagine that the weight is at the origin and that the dashed line is the *x*-axis. Then cable **v** is represented by the vector

$$(c \cos 65°)\mathbf{i} + (c \sin 65°)\mathbf{j}$$

which has magnitude c. (Why?) Represent cable **u** similarly, denoting its magnitude as d. Use the fact that $\mathbf{u} + \mathbf{v} = 0\mathbf{i} + 400\mathbf{j}$ (why?) to set up a system of two equations in the unknowns c and d.

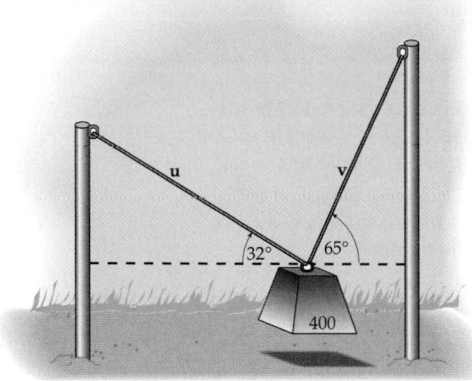

51. A 175-pound high-wire artist stands balanced on a tightrope, which sags slightly at the point where he is standing. The rope in front of him makes a 6° angle with the horizontal and the rope behind him makes a 4° angle with the horizontal. Find the force on each end of the rope. *Hint:* Use a picture and procedure similar to that in Exercise 50.

52. Let **v** be the vector with initial point (x_1, y_1) and terminal point (x_2, y_2), and let k be any real number.
  a. Show that $\tan \theta = \tan \beta$ where θ is the direction angle of **v** and β is the direction angle of $k\mathbf{v}$. Use the fact that $\tan t = \tan(t + 180°)$ to conclude that **v** and $k\mathbf{v}$ have either the same or opposite directions.
  b. Use the fact that (c, d) and $(-c, -d)$ lie on the same straight line on opposite sides of the origin to verify that **v** and $k\mathbf{v}$ have the same direction if $k > 0$ and opposite directions if $k < 0$.

53. Let $\mathbf{u} = \langle a, b \rangle$ and $\mathbf{v} = \langle c, d \rangle$. In Exercise 34 of Section 10.5, $\|\mathbf{u} - \mathbf{v}\| = \|\mathbf{w}\|$ was shown (see the figure with Exercise 34 of Section 10.5). Show that $\mathbf{u} - \mathbf{v}$ is equivalent to the vector **w** with initial point (c, d) and terminal point (a, b) by now showing that $\mathbf{u} - \mathbf{v}$ and **w** have the same direction.

45. ground speed: 448.6 mph; course: 174.2°

46. air speed: 424.3 mph; direction: 62.4°

47. air speed: 96.6 mph; direction: 326°

48. 69.08°

49. 0.8023 mph

50. $c \approx 341.77$ lb; $d \approx 170.32$ lb

51. 1005 lb on 6°; 1002 lb on 4°

52. a. $\tan \theta = \dfrac{y_2 - y_1}{x_2 - x_1}$

  $= \dfrac{ky_2 - ky_1}{kx_2 - kx_1} = \tan \beta$

  Since the angles have the same tangent, they may only differ by a multiple of π, and so are parallel. They have either the same direction or opposite directions.

  b. If $k > 0$, the signs of the components of $k\mathbf{v}$, the same as those of **v**, so the two vectors lie in the same quadrant. Therefore, they must have the same direction. If $k < 0$, then the components of $k\mathbf{v}$ and the components of **v** must have opposite signs and the two vectors do not lie in the same quadrant. Therefore, they do not have the same direction and must have opposite directions.

53. $\mathbf{u} - \mathbf{v}$ lies on the straight line through $(0, 0)$ and $(a - c, b - d)$ which has slope $\dfrac{(a - c) - 0}{(b - d) - 0} = \dfrac{a - c}{b - d}$. Similarly, **w** lies on the line through (a, b) and (c, d), which also has slope $\dfrac{a - c}{b - d}$. So, $\mathbf{u} - \mathbf{v}$ and **w** are parallel. Verify that they actually have the same direction by considering the relative positions of (a, b), (c, d), and $(a - c, b - d)$. For instance, if $\mathbf{u} - \mathbf{v}$ points upward to the right, then (a, b) lies to the right and above (c, d). Hence $c < a$ and $d < b$, so that $a - c > 0$ and $b - d > 0$, which means that the endpoint of **w** lies in the first quadrant, that is, **w** points upward to the right.

Teaching Notes

The section title is **The Dot Product,** but notice that after the dot product and its properties are discussed, there are many topics:

- angles between vectors
- parallel vectors
- the Schwarz Inequality
- orthogonal vectors
- projections and components
- work

As students learn about these topics, they will see that the dot product of two vectors **u** and **v**, denoted **u · v,** is used directly or indirectly in every topic.

Remind students that in each expression in Property 4, k is a scalar.

In Property 5, the first **0** is the zero vector $\langle 0, 0 \rangle$, and the second 0 is the number 0.

Illustrate Property 5 as follows:
Let $\mathbf{u} = \langle 2, 5 \rangle$. Then
$$\mathbf{0 \cdot u} = \langle 0, 0 \rangle \cdot \langle 2, 5 \rangle$$
$$= (0)(2) + (0)(5) = 0$$

Parallel Vectors are described as vectors that lie on the same line through the origin and have either the same or opposite directions. This description is probably not consistent with students' understanding of the meaning of *parallel*. Explain as follows:

1. Have students look at Figure 10.5-3 on page 653. Explain that **u** and **v** are parallel in each of the first three diagrams.
2. Remind students that every vector is equivalent to some vector whose initial point is the origin (see Equivalent Vectors on page 654).
3. Looking back at Figure 10.5-3 on page 653, have students "mentally place" every vector so that its initial point is the origin of a coordinate system.

10.6.A

Excursion: The Dot Product

Objectives

- Find the dot product of two vectors and the angle between two vectors
- Determine projection and component vectors and use them in physical applications

Dot Product

Unlike multiplication of real numbers where there is only one type of multiplication, vector operations include three types of multiplication: scalar multiplication, dot products, and cross products. This section discusses the vector operation called the **dot product.** Unlike scalar multiplication of vectors, the dot product is not a vector.

The dot product of two vectors is a *real number*.

> The *dot product* of vectors $\mathbf{u} = \langle a, b \rangle = a\mathbf{i} + b\mathbf{j}$ and $\mathbf{v} = \langle c, d \rangle = c\mathbf{i} + d\mathbf{j}$ is denoted $\mathbf{u \cdot v}$ and is defined to be the real number $ac + bd$. Thus,
> $$\mathbf{u \cdot v} = ac + bd.$$

NOTE The dot product of two vectors is found by multiplying corresponding components and finding the sum of the products.

Example 1   **Find Dot Product of Two Vectors**

Find the dot product $\mathbf{u \cdot v}$ for the given vectors **u** and **v**.

a. $\mathbf{u} = \langle 5, 3 \rangle$ and $\mathbf{v} = \langle -2, 6 \rangle$
b. $\mathbf{u} = 4\mathbf{i} - 2\mathbf{j}$ and $\mathbf{v} = 3\mathbf{i} - \mathbf{j}$
c. $\mathbf{u} = \langle 2, -4 \rangle$ and $\mathbf{v} = \langle 6, 3 \rangle$

Solution

a. $\mathbf{u \cdot v} = \langle 5, 3 \rangle \cdot \langle -2, 6 \rangle = 5(-2) + 3(6) = 8$
b. $\mathbf{u \cdot v} = (4\mathbf{i} - 2\mathbf{j}) \cdot (3\mathbf{i} - \mathbf{j}) = 4(3) + (-2)(-1) = 14$
c. $\mathbf{u \cdot v} = \langle 2, -4 \rangle \cdot \langle 6, 3 \rangle = 2(6) + (-4)(3) = 0$

The dot product has a number of useful properties.

Properties of the Dot Product

> If u, v, and w are vectors, and k is a real number, then:
> 1. $\mathbf{u \cdot u} = \|\mathbf{u}\|^2$
> 2. $\mathbf{u \cdot v} = \mathbf{v \cdot u}$ *commutative*
> 3. $\mathbf{u \cdot (v + w)} = \mathbf{u \cdot v} + \mathbf{u \cdot w}$ *distributive*
> 4. $k\mathbf{u \cdot v} = k(\mathbf{u \cdot v}) = \mathbf{u} \cdot k\mathbf{v}$
> 5. $\mathbf{0 \cdot u} = 0$

Proof Let a, b, c, and d be real numbers.

1. If $\mathbf{u} = \langle a, b \rangle$, then $\|\mathbf{u}\| = \sqrt{a^2 + b^2}$. Therefore,

$$\mathbf{u} \cdot \mathbf{u} = \langle a, b \rangle \cdot \langle a, b \rangle = a(a) + b(b) = a^2 + b^2 = \left(\sqrt{a^2 + b^2}\right)^2 = \|\mathbf{u}\|^2.$$

2. If $\mathbf{u} = \langle a, b \rangle$ and $\mathbf{v} = \langle c, d \rangle$, then

$$\mathbf{u} \cdot \mathbf{v} = \langle a, b \rangle \cdot \langle c, d \rangle = ac + bd = ca + db = \langle c, d \rangle \cdot \langle a, b \rangle = \mathbf{v} \cdot \mathbf{u}.$$

The proofs of the last three statements are asked for in the exercises.

Angles Between Vectors

If $\mathbf{u} = \langle a, b \rangle$ and $\mathbf{v} = \langle c, d \rangle$ are any nonzero vectors, then **the angle between $\mathbf{u}$ and $\mathbf{v}$** is the smallest angle θ formed by these two vectors, as shown in Figure 10.6.A-1. The clockwise or counterclockwise rotation is ignored, and the angle between $\mathbf{v}$ and $\mathbf{u}$ is considered to be the same as the angle between $\mathbf{u}$ and $\mathbf{v}$. Thus, the radian measure of θ is in the interval $[0, \pi]$.

Nonzero vectors $\mathbf{u}$ and $\mathbf{v}$ are said to be **parallel** if the angle between them is either 0 or π radians. In other words, $\mathbf{u}$ and $\mathbf{v}$ are parallel if they lie on the same straight line through the origin and have either the same or opposite directions. The zero vector $\mathbf{0}$ is considered to be parallel to every vector.

Any scalar multiple of $\mathbf{u}$ is parallel to $\mathbf{u}$ because it lies on the same straight line as $\mathbf{u}$. Conversely, if $\mathbf{v}$ is parallel to $\mathbf{u}$, it is easy to show that $\mathbf{v}$ must be a scalar multiple of $\mathbf{u}$. This is shown in the exercises.

Figure 10.6.A-1

Parallel Vectors

> Vectors $\mathbf{u}$ and $\mathbf{v}$ are parallel exactly when
>
> $\mathbf{v} = k\mathbf{u}$, for some real number k.

Example 2   Determine Parallel Vectors

Determine whether the vectors $\mathbf{u} = \langle 2, 3 \rangle$ and $\mathbf{v} = \langle 8, 12 \rangle$ are parallel.

Solution

Vector $\mathbf{v}$ is a scalar multiple of $\mathbf{u}$.

$$\mathbf{v} = \langle 8, 12 \rangle = 4\langle 2, 3 \rangle = 4\mathbf{u}$$

Thus, vectors $\mathbf{u}$ and $\mathbf{v}$ are parallel.   ∎

The angle between nonzero vectors $\mathbf{u}$ and $\mathbf{v}$ is closely related to their dot product

---

Teaching Notes

Note the following for the equation $\mathbf{v} = k\mathbf{u}$ in **Parallel Vectors:**

If $k = 1$, vectors $\mathbf{u}$ and $\mathbf{v}$ are equivalent.

If $k = -1$, vectors $\mathbf{u}$ and $\mathbf{v}$ are opposite.

If $k = 0$, $\mathbf{v} = k\mathbf{u}$ becomes $\mathbf{v} = 0 \cdot \mathbf{u}$; so in this case, $\mathbf{v} = \mathbf{0} = \langle 0, 0 \rangle$. This explains why the zero vector is considered to be parallel to every vector.

COMMON ERROR ALERT

Students might incorrectly write a dot product as a vector. If $\mathbf{u} = \langle a, b \rangle$ and $\mathbf{v} = \langle c, d \rangle$, they might write $\mathbf{u} \cdot \mathbf{v}$ incorrectly as $\langle ac, bd \rangle$. The correct expression is the real number $ac + bd$.

Example Notes

In **Example 1b**, alternate vector notation is used. $4\mathbf{i} - 2\mathbf{j}$ is the vector $\langle 4, -2 \rangle$.

ADDITIONAL EXAMPLES

Example 1

Find the dot product $\mathbf{u} \cdot \mathbf{v}$ for the given vectors $\mathbf{u}$ and $\mathbf{v}$.

a. $\mathbf{u} = \langle 3, -5 \rangle$ and $\mathbf{v} = \langle -4, 3 \rangle$

$\mathbf{u} \cdot \mathbf{v} = \langle 3, -5 \rangle \cdot \langle -4, 3 \rangle$

$= 3(-4) + (-5)(3) = -27$

b. $\mathbf{u} = 5\mathbf{i} + 2\mathbf{j}$ and $\mathbf{v} = -2\mathbf{i} + 5\mathbf{j}$

$\mathbf{u} \cdot \mathbf{v} = (5\mathbf{i} + 2\mathbf{j}) \cdot (-2\mathbf{i} + 5\mathbf{j})$

$= 5(-2) + (2)(5) = 0$

c. $\mathbf{u} = \langle -2, 7 \rangle$ and $\mathbf{v} = \langle 6, -1 \rangle$

$\mathbf{u} \cdot \mathbf{v} = \langle -2, 7 \rangle \cdot \langle 6, -1 \rangle$

$= (-2)(6) + 7(-1) = -19$

Example 2

Determine whether the vectors $\mathbf{u} = \langle 5, 4 \rangle$ and $\mathbf{v} = \langle 15, 12 \rangle$ are parallel.

Vector $\mathbf{v}$ is a scalar multiple of $\mathbf{u}$.

$\mathbf{v} = \langle 15, 12 \rangle = 3\langle 5, 4 \rangle = 3\mathbf{u}$

So, vectors $\mathbf{u}$ and $\mathbf{v}$ are parallel.

Teaching Notes

The **Angle Theorem** states that for nonzero vectors **u** and **v**, $\cos \theta = \frac{\mathbf{u} \cdot \mathbf{v}}{\|\mathbf{u}\|\|\mathbf{v}\|}$. The denominator $\|\mathbf{u}\|\|\mathbf{v}\|$ is positive because the vectors **u** and **v** are both nonzero and the magnitude of any nonzero vector is positive. Therefore, the signs of $\cos \theta$ and $\mathbf{u} \cdot \mathbf{v}$ must be the same. Ask students to give the sign of $\mathbf{u} \cdot \mathbf{v}$ in each of the following cases and justify their answers:

θ is acute   sign of $\mathbf{u} \cdot \mathbf{v}$ is positive because $\cos \theta$ is positive for any acute angle θ

θ is obtuse   sign of $\mathbf{u} \cdot \mathbf{v}$ is negative because $\cos \theta$ is negative for any obtuse angle θ

θ is a right angle $\mathbf{u} \cdot \mathbf{v}$ has no sign; $\mathbf{u} \cdot \mathbf{v} = 0$ because $\cos 90° = 0$

When $\theta = 0°$, the vectors have the same direction; when $\theta = 180°$, the vectors have opposite directions. In both cases, the vectors are parallel. The diagram below shows both cases.

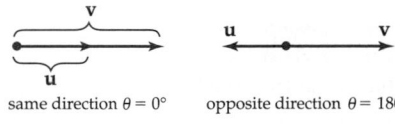

same direction $\theta = 0°$ opposite direction $\theta = 180°$

Parallel Vectors

COMMON ERROR ALERT

When working with vectors, students might be confused about whether a computation results in a vector or a real number. Remind students that in the formula $\cos \theta = \frac{\mathbf{u} \cdot \mathbf{v}}{\|\mathbf{u}\|\|\mathbf{v}\|}$, $\cos \theta$ is always a real number. Therefore, the value of the expression on the right side is also a real number.

Angle Theorem

> If θ is the angle between the nonzero vectors **u** and **v**, then
> $$\mathbf{u} \cdot \mathbf{v} = \|\mathbf{u}\| \|\mathbf{v}\| \cos \theta,$$
> or equivalently,
> $$\cos \theta = \frac{\mathbf{u} \cdot \mathbf{v}}{\|\mathbf{u}\| \|\mathbf{v}\|}.$$

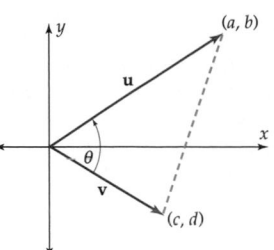

Figure 10.6.A-2

Proof Let a, b, c, and d be real numbers, and suppose that $\|\mathbf{u}\| \neq 0$ and $\|\mathbf{v}\| \neq 0$. If $\mathbf{u} = \langle a, b \rangle$, $\mathbf{v} = \langle c, d \rangle$, and the angle θ is not 0 or π, then **u** and **v** form two sides of a triangle, as shown in Figure 10.6.A-2.

The lengths of two sides of the triangle are $\|\mathbf{u}\| = \sqrt{a^2 + b^2}$ and $\|\mathbf{v}\| = \sqrt{c^2 + d^2}$. The distance formula shows that the length of the third side (opposite angle θ) is $\sqrt{(a - c)^2 + (b - d)^2}$. Therefore, the Law of Cosines produces the following result.

$$\left[\sqrt{(a - c)^2 + (b - d)^2}\right]^2 = \|\mathbf{u}\|^2 + \|\mathbf{v}\|^2 - 2\|\mathbf{u}\| \|\mathbf{v}\| \cos \theta$$
$$(a - c)^2 + (b - d)^2 = (a^2 + b^2) + (c^2 + d^2) - 2\|\mathbf{u}\| \|\mathbf{v}\| \cos \theta$$
$$a^2 - 2ac + c^2 + b^2 - 2bd + d^2 = a^2 + b^2 + c^2 + d^2 - 2\|\mathbf{u}\| \|\mathbf{v}\| \cos \theta$$
$$-2ac - 2bd = -2\|\mathbf{u}\| \|\mathbf{v}\| \cos \theta$$
$$-2(ac + bd) = -2\|\mathbf{u}\| \|\mathbf{v}\| \cos \theta$$
$$ac + bd = \|\mathbf{u}\| \|\mathbf{v}\| \cos \theta$$
$$\mathbf{u} \cdot \mathbf{v} = \|\mathbf{u}\| \|\mathbf{v}\| \cos \theta \qquad \mathbf{u} \cdot \mathbf{v} = ac + bd$$
$$\frac{\mathbf{u} \cdot \mathbf{v}}{\|\mathbf{u}\|\|\mathbf{v}\|} = \cos \theta$$

The proof when θ is 0 or π is exercise 41.

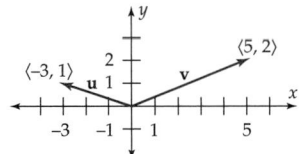

Figure 10.6.A-3

Example 3   Find the Angle Between Vectors

Find the angle θ between the vectors $\langle -3, 1 \rangle$ and $\langle 5, 2 \rangle$, which are shown in Figure 10.6.A-3.

Solution

Apply the formula from the Angle Theorem with $\mathbf{u} = \langle -3, 1 \rangle$ and $\mathbf{v} = \langle 5, 2 \rangle$.

$$\cos \theta = \frac{\mathbf{u} \cdot \mathbf{v}}{\|\mathbf{u}\| \|\mathbf{v}\|} = \frac{(-3)(5) + 1(2)}{(\sqrt{(-3)^2 + 1^2})(\sqrt{5^2 + 2^2})} = \frac{-13}{\sqrt{10} \sqrt{29}} = \frac{-13}{\sqrt{290}}$$

Using the $\cos^{-1}$ key shows that

$$\theta \approx 2.4393 \text{ radians, or} \approx 139.76°.$$

■

The Angle Theorem has several useful consequences. For instance, taking the absolute value of each side of $\mathbf{u} \cdot \mathbf{v} = \|\mathbf{u}\| \|\mathbf{v}\| \cos \theta$, and using the fact

---

that $\|\,\|\mathbf{u}\|\ \|\mathbf{v}\|\,\| = \|\mathbf{u}\|\ \|\mathbf{v}\|$ (because $\|\mathbf{u}\|\ \|\mathbf{v}\|$ is always positive), produces the following results.

$$|\,\mathbf{u}\cdot\mathbf{v}\,| = |\,\|\mathbf{u}\|\ \|\mathbf{v}\|\cos\theta\,| = \|\,\|\mathbf{u}\|\ \|\mathbf{v}\|\,\|\,|\cos\theta| = \|\mathbf{u}\|\ \|\mathbf{v}\|\,|\cos\theta|$$

For any angle θ, $|\cos\theta| \le 1$; therefore,

$$|\,\mathbf{u}\cdot\mathbf{v}\,| = \|\mathbf{u}\|\ \|\mathbf{v}\|\,|\cos\theta| \le \|\mathbf{u}\|\ \|\mathbf{v}\|.$$

This proves the Schwarz inequality.

Schwarz Inequality

For any vectors **u** and **v**,

$$|\,\mathbf{u}\cdot\mathbf{v}\,| \le \|\mathbf{u}\|\ \|\mathbf{v}\|.$$

Vectors **u** and **v** are said to be **orthogonal** (or perpendicular) if the angle between them is $\frac{\pi}{2}$ radians (90°), or if at least one of them is **0**. The key fact about orthogonal vectors follows.

Orthogonal Vectors

Let **u** and **v** be vectors. Then

u and **v** are orthogonal exactly when **u·v** = 0.

Proof If **u** or **v** is **0**, then $\mathbf{u}\cdot\mathbf{v} = 0$. If **u** and **v** are nonzero orthogonal vectors, then by the Angle Theorem:

$$\mathbf{u}\cdot\mathbf{v} = \|\mathbf{u}\|\ \|\mathbf{v}\|\cos\theta = \|\mathbf{u}\|\ \|\mathbf{v}\|\cos\frac{\pi}{2} = \|\mathbf{u}\|\ \|\mathbf{v}\|\,(0) = 0$$

Conversely, if **u** and **v** are vectors such that $\mathbf{u}\cdot\mathbf{v} = 0$, then Exercise 42 asks for a proof that **u** and **v** are orthogonal.

Example 4   Find Orthogonal Vectors

Determine whether the given vectors are orthogonal.

a. $\mathbf{u} = \langle 2,-6\rangle$ and $\mathbf{v} = \langle 9, 3\rangle$ **b.** $\mathbf{u} = \frac{1}{2}\mathbf{i} + 5\mathbf{j}$ and $\mathbf{v} = 10\mathbf{i} - \mathbf{j}$

Solution

a. $\mathbf{u}\cdot\mathbf{v} = \langle 2,-6\rangle\cdot\langle 9,3\rangle$

$= 2\,(9) + (-6)\,(3)$

$= 18 - 18 = 0$

Vectors **u** and **v** are orthogonal.

b. $\mathbf{u}\cdot\mathbf{v} = \left(\frac{1}{2}\mathbf{i} + 5\mathbf{j}\right)\cdot(10\mathbf{i} - \mathbf{j})$

$= \frac{1}{2}\,(10) + 5\,(-1)$

$= 5 - 5 = 0$

Vectors **u** and **v** are orthogonal.

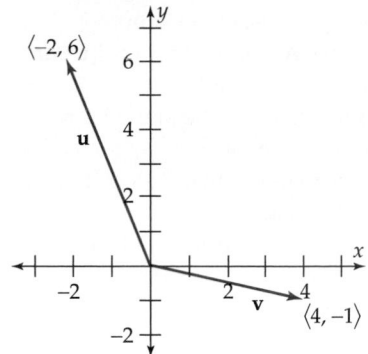

The magnitude of $\text{proj}_v\mathbf{u}$, is determined by three quantities:
- the magnitude (length) of $\mathbf{u}$
- the magnitude (length) of $\mathbf{v}$
- the angle between $\mathbf{u}$ and $\mathbf{v}$

The three representations in Figure 10.6.A-4 show that $\text{proj}_v\mathbf{u}$ can be (from left to right):
- shorter than $\mathbf{v}$ if the angle between $\mathbf{u}$ and $\mathbf{v}$ is acute
- longer than $\mathbf{v}$ if the angle between $\mathbf{u}$ and $\mathbf{v}$ is acute
- in the opposite direction from $\mathbf{v}$ if the angle between $\mathbf{u}$ and $\mathbf{v}$ is obtuse

For an acute angle between $\mathbf{u}$ and $\mathbf{v}$, it is also possible for $\text{proj}_v\mathbf{u}$ to be the same length as $\mathbf{v}$ (see diagram below):

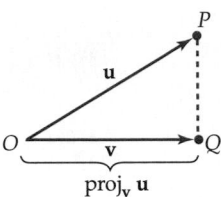

Note that in the first two representations in Figure 10.6.A-4, the length of $\mathbf{v}$ is varied to show two different possibilities. Use the two figures below to show different possibilities that can result by varying the angle between the vectors instead of varying the length of one of the vectors. Notice that for a greater acute angle, $\text{proj}_v\mathbf{u}$ is shorter:

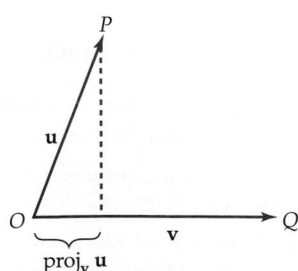

Projections and Components

If $\mathbf{u}$ and $\mathbf{v}$ are nonzero vectors, and θ is the angle between them, construct the perpendicular line segment from the terminal point P of $\mathbf{u}$ to the straight line on which $\mathbf{v}$ lies. This perpendicular segment intersects the line at a point Q. The three possibilities are shown in Figure 10.6.A-4.

The vector $\overrightarrow{OQ}$ is called the **projection of u onto v** and is denoted $\text{proj}_v\mathbf{u}$. A useful description of $\text{proj}_v\mathbf{u}$ follows.

Figure 10.6.A-4

Projection of u *onto* v

> **If u and v are nonzero vectors, then the projection of u onto v is the vector**
>
> $$\text{proj}_v\mathbf{u} = \left(\frac{\mathbf{u}\cdot\mathbf{v}}{\|\mathbf{v}\|^2}\right)\mathbf{v}.$$

Proof Because $\text{proj}_v\mathbf{u}$ and $\mathbf{v}$ lie on the same straight line, they are parallel. Therefore, $\text{proj}_v\mathbf{u} = k\mathbf{v}$ for some real number k. Construct the orthogonal vector from a point Q on $\mathbf{v}$ through point P, the terminal point of $\mathbf{u}$. Let $\mathbf{w}$ be the vector with its initial point at the origin and the same length and direction as $\overrightarrow{QP}$, as in the two cases shown in Figure 10.6.A-5.

 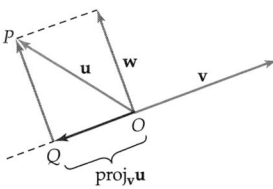

Figure 10.6.A-5

Because $\mathbf{w}$ is parallel to $\overrightarrow{QP}$ it is orthogonal to $\mathbf{v}$. As shown in Figure 10.6.A-5, $\mathbf{u} = \text{proj}_v\mathbf{u} + \mathbf{w} = k\mathbf{v} + \mathbf{w}$. Consequently, by the properties of the dot product:

$$\mathbf{u} \cdot \mathbf{v} = (k\mathbf{v} + \mathbf{w}) \cdot \mathbf{v} \qquad \textit{substitution}$$
$$= (k\mathbf{v}) \cdot \mathbf{v} + \mathbf{w} \cdot \mathbf{v} \qquad \textit{distributive}$$
$$= k(\mathbf{v} \cdot \mathbf{v}) + \mathbf{w} \cdot \mathbf{v}$$
$$= k\|\mathbf{v}\|^2 + \mathbf{w} \cdot \mathbf{v} \qquad \mathbf{v} \cdot \mathbf{v} = \|\mathbf{v}\|^2$$

But $\mathbf{w} \cdot \mathbf{v} = 0$ because $\mathbf{w}$ and $\mathbf{v}$ are orthogonal. So,

$$\mathbf{u} \cdot \mathbf{v} = k\|\mathbf{v}\|^2 \qquad \text{or equivalently,} \qquad k = \frac{\mathbf{u} \cdot \mathbf{v}}{\|\mathbf{v}\|^2}.$$

Finally, multiplying both sides of the last statement by $\mathbf{v}$, and substituting $\text{proj}_v\mathbf{u}$ for $k\mathbf{v}$, the desired result is proved.

$$\text{proj}_v\mathbf{u} = k\mathbf{v} = \left(\frac{\mathbf{u} \cdot \mathbf{v}}{\|\mathbf{v}\|^2}\right)\mathbf{v}$$

Example 5   **Find Projection Vectors**

If $\mathbf{u} = 8\mathbf{i} + 3\mathbf{j}$ and $\mathbf{v} = 4\mathbf{i} - 2\mathbf{j}$, find $\text{proj}_v\mathbf{u}$ and $\text{proj}_u\mathbf{v}$.

Solution

$$\mathbf{u} \cdot \mathbf{v} = 8(4) + 3(-2) = 26 = \mathbf{v} \cdot \mathbf{u}$$
$$\|\mathbf{v}\|^2 = \mathbf{v} \cdot \mathbf{v} = 4^2 + (-2)^2 = 20 \qquad \text{and} \qquad \|\mathbf{u}\|^2 = \mathbf{u} \cdot \mathbf{u} = 8^2 + 3^2 = 73$$

Therefore,

$$\text{proj}_v\mathbf{u} = \left(\frac{\mathbf{u} \cdot \mathbf{v}}{\|\mathbf{v}\|^2}\right)\mathbf{v} = \left(\frac{26}{20}\right)(4\mathbf{i} - 2\mathbf{j}) = \frac{26}{5}\mathbf{i} - \frac{13}{5}\mathbf{j}$$

and

$$\text{proj}_u\mathbf{v} = \left(\frac{\mathbf{v} \cdot \mathbf{u}}{\|\mathbf{u}\|^2}\right)\mathbf{u} = \left(\frac{26}{73}\right)(8\mathbf{i} + 3\mathbf{j}) = \frac{208}{73}\mathbf{i} + \frac{78}{73}\mathbf{j}$$

The projection vectors from Example 5 are shown in Figure 10.6.A-6.

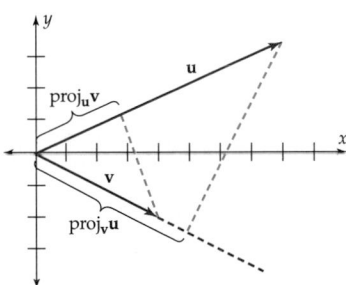

Figure 10.6.A-6

Example Notes

Because $\dfrac{\mathbf{u} \cdot \mathbf{v}}{\|\mathbf{v}\|^2}$ is a scalar,

$$\text{proj}_v\mathbf{u} = \left(\frac{\mathbf{u} \cdot \mathbf{v}}{\|\mathbf{v}\|^2}\right)\mathbf{v} \text{ has the form}$$

$\text{proj}_v\mathbf{u} = k\mathbf{v}$. This means that $\text{proj}_v\mathbf{u}$ is a vector whose direction is the same as the direction of $\mathbf{v}$.

In **Example 5,** point out in Figure 10.6.A-6 that $\text{proj}_v\mathbf{u}$ is a vector with the same direction as vector $\mathbf{v}$, and $\text{proj}_u\mathbf{v}$ is a vector with the same direction as vector $\mathbf{u}$.

ADDITIONAL EXAMPLES

Example 5

If $\mathbf{u} = 7\mathbf{i} - 2\mathbf{j}$ and $\mathbf{v} = 9\mathbf{i} + 4\mathbf{j}$, find $\text{proj}_v\mathbf{u}$ and $\text{proj}_u\mathbf{v}$.

$$\mathbf{u} \cdot \mathbf{v} = 7(9) + (-2)(4) = 55 = \mathbf{v} \cdot \mathbf{u}$$
$$\|\mathbf{v}\|^2 = \mathbf{v} \cdot \mathbf{v} = 9^2 + 4^2 = 97$$
$$\|\mathbf{u}\|^2 = \mathbf{u} \cdot \mathbf{u} = 7^2 + (-2)^2 = 53$$

Therefore, $\text{proj}_v\mathbf{u} = \left(\dfrac{\mathbf{u} \cdot \mathbf{v}}{\|\mathbf{v}\|^2}\right)\mathbf{v}$

$$= \left(\frac{55}{97}\right)(9\mathbf{i} + 4\mathbf{j})$$

$$= \frac{495}{97}\mathbf{i} + \frac{220}{97}\mathbf{j}$$

and $\text{proj}_u\mathbf{v} = \left(\dfrac{\mathbf{v} \cdot \mathbf{u}}{\|\mathbf{u}\|^2}\right)\mathbf{u}$

$$= \left(\frac{55}{53}\right)(7\mathbf{i} - 2\mathbf{j})$$

$$= \frac{385}{53}\mathbf{i} - \frac{110}{53}\mathbf{j}$$

The projection vectors $\dfrac{495}{97}\mathbf{i} + \dfrac{220}{97}\mathbf{j}$ and $\dfrac{385}{53}\mathbf{i} - \dfrac{110}{53}\mathbf{j}$ are shown in the figure below.

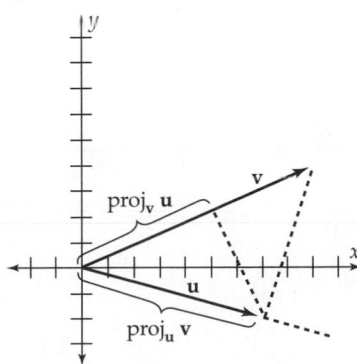

Teaching Notes

Make sure students understand that $\text{proj}_v\mathbf{u}$ is a vector, but all of the following are scalars:

- $\text{comp}_v\mathbf{u}$ (can be positive, negative, or zero)
- $|\text{comp}_v\mathbf{u}|$ (absolute value of $\text{comp}_v\mathbf{u}$; can be positive or zero)
- $\|\text{proj}_v\mathbf{u}\|$ (magnitude of the vector $\text{proj}_v\mathbf{u}$)

Show the following three diagrams to help students understand the relationships discussed on this page:

$$\text{comp}_v\mathbf{u} = \frac{\mathbf{u} \cdot \mathbf{v}}{\|\mathbf{v}\|} = \frac{32 + 0}{8} = 4$$

$$\cos\theta = \frac{\text{comp}_v\mathbf{u}}{\|\mathbf{u}\|} = \frac{4}{5}$$

$$\text{proj}_v\mathbf{u} = \left(\frac{\mathbf{u} \cdot \mathbf{v}}{\|\mathbf{v}\|^2}\right)\mathbf{v} = \frac{32}{64}\langle 8 \rangle = \langle 4, 0 \rangle$$

$$\|\text{proj}_v\mathbf{u}\| = 4$$

$$\text{comp}_v\mathbf{u} = \frac{\mathbf{u} \cdot \mathbf{v}}{\|\mathbf{v}\|} = \frac{0 + 0}{8} = 0$$

$$\cos\theta = \cos 90° = \frac{0}{5} = 0$$

$$\text{proj}_v\mathbf{u} = \left(\frac{\mathbf{u} \cdot \mathbf{v}}{\|\mathbf{v}\|^2}\right)\mathbf{v} = \frac{0}{64}\langle 8, 0 \rangle = \langle 0, 0 \rangle$$

$$\|\text{proj}_v\mathbf{u}\| = 0$$

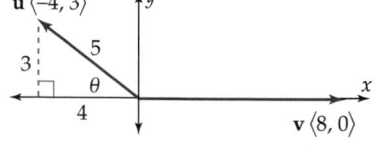

$$\text{comp}_v\mathbf{u} = \frac{\mathbf{u} \cdot \mathbf{v}}{\|\mathbf{v}\|} = \frac{-32 + 0}{8} = -4$$

$$\cos\theta = \frac{\text{comp}_v\mathbf{u}}{\|\mathbf{u}\|} = \frac{-4}{5}$$

$$\text{proj}_v\mathbf{u} = \left(\frac{\mathbf{u} \cdot \mathbf{v}}{\|\mathbf{v}\|^2}\right)\mathbf{v} = \frac{-32}{64}\langle 8, 0 \rangle = \langle -4, 0 \rangle$$

$$\|\text{proj}_v\mathbf{u}\| = 4$$

Projections and Components

Recall from Section 10.6 that $\frac{1}{\|\mathbf{v}\|}\mathbf{v}$ is a unit vector in the direction of $\mathbf{v}$. Then, $\text{proj}_v\mathbf{u}$ can be expressed as a scalar multiple of this unit vector.

$$\text{proj}_v\mathbf{u} = \left(\frac{\mathbf{u} \cdot \mathbf{v}}{\|\mathbf{v}\|^2}\right)\mathbf{v} = \left(\frac{\mathbf{u} \cdot \mathbf{v}}{\|\mathbf{v}\|}\right)\left(\frac{1}{\|\mathbf{v}\|}\mathbf{v}\right)$$

The scalar $\frac{\mathbf{u} \cdot \mathbf{v}}{\|\mathbf{v}\|}$ is called the **component of u along v**, and is denoted $\text{comp}_v\mathbf{u}$.

$$\text{proj}_v\mathbf{u} = \left(\frac{\mathbf{u} \cdot \mathbf{v}}{\|\mathbf{v}\|}\right)\left(\frac{1}{\|\mathbf{v}\|}\mathbf{v}\right) = \text{comp}_v\mathbf{u}\left(\frac{1}{\|\mathbf{v}\|}\mathbf{v}\right)$$

Because $\frac{1}{\|\mathbf{v}\|}\mathbf{v}$ is a unit vector, it can be used to find the length of $\text{proj}_v\mathbf{u}$.

$$\|\text{proj}_v\mathbf{u}\| = \left\|\text{comp}_v\mathbf{u}\left(\frac{1}{\|\mathbf{v}\|}\mathbf{v}\right)\right\| = |\text{comp}_v\mathbf{u}|\left\|\left(\frac{1}{\|\mathbf{v}\|}\mathbf{v}\right)\right\| = |\text{comp}_v\mathbf{u}|.$$

Also, because $\mathbf{u} \cdot \mathbf{v} = \|\mathbf{u}\| \|\mathbf{v}\| \cos\theta$, where θ is the angle between $\mathbf{u}$ and $\mathbf{v}$,

$$\begin{aligned}\text{comp}_v\mathbf{u} &= \frac{\mathbf{u} \cdot \mathbf{v}}{\|\mathbf{v}\|}\\ &= \frac{\|\mathbf{u}\| \|\mathbf{v}\| \cos\theta}{\|\mathbf{v}\|}\\ &= \|\mathbf{u}\| \cos\theta\end{aligned}$$

This result is stated formally as follows.

Projections and Components

> If u and v are nonzero vectors, and θ is the angle between them, then
>
> $$\text{comp}_v\mathbf{u} = \frac{\mathbf{u} \cdot \mathbf{v}}{\|\mathbf{v}\|} = \|\mathbf{u}\| \cos\theta$$
>
> and
>
> $$\|\text{proj}_v\mathbf{u}\| = |\text{comp}_v\mathbf{u}|.$$

Example 6 **Find Component Vectors**

If $\mathbf{u} = 2\mathbf{i} + 3\mathbf{j}$ and $\mathbf{v} = -5\mathbf{i} + 2\mathbf{j}$, find $\text{comp}_v\mathbf{u}$ and $\text{comp}_u\mathbf{v}$.

Solution

$$\mathbf{u} \cdot \mathbf{v} = 2(-5) + 3(2) = -4 = \mathbf{v} \cdot \mathbf{u}$$

$$\|\mathbf{v}\| = \sqrt{(-5)^2 + 2^2} = \sqrt{29} \quad \text{and} \quad \|\mathbf{u}\| = \sqrt{2^2 + 3^2} = \sqrt{13}$$

Example Notes

Show the results of **Example 6**.

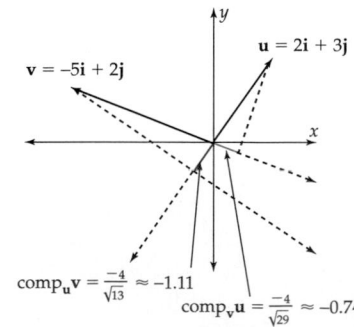

Therefore,

$$\text{comp}_\mathbf{v}\mathbf{u} = \frac{\mathbf{u} \cdot \mathbf{v}}{\|\mathbf{v}\|} = \frac{-4}{\sqrt{29}} \quad \text{and} \quad \text{comp}_\mathbf{u}\mathbf{v} = \frac{\mathbf{v} \cdot \mathbf{u}}{\|\mathbf{u}\|} = \frac{-4}{\sqrt{13}}$$

∎

Applications

Vectors and the dot product can be used to solve a variety of problems.

Example 7   Find Forces Due to Gravity

A 4000-pound automobile is on an inclined ramp that makes a 15° angle with the horizontal. Find the force required to keep it from rolling down the ramp, assuming that the only force that must be overcome is that due to gravity.

Solution

The situation is shown in Figure 10.6.A-7, where the coordinate system is chosen so that the car is at the origin, the vector **F** representing the downward force of gravity is on the y-axis, and **v** is a unit vector from the origin down the ramp.

Because the car weighs 4000 pounds, $\mathbf{F} = -4000\mathbf{j}$. The angle between **v** and **F** is $90° - 15° = 75°$. The vector $\text{proj}_\mathbf{v}\mathbf{F}$ is the force pulling the car down the ramp, so a force of the same magnitude in the opposite direction is needed to keep the car motionless.

$$\|\text{proj}_\mathbf{v}\mathbf{F}\| = |\text{comp}_\mathbf{v}\mathbf{F}|$$
$$= |\|\mathbf{F}\| \cos 75°|$$
$$= 4000 \cos 75°$$
$$\approx 1035.3$$

Therefore, a force of 1035.3 pounds is required to hold the car in place.

Figure 10.6.A-7

If a constant force **F** is applied to an object, pushing or pulling it a distance d in the direction of the force, as shown in Figure 10.6.A-8, the amount of **work** done by the force is defined to be the product of the magnitude of the force and the distance.

$$W = (\text{magnitude of force})(\text{distance}) = \|\mathbf{F}\|(d)$$

If the magnitude of **F** is measured in pounds and d in feet, then the units for W are foot-pounds. For example, if you push a car for 35 feet along a level driveway by exerting a constant force of 110 pounds, the amount of work done is $110(35) = 3850$ foot-pounds.

When a force **F** moves an object in the direction of a vector **d** rather than in the direction of **F**, as shown in Figure 10.6.A-9, then the motion of the object can be considered as the result of the vector $\text{proj}_\mathbf{d}\mathbf{F}$, which is a force in the same direction as **d**.

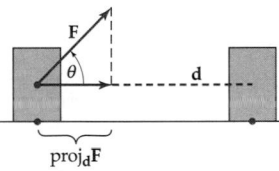

Figure 10.6.A-8

Figure 10.6.A-9

Section 10.6.A   *Excursion:* **The Dot Product**   **677**

ADDITIONAL EXAMPLES

Example 6

If $\mathbf{u} = 7\mathbf{i} + 3\mathbf{j}$ and $\mathbf{v} = -3\mathbf{i} + 4\mathbf{j}$, find $\text{comp}_\mathbf{v}\mathbf{u}$ and $\text{comp}_\mathbf{u}\mathbf{v}$.

$\mathbf{u} \cdot \mathbf{v} = 7(-3) + 3(4) = -9 = \mathbf{v} \cdot \mathbf{u}$

$\|\mathbf{v}\| = \sqrt{(-3)^2 + 4^2} = \sqrt{25} = 5$

$\|\mathbf{u}\| = \sqrt{7^2 + 3^2} = \sqrt{58}$

Therefore, $\text{comp}_\mathbf{v}\mathbf{u} = \dfrac{\mathbf{u} \cdot \mathbf{v}}{\|\mathbf{v}\|} = \dfrac{-9}{5}$ and

$\text{comp}_\mathbf{u}\mathbf{v} = \dfrac{\mathbf{v} \cdot \mathbf{u}}{\|\mathbf{u}\|} = \dfrac{-9}{\sqrt{58}}$.

Example 7

A boat weights 700 pounds and is on a ramp that makes an angle of 20° with the horizontal. Suppose that there is no force on the boat other than gravity. How much force is needed to keep the boat in place?

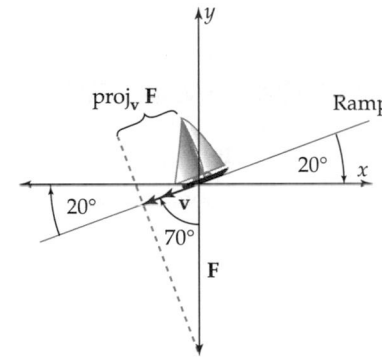

Because the boat weighs 700 pounds, $\mathbf{F} = -700\mathbf{j}$. The angle between **v** and **F** is $90° - 20° = 70°$. The vector $\text{proj}_\mathbf{v}\mathbf{F}$ is the force pulling the boat down the ramp, so a force of the same magnitude in the opposite direction is needed to keep the boat motionless on the ramp.

$$\|\text{proj}_\mathbf{v}\mathbf{F}\| = |\text{comp}_\mathbf{v}\mathbf{F}|$$
$$= |\|\mathbf{F}\| \cos 70°|$$
$$= 700 \cos 70°$$
$$\approx 239.4$$

Therefore, a force of about 239.4 pounds is required to hold the boat in place.

Teaching Notes

The meaning of work in physics and mathematics is not the same as the everyday meaning.

Recall that every force can be represented by a vector (page 664). **Work**, however, is a scalar. Note that the equation $W = (\text{magnitude of force})(\text{distance})$ has the form $W = (\text{scalar})(\text{scalar})$.

Real-World Application

In **Example 8,** we find the amount of work done in moving a sled horizontally by pulling in a direction that is not horizontal. This type of real-world application is a part of almost every student's experience. Ask your students to conjecture, and then find, the amount of work done if the angle with the horizontal is 0° (that is, if the child pulls in the direction of the vector **d**).

$$W = 20 \cdot 100 \cdot \cos 0° = 20 \cdot 100 \cdot 1$$
$$= 2000 \text{ ft-lb}$$

Note that the greatest possible amount of work is done when the force is in the direction of **d.** Why? The greatest possible value of $\cos \theta$ is 1.

ADDITIONAL EXAMPLES

Example 8

A toy boat is pulled horizontally by pulling a rope as shown below. The rope makes a 60° angle with the horizontal. The force pulling the rope is a constant 40 pounds. How much work is done in moving the boat 7.5 feet horizontally?

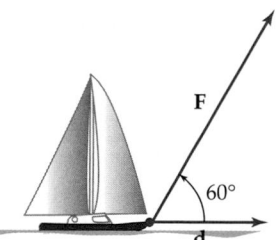

The magnitude of force **F** on the rope is 40 pounds, and the boat moves along vector **d** of length 7.5 feet.

$$W = \mathbf{F} \cdot \mathbf{d}$$
$$= \|\mathbf{F}\| \|\mathbf{d}\| \cdot \cos \theta$$
$$= 40 \cdot (7.5) \cdot \frac{1}{2}$$
$$= 150$$

Therefore, the work done is 150 foot-pounds.

NOTE This formula reduces to the previous one when **F** and **d** have the same direction because in that case, $\cos \theta = \cos 0 = 1$, so that
$W = \|\mathbf{F}\| \|\mathbf{d}\| = $ magnitude of force times distance moved.

Work

Therefore, the amount of work done by **F** is the same as the amount of work done by $\text{proj}_\mathbf{d}\mathbf{F}$, as shown below.

$$W = \|\text{proj}_\mathbf{d}\mathbf{F}\| \|\mathbf{d}\|$$
$$= |\text{comp}_\mathbf{d}\mathbf{F}| \|\mathbf{d}\|$$
$$= \|\mathbf{F}\| (\cos \theta) \|\mathbf{d}\|$$
$$= \mathbf{F} \cdot \mathbf{d} \qquad \textit{See note.}$$

Consequently, work can be described as follows.

> **The work W done by a constant force F as its point of application moves along the vector d is**
>
> $$W = |\text{comp}_\mathbf{d}\mathbf{F}| \|\mathbf{d}\| \qquad \text{or equivalently,} \qquad W = \mathbf{F} \cdot \mathbf{d}.$$

Example 8　Compute Work

How much work is done by a child who pulls a sled 100 feet over level ground by exerting a constant 20-pound force on a rope that makes a 45° angle with the ground?

Figure 10.6.A-10

Solution

The situation is shown in Figure 10.6.A-10, where force **F** on the rope has magnitude 20, and the sled moves along vector **d** of length 100.

$$W = \mathbf{F} \cdot \mathbf{d}$$
$$= \|\mathbf{F}\| \|\mathbf{d}\| \cdot \cos \theta$$
$$= 20 \cdot 100 \cdot \frac{\sqrt{2}}{2}$$
$$= 1000\sqrt{2}$$
$$\approx 1414.2$$

Therefore, the work done is 1414.2 foot-pounds. ∎

Exercises 10.6.A

In Exercises 1–6, find $u \cdot v$, $u \cdot u$, and $v \cdot v$.

1. $u = \langle 3, 4 \rangle$, $v = \langle -5, 2 \rangle$
-7; 25; 29

2. $u = \langle -1, 6 \rangle$, $v = \left\langle -4, \dfrac{1}{3} \right\rangle$ 6; 37; $\dfrac{145}{9}$

3. $u = 2i + j$, $v = 3i$
6; 5; 9

4. $u = i - j$, $v = 5j$
-5; 2; 25

5. $u = 3i + 2j$, $v = 2i + 3j$
12; 13; 13

6. $u = 4i - j$, $v = -i + 2j$
-6; 17; 5

In Exercises 7–12, find the dot product when $u = \langle 2, 5 \rangle$, $v = \langle -4, 3 \rangle$, and $w = \langle 2, -1 \rangle$.

7. $u \cdot (v + w)$
6

8. $u \cdot (v - w)$
8

9. $(u + v) \cdot (v + w)$
20

10. $(u + v) \cdot (u - v)$
4

11. $(3u + v) \cdot 2w$
-28

12. $(u + 4v) \cdot (2u + w)$
69

In Exercises 13–18, find the angle between vectors u and v.

13. $u = \langle 4, -3 \rangle$, $v = \langle 1, 2 \rangle$ **1.75065 radians**

14. $u = \langle 2, 4 \rangle$, $v = \langle 0, -5 \rangle$ **2.6779 radians**

15. $u = 2i - 3j$, $v = -i$ **2.1588 radians**

16. $u = 2j$, $v = 4i + j$ **1.3258 radians**

17. $u = \sqrt{2}\,i + \sqrt{2}\,j$, $v = i - j$ $\dfrac{\pi}{2}$ **radians**

18. $u = 3i - 5j$, $v = -2i + 3j$ **3.0940 radians**

In Exercises 19–24, determine whether the vectors u and v are parallel, orthogonal, or neither.

19. $u = \langle 2, 6 \rangle$, $v = \langle 3, -1 \rangle$
orthogonal

20. $u = \langle -5, 3 \rangle$, $v = \langle 2, 6 \rangle$
neither

21. $u = \langle 9, -6 \rangle$, $v = \langle -6, 4 \rangle$
parallel

22. $u = -i + 2j$, $v = 2i - 4j$
parallel

23. $u = 2i - 2j$, $v = 5i + 8j$
neither

24. $u = 6i - 4j$, $v = 2i + 3j$
orthogonal

In Exercises 25–28, find a real number k such that vectors u and v are orthogonal.

25. $u = 2i + 3j$, $v = 3i - kj$ $k = 2$

26. $u = -3i + j$, $v = 2ki - 4j$ $k = -\dfrac{2}{3}$

27. $u = i - j$, $v = ki + \sqrt{2}\,j$ $k = \sqrt{2}$

28. $u = -4i + 5j$, $v = 2i + 2kj$ $k = \dfrac{4}{5}$

In Exercises 29–32, find $\text{proj}_u v$ and $\text{proj}_v u$.

29. $u = 3i - 5j$, $v = 6i + 2j$

30. $u = 2i - 3j$, $v = i + 2j$

31. $u = i + j$, $v = i - j$

32. $u = 5i + j$, $v = -2i + 3j$

In Exercises 33–36, find $\text{comp}_v u$.

33. $u = 10i + 4j$, $v = 3i - 2j$

34. $u = i - 2j$, $v = 3i + j$

35. $u = 3i + 2j$, $v = -i + 3j$

36. $u = i + j$, $v = -3i - 2j$

In Exercises 37–39, let $u = \langle a, b \rangle$, $v = \langle c, d \rangle$ and $w = \langle r, s \rangle$. Verify that the given property of dot products is valid by calculating the quantities on each side of the equal sign.

37. $u \cdot (v + w) = u \cdot v + u \cdot w$

38. $ku \cdot v = k(u \cdot v) = u \cdot kv$

39. $0 \cdot u = 0$

40. Suppose $u = \langle a, b \rangle$ and $v = \langle c, d \rangle$ are nonzero parallel vectors.
a. If $c \neq 0$, show that u and v lie on the same nonvertical straight line through the origin.
b. If $a \neq 0$, show that $v = \dfrac{c}{a}u$ (that is, v is a scalar multiple of u). *Hint:* The equation of the line on which u and v lie is $y = mx$ for some constant m (why?), which implies that $b = ma$ and $d = mc$.
c. If $c = 0$, show that v is a scalar multiple of u. *Hint:* If $c = 0$ then $a = 0$ (why?) and so $b \neq 0$ (otherwise $u = 0$).

c. Let $c = 0$ and $d \neq 0$ since v is not the zero vector. The line containing v and u is the vertical line $x = 0$. (a, b) is on this line so $a = 0$. Then, since u is not the zero vector $b \neq 0$
and $v = \langle 0, d \rangle = \dfrac{d}{b}\langle 0, b \rangle = \dfrac{d}{b}u$.

29. $\left\langle \dfrac{12}{17}, -\dfrac{20}{17} \right\rangle$; $\left\langle \dfrac{6}{5}, \dfrac{2}{5} \right\rangle$

30. $\left\langle -\dfrac{8}{13}, \dfrac{12}{13} \right\rangle$; $\left\langle -\dfrac{4}{5}, -\dfrac{8}{5} \right\rangle$

31. $\langle 0, 0 \rangle$; $\langle 0, 0 \rangle$

32. $\left\langle -\dfrac{35}{26}, -\dfrac{7}{26} \right\rangle$; $\left\langle \dfrac{14}{13}, -\dfrac{21}{13} \right\rangle$

33. $\dfrac{22}{\sqrt{13}}$

34. $\dfrac{1}{\sqrt{10}}$

35. $\dfrac{3}{\sqrt{10}}$

36. $-\dfrac{5}{\sqrt{13}}$

37. $u \cdot (v + w)$
$$= \langle a, b \rangle \cdot (\langle c, d \rangle + \langle r, s \rangle)$$
$$= \langle a, b \rangle \cdot \langle c + r, d + s \rangle$$
$$= a(c + r) + b(d + s)$$
$$= ac + ar + bd + bs$$

$u \cdot v + u \cdot w$
$$= \langle a, b \rangle \cdot \langle c, d \rangle + \langle a, b \rangle \cdot \langle r, s \rangle$$
$$= (ac + bd) + (ar + bs)$$
$$= ac + ar + bd + bs$$

38. $ku \cdot v = \langle ka, kb \rangle \cdot \langle c, d \rangle$
$$= kac + kbd,$$
$k(u \cdot v) = k(ac + bd)$
$$= kac + kbd$$
$u \cdot kv = \langle a, b \rangle \cdot \langle kc, kd \rangle$
$$= kac + kbd$$

39. $0 \cdot u = \langle 0, 0 \rangle \cdot \langle a, b \rangle = 0a + 0b = 0$

40. a. The slope of v is $\dfrac{d}{c}$. The vectors also have the same initial point, the origin. Thus the lines that contain the vectors share a point and have the same slope and must be on the same line.

b. Let $y = mx$ be the line containing u and v. Then (a, b) and (c, d) are points on this line and $b = ma$, $d = mc$, $m = \dfrac{b}{a} = \dfrac{d}{c}$ and $\dfrac{c}{a} = \dfrac{d}{b}$.
$$\dfrac{c}{a}u = \dfrac{c}{a}\langle a, b \rangle = \left\langle c, \dfrac{c}{a}b \right\rangle$$
$$= \left\langle c, \dfrac{d}{b}b \right\rangle = \langle c, d \rangle = v$$

41. If $\theta = 0$ or π, then **u** and **v** are parallel, so **v** = k**u** for some real number k. We know that $\|\mathbf{v}\| = |k|\,\|\mathbf{u}\|$. If $\theta = 0$, then $\cos\theta = 1$ and $k > 0$. Since $k > 0$, $|k| = k$ and so $\|\mathbf{v}\| = k\|\mathbf{u}\|$. Therefore, $\mathbf{u}\cdot\mathbf{v} = \mathbf{u}\cdot k\mathbf{u} = k\mathbf{u}\cdot\mathbf{u}$ $= k\|\mathbf{u}\|^2 = \|\mathbf{u}\|(k\|\mathbf{u}\|) = \|\mathbf{u}\|\|\mathbf{v}\|$ $= \|\mathbf{u}\|\|\mathbf{v}\|\cos\theta$. On the other hand, if $\theta = \pi$, then $\cos\theta = -1$ and $k < 0$. Since $k < 0$, $|k| = -k$ and so $\|\mathbf{v}\| = -k\|\mathbf{u}\|$. Then $\mathbf{u}\cdot\mathbf{v} = \mathbf{u}\cdot k\mathbf{u}, = k\mathbf{u}\cdot\mathbf{u}$ $= k\|\mathbf{u}\|^2 = \|\mathbf{u}\|(-k\|\mathbf{u}\|)$ $= -\|\mathbf{u}\|\|\mathbf{v}\| = \|\mathbf{u}\|\|\mathbf{v}\|\cos\theta$. In both cases we have shown $\mathbf{u}\cdot\mathbf{v} = \|\mathbf{u}\|\|\mathbf{v}\|\cos\theta$.

42. Let θ be the angle between **u** and **v**, then $\cos\theta = 0$ and so, $\theta = \dfrac{\pi}{2} + k\pi$ where k is any integer. For any choice of k this is a right angle and the vectors are orthogonal.

43. If $A = (1, 2)$, $B = (3, 4)$, and $C = (5, 2)$, then the vector $\overrightarrow{AB} = \langle 2, 2\rangle$, $\overrightarrow{AC} = \langle 4, 0\rangle$, and $\overrightarrow{BC} = \langle 2, -2\rangle$. Since $\overrightarrow{AB}\cdot\overrightarrow{BC} = 0$, $\overrightarrow{AB}$ and $\overrightarrow{BC}$ are perpendicular, so the angle at vertex B is a right angle.

44. $x = 0$

45. possible answer:
$\mathbf{u} = \langle 1, 0\rangle$, $\mathbf{v} = \langle 1, 1\rangle$,
$\mathbf{w} = \langle 1, -1\rangle$

46. $(\|\mathbf{u}\|\mathbf{v} + \|\mathbf{v}\|\mathbf{u})\cdot(\|\mathbf{u}\|\mathbf{v} - \|\mathbf{v}\|\mathbf{u})$
$= \|\mathbf{u}\|^2(\mathbf{v}\cdot\mathbf{v}) - \|\mathbf{v}\|^2(\mathbf{u}\cdot\mathbf{u})$
$= \|\mathbf{u}\|^2\|\mathbf{v}\|^2 - \|\mathbf{u}\|^2\|\mathbf{v}\|^2 = 0$.
Since the dot product is 0, the vectors are orthogonal.

47. 300 lb

48. $\langle 1000, 267.95\rangle$

49. 13

50. -9

51. 24

52. 20

53. The force in the direction of the lawnmower's motion is $30\cos 60° = 15$ lb. Thus, the work done is $15(75) = 1125$ ft-lb.

54. 3262.7 ft-lb

55. 1368 ft-lb

56. 2447.0 ft-lb

41. Prove the Angle Theorem in the case when θ is 0 or π.

42. If **u** and **v** are nonzero vectors such that $\mathbf{u}\cdot\mathbf{v} = 0$, show that **u** and **v** are orthogonal. *Hint:* If θ is the angle between **u** and **v**, what is $\cos\theta$ and what does this say about θ?

43. Show that $(1, 2), (3, 4), (5, 2)$ are the vertices of a right triangle by considering the sides of the triangle as vectors.

44. Find a number x such that the angle between the vectors $\langle 1, 1\rangle$ and $\langle x, 1\rangle$ is $\dfrac{\pi}{4}$ radians.

45. Find nonzero vectors **u**, **v**, and **w** such that $\mathbf{u}\cdot\mathbf{v} = \mathbf{u}\cdot\mathbf{w}$, $\mathbf{v}\neq\mathbf{w}$, and neither **v** nor **w** is orthogonal to **u**.

46. If **u** and **v** are nonzero vectors, show that the vectors $\|\mathbf{u}\|\mathbf{v} + \|\mathbf{v}\|\mathbf{u}$, $\|\mathbf{u}\|\mathbf{v} - \|\mathbf{v}\|\mathbf{u}$ are orthogonal.

47. A 600-pound trailer is on an inclined ramp that makes a 30° angle with the horizontal. Find the force required to keep it from rolling down the ramp, assuming that the only force that must be overcome is due to gravity.

48. In Example 7, find the vector that represents the force necessary to keep the car motionless.

In Exercises 49–52, find the work done by a constant force F as the point of application of F moves along the vector $\overrightarrow{PQ}$.

49. $\mathbf{F} = 2\mathbf{i} + 5\mathbf{j}$, $P = (0, 0)$, $Q = (4, 1)$

50. $\mathbf{F} = \mathbf{i} - 2\mathbf{j}$, $P = (0, 0)$, $Q = (-5, 2)$

51. $\mathbf{F} = 2\mathbf{i} + 3\mathbf{j}$, $P = (2, 3)$, $Q = (5, 9)$ *Hint:* Find the component form of $\overrightarrow{PQ}$.

52. $\mathbf{F} = 5\mathbf{i} + \mathbf{j}$, $P = (-1, 2)$, $Q = (4, -3)$

53. A lawn mower handle makes an angle of 60° with the ground. A woman pushes on the handle with a force of 30 pounds. How much work is done as she moves the lawn mower a distance of 75 feet on level ground?

54. A child pulls a wagon along a level sidewalk by exerting a force of 18 pounds on the wagon handle, which makes an angle of 25° with the horizontal. How much work is done as she pulls the wagon 200 feet?

55. A 40-pound cart is pushed 100 feet up a ramp that makes a 20° angle with the horizontal. How much work is done against gravity? *Hint:* The amount of work done against gravity is the negative of the amount of work done by gravity. Position the cart on a coordinate plane so that the cart is at the origin. Then the cart moves along vector $\mathbf{d} = (100\cos 20°)\mathbf{i} + (100\sin 20°)\mathbf{j}$ and the downward force of gravity is $\mathbf{F} = 0\mathbf{i} - 40\mathbf{j}$.

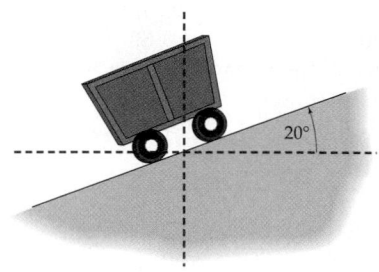

56. Suppose the child in Exercise 54 is pulling the wagon up a hill that makes an angle of 20° with the horizontal, and all other conditions remain the same. How much work is done in pulling the wagon 150 feet?

CHAPTER 10 REVIEW

Important Concepts

681

Important Facts and Formulas

Law of Cosines $a^2 = b^2 + c^2 - 2bc \cos A$

Law of Cosines, *Alternate Form:* $\cos A = \dfrac{b^2 + c^2 - a^2}{2bc}$

Law of Sines $\dfrac{a}{\sin A} = \dfrac{b}{\sin B} = \dfrac{c}{\sin C}$

Area of triangle ABC**:** $\dfrac{ab \sin C}{2}$

Heron's Formula Area of triangle $ABC = \sqrt{s(s-a)(s-b)(s-c)}$, where $s = \dfrac{1}{2}(a + b + c)$.

$|a + bi| = \sqrt{a^2 + b^2}$

$a + bi = r(\cos \theta + i \sin \theta)$, where
$$r = \sqrt{a^2 + b^2}, a = r \cos \theta, b = r \sin \theta$$

$r_1(\cos \theta_1 + i \sin \theta_1) \cdot r_2(\cos \theta_2 + i \sin \theta_2) =$
$$r_1 r_2 [\cos(\theta_1 + \theta_2) + i \sin(\theta_1 + \theta_2)]$$

$\dfrac{r_1(\cos \theta_1 + i \sin \theta_1)}{r_2(\cos \theta_2 + i \sin \theta_2)} = \dfrac{r_1}{r_2} [\cos(\theta_1 - \theta_2) + i \sin(\theta_1 - \theta_2)]$

DeMoivre's Theorem
$$[r(\cos \theta + i \sin \theta)]^n = r^n [\cos n\theta + i \sin n\theta]$$

The distinct nth roots of $r(\cos \theta + i \sin \theta)$ are:
$$\sqrt[n]{r}\left[\cos\left(\frac{\theta + 2k\pi}{n}\right) + i \sin\left(\frac{\theta + 2k\pi}{n}\right)\right] \qquad (k = 0, 1, 2, \dots, n - 1)$$

The distinct nth roots of unity are:
$$\cos \frac{2k\pi}{n} + i \sin \frac{2k\pi}{n} \qquad (k = 0, 1, 2, \dots, n - 1)$$

If $P = (x_1, y_1)$ and $Q = (x_2, y_2)$, then $\overrightarrow{PQ} = \langle x_2 - x_1, y_2 - y_1 \rangle$.

$\|\langle a, b \rangle\| = \sqrt{a^2 + b^2}$

If $\mathbf{u} = \langle a, b \rangle$ and k is a scalar, then $k\mathbf{u} = \langle ka, kb \rangle$.

If $\mathbf{u} = \langle a, b \rangle$ and $\mathbf{v} = \langle c, d \rangle$, then
$$\mathbf{u} + \mathbf{v} = \langle a + c, b + d \rangle \text{ and } \mathbf{u} - \mathbf{v} = \langle a - c, b - d \rangle.$$

Properties of Vector Addition and Scalar Multiplication
For any vectors **u**, **v**, and **w** and any scalars r and s:

1. $\mathbf{u} + (\mathbf{v} + \mathbf{w}) = (\mathbf{u} + \mathbf{v}) + \mathbf{w}$
2. $\mathbf{u} + \mathbf{v} = \mathbf{v} + \mathbf{u}$
3. $\mathbf{v} + \mathbf{0} = \mathbf{v} = \mathbf{0} + \mathbf{v}$
4. $\mathbf{v} + (-\mathbf{v}) = \mathbf{0}$
5. $r(\mathbf{u} + \mathbf{v}) = r\mathbf{u} + r\mathbf{v}$
6. $(r + s)\mathbf{v} = r\mathbf{v} + s\mathbf{v}$
7. $(rs)\mathbf{v} = r(s\mathbf{v}) = s(r\mathbf{v})$
8. $1\mathbf{v} = \mathbf{v}$
9. $0\mathbf{v} = \mathbf{0} = r\mathbf{0}$

If $\mathbf{u} = \langle a, b \rangle = a\mathbf{i} + b\mathbf{j}$, then

$$a = \|\mathbf{u}\| \cos \theta \qquad \text{and} \qquad b = \|\mathbf{u}\| \sin \theta,$$

where θ is the direction angle of **u**.

If $\mathbf{u} = \langle a, b \rangle = a\mathbf{i} + b\mathbf{j} \qquad \text{and} \qquad \mathbf{v} = \langle c, d \rangle = c\mathbf{i} + d\mathbf{j}$, then

$$\mathbf{u} \cdot \mathbf{v} = ac + bd.$$

If θ is the angle between nonzero vectors **u** and **v**, then

$$\mathbf{u} \cdot \mathbf{v} = \|\mathbf{u}\| \|\mathbf{v}\| \cos \theta.$$

Schwarz Inequality $|\mathbf{u} \cdot \mathbf{v}| \leq \|\mathbf{u}\| \|\mathbf{v}\|$

Vectors **u** and **v** are orthogonal exactly when $\mathbf{u} \cdot \mathbf{v} = 0$.

$$\text{proj}_{\mathbf{v}}\mathbf{u} = \left(\frac{\mathbf{u} \cdot \mathbf{v}}{\|\mathbf{v}\|^2} \right) \mathbf{v}$$

$$\text{comp}_{\mathbf{v}}\mathbf{u} = \frac{\mathbf{u} \cdot \mathbf{v}}{\|\mathbf{v}\|} = \|\mathbf{u}\| \cos \theta, \text{ where } \theta \text{ is the angle between } \mathbf{u} \text{ and } \mathbf{v}.$$

Properties of Dot Products
If **u**, **v**, and **w** are vectors, and k is a real number, then:

1. $\mathbf{u} \cdot \mathbf{u} = \|\mathbf{u}\|^2$
2. $\mathbf{u} \cdot \mathbf{v} = \mathbf{v} \cdot \mathbf{u}$
3. $\mathbf{u} \cdot (\mathbf{v} + \mathbf{w}) = \mathbf{u} \cdot \mathbf{v} + \mathbf{u} \cdot \mathbf{w}$
4. $k\mathbf{u} \cdot \mathbf{v} = k(\mathbf{u} \cdot \mathbf{v}) = \mathbf{u} \cdot k\mathbf{v}$
5. $\mathbf{0} \cdot \mathbf{u} = 0$

Review Exercises

ANSWERS

1. $A \approx 52.9°$, $B \approx 41.6°$, $C \approx 85.5°$
2. $A \approx 97.1°$, $B \approx 25.1°$, $C \approx 57.8°$
3. $A \approx 20.6°$, $b \approx 21.8$, $C \approx 29.4°$
4. $c \approx 9.3$, $A \approx 45.8°$, $B \approx 61.8°$
5. $A \approx 35.5°$, $b \approx 8.3$, $C \approx 68.5°$
6. $A \approx 106.6°$, $B \approx 48.2°$, $C \approx 25.2°$
11. $A = 25°$, $a \approx 2.9$, $b \approx 5.6$
12. $C = 40°$; $a \approx 17.2$, $c \approx 11.1$
13. $A \approx 52.03°$, $B \approx 65.97°$, $b \approx 86.9$
14. $A = 90°$, $B = 60°$, $b \approx 4.3$
15. $B \approx 81.8°$, $C \approx 38.2°$, $c \approx 2.5$ and $B \approx 98.2°$, $C \approx 21.8°$, $c \approx 1.5$
16. $A \approx 62.9°$, $B \approx 76.1°$, $b \approx 4.1$ and $A \approx 117.1°$, $B \approx 21.9°$, $b \approx 1.6$
17. $a \approx 41.6$; $C = 75°$, $c \approx 54.1$
18. no such triangle

Review Exercises

Note: Standard notation is used for triangles.

Section   **10.1**

In Exercises 1–6, use the Law of Cosines to solve triangle *ABC*.

1. $a = 12$, $b = 10$, $c = 15$
2. $a = 7.5$, $b = 3.2$, $c = 6.4$
3. $a = 10$, $c = 14$, $B = 130°$
4. $a = 7$, $b = 8.6$, $C = 72.4°$
5. $a = 5$, $c = 8$, $B = 76°$
6. $a = 90$, $b = 70$, $c = 40$

7. Two trains depart simultaneously from the same station. The angle between their two tracks is 120°. One train travels at an average speed of 45 miles per hour and the other at 70 miles per hour. How far apart are the trains after 3 hours?
   ≈301 mi

8. A 40-foot flagpole sits on the side of a hill. The hillside makes a 17° angle with the horizontal. How long is a wire that runs from the top of the pole to a point 72 feet downhill from the base of the pole?
   ≈92.0 ft

9. Find angle *ABC* in the figure below.
   ≈71.89°

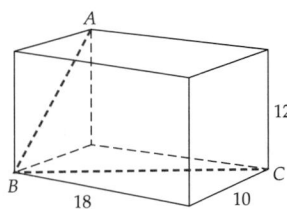

10. A surveyor stakes out points *A* and *B* on opposite sides of a building. Point *C* is 300 feet from *A* and 440 feet from *B*. Angle *ACB* measures 38°. What is the distance from *A* to *B*?
    ≈274.9 ft

Section   **10.2**

In Exercises 11–18, use the Law of Sines to solve triangle *ABC*.

11. $B = 124°$, $C = 31°$, $c = 3.5$
12. $A = 96°$, $B = 44°$, $b = 12$
13. $a = 75$, $c = 84$, $C = 62°$
14. $a = 5$, $c = 2.5$, $C = 30°$
15. $a = 3.5$, $b = 4$, $A = 60°$
16. $a = 3.8$, $c = 2.8$, $C = 41°$
17. $A = 48°$, $B = 57°$, $b = 47$
18. $A = 67°$, $c = 125$, $a = 100$

19. Find the area of triangle *ABC* if $b = 24$, $c = 15$, and $A = 55°$.
    ≈147.4 sq units

20. Find the area of triangle *ABC* if $a = 10$, $c = 14$, and $B = 75°$.
    ≈67.6 sq units

21. A boat travels for 8 kilometers in a straight line from the dock. It is then sighted from a lighthouse which is 6.5 kilometers from the dock. The angle determined by the dock, the lighthouse (vertex), and the boat is 25°. How far is the boat from the lighthouse?
    ≈13.4 km

22. A pole tilts 12° from the vertical, away from the sun, and casts a 34-foot shadow on level ground. The angle of elevation from the end of the shadow to the top of the pole is 64°. How long is the pole?
    ≈49.6 ft

23. Two surveyors, Joe and Alice, are 240 meters apart on a riverbank. Each sights a flagpole on the opposite bank. The angle from the pole to Joe (vertex) to Alice is 63°. The angle from the pole to Alice (vertex) to Joe is 54°. How far are Joe and Alice from the pole?

24. A straight road slopes at an angle of 10° with the horizontal. When the angle of elevation of the sun is 62.5°, a telephone pole at the side of the road casts a 15-foot shadow downhill, parallel to the road. How high is the telephone pole?
≈25.8 ft

25. A woman on the top of a 448-foot building spots a small plane. As she views the plane, its angle of elevation is 62°. At the same instant a man at the ground-level entrance to the building sees the plane and notes that its angle of elevation is 65°.
  a. How far is the woman from the plane? **≈3617.65 ft**
  b. How far is the man from the plane? **≈4018.71 ft**
  c. How high is the plane? **≈3642.19 ft**

26. Use the Law of Sines to prove Engelsohn's equations given below: For any triangle ABC (standard notation),

$$\frac{a + b}{c} = \frac{\sin A + \sin B}{\sin C} \quad \text{and} \quad \frac{a - b}{c} = \frac{\sin A - \sin B}{\sin C}.$$

In Exercises 27–30, find the area of the triangle described.

27. angle of 30°, adjacent side lengths 5 and 8 **10 sq units**

28. angle of 40°, adjacent side lengths 3 and 12 **≈11.6 sq units**

29. side lengths 7, 11, and 14 **≈37.95 sq units**

30. side lengths 4, 8, and 10 **≈15.2 sq units**

Section 10.3

31. Simplify $|i(4 + 2i)| + |3 - i|$. **$\sqrt{10} + 2\sqrt{5}$**

32. Simplify $|3 + 2i| - |1 - 2i|$. **$\sqrt{13} - \sqrt{5}$**

33. Graph the equation $|z| = 2$ in the complex plane.

34. Graph the equation $|z - 3| = 1$ in the complex plane.

35. Express $1 + i\sqrt{3}$ in polar form. **$2\left(\cos \frac{\pi}{3} + i \sin \frac{\pi}{3}\right)$**

36. Express $4 - 5i$ in polar form.
$\sqrt{41}(\cos -0.8961 + i \sin -0.8961)$

In Exercises 37–41, express the given number in the form $a + bi$.

37. $2\left(\cos \frac{\pi}{12} + i \sin \frac{\pi}{12}\right) \cdot 4\left(\cos \frac{\pi}{6} + i \sin \frac{\pi}{6}\right)$ **$4\sqrt{2} + 4i\sqrt{2}$**

38. $3\left(\cos \frac{\pi}{8} + i \sin \frac{\pi}{8}\right) \cdot 2\left(\cos \frac{3\pi}{8} + i \sin \frac{3\pi}{8}\right)$ **$6i$**

23. Joe is about 217.9 m from the pole and Alice is about 240 m from the pole.

26. From the Law of Sines,

$$\sin A = \frac{a \sin C}{c} \text{ and}$$

$$\sin B = \frac{b \sin C}{c}.$$

Add these two to get

$$\sin A + \sin B = \sin C\left(\frac{a + b}{c}\right),$$

so $\dfrac{\sin A + \sin B}{\sin C} = \dfrac{a + b}{c}$.

Use the same two initial equations but subtract instead of adding

to get $\dfrac{\sin A - \sin B}{\sin C} = \dfrac{a - b}{c}$.

33. The graph is a circle of radius 2 centered at the origin.

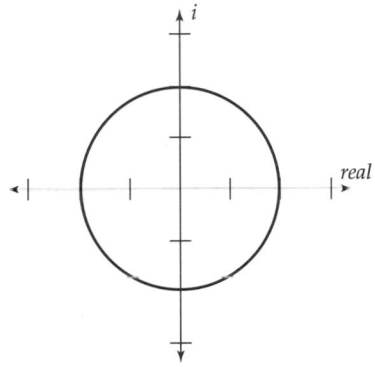

34. The graph is a circle of radius 1 centered at (3, 0).

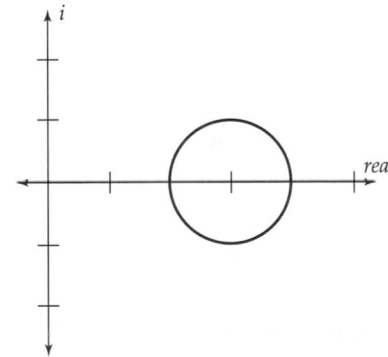

42. $\cos\dfrac{\pi}{6} + i\sin\dfrac{\pi}{6}$,

$\cos\dfrac{5\pi}{6} + i\sin\dfrac{5\pi}{6}$,

$\cos\dfrac{9\pi}{6} + i\sin\dfrac{9\pi}{6}$

43. 1, $\cos\dfrac{\pi}{3} + i\sin\dfrac{\pi}{3}$,

$\cos\dfrac{2\pi}{3} + i\sin\dfrac{2\pi}{3}$, -1,

$\cos\dfrac{4\pi}{3} + i\sin\dfrac{4\pi}{3}$, $\cos\dfrac{5\pi}{3} + i\sin\dfrac{5\pi}{3}$

44. $12^{\frac{1}{16}}\left(\cos\dfrac{\pi}{6} + i\sin\dfrac{\pi}{6}\right)$,

$12^{\frac{1}{16}}\left(\cos\dfrac{5\pi}{12} + i\sin\dfrac{5\pi}{12}\right)$,

$12^{\frac{1}{16}}\left(\cos\dfrac{2\pi}{3} + i\sin\dfrac{2\pi}{3}\right)$,

$12^{\frac{1}{16}}\left(\cos\dfrac{11\pi}{12} + i\sin\dfrac{11\pi}{12}\right)$,

$12^{\frac{1}{16}}\left(\cos\dfrac{7\pi}{6} + i\sin\dfrac{7\pi}{6}\right)$,

$12^{\frac{1}{16}}\left(\cos\dfrac{17\pi}{12} + i\sin\dfrac{17\pi}{12}\right)$,

$12^{\frac{1}{16}}\left(\cos\dfrac{5\pi}{3} + i\sin\dfrac{5\pi}{3}\right)$,

$12^{\frac{1}{16}}\left(\cos\dfrac{23\pi}{12} + i\sin\dfrac{23\pi}{12}\right)$

45. $\cos\dfrac{\pi}{8} + i\sin\dfrac{\pi}{8}$, $\cos\dfrac{5\pi}{8} + i\sin\dfrac{5\pi}{8}$,

$\cos\dfrac{9\pi}{8} + i\sin\dfrac{9\pi}{8}$,

$\cos\dfrac{13\pi}{8} + i\sin\dfrac{13\pi}{8}$

46. $2^{\frac{1}{6}}\left(\cos\dfrac{7\pi}{12} + i\sin\dfrac{7\pi}{12}\right)$,

$2^{\frac{1}{6}}\left(\cos\dfrac{5\pi}{4} + i\sin\dfrac{5\pi}{4}\right)$,

$2^{\frac{1}{6}}\left(\cos\dfrac{23\pi}{12} + i\sin\dfrac{23\pi}{12}\right)$

56. 5; ≈ 0.9273 radians

57. $-\dfrac{1}{\sqrt{5}}\mathbf{i} + \dfrac{2}{\sqrt{5}}\mathbf{j}$

58. magnitude: ≈ 26.5 lb;
direction: $\approx 49.1°$

59. ground speed: ≈ 321.87 mph;
course: $\approx 126.18°$

60. parallel component is 20 lb;
perpendicular component is
$20\sqrt{3}$ lb

39. $\dfrac{12\left(\cos\dfrac{7\pi}{12} + i\sin\dfrac{7\pi}{12}\right)}{3\left(\cos\dfrac{5\pi}{12} + i\sin\dfrac{5\pi}{12}\right)}$ $2\sqrt{3} + 2i$

Section **10.4**

40. $\left(\cos\dfrac{\pi}{12} + i\sin\dfrac{\pi}{12}\right)^{18}$ **41.** $\left[\sqrt[3]{3}\left(\cos\dfrac{5\pi}{36} + i\sin\dfrac{5\pi}{36}\right)\right]^{12}$ $\dfrac{81}{2} - \dfrac{81\sqrt{3}}{2}i$

$-i$

In Exercises 42–46, solve the given equation in the complex number system, and express your answers in polar form.

42. $x^3 = i$ **43.** $x^6 = 1$ **44.** $x^8 = -\sqrt{3} - 3i$

45. $x^4 = i$ **46.** $x^3 = 1 - i$

Section **10.5**

In Exercises 47–50, let $\mathbf{u} = \langle 3, -2\rangle$ and $\mathbf{v} = \langle 8, 1\rangle$. Find each of the following:

47. $\mathbf{u} + \mathbf{v}$ **48.** $\|-3\mathbf{v}\|$ **49.** $\|2\mathbf{v} - 4\mathbf{u}\|$ **50.** $3\mathbf{u} - \dfrac{1}{2}\mathbf{v}$

   $11\mathbf{i} - \mathbf{j}$ $3\sqrt{65}$ $2\sqrt{29}$ $5\mathbf{i} - \dfrac{13}{2}\mathbf{j}$

In Exercises 51–54, let $\mathbf{u} = -2\mathbf{i} + \mathbf{j}$ and $\mathbf{v} = 3\mathbf{i} - 4\mathbf{j}$. Find each of the following:

51. $4\mathbf{u} - \mathbf{v}$ **52.** $\mathbf{u} + 2\mathbf{v}$ **53.** $\|\mathbf{u} + \mathbf{v}\|$ **54.** $\|\mathbf{u}\| + \|\mathbf{v}\|$

   $-11\mathbf{i} + 8\mathbf{j}$ $4\mathbf{i} - 7\mathbf{j}$ $\sqrt{10}$ $\sqrt{5} + 5$

55. Find the components of the vector $\mathbf{v}$ such that $\|\mathbf{v}\| = 5$ and the direction angle of $\mathbf{v}$ is $45°$. $\left\langle\dfrac{5\sqrt{2}}{2}, \dfrac{5\sqrt{2}}{2}\right\rangle$

Section **10.6**

56. Find the magnitude and direction angle of $3\mathbf{i} + 4\mathbf{j}$.

57. Find a unit vector whose direction is opposite the direction of $3\mathbf{i} - 6\mathbf{j}$.

58. An object at the origin is acted upon by a 10-pound force with direction angle $90°$ and a 20-pound force with direction angle $30°$. Find the magnitude and direction of the resultant force.

59. A plane flies in the direction $120°$, with an air speed of 300 miles per hour. The wind is blowing from north to south at 40 miles per hour. Find the course and ground speed of the plane.

60. An object weighing 40 pounds lies on an inclined plane that makes a $30°$ angle with the horizontal. Find the components of the weight parallel and perpendicular to the plane.

Section **10.6.A**

In Exercises 61–64, let $\mathbf{u} = \langle 3, -4\rangle$, $\mathbf{v} = \langle -2, 5\rangle$, and $\mathbf{w} = \langle 0, 3\rangle$. Find each of the following:

61. $\mathbf{u} \cdot \mathbf{v}$ **-26**   **62.** $\mathbf{u} \cdot \mathbf{u} - \mathbf{v} \cdot \mathbf{v}$ **-4**   **63.** $(\mathbf{u} + \mathbf{v}) \cdot \mathbf{w}$ **3**

64. $(\mathbf{u} + \mathbf{w}) \cdot (\mathbf{w} - 3\mathbf{v})$ **30**

65. What is the angle between the vectors $5\mathbf{i} - 2\mathbf{j}$ and $3\mathbf{i} + \mathbf{j}$?   **0.70 radians**

66. Is $3\mathbf{i} - 2\mathbf{j}$ orthogonal to $4\mathbf{i} + 6\mathbf{j}$?   **yes**

In Exercises 67 and 68, let $u = 4i - 3j$ and $v = 2i + j$. Find each of the following:

67. $\text{proj}_v u$
    $2i + j = v$

68. $\text{comp}_u v$ **1**

69. If u and v have the same magnitude, show that $u + v$ and $u - v$ are orthogonal.

70. If u and v are nonzero vectors, show that the vector $u - kv$ is orthogonal to v, where $k = \dfrac{u \cdot v}{\|v\|^2}$.

71. A 3500-pound automobile is on an inclined ramp that makes a 30° angle with the horizontal. Find the force required to keep it from rolling down the ramp, assuming the only force that must be overcome is due to gravity.
    1750 lb

72. A sled is pulled along level ground by a rope that makes a 50° angle with the horizontal. If a force of 40 pounds is used to pull the sled, how much work is done in pulling it 100 feet?
    2571.2 ft-lb

69. $(u + v) \cdot (u - v)$
    $= u \cdot u - u \cdot v + v \cdot u - v \cdot v$
    $= u \cdot u - v \cdot v$
    $= \|u^2\| - \|v^2\| = 0$ since u and v have the same magnitude.

70. $v \cdot (u - kv) = v \cdot u - kv \cdot v$
    $= v \cdot u - \dfrac{u \cdot v}{\|v\|^2} v \cdot v$
    $= v \cdot u - \dfrac{u \cdot v}{\|v\|^2} \|v\|^2$
    $= v \cdot u - u \cdot v = 0$

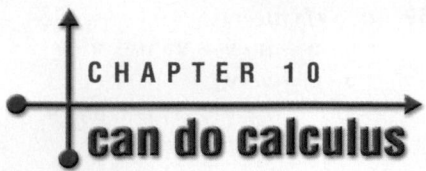

Example Notes

For **Example 3**, remind students to store unrounded values and use them to compute the approximate value of $e^{\pi+2i}$.

```
e^(π)→P
        23.14069263
cos(2)→Q
        -.4161468365
sin(2)→R
        .9092974268
```

Then, instead of using $23.14(-0.4161 + 0.9093i)$, they can use $P(Q + Ri)$ to get the approximate value shown.

ADDITIONAL EXAMPLES

Example 1

Evaluate $e^{\frac{3\pi}{2}i}$.

$$e^{\frac{3\pi}{2}i} = \cos\left(\frac{3\pi}{2}\right) + i\sin\left(\frac{3\pi}{2}\right)$$

$$= 0 + i(-1) = -i$$

Therefore, $e^{\frac{3\pi}{2}i} = -i$.

Example 2

Show that $-i = e^{-\frac{\pi}{2}i}$ and find $(-i)^i$.

$$e^{-\frac{\pi}{2}i} = \cos\left(-\frac{\pi}{2}\right) + i\sin\left(-\frac{\pi}{2}\right)$$

$$= 0 + i(-1)$$

$$= -i$$

To find $(-i)^i$, raise both sides of the identity $-i = e^{-\frac{\pi}{2}i}$ to the power i.

$$(-i)^i = \left(e^{-\frac{\pi}{2}i}\right)^i = e^{-\frac{\pi}{2}i^2} = e^{-\frac{\pi}{2}(-1)} = e^{\frac{\pi}{2}}$$

A calculator computes the value of $e^{\frac{\pi}{2}}$ to be 4.810477381. So $(-i)^i \approx 4.8105$.

can do calculus

Euler's Formula

One of the most interesting and surprising identities in all of mathematics is one that relates the exponential function e^x to the trigonometric functions $\sin x$ and $\cos x$ and the imaginary number i.

$$e^{ix} = \cos x + i \sin x$$

The identity, known as Euler's formula, is named after the mathematician Leonhard Euler (1707–1783), who discovered it in 1748. The formula is used in many areas of calculus—most notably differential equations.

Euler's formula is true for any real number x, and many real numbers produce surprising results.

Example 1   Evaluating Euler's Formula

Evaluate $e^{i\pi}$.

Solution

Substitute π for x in the formula and simplify.

$$e^{i\pi} = \cos\pi + i\sin\pi = -1 + i(0) = -1$$

Therefore, $e^{i\pi} = -1$. ∎

Rewriting the last equation connects the five most common constants of mathematics: $e, \pi, i, 0$, and 1.

$$e^{i\pi} + 1 = 0$$

One of the most surprising aspects of this displayed equation is that raising an irrational number to an irrational power results in an *integer*. In fact, raising an imaginary number to an imaginary power can also give a real number, as shown in the next example.

Example 2   Imaginary Numbers Raised to Imaginary Powers

Show that $i = e^{\frac{\pi}{2}i}$ and find i^i.

Solution

Substitute $x = \frac{\pi}{2}$ into Euler's formula and simplify.

$$e^{\frac{\pi}{2}i} = \cos\frac{\pi}{2} + i\sin\frac{\pi}{2} = 0 + i(1) = i$$

688

```
e^(-π/2)
        .2078795764
```

Figure 10.C-1

To find i^i, raise both sides of the identity $i = e^{\frac{\pi}{2}i}$ to the power i.

$$i^i = \left(e^{\frac{\pi}{2}i}\right)^i = e^{\frac{\pi}{2}i^2} = e^{\frac{\pi}{2}(-1)} = e^{-\frac{\pi}{2}}$$

A calculator computes the value of $e^{-\frac{\pi}{2}}$ to be 0.2078795764, as shown in Figure 10.C-1. So $i^i \approx 0.2079$. ∎

Euler's formula can be used to define complex powers of e, that is, e^{x+iy}.

$$e^z = e^{x+iy} = e^x \cdot e^{iy} = e^x(\cos y + i \sin y)$$

The equation $e^{x+iy} = e^x(\cos y + i \sin y)$ defines a complex power of e in terms of a real power of e and the cosine and sine of a real number.

Example 3   Complex Power of e

Find the exact value and approximate value of $e^{\pi+2i}$.

Solution

Substitute $x = \pi$ and $y = 2$ into the formula $e^z = e^x(\cos y + i \sin y)$.

$$e^{\pi+2i} = e^{\pi}(\cos 2 + i \sin 2) \quad\quad \textit{exact value}$$
$$\approx 23.14(-0.4161 + 0.9093i)$$
$$\approx -9.629926 + 21.041772i \quad \textit{approximate value}$$ ∎

Exercises

Find the exact value and the approximate value of the following powers of e.

1. $e^{-\pi i}e^{-\pi i}$

2. $\left(e^{3i}\right)^{3i}$

3. $e^{-i}e^{-i}$

4. $e^{\frac{\pi}{4}i}$

5. $e^{1+i\pi}$

6. $e^{2\pi i}$

7. $e^{1-\frac{\pi}{3}i}$

8. $e^{\pi+i}$

689

Exercises

ANSWERS

1. 1

2. e^{-9}; 0.00012

3. $\cos(-2) + i\sin(-2)$;
$-0.4161 - 0.9093i$

4. $\cos\left(\dfrac{\pi}{4}\right) + i\sin\left(\dfrac{\pi}{4}\right)$;
$0.7071 + 0.7071i$

5. $e(\cos\pi + i\sin\pi) = -e$; -2.7183

6. 1

7. $e\left(\cos-\dfrac{\pi}{3} + i\sin-\dfrac{\pi}{3}\right)$;
$1.3591 - 2.3541i$

8. $e^{\pi}(\cos 1 + i\sin 1)$;
$12.5030 + 19.4722i$

Example 3

Find the exact value and approximate value of $e^{\frac{\pi}{4}+4i}$.

Substitute $x = \dfrac{\pi}{4}$ and $y = 4$ into the formula $e^z = e^x(\cos y + i\sin y)$.

$$e^{\frac{\pi}{4}+4i} = e^{\frac{\pi}{4}}(\cos 4 + i\sin 4)$$
$$\approx 2.19(-0.6536 - 0.7568i)$$
$$\approx -1.433624 - 1.659880i$$

 Math Background

In Section 10.3, students learned how to graph a complex number $a + bi$ in the complex plane and to write $a + bi$ in polar form as $r(\cos\theta + i\sin\theta)$. In this section they learn that
$$e^{ix} = \cos x + i\sin x.$$
The graph of e^{ix} for any value of x is a point on the unit circle in the complex plane, as shown below.

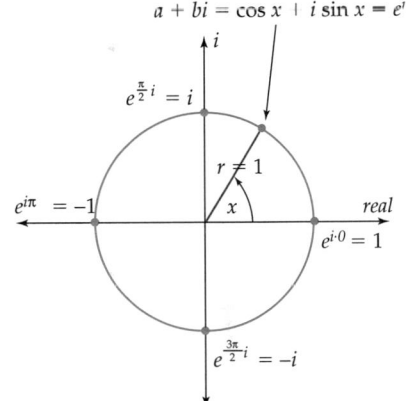

Note that if $r = 1$,
$$a + bi = r(\cos x + i\sin x)$$
$$= 1(\cos x + i\sin x)$$
$$= \cos x + i\sin x$$
$$= e^{ix}$$

The graph shows these values of e^{ix}:

$e^{i\pi} = -1$ (from Example 1)

$e^{\frac{\pi}{2}i} = i$ (from Example 2)

$e^{\frac{3\pi}{2}i} = -i$ (from Additional Example 1)

$e^{i\cdot 0} = \cos 0 + i\sin 0 = 1$

can do calculus   **689**

Analytic Geometry

In this chapter, students will study the conic sections, beginning with the standard rectangular equations for ellipses, hyperbolas, and parabolas (and their translations and rotations). They will then study the polar coordinate system and learn how to represent the conic sections by using polar equations. Finally, they will learn about parametric equations and learn how to use them to provide yet another representation of the conic sections.

CHAPTER

11

Analytic Geometry

You are there!

All planets travel in elliptical orbits around the sun, moons travel in elliptical orbits around planets, and satellites follow elliptical paths around the earth. Parabolic reflectors are used in spotlights, radar antennas, and satellite dishes. The long-range navigation system (LORAN) uses hyperbolas to enable a ship to determine its exact location. See Exercise 68 in Section 11.4.

690

Chapter Outline

can do calculus Arc Length of a Polar Graph

Interdependence of Sections

Sections 3.1, 3.2, and 3.4 are prerequisites for this chapter. Except for the discussion of standard equations for conics in Sections 11.1–11.4, Chapter 6 (Trigonometry) is also a prerequisite.

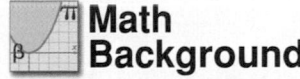

Math Background

Conic sections were first described by the ancient Greek mathematician Apollonius of Perga (c. 262 B.C.–190 B.C.). In his eight-volume work *Conics,* Apollonius defined conic sections geometrically in terms of the intersection of a plane and a cone, outlined many of their properties, and is credited for coining the terms *ellipse, hyperbola,* and *parabola.* He also developed a hemicyclium—a more-accurate sundial, with hour lines inscribed onto the surface of a conic section.

When a right circular cone is cut by a plane, the intersection is a curve called a **conic section,** as shown in the figure below. (A point, a line, or two intersecting lines are sometimes called **degenerate conic sections.)** Conic sections were studied by the ancient Greeks and are still of interest. For example, the orbits of planets are ellipses, parabolic mirrors are used in telescopes, and certain atomic particles follow hyperbolic paths.

Circle   Ellipse   Hyperbola   Parabola   Point   Line   Two intersecting lines

Although the Greeks studied conic sections from a purely geometric point of view, the modern approach is to describe them in terms of the coordinate plane and distance, or as the graphs of certain types of equations. The study of the geometric properties of objects using a coordinate system is called **analytic geometry.** Circles are discussed in the appendix and used in prior sections. In this chapter, ellipses, hyperbolas, and parabolas are defined in terms of points and distances, and their equations are determined. The standard form of the equation of a conic includes the key information necessary for a rough sketch of its graph. Techniques for graphing conic sections with a calculator are discussed in the sections that define each conic section, and applications are given.

691

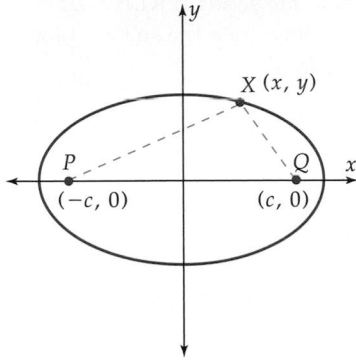

Section
11.1 Ellipses

Teaching Notes

Point out that the major axis and minor axis of an ellipse are *line segments*, not lines.

To help students understand the derivation of the **Equation of an Ellipse,** show the following sketch:

You may want to have students supply these missing steps to get Equation [1]:

$$\left(\sqrt{(x+c)^2 + y^2}\right)^2$$

$$= \left(2a - \sqrt{(x-c)^2 + y^2}\right)^2$$

$$(x+c)^2 + y^2 = 4a^2 -$$
$$\quad 4a\sqrt{(x-c)^2 + y^2} + (x-c)^2 + y^2$$

$$x^2 + 2cx + c^2 + y^2 = 4a^2 -$$
$$\quad 4a\sqrt{(x-c)^2 + y^2} + x^2 -$$
$$\quad\quad 2cx + c^2 + y^2$$

$$4a\sqrt{(x-c)^2 + y^2} = 4a^2 - 4cx$$

$$a\sqrt{(x-c)^2 + y^2} = a^2 - cx$$

$$a^2(x-c)^2 + a^2 y^2 = a^4 - 2a^2 cx + c^2 x^2$$

$$a^2(x^2 - 2cx + c^2) + a^2 y^2$$
$$\quad = a^4 - 2a^2 cx + c^2 x^2$$

$$a^2 x^2 - 2a^2 cx + a^2 c^2 + a^2 y^2$$
$$\quad = a^4 - 2a^2 cx + c^2 x^2$$

$$a^2 x^2 + a^2 c^2 + a^2 y^2 = a^4 + c^2 x^2$$

$$a^2 x^2 - c^2 x^2 + a^2 y^2 = a^4 - a^2 c^2$$

$$(a^2 - c^2)x^2 + a^2 y^2 = a^2(a^2 - c^2) \quad \textbf{[1]}$$

11.1 Ellipses

Objectives

- Define an ellipse
- Write the equation of an ellipse
- Identify important characteristics of ellipses
- Graph ellipses

An ellipse is a closed figure that can be thought of as a circle that has been elongated along a line of symmetry through its center. In this section, ellipses are defined in terms of points and distances, and then their equations are derived from the definition.

Definition of an Ellipse

Let P and Q be points in the plane and k a number greater than the distance from P to Q. The **ellipse** with **foci** (singular: **focus**) P and Q is

the set of all points X such that the *sum* of the distance from X to P and the distance from X to Q is k.

Written algebraically with X representing a point (x, y) on the ellipse,

$$XP + XQ = k$$

To draw the ellipse, pin the ends of a string of length k at points P and Q, as shown in Figure 11.1-1. Place a pencil against the string, and keep the string taut while moving the pencil.

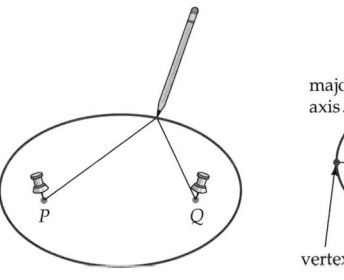

Figure 11.1-1   **Figure 11.1-2**

The midpoint of the segment $\overline{PQ}$ joining the foci is the **center** of the ellipse. The points where the line through the foci intercept the ellipse are its **vertices.** The segment connecting the vertices is the **major axis,** and the segment through the center of the ellipse perpendicular to the major axis is the **minor axis,** as shown in Figure 11.1-2.

If the points P and Q coincide, the ellipse generated is a circle with radius $\dfrac{k}{2}$. Thus, a circle is a special case of an ellipse.

Equation of an Ellipse

The simplest case is an ellipse centered at the origin, with its foci on the x- or y-axis. Suppose that the foci are on the x-axis at the points $P(-c, 0)$

If the equation of an ellipse is in standard form and the denominators are equal, then the ellipse is a circle.

For example, $\dfrac{x^2}{9} + \dfrac{y^2}{9} = 1$ is a circle with radius 3. Multiplying both sides by 9 gives the form $x^2 + y^2 = 9$, which may be familiar to students already.

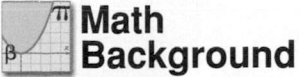

and $Q(c, 0)$, where $c > 0$. Let $a = \dfrac{k}{2}$, so that $k = 2a$. Then (x, y) is on the ellipse exactly when

[distance from (x, y) to P] + [distance from (x, y) to Q] $= k = 2a$.

Written algebraically,

$$\sqrt{(x + c)^2 + (y - 0)^2} + \sqrt{(x - c)^2 + (y - 0)^2} = 2a$$

which can be rewritten as

$$\sqrt{(x + c)^2 + y^2} = 2a - \sqrt{(x - c)^2 + y^2}.$$

Square both sides and simplify the result.

$$a\sqrt{(x - c)^2 + y^2} = a^2 - cx$$

Square both sides again and simplify.

$$(a^2 - c^2)x^2 + a^2y^2 = a^2(a^2 - c^2) \qquad \text{[1]}$$

To simplify the last equation, let $b = \sqrt{a^2 - c^2}$, so that

$$b^2 = a^2 - c^2$$

Equation [1] then becomes

$$b^2x^2 + a^2y^2 = a^2b^2$$

Dividing both sides by a^2b^2 shows that the coordinates of every point on the ellipse satisfy the equation

$$\frac{x^2}{a^2} + \frac{y^2}{b^2} = 1 \qquad \textit{Standard form of an ellipse}$$

Conversely, it can be shown that every point whose coordinates satisfy the equation is on the ellipse. The equation for an ellipse with foci $(0, c)$ and $(0, -c)$ on the y-axis is developed similarly.

Standard Equation of an Ellipse Centered at the Origin

Let a and b be real numbers such that $0 < b < a$. Then the graph of each of the following equations is an ellipse centered at the origin.

Foci on the x-axis:

$$\frac{x^2}{a^2} + \frac{y^2}{b^2} = 1$$

Foci on the y-axis:

$$\frac{x^2}{b^2} + \frac{y^2}{a^2} = 1$$

The definition of an ellipse refers to fixed points P and Q, a set of points X, and a number k. The first equation in standard form, $\dfrac{x^2}{a^2} + \dfrac{y^2}{b^2} = 1$, contains variables x, y and constants a, b. To see how the equation is based on the definition, note the following relationships that connect x, y, a, and b to P, Q, X, and k:

- x and y are the coordinates of X.
- a is half of k.
- c is half the distance between P and Q, and $b = \sqrt{a^2 - c^2}$.

So, the equation $\dfrac{x^2}{a^2} + \dfrac{y^2}{b^2} = 1$ is really a statement that says (x, y) is a point on the ellipse if and only if it satisfies the definition.

Note that because of the condition $b = \sqrt{a^2 - c^2}$, the Pythagorean relationship $b^2 + c^2 = a^2$ is satisfied, as shown below:

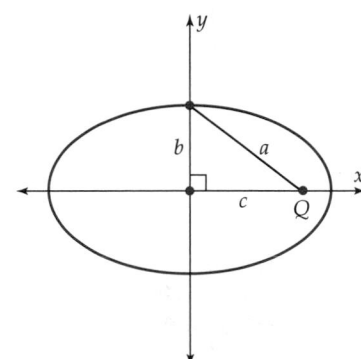

Recall that $2a = k$, and k is the sum of the distances from any point on the ellipse to the foci (the length of string in Figure 11.1-1). You can use the diagram below to demonstrate why the vertices of an ellipse have coordinates $(-a, 0)$ and $(a, 0)$. (Actually using pins and a length of string is useful.)

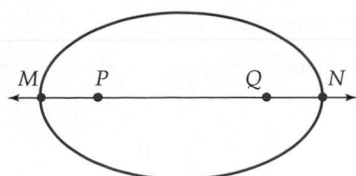

Consider the value of k measured at vertex N:

$$QN + NP = k$$

Then, by a sequence of substitutions, we get:

$$QN + PQ + QN = k$$
$$MP + PQ + QN = k$$
$$MN = k$$

So the distance between the vertices is k, or $2a$. Therefore, the distance from each vertex to the center is a.

Math Background

Note that because of the characteristics of an ellipse, $0 \le c < a$. Therefore, $0 \le \frac{c}{a} < 1$. The ratio $\frac{c}{a}$ is called the *eccentricity* of an ellipse, and it determines the shape of the ellipse as described below.

If $\frac{c}{a}$ is close to 0, then c is close to 0, each focus is near the center, and the ellipse is nearly round. (If $c = 0$, each focus coincides with the center, and the ellipse is a circle.)

If $\frac{c}{a}$ is close to 1, then c is close to a, each focus is near a vertex, and the ellipse is elongated. (If we allow $c = a$, then each focus coincides with a vertex, and the resulting set of points is just a line segment.)

Example Notes

For **Example 2,** encourage students to verify their calculator graph by getting the equation in standard form and locating the vertices and endpoints of the minor axis:

$$4x^2 + 9y^2 = 36$$
$$\frac{4x^2}{36} + \frac{9y^2}{36} = \frac{36}{36}$$
$$\frac{x^2}{9} + \frac{y^2}{4} = 1$$

The major axis is on the x-axis, $a = \pm 3$ and $b = \pm 2$. The vertices are $(3, 0)$ and $(-3, 0)$ and the endpoints of the minor axis are $(0, 2)$ and $(0, -2)$.

COMMON ERROR ALERT

Students sometimes simplify radical expressions incorrectly. In **Example 2,** they might forget to take the square root of $\frac{4}{9}$ and write

$$\pm\sqrt{\frac{36 - 4x^2}{9}} = \pm\frac{4}{9}\sqrt{9 - x^2}.$$

Remind them that:

$$\pm\sqrt{\frac{36 - 4x^2}{9}} = \pm\sqrt{\frac{4}{9}(9 - x^2)}$$

$$= \pm\sqrt{\frac{4}{9}} \cdot \sqrt{9 - x^2}$$

$$= \pm\frac{2}{3}\sqrt{9 - x^2}$$

When the equation is in standard form, the x- and y-intercepts are easily found.

x-intercepts $(y = 0)$	y-intercepts $(x = 0)$
$\dfrac{x^2}{a^2} + \dfrac{0^2}{b^2} = 1$	$\dfrac{0^2}{a^2} + \dfrac{y^2}{b^2} = 1$
$x^2 = a^2$	$y^2 = b^2$
$x = \pm a$	$y = \pm b$

The characteristics of the graph of an ellipse centered at the origin are shown in the following box.

Characteristics of Ellipses

For $0 < b < a$,

Foci on the x-axis:
$$\frac{x^2}{a^2} + \frac{y^2}{b^2} = 1$$

Foci on the y-axis:
$$\frac{x^2}{b^2} + \frac{y^2}{a^2} = 1$$

x-intercepts: $\pm a$
y-intercepts: $\pm b$
major axis is on the x-axis
vertices $(-a, 0)$ and $(a, 0)$
foci $(-c, 0)$ and $(c, 0)$, where
$c = \sqrt{a^2 - b^2}$

x-intercepts: $\pm b$
y-intercepts: $\pm a$
major axis is on the y-axis
vertices $(0, -a)$ and $(0, a)$
foci $(0, -c)$ and $(0, c)$, where
$c = \sqrt{a^2 - b^2}$

Notice the following facts in both cases.

- the foci are within the ellipse
- the major axis always contains the foci and is determined by which denominator is larger
- the distance between the foci is $2c$
- the center is the midpoint between the foci and the midpoint between the vertices
- the distance between the vertices is $2a$
- $c^2 = a^2 - b^2$

When the equation of an ellipse centered at the origin is in standard form, the denominator of the x term always gives the x-intercepts and the denominator of the y term always gives the y-intercepts.

Graphing an Ellipse

Example 1   **Graph an Ellipse**

Show that the graph of the equation $25x^2 + 16y^2 = 400$ is an ellipse. Label the foci, the vertices, the major axis, and the minor axis.

Solution

Put the equation in standard form by dividing both sides by 400.

$$\frac{x^2}{16} + \frac{y^2}{25} = 1$$

This is the equation of an ellipse with its center at the origin. The foci are on the y-axis because the denominator of y^2 is larger. Since $a^2 = 25$ and $b^2 = 16$, the x-intercepts are $\pm b = \pm 4$ and the y-intercepts are $\pm a = \pm 5$. To graph the ellipse, plot the intercepts and draw the ellipse, as shown in Figure 11.1-3.

To locate the foci, note that $c = \sqrt{25 - 16} = \sqrt{9} = 3$ and that the foci are on the y-axis. Therefore, the foci are $(0, -3)$ and $(0, 3)$.

The vertices are $(0, -5)$ and $(0, 5)$, and the major axis lies on the y-axis with endpoints at the vertices.

The minor axis lies on the x-axis, with endpoints $(-4, 0)$ and $(4, 0)$. ∎

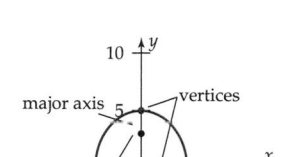

Figure 11.1-3

Example 2   **Graph an Ellipse on a Calculator**

Graph the ellipse with equation $4x^2 + 9y^2 = 36$ on a calculator.

Solution

Solve the equation for y.

$$9y^2 = 36 - 4x^2$$

$$y^2 = \frac{36 - 4x^2}{9}$$

$$y = \pm\sqrt{\frac{36 - 4x^2}{9}} = \pm\frac{2}{3}\sqrt{9 - x^2}$$

The ellipse is defined by the two functions

$$Y_1 = \frac{2}{3}\sqrt{9 - x^2} \quad \text{and} \quad Y_2 = -\frac{2}{3}\sqrt{9 - x^2},$$

whose graphs are shown in Figure 11.1-4. ∎

Figure 11.1-4

NOTE Graph all conic sections using a square window to see the correct shape.

Example 1

Show that the graph of the equation $9x^2 + 25y^2 = 225$ is an ellipse. Label the foci, the vertices, the major axis, and the minor axis.

Divide by 225 to get $\frac{x^2}{25} + \frac{y^2}{9} = 1$.

This is the equation of an ellipse with its center at the orgin.

The foci are on the x-axis because the denominator of x^2 is larger.

$a^2 = 25$ and $b^2 = 9$

$a = \pm 5$ and $b = \pm 3$

$c = \sqrt{25 - 9} = \sqrt{16} = 4$

The foci are $(4, 0)$ and $(-4, 0)$.
The vertices are $(5, 0)$ and $(-5, 0)$.
The major axis is the x-axis and the minor axis is the y-axis.

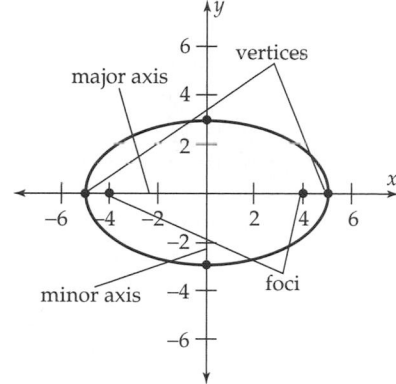

Example 2

Graph the ellipse with equation $25x^2 + 4y^2 = 100$ on a calculator.

$4y^2 = 100 - 25x^2$

$y^2 = \frac{100 - 25x^2}{4}$

$y = \pm\sqrt{\frac{100 - 25x^2}{4}} = \pm\frac{5}{2}\sqrt{4 - x^2}$

Let $Y_1 = \frac{5}{2}\sqrt{4 - x^2}$ and

$Y_2 = -\frac{5}{2}\sqrt{4 - x^2}$.

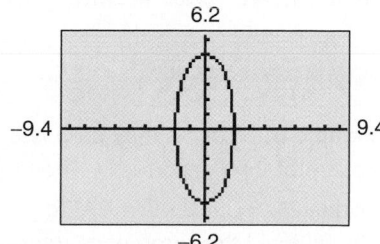

Teaching Notes

Most students can understand intuitively that the minimum and maximum distances from a focus to a point on an ellipse occur when that point on the ellipse is an endpoint of the major axis (a vertex). Refer to Figure 11.1-1 on page 692. As the pencil is moved along its path to the right, it gets farther from focus P and closer to focus Q; it will be farthest from P and closest to Q when it is at the right vertex.

Example Notes

In **Example 4**, the dimensions of the ellipse are given as length and width; these are common sense dimensions. That is, the length is understood to be the length of the major axis and the width is understood to be the length of the minor axis.

In **Example 5**, the minimum and maximum distances found are approximate distances from the *center* of the Earth to the *center* of the Sun. The radius of the Earth is about 3960 miles and the radius of the Sun is about 435,000 miles. The approximate minimum and maximum distances between the points on the Earth and Sun's surfaces that are nearest to each other are:

minimum:
91,200,000 − (3960 + 435,000)
    = 90,761,040 ≈ 90.8 million miles
maximum:
94,300,000 − (3960 + 435,000)
    = 93,861,040 ≈ 93.4 million miles

Similarly, in **Additional Example 5** (page 698), the approximate minimum and maximum distances from the satellite to the nearest point on the Earth's surface are:

minimum: 18,859 − 3960 = 14,899 miles
maximum: 33,141 − 3960 = 29,181 miles

COMMON ERROR ALERT

In **Example 3**, students may calculate the square of $2\sqrt{6}$ incorrectly. They may write $\left(2\sqrt{6}\right)^2 = 2 \cdot 6 = 12$. To help them avoid this error, encourage students to write the expression as a product: $\left(2\sqrt{6}\right)^2 = \left(2\sqrt{6}\right)\left(2\sqrt{6}\right)$
$= 4 \cdot 6 = 24$

Ellipse Equations

Example 3   Find the Equation of an Ellipse

Find the equation of the ellipse that has vertices at $(0, \pm 6)$ and foci at $\left(0, \pm 2\sqrt{6}\right)$. Then sketch its graph by using the intercepts.

Solution

The foci of the ellipse lie on the y-axis, and its center is the origin. Thus, the equation has the form

$$\frac{x^2}{b^2} + \frac{y^2}{a^2} = 1$$

Find b by letting $a = 6$ and $c = 2\sqrt{6}$ and by using the relationship among the values for an ellipse.

$$c^2 = a^2 - b^2$$
$$\left(2\sqrt{6}\right)^2 = (6)^2 - b^2$$
$$24 = 36 - b^2$$
$$b^2 = 12$$
$$b = \sqrt{12} \approx 3.5$$

Thus, the equation is

$$\frac{x^2}{\left(\sqrt{12}\right)^2} + \frac{y^2}{6^2} = 1 \quad \text{or} \quad \frac{x^2}{12} + \frac{y^2}{36} = 1$$

and the intercepts are $(0, \pm 6)$ and $\left(\pm\sqrt{12}, 0\right)$. See Figure 11.1-5. ∎

Figure 11.1-5

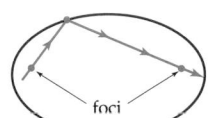

Figure 11.1-6

NOTE The area of an ellipse is $A = \pi ab$, where $2a$ is the length of the major axis and $2b$ is the length of the minor axis. See Exercise 24 for a method to estimate the circumference of an ellipse.

Applications of Ellipses

Elliptical surfaces have interesting reflective properties. A sound wave or light ray that passes through one focus and reflects off an ellipse will always pass through the other focus, as shown in Figure 11.1-6.

Example 4   Finding the Foci

The Whispering Gallery at the Museum of Science and Industry in Chicago is elliptical in shape, with a parabolic dish at each focus. (Parabolas are discussed in Section 11.3.) The shape of the room and two parabolic dishes carry the quietest sound from one focus to the other. The width of the ellipse is 13 feet 6 inches and the length of the ellipse is 47 feet 4 inches. Assume that the ellipse is centered at the origin. Find its equation, sketch its graph, and locate the foci.

Solution

Because the length of the ellipse is 47 feet 4 inches, the value of a is half that amount, or $23\frac{2}{3}$ feet. Because the width is 13 feet 6 inches, the value

Real-World Application

Example 5 is about the elliptical orbit of Earth around the Sun. Have students choose another planet in our solar system and research its orbit, finding lengths of the major axis, minor axis, and minimum and maximum distances from the Sun.

of b is half that, or $6\frac{3}{4}$ feet. Therefore, the equation of the ellipse is

$$\frac{x^2}{\left(23\frac{2}{3}\right)^2} + \frac{y^2}{\left(6\frac{3}{4}\right)^2} = 1$$

$$\frac{x^2}{\frac{5041}{9}} + \frac{y^2}{\frac{729}{16}} = 1$$

$$\frac{9x^2}{5041} + \frac{16y^2}{729} = 1$$

The distance from the center to each focus is c, which is given by

$$c^2 = a^2 - b^2 = \frac{5041}{9} - \frac{729}{16} = \frac{74{,}095}{144}$$

$$c = \sqrt{\frac{74{,}095}{144}} \approx 22.7$$

Therefore, the foci are approximately $F_1(-22.7, 0)$ and $F_2(22.7, 0)$, as shown in Figure 11.1-7. ■

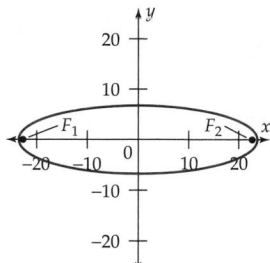

Figure 11.1-7

The planets and many comets have elliptical orbits, with the Sun at one focus. The Moon travels in an elliptical orbit with Earth at one focus, and man-made satellites usually travel in elliptical orbits around Earth.

Example 5 Elliptical Orbits

Earth's orbit around the Sun is an ellipse that is almost a circle. The Sun is at one focus, the major axis is 299,190,000 km in length, and the minor axis is 299,148,000 km in length. What are the minimum and maximum distances from Earth to the Sun?

Solution

Choose a coordinate system with the center of the ellipse at the origin and the Sun at the point $(c, 0)$ to get a diagram of the orbit. See Figure 11.1-8a.

Figure 11.1-8a

Figure 11.1-8b

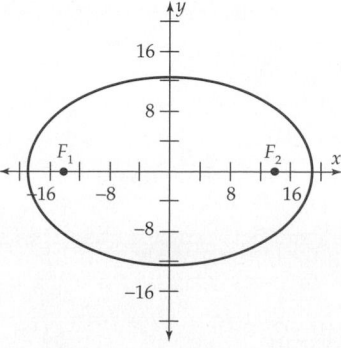

Example 3

Find the equation of the ellipse that has vertices at $(\pm 8, 0)$ and foci at $(\pm 3\sqrt{5}, 0)$. Then sketch its graph by using the intercepts.

The foci lie on the *x*-axis and the center is the origin, so the equation has the form

$$\frac{x^2}{a^2} + \frac{y^2}{b^2} = 1.$$

$$c^2 = a^2 - b^2$$

$$\left(3\sqrt{5}\right)^2 = (8)^2 - b^2$$

$$45 = 64 - b^2$$

$$b^2 = 19$$

$$b = \sqrt{19} \approx 4.4$$

equation: $\dfrac{x^2}{64} + \dfrac{y^2}{19} = 1$

intercepts: $(\pm 8, 0)$ and $(0, \pm\sqrt{19})$

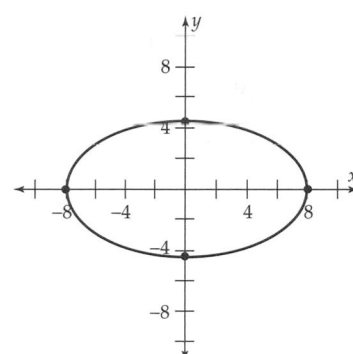

Example 4

A furniture maker has a rectangular block of wood that measures $37\frac{1}{2}$ inches by 25 inches. She wants to cut it to make the largest elliptical table top possible. Find an equation of the ellipse she can use, placing the center at the origin and the major axis on the *x*-axis. Locate the foci and sketch the graph.

$a = 18\frac{3}{4}$ in., $b = 12\frac{1}{2}$ in.

Equation: $\dfrac{x^2}{\left(18\frac{3}{4}\right)^2} + \dfrac{y^2}{\left(12\frac{1}{2}\right)^2} = 1$

$$\frac{x^2}{\frac{5625}{16}} + \frac{y^2}{\frac{625}{4}} = 1$$

$$\frac{16x^2}{5625} + \frac{4y^2}{625} = 1$$

$$c^2 = a^2 - b^2 = \frac{5625}{16} - \frac{625}{4} = \frac{3125}{16}$$

$$c = \sqrt{\frac{3125}{16}} \approx 14.0$$

approximate foci: $F_1(-14.0, 0)$ and $F_2(14.0, 0)$

ADDITIONAL EXAMPLES

Example 5

Sirius Radio has three satellites that travel in the same elliptical orbit around Earth. The length of the major axis of the elliptical orbit is about 52,000 miles, the length of the minor axis is about 50,000 miles, and Earth is at one focus. Find the minimum and maximum distances from any one of the three satellites to Earth.

$2a = 52{,}000$, so $a = 26{,}000$

$2b = 50{,}000$, so $b = 25{,}000$

$c = \sqrt{a^2 - b^2}$

$c = \sqrt{26{,}000^2 - 25{,}000^2}$

$c \approx 7141$

minimum distance
$= a - c \approx 26{,}000 - 7141$
$\approx 18{,}859$ miles

maximum distance
$= a + c \approx 26{,}000 + 7141$
$\approx 33{,}141$ miles

Exercises 11.1

ANSWERS

The length of the major axis is $2a$ and the length of the minor axis is $2b$, so

$$2a = 299{,}190{,}000 \qquad 2b = 299{,}148{,}000$$
$$a = 149{,}595{,}000 \qquad b = 149{,}574{,}000$$

Therefore, the distance from each focus to the center is given by

$$c = \sqrt{a^2 - b^2} \approx 2{,}507{,}000$$

It can be proved algebraically that the minimum and maximum distances from a focus to a point on the ellipse are at the endpoints of the major axis. That is, the maximum distance is $a + c$ and the minimum distance is $a - c$. See Figure 11.1-8b.

* minimum distance $= a - c \approx 147{,}088{,}000$ km ≈ 91.2 million miles
* maximum distance $= a + c \approx 152{,}102{,}000$ km ≈ 94.3 million miles

---

Exercises 11.1

In Exercises 1–6, find the equation of the ellipse centered at the origin that satisfies the given conditions.

1. foci on x-axis; x-intercepts ± 7, y-intercepts ± 2 $\quad \dfrac{x^2}{49} + \dfrac{y^2}{4} = 1$

2. foci on y-axis; x-intercepts ± 1, y-intercepts ± 8 $\quad \dfrac{x^2}{1} + \dfrac{y^2}{64} = 1$

3. foci on x-axis; major axis of length 12; minor axis of length 8 $\quad \dfrac{x^2}{36} + \dfrac{y^2}{16} = 1$

4. foci on y-axis; major axis of length 20; minor axis of length 18 $\quad \dfrac{x^2}{81} + \dfrac{y^2}{100} = 1$

5. endpoints of major and minor axes: $(0, -7), (0, 7)$, $(-3, 0), (3, 0)$ $\quad \dfrac{x^2}{9} + \dfrac{y^2}{49} = 1$

6. vertices $(8, 0)$ and $(-8, 0)$, minor axis of length 8 $\quad \dfrac{x^2}{64} + \dfrac{y^2}{16} = 1$

In Exercises 7–12, match one of the following equations to the given graph.

$$\dfrac{x^2}{9} + \dfrac{y^2}{16} = 1 \qquad \dfrac{x^2}{16} + \dfrac{y^2}{9} = 1$$

$$\dfrac{x^2}{4} + \dfrac{y^2}{25} = 1 \qquad \dfrac{x^2}{25} + \dfrac{y^2}{4} = 1$$

$$2x^2 + y^2 = 12 \qquad x^2 + 6y^2 = 18$$

7.
$x^2 + 6y^2 = 18$

8.
$\dfrac{x^2}{4} + \dfrac{y^2}{25} = 1$

9.

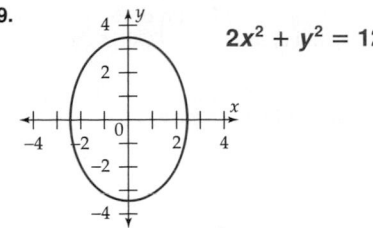

$$2x^2 + y^2 = 12$$

10.

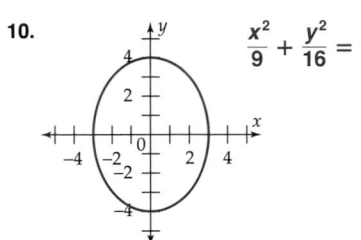

$$\frac{x^2}{9} + \frac{y^2}{16} = 1$$

11.

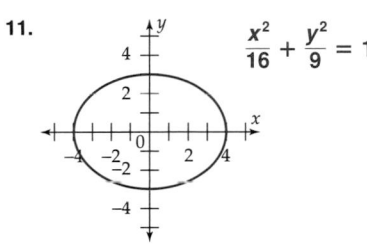

$$\frac{x^2}{16} + \frac{y^2}{9} = 1$$

12.

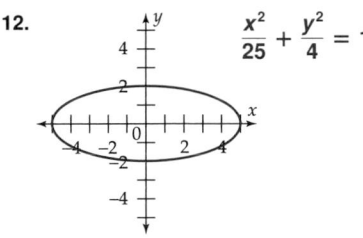

$$\frac{x^2}{25} + \frac{y^2}{4} = 1$$

In Exercises 13–16, find a complete graph of the equation.

13. $\dfrac{x^2}{25} + \dfrac{y^2}{4} = 1$ **14.** $\dfrac{x^2}{6} + \dfrac{y^2}{16} = 1$

15. $4x^2 + 3y^2 = 12$ **16.** $9x^2 + 4y^2 = 72$

Calculus can be used to show that the area of the ellipse with equation $\dfrac{x^2}{a^2} + \dfrac{y^2}{b^2} = 1$ is πab. Use this fact to find the area of each ellipse in Exercises 17–22.

17. $\dfrac{x^2}{16} + \dfrac{y^2}{4} = 1$ **8π**   **18.** $\dfrac{x^2}{9} + \dfrac{y^2}{5} = 1$ **$3\pi\sqrt{5}$**

19. $3x^2 + 4y^2 = 12$ **20.** $7x^2 + 5y^2 = 35$ **$\pi\sqrt{35}$**
 $2\pi\sqrt{3}$
21. $6x^2 + 2y^2 = 14$ **$\dfrac{7\pi}{\sqrt{3}}$**   **22.** $5x^2 + y^2 = 5$ **$\pi\sqrt{5}$**

23. Washington, D.C. has a park located next to the White House called The Ellipse. Letting the center of the ellipse be at the origin of a coordinate system, the equation that defines the boundary of the park is

$$\frac{x^2}{562,500} + \frac{y^2}{409,600} = 1$$

Find how many square feet of grass is needed to cover the entire park.
≈1,507,964 sq ft

24. The Indian mathematician Ramanujan is credited with developing the following formula that approximates the circumference of an ellipse. If $2a$ and $2b$ are the lengths of the major and minor axes of the ellipse, the circumference can be approximated by

$$\pi(3a + 3b) - \sqrt{(a + 3b)(b + 3a)}$$

Estimate the amount of fencing needed to enclose The Ellipse park described in Exercise 23.
≈10,323 ft

25. Consider the ellipse whose equation is $\dfrac{x^2}{a^2} + \dfrac{y^2}{b^2} = 1$.

Show that if $a = b$, then the graph is actually a circle.

26. Complete the derivation of the equation of the ellipse as follows.
 a. By squaring both sides, show that the equation

$$\sqrt{(x + c)^2 + y^2} = 2a - \sqrt{(x - c)^2 + y^2}$$

 may be simplified as

$$a\sqrt{(x - c)^2 + y^2} = a^2 - cx.$$

 b. Show that the last equation in part **a** may be further simplified as

$$(a^2 - c^2)x^2 + a^2y^2 = a^2(a^2 - c^2).$$

27. Sketch the graph of $\dfrac{y^2}{4} + \dfrac{x^2}{b^2} = 1$ for $b = 2, b = 4,$ $b = 8, b = 12,$ and $b = 20$. What happens to the

---

13.

14.

15.

16.

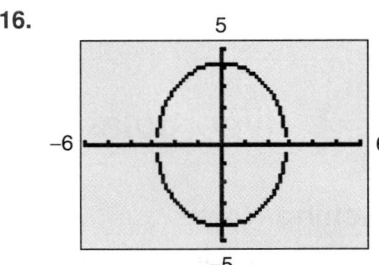

25. If $a = b$, then $\dfrac{x^2}{a^2} + \dfrac{y^2}{a^2} = 1$.

Multiplying both sides by a^2 gives $x^2 + y^2 = a^2$, the equation of a circle of radius a with center at the origin.

---

26. a. $\left(\sqrt{(x + c)^2 + y^2}\right)^2$

$\qquad = \left(2a - \sqrt{(x - c)^2 + y^2}\right)^2$

$(x + c)^2 + y^2$

$\qquad = 4a^2 - 4a\sqrt{(x - c)^2 + y^2} +$

$\qquad\qquad (x - c)^2 + y^2$

$4a\sqrt{(x - c)^2 + y^2} = 4a^2 - 4xc$

$a\sqrt{(x - c)^2 + y^2} = a^2 - xc$

26. b. $\left(a\sqrt{(x - c)^2 + y^2}\right)^2 = (a^2 - cx)^2$

$a^2((x - c)^2 + y^2) = a^4 - 2a^2cx + c^2x^2$

$a^2x^2 - 2a^2cx + a^2c^2 + a^2y^2$

$\qquad\qquad = a^4 - 2a^2cx + c^2x^2$

$a^2x^2 - c^2x^2 + a^2y^2 = a^4 - a^2c^2$

$(a^2 - c^2)x^2 + a^2y^2 = a^2(a^2 - c^2)$

27. As b gets larger, the ellipse becomes more elongated horizontally. As b gets closer to 0, the graph becomes very close to being a vertical line. However, it will never be a vertical line, because b cannot have a value of 0.

ellipse as b takes larger and larger values? Could the graph ever degenerate into a vertical line?

28. Halley's Comet has an elliptical orbit with the sun at one focus and a major axis of 1,636,484,848 miles. The closest the comet comes to the sun is 54,004,000 miles. What is the maximum distance from the comet to the sun?
≈1,582,480,848 mi

29. The orbit of the Moon around Earth is an ellipse with Earth at one focus. If the length of the major axis of the orbit is 477,736 miles and the length of the minor axis is 477,078 miles, find the minimum and maximum distances from Earth to the Moon.
≈226,335 mi and 251,401 mi

30. *Critical Thinking* An arched footbridge over a 100-foot river is shaped like half an ellipse. The maximum height of the bridge over the river is 20 feet. Find the height of the bridge over a point in the river exactly 25 feet from the center of the river.
≈17.32 ft

31. *Critical Thinking* Find the length of the sides (in terms of a, b, and c) of triangle FOC in the following ellipse. Its equation is $\dfrac{x^2}{a^2} + \dfrac{y^2}{b^2} = 1$ and F is one focus. Justify your answer.

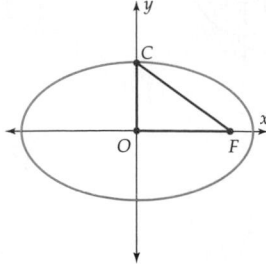

b = length of OC; c = length of OF; since $c = \sqrt{a^2 - b^2}$, $c^2 = a^2 - b^2$ or $a^2 = b^2 + c^2$; by the Pythagorean Theorem a = length of CF.

Teaching Notes

Point out the following differences between the **Definition of a Hyperbola** and the **Definition of an Ellipse** (page 692):

For an ellipse, $k > PQ$.

For a hyperbola, $k > 0$.

For an ellipse, k represents a sum.

For a hyperbola, k represents the absolute value of a difference.

 Hyperbolas

Objectives

- Define a hyperbola
- Write the equation of a hyperbola
- Identify important characteristics of hyperbolas
- Graph hyperbolas

Like an ellipse, a hyperbola has two foci, two vertices, and a center; but its shape is quite different.

Definition of a Hyperbola

Let P and Q be points in the plane and k be a positive number. The **hyperbola** with **foci** P and Q is the set of all points X such that

the absolute value of the *difference* of the distance from X to P and the distance from X to Q is k.

That is,

$$|XP - XQ| = k,$$

where X represents the point (x, y) and k is called the **distance difference.**

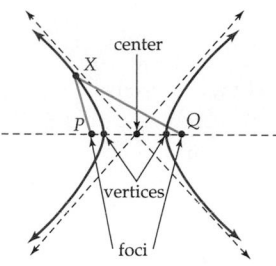

Figure 11.2-1

As shown in Figure 11.2-1, a hyperbola consists of two separate branches (shown in red). The distances XP and XQ are shown in blue. The dotted straight lines are the **asymptotes** of the hyperbola. The asymptotes are not part of the hyperbola but are useful in graphing. A hyperbola approaches its asymptotes, but it never touches them.

The midpoint of the segment joining the foci, $\overline{PQ}$, is the **center** of the hyperbola, and the line through P and Q is called the **focal axis.** The points where the focal axis intercepts the hyperbola are its **vertices.**

Equation of a Hyperbola

The simplest case is a hyperbola centered at the origin with its foci on the x- or y-axis. The equation of a hyperbola is derived by using the distance formula, and it is left as an exercise.

Standard Equation of a Hyperbola Centered at the Origin

Let a and b be positive real numbers. Then the graph of each of the following equations is a hyperbola centered at the origin.

foci on the x-axis:	foci on the y-axis:
$$\dfrac{x^2}{a^2} - \dfrac{y^2}{b^2} = 1$$	$$\dfrac{y^2}{a^2} - \dfrac{x^2}{b^2} = 1$$

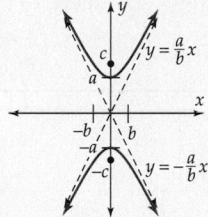

The characteristics of the graph of a hyperbola centered at the origin are shown in the following list. Notice in both cases that

- the hyperbola bends toward the foci
- the positive term determines which way the hyperbola opens
- the distance between the foci is $2c$
- the distance between the vertices is $2a$
- the center is the midpoint between the foci and the midpoint between the vertices
- $c^2 = a^2 + b^2$

When the equation is in standard form with the x term positive and y term negative, the hyperbola intersects the x-axis and opens left and right.

When the x term is negative and the y term is positive, the hyperbola intersects the y-axis and opens up and down.

Teaching Notes

It is not easy to use the definition to draw a hyperbola. An alternative is to accurately graph a hyperbola on graph paper by plotting points and then use a ruler to verify that the definition is satisfied. That is, measure the distances from some point on the hyperbola to the foci, then find the absolute value of the difference. Then repeat the process for other points on the hyperbola. Finally, compare the results to see if they are approximately the same. (You can have students do this for **Example 1,** pages 702–703).

Point out the following differences between the **Standard Equation of a Hyperbola Centered at the Origin** and the **Standard Equation of an Ellipse Centered at the Origin** (page 693):

For an ellipse, $b < a$.

For a hyperbola, $b < a$, $b > a$, or $b = a$.

The equation of an ellipse uses $+$.

The equation of a hyperbola uses $-$.

π Math Background

As with an ellipse, the ratio $\frac{c}{a}$ for a hyperbola is called its *eccentricity,* and it determines the shape of the hyperbola. For a hyperbola, $c > a$, so $\frac{c}{a} > 1$. If $\frac{c}{a}$ is close to 1, the branches of the hyperbola are narrow and "pointed." As $\frac{c}{a}$ increases, the branches get wider and "flatter."

In Example 2,

$c = \sqrt{a^2 + b^2} = \sqrt{9 + 4} = \sqrt{13}$ and $a = 3$, so $\frac{c}{a} = \frac{\sqrt{13}}{3} \approx 1.2$.

In **Example 3,** $\frac{c}{a} = \frac{\sqrt{10}}{1} \approx 3.2$.

Note that the branches of the hyperbola in Example 3 are wider and flatter than those in Example 2 (page 704).

Teaching Notes

It will be helpful to give students plenty of practice in identifying a, b, and c from an equation in standard form, and then sketching the auxiliary box, asymptotes, and finally the hyperbola. Samples are shown below.

$$\frac{x^2}{25} - \frac{y^2}{4} = 1$$

$$a = 5, b = 2, c = \sqrt{25 + 4}$$
$$= \sqrt{29} \approx 5.4$$

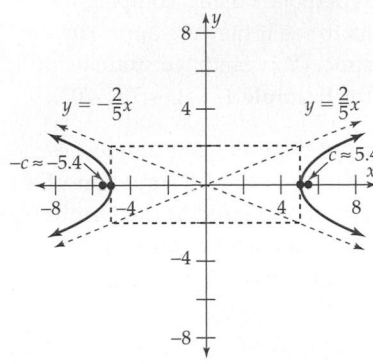

For the remaining samples, have students sketch as shown above.

$$\frac{y^2}{1} - \frac{x^2}{9} = 1$$

$$a = 1, b = 3, c = \sqrt{1 + 9}$$
$$= \sqrt{10} \approx 3.2$$
(hyperbola opens up and down)

$$\frac{y^2}{20} - \frac{x^2}{9} = 1$$

$$a = 2\sqrt{5}, b = 3, c = \sqrt{20 + 9}$$
$$= \sqrt{29} \approx 5.4$$
(hyperbola opens up and down)

$$\frac{x^2}{8} - \frac{y^2}{8} = 1$$

$$a = 2\sqrt{2}, b = 2\sqrt{2}, c = \sqrt{8 + 8}$$
$$= \sqrt{16} = 4$$
(hyperbola opens left and right)

Characteristics of Hyperbolas

For positive numbers a and b,

Foci on the x-axis:
$$\frac{x^2}{a^2} - \frac{y^2}{b^2} = 1$$

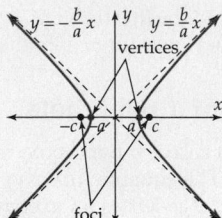

Foci on the y-axis:
$$\frac{y^2}{a^2} - \frac{x^2}{b^2} = 1$$

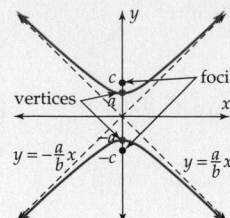

x-intercepts: $\pm a$
y-intercepts: none
focal axis is on the x-axis
vertices $(-a, 0)$ and $(a, 0)$
foci $(-c, 0)$ and $(c, 0)$, where
$c = \sqrt{a^2 + b^2}$
asymptotes: $y = \frac{b}{a}x$ and
$y = -\frac{b}{a}x$

x-intercepts: none
y-intercepts: $\pm a$
focal axis is on the y-axis
vertices $(0, -a)$ and $(0, a)$
foci $(0, -c)$ and $(0, c)$, where
$c = \sqrt{a^2 + b^2}$
asymptotes: $y = \frac{a}{b}x$ and
$y = -\frac{a}{b}x$

Graphing a Hyperbola

Example 1 Graph a Hyperbola

Show that the graph of the equation $9x^2 - 4y^2 = 36$ is a hyperbola. Graph it and its asymptotes. Find the equations of the asymptotes, and label the foci and the vertices.

Solution

Put the equation in standard form by dividing both sides by 36 and simplifying.

$$\frac{9x^2}{36} - \frac{4y^2}{36} = 1$$

$$\frac{x^2}{4} - \frac{y^2}{9} = 1$$

$$\frac{x^2}{2^2} - \frac{y^2}{3^2} = 1$$

COMMON ERROR ALERT

When students graph a hyperbola with paper and pencil they often make the error illustrated below:

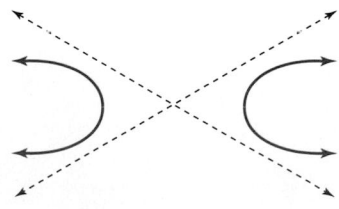

Note how the drawing incorrectly suggests that the branches get close to the asymptotes and then get farther from the asymptotes. Using Figure 11.2-2 as a reference, emphasize that if any branch is extended, it will get closer and closer to the asymptote.

Applying the fact in the box with $a = 2$ and $b = 3$ shows that the graph is a hyperbola centered at the origin with vertices $(2, 0)$ and $(-2, 0)$ and has asymptotes $y = \frac{3}{2}x$ and $y = -\frac{3}{2}x$. First plot the vertices and sketch the **auxiliary rectangle** determined by the vertical lines $x = \pm a = \pm 2$ and the horizontal lines $y = \pm b = \pm 3$. The asymptotes go through the origin and the corners of this rectangle, as shown on the left in Figure 11.2-2. It is then easy to sketch the hyperbola by drawing curves that are asymptotic to the dashed lines.

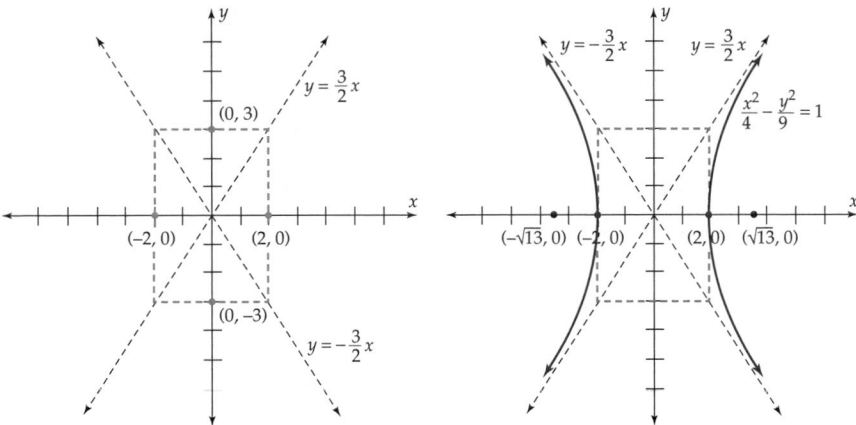

Figure 11.2-2

Locate the foci by using the formula $c = \sqrt{a^2 + b^2}$ with $a = 2$ and $b = 3$.

$$c = \sqrt{2^2 + 3^3}$$
$$= \sqrt{4 + 9} = \sqrt{13} \approx 3.6$$

Therefore, the foci are $\left(\sqrt{13}, 0\right)$ and $\left(-\sqrt{13}, 0\right)$, as shown on the graph on the right in Figure 11.2-2.   ∎

Example 2   **Graph a Hyperbola on a Calculator**

Identify the graph of $4x^2 - 9y^2 = 36$, and then graph it on a calculator.

Solution

Dividing both sides of $4x^2 - 9y^2 = 36$ by 36 shows that it is the equation of a hyperbola.

$$\frac{x^2}{9} - \frac{y^2}{4} = 1$$

Example Notes

Students will need a straightedge to draw the asymptotes in **Example 1**.

After completing **Example 2**, have students use the Table feature of their calculator to show that $y = \frac{2}{3}x$ is an asymptote.

Let $Y_1 = \frac{2}{3}\sqrt{x^2 - 9}$ and $Y_2 = \frac{2}{3}x$. As seen in the table, Y_1-values get closer and closer to the corresponding Y_2-values.

X	Y₁	Y₂
0	ERROR	0
5	2.6667	3.3333
10	6.3596	6.6667
15	9.798	10
20	13.182	13.333
25	16.546	16.667
30	19.9	20

X=0

Note that Y_2 above is *not* $Y_2 = -\frac{2}{3}\sqrt{x^2 - 9}$.

ADDITIONAL EXAMPLES

Example 1

Show that the graph of the equation $4y^2 - 16x^2 = 64$ is a hyperbola. Graph it and its asymptotes. Find the equations of the asymptotes, and label the foci and the vertices.

Put the equation in standard form.

$$\frac{4y^2}{64} - \frac{16x^2}{64} = 1$$
$$\frac{y^2}{16} - \frac{x^2}{4} = 1$$
$$\frac{y^2}{4^2} - \frac{x^2}{2^2} = 1$$

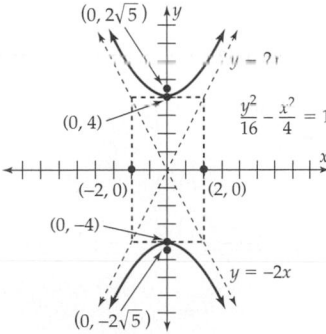

$a = 4$, $b = 2$
equations of the asymptotes:
$y = 2x$, $y = -2x$
vertices: $(0, 4)$, $(0, -4)$
$c = \sqrt{a^2 + b^2} = \sqrt{4^2 + 2^2}$
$\quad = \sqrt{20} = 2\sqrt{5} \approx 4.5$
foci: $(0, 2\sqrt{5})$, $(0, -2\sqrt{5})$

Example 2

Identify the graph of $5x^2 - 4y^2 = 20$, and then graph it on a calculator.

Dividing both sides of $5x^2 - 4y^2 = 20$ by 20 shows that it is the equation of a hyperbola.

$$\frac{5x^2}{20} - \frac{4y^2}{20} = 1$$

$$\frac{x^2}{4} - \frac{y^2}{5} = 1$$

To graph the hyperbola on a calculator, solve the original equation for y.

$$5x^2 - 4y^2 = 20$$

$$-4y^2 = -5x^2 + 20$$

$$y^2 = \frac{5x^2 - 20}{4}$$

$$y = \pm\frac{\sqrt{5x^2 - 20}}{2}$$

The hyperbola is defined by the two functions $Y_1 = \frac{1}{2}\sqrt{5x^2 - 20}$ and $Y_2 = -\frac{1}{2}\sqrt{5x^2 - 20}$.

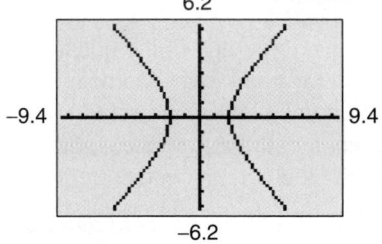

Example 3

Find the equation of the hyperbola that has vertices at $(2, 0)$ and $(-2, 0)$ and passes through the point $(4, \sqrt{3})$. Then sketch its graph by using the asymptotes, and label the foci.

The vertices are on the x-axis and the equation has the form $\frac{x^2}{a^2} - \frac{y^2}{b^2} = 1$, with $a = 2$.

Because $(4, \sqrt{3})$ is on the graph,

$$\frac{4^2}{2^2} - \frac{(\sqrt{3})^2}{b^2} = 1$$

$$4 - \frac{3}{b^2} = 1$$

$$-\frac{3}{b^2} = -3$$

$$b^2 = 1$$

Therefore, $b = 1$.

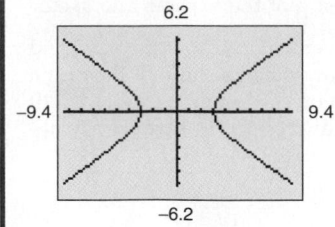

Figure 11.2-3

NOTE The two branches of the hyperbola in Figure 11.2-3 do not correspond to the two functions shown in Example 2. One function gives the part above the x-axis and the other gives the part below the x-axis.

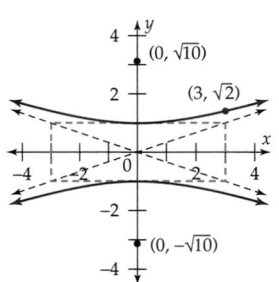

Figure 11.2-4

To graph this hyperbola on a calculator, solve the original equation for y.

$$9y^2 = 4x^2 - 36$$

$$y^2 = \frac{4x^2 - 36}{9}$$

$$y = \pm\sqrt{\frac{4x^2 - 36}{9}} = \pm\frac{2}{3}\sqrt{x^2 - 9}$$

The hyperbola is defined by the two functions

$$Y_1 = \frac{2}{3}\sqrt{x^2 - 9} \quad \text{and} \quad Y_2 = -\frac{2}{3}\sqrt{x^2 - 9}$$

whose graphs are shown in Figure 11.2-3.

Writing the Equation of a Hyperbola

Example 3   Find the Equation of a Hyperbola

Find the equation of the hyperbola that has vertices at $(0, 1)$ and $(0, -1)$ and passes through the point $(3, \sqrt{2})$. Then sketch its graph by using the asymptotes, and label the foci.

Solution

The vertices are on the y-axis and the equation has the form

$$\frac{y^2}{a^2} - \frac{x^2}{b^2} = 1,$$

with $a = 1$. Because $(3, \sqrt{2})$ is on the graph,

$$\frac{(\sqrt{2})^2}{1^2} - \frac{3^2}{b^2} = 1$$

$$2 - \frac{9}{b^2} = 1$$

$$b^2 = 9.$$

Therefore, $b = 3$ and the equation of the hyperbola is

$$\frac{y^2}{1^2} - \frac{x^2}{3^2} = 1 \quad \text{or} \quad y^2 - \frac{x^2}{9} = 1$$

The asymptotes of the hyperbola are the lines $y = \pm\frac{1}{3}x$.

The foci are on the y-axis c units away from the center, $(0, 0)$, where

$$c = \sqrt{1^2 + 3^3} = \sqrt{1 + 9} = \sqrt{10}$$

Thus, the foci are at $(0, \sqrt{10})$ and $(0, -\sqrt{10})$, as shown in Figure 11.2-4.

Applications of Hyperbolas

Applications modeled by hyperbolas occur in science, business, and economics. Unlike Halley's comet, which as an elliptical orbit, some comets have hyperbolic orbits. These comets pass through the solar system once and never return.

Additionally, the reflective properties of hyperbolas are used in the design of camera and telescope lenses. The Hubble Space Telescope incorporates a Cassegrain telescope (invented in 1672), which has both a hyperbolic mirror and a parabolic mirror. If a light ray passes through one focus of a hyperbola and reflects off the hyperbola at a point P, then the reflected ray moves along the straight line determined by P and the other focus, as shown in Figure 11.2-5.

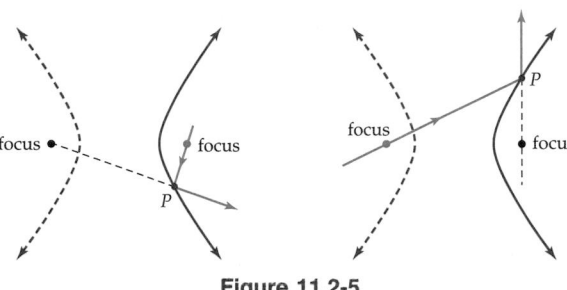

Figure 11.2-5

The next example illustrates the way hyperbolas are used in location systems.

Example 4   Determine Locations

An explosion was heard on a passenger ship and on a naval ship that are $\frac{1}{2}$ mile apart. Passengers on Ship A heard the sound $\frac{1}{2}$ second before sailors on Ship B. The speed of sound in air is approximately 1100 feet per second. Describe the possible locations of the explosion.

Solution

In $\frac{1}{2}$ second, the sound traveled $\frac{1}{2}(1100)$, or 550 feet. Therefore, the explosion occurred at a point 550 feet closer to ship A than to ship B. That is, the difference between the distance from the explosion to ship B and from the explosion to ship A is 550 feet. Whenever a difference is constant, a hyperbola is usually a good model.

Draw a coordinate system and place A and B on the x-axis equidistant from the origin. The locations of the ships are the foci of the hyperbola, and the hyperbola contains all possible locations of the explosion.

continued from page 704

The equation of the hyperbola is
$$\frac{x^2}{2^2} - \frac{y^2}{1^2} = 1 \text{ or } \frac{x^2}{4} - y^2 = 1$$

The asymptotes of the hyperbola are the lines $y = \pm\frac{1}{2}x$.

The foci are on the x-axis c units away from the center, $(0, 0)$ where
$$c = \sqrt{2^2 + 1^2} = \sqrt{4 + 1} = \sqrt{5} \approx 2.2$$

Thus, the foci are at $(\sqrt{5}, 0)$ and $(-\sqrt{5}, 0)$.

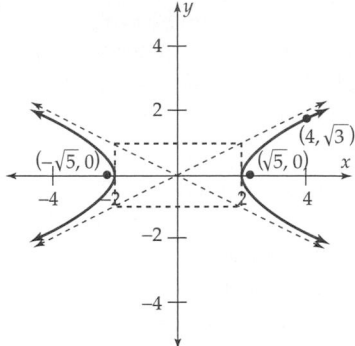

Teaching Notes

Figure 11.2-5 has two cases. Each case shows the path of a light ray hitting a hyperbola and the path of the resulting reflected ray. It appears that in the first case, the paths are perpendicular. While it is certainly possible that the paths turn out to be perpendicular, whether or not it happens that way depends on the location of point P.

Real-World Application

The real-world applications mentioned at the top of page 705 involve objects that have shapes like hyperbolas or that travel in paths like hyperbolas.

The application in **Example 4**, however, involves a hyperbola in a very different way. In Example 4, a sound originates somewhere that is 550 feet closer to one ship than to another ship. The origin of the sound can be any location that satisfies that condition, so all possible locations form a set of points that is a hyperbola. So, in this case, a hyperbola is used to describe a solution to a problem. Exercises 27 and 28 on page 708 are similar real-world applications.

ADDITIONAL EXAMPLES

Example 4

An airplane crashed and was heard by a park ranger and by a family camping in a park. The park ranger and the family are $\frac{1}{4}$ mile apart and the ranger heard the sound 1 second before the family. The speed of sound in air is approximately 1100 feet per second. Describe the possible locations of the plane crash.

In 1 second, the sound traveled 1100 feet. The crash occurred at a point 1100 feet closer to the ranger than the family.

Draw a coordinate system and place *A* (ranger) and *B* (family) on the *x*-axis equidistant from the origin. The location of the park ranger and the family are the foci of the hyperbola and the hyperbola contains all possible locations of the crash.

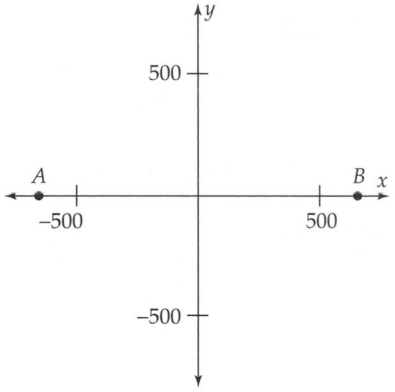

The distance between *A* and *B* is $\frac{1}{4}$ mile, or 1320 feet, so the coordinates of *A* and *B* are $(-660, 0)$ and $(660, 0)$.

The crash occurred on one branch of the hyperbola with foci $(-660, 0)$ and $(660, 0)$ such that $|XB - XA| = 1100$.

Let V_1 be the vertex closer to focus *A*. (Refer to Figure 11.2-6b)

$$|BV_1 - AV_1| = 1100$$
$$|(c + a) - (c - a)| = 1100$$
$$|2a| = 1100$$
$$a = 550$$

$a = 550$, $c = 660$
$$b^2 = c^2 - a^2$$
$$= 660^2 - 550^2$$
$$= 133,100$$

The equation of the hyperbola is
$$\frac{x^2}{a^2} - \frac{y^2}{b^2} = \frac{x^2}{302,500} - \frac{y^2}{133,100} = 1$$

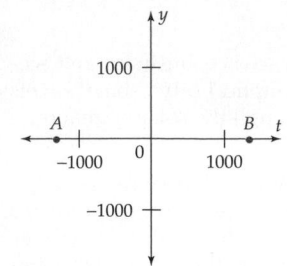

Figure 11.2-6a

NOTE For every point *X* on the branch of the hyperbola closer to *A*,

$$XB - XA = 550.$$

For every point *X* on the branch of the hyperbola closer to *B*,

$$XB - XA = -550.$$

Because the distance from *A* to *B* is $\frac{1}{2}$ mile, or 2640 feet, the coordinates of *A* and *B* are $(-1320, 0)$ and $(1320, 0)$, as shown in Figure 11.2-6a.

The explosion occurred on one branch of the hyperbola with foci $(-1320, 0)$ and $(1320, 0)$ such that $|XB - XA| = 550$ for every point *X* on the hyperbola.

Let V_1 be the vertex of the hyperbola closer to focus *A*. Because V_1 is on the hyperbola, the difference between the distances AV_1 and BV_1 is 550 feet. As shown in Figure 11.2-6b,

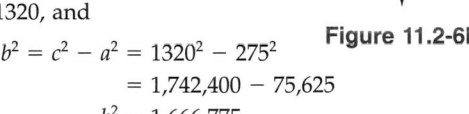

$$|BV_1 - AV_1| = 550$$
$$|(c + a) - (c - a)| = 550$$
$$|2a| = 550$$

Because $a > 0$, $a = 275$

Figure 11.2-6b

Thus, $a = 275$, $c = 1320$, and
$$b^2 = c^2 - a^2 = 1320^2 - 275^2$$
$$= 1,742,400 - 75,625$$
$$b^2 = 1,666,775$$

Therefore, the equation of the hyperbola is
$$\frac{x^2}{a^2} - \frac{y^2}{b^2} = \frac{x^2}{75,625} - \frac{y^2}{1,666,775} = 1.$$

The explosion occurred somewhere on the branch of the hyperbola closer to the passenger ship at *A*, as illustrated in Figure 11.2-6c.

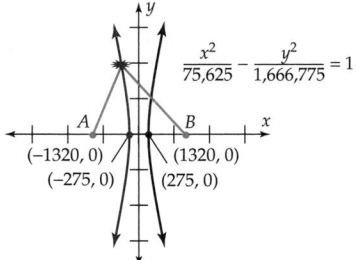

Figure 11.2-6c

To find the exact location of the explosion, the sound must be detected at a third location that is the focus of another hyperbola that shares one of the two foci given in the original problem. The intersection of the two hyperbolas will identify the precise location of the explosion, but the second hyperbola will not have its center at the origin. See Example 10 in Section 11.4, which gives the procedure for finding the exact location. ∎

The plane crashed on the branch of the hyperbola closer to the park ranger.

Exercises 11.2

In Exercises 1–6, find the equation of the hyperbola centered at the origin that satisfies the given conditions.

1. x-intercepts ±3, asymptote $y = 2x$ $\dfrac{x^2}{9} - \dfrac{y^2}{36} = 1$

2. y-intercepts ±12, asymptote $y = \dfrac{3x}{2}$ $\dfrac{y^2}{144} - \dfrac{x^2}{64} = 1$

3. vertex $(2, 0)$, passing through $\left(4, \sqrt{3}\right)$ $\dfrac{x^2}{4} - y^2 = 1$

4. vertex $\left(0, \sqrt{12}\right)$, passing through $\left(2\sqrt{3}, 6\right)$ $\dfrac{y^2}{12} - \dfrac{x^2}{6} = 1$

5. focus $(-3, 0)$ and vertex $(-2, 0)$ $\dfrac{x^2}{4} - \dfrac{y^2}{5} = 1$

6. focus $(0, 4)$ and vertex $\left(0, \sqrt{12}\right)$ $\dfrac{y^2}{12} - \dfrac{x^2}{4} = 1$

In Exercises 7–12, match one of the following equations to the given graph.

$\dfrac{x^2}{9} + \dfrac{y^2}{4} = 1$ $\dfrac{y^2}{16} - \dfrac{x^2}{9} = 1$

$8x^2 + y^2 = 8$ $8x^2 - y^2 = 8$

$\dfrac{x^2}{9} - \dfrac{y^2}{4} = 1$ $16y^2 - \dfrac{25x^2}{9} = 1$

7. 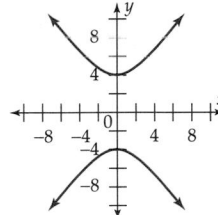 $\dfrac{y^2}{16} - \dfrac{x^2}{9} = 1$

8. 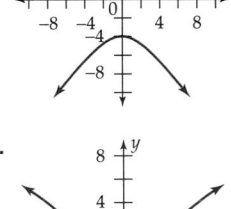 $\dfrac{x^2}{9} - \dfrac{y^2}{4} = 1$

9. $8x^2 - y^2 = 8$

10. 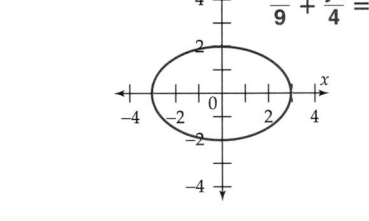 $16y^2 - \dfrac{25x^2}{9} = 1$

11. $8x^2 + y^2 = 8$

12. $\dfrac{x^2}{9} + \dfrac{y^2}{4} = 1$

In Exercises 13–18, sketch a complete graph of the equation. Label the foci and the asymptote equations.

13. $\dfrac{x^2}{6} - \dfrac{y^2}{16} = 1$ **14.** $\dfrac{x^2}{4} - y^2 = 1$

15. $4x^2 - y^2 = 16$ **16.** $3y^2 - 5x^2 = 15$

17. $18y^2 - 8x^2 - 2 = 0$ **18.** $x^2 - 2y^2 = 1$

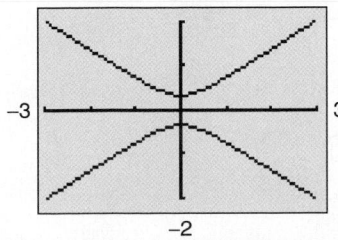

foci are at $\left(0, \dfrac{\sqrt{13}}{6}\right)$ and $\left(0, -\dfrac{\sqrt{13}}{6}\right)$; asymptotes are $y = \dfrac{2}{3}x$ and $y = -\dfrac{2}{3}x$

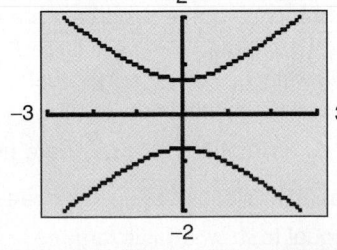

foci are at $\left(0, \sqrt{\dfrac{3}{2}}\right)$ and $\left(0, -\sqrt{\dfrac{3}{2}}\right)$; asymptotes are $y = \sqrt{\dfrac{1}{2}}x$ and $y = -\sqrt{\dfrac{1}{2}}x$

Exercises 11.2

ANSWERS

13.

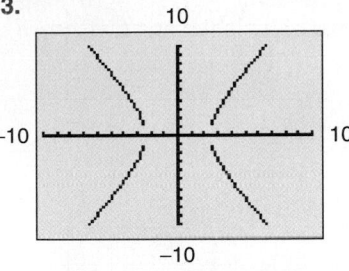

foci are at $\left(\sqrt{22}, 0\right)$ and $\left(-\sqrt{22}, 0\right)$; asymptotes are $y = \dfrac{4}{\sqrt{6}}x$ and $y = -\dfrac{4}{\sqrt{6}}x$

14.

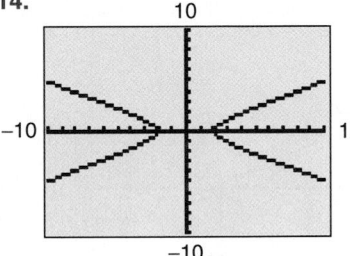

foci are at $\left(\sqrt{5}, 0\right)$ and $\left(-\sqrt{5}, 0\right)$; asymptotes are $y = \dfrac{1}{2}x$ and $y = -\dfrac{1}{2}x$

15.

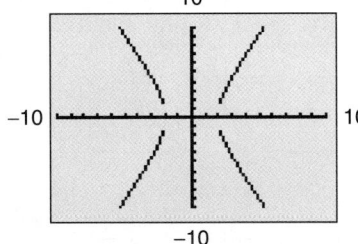

foci are at $\left(\sqrt{20}, 0\right)$ and $\left(-\sqrt{20}, 0\right)$; asymptotes are $y = 2x$ and $y = -2x$

16.

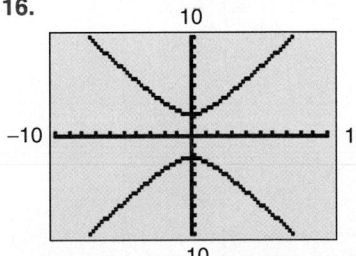

foci are at $\left(0, \sqrt{8}\right)$ and $\left(0, -\sqrt{8}\right)$; asymptotes are $y = \sqrt{\dfrac{5}{3}}x$ and $y = -\sqrt{\dfrac{5}{3}}x$

19.

20.

21.

22.

23.

24.

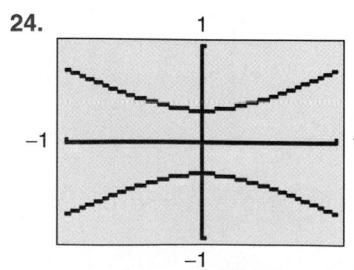

In Exercises 19–24, graph each equation using a graphing calculator.

19. $4x^2 - y^2 = 16$

20. $\dfrac{x^2}{4} - y^2 = 1$

21. $x^2 - 2y^2 = -1$

22. $\dfrac{x^2}{6} - \dfrac{y^2}{16} = 1$

23. $3y^2 - 5x^2 = 15$

24. $18y^2 - 8x^2 - 2 = 0$

25. Sketch the graph of $\dfrac{y^2}{4} - \dfrac{x^2}{b^2} = 1$ for $b = 2, b = 4,$ $b = 8, b = 12,$ and $b = 20.$ What happens to the hyperbola as b takes larger and larger values? Could the graph ever degenerate into a pair of horizontal lines?

26. Sketch the graph of $\dfrac{y^2}{a^2} - \dfrac{x^2}{16} = 1$ for $a = 8, a = 4,$ $a = 2, a = 1,$ and $a = 0.5.$ What happens to the hyperbola as a takes smaller and smaller values? Could the graph ever degenerate into a pair of horizontal lines?

27. April and Marty, 2 miles apart, are talking on the phone when lightning strikes nearby. They each hear the thunder, but April hears it 2.4 seconds after Marty. Sketch a graph of the locations where the lightning could have struck. [Sound travels at approximately 1100 feet per second.]

28. In Exercise 27, suppose that later in the conversation Marty hears the thunder 3 seconds after April. Sketch a graph of the locations where the lightning could have struck.

For Exercises 29–30, write the equation of the tangent line to the given curve at the given point by using the following facts. The slope m of the tangent line to a hyperbola at the point (x, y) is

$$m = \dfrac{b^2 x}{a^2 y} \quad \text{for} \quad \dfrac{x^2}{a^2} - \dfrac{y^2}{b^2} = 1$$

$$m = \dfrac{a^2 x}{b^2 y} \quad \text{for} \quad \dfrac{y^2}{a^2} - \dfrac{x^2}{b^2} = 1$$

29. $\dfrac{x^2}{8} - \dfrac{y^2}{4} = 1$ at $(4, 2)$

30. $\dfrac{y^2}{8} - \dfrac{x^2}{36} = 1$ at $(6, 4)$

31. Show that the difference between the distance from each focus to any point on a hyperbola is equal to the distance between the vertices.

32. Derive the equation of a hyperbola centered at the origin as follows.

   a. Let $P(x, y)$ be a point on the hyperbola with foci $F_1(-c, 0)$ and $F_2(c, 0)$. Assume that $F_1 P > F_2 P.$ By the definition of a hyperbola, the distance formula, and Exercise 31,

$$F_1 P - F_2 P = k$$
$$\sqrt{(x + c)^2 + y^2} - \sqrt{(x - c)^2 + y^2} = 2a$$

   Show that the last equation simplifies as shown.

$$cx - a^2 = a\sqrt{(x - c)^2 + y^2}$$

   b. Show that the last equation in part **a** may be further simplified as shown.

$$x^2(c^2 - a^2) - a^2 y^2 = a^2(c^2 - a^2)$$

   c. Let $b^2 = c^2 - a^2$ and show that the equation in **b** simplifies to the standard form of a hyperbola centered at the origin.

33. *Critical Thinking* The following hyperbola is centered at the origin with vertex V and the auxiliary rectangle as shown. Use the length of one of the sides of triangle POV to locate the foci. Justify your answer.

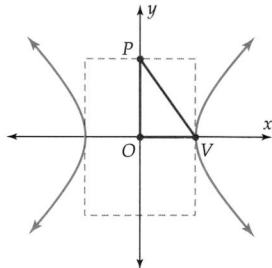

OV = a, OP = b; since in the right triangle $a^2 + b^2 = c^2$ and in the equation of a hyperbola $c^2 = a^2 + b^2$, $PV = c$, which is the distance from each focus to the center O.

25. The two branches of the hyperbola are very "flat" when b is large. With very large b and a small viewing window, the hyperbola may look like two horizontal lines, but it isn't because its asymptotes $y = \pm\dfrac{2}{b}x$ are not horizontal (their slopes, $\pm\dfrac{2}{b}$, are close to, but not equal to, 0 when b is large).

26–28. *See pp.* 1074–1075

29. $y = x - 2$

30. $y = \dfrac{1}{3}x + 2$

31–32. *See p.* 1075.

11.3 Parabolas

Objectives

- Define a parabola
- Write the equation of a parabola
- Identify important characteristics of parabolas
- Graph parabolas

Parabolas appeared in Section 3.3 as the graphs of quadratic functions, which are a special case of the following more general definition.

Definition of a Parabola

Let L be a line in the plane and P be a point not on L. If X is any point not on L, the distance from X to L is defined to be the length of the perpendicular line segment from X to L. The **parabola** with **focus** P and **directrix** L is the set of all points X such that

$$\text{distance from } X \text{ to } P = \text{distance from } X \text{ to } L$$

as shown in Figure 11.3-1.

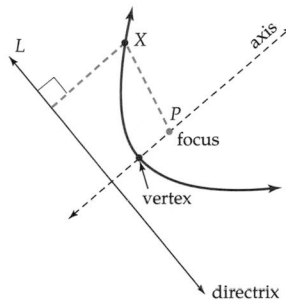

Figure 11.3-1

The line through P perpendicular to L is called the **axis.** The intersection of the axis with the parabola, which is the midpoint of the segment of the axis from P to L, is the **vertex of the parabola,** as shown in Figure 11.3-1.

Equation of a Parabola

Suppose that the focus is on the y-axis at the point $(0, p)$, where p is a nonzero constant, and that the directrix is the horizontal line $y = -p$. If (x, y) is any point on the parabola, then the distance from (x, y) to the horizontal line $y = -p$ is the length of the vertical segment from (x, y) to $(x, -p)$, as shown in Figure 11.3-2.

By the definition of a parabola,

$$\text{distance from } (x, y) \text{ to } (0, p) = \text{distance from } (x, y) \text{ to } y = -p$$
$$\text{distance from } (x, y) \text{ to } (0, p) = \text{distance from } (x, y) \text{ to } (x, -p)$$
$$\sqrt{(x - 0)^2 + (y - p)^2} = \sqrt{(x - x)^2 + [y - (-p)]^2}$$

Figure 11.3-2

Challenge students to derive the standard equation for a parabola with focus $(p, 0)$ and directrix $x = -p$.

$$\sqrt{(x - p)^2 + (y - 0)^2} = \sqrt{[x - (-p)]^2 + (y - y)^2}$$
$$(x - p)^2 + (y - 0)^2 = (x + p)^2 + (y - y)^2$$
$$x^2 - 2px + p^2 + y^2 = x^2 + 2px + p^2 + 0^2$$
$$y^2 = 4px$$

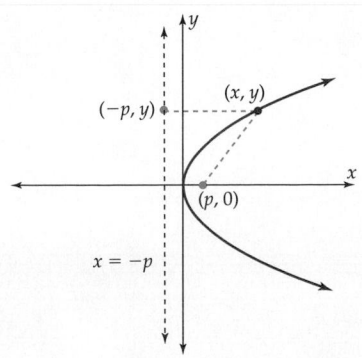

Section 11.3 Parabolas

Teaching Notes

The definitions of ellipses and hyperbolas involve distances to two fixed points (foci). The definition of a parabola involves distances to one fixed point (focus) and to a fixed line (directrix).

The distance from a point to a line is the length of the perpendicular segment from the point to the line. That fact is included in the **Definition of a Parabola** for emphasis.

After graphing a parabola (as in **Example 1,** pages 711–712), students can verify that the definition is satisfied. They can measure to verify that the distance from a point on the parabola to the focus equals the distance from the same point on the parabola to the directrix. This can be repeated for several other points on the parabola.

After discussing the derivation of the **Equation of a Parabola** (ending with $x^2 = 4py$ on page 710), point out that p can be negative, and show the following sketch:

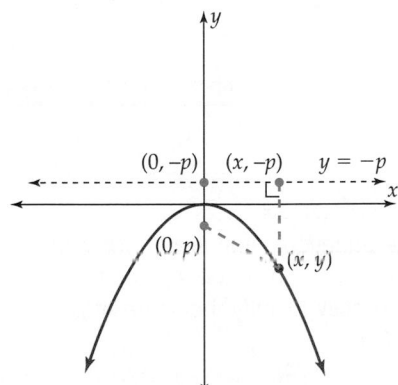

Note that if p is negative, then $-p$ is positive. Also note that the entire derivation of $x^2 = 4py$ is the same, using the sketch above.

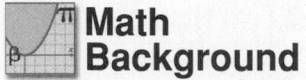

Math Background

In Section 3.3 (page 164), the polynomial form of a quadratic function is given as $f(x) = ax^2 + bx + c$. If $a = \frac{1}{4p}$, $b = 0$, and $c = 0$, the function is $f(x) = \frac{1}{4p}x^2$.

This function is equivalent to $y = \frac{1}{4p}x^2$, one of the alternate forms of the equation of a parabola in the **NOTE** on this page.

If $p = \frac{1}{4}$, then $y = \frac{1}{4p}x^2 = \frac{1}{4 \cdot \frac{1}{4}}x^2 = x^2$,

which is the parent quadratic function shown on page 173.

The other alternate form of an equation of a parabola is $x = \frac{1}{4p}y^2$, which is not a function.

Teaching Notes

Compare some of the facts about ellipses, hyperbolas, and parabolas:

Ellipse	Hyperbola	Parabola
definition uses 2 fixed points	definition uses 2 fixed points	definition uses a fixed point and a fixed line
2 foci	2 foci	1 focus
2 vertices	2 vertices	1 vertex
1 center	1 center	no center
major axis minor axis	focal axis	axis of symmetry
no asymptotes	2 asymptotes	no asymptotes

COMMON ERROR ALERT

The equation given in **Example 1** is $x^2 + 8y = 0$; students might incorrectly identify the value of p as follows:

$$4p = 8$$
$$p = 2$$

Remind them that they need the equation in standard form to get the correct value of p:

standard form: $x^2 = -8y$
correct value of p: $p = -2$

Square both sides of the equation and simplify.

$$(x - 0)^2 + (y - p)^2 = (x - x)^2 + (y + p)^2$$
$$x^2 + y^2 - 2py + p^2 = 0^2 + y^2 + 2py + p^2$$
$$x^2 = 4py \quad \text{standard form of a parabola}$$

Conversely, it can be shown that every point whose coordinates satisfy this equation is on the parabola. A similar argument works for the parabola with focus $(p, 0)$ on the x-axis and directrix the vertical line $x = -p$, and leads to the following conclusion.

Standard Equation of a Parabola with Vertex at the Origin

Let p be a nonzero real number. Then the graph of each of the following equations is a parabola with vertex at the origin.

focus at $(0, p)$	focus at $(p, 0)$
directrix: $y = -p$	directrix: $x = -p$
$x^2 = 4py$	$y^2 = 4px$

NOTE The equations of a parabola in standard form can also be written as

$$y = \frac{1}{4p}x^2$$

and

$$x = \frac{1}{4p}y^2.$$

One of the variables is quadratic and the other variable is linear. When the y term is linear, the parabola opens up or down; when the x term is linear, the parabola opens left or right. The characteristics of the graph of a parabola with vertex at the origin are shown in the following box. Notice the following facts in both cases.

- the parabola bends toward the focus and away from the directrix
- the linear term determines the orientation of the parabola and the axis of symmetry—left/right or up/down
- the sign of p determines which way the parabola opens
- the distance between the focus and the directrix is $2p$
- the distance from the vertex to the focus and the distance from the vertex to the directrix is p
- the vertex is the midpoint of the line segment joining the focus and the directrix

Characteristics of Parabolas

For a nonzero real number p, parabolas have the following characteristics.

$$x^2 = 4py \qquad\qquad y^2 = 4px$$

• focus on the y axis at $(0, p)$
• directrix $y = -p$
• axis of symmetry is the y-axis

• focus on the x-axis at $(p, 0)$
• directrix $x = -p$
• axis of symmetry is the x-axis

• If $p > 0$, then the parabola:

opens up   opens right

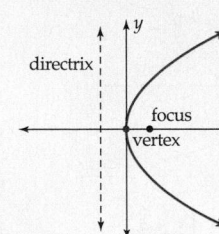

• If $p < 0$, then the parabola:

opens down   opens left

Example 1   Graphing a Parabola

Show that the graph of the equation $x^2 + 8y = 0$ is a parabola. Draw its graph, and then find and label its focus and directrix.

Solution

Write the equation in standard form: $x^2 = -8y$. This equation is of the form $x^2 = 4py$, so the graph is a parabola. To find the value of p, note that

$$4p = -8$$
$$p = -2$$

Example Notes

To get the proper "width" of a parabola, you can plot points. In **Example 1**, ask students to supply the y-values in the following ordered pairs and then plot those points for the graph:

$$\left(2, -\frac{1}{2}\right), \left(-2, -\frac{1}{2}\right), (4, -2), (-4, -2),$$
$$(8, -8), (-8, -8)$$

Math Background

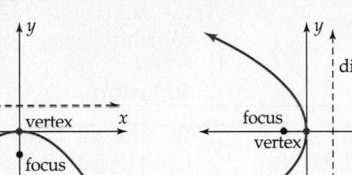

The length of the segment through the focus and perpendicular to the axis of symmetry is called the *focal width* of the parabola. The focal width of $x^2 = 4py$ and $y^2 = 4px$ is $|4p|$. The focal width of $x^2 = -8y$ (from Example 1), is $|-8| = 8$, as shown below.

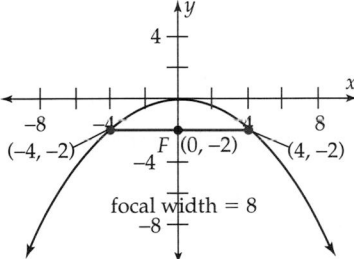

ADDITIONAL EXAMPLES

Example 1

Show that the graph of the equation $y^2 - 16x = 0$ is a parabola. Draw its graph, and then find and label its focus and directrix.

standard form: $y^2 = 16x$

This equation is of the form $y^2 = 4px$.

$4p = 16$, so $p = 4$.

The focus is $(p, 0) = (4, 0)$.

The directrix is $x = -p = -4$

The parabola opens to the right because p is positive.

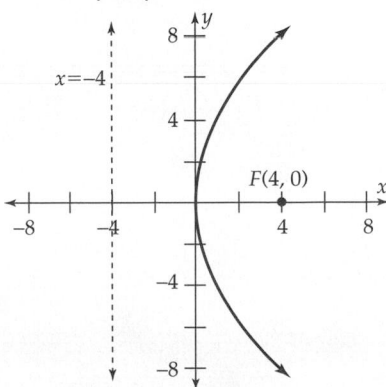

Example Notes

Have students check answers in **Example 3** by verifying that the distance from the focus to the given point is equal to the distance from the directrix to the given point.

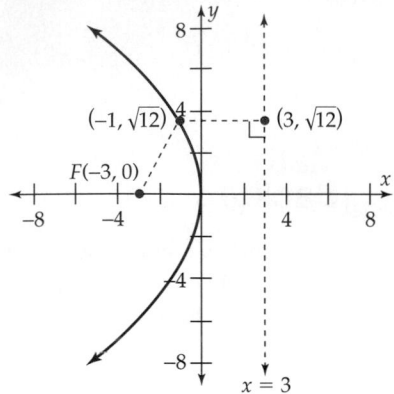

focus $(-3, 0)$ to given point $\left(-1, \sqrt{12}\right)$:

$$\sqrt{(-1 - (-3))^2 + \left(\sqrt{12} - 0\right)^2}$$
$$= \sqrt{4 + 12} = \sqrt{16} = 4$$

directrix $x = 3$ to given point $\left(-1, \sqrt{12}\right)$:

$$\sqrt{(-1 - 3)^2 + \left(\sqrt{12} - \sqrt{12}\right)^2}$$
$$= \sqrt{16 + 0} = \sqrt{16} = 4$$

The parabola for **Example 4** is shown in Figure 11.3-8b on page 714. It is a cross section of the parabolic dish radio telescope in Figure 11.3-8a. To help students visualize the parabola as a cross section of the parabolic dish, you can make a vertical cut through a cardboard dessert bowl. (If you do this, point out that the bowl is probably not an actual parabolic dish).

Figure 11.3-3

Figure 11.3-4

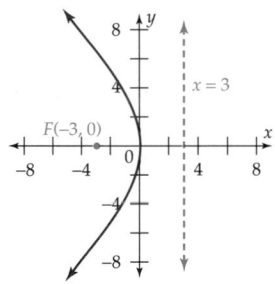

Figure 11.3-5

Therefore, the following statements are true, as shown in Figure 11.3-3.

- the focus is $(0, p) = (0, -2)$
- the directrix is $y = -p = -(-2) = 2$
- the parabola opens downward because p is negative

Example 2   Graph a Parabola on a Calculator

On a calculator, graph the parabola $y^2 = 12x$.

Solution

Solve the equation for y and enter both functions into a calculator.

$$y = \pm\sqrt{12x}$$

The graphs of $Y_1 = \sqrt{12x}$ and $Y_2 = -\sqrt{12x}$ are shown in Figure 11.3-4.

Writing the Equation of a Parabola

Example 3   Find the Equation of a Parabola

Find the focus, directrix, and equation of the parabola that passes through the point $\left(-1, \sqrt{12}\right)$, has vertex $(0, 0)$, and has its focus on the x-axis. Sketch the graph of the parabola, and label its focus and directrix.

Solution

Because the focus is on the x-axis, the equation has the form $y^2 = 4px$. Since $\left(-1, \sqrt{12}\right)$ is on the graph,

$$\left(\sqrt{12}\right)^2 = 4p(-1)$$
$$12 = -4p$$
$$-3 = p$$

Therefore, the focus is $(-3, 0)$ and the directrix is the vertical line $x = 3$. The equation of the parabola is $y^2 = -12x$, whose graph is shown in Figure 11.3-5.

Applications of Parabolas

Projectiles follow a parabolic curve, a fact that is used in the design of water slides in which the rider slides down a sharp incline, then up and over a hill, before plunging downward into a pool. At the peak of the hill, the rider shoots up along a parabolic arc several inches above the slide, experiencing a sensation of weightlessness.

Real-World Application

The radio telescope in **Example 4** has the shape of a parabolic dish (also called a paraboloid) because a cross section through the center of the dish is a parabola. Another way of describing the relationship between the two-dimensional parabola and the three-dimensional paraboloid is to describe how to use a parabola to get a paraboloid.

If a parabola is revolved about its axis of symmetry, the result is a *paraboloid of revolution*. The parabola and the paraboloid share the same axis of symmetry, the same focus, and the same vertex. The reflection properties diagrammed in Figures 11.3-6 and 11.3-7 apply in headlights, searchlights, antennas, satellite dishes, telescopes, and microphones, which are all three-dimensional paraboloids.

Certain laws of physics show that sound waves or light rays from a source at the focus of a parabola will reflect off the parabola in rays parallel to the axis of the parabola, as shown in Figure 11.3-6. This is the reason that parabolas are used in automobile headlights and searchlights.

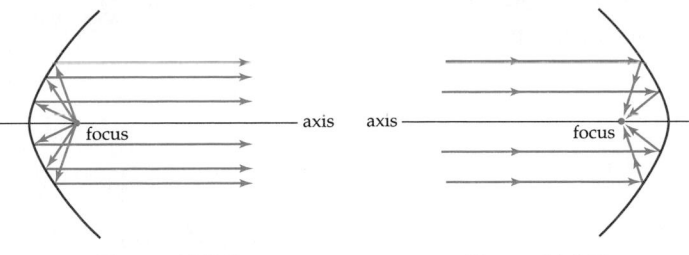

Figure 11.3-6   **Figure 11.3-7**

Conversely, a sound wave or light ray coming toward a parabola will be reflected into the focus, as shown in Figure 11.3-7. This fact is used in the design of radar antennas, satellite dishes, and field microphones used at outdoor sporting events to pick up conversations on the field.

Example 4   **Parabola Application**

A radio telescope in the Very Large Array at Socorro, New Mexico, shown in Figure 11.3-8a, has the shape of a parabolic dish (a cross section through the center of the dish is a parabola). It is approximately 12 feet deep at the center and has a diameter of 82 feet. How far from the vertex of the parabolic dish should the receiver be placed in order to "catch" all the radio waves that hit the dish?

Figure 11.3-8a

ADDITIONAL EXAMPLES

Example 2

On a calculator, graph the parabola $y^2 = 3x$.
Solve the equation for y and enter both functions into a calculator.
$y = \pm\sqrt{3x}$
$Y_1 = \sqrt{3x}$ and $Y_2 = -\sqrt{3x}$

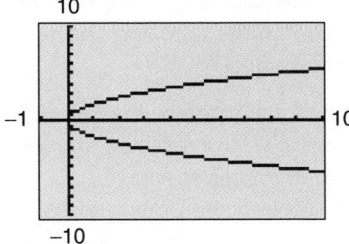

Example 3

Find the focus, directrix, and equation of the parabola that passes through the point $\left(\sqrt{20}, 5\right)$, has vertex $(0, 0)$, and has its focus on the y-axis. Sketch the graph of the parabola, and label its focus and directrix.

Because the focus is on the y-axis, the equation has the form $x^2 = 4py$. Since $\left(\sqrt{20}, 5\right)$ is on the graph,

$$\left(\sqrt{20}\right)^2 = 4p(5)$$
$$20 = 20p$$
$$1 = p$$

Therefore, the focus is $(0, 1)$ and the directrix is the horizontal line $y = -1$. The equation of the parabola is $x^2 = 4y$.

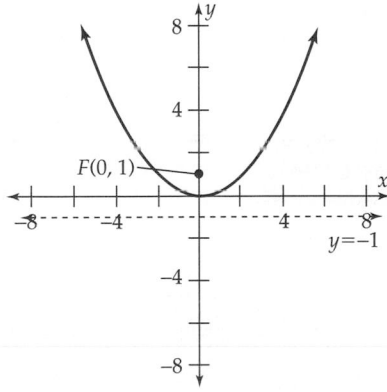

ADDITIONAL EXAMPLES

Example 4

A certain satellite dish has the shape of a parabolic dish (a cross section through the center of the dish is a parabola). It is 45 cm deep at the center and has a diameter of 274 cm. How far from the vertex of the parabolic dish should the receiver be placed in order to "catch" the transmitted signal?

All waves transmitted by the satellite that hit the dish are reflected into the focus, so the receiver should be located at the focus. Draw a cross-section of the dish with the vertex at the origin:

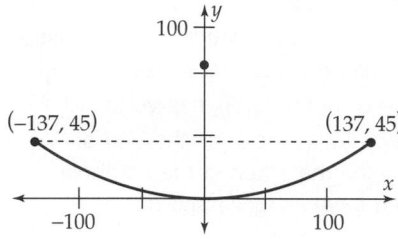

The equation of the parabola is in the form $x^2 = 4py$. Because the point (137, 45) is on the parabola,

$$x^2 = 4py$$
$$137^2 = 4p(45)$$
$$137^2 = 180p$$
$$p = \frac{137^2}{180} \approx 104 \text{ cm}$$

The focus is at the point $(0, p)$, so in this case it is at $(0, 104)$. The receiver should be placed about 104 cm from the vertex.

Exercises 11.3

ANSWERS

Figure 11.3-8b

All radio waves hitting the dish are reflected into the focus, so the receiver should be located there. To find the focus, draw a cross section of the dish, with the vertex at the origin, as shown in Figure 11.3-8b. The equation of this parabola is of the form $x^2 = 4py$. Because the point (41, 12) is on the parabola,

$$x^2 = 4py$$
$$41^2 = 4p(12) \qquad \textit{Substitute}$$
$$41^2 = 48p \qquad \textit{Simplify}$$
$$p = \frac{41^2}{48} \qquad \textit{Divide both sides by 48}$$
$$p = \frac{1681}{48} \approx 35 \text{ feet}$$

The focus is the point $(0, p)$, which is p units from the vertex $(0, 0)$. Therefore, the receiver should be placed about 35 feet from the vertex. ∎

Exercises 11.3

In Exercises 1–6, find the equation of the parabola with vertex at the origin that satisfies the given condition.

1. axis $x = 0$, passing through (2, 12) $y = 3x^2$

2. axis $y = 0$, passing through (2, 12) $y^2 = 72x$

3. focus (5, 0) $y^2 = 20x$

4. focus (0, 3.5) $x^2 = 14y$

5. directrix $x = -2$ $y^2 = 8x$

6. directrix $y = 3$ $x^2 = -12y$

In Exercises 7–10, match one of the following equations to the given graph.

$$6x = y^2 \qquad y^2 = -4x$$
$$y = \frac{x^2}{4} \qquad x^2 = -8y$$

7.

$y = \dfrac{x^2}{4}$

8.

$y^2 = -4x$

9.

$x^2 = -8y$

10.

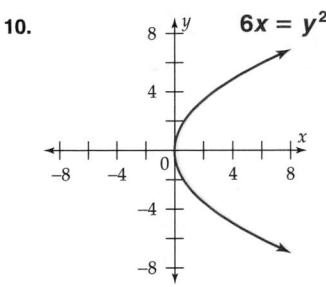

$6x = y^2$

In Exercises 11–14, sketch a complete graph of the equation.

11. $x = -6y^2$ **12.** $\frac{1}{2}y^2 = 2x$

13. $8x = 2y^2$ **14.** $4y = x^2$

In Exercises 15–18, find the focus and directrix of the parabola.

15. $y = 3x^2$ **16.** $x = \frac{1}{2}y^2$

17. $y = \frac{1}{4}x^2$ **18.** $x = -6y^2$

In Exercises 19–22, find the equation of the parabola with vertex at the origin passing through the given points.

19. $(-1, 2)$ and $(1, 2)$ **20.** $\left(3, -\frac{3}{2}\right)$ and $\left(3, \frac{3}{2}\right)$

21. $(-1, -2)$ and $(-1, 2)$ **22.** $(-2, -5)$ and $(2, -5)$

23. Find the point on the graph of $y^2 = 8x$ that is closest to the focus of the parabola.
the vertex: (0, 0)

24. Find the point on the graph of $x^2 = -3y$ that is closest to the focus of the parabola.
the vertex: (0, 0)

25. The receiver in a parabolic television dish is 2 feet from the vertex and is located at the focus. Find an equation of a cross section of the receiver. (Assume that the dish is directed to the right and that the vertex is at the origin.) $y^2 = 8x$

26. The receiver in a parabolic television dish is 1.5 feet from the vertex and is located at the focus. Find an equation of a cross section of the receiver. (Assume that the dish is directed upward and that the vertex is at the origin.) $x^2 = 6y$

27. The filament of a flashlight bulb is located at the focus, which is $\frac{1}{2}$ inch from the vertex of a parabolic reflector. Find an equation of a cross section of the reflector. (Assume that the flashlight is directed to the left and that the vertex is at the origin.)
$y^2 = -2x$

28. The filament of a flashlight bulb is located at the focus, which is $\frac{1}{4}$ inch from the vertex of a parabolic reflector. Find an equation of a cross section of the reflector. (Assume that the flashlight is directed downward and that the vertex is at the origin.)
$x^2 = -y$

ADDITIONAL EXAMPLES

Example 4

A certain satellite dish has the shape of a parabolic dish (a cross section through the center of the dish is a parabola). It is 45 cm deep at the center and has a diameter of 274 cm. How far from the vertex of the

Section
11.4 Translations and Rotations of Conics

Teaching Notes

The title of this section can be connected to the first paragraph as follows:

- Conics centered at points other than the origin are **Translations.**
- Conics with axes not parallel to the coordinate axes are **Rotations.**

You can point out that translations and rotations are types of transformations and that students have already studied various types of transformations. In particular, they have studied transformations of parabolas in Section 3.3 (page 164), where they applied the transformation form of a quadratic function $f(x) = a(x - h)^2 + k$.

Example Notes

In **Example 1,** the following table can be used to summarize the translated conic:

$\dfrac{x^2}{9} + \dfrac{y^2}{36} = 1$	$\dfrac{(x-5)^2}{9} + \dfrac{(y+4)^2}{36} = 1$
center	center
$(0, 0)$	$(5, -4)$
endpoints of major axis	endpoints of major axis
$(0, 6)$ and $(0, -6)$	$(5, 2)$ and $(5, -10)$
endpoints of minor axis	endpoints of minor axis
$(3, 0)$ and $(-3, 0)$	$(8, -4)$ and $(2, -4)$

Point out that the translation results in each x-coordinate increasing by 5, and each y-coordinate decreasing by 4.

In **Example 2,** ask students why $4x^2 - 32x$ is rewritten as $4(x^2 - 8x)$ and why $9y^2 - 90y$ is rewritten as $9(y^2 - 10y)$.

The process of completing the square requires that the leading coefficient be 1.

11.4 Translations and Rotations of Conics

Objectives

- Write the equation of a translated conic
- Graph a translated conic
- Determine the shape of a translated conic without graphing
- Apply translated conics to real-world problems

Horizontal and Vertical Shifts

Now that you are familiar with conic sections centered at the origin, the discussion will be expanded to include both conics centered at other points in the plane and ones with axes that may not be parallel to the coordinate axes.

As you saw in Section 3.4, replacing a variable x with $x - 5$ in the rule of a function $y = f(x)$ shifts the graph of the function 5 units to the right, whereas replacing x with $x + 5$, that is, $x - (-5)$, shifts the graph 5 units to the left. Similarly, if the rule of a function is given by $y = f(x)$, then replacing y with $y - 4$ shifts the graph 4 units upward, because $y - 4 = f(x)$ is equivalent to $y = f(x) + 4$. For equations that are not functions, a similar result applies.

> Let h and k be constant. Replacing x with $x - h$ and y with $y - k$ in an equation shifts the graph of the equation:
>
> - $|h|$ **units to the right for positive h and to the left for negative h**
> - $|k|$ **units upward for positive k and downward for negative k**

The process of writing the equation of a conic is the same as that discussed in Sections 11.1 through 11.3, except that x and y are replaced with $x - h$ and $y - k$, where (h, k) is the vertex of a parabola or the center of an ellipse or a hyperbola.

Example 1 Graph a Translated Conic

Identify and sketch the graph of

$$\frac{(x - 5)^2}{9} + \frac{(y + 4)^2}{36} = 1$$

and find its center, major axis, and minor axis.

Solution

The given equation can be obtained from the equation $\dfrac{x^2}{9} + \dfrac{y^2}{36} = 1$, whose graph is known to be an ellipse, as follows:

replace x by $x - 5$ and replace y by $y - (-4) = y + 4$.

This is the situation described in the previous box with $h = 5$ and $k = -4$. Therefore, the graph is the ellipse $\dfrac{x^2}{9} + \dfrac{y^2}{36} = 1$ shifted 5 units to the right and 4 units downward, as shown in Figure 11.4-1.

- The center of the ellipse is $(5, -4)$.
- The major axis lies on the vertical line $x = 5$.
- The minor axis is on the horizontal line $y = -4$.

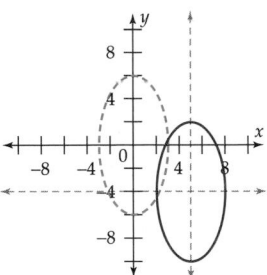

Figure 11.4-1

Before identifying a conic section and determining its characteristics, the corresponding equation should be rewritten in standard form.

Example 2 **Identify a Conic**

Identify and sketch the graph of
$$4x^2 + 9y^2 - 32x - 90y + 253 = 0.$$

Solution

Rewrite the equation as
$$(4x^2 - 32x) + (9y^2 - 90y) = -253$$
$$4(x^2 - 8x) + 9(y^2 - 10y) = -253$$

Complete the square in $x^2 - 8x$ and $y^2 - 10y$.

$$4(x^2 - 8x + 16) + 9(y^2 - 10y + 25) = -253 + ? + ?$$

NOTE Review the technique of completing the square in Section 2.2, if needed.

Be careful here: 16 and 25 were not added to the left side of the equation. Actually $4 \cdot 16 = 64$ and $9 \cdot 25 = 225$ were added, when the left side is multiplied out. Therefore, to leave the original equation unchanged, 64 and 225 must be added to the right side.

$$4(x^2 - 8x + 16) + 9(y^2 - 10y + 25) = -253 + 64 + 225$$
$$4(x - 4)^2 + 9(y - 5)^2 = 36$$
$$\frac{4(x - 4)^2}{36} + \frac{9(y - 5)^2}{36} = 1$$
$$\frac{(x - 4)^2}{9} + \frac{(y - 5)^2}{4} = 1$$

Example 1

Identify and sketch the graph of
$\dfrac{(x + 3)^2}{25} + \dfrac{(y - 6)^2}{9} = 1$ and find its
center, major axis, and minor axis.

The given equation can be obtained from the equation of the ellipse
$\dfrac{x^2}{25} + \dfrac{y^2}{9} = 1$ as follows:

replace x by $x - (-3) = x + 3$

replace y by $y - 6$

$h = -3, k = 6$

Therefore, the graph is the ellipse
$\dfrac{x^2}{25} + \dfrac{y^2}{9} = 1$ shifted 3 units left and
6 units up. So

- The center is $(-3, 6)$.
- The major axis lies on the horizontal line $y = 6$.
- The minor axis lies on the vertical line $x = -3$.

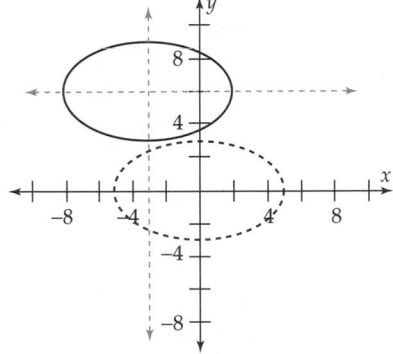

Example 2

Identify and sketch the graph of
$9x^2 + 16y^2 + 72x + 96y + 144 = 0$.

$$(9x^2 + 72x) + (16y^2 + 96y) = -144$$
$$9(x^2 + 8x) + 16(y^2 + 6y) = -144$$
$$9(x^2 + 8x + 16) + 16(y^2 + 6y + 9)$$
$$= -144 + 144 + 144$$
$$9(x + 4)^2 + 16(y + 3)^2 = 144$$
$$\frac{9(x + 4)^2}{144} + \frac{16(y + 3)^2}{144} = 1$$
$$\frac{(x + 4)^2}{16} + \frac{(y + 3)^2}{9} = 1$$

The graph of the equation is the
ellipse $\dfrac{x^2}{16} + \dfrac{y^2}{9} = 1$ shifted 4 units left
and 3 units down. Its center is
$(-4, -3)$, its major axis lies on the
line $x = -4$, and its minor axis lies on
the line $y = -3$.

Example Notes

For **Example 3**, have students plot all five given points (or identify them in Figure 11.4-3). This will help them understand the discussion in the Solution.

Ask students to give the equation of the dotted blue ellipse and the coordinates of its foci.

$$\frac{x^2}{9} + \frac{y^2}{36} = 1; \left(0, -3\sqrt{3}\right) \text{ and } \left(0, 3\sqrt{3}\right)$$

Then, ask how the blue dotted ellipse is translated to get the red ellipse.

The blue dotted ellipse is shifted 5 units to the right and 4 units down.

ADDITIONAL EXAMPLES

Example 3

Find the equation of an ellipse with center at $(-6, 5)$ such that the endpoints of its major and minor axes are $(-9, 5)$, $(-3, 5)$, $(-6, 7)$, and $(-6, 3)$. Find the coordinates of the foci. The major axis has a length of 6 and is parallel to the x-axis. The minor axis has a length of 4 and is parallel to the y-axis. Therefore, $a = 3$ and $b = 2$, and the equation of the ellipse has the form

$$\frac{(x - h)^2}{3^2} + \frac{(y - k)^2}{2^2} = 1.$$

Because its center is $(-6, 5)$, the equation has the form

$$\frac{(x - (-6))^2}{3^2} + \frac{(y - 5)^2}{2^2} = 1$$

$$\frac{(x + 6)^2}{9} + \frac{(y - 5)^2}{4} = 1.$$

Since $a = 3$ and $b = 2$,

$$c = \sqrt{3^2 - 2^2} = \sqrt{9 - 4} = \sqrt{5}.$$

The foci of $\dfrac{(x + 6)^2}{9} + \dfrac{(y - 5)^2}{4} = 1$ are $\sqrt{5}$ units from the center $(-6, 5)$ on the major axis. So, the foci are

$$\left(-6 + \sqrt{5}, 5\right) \text{ and } \left(-6 - \sqrt{5}, 5\right),$$

as shown in the figure.

The graph of this equation is the ellipse $\dfrac{x^2}{9} + \dfrac{y^2}{4} = 1$ shifted 4 units to the right and 5 units upward. Its center is at $(4, 5)$, its major axis lies on the horizontal line $y = 5$, and its minor axis lies on the vertical line $x = 4$, as shown in Figure 11.4-2.

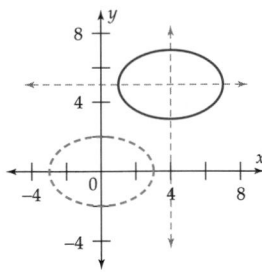

Figure 11.4-2

Example 3   **Writing the Equation of a Translated Conic**

Find the equation of an ellipse with center at $(5, -4)$ such that the endpoints of its major and minor axes are $(5, 2)$, $(5, -10)$, $(2, -4)$, and $(8, -4)$. Find the coordinates of the foci.

Solution

The major axis has length 12 and is parallel to the y-axis. The minor axis has length 6 and is parallel to the x-axis. Therefore, $a = 6$, $b = 3$, and the equation of the ellipse has the form

$$\frac{(x - h)^2}{3^2} + \frac{(y - k)^2}{6^2} = 1$$

Because it has its center at $(5, -4)$, the equation of the ellipse has the form

$$\frac{(x - 5)^2}{3^2} + \frac{(y - (-4))^2}{6^2} = 1$$

$$\frac{(x - 5)^2}{9} + \frac{(y + 4)^2}{36} = 1.$$

Since $a = 6$ and $b = 3$, and in an ellipse, $c = \sqrt{a^2 - b^2}$,

$$c = \sqrt{6^2 - 3^2} = \sqrt{36 - 9} = \sqrt{27} = 3\sqrt{3}$$

The foci of $\dfrac{(x - 5)^2}{9} + \dfrac{(y + 4)^2}{36} = 1$ are $3\sqrt{3}$ units from the center $(5, -4)$ on the major axis. That is, the foci are $\left(5, -4 + 3\sqrt{3}\right)$ and $\left(5, -4 - 3\sqrt{3}\right)$, as shown in Figure 11.4-3.

Figure 11.4-3

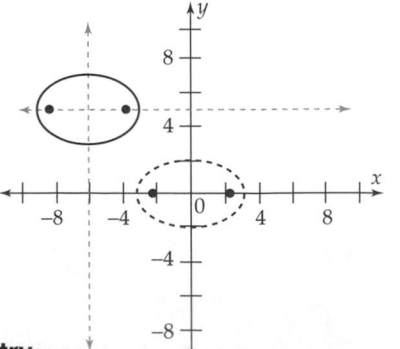

Example 4 **Identify a Translated Conic**

Identify and sketch the graph of $x = 2y^2 + 12y + 14$. Label all characteristics of the conic.

Solution

Rewrite the equation and complete the square in y, being careful to add the appropriate amounts to both sides of the equation.

$$2y^2 + 12y = x - 14$$
$$2(y^2 + 6y) = x - 14$$
$$2(y^2 + 6y + 9) = x - 14 + 2(9)$$
$$2(y + 3)^2 = x + 4$$
$$(y + 3)^2 = \frac{1}{2}(x + 4)$$
$$(y - (-3))^2 = \frac{1}{2}(x - (-4))$$

Thus, the graph is the graph of the parabola $y^2 = \frac{1}{2}x$ shifted 4 units to the left and 3 units downward, as shown in Figure 11.4-4.

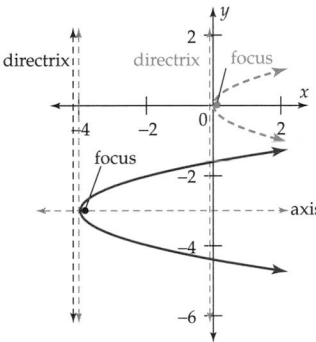

Figure 11.4-4

The parabola $y^2 = \frac{1}{2}x$ has its vertex at $(0, 0)$, the x-axis as its axis of symmetry, $\left(\frac{1}{8}, 0\right)$ as its focus, and $x = -\frac{1}{8}$ as its directrix. After the graph is shifted, the parabola will have its vertex at $(-4, -3)$ and the horizontal line $y = -3$ as its axis.

The translated parabola has its focus at $\left(\frac{1}{8} - 4, -3\right)$, or $\left(-\frac{31}{8}, -3\right)$ and directrix $x = -\frac{1}{8} - 4 = -\frac{33}{8}$.

Example 4

Identify and sketch the graph of $y = 3x^2 - 12x + 10$. Label all characteristics of the conic.

$$3x^2 - 12x = y - 10$$
$$3(x^2 - 4x) = y - 10$$
$$3(x^2 - 4x + 4) = y - 10 + 3(4)$$
$$3(x - 2)^2 = y + 2$$
$$(x - 2)^2 = \frac{1}{3}(y + 2)$$
$$(x - 2)^2 = \frac{1}{3}(y - (-2))$$

This graph is the graph of $x^2 = \frac{1}{3}y$ shifted 2 units to the right and 2 units down.

The parabola $x^2 = \frac{1}{3}y$ has its vertex at $(0, 0)$, the y-axis as its axis of symmetry, $\left(0, \frac{1}{12}\right)$ as its focus, and $y = -\frac{1}{12}$ as its directrix. After the graph is shifted, the parabola will have its vertex at $(2, -2)$ and the vertical line $x = 2$ as its axis.

The translated parabola has its focus at $\left(2, -2 + \frac{1}{12}\right)$, or $\left(2, -\frac{23}{12}\right)$ and directrix $y = -\frac{25}{12}$.

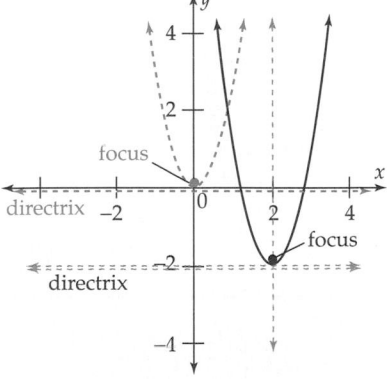

COMMON ERROR ALERT

Students often make sign errors when working with translations. In **Example 3,** a common error is to use the center $(5, -4)$ and write the incorrect equation $\frac{(x + 5)^2}{9} + \frac{(y - 4)^2}{36} = 1$. In **Example 4,** a common error is to use the equation $(y + 3)^2 = \frac{1}{2}(x + 4)$ and write the incorrect vertex $(4, 3)$.

Teaching Notes

This page is a summary of standard equations of conic sections whose axes are parallel to the coordinate axes. The phrase *axes are parallel to the coordinate axes* means that the conics addressed on this page are *translated conics*. The figures below show the types of graphs that correspond to the equations.

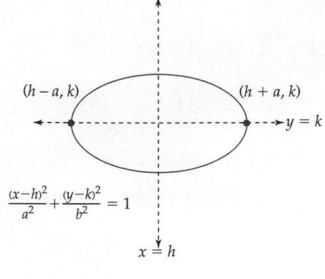

$$\frac{(x-h)^2}{a^2} + \frac{(y-k)^2}{b^2} = 1$$

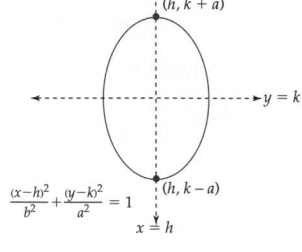

$$\frac{(x-h)^2}{b^2} + \frac{(y-k)^2}{a^2} = 1$$

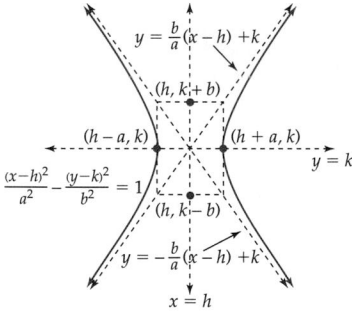

$$\frac{(x-h)^2}{a^2} - \frac{(y-k)^2}{b^2} = 1$$

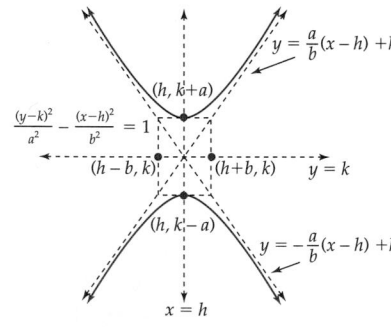

$$\frac{(y-k)^2}{a^2} - \frac{(x-h)^2}{b^2} = 1$$

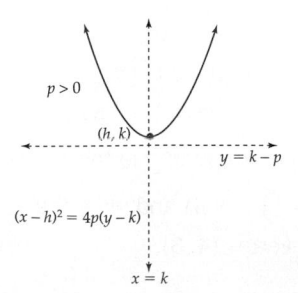

$$(x-h)^2 = 4p(y-k)$$

Standard Equations of Conic Sections

The following is a summary of the standard equations of conic sections whose axes are parallel to the coordinate axes.

Let (h, k) be any point in the plane.

- If a and b are real numbers with $a > b > 0$, then the graph of each of the following equations is an ellipse with center (h, k).

$$\frac{(x-h)^2}{a^2} + \frac{(y-k)^2}{b^2} = 1$$
$\begin{cases} \text{major axis on the horizontal line } y = k \\ \text{minor axis on the vertical line } x = h \\ \text{vertices: } (h \pm a, k) \\ \text{foci: } (h - c, k) \text{ and } (h + c, k), \text{ where} \\ \quad c = \sqrt{a^2 - b^2} \end{cases}$

$$\frac{(x-h)^2}{b^2} + \frac{(y-k)^2}{a^2} = 1$$
$\begin{cases} \text{major axis on the vertical line } x = h \\ \text{minor axis on the horizontal line } y = k \\ \text{vertices: } (h, k \pm a) \\ \text{foci: } (h, k - c) \text{ and } (h, k + c), \text{ where} \\ \quad c = \sqrt{a^2 - b^2} \end{cases}$

- If a and b are positive real numbers, then the graph of each of the following equations is a hyperbola with center (h, k).

$$\frac{(x-h)^2}{a^2} - \frac{(y-k)^2}{b^2} = 1$$
$\begin{cases} \text{focal axis on the horizontal line } y = k \\ \text{vertices: } (h - a, k) \text{ and } (h + a, k) \\ \text{foci: } (h - c, k) \text{ and } (h + c, k), \text{ where} \\ \quad c = \sqrt{a^2 + b^2} \\ \text{asymptotes: } y = \pm\frac{b}{a}(x - h) + k \end{cases}$

$$\frac{(y-k)^2}{a^2} - \frac{(x-h)^2}{b^2} = 1$$
$\begin{cases} \text{focal axis on the vertical line } x = h \\ \text{vertices: } (h, k - a) \text{ and } (h, k + a) \\ \text{foci: } (h, k - c) \text{ and } (h, k + c), \text{ where} \\ \quad c = \sqrt{a^2 + b^2} \\ \text{asymptotes: } y = \pm\frac{a}{b}(x - h) + k \end{cases}$

- If p is a nonzero real number, then the graph of each of the following equations is a parabola with vertex (h, k).

$$(x - h)^2 = 4p(y - k)$$
$\begin{cases} \text{focus: } (h, k + p) \\ \text{directrix: the horizontal line } y = k - p \\ \text{axis: the vertical line } x = h \\ \text{opens upward if } p > 0, \text{downward if } p < 0 \end{cases}$

$$(y - k)^2 = 4p(x - h)$$
$\begin{cases} \text{focus: } (h + p, k) \\ \text{directrix: the vertical line } x = h - p \\ \text{axis: the horizontal line } y = k \\ \text{opens to right if } p > 0, \text{to left if } p < 0 \end{cases}$

When the equation of a conic section is in standard form, the techniques in previous sections can be used to obtain its graph on a calculator.

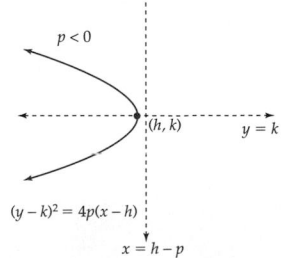

Technology Tip

● Casio has a conic section grapher, on the main menu, that produces the graphs of equations in standard form when the various coefficients are entered.

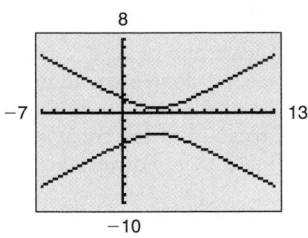

Figure 11.4-5

Example 5   Calculator Graph of a Conic

Graph the equation $\dfrac{(y + 1)^2}{2} - \dfrac{(x - 3)^2}{4} = 1$.

Solution

The graph is a hyperbola centered at $(3, -1)$. To graph on a calculator, solve the equation for y.

$$\frac{(y + 1)^2}{2} = 1 + \frac{(x - 3)^2}{4}$$

$$(y + 1)^2 = 2\left[1 + \frac{(x - 3)^2}{4}\right] = 2 + \frac{(x - 3)^2}{2}$$

$$y + 1 = \pm\sqrt{2 + \frac{(x - 3)^2}{2}}$$

$$Y_1 = \sqrt{2 + \frac{(x - 3)^2}{2}} - 1 \quad \text{or} \quad Y_2 = -\sqrt{2 + \frac{(x - 3)^2}{2}} - 1$$

Graph the last two functions on the same screen. The graph of the first is the top half and the graph of the second is the bottom half of the graph of the original equation, as shown in Figure 11.4-5. ■

When a second-degree equation is not in standard form, the fastest way to graph it is to use the method in Example 5, modified as in the next example.

Example 6   Graph a Conic Not in Standard Form

Graph the equation $x^2 + 8y^2 + 6x + 9y + 4 = 0$ without putting it in standard form.

Solution

Write the equation as

$$8y^2 + 9y + (x^2 + 6x + 4) = 0.$$

This is a quadratic equation of the form $ay^2 + by + c = 0$, with

$$a = 8, \quad b = 9, \quad \text{and} \quad c = x^2 + 6x + 4,$$

which can be solved by using the quadratic formula.

$$y = \frac{-b \pm \sqrt{b^2 - 4ac}}{2a}$$

$$= \frac{-9 \pm \sqrt{9^2 - 4 \cdot 8(x^2 + 6x + 4)}}{2 \cdot 8}$$

$$= \frac{-9 \pm \sqrt{81 - 32(x^2 + 6x + 4)}}{16}$$

Example Notes

In **Example 5** (and **Additional Example 5**), make sure students understand that they cannot enter $Y_2 = -Y_1$ as is possible for an ellipse centered at the origin.

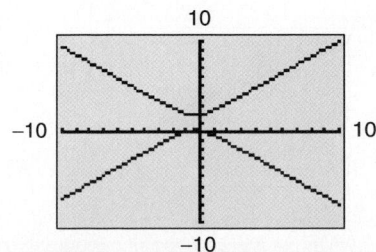

The conic is a hyperbola.

Example 5

Graph the equation

$$\frac{(x - 2)^2}{9} + \frac{(y + 3)^2}{3} = 1.$$

The graph is an ellipse centered at $(2, -3)$. Solve the equation for y:

$$\frac{(y + 3)^2}{3} = 1 - \frac{(x - 2)^2}{9}$$

$$(y + 3)^2 = 3\left[1 - \frac{(x - 2)^2}{9}\right]$$

$$= 3 - \frac{(x - 2)^2}{3}$$

$$y + 3 = \pm\sqrt{3 - \frac{(x - 2)^2}{3}}$$

$$Y_1 = \sqrt{3 - \frac{(x - 2)^2}{3}} - 3,$$

$$Y_2 = -\sqrt{3 - \frac{(x - 2)^2}{3}} - 3$$

The graphs of Y_1 and Y_2 combined form the graph of the original equation, as shown below.

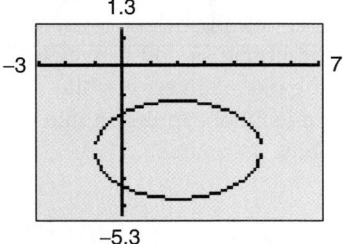

Example 6

Graph the equation $3x^2 - 4y^2 + 2x + 8y - 1 = 0$ without putting it in standard form.

Write in quadratic form $ay^2 + by + c = 0$:

$$-4y^2 + 8y + (3x^2 + 2x - 1) = 0$$

$a = -4, b = 8, c = 3x^2 + 2x - 1$

Use the quadratic formula:

$$y = \frac{-b \pm \sqrt{b^2 - 4ac}}{2a}$$

$$= \frac{-8 \pm \sqrt{8^2 - 4(-4)(3x^2 + 2x - 1)}}{2(-4)}$$

$$= \frac{-8 \pm \sqrt{64 + 16(3x^2 + 2x - 1)}}{-8}$$

Graph the functions

$$Y_1 = \frac{-8 + \sqrt{64 + 16(3x^2 + 2x - 1)}}{-8}$$

and

$$Y_2 = \frac{-8 - \sqrt{64 + 16(3x^2 + 2x - 1)}}{-8}.$$

Teaching Notes

The task of entering functions such as Y_1 and Y_2 shown at the top of this page in a calculator requires great care, especially with the placement of parentheses. Suggest that students write the functions on paper first and then enter them in the calculator. The method is shown below for Y_1.

$Y_1 = (-9 + \sqrt{(81 - 32(x^2 + 6x + 4))})/16$

Example Notes

In **Example 7**, note that there is no need to simplify the radical expressions for Y_1 and Y_2 (they could be simplified into quadratic trinomials). However, there is nothing wrong with simplifying the expressions; the risk of an error while simplifying should be weighed against the risk of an error while entering a lengthy expression into the graphing calculator.

ADDITIONAL EXAMPLES

Example 7

Graph the equation
$5x^2 + 6xy + 4y^2 + 2x + 3y - 8 = 0$
and identify the conic.
Rewrite the equation as
$4y^2 + (6x + 3)y + (5x^2 + 2x - 8) = 0$.
Solve using the quadratic equation
with $a = 4$, $b = 6x + 3$, and
$c = 5x^2 + 2x - 8$.

$y = \dfrac{-b \pm \sqrt{b^2 - 4ac}}{2a}$

$y = \dfrac{-(6x + 3) \pm \sqrt{(6x + 3)^2 - 4(4)(5x^2 + 2x - 8)}}{2(4)}$

$y = \dfrac{-(6x + 3) \pm \sqrt{(6x + 3)^2 - 16(5x^2 + 2x - 8)}}{8}$

Graph the functions

$Y_1 = \dfrac{-(6x + 3) + \sqrt{(6x + 3)^2 - 16(5x^2 + 2x - 8)}}{8}$

and

$Y_2 = \dfrac{-(6x + 3) - \sqrt{(6x + 3)^2 - 16(5x^2 + 2x - 8)}}{8}$.

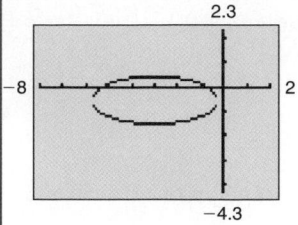

Figure 11.4-6

The graphs of both of the functions

$$Y_1 = \frac{-9 + \sqrt{81 - 32(x^2 + 6x + 4)}}{16} \quad \text{and}$$

$$Y_2 = \frac{-9 - \sqrt{81 - 32(x^2 + 6x + 4)}}{16}$$

are shown on the same screen in Figure 11.4-6. The conic is an ellipse. ∎

Rotations and Second-Degree Equations

A second-degree equation in x and y is one that can be written in the form

$$Ax^2 + Bxy + Cy^2 + Dx + Ey + F = 0 \qquad \textbf{[1]}$$

for some constants A, B, C, D, E, and F, with at least one of A, B, or C nonzero. Every conic section is the graph of a second-degree equation. The terms Dx, Ey, and F determine the translation of the conic from the origin. When $B \neq 0$, the term Bxy determines a rotation of the conic so that its axes are no longer parallel to the coordinate axes. For instance, the ellipse equation $\dfrac{x^2}{4} + \dfrac{(y - 3)^2}{6} = 1$ can be written as

$$12\left(\frac{x^2}{4}\right) + 12\left[\frac{(y - 3)^2}{6}\right] = 12$$
$$3x^2 + 2(y - 3)^2 = 12$$
$$3x^2 + 2(y^2 - 6y + 9) = 12$$
$$3x^2 + 2y^2 - 12y + 18 = 12$$
$$3x^2 + 2y^2 - 12y + 6 = 0$$

The last equation above has the form of equation [1] with $A = 3$, $B = 0$, $C = 2$, $D = 0$, $E = -12$, and $F = 6$.

Conversely, it can be shown that the graph of every second-degree equation is a conic section (possibly degenerate—see page 691). When the equation has an xy term, the conic may be rotated from standard position such that its axis or axes are not parallel to the coordinate axes.

Example 7 Identify a Conic

Graph the equation $3x^2 + 6xy + y^2 + x - 2y + 7 = 0$ and identify the conic.

Solution

Rewrite the equation as

$$y^2 + 6xy - 2y + 3x^2 + x + 7 = 0$$
$$y^2 + (6x - 2)y + (3x^2 + x + 7) = 0$$

The last equation has the form $ay^2 + by + c = 0$, with $a = 1$, $b = 6x - 2$, and $c = 3x^2 + x + 7$. It can be solved for y by using the quadratic formula.

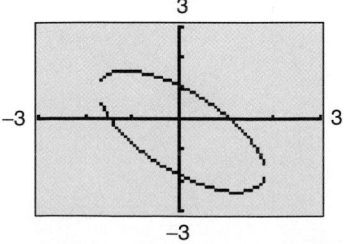

The graph is an ellipse with its axes tilted.

$$y = \frac{-b \pm \sqrt{b^2 - 4ac}}{2a}$$

$$y = \frac{-(6x - 2) \pm \sqrt{(6x - 2)^2 - 4 \cdot 1 \cdot (3x^2 + x + 7)}}{2 \cdot 1}$$

Half of the graph is obtained by graphing

$$Y_1 = \frac{-(6x - 2) + \sqrt{(6x - 2)^2 - 4 \cdot 1 \cdot (3x^2 + x + 7)}}{2}$$

and the other half by graphing

$$Y_2 = \frac{-(6x - 2) - \sqrt{(6x - 2)^2 - 4 \cdot 1 \cdot (3x^2 + x + 7)}}{2}$$

The graph is a hyperbola whose focal axis is tilted.

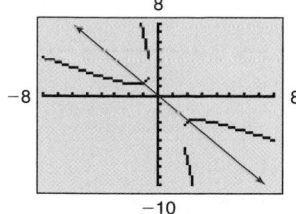

Figure 11.4-7

The Discriminant

The following fact makes it easy to identify the graphs of second-degree equations without graphing.

Graphs of Second-Degree Equations

> The graph of the equation
>
> $Ax^2 + Bxy + Cy^2 + Dx + Ey + F = 0$, with A, B, C not all zero,
>
> • is a circle, an ellipse, or a point, if $B^2 - 4AC < 0$
> • is a parabola, a line, or two parallel lines, if $B^2 - 4AC = 0$
> • is a hyperbola or two intersecting lines, if $B^2 - 4AC > 0$
>
> The expression $B^2 - 4AC$ is called the discriminant.

Example 8   Identify a Conic

Identify the graph of $2x^2 - 4xy + 3y^2 + 5x + 6y - 8 = 0$ and confirm your conclusions by graphing.

Solution

Compute the discriminant with $A = 2$, $B = -4$, and $C = 3$.

$$B^2 - 4AC = (-4)^2 - 4 \cdot 2 \cdot 3 = 16 - 24 = -8$$

Hence, the graph is an ellipse, a circle, or a single point. Use the quadratic formula to solve for y.

$$3y^2 + (-4x + 6)y + (2x^2 + 5x - 8) = 0$$

Graph both solutions on the same screen, as shown in Figure 11.4–8.

$$y = \frac{-(-4x + 6) \pm \sqrt{(-4x + 6)^2 - 4 \cdot 3 \cdot (2x^2 + 5x - 8)}}{2 \cdot 3}$$

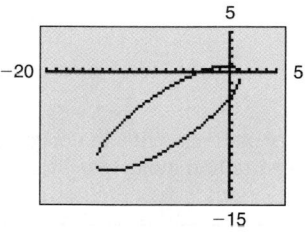

Figure 11.4-8

ADDITIONAL EXAMPLES

Example 8

Identify the graph of
$3x^2 + 4xy - 2y^2 - x + 2y - 4 = 0$
and confirm your conclusions by graphing.
$A = 3$, $B = 4$, and $C = -2$
discriminant:
$B^2 - 4AC = 4^2 - 4(3)(-2) = 16 + 24$
        $= 40$

Since $40 > 0$, the conic is a hyperbola or two intersecting lines. Use the quadratic formula to solve for y:

$$3x^2 + 4xy - 2y^2 - x + 2y - 4 = 0$$
$$-2y^2 + 4xy + 2y + 3x^2 - x - 4 = 0$$
$$-2y^2 + (4x + 2)y + (3x^2 - x - 4) = 0$$
$$y = \frac{-(4x + 2) \pm \sqrt{(4x + 2)^2 - 4(-2)(3x^2 - x - 4)}}{2(-2)}$$

Real-World Application

Example 10 on page 724 is a real-world application that uses hyperbolas. It is about a long range navigation system called LORAN. LORAN is used to determine locations of vessels at sea. For example, navigators of deep sea fishing vessels use LORAN to help them repeatedly return to the most fertile fishing waters. However, the LORAN system has limitations. The Global Positioning System (GPS), a network of 24 solar-powered satellites, is another commonly used navigation and location tool, particularly in military and high-tech applications. Have students research and compare the functioning and capabilities of GPS and LORAN.

Example 9

Identify the graph of
$15x^2 + 11xy + 2y^2 + y + 3 = 0$,
and sketch a complete graph.
The discriminant of the equation is

$B^2 - 4AC = 11^2 - 4(15)(2)$

$= 121 - 120 = 1$,

so the graph is a hyperbola. Write the
equation in quadratic form in y:

$2y^2 + 11xy + y + 15x^2 + 3 = 0$

$2y^2 + (11x + 1)y + (15x^2 + 3) = 0$

Solve using the quadratic formula:

$y = \frac{-(11x + 1) \pm \sqrt{(11x + 1)^2 - 4(2)(15x^2 + 3)}}{2(2)}$

Graph in a standard viewing window:

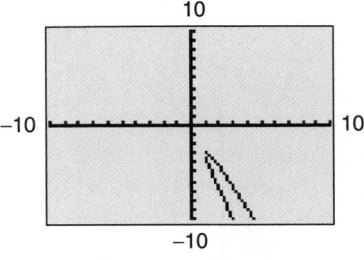

The graph must be either a hyperbola
or two intersecting lines, so the graph
in the standard viewing widow is
incomplete.

A larger window shows that it is a
hyperbola:

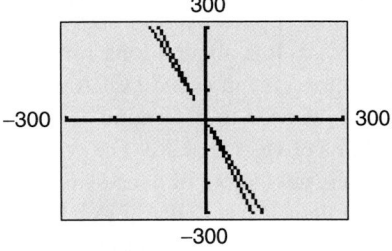

Example 10

Three LORAN transmission stations
(B, A, and C) are located 400 miles
apart in a straight line along a coast,
transmitting signals that travel at a
rate of 980 feet per microsecond.
Each station transmits a signal at
the same instant to a ship S that is
located offshore. The ship receives the
signal from station A first. It receives
the signal from C 792 microseconds
after receiving it from A. It receives
the signal from B 1056 microseconds
after receiving it from A. Determine
the ship's location.

Figure 11.4-9a

Figure 11.4-9b

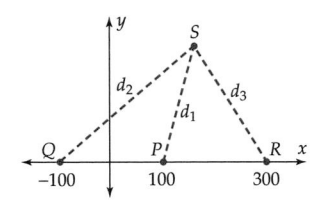

Figure 11.4-10

Example 9   Use the Discriminant

Identify the graph of $3x^2 + 5xy + 2y^2 - 8y - 1 = 0$, and sketch a complete graph.

Solution

The discriminant of the equation is $B^2 - 4AC = 5^2 - 4 \cdot 3 \cdot 2 = 1$. So the graph is a hyperbola—or two intersecting lines in the degenerate case.

To graph the equation, write the equation in quadratic form in y.

$$3x^2 + 5xy + 2y^2 - 8y - 1 = 0$$
$$2y^2 + 5xy - 8y + 3x^2 - 1 = 0$$
$$2y^2 + (5x - 8)y + (3x^2 - 1) = 0$$

Then use the quadratic formula to solve for y.

$$y = \frac{-(5x - 8) \pm \sqrt{(5x - 8)^2 - 4 \cdot 2 \cdot (3x^2 - 1)}}{4}$$

Graphing these two functions in the standard window produces Figure 11.4-9a, which looks like a parabola. This cannot be correct: because the discriminant is positive, the graph must be a hyperbola. A different viewing window is needed for a complete graph of this hyperbola, which is shown in Figure 11.4-9b. ∎

Applications

The long-range navigation system (LORAN) uses hyperbolas to enable a ship to determine its exact location by radio, as illustrated in the following example.

Example 10   LORAN Application

Three LORAN radio transmitters Q, P, and R are located 200 miles apart along a straight line and simultaneously transmit signals at regular intervals. These signals travel at a speed of 980 feet per microsecond, the speed of light. Ship S receives a signal from P and, 528 microseconds later, a signal from Q. It also receives a signal from R 305 microseconds after the one from P. Determine the ship's location.

Solution

Let the x-axis be the line through the LORAN stations, with the origin located midway between Q and P, so that the situation looks like Figure 11.4-10. If the signal takes t microseconds to go from P to S, then

$$d_1 = 980t \qquad \text{and} \qquad d_2 = 980(t + 528)$$

so that

$$|d_1 - d_2| = |980t - 980(t + 528)| = 980 \cdot 528 = 517{,}440 \text{ feet.}$$

Let the x-axis be the line through the LORAN
stations, with the origin midway between B and
A, so that the coordinates of B, A, and C are
$(-200, 0)$, $(200, 0)$, and $(600, 0)$ respectively.

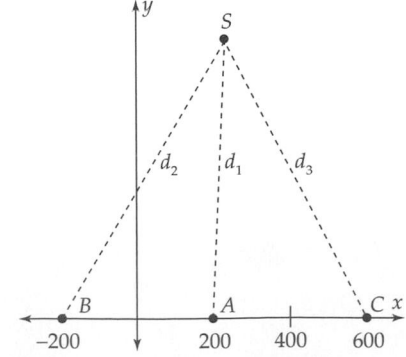

continued from page 724

Since one mile is 5280 feet,

$$|d_1 - d_2| = \frac{517{,}440}{5280} = 98 \text{ miles.}$$

In other words,

$$|(\text{distance from } P \text{ to } S) - (\text{distance from } Q \text{ to } S)| = 98 \text{ miles.}$$

This is the definition of a hyperbola given in Section 11.2; thus, S is on the hyperbola with foci $P = (100, 0)$ and $Q = (-100, 0)$ and distance difference $r = 98$. This hyperbola has an equation of the form

$$\frac{x^2}{a^2} - \frac{y^2}{b^2} = 1,$$

where $(-a, 0)$ are the vertices, $(-c, 0) = (-100, 0)$ are the foci and $c^2 = a^2 + b^2$.

Figure 11.4-11 and the fact that the vertex $(a, 0)$ is on the hyperbola show that

$$|[\text{distance from } P \text{ to } (a, 0)] - [\text{distance } Q \text{ to } (a, 0)]| = r = 98$$
$$|(100 - a) - (100 + a)| = 98$$
$$|-2a| = 98$$
$$|a| = 49$$

Consequently, $a^2 = 49^2 = 2401$ and $b^2 = c^2 - a^2 = 100^2 - 49^2 = 7599$. Thus, the ship lies on the hyperbola

$$\frac{x^2}{2401} - \frac{y^2}{7599} = 1. \qquad [2]$$

A similar argument using P and R as foci shows that the ship also lies on the hyperbola with foci $P = (100, 0)$ and $R = (300, 0)$ and center $(200, 0)$, whose distance difference r is

$$|d_1 - d_3| = 980 \cdot 305 = 298{,}900 \text{ feet} \approx 56.61 \text{ miles.}$$

As before, you can verify that $a = \dfrac{56.61}{2} = 28.305$ and $a^2 = 28.305^2 = 801.17$. This hyperbola has center $(200, 0)$ and its foci are $(200 - c, k) = (100, 0)$ and $(200 + c, k) = (300, 0)$, which implies that $c = 100$.

$$b^2 = c^2 - a^2 = 100^2 - 801.17 = 9198.83$$

The ship also lies on the hyperbola

$$\frac{(x - 200)^2}{801.17} - \frac{y^2}{9198.83} = 1. \qquad [3]$$

Since the ship lies on both hyperbolas, its coordinates are solutions of both equations [2] and [3]. They can be found algebraically by solving each of the equations for y^2, setting the results equal, and solving for x. They can be found geometrically by graphing both hyperbolas and finding the points of intersection. Since the signal from P was received first, the ship is closer to P. So it is located at the point S in Figure 11.4-12 or at the intersection point directly below it. A graphical intersection finder shows that point S is at approximately $(130.48, 215.14)$, where the coordinates are in miles from the origin.

Figure 11.4-11

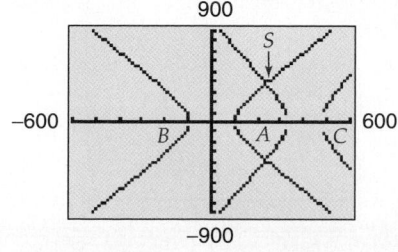

Figure 11.4-12

If the signal takes t microseconds to go from A to S, then $d_1 = 980t$ and $d_2 = 980(t + 1056)$.

$$|d_1 - d_2| = |980t - 980(t + 1056)|$$
$$= 980 \cdot 1056 = 1{,}034{,}880 \text{ feet, or}$$

$1{,}034{,}880 \div 5{,}280 = 196$ miles.

So, $|(\text{distance from } A \text{ to } S) - (\text{distance from } B \text{ to } S)| = 196$ miles, and S lies on the hyperbola with foci at $B = (-200, 0)$ and $A = (200, 0)$.

The hyperbola has an equation of the form $\dfrac{x^2}{a^2} - \dfrac{y^2}{b^2} = 1$.

The vertex $(a, 0)$ lies on the hyperbola with foci

$(-200, 0)$ and $(200, 0)$,

$$|[\text{distance from } (200, 0) \text{ to } (a, 0)]$$
$$- [\text{distance from } (-200, 0) \text{ to } (a, 0)]|$$
$$= 196$$

$$|(200 - a) - (200 + a)| = 196$$
$$|200 - a - 200 - a| = 196$$
$$|-2a| = 196$$
$$|a| = 98$$

$$a^2 = 98^2 = 9604$$
$$b^2 = c^2 - a^2$$
$$b^2 = 200^2 - 98^2$$
$$b^2 = 30{,}396$$

So, the ship lies on the hyperbola given by $\dfrac{x^2}{9604} - \dfrac{y^2}{30{,}396} = 1$.

Using A and C as foci shows that the ship also lies on the hyperbola with foci $A = (200, 0)$, and $C = (600, 0)$ and center $(400, 0)$ whose distance difference r is

$$|d_1 - d_3| = 980 \cdot 792 = 776{,}160 \text{ feet}$$
$$= 147 \text{ miles.}$$

As before, $a = \dfrac{147}{2} = 73.5$ and $a^2 = (73.5)^2 = 5402.25$. This hyperbola has center $(400, 0)$ and its foci are $(400 - c, k) = (200, 0)$ and $(400 + c, k) = (600, 0)$, so $c = 200$.

$$b^2 = c^2 - a^2 = 200^2 - 5402.25$$
$$= 34{,}597.75$$

The ship also lies on the hyperbola given by $\dfrac{(x - 400)^2}{5402.25} - \dfrac{y^2}{34{,}597.75} = 1$.

The intersection of the hyperbolas is at approximately $(233.72, 377.47)$, where the coordinates are in miles from the origin.

Exercises 11.4

ANSWERS

1. $\dfrac{(x-2)^2}{4} + \dfrac{(y-3)^2}{16} = 1$

2. $\dfrac{(x+5)^2}{25} + \dfrac{(y-2)^2}{225} = 1$

3. $\dfrac{4(x-7)^2}{25} + \dfrac{(y+4)^2}{36} = 1$

4. $\dfrac{4(x+3)^2}{225} + \dfrac{4(y+9)^2}{49} = 1$

5. $\dfrac{(y-3)^2}{4} - \dfrac{(x+2)^2}{6} = 1$

6. $\dfrac{(x+5)^2}{4} - \dfrac{(y-1)^2}{16} = 1$

7. $\dfrac{(x-4)^2}{9} - \dfrac{(y-2)^2}{16} = 1$

8. $\dfrac{(y+5)^2}{25} - \dfrac{(x+3)^2}{36} = 1$

23.

24.

25.

26.
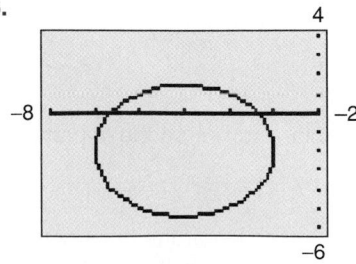

Exercises 11.4

In Exercises 1–16, find the equation of the conic sections satisfying the given conditions.

1. ellipse with center $(2, 3)$; endpoints of major and minor axes: $(2, -1), (0, 3), (2, 7), (4, 3)$

2. ellipse with center $(-5, 2)$ endpoints of major and minor axes: $(0, 2), (-5, 17), (-10, 2), (-5, -13)$

3. ellipse with center $(7, -4)$ foci on the line $x = 7$; major axis of length 12; minor axis of length 5

4. ellipse with center $(-3, -9)$; foci on the line $y = -9$; major axis of length 15; minor axis of length 7

5. hyperbola with center $(-2, 3)$; vertex $(-2, 1)$; passing through $\left(-2 + 3\sqrt{10}, 11\right)$

6. hyperbola with center $(-5, 1)$; vertex $(-3, 1)$; passing through $\left(-1, 1 - 4\sqrt{3}\right)$

7. hyperbola with center $(4, 2)$; vertex $(7, 2)$; asymptote $3y = 4x - 10$

8. hyperbola with center $(-3, -5)$; vertex $(-3, 0)$; asymptote $6y = 5x - 15$

9. parabola with vertex $(1, 0)$; axis $x = 1$; passing through $(2, 13)$ $\quad y = 13(x - 1)^2$

10. parabola with vertex $(-3, 0)$; axis $y = 0$; passing through $(-1, 1)$ $\quad x + 3 = 2y^2$

11. parabola with vertex $(2, 1)$; axis $y = 1$; passing through $(5, 0)$ $\quad x - 2 = 3(y - 1)^2$

12. parabola with vertex $(1, -3)$; axis $y = -3$; passing through $(-1, -4)$ $\quad x - 1 = -2(y + 3)^2$

13. ellipse with center $(3, -2)$; passing through $(3, -6)$ and $(9, -2)$ $\quad \dfrac{(x-3)^2}{36} + \dfrac{(y+2)^2}{16} = 1$

14. ellipse with center $(2, 5)$; passing through $(2, 4)$ and $(-3, 5)$ $\quad \dfrac{(x-2)^2}{25} + \dfrac{(y-5)^2}{1} = 1$

15. parabola with vertex $(-3, -2)$ and focus $\left(-\dfrac{47}{16}, -2\right)$ $\quad x + 3 = 4(y + 2)^2$

16. parabola with vertex $(-5, -5)$ and focus $\left(-5, -\dfrac{99}{20}\right)$ $\quad y + 5 = 5(x + 5)^2$

In Exercises 17–22, assume that the graph of the equation is a nondegenerate conic section. Without graphing, determine whether the graph is a circle, ellipse, hyperbola, or parabola.

17. $x^2 - 2xy + 3y^2 - 1 = 0$
ellipse

18. $xy - 1 = 0$
hyperbola

19. $x^2 + 2xy + y^2 + 2\sqrt{2}x - 2\sqrt{2}y = 0$
parabola

20. $2x^2 - 4xy + 5y^2 - 6 = 0$
ellipse

21. $17x^2 - 48xy + 31y^2 + 50 = 0$
hyperbola

22. $2x^2 - 4xy - 2y^2 + 3x + 5y - 10 = 0$
hyperbola

In Exercises 23–34, sketch a complete graph of each conic section.

23. $\dfrac{(x-1)^2}{4} + \dfrac{(y-5)^2}{9} = 1$

24. $\dfrac{(x-2)^2}{16} + \dfrac{(y+3)^2}{12} = 1$

25. $\dfrac{(x+1)^2}{16} + \dfrac{(y-4)^2}{8} = 1$

26. $\dfrac{(x+5)^2}{4} + \dfrac{(y+2)^2}{12} = 1$

27. $y = 4(x - 1)^2 + 2$ 28. $y = 3(x - 2)^2 - 3$

29. $x = 2(y - 2)^2$ 30. $x = -3(y - 1)^2 - 2$

31. $\dfrac{(y+3)^2}{25} - \dfrac{(x+1)^2}{16} = 1$

32. $\dfrac{(y+1)^2}{9} - \dfrac{(x-1)^2}{25} = 1$

33. $\dfrac{(x+3)^2}{1} - \dfrac{(y-2)^2}{4} = 1$

34. $\dfrac{(y+5)^2}{9} - \dfrac{(x-2)^2}{1} = 1$

In Exercises 35–52, use the discriminant to identify the conic section whose equation is given, and find a viewing window that shows a complete graph.
35–52. Viewing windows may vary.

35. $9x^2 + 4y^2 + 54x - 8y + 49 = 0$
ellipse; $-6 \le x \le 3$, $-2 \le y \le 4$

36. $4x^2 + 5y^2 - 8x + 30y + 29 = 0$
ellipse; $-3 \le x \le 5$, $-6 \le y \le 0$

27.

28.
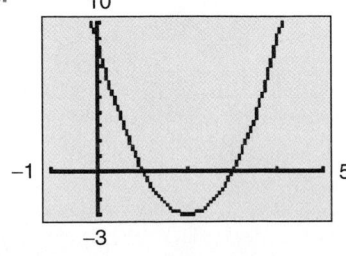

29–34. See p. 1075.

37. $4y^2 - x^2 + 6x - 24y + 11 = 0$
hyperbola; $-7 \leq x \leq 13$, $-3 \leq y \leq 9$

38. $x^2 - 16y^2 = 0$ **two lines intersecting at the origin; $-10 \leq x \leq 10$, $-10 \leq y \leq 10$**

39. $3y^2 - x - 2y + 1 = 0$
parabola; $-1 \leq x \leq 8$, $-3 \leq y \leq 3$

40. $x^2 - 6x + y + 5 = 0$
parabola; $-5 \leq x \leq 10$, $-10 \leq y \leq 7$

41. $41x^2 - 24xy + 34y^2 - 25 = 0$
ellipse; $-1.5 \leq x \leq 1.5$, $-1 \leq y \leq 1$

42. $x^2 + 2\sqrt{3}xy + 3y^2 + 8\sqrt{3}x - 8y + 32 = 0$
parabola; $-20 \leq x \leq 0$, $-4 \leq y \leq 20$

43. $17x^2 - 48xy + 31y^2 + 49 = 0$
hyperbola; $-15 \leq x \leq 15$, $-10 \leq y \leq 10$

44. $52x^2 - 72xy + 73y^2 = 200$
ellipse; $-3 \leq x \leq 3$, $-3 \leq y \leq 3$

45. $9x^2 + 24xy + 16y^2 + 90x - 130y = 0$
parabola; $-19 \leq x \leq 2$, $-1 \leq y \leq 13$

46. $x^2 + 10xy + y^2 + 1 = 0$
hyperbola; $-3 \leq x \leq 3$, $-3 \leq y \leq 3$

47. $23x^2 + 26\sqrt{3}xy - 3y^2 - 16x + 16\sqrt{3}y + 128 = 0$
hyperbola; $-15 \leq x \leq 15$, $-15 \leq y \leq 15$

48. $x^2 + 2xy + y^2 + 12\sqrt{2}x - 12\sqrt{2}y = 0$
parabola; $-20 \leq x \leq 4$, $-4 \leq y \leq 20$

49. $17x^2 - 12xy + 8y^2 - 80 = 0$
ellipse; $-6 \leq x \leq 6$, $-4 \leq y \leq 4$

50. $11x^2 - 24xy + 4y^2 + 30x + 40y - 45 = 0$
hyperbola; $-20 \leq x \leq 20$, $-20 \leq y \leq 20$

51. $3x^2 + 2\sqrt{3}xy + y^2 + 4x - 4\sqrt{3}y - 16 = 0$
parabola; $-9 \leq x \leq 4$, $-2 \leq y \leq 10$

52. $3x^2 + 2\sqrt{2}xy + 2y^2 - 12 = 0$
ellipse; $-3 \leq x \leq 3$, $-3 \leq y \leq 3$

In Exercises 53 and 54, find the equations of two distinct ellipses satisfying the given conditions.

53. Center at $(-5, 3)$; major axis of length 14; minor axis of length 8.

54. Center at $(2, -6)$; major axis of length 15; minor axis of length 6.

55. *Critical Thinking* Show that the asymptotes of the hyperbola $\dfrac{x^2}{a^2} - \dfrac{y^2}{a^2} = 1$ are perpendicular to each other.

56. Find a number k such that $(-2, 1)$ is on the graph of $3x^2 + ky^2 = 4$. Then graph the equation.

57. Find the number b such that the vertex of the parabola $y = x^2 + bx + c$ lies on the y-axis.
$b = 0$

58. Find the number d such that the parabola $(y + 1)^2 = dx + 4$ passes through $(-6, 3)$.
$d = -2$

59. Find the points of intersection of the parabola $4y^2 + 4y = 5x - 12$ and the line $x = 9$.
$\left(9, -\dfrac{1}{2} - \dfrac{1}{2}\sqrt{34}\right)$

60. Find the points of intersection of the parabola $4x^2 - 8x = 2y + 5$ and the line $y = 15$.
$\left(1 - \dfrac{\sqrt{39}}{2}, 15\right)$

In Exercises 61–64, write the resulting equation in standard form.

61. Translate the hyperbola defined by the equation $3y^2 + 20x = 23 + 5x^2 + 12y$ up 3 units and to the right 5 units. $\dfrac{(y - 5)^2}{5} - \dfrac{(x - 7)^2}{3} = 1$

62. Translate the hyperbola defined by the equation $16x^2 - 9y^2 + 64x = 89 - 18y$ down 2 units and to the right 3 units. $\dfrac{(x - 1)^2}{9} - \dfrac{(y + 1)^2}{16} = 1$

63. Translate the hyperbola defined by the equation $4x^2 - 9y^2 - 8x + 54y = 113$ up 1 unit and to the left 4 units. $\dfrac{(x + 3)^2}{9} - \dfrac{(y - 4)^2}{4} = 1$

64. Translate the hyperbola defined by the equation $7x^2 - 5y^2 = 48 - 20y - 14x$ down 5 units and to the left 4 units. $\dfrac{(x + 5)^2}{5} - \dfrac{(y + 3)^2}{7} = 1$

65. Suppose a golf ball driven off the tee travels 210 yards down the fairway. During flight it reaches a maximum height of 55 yards. Find an equation that describes the ball's parabolic path if the tee is at the origin and the positive x-axis is along the ground in the direction of the drive. $(x - 105)^2 = -200.45(y - 55)$

66. Suppose a golf ball driven off the tee travels 175 yards down the fairway. During flight it reaches a maximum height of 40 yards. Find an equation that describes the ball's parabolic path if the tee is at the origin and the positive x-axis is along the ground in the direction of the drive. $(x - 87.5)^2 = -191.4(y - 40)$

67. Two listening stations 1 mile apart record an explosion. One microphone receives the sound 2 seconds after the other does. Use the line through the microphones as the x-axis, with the origin midway between the microphones, and the fact that sound travels at 1100 feet/second to find the equation of the hyperbola on which the explosion is located. Can you determine the exact location of the explosion?

68. Two transmission stations P and Q are located 200 miles apart on a straight shoreline. A ship 50 miles from shore is moving parallel to the shoreline. A signal from Q reaches the ship 400 microseconds after a signal from P. If the signals travel at 980 feet per microsecond, find the location of the ship (in terms of miles) in the coordinate system with x-axis through P and Q, and origin midway between them.

53. $\dfrac{(x + 5)^2}{49} + \dfrac{(y - 3)^2}{16} = 1$;
$\dfrac{(x + 5)^2}{16} + \dfrac{(y - 3)^2}{49} = 1$

54. $\dfrac{(x - 2)^2}{\left(\dfrac{15}{2}\right)^2} + \dfrac{(y + 6)^2}{3^2} = 1$;
$\dfrac{(x - 2)^2}{3^2} + \dfrac{(y + 6)^2}{\left(\dfrac{15}{2}\right)^2} = 1$

55. The asymptotes of $\dfrac{x^2}{a^2} - \dfrac{y^2}{a^2} = 1$ are $y = \pm\dfrac{a}{a}x$ or $y = \pm x$, with slopes $+1$ and -1. Since $(+1)(-1) = -1$, these lines are perpendicular.

56. $k = -8$

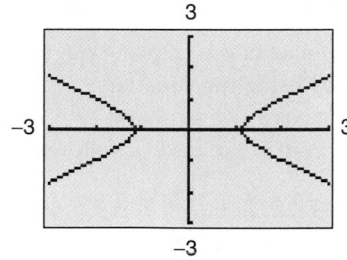

67. $\dfrac{x^2}{1{,}210{,}000} - \dfrac{y^2}{5{,}759{,}600} = 1$
(measurement in feet). The exact location cannot be determined from the given information.

68. $\dfrac{x^2}{(37.12)^2} - \dfrac{y^2}{(92.85)^2} = 1$
(measurement in miles). The ship is at the point $(42.16, 50)$.

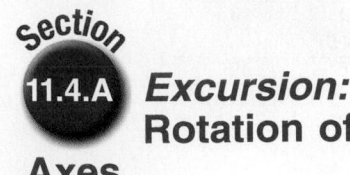

Section 11.4.A Excursion: Rotation of Axes

Math Background

After the information about centers, vertices, etc. is obtained in the uv system, the information can be expressed in the xy system using the Rotation Equations. For example, consider the parabola in **Example 1.**

Its focus in the uv plane is at $\left(0, \frac{1}{8}\right)$.

The focus in the xy plane can be found using the equations $x = u \cos \theta - v \sin \theta$ and $y = u \sin \theta + v \cos \theta$ as follows.

Using $\theta = \frac{\pi}{6}$, $u = 0$, and $v = \frac{1}{8}$:

$x = u \cos \theta - v \sin \theta \quad | \quad y = u \sin \theta + v \cos \theta$

$x = 0\left(\frac{\sqrt{3}}{2}\right) - \frac{1}{8}\left(\frac{1}{2}\right) \quad | \quad y = 0\left(\frac{1}{2}\right) + \frac{1}{8}\left(\frac{\sqrt{3}}{2}\right)$

$x = -\frac{1}{16} \quad \left| \quad y = \frac{\sqrt{3}}{16}\right.$

So, the focus in the xy plane is $\left(-\frac{1}{16}, \frac{\sqrt{3}}{16}\right)$.

Teaching Notes

After discussing how to derive the first equation in **The Rotation Equations** box, have students derive the second equation.

$y = r \sin(\theta + \beta)$
$\quad = r(\sin \theta \cos \beta + \cos \theta \sin \beta)$
$\quad = (r \cos \beta) \sin \theta + (r \sin \beta) \cos \theta$
$\quad = u \sin \theta + v \cos \theta$

Example Notes

Some steps are omitted on page 730 for **Example 1,** but all steps are included for **Additional Example 1.**

Excursion: Rotation of Axes

Objectives

- Write the equation of a rotated conic section in terms of u and v
- Determine the angle of rotation of a rotated conic section

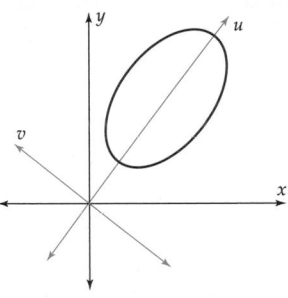

Figure 11.4.A-1

The graph of an equation of the form

$$Ax^2 + Bxy + Cy^2 + Dx + Ey + F = 0,$$

with $B \neq 0$, is a conic section that is rotated so that its axes are not parallel to the coordinate axes, as in Figure 11.4.A-1. Although the graph is readily obtained with a calculator, as in Examples 7–9 of Section 11.4, useful information about the center, vertices, etc., cannot be read directly from the equation, as it can be with an equation in standard form. However, if the xy coordinate system is replaced by a new coordinate system, as indicated by the blue uv axes in Figure 11.4.A-1, then the conic is not rotated in the new system and has a uv equation in standard form that will provide the desired information.

Rotation Equations

In order to use this approach, first determine the relationship between the xy coordinates of a point and its coordinates in the uv system. Suppose the uv coordinate system is obtained by rotating the xy axes about the origin, counterclockwise through an angle θ. If a point P has coordinates (x, y) in the xy system, its coordinates (u, v) can be found in the rotated coordinate system by using Figure 11.4.A-2.

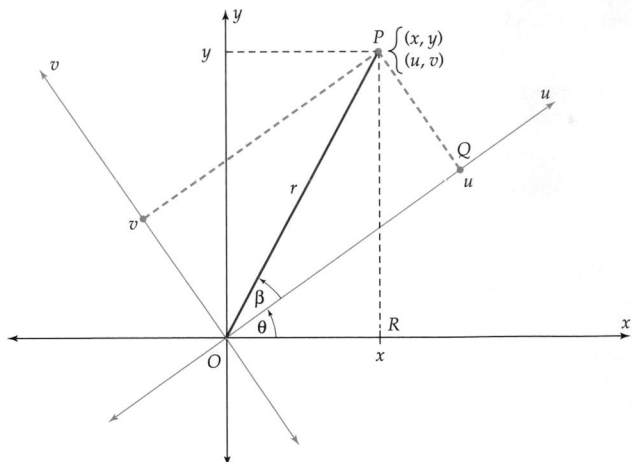

Figure 11.4.A-2

Triangle OPQ shows that

$$\cos \beta = \frac{OQ}{OP} = \frac{u}{r} \quad \text{and} \quad \sin \beta = \frac{PQ}{OP} = \frac{v}{r}$$

Therefore,

$$u = r \cos \beta \quad \text{and} \quad v = r \sin \beta$$

Similarly, triangle OPR shows that

$$\cos(\theta + \beta) = \frac{OR}{OP} = \frac{x}{r} \quad \text{and} \quad \sin(\theta + \beta) = \frac{PR}{OP} = \frac{y}{r}$$

so that

$$x = r \cos(\theta + \beta) \quad \text{and} \quad y = r \sin(\theta + \beta)$$

Applying the addition identity for cosine shows that

$$\begin{aligned} x &= r \cos(\theta + \beta) \\ &= r(\cos \theta \cos \beta - \sin \theta \sin \beta) \\ &= (r \cos \beta)\cos \theta - (r \sin \beta)\sin \theta \\ &= u \cos \theta - v \sin \theta \end{aligned}$$

A similar argument with $y = r \sin(\theta + \beta)$ and the addition identity for sine leads to the following result.

The Rotation Equations

> If the xy coordinate axes are rotated through an angle θ to produce the uv coordinate axes, then the coordinates (x, y) and (u, v) of a point are related by the following equations.
>
> $$x = u \cos \theta - v \sin \theta$$
> $$y = u \sin \theta + v \cos \theta$$

Example 1 A Rotated Conic in the uv System

If the xy axes are rotated $\frac{\pi}{6}$ radians, find the equation relative to the uv axes of the graph of

$$3x^2 + 2\sqrt{3}xy + y^2 + x - \sqrt{3}y = 0$$

Identify and graph the equation.

Solution

NOTE Recall that $\frac{\pi}{6}$ represents about 0.5236 radians, or 30°.

Because $\sin \frac{\pi}{6} = \frac{1}{2}$ and $\cos \frac{\pi}{6} = \frac{\sqrt{3}}{2}$, the rotation equations are

$$x = u \cos \frac{\pi}{6} - v \sin \frac{\pi}{6} = \frac{\sqrt{3}}{2}u - \frac{1}{2}v$$

$$y = u \sin \frac{\pi}{6} + v \cos \frac{\pi}{6} = \frac{1}{2}u + \frac{\sqrt{3}}{2}v$$

ADDITIONAL EXAMPLES

Example 1

If the xy axes are rotated $\frac{\pi}{3}$ radians, find the equation relative to the uv axes of the graph of $x^2 + 2\sqrt{3}xy + 3y^2 + 2\sqrt{3}x - 2y = 0$. Identify and graph the equation.

$\sin \frac{\pi}{3} = \frac{\sqrt{3}}{2}$ and $\cos \frac{\pi}{3} = \frac{1}{2}$, so the rotation equations are:

$$x = u \cos \theta - v \sin \theta = \frac{1}{2}u - \frac{\sqrt{3}}{2}v$$

$$y = u \sin \theta + v \cos \theta = \frac{\sqrt{3}}{2}u + \frac{1}{2}v$$

When rotated into the uv plane, the equation

$$x^2 + 2\sqrt{3}xy + 3y^2 + 2\sqrt{3}x - 2y = 0$$

becomes

$$\left(\frac{1}{2}u - \frac{\sqrt{3}}{2}v\right)^2$$

$$+ 2\sqrt{3}\left(\frac{1}{2}u - \frac{\sqrt{3}}{2}v\right)\left(\frac{\sqrt{3}}{2}u + \frac{1}{2}v\right)$$

$$+ 3\left(\frac{\sqrt{3}}{2}u + \frac{1}{2}v\right)^2 + 2\sqrt{3}\left(\frac{1}{2}u - \frac{\sqrt{3}}{2}v\right)$$

$$- 2\left(\frac{\sqrt{3}}{2}u + \frac{1}{2}v\right) = 0$$

$$\frac{1}{4}u^2 - \frac{\sqrt{3}}{2}uv + \frac{3}{4}v^2$$

$$+ 2\sqrt{3}\left(\frac{\sqrt{3}}{4}u^2 - \frac{1}{2}uv - \frac{\sqrt{3}}{4}v^2\right)$$

$$+ 3\left(\frac{3}{4}u^2 + \frac{\sqrt{3}}{2}uv + \frac{1}{4}v^2\right)$$

$$+ 2\sqrt{3}\left(\frac{1}{2}u - \frac{\sqrt{3}}{2}v\right)$$

$$- 2\left(\frac{\sqrt{3}}{2}u + \frac{1}{2}v\right) = 0$$

The left side can be simplified as follows:

$$\frac{1}{4}u^2 - \frac{\sqrt{3}}{2}uv + \frac{3}{4}v^2$$

$$+\frac{3}{2}u^2 - \sqrt{3}uv - \frac{3}{2}v^2$$

$$+\frac{9}{4}u^2 + \frac{3\sqrt{3}}{2}uv + \frac{3}{4}v^2$$

$$+ \sqrt{3}u - 3v$$

$$- \sqrt{3}u - v$$

$$\overline{4u^2 \quad + 0v \quad + 0v^2 + \quad 0u - 4v}$$

So, the simplified equation is:

$$4u^2 - 4v = 0$$

$$u^2 = v$$

The graph is a parabola in the uv plane with vertex at $(0, 0)$, focus at $\left(0, \frac{1}{4}\right)$, and directrix $v = -\frac{1}{4}$.

Example Notes

Another way to find θ in **Example 2** is shown below:

$\cot 2\theta = \dfrac{7}{2}$, so $\dfrac{1}{\tan 2\theta} = \dfrac{7}{24}$, and

$\tan 2\theta = \dfrac{24}{7}$. Use the TAN^{-1} key on a calculator to find $2\theta \approx 73.74°$, so $\theta \approx 36.87°$.

ADDITIONAL EXAMPLES

Example 2

What angle of rotation will eliminate the xy term in the equation $73x^2 - 72xy + 52y^2 + 420x - 440y + 900 = 0$, and what are the rotation equations?

Let $A = 73$, $B = -72$, and $C = 52$. The figure should be rotated through an angle θ such that

$$\cot 2\theta = \frac{A - C}{B} = \frac{73 - 52}{-72} = \frac{21}{-72}$$
$$= -\frac{7}{24}.$$

Because $0 < 2\theta < \pi$ and $\cot 2\theta$ is negative, the terminal side of the angle 2θ must lie in the second quadrant, as shown below.

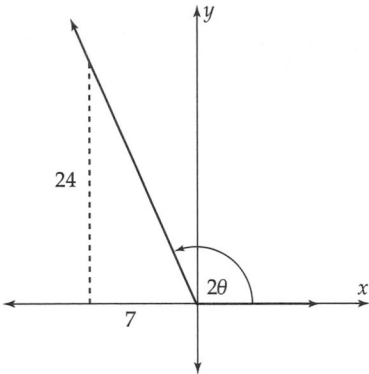

The hypotenuse has length 25.
$\cos 2\theta = -\dfrac{7}{25}$. Use half-angle identities to find $\sin \theta$ and $\cos \theta$:

$$\sin \theta = \sqrt{\frac{1 - \cos 2\theta}{2}} = \sqrt{\frac{1 - \left(-\frac{7}{25}\right)}{2}}$$
$$= \sqrt{\frac{16}{25}} = \frac{4}{5}$$

$$\cos \theta = \sqrt{\frac{1 + \cos 2\theta}{2}} = \sqrt{\frac{1 + \left(-\frac{7}{25}\right)}{2}}$$
$$= \sqrt{\frac{9}{25}} = \frac{3}{5}$$

$\sin^{-1}\dfrac{4}{5} \approx 0.9273$ radians, or about 53.13°.

Substitute these expressions into the original equation.

$$3x^2 + 2\sqrt{3}xy + y^2 + x - \sqrt{3}y = 0$$

$$3\left(\frac{\sqrt{3}}{2}u - \frac{1}{2}v\right)^2 + 2\sqrt{3}\left(\frac{\sqrt{3}}{2}u - \frac{1}{2}v\right)\left(\frac{1}{2}u + \frac{\sqrt{3}}{2}v\right)$$

$$+ \left(\frac{1}{2}u + \frac{\sqrt{3}}{2}v\right)^2 + \left(\frac{\sqrt{3}}{2}u - \frac{1}{2}v\right) - \sqrt{3}\left(\frac{1}{2}u + \frac{\sqrt{3}}{2}v\right) = 0$$

Then multiply out the result.

$$3\left(\frac{3}{4}u^2 - \frac{\sqrt{3}}{2}uv + \frac{1}{4}v^2\right) + 2\sqrt{3}\left(\frac{\sqrt{3}}{4}u^2 + \frac{1}{2}uv - \frac{\sqrt{3}}{4}v^2\right)$$

$$+ \left(\frac{1}{4}u^2 + \frac{\sqrt{3}}{2}uv + \frac{3}{4}v^2\right) + \left(\frac{\sqrt{3}}{2}u - \frac{1}{2}v\right) - \sqrt{3}\left(\frac{1}{2}u + \frac{\sqrt{3}}{2}v\right) = 0$$

You can verify that the last equation simplifies to

$$4u^2 - 2v = 0 \qquad \text{or equivalently, } u^2 = \frac{1}{2}v = 4\left(\frac{1}{8}\right)v$$

In the uv system, $u^2 = \dfrac{1}{2}v$ is the equation of an upward-opening parabola with vertex at $(0, 0)$, focus at $\left(0, \dfrac{1}{8}\right)$, and directrix $v = -\dfrac{1}{8}$, as shown in Figure 11.4.A-3.

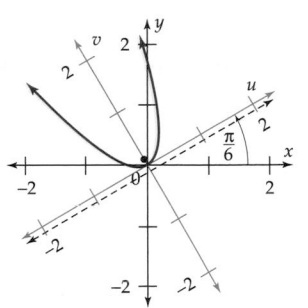

Figure 11.4.A-3

Rotation Angle to Eliminate xy Term

Rotating the axes in the preceding example changed the original equation, which included an xy term, to an equation that had no uv term. This can be done for any second-degree equation by choosing an angle of rotation that will eliminate the xy term.

Rotation Angle

> The equation $Ax^2 + Bxy + Cy^2 + Dx + Ey + F = 0$ $(B \neq 0)$ can be rewritten as $A'u^2 + C'v^2 + D'u + E'v + F = 0$ by rotating the xy axes through an angle θ such that
>
> $$\cot 2\theta = \frac{A - C}{B} \qquad \left(0 < \theta < \frac{\pi}{2}\right)$$

The restriction $0 < \theta < \dfrac{\pi}{2}$ insures that $0 < 2\theta < \pi$.

Example 2   Find the Rotation Angle

What angle of rotation will eliminate the xy term in the equation

$$153x^2 + 192xy + 97y^2 - 1710x - 1470y + 5625 = 0,$$

and what are the rotation equations?

The rotation equations are

$$x = u \cos \theta - v \sin \theta = \frac{3}{5}u - \frac{4}{5}v$$

$$y = u \sin \theta + v \cos \theta = \frac{4}{5}u + \frac{3}{5}v.$$

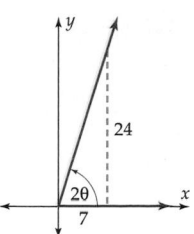

Figure 11.4.A-4

Solution

Letting $A = 153$, $B = 192$, and $C = 97$, the figure should be rotated through an angle of θ, where

$$\cot 2\theta = \frac{153 - 97}{192} = \frac{56}{192} = \frac{7}{24}$$

Because $0 < 2\theta < \pi$ and $\cot 2\theta$ is positive, the terminal side of the angle 2θ lies in the first quadrant, as shown in Figure 11.4.A-4. The hypotenuse of the triangle shown has length $\sqrt{7^2 + 24^2} = \sqrt{625} = 25$.

Hence, $\cos 2\theta = \frac{7}{25}$. The half-angle identities show that

$$\sin \theta = \sqrt{\frac{1 - \cos 2\theta}{2}} = \sqrt{\frac{1 - \frac{7}{25}}{2}} = \sqrt{\frac{9}{25}} = \frac{3}{5}$$

$$\cos \theta = \sqrt{\frac{1 + \cos 2\theta}{2}} = \sqrt{\frac{1 + \frac{7}{25}}{2}} = \sqrt{\frac{16}{25}} = \frac{4}{5}$$

Using $\sin \theta = \frac{3}{5}$ and the SIN^{-1} key on a calculator, the angle θ of rotation is approximately 0.6435 radians, or about 36.87°. The rotation equations are

$$x = u \cos \theta - v \sin \theta = \frac{4}{5}u - \frac{3}{5}v$$

$$y = u \sin \theta + v \cos \theta = \frac{3}{5}u + \frac{4}{5}v.$$

■

Identifying Rotated Conics

The rotation equations can be used to find the equation of the rotated conic in the uv coordinate system. Substitute the x rotation equation for x and the y rotation equation for y, and simplify the result to eliminate the xy term.

Example 3   Graph a Rotated Conic

Graph the equation without using a calculator.

$$153x^2 + 192xy + 97y^2 - 1710x - 1470y + 5625 = 0$$

Solution

The angle θ and the rotation equations for eliminating the xy term were found in the preceding example. Substitute the rotation equations into the given equation and simplify the result to eliminate the xy term.

Real-World Application

Graphic design often involves the placement of various figures such that the figures together form a particular image. For example, the symbol for atomic energy shown below, is a collection of four ellipses:

- 1 ellipse in standard position with major axis horizontal
- 1 ellipse, a 45° rotation of the ellipse with major axis horizontal
- 1 ellipse in standard position with major axis vertical
- 1 ellipse that is a 45° rotation of the ellipse with major axis vertical

A graphic designer may have to determine equations for each ellipse in order to create an electronic image of the symbol.

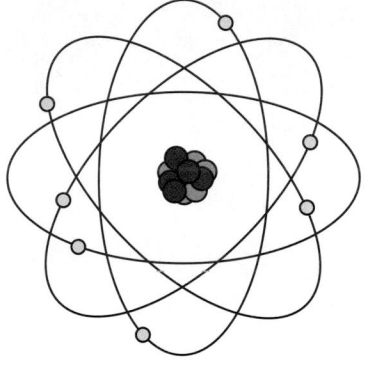

$$153x^2 + 192xy + 97y^2 - 1710x - 1470y + 5625 = 0$$

$$153\left(\frac{4}{5}u - \frac{3}{5}v\right)^2 + 192\left(\frac{4}{5}u - \frac{3}{5}v\right)\left(\frac{3}{5}u + \frac{4}{5}v\right)$$

$$+ 97\left(\frac{3}{5}u + \frac{4}{5}v\right)^2 - 1710\left(\frac{4}{5}u - \frac{3}{5}v\right) - 1470\left(\frac{3}{5}u + \frac{4}{5}v\right) + 5625 = 0$$

$$153\left(\frac{16}{25}u^2 - \frac{24}{25}uv + \frac{9}{25}v^2\right) + 192\left(\frac{12}{25}u^2 + \frac{7}{25}uv - \frac{12}{25}v^2\right)$$

$$+ 97\left(\frac{9}{25}u^2 + \frac{24}{25}uv + \frac{16}{25}v^2\right) - 2250u - 150v + 5625 = 0$$

$$225u^2 + 25v^2 - 2250u - 150v + 5625 = 0$$

$$9u^2 + v^2 - 90u - 6v + 225 = 0$$

$$9(u^2 - 10u) + (v^2 - 6v) = -225$$

Finally, complete the square in u and v by adding the appropriate amounts to the right side so as not to change the equation.

$$9(u^2 - 10u + 25) + (v^2 - 6v + 9) = -225 + 9(25) + 9$$

$$9(u - 5)^2 + (v - 3)^2 = 9$$

$$\frac{(u - 5)^2}{1} + \frac{(v - 3)^2}{9} = 1$$

Therefore, the graph is an ellipse centered at (5, 3) in the uv coordinate system, as shown in Figure 11.4.A-5.

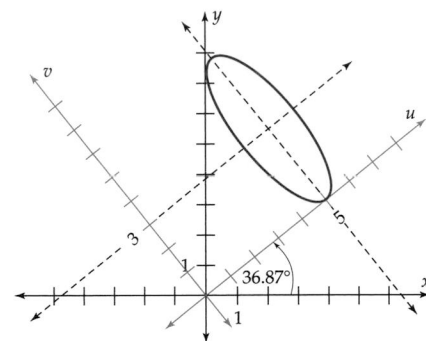

Figure 11.4.A-5

Exercises 11.4.A

ANSWERS

5. $\theta \approx 53.13°$; $x = \frac{3}{5}u - \frac{4}{5}v$;

$y = \frac{4}{5}u + \frac{3}{5}v$

6. $\theta = 60°$; $x = \frac{1}{2}u - \frac{\sqrt{3}}{2}v$;

$y = \frac{\sqrt{3}}{2}u + \frac{1}{2}v$

7. $\theta \approx 36.87°$; $x = \frac{4}{5}u - \frac{3}{5}v$;

$y = \frac{3}{5}u + \frac{4}{5}v$

8. $\theta \approx 36.87°$; $x = \frac{4}{5}u - \frac{3}{5}v$;

$y = \frac{3}{5}u + \frac{4}{5}v$

9. a. $(A\cos^2\theta + B\cos\theta\sin\theta + C\sin^2\theta)u^2 + (B\cos^2\theta - 2A\cos\theta\sin\theta + 2C\cos\theta\sin\theta - B\sin^2\theta)uv + (C\cos^2\theta - B\cos\theta\sin\theta + A\sin^2\theta)v^2 + (D\cos\theta + E\sin\theta)u + (E\cos\theta - D\sin\theta)v + F = 0$

b. $B' = B\cos^2\theta - 2A\cos\theta\sin\theta + 2C\cos\theta\sin\theta - B\sin^2\theta$
$= 2(C - A)\sin\theta\cos\theta + B(\cos^2\theta - \sin^2\theta)$ since B' is the coefficient of uv

c. Since $\sin 2\theta = 2\sin\theta\cos\theta$ and $\cos 2\theta = \cos^2\theta - \sin^2\theta$,
$B' = (C - A)\sin 2\theta + B\cos 2\theta$.

d. If $\cot 2\theta - \frac{A - C}{B}$ then $A - C = B\cot 2\theta$ and we have $B' = (-B\cot 2\theta)\sin 2\theta + B\cos 2\theta = -B\cos 2\theta + B\cos 2\theta = 0$.

Exercises 11.4.A

In Exercises 1–4, rotate the axes through the given angle to form the uv coordinate system. Express the given equation in terms of the uv coordinate system.

1. $\theta - \dfrac{\pi}{4}$; $xy - 1$ $\dfrac{u^2}{2} - \dfrac{v^2}{2} = 1$

2. $\theta = \dfrac{\pi}{4}$; $13x^2 + 10xy + 13y^2 = 72$ $\dfrac{u^2}{4} + \dfrac{v^2}{9} = 1$

3. $\theta = \dfrac{\pi}{6}$; $7x^2 - 6\sqrt{3}xy + 13y^2 - 16 = 0$ $\dfrac{u^2}{4} + v^2 = 1$

4. $\sin\theta = \dfrac{1}{\sqrt{5}}$; $x^2 - 4xy + 4y^2 + 5\sqrt{5}y + 1 = 0$
$5v^2 + 5u + 10v + 1 = 0$

In Exercises 5–8 find the angle of rotation that will eliminate the xy term of the equation and list the rotation equations in this case.

5. $41x^2 - 24xy + 34y^2 - 25 = 0$

6. $x^2 + 2\sqrt{3}xy + 3y^2 + 8\sqrt{3}x - 8y + 32 = 0$

7. $17x^2 - 48xy + 31y^2 + 49 = 0$

8. $52x^2 - 72xy + 73y^2 = 200$

9. *Critical Thinking*
 a. Given an equation
$$Ax^2 + Bxy + Cy^2 + Dx + Ey + F = 0$$
 with $B \neq 0$ and an angle θ, use the rotation equations to rewrite the equation in the form
$$A'u^2 + B'uv + C'v^2 + D'u + E'v + F' = 0,$$
 where $A', \dots, F'$ are expressions involving $\sin\theta$, $\cos\theta$ and the constants $A, \dots, F$.
 b. Verify that
 $B' = 2(C - A)\sin\theta\cos\theta + B(\cos^2\theta - \sin^2\theta)$
 c. Use the double-angle identities to show that
 $B' = (C - A)\sin 2\theta + B\cos 2\theta$
 d. If θ is chosen so that $\cot 2\theta = \dfrac{A - C}{B}$, show that $B' = 0$. This proves the rotation angle formula.

10. *Critical Thinking* Assume that the graph of $A'u^2 + C'v^2 + D'u + E'v + F' = 0$ (with at least one of A' or C' nonzero) in the uv coordinate system is a nondegenerate conic. Show that its graph is an ellipse if $A'C' > 0$ (A' and C' have the same sign), a hyperbola if $A'C' < 0$ (A' and C' have opposite signs), or a parabola if $A'C' = 0$.

11. *Critical Thinking* Assume the graph of
$$Ax^2 + Bxy + Cy^2 + Dx + Ey + F = 0$$
 is a nondegenerate conic section. Prove the statement in the box on page 723 as follows.
 a. In Exercise 9 **a.** show that
 $(B')^2 - 4A'C' = B^2 - 4AC.$
 b. Assume θ has been chosen so that $B' = 0$. Use Exercise 10 to show that the graph of the original equation is
 an ellipse if $B^2 - 4AC < 0$,
 a parabola if $B^2 - 4AC = 0$, and
 a hyperbola if $B^2 - 4AC > 0$.

12. *Critical Thinking* Suppose an xy- and uv-coordinate system have the same origin and θ is the angle between the positive x-axis and the positive u-axis. Show that the point (u, v) in the rotated system is related to the point (x, y) by the following equations. *Hint:* If the rotation from the xy-coordinate system to the uv-coordinate system is positive, then the rotation from the uv-coordinate system to the xy-coordinate system is negative.
$$u = x\cos\theta + y\sin\theta$$
$$v = y\cos\theta - x\sin\theta.$$

In Exercises 13–16, find the new coordinates of the point when the coordinate axes are rotated through the given angle by using the equations in Exercise 12.

13. $(3, 2)$; $\theta = \dfrac{\pi}{4}$
$\left(\dfrac{5\sqrt{2}}{2}, -\dfrac{\sqrt{2}}{2} \right)$

14. $(-2, 4)$; $\theta = \dfrac{\pi}{3}$
$(-1 + 2\sqrt{3}, 2 + \sqrt{3})$

15. $(1, 0)$; $\theta = \dfrac{\pi}{6}$
$\left(\dfrac{\sqrt{3}}{2}, -\dfrac{1}{2} \right)$

16. $(3, 3)$; $\sin\theta = \dfrac{5}{13}$
$\left(\dfrac{51}{13}, \dfrac{21}{13} \right)$

---

10. The discriminant is $B^2 - 4A'C'$ and $B = 0$. If $A'C' > 0$, the discriminant is negative and therefore an ellipse. If $A'C' < 0$, the discriminant is positive and therefore a hyperbola. If $A'C' = 0$, the discriminant is zero and therefore a parabola.

11. a. From Exercise 9 (a) we have $(B')^2 - 4A'C' =$
$(B\cos^2\theta - 2A\cos\theta\sin\theta + 2C\cos\theta\sin\theta - B\sin^2\theta)^2 -$
$4(A\cos^2\theta + B\cos\theta\sin\theta + C\sin^2\theta)(C\cos^2\theta - B\cos\theta\sin\theta + A\sin^2\theta) =$
$[B(\cos^2\theta - \sin^2\theta) + 2(C - A)\cos\theta\sin\theta]^2 -$
$4(A\cos^2\theta + B\cos\theta\sin\theta + C\sin^2\theta)(C\cos^2\theta - B\cos\theta\sin\theta + A\sin^2\theta) =$
$B^2(\cos^2\theta - \sin^2\theta)^2 +$
$4(C - A)^2\cos^2\theta\sin^2\theta +$
$4B(C - A)(\cos^2\theta \sin^2\theta)\cos\theta\sin\theta -$
$[4AC(\cos^4\theta + \sin^4\theta) +$
$4(A^2 + C^2 - B^2)\cos^2\theta\sin^2\theta -$
$4AB(\cos^3\theta\sin\theta -$
$\cos\theta\sin^3\theta) +$
$4BC(\cos^3\theta\sin\theta -$
$\cos\theta\sin^3\theta)] = B^2(\cos^4\theta -$
$2\cos^2\theta\sin^2\theta + \sin^4\theta +$
$4\cos^2\theta\sin^2\theta) -$
$4AC(2\cos^2\theta\sin^2\theta +$
$\cos^4\theta + \sin^4\theta)$
(everything else cancels) $=$
$(B^2 - 4AC)(\cos^4\theta +$
$2\cos^2\theta\sin^2\theta + \sin^4\theta) =$
$(B^2 - 4AC)(\cos^2\theta + \sin^2\theta)^2 =$
$B^2 - 4AC$

b. If $B^2 - 4AC < 0$, then also $(B')^2 - 4A'C' < 0$.
Since $B' = 0$, $-4A'C' < 0$ and so $A'C' > 0$. By Exercise 10, the graph is an ellipse. The other two cases are proved in the same way.

---

12. In the equations
$$x = u\cos\theta - v\sin\theta$$
$$y = u\sin\theta + v\cos\theta$$
replace (x, y) with (u, v) and vice versa; replace θ with $-\theta$,
$$u = x\cos(-\theta) - y\sin(-\theta)$$
$$v = x\sin(-\theta) + y\cos(-\theta)$$

Since $\cos(-\theta) = \cos\theta$ and $\sin(-\theta) = -\sin\theta$,
$$u = x\cos\theta + y\sin\theta$$
$$v = -x\sin\theta + y\cos\theta \text{ or }$$
$$v = y\cos\theta - x\sin\theta$$

Section 11.5 Polar Coordinates

Teaching Notes

Students may ask what the need is for an alternate coordinate system. It will be pointed out later in this section that polar equations of certain types of graphs are much simpler than rectangular equations of the same graphs. Have them glance at the graphs on pages 740–743 to see examples.

Note the following characteristics of a **Polar Coordinate System**:
- There is only one axis, the polar axis.
- The polar axis is a ray, not a line.
- The origin is also called the pole. (Tell students that the label in Figure 11.5-1 means Origin *or* Pole, not Origin Pole.
- Polar coordinates of a point are not unique. In fact, every point in a polar coordinate system has infinitely many ordered pair coordinates.

All the points shown in Figure 11.5-2 have whole numbers as first coordinates and familiar radian measures as second coordinates. Point out that r and θ can both be any real number. Ask students which point in Figure 11.5-2 each of the following is near:

$$\left(4.7, \frac{7\pi}{13}\right) \left(5, \frac{\pi}{2}\right)$$

$$\left(\sqrt{10}, 5.51\right) \left(3, -\frac{\pi}{4}\right)$$

Figure 11.5-3 demonstrates that polar coordinates of a point are not unique. Note that there are infinitely many angles that are coterminal with $\frac{\pi}{3}$.

In Figure 11.5-4, point out that different coordinates for the same point can also be obtained by using the opposite of r and $\theta + \frac{\pi}{2}$. That is, $\left(-2, \frac{3\pi}{4}\right)$ is the same point as $\left(2, \frac{\pi}{4}\right)$.

11.5 Polar Coordinates

Objectives
- Locate points in a polar coordinate system
- Convert between coordinates in rectangular and polar systems
- Create graphs of equations in polar coordinates
- Recognize equations and graphs of:
  - cardioid
  - rose
  - circle
  - lemniscate
  - limaçon

The coordinate system most commonly used is the rectangular coordinate system, which is based on two perpendicular axes. However, other coordinate systems are possible.

The Polar Coordinate System

Choose a point O in the plane, called the **origin**, or **pole.** The horizontal ray extending to the right with endpoint O is called the **polar axis.** A point P in the plane has **polar coordinates**

$$(r, \theta)$$

where r is the length of $\overline{OP}$ and θ is the angle with the polar axis as its initial side and $\overline{OP}$ as its terminal side, as shown in Figure 11.5-1. Unless otherwise stated, θ will be measured in radians.

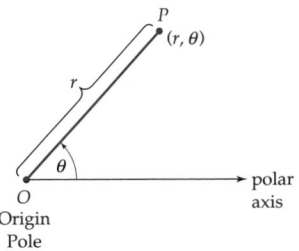

Figure 11.5-1

NOTE The coordinates of the origin can be written as $(0, \theta)$, where θ is any angle.

The θ-coordinate may be either positive or negative, depending on whether it is measured as a counterclockwise or clockwise rotation. Figure 11.5-2 shows some points in a polar coordinate system, and the "circular grid" that a polar coordinate system imposes on the plane.

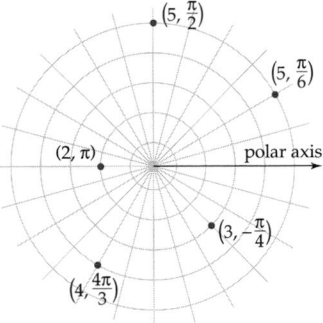

Figure 11.5-2

The polar coordinates of a point P are *not* unique. For example, because $\frac{\pi}{3}$, $\frac{7\pi}{3}$, and $\frac{-5\pi}{3}$ are coterminal angles, the coordinates $\left(2, \frac{\pi}{3}\right)$, $\left(2, \frac{7\pi}{3}\right)$, and $\left(2, \frac{-5\pi}{3}\right)$ all represent the same point, as shown in Figure 11.5-3.

      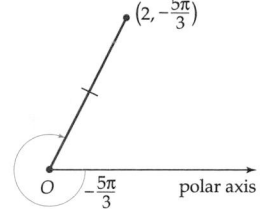

Figure 11.5-3

The r-coordinate may also be negative, as shown in Figure 11.5-4. For $r > 0$, the point $(-r, \theta)$ lies on the line containing the terminal side of θ at a distance r from the origin—but on the *opposite* side of the origin from the point (r, θ).

      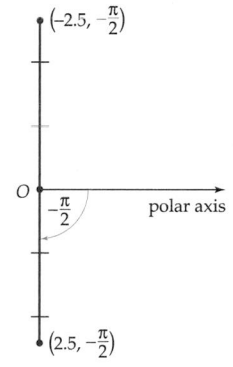

Figure 11.5-4

| **Example 1** | **Polar Coordinates of a Point** |

Determine if the given coordinates represent the same point as $\left(3, \frac{\pi}{6}\right)$ in a polar coordinate system.

a. $\left(3, \frac{13\pi}{6}\right)$ **b.** $\left(3, \frac{-5\pi}{6}\right)$ **c.** $\left(-3, \frac{7\pi}{6}\right)$

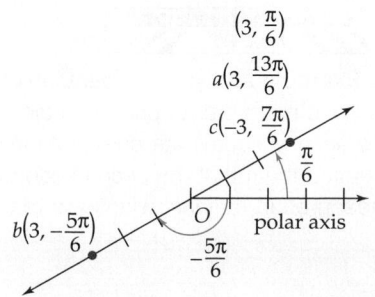

---

continued from page 734

Many students will find it is easier to plot a point (r, θ) in a polar coordinate system by first using θ, and then using r. Trying to use r first to plot a point might be confusing, especially when r is negative.

To explain plotting points with negative r-values, remind students of *opposite rays* from geometry. Plot the point $\left(2, \frac{\pi}{4}\right)$ as shown below. Then plot $\left(-2, \frac{\pi}{4}\right)$ by counting 2 units from the origin on the opposite ray.

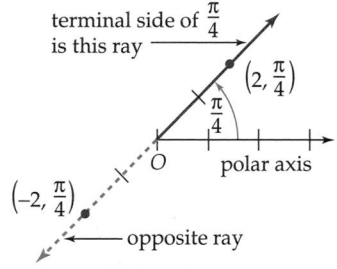

Math Background

Just as rectangular coordinates can be extended to three dimensions to describe points in space, polar coordinates can be extended in a similar manner, forming a *cylindrical coordinate system*. A point in space can be represented as follows:
- rectangular coordinates (x, y, z)
- cylindrical coordinates (r, θ, z)

In rectangular coordinates, z is the perpendicular distance from a point (x, y) in the x-y plane to the point (x, y, z).

In cylindrical coordinates, z is the perpendicular distance from a point (r, θ) in the r-θ plane to the point (r, θ, z).

Example Notes

For **Example 1,** have students plot all 4 points and label as shown below so that they have it for reference when they turn to page 736.

Students can check to see that the answers to **Example 2b** are reasonable as follows:

$(3, 4)$

$\theta = 4$, and 4 radians is approximately 1 radian past θ.

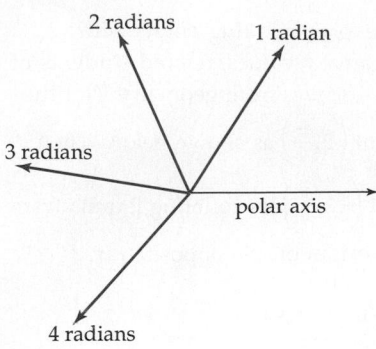

$r = 3$,

$\sqrt{(-1.96)^2 + (-2.27)^2} \approx 2.999 \approx 3$

Have students use the calculator, as suggested in the **Technology Tip**, to convert the polar coordinates $(3, 4)$ in **Example 2b** to rectangular coordinates.

Math Background

Figure 11.5-7 shows both a rectangular grid and a polar grid. Polar graph paper, as shown below, generally consists of concentric circles with the pole as the center and line segments forming equal central angles.

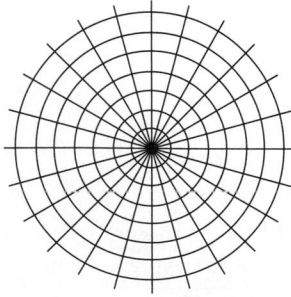

The angles may be measured in degrees or in radians. There are several Internet sites that have polar graph paper available to download. To find one, search the Internet for "polar graph paper."

Solution

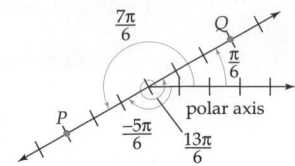

Figure 11.5-5

The point labeled Q in Figure 11.5-5 can be represented by the coordinates $\left(3, \dfrac{\pi}{6}\right)$, $\left(3, \dfrac{13\pi}{6}\right)$, or $\left(-3, \dfrac{7\pi}{6}\right)$. The point labeled P can be represented by the coordinates $\left(3, \dfrac{-5\pi}{6}\right)$. Thus, the coordinates in **a** and **c** represent the same point as $\left(3, \dfrac{\pi}{6}\right)$, but the coordinates in **b** do not. ∎

Polar and Rectangular Coordinates

Suppose that a polar and rectangular system of coordinates are drawn in the same plane, with the origins at the same point, so that the polar axis is the positive x-axis, and the polar line $\theta = \dfrac{\pi}{2}$ is the y-axis. The coordinates of point P in the plane can be written as (r, θ) or as (x, y), as shown in Figure 11.5-6.

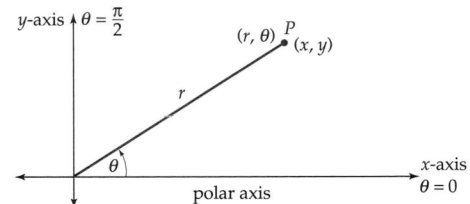

Figure 11.5-6

Let r be as shown in Figure 11.5-6, with r positive. Since r is the distance from $(0, 0)$ to (x, y), the distance formula shows that

$$r = \sqrt{x^2 + y^2}$$

Also, by the definitions of the trigonometric functions in the coordinate plane,

$$\cos \theta = \frac{x}{r} \qquad \sin \theta = \frac{y}{r} \qquad \tan \theta = \frac{y}{x}$$

These equations can be used to obtain the relationship between polar and rectangular coordinates.

COMMON ERROR ALERT

In **Example 2b,** some students might think that $(3, 4)$ is not a pair of polar coordinates because the second coordinate does not have π in it. Remind them that the second coordinate is measured in radians, which are real numbers.

Coordinate Conversion Formulas

Polar → Rectangular
Point P with polar coordinates (r, θ) has rectangular coordinates (x, y), where

$$x = r \cos \theta \qquad \text{and} \qquad y = r \sin \theta$$

Rectangular → Polar
Point P with rectangular coordinates (x, y) has polar coordinates (r, θ), where

$$r^2 = x^2 + y^2 \qquad \text{and} \qquad \tan \theta = \frac{y}{x}$$

Technology Tip

Keys to convert from rectangular to polar coordinates, or vice versa, are in the TI ANGLE menu and in the ANGLE submenu of the Casio OPTN menu.

The conversion formulas from polar to rectangular coordinates give a unique solution for all values of r and θ.

Example 2   Polar → Rectangular

Convert each point from polar coordinates to rectangular coordinates.

a. $\left(2, \dfrac{\pi}{6}\right)$

b. $(3, 4)$

Solution

a. For $\left(2, \dfrac{\pi}{6}\right)$, apply the conversion formulas using $r = 2$ and $\theta = \dfrac{\pi}{6}$.

$$x = 2 \cos \frac{\pi}{6} = 2 \cdot \frac{\sqrt{3}}{2} = \sqrt{3}$$

$$y = 2 \sin \frac{\pi}{6} = 2 \cdot \frac{1}{2} = 1$$

So the rectangular coordinates are $\left(\sqrt{3}, 1\right)$.

b. For $(3, 4)$, apply the conversion formulas using $r = 3$ and $\theta = 4$.

$$x = 3 \cos 4 \approx -1.96$$
$$y = 3 \sin 4 \approx -2.27$$

So the approximate rectangular coordinates are $(-1.96, -2.27)$.

Figure 11.5-7 displays the rectangular coordinates of the points in part **a** and part **b**, along with both a rectangular grid and a polar grid. ∎

The conversion formulas from rectangular to polar coordinates do not have unique solutions for r and θ. In particular, the equation $\tan \theta = \dfrac{y}{x}$ has no solutions when $x = 0$ and infinitely many solutions when $x \neq 0$.

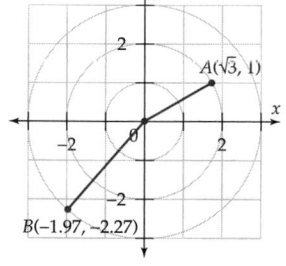

$A(\sqrt{3}, 1)$

$B(-1.97, -2.27)$

Figure 11.5-7

$B(-1.25, 2.73)$

$A(\sqrt{2}, \sqrt{2})$

Example 1

Determine if the given coordinates represent the same point as $\left(2, \dfrac{4\pi}{3}\right)$.

a. $\left(2, -\dfrac{2\pi}{3}\right)$ yes

b. $\left(-2, \dfrac{\pi}{3}\right)$ yes

c. $\left(-2, \dfrac{10\pi}{3}\right)$ no

The point Q below can be represented by the coordinates $\left(2, \dfrac{4\pi}{3}\right)$, $\left(2, -\dfrac{2\pi}{3}\right)$ and $\left(-2, \dfrac{\pi}{3}\right)$. The point P can be represented by the coordinates $\left(-2, \dfrac{10\pi}{3}\right)$. So, the coordinates in **a** and **b** represent the same point as $\left(2, \dfrac{4\pi}{3}\right)$, but the coordinates in **c** do not.

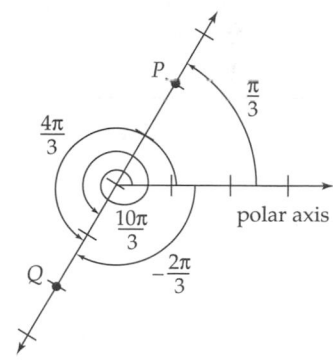

Example 2

Convert each point from polar coordinates to rectangular coordinates.

a. $\left(2, \dfrac{\pi}{4}\right)$

$$x = 2 \cos \frac{\pi}{4} = 2 \cdot \frac{\sqrt{2}}{2} = \sqrt{2}$$

$$y = 2 \sin \frac{\pi}{4} = 2 \cdot \frac{\sqrt{2}}{2} = \sqrt{2}$$

rectangular coordinates: $\left(\sqrt{2}, \sqrt{2}\right)$
(shown in the figure by point A)

b. $(3, 2)$
$$x = 3 \cos 2 \approx -1.25$$
$$y = 3 \sin 2 \approx 2.73$$
approximate rectangular coordinates: $(-1.25, 2.73)$
(shown in the figure by point B)

Example Notes

For **Example 3**, in Figure 11.5-8, point A corresponds to part **a**, point B corresponds to part **b**, etc. For each point, one possible answer is shown in the Figure.

Have students name several other possible pairs of polar coordinates for the points, using positive and negative values of r. For example, in part **a**, other possible answers are $\left(2\sqrt{2}, \frac{15\pi}{4}\right)$ and $\left(-2\sqrt{2}, \frac{3\pi}{4}\right)$.

Generally, any point of the form $\left(2\sqrt{2}, \frac{7\pi}{4} + 2k\pi\right)$, where k is any integer, is a correct description of the point.

For any point (r, θ) and any integer k, the following all name the same point:
$$(r, \theta)$$
$$(r, \theta + 2k\pi)$$
$$(-r, \theta + (2k + 1)\pi)$$

In part **3c**, $\tan^{-1}$ cannot be used because $\tan^{-1}\frac{-5}{0}$ is undefined. Students must know that when $x = 0$ and $y \neq 0$, the point lies on the positive y-axis or negative y-axis and $\theta = \frac{\pi}{2}$ or $\theta = \frac{3\pi}{2}$, respectively.

In **Example 4b**, the graph is a line, not a ray. For example, $\left(-2, \frac{\pi}{6}\right)$ satisfies $\theta = \frac{\pi}{6}$.

Teaching Notes

When a Cartesian equation of degree one contains only one variable (e.g. $y = 4$ or $x = 7$), its graph is a line that is parallel to the x-axis or y-axis. When a polar equation of degree one contains only one variable (e.g. $r = 3$ or $\theta = \frac{\pi}{6}$), its graph is a circle of radius r or a line that makes an angle of θ with the polar axis.

$$\theta = \tan^{-1}\frac{y}{x} + k\pi \qquad\qquad (k \text{ is any integer})$$

Not every solution works for a specific point P. To find solutions that represent the point P, you need to know which quadrant contains P.

$\theta = \tan^{-1}\frac{y}{x}$ can be used for points in Quadrants I and IV because it would be an angle between $-\frac{\pi}{2}$ and $\frac{\pi}{2}$. Similarly, $\theta = \tan^{-1}\frac{y}{x} + \pi$ can be used for points in Quadrants II and III because it would be an angle between $\frac{\pi}{2}$ and $\frac{3\pi}{2}$.

Example 3   Rectangular → Polar

Convert each point from rectangular coordinates to polar coordinates.

a. $(2, -2)$ **b.** $(-3, -5)$ **c.** $(0, -5)$ **d.** $(-2, 4)$

Solution

a. For $(2, -2)$, the second set of equations of the coordinate conversion formulas with $x = 2$ and $y = -2$ shows that
$$r = \sqrt{2^2 + (-2)^2} = \sqrt{8} = 2\sqrt{2} \quad \text{and} \quad \tan\theta = \frac{-2}{2} = -1, \quad \text{or}$$
$\theta = \tan^{-1}\frac{-2}{2} = -\frac{\pi}{4}$. The point is in Quadrant IV, so two possible answers are $\left(2\sqrt{2}, -\frac{\pi}{4}\right)$ or $\left(2\sqrt{2}, \frac{7\pi}{4}\right)$.

b. For $(-3, -5)$, $r = \sqrt{(-3)^2 + (-5)^2} = \sqrt{34}$. A calculator shows that
$$\tan^{-1}\frac{-5}{-3} \approx 1.0304$$
Because the point $(-3, -5)$ is in Quadrant III, $\theta \approx 1.0304 + \pi \approx 4.17$. Therefore, one possible answer is $\left(\sqrt{34}, 4.17\right)$.

c. For $(0, -5)$, $r = \sqrt{0^2 + (-5)^2} = 5$. Because the point is on the negative y-axis, $\theta = \frac{3\pi}{2}$. Therefore, two possible answers are $\left(5, \frac{3\pi}{2}\right)$ or $\left(5, -\frac{\pi}{2}\right)$.

d. For $(-2, 4)$, $r = \sqrt{(-2)^2 + 4^2} = \sqrt{4 + 16} = \sqrt{20} = 2\sqrt{5}$.
$\tan\theta = -\frac{4}{2} = -2$, and $\tan^{-1}(-2) \approx -1.11$, which is in Quadrant IV.

Because $(-2, 4)$ is in Quadrant II, $\theta \approx -1.11 + \pi \approx 2.03$.

Therefore, one possible answer is $(2\sqrt{5}, 2.03)$.

Figure 11.5-8 displays the polar coordinates of the points in parts **a–d**, along with both a rectangular grid and a polar grid.

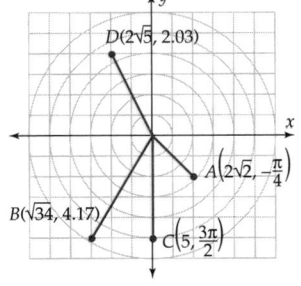

Figure 11.5-8

Polar Graphs

An equation like $r = 2\cos\theta$, where r and θ are the variables, is a **polar equation**. Equations in x and y are called **rectangular** or **Cartesian equations**. Many useful curves have simple polar equations, although they may have complicated rectangular equations.

Like other graphs, the graph of a polar equation in r and θ is the set of points (r, θ) in the plane that make the equation true. It is possible to write a polar equation in rectangular form or a rectangular equation in polar form by using the coordinate conversion formulas, definitions, and basic facts about trigonometric functions.

Graphs of the Form r = a and θ = b

Several types of graphs have equations that are simpler in polar form than in rectangular form. For example, the graph of $r = 1$ consists of points of the form $(1, \theta)$, which is all points that are 1 unit from the pole. That is, the graph of $r = 1$ is the unit circle centered at the pole. The equation $\theta = \dfrac{\pi}{4}$ consists of all points of the form $\left(r, \dfrac{\pi}{4}\right)$. That is, all points that lie on the line that makes a $\dfrac{\pi}{4}$, or 45°, angle with the polar axis.

Example 4   Polar Graphs

Graph each polar equation below.

a. $r = 3$ **b.** $\theta = \dfrac{\pi}{6}$

Solution

a. The graph consists of all points $(3, \theta)$, that is, all points whose distance from the pole is 3. So, the graph is a circle of radius 3 with its center at the pole.

b. The graph consists of all points $\left(r, \dfrac{\pi}{6}\right)$. These points lie on the straight line that contains the terminal side of an angle of $\dfrac{\pi}{6}$ radians, whose initial side is the polar axis.

Figure 11.5-9   **Figure 11.5-10**

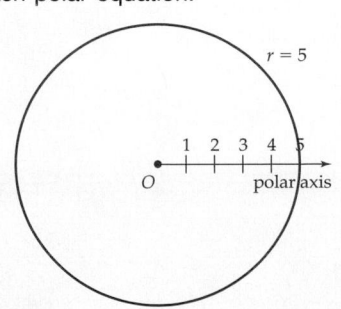

For **Example 5,** ask students for the minimum and maximum values of $\sin \theta$. $-1, 1$

Ask for the minimum and maximum values of r.

minimum: $r = 1 + (-1) = 0$

maximum: $r = 1 + 1 = 2$

Have students complete the table:

θ	$\sin \theta$	$r = 1 + \sin \theta$
0	0	1
$\frac{\pi}{2}$	1	2
π	0	1
$\frac{3\pi}{2}$	-1	0
2π	0	1

Have students use the table values to label the points (r, θ) on the figure below.

Math Background

A cardioid can be formed by tracing the path of a particular point of a circle O as circle O rolls around another circle P, where circles O and P have the same radius.

Graphs of Other Polar Equations

Other types of graphs have simple equations in polar form. Several types of polar graphs have specific forms that can be classified by special names like cardioid, limaçon, and rose.

Many polar equations are functions, with independent variable θ, and dependent variable r. Therefore, polar functions are written as $r = f(\theta)$.

Example 5 Polar Graphs

Graph $r = 1 + \sin \theta$.

Solution

Consider the behavior of $\sin \theta$ in each quadrant.

As θ increases from 0 to $\frac{\pi}{2}$, $\sin \theta$ increases from 0 to 1. So $r = 1 + \sin \theta$ increases from 1 to 2.

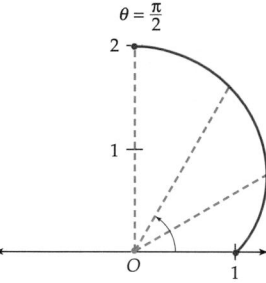

As θ increases from $\frac{\pi}{2}$ to π, $\sin \theta$ decreases from 1 to 0. So $r = 1 + \sin \theta$ decreases from 2 to 1.

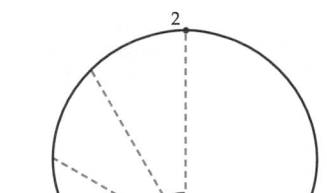

As θ increases from π to $\frac{3\pi}{2}$, $\sin \theta$ decreases from 0 to -1. So $r = 1 + \sin \theta$ decreases from 1 to 0.

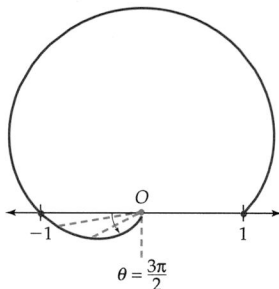

As θ increases from $\frac{3\pi}{2}$ to 2π, $\sin \theta$ increases from -1 to 0. So $r = 1 + \sin \theta$ increases from 0 to 1.

Figure 11.5-11

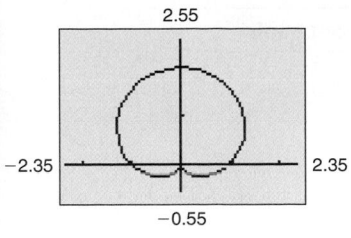

2.55

−2.35 | 2.35

−0.55

Figure 11.5-12

For $\theta > 2\pi$ and $\theta < 0$, $\sin\theta$ repeats the same pattern, so the full graph, as shown in the lower right drawing of Figure 11.5-11, is called a **cardioid.** The graph of $r = 1 + \sin\theta$ displayed on a graphing calculator is shown in Figure 11.5-12.

■

The easiest way to graph a polar function of the form $r = f(\theta)$ is to use a calculator in polar graphing mode. The following Tip should be helpful.

Technology Tip

The viewing window of a calculator in polar graphing mode has the usual settings for the x- and y-values, and also θ min, θ max, and θ step. (Casio has θ pitch instead of θ step.) For a complete graph of a polar equation that contains a trigonometric function, the interval from θ min to θ max should be at least as large as the period of the function.

The value of θ step determines the number of points plotted by the calculator. A smaller value of θ step will generally result in a more accurate curve but will also take longer to graph.

To view the polar coordinates using the Trace feature, from the Format menu choose PolarGC on TI models. Casio models automatically display coordinates for the type of graph shown.

Graphing Exploration ●

Graph $r = 2 + 4\cos\theta$ on a calculator in polar graphing mode. Experiment with the size of the window and the values of θ min, θ max, and θ step to find (approximately) the graph shown in Figure 11.5-13. What window settings did you use to obtain the graph?

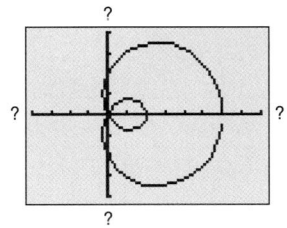

Figure 11.5-13

Common Polar Graphs

The following is a summary of commonly encountered polar graphs. In each case, a and b are constants, and θ is measured in radians.

Depending on the plus or minus sign and whether sine or cosine is used, the basic shape of each graph may differ from those shown by a rotation, reflection, or horizontal or vertical shift.

ADDITIONAL EXAMPLES

Example 5

Graph $r = 1 + \cos\theta$.

As θ increases from 0 to $\frac{\pi}{2}$, $\cos\theta$ decreases from 1 to 0, so $r = 1 + \cos\theta$ decreases from 2 to 1. (This change is shown by the dotted line segments below).

As θ increases from $\frac{\pi}{2}$ to π, $\cos\theta$ decreases from 0 to −1, so $r = 1 + \cos\theta$ decreases from 1 to 0.

As θ increases from π to $\frac{3\pi}{2}$, $\cos\theta$ increases from −1 to 0, so $r = 1 + \cos\theta$ increases from 0 to 1.

As θ increases from $\frac{3\pi}{2}$ to 2π, $\cos\theta$ increases from 0 to 1, so $r = 1 + \cos\theta$ increases from 1 to 2.

For $\theta > 2\pi$ and $\theta < 0$, $\cos\theta$ repeats the same pattern, so the full graph is obtained by letting θ take on all values in the interval $[0, 2\pi)$. The full graph is the cardioid shown below.

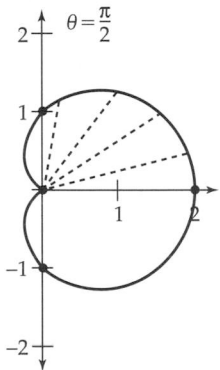

The graph of $r = 1 + \cos\theta$ displayed on a graphing calculator:

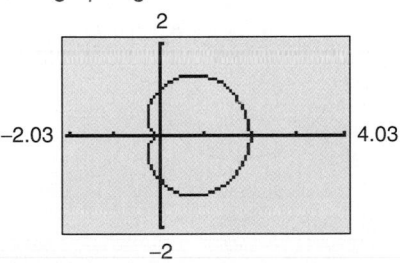

2

−2.03 | 4.03

−2

Teaching Notes

Solution to the **Graphing Exploration:** Possible window settings used to obtain the graph in Figure 11.5-13 are as follows:

θmin = 0 θmax = 2π
θstep = $\pi/24 \approx 0.1308996$
Xmin = −4   Ymin = −4
Xmax = 8   Ymax = 4

Teaching Notes

Note that the graphs on pages 742–743 are generalized; that is they do not show specific *r*-values.

Show students the following rough sketch of $r = 2\theta$:

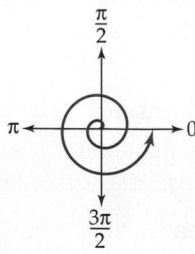

Ask them to display the graph on their calculators and describe the window they use. **possible window**

$\theta\text{min} = 0$
$\theta\text{max} = 4\pi$
$\theta\text{step} = \pi/24 \approx 0.1308996$
$\text{Xmin} = -36$
$\text{Xmax} = 36$
$\text{Ymin} = -24$
$\text{Ymax} = 24$

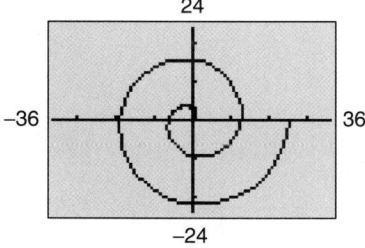

Repeat the activity for $r = -2\theta$:

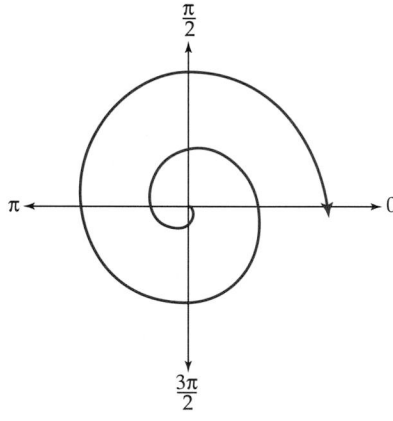

possible window

$\theta\text{min} = -4\pi$
$\theta\text{max} = 0$
$\theta\text{step} = \pi/24 \approx 0.1308996$
$\text{Xmin} - -36$
$\text{Xmax} = 36$
$\text{Ymin} = -24$
$\text{Ymax} = 24$

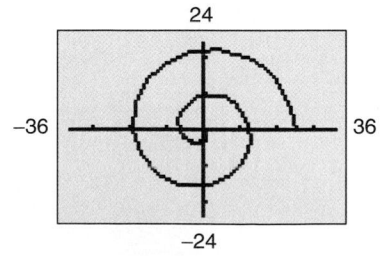

Equation	Name of Graph	Shape of Graph
$r = a\theta \quad (\theta \geq 0)$ $r = a\theta \quad (\theta \leq 0)$	Archimedian spiral	$r = a\theta\ (\theta \geq 0)$ $r = a\theta\ (\theta \leq 0)$
$r = a(1 - \sin\theta)$ $r = a(1 - \cos\theta)$	cardioid	$r = a(1 + \cos\theta)$ $r = a(1 - \sin\theta)$
$r = a\sin n\theta$ $r = a\cos n\theta$ $(n \geq 2)$	rose For *n* odd, there are *n* petals. For *n* even, there are 2*n* petals.	$n = 4$ $n = 5$ $r = a\cos n\theta$ $r = a\sin n\theta$
$r = a\sin\theta$ $r = a\cos\theta$	circle	$r = a\cos\theta$ $r = a\sin\theta$

Equation	Name of Graph	Shape of Graph
$r^2 = -a^2 \sin 2\theta$ $r^2 = -a^2 \cos 2\theta$	lemniscate	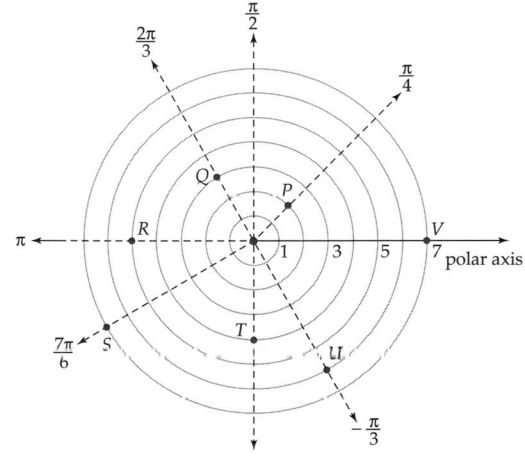 $r^2 = a^2 \sin 2\theta$ $r^2 = a^2 \cos 2\theta$
$r = a + b \sin \theta$ $r = a + b \sin \theta$ $(a, b > 0, a \neq b)$	limaçon	$a < b$ $b < a < 2b$ $a \geq 2b$ $r = a + b \cos \theta$ $r = a + b \sin \theta$ $r = a - b \sin \theta$

Teaching Notes

Have students graph the polar equations below and identify each with a type shown on pages 742–743:

$r = 3 \cos 2\theta$ $r = a \cos n\theta$, rose

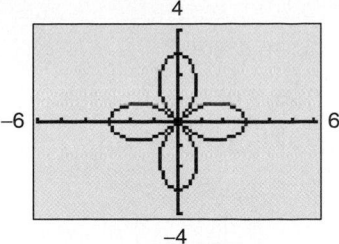

$r = 2 - 2 \cos \theta$
$r = a(1 \pm \cos \theta)$, cardioid

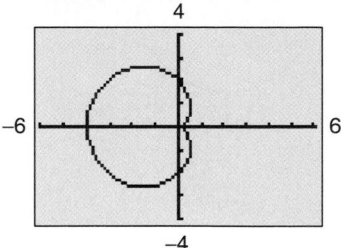

Finally, have students create their own equations and graph them.

Exercises 11.5

1. What is one possible pair of polar coordinates of each of the points P, Q, R, S, T, U, V in the figure?

In Exercises 2–6, list four other pairs of polar coordinates for the given point, each with a different combination of signs (that is, $r > 0$, $\theta > 0$; $r > 0$, $\theta < 0$; $r < 0$, $\theta > 0$; and $r < 0$, $\theta < 0$).

2. $\left(3, \dfrac{\pi}{3}\right)$ **3.** $(-5, \pi)$ **4.** $\left(2, -\dfrac{2\pi}{3}\right)$

5. $\left(-1, -\dfrac{\pi}{6}\right)$ **6.** $\left(\sqrt{3}, \dfrac{3\pi}{4}\right)$

In Exercises 7–10, convert the polar coordinates to rectangular coordinates.

7. $\left(3, \dfrac{\pi}{3}\right)$ **8.** $\left(-2, \dfrac{\pi}{4}\right)$

9. $\left(-1, \dfrac{5\pi}{6}\right)$ **10.** $(2, 0)$

6. $\left(\sqrt{3}, \dfrac{11\pi}{4}\right), \left(\sqrt{3}, -\dfrac{5\pi}{4}\right),$
   $\left(-\sqrt{3}, \dfrac{7\pi}{4}\right), \left(-\sqrt{3}, -\dfrac{\pi}{4}\right)$

7. $\left(\dfrac{3}{2}, \dfrac{3\sqrt{3}}{2}\right)$

8. $\left(-\sqrt{2}, -\sqrt{2}\right)$

9. $\left(\dfrac{\sqrt{3}}{2}, -\dfrac{1}{2}\right)$

10. $(2, 0)$

Exercises 11.5

ANSWERS

1. $P = \left(2, \dfrac{\pi}{4}\right), Q = \left(3, \dfrac{2\pi}{3}\right),$

   $R = (5, \pi), S = \left(7, \dfrac{7\pi}{6}\right),$

   $T = \left(4, \dfrac{3\pi}{2}\right), U = \left(6, -\dfrac{\pi}{3}\right)$

   or $\left(6, \dfrac{5\pi}{3}\right), V = (7, 0)$

2. $\left(3, \dfrac{7\pi}{3}\right), \left(3, -\dfrac{5\pi}{3}\right), \left(-3, \dfrac{4\pi}{3}\right),$

   $\left(-3, -\dfrac{2\pi}{3}\right)$

3. $(5, 2\pi), (5, -2\pi), (-5, 3\pi),$

   $(-5, -\pi)$

4. $\left(2, \dfrac{4\pi}{3}\right), \left(2, -\dfrac{8\pi}{3}\right),$

   $\left(-2, \dfrac{\pi}{3}\right), \left(-2, -\dfrac{5\pi}{3}\right)$

5. $\left(1, \dfrac{5\pi}{6}\right), \left(1, -\dfrac{7\pi}{6}\right), \left(-1, \dfrac{11\pi}{6}\right),$

   $\left(-1, -\dfrac{13\pi}{6}\right)$

11. $\left(6, -\dfrac{\pi}{6}\right)$

12. $\left(4, -\dfrac{\pi}{6}\right)$

13. $\left(2\sqrt{5}, 1.1071\right)$

14. $\left(\sqrt{13}, -0.5880\right)$

15. $\left(\sqrt{31.25}, 2.6779\right)$

16. $\left(\sqrt{47.44}, 3.59\right)$

17.

18.

19.

20.

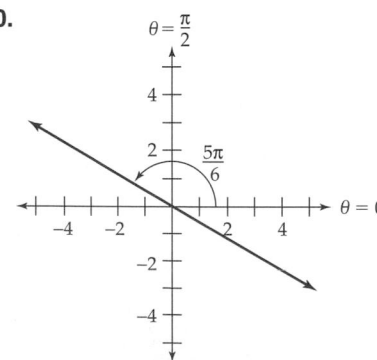

In Exercises 11–16, convert the rectangular coordinates to polar coordinates.

11. $\left(3\sqrt{3}, -3\right)$ **12.** $\left(2\sqrt{3}, -2\right)$ **13.** $(2, 4)$

14. $(3, -2)$ **15.** $(-5, 2.5)$ **16.** $(-6.2, -3)$

In Exercises 17–22, sketch the graph of the equation without using a calculator.

17. $r = 4$ **18.** $r = -1$ **19.** $\theta = -\dfrac{\pi}{3}$

20. $\theta = \dfrac{5\pi}{6}$ **21.** $\theta = 1$ **22.** $\theta = -4$

In Exercises 23–46, sketch the graph of the equation.

23. $r = \theta$ $(\theta \le 0)$ **24.** $r = 3\theta$ $(\theta \ge 0)$

25. $r = 1 - \sin\theta$ **26.** $r = 3 - 3\cos\theta$

27. $r = -2\cos\theta$ **28.** $r = -6\sin\theta$

29. $r = \cos 2\theta$ **30.** $r = \cos 3\theta$

31. $r = \sin 3\theta$ **32.** $r = \sin 4\theta$

33. $r^2 = 4\cos 2\theta$ **34.** $r^2 = \sin 2\theta$

35. $r = 2 + 4\cos\theta$ **36.** $r = 1 + 2\cos\theta$

37. $r = \sin\theta + \cos\theta$ **38.** $r = 4\cos\theta + 4\sin\theta$

39. $r = \sin\dfrac{\theta}{2}$ **40.** $r = 4\tan\theta$

41. $r = \sin\theta\tan\theta$ (cissoid)

42. $r = 4 + 2\sec\theta$ (conchoid)

43. $r = e^{\theta}$ (logarithmic spiral)

44. $r^2 = \dfrac{1}{\theta}$ **45.** $r = \dfrac{1}{\theta}$ $(\theta > 0)$ **46.** $r^2 = \theta$

47. a. Find a complete graph of $r = 1 - 2\sin 3\theta$.
   b. Predict what the graph of $r = 1 - 2\sin 4\theta$ will look like. Then check your prediction with a calculator.
   c. Predict what the graph of $r = 1 - 2\sin 5\theta$ will look like. Then check your prediction with a calculator.

48. a. Find a complete graph of $r = 1 - 3\sin 2\theta$.
   b. Predict what the graph of $r = 1 - 3\sin 3\theta$ will look like. Then check your prediction with a calculator.
   c. Predict what the graph of $r = 1 - 3\sin 4\theta$ will look like. Then check your prediction with a calculator.

49. If a and b are constants such that $ab \ne 0$, show that the graph of $r = a\sin\theta + b\cos\theta$ is a circle. *Hint*: Multiply both sides by r and convert to rectangular coordinates.

50. *Critical Thinking* Prove that the coordinate conversion formulas are valid when $r < 0$. *Hint*: If P has coordinates (x, y) and (r, θ), with $r < 0$, verify that the point Q with rectangular coordinates $(-x, -y)$ has polar coordinates $(-r, \theta)$. Since $r < 0$, $-r$ is positive and the conversion formulas proved in the text apply to Q. For instance, $-x = -r\cos\theta$, which implies that $x = r\cos\theta$.

51. *Critical Thinking* Distance Formula for Polar Coordinates: Prove that the distance from (r, θ) to (s, β) is $\sqrt{r^2 + s^2 - 2rs\cos(\theta - \beta)}$. *Hint*: If $r > 0$, $s > 0$, and $\theta > \beta$, then the triangle with vertices $(r, \theta), (s, \beta), (0, 0)$ has an angle of $\theta - \beta$, whose sides have lengths r and s. Use the Law of Cosines.

52. *Critical Thinking* Explain why the following symmetry tests for the graphs of polar equations are valid.
   a. If replacing θ by $-\theta$ produces an equivalent equation, then the graph is symmetric with respect to the line $\theta = 0$ (the x-axis).
   b. If replacing θ by $\pi - \theta$ produces an equivalent equation, then the graph is symmetric with respect to the line $\theta = \pi/2$ (the y-axis).
   c. If replacing r by $-r$ produces an equivalent equation, then the graph is symmetric with respect to the pole (origin).

21.

22–52. *See pp. 1075–1078.*

Polar Equations of Conics

Section 11.6 Polar Equations of Conics

Objectives

- Define eccentricity of an ellipse, a parabola, and a hyperbola
- Develop and use the general polar equation of a conic section

In a rectangular coordinate system, each type of conic section has a different definition. By using polar coordinates, it is possible to give a unified treatment of conics and their equations. A key concept in this development is *eccentricity*.

Eccentricity

Recall that ellipses and hyperbolas are defined in terms of two foci, and both have two vertices that lie on the line through the foci. The **eccentricity**, *e*, of an ellipse or a hyperbola is the ratio

$$e = \frac{\text{distance between the foci}}{\text{distance between the vertices}}$$

> **NOTE** Do not confuse the eccentricity of a conic section, which is denoted as e and whose value varies, with the number e, which is the constant 2.718281828.... The meaning should be clear in context.

If a conic is centered at the origin with foci on the *x*-axis, the situation is as follows.

Ellipse	**Hyperbola**
$\dfrac{x^2}{a^2} + \dfrac{y^2}{b^2} = 1$	$\dfrac{x^2}{a^2} - \dfrac{y^2}{b^2} = 1$

For $a > b$,

foci: $(\pm c, 0)$ vertices: $(\pm a, 0)$ foci: $(\pm c, 0)$ vertices: $(\pm a, 0)$

$c = \sqrt{a^2 - b^2}$ $c = \sqrt{a^2 + b^2}$

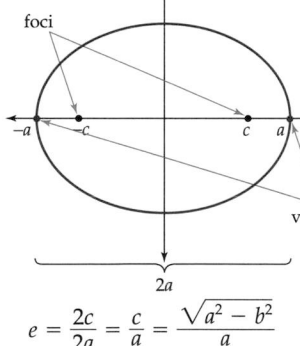

$$e = \frac{2c}{2a} = \frac{c}{a} = \frac{\sqrt{a^2 - b^2}}{a}$$

Figure 11.6-1

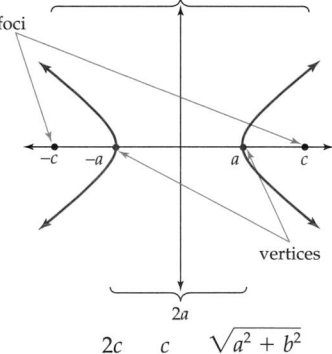

$$e = \frac{2c}{2a} = \frac{c}{a} = \frac{\sqrt{a^2 + b^2}}{a}$$

Figure 11.6-2

Teaching Notes

Remind students that they have studied standard equations of translated (but not rotated) conics (page 720). In this section, **Polar Equations of Conics** will be developed for the same cases (i.e, no rotation).

The eccentricity of parabolas is not discussed here because a parabola has only one focus, and the definition of **Eccentricity** as presented here requires a distance between *two* foci. On page 747, you will see that the eccentricity of a parabola is 1.

The definition of eccentricity is

$$e = \frac{\text{distance between the foci}}{\text{distance between the vertices}}.$$

Note that distance between the foci $= 2c$ and distance between the vertices $= 2a$.

Therefore, $e = \frac{2c}{2a} = \frac{c}{a}$, as shown at the bottom of the page.

Recall that $a > b$ for every ellipse, but not for every hyperbola. The condition $a > b$ is stated here because it applies to ellipses and hyperbolas with foci on the *x*-axis.

Real-World Application

As noted on page 691, the orbits of planets around the sun are ellipses. The orbits of some comets are also ellipses. The orbits of the planets are ellipses with relatively low eccentricities (i.e. the orbital paths are nearly circular); comets generally have eccentricities near 1.

Contrast the eccentricity of Earth's orbital path (0.017) with that of Halley's comet (0.97) in the diagram.

continued from page 745

A comet or planet that elliptically orbits the sun achieves *perihelion* when its distance to the sun is the least and *aphelion* when it is greatest. Both states occur at endpoints of the major axis. Because of its near-circular orbit, the distances from Earth to the Sun at perihelion and aphelion are not greatly different. However, for comets like Halley's comet, the difference is measured in billions of kilometers.

Some comets have elliptical orbits; other comets have orbits that are parabolas. Exercises 47 and 48 on pages 753–754 are about a parabolic orbit and an elliptical orbit. The diagrams shown below will be helpful to students when they work on these exercises.

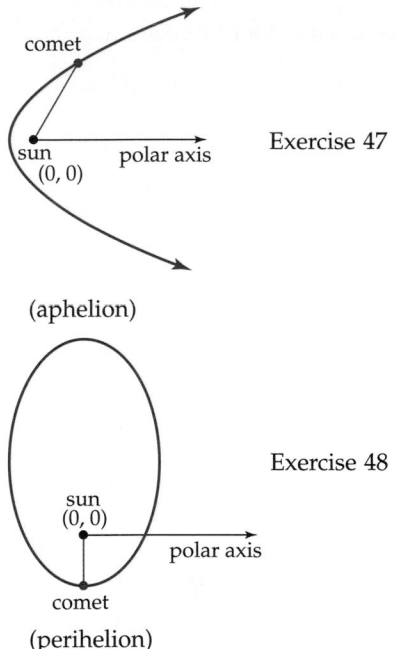

Exercise 47

Exercise 48

Teaching Notes

Use the diagrams at the bottom of page 747 to emphasize the differences in the value of e for each type of figure. Have students explore one figure at a time. For example, have them select another point X on the ellipse and confirm that the distance to the focus is less than the distance to the directrix. Emphasize that in the ellipse shown, the ratio $\frac{XP}{XL}$ will be equal to $\frac{3}{4}$ for any point X.

A similar analysis shows that the formulas for e are also valid for conics whose foci lie on the y-axis. These formulas can be used to compute the eccentricity of any ellipse or hyperbola whose equation is in standard form.

As Figure 11.6-1 shows, the distance between the foci of an ellipse is always less than the distance between its vertices, so that

$$0 < e < 1 \text{ for all ellipses.}$$

Similarly, the distance between the foci of a hyperbola is greater than the distance between its vertices, as shown in Figure 11.6-2, so that

$$e > 1 \text{ for all hyperbolas.}$$

Example 1 Eccentricity of a Conic

Find the eccentricity of each given conic.

a. $\dfrac{y^2}{4} - \dfrac{x^2}{21} = 1$ **b.** $4x^2 + 9y^2 - 32x - 90y + 253 = 0$

Solution

a. $\dfrac{y^2}{4} - \dfrac{x^2}{21} = 1$ represents a hyperbola with $a^2 = 4$ and $b^2 = 21$, so

$$e = \frac{\sqrt{a^2 + b^2}}{a} = \frac{\sqrt{4 + 21}}{2} = \frac{\sqrt{25}}{2} = \frac{5}{2} = 2.5$$

b. From Example 2 in Section 11.4, $4x^2 + 9y^2 - 32x - 90y + 253 = 0$ can be written in standard form, as

$$\frac{(x - 4)^2}{9} + \frac{(y - 5)^2}{4} = 1$$

The graph of this equation has the same shape as the ellipse

$$\frac{x^2}{9} + \frac{y^2}{4} = 1$$

with a horizontal and a vertical shift. Since the distances between the foci or vertices are the same in both ellipses, the eccentricity is the same for both. Using $a^2 = 9$ and $b^2 = 4$, the eccentricity is

$$e = \frac{\sqrt{a^2 - b^2}}{a} = \frac{\sqrt{9 - 4}}{3} = \frac{\sqrt{5}}{3} \approx 0.745$$

∎

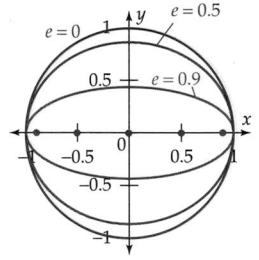

Figure 11.6-3

The eccentricity of an ellipse measures its distortion from a circle, which is a special case of an ellipse. In a circle, the two foci coincide at the center, so the distance between the foci is 0 and its eccentricity is 0. As the foci move farther apart, the eccentricity increases, and the ellipse becomes more distorted from a circle. In Figure 11.6-3, the foci and eccentricities are shown in the same color as the corresponding ellipse.

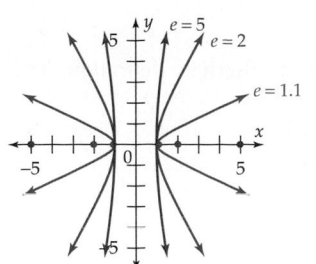

Figure 11.6-4

In Figure 11.6-4, colors of the foci and the eccentricities correspond to each hyperbola. As the foci move farther from the vertices, the branches of the hyperbola become straighter and approach vertical lines.

The preceding discussion does not apply to parabolas because they have only one focus. For reasons explained below, the eccentricity of any parabola is defined to be the number 1.

Alternate Definition of Conics

The following description, whose proof is omitted, is sometimes used to define the conic sections because it provides a unified approach instead of the variety of descriptions given in Sections 11.1, 11.2, and 11.3. It is also used to determine the polar equations of conic sections.

Alternate Definition of Conic Sections

NOTE Recall that the distance from a point to a line is measured along the perpendicular segment from the point to the line.

> Let L be a fixed line called a directrix, P a fixed point not on L, and e a positive constant. The set of all points X in the plane such that
>
> $$\frac{\text{distance between } X \text{ and the fixed point}}{\text{distance between } X \text{ and the fixed line}} = \frac{XP}{XL} = e$$
>
> is a conic section with P as one focus.
>
> - For $0 < e < 1$, the conic is an ellipse.
> - For $e = 1$, the conic is a parabola.
> - For $e > 1$, the conic is a hyperbola.

Recall that the definition of a parabola was all points equidistant from a fixed point and a fixed line. Therefore, the alternate definition coincides with the original definition given in Section 11.3. Examples of this definition are shown in the following diagram.

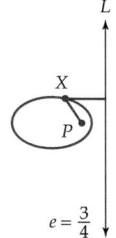

$$\frac{XP}{XL} = \frac{3}{4} \rightarrow XP = \frac{3}{4}XL$$

The distance from X to P is $\frac{3}{4}$ the distance from X to L. The conic is an ellipse.

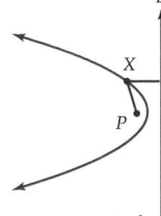

$$\frac{XP}{XL} = 1 \rightarrow XP = XL$$

The distance from X to P equals the distance from X to L. The conic is a parabola.

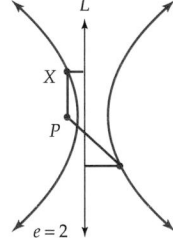

$$\frac{XP}{XL} = 2 \rightarrow XP = 2XL$$

The distance from X to P is twice the distance from X to L. The conic is a hyperbola.

Example Notes

In **Example 1b**, the ellipse is not centered at the origin. Recall that such ellipses can be described as the result of one or more translations of an ellipse that *is* centered at the origin. Ask students how the graph of $\frac{x^2}{9} + \frac{y^2}{4} = 1$ is translated to form the graph of $\frac{(x-4)^2}{9} + \frac{(y-5)^2}{4} = 1$.

The graph of $\frac{x^2}{9} + \frac{y^2}{4} = 1$ is shifted 4 units to the right and 5 units up.

ADDITIONAL EXAMPLES

Example 1

Find the eccentricity of each given conic.

a. $\frac{x^2}{25} + \frac{y^2}{16} = 1$

This equation represents an ellipse with $a^2 = 25$ and $b^2 = 16$, so

$$e = \frac{\sqrt{a^2 - b^2}}{a} = \frac{\sqrt{25 - 16}}{5} = \frac{3}{5}$$

b. $9x^2 - y^2 - 18x + 6y - 36 = 0$

Write the equation in standard form:

$$9x^2 - y^2 - 18x + 6y - 36 = 0$$
$$9x^2 - 18x - y^2 + 6y = 36$$
$$9(x^2 - 2x) - (y^2 - 6y) = 36$$
$$9(x^2 - 2x + 1) - (y^2 - 6y + 9)$$
$$= 36 + 9(1) - 9$$
$$9(x - 1)^2 - (y - 3)^2 = 36$$
$$\frac{(x-1)^2}{4} - \frac{(y-3)^2}{36} = 1$$

The graph of this hyperbola has the same shape as the hyperbola $\frac{x^2}{4} - \frac{y^2}{36} = 1$. Since the distances between the foci or vertices are the same in both hyperbolas, their eccentricities are the same. Using $a^2 = 4$ and $b^2 = 36$,

$$e = \frac{\sqrt{a^2 + b^2}}{a} = \frac{\sqrt{4 + 36}}{2}$$
$$= \frac{\sqrt{40}}{2} = \sqrt{10} \approx 3.162$$

Math Background

The image of a figure following a translation is *congruent* to its preimage, and thus all distances are preserved. It is because of this fact that we can conclude that the eccentricities of translated conics are equal.

Teaching Notes

At the bottom of page 748, the *eccentricity* of a conic section whose equation is of the form $r = \dfrac{ed}{1 \pm e \cos \theta}$ or $r = \dfrac{ed}{1 \pm e \sin \theta}$ is defined to be the coefficient e of the trigonometric function in the denominator. It can be shown that this definition agrees with the one given on page 745 for ellipses and hyperbolas.

When studying the information given on page 749, point out that the polar equation of any of the three types of conics can contain either a cosine expression *or* a sine expression. All 4 forms of equations apply to all 3 types of conics. For example, the equation of an ellipse might take any of the forms listed in the first column. The difference between a conic whose polar equation has a sine expression and one with a cosine expression lies in the orientation of the conic on the polar plane. If the equation contains *cosine*, any foci and vertices will be on a *horizontal* axis. If the equation contains *sine*, any foci and vertices will be on a *vertical* axis.

Point out that for each graph in the Example column, the ray is the polar axis and the endpoint of the ray is the pole (origin) $(0, 0)$. In each case, $(0, 0)$ is a focus of the conic.

pole
(origin)
$(0, 0)$ polar axis

For an ellipse or a hyperbola, Vertices $\theta = 0$ and $\theta = \pi$ means the vertices will have the form $(\ , 0)$ and $(\ , \pi)$.

For a parabola, Vertex $\theta = 0$ or $\theta = \pi$ means the vertex has the form $(\ , 0)$ and $(\ , \pi)$.

The following diagrams show all the possible orientations of the graphs from the table on page 749.

Polar Equations of Conics

To generate polar equations of conics from the alternate definition, let P be the pole, and L be a vertical line d units to the left of the pole, as shown in Figure 11.6-5.

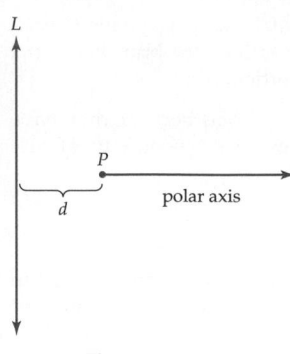

Figure 11.6-5

A point $X = (r, \theta)$ on a general conic satisfies the condition

$$\frac{XP}{XL} = e$$

By the definition of polar coordinates, the r-coordinate of X, shown in Figure 11.6–6, is the distance from the origin to X.

$$XP = r$$

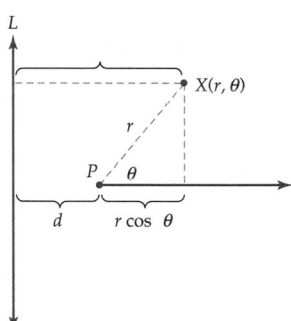

Figure 11.6-6

Figure 11.6-6 also shows that

$$XL = d + r \cos \theta$$

So the polar equation of the conic is given by

$$\frac{XP}{XL} = \frac{r}{d + r \cos \theta} = e$$

$$r = ed + e\,r \cos \theta$$

$$r - e\,r \cos \theta = ed$$

$$r(1 - e \cos \theta) = ed$$

$$r = \frac{ed}{1 - e \cos \theta}$$

If L is to the right of the pole, it can be shown that

$$r = \frac{ed}{1 + e \cos \theta}$$

If L is a horizontal line, it can also be shown that

$$r = \frac{ed}{1 - e \sin \theta} \quad \text{or} \quad r = \frac{ed}{1 + e \sin \theta}$$

depending on whether L is below the pole or above it.

If an equation has another value in place of 1, divide both numerator and denominator by that number to rewrite the equation in the desired form. When the constant term in the denominator is 1, the eccentricity is the coefficient of the trigonometric function. For example, suppose a conic is given by

$$r = \frac{20}{4 - 8 \cos \theta}$$

Divide both numerator and denominator by 4.

$$r = \frac{5}{1 - 2 \cos \theta}$$

The conic is a hyperbola because the eccentricity is 2.

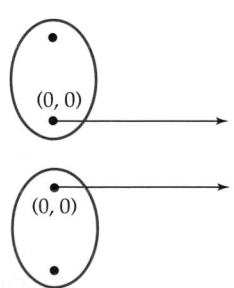

continued from page 746

Polar Equations of Conic Sections

NOTE d is the distance from the focus at the pole to the directrix.

Equations	Graph	Example
$r = \dfrac{ed}{1 + e \cos \theta}$	$0 < e < 1$ *Ellipse* • Vertices $\theta = 0$ and $\theta = \pi$ • One focus at $(0, 0)$	
	$e = 1$ *Parabola* • Vertex $\theta = 0$ or $\theta = \pi$; r is not defined for the other value of θ • Focus at $(0, 0)$	
$r = \dfrac{ed}{1 - e \cos \theta}$	$e > 1$ *Hyperbola* • Vertices $\theta = 0$ and $\theta = \pi$ • One focus at $(0, 0)$	
$r = \dfrac{ed}{1 + e \sin \theta}$	$0 < e < 1$ *Ellipse* • Vertices $\theta = \dfrac{\pi}{2}$ and $\theta = \dfrac{3\pi}{2}$ • One focus at $(0, 0)$	
	$e = 1$ *Parabola* • Vertices $\theta = \dfrac{\pi}{2}$ or $\theta = \dfrac{3\pi}{2}$; r is not defined for the other value of θ • Focus at $(0, 0)$	
$r = \dfrac{ed}{1 - e \sin \theta}$	$e > 1$ *Hyperbola* • Vertices $\theta = \dfrac{\pi}{2}$ and and $\theta = \dfrac{3\pi}{2}$ • One focus at $(0, 0)$	

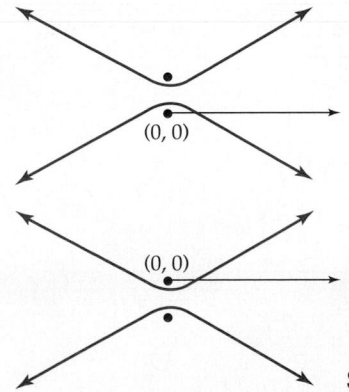

Example 2

Find a complete graph of $r = \dfrac{2e}{1 + e\sin\theta}$ for the following eccentricities.

a. $e = 0.5$

ellipse:

$r = \dfrac{2(0.5)}{1 + 0.5\sin\theta} = \dfrac{1}{1 + 0.5\sin\theta}$

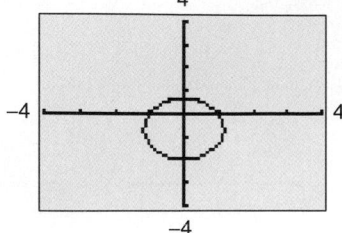

b. $e = 1$

parabola: $r = \dfrac{2(1)}{1 + 1\sin\theta} = \dfrac{2}{1 + \sin\theta}$

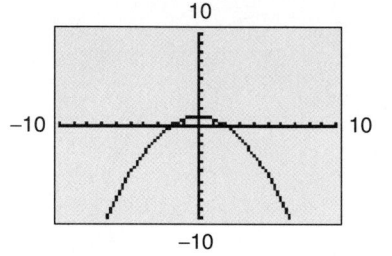

c. $e = 3$

hyperbola:

$r = \dfrac{2(3)}{1 + 3\sin\theta} = \dfrac{6}{1 + 3\sin\theta}$

Example 3

Identify the conic section that is the graph of $r = \dfrac{12}{6 + 18\cos\theta}$ and find its eccentricity and vertices.

Rewrite the equation:

$r = \dfrac{12}{6 + 18\cos\theta} = \dfrac{12}{6(1 + 3\cos\theta)}$

$= \dfrac{2}{1 + 3\cos\theta}$

The graph of the equation is a hyperbola with eccentricity 3.

The vertices occur when $\theta = 0$ and $\theta = \pi$.

Example 2 Polar Equations of Conic Sections

Find a complete graph of $r = \dfrac{3e}{1 + e\cos\theta}$ for the following eccentricities.

a. $e = 0.7$ **b.** $e = 1$ **c.** $e = 2$

Solution

From the first equation in the preceding chart, with $d = 3$, the graphs are an ellipse, a parabola, and a hyperbola, respectively, as shown in Figure 11.6-7. In each case, $0 \le \theta \le 2\pi$.

a. $e = 0.7$

$r = \dfrac{3(0.7)}{1 + 0.7\cos\theta} = \dfrac{2.1}{1 + 0.7\cos\theta}$

ellipse

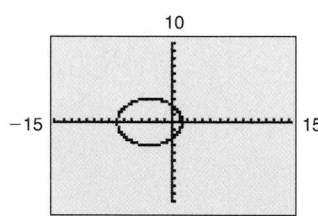

b. $e = 1$

$r = \dfrac{3(1)}{1 + 1\cdot\cos\theta} = \dfrac{3}{1 + \cos\theta}$

parabola

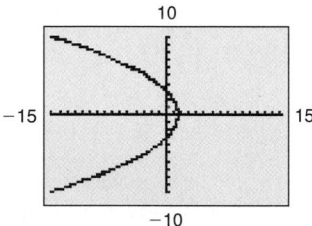

c. $e = 2$

$r = \dfrac{3(2)}{1 + 2\cos\theta} = \dfrac{6}{1 + 2\cos\theta}$

hyperbola

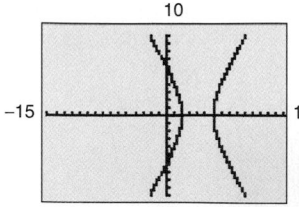

Figure 11.6-7

Example 3 Polar Equations of Conic Sections

Identify the conic section that is the graph of

$$r = \dfrac{20}{4 - 10\sin\theta}$$

and find its eccentricity and vertices.

Solution

First, rewrite the equation in one of the forms listed in the preceding box.

$$r = \dfrac{20}{4 - 10\sin\theta} = \dfrac{20}{4(1 - 2.5\sin\theta)} = \dfrac{5}{1 - 2.5\sin\theta}$$

According to the equation, $e = 2.5$. Thus, the graph is a hyperbola with eccentricity 2.5.

Substitute these values for θ in the original equation to find r:

$r = \dfrac{12}{6 + 18\cos(0)} = \dfrac{12}{6 + 18(1)} = \dfrac{1}{2}$

$r = \dfrac{12}{6 + 18\cos(\pi)} = \dfrac{12}{6 + 18(-1)} = -1$

The vertices are $\left(\dfrac{1}{2}, 0\right)$ and $(-1, \pi)$.

COMMON ERROR ALERT

In **Example 3**, students might rewrite the equation $r = \dfrac{20}{4 - 10\sin\theta}$ as $r = \dfrac{10(2)}{4 - 10\sin\theta}$ and conclude that the eccentricity is 10. Remind them that the constant term in the denominator must be 1, so 4 must be factored out of both numerator and denominator.

The vertices occur when $\theta = \frac{\pi}{2}$ and $\theta = \frac{3\pi}{2}$. To find the r-coordinates, substitute into the original equation.

$$\theta = \frac{\pi}{2} \rightarrow r = \frac{20}{4 - 10\sin\frac{\pi}{2}} = \frac{20}{4 - 10 \cdot 1} = \frac{20}{-6} = -\frac{10}{3}$$

$$\theta = \frac{3\pi}{2} \rightarrow r = \frac{20}{4 - 10\sin\frac{3\pi}{2}} = \frac{20}{4 - 10(-1)} = \frac{20}{14} = \frac{10}{7}$$

The vertices are $\left(-\frac{10}{3}, \frac{\pi}{2}\right)$ and $\left(\frac{10}{7}, \frac{3\pi}{2}\right)$. ∎

> ## Graphing Exploration
>
> Find a viewing window that shows a complete graph of the hyperbola in Example 3.

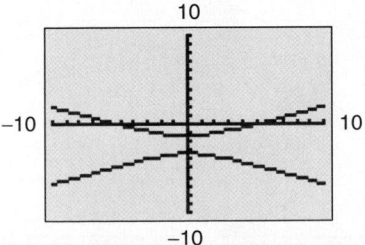

Figure 11.6-8

Example 4 Polar Equations of Conic Sections

Find a polar equation of the ellipse with one focus at $(0, 0)$ and vertices $(3, 0)$ and $(6, \pi)$.

Solution

Because the vertices occur when $\theta = 0$ and $\theta = \pi$, the polar equation is of the form

$$r = \frac{ed}{1 + e\cos\theta} \qquad \text{or} \qquad r = \frac{ed}{1 - e\cos\theta}.$$

Select one of these equations, say

$$r = \frac{ed}{1 + e\cos\theta}$$

and proceed as follows. If the selected equation leads to a contradiction, start again with the other form.

Substitute the values of r and θ given by the vertices to obtain two equations.

$(3, 0)$ | $(6, \pi)$

$$3 = \frac{ed}{1 + e\cos 0} \qquad\qquad 6 = \frac{ed}{1 + e\cos\pi}$$

$$3 = \frac{ed}{1 + e} \qquad\qquad 6 = \frac{ed}{1 - e}$$

$$3(1 + e) = ed \qquad \text{and} \qquad 6(1 - e) = ed$$

Teaching Notes

Solution to the Graphing Exploration: The standard viewing window produces a complete graph of $r = \frac{20}{4 - 10\sin\theta}$ as shown to the right.

Recent Texas Instruments calculators come with a graphing application for conics that can generate correct graphs of conic sections without showing extraneous lines at the asymptotes. The "Conics" application can be found in the "APPS" menu.

Example 4

Find a polar equation of the hyperbola with one focus at $(0, 0)$ and vertices at $\left(2, \frac{\pi}{2}\right)$ and $\left(-6, \frac{3\pi}{2}\right)$.

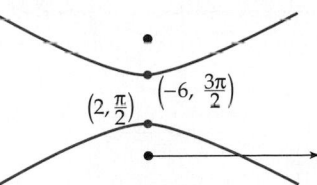

Because the vertices occur when $\theta = \frac{\pi}{2}$ and $\theta = \frac{3\pi}{2}$, the polar equation takes one of the following forms:

$$r = \frac{ed}{1 + e\sin\theta} \qquad \text{or} \qquad r = \frac{ed}{1 - e\sin\theta}$$

Select $r = \frac{ed}{1 - e\sin\theta}$ and substitute the coordinates of the vertices:

$$2 = \frac{ed}{1 - e\sin\left(\frac{\pi}{2}\right)} \qquad -6 = \frac{ed}{1 - e\sin\left(\frac{3\pi}{2}\right)}$$

$$2 = \frac{ed}{1 - e} \qquad\qquad -6 = \frac{ed}{1 + e}$$

$$2(1 - e) = ed \qquad -6(1 + e) = ed$$

$$2(1 - e) = -6(1 + e)$$

$$2 - 2e = -6 - 6e$$

$$4e = -8$$

$$e = -2$$

Since eccentricity must be greater than 0, the wrong form was selected. Select the form $r = \frac{ed}{1 + e\sin\theta}$ and repeat:

$$2 = \frac{ed}{1 + e\sin\left(\frac{\pi}{2}\right)} \qquad -6 = \frac{ed}{1 + e\sin\left(\frac{3\pi}{2}\right)}$$

$$2 = \frac{ed}{1 + e} \qquad\qquad -6 = \frac{ed}{1 - e}$$

$$2(1 + e) = ed \qquad -6(1 - e) = ed$$

$$2(1 + e) = -6(1 - e)$$

$$2 + 2e = -6 + 6e$$

$$8 = 4e$$

$$2 = e$$

Use the equation $2(1 + e) = ed$ and $e = 2$ to find d:

$$2(1 + e) = ed$$

$$2(1 + 2) = 2d$$

$$6 = 2d$$

$$3 = d$$

Use the values of e and d to write the equation of the hyperbola:

$$r = \frac{ed}{1 + e\sin\theta}$$

$$r = \frac{2 \cdot 3}{1 + 2\sin\theta}$$

$$r = \frac{6}{1 + 2\sin\theta}$$

19. a.

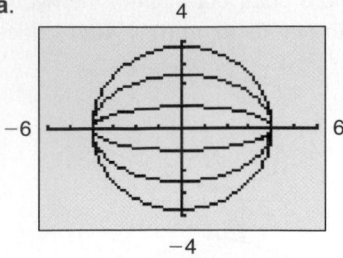

b. $\dfrac{\sqrt{15}}{4}, \dfrac{\sqrt{10}}{4}, \dfrac{\sqrt{2}}{4}$

c. The smaller the eccentricity, the closer the shape is to circular.

20. a.

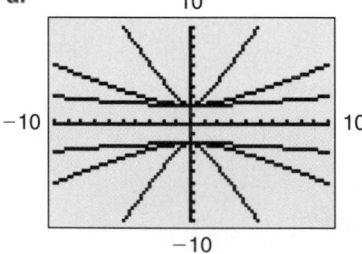

b. ≈1.1180, 2, 55

c. As the eccentricity increases, the hyperbola gets flatter.

21.

22.

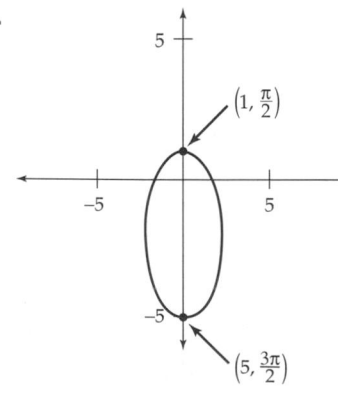

Therefore,

$$3(1 + e) = 6(1 - e)$$
$$3 + 3e = 6 - 6e$$
$$9e = 3$$
$$e = \frac{1}{3}$$

Substituting this value of e into the equation $3(1 + e) = ed$ and solving for d shows that $d = 12$. Hence, $ed = 4$ and the equation of the ellipse is

$$r = \frac{4}{1 + \dfrac{1}{3}\cos\theta} \qquad \text{or equivalently,} \qquad r = \frac{12}{3 + \cos\theta}$$

If you had started this process with the equation $r = \dfrac{ed}{1 - e\cos\theta}$, you would have obtained $e = -\dfrac{1}{3}$, which is impossible since the eccentricity is always positive.   ∎

Exercises 11.6

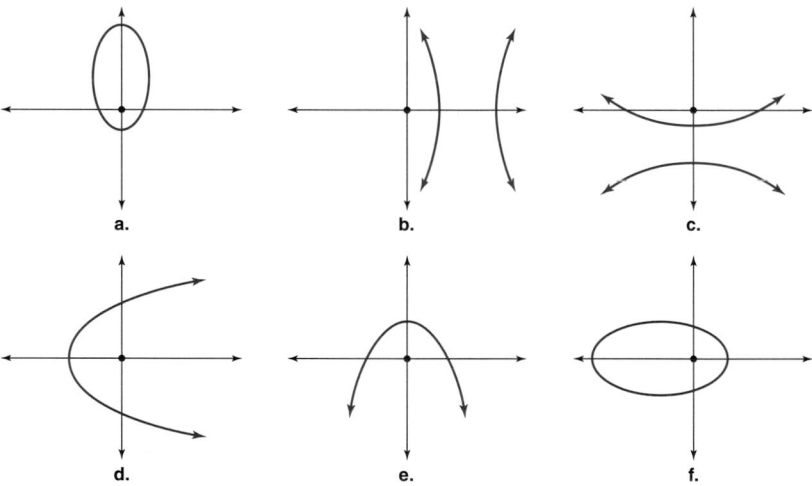

a.   b.   c.

d.   e.   f.

In Exercises 1–6, which of the graphs a–f above could be the graph of the given equation?

1. $r = \dfrac{3}{1 - \cos\theta}$ **d**

2. $r = \dfrac{6}{2 + \cos\theta}$ **f**

3. $r = \dfrac{6}{2 - 4\sin\theta}$ **c**

4. $r = \dfrac{15}{1 + 4\cos\theta}$ **b**

5. $r = \dfrac{6}{3 - 2\sin\theta}$ **a**

6. $r = \dfrac{6}{\dfrac{3}{2} + \dfrac{3}{2}\sin\theta}$ **e**

23.

24.

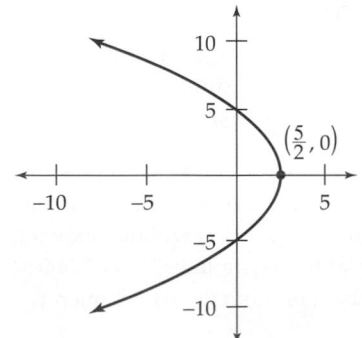

In Exercises 7–12, identify the conic section whose equation is given; if it is an ellipse or hyperbola, state its eccentricity.

7. $r = \dfrac{12}{3 + 4\sin\theta}$
hyperbola, $e = \dfrac{4}{3}$

8. $r = \dfrac{-10}{2 + 3\cos\theta}$
hyperbola, $e = \dfrac{3}{2}$

9. $r = \dfrac{8}{3 + 3\sin\theta}$
parabola, $e = 1$

10. $r = \dfrac{20}{5 - 10\sin\theta}$
hyperbola, $e = 2$

11. $r = \dfrac{2}{6 - 4\cos\theta}$
ellipse, $e = \dfrac{2}{3}$

12. $r = \dfrac{-6}{5 + 2\cos\theta}$
ellipse, $e = \dfrac{2}{5}$

In Exercises 13–18, find the eccentricity of the conic whose equation is given.

13. $\dfrac{x^2}{100} + \dfrac{y^2}{99} = 1$ 0.1

14. $\dfrac{(x-4)^2}{18} + \dfrac{(y+5)^2}{25} = 1$ $\dfrac{\sqrt{7}}{5}$

15. $\dfrac{(x-6)^2}{10} - \dfrac{y^2}{40} = 1$ $\sqrt{5}$

16. $4x^2 + 9y^2 - 24x + 36y + 36 = 0$ $\dfrac{\sqrt{5}}{3}$

17. $16x^2 - 9y^2 - 32x + 36y + 124 = 0$ $\dfrac{5}{4}$

18. $4x^2 - 5y^2 - 16x - 50y + 71 = 0$ $\dfrac{3}{2}$

19. a. Using a square viewing window, graph these ellipses on the same screen, if possible.
$$\dfrac{x^2}{16} + \dfrac{y^2}{1} = 1 \quad \dfrac{x^2}{16} + \dfrac{y^2}{6} = 1 \quad \dfrac{x^2}{16} + \dfrac{y^2}{14} = 1$$
b. Compute the eccentricity of each ellipse in part **a.**
c. Based on parts **a** and **b**, how is the shape of an ellipse related to its eccentricity?

20. a. Graph these hyperbolas on the same screen, if possible.
$$\dfrac{y^2}{4} - \dfrac{x^2}{1} = 1 \quad \dfrac{y^2}{4} - \dfrac{x^2}{12} = 1 \quad \dfrac{y^2}{4} - \dfrac{x^2}{96} = 1$$
b. Compute the eccentricity of each hyperbola in part **a.**
c. Based on parts **a** and **b**, how is the shape of a hyperbola related to its eccentricity?

In Exercises 21–32, sketch the graph of the equation and label the vertices.

21. $r = \dfrac{8}{1 - \cos\theta}$

22. $r = \dfrac{5}{3 + 2\sin\theta}$

23. $r = \dfrac{4}{2 - 4\cos\theta}$

24. $r = \dfrac{5}{1 + \cos\theta}$

25. $r = \dfrac{10}{4 - 3\sin\theta}$

26. $r = \dfrac{12}{3 + 4\sin\theta}$

27. $r = \dfrac{15}{3 - 2\cos\theta}$

28. $r = \dfrac{32}{3 + 5\sin\theta}$

29. $r = \dfrac{3}{1 + \sin\theta}$

30. $r = \dfrac{10}{3 + 2\cos\theta}$

31. $r = \dfrac{10}{2 + 3\sin\theta}$

32. $r = \dfrac{15}{4 - 4\cos\theta}$

In Exercises 33–46, find the polar equation of the conic section that has focus (0, 0) and satisfies the given conditions.

33. parabola; vertex $(3, \pi)$ $r = \dfrac{6}{1 - \cos\theta}$

34. parabola; vertex $\left(2, \dfrac{\pi}{2}\right)$ $r = \dfrac{4}{1 + \sin\theta}$

35. ellipse; vertices $\left(2, \dfrac{\pi}{2}\right)$ and $\left(8, \dfrac{3\pi}{2}\right)$ $r = \dfrac{16}{5 + 3\sin\theta}$

36. ellipse; vertices $(2, 0)$ and $(4, \pi)$ $r = \dfrac{8}{3 + \cos\theta}$

37. hyperbola; vertices $(1, 0)$ and $(-3, \pi)$
$r = \dfrac{3}{1 + 2\cos\theta}$

38. hyperbola; vertices $\left(-2, \dfrac{\pi}{2}\right)$ and $\left(4, \dfrac{3\pi}{2}\right)$
$r = \dfrac{-8}{1 + 3\sin\theta}$

39. eccentricity 4; directrix $r = -2\sec\theta$
$r = \dfrac{8}{1 - 4\cos\theta}$

40. eccentricity 2; directrix $r = 4\csc\theta$
$r = \dfrac{8}{1 + 2\sin\theta}$

41. eccentricity 1; directrix $r = -3\csc\theta$
$r = \dfrac{3}{1 - \sin\theta}$

42. eccentricity 1; directrix $r = 5\sec\theta$
$r = \dfrac{5}{1 + \cos\theta}$

43. eccentricity $\dfrac{1}{2}$; directrix $r = 2\sec\theta$
$r = \dfrac{2}{2 + \cos\theta}$

44. eccentricity $\dfrac{4}{5}$; directrix $r = 3\csc\theta$
$r = \dfrac{12}{5 + 4\sin\theta}$

45. hyperbola; vertical directrix to the left of the pole; eccentricity 2; $\left(1, \dfrac{2\pi}{3}\right)$ is on the graph.
$r = \dfrac{2}{1 - 2\cos\theta}$

46. hyperbola; horizontal directrix above the pole; eccentricity 2; $\left(1, \dfrac{2\pi}{3}\right)$ is on the graph.
$r = \dfrac{1 + \sqrt{3}}{1 + 2\sin\theta}$

47. A comet travels in a parabolic orbit with the sun as the focus. When the comet is 60 million miles from the sun, the line segment from the sun to the comet makes an angle of $\dfrac{\pi}{3}$ radians with the axis of the parabolic orbit. Using the sun as the pole

25.

26.

27.

28.

29.

30.

31.

32.

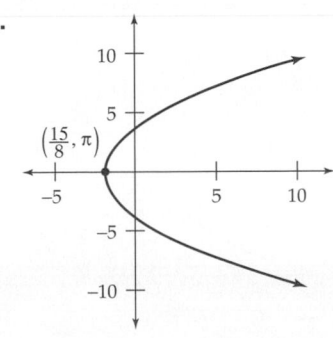

$$r = \frac{30}{1 - \cos \theta},$$

and assuming the axis of the orbit lies along the polar axis, find a polar equation for the orbit. **where r is in millions of miles**

48. Halley's Comet has an elliptical orbit, with eccentricity 0.97 and the sun as a focus. The length of the major axis of the orbit is 3364.74 million miles. Using the sun as the pole and assuming the major axis of the orbit is perpendicular to the polar axis, find a polar equation for the orbit.

$$r = \frac{96.45}{1 - 0.97 \sin \theta}, \text{ where } r \text{ is millions of miles}$$

Section
11.7 Plane Curves and Parametric Equations

Teaching Notes

Students have learned to graph functions and relations in both rectangular and polar coordinate systems. However, neither of these methods is suitable for some graphs, such as the graph shown in Figure 11.7-1. The graph shown in Figure 11.7-1 is the graph of two **Parametric Equations.** Parametric equations were briefly introduced on pages 157–159.

All graphs in this section are in the xy rectangular coordinate plane. In a graph of parametric equations, the coordinates x and y are defined as functions of a third variable, usually t.

The variable t used in parametric equations often represents time. When a point is considered to be the location of a particle traveling along the curve, it tells three pieces of information: the time t, the x-coordinate of the particle's location, and the y-coordinate of the particle's location. This description is well suited to many real-world applications, from the simple (such as the location of an aircraft t minutes after taking off) to the complex (such as the location of a particle in an electro-magnetic field).

Since parametric equations are often used to describe motion, arrows are sometimes added to their graphs to display the direction of motion as t increases. This is shown in Figure 11.7-1. In Figure 11.7-2a on page 756, arrows are used to show how plotted points would be connected to draw the graph.

11.7 Plane Curves and Parametric Equations

Objectives

- Define plane curves and parameterizations

- Find parametric equations for projectile motion and cycloids

Many curves in the plane cannot be represented as the graph of a function $y = f(x)$. Parametric graphing makes it possible to represent such curves in terms of functions and also provides a formal definition of a curve in the plane.

Plane Curves

Consider an object moving in the plane during a particular time interval. In order to describe both the path of the object and its location at a particular time, three variables are needed: the time t, and the coordinates (x, y) of the object at time t. For example, the coordinates might be given by

$$x = 4 \cos t + 5 \cos 3t \quad \text{and} \quad y = \sin 3t + t$$

During the time interval $0 \le t \le 12.5$, the object traces out the curve shown in Figure 11.7-1. The points labeled on the graph show the location of the point at various times. Note that the object may be at the same location at different times, the points where the graph crosses itself.

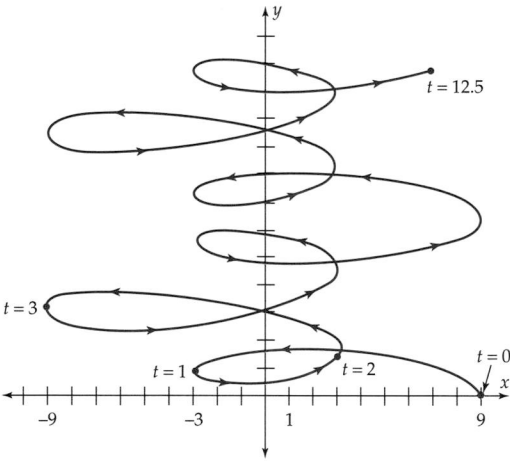

Figure 11.7-1

Definition of a Plane Curve

> Let f and g be continuous functions of t on an interval I. The set of all points (x, y), where
>
> $$x = f(t) \quad \text{and} \quad y = g(t)$$
>
> is called a *plane curve*. The variable t is called a *parameter* and the equations that define x and y are called *parametric equations*.

A pair of parametric equations that describe a given curve is called a **parameterization** of the curve. More than one parameterization is possible for a given curve.

Example 1   Parameterizations of a Line

Find three parameterizations of the line through $(1, -3)$ with slope -2.

Solution

The equation of the line in rectangular coordinates is

$$y + 3 = -2(x - 1) \quad \text{or equivalently} \quad y = -2x - 1 \quad \text{[1]}$$

Choose three expressions in terms of t to represent x, and substitute each into equation [1] to find corresponding expressions for y.

a. $x = t$

$y = -2t - 1$

for any t

b. $x = t + 1$

$y = -2(t + 1) - 1$

$= -2t - 3$

for any t

c. $x = \tan t$

$y = -2\tan t - 1$

$-\dfrac{\pi}{2} < t < \dfrac{\pi}{2}$

Notice in **a** and **b** that when t runs through all real numbers, both x and y take on all real numbers as well. In **c** when t runs from $-\dfrac{\pi}{2}$ to $\dfrac{\pi}{2}$, $x = \tan t$ takes all possible real number values, and hence so does y. Therefore, each parameterization represents the entire line. ∎

Graphing Parametric Equations

Parametric equations may be graphed by hand by plotting points, or by using a calculator in parametric mode. When choosing a viewing window, you must specify values not only for x and y, but also for t. You must also choose a t-step (or t-pitch), which determines how much t changes each time a point is plotted. A t-step between 0.05 and 0.15 usually produces a relatively smooth graph in a reasonable amount of time.

Example Notes

In **Example 1**, the equation in rectangular coordinates is first given in point-slope form and then slope-intercept form:

$$y - y_1 = m(x - x_1) \quad y = mx + b$$

Point out that the expressions in t that are used to represent x are selected at random. An infinite number of choices is possible here. However, as stated in the **CAUTION** box, not every choice will produce a complete graph. For example, the parametric equations

$$x = t^2$$
$$y = -2t^2 - 1$$

produce only the red portion of the entire line, as shown below:

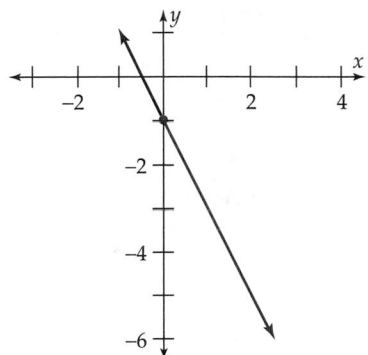

ADDITIONAL EXAMPLES

Example 1

Find three parameterizations of the line through $(4, 1)$ with slope -3.

The equation of the line in rectangular coordinates is

$$(y - 1) = -3(x - 4)$$
$$\text{or}$$
$$y = -3x + 13$$

Choose 3 expressions for x and substitute to get 3 possible answers:

a. $x = t$

$y = -3t + 13$ for any t

b. $x = 5t$

$y = -3(5t) + 13$

$= -15t + 13$ for any t

c. $x = \tan t$

$y = -3\tan t + 13$

$-\dfrac{\pi}{2} < t < \dfrac{\pi}{2}$

Teaching Notes

Using a *t*-step of 0.1, the graph resembles Figure 11.7-1.

Using a *t*-step of 1.5:

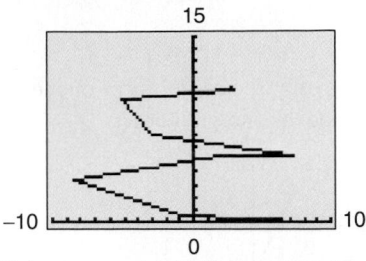

Using a *t*-step of 1.5, the resemblance to Figure 11.7-1 is not as close.

A possible *t*-step is 0.05, used below:

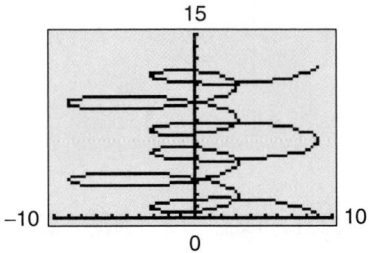

Using a *t*-step of 0.05, the graph does not obviously differ from using a *t*-step of 0.1.

Generally, decreasing the *t*-step gives a more accurate graph, down to a particular *t*-step value. That is, it may not be possible to see the improvement in accuracy when the *t*-step is decreased below a certain value. Furthermore, a very small *t*-step may result in very slow graphing on a calculator.

Example Notes

In **Example 2,** only integer values of *t* are used to get the graph shown in Figure 11.7-2a. The calculator graph in Figure 11.7-2b uses many more values of *t* by using a *t*-step that is much less than 1. A calculator graph using a *t*-step equal to 1 is shown on the right. It consists of only three line segments, corresponding to the three arrows in Figure 11.7-2a.

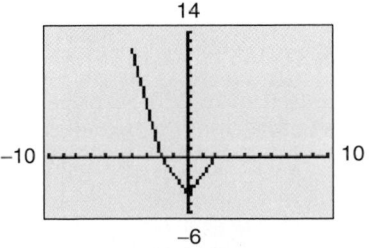

Technology Tip

For parametric graphing mode, choose **PAR** or **PARM** respectively in the TI MODE menu or the TYPE submenu of the Casio **GRAPH** menu.

> **Graphing Exploration** ●
>
> Graph the curve shown in Figure 11.7-1 at the beginning of this section using the window
>
> $$0 \le t \le 12.5 \qquad -10 \le x \le 10 \qquad 0 \le y \le 15$$
>
> and *t*-step 0.1. Does the graph look like Figure 11.7-1? Now change the *t*-step to 1.5 and graph the equations again. Now how does the graph look? Experiment with different *t*-steps to see how they affect the graph.

Example 2   Parameterization of a Parabola

By hand, graph the curve given by

$$x = -2t \qquad \text{and} \qquad y = 4t^2 - 4, \qquad -1 \le t \le 2.$$

Confirm your sketch by using the parametric mode on a calculator.

Solution

For $-1 \le t \le 2$, there is a value of x and a value of y that corresponds to each specific value of t. Find several points by picking values for t, finding the corresponding values of x and y, plotting the points, and connecting the points in the order determined by the least to greatest values of t.

t	$x = -2t$	$y = 4t^2 - 4$	(x, y)
-1	2	0	$(2, 0)$
0	0	-4	$(0, -4)$
1	-2	0	$(-2, 0)$
2	-4	12	$(-4, 12)$

Figure 11.7-2a

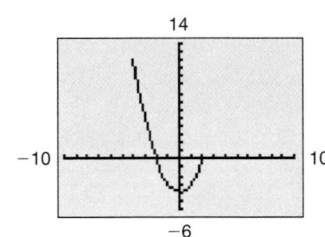

Figure 11.7-2b

The points are plotted and the direction of the curve is indicated in Figure 11.7-2a, and a calculator-generated graph is shown in Figure 11.7-2b.

The direction in which a parametric curve is traced is called its **orientation.**

Eliminating the Parameter

Some curves given by parametric equations can also be expressed as part of the graph of an equation in x and y. The process for doing this, called **eliminating the parameter,** is as follows.

> **Solve one of the parametric equations for the parameter t and substitute this result in the other parametric equation.**

Example 3 Eliminate the Parameter

Consider the curve given in Example 2.

$$x = -2t \qquad \text{and} \qquad y = 4t^2 - 4, \qquad -1 \le t \le 2$$

Find an equation in x and y whose graph includes the graph of the given curve.

Solution

Solve one of the parametric equations for t and substitute the result into the other equation. Solving $x = -2t$ for t shows that $t = -\dfrac{x}{2}$. Substituting this into the equation for y and simplifying the result will eliminate t.

$$y = 4t^2 - 4 = 4\left(-\frac{x}{2}\right)^2 - 4 = 4\left(\frac{x^2}{4}\right) - 4 = x^2 - 4$$

The graph of $y = x^2 - 4$ is the parabola shown in Figure 11.7-3.

Every point on the curve given by the parametric equations is also on the graph of $y = x^2 - 4$. However, the curve given by the parametric equation is *not* the entire parabola, but only the part shown in red, which joins the points $(2, 0)$ and $(-4, 12)$. These points correspond to the minimum and maximum values of t, $t = -1$ and $t = 2$.

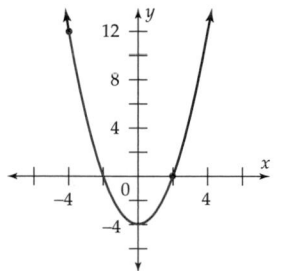

Figure 11.7-3

Example 4 Parameterization of Transformations

Given the parent relation $x = y^2$, write a set of parametric equations to represent the relation, and sketch the graph.

Then write the parametric equations of the following successive transformations of the parent relation, and sketch each graph.

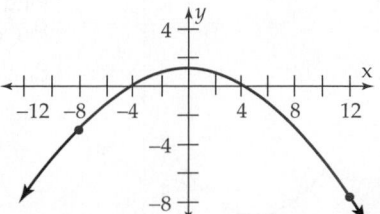

Example 2

By hand, graph the curve given by

$x = 4t$ and $y = -t^2 + 1$, $-2 \le t \le 3$.

Confirm your sketch by using the parametric mode on a calculator. Select several values of t and generate ordered pairs (x, y):

t	$x = 4t$	$y = -t^2 + 1$	(x, y)
-2	-8	-3	$(-8, -3)$
-1	-4	0	$(-4, 0)$
0	0	1	$(0, 1)$
1	4	0	$(4, 0)$
2	8	-3	$(8, -3)$
3	12	-8	$(12, -8)$

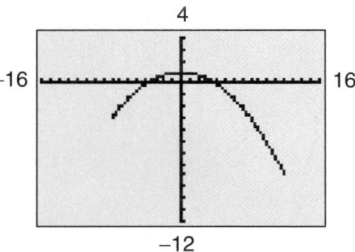

Example 3

Consider the curve given in **Additional Example 2.**

$x = 4t$ and $y = -t^2 + 1$, $-2 \le t \le 3$.

Find an equation in x and y whose graph includes the graph of the given curve.

Solve one equation for t:

$$x = 4t$$
$$t = \frac{x}{4}$$

Substitute into the other equation:

$$y = -t^2 + 1 = -\left(\frac{x}{4}\right)^2 + 1$$
$$= -\frac{1}{16}x^2 + 1$$

The graph of $y = -\dfrac{1}{16}x^2 + 1$ is shown in black; it includes the graph of the given curve, shown in red from $(-8, -3)$ to $(12, -8)$.

ADDITIONAL EXAMPLES

Example 4

Given the parent function $f(x) = x^2$, write a set of parametric equations to represent the function, and sketch the graph.

The parent function can be parameterized as:

$x = t$ $y = t^2$, where t is any real number.

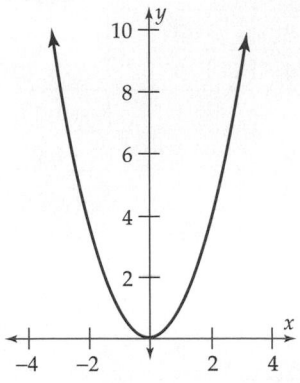

Write the parametric equations of the following successive transformations of the parent function, and sketch each graph.

a. a vertical shift up 3 units

$x = t$ $y = t^2 + 3$ for any t

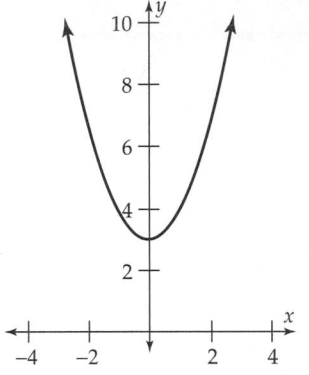

b. then a horizontal stretch by a factor of 2

$x = 2t$ $y = t^2 + 3$ for any t

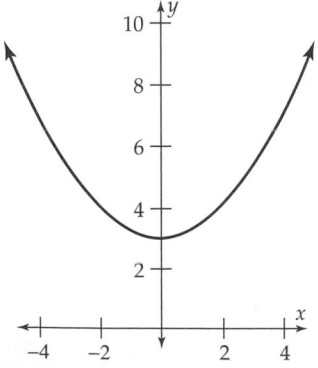

c. then a horizontal shift left 4 units.

$x = 2t - 4$ $y = t^2 + 3$ for any t

758 Chapter 11 **Analytic Geometry**

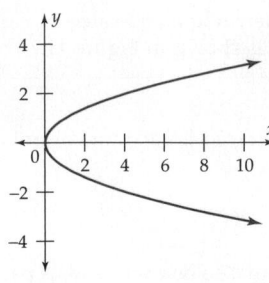

Figure 11.7-4a

a. A horizontal stretch by a factor of 5

$x = 5t^2$
$y = t$
for any t

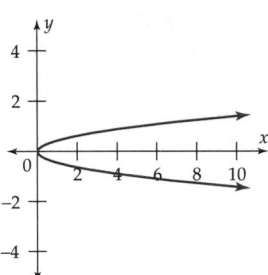

Figure 11.7-4b

b. Then a horizontal shift 3 units to the right

$x = 5t^2 + 3$
$y = t$
for any t

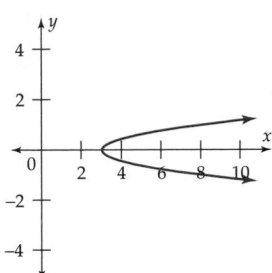

Figure 11.7-4c

c. Then a vertical shift down 2 units

$x = 5t^2 + 3$
$y = t - 2$
for any t

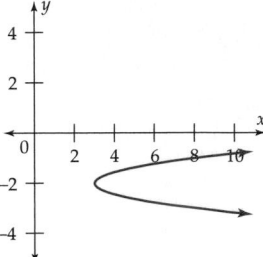

Figure 11.7-4d

a. a horizontal stretch by a factor of 5

b. then a horizontal shift 3 units to the right

c. then a vertical shift down 2 units

Finally, find the focus and a parameterization of the directrix of the parabola found in step **c**.

Solution

The parent relation can be parameterized as

$$x = t^2 \quad \text{and} \quad y = t \quad t \text{ any real number,}$$

whose graph is shown in Figure 11.7-4a.

Recall that the equation of a parabola has the form $y^2 = 4px$. Solving for x, the equation can be written as

$$x = \frac{1}{4p} y^2$$

Therefore, the coefficient of the squared term can be used to find the value of p, which in turn can be used to find both the focus and the directrix of the parabola.

Setting the coefficient of the squared term, 5, equal to $\frac{1}{4p}$ yields

$$5 = \frac{1}{4p} \quad \text{or} \quad p = \frac{1}{20}$$

Find the focus and a parameterization of the directrix of the parabola found in step **c**.

Since the parabola's equation will take the form $y = \frac{1}{4p} x^2$, the coefficient of the t^2 term can be used to find the value of p. So, $1 = \frac{1}{4p}$ or $p = \frac{1}{4}$.

The vertex is located at $(-4, 3)$, and the focus is $\frac{1}{4}$ of a unit above it, so the focus is located at $\left(-4, 3 + \frac{1}{4}\right)$ or $\left(-4, \frac{13}{4}\right)$. The directrix is a horizontal line $\frac{1}{4}$ of a unit below the vertex, $y = 3 - \frac{1}{4} = \frac{11}{4}$.

Note that the vertex has been translated to $(3, -2)$ and that the focus is $\frac{1}{20}$ of a unit to the right of the vertex. Thus, the focus is at $\left(3 + \frac{1}{20}, -2\right)$, or $\left(\frac{61}{20}, -2\right)$. The directrix is the vertical line that is $\frac{1}{20}$ of a unit to the left of the vertex, that is, $x = 3 - \frac{1}{20} = \frac{59}{20}$.

NOTE In the applications in this section, air resistance is ignored and some facts about gravity that are proved in physics are assumed.

Applications

Example 5 Application of Parameterization of a Parabola

A golfer hits a ball with an initial velocity of 140 feet per second so that its path as it leaves the ground makes an angle of 31° with the horizontal.

a. When does the ball hit the ground?

b. How far from its starting point does it land?

c. What is the maximum height of the ball during its flight?

Solution

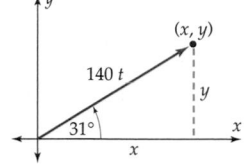

Figure 11.7-5a

Imagine that the golf ball starts at the origin and travels in the direction of the positive x-axis. If there were no gravity, the distance traveled by the ball in t seconds would be $140t$ feet. As shown in Figure 11.7-5a, the coordinates (x, y) of the ball would satisfy

$$\frac{x}{140t} = \cos 31° \qquad \frac{y}{140t} = \sin 31°$$
$$x = (140 \cos 31°)t \qquad y = (140 \sin 31°)t.$$

However, gravity at time t exerts a force of $16t^2$ feet per second per second downward, that is, in the negative direction on the y-axis. Consequently, the coordinates of the golf ball at time t are

$$x = (140 \cos 31°)t \quad \text{and} \quad y = (140 \sin 31°)t - 16t^2.$$

The path given by these parametric equations is shown in Figure 11.7-5b.

Figure 11.7-5b

a. The ball is on the ground when $y = 0$, that is, at the x-intercepts of the graph, which can be found geometrically by using trace and zoom-in. To find the intercepts algebraically, set $y = 0$ and solve for t.

$$(140 \sin 31°)t - 16t^2 = 0$$
$$t(140 \sin 31° - 16t) = 0$$
$$t = 0 \quad \text{or} \quad 140 \sin 31° - 16t = 0$$
$$t = \frac{140 \sin 31°}{16} \approx 4.5066$$

Thus, the ball hits the ground after approximately 4.5066 seconds.

Suggest that students use a square window such as:

$0 \le x \le 600, 0 \le y \le 400$ to see a more accurate representation of the entire path, or

$0 \le x \le 100, 0 \le y \le 67$ to see a more accurate representation of the beginning of the path.

In **Example 4,** students may recall what they learned in Section 3.4 regarding transformations. In particular, the information presented in the boxes on pages 179 and 180 states that a horizontal stretch by a factor of 5 is produced by multiplying x by $\frac{1}{5}$. Therefore, students might think that the equation $x = \frac{1}{5}t^2$ should be used in part **4a.** However, remind the students that the rules on pages 179–180 apply when y is a function of x. In parametric equations, the rules on pages 179–180 must be applied to x, not t, as follows:

$$\frac{1}{5}x = t^2; x = 5t^2$$

Likewise, for parts **4b** and **4c:**

- To shift 3 units right, they need to replace x with $x - 3$. This gives $x - 3 = 5t^2$, or $x = 5t^2 + 3$.

- To shift 2 units down, they need to replace y with $y + 2$. This gives $y + 2 - t$, or $y - t - 2$.

Example Notes

In **Example 5,** an equation in x and y can be found as follows:

$$x = (140 \cos 31°)t$$

$$t = \frac{x}{140 \cos 31°}$$

$$y = (140 \sin 31°)t - 16t^2$$

$$y = (140 \sin 31°)\left(\frac{x}{140 \cos 31°}\right) - 16\left(\frac{x}{140 \cos 31°}\right)^2$$

$$y = \left(\frac{\sin 31°}{\cos 31°}\right)x - \frac{16}{(140 \cos 31°)^2}x^2$$

$$y \approx 0.6009x - 0.0011x^2$$

Ask students to graph this equation and compare it to Figure 11.7-5b; they should get the same graph.

Point out that the graph in Figure 11.7-5b represents the path of the golf ball. The beginning of the path (the portion of the graph near the origin) appears to be nearly a straight line. Ask students why the angle appears to be not nearly equal to 31°. The viewing window is not square.

Example 5

A cannonball is launched from ground level with an initial velocity of 160 feet per second so that its path as it leaves the ground makes an angle of 45° with the horizontal.

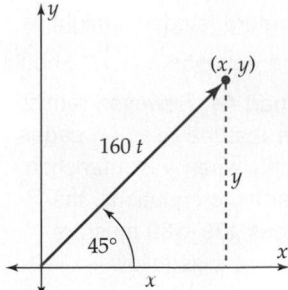

a. When does the cannonball hit the ground?

The path of the cannonball is described by the parametric equations

$x = (160 \cos 45°)t$ and
$y = (160 \sin 45°)t - 16t^2$.

The graph of these equations is shown below:

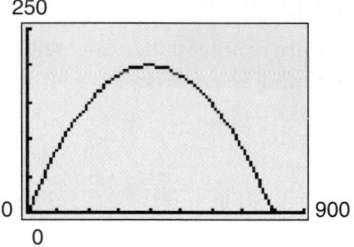

Find t when $y = 0$:

$y = (160 \sin 45°)t - 16t^2$
$0 = (160 \sin 45°)t - 16t^2$
$0 = t(160 \sin 45° - 16t)$
$t = 0$ or $160 \sin 45° - 16t = 0$
$t = 0$ or $t = \dfrac{160 \sin 45°}{16} \approx 7.0711$

The solution $t = 0$ represents the moment when the cannonball was fired. The other solution represents the time elapsed when the cannonball hits the ground. Thus, the cannonball hits the ground after approximately 7.0711 seconds.

b. How far from its starting point does it land?

At $t = 7.0711$, the x-coordinate is

$x = (160 \cos 45°)7.0711$
≈ 800.00 feet

c. What is the maximum height of the cannonball during its flight?

The vertex of the parabola is halfway between the x-intercepts, that is, when

$x = \dfrac{0 + 800}{2} = 400.$

$(160 \cos 45°)t = x = 400$

$t = \dfrac{400}{160 \cos 45°}$

$t \approx 3.5355$

The y-coordinate of the vertex, which is the maximum height, is:

$y = (160 \sin 45°)t - 16t^2$
$y = (160 \sin 45°)(3.5355) - 16(3.536)^2$
$y \approx 200$ feet

Technology Tip

● The graphical root finder and maximum finder do not operate in parametric mode.

Figure 11.7-6a

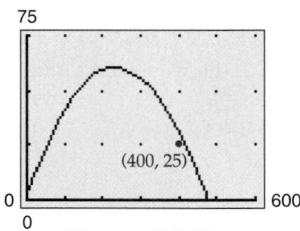

Figure 11.7-6b

---

b. The horizontal distance traveled by the ball is given by the x-coordinate of the second intercept. The x-coordinate when $t \approx 4.5066$ is

$$x = (140 \cos 31°)(4.5066) \approx 540.81 \text{ feet.}$$

c. The graph in Figure 11.7-5 looks like a parabola—and it is, as you can verify by eliminating the parameter t (see Exercise 40). The y-coordinate of the vertex is the maximum height of the ball. It can be found graphically by using trace and zoom-in, or algebraically as follows.

The vertex occurs halfway between the two x-intercepts at $x = 0$ and $x = 540.81$, that is, when $x \approx \dfrac{0 + 540.81}{2} = 270.405$.

$$(140 \cos 31°)t = x = 270.405$$

$$t = \dfrac{270.405}{140 \cos 31°}$$

$$\approx 2.2533$$

Therefore, the y-coordinate of the vertex, which is the maximum height of the ball, is

$$y = (140 \sin 31°)(2.2533) - 16(2.2533)^2 \approx 81.237 \text{ feet.} \quad ■$$

Example 6   Projectile Motion

A batter hits a ball that is 3 feet above the ground. The ball leaves the bat with an initial velocity of 138 feet per second, making an angle of 26° with the horizontal and heading toward a 25-foot fence that is 400 feet away. Will the ball go over the fence?

Solution

Suppose that home plate is at the origin and that the ball travels in the direction of the positive x-axis. The vertical and horizontal distances traveled by the ball, disregarding gravity, are

$$\dfrac{x}{138t} = \cos 26° \qquad \dfrac{y - 3}{138t} = \sin 26°$$

$$x = (138 \cos 26°)t \qquad y = (138 \sin 26°)t + 3,$$

as shown in Figure 11.7-6a.

Allowing for the effect of gravity on the y-coordinate, the ball's path is given by the parametric equations

$$x = (138 \cos 26°)t \qquad \text{and} \qquad y = (138 \sin 26°)t + 3 - 16t^2.$$

The graph of the ball's path, shown in Figure 11.7-6b, was made with the grid-on feature and vertical tick marks 25 units apart. It shows that the y-coordinate of the ball is greater than 25 when its x-coordinate is 400. So, the ball goes over the fence. ■

The procedure used in Example 6 applies to the general case. Replacing 3 by k, 26° by θ, and 138 by v leads to the following conclusion.

Projectile Motion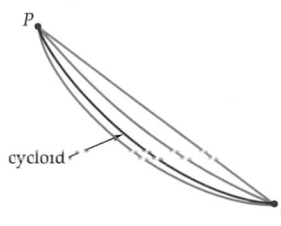

> **When a projectile**
>
> * **is fired from the position $(0, k)$ on the positive y-axis at an angle θ with the horizontal,**
> * **in the direction of the positive x-axis,**
> * **with initial velocity v feet per second,**
> * **with negligible air resistance,**
>
> **then its position at time t seconds is given by the parametric equations**
>
> $$x = (v \cos \theta)t \quad \text{and} \quad y = (v \sin \theta)t + k - 16t^2.$$

Technology Tip

In parametric graphing zoom-in can be very time-consuming. It is often more effective to limit the t range to the values near the points you are interested in and set the t step very small. The picture may be hard to read, but trace can be used to determine coordinates.

Graphing Exploration

Will the ball in Example 6 go over the fence if its initial velocity is 135 feet per second? Use degree mode and the viewing window of Figure 11.7-6b with $0 \le t \le 4$ and t step = 0.1 to graph the ball's path. You may need to use trace if the graph is hard to read. If the answer still is not clear, try changing the t step to 0.02.

Cycloids

Imagine a bug that is sitting at a point P at the edge of a wheel. The path traced out by the bug as the wheel rolls is a curve called a **cycloid**, as shown in Figure 11.7-7.

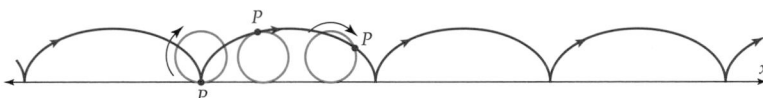

Figure 11.7-7

Cycloids have a number of interesting applications. For example, of all the possible paths joining P and Q in Figure 11.7-8, an arch of an inverted cycloid (in red) is the curve along which a particle subject only to gravity will slide from P to Q in the shortest possible time.

The Dutch physicist Christiaan Huygens, who invented the pendulum clock, proved that a particle takes the same amount of time to slide to the bottom point, Q, of an inverted cycloid (see Figure 11.7-9) starting from *any* point P on the curve.

Figure 11.7-8

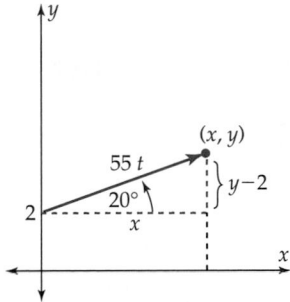

Example Notes

In **Example 7**, note that t represents angle measure, not time. The x and y coordinates are functions of the amount of rotation of the circle.

Recall that $\frac{\pi}{2} = 90°$. In Figure 11.7-11, the condition $0 < t < \frac{\pi}{2}$ is required because t represents an acute angle of a right triangle.

To get the graph shown in Figure 11.7-12, the following window settings can be used for the parameter t: $0 \le t \le 15$, t-step $= 0.1$

ADDITIONAL EXAMPLES

Example 7

Find a parameterization of a cycloid generated by point P on a circle of radius 5 that rolls along the x-axis.

$x = 5(t - \sin t)$ and $y = 5(1 - \cos t)$ for any t.

Real-World Application

This lesson introduces a curve called a **cycloid,** formed by a point on a circle when the circle is "rolled" along a straight line. A cycloid is a special case of a *roulette* (also known as a *spirograph curve*). A roulette is formed by a point on a curve when the curve is rolled along a straight line or another curve.

The Spirograph™ is a toy that is used to create designs by inserting a pencil through a hole in one figure (a circle or oval) and rolling the figure around or along another figure (a line or circle). Students can experiment with making spirograph designs. Since the toy version may not be readily available, have them search the Internet for applets that can be used to create computer-generated spirograph designs.

Figure 11.7-9

Example 7   Parameterization of a Cycloid

Find a parameterization of a cycloid generated by point P on a circle of radius 3 that rolls along the x-axis.

Solution

Begin with P at the origin and the center C of the circle at $(0, 3)$. As the circle rolls along the x-axis, the segment $\overline{CP}$ rotates through an angle of t radians, as shown in Figure 11.7-10.

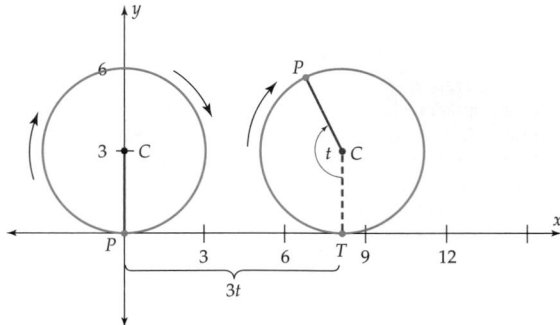

Figure 11.7-10

The distance from T to the origin is the length of the arc of the circle from T to P. From the formula for arc length in Section 6.3, $\ell = r\theta = 3t$.

Therefore, the center C has coordinates $(3t, 3)$. For $0 < t < \frac{\pi}{2}$, triangle PQC in Figure 11.7-11 shows that

$$\sin t = \frac{PQ}{3} \quad \text{and} \quad \cos t = \frac{CQ}{3}$$

or, equivalently,

$$PQ = 3 \sin t \quad \text{and} \quad CQ = 3 \cos t$$

Thus, the point (x, y) in Figure 11.7-11 has the following coordinates.

$$x = OT - PQ = 3t - 3\sin t = 3(t - \sin t)$$
$$y = CT - CQ = 3 - 3\cos t = 3(1 - \cos t)$$

Figure 11.7-11

20

0

14π

−10

Figure 11.7-12

A similar analysis for other values of t shows that these equations are valid for all values of t. (See Exercises 44–46.) Therefore, the parametric equations of the cycloid are

$$x = 3(t - \sin t) \quad \text{and} \quad y = 3(1 - \cos t), \text{ for any } t.$$ ∎

In general, a cycloid generated by a point on a circle of radius r has the following parameterization.

$$x = r(t - \sin t) \quad \text{and} \quad y = r(1 - \cos t), \quad \text{for any } t$$

Exercises 11.7

In Exercises 1–14, find a viewing window that shows a complete graph of the curve.

1–14: Viewing windows may vary.

1. $x = t^2 - 4, \quad y = \dfrac{t}{2}, \quad -2 \le t \le 3$

  $-5 \le x \le 6$ **and** $-2 \le y \le 2$

2. $x = 3t^2, \quad y = 2 + 5t, \quad 0 \le t \le 2$

  $-1 \le x \le 15$ **and** $0 \le y \le 15$

3. $x = 2t, \quad y = t^2 - 1, \quad -1 \le t \le 2$

  $-3 \le x \le 4$ **and** $-2 \le y \le 3$

4. $x = t - 1, \quad y = \dfrac{t+1}{t-1}, \quad t \ge 1$

  $0 \le x \le 20$ **and** $0 \le y \le 10$

5. $x = 4\sin 2t + 9, \quad y = 6\cos t - 8, \quad 0 \le t \le 2\pi$

  $0 \le x \le 14$ **and** $-15 \le y \le 0$

6. $x = t^3 - 3t - 8, \quad y = 3t^2 - 15, \quad -4 \le t \le 4$

  $-20 \le x \le 10$ **and** $-20 \le y \le 10$

7. $x = 6\cos t + 12\cos^2 t, \quad y = 8\sin t + 8\sin t \cos t,$
  $0 \le t \le 2\pi$

  $-2 \le x \le 20$ **and** $-11 \le y \le 11$

8. $x = 12\cos t, \quad y = 12\sin 2t, \quad 0 \le t \le 2\pi$

  $-12 \le x \le 12$ **and** $-12 \le y \le 12$

9. $x = 6\cos t + 5\cos 3t, \quad y = 6\sin t - 5\sin 3t,$
  $0 \le t \le 2\pi$

  $-12 \le x \le 12$ **and** $-12 \le y \le 12$

10. $x = 3t^2 + 10, \quad y = 4t^3, \quad t$ any real number

  $10 \le x \le 20$ **and** $-20 \le y \le 20$

11. $x = 12\cos 3t \cos t + 6, \quad y = 12\cos 3t \sin t - 7,$
  $0 \le t \le 2\pi$

  $-2 \le x \le 20$ **and** $-20 \le y \le 4$

12. $x = 2\cos 3t - 6, \quad y = 2\cos 3t \sin t + 7,$
  $0 \le t \le 2\pi$

  $-9 \le x \le -3$ **and** $4 \le y \le 10$

13. $x = t\sin t, \quad y = t\cos t, \quad 0 \le t \le 8\pi$

  $-25 \le x \le 22$ **and** $-25 \le y \le 26$

14. $x = 9\sin t, \quad y = 9t\cos t, \quad 0 \le t \le 20$

  $-10 \le x \le 10$ **and** $-200 \le y \le 200$

In Exercises 15–24, the given curve is part of the graph of an equation in x and y. Eliminate the parameter by solving one equation for t and substituting the result into the other equation.

15. $x = t - 3, \quad y = 2t + 1, \quad t \ge 0$

  $y = 2x + 7$

16. $x = t + 5, \quad y = \sqrt{t}, \quad t \ge 0$

  $y = \sqrt{x - 5}$

17. $x = -2 + t^2, \quad y = 1 + 2t^2, \quad$ for any t

  $y = 2x + 5$

18. $x = t^2 + 1, \quad y = t^2 - 1, \quad$ for any t

  $y = x - 2$

19. $x = e^t, \quad y = t, \quad$ for any t

  $y = \ln x$

20. $x = 2e^t, \quad y = 1 - e^t, \quad t \ge 0$

  $x + 2y = 2$

21. $x = 3\cos t, \quad y = 3\sin t, \quad 0 \le t \le 2\pi$

  $x^2 + y^2 = 9$

22. $x = 4\sin 2t, \quad y = 2\cos 2t, \quad 0 \le t \le 2\pi$

  $x^2 + 4y^2 = 16$

23. $x = 3\cos t, \quad y = 4\sin t, \quad 0 \le t \le 2\pi$

  $16x^2 + 9y^2 = 144$

24. $x = 2\sin t - 3, \quad y = 2\cos t + 1, \quad 0 \le t \le \pi$

  $(x + 3)^2 + (y - 1)^2 = 4$

In Exercises 25 and 26, sketch the graphs of the given curves and compare them. Do they differ? If so, how?

25. a. $x = -4 + 6t, \quad y = 7 - 12t, \quad 0 \le t \le 1$
  b. $x = 2 - 6t, \quad y = -5 + 12t, \quad 0 \le t \le 1$

26. a. $x = t, \quad y = t^2, \quad$ for any t
  b. $x = \sqrt{t}, \quad y = t, \quad$ for any t
  c. $x = e^t, \quad y = e^{2t}, \quad$ for any t

27. By eliminating the parameter, show that the curve with parametric equations
$$x = a + (c - a)t, \quad y = b + (d - b)t$$
$$\text{for any } t$$
is a straight line.

In Exercises 28–30, find a parameterization of the given curve. Confirm your answer by graphing.

28. line segment from $(14, -5)$ to $(5, -14)$ *Hint:* See Exercise 27.

---

27. Solving $x = a + (c - a)t$ for t

gives $t = \dfrac{x - a}{c - a}$ and substituting

in $y = b + (d - b)t$ then gives

$y = b + (d - b)\dfrac{x - a}{c - a}$, or

$y = b + \dfrac{d - b}{c - a}(x - a)$.

This is a linear equation and therefore gives a straight line. You can check by substitution that (a, b) and (c, d) lie on this straight line; in fact, these points correspond to $t = 0$ and $t = 1$, respectively.

28. $x = 14 - 9t, \; y = -5 - 9t$

  $(0 \le t \le 1)$

ANSWERS

25. a.

8

X1ₜ=⁻4+6T   Y1ₜ=7−12T

−5   3

T=.6
X=⁻.4   Y=⁻.2

−6

b.

8

X1ₜ=2−6T   Y1ₜ=⁻5+12T

−5   3

T=.6
X=⁻1.6   Y=2.2

−6

Both give a straight line segment between $P = (-4, 7)$ and $Q = (2, -5)$. The parametric equations in **a** move from P to Q, and the parametric equations in **b** move from Q to P.

26. a.

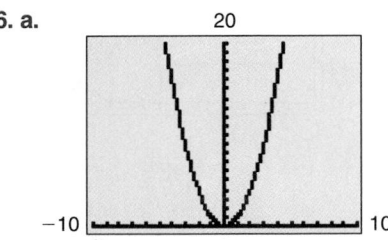

20

−10   10

0

b.

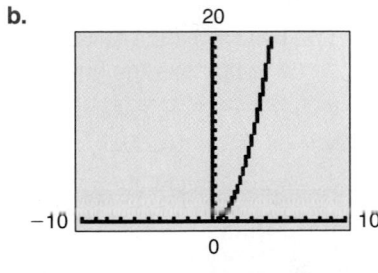

20

−10   10

0

c.

20

−10   10

0

All three are portions of the same parabola $y = x^2$. Parts **b** and **c** only include the values for $x \ge 0$.

35. Solve the first equation for

$$t = \frac{x}{140 \cos 31°}.$$

Substitute into the second to get

$$y = (140 \sin 31°)\left(\frac{x}{140 \cos 31°}\right) -$$

$$16\left(\frac{x}{140 \cos 31°}\right)^2, \text{ which is the}$$

equation of a parabola.

36. a. $x = (60 \cos 50°)t,$

$y = (60 \sin 50°)t - 16t^2 + 5$

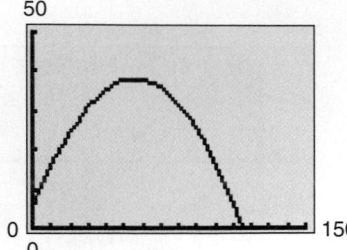

b. approximately 2.98 sec;
approximately 115 ft

37. a. 120

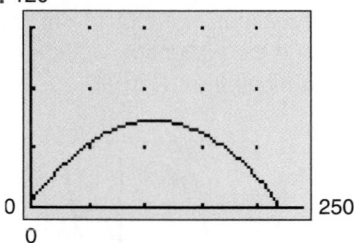

$x = (88 \cos 48°)t$

$y = (88 \sin 48°)t - 16t^2 + 4$

$0 \le t \le 4.5$

b. Yes

38. The ball will hit the fence about 31.56 feet above the ground so it won't quite go over it.

39. $v = 80\sqrt[4]{3} \approx 105.29$ ft/sec

40. a. approximately 30°

b. 29.3°

41. a. 50

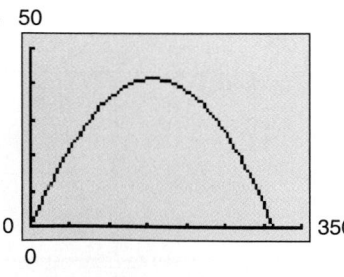

$x = (110 \cos 28°)t$

$y = (110 \sin 28°)t - 16t^2$

$0 \le t \le 3.5$

b. about 3.2 sec

c. ≈ 41.67 ft

---

29. line segment from $(-6, 12)$ to $(12, -10)$
$x = -6 + 18t, \ y = 12 - 22t \quad (0 \le t \le 1)$

30. line segment from $(18, 4)$ to $(-16, 14)$
$x = 18 - 34t, \ y = 4 + 10t$

In Exercises 31–34, locate all local maxima and minima (other than endpoints) of the curve.

31. $x = 4t - 6, \quad y = 3t^2 + 2, \quad -10 \le t \le 10$
local minimum at $(-6, 2)$

32. $x = t^3 + \sin t + 4, \quad y = \cos t, \quad -1.5 \le t \le 2$
local maximum at $(4, 1)$

33. $x = 4t^3 - t + 4, \quad y = -3t^2 + 5, \quad -2 \le t \le 2$
local maximum at $(4, 5)$

34. $x = 4t^3 - \cos t - 5, \quad y = 3t^2 - 8, \quad -2 \le t \le 2$
local minimum at $(-6, -8)$

35. Show that the ball's path in Example 5 is a parabola by eliminating the parameter in the parametric equations below.
$$x = (140 \cos 31°)t$$
$$y = (140 \sin 31°)t - 16t^2$$

In Exercises 36–41, use a calculator in degree mode, and assume that air resistance is negligible.

36. A ball is thrown from a height of 5 feet above the ground with an initial velocity of 60 feet/second at an angle of 50° with the horizontal.
a. Graph the ball's path.
b. When and where does the ball hit ground?

37. A medieval bowman shoots an arrow which leaves the bow 4 feet above the ground with an initial velocity of 88 feet/second at an angle of 48° with the horizontal.
a. Graph the arrow's path.
b. Will the arrow go over the 40-foot-high castle wall that is 200 feet from the archer?

38. A golfer at a driving range stands on a platform 2 feet above the ground and hits the ball with an initial velocity of 120 feet/second at an angle of 39° with the horizontal. There is a 32-foot-high fence 400 feet away. Will the ball fall short, hit the fence, or go over it?

39. A golf ball is hit off the tee at an angle of 30° and lands 300 feet away. What was its initial velocity? *Hint:* The ball lands when $x = 300$ and $y = 0$. Use this fact and the parametric equations for the ball's path to find two equations in the variables t and v. Solve for v.

40. A football kicked from the ground has an initial velocity of 75 feet/second.
a. Set up the parametric equations that describe the ball's path. Experiment graphically with different angles to find the smallest angle

---

(within one degree) needed so that the ball travels at least 150 feet.
b. Use algebra and trigonometry to find the angle needed for the ball to travel exactly 150 feet. *Hint:* The ball lands when $x = 150$ and $y = 0$. Use this fact and the parametric equations for the ball's path to find two equations in the variables t and θ. Solve the "x equation" for t and substitute this result into the other one; then solve for θ. The double-angle identity may be helpful for putting this equation into a form that is easy to solve.

41. A skeet is fired from the ground with an initial velocity of 110 feet/second at an angle of 28°.
a. Graph the skeet's path.
b. How long is the skeet in the air?
c. How high does it go?

42. A golf ball is hit off the ground at an angle of θ degrees with an initial velocity of 100 feet/second.
a. Graph the path of the ball when $\theta = 30°$ and when $\theta = 60°$. In which case does the ball land farthest away?
b. Do part **a** when $\theta = 25°$ and $\theta = 65°$.
c. Experiment further and make a conjecture as to the results when the sum of the two angles is 90°.
d. Prove your conjecture algebraically. *Hint:* Find the value of t at which a ball hit at angle θ hits the ground (which occurs when $y = 0$); this value of t will be an expression involving θ. Find the corresponding value of x (which is the distance of the ball from the starting point). Then do the same for an angle of $90° - \theta$, and use the cofunction identities (in degrees) to show that you get the same value of x.

43. A golf ball is hit off the ground at an angle of θ degrees with an initial velocity of 100 feet/second.
a. Graph the path of the ball when $\theta = 20°$, $\theta = 40°$, $\theta = 60°$, and $\theta = 80°$.
b. For what angle in part **a** does the ball land farthest from where it started?
c. Experiment with different angles, as in parts **a** and **b**, and make a conjecture as to which angle results in the ball landing farthest from its starting point.

In Exercises 44–46, complete the derivation of the parametric equations of the cycloid in Example 7.

44. a. If $\frac{\pi}{2} < t < \pi$, verify that angle θ in the figure has measure $t - \frac{\pi}{2}$ and that

---

42. a. The balls travel the same distance.

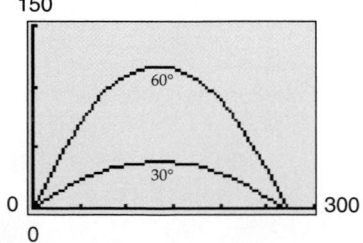

b. The balls travel the same distance.

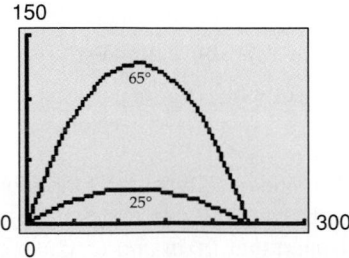

$$x = OT - CQ = 3t - 3\cos\left(t - \frac{\pi}{2}\right)$$

$$y = CT + PQ = 3 + 3\sin\left(t - \frac{\pi}{2}\right).$$

b. Use the addition and subtraction identities for sine and cosine to show that in this case
$x = 3(t - \sin t)$ and $y = 3(1 - \cos t)$.

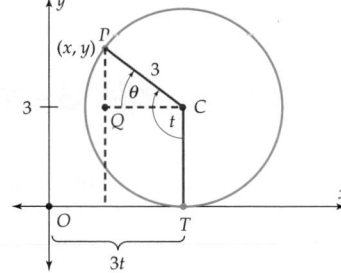

45. a. If $\frac{3\pi}{2} < t < 2\pi$, verify that angle θ in the figure has measure $t - \frac{3\pi}{2}$ and that

$$x = OT + CQ = 3t + 3\cos\left(t - \frac{3\pi}{2}\right)$$

$$y = CT - PQ = 3 - 3\sin\left(t - \frac{3\pi}{2}\right).$$

b. Use the addition and subtraction identities for sine and cosine to show that in this case

$$x = 3(t - \sin t) \quad \text{and} \quad y = 3(1 - \cos t).$$

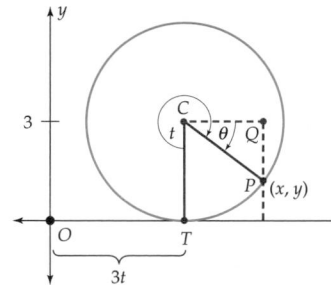

46. a. If $\pi < t < \frac{3\pi}{2}$, verify that angle θ in the figure measures $\frac{3\pi}{2} - t$ and that

$$x = OT + CQ = 3t + 3\cos\left(\frac{3\pi}{2} - t\right)$$

$$y = CT + PQ = 3 + 3\sin\left(\frac{3\pi}{2} - t\right).$$

b. Use the addition and subtraction identities for sine and cosine to show that in this case

$$x = 3(t - \sin t) \quad \text{and} \quad y = 3(1 - \cos t).$$

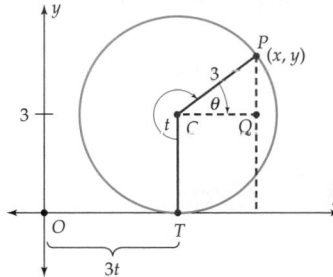

47. *Critical Thinking* Set your calculator for radian mode and for simultaneous graphing mode. Check your instruction manual for how to do this. Particles *A*, *B*, and *C* are moving in the plane, with their positions at time *t* seconds given by:
A: $x = 8\cos t$ and $y = 5\sin t$
B: $x = 3t$ and $y = 5t$
C: $x = 3t$ and $y = 4t$
a. Graph the paths of *A* and *B* in the window with $0 \le x \le 12, 0 \le y \le 6$, and $0 \le t \le 2$. The paths intersect, but do the particles actually collide? That is, are they at the same point at the same time? For slow motion, choose a very small *t*-step, such as 0.01.
b. Set *t*-step $= 0.05$ and trace to estimate the time at which *A* and *B* are closest to each other.
c. Graph the paths of *A* and *C* and determine geometrically, as in part **b**, whether they collide. Approximately when are they closest?
d. Confirm your answers in part **c** as follows. Explain why the distance between particles *A* and *C* at time *t* is given by

$$d = \sqrt{(8\cos t - 3t)^2 + (5\sin t - 4t)^2}.$$

A and *C* will collide if $d = 0$ at some time. Using function graphing mode, graph this distance function when $0 \le t \le 2$. Zoom-in if necessary, and show that *d* is always positive. Find the value of *t* for which *d* is smallest.

48. *Critical Thinking* A particle moves on the horizontal line $y = 3$. Its *x*-coordinate at time *t* seconds is given by $x = 2t^3 - 13t^2 + 23t - 8$. This exercise explores the motion of the particle.
a. Graph the path of the particle in the viewing window with $-10 \le x \le 10, -2 \le y \le 4$, $0 \le t \le 4.3$, and *t*-step $= 0.05$. Note that the calculator seems to pause before completing the graph.

42. c. Balls hit with angles of elevation θ and θ_1 will travel the same distance if $\theta + \theta_1 = 90°$.
d. A ball hit with initial velocity v_o and angle of elevation θ will hit the ground at

$$x = \frac{v_o^2}{16} \sin\theta \cos\theta.$$

Balls hit with complementary angles of elevation will travel the same distance.

43. a. 200

b. 40°

c. 200

An angle of 45° seems to result in the longest distance.

44. a. Since $\angle QCT = \frac{\pi}{2}$, $t = \theta + \frac{\pi}{2}$. Therefore, $\theta = t - \frac{\pi}{2}$.

$$x = OT - CQ = 3t - 3\cos\theta$$

$$= 3t - 3\cos\left(t - \frac{\pi}{2}\right)$$

$$y = CT + PQ = 3 + 3\sin\theta$$

$$= 3 + 3\sin\left(t - \frac{\pi}{2}\right)$$

b. $x = 3t - 3\left(\cos t \cos\frac{\pi}{2} + \sin t \sin\frac{\pi}{2}\right)$

$$= 3(t - \sin t)$$

$$y = 3 + 3\left(\sin t \cos\frac{\pi}{2} - \cos t \sin\frac{\pi}{2}\right)$$

$$= 3(1 - \cos t)$$

45–48. *See pp. 1078–1079.*

b. Use trace (starting with $t = 0$) and watch the path of the particle as you press the right arrow key at regular intervals. How many times does it change direction? When does it appear to be moving the fastest?

c. At what times t does the particle change direction? What are its x-coordinates at these times?

Parameterizations of Conic Sections

Teaching Notes

To verify that parameterizations given in **Example 1** trace out the circle at different speeds, have students graph both parameterizations in a graphing calculator with $0 \le t \le \frac{\pi}{2}$ as shown below.

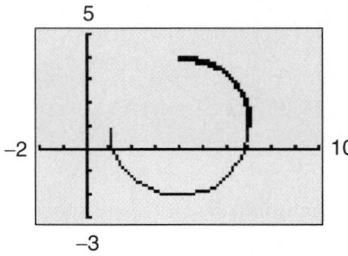

The parameterization $x = 3 \cos t + 4$ and $y = 3 \sin t + 1$ traces a quarter circle in the counterclockwise direction, while the parameterization $x = 3 \cos 2t + 4$ and $y = -3 \sin 2t + 1$ traces a *semicircle* in the *clockwise* direction. The table below $\left(\Delta \text{Tbl} = \frac{\pi}{4} \right)$ shows that the second parameterization returns to $(7, 1)$ when $t = 3.1416$ (or π).

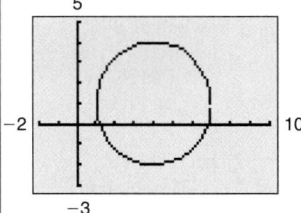

In **Parametric Equations of an Ellipse**, point out that the letters a and b are used somewhat differently here than in the rectangular equations for ellipses in Sections 11.1 (page 693)

11.7.A   *Excursion:* **Parameterizations of Conic Sections**

Objectives

- Define parametric equations for a circle, an ellipse, a hyperbola, and a parabola

Conic sections can often be graphed more conveniently in parametric mode. Parameterizations for conic sections can be found by using Pythagorean identities, as shown in the following examples.

Circles

> **Example 1**   **Parameterization of a Circle**

The equation of the circle with center $(4, 1)$ and radius 3 is

$$(x - 4)^2 + (y - 1)^2 = 9.$$

Show that the following equations provide a parameterization of this circle.

$$x = 3 \cos t + 4 \quad \text{and} \quad y = 3 \sin t + 1, \quad 0 \le t \le 2\pi \quad \textbf{[1]}$$

Solution

To show that the parametric equations satisfy the circle equation, substitute into the equation of the circle and use the Pythagorean identity.

$$
\begin{aligned}
(x - 4)^2 + (y - 1)^2 &= (3 \cos t + 4 - 4)^2 + (3 \sin t + 1 - 1)^2 \\
&= (3 \cos t)^2 + (3 \sin t)^2 \\
&= 9 \cos^2 t + 9 \sin^2 t \\
&= 9(\cos^2 t + \sin^2 t) \\
&= 9(1) \\
&= 9
\end{aligned}
$$

With this parameterization the circle is traced out in a counterclockwise direction from the point $(7, 1)$, as shown in Figure 11.7.A-1. Another parameterization is given by

$$x = 3 \cos 2t + 4 \quad \text{and} \quad y = -3 \sin 2t + 1, \quad 0 \le t \le \pi$$

Verify that this last parameterization traces out the circle in a clockwise direction twice as fast as the parameterization given in [1], because t runs from 0 to π, rather than to 2π. ∎

Figure 11.7.A-1

> **NOTE** When the values of t are given in radian measure, such as 2π, make sure your calculator is in radian mode when graphing.

and 11.4 (page 720). In the rectangular equations, it is specified that $a > b$ and the major (longer) axis of an ellipse has length $2a$ and the minor (shorter) axis has length $2b$. In the parametric equations for ellipses given here, there are no restrictions on the size of b. The *horizontal axis* of the ellipse has length $2a$; it is the major axis when $a > b$ and the minor axis when $a < b$. The *vertical axis* has length $2b$; it is the minor axis when $a > b$ and the major axis when $a < b$.

Example Notes

In **Example 1**, ask students why the parameterization starts from $(7, 1)$.
When $t = 0$,
$x = 3 \cos t + 4 = 3 \cos 0 + 4 = 3 + 4 = 7$
$y = 3 \sin t + 1 = 3 \sin 0 + 1 = 0 + 1 = 1$

In **Example 2**, ask students which point the parameterization starts from. $(5, 0)$

Parametric Equations of a Circle

> The circle with center (c, d) and radius r is given by the parametric equations
>
> $$x = r \cos t + c \quad \text{and} \quad y = r \sin t + d \quad (0 \le t \le 2\pi).$$

The procedure used in Example 1 works in the general case. Example 1 is the special case where $r = 3$ and $(c, d) = (4, 1)$.

Ellipses

Because an ellipse is a generalization of a circle, a similar parameterization can be used.

Example 2   Parameterization of an Ellipse

Find a parameterization of the following ellipse.

$$\frac{x^2}{25} + \frac{y^2}{4} = 1$$

Solution

Let

$$x = 5 \cos t \quad \text{and} \quad y = 2 \sin t, \quad 0 \le t \le 2\pi.$$

Use the Pythagorean identity to show that these parametric equations satisfy the equation of an ellipse.

$$\begin{aligned}
\frac{x^2}{25} + \frac{y^2}{4} &= \frac{(5 \cos t)^2}{25} + \frac{(2 \sin t)^2}{4} \\
&= \frac{25 \cos^2 t}{25} + \frac{4 \sin^2 t}{4} \\
&= \cos^2 t + \sin^2 t \\
&= 1
\end{aligned}$$

Figure 11.7.A-2

The graph is shown in Figure 11.7.A-2. Its major axis has length $2 \cdot 5 = 10$, and its minor axis has length $2 \cdot 2 = 4$. ∎

The parameterization in Example 2, where the center of the ellipse is at $(0, 0)$, can be extended to the general case.

Parametric Equations of an Ellipse

> The ellipse with center (c, d) and a horizontal axis of length $2a$ and a vertical axis of length $2b$ is given by the parametric equations
>
> $$x = a \cos t + c \quad \text{and} \quad y = b \sin t + d \quad (0 \le t \le 2\pi).$$

Teaching Notes

Have students show that the equations $x = b \tan t + c$ and $y = a \sec t + d$ $(0 \le t \le 2\pi)$ provide a parameterization for the hyperbola $\dfrac{(y - d)^2}{a^2} - \dfrac{(x - c)^2}{b^2} = 1$.

$$\dfrac{(y - d)^2}{a^2} - \dfrac{(x - c)^2}{b^2}$$

$$= \dfrac{(a \sec t + d - d)^2}{a^2} - \dfrac{(b \tan t + c - c)^2}{b^2}$$

$$= \dfrac{(a \sec t)^2}{a^2} - \dfrac{(b \tan t)^2}{b^2}$$

$$= \dfrac{a^2 \sec^2 t}{a^2} - \dfrac{b^2 \tan^2 t}{b^2}$$

$$= \sec^2 t - \tan^2 t$$

$$= 1$$

Example Notes

In **Example 3**, if students try to graph the hyperbola with the given parameterization on their calculators, they will most likely get erroneous lines because when $t = \dfrac{\pi}{2}$ and $t = \dfrac{3\pi}{2}$, both x and y are undefined (since $\tan \dfrac{\pi}{2}$, $\sec \dfrac{\pi}{2}$, $\tan \dfrac{3\pi}{2}$ and $\sec \dfrac{3\pi}{2}$ are undefined). Show them the following sketch of the hyperbola for Example 3.

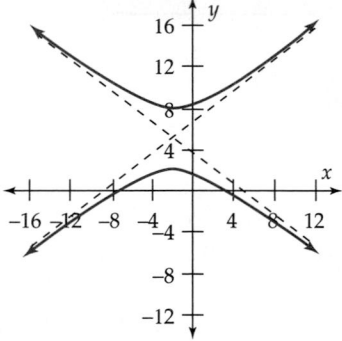

ADDITIONAL EXAMPLES

Example 3

Identify the conic section whose equation is given below, and find a parameterization for it.

$$\dfrac{(x - 3)^2}{25} - \dfrac{(y + 1)^2}{4} = 1$$

The equation is a hyperbola with center $(3, -1)$. Using the first equation from the box on page 768, with $a = 5$, $b = 2$, and $(c, d) = (3, -1)$, the parametric equations are $x = 5 \sec t + 3$ and $y = 2 \tan t - 1$, $0 \le t \le 2\pi$.

Hyperbolas

The hyperbola centered at (c, d) with equation

$$\dfrac{(x - c)^2}{a^2} - \dfrac{(y - d)^2}{b^2} = 1$$

can be obtained from the following parameterization.

$$x = a \sec t + c \qquad y = b \tan t + d, \qquad 0 \le t \le 2\pi$$

By a Pythagorean identity, $1 + \tan^2 t = \sec^2 t$. Therefore,

$$\dfrac{(x - c)^2}{a^2} - \dfrac{(y - d)^2}{b^2} = \dfrac{(a \sec t + c - c)^2}{a^2} - \dfrac{(b \tan t + d - d)^2}{b^2}$$

$$= \dfrac{(a \sec t)^2}{a^2} - \dfrac{(b \tan t)^2}{b^2}$$

$$= \dfrac{a^2 \sec^2 t}{a^2} - \dfrac{b^2 \tan^2 t}{b^2}$$

$$= \sec^2 t - \tan^2 t = 1$$

A similar argument works for other hyperbolas and leads to the following conclusion.

Parametric Equations of a Hyperbola

Hyperbolas with center at (c, d) have the following parameterizations.

Equation	Parameterization
$\dfrac{(x - c)^2}{a^2} - \dfrac{(y - d)^2}{b^2} = 1$	$x = a \sec t + c \qquad y = b \tan t + d$ $(0 \le t \le 2\pi)$
$\dfrac{(y - d)^2}{a^2} - \dfrac{(x - c)^2}{b^2} = 1$	$x = b \tan t + c \qquad y = a \sec t + d$ $(0 \le t \le 2\pi)$

Example 3 Parameterization of a Conic

Identify the conic section whose equation is given below, and find a parameterization for it.

$$\dfrac{(y - 5)^2}{9} - \dfrac{(x + 2)^2}{16} = 1$$

Solution

The equation is a hyperbola with center at $(-2, 5)$. It has the same form as the second equation in the preceding box, with $a = 3$, $b = 4$, and $(c, d) = (-2, 5)$. Therefore, its parametric equations are

$$x = 4 \tan t - 2 \qquad y = 3 \sec t + 5, \qquad 0 \le t \le 2\pi.$$

Parametric Equations of a Parabola

When a parabola has an equation such as

$$y = 4(x - 5)^2 + 7,$$

in which y is a function of x, then it can be graphed on a calculator either in function mode or in parametric mode with

$$x = t \quad \text{and} \quad y = 4(t - 5)^2 + 7.$$

A parabola with an equation such as

$$x = 2(y + 3)^2 - 4,$$

in which x is a function of y, cannot be graphed (by using a single equation) in function mode on a calculator, but it can be graphed in parametric mode by letting

$$x = 2(t + 3)^2 - 4 \quad \text{and} \quad y = t.$$

Similar techniques work for other parabolas.

Exercises 11.7.A

In Exercises 1–4, find a parameterization of the given curve. Confirm your answer by graphing.

1. circle with center $(9, 12)$ and radius 5

2. $x^2 + y^2 - 14x + 8y + 29 = 0$ *Hint*: see Example 2 in Section 11.4.

3. $x^2 + y^2 - 4x - 6y + 9 = 0$

4. circle with center $(7, -4)$ and radius 6

In Exercises 5–26, find parametric equations for the curve whose equation is given, and use these parametric equations to find a complete graph of the curve.

5. $\dfrac{x^2}{10} - 1 = \dfrac{-y^2}{36}$

6. $\dfrac{y^2}{49} + \dfrac{x^2}{81} = 1$

7. $4x^2 + 4y^2 = 1$

8. $x^2 + 4y^2 = 1$

9. $\dfrac{x^2}{10} - \dfrac{y^2}{36} = 1$

10. $\dfrac{y^2}{9} - \dfrac{x^2}{16} = 1$

11. $x^2 - 4y^2 = 1$

12. $2x^2 - y^2 = 4$

13. $8x = 2y^2$

14. $4y = x^2$

15. $\dfrac{(x - 1)^2}{4} + \dfrac{(y - 5)^2}{9} = 1$

16. $\dfrac{(x - 2)^2}{16} + \dfrac{(y + 3)^2}{12} = 1$

17. $\dfrac{(x + 1)^2}{16} + \dfrac{(y - 4)^2}{8} = 1$

18. $\dfrac{(x + 5)^2}{4} + \dfrac{(y + 2)^2}{12} = 1$

19. $y = 4(x - 1)^2 + 2$

20. $y = 3(x - 2)^2 - 3$

21. $x = 2(y - 2)^2$

22. $x = -3(y - 1)^2 - 2$

23. $\dfrac{(y + 3)^2}{25} - \dfrac{(x + 1)^2}{16} = 1$

24. $\dfrac{(y + 1)^2}{9} - \dfrac{(x - 1)^2}{25} = 1$

25. $\dfrac{(x + 3)^2}{1} - \dfrac{(y - 2)^2}{4} = 1$

26. $\dfrac{(y + 5)^2}{9} - \dfrac{(x - 2)^2}{1} = 1$

CHAPTER 11

Review

CHAPTER 11 REVIEW

Important Concepts

Important Facts and Formulas

Equation of an **ellipse** with center (h, k) and axes on the lines $x = h, y = k$:

$$\frac{(x - h)^2}{a^2} + \frac{(y - k)^2}{b^2} = 1$$

Equation of a **hyperbola** with center (h, k) and vertices on the line $y = k$:

$$\frac{(x - h)^2}{a^2} - \frac{(y - k)^2}{b^2} = 1$$

Equation of **hyperbola** with center (h, k) and vertices on the line $x = h$:

$$\frac{(y - k)^2}{a^2} - \frac{(x - h)^2}{b^2} = 1$$

Equation of a **parabola** with vertex (h, k) and axis $x = h$:

$$(x - h)^2 = 4p(y - k)$$

Equation of a **parabola** with vertex (h, k) and axis $y = k$:

$$(y - k)^2 = 4p(x - h)$$

Rotation equations:

$$x = u \cos \theta - v \sin \theta$$
$$y = u \sin \theta + v \cos \theta$$

Rotation Angle:

To eliminate the xy term in $Ax^2 + Bxy + Cy^2 + Dx + Ey + F = 0$, rotate the axes through an angle θ such that $\cot 2\theta = \dfrac{A - C}{B}$.

The rectangular and polar coordinates of a point are related by

$$x = r \cos \theta \qquad \text{and} \qquad y = r \sin \theta$$
$$r^2 = x^2 + y^2 \qquad \text{and} \qquad \tan \theta = \frac{y}{x}$$

Review Exercises

ANSWERS

1. ellipse; foci at $(0, \pm2)$;
   vertices at $\left(0, \pm2\sqrt{5}\right)$

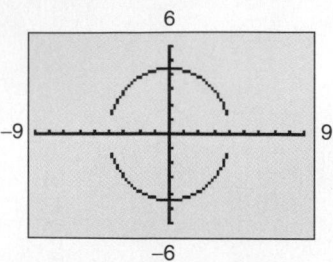

2. ellipse; foci at $\left(0, \pm\sqrt{21}\right)$;
   vertices at $(0, \pm5)$

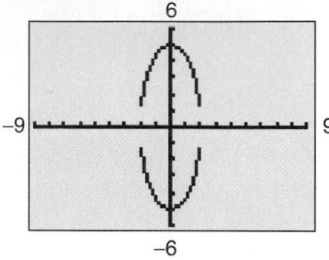

3. This is the same graph as in Exercise 2; the equations are equivalent.

4. ellipse; foci at $\left(\pm\sqrt{5}, 0\right)$;
   vertices at $(\pm3, 0)$

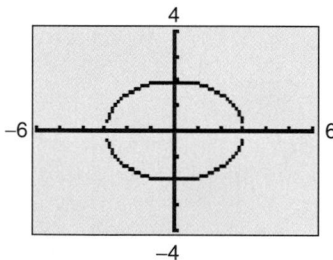

5. $\dfrac{x^2}{12} + \dfrac{y^2}{16} = 1$; ellipse;
   foci at $(0, \pm2)$;
   vertices at $(0, \pm4)$

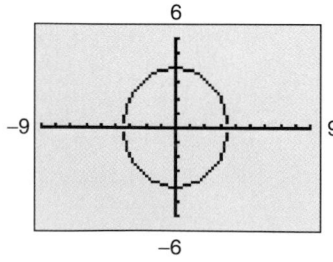

6. $\dfrac{x^2}{9} + \dfrac{y^2}{1} = 1$; ellipse; foci at $\left(\pm\sqrt{8}, 0\right)$;
   vertices at $(\pm3, 0)$

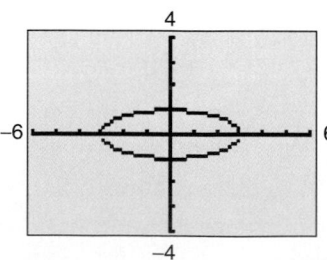

If e and d are constants with $e > 0$, then the graph of a polar equation of the form

$$r = \frac{ed}{1 \pm e\cos\theta} \quad \text{or} \quad r = \frac{ed}{1 \pm e\sin\theta}$$

is an ellipse if $0 < e < 1$, a parabola if $e = 1$, and a hyperbola if $e > 1$.

Review Exercises

In Exercises 1–10, find the foci and vertices of the conic, and find a viewing window that shows a complete graph of the equation.   **1–10: Viewing windows may vary.**

Section 11.1

1. $\dfrac{x^2}{16} + \dfrac{y^2}{20} = 1$

2. $\dfrac{x^2}{4} + \dfrac{y^2}{25} = 1$

3. $25x^2 + 4y^2 = 100$

4. $4x^2 + 9y^2 = 36$

5. Find the equation of the ellipse with center at the origin, one vertex at $(0, 4)$, passing through $\left(\sqrt{3}, 2\sqrt{3}\right)$.

6. Find the equation of the ellipse with center at the origin, one vertex at $(3, 0)$, passing through $\left(1, \dfrac{2\sqrt{2}}{3}\right)$.

Section 11.2

7. $\dfrac{x^2}{9} - \dfrac{y^2}{16} = 1$

8. $\dfrac{x^2}{16} - \dfrac{y^2}{4} = 1$

9. Find the equation of the hyperbola with center at the origin, one vertex at $(0, -2)$, passing through $\left(-1, 2\sqrt{2}\right)$.

10. Find the equation of the hyperbola with center at the origin, one vertex at $(3, 0)$, passing through $\left(5, -\dfrac{8}{3}\right)$.

Section 11.3

In Exercises 11–16, find the equation of the parabola with vertex at the origin that satisfies the given condition

11. axis $x = 0$, passing through $(-1, 5)$ $y^2 = -25x$

12. axis $y = 0$, passing through $(-1, 5)$ $x^2 = \dfrac{1}{5}y$

13. focus $(-4, 0)$ $y^2 = -16x$

14. focus $(0, -3)$ $x^2 = -12y$

15. directrix $x = -4$ $y^2 = 16x$

16. directrix $y = 2$ $x^2 = -8y$

17. Find the focus and directrix of the parabola $10y = 7x^2$.   **focus:** $\left(0, \dfrac{5}{14}\right)$, **directrix:** $y = -\dfrac{5}{14}$

18. Find the focus and directrix of the parabola $3y^2 - x - 4y + 4 = 0$.   **focus:** $\left(\dfrac{33}{12}, \dfrac{2}{3}\right)$, **directrix:** $x = \dfrac{31}{12}$

7–10. See p. 1080.

Section   11.4

In Exercises 19–28, sketch the graph of the equation and identify the conic. If there are asymptotes, give their equations and label all characteristic points.

19. $\dfrac{(x-1)^2}{7} + \dfrac{(y-3)^2}{16} = 1$

20. $3x^2 = 1 + 2y^2$

21. $\dfrac{(x-3)^2}{9} + \dfrac{(y+5)^2}{4} = 1$

22. $\dfrac{(y+4)^2}{25} - \dfrac{(x-1)^2}{4} = 1$

23. $4x^2 - 9y^2 = 144$

24. $x^2 + 4y^2 - 10x + 9 = 0$

25. $2y = 4(x-3)^2 + 6$

26. $3y = 6(x+1)^2 - 9$

27. $x = y^2 + 2y + 2$

28. $y = x^2 - 2x + 3$

29. What is the center of the ellipse $4x^2 + 3y^2 - 32x + 36y + 124 = 0$?
(4, −6)

30. Find the equation of the hyperbola with center at the origin, one vertex at $(0, 5)$, passing through $\left(1, 3\sqrt{5}\right)$. $\dfrac{y^2}{25} - \dfrac{4x^2}{5} = 1$

31. Find the equation of the hyperbola with center at $(3, 0)$, one vertex at $(3, 2)$, passing through $\left(1, \sqrt{5}\right)$. $\dfrac{y^2}{4} - \dfrac{(x-3)^2}{16} = 1$

32. Find the equation of the parabola with vertex $(2, 5)$, axis $x = 2$, passing through $(3, 12)$.
$(x-2)^2 = \dfrac{1}{7}(y-5)$

33. Find the equation of the parabola with vertex $\left(\dfrac{3}{2}, -\dfrac{1}{2}\right)$, axis $y = -\dfrac{1}{2}$, passing through $(-3, 1)$. $\left(y + \dfrac{1}{2}\right)^2 = -\dfrac{1}{2}\left(x - \dfrac{3}{2}\right)$

34. Find the equation of the parabola with vertex $(5, 2)$ that passes through the points $(7, 3)$ and $(9, 6)$.
$(x-5)^2 = 4(y-2)$

35. Find the equation of the ellipse with center at $(3, 1)$, one vertex at $(1, 1)$, passing through $\left(2, 1 + \sqrt{\dfrac{3}{2}}\right)$. $\dfrac{(x-3)^2}{4} + \dfrac{(y-1)^2}{2} = 1$

In Exercises 36–39, assume that the graph of the equation is a nondegenerate conic. Use the discriminant to identify the graph.

36. $x^2 + y^2 - xy - 4y = 0$
ellipse

37. $4xy - 3x^2 - 20 = 0$
hyperbola

38. $4x^2 - 4xy + y^2 - \sqrt{5}x - 2\sqrt{5}y = 0$
parabola

39. $3x^2 + 2\sqrt{2}xy + 2y^2 - 12 = 0$
ellipse

In Exercises 40–45, find a viewing window that shows a complete graph of the equation.   **40–45: Viewing windows may vary.**

40. $x^2 + xy + y^2 - 3y - 6 = 0$

41. $x^2 + xy - 2 = 0$

42. $x^2 - 4xy + y^2 + 5 = 0$

43. $x^2 + 3xy + y^2 - 2\sqrt{2}x + 2\sqrt{2}y = 0$

44. $x^2 + 2xy + y^2 - 4\sqrt{2}y = 0$

45. $x^2 - xy + y^2 - 6 = 0$

19. ellipse, center: $(1, 3)$ foci: $(1, 6)$, $(1, 0)$, vertices: $(1, 7)$, $(1, -1)$

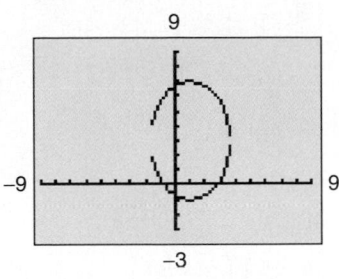

20. hyperbola, center: $(0, 0)$,

vertices: $\left(\pm\dfrac{1}{\sqrt{3}}, 0\right)$,

foci: $\left(\pm\sqrt{\dfrac{5}{6}}, 0\right)$,

asymptotes: $y = \pm\sqrt{\dfrac{3}{2}}\,x$

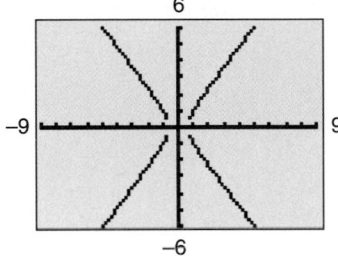

21. ellipse, center: $(3, -5)$,
vertices: $(0, -5)$ and $(6, -5)$,
foci: $\left(3 \pm \sqrt{5}, -5\right)$

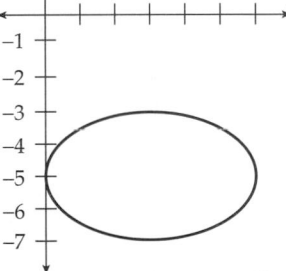

22–28. *See p.* 1081.

40. $-5 \le x \le 3$ and $-2 \le y \le 6$

41. $-9 \le x \le 9$ and $-6 \le y \le 6$

42. $-5 \le x \le 5$ and $-15 \le y \le 15$

43. $-15 \le x \le 10$ and $-10 \le y \le 20$

44. $-10 \le x \le 2$ and $-1 \le y \le 10$

45. $-6 \le x \le 6$ and $-4 \le y \le 4$

46. $x = \frac{\sqrt{2}}{2}u - \frac{\sqrt{2}}{2}v$

$y = \frac{\sqrt{2}}{2}u + \frac{\sqrt{2}}{2}v$

47. $x = \frac{1}{2}u - \frac{\sqrt{3}}{2}v$

$y = \frac{\sqrt{3}}{2}u + \frac{1}{2}v$

48. $45°$

49. $45°$

50. $\left(2, \frac{5\pi}{4}\right), \left(2, -\frac{3\pi}{4}\right),$

$\left(-2, \frac{9\pi}{4}\right), \left(-2, \frac{17\pi}{4}\right)$

51.

52.

53.

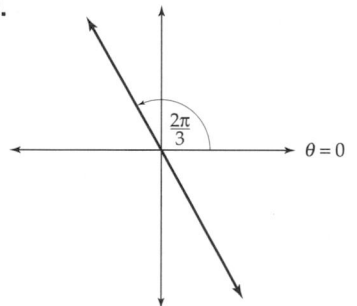

54–61. *See pp.* 1081–1082.

62. $\left(\sqrt{12}, \frac{\pi}{6}\right)$

63. $\left(-\frac{3}{2}, -\frac{3\sqrt{3}}{2}\right)$

64. Eccentricity $= \frac{1}{\sqrt{5}} \approx 0.4472$

65. Eccentricity $= \sqrt{\frac{2}{3}} \approx 0.8165$

66–69. *See p.* 1082.

70. $r = \frac{-15}{1 - 4\sin\theta}$

71. $r = \frac{2}{1 + \cos\theta}$

72. $r = \frac{9}{4 - 3\sin\theta}$

73. $r = \frac{24}{5 + \cos\theta}$

Section 11.4.A — In Exercises 46–47, find the rotation equations when the x- and y-axes are rotated through the given angle.

46. $45°$

47. $60°$

In Exercises 48–49, find the angle through which the x- and y-axes should be rotated to eliminate the xy term in the equation.

48. $x^2 - 4xy + y^2 + 5 = 0$

49. $x^2 + xy + y^2 - 3y - 6 = 0$

Section 11.5 — **50.** List four other pairs of polar coordinates for the point $\left(-2, \frac{\pi}{4}\right)$.

51. Plot the points $\left(2, \frac{3\pi}{4}\right)$ and $\left(-3, -\frac{2\pi}{3}\right)$ on a polar coordinate graph.

In Exercises 52–61, sketch the graph of the polar equation.

52. $r = -2$

53. $\theta = \frac{2\pi}{3}$

54. $\theta = -\frac{5\pi}{6}$

55. $r = 2\theta \ (\theta \le 0)$

56. $r = 4\cos\theta$

57. $r = 2 - 2\sin\theta$

58. $r = \cos 3\theta$

59. $r^2 = \cos 2\theta$

60. $r = 1 + 2\sin\theta$

61. $r = 5$

62. Convert $\left(3, \sqrt{3}\right)$ from rectangular to polar coordinates.

63. Convert $\left(3, -\frac{2\pi}{3}\right)$ from polar to rectangular coordinates.

Section 11.6 — **64.** What is the eccentricity of the ellipse $24x^2 + 30y^2 = 120$?

65. What is the eccentricity of the ellipse $3x^2 + y^2 = 84$?

In Exercises 66–69, sketch the graph of the equation, labeling the vertices and identifying the conic.

66. $r = \frac{14}{7 + 7\cos\theta}$

67. $r = \frac{-24}{3 - 9\cos\theta}$

68. $r = \frac{10}{3 + 4\sin\theta}$

69. $r = \frac{12}{2 - \sin\theta}$

In Exercises 70–73, find a polar equation of the conic that has focus $(0, 0)$ and satisfies the given conditions.

70. hyperbola; vertices $\left(5, \frac{\pi}{2}\right)$ and $\left(-3, \frac{3\pi}{2}\right)$

71. eccentricity 1; directrix $r = 2\sec\theta$

72. eccentricity 0.75; directrix $r = -3\csc\theta$

73. ellipse; vertices $(4, 0)$ and $(6, \pi)$

In Exercises 74–77, find a viewing window that shows a complete graph of the curve with the given parametric equations.   **74–77: Viewing windows may vary**

74. $x = [64 \cos(\pi/6)]t$ and $y = -16t^2 + \left[64 \sin\dfrac{\pi}{6}\right]t,\;\; 0 \le t \le \pi$

75. $x = t^3 + t + 1$ and $y = t^2 + 2t,\;\; -3 \le t \le 3$

76. $x = t^2 - t + 3$ and $y = t^3 - 5t,\;\; -3 \le t \le 3$

77. $x = 8 \cos t + \cos 8t$ and $y = 8 \sin t - \sin 8t,\;\; 0 \le t \le 2\pi$

Section 11.7   In Exercises 78–81, sketch the graph of the curve whose parametric equations are given, and by eliminating the parameter, find an equation in x and y whose graph contains the given curve.

78. $x = 3 \cos t,\;\; y = 5 \sin t,\;\; 0 \le t \le 2\pi$

79. $x = \cos t,\;\; y = 2 \sin^2 t,\;\; 0 \le t \le 2\pi$

80. $x = e^t,\;\; y = \sqrt{t + 1},\;\; t \ge 1$

81. $x = 2t - 1,\;\; y = 2 - t,\;\; -3 \le t \le 3$

82. Which of the following is not a parameterization of the curve $x = y^2 + 1$?
    a. $x = t^2 + 1,$ $y = t,$ any real number t
    b. $x = \sin^2 t + 1,$ $y = \sin t,$ any real number t
    c. $x = t^4 + 1,$ $y = t^2,$ any real number t
    d. $x = t^6 + 1,$ $y = t^3,$ any real number t

83. Which of the curves in Questions 74–77 appear to be the graphs of functions of the form $y = f(x)$?

Section 11.7.A   In Exercises 84–87, find a parameterization of the given curve. Confirm your answer by graphing.

84. circle with center $(3, -2)$ and radius 4

85. circle with center $(-3, 5)$ and radius 5

86. $9x^2 + 4y^2 - 54x + 16y + 61 = 0$ **87.** $4x^2 + y^2 + 16x - 6y + 21 = 0$

In Exercises 88–97, find parametric equations for the curve whose equation is given, and use these parametric equations to find a complete graph of the curve.

88. $9x^2 + 9y^2 = 1$ **89.** $4x^2 + 9y^2 = 1$

90. $16x^2 - y^2 = 1$ **91.** $x^2 - 36y^2 = 1$

92. $\dfrac{(x - 3)^2}{9} + \dfrac{(y + 4)^2}{25} = 1$ **93.** $\dfrac{(x + 2)^2}{49} + \dfrac{(y - 5)^2}{64} = 1$

94. $\dfrac{(x - 2)^2}{81} - \dfrac{(y - 5)^2}{100} = 1$ **95.** $\dfrac{(y + 3)^2}{4} - \dfrac{(x - 2)^2}{12} = 1$

96. $y = 3(x + 2)^2 - 5$ **97.** $x = -32(y + 4)^2 - 5$

74. $0 \le x \le 200$ and $-100 \le y \le 50$

75. $-35 \le x \le 32$ and $-2 \le y \le 16$

76. $0 \le x \le 15$ and $-15 \le y \le 15$

77. $-15 \le x \le 15$ and $-10 \le y \le 10$

78. $\left(\dfrac{x}{3}\right)^2 + \left(\dfrac{y}{5}\right)^2 = 1$

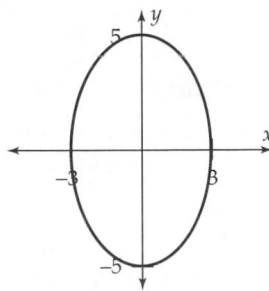

79. $y = -2x^2 + 2$

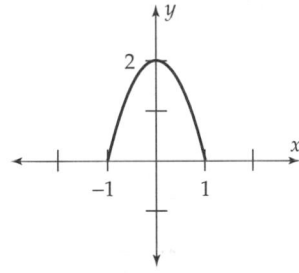

Point moves from $(1, 0)$ to $(-1, 0)$ as t goes from 0 to π. Then point retraces its path, moving from $(-1, 0)$ to $(1, 0)$ as t goes from π to 2π.

80. In $x = y^2 - 1$

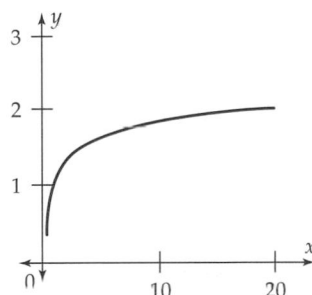

81. $x = 3 - 2y$ or $y = -\dfrac{1}{2}x + \dfrac{3}{2}$

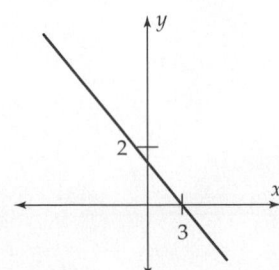

82. b and c

83. 74 and 75

84–97. *See pp. 1082–1083.*

can do calculus

Arc Length of a Polar Graph

Example Notes

Have students recall the first form of the Law of Cosines (page 617):

$$a^2 = b^2 + c^2 - 2bc \cos A$$

Ask them to give the corresponding equation that applies to Figure 11.C-3, and then solve it for a.

$$a^2 = r_1^2 + r_2^2 - 2r_1r_2 \cos \frac{\pi}{3}$$

$$a^2 = r_1^2 + r_2^2 - 2r_1r_2 \cdot \frac{1}{2}$$

$$a = \sqrt{r_1^2 + r_2^2 - r_1r}$$

Point out this equation at the bottom of the page.

Note that using a smaller angle than $\frac{\pi}{3}$ would result in more blue segments in Figure 11.C-2, and therefore a more accurate estimate for the length of the curve, but $\frac{\pi}{3}$ leads to the simplest expression for a.

The radical expressions on page 777 form an iterative pattern. Each has the form $\sqrt{x^2 + \left(x + \frac{2\pi}{3}\right)^2 - x\left(x + \frac{2\pi}{3}\right)}$.

Ask students to simplify this expression:

$$\sqrt{x^2 + x^2 + \frac{4\pi}{3}x + \frac{4\pi^2}{9} - x^2 - \frac{2\pi}{3}x}$$

$$= \sqrt{x^2 + \frac{2\pi}{3}x + \frac{4\pi^2}{9}}$$

To easily evaluate the radical expressions on page 777, have students do the following on their calculators:

Set $Y_1 = \sqrt{(x^2 + 2\pi x/3 + 4\pi^2/9)}$. Then, to evaluate each expression, use the table function $\left(\Delta \text{Tbl} = \frac{2\pi}{3}\right)$ as shown below:

---

can do calculus

Arc Length of a Polar Graph

Many applications of calculus involve finding the distance along a curve, or **arc length.** Although calculus is usually needed to find the exact value of the arc length, approximations are often sufficient.

A curve may be approximated by straight segments with endpoints on the curve, as shown in Figure 11.C-1. In polar coordinates, the curve, which is a circle, can be represented by the function $r = c$ for some constant c. The circumference of the circle is $2\pi c \approx 6.28c$. The length of each blue segment is also c, since the dashed lines form equilateral triangles. Thus, the approximate length of the curve is the total length of the blue segments, or $6c$.

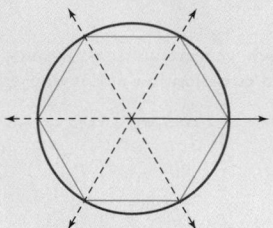

Figure 11.C-1

In general, the Law of Cosines may be used to find the length of a segment with two endpoints on the curve, as shown in the following example.

Example 1   Estimating the Length of a Curve

Estimate the length of the spiral with the equation $r = 2\theta$ from 0 to 2π.

Solution

The dashed lines in Figure 11.C-2 divide the spiral into triangles with an angle of $\frac{\pi}{3}$ at the origin. The table below shows the value of r for each value of θ that is an endpoint of a segment.

Figure 11.C-2

θ	0	$\frac{\pi}{3}$	$\frac{2\pi}{3}$	π	$\frac{4\pi}{3}$	$\frac{5\pi}{3}$	2π
r	0	$\frac{2\pi}{3}$	$\frac{4\pi}{3}$	2π	$\frac{8\pi}{3}$	$\frac{10\pi}{3}$	4π

The first segment has one endpoint at the origin, so its length is the value of r at the other endpoint, which is $\frac{2\pi}{3}$.

Every remaining segment is the side of a triangle that is opposite an angle at the origin of $\frac{\pi}{3}$, as shown in Figure 11.C-3.

Figure 11.C-3

By the Law of Cosines,

$$a^2 = r_1^2 + r_2^2 - 2r_1r_2 \cos \frac{\pi}{3}$$

$$a = \sqrt{r_1^2 + r_2^2 - r_1r_2}$$

The lengths of the segments can be calculated using this formula.

Segment from $\theta = 0$ to $\theta = \frac{\pi}{3}$: $\frac{2\pi}{3} \approx 2.09$

Segment from $\theta = \frac{\pi}{3}$ to $\theta = \frac{2\pi}{3}$: $\sqrt{\left(\frac{2\pi}{3}\right)^2 + \left(\frac{4\pi}{3}\right)^2 - \left(\frac{2\pi}{3}\right)\left(\frac{4\pi}{3}\right)} \approx 3.63$

Segment from $\theta = \frac{2\pi}{3}$ to $\theta = \pi$: $\sqrt{\left(\frac{4\pi}{3}\right)^2 + (2\pi)^2 - \left(\frac{4\pi}{3}\right)(2\pi)} \approx 5.54$

Segment from $\theta = \pi$ to $\theta = \frac{4\pi}{3}$: $\sqrt{(2\pi)^2 + \left(\frac{8\pi}{3}\right)^2 - (2\pi)\left(\frac{8\pi}{3}\right)} \approx 7.55$

Segment from $\theta = \frac{4\pi}{3}$ to $\theta = \frac{5\pi}{3}$: $\sqrt{\left(\frac{8\pi}{3}\right)^2 + \left(\frac{10\pi}{3}\right)^2 - \left(\frac{8\pi}{3}\right)\left(\frac{10\pi}{3}\right)} \approx 9.60$

Segment from $\theta = \frac{5\pi}{3}$ to $\theta = 2\pi$: $\sqrt{\left(\frac{10\pi}{3}\right)^2 + (4\pi)^2 - \left(\frac{10\pi}{3}\right)(4\pi)} \approx 11.66$

The approximate length of the spiral is the sum of the segments.

arc length $\approx 2.09 + 3.63 + 5.54 + 7.55 + 9.60 + 11.66 \approx 40.07$ ∎

Exercises

In Exercises 1–4, approximate each curve for $0 \le \theta \le 2\pi$ by six segments and estimate each arc length.

1. $r = 1.5\theta$ **< 30**

2. $r = 3 + 2\cos\theta$ **< 20**

3. $r = 1 + \cos\theta$ **< 8**

4. $r = \dfrac{1}{2 + \sin\theta}$ **< 4**

5. Use the figure to estimate the length of the cardioid with the equation $r = 1 + \sin\theta$.
  < 10

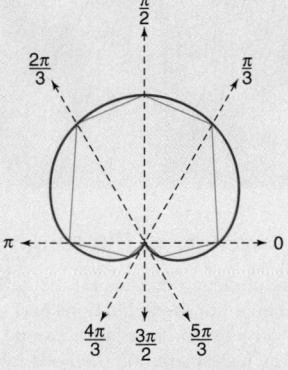

6. Use Heron's formula for the area of a triangle (see page 633) and your results from Exercise 5 to estimate the area of the cardioid with the equation $r = 1 + \sin\theta$ **< 5**

777

Example 1

Estimate the length of the spiral with the equation $r = \frac{1}{2}\theta$ from 0 to 2π.

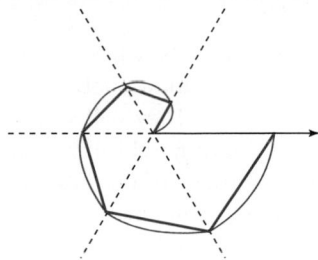

The endpoints of the red segments are at points (r, θ) shown in the table:

θ	0	$\frac{\pi}{3}$	$\frac{2\pi}{3}$	π	$\frac{4\pi}{3}$	$\frac{5\pi}{3}$	2π
r	0	$\frac{\pi}{6}$	$\frac{\pi}{3}$	$\frac{\pi}{2}$	$\frac{2\pi}{3}$	$\frac{5\pi}{6}$	π

Find the length of each red segment.

Segment from $\theta = 0$ to $\theta = \frac{\pi}{3}$:

$\frac{\pi}{6} \approx 0.52$

Segment from:

$\theta = \frac{\pi}{3}$ to $\theta = \frac{2\pi}{3}$:

$\sqrt{\left(\frac{\pi}{6}\right)^2 + \left(\frac{\pi}{3}\right)^2 - \left(\frac{\pi}{6}\right)\left(\frac{\pi}{3}\right)} \approx 0.91$

$\theta = \frac{2\pi}{3}$ to $\theta = \pi$:

$\sqrt{\left(\frac{\pi}{3}\right)^2 + \left(\frac{\pi}{2}\right)^2 - \left(\frac{\pi}{3}\right)\left(\frac{\pi}{2}\right)} \approx 1.39$

$\theta = \pi$ to $\theta = \frac{4\pi}{3}$:

$\sqrt{\left(\frac{\pi}{2}\right)^2 + \left(\frac{2\pi}{3}\right)^2 - \left(\frac{\pi}{2}\right)\left(\frac{2\pi}{3}\right)} \approx 1.89$

$\theta = \frac{4\pi}{3}$ to $\theta = \frac{5\pi}{3}$:

$\sqrt{\left(\frac{2\pi}{3}\right)^2 + \left(\frac{5\pi}{6}\right)^2 - \left(\frac{2\pi}{3}\right)\left(\frac{5\pi}{6}\right)} \approx 2.40$

$\theta = \frac{5\pi}{3}$ to $\theta = 2\pi$:

$\sqrt{\left(\frac{5\pi}{6}\right)^2 + \pi^2 - \left(\frac{5\pi}{6}\right)(\pi)} \approx 2.92$

The approximate length of the spiral is the sum of the segments:
arc length $\approx 0.52 + 0.91 + 1.39 + 1.89 + 2.40 + 2.92 \approx 10.03$

Exercises

ANSWERS

CHAPTER 12

Systems and Matrices

In this chapter, students will learn to solve systems of equations, both linear and nonlinear. They will solve systems numerically, graphically, and algebraically, with two of the algebraic methods using matrices. There are two Excursions—graphing in three dimensions and solving systems of inequalities.

CHAPTER 12 | Systems and Matrices

Is this a diamond in the rough?

The structure of certain crystals can be defined by a large system of linear equations with more than a hundred equations and variables. A variety of resource allocation problems involving many variables can be handled by solving an appropriate system of equations. The fastest solution methods involve matrices and are easily implemented on a computer or calculator. See Exercise 36 in Section 12.2.

778

Interdependence of Sections

Readers who are familiar with solving systems of linear equations may omit section 12.1.

$$12.1 \rightarrow 12.2 \rightarrow 12.3 \rightarrow 12.4$$
$$\searrow$$
$$12.5$$

$\mathbb{R}$eal-world situations often require a common solution to several equations with multiple variables. Such a collection of equations is known as a *system of equations.* Solutions to a system of equations in two or three variables may be represented geometrically by intersections of lines or planes. In this chapter, systems will be solved graphically, algebraically by substitution or elimination, and by two matrix methods: row reduction and inverse matrices.

12.1 Solving Systems of Equations

Objectives

• Solve systems of equations by graphing, substitution, and elimination

• Recognize consistent and inconsistent systems

• Solve applications using systems

A **system of equations** is a set of two or more equations in two or more variables. When a system has 3 equations in 2 variables, it is called a 3×2 system. In the examples of systems of equations shown below, the first is a 3×3 system, the second is a 3×4 system, and the third is a 2×2 system.

$$
\begin{array}{lll}
2x - 5y + 3z = 1 & 2x + 5y + z + w = 0 & x^2 + y^2 = 25 \\
x + 2y - z = 2 & 2y - 4z + 41w = 5 & x^2 - y = 7 \\
3x + y + 2z = 11 & 3x + 7y + 5z - 8w = -6 &
\end{array}
$$

| *Three equations in three variables* | *Three equations in four variables* | *Two equations in two variables* |

The first two systems above are called **linear systems** because the variables in each equation are all to the power of one, thus they are all linear. The third is a **nonlinear system** because at least one equation is nonlinear—in this case, quadratic.

779

Section
12.1 Solving Systems of Equations

Teaching Notes

Emphasize to students that order is important when giving the number of equations and variables in a system. For example, a 3×4 system is different than a 4×3 system.

• 3×4: 3 equations, 4 variables

• 4×3: 4 equations, 3 variables

This terminology will be helpful in the next section (12.2) when matrices are introduced. Matrices are important and useful in solving some types of linear systems.

When using a matrix to represent a system of equations, the number of equations determines the number of rows in the matrix. Similarly, the number of variables determines the number of columns in the matrix (augmented matrices have an additional column for the constants). Thus, a 3×4 system of equations can be written as a 3×4 matrix (or a 3×5 augmented matrix).

Example Notes

For **Example 1,** you can suggest that students check the solution by substituting into each equation as shown below:

$$2x - y = 1 \qquad 3x + 2y = 12$$
$$2(2) - 3 \mid 1 \qquad 3(1) + 2(3) \mid 12$$
$$1 \mid 1 \qquad\qquad 12 \mid 12$$

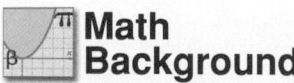

Math Background

The exact solution for **Example 2** can be found algebraically. Two algebraic methods are shown on the following pages—substitution and elimination. The elimination method is outlined below for Example 2.

$$2x - y = 1$$
$$3x + 2y = 4$$

Multiply the first equation by 2 to get opposite y-coefficients.

$$4x - 2y = 2$$
$$3x + 2y = 4$$

Add the equations to eliminate y, and then solve the resulting equation ($7x = 6$) to find that $x = \frac{6}{7}$. Substitute $\frac{6}{7}$ for x in one of the original equations and solve for y to find that $y = \frac{5}{7}$.

Teaching Notes

To determine the **Type of System and Number of Solutions** for a system, you can solve each equation for y, which results in slope-intercept form. An example of each case in Figure 12.1-3 is shown below: Parallel lines have the same slope and different y-intercepts, such as:

$$y = \frac{1}{2}x - 1 \text{ and } y = \frac{1}{2}x - 4$$

Lines that intersect at a single point have different slopes and different y-intercepts, such as the equations in **Example 2:**

$$y = 2x - 1 \text{ and } y = -\frac{3}{2}x + 2$$

Lines that coincide have identical equations when their equations are solved for y and therefore have the same slope and the same y-intercept, such as:

$$y = \frac{1}{2}x - 1 \text{ and } y = \frac{1}{2}x - 1$$

Table setup is accessed from the TBLSET key of TI and RANG in the Casio TABLE menu.

The increment is ΔTBL on TI and PITCH on Casio. The table type is labeled INDPNT on TI.

Figure 12.1-1

Solutions of a System of Equations

A **solution of a system of equations** is a set of values that satisfy all the equations in the system. In the first system of equations on the previous page, substituting $x = 1$, $y = 2$, and $z = 3$ gives the following:

$$2x - 5y + 3z = 2(1) - 5(2) + 3(3) = 2 - 10 + 9 = 1$$
$$x + 2y - z = (1) + 2(2) - 3 = 1 + 4 - 3 = 2$$
$$3x + y + 2z = 3(1) + (2) + 2(3) = 3 + 2 + 6 = 11$$

Because the set of values $x = 1$, $y = 2$, $z = 3$ makes all equations true, the set is a solution of the system. The set of values $x = 0$, $y = 7$, $z = 12$ is a solution of the first two equations, but not the third, so it is not a solution of the system.

Solutions of systems of equations in two variables can be found numerically by comparing tables of values for the equations.

Example 1 Solving a System Numerically

Find a solution of the system of equations below by using tables of values for the equations.

$$2x - y = 1$$
$$3x + 2y = 12$$

Solution

First, solve each equation for y. Then create a table of values for each equation. The table in Figure 12.1-1 shows solutions to each equation. To solve the system, find a common output.

$$y = 2x - 1$$
$$y = -\frac{3}{2}x + 6$$

Notice that at $x = 2$, the y-values are the same for the two equations. Thus, $x = 2$, $y = 3$ is a solution of the system of equations. ∎

Solving systems numerically has several disadvantages. First, there is no way of knowing whether all possible solutions have been found. Second, many values may have to be checked before a solution is found. And third, if a solution lies between the values in the table, it may be missed.

Solving Systems with Graphs

One method of solving systems of equations in two variables is graphing the equations and finding the point(s) of intersection. Since the graph of each equation represents all possible solutions of that equation, a point of intersection of two graphs represents a solution of both equations. The advantage of solving a system graphically is that the solution is shown visually, but solving systems graphically is limited to two-variable systems.

Example 2   Graphical Solutions of a Linear System

Find a solution of the system of equations below by graphing the equations.

$$2x - y = 1$$
$$3x + 2y = 4$$

Figure 12.1-2

Solution

Solve each equation for y, graph each equation, and find the coordinates of all points of intersection.

$$y = 2x - 1$$
$$y = -\frac{3}{2}x + 2$$

The system of equations has exactly one solution, $x \approx 0.86$ and $y \approx 0.71$, as shown in Figure 12.1-2.

■

Type of System and Number of Solutions

Systems of equations may be classified according to the number of solutions. A system with no solutions is called **inconsistent,** and a system with at least one solution is called **consistent.**

Linear Systems

Because the graphs in a linear system with two variables are lines, there are exactly three geometric possibilities.

- the lines can be parallel and have no point of intersection
- the lines can intersect at a single point
- the lines can coincide

Each of these possibilities leads to a different number of solutions for the system. The three types of 2 × 2 linear systems are shown below.

Figure 12.1-3

Example Notes

Remind students that for the first step in **Solving Systems with Substitution,** they can solve *either* equation for *either* variable. In **Example 3,** solving the first equation for y is a good choice because it delays introducing fractions.

Remind students that when **Solving Systems by Elimination,** they can choose to multiply by an appropriate nonzero constant so that they can eliminate *either* variable. In **Example 4,** ask how you could eliminate y. Multiply the second equation by 3 and then add the equations.

The last step in solving a system algebraically is to verify the solution in each equation. In **Examples 3** and **4,** point out that confirming a solution graphically is not the same as verifying a solution. To verify means to check algebraically. Ask students to check the solution in **Example 3** algebraically.

$$
\begin{array}{c|c|c|c}
3x \;-\; y = 12 & & 2x \;+\; 3y = 2 & \\
3\left(\frac{38}{11}\right) - \left(-\frac{18}{11}\right) & 12 & 2\left(\frac{38}{11}\right) + 3\left(-\frac{18}{11}\right) & 2 \\
\frac{114}{11} \;+\; \frac{18}{11} & 12 & \frac{76}{11} \;-\; \frac{54}{11} & 2 \\
\frac{132}{11} & 12 & \frac{22}{11} & 2 \\
12 & 12 & 2 & 2
\end{array}
$$

COMMON ERROR ALERT

Students sometimes make sign errors when solving systems of equations.

A common error in **Example 3** is to "drop" the negative sign in front of y:

$3x - y = 12$
$\quad y = -3x + 12 \quad$ *incorrect*

Remind students to multiply both sides by -1 after subtracting $3x$ from both sides:

$3x - y = 12$
$\quad -y = -3x + 12$
$\quad\;\; y = 3x - 12 \quad$ *correct*

Number of Solutions of a Linear System

There are exactly three possibilities for the number of solutions of a 2×2 system of *linear* equations.

- no solutions (inconsistent system)
- one solution (consistent system)
- infinitely many solutions (consistent system)

Solving Systems Algebraically

Solving systems of equations by graphing often gives approximate solutions, while algebraic methods produce exact solutions. Furthermore, algebraic methods are often as easy to use as graphical methods. Two common algebraic methods are **substitution** and **elimination.**

Substitution Method

Solving Systems with Substitution

To solve a system using the substitution method:

1. Solve one equation for x (or y).
2. Substitute the expression for x (or y) into the other equation.
3. Solve for the remaining variable.
4. Substitute the value found in Step 3 into one of the original equations, and solve for the other variable.
5. Verify the solution in each equation.

Example 3   Solving a System by Substitution

Solve the system of equations below by substitution.

$$3x \;-\; y = 12$$
$$2x + 3y = \;\;2$$

Solution

Solve the first equation for y.

$$y = 3x - 12$$

Substitute the expression $3x - 12$ for y in the second equation and solve for x.

$$
\begin{aligned}
2x + 3(3x - 12) &= 2 \\
2x + \;9x - 36 &= 2 \\
11x &= 38 \\
x &= \frac{38}{11} \approx 3.45
\end{aligned}
$$

> **CAUTION**
>
> When solving a system of equations, remember to find values for *all* of the variables.

To find the value of y, substitute $\frac{38}{11}$, the value of x, into $y = 3x - 12$ and simplify.

$$y = 3\left(\frac{38}{11}\right) - 12 = -\frac{18}{11} \approx -1.64$$

The exact solution to the system is $x = \frac{38}{11}$, $y = -\frac{18}{11}$, and the approximate solution is $x \approx 3.45$, $y \approx -1.64$.

Figure 12.1-4

The solution may be confirmed by graphing, as shown in Figure 12.1-4, where $x \approx 3.45$ and $y \approx -1.64$.

Elimination Method

Elimination is another algebraic method used to solve systems.

Solving Systems by Elimination

> **To solve a system using the elimination method:**
>
> 1. **Multiply one or both of the equations by a nonzero constant so that the coefficients of x (or y) are opposites of each other.**
> 2. **Eliminate x (or y) by adding the equations, and solve for the remaining variable.**
> 3. **Substitute the value found in Step 2 into one of the original equations, and solve for the other variable.**
> 4. **Verify the solution in each equation.**

Example 4   **Solving a System by Elimination**

Solve the system of equations below by elimination.

$$x - 3y = 4$$
$$2x + y = 1$$

Solution

Multiply the first equation by -2.

$$-2x + 6y = -8$$
$$2x + y = 1$$

Add the equations to eliminate x, and solve the resulting equation.

$$
\begin{array}{r}
-2x + 6y = -8 \\
+\quad 2x + y = 1 \\
\hline
7y = -7 \\
y = -1
\end{array}
$$

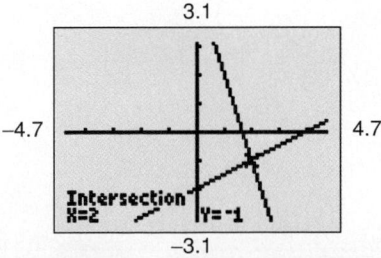

Example 3

Solve the system of equations below by substitution.

$$2x + y = 2$$
$$3x - 2y = 4$$

Solve the first equation for y:

$$y = 2 - 2x$$

Substitute $2 - 2x$ for y into the second equation and solve for x:

$$3x - 2y = 4$$
$$3x - 2(2 - 2x) = 4$$
$$3x - 4 + 4x = 4$$
$$7x = 8$$
$$x = \frac{8}{7}$$

Substitute $x = \frac{8}{7}$ into $y = 2 - 2x$ and simplify:

$$y = 2 - 2\left(\frac{8}{7}\right) = \frac{14}{7} - \frac{16}{7} = -\frac{2}{7}$$

The exact solution is $x = \frac{8}{7}$, $y = -\frac{2}{7}$.

The approximate solution is $x \approx 1.14$, $y \approx -0.29$.

Example 4

Solve the system of equations below by elimination.

$$3x + y = 5$$
$$x - 2y = 4$$

Multiply the first equation by 2.

$$6x + 2y = 10$$
$$x - 2y = 4$$

Add the equations to eliminate y; solve for x:

$$
\begin{array}{r}
6x + 2y = 10 \\
+\quad x - 2y = 4 \\
\hline
7x = 14 \\
x = 2
\end{array}
$$

Substitute $x = 2$ into the second equation; solve for y:

$$2 - 2y = 4$$
$$-2y = 2$$
$$y = -1$$

The solution is $x = 2$, $y = -1$.

Solution to the **Graphing Exploration:**
Solve each equation from **Example 5** for y and then graph as shown:

$$Y_1 = \frac{2}{3}x - \frac{5}{3}, \quad Y_2 = \frac{2}{3}x - \frac{1}{6}$$

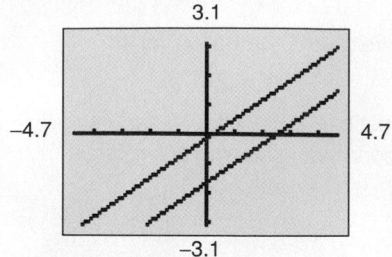

The lines are parallel, which confirms that the system has no solution.

COMMON ERROR ALERT

In **Example 6,** there are infinitely many solutions because a true statement, $0 = 0$, is obtained. Students may incorrectly think that $0 = 0$ is the statement needed to conclude that there are infinitely many solutions. Emphasize that *any true statement implies that there are infinitely many solutions* (if all the preceding work is correct). For example, the system

$$x + 3 = 2y$$
$$-x = -2y + 3$$

has infinitely many solutions because the true statement $3 = 3$ is obtained by adding the equations:

$$\begin{array}{rl} x + 3 = & 2y \\ + \; -x \quad = & -2y + 3 \\ \hline 3 = & 3 \end{array}$$

ADDITIONAL EXAMPLES

Example 5

Solve the system of equations below by elimination.

$$3x - 2y = 7$$
$$9x - 6y = -3$$

Multiply the first equation by -3 and add the two equations:

$$\begin{array}{rl} -9x + 6y = & -21 \\ + \; 9x - 6y = & -3 \\ \hline 0 = & -24 \end{array}$$

Because the statement $0 = -24$ is always false, the system has no solution; it is inconsistent.

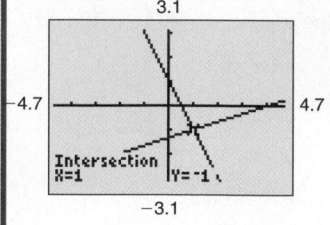

Figure 12.1-5

Substitute -1 for y in one of the original equations and solve for x.

$$x - 3(-1) = 4$$
$$x = 1$$

The solution of the system is $x = 1$, $y = -1$. The solution is confirmed graphically in Figure 12.1-5.

Solutions of Consistent and Inconsistent Systems

The following examples show how the elimination method may be used to solve consistent systems with infinitely many solutions or inconsistent systems.

Example 5   **Recognizing an Inconsistent System**

Solve the system of equations below by elimination.

$$2x - 3y = 5$$
$$4x - 6y = 1$$

Solution

Multiply the first equation by -2, then add the two equations.

$$\begin{array}{rl} -4x + 6y = & -10 \\ + \quad 4x - 6y = & 1 \\ \hline 0 = & -9 \end{array}$$

The last statement, $0 = -9$, is always false. This indicates that the original system has no solutions. Thus, the system is inconsistent.

Graphing Exploration

Confirm the result of Example 5 geometrically by graphing the two equations in the system. Do the lines intersect, or are they parallel?

Example 6   **Recognizing a System with Infinitely Many Solutions**

Solve the system of equations below by elimination.

$$2x - 4y = 6$$
$$-3x + 6y = -9$$

Solution

Multiply the first equation by 3 and the second equation by 2, then add the two equations.

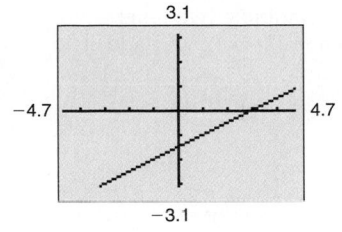

Figure 12.1-6

$$6x - 12y = 18$$
$$+ \ -6x + 12y = -18$$
$$0 = 0$$

The last equation, $0 = 0$, is always true. This indicates that the two equations represent the same line, and every ordered pair that satisfies the first equation must also satisfy the second equation. Thus, the system has infinitely many solutions. ∎

Using a Parameter to Write Solutions

It is common to represent solutions of consistent systems that have infinitely many solutions in terms of a variable called a **parameter**, which represents any real number. In Example 6, let $y = t$ and substitute this value into one of the equations.

$$2x - 4t = 6 \qquad \textit{t is any real number.}$$
$$x = 3 + 2t \qquad \textit{Solve for x.}$$

The solutions can be written as $x = 3 + 2t$, $y = t$. Individual numerical solutions can be found by substituting real values for t, as follows.

$t = 1$	$x = 5, y = 1$
$t = -2$	$x = -1, y = -2$
$t = 0$	$x = 3, y = 0$

Solving Larger Systems by Elimination

It is possible to use elimination to solve larger systems. Equations are combined in pairs to create a system of equations with one fewer variable that can be solved using the techniques discussed in this section. The solutions of the reduced system are then substituted back into the original equations to find the remaining variables.

Example 7　Solving a 3 × 3 System by Elimination

Solve the system of equations below by elimination.

$$2x + y - z = -1 \qquad [1]$$
$$-x - 3y + z = 5 \qquad [2]$$
$$x + 4y - 2z = -10 \qquad [3]$$

Solution

Eliminate z by adding equations [1] and [2].

$$2x + y - z = -1 \qquad [1]$$
$$+ \ -x - 3y + z = 5 \qquad [2]$$
$$x - 2y = 4 \qquad [4]$$

Substitute into [1] to find z:
$$1 + 2 - z = 6$$
$$-z = 3$$
$$z = -3$$
The solution is $x = 1$, $y = 2$, $z = -3$.

Example 6

Solve the following system of equations below by elimination.

$$3x - 6y = 3$$
$$-4x + 8y = -4$$

Multiply the first equation by 4 and the second equation by 3. Then add the two equations.

$$12x - 24y = 12$$
$$+ \ -12x + 24y = -12$$
$$0 = 0$$

Since the statement $0 = 0$ is always true, the system has infinitely many solutions.

The two equations represent the same line, as shown in the graph below.

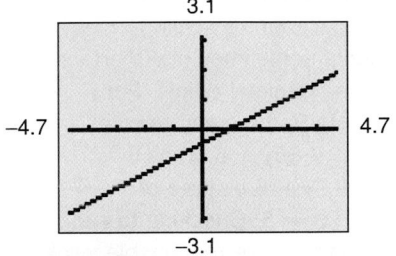

Example 7

Solve the system of equations below by elimination.

$$x + y - z = 6 \qquad [1]$$
$$2x + 3y + z = 5 \qquad [2]$$
$$-x + 2y + 4z = -9 \qquad [3]$$

Add [1] and [2] to eliminate z:

$$x + y - z = 6 \qquad [1]$$
$$+ \ 2x + 3y + z = 5 \qquad [2]$$
$$3x + 4y = 11 \qquad [4]$$

Add 4 times [1] and [3] to eliminate z:

$$4x + 4y - 4z = 24 \qquad 4 \cdot [1]$$
$$+ \ -x + 2y + 4z = -9 \qquad [3]$$
$$3x + 6y = 15 \qquad [5]$$

Add -1 times [4] and [5] to solve for y:

$$-3x - 4y = -11 \qquad -1 \cdot [4]$$
$$+ \ 3x + 6y = 15 \qquad [5]$$
$$2y = 4$$
$$y = 2$$

Substitute into [4] to find x:

$$3x + 4(2) = 11$$
$$3x = 3$$
$$x = 1$$

Teaching Notes

For application problems, students may find it difficult to translate verbal information into equations. Remind them that each term in an equation must represent the same kind of quantity.

In the first equation in **Example 8**, $x + y = 575$, each term represents *a number of people*. In the second equation, $5x + 3y = 2575$, each term represents *an amount of money*.

In the first equation in **Example 9**, $x + y = 1$, each term represents *an amount of coffee*. In the second equation, $4.50x + 7.00y = 5.00$, each term represents *an amount of money*.

COMMON ERROR ALERT

For applications involving money, students sometimes make errors involving decimal points. For **Example 9**, they may rewrite $4.50x + 7.00y = 5.00$ as $450x + 7y = 5$ instead of $4.5x + 7y = 5$. Checking to see that answers are reasonable will be helpful in identifying such errors.

Real-World Application

Example 8 is a real-world problem that can be solved by using a 2×2 linear system. Some real-world problems require a system that has more variables than equations. If the ball game in Example 8 was attended by adults (x), children (y), and seniors (z), and if senior tickets were $4 each, the system would be:

$$x + y + z = 575$$
$$5x + 3y + 4z = 2575$$

If we eliminate a variable, say z, we get an equation with 2 variables:

$$
\begin{array}{r}
-4x - 4y - 4z = -2300 \\
+\ 5x + 3y + 4z = \ \ \ 2575 \\
\hline
x - y \ \ \ \ \ \ \ = \ \ \ \ 275
\end{array}
$$

This means that the system cannot be solved algebraically.

Eliminate *the same* variable, in this case z, by combining two other equations. One possible way is to multiply equation [2] by 2 and add it to equation [3].

$$
\begin{array}{rrll}
-2x - 6y + 2z = & 10 & & 2 \cdot [2] \\
+\ \ \ x + 4y - 2z = & -10 & & [3] \\
\hline
-x - 2y \ \ \ \ \ \ \ \ = & 0 & & [5]
\end{array}
$$

The two resulting equations, [4] and [5], form a system of two equations in two variables, which can be solved by elimination, substitution, or graphing.

$$
\begin{array}{rrl}
x - 2y = & 4 & [4] \\
+\ -x - 2y = & 0 & [5] \\
\hline
-4y = & 4 & \\
y = & -1 &
\end{array}
$$

Find the value of x by substituting $y = -1$ into equation [4].

$$x - 2(-1) = 4$$
$$x \ \ \ \ \ \ \ \ \ \ = 2$$

To find the value of z, substitute the values $x = 2$ and $y = -1$ into equation [1] from the original system, and solve.

$$2(2) + (-1) - z = -1$$
$$z = 4$$

The solution is $x = 2$, $y = -1$, $z = 4$.

The solution should be checked in *all* equations of the original system. ∎

Applications of Systems

Systems of equations occur in many real-world applications. The simplest situations involve two quantities and two linear relationships between these quantities, as shown in the following example.

Example 8   **2×2 Linear System Application**

A ball game is attended by 575 people, and total ticket sales are $2575. If tickets cost $5 for adults and $3 for children, how many adults and how many children attended the game?

Solution

Let x be the number of adults and y be the number of children. The first equation is based on the total number of people at the game.

$$
\begin{array}{ccc}
\textit{number of adults} & \textit{number of children} & \textit{total attendance} \\
x & +\ \ \ \ \ y & =\ \ \ \ \ 575
\end{array}
$$

The second equation is based on the ticket sales. Notice that the term for each type of ticket sales is found by multiplying the price per ticket by the number of tickets sold, and total ticket sales is the sum of the sales of the different types of tickets.

adult ticket sales + child ticket sales = total ticket sales

$$\left(\begin{array}{c} price \\ per \\ ticket \end{array}\right)\left(\begin{array}{c} number \\ of \\ adults \end{array}\right) \quad \left(\begin{array}{c} price \\ per \\ child \end{array}\right)\left(\begin{array}{c} number \\ of \\ children \end{array}\right)$$

$$5x \qquad + \qquad 3y \qquad = \qquad 2575$$

Solve the system of equations.

$$x + y = 575 \qquad \textit{number of tickets}$$
$$5x + 3y = 2575 \qquad \textit{total ticket sales}$$

Multiply the first equation by -3 and add the result to the second equation.

$$\begin{array}{rcl} -3x - 3y &=& -1725 \\ + \quad 5x + 3y &=& 2575 \\ \hline 2x &=& 850 \\ x &=& 425 \end{array}$$

So 425 adults and $y = 575 - 425 = 150$ children attended the game. Confirm by graphing, as shown in Figure 12.1-7.

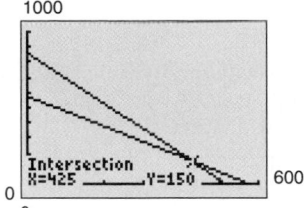

Figure 12.1-7

Example 9 **Mixture Application**

A cafe sells two kinds of coffee in bulk. The Costa Rican sells for $4.50 per pound, and the Kenyan sells for $7.00 per pound. The owner wishes to mix a blend that would sell for $5.00 per pound. How much of each type of coffee should be used in the blend?

Solution

Let x be the amount of Costa Rican coffee and y be the amount of Kenyan coffee in each pound of the blend. The first equation is based on the weight of the coffee.

weight of Costa + weight of = one pound of blend
Rican   Kenyan
$$x \qquad + \qquad y \qquad = \qquad 1$$

The second equation is based on the price of the coffee.

price of Costa Rican + price of Kenyan = price of blend

$$\left(\begin{array}{c} price \\ per \\ pound \end{array}\right)\left(\begin{array}{c} weight \\ of \\ coffee \end{array}\right) \quad \left(\begin{array}{c} price \\ per \\ pound \end{array}\right)\left(\begin{array}{c} weight \\ of \\ coffee \end{array}\right)$$

$$4.50x \qquad + \qquad 7.00y \qquad = \qquad \$5.00$$

A pound of mix should contain 0.6 lb of macadamia nuts and 0.4 lb of almonds.

Example 8

The revenue from ticket sales for a concert was $7050, and 910 tickets were sold. Reserved seat tickets cost $9 and lawn seat tickets cost $5. How many of each type of ticket were sold?

Write a system of equations.

$$x + y = 910$$
$$9x + 5y = 7050$$

Multiply the first equation by -5 and add the result to the second equation to find x, the number of reserved tickets:

$$\begin{array}{rcl} -5x - 5y &=& -4550 \\ + \quad 9x + 5y &=& 7050 \\ \hline 4x &=& 2500 \\ x &=& 625 \end{array}$$

Find y, the number of lawn seat tickets:
$$625 + y = 910$$
$$y = 285$$

Example 9

A market sells macadamia nuts for $8.00 a pound and almonds for $5.50 a pound. A customer wishes to make a mix that would cost $7.00 a pound. How much of each type of nut will be used in a pound of mix?

Write a system of equations.
$$x + y = 1$$
$$8.00x + 5.50y = 7.00$$

Multiply the first equation by -5.5 and add the result to the second equation to find x, the number of pounds of macadamia nuts:

$$\begin{array}{rcl} -5.5x - 5.5y &=& -5.5 \\ + \quad 8x + 5.5y &=& 7 \\ \hline 2.5x &=& 1.5 \\ x &=& 0.6 \end{array}$$

Find y, the number of pounds of almonds:
$$0.6 + y = 1.0$$
$$y = 0.4$$

Exercises 12.1

ANSWERS

7. $x = \frac{11}{5}, y = -\frac{7}{5}$

8. $x = \frac{6}{5}, y = \frac{13}{5}$

9. $x = \frac{2}{7}, y = -\frac{11}{7}$

10. $x = \frac{5}{7}, y = \frac{13}{7}$

21. $x = b, y = \frac{3b - 4}{2}$, where b is any real number

22. $x = b, y = \frac{b - 1}{4}$, where b is any real number

23. $x = b, y = \frac{3b - 2}{4}$, where b is any real number

24. $x = b, y = \frac{5 - 10b}{12}$, where b is any real number

Figure 12.1-8

Solve the system of equations.

$$x + y = 1$$
$$4.5x + 7y = 5$$

Multiply the first equation by -7 and add it to the second equation.

$$\begin{aligned}
-7x - 7y &= -7 \\
+ \quad 4.5x + 7y &= 5 \\
\hline
-2.5x &= -2 \\
x &= 0.8
\end{aligned}$$

The owner should use 0.8 pounds of Costa Rican coffee and $1 - 0.8 = 0.2$ pounds of Kenyan coffee in each pound of blend, or 80% Costa Rican and 20% Kenyan. See Figure 12.1-8 for graphical confirmation. ∎

Exercises 12.1

In Exercises 1–6, determine whether the given values of x, y, and z are a solution of the system of equations.

1. $x = -1, y = 3$

$$2x + y = 1$$
$$-3x + 2y = 9$$

yes

2. $x = 3, y = 4$

$$2x + 6y = 30$$
$$x + 2y = 11$$

yes

3. $x = 2, y = -1$

$$\frac{1}{3}x + \frac{1}{2}y = \frac{1}{6}$$
$$\frac{1}{2}x + \frac{1}{3}y = \frac{2}{3}$$

yes

4. $x = 0.4, y = 0.7$

$$3.1x - 2y = -0.16$$
$$5x - 3.5y = -0.48$$

no

5. $x = \frac{1}{2}, y = 3, z = -1$

$$2x - y + 4z = -6$$
$$3y + 3z = 6$$
$$2z = 2$$

no

6. $x = 2, y = \frac{3}{2}, z = -\frac{1}{2}$

$$3x + 4y - 2z = 13$$
$$x - 3y + 5z = -5$$
$$\frac{1}{2}x + 8z = -3$$

yes

In Exercises 7–14, use substitution to solve the system.

7. $x - 2y = 5$
$ 2x + y = 3$

8. $3x - y = 1$
$ -x + 2y = 4$

9. $3x - 2y = 4$
$ 2x + y = -1$

10. $5x - 3y = -2$
$ -x + 2y = 3$

11. $r + s = 0$
$ r - s = 5$

$r = \frac{5}{2}, s = -\frac{5}{2}$

12. $t = 3u + 5$
$ t = u + 5$

$t = 5, u = 0$

13. $x + y = c + d$ (where c, d are constants)
$x - y = 2c - d$ $\quad x = \frac{3c}{2}, y = \frac{-c + 2d}{2}$

14. $x + 3y = c - d$ (where c, d are constants)
$2x - y = c + d$ $\quad x = \frac{4c + 2d}{7}, y = \frac{c - 3d}{7}$

In Exercises 15–34, use the elimination method to solve the system.

15. $2x - 2y = 12$
$ -2x + 3y = 10$
$x = 28, y = 22$

16. $3x + 2y = -4$
$ 4x - 2y = -10$
$x = -2, y = 1$

17. $x + 3y = -1$
$ 2x - y = 5$
$x = 2, y = -1$

18. $4x - 3y = -1$
$ x + 2y = 19$
$x = 5, y = 7$

19. $2x + 3y = 15$
$ 8x + 12y = 40$
inconsistent

20. $2x + 5y = 8$
$ 6x + 15y = 18$
inconsistent

21. $3x - 2y = 4$
$ 6x - 4y = 8$

22. $2x - 8y = 2$
$ 3x - 12y = 3$

23. $12x - 16y = 8$
$ 42x - 56y = 28$

24. $\frac{1}{3}x + \frac{2}{5}y = \frac{1}{6}$
$\phantom{\frac{1}{3}} 20x + 24y = 10$

25. $9x - 3y = 1$
$ 6x - 2y = -5$
inconsistent

26. $8x + 4y = 3$
$ 10x + 5y = 1$
inconsistent

27. $\frac{x}{3} - \frac{y}{2} = -3$
$\frac{2x}{5} + \frac{y}{5} = -2$
$x = -6, y = 2$

28. $\frac{x}{3} + \frac{3y}{5} = 4$
$\frac{x}{6} - \frac{y}{2} = -3$
$x = \frac{3}{4}, y = \frac{25}{4}$

29. $\dfrac{x+y}{4} - \dfrac{x-y}{3} = 1$ $x = \dfrac{66}{5}, y = \dfrac{18}{5}$

$\dfrac{x+y}{4} + \dfrac{x-y}{2} = 9$

30. $\dfrac{x-y}{4} + \dfrac{x+y}{3} = 1$ $x = -6, y = 54$

$\dfrac{x+2y}{3} + \dfrac{3x-y}{2} = -2$

31. $3.5x - 2.18y = 2.00782$ $x = 0.185, y = -0.624$
$1.92x + 6.77y = -3.86928$

32. $463x - 80y = -13781.6$ $x = -20, y = 56.52$
$0.0375x + 0.912y = 50.79624$

33. $2x - 4y + z = 14$ $x = 3, y = -1, z = 4$
$-2x + y - 6z = -31$
$x - 3y + 2z = 14$

34. $x + 3y - 2z = 8$ $x = -2, y = 0, z = -5$
$-4x - 3y + z = 3$
$5x - y - 6z = 20$

In Exercises 35 and 36, find the values of c and d for which both given points lie on the given straight line. *Hint:* Substitute the x- and y-values of each of the given points into the equation to create a 2×2 system.

35. $cx + dy = 2; (0, 4)$ and $(2, 16)$ $c = -3, d = \dfrac{1}{2}$

36. $cx + dy = -6; (1, 3)$ and $(-2, 12)$ $c = -3, d = -1$

37. Bill and Ann plan to install a heating system for their swimming pool. They have gathered the following cost information.

System	Installation cost	Monthly operational cost
Electric	$2000	$80.00
Solar	$14,000	$ 9.50

a. Write a linear equation for each heating system that expresses its total cost y in terms of x, the number of years of operation.
b. What is the five-year total cost of electric heat? of solar heat?
c. In what year will the total cost of the two heating systems be the same? Which is the cheapest system before that time?

38. One parcel of land is worth $100,000 now and is increasing in value at the rate of $3000 per year. A second parcel is now worth $60,000 and is increasing in value at the rate of $7500 per year.
a. For each parcel of land, write an equation that expresses the value y of the land in year x.
b. Graph the equations in part **a**.
c. Where do the lines intersect? What is the significance of this point?
d. Which parcel will be worth more in five years? in 15 years?

39. A toy company makes dolls, as well as collector cases for each doll. To make x cases costs the company $5000 in fixed overhead, plus $7.50 per case. An outside supplier has offered to produce any desired volume of cases for $8.20 per case.
a. Write an equation that expresses the company's cost to make x cases itself.
b. Write an equation that expresses the cost of buying x cases from the outside supplier.
c. Graph both equations on the same axes and determine when the two costs are the same.
d. When should the company make the cases themselves, and when should they buy them from the outside supplier?

40. The sum of two numbers is 40. The difference of twice the first number and the second is 11. What are the numbers?
17 and 23

41. A 200-seat theater charges $3 for adults and $1.50 for children. If all seats were filled and the total ticket income was $510, how many adults and how many children were in the audience?
140 adults, 60 children

42. A theater charges $4 for main floor seats and $2.50 for balcony seats. If all seats are sold, the ticket income is $2100. At one show, 25% of the main floor seats and 40% of the balcony seats were sold, and ticket income was $600. How many seats are on the main floor and how many in the balcony? **400 seats on main floor, 200 seats in balcony**

43. An investor has part of her money in an account that pays 2% annual interest, and the rest in an account that pays 4% annual interest. If she has $4000 less in the higher paying account than in the lower paying one and her total annual interest income is $1010, how much does she have invested in each account?
$19,500 at 2% and $15,500 at 4%

37. a. electric: $y = 960x + 2000$;
solar: $y = 114x + 14{,}000$
b. electric: $6800; solar: $14,570
c. fourteenth year; electric

38. a. $y = 3000x + 100{,}000$;
$y = 7500x + 60{,}000$
b.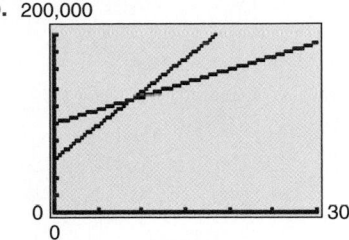
c. (8.889, 126,667); The parcels are worth the same amount after about 8.889 years.
d. In 5 years, the first parcel will still be worth more, but in 15 years, the second parcel will have passed it.

39. a. $y = 7.50x + 5000$
b. $y = 8.20x$
c.
costs equal at approximately 7143 cases
d. The company should buy from the supplier any number of cases less than 7143 and produce their own beyond that quantity.

44. The death rate per 100,000 population y in year x for heart disease and cancer is approximated by these equations:

   Heart Disease: $\quad 6.9x + 2y = 728.4$
   Cancer: $\qquad -1.3x + \ y = 167.5$,

where $x = 0$ corresponds to 1970. If the equations remain accurate, when will the death rates for heart disease and cancer be the same? (Source: U.S. Department of Health and Human Services) **≈2011**

45. At a certain store, cashews cost $4.40 per pound and peanuts cost $1.20 per pound. If you want to buy exactly 3 pounds of nuts for $6.00, how many pounds of each kind of nuts should you buy? *Hint:* If you buy x pounds of cashews and y pounds of peanuts, then $x + y = 3$. Find a second equation by considering cost and solve the resulting system. **$\frac{3}{4}$ lb cashews and $2\frac{1}{4}$ lb peanuts**

46. A store sells deluxe tape recorders for $150. The regular model costs $120. The total tape recorder inventory would sell for $43,800. But during a **100 deluxe model, 240 regular model**

recent month the store actually sold half of its deluxe models and two-thirds of the regular models and took in a total of $26,700. How many of each kind of tape recorder did they have at the beginning of the month?

47. How many cubic centimeters (cm^3) of a solution that is 20% acid and of another solution that is 45% acid should be mixed to produce 100 cm^3 of a solution that is 30% acid? **60cc of 20% and 40cc of 45%**

48. How many grams of a 50%-silver alloy should be mixed with a 75%-silver alloy to obtain 40 grams of a 60%-silver alloy? **24 g 50% silver alloy, 16 g 75% silver alloy**

49. A machine in a pottery factory takes 3 minutes to form a bowl and 2 minutes to form a plate. The material for a bowl costs $0.25 and the material for a plate costs $0.20. If the machine runs for 8 hours straight and exactly $44 is spent for material, how many bowls and plates can be produced? **80 bowls; 120 plates**

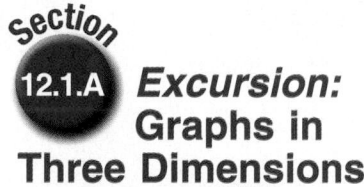

Section
12.1.A *Excursion:* Graphs in Three Dimensions

Teaching Notes

To help students visualize the three axes in Figure 12.1.A-1, tell them to draw a pair of perpendicular axes on paper and then place a pencil at the origin, perpendicular to the paper (i.e. "standing straight up" from the paper on the desk).

Next, have them look at Figure 12.1.A-2 on page 791. The paper they drew on represents the familiar xy-plane (green) and the pencil represents the z-axis.

 12.1.A *Excursion:* **Graphs in Three Dimensions**

Objectives

- Plot points in three dimensions

- Graph planes in three dimensions

- Use graphs of planes to visualize the number of solutions to a 3×3 system of equations

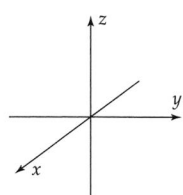

Figure 12.1.A-1

In section 12.1, two-dimensional graphs were used to interpret and solve systems of equations in two variables. Systems of equations in three variables can be represented by three-dimensional graphs, as shown in this excursion. However, finding the solutions of such systems requires algebraic techniques that are presented in the following sections.

Three-Dimensional Coordinates

Just as ordered pairs of real numbers (x, y) are identified with points in a plane, ordered triples (x, y, z) of real numbers can be identified with points in three-dimensional space. To do this, draw three coordinate axes as shown in Figure 12.1.A-1. The axes in three-dimensional space are usually called the x-axis, the y-axis, and the z-axis. In three-dimensional coordinates, the arrowhead on each axis indicates the positive direction.

Each pair of axes determines a **coordinate plane,** which is named by the axes that determine it. There are three coordinate planes, the xy-plane, the yz-plane, and the xz-plane, which divide the three-dimensional space into eight regions, called **octants,** shown in Figure 12.1.A-2. The octant in which all coordinates are positive is called the **first octant.**

Teaching Notes

Point out:
- An arrowhead on an axis indicates the positive direction.
- The three coordinate planes divide three-dimensional space into 8 **octants.**
- The perspective of Figure 12.1.A-2 is from the first octant. In other words, it is as if the viewer is in the first octant, "above" the green xy-plane, "in front of" the blue yz-plane, and "to the right of" the yellow xz-plane.

> **NOTE** The octants can be considered as the regions above and below each quadrant of the xy-plane.

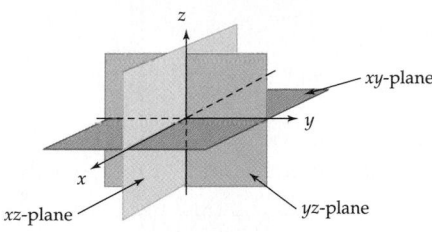

Figure 12.1.A-2

Plotting Points in Three Dimensions

To plot the point (a, b, c) in a three-dimensional coordinate system, move a units from the origin along the x-axis, move b units parallel to the y-axis, then move c units parallel to the z-axis. Dashed lines are used to indicate the distances parallel to the y- and z-axes.

COMMON ERROR ALERT

Students often identify or label axes incorrectly in a three-dimensional coordinate system because it appears that "the y-axis is where the x-axis used to be and the z-axis is where the y-axis used to be."

The following activity might help some students remember how to label the axes: Have them draw the customary x-axis and y-axis on paper and place a pencil at the origin perpendicular to the paper, as described earlier. The pencil is the z-axis (the new axis). Next, have them rotate the paper clockwise, holding the pencil in place, until they have the perspective shown in Figure 12.1.A-2.

Example 1   Points in Space

Plot the given points in a three-dimensional coordinate system.

$$(1, 3, 4), (0, -2, 0), (2, -2, -3)$$

Solution

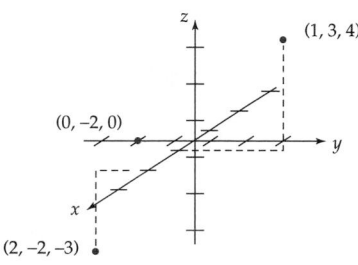

Figure 12.1.A-3 ∎

Graphs in Three Dimensions

A function in three dimensions can be written in terms of x, y, and z, or as a function of two variables, x and y. The graph of a linear equation in three dimensions is a plane. A comparison of two-dimensional and three-dimensional forms follows.

ADDITIONAL EXAMPLES

Example 1

Plot the given points in a three-dimensional coordinate system.

$$(-2, 1, -4), (2, 0, 0), (-1, -3, 1)$$

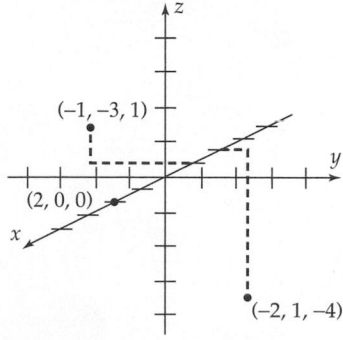

Math Background

Although French mathematician Rene Descartes (1596–1650) is well known as the founder of modern analytic geometry in the plane, he did not write in any detail about extending his ideas to three dimensions. The Dutch mathematician Frans van Schooten (1615–1660), one of the chief early promoters of Descartes' geometry, suggested using Cartesian coordinates to describe three-dimensional space. The subject was not systematically developed, however, until French mathematician Antoine Parent (1666–1716) presented a paper on it to the French Academy in 1700.

ADDITIONAL EXAMPLES

Example 2

Graph the plane $3x + 6y + 4z = 12$. Find the intercepts.

x-intercept:
$$3x + 6(0) + 4(0) = 12$$
$$x = 4$$

y-intercept:
$$3(0) + 6y + 4(0) = 12$$
$$y = 2$$

z-intercept:
$$3(0) + 6(0) + 4z = 12$$
$$z = 3$$

Plot the intercepts, and sketch the plane that contains them.

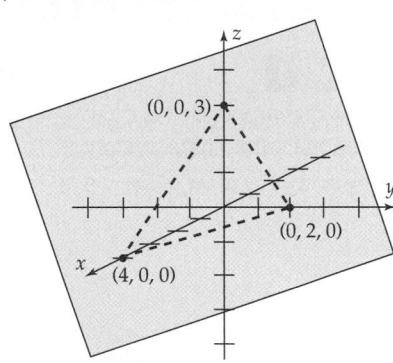

Two dimensions		Three dimensions	
$y = mx + b$ $f(x) = mx + b$	slope-intercept form of a line	$z = mx + ny + b$ $F(x, y) = mx + ny + b$	slope-intercept form of a plane
$m = \dfrac{y_2 - y_1}{x_2 - x_1}$	slope	$m = \dfrac{z_2 - z_1}{x_2 - x_1}$	slope in x-direction
b	y-intercept	$n = \dfrac{z_2 - z_1}{y_2 - y_1}$	slope in y-direction
		b	z-intercept
$Ax + By = C$	general form of a line	$Ax + By + Cz = D$	general form of a plane
$y - y_0 = m(x - x_0)$	point-slope form of a line	$z - z_0 = m(x - x_0) + n(y - y_0)$	point-slope form of a plane
$x = 0$ $y = 0$	y-axis x-axis	$x = 0$ $y = 0$ $z = 0$	yz-plane xz-plane xy-plane
$x = a$ $y = b$	vertical line horizontal line	$x = a$ $y = b$ $z = c$	plane: parallel to yz-plane parallel to xz-plane parallel to xy-plane

Graphing Planes

One method of graphing a plane in three dimensions is to find the x-, y-, and z-intercepts, plot the intercepts on the axes, and then sketch the plane. To find the x-intercept, set y and z equal to 0, and solve for x. The y-intercept and z-intercept are found in a similar manner.

Example 2 Graphing a Plane in General Form

Graph the plane $2x + 3y + 4z = 12$.

Solution

First, find the intercepts.

$$x\text{-intercept:}\quad 2x + 3(0) + 4(0) = 12$$
$$x = 6$$
$$y\text{-intercept:}\quad 2(0) + 3y + 4(0) = 12$$
$$y = 4$$
$$z\text{-intercept:}\quad 2(0) + 3(0) + 4z = 12$$
$$z = 3$$

Plot the intercepts, and sketch the plane that contains them, as shown in Figure 12.1.A-4.

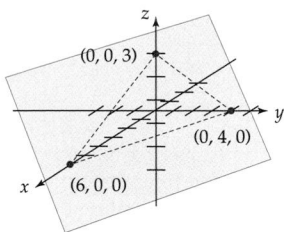

Figure 12.1.A-4

Example 3   Graphing a Plane in Slope-Intercept Form

Graph the plane $F(x, y) = x + 2y - 2$.

Solution

First, find the intercepts. Use the fact that $z = F(x, y)$ to find the z-intercept.

x-intercept: $0 = x + 2(0) - 2$
$\qquad\qquad\quad x = 2$

y-intercept: $0 = 0 + 2y - 2$
$\qquad\qquad\quad y = 1$

z-intercept: $z = 0 + 2(0) - 2$
$\qquad\qquad\quad z = -2$

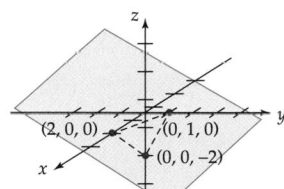

Figure 12.1.A-5

Plot the intercepts and sketch the plane that contains them, as shown in Figure 12.1.A-5.

Example 4   Graphing a Plane Parallel to an Axis

Graph the plane $z - 4 = 2(x - 1)$.

Solution

First, find the intercepts. There is no y term; thus, the plane has no y-intercept. It is parallel to the y-axis.

x-intercept: $0 - 4 = 2(x - 1)$
$\qquad\qquad\quad x = -1$

z-intercept: $z - 4 = 2(0 - 1)$
$\qquad\qquad\quad z = 2$

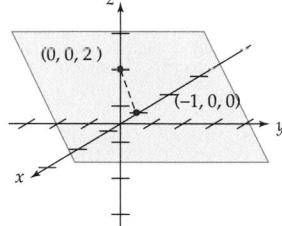

Figure 12.1.A-6

Plot the intercepts and sketch the plane that contains them, as shown in Figure 12.1.A-6.

Graphical Representations of 3 × 3 Systems

A linear system of equations in three variables is represented graphically by three planes. A solution of a 3 × 3 linear system is a point of intersection of *all three* planes. As in two variables, a linear system in three variables can have no solutions, one solution, or infinitely many solutions.

Example 3

Graph the plane $F(x, y) = 2x + y - 4$.
Find the intercepts.
x-intercept:
$\qquad 0 = 2x + (0) - 4$
$\qquad x = 2$
y-intercept:
$\qquad 0 = 2(0) + y - 4$
$\qquad y = 4$
z-intercept:
$\qquad z = 2(0) + (0) - 4$
$\qquad z = -4$
Plot the intercepts, and sketch the plane that contains them.

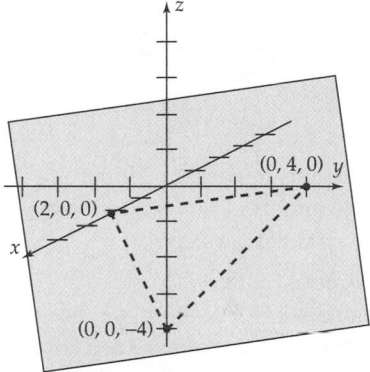

Example 4

Graph the plane $z + 1 = y - 2$.
Find the intercepts. There is no x term, thus, the plane has no x-intercept. It is parallel to the x-axis.
y-intercept:
$\qquad 0 + 1 = y - 2$
$\qquad y = 3$
z-intercept:
$\qquad z + 1 = 0 - 2$
$\qquad z = -3$
Plot the intercepts and sketch the plane that contains them.

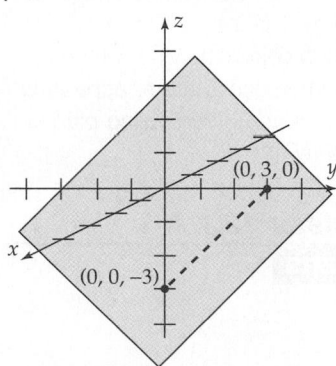

Teaching Notes

In the figure that illustrates one solution, the planes appear to be perpendicular two at a time, as in Figure 12.1.A-2 on page 791. Make sure students understand that to have one solution, it is only necessary that three planes intersect in one point; it is not necessary that any of the planes be perpendicular. The vertex of a triangular pyramid is an example from geometry that you could use to demonstrate this.

Ask students to describe all the possible graphical representations of a 3×3 linear system.

no solutions
- 3 parallel planes
- 2 parallel planes intersected by a third plane, forming 2 parallel lines of intersection
- 3 planes intersecting two at a time, forming 3 parallel lines of intersection
- 2 planes coinciding and a third plane parallel to them, appearing the same as 2 parallel planes (not shown)

one solution
- 3 planes intersecting in one point

infinitely many solutions
- 3 planes intersecting, forming 1 line of intersection
- 3 planes coinciding, appearing the same as 1 plane (not shown)
- 2 planes coinciding and a third plane intersecting them, appearing the same as 2 intersecting planes (not shown)

Exercises 12.1.A

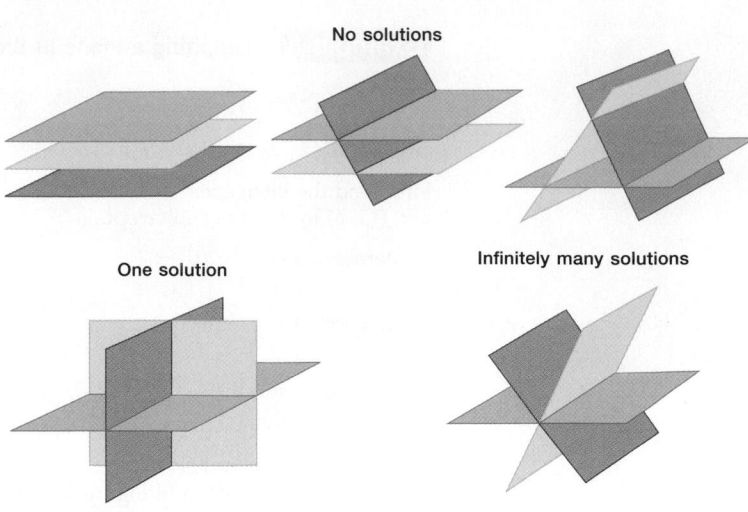

No solutions

One solution

Infinitely many solutions

Figure 12.1.A-7

All remaining possibilities not shown are listed below:

- three planes coincide (infinitely many solutions)
- two planes coincide and the third plane intersects them (infinitely many solutions)
- two planes coincide and the third plane is parallel (no solutions)

Exercises 12.1.A

In Exercises 1–8, plot the given point in a three-dimensional coordinate system.

1. $(1, 4, 5)$ **2.** $(-3, 2, 4)$

3. $(0, 2, -3)$ **4.** $(4, 0, 6)$

5. $(3, 0, 0)$ **6.** $(0, 0, -4)$

7. $(2, -3, -1)$ **8.** $(-3, -1, 5)$

In Exercises 9–20, graph the plane described by the given equation.

9. $x + 3y - z = 6$ **10.** $5x + 2y - 4z = 10$

11. $3x - 4y + 6z = 9$ **12.** $-2x + 4y + 5z = 8$

13. $z = x + y - 3$ **14.** $z = 2x - y + 6$

15. $F(x, y) = 2x + 4y - 8$ **16.** $F(x, y) = 3x - 5y + 9$

17. $z + 6 = 3(x - 2)$ **18.** $z - 8 = 4(y - 3)$

19. $3x + 2z = -6$ **20.** $4x + z = 2$

21. *Critical Thinking* Describe the possibilities for the number of solutions of a linear system of equations with 2 equations in 3 variables. Explain your answers in terms of intersections of two planes. You may include a sketch in your answer.

1.

2.

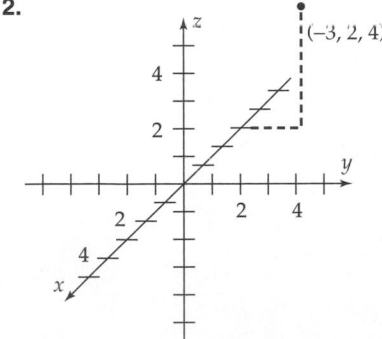

3–21. *See pp.* **1083–1084.**

12.2   Matrices

Objectives

- Represent systems of equations by augmented matrices

- Solve systems of equations by row reduction

- Solve systems by using a calculator to obtain reduced row echelon form matrices

- Solve applications by using matrices

Augmented Matrices

It is often convenient to use an array of numbers, called a **matrix,** as a method to represent a system of equations. For example, the system

$$x + 2y = -2$$
$$2x + 6y = 2$$

is written in matrix form as

$$\begin{pmatrix} 1 & 2 & -2 \\ 2 & 6 & 2 \end{pmatrix}$$

In this shorthand, only the coefficients of the variables are written. This representation is called an **augmented matrix** where each row of the matrix represents an equation of the system. The numbers in the first column are coefficients of x, the numbers in the second column are coefficients of y, and the third column's numbers are the constant terms. A vertical dashed line is often used to represent the equal signs.

Example 1   Writing a System as an Augmented Matrix

Write an augmented matrix for the system of equations.

$$x + 2y + 3z = -2$$
$$2y - 5z = 6$$
$$3x + 3y + 10z = -2$$

Solution

The augmented matrix is $\begin{pmatrix} 1 & 2 & 3 & -2 \\ 0 & 2 & -5 & 6 \\ 3 & 3 & 10 & -2 \end{pmatrix}$.

Notice that 0 is the x-coefficient in the second equation. ∎

Solving Systems Using Augmented Matrices

Recall that in the elimination method, an equation may be multiplied by a nonzero constant, or two equations may be added together. Also, the order of the equations is irrelevant, so equations may be interchanged. Performing any of these operations produces an **equivalent system,** that is, a system with the same solutions.

Augmented matrices can be used to solve linear systems. When dealing with matrices, operations similar to those used in the elimination method are called **elementary row operations.**

Section
12.2 Matrices

Math Background

The system in **Example 1** is a 3×3 linear system that can be solved by various methods.

The system can be solved algebraically using elimination, as shown in Section 12.1. Elementary row operations can be used to produce a reduced row-echelon form of the matrix. Have students use elimination to solve the system of equations in Example 1.
$x = 8$, $y = -2$, $z = -2$
Likewise, the system in Additional Example 1 can also be solved using elimination.
$x = \frac{1}{51} \approx 0.0196$, $y = -\frac{11}{51} \approx -0.2157$,
$z = -\frac{28}{17} \approx -1.0471$

A method using matrices not shown in this text is Cramer's Rule, named after Swiss mathematician Gabriel Cramer (1704–1752). Cramer's Rule uses *determinants*.

ADDITIONAL EXAMPLES

Example 1

Write an augmented matrix for the system of equations.
$$3y - z = 1$$
$$x + 2y + 4z = -7$$
$$-5x - y - 6z = 10$$
$$\begin{pmatrix} 0 & 3 & -1 & 1 \\ 1 & 2 & 4 & -7 \\ -5 & -1 & -6 & 10 \end{pmatrix}$$

Teaching Notes

Use **Example 2** to compare the previous elimination method and the new elimination method. The difference is that in the new method, we rewrite one of the original equations along with the new equation.

previous method	new method
$x + 2y = -2$	$x + 2y = -2$
$2x + 6y = 2$	$2x + 6y = 2$
$\downarrow$	$\downarrow$

$$\begin{array}{r} -2x - 4y = 4 \\ +\ 2x + 6y = 2 \\ \hline 2y = 6 \end{array}$$

$$\begin{array}{r} x + 2y = -2 \\ 2y = 6 \end{array}$$

ADDITIONAL EXAMPLES

Example 2

Solve the system of equations.

$$x + 2y = 1$$
$$4x + 3y = -6$$

Elimination method:

Replace the second row by the sum of itself and -4 times the first row.

$$x + 2y = 1$$
$$-5y = -10$$

Multiply the second row by $-\frac{1}{5}$.

$$x + 2y = 1$$
$$y = 2$$

Replace the first row by the sum of itself and -2 times the second row.

$$x = -3$$
$$y = 2$$

Augmented matrix method:

$$\begin{pmatrix} 1 & 2 & | & 1 \\ 4 & 3 & | & -6 \end{pmatrix}$$

$$-4r_1 + r_2 \rightarrow r_2$$

$$\begin{pmatrix} 1 & 2 & | & 1 \\ 0 & -5 & | & -10 \end{pmatrix}$$

$$-\frac{1}{5}r_2 \rightarrow r_2$$

$$\begin{pmatrix} 1 & 2 & | & 1 \\ 0 & 1 & | & 2 \end{pmatrix}$$

$$-2r_2 + r_1 \rightarrow r_1$$

$$\begin{pmatrix} 1 & 0 & | & -3 \\ 0 & 1 & | & 2 \end{pmatrix}$$

$$x = -3, y = 2$$

Elementary Row Operations

Performing any of the following operations on an augmented matrix produces an augmented matrix of an equivalent system:

- **Interchange any two rows.**
- **Replace any row by a nonzero constant multiple of itself.**
- **Replace any row by the sum of itself and a nonzero constant multiple of another row.**

Example 2 shows the use of the elementary row operations in solving a system. To solve a system of two equations in two variables using elementary row operations, produce an equivalent matrix that has one row with an x-coefficient of 1 and a y-coefficient of 0, and the other row with an x-coefficient of 0 and a y-coefficient of 1. The desired equivalent matrix and its corresponding system are shown below.

$$\begin{pmatrix} 1 & 0 & | & a \\ 0 & 1 & | & b \end{pmatrix} \quad \longleftrightarrow \quad \begin{array}{l} x = a \\ y = b \end{array}$$

Example 2 Using an Augmented Matrix

Solve the system of equations

$$x + 2y = -2$$
$$2x + 6y = 2$$

Solution

The system is solved below by using elementary row operations in the elimination method on the left and the augmented matrix method on the right. Compare the steps performed in each method.

$$\begin{array}{l} x + 2y = -2 \\ 2x + 6y = 2 \end{array} \qquad \begin{pmatrix} 1 & 2 & | & -2 \\ 2 & 6 & | & 2 \end{pmatrix}$$

Replace the second row by the sum of itself and -2 times the first row.

$$-2r_1 + r_2 \rightarrow r_2$$

$$\begin{array}{l} x + 2y = -2 \\ 2y = 6 \end{array} \qquad \begin{pmatrix} 1 & 2 & | & -2 \\ 0 & 2 & | & 6 \end{pmatrix}$$

Multiply the second row by $\frac{1}{2}$.

$$\frac{1}{2}r_2 \rightarrow r_2$$

$$\begin{array}{l} x + 2y = -2 \\ y = 3 \end{array} \qquad \begin{pmatrix} 1 & 2 & | & -2 \\ 0 & 1 & | & 3 \end{pmatrix}$$

Replace the first row by the sum of itself and -2 times the second row.

$$-2r_2 + r_1 \rightarrow r_1$$

$$\begin{array}{l} x = -8 \\ y = 3 \end{array} \qquad \begin{pmatrix} 1 & 0 & | & -8 \\ 0 & 1 & | & 3 \end{pmatrix}$$

NOTE In previous methods, the step to replace a row with the sum of itself and a multiple of another row was done in two or more steps.

This last augmented matrix $\begin{pmatrix} 1 & 0 & -8 \\ 0 & 1 & 3 \end{pmatrix}$ represents the same solution of the system as the solution obtained by using the elimination method. The solution of the system is $x = -8$, $y = 3$. ∎

Reduced Row-Echelon Form

The last matrix of Example 2 is in **reduced row-echelon form,** which is summarized as follows.

Reduced Row-Echelon Form

> A matrix is in reduced row-echelon form if it satisfies the following conditions.
>
> - All rows consisting entirely of zeros (if any) are at the bottom.
> - The first nonzero entry in each nonzero row is a 1 (called a *leading* 1).
> - Any column containing a leading 1 has zeros as all other entries.
> - Each leading 1 appears to the right of leading 1's in any preceding row.

Gauss-Jordan Elimination

The method of using elementary row operations to produce an equivalent matrix in reduced row-echelon form is called **Gauss-Jordan elimination.** When an augmented matrix is in reduced row-echelon form, the solutions of the system it represents can be read immediately, as in the last step of Example 2.

Example 3 Using Gauss-Jordan Elimination

The matrices below are in reduced row-echelon form. Write the system represented by each matrix, find the solutions, if any, and classify each system as consistent, consistent with infinitely many solutions, or inconsistent.

a. $\begin{pmatrix} 1 & -3 & 4 \\ 0 & 0 & 0 \end{pmatrix}$ **b.** $\begin{pmatrix} 1 & 0 & 0 & 3 \\ 0 & 1 & 0 & -7 \\ 0 & 0 & 1 & 4 \end{pmatrix}$ **c.** $\begin{pmatrix} 1 & 2 & -1 \\ 0 & 0 & 3 \end{pmatrix}$

Solution

a. The system represented by the augmented matrix is

$$x - 3y = 4$$
$$0x + 0y = 0$$

NOTE A matrix can represent a system of equations that has variables other than x, y, and z. When given a matrix without the corresponding system, the choice of letters used to represent the variables is arbitrary. Another common choice is x_1, x_2, and x_3.

Example 3

The matrices below are in reduced row-echelon form. Write the system represented by each matrix, find the solutions, if any, and classify each system as consistent, consistent with infinitely many solutions, or inconsistent.

a. $\begin{pmatrix} 0 & 0 & 0 \\ -2 & 1 & 3 \end{pmatrix}$

system:

$$0x + 0y = 0$$
$$-2x + y = 3$$

The equation $0 = 0$ is always true. The system is consistent with infinitely many solutions. All solutions lie on the line $-2x + y = 3$.

Represent the solutions using the parameter t. Letting $x = t$ yields $-2t + y = 3$, so $y = 2t + 3$. Some individual solutions are:

For $t - 2$, $x - 2$ and $y = 7$.

For $t = 0$, $x = 0$ and $y = 3$.

For $t = -3$, $x = -3$ and $y = -3$.

b. $\begin{pmatrix} 1 & 0 & 0 & 2 \\ 0 & 1 & 0 & -1 \\ 0 & 0 & 1 & 5 \end{pmatrix}$

system:

$$x \qquad = 2$$
$$\quad y \quad = -1$$
$$\qquad z = 5$$

The solution is $x = 2$, $y = -1$, $z = 5$, so the system is consistent.

c. $\begin{pmatrix} 3 & -1 & 4 \\ 0 & 0 & 2 \end{pmatrix}$

system:

$$3x - y = 4$$
$$0x + 0y = 2$$

The equation $0 = 2$ is always false; the system is inconsistent because it has no solutions.

Students might enter the dimensions of an augmented matrix incorrectly into a calculator because they confuse it with the description of the system represented by the matrix. For instance, the system in **Example 4a** is called a 2×2 system because it has 2 equations in 2 variables (see page 779). However, the augmented matrix that represents the system is a 2×3 matrix because it has 2 rows and 3 columns. Make sure students *enter the number of rows and columns of the augmented matrix* in the calculator.

ADDITIONAL EXAMPLES

Example 4

Solve the following systems of equations using a calculator's reduced row-echelon form feature.

a. $3x + 2y = -2$
$\quad 2x + y = 0$

augmented matrix:

$$\begin{pmatrix} 3 & 2 & -2 \\ 2 & 1 & 0 \end{pmatrix}$$

```
[A]
        [[3 2 -2]
         [2 1 0 ]]
rref([A])
        [[1 0 2 ]
         [0 1 -4]]
```

The solution is $x = 2$, $y = -4$.

b. $-5x + 2y - 3z = 1$
$\quad 4x - y - z = 6$
$\quad 3y + 2z = -4$

augmented matrix:

$$\begin{pmatrix} -5 & 2 & -3 & 1 \\ 4 & -1 & -1 & 6 \\ 0 & 3 & 2 & -4 \end{pmatrix}$$

```
[[ -5 2  -3 1 ]
 [4  -1 -1 6 ]
 [0  3  2  -4]]
rref([B])
   [[1 0 0 1 ]
    [0 1 0 0 ]
    [0 0 1 -2]]
```

The solution is $x = 1$, $y = 0$, $z = -2$.

The second equation, $0 = 0$, is always true. The system is consistent with infinitely many solutions. All solutions lie on the line represented by $x - 3y = 4$.

Represent the solutions of the system using the parameter t. Letting $y = t$ yields $x - 3t = 4$, so $x = 4 + 3t$. Individual solutions may then be found by substituting real values for t.

t (a real number)	$x = 4 + 3t$	$y = t$
$t = 1$	$x = 7$	$y = 1$
$t = -2$	$x = -2,$	$y = -2$
$t = 0$	$x = 4$	$y = 0$

b. The system represented by the matrix is

$$\begin{aligned} x \quad\quad &= 3 \\ y \quad &= -7 \\ z &= 4 \end{aligned}$$

The solution of the system is $x = 3$, $y = -7$, $z = 4$, so the system is consistent.

c. The system represented by the matrix is

$$\begin{aligned} x + 2y &= -1 \\ 0x + 0y &= 3 \end{aligned}$$

The second equation, $0 = 3$, is always false. This indicates that the system is inconsistent because it has no solutions. ∎

Calculators and Reduced Row-Echelon Form

Most graphing calculators have a command that uses elementary row operations to put a given matrix into reduced row-echelon form.

Example 4 **Using Reduced Row-Echelon Form**

Solve the following systems of equations using a calculator's reduced row-echelon form feature:

a. $\begin{aligned} 2x + y &= 0 \\ -4x + y &= 18 \end{aligned}$

b. $\begin{aligned} -x + 2y - 3z &= 5 \\ 3x - y + 5z &= -3 \\ y - 2z &= 6 \end{aligned}$

Solution

Write the augmented matrix for each system, enter each system into a calculator as a matrix, then reduce to reduced row-echelon form (see Technology Tip).

a. $\begin{pmatrix} 2 & 1 & 0 \\ -4 & 1 & 18 \end{pmatrix}$

b. $\begin{pmatrix} -1 & 2 & -3 & 5 \\ 3 & -1 & 5 & -3 \\ 0 & 1 & -2 & 6 \end{pmatrix}$

Figure 12.2-1a   **Figure 12.2-1b**

The solution is $x = -3, y = 6$.   The solution is $x = 4, y = 0, z = -3$.

Example 5   Calculator Solution to an Inconsistent System

Solve the system of equations.

$$x + y + 2z = 1$$
$$2x + 4y + 5z = 2$$
$$3x + 5y + 7z = 4$$

Solution

Write the augmented matrix for the system, enter the matrix into a calculator, then reduce to reduced row-echelon form, as shown in Figure 12.2-2.

The last row of the reduced matrix represents the equation

$$0x + 0y + 0z = 1.$$

Because the equation has no solution, the original system has no solution and is therefore inconsistent.

$$\begin{pmatrix} 1 & 1 & 2 & | & 1 \\ 2 & 4 & 5 & | & 2 \\ 3 & 5 & 7 & | & 4 \end{pmatrix}$$

Figure 12.2-2

Example 6   Calculator Solution of a System

Solve the system of equations below.

$$2x + 5y + z + 3w = 0$$
$$2y - 4z + 6w = 0$$
$$2x + 17y - 23z + 40w = 0$$

Solution

Notice that all of the constant terms in the system are zero. A system like this has at least one solution, namely, $x = 0, y = 0, z = 0, w = 0$, which is called the *trivial solution*. However, there may be nonzero solutions as well.

Write the augmented matrix for the system, then enter and reduce it to reduced row-echelon form using a calculator, as shown in Figure 12.2-3.

$$\begin{pmatrix} 2 & 5 & 1 & 3 & | & 0 \\ 0 & 2 & -4 & 6 & | & 0 \\ 2 & 17 & -23 & 40 & | & 0 \end{pmatrix}$$

Figure 12.2-3

Example 5

Solve the system of equations.

$$x + 2y + 4z = 3$$
$$2x + 3y + z = 4$$
$$3x + 5y + 5z = 5$$

augmented matrix:

$$\begin{pmatrix} 1 & 2 & 4 & | & 3 \\ 2 & 3 & 1 & | & 4 \\ 3 & 5 & 5 & | & 5 \end{pmatrix}$$

Because the equation $0x + 0y + 0z = 1$ has no solution, the original system has no solution and is therefore inconsistent.

Example 6

Solve the system of equations below.

$$2x + 3y + 2z + 2w = 0$$
$$y - 2z - 9w = 0$$
$$x + 12y - 20z + 10w = 0$$

augmented matrix:

$$\begin{pmatrix} 2 & 3 & 2 & 2 & | & 0 \\ 0 & 1 & -2 & -9 & | & 0 \\ 1 & 12 & -20 & 10 & | & 0 \end{pmatrix}$$

The system corresponding to the reduced matrix is:

$$x + 4z = 0$$
$$y - 2z = 0$$
$$w = 0$$

The system is consistent with infinitely many solutions.

$x = -4z, y = 2z, w = 0$

Letting $z = t$, the solutions all have the form

$x = -4t, y = 2t, z = t, w = 0$.

Some individual solutions are:

$t = 0, x = 0, y = 0, z = 0, w = 0$
$t = 1, x = -4, y = 2, z = 1, w = 0$
$t = -2, x = 8, y = -4, z = -2, w = 0$

Real-World Application

In **Example 7**, someone is borrowing money to start a small business using credit cards that have different interest rates. Have students investigate the interest rates for various types of credit cards, such as personal and business. Which types have lower interest rates? Why? Have them compare credit card interest rates with interest rates on small business loans.

Similar applications are in Exercises 39–41. These applications are summarized below, along with possible questions for research or discussion.

39. Lillian borrows money from different sources at different interest rates. Why do you think the rate from the insurance company is the lowest? possible answer: The loan from the insurance company is secured by the cash value of the policy.

40. Someone invests in stocks, and the stocks increase in value at different rates. Are these rates predetermined, as are the loan rates in Exercise 39? Explain your answer. possible answer: no; Changes in the value of a stock cannot be predicted.

41. Someone invests in a mutual fund, bonds, and a fast food franchise that pay different dividend rates. Her total income is $4800. Point out the word *income* in this problem, then refer students back to Exercise 40. Did the investor in Exercise 40 receive income? Explain your answer. possible answer: no; Exercise 40 states only that the investment is now worth $29,440, which is $4440 more than the original investment of $25,000. The investor would receive income only if she sold the stock. (And her income would likely be reduced by a broker's commission.)

The system corresponding to the reduced matrix is

$$
\begin{aligned}
x + \quad 5.5z &= 0 \\
y - \quad 2z &= 0 \\
w &= 0
\end{aligned}
$$

The system is consistent with infinitely many solutions. The value of w is always 0, and the first two equations can be solved for x and y in terms of z.

$$
\begin{aligned}
x &= -5.5z \\
y &= 2z \\
w &= 0
\end{aligned}
$$

Letting $z = t$, the solutions of the system all have the form

$$
x = -5.5t, \qquad y = 2t, \qquad z = t, \qquad w = 0.
$$

Individual solutions may be found by substituting real values for t.

$t = 0$	$x = 0,$	$y = 0,$	$z = 0,$	$w = 0$
$t = 1$	$x = -5.5,$	$y = 2,$	$z = 1,$	$w = 0$
$t = -3$	$x = 16.5,$	$y = -6,$	$z = -3,$	$w = 0$

Example 7 Application Using Calculator Reduced Row-Echelon Form

Charlie is starting a small business and borrows $10,000 on three different credit cards, with annual interest rates of 18%, 15%, and 9%, respectively. He borrows three times as much on the 15% card as he does on the 18% card, and his total annual interest on all three cards is $1244.25. How much did he borrow on each credit card?

Solution

Let x be the amount borrowed on the 18% card, y the amount borrowed on the 15% card, and z the amount borrowed on the 9% card. The total amount borrowed is $10,000.

$$
x + y + z = 10,000
$$

Total interest is the sum of the amounts of interest on the three cards.

Interest on 18% card		*Interest on 15% card*		*Interest on 9% card*		*Total interest*
$0.18x$	$+$	$0.15y$	$+$	$0.09z$	$=$	1244.25

The amounts on the cards are related by a third equation.

Amount on 15% card		*3 times amount on 18% card*
y	$=$	$3x$

The equation $y = 3x$ is equivalent to $3x - y = 0$. Therefore, the system of equations is

$$\begin{array}{rcrcrcr} x &+& y &+& z &=& 10{,}000 \\ 0.18x &+& 0.15y &+& 0.09z &=& 1244.25 \\ 3x &-& y & & &=& 0 \end{array}$$

The corresponding matrix and its reduced row-echelon form are shown in Figure 12.2-4.

$$\left(\begin{array}{ccc|c} 1 & 1 & 1 & 10{,}000 \\ 0.18 & 0.15 & 0.09 & 1244.25 \\ 3 & -1 & 0 & 0 \end{array}\right)$$

Figure 12.2-4

The solution is $x = 1275$, $y = 3825$, and $z = 4900$. Charlie borrowed $1275 on the 18% card, $3825 on the 15% card, and $4900 on the 9% card. ∎

Exercises 12.2

In Exercises 1–4, write the augmented matrix of the system.

1. $2x - 3y + 4z = 1$
$x + 2y - 6z = 0$
$3x - 7y + 4z = -3$

2. $x + 2y - 3w + 7z = -5$
$2x - y - 3w + 2z = 4$
$3x + 2y + 7w - 6z = 0$

3. $x - \dfrac{1}{2}y + \dfrac{7}{4}z = 0$

$2x - \dfrac{3}{2}y + 5z = 0$

$-2y + \dfrac{1}{3}z = 0$

4. $2x - \dfrac{1}{2}y + \dfrac{7}{2}w - 6z = 1$

$\dfrac{1}{4}x - 6y + 2w - z = 2$

$4y - \dfrac{1}{2}w + 6z = 3$

$2x + 3y - 2w + \dfrac{1}{2}z = 4$

In Exercises 5–8, the augmented matrix of a system of equations is given. Express the system in equation notation.

5. $\left(\begin{array}{cc|c} 2 & -3 & 1 \\ 4 & 7 & 2 \end{array}\right)$

6. $\left(\begin{array}{ccc|c} 2 & 3 & 5 & 2 \\ 1 & 6 & 9 & 0 \end{array}\right)$

7. $\left(\begin{array}{cccc|c} 1 & 0 & 1 & 0 & 1 \\ 1 & -1 & 4 & -2 & 3 \\ 4 & 2 & 5 & 0 & 2 \end{array}\right)$

8. $\left(\begin{array}{ccc|c} 1 & 7 & 0 & 4 \\ 2 & 3 & 1 & 6 \\ -1 & 0 & 2 & 3 \end{array}\right)$

In Exercises 9–12, the reduced row-echelon form of the augmented matrix of a system of equations is given. Find the solutions of the system.

9. $\left(\begin{array}{cccc|c} 1 & 0 & 0 & 0 & \frac{3}{2} \\ 0 & 1 & 0 & 0 & 5 \\ 0 & 0 & 1 & 0 & -2 \\ 0 & 0 & 0 & 1 & 0 \end{array}\right)$

10. $\left(\begin{array}{ccccc|c} 1 & 0 & 0 & 0 & 0 & 5 \\ 0 & 1 & 0 & 0 & 0 & 4 \\ 0 & 0 & 1 & 0 & 0 & 3 \\ 0 & 0 & 0 & 0 & 1 & 2 \\ 0 & 0 & 0 & 0 & 0 & 1 \end{array}\right)$

11. $\left(\begin{array}{cccc|c} 1 & 0 & 0 & 1 & 2 \\ 0 & 1 & 0 & 2 & -3 \\ 0 & 0 & 1 & 0 & 4 \\ 0 & 0 & 0 & 0 & 0 \end{array}\right)$

12. $\left(\begin{array}{cccc|c} 1 & 0 & 0 & 0 & 7 \\ 0 & 1 & 0 & 0 & 1 \\ 0 & 0 & 1 & 0 & -5 \\ 0 & 0 & 0 & 1 & 4 \\ 0 & 0 & 0 & 0 & 0 \\ 0 & 0 & 0 & 0 & 0 \end{array}\right)$

---

4. $\left(\begin{array}{cccc|c} 2 & -\frac{1}{2} & \frac{7}{2} & -6 & 1 \\ \frac{1}{4} & -6 & 2 & -1 & 2 \\ 0 & 4 & -\frac{1}{2} & 6 & 3 \\ 2 & 3 & -2 & \frac{1}{2} & 4 \end{array}\right)$

5. $2x - 3y = 1$
$4x + 7y = 2$

6. $2x + 3y + 5z = 2$
$x + 6y + 9z = 0$

7. $x + z = 1$
$x - y + 4z - 2w = 3$
$4x + 2y + 5z = 2$

8. $x + 7y = 4$
$2x + 3y + z = 6$
$-x + 2z = 3$

9. $x = \dfrac{3}{2}$, $y = 5$, $z = -2$, $w = 0$

10. $x = 5$, $y = 4$, $z = 3$, $v = 2$, $w = 1$

11–12. *See p. 802.*

ADDITIONAL EXAMPLES

Example 7

Samantha invests $25,000 in three different mutual funds, *A*, *B*, and *C*. She invests four times as much in Fund *A* as in Fund *B*. Fund *A* increases 10% in value, *B* increases 18%, and *C* increases 15%. Her total investment in the funds is now worth $28,070. How much did she invest in each fund?

Let *x* be the amount invested in Fund *A* (at 10%), *y* the amount invested in Fund *B* (at 18%), and *z* the amount invested in Fund *C* (at 15%):

The total amount invested is 25,000.

The total increase in value is $28{,}070 - 25{,}000 = 3070$.

x is 4 times *y*, so $x = 4y$, and $x - 4y = 0$.

The system is:

$$\begin{array}{rcrcrcr} x &+& y &+& z &=& 25{,}000 \\ 0.1x &+& 0.18y &+& 0.15z &=& 3070 \\ x &-& 4y & & &=& 0 \end{array}$$

augmented matrix:

$$\left(\begin{array}{ccc|c} 1 & 1 & 1 & 25{,}000 \\ 0.1 & 0.18 & 0.15 & 3070 \\ 1 & -4 & 0 & 0 \end{array}\right)$$

The solution is $x = 16{,}000$, $y = 4000$, $z = 5000$. Samantha invested $16,000 in Fund *A*, $4000 in Fund *B*, and $5000 in Fund *C*.

Exercises 12.2

ANSWERS

1. $\left(\begin{array}{ccc|c} 2 & -3 & 4 & 1 \\ 1 & 2 & -6 & 0 \\ 3 & -7 & 4 & -3 \end{array}\right)$

2. $\left(\begin{array}{cccc|c} 1 & 2 & -3 & 7 & -5 \\ 2 & -1 & -3 & 2 & 4 \\ 3 & 2 & 7 & -6 & 0 \end{array}\right)$

3. $\left(\begin{array}{ccc|c} 1 & -\frac{1}{2} & \frac{7}{4} & 0 \\ 2 & -\frac{3}{2} & 5 & 0 \\ 0 & -2 & \frac{1}{3} & 0 \end{array}\right)$

11. $x = 2 - t$, $y = -3 - 2t$, $z = 4$,
$w = t$, where t is any real number

12. $x = 7$, $y = 1$, $z = -5$, $w = 4$

13. $x = -1$, $y = -1$, $z = 1$

14. $x = 32$, $y = -6$, $z = -6$

15. $x = -\dfrac{1}{2}$, $y = -\dfrac{3}{4}$, $z = \dfrac{3}{2}$

16. $x = \dfrac{1}{5}$, $y = -\dfrac{3}{5}$, $z = 0$

17. $x = -14$, $y = -6$, $z = 2$

18. $x = 1$, $y = 2$, $z = -1$

19. no solution

20. $x = \dfrac{12}{7} - \dfrac{1}{7}t$, $y = -\dfrac{6}{7} + \dfrac{4}{7}t$, $z = t$,
where t is any real number

21. $x = t$, $y = \dfrac{1}{2} - 2t$, $z = t$, where t
is any real number

22. $x = 0$, $y = t + \dfrac{1}{10}$, $z = 2t - \dfrac{13}{5}$,
$w = t$, where t is any real
number

23. $x = 1$, $y = 2$

24. $x = 1$, $y = 1$, $z = 1$

25. no solution

26. no solution

27. $x = -t + 2$, $y = t - 1$, $z = t$,
where t is any real number

28. $x = 1 + t$, $y = \dfrac{1}{2} - \dfrac{1}{2}t$, $z = t$,
where t is any real number

29. $x = 0$, $y = 0$, $z = 0$

30. $x = 0$, $y = 0$, $z = 0$

31. $x = -1$, $y = 1$, $z = -3$, $w = -2$

32. $x = 1$, $y = -1$, $z = 2$, $w = -3$

33. $x = 3$, $y = 1$, $z = -2$, $w = -5$

34. $x = 0$, $y = 0$, $z = 0$, $w = 0$

35. $x = -\dfrac{3}{4}$, $y = \dfrac{10}{3}$, $z = \dfrac{5}{2}$

36.

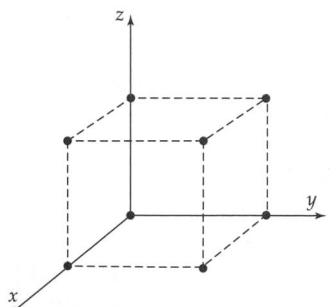

In Exercises 13–20, use Gauss-Jordan elimination to solve the system.

13. $-x + 3y + 2z = 0$
$-2x - 3y - 2z = 3$
$x + 2y + 3z = 0$

14. $3x + 7y + 9z = 0$
$x + 2y + 3z = 2$
$x + 4y + z = 2$

15. $x + 2y + 2z = 1$
$x - 2y + 2z = 4$
$2x - 2y + 3z = 5$

16. $2x - y + 2z = 1$
$3x + y + 2z = 0$
$7x - y + 3z = 2$

17. $x - 2y + 4z = 6$
$x + y + 13z = 6$
$-2x + 6y - z = -10$

18. $x - y + 5z = -6$
$3x + 3y - z = 10$
$x + 3y + 2z = 5$

19. $x + y + z = 200$
$x - 2y + 2z = 0$
$2x + 3y + 5z = 600$
$2x - y + z = 200$

20. $3x - y + z = 6$
$x + 2y - z = 0$

In Exercises 21–35, solve the system by any method.

21. $11x + 10y + 9z = 5$
$x + 2y + 3z = 1$
$3x + 2y + z = 1$

22. $-x + 2y - 3z + 4w = 8$
$2x - 4y + z + 2w = -3$
$5x - 4y + z + 2w = -3$

23. $x + y = 3$
$5x - y = 3$
$9x - 4y = 1$

24. $2x - y + 2z = 3$
$-x + 2y - z = 0$
$x + y - z = 1$

25. $x - 4y - 13z = 4$
$x - 2y - 3z = 2$
$-3x + 5y + 4z = 2$

26. $2x - 4y + z = 3$
$x + 3y - 7z = 1$
$-2x + 4y - z = 10$

27. $4x + y + 3z = 7$
$x - y + 2z = 3$
$3x + 2y + z = 4$

28. $x + 4y + z = 3$
$-x + 2y + 2z = 0$
$2x + 2y - z = 3$

29. $x + y + z = 0$
$3x - y + z = 0$
$-5x - y + z = 0$

30. $x + y + z = 0$
$x - y - z = 0$
$x - y + z = 0$

31. $2x + y + 3z - 2w = -6$
$4x + 3y + z - w = -2$
$x + y + z + w = -5$
$-2x - 2y + 2z + 2w = -10$

32. $x + y + z + w = -1$
$-x + 4y + z - w = 0$
$x - 2y + z - 2w = 11$
$-x - 2y + z + 2w = -3$

33. $x - 2y - z - 3w = 18$
$-x + y + 3z - 3w = 7$
$4y + 3z - 2w = 8$
$2x - 2y + 3z + w = -7$

34. $3x - y + 2z + 5w = 0$
$-x + 3y + 2z + 5w = 0$
$x + 2y + 5z - 4w = 0$
$2x - y + 5z + 3w = 0$

35. $\dfrac{1}{x + 1} - \dfrac{2}{y - 3} + \dfrac{3}{z - 2} = 4$

$\dfrac{5}{y - 3} - \dfrac{10}{z - 2} = -5$

$\dfrac{-3}{x + 1} + \dfrac{4}{y - 3} - \dfrac{1}{z - 2} = -2$

Hint: Let $u = \dfrac{1}{x + 1}$, $v = \dfrac{1}{y - 3}$, $w = \dfrac{1}{z - 2}$.

36. A matrix can be used to represent a set of points in space, with the x-coordinates in the first column, the y-coordinates in the second column, and the z-coordinates in the third column. Each row represents a point. A *crystal lattice* is used to represent the atomic structure of a crystal. The two matrices below represent simple cubic and A10 crystal lattices, in which the atoms of the crystal are at the points represented by the rows of the matrix.

Simple Cubic			A10		
x	y	z	x	y	z
0	0	0	0	0	0
3.35	0	0	2.93	0.48	0.48
0	3.35	0	0.48	2.93	0.48
3.35	3.35	0	0.48	0.48	2.93
0	0	3.35	3.40	3.40	0.95
3.35	0	3.35	3.40	0.95	3.40
0	3.35	3.35	0.95	3.40	3.40
3.35	3.35	3.35	3.88	3.88	3.88

In two different three-dimensional coordinate systems, plot the points in each matrix and connect them to form two prisms. How are the two lattices alike? How are they different?

37. A collection of nickels, dimes, and quarters totals $6.00. If there are 52 coins altogether and twice as many dimes as nickels, how many of each kind of coin are there?

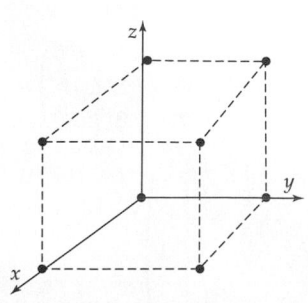

They both have 6 faces and 12 edges; one has square faces while the other has faces that are parallelograms.

37. 10 quarters; 28 dimes; 14 nickels

38. A collection of nickels, dimes, and quarters totals $8.20. The number of nickels and dimes together is twice the number of quarters. The value of the nickels is one-third of the value of the dimes. How many of each kind of coin are there?

39. Lillian borrows $10,000. She borrows some from her friend at 8% annual interest, twice as much as that from her bank at 9%, and the remainder from her insurance company at 5%. She pays a total of $830 in interest for the first year. How much did she borrow from each source?

40. An investor puts a total of $25,000 into three stocks. She invests some of it in stock A and $2000 more than one-half that amount in stock B. The remainder is invested in stock C. Stock A rises 16% in value, stock B 20%, and stock C 18%. Her investment in the three stocks is now worth $29,440. How much was originally invested in each stock?

41. An investor has $70,000 invested in a mutual fund, bonds, and a fast food franchise. She has twice as much invested in bonds as in the mutual fund. Last year the mutual fund paid a 2% dividend, the bonds 10%, and the fast food franchise 6%; her dividend income was $4800. How much is invested in each of the three investments?

42. Tickets to a concert cost $2 for children, $3 for teenagers, and $5 for adults. When 570 people attended the concert, the total ticket receipts were $1950. Three-fourths as many teenagers as children attended. How many children, adults, and teenagers attended?

43. A company sells three models of humidifiers: the bedroom model weighs 10 pounds and comes in an 8-cubic-foot box; the living room model weighs 20 pounds and comes in an 8-cubic-foot box; the whole-house model weighs 60 pounds and comes in a 28-cubic-foot box. Each of their delivery vans has 248 cubic feet of space and can hold a maximum of 440 pounds. In order for a van to be as fully loaded as possible, how many of each model should it carry?

44. Peanuts cost $3 per pound, almonds $4 per pound, and cashews $8 per pound. How many pounds of each should be used to produce 140 pounds of a mixture costing $6 per pound, in which there are twice as many peanuts as almonds?

45. If Tom, George, and Mario work together, they can paint a large room in 4 hours. When only George and Mario work together, it takes 8 hours to paint the room. Tom and George, working together, take 6 hours to paint the room. How long would it take each of them to paint the room alone? *Hint:* If x is the amount of the room painted in 1 hour by Tom, y is the amount painted by George, and z the amount painted by Mario, then $x + y + z = \dfrac{1}{4}$.

46. Pipes R, S, and T are connected to the same tank. When all three pipes are running, they can fill the tank in 2 hours. When only pipes S and T are running, they can fill the tank in 4 hours. When only R and T are running, they can fill the tank in 2.4 hours. How long would it take each pipe running alone to fill the tank?

47. A furniture manufacturer has 1950 hours available each week in the cutting department, 1490 hours in the assembly department, and 2160 in the finishing department. Manufacturing a chair requires 0.2 hours of cutting, 0.3 hours of assembly, and 0.1 hours of finishing. A chest requires 0.5 hours of cutting, 0.4 hours of assembly, and 0.6 hours of finishing. A table requires 0.3 hours of cutting, 0.1 hours of assembly, and 0.4 hours of finishing. How many chairs, chests, and tables should be produced in order to use all the available production capacity?

48. A stereo equipment manufacturer produces three models of speakers, R, S, and T, and has three kinds of delivery vehicles: trucks, vans, and station wagons. A truck holds 2 boxes of model R, 1 of model S, and 3 of model T. A van holds 1 box of model R, 3 of model S, and 2 of model T. A station wagon holds 1 box of model R, 3 of model S, and 1 of model T. If 15 boxes of model R, 20 of model S, and 22 of model T are to be delivered, how many vehicles of each type should be used so that all operate at full capacity?

49. A company produces three camera models: A, B, and C. Each model A requires 3 hours of lens polishing, 2 hours of assembly time, and 2 hours of finishing time. Each model B requires 2, 2, and 1 hours of lens polishing, assembly, and finishing time, and each model C requires 1, 3, and 1 hours, respectively. There are 100 hours available for lens polishing, 100 hours for assembly, and 65 hours for finishing each week. How many of each model should be produced if all available time is used?

38. 16 nickels;
24 dimes;
20 quarters

39. $3000 from her friend;
$6000 from the bank;
$1000 from the insurance company

40. $10,000 stock A;
$7,000 stock B;
$8,000 stock C

41. $15,000 in the mutual fund;
$30,000 in bonds;
$25,000 in food franchise

42. 200 children;
150 teens;
220 adults

43. Three possible solutions:

18 bedroom;
13 living room;
0 whole house

16 bedroom;
8 living room;
2 whole house

14 bedroom;
3 living room;
4 whole house

44. 40 lb peanuts;
20 lb almonds;
80 lb cashews

45. Tom: 8 hours;
George: 24 hours;
Mario: 12 hours

46. 4 hours to fill pipe R;
12 hours to fill pipe S;
6 hours to fill pipe T

47. 2000 chairs;
1600 chests;
2500 tables

48. 5 trucks;
2 vans;
3 station wagons

49. 20 model A;
15 model B;
10 model C

Section 12.3 Matrix Operations

Teaching Notes

In this section, students will add and subtract matrices. They will also multiply matrices by scalars (real numbers) and multiply matrices by matrices.

All of the operations mentioned above are accomplished by appropriate operations with real numbers. Emphasize the following points at the appropriate times (a and b represent real numbers; A and B represent matrices):

- Addition of real numbers is commutative. $a + b = b + a$
  Addition of matrices is also commutative. $A + B = B + A$
- Subtraction of real numbers is not commutative.
  $a - b \neq b - a$ in general.
  Subtraction of matrices is also not commutative.
  $A - B \neq B - A$ in general.
- Multiplication of real numbers is commutative.
  $ab = ba$
  Multiplication of matrices is **not** commutative.
  $AB \neq BA$ in general.

You may want to relate multiplying a matrix by a scalar to multiplying a vector by a scalar (page 655). The product of a scalar k and a vector $\mathbf{v} = \langle a, b \rangle$ is $k\mathbf{v} = \langle ka, kb \rangle$. This definition is consistent with the definition of the product of a scalar and a matrix.

COMMON ERROR ALERT

Subtracting matrices with many entries requires many real number subtractions, which could lead to sign errors. For instance, there are 9 real number subtractions required in **Example 1.** A strategy that may help students avoid errors is to use the property $A - B = A + (-B)$. That is, first change the signs of all the elements in matrix B, and then add the matrices.

12.3 Matrix Operations

Objectives

- Add and subtract matrices
- Multiply a matrix by a scalar factor
- Multiply two matrices
- Use matrix multiplication to solve problems
- Use matrices to represent directed networks

Matrices were used in Section 12.2 to solve systems of linear equations. However, matrices are also useful for organizing data. The arithmetic of matrices has practical applications in the natural sciences, engineering, the social sciences, and management. Matrices are now considered in a more general setting.

A matrix has been defined as an array of numbers. The **dimensions** of a matrix indicate the number of rows and columns in the matrix. An $m \times n$ **matrix** has m rows and n columns. For example:

$$A = \begin{pmatrix} 3 & 2 & -5 \\ 6 & 1 & 7 \\ -2 & 0 & 5 \end{pmatrix} \qquad B = \begin{pmatrix} \frac{3}{2} \\ -5 \\ 0 \\ 12 \end{pmatrix}$$

3×3 *matrix*
3 rows, 3 columns

4×1 *matrix*
4 rows, 1 column

Each entry of a matrix can be located by stating the row and column in which it appears. An entry a_{ij} is the entry in row i and column j of its corresponding matrix. In the matrices above, $a_{13} = -5$ and $b_{41} = 12$. Two matrices are said to be **equal** if they have the same dimensions and the corresponding entries are equal.

The general form of a matrix can be written as shown below.

$$A = \begin{pmatrix} a_{11} & a_{12} & a_{13} & \cdots & a_{1n} \\ a_{21} & a_{22} & a_{23} & \cdots & a_{2n} \\ a_{31} & a_{32} & a_{33} & \cdots & a_{3n} \\ \vdots & \vdots & \vdots & & \vdots \\ a_{m1} & a_{m2} & a_{m3} & \cdots & a_{mn} \end{pmatrix}$$

Matrix Addition and Subtraction

Matrices may be added or subtracted, but unlike real numbers, not all sums and differences are defined. It is only possible to add or subtract matrices that have the same dimensions.

Matrix Addition and Subtraction

> Matrices that have the same dimensions may be added or subtracted by adding or subtracting the corresponding entries.
>
> For matrices that have different dimensions, addition and subtraction are not defined.

```
[A]+[B]
[[8  -4 -3]
 [10 6   3]
 [-1 -1 5 ]]
```

Figure 12.3-1a

```
[A]-[B]
[[-2 8  -7]
 [2  -4 11]
 [-3 1  5 ]]
```

Figure 12.3-1b

Example 1   Adding and Subtracting Matrices

For the given matrices, find $A + B$ and $A - B$.

$$A = \begin{pmatrix} 3 & 2 & -5 \\ 6 & 1 & 7 \\ -2 & 0 & 5 \end{pmatrix} \qquad B = \begin{pmatrix} 5 & -6 & 2 \\ 4 & 5 & -4 \\ 1 & -1 & 0 \end{pmatrix}$$

Solution

Both are 3×3 matrices, so add or subtract the corresponding entries.

$$A + B = \begin{pmatrix} 3 & 2 & -5 \\ 6 & 1 & 7 \\ -2 & 0 & 5 \end{pmatrix} + \begin{pmatrix} 5 & -6 & 2 \\ 4 & 5 & -4 \\ 1 & -1 & 0 \end{pmatrix} = \begin{pmatrix} 8 & -4 & -3 \\ 10 & 6 & 3 \\ -1 & -1 & 5 \end{pmatrix}$$

$$A - B = \begin{pmatrix} 3 & 2 & -5 \\ 6 & 1 & 7 \\ -2 & 0 & 5 \end{pmatrix} - \begin{pmatrix} 5 & -6 & 2 \\ 4 & 5 & -4 \\ 1 & -1 & 0 \end{pmatrix} = \begin{pmatrix} -2 & 8 & -7 \\ 2 & -4 & 11 \\ -3 & 1 & 5 \end{pmatrix}$$

The results are confirmed in Figures 12.3-1a and 12.3-1b. ∎

Multiplication and Matrices

Scalar Multiplication

There are two different types of multiplication associated with matrices: scalar multiplication and matrix multiplication. **Scalar multiplication** is the product of a real number and a matrix, while **matrix multiplication** is the product of two matrices.

Scalar Multiplication

> Scalar multiplication is the product of a *scalar*, or real number, and a matrix. If A is an $m \times n$ matrix and k is a real number, then kA is the $m \times n$ matrix formed by multiplying each entry of A by k.
>
> $$k \begin{pmatrix} a_{11} & \cdots & a_{1n} \\ \vdots & \ddots & \vdots \\ a_{m1} & \cdots & a_{mn} \end{pmatrix} = \begin{pmatrix} ka_{11} & \cdots & ka_{1n} \\ \vdots & \ddots & \vdots \\ ka_{m1} & \cdots & ka_{mn} \end{pmatrix}$$

Example 2   Scalar Multiplication

For the matrix $A = \begin{pmatrix} 3 & 2 & -5 \\ 6 & 1 & 7 \\ -2 & 0 & 5 \end{pmatrix}$, find $3A$.

Example 1

For the given matrices, find $A + B$ and $A - B$.

$$A = \begin{pmatrix} 2 & -1 & 3 \\ -4 & 6 & 1 \\ 0 & -5 & -2 \end{pmatrix} \quad B = \begin{pmatrix} 4 & 3 & -1 \\ -4 & 5 & 7 \\ 2 & 7 & -5 \end{pmatrix}$$

$$A + B = \begin{pmatrix} 6 & 2 & 2 \\ -8 & 11 & 8 \\ 2 & 2 & -7 \end{pmatrix}$$

```
[A]+[B]
[[6  2  2 ]
 [-8 11 8 ]
 [2  2  -7]]
```

$$A - B = \begin{pmatrix} -2 & -4 & 4 \\ 0 & 1 & -6 \\ -2 & -12 & 3 \end{pmatrix}$$

```
[A]-[B]
[[-2 -4  4 ]
 [0  1   -6]
 [-2 -12 3 ]]
```

Example 2

For the matrix $A = \begin{pmatrix} 4 & -2 & 5 \\ 1 & 0 & -1 \\ 3 & -5 & -4 \end{pmatrix}$, find $4A$.

$$4A = \begin{pmatrix} 16 & -8 & 20 \\ 4 & 0 & 4 \\ 12 & -20 & -16 \end{pmatrix}$$

```
4[A]
[[16 -8  20 ]
 [4  0   -4 ]
 [12 -20 -16]]
```

Teaching Notes

Emphasize that for **Matrix Multiplication,** a product is defined only if the number of columns in the first matrix equals the number of rows in the second matrix. In the diagram below, the product AB is defined, and the product is an $m \times p$ matrix.

$$
\begin{array}{cc}
A & B \\
m \times n & n \times p
\end{array}
$$

equal

product AB is $m \times p$

Use A and B in **Example 3** to illustrate the same point.

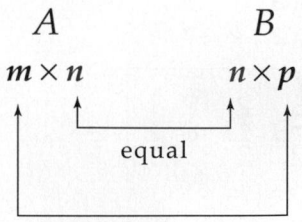

$$
\begin{array}{cc}
A & B \\
\begin{pmatrix} 3 & 1 & 2 \\ -1 & 0 & 4 \end{pmatrix} & \begin{pmatrix} 2 & -3 \\ 0 & 5 \\ 1 & 8 \end{pmatrix} = \begin{pmatrix} & \\ & \end{pmatrix}
\end{array}
$$

$$
\begin{array}{ccc}
2 \times 3 & 3 \times 2 & 2 \times 2
\end{array}
$$

equal

product AB is 2×2

Make sure students understand that the "ijth entry" in a product matrix is the number that results when *row i* in the first matrix and *column j* in the second matrix are multiplied.

Illustrate with the diagram below, where P is the product of matrices A and B, and p_{23} is the result of multiplying row 2 of matrix A and column 3 of matrix B.

$$
\begin{array}{ccccc}
A & \cdot & B & = & P
\end{array}
$$

$$
\begin{pmatrix} * & * & * \\ * & * & * \end{pmatrix}\begin{pmatrix} * & * & * & * \\ * & * & * & * \\ * & * & * & * \end{pmatrix}=\begin{pmatrix} * & * & * \\ * & * & * \end{pmatrix}
$$

row 2   column 3 p_{23} is in
                                    row 2, column 3

Example Notes

Remind students that matrix multiplication is not commutative. Note that in **Example 3,** not only do AB and BA have different entries, but they also have different dimensions. AB is 2×2 and BA is 3×3.

```
3[A]
  [[9   6  -15]
   [18  3  21 ]
   [-6  0  15 ]]
```

Figure 12.3-2

Solution

Multiply each entry of A by 3.

$$
3A = 3\begin{pmatrix} 3 & 2 & -5 \\ 6 & 1 & 7 \\ -2 & 0 & 5 \end{pmatrix} = \begin{pmatrix} 3(3) & 3(2) & 3(-5) \\ 3(6) & 3(1) & 3(7) \\ 3(-2) & 3(0) & 3(5) \end{pmatrix} = \begin{pmatrix} 9 & 6 & -15 \\ 18 & 3 & 21 \\ -6 & 0 & 15 \end{pmatrix}
$$

The results are confirmed in Figure 12.3-2. ∎

Matrix Multiplication

To multiply two matrices, multiply the rows of the first matrix by columns of the second matrix.

The number of entries in each row of the first matrix must be the same as the number of entries in each column of the second matrix.

To multiply a row by a column, multiply the corresponding entries, then add the results. In the following illustration, row 2 of the first matrix is multiplied by column 1 of the second matrix to produce the entry in row 2 column 1 of the product matrix. Note that the product of a row and a column is a single number.

$$
\begin{pmatrix} * & * & * \\ 3 & 1 & 2 \\ * & * & * \end{pmatrix}\begin{pmatrix} 2 & * & * \\ 0 & * & * \\ 1 & * & * \end{pmatrix} = \begin{pmatrix} & * & \\ 3\cdot 2 & + & 1\cdot 0 & + & 2\cdot 1 & * & * \\ & * & \end{pmatrix} = \begin{pmatrix} * & * & * \\ 8 & * & * \\ * & * & * \end{pmatrix}
$$

$$
\underset{a_{21}b_{11}}{\uparrow} \quad \underset{a_{22}b_{21}}{\uparrow} \quad \underset{a_{23}b_{31}}{\uparrow}
$$

Matrix Multiplication

> The product AB is defined only when the number of columns of A is the same as the number of rows of B.
>
> If A is an $m \times n$ matrix and B is an $n \times p$ matrix, then AB is an $m \times p$ matrix C where the entry in the ith row, jth column is
>
> $$c_{ij} = a_{i1}b_{1j} + a_{i2}b_{2j} + \dots + a_{in}b_{nj}$$

The following diagram shows how the dimensions of the product matrix are related to the dimensions of the factor matrices:

$$(m \times n \text{ matrix}) \cdot (n \times p \text{ matrix}) = (m \times p \text{ matrix})$$

CAUTION

Before finding the entries of a product matrix, check the dimensions of the factor matrices to make sure that the product is defined.

Example 3 Matrix Multiplication

For the given matrices, find AB, BA, AC, and CA when defined.

$$A = \begin{pmatrix} 3 & 1 & 2 \\ -1 & 0 & 4 \end{pmatrix} \qquad B = \begin{pmatrix} 2 & -3 \\ 0 & 5 \\ 1 & 8 \end{pmatrix} \qquad C = \begin{pmatrix} 1 & 3 \\ 0 & -1 \end{pmatrix}$$

Solution

First, verify that each product is defined.

A is 2×3 and B is 3×2, so AB is defined.

B is 3×2 and A is 2×3, so BA is defined.

A is 2×3 and C is 2×2, so AC is *not* defined.

C is 2×2 and A is 2×3, so CA is defined.

AB is a 2×2 matrix.

> **CAUTION**
>
> Matrix multiplication is not commutative, that is, $AB \neq BA$ in general. AB and BA may have different dimensions, as in Example 3, or BA may not be defined when AB is. Even when AB and BA are both defined and have the same dimensions, they may not be equal.

$$AB = \begin{pmatrix} 3 & 1 & 2 \\ -1 & 0 & 4 \end{pmatrix}\begin{pmatrix} 2 & -3 \\ 0 & 5 \\ 1 & 8 \end{pmatrix}$$

$$= \begin{pmatrix} \overbrace{3(2) + 1(0) + 2(1)}^{\text{row 1 of } A \times \text{ column 1 of } B} & \overbrace{3(-3) + 1(5) + 2(8)}^{\text{row 1 of } A \times \text{ column 2 of } B} \\ \underbrace{(-1)2 + 0(0) + 4(1)}_{\text{row 2 of } A \times \text{ column 1 of } B} & \underbrace{(-1)(-3) + 0(5) + 4(8)}_{\text{row 2 of } A \times \text{ column 2 of } B} \end{pmatrix}$$

$$= \begin{pmatrix} 8 & 12 \\ 2 & 35 \end{pmatrix}$$

BA is a 3×3 matrix.

$$BA = \begin{pmatrix} 2 & -3 \\ 0 & 5 \\ 1 & 8 \end{pmatrix}\begin{pmatrix} 3 & 1 & 2 \\ -1 & 0 & 4 \end{pmatrix}$$

$$= \begin{pmatrix} 2(3) + (-3)(-1) & 2(1) + (-3)(0) & 2(2) + (-3)(4) \\ 0(3) + 5(-1) & 0(1) + 5(0) & 0(2) + 5(4) \\ 1(3) + 8(-1) & 1(1) + 8(0) & 1(2) + 8(4) \end{pmatrix}$$

$$= \begin{pmatrix} 9 & 2 & -8 \\ -5 & 0 & 20 \\ -5 & 1 & 34 \end{pmatrix}$$

Note that $AB \neq BA$.

Example 3

For the given matrices, find AB, BA, AC, and CA when defined.

$$A = \begin{pmatrix} -1 & 2 \\ 3 & 0 \\ 1 & 5 \end{pmatrix} \quad B = \begin{pmatrix} 2 & 3 & -1 \\ 4 & 1 & 0 \end{pmatrix}$$

$$C = \begin{pmatrix} 0 & 1 \\ -2 & 3 \end{pmatrix}$$

AB:
$(3 \times 2) \cdot (2 \times 3)$; AB is defined.

BA:
$(2 \times 3) \cdot (3 \times 2)$; BA is defined.

AC:
$(3 \times 2) \cdot (2 \times 2)$; AC is defined.

CA:
$(2 \times 2) \cdot (3 \times 2)$; CA is not defined.

$$AB = \begin{pmatrix} 6 & -1 & 1 \\ 6 & 9 & -3 \\ 22 & 8 & -1 \end{pmatrix}$$

$$BA = \begin{pmatrix} 6 & -1 \\ -1 & 8 \end{pmatrix}$$

```
[A] [B]
    [[6   -1  1 ]
     [6    9  -3]
     [22   8  -1]]
[B] [A]
        [[6   -1]
         [-1  8 ]]
```

$$AC = \begin{pmatrix} -4 & 5 \\ 0 & 3 \\ -10 & 16 \end{pmatrix}$$

The matrix multiplication in **Example 4** could be extended. Suppose the furniture restorer has an assistant whose hourly rates are different. The cost per hour matrix and the total cost matrix would then each have another column, as shown below. Have students find the total cost entries for the assistant.

$$\begin{pmatrix} 0.5\,\text{hr} & 2.5\,\text{hr} & 1\text{hr} \\ 1\,\text{hr} & 4\,\text{hr} & 1.5\,\text{hr} \\ 3\,\text{hr} & 7\,\text{hr} & 4.5\,\text{hr} \end{pmatrix}\begin{pmatrix} \$7 & \$6 \\ \$18 & \$15 \\ \$10 & \$8 \end{pmatrix}$$

$$= \begin{pmatrix} \$58.50 & \$48.50 \\ \$94 & \$78 \\ \$192 & \$159 \end{pmatrix}$$

You might want to extend the problem by including other furniture items (blanket chest, bookcase, etc.) or processes (painting, repairing, etc.).

ADDITIONAL EXAMPLES

Example 4

Brett runs a small business cleaning and detailing vehicles for hotel customers. He offers three services—cleaning the interior, cleaning the exterior, and waxing. The number of hours required and the cost per hour of each service are given by the following matrices. Find the product of the matrices and interpret the results.

	Hours				Hourly rate
	Int.	Ext.	Wax		
Small car	0.5	0.25	1	Int.	$24
Large car	0.75	0.5	1.5	Ext.	$30
SUV	1	0.5	2	Wax	$24

$$\begin{pmatrix} 0.5 & 0.25 & 1 \\ 0.75 & 0.5 & 1.5 \\ 1 & 0.5 & 2 \end{pmatrix}\begin{pmatrix} \$24 \\ \$30 \\ \$24 \end{pmatrix}$$

$$= \begin{array}{l} \text{S.C.} \\ \text{L.C.} \\ \text{SUV} \end{array}\begin{pmatrix} \$43.5 \\ \$69 \\ \$87 \end{pmatrix} \quad \text{total cost}$$

The product matrix shows the total cost of an interior cleaning, an exterior cleaning, and waxing for each vehicle type.

AC is not defined.

CA is a 2×3 matrix.

$$CA = \begin{pmatrix} 1 & 3 \\ 0 & -1 \end{pmatrix}\begin{pmatrix} 3 & 1 & 2 \\ -1 & 0 & 4 \end{pmatrix}$$

$$= \begin{pmatrix} 1(3) + 3(-1) & 1(1) + 3(0) & 1(2) + 3(4) \\ 0(3) + (-1)(-1) & 0(1) + (-1)(0) & 0(2) + (-1)(4) \end{pmatrix}$$

$$= \begin{pmatrix} 0 & 1 & 14 \\ 1 & 0 & -4 \end{pmatrix}$$

Matrices can also be multiplied on a calculator, as shown below.

Figure 12.3-3

Applications

Matrices are a convenient way to handle data that is grouped into categories. If the categories of the rows of one matrix are the same as those of the columns of another, the matrices can often be multiplied to form a meaningful product.

Example 4 Using Matrix Multiplication

A furniture restorer refinishes chairs, tables, and dressers. The amount of time required to complete each step of refinishing and the cost per hour of each step are given by the following matrices. Find the product of the two matrices and interpret the result.

	Hours				cost per hour
	removing finish	sanding	finishing		
chair	0.5 hr	2.5 hr	1 hr	removing finish	$7
table	1 hr	4 hr	1.5 hr	sanding	$18
dresser	3 hr	7 hr	4.5 hr	finishing	$10

To multiply matrices on a calculator, enter the matrices in the memory and recall them as needed. If the product of two matrices is not defined, the calculator will give an error message.

Figure 12.3-4

Figure 12.3-5

Solution

The first matrix is 3×3 and the second is 3×1, so multiplication of the first matrix by the second matrix is defined, and the product is a 3×1 matrix. In the product of a row and a column, the amount of time for each step is multiplied by the cost per hour for that step, giving the cost for that step. The costs are then added, giving the total cost for the item. The product matrix will give the total cost for refinishing each item.

$$\begin{pmatrix} 0.5\,\text{hr} & 2.5\,\text{hr} & 1\,\text{hr} \\ 1\,\text{hr} & 4\,\text{hr} & 1.5\,\text{hr} \\ 3\,\text{hr} & 7\,\text{hr} & 4.5\,\text{hr} \end{pmatrix} \begin{pmatrix} \$7 \\ \$18 \\ \$10 \end{pmatrix} = \begin{matrix} \text{chair} \\ \text{table} \\ \text{dresser} \end{matrix} \overset{\text{total cost}}{\begin{pmatrix} \$58.50 \\ \$94 \\ \$192 \end{pmatrix}}$$ ∎

Directed Networks

The following figure is a **directed network.** The points that are labeled by capital letters are called **vertices,** and the arrows indicate the direction in which the paths between the vertices can be traveled. For example, from vertex L there is 1 path to M and 2 paths to K, but from K, there are 0 paths to L or to M.

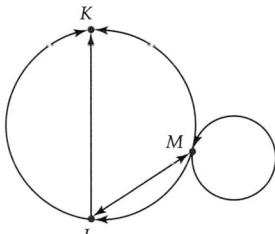

Figure 12.3-6

From	To	Number of paths
K	K	0
K	L	0
K	M	0
L	K	2
L	L	0
L	M	1
M	K	1
M	L	2
M	M	1

An **adjacency matrix** can be used to represent the connections between the vertices, as shown at right. The entries in the matrix are the number of direct paths, called **one-stage paths,** from one vertex to another.

$$\text{From:} \begin{matrix} K \\ L \\ M \end{matrix} \overset{\begin{matrix} \quad K & L & M \end{matrix}}{\begin{pmatrix} 0 & 0 & 0 \\ 2 & 0 & 1 \\ 1 & 2 & 1 \end{pmatrix}}$$

To:

Scientists can use directed networks and associated adjacency matrices to interpret relationships among animals in a food web (see pages 810–811).

In the adjacency matrix in **Example 6,** the last row of 0's indicates that killer whales are at the top of the food chain. That is, killer whales are not the prey of any other animal in the food web.

A column with one 1 indicates that the animal has only one direct source of food. For example, the only food for sea otters is shellfish. If the supply of shellfish is depleted or eradicated, then sea otters lose their only food source. However, if the supply of shellfish is depleted or eradicated, animals in the web other than sea otters will be affected *indirectly.* To see indirect relationships, use the *squared* adjacency matrix shown below.

To:

$$\text{From:} \begin{matrix} s \\ f \\ so \\ sl \\ kw \end{matrix} \overset{\begin{matrix} \; s & f & so & sl & kw \end{matrix}}{\begin{pmatrix} \mathbf{1} & \mathbf{2} & \mathbf{1} & \mathbf{1} & \mathbf{2} \\ 0 & 1 & 0 & 1 & 2 \\ 0 & 0 & 0 & 0 & 0 \\ 0 & 0 & 0 & 0 & 0 \\ 0 & 0 & 0 & 0 & 0 \end{pmatrix}}$$

The squared matrix shows the number of two-stage paths in the network (paths from animal to animal to animal).

The bold red numbers in the first row of the squared matrix represent these two-stage paths that can be verified in Figure 12.3-7:

1	shellfish to shellfish to shellfish
2	shellfish to shellfish to fish; shellfish to fish to fish
2	shellfish to sea otters to killer whales; shellfish to fish to killer whales

The 2 two-stage paths above that end at killer whales have these meanings:
- Killer whales eat sea otters, and sea otters eat shellfish.
- Killer whales eat fish, and fish eat shellfish.

Students can use the internet or library to do further research on the use of matrices to study directed networks, food webs, and ecosystems.

Example 5

Find the matrix for the number of two-stage paths for the directed network shown below, and interpret the result.

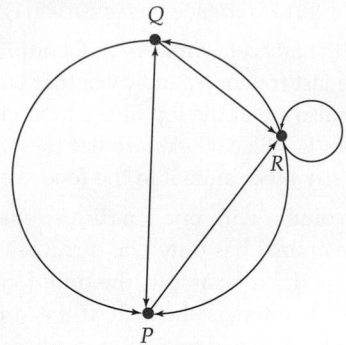

adjacency matrix for one-stage paths:

$$\begin{array}{c} \\ \\ \text{From:} \\ \\ \end{array} \begin{array}{cc} & \text{To:} \\ & \begin{array}{ccc} P & Q & R \end{array} \\ \begin{array}{c} P \\ Q \\ R \end{array} & \begin{pmatrix} 0 & 1 & 1 \\ 2 & 0 & 1 \\ 1 & 1 & 1 \end{pmatrix} \end{array}$$

adjacency matrix for two-stage paths:

$$\begin{pmatrix} 0 & 1 & 1 \\ 2 & 0 & 1 \\ 1 & 1 & 1 \end{pmatrix}^2 = \begin{pmatrix} 3 & 1 & 2 \\ 1 & 3 & 3 \\ 3 & 2 & 3 \end{pmatrix}$$

The last matrix above gives the number of two-stage paths for the network; the paths are described in the table below.

From	To	No. of 2-stage paths	Paths
P	P	3	$P \to Q \to P$; $P \to Q \to P$; $P \to R \to P$
P	Q	1	$P \to R \to Q$
P	R	2	$P \to Q \to R$; $P \to R \to R$
Q	P	1	$Q \to R \to P$
Q	Q	3	$Q \to P \to Q$; $Q \to P \to Q$; $Q \to R \to Q$
Q	R	3	$Q \to P \to R$; $Q \to P \to R$; $Q \to R \to R$
R	P	3	$R \to Q \to P$; $R \to Q \to P$; $R \to R \to P$
R	Q	2	$R \to P \to Q$; $R \to R \to Q$
R	R	3	$R \to P \to R$; $R \to Q \to R$; $R \to R \to R$

Multiplying Adjacency Matrices

If A is the adjacency matrix of a network, then the product $A \times A = A^2$ is a matrix for the number of two-stage paths, that is, paths from one vertex to another through one intermediate vertex.

Example 5   Using an Adjacency Matrix

Find the matrix for the number of two-stage paths for the directed network on page 809, and interpret the result.

Solution

The matrix for the number of two-stage paths is

$$\begin{pmatrix} 0 & 0 & 0 \\ 2 & 0 & 1 \\ 1 & 2 & 1 \end{pmatrix}^2 = \begin{pmatrix} 0 & 0 & 0 \\ 2 & 0 & 1 \\ 1 & 2 & 1 \end{pmatrix}\begin{pmatrix} 0 & 0 & 0 \\ 2 & 0 & 1 \\ 1 & 2 & 1 \end{pmatrix} = \begin{pmatrix} 0 & 0 & 0 \\ 1 & 2 & 1 \\ 5 & 2 & 3 \end{pmatrix}$$

The matrix gives the number of two-stage paths, which are given in the table below.

From	To	Number of two-stage paths	Paths
K	K	0	none
K	L	0	none
K	M	0	none
L	K	1	$L \to M \to K$
L	L	2	$L \to M \to L$; $L \to M \to L$ (see Note)
L	M	1	$L \to M \to M$
M	K	5	$M \to L \to K$; $M \to L \to K$; $M \to L \to K$ $M \to L \to K$; $M \to M \to K$
M	L	2	$M \to M \to L$; $M \to M \to L$
M	M	3	$M \to L \to M$; $M \to L \to M$; $M \to M \to M$

Example 6   Food Webs

A *food web* shows the relationships between certain predators and prey in an ecosystem. A directed network can be used to represent a food web, with the arrows pointing in the direction of prey to predator. Write an adjacency matrix for the following food web.

NOTE Two different two-stage paths may pass through the same vertices in the same order, as shown below.

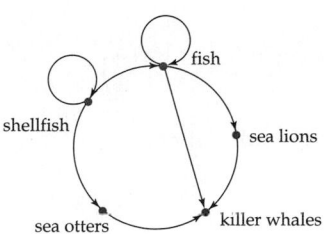

Figure 12.3-7

Solution

The matrix is given below.

To:

		s	f	so	sl	kw
From:	s	1	1	1	0	0
	f	0	1	0	1	1
	so	0	0	0	0	1
	sl	0	0	0	0	1
	kw	0	0	0	0	0

Exercises 12.3

In Exercises 1–6, refer to matrices *A*, *B*, and *C* below.

$$A = \begin{pmatrix} 2 & -6 & 3 \\ 4 & -2 & 1 \\ 3 & 5 & -5 \end{pmatrix} \qquad B = \begin{pmatrix} -4 & 4 & 7 \\ 5 & 3 & 2 \\ -1 & -6 & 6 \end{pmatrix}$$

$$C = \begin{pmatrix} 4 & 3 & -5 \\ -2 & -1 & 7 \\ 4 & 6 & 1 \end{pmatrix}$$

Find each of the following:

1. $A + B$ **2.** AB

3. $A + C$ **4.** $3A$

5. $2C$ **6.** $2B + 3C$

In Exercises 7–12, determine if the product *AB* or *BA* is defined. If a product is defined, state its dimensions. Do not calculate the products.

7. $A = \begin{pmatrix} 3 & 6 & 7 \\ 8 & 0 & 1 \end{pmatrix}$ $B = \begin{pmatrix} 2 & 5 & 9 & 1 \\ 7 & 0 & 0 & 6 \\ -1 & 3 & 8 & 7 \end{pmatrix}$

AB **defined, 2 × 4;** *BA* **not defined**

8. $A = \begin{pmatrix} -1 & -2 & -5 \\ 9 & 2 & -1 \\ 10 & 34 & 5 \end{pmatrix}$ $B = \begin{pmatrix} 17 & -9 \\ -6 & 12 \\ 3 & 5 \end{pmatrix}$

AB **defined, 3 × 2;** *BA* **not defined**

9. $A = \begin{pmatrix} 1 & 0 \\ 1 & 1 \\ 0 & 1 \end{pmatrix}$ $B = \begin{pmatrix} 5 & 6 & 11 \\ 7 & 8 & 15 \end{pmatrix}$

AB **defined, 3 × 3;** *BA* **defined, 2 × 2**

10. $A = \begin{pmatrix} 1 & -5 & 7 \\ 2 & 4 & 8 \\ 1 & -1 & 2 \end{pmatrix}$ $B = \begin{pmatrix} -2 & 4 & 9 \\ 13 & -2 & 1 \\ 5 & 25 & 0 \end{pmatrix}$

AB **defined 3 × 3;** *BA* **defined 3 × 3**

11. $A = \begin{pmatrix} -4 & 15 \\ 3 & -7 \\ 2 & 10 \end{pmatrix}$ $B = \begin{pmatrix} 1 & 2 \\ 3 & 4 \end{pmatrix}$

AB **defined, 3 × 2;** *BA* **not defined**

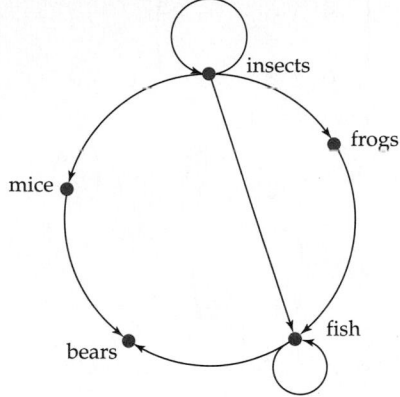

16.
$$\begin{pmatrix} -13 & 1 & -2 & 4 \\ -3 & 9 & -6 & 0 \\ -6 & -1 & 0 & 2 \\ 4 & 7 & -4 & -2 \end{pmatrix}$$

17.
$$\begin{pmatrix} 1 & -1 & 1 & 2 \\ 4 & 3 & 3 & 2 \\ -1 & -1 & -3 & 2 \\ 5 & 3 & 2 & 5 \end{pmatrix}$$

18. not defined

19. $AB = \begin{pmatrix} 17 & -3 \\ 33 & -19 \end{pmatrix}$; $BA = \begin{pmatrix} -4 & 9 \\ 24 & 2 \end{pmatrix}$

20. $AB = \begin{pmatrix} \frac{13}{2} & -\frac{1}{4} \\ \frac{51}{4} & -\frac{5}{2} \end{pmatrix}$;

$BA = \begin{pmatrix} -\frac{9}{2} & -\frac{13}{4} \\ \frac{31}{4} & \frac{17}{2} \end{pmatrix}$

21. $AB = \begin{pmatrix} 8 & 24 & -8 \\ 2 & -2 & 6 \\ -3 & -21 & 15 \end{pmatrix}$;

$BA = \begin{pmatrix} 19 & 9 & 8 \\ -10 & 2 & 0 \\ 0 & 0 & 0 \end{pmatrix}$

22. $AB = \begin{pmatrix} -4 & 4 & 5 & 8 \\ 13 & 2 & 19 & 14 \\ -1 & -3 & -20 & -21 \\ 1 & -2 & 12 & 6 \end{pmatrix}$;

$BA = \begin{pmatrix} -12 & -7 & 10 & 23 \\ 15 & 1 & 8 & 8 \\ 2 & 5 & -5 & 6 \\ -4 & -1 & 1 & 0 \end{pmatrix}$

23.

To:

$$\begin{array}{cc} & J\ \ K\ \ L \\ \text{From:}\ \begin{matrix} J \\ K \\ L \end{matrix} & \begin{pmatrix} 0 & 1 & 1 \\ 1 & 1 & 2 \\ 0 & 1 & 0 \end{pmatrix} \end{array}$$

24.

To:

$$\begin{array}{cc} & M\ \ N\ \ P \\ \text{From:}\ \begin{matrix} M \\ N \\ P \end{matrix} & \begin{pmatrix} 1 & 2 & 1 \\ 1 & 0 & 1 \\ 0 & 0 & 0 \end{pmatrix} \end{array}$$

25. $\begin{pmatrix} 0 & 1 & 1 \\ 1 & 1 & 2 \\ 0 & 1 & 0 \end{pmatrix}^2 = \begin{pmatrix} 1 & 2 & 2 \\ 1 & 4 & 3 \\ 1 & 1 & 2 \end{pmatrix}$

26. $\begin{pmatrix} 1 & 2 & 1 \\ 1 & 0 & 1 \\ 0 & 0 & 0 \end{pmatrix}^2 = \begin{pmatrix} 3 & 2 & 3 \\ 1 & 2 & 1 \\ 0 & 0 & 0 \end{pmatrix}$

---

12. $A = \begin{pmatrix} 10 & 12 \\ -6 & 0 \\ 1 & 23 \\ -4 & 3 \end{pmatrix}$ $B = \begin{pmatrix} 1 & 2 & 3 \\ 3 & 2 & 1 \end{pmatrix}$

AB defined 4 × 3; BA not defined
In Exercises 13–18, find AB.

13. $A = \begin{pmatrix} 3 & 2 \\ 2 & 4 \end{pmatrix}$ $B = \begin{pmatrix} 1 & -2 & 3 \\ 0 & 3 & 1 \end{pmatrix}\begin{pmatrix} 3 & 0 & 11 \\ 2 & 8 & 10 \end{pmatrix}$

14. $A = \begin{pmatrix} -1 & 2 & 3 \\ 0 & -1 & 2 \\ 1 & 2 & 0 \end{pmatrix}$ $B = \begin{pmatrix} 3 & -2 & -1 \\ 1 & 0 & 5 \\ 1 & -1 & -1 \end{pmatrix}\begin{pmatrix} 2 & -1 & 8 \\ 1 & -2 & -7 \\ 5 & -2 & 9 \end{pmatrix}$

15. $A = \begin{pmatrix} 1 & 0 & -4 \\ 0 & 2 & -1 \\ 2 & 3 & 4 \end{pmatrix}$ $B = \begin{pmatrix} 1 & 1 \\ 1 & 0 \\ 0 & 1 \end{pmatrix}\begin{pmatrix} 1 & -3 \\ 2 & -1 \\ 5 & 6 \end{pmatrix}$

16. $A = \begin{pmatrix} 1 & -2 \\ 3 & 0 \\ 0 & -1 \\ 2 & 1 \end{pmatrix}$ $B = \begin{pmatrix} -1 & 3 & -2 & 0 \\ 6 & 1 & 0 & -2 \end{pmatrix}$

17. $A = \begin{pmatrix} 2 & 0 & -1 \\ 1 & 1 & 2 \\ 0 & 2 & -3 \\ 2 & 3 & 0 \end{pmatrix}$ $B = \begin{pmatrix} 1 & 0 & 1 & 1 \\ 1 & 1 & 0 & 1 \\ 1 & 1 & 1 & 0 \end{pmatrix}$

18. $A = \begin{pmatrix} 10 & 0 & 1 & 0 \\ -1 & 1 & 0 & 1 \end{pmatrix}$ $B = \begin{pmatrix} 2 & -1 & 0 & 1 \\ -2 & 3 & 1 & -4 \\ 3 & 5 & 2 & -5 \end{pmatrix}$

In Exercises 19–22, show that AB is not equal to BA by computing both products.

19. $A = \begin{pmatrix} 3 & 2 \\ 5 & 1 \end{pmatrix}$ $B = \begin{pmatrix} 7 & -5 \\ -2 & 6 \end{pmatrix}$

20. $A = \begin{pmatrix} \frac{3}{2} & 2 \\ 4 & \frac{7}{2} \end{pmatrix}$ $B = \begin{pmatrix} 1 & -\frac{3}{2} \\ \frac{5}{2} & 1 \end{pmatrix}$

21. $A = \begin{pmatrix} 4 & 2 & -1 \\ 0 & 1 & 2 \\ -3 & 0 & 1 \end{pmatrix}$ $B = \begin{pmatrix} 1 & 7 & -5 \\ 2 & -2 & 6 \\ 0 & 0 & 0 \end{pmatrix}$

22. $A = \begin{pmatrix} 1 & 1 & -1 & 1 \\ 2 & 0 & 3 & 2 \\ -3 & 0 & 0 & 1 \\ 1 & -1 & 1 & 2 \end{pmatrix}$ $B = \begin{pmatrix} 0 & 1 & 7 & 7 \\ 2 & 3 & -2 & 1 \\ 5 & 0 & 1 & 0 \\ -1 & 0 & 1 & 0 \end{pmatrix}$

27. $\begin{pmatrix} 3.75 \\ 6.5 \\ 14.75 \end{pmatrix}$

The total cost to bake and decorate each giant cookie is $3.75; sheet cake: $6.50; 3-tiered cake: $14.75.

---

23. Write an adjacency matrix for the directed network below.

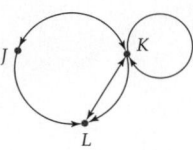

24. Write an adjacency matrix for the directed network below.

25. Find a matrix for the directed network in Exercise 23 that represents the number of two-stage paths.

26. Find a matrix for the directed network in Exercise 24 that represents the number of two-stage paths.

27. A bakery sells giant cookies, sheet cakes, and 3-tiered cakes. The time required for each step is given in the matrix below.

	baking	decorating
giant cookie	0.5 hr	0.25 hr
sheet cake	0.75 hr	0.5 hr
3-tiered cake	1.5 hr	1.25 hr

The cost per hour for baking and decorating is given by the matrix below. Find the product of the two matrices and interpret the result.

cost per hour

$$\begin{matrix} \text{baking} \\ \text{decorating} \end{matrix} \begin{pmatrix} \$4 \\ \$7 \end{pmatrix}$$

28. A boutique sells shirts, pants, and dresses. The time required for each step is given in the matrix below.

	cutting	sewing
shirt	1 hr	1 hr
pants	1.5 hr	1.25 hr
dress	2 hr	1.75 hr

28. $\begin{pmatrix} 14 \\ 18.75 \\ 25.75 \end{pmatrix}$

The total cost to cut and sew each shirt: $14; pants: $18.75; dress: $25.75.

The cost per hour for cutting and sewing is given by the matrix below. Find the product of the two matrices and interpret the result.

$$\begin{matrix} & \text{cost per} \\ & \text{hour} \\ \text{cutting} & \begin{pmatrix} \$5 \\ \$9 \end{pmatrix} \\ \text{sewing} & \end{matrix}$$

29. A small college offers lecture and lab courses. The class sizes are given in the matrix below.

$$\begin{matrix} & \text{freshman} & \text{sophomore} & \text{junior} & \text{senior} \\ & \text{level} & \text{level} & \text{level} & \text{level} \\ \text{lecture} & \begin{pmatrix} 150 & 100 & 75 & 50 \\ 30 & 25 & 25 & 20 \end{pmatrix} \\ \text{lab} & \end{matrix}$$

The tuition for each course is given by the matrix below. Find the product of the two matrices. Interpret all meaningful entries in the product.

$$\begin{matrix} & \text{lecture} & \text{lab} \\ \text{freshman level} & \begin{pmatrix} \$200 & \$40 \\ \$240 & \$48 \\ \$280 & \$56 \\ \$320 & \$64 \end{pmatrix} \\ \text{sophomore level} & \\ \text{junior level} & \\ \text{senior level} & \end{matrix}$$

30. A store sells trail mixes made of nuts and dried fruit. The nutritional information per serving is given in the matrix below.

$$\begin{matrix} & \text{nuts} & \text{fruit} \\ \text{fat} & \begin{pmatrix} 1\text{ g} & 52\text{ g} \\ 3\text{ g} & 20\text{ g} \\ 65\text{ g} & 21\text{ g} \end{pmatrix} \\ \text{protein} & \\ \text{carbohydrates} & \end{matrix}$$

The percent of fruit and nuts per serving in each mix is given below. Find the product of the two matrices, and interpret the result.

$$\begin{matrix} & \text{mix A} & \text{mix B} \\ \text{nuts} & \begin{pmatrix} 30\% & 45\% \\ 70\% & 55\% \end{pmatrix} \\ \text{fruit} & \end{matrix}$$

31. Write an adjacency matrix for the food web represented by the directed network below.

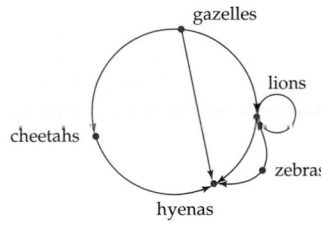

32. Write an adjacency matrix for the food web represented by the directed network below.

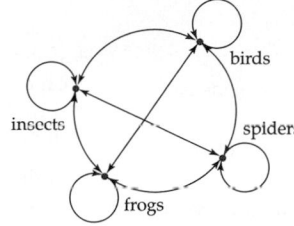

33. An airline offers nonstop flights between certain cities, as shown on the directed network below.

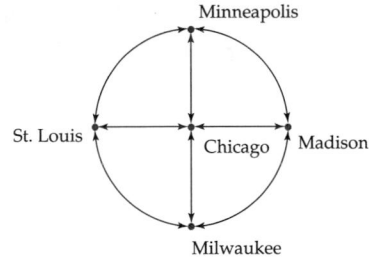

a. Write an adjacency matrix A for the directed network above.
b. Find the matrix A^2, which represents the number of flights between cities with exactly 1 layover. Find the matrix A^3, which represents the number of flights between cities with exactly 2 layovers.
c. Find the matrix $A + A^2 + A^3$, and interpret the result.

34. A delivery company ships packages between certain locations, as shown by the directed network below.

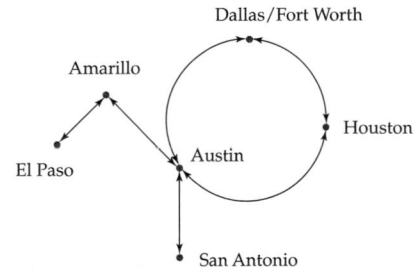

a. Write an adjacency matrix A for the directed network above.
b. Find the matrix $A + A^2 + A^3$, and interpret the result.

29. $\begin{pmatrix} 91{,}000 & 18{,}200 \\ 25{,}400 & 5080 \end{pmatrix}$; $a_{11} = \$91{,}000$

represents the total amount of tuition the college got from lecture; $a_{22} = \$5080$ represents the total amount of tuition the college got from lab; a_{12} and a_{21} are not meaningful in the context of the problem.

30. $\begin{pmatrix} 36.7 & 29.05 \\ 14.9 & 12.35 \\ 34.2 & 40.8 \end{pmatrix}$

A serving of Mix A has 36.7 g of fat, 14.9 g of protein, and 34.2 g of carbohydrates. A serving of Mix B has 29.05 g of fat, 12.35 g of protein, and 40.8 g of carbohydrates.

31.

$$\begin{matrix} & C & G & H & L & Z \\ C & \begin{pmatrix} 0 & 0 & 1 & 0 & 0 \\ 1 & 0 & 1 & 1 & 0 \\ 0 & 0 & 0 & 0 & 0 \\ 0 & 0 & 1 & 1 & 0 \\ 0 & 0 & 1 & 1 & 0 \end{pmatrix} \\ G & \\ H & \\ L & \\ Z & \end{matrix}$$

32.

$$\begin{matrix} & B & F & I & S \\ B & \begin{pmatrix} 1 & 1 & 1 & 1 \\ 1 & 1 & 1 & 1 \\ 1 & 1 & 1 & 1 \\ 1 & 1 & 1 & 1 \end{pmatrix} \\ F & \\ I & \\ S & \end{matrix}$$

33. a.

$$\begin{matrix} & C & Ma & Mil & Min & SL \\ C & \begin{pmatrix} 0 & 1 & 1 & 1 & 1 \\ 1 & 0 & 1 & 1 & 0 \\ 1 & 1 & 0 & 0 & 1 \\ 1 & 1 & 0 & 0 & 1 \\ 1 & 0 & 1 & 1 & 0 \end{pmatrix} \\ Ma & \\ Mil & \\ Min & \\ SL & \end{matrix}$$

b.

$$A^2 = \begin{pmatrix} 4 & 2 & 2 & 2 & 2 \\ 2 & 3 & 1 & 1 & 3 \\ 2 & 1 & 3 & 3 & 1 \\ 2 & 1 & 3 & 3 & 1 \\ 2 & 3 & 1 & 1 & 3 \end{pmatrix};$$

$$A^3 = \begin{pmatrix} 8 & 8 & 8 & 8 & 8 \\ 8 & 4 & 8 & 8 & 4 \\ 8 & 8 & 4 & 4 & 8 \\ 8 & 8 & 4 & 4 & 8 \\ 8 & 4 & 8 & 8 & 4 \end{pmatrix}$$

c.

$$A + A^2 + A^3 = \begin{pmatrix} 12 & 11 & 11 & 11 & 11 \\ 11 & 7 & 10 & 10 & 7 \\ 11 & 10 & 7 & 7 & 10 \\ 11 & 10 & 7 & 7 & 10 \\ 11 & 7 & 10 & 10 & 7 \end{pmatrix}$$

This matrix represents the total number of flights that are direct, have one layover, or have two layovers between each pair of cities.

34. a.

$$\begin{matrix} & Am & Au & DFW & EP & H & SA \\ Am & \begin{pmatrix} 0 & 1 & 0 & 1 & 0 & 0 \\ 1 & 0 & 1 & 0 & 1 & 1 \\ 0 & 1 & 0 & 0 & 1 & 0 \\ 1 & 0 & 0 & 0 & 0 & 0 \\ 0 & 1 & 1 & 0 & 0 & 0 \\ 0 & 1 & 0 & 0 & 0 & 0 \end{pmatrix} \\ Au & \\ DFW & \\ EP & \\ H & \\ SA & \end{matrix}$$

b.

$$A + A^2 + A^3 = \begin{pmatrix} 2 & 6 & 2 & 3 & 2 & 1 \\ 6 & 6 & 7 & 1 & 7 & 5 \\ 2 & 7 & 4 & 1 & 5 & 2 \\ 3 & 1 & 1 & 1 & 1 & 1 \\ 2 & 7 & 5 & 1 & 4 & 2 \\ 1 & 5 & 2 & 1 & 2 & 1 \end{pmatrix}$$

This matrix represents the total number of shipments that are direct or go through one or two intermediary cities for each pair of cities.

12.4 Matrix Methods for Square Systems

Section

12.4 Matrix Methods for Square Systems

Teaching Notes

Make sure students understand the following facts about a **square system** of equations:

- The number of variables = the number of equations in the system.
- The coefficient matrix is square (matrix A on this page is 3×3).
- The *augmented* matrix is *not* square (the augmented matrix for the system on this page is 3×4; see page 795).

Math Background

Students will find the inverse of a 2×2 matrix in **Example 4**. They will use inverse matrices to solve systems of equations in **Examples 5, 6,** and **7**.

The method of finding the inverse of a matrix using determinants is not shown in this text. Although determinants provide useful notation and concepts in the theory of matrices, they are an inefficient tool for solving large systems of linear equations. For that reason, computer programs and calculators solve systems of linear equations using row reduction of matrices, similar to the method presented in this book.

Objectives

- Define the $n \times n$ identity matrix
- Find the inverse of an invertible matrix
- Solve square systems of equations using inverse matrices

Matrix Methods for Square Systems

A system of equations that has the same number of equations as variables is called a **square system.** There is a method of solving this type of system that does not require row reduction. This method only works if the system has a unique solution.

Examine the system of equations below.

$$\left. \begin{array}{rcr} x + y + z = & 2 \\ 2x + 3y & = & 5 \\ x + 2y + z = & -1 \end{array} \right\} \qquad [1]$$

Instead of using a single matrix to represent the system, we can consider the system as having three parts: the coefficients, the variables, and the constants. A matrix can be used to represent each part.

$$A = \begin{pmatrix} 1 & 1 & 1 \\ 2 & 3 & 0 \\ 1 & 2 & 1 \end{pmatrix} \qquad X = \begin{pmatrix} x \\ y \\ z \end{pmatrix} \qquad B = \begin{pmatrix} 2 \\ 5 \\ -1 \end{pmatrix}$$

$\qquad\qquad$ *coefficients* $\qquad\qquad$ *variables* $\qquad\qquad$ *constants*

The relationship between the three matrices and the system is shown in the following example.

Example 1   A Matrix Equation

For the system of equations and the three matrices above, verify that $AX = B$.

Solution

By the definition of matrix multiplication:

$$AX = \begin{pmatrix} 1 & 1 & 1 \\ 2 & 3 & 0 \\ 1 & 2 & 1 \end{pmatrix} \begin{pmatrix} x \\ y \\ z \end{pmatrix} = \begin{pmatrix} x + y + z \\ 2x + 3y \\ x + 2y + z \end{pmatrix}$$

According to the system of equations [1], the entries of the matrix AX are equal to the corresponding entries of B, so the two matrices are equal, that is, $AX = B$. ∎

Example 1 shows that a square system can be represented by the **matrix equation** $AX = B$, where A is the matrix of the system's coefficients and B is the matrix of the system's constants. Thus, the system can be solved by solving the corresponding matrix equation. Solving the equation $AX = B$ means finding the entries of the matrix X, which are the variables of the system.

Identity Matrices and Inverse Matrices

To solve a matrix equation $AX = B$, it is necessary to "undo" the matrix multiplication. One method of solving similar equations with real numbers is by multiplying both sides of the equation by the inverse of a.

$$ax = b$$
$$a^{-1}ax = a^{-1}b \qquad [2]$$
$$x = a^{-1}b$$

The solution of equation [2] depends on the fact that $aa^{-1} = 1$, which is the identity for multiplication of real numbers. Thus, in order to define the inverse of a matrix, we must first define the identity for matrix multiplication.

The $n \times n$ **identity matrix** I_n is the matrix with n rows and n columns that has 1's on the diagonal from the top left to the bottom right and 0's as all its other entries.

$$I_2 = \begin{pmatrix} 1 & 0 \\ 0 & 1 \end{pmatrix} \qquad I_3 = \begin{pmatrix} 1 & 0 & 0 \\ 0 & 1 & 0 \\ 0 & 0 & 1 \end{pmatrix} \qquad I_4 = \begin{pmatrix} 1 & 0 & 0 & 0 \\ 0 & 1 & 0 & 0 \\ 0 & 0 & 1 & 0 \\ 0 & 0 & 0 & 1 \end{pmatrix}$$

The identity matrix, I_n, is the identity for multiplication of $n \times n$ matrices.

Identity Matrix

For any $n \times n$ matrix A,

$$AI_n = I_nA = A.$$

Example 2   Verifying the Identity Matrix Property

For matrix C, verify that $CI_2 = I_2C = C$.

$$C = \begin{pmatrix} 3 & 2 \\ 5 & 7 \end{pmatrix}$$

Solution

By the definition of matrix multiplication,

$$CI_2 = \begin{pmatrix} 3 & 2 \\ 5 & 7 \end{pmatrix}\begin{pmatrix} 1 & 0 \\ 0 & 1 \end{pmatrix} = \begin{pmatrix} 3(1) + 2(0) & 3(0) + 2(1) \\ 5(1) + 7(0) & 5(0) + 7(1) \end{pmatrix} = \begin{pmatrix} 3 & 2 \\ 5 & 7 \end{pmatrix} = C$$

$$I_2C = \begin{pmatrix} 1 & 0 \\ 0 & 1 \end{pmatrix}\begin{pmatrix} 3 & 2 \\ 5 & 7 \end{pmatrix} = \begin{pmatrix} 1(3) + 0(5) & 1(2) + 0(7) \\ 0(3) + 1(5) & 0(2) + 1(7) \end{pmatrix} = \begin{pmatrix} 3 & 2 \\ 5 & 7 \end{pmatrix} = C$$

Inverse Matrices

An $n \times n$ matrix A is called **invertible,** or **nonsingular,** if there exists an $n \times n$ matrix B such that $AB = I_n$. (In this case it is also true that $BA = I_n$.)

ADDITIONAL EXAMPLES

Example 1

For the system of equations and the three matrices below, verify that $AX = B$.

$$\begin{array}{rrrcr} x & -\ y & +\ z & = & 0 \\ 2x & +\ y & -\ 3z & = & 7 \\ 3x & -\ 2y & & = & -4 \end{array}$$

$$A = \begin{pmatrix} 1 & -1 & 1 \\ 2 & 1 & -3 \\ 3 & -2 & 0 \end{pmatrix} \quad X = \begin{pmatrix} x \\ y \\ z \end{pmatrix} \quad B = \begin{pmatrix} 0 \\ 7 \\ -4 \end{pmatrix}$$

$$AX = \begin{pmatrix} 1 & -1 & 1 \\ 2 & 1 & -3 \\ 3 & -2 & 0 \end{pmatrix}\begin{pmatrix} x \\ y \\ z \end{pmatrix} = \begin{pmatrix} x - y + z \\ 2x + y - 3z \\ 3x - 2y \end{pmatrix}$$

According to the system of equations, the entries of the matrix AX are equal to the corresponding entries of B, so the two matrices are equal, i.e., $AX = B$.

Example 2

For the matrix C, verify that $CI_3 = I_3C = C$.

$$C = \begin{pmatrix} 4 & -2 & 1 \\ 6 & 3 & 0 \\ 2 & 1 & 3 \end{pmatrix}$$

$$CI_3 = \begin{pmatrix} 4 & -2 & 1 \\ 6 & 3 & 0 \\ 2 & 1 & 3 \end{pmatrix}\begin{pmatrix} 1 & 0 & 0 \\ 0 & 1 & 0 \\ 0 & 0 & 1 \end{pmatrix}$$

$$= \begin{pmatrix} 4(1) & -2(1) & 1(1) \\ 6(1) & 3(1) & 0(1) \\ 2(1) & 1(1) & 3(1) \end{pmatrix}$$

$$= \begin{pmatrix} 4 & -2 & 1 \\ 6 & 3 & 0 \\ 2 & 1 & 3 \end{pmatrix} = C$$

$$I_3C = \begin{pmatrix} 1 & 0 & 0 \\ 0 & 1 & 0 \\ 0 & 0 & 1 \end{pmatrix}\begin{pmatrix} 4 & -2 & 1 \\ 6 & 3 & 0 \\ 2 & 1 & 3 \end{pmatrix}$$

$$= \begin{pmatrix} 1(4) & 1(-2) & 1(1) \\ 1(6) & 1(3) & 1(0) \\ 1(2) & 1(1) & 1(3) \end{pmatrix}$$

$$= \begin{pmatrix} 4 & -2 & 1 \\ 6 & 3 & 0 \\ 2 & 1 & 3 \end{pmatrix} = C$$

Example 3

For the given matrices, verify that B is the inverse of A.

$$A = \begin{pmatrix} 1 & 3 \\ 1 & 2 \end{pmatrix} \quad B = \begin{pmatrix} -2 & 3 \\ 1 & -1 \end{pmatrix}$$

$$AB = \begin{pmatrix} 1 & 3 \\ 1 & 2 \end{pmatrix}\begin{pmatrix} -2 & 3 \\ 1 & -1 \end{pmatrix}$$

$$= \begin{pmatrix} 1(-2) + 3(1) & 1(3) + 3(-1) \\ 1(-2) + 2(1) & 1(3) + 2(-1) \end{pmatrix}$$

$$= \begin{pmatrix} 1 & 0 \\ 0 & 1 \end{pmatrix} = I_2$$

$$BA = \begin{pmatrix} -2 & 3 \\ 1 & -1 \end{pmatrix}\begin{pmatrix} 1 & 3 \\ 1 & 2 \end{pmatrix}$$

$$= \begin{pmatrix} (-2)(1) + 3(1) & (-2)(3) + 3(2) \\ 1(1) - (-1)(1) & 1(3) + (-1)(2) \end{pmatrix}$$

$$= \begin{pmatrix} 1 & 0 \\ 0 & 1 \end{pmatrix} = I_2$$

Example 4

Find the inverse of matrix

$$A = \begin{pmatrix} 2 & 4 \\ 1 & 3 \end{pmatrix}.$$

Suppose $A^{-1} = \begin{pmatrix} x & u \\ y & v \end{pmatrix}.$

Then $AA^{-1} = I_2$.

$$AA^{-1} = \begin{pmatrix} 2 & 4 \\ 1 & 3 \end{pmatrix}\begin{pmatrix} x & u \\ y & v \end{pmatrix}$$

$$= \begin{pmatrix} 2x + 4y & 2u + 4v \\ x + 3y & u + 3v \end{pmatrix}$$

$$= \begin{pmatrix} 1 & 0 \\ 0 & 1 \end{pmatrix} = I_2$$

Set the corresponding entries of AA^{-1} and I_2 equal to each other to obtain the following systems of equations.

$2x + 4y = 1 \quad 2u + 4v = 0$

$x + 3y = 0 \quad u + 3v = 1$

Solving these two systems yields:

$x = \dfrac{3}{2}, \; y = -\dfrac{1}{2}, \; u = -2, \; v = 1$

Thus, $A^{-1} = \begin{pmatrix} \frac{3}{2} & -2 \\ -\frac{1}{2} & 1 \end{pmatrix}.$

```
[A]
          [[2 4]
           [1 3]]
[A]-1
          [[1.5 -2]
           [-.5 1 ]]
```

The matrix B is called the **inverse** of A, and is written as A^{-1}, where $AA^{-1} = A^{-1}A = I_n$. Not all matrices have a multiplicative inverse.

Example 3   Verifying an Inverse Matrix

For the given matrices, verify that B is the inverse of A.

$$A = \begin{pmatrix} 2 & 1 \\ 3 & 1 \end{pmatrix} \qquad B = \begin{pmatrix} -1 & 1 \\ 3 & -2 \end{pmatrix}$$

Solution

By the definition of matrix multiplication,

$$AB = \begin{pmatrix} 2 & 1 \\ 3 & 1 \end{pmatrix}\begin{pmatrix} -1 & 1 \\ 3 & -2 \end{pmatrix} = \begin{pmatrix} 2(-1) + 1(3) & 2(1) + 1(-2) \\ 3(-1) + 1(3) & 3(1) + 1(-2) \end{pmatrix} = \begin{pmatrix} 1 & 0 \\ 0 & 1 \end{pmatrix} = I_2$$

Notice also that

$$BA = \begin{pmatrix} -1 & 1 \\ 3 & -2 \end{pmatrix}\begin{pmatrix} 2 & 1 \\ 3 & 1 \end{pmatrix} = \begin{pmatrix} (-1)(2) + 1(3) & (-1)(1) + 1(1) \\ 3(2) + (-2)(3) & 3(1) + (-2)(1) \end{pmatrix}$$

$$= \begin{pmatrix} 1 & 0 \\ 0 & 1 \end{pmatrix} = I_2$$

There are several methods of finding the inverse of an invertible matrix.

Example 4   Finding an Inverse Matrix

Find the inverse of matrix $A = \begin{pmatrix} 2 & 6 \\ 1 & 4 \end{pmatrix}.$

Solution

Suppose $A^{-1} = \begin{pmatrix} x & u \\ y & v \end{pmatrix}.$ Then $AA^{-1} = I_2$.

$$AA^{-1} = \begin{pmatrix} 2 & 6 \\ 1 & 4 \end{pmatrix}\begin{pmatrix} x & u \\ y & v \end{pmatrix} = \begin{pmatrix} 2x + 6y & 2u + 6v \\ x + 4y & u + 4v \end{pmatrix} = \begin{pmatrix} 1 & 0 \\ 0 & 1 \end{pmatrix} = I_2$$

Setting the corresponding entries of AA^{-1} and I_2 equal to each other results in two systems of equations, one for each column.

$$2x + 6y = 1 \qquad 2u + 6v = 0$$
$$x + 4y = 0 \qquad u + 4v = 1$$

The solutions of the two systems are $x = 2$, $y = -\dfrac{1}{2}$ and $u = -3$, $v = 1$.

Thus, $A^{-1} = \begin{pmatrix} 2 & -3 \\ -\frac{1}{2} & 1 \end{pmatrix}.$ Check this by verifying that $AA^{-1} = I_2$.

[A]
          [[2 6]
           [1 4]]
[A]⁻¹
        [[2   -3]
         [-.5 1]]

Figure 12.4-1

Most graphing calculators can also be used to find inverse matrices directly by using the x^{-1} key, as shown in Figure 12.4-1.

Solving Square Systems Using Inverse Matrices

Recall that the need for inverse matrices arose out of the matrix equation $AX = B$, which represents a square system of equations. The equation can now be easily solved by multiplying both sides by the inverse of the coefficient matrix A.

$$AX = B$$
$$A^{-1}AX = A^{-1}B \qquad \textit{Multiply both sides by } A^{-1}.$$
$$I_nX = A^{-1}B \qquad \textit{A}^{-1}A = I_n \textit{ by definition of inverse.}$$
$$X = A^{-1}B \qquad I_nX = X \textit{ by definition of identity.}$$

Thus, the solution of a square system of equations with an invertible coefficient matrix A and constant matrix B is $X = A^{-1}B$.

CAUTION

Because matrix multiplication is not commutative, it is important to always multiply in the same order on both sides of the equation.

Matrix Solution of a Square System

Suppose that a square system of equations can be represented by the matrix equation $AX = B$, where A is the matrix of the coefficients, X is the matrix of the variables, and B is the matrix of the constants. If A is invertible, then the unique solution of the system is

$$X = A^{-1}B$$

If A is not invertible, then the system is either consistent with infinitely many solutions or inconsistent. Its solutions (if any) may be found by using Gauss-Jordan elimination.

Example 5   Solving a 2 × 2 System Using a Matrix Equation

Use an inverse matrix to solve
$$\begin{array}{r} x + y = 2 \\ 2x - 9y = 15 \end{array}$$

[A]⁻¹[B]
        [[3]
         [-1]]

Figure 12.4-2

Solution

The coefficient matrix $A = \begin{pmatrix} 1 & 1 \\ 2 & -9 \end{pmatrix}$ and the constant matrix $B = \begin{pmatrix} 2 \\ 15 \end{pmatrix}$.

Then $X = A^{-1}B = \begin{pmatrix} 3 \\ -1 \end{pmatrix}$, so the solution is $x = 3$, $y = -1$. ∎

Example 5

Use an inverse matrix to solve
$$\begin{array}{r} x - y = 1 \\ 2x + 3y = 7 \end{array}$$

The coefficient matrix is $A = \begin{pmatrix} 1 & -1 \\ 2 & 3 \end{pmatrix}$

and the constant matrix is

$$B = \begin{pmatrix} 1 \\ 7 \end{pmatrix}.$$

$$X = A^{-1}B = \begin{pmatrix} 2 \\ 1 \end{pmatrix}$$

[A]⁻¹[B]
          [[2]
           [1]]

The solution is $x = 2$, $y = 1$.

Example Notes

You might want to have your students use the method shown in **Example 4** to find A^{-1} in **Example 5**.

Suppose $A^{-1} = \begin{pmatrix} x & u \\ y & v \end{pmatrix}$.

Then $AA^{-1} = I_2$.

$$AA^{-1} = \begin{pmatrix} 1 & 1 \\ 2 & -9 \end{pmatrix}\begin{pmatrix} x & u \\ y & v \end{pmatrix}$$
$$= \begin{pmatrix} x + y & u + v \\ 2x - 9y & 2u - 9v \end{pmatrix}$$
$$= \begin{pmatrix} 1 & 0 \\ 0 & 1 \end{pmatrix} = I_2$$

$x + y = 1$	$u + v = 0$
$2x - 9y = 0$	$2u - 9v = 1$
Solve and get:	Solve and get:
$x = \dfrac{9}{11}, y = \dfrac{2}{11}$	$u = \dfrac{1}{11}, v = -\dfrac{1}{11}$

Therefore, $A^{-1} = \begin{pmatrix} \dfrac{9}{11} & \dfrac{1}{11} \\ \dfrac{2}{11} & -\dfrac{1}{11} \end{pmatrix}$

Example 6

Use an inverse matrix to solve

$$x - y + z = 7$$
$$3x + 2y \quad\;\; = 4$$
$$x - 2y + 2z = 12$$

The coefficient matrix is

$$A = \begin{pmatrix} 1 & -1 & 1 \\ 3 & 2 & 0 \\ 1 & -2 & 2 \end{pmatrix}$$ and the constant

matrix is $B = \begin{pmatrix} 7 \\ 4 \\ 12 \end{pmatrix}$.

$$X = A^{-1}B = \begin{pmatrix} 2 \\ -1 \\ 4 \end{pmatrix}$$

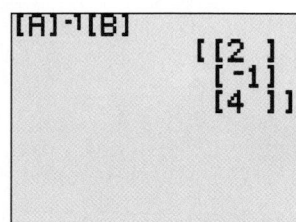

```
[A]⁻¹[B]
          [[2 ]
           [-1]
           [4 ]]
```

The solution is $x = 2$, $y = -1$, $z = 4$.

Example 7

Find the equation of the parabola that passes through the points $(0, -1)$, $(-1, 4)$, and $(4, 19)$.

Substitute the values of x and y from each point into the equation $y = ax^2 + bx + c$ to form a system of equations in a, b, and c.

(x, y)	$y = ax^2 + bx + c$
$(0, -1)$	$-1 = \qquad\qquad c$
$(-1, 4)$	$4 = a - b + c$
$(4, 19)$	$19 = 16a + 4b + c$

Find the values of a, b, and c by solving the matrix equation $AX = B$, with

$$A = \begin{pmatrix} 0 & 0 & 1 \\ 1 & -1 & 1 \\ 16 & 4 & 1 \end{pmatrix}, X = \begin{pmatrix} a \\ b \\ c \end{pmatrix}, \text{and } B = \begin{pmatrix} -1 \\ 4 \\ 19 \end{pmatrix}.$$

```
[A]⁻¹[B]
          [[2 ]
           [-3]
           [-1]]
```

The solution is $a = 2$, $b = -3$, $c = -1$ so the equation of the parabola is $y = 2x^2 - 3x - 1$.

---

818 Chapter 12 **Systems and Matrices**

Example 6 **Solving a 3 × 3 System Using a Matrix Equation**

$$x + y + z = 2$$
Use an inverse matrix to solve $\quad 2x + 3y \quad\;\; = 5$
$$x + 2y + z = -1$$

Solution

The coefficient matrix is $A = \begin{pmatrix} 1 & 1 & 1 \\ 2 & 3 & 0 \\ 1 & 2 & 1 \end{pmatrix}$ and the constant matrix is

$B = \begin{pmatrix} 2 \\ 5 \\ -1 \end{pmatrix}$. Then $X = A^{-1}B = \begin{pmatrix} 7 \\ -3 \\ -2 \end{pmatrix}$, so the solution is $x = 7$, $y = -3$,

$z = -2$, as shown in Figure 12.4-3. ∎

```
[A]⁻¹[B]
          [[7 ]
           [-3]
           [-2]]
```

Figure 12.4-3

Curve Fitting

Just as two points determine a unique line, three noncollinear points determine a unique parabola. In general, a polynomial of degree n can be determined by $n + 1$ noncollinear points, a circle by three noncollinear points, and a general conic by five noncollinear points. Matrix methods can be used to find curves that pass through a given set of points.

Example 7 **Finding the Parabola Through Three Points**

Find the equation of the parabola that passes through the points $(1, -4)$, $(-1, -10)$, and $(4, -25)$.

Solution

The equation of a parabola can be written as $y - ax^2 + bx + c$.

Substitute the values of x and y from each point into the equation to form a system of equations with the variables a, b, and c.

(x, y)	$y = ax^2 + bx + c$
$(1, -4)$	$-4 = a + b + c$
$(-1, -10)$	$-10 = a - b + c$
$(4, -25)$	$-25 = 16a + 4b + c$

Find the values of a, b, and c by solving the matrix equation $AX = B$.

$$A = \begin{pmatrix} 1 & 1 & 1 \\ 1 & -1 & 1 \\ 16 & 4 & 1 \end{pmatrix}, X = \begin{pmatrix} a \\ b \\ c \end{pmatrix}, \text{and } B = \begin{pmatrix} -4 \\ -10 \\ -25 \end{pmatrix}$$

```
[A]⁻¹[B]
          [[-2]
           [3 ]
           [-5]]
```

Figure 12.4-4

The solution is $a = -2$, $b = 3$, $c = -5$, as shown in Figure 12.4-4. Thus, the equation of the parabola is $y = -2x^2 + 3x - 5$. ∎

Exercises 12.4

ANSWERS

1. $I_2 = \begin{pmatrix} 1 & 0 \\ 0 & 1 \end{pmatrix}$

2. $I_2 = \begin{pmatrix} 1 & 0 \\ 0 & 1 \end{pmatrix}$

3. $I_3 = \begin{pmatrix} 1 & 0 & 0 \\ 0 & 1 & 0 \\ 0 & 0 & 1 \end{pmatrix}$

4. $I_3 = \begin{pmatrix} 1 & 0 & 0 \\ 0 & 1 & 0 \\ 0 & 0 & 1 \end{pmatrix}$

Exercises 12.4

In Exercises 1–4, write the identity matrix I_n for each matrix, and verify that $CI_n = I_nC = C$.

1. $C = \begin{pmatrix} 3 & -2 \\ 1 & 4 \end{pmatrix}$ **2.** $C = \begin{pmatrix} 6 & 4 \\ -3 & 2 \end{pmatrix}$

3. $C = \begin{pmatrix} 2 & 1 & 0 \\ 0 & 3 & 2 \\ 4 & -1 & 0 \end{pmatrix}$ **4.** $C = \begin{pmatrix} 0 & 0 & 1 \\ -2 & 4 & 1 \\ 1 & 3 & 5 \end{pmatrix}$

In Exercises 5–8, verify that B is the inverse of A.

5. $A = \begin{pmatrix} 3 & 1 \\ 5 & 2 \end{pmatrix}$ $B = \begin{pmatrix} 2 & -1 \\ -5 & 3 \end{pmatrix}$

6. $A = \begin{pmatrix} 4 & 8 \\ 2 & 6 \end{pmatrix}$ $B = \begin{pmatrix} \frac{3}{4} & -1 \\ -\frac{1}{4} & \frac{1}{2} \end{pmatrix}$

7. $A = \begin{pmatrix} 1 & 0 & 1 \\ -1 & 0 & 1 \\ 1 & 1 & -1 \end{pmatrix}$ $B = \begin{pmatrix} \frac{1}{2} & -\frac{1}{2} & 0 \\ 0 & 1 & 1 \\ \frac{1}{2} & \frac{1}{2} & 0 \end{pmatrix}$

8. $A = \begin{pmatrix} 2 & 1 & 0 \\ 1 & 2 & 2 \\ 1 & 0 & 0 \end{pmatrix}$ $B = \begin{pmatrix} 0 & 0 & 1 \\ 1 & 0 & -2 \\ -1 & \frac{1}{2} & \frac{3}{2} \end{pmatrix}$

In Exercises 9–12, write a set of systems of equations that represent the solution of the matrix equation $AA^{-1} = I_n$. (See Example 4.) Do not solve the systems.

9. $A = \begin{pmatrix} 2 & 0 \\ 4 & 1 \end{pmatrix}$ **10.** $A = \begin{pmatrix} -1 & 3 \\ 2 & -5 \end{pmatrix}$

11. $A = \begin{pmatrix} 1 & 2 & -1 \\ 0 & 1 & 2 \\ 3 & 2 & 1 \end{pmatrix}$ **12.** $A = \begin{pmatrix} 4 & -3 & 2 \\ 2 & 0 & 1 \\ -1 & 0 & 5 \end{pmatrix}$

In Exercises 13–20, find the inverse of the matrix, if it exists.

13. $\begin{pmatrix} 1 & 2 \\ 3 & 4 \end{pmatrix}$ **14.** $\begin{pmatrix} 3 & 5 \\ 1 & 4 \end{pmatrix}$

15. $\begin{pmatrix} 3 & -1 \\ -6 & 2 \end{pmatrix}$ **16.** $\begin{pmatrix} 1 & -1 & 0 \\ 1 & 0 & -1 \\ 6 & -2 & -3 \end{pmatrix}$

17. $\begin{pmatrix} 1 & 2 & 0 \\ 3 & -1 & 2 \\ -2 & 3 & -2 \end{pmatrix}$ **18.** $\begin{pmatrix} 1 & -3 & 4 \\ 2 & -5 & 7 \\ 0 & -1 & 1 \end{pmatrix}$

19. $\begin{pmatrix} 5 & 0 & 2 \\ 2 & 2 & 1 \\ -3 & 1 & -1 \end{pmatrix}$ **20.** $\begin{pmatrix} -1 & 3 & 1 \\ 2 & 5 & 0 \\ 3 & 1 & -2 \end{pmatrix}$

In Exercises 21–26, solve the system of equations by using inverse matrices. (See Examples 5 and 6.)

21. $3x + 5y = 4$
$2x - 6y = 12$
$x = 3,\ y = -1$

22. $3x - 5y = -23$
$-8x + 6y = 10$
$x = 4,\ y = 7$

23. $-x + y\quad = 1$
$-x\quad + z = -2$
$6x - 2y - 3z = 3$
$x = -1,\ y = 0,\ z = -3$

24. $x + 2y + 3z = 1$
$2x + 5y + 3z = 0$
$x\quad + 8z = -1$
$x = -49,\ y = 16,\ z = 6$

25. $2x + y\quad = 0$
$-4x - y - 3z = 1$
$3x + y + 2z = 2$
$x = -8,\ y = 16,\ z = 5$

26. $-3x - 3y - 4z = 2$
$y + z = 1$
$4x + 3y + 4z = 3$
$x = 5,\ y = 21,\ z = -20$

In Exercises 27–34, solve the system by any method.

27. $x + y + \quad 2w = 3$
$2x - y + z - w = 5$
$3x + 3y + 2z - 2w = 0$
$x + 2y + z\quad = 2$
$x = -0.5,\ y = -2.1,$
$z = 6.7,\ w = 2.8$

28. $x - 2y + 3z\quad = 1$
$y - z + w = -2$
$-2x + 2y - 2z + 4w = 5$
$2y - 3z + w - 8$
$x = \frac{9}{4},\ y = \frac{-55}{2},$
$z = \frac{-75}{4},\ w = \frac{27}{4}$

29. $x + 2y + 4z = 6$
$y + z = 1$
$x + 3y + 5z = 10$
no solution

30. $x + 4y + 5z + 2w = 0$
$2x + y + 4z - 2w = 0$
$-x + 7y + 10z + 5w = 0$
$-4x + 2y + z + 5w = 0$
$x = 0,\ y = 0,$
$z = 0,\ w = 0$

31. $x + 2y + 3z\quad = 6$
$3x + 2y + 4z\quad = 9$
$2x + 6y + 8z + w = 17$
$2x + \quad 2z - 2w = 2$
$x = 2 - t,$
$y = 3.5 - 2.5t,$
$z = -1 + 2t,\ w = t,$
where t is any real number

32. $x \quad + 3w = -2$
$x - 4y - z + 3w = -7$
$4y + z\quad = 5$
$-x + 12y + 3z - 3w = 17$
$x = -2 - 3t,$
$y = \frac{5}{4} - \frac{1}{4}s,\ z = s,$
$w = t,$ where s and t are any real numbers.

33. $x + 2y + 2z - 2w - -23$
$4x + 4y - z + 5w = 7$
$-2x + 5y + 6z + 4w = 0$
$5x + 13y + 7z + 12w = -7$
$x = -\frac{1149}{161},\ y = \frac{426}{161},\ z = -\frac{1124}{161},\ w = \frac{579}{161}$

5. $AB = \begin{pmatrix} 3 & 1 \\ 5 & 2 \end{pmatrix}\begin{pmatrix} 2 & -1 \\ -5 & 3 \end{pmatrix}$
$= \begin{pmatrix} 1 & 0 \\ 0 & 1 \end{pmatrix} = I_2$

6. $AB = \begin{pmatrix} 4 & 8 \\ 2 & 6 \end{pmatrix}\begin{pmatrix} \frac{3}{4} & -1 \\ -\frac{1}{4} & \frac{1}{2} \end{pmatrix}$
$= \begin{pmatrix} 1 & 0 \\ 0 & 1 \end{pmatrix} = I_2$

7. $AB = \begin{pmatrix} 1 & 0 & 1 \\ -1 & 0 & 1 \\ 1 & 1 & -1 \end{pmatrix}\begin{pmatrix} \frac{1}{2} & -\frac{1}{2} & 0 \\ 0 & 1 & 1 \\ \frac{1}{2} & \frac{1}{2} & 0 \end{pmatrix}$
$= \begin{pmatrix} 1 & 0 & 0 \\ 0 & 1 & 0 \\ 0 & 0 & 1 \end{pmatrix} = I_3$

8. $AB = \begin{pmatrix} 2 & 1 & 0 \\ 1 & 2 & 2 \\ 1 & 0 & 0 \end{pmatrix}\begin{pmatrix} 0 & 0 & 1 \\ 1 & 0 & -2 \\ -1 & \frac{1}{2} & \frac{3}{2} \end{pmatrix}$
$= \begin{pmatrix} 1 & 0 & 0 \\ 0 & 1 & 0 \\ 0 & 0 & 1 \end{pmatrix} = I_3$

9. $2x = 1$ $2u = 0$
$4x + y = 0$ $4u + v = 1$

10. $-x + 3y = 1$ $-u + 3v = 0$
$2x - 5y = 0$ $2u - 5v = 1$

11. $x + 2y - z = 1$
$y + 2z = 0$
$3x + 2y + z = 0$

$u + 2v - w = 0$
$v + 2w = 1$
$3u + 2v + w = 0$

$r + 2s - t = 0$
$s + 2t = 0$
$3r + 2s + t = 1$

12. $4x - 3y + 2z = 1$
$2x\quad + z = 0$
$-x\quad + 5z = 0$

$4u - 3v + 2w = 0$
$2u\quad + w = 1$
$-u\quad + 5w = 0$

$4r - 3s + 2t = 0$
$2r\quad + t = 0$
$-r\quad + 5t = 1$

13. $\begin{pmatrix} -2 & 1 \\ \frac{3}{2} & -\frac{1}{2} \end{pmatrix}$

14. $\begin{pmatrix} \frac{4}{7} & -\frac{5}{7} \\ -\frac{1}{7} & \frac{3}{7} \end{pmatrix}$

15. no inverse

16. $\begin{pmatrix} -2 & -3 & 1 \\ -3 & -3 & 1 \\ -2 & -4 & 1 \end{pmatrix}$

17. no inverse

18. no inverse

19. $\begin{pmatrix} -3 & 2 & -4 \\ -1 & 1 & -1 \\ 8 & -5 & 10 \end{pmatrix}$

20. $\begin{pmatrix} -\frac{10}{9} & \frac{7}{9} & -\frac{5}{9} \\ \frac{4}{9} & -\frac{1}{9} & \frac{2}{9} \\ -\frac{13}{9} & \frac{10}{9} & -\frac{11}{9} \end{pmatrix}$

34. $x = 0, y = 0, z = 0, v = 0, w = 0$

35. a. $\begin{pmatrix} 1 & -2 \\ -3 & 6 \end{pmatrix}\begin{pmatrix} x \\ y \end{pmatrix} = \begin{pmatrix} 3 \\ -9 \end{pmatrix};$

$\begin{pmatrix} 1 & -2 \\ -3 & 6 \end{pmatrix}\begin{pmatrix} x \\ y \end{pmatrix} = \begin{pmatrix} 4 \\ -7 \end{pmatrix}$

A and X; no

b. The first system has an infinite number of solutions of the form $x = t$, $y = \frac{1}{2}t - \frac{3}{2}$; the second system has no solution. If a coefficient matrix does not have an inverse, then any system with those coefficients will have an infinite number of solutions or no solution.

36. a. $\begin{pmatrix} 1 & 2 & -3 & | & -4 \\ 2 & 4 & 1 & | & -1 \\ 1 & -5 & 2 & | & 15 \end{pmatrix}$

in reduced row echelon form is

$\begin{pmatrix} 1 & 0 & 0 & | & 3 \\ 0 & 1 & 0 & | & -2 \\ 0 & 0 & 1 & | & 1 \end{pmatrix}$

b. $\begin{pmatrix} 1 & 2 & -3 \\ 2 & 4 & 1 \\ 1 & -5 & 2 \end{pmatrix}\begin{pmatrix} x \\ y \\ z \end{pmatrix} = \begin{pmatrix} -4 \\ -1 \\ 15 \end{pmatrix};$

$X = A^{-1}B = \begin{pmatrix} 3 \\ -2 \\ 1 \end{pmatrix};$

$x = 3, y = -2, z = 1$

The last column of the reduced row echelon form represents the solution of the system.

37. $a = 1, b = 0, c = -1; y = x^2 - 1$

38. $a = 0.5, b = -1.5, c = 2;$
$y = 0.5x^2 - 1.5x + 2$

39. $a = 0.5, b = -1.5, c = 2;$
$y = 0.5x^2 - 1.5x + 2$

40. $a = \frac{14}{3}, b = -17, c = \frac{55}{3};$
$y = \frac{14}{3}x^2 - 17x + \frac{55}{3}$

34.
$x + 2y + 5z - 2v + 4w = 0$
$2x - 4y + 6z + v + 4w = 0$
$5x + 2y - 3z + 2v + 3w = 0$
$6x - 5y - 2z + 5v + 3w = 0$
$x + 2y - z - 2v + 4w = 0$

35. *Critical Thinking* Consider the two systems of equations below.

$\begin{aligned} x - 2y &= 3 \\ -3x + 6y &= -9 \end{aligned}$ $\begin{aligned} x - 2y &= 4 \\ -3x + 6y &= -7 \end{aligned}$

a. Write a matrix equation that represents each system. Which matrices in the two equations are the same? Does either matrix equation have a solution?

b. Solve each system by any method. Make a conjecture about the relationship between the existence of an inverse coefficient matrix and the nature of the solutions to any system with those coefficients.

36. *Critical Thinking* Consider the system of equations below.

$\begin{aligned} x + 2y - 3z &= -4 \\ 2x + 4y + z &= -1 \\ x - 5y + 2z &= 15 \end{aligned}$

a. Write an augmented matrix that represents the system, and reduce it to reduced row echelon form.

b. Write a matrix equation that represents the system, and solve it using an inverse matrix.

c. Describe your results in part **a** in terms of the matrix equation from part **b**.

In Exercises 37–40, find constants a, b, c such that the three given points lie on the parabola $y = ax^2 + bx + c$. (See Example 7.)

37. $(1, 0), (2, 3), (3, 8)$ **38.** $(1, 1), (2, 1), (3, 2)$

39. $(3, 2), (1, 1), (2, 1)$ **40.** $(1, 6), (2, 3), (4, 25)$

In Exercises 41–43, write a system of equations that determines the polynomial of the given type that passes through the given points. Do not solve the system.

41. cubic; $(0, 5), (2, 1), (4, -7), (8, 3)$

42. cubic; $(-3, 1), (-1, -2), (0, 6), (3, 0)$

43. quartic; $(-5, -1), (-2, 0), (1, 3), (2, 5), (10, -4)$

---

44. Concentrations of the greenhouse gas carbon dioxide, CO_2, have increased quadratically over the past half century. The concentration y of CO_2, in parts per million, in year x is given by an equation of the form

$$y = ax^2 + bx + c.$$

a. Let $x = 0$ correspond to 1958 and use the following data to find a, b, and c.

Year	1958	1979	2001
CO_2 Concentration	315	337	371

b. Use this equation to estimate the CO_2 concentration in the years 1983, 1993, and 2003. For comparison purposes, the actual concentrations in 1983 and 1993 were 343 ppm and 357 ppm respectively.

45. Find constants a, b, and c such that the points $(0, -2)$ $(\ln 2, 1)$, and $(\ln 4, 4)$ lie on the graph of $f(x) = ae^x + be^{-x} + c$. (See Example 7.)

46. Find constants a, b, and c such that the points $(0, -1)$ $(\ln 2, 4)$, and $(\ln 3, 7)$ lie on the graph of $f(x) = ae^x + be^{-x} + c$.

47. A conic section has the equation $Ax^2 + Bxy + Cy^2 + Dx + Ey + F = 0$. Find the values of A, B, C, D, E, and F for the conic section that passes through the six given points: $(3, 4), (6, 2), (2, 6), (12, 1), (4, 3), (1, 12)$. Write the equation and identify the type of conic section.

48. A candy company produces three types of gift boxes: A, B, and C. A box of variety A contains 0.6 lb of chocolates and 0.4 lb of mints. A box of variety B contains 0.3 lb of chocolates, 0.4 lb of mints, and 0.3 lb of caramels. A box of variety C contains 0.5 lb of chocolates, 0.3 lb of mints, and 0.2 lb of caramels. The company has 41,400 lb of chocolates, 29,400 lb of mints, and 16,200 lb of caramels in stock. How many boxes of each kind should be made in order to use up all their stock?

49. Certain circus animals are fed the same three food mixes: R, S, and T. Lions receive 1.1 units of mix R, 2.4 units of mix S, and 3.7 units of mix T each day. Horses receive 8.1 units of mix R, 2.9 units of mix S, and 5.1 units of mix T each day. Bears receive 1.3 units of mix R, 1.3 units of mix S, and 2.3 units of mix T each day. If 16,000 units of mix R, 28,000 units of mix S, and 44,000 units of mix T are available each day, how many of each type of animal can be supported?

41.
(x, y)	$y = ax^3 + bx^2 + cx + d$
$(0, 5)$	$5 = d$
$(2, 1)$	$1 = 8a + 4b + 2c + d$
$(4, -7)$	$-7 = 64a + 16b + 4c + d$
$(8, 3)$	$3 = 512a + 64b + 8c + d$

42.
(x, y)	$y = ax^3 + bx^2 + cx + d$
$(-3, 1)$	$1 = -27a + 9b - 3c + d$
$(-1, -2)$	$-2 = -a + b - c + d$
$(0, 6)$	$6 = d$
$(3, 0)$	$0 = 27a + 9b + 3c + d$

43.
(x, y)	$y = ax^4 + bx^3 + cx^2 + dx + e$
$(-5, -1)$	$-1 = 625a - 125b + 25c - 5d + e$
$(-2, 0)$	$0 = 16a - 8b + 4c - 2d + e$
$(1, 3)$	$3 = a + b + c + d + e$
$(2, 5)$	$5 = 16a + 8b + 4c + 2d + e$
$(10, -4)$	$-4 = 10,000a + 1000b + 100c + 10d + e$

12.5 Nonlinear Systems

Objectives

- Solve nonlinear systems algebraically
- Solve nonlinear systems graphically

The matrix methods discussed in Section 12.2 and Section 12.4 can only be used for linear systems. Sometimes, however, it is necessary to solve nonlinear systems. Some nonlinear systems may be solved algebraically, by substitution or elimination.

Example 1 Solving a Nonlinear System by Elimination

Solve the system of equations.

$$x^2 - y^2 = 5$$
$$x^2 + y^2 = 13$$

Solution

This system can easily be solved by elimination. Add the two equations to eliminate y^2, and solve the resulting equation.

$$
\begin{array}{rcl}
x^2 - y^2 &=& 5 \\
+\ x^2 + y^2 &=& 13 \\
\hline
2x^2 &=& 18 \\
x^2 &=& 9 \\
x &=& \pm 3
\end{array}
$$

> **NOTE** Nonlinear systems can have any number of solutions, including solutions with the same x-value but different y-values—and vice versa. Thus, it is convenient to write the solutions as ordered pairs, (x, y).

Substitute each value of x into one of the original equations and solve for y. The x term is squared in both equations, so it is not necessary to substitute both 3 and -3, because $3^2 = (-3)^2$.

$$
\begin{array}{rcl}
3^2 - y^2 &=& 5 \\
y^2 &=& 4 \\
y &=& \pm 2
\end{array}
$$

The system has four solutions: $x = 3, y = 2; x = 3, y = -2; x = -3, y = 2$; and $x = -3, y = -2$. Written as ordered pairs, the solutions are $(3, 2)$, $(3, -2)$, $(-3, 2)$, and $(-3, -2)$. ∎

Example 2 Solving a Nonlinear System by Substitution

Solve the system of equations.

$$2x^2 - y^2 = 1$$
$$x + y = 12$$

---

44. a. $a \approx 0.01158, b \approx 0.80449, c = 315$
   b. 1983: ≈ 342.35; 1993: ≈ 357.34;
      2003: ≈ 374.65

45. $y = e^x - 4e^{-x} + 1$

46. $y = 2e^x - 6e^{-x} + 3$

47. $A = 0, B = -\frac{1}{12}F, C = 0, D = 0,$
   $E = 0,$ and $F = t,$ where t is
   any real number; $-\frac{t}{12}xy + t = 0,$
   which reduces to $xy = 12$; hyperbola

48. 15,000 gift box A; 18,000 gift box B;
   54,000 gift box C

49. 10,128 lions; 224 horses, 2339 bears

Section 12.5 Nonlinear Systems

Example Notes

Refer students to the box on page 723. Have them use the discriminant to identify the type of graphs in Example 1.

$x^2 - y^2 = 5$ hyperbola
$x^2 + y^2 = 13$ circle

Students can confirm the solutions graphically.
Solve each equation for y:

$$y = \pm\sqrt{x^2 - 5}$$
$$y = \pm\sqrt{13 - x^2}$$

Graph the four associated functions and trace or use an intersection finder.

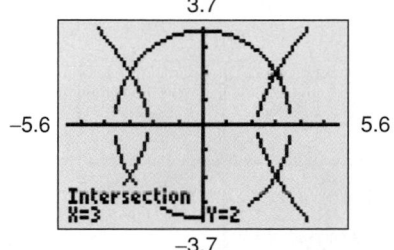

ADDITIONAL EXAMPLES

Example 1

Solve the system of equations.
$$x^2 - y^2 = -15$$
$$2x^2 + y^2 = 18$$
Solve by elimination. Add the two equations to eliminate y, and solve the resulting equation.

$$
\begin{array}{rcl}
x^2 - y^2 &=& -15 \\
+\ 2x^2 + y^2 &=& 18 \\
\hline
3x^2 &=& 3 \\
x^2 &=& 1 \\
x &=& \pm 1
\end{array}
$$

Substitute into one of the original equations and solve for y. The x term is squared in both equations; it is not necessary to substitute both 1 and -1, since $1^2 = (-1)^2$.

$$
\begin{array}{rcl}
1^2 - y^2 &=& -15 \\
-y^2 &=& -16 \\
y^2 &=& 16 \\
y &=& \pm 4
\end{array}
$$

The solutions are $(1, 4)$, $(1, -4)$, $(-1, 4)$, and $(-1, -4)$.

EXAMPLE NOTES

If you have students confirm the solutions in **Example 2** graphically, they will need to experiment to find an appropriate viewing window. Students should be able to predict from the equations that the graphs are a hyperbola and a line. The standard viewing window shows only one point of intersection at (5, 7).

The larger window below shows both points of intersection, and the intersection finder confirms the other solution, (−29, 41).

To solve a system graphically, you need to be sure that complete graphs are displayed. For **Example 3**, have students review *end behavior of polynomial functions* (page 263) and *number of local extrema* (page 266) for this purpose.

ADDITIONAL EXAMPLES

Example 2

Solve the system of equations.

$$x^2 + y^2 = 25$$
$$2x + y = 10$$

Solve by substitution. Solve the second equation for y, and substitute into the first equation.

$$y = 10 - 2x$$
$$x^2 + (10 - 2x)^2 = 25$$
$$x^2 + 100 - 40x + 4x^2 = 25$$
$$5x^2 - 40x + 75 = 0$$
$$5(x^2 - 8x + 15) = 0$$
$$5(x - 3)(x - 5) = 0$$
$$x = 3 \text{ or } x = 5$$

Substitute these values of x into the second equation.

$$2x + y = 10 \qquad 2x + y = 10$$
$$2(3) + y = 10 \qquad 2(5) + y = 10$$
$$y = 4 \qquad\qquad y = 0$$

The solutions are (3, 4) and (5, 0).

CAUTION

When solving non-linear systems algebraically, extraneous solutions can result. Check all solutions in all of the original equations.

Solution

This system can be solved by substitution. Solve the second equation for y, and substitute into the first equation.

$$y = 12 - x$$
$$2x^2 - (12 - x)^2 = 1$$
$$2x^2 - 144 + 24x - x^2 = 1$$
$$x^2 + 24x - 145 = 0$$
$$x = 5 \text{ or } x = -29$$

If these values of x are substituted back into the second equation, the resulting solutions are $y = 7$ or $y = 41$, respectively. This gives two solutions, (5, 7) and (−29, 41).

Notice that if the values for x were substituted into the first equation instead, the resulting solutions would be $y = \pm7$ or $y = \pm41$. This would give 4 solutions, (5, 7), (5, −7), (−29, 41), and (−29, −41). However, the solutions (5, −7) and (−29, −41) do not satisfy the second equation; they are extraneous.

Thus, the solutions of the system are (5, 7) and (−29, 41).   ■

Solving Nonlinear Systems Graphically

Consider the system below.

$$y = x^4 - 4x^3 + 9x - 1$$
$$y = 3x^2 - 3x - 7$$

Substitution may seem like an appropriate method for solving the system. However, if the expression for y in the first equation is substituted for y in the second equation, the result is

$$x^4 - 4x^3 + 9x - 1 = 3x^2 - 3x - 7$$
$$x^4 - 4x^3 - 3x^2 + 12x + 6 = 0$$

This fourth-degree equation cannot be readily solved algebraically, so a graphical approach is appropriate.

Example 3   Solving a Nonlinear System Graphically

Solve the following system of equations graphically.

$$y = x^4 - 4x^3 + 9x - 1$$
$$y = 3x^2 - 3x - 7$$

Solution

Graph both equations on the same screen. Trace or use an intersection finder to determine the coordinates of the intersections.

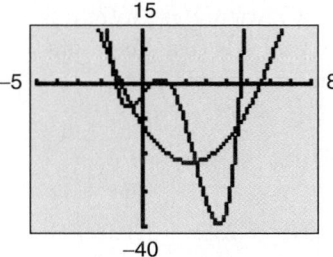

Figure 12.5-1

The graphs intersect at four points. The approximate solutions are $(-1.5, 4.4)$, $(-0.5, -4.8)$, $(2.1, 0.1)$, and $(3.9, 26.3)$.

Example 4 Solving a Nonlinear System Graphically

Solve the following system of equations graphically.

$$2x^2 \qquad + 3y^2 = 30$$
$$2x^2 - xy - \ y^2 = \ 8$$

Solution

In order to graph the equations, they must both be solved for y.

$$2x^2 + 3y^2 = 30$$
$$y^2 = 10 \ - \ \frac{2}{3}x^2$$
$$y = \pm\sqrt{10 - \frac{2}{3}x^2}$$

To solve the second equation for y, use the quadratic formula with y as the variable.

$$2x^2 - xy - y^2 = 8$$
$$-y^2 - xy + (2x^2 - 8) = 0$$

$a = -1$, $b = -x$, and $c = 2x^2 - 8$

$$y = \frac{x \pm \sqrt{x^2 + 4(2x^2 - 8)}}{-2}$$
$$= \frac{x \pm \sqrt{9x^2 - 32}}{-2}$$

Graph the four equations and then trace or use an intersection finder.

There are four solutions: $(3, 2)$, $(-3, -2)$, $(-2.2, 2.6)$, and $(2.2, -2.6)$. The first two are exact solutions, a fact that can be confirmed by substituting the values into the original equations.

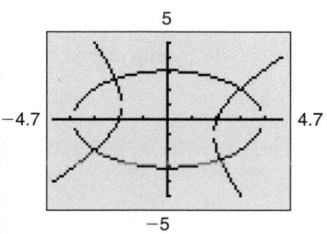

Figure 12.5-2

Example 3

Solve the following system of equations graphically.

$$y = x^4 - 5x^3 + 8x - 3$$
$$y = 2x^2 - 9x - 12$$

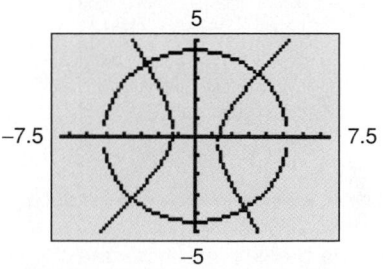

The graphs intersect at four points. The approximate solutions are $(-1.5, 5.4)$, $(-0.5, -6.5)$, $(2.5, -22.0)$, and $(4.5, -11.9)$.

Example 4

Solve the following system of equations graphically.

$$3x^2 \qquad + 4y^2 = 80$$
$$3x^2 - xy - 2y^2 = \ 5$$

Solve both equations for y:

- $3x^2 + 4y^2 = 80$

$$y^2 = 20 - \frac{3}{4}x^2$$
$$y = \pm\sqrt{20 - \frac{3}{4}x^2}$$

- $3x^2 - xy - 2y^2 = 5$

Use the quadratic formula with y as the variable:

$$-2y^2 - xy + (3x^2 - 5) = 0$$

$a = -2$, $b = -x$, $c = 3x^2 - 5$

$$y = \frac{x \pm \sqrt{x^2 - 4(-2)(3x^2 - 5)}}{2(-2)}$$
$$= \frac{x \pm \sqrt{25x^2 - 40}}{-4}$$

Graph the four associated equations:

The approximate solutions are $(2.8, -3.8)$, $(-2.8, 3.8)$, $(3.5, 3.3)$, and $(-3.5, -3.3)$.

Real-World Application

The application in **Example 5** involves revenue, cost, and profit. Profits and break-even points in business applications such as this are often found by using the profit function, $P = R - C$, where P is profit, R is revenue, and C is cost. The profit function for Example 5 is:

$P = R - C$

$P = (-0.04x^2 + 320x) -$
$$(85x + 120,000)$$

$P = -0.04x^2 + 235x - 120,000$

At the break-even points, $P = 0$. You can find the number of bicycles, x, when $P = 0$ by graphing the profit function P and finding the x-intercepts, or you can use the quadratic formula as shown below.

$x = \dfrac{-235 \pm \sqrt{235^2 - 4(-0.04)(-120,000)}}{2(-0.04)}$

$= \dfrac{-235 \pm \sqrt{55,225 - 19,200}}{-0.08}$

$= \dfrac{-235 \pm \sqrt{36,025}}{-0.08}$

$x \approx 565, \ x \approx 5310$

ADDITIONAL EXAMPLES

Example 5

The revenue and cost (in dollars) for manufacturing and selling x snowboards are given by the following equations:

cost: $y = 50x + 90,000$
revenue: $y = -0.05x^2 + 345x$

Find all break-even points of the system.

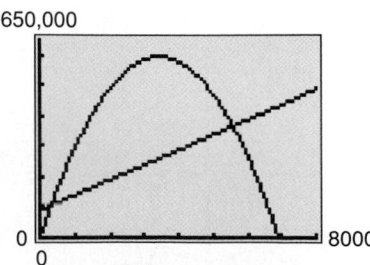

The two break even points are approximately (323, 106,137) and (5577, 368,863). By manufacturing and selling between 323 and 5577 snowboards, the company will make a profit.

Example 5   Application of a Nonlinear System

The revenue and cost (in dollars) for manufacturing x bicycles are given by the following equations:

cost: $y = 85x + 120,000$
revenue: $y = -0.04x^2 + 320x$

A solution of this system is called a *break-even point*, which occurs when the cost and revenue are equal. Find all break-even points of this system.

Solution

Graph both equations on the same screen. To choose a window, notice that the graph of the revenue equation is a parabola with vertex (4000, 640,000).

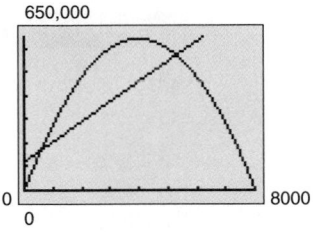

Figure 12.5-3

There are two break-even points: approximately (565, 168,022) and (5310, 571,353). This means that if the manufacturer makes and sells 565 or 5310 bicycles, the cost and revenue will be the same. That is, the manufacturer will break even. From the graph, you can see that between 565 and 5310, the revenue is greater than the cost, so the manufacturer will make a profit when producing between 565 and 5310 bicycles.

Exercises 12.5

In Exercises 1–12, solve the system algebraically.

1. $x^2 - y = 0$
        $-2x + y = 3$

2. $x^2 - y = 0$
        $-3x + y = -2$

3. $x^2 - y = 0$
      $x^2 + 3y = 6$

4. $x^2 - y = 0$
      $x^2 + 4y = 4$

5. $x + y = 10$
      $xy = 21$

6. $2x + y = 4$
      $xy = 2$

7. $xy + 2y^2 = 8$
      $x - 2y = 4$

8. $xy + 4x^2 = 3$
      $3x + y = 2$

9. $x^2 + y^2 - 4x - 4y = -4$
      $x - y = 2$

10. $x^2 + y^2 - 4x - 2y = -1$
       $x + 2y = 2$

11. $x^2 + y^2 = 25$
       $x^2 + y = 19$

12. $x^2 + y^2 = 1$
       $x^2 - y = 5$

In Exercises 13–28, solve the system by any means.

13. $y = x^3 - 3x^2 + 4$
       $y = -0.5x^2 + 3x - 2$

14. $y = -x^3 + 3x^2 + x - 3$
       $y = -2x^2 + 5$

15. $y = x^3 - 3x + 2$
       $y = \dfrac{3}{x^2 + 3}$

Exercises 12.5

ANSWERS

1. $x = 3, y = 9$ or $x = -1, y = 1$

2. $x = 2, y = 4$ or $x = 1, y = 1$

3. $x = \sqrt{\dfrac{3}{2}}, y = \dfrac{3}{2}$ or $x = -\sqrt{\dfrac{3}{2}}, y = \dfrac{3}{2}$

4. $x = \sqrt{\dfrac{4}{5}}, y = \dfrac{4}{5}$ or $x = -\sqrt{\dfrac{4}{5}}, y = \dfrac{4}{5}$

5. $x = 7, y = 3$ or $x = 3, y = 7$

6. $x = 1, y = 2$

7. $x = 0, y = -2$ or $x = 6, y = 1$

8. $x = -3, y = 11$ or $x = 1, y = -1$

9. $x = 2, y = 0$ or $x = 4, y = 2$

10. $x = 0, y = 1$ or $x = \dfrac{16}{5}, y = -\dfrac{3}{5}$

11. $x = 4, y = 3$ or $x = -4, y = 3$ or
       $x = \sqrt{21}, y = -2$ or $x = -\sqrt{21}, y = -2$

12. no solution

16. $y = 0.25x^4 - 2x^2 + 4$
$y = x^3 - x^2 - 2x + 1$

17. $y = x^3 + x + 1$
$y = \sin x$

18. $y = x^2 - 4$
$y = \cos x$

19. $25x^2 - 16y^2 = 400$
$-9x^2 + 4y^2 = -36$

20. $9x^2 + 16y^2 = 140$
$-x^2 + 4y^2 = -4$

21. $5x^2 + 3y^2 - 20x + 6y = -8$
$x - y = 2$

22. $4x^2 + 9y^2 = 36$
$2x - y = -1$

23. $x^2 + 4xy + 4y^2 - 30x - 90y + 450 = 0$
$x^2 + x - y + 1 = 0$

24. $3x^2 + 4xy + 3y^2 - 12x + 2y + 7 = 0$
$x^2 - 10x - y + 21 = 0$

25. $4x^2 - 6xy + 2y^2 - 3x + 10y = 6$
$4x^2 + y^2 = 64$

26. $5x^2 + xy + 6y^2 - 79x - 73y + 196 = 0$
$x^2 - 2xy + y^2 - 8x - 8y + 48 = 0$

27. $x^2 + 3xy + y^2 = 2$
$3x^2 - 5xy + 3y^2 = 7$

28. $2x^2 - 8xy + 8y^2 + 2x - 5 = 0$
$16x^2 - 24xy + 9y^2 + 100x - 200y + 100 = 0$

In Exercises 29–32, find the center (h, k) and radius r of the circle $(x - h)^2 + (y - k)^2 = r^2$ that passes through the three given points.

29. $(0, 5)$, $(3, 4)$, $(4, 3)$ **30.** $(3, 4)$, $(2, 5)$, $(3, 6)$

31. $(5, 25)$, $(17, 21)$, $(2, 24)$

32. $(8, 12)$, $(14, 4)$, $(6.4, 12.8)$

33. Find the break-even points for the following revenue and cost functions. (See Example 5.)

cost: $y = 30x + 25{,}000$
revenue: $y = -0.03x^2 + 100x$

34. A 52-foot-long piece of wire is to be cut into three pieces, two of which are the same length. The two equal pieces are to be bent into circles and the third piece into a square. What should the length of each piece be if the total area enclosed by the two circles and the square is 100 square feet?

35. A rectangular box (including top) with square ends and a volume of 16 cubic meters is to be constructed from 40 square meters of cardboard. What should its dimensions be?

36. A rectangular sheet of metal is to be rolled into a circular tube. If the tube is to have a surface area (excluding ends) of 210 square inches and a volume of 252 cubic inches, what size of metal sheet should be used? (Recall that the circumference of a circle with radius r is $2pr$ and that the volume of a cylinder with radius r and height h is pr^2h.)
15.08 in. by 13.93 in.

37. Find two real numbers whose sum is -16 and whose product is 48.
-4 and -12

38. Find two real numbers whose sum is 34.5 and whose product is 297.
16.5 and 18

39. Find two positive real numbers whose difference is 1 and whose product is 4.16.
1.6 and 2.6

40. Find two real numbers whose difference is 25.75 and whose product is 127.5.
30 and 4.25 or -4.25 and -30

41. Find two real numbers whose sum is 3 such that the sum of their squares is 369.
15 and -12

42. Find two real numbers whose sum is 2 such that the difference of their squares is 60.
16 and -14

43. Find the dimensions of a rectangular room whose perimeter is 58 feet and whose area is 204 square feet.
12 ft by 17 ft

44. Find the dimensions of a rectangular room whose perimeter is 53 feet and whose area is 165 square feet.
16.5 ft by 10 ft

45. A rectangle has an area of 120 square inches and a diagonal 17 inches in length. What are its dimensions?
8 in. by 15 in.

46. A right triangle has an area of 225 square centimeters and a hypotenuse 35 centimeters in length. To the nearest hundredth of a centimeter, how long are the legs of the triangle?
32.06 cm and 14.03 cm

47. Find the equation of the straight line that intersects the parabola $y = x^2$ only at the point $(3, 9)$. *Hint:* What condition on the discriminant guarantees that a quadratic equation has exactly one real solution?
$y = 6x - 9$

13. $x = -1.6237$, $y = -8.1891$ or
$x = 1.3163$, $y = 1.0826$ or
$x = 2.8073$, $y = 2.4814$

14. $x = -1.2176$, $y = 2.035$ or
$x = 1.3498$, $y = 1.3563$

15. $x = -1.9493$, $y = 0.4412$ or
$x = 0.3634$, $y = 0.9578$ or
$x = 1.4184$, $y = 0.5986$

16. $x = 1.8276$, $y = 0.1089$

17. $x = -0.9519$, $y = -0.8145$

18. $x = -1.9140$ $y = -0.3365$ or
$x = 1.9140$, $y = -0.3365$

19. no solution

20. $x = -3.4641$, $y = -1.4142$ or
$x = -3.4641$, $y = 1.4142$ or
$x = 3.4641$, $y = -1.4142$ or
$x = 3.4641$, $y = 1.4142$

21. $x = \dfrac{13 - \sqrt{105}}{8}$, $y = \dfrac{-3 - \sqrt{105}}{8}$ or
$x = \dfrac{13 + \sqrt{105}}{8}$, $y = \dfrac{-3 + \sqrt{105}}{8}$

22. $x = \dfrac{-9 + 3\sqrt{39}}{20}$, $y = \dfrac{1 + 3\sqrt{39}}{10}$ or
$x = \dfrac{-9 - 3\sqrt{39}}{20}$, $y = \dfrac{1 - 3\sqrt{39}}{10}$

23. $x = -4.8093$, $y = 19.3201$ or
$x = -3.1434$, $y = 7.7374$ or
$x = 2.1407$, $y = 7.7230$ or
$x = 2.8120$, $y = 11.7195$

24. $x = 2.9615$, $y = 0.1556$, or
$x = 6.2237$, $y = -2.5026$

25. $x = -3.8371$, $y = -2.2596$ or
$x = -0.9324$, $y = -7.7796$

26. $x = 3.2568$, $y = 11.7410$ or
$x = 15.0506$, $y = 4.6004$

27. $x = -1.4873$, $y = 0.0480$ or
$x = -0.0480$, $y = 1.4873$ or
$x = 0.0480$, $y = -1.4873$ or
$x = 1.4873$, $y = -0.0480$

28. $x = -3.3025$, $y = -0.4468$ or
$x = 1.4193$, $y = 1.2294$

29. center $(0, 0)$; $r = 5$

30. center $(3, 5)$; $r = 1$

31. center $(7.5, 12.5)$; $r \approx 12.75$

32. center $(1.4, 0.8)$; $r = 13$

33. $(440.2, 38{,}205.5)$ and
$(1893.1, 81{,}794.5)$

34. $(25.0372, 1.9256)$ and
$(6.7356, 38.5288)$

35. possible answers: 2 by 2 by 4 m; approximately 3.123 by 3.123 by 1.640 m

Excursion: Systems of Inequalities

Section 12.5.A Excursion: Systems of Inequalities

Teaching Notes

The directions in Examples 1–3 all use the word *solve*. Point out that the inequalities in **Examples 1** and **2** and the system in **Example 3** all have an infinite number of ordered pair solutions, so they cannot all be listed. To *solve* an inequality, we use shading in a coordinate plane to show where all the ordered pair solutions are located.

The box at the bottom of page 827 contains inequalities of the form $y > mx + b$, $y \geq mx + b$, etc. It also contains the equation $y = mx + b$. Remind students that $y = mx + b$ is the slope-intercept form of the equation of a line with slope m and y-intercept b.

Example Notes

Before students graph the solution to **Example 2**, have them read the **Technology Tip** on page 828 to find out how to display shading on their calculators.

ADDITIONAL EXAMPLES

Example 1

Solve the inequality $y \leq \frac{1}{2}x + 4$.

Graph the line $y = \frac{1}{2}x + 4$.

Choose point (0, 0) and test it in the inequality.

$0 \stackrel{?}{\leq} \frac{1}{2}(0) + 4$ *True*

The inequality is true for the test point, so shade the region that *does* contain the point, in this case, the region below the line.

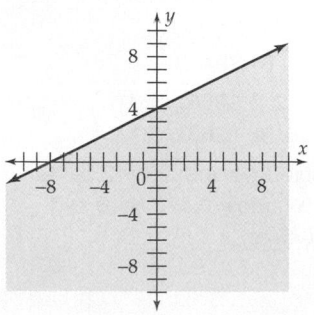

Objectives

- Solve inequalities in two variables
- Solve systems of inequalities by graphing
- Solve linear programming problems

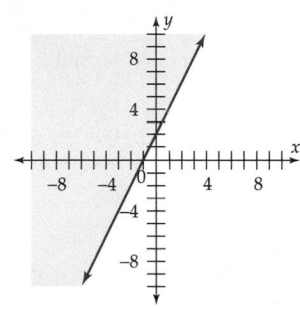

Figure 12.5.A-1

Test-Point Method for Solving Inequalities in Two Variables

Inequalities in two variables are solved by graphing. The solution to an inequality in two variables is the region in the coordinate plane consisting of all points whose coordinates satisfy the inequality.

> **Example 1**   **Solving an Inequality in Two Variables**

Solve the inequality $y \geq 2x + 2$.

Solution

First, graph the line $y = 2x + 2$. The solution to the inequality is the set of all points on the line, plus all points in either the region above or the region below the line. To determine which region is the solution, choose a point that is not on the line, such as (0, 0), and test it in the inequality.

$$0 \stackrel{?}{\geq} 2(0) + 2 \qquad \textit{False}$$

The inequality is false for the test point, so shade the region that does not contain that point—in this case, the region above the line. ∎

The method used in Example 1 can be summarized as follows.

> Replace the inequality symbol by an equal sign, and graph the resulting line.
>
> - For $\leq$ and $\geq$ inequalities, use a solid line to indicate that the line is part of the solution.
> - For $>$ and $<$ inequalities, use a dashed line to indicate that the line is *not* part of the solution.
>
> Choose a test point that is not on the line, and substitute its coordinates in the inequality.
>
> - If the coordinates of the test point make the inequality true, then the solution includes the region on the side of the line containing the test point.
> - If the coordinates of the test point make the inequality false, then the solution includes the region on the side of the line that does not contain the test point.

The test-point method can be used to solve any inequality, but the following technique for linear inequalities with two variables is often easier, especially when using a calculator.

| **Example 2** | Solving a Linear Inequality |

Solve the inequality $6x + 3y < 6$.

Solution

First, solve the inequality for y.

$$3y < -6x + 6$$
$$y < -2x + 2$$

If the point (x, y) satisfies this inequality, then it lies below the line $y = -2x + 2$. Thus, the solution of the inequality is the set of all points that lie below the line $y = -2x + 2$, as shown in Figure 12.5.A-2. The line $y = -2x + 2$ is not part of the solution.

Figure 12.5.A-2

CAUTION

Graphing calculators do not display a dashed line with the shade feature. The line in Figure 12.5.A-2 is not part of the solution.

The solution method used in Example 2 can be summarized as follows.

Solving Linear Inequalities in Two Variables

Solve the inequality for y so that it has one of the following forms:

$$y > mx + b \qquad y \ge mx + b \qquad y < mx + b \qquad y \le mx + b$$

• The solution of $y > mx + b$ is the half-plane *above* the line.

• The solution of $y < mx + b$ is the half-plane *below* the line.

For $y \ge mx + b$ and $y \le mx + b$, the line $y = mx + b$ is also part of the solution.

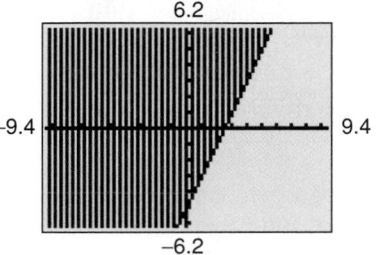

ADDITIONAL EXAMPLES

Example 3

Solve the system of inequalities.

$$y \geq -x - 4$$
$$y < x + 2$$

Graph the two inequalities together, as shown in the graphs below.

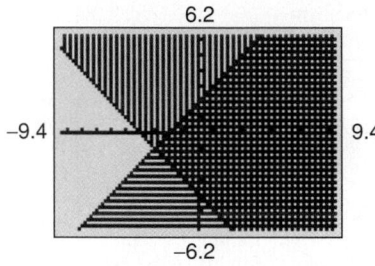

The area where the shaded regions intersect is the solution of the system. Any point in this shaded region of the plane is a solution of both inequalities. For example, the point (0, 0) in the solution satisfies both inequalities, as shown below.

$$0 \geq -(0) - 4 = -4$$
$$0 < (0) + 2 = 2$$

Technology Tip

To display shading on TI models, select the graph style for a function by moving the cursor to the left of the equal sign in the function editor to the graph's style icon, shown in the first column. Press ENTER repeatedly to rotate through the graph styles until the desired style is shown. Then graph the function as usual. There is also a SHADE option in the DRAW menu.

In the function memory of CASIO models, select Type(F3) ▶(F6) and then the inequality sign desired.

Systems of Inequalities in Two Variables

The solution of a system of inequalities in two variables is found by graphing all the inequalities on the same coordinate plane. The solution is the region that is common to the solutions of all the graphs.

Example 3   Solving a System of Inequalities

Solve the system of inequalities.

$$y \leq x + 3$$
$$y > -x + 1$$

Solution

Graph the two inequalities together, as shown in Figure 12.5.A-3. Figure 12.5.A-4 shows a calculator screen with regions shaded.

Figure 12.5.A-3

Figure 12.5.A-4

The area where the shaded regions intersect is the solution of the system. Any point in this shaded region of the plane is a solution of both inequalities. For example, the point (5, 2) in the solution satisfies both inequalities, as shown below.

$$2 \leq 5 + 3 = 8$$
$$2 > -5 + 1 = -4$$

Linear Programming

Linear programming is a process that involves finding the maximum or minimum output of a linear function, called the **objective function,** subject to certain restrictions, called **constraints.**

For linear programming problems in two variables, the objective function has the form $F(x, y) = ax + by$, and the constraints are linear inequalities. The solution of the system of linear inequalities formed by the constraints is called the **feasible region.**

The feasible region is a region in the plane that is bounded by straight lines, such as those shown in Figure 12.5.A-5. The first figure is bounded on all four sides and the two other figures have one side that is not bounded.

Figure 12.5.A-5

A **corner point** of such a region is any point where two of the sides intersect, such as points P, Q, R, and S in the first region in Figure 12.5.A-5.

The key to solving linear programming problems is the following theorem, which will not be proved here.

Fundamental Theorem of Linear Programming

> The maximum value or minimum value of the objective function (if it exists) always occurs at one or more of the corner points of the feasible region. Thus, the solution may be found by graphing the feasible region, and testing the coordinates of the corner points in the objective function to find the maximum or minimum value of the function.

Students may shade the wrong half-plane when they isolate y on the right hand side of the inequality.

For instance, in **Example 4,** the second constraint is $2x - y \leq 9$. Students might simplify this inequality as follows:

$$2x - y \leq 9$$
$$2x \quad\, \leq 9 + y$$
$$2x - 9 \leq y$$

Since the *less than* or equal to symbol is used, they may incorrectly shade the region *below* the line. Encourage students to rewrite the inequality with y on the left hand side as $y \geq 2x - 9$. Then they can refer to the box on the bottom of page 827 to find that they should shade *above* the line.

 Math Background

Russian-American mathematician George Dantzig (1914–) is often considered to be the "father of linear programming." His most important contribution to the subject is the simplex method of optimization, which he first elaborated in 1947. Dantzig's ideas evolved from work he did on planning and logistics for the United States Air Force during World War II.

Example 4

Find the maximum value of the function $F(x, y) = 5x + 2y$ subject to the constraints below.

$$\begin{cases} 3x + 5y \le 25 \\ x - y \le 3 \\ x \ge 0 \\ y \ge 0 \end{cases}$$

Graph the feasible region, the solution to the system of inequalities:

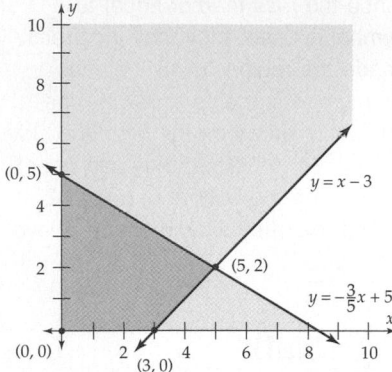

Find the corner points of the feasible region from the graph:

(0, 0), (0, 5), (3, 0), (5, 2)

Evaluate the objective function at each of the corner points:

Corner point	$F(x,y) = 5x + 2y$
(0, 0)	5(0) + 2(0) = 0
(0, 5)	5(0) + 2(5) = 10
(3, 0)	5(3) + 2(0) = 15
(5, 2)	5(5) + 2(2) = 29

The corner point (5, 2) yields the maximum value of the objective function, 29.

COMMON ERROR ALERT

Students may think that the corner point with the "minimum" coordinates yields the minimum value of the objective function and the point with the "maximum" coordinates yields the maximum value of the objective function. This is not necessarily the case, as illustrated.

To see why the Fundamental Theorem above is true, notice that the graph of the objective function is a plane in three dimensions. The portion of the plane that lies above the feasible region must have its high point and low point at a corner, as shown in Figure 12.5.A-6.

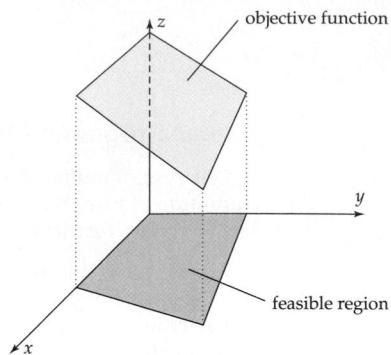

Figure 12.5.A-6

Example 4   **A Linear Programming Problem**

Find the maximum value of the function $F(x, y) = 3x + 2y$ subject to the constraints below.

$$\begin{cases} x + 4y \le 18 \\ 2x - y \le 9 \\ x \ge 0 \\ y \ge 0 \end{cases}$$

Solution

First, graph the feasible region. This is the solution of the system of inequalities.

NOTE In linear programming problems with a feasible region that is unbounded on one or more sides, there may be a minimum or maximum value of the objective function, but (usually) not both.

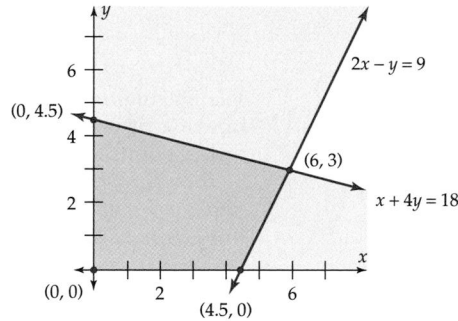

Figure 12.5.A-7

- Note in Figure 12.5.A-6, the maximum value of the objective function appears to be directly above corner point (0, 0), and the minimum above the point with both coordinates nonzero.

- Also, suppose the objective function $F(x, y) = -3x + 2y$ was subject to the same constraints as in **Example 4.** Then we would have:

Corner point	$F(x, y) = -3x + 2y$
(0, 0)	-3(0) + 2(0) = 0
(0, 4.5)	-3(0) + 2(4.5) = 9
(4.5, 0)	-3(4.5) + 2(0) = -13.5
(6, 3)	-3(6) + 2(3) = -12

Here, the objective function is minimized at (4.5, 0) and maximized at (0, 4.5).

Second, find the corner points of the feasible region from the graph. They are (0, 0), (0, 4.5), (4.5, 0), and (6, 3).

Third, evaluate the objective function at each of the corner points.

Corner point	$F(x, y) = 3x + 2y$
(0, 0)	$3(0) + 2(0) = 0$
(0, 4.5)	$3(0) + 2(4.5) = 9$
(4.5, 0)	$3(4.5) + 2(0) = 13.5$
(6, 3)	$3(6) + 2(3) = 24$

The solution is the corner point (6, 3), which yields the largest value of the objective function, 24. This is the maximum value of the objective function.

∎

Example 5   Application

Carla is making earrings and necklaces to sell at a craft fair. The profit from each pair of earrings is $3, and the profit from each necklace is $5. She has 12 hours to make all of the jewelry she plans to sell. Each pair of earrings takes 15 minutes to make, and each necklace takes 40 minutes to make. She also has $80 for supplies. The supplies for a pair of earrings cost $2, and the supplies for a necklace cost $4. How many pairs of earrings and how many necklaces should she make to maximize her profit?

Solution

Let x be the number of pairs of earrings and y be the number of necklaces. The objective function, which represents the profit, is $P(x, y) = 3x + 5y$. The constraints are inequalities involving time and cost. In addition, there is an implied constraint that neither quantity can be negative. This gives the following linear programming problem:

$$\text{Maximize } P(x, y) = 3x + 5y$$

$$\text{Subject to: } \begin{cases} 15x + 40y \le 720 & time \\ 2x + 4y \le 80 & cost \\ x \ge 0 \\ y \ge 0 \end{cases}$$

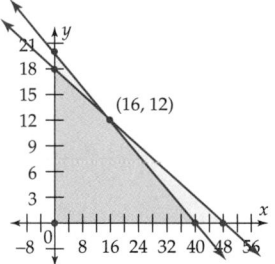

Figure 12.5.A-8

The feasible region is shown in Figure 12.5.A-8.

Example 5

Joseph is making toy boats and trucks to sell at a carnival. The profit from each boat is $5 and the profit from each truck is $4. He has 10 hours to make all of the toys he plans to sell. It takes him 30 minutes to make each boat and 20 minutes to make each truck. He has $105 for supplies. The supplies for a boat cost $3 and the supplies for a truck cost $5.

How many boats and trucks should he make to maximize his profit?

Let x be the number of boats and y be the number of trucks.

Objective (profit) function:
$$P(x, y) = 5x + 4y$$

Constraints involve time and cost, and also that neither the number of boats nor trucks can be negative.

Linear programming problem:

Maximize $P(x, y) = 5x + 4y$

$$\text{Subject to: } \begin{cases} 30x + 20y \le 600 & time \\ 3x + 5y \le 105 & cost \\ x \ge 0 \\ y \ge 0 \end{cases}$$

Graph the feasible region.

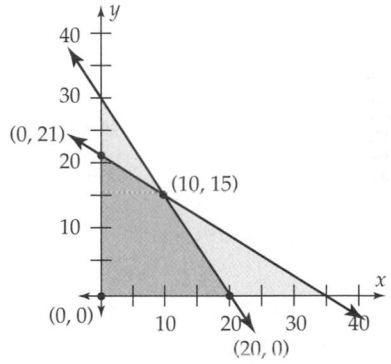

Corner point	$P(x, y) = 5x + 4y$
(0, 0)	$5(0) + 4(0) = 0$
(0, 21)	$5(0) + 4(21) = 84$
(20, 0)	$5(20) + 4(0) = 100$
(10, 15)	$5(10) + 4(15) = 110$

To maximize his profit, Joseph should make 10 boats and 15 trucks. His maximum profit will be $110.

Example Notes

In **Example 5**, the time constraint is $15x + 40y \le 720$, where all of the quantities are in minutes ($12 \text{ hr} = 12 \times 60 = 720 \text{ min}$).

The constraint could have also been written with all of the quantities in hours:

$15 \text{ min} = \frac{1}{4} \text{ hr}$ and $40 \text{ min} = \frac{2}{3} \text{ hr}$, so $\frac{1}{4}x + \frac{2}{3}y \le 12$.

These inequalities are equivalent.

Real-World Application

Example 5 uses linear programming to find out how to maximize a profit, subject to certain constraints that involve time and money. Linear programming can be used to solve the same type of problem when there are additional constraints, as illustrated below.

Suppose Carla wants to sell earrings and necklaces at another craft fair, but she is too busy to make them. She hires two helpers: Amy to make earrings and Bess to make necklaces. Carla allows a total of 12 hours working time for Amy and Bess. She budgets $60 for supplies and $156 to pay Amy and Bess.

The costs and times involved are shown in the table below:

	Per pair of earrings	Per necklace
Time	20 min	60 min
Cost of supplies	$2	$4
Cost of labor	$6	$6

How many pairs of earrings (x) and how many necklaces (y) should be made and sold to maximize profit (with the same profit function) in this situation?

The constraints are:

Time: $20x + 60y \leq 720$

Cost of supplies: $2x + 4y \leq 60$

Cost of labor: $6x + 6y \leq 156$

Implied: $x \geq 0, y \geq 0$

Graph the feasible region.

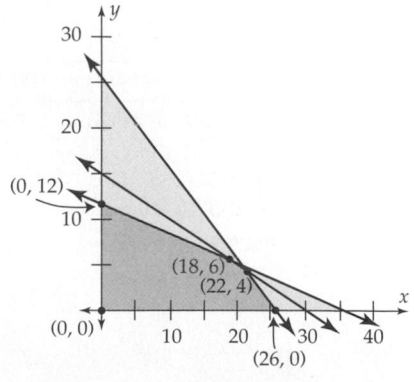

The corner points are shown below, with the objective function evaluated at each point.

Corner point	$P(x, y) = 3x + 5y$
(0, 0)	$3(0) + 5(0) = 0$
(0, 18)	$3(0) + 5(18) = 90$
(40, 0)	$3(40) + 5(0) = 120$
(16, 12)	$3(16) + 5(12) = 108$

The maximum value occurs at (40, 0). To make the maximum profit, Carla should make 40 pairs of earrings and 0 necklaces. Her maximum profit will be $120.

Summary: Solving Linear Programming Problems

To solve a linear programming problem:

- **Graph the feasible region. This is the solution of the system of inequalities formed by the constraints.**
- **Find the corner points of the feasible region from the graph.**
- **Evaluate the objective function at each corner point.**
- **Choose the corner point which yields the greatest (or least) value of the objective function. This is the maximum (or minimum) value of the function on the feasible region.**

Exercises 12.5.A

In Exercises 1–12, solve the system of inequalities.

1. $y \leq 2x + 4$
$y > x - 2$

2. $y \geq x - 3$
$y \geq 4x + 2$

3. $y > 3x - 1$
$y < \frac{1}{2}x + 3$

4. $y \leq \frac{1}{4}x + 1$
$y > 4x - 1$

5. $2x + 3y > 6$
$x - 2y \leq 5$

6. $2x + 4y \leq 5$
$3x + 2y \leq 8$

7. $7 \geq 2x + 1$
$y \leq x$

8. $y \geq x$
$y < 2x + 3$

Corner point	$P(x, y) = 3x + 5y$
(0, 0)	$3(0) + 5(0) = 0$
(0, 12)	$3(0) + 5(12) = 60$
(18, 6)	$3(18) + 5(6) = 84$
(22, 4)	$3(22) + 5(4) = 86$
(26, 0)	$3(26) + 5(0) = 78$

To maximize profit, Amy should make 22 pairs of earrings and Bess should make 4 necklaces. Carla's maximum profit will be $86.

9. $y > 2x - 1$
$x + y < 16$

10. $y \leq x + 3$
$x - y < 1$

11. $y \leq 1$
$x \leq -1$

12. $4x + 9y \leq 36$
$4y - x < 16$

In Exercises 13–16, graph the feasible region described by the system of inequalities, and find all of its corner points.

13. $3x + 4y \leq 24$
$9x - 2y \leq 30$
$x \geq 0$
$y \geq 0$

14. $x + y \leq 7$
$7x + 2y \leq 24$
$x \geq 0$
$y \geq 0$

15. $x + 2y \leq 8$
$3x - y \leq 6$
$x \geq 0$
$y \geq 0$

16. $2x + 3y \leq 12$
$5x + 2y \leq 10$
$x \geq 0$
$y \geq 0$

Solve the following linear programming problems.

17. Maximize: $F(x, y) = 2x + 5y$

Subject to:
$\begin{cases} x + y \leq 6 \\ x - y \leq 4 \\ x \geq 0 \\ y \geq 0 \end{cases}$

18. Maxmimize: $F(x, y) = 3x + 7y$

Subject to:
$\begin{cases} -x + 2y \leq 10 \\ 7x + 11y \leq 105 \\ x \geq 0 \\ y \geq 0 \end{cases}$

19. Minimize: $F(x, y) = \frac{1}{2}x + \frac{3}{4}y$

Subject to:
$\begin{cases} 3x + 4y \leq 32 \\ 4x + 2y \leq 36 \\ x \geq 0 \\ y \geq 0 \end{cases}$

20. Minimize: $F(x, y) = 4x + 2y$

Subject to:
$\begin{cases} -3x + 12y \leq 60 \\ 8x - 5y \leq 56 \\ x \geq 0 \\ y \geq 0 \end{cases}$

21. A lunch counter sells two types of sandwiches, roast beef and chicken salad. The profit on the sandwiches is $2 for chicken salad and $3 for roast beef. The amount of bread available is enough for 30 sandwiches. There are 4 hours available to prepare sandwiches. If chicken salad sandwiches take 7 minutes to prepare and roast beef sandwiches take 10 minutes, how many of each type of sandwich should be prepared to maximize the profit?

22. A dealer has a lot that can hold 30 vehicles. In this lot, there are two available models, A and B. The dealer normally sells at least twice as many model A cars as model B cars. If the dealer makes a profit of $1300 on model A cars and $1700 on model B cars, how many of each car should the dealer have in the lot?

23. A 30-acre orchard is to contain two types of trees, peach and almond. The profit per year is $16.80 per peach tree and $21.60 per almond tree. An acre can sustain 1080 peach trees or 900 almond trees. If the grower has available labor to plant a maximum of 30,000 trees, how many of each type of tree should be planted?

24. An investor has $12,000 to invest into two different funds. Fund A, which is a high-risk fund, yields an average return of 14%. Fund B, which is a low-risk fund, yields an average return of 6%. To reduce the risk, the investor wants the amount in fund B to be at least twice the amount in fund A. How much should be invested in each fund to maximize the return? What is the maximum return?

1.

2.

3.

4.

5.

6.

7.

8.

9–24. *See p.* **1085.**

CHAPTER 12

Review

Important Concepts

834

Review Exercises

Section 12.1

In Exercises 1–10, solve the system of linear equations by any method.

1. $-5x + 3y = 4$
$2x - y = -3$ $\quad x = -5, \ y = -7$

2. $3x - y = 6$
$2x + 3y = 7$ $\quad x = \dfrac{25}{11}, \ y = \dfrac{9}{11}$

3. $3x - 5y = 10$
$4x - 3y = 6$ $\quad x = 0, \ y = -2$

4. $\dfrac{1}{4}x - \dfrac{1}{3}y = -\dfrac{1}{4}$
$\dfrac{1}{10}x + \dfrac{2}{5}y = \dfrac{2}{5}$ $\quad x = \dfrac{1}{4}, \ y = \dfrac{15}{16}$

5. $3x + y - z = 13$
$x + y + 2z = 9$
$-3x - y + 2z = 9$
$x = 35, \ y = -70, \ z = 22$

6. $x + 2y + 3z = 1$
$4x + 4y + 4z = 2$
$10x + 8y + 5z = 4$
$x = 0, \ y = 0.5, \ z = 0$

7. $4x + 3y - 3z = 2$
$5x - 3y + 2z = 10$
$2x - 2y + 3z = 14$
$x = 2, \ y = 4, \ z = 6$

8. $x + y - 4z = 0$
$2x + y - 3z = 2$
$-3x - y + 2z = -4$
$x = 2 - t,$
$y = -2 + 5t,$
$z = t$
for any real number t

9. $x - 2y - 3z = 1$
$5y + 10z = 0$
$8x - 6y - 4z = 8$
$x = -t + 1,$
$y = -2t,$
$z = t$
for any real number t

10. $4x - y - 2z = 4$
$x - y - \dfrac{1}{2}z = 1$
$2x - y - z = 8$
no solution

11. The sum of one number and three times a second number is -20. The sum of the second number and two times the first number is 55. Find the two numbers. **37 and -19**

12. You are given $144 in $1, $5, and $10 bills. There are 35 bills. There are two more $10 bills than $5 bills. How many bills of each type do you have? **19 ones, 7 fives, 9 tens**

13. Let L be the line with equation $4x - 2y = 6$ and M the line with equation $-10x + 5y = -15$. Which of the following statements is true? **c**
   a. L and M do not intersect.
   b. L and M intersect at a single point.
   c. L and M are the same line.
   d. All of the above are true.
   e. None of the above are true.

14. Which of the following statements about the given system of equations are *false*? **c**

$$x \quad\ + \ z = 2$$
$$6x + 4y + 14z = 24$$
$$2x + \ y + \ 4z = 7$$

   a. $x = 2, y = 3, z = 0$ is a solution.
   b. $x = 1, y = 1, z = 1$ is a solution.
   c. $x = 1, y = -3, z = 3$ is a solution.
   d. The system has an infinite number of solutions.
   e. $x = 2, y = 5, z = -1$ is not a solution.

15. Tickets to a lecture cost $1 for students, $1.50 for faculty, and $2 for others. Total attendance at the lecture was 460, and the total income from tickets was $570. Three times as many students as faculty attended. How many faculty members attended the lecture? **100**

16. An alloy containing 40% gold and an alloy containing 70% gold are to be mixed to produce 50 pounds of an alloy containing 60% gold. How much of each alloy is needed?

$\dfrac{50}{3}$ **lb 40% alloy,** $\dfrac{100}{3}$ **lb 70% alloy**

17. $2x + 6y = 16$
$2x + 3y = 7$

18. $2x - y = 4$
$3x + 2y = -1$

19. $2x + 3z = -2$
$4x - 3y + 7z = 1$
$8x - 9y + 10z = -3$

20. $x + y - 5z = 2$
$x - 2z = 0$
$2x - y - z = 1$

21. $x = \frac{26}{9},\ y = -\frac{11}{9}$; consistent

22. $x = t,\ y = \frac{3}{2}t - \frac{1}{2}$ for any real number t

23. no solution; inconsistent

24. $x = 2,\ y = 0,\ z = 6$; consistent

25. $x = \frac{1}{11}t + \frac{37}{11},\ y = \frac{3}{11}t - \frac{10}{11},$
$z = t$, for any real number t; consistent

26. no solution; inconsistent

27. $\begin{pmatrix} -2 & 3 \\ -4 & -1 \end{pmatrix}$

28. $\begin{pmatrix} -7 & 3 & 14 \\ -2 & 2 & 20 \end{pmatrix}$

29. not defined

30. $\begin{pmatrix} 12 & -4 \\ 26 & 7 \end{pmatrix}$

31. $\begin{pmatrix} -9 & 7 \\ -4 & 3 \end{pmatrix}$

32. no inverse

33. $\begin{pmatrix} 1 & 2 & -2 \\ -1 & 3 & 0 \\ 0 & -2 & 1 \end{pmatrix}$

34. $\begin{pmatrix} 3 & -\frac{7}{5} & -\frac{1}{5} \\ 2 & -1 & 0 \\ 0 & \frac{2}{5} & \frac{1}{5} \end{pmatrix}$

35. $x = 4,\ y = 3,\ z = 2$

36. $x = 0,\ y = 0,\ z = 0,\ u = 0$

Section 12.2

For Exercises 17–20, write the system of linear equations represented by the augmented matrix.

17. $\left(\begin{array}{cc|c} 2 & 6 & 16 \\ 2 & 3 & 7 \end{array}\right)$ 　　　　**18.** $\left(\begin{array}{cc|c} 2 & -1 & 4 \\ 3 & 2 & -1 \end{array}\right)$

19. $\left(\begin{array}{ccc|c} 2 & 0 & 3 & -2 \\ 4 & -3 & 7 & 1 \\ 8 & -9 & 10 & -3 \end{array}\right)$ 　　**20.** $\left(\begin{array}{ccc|c} 1 & 1 & -5 & 2 \\ 1 & 0 & -2 & 0 \\ 2 & -1 & -1 & 1 \end{array}\right)$

For Exercises 21–26, write the system represented by each matrix, find the solutions, if any, and classify each system as consistent or inconsistent.

21. $\left(\begin{array}{cc|c} 4 & -2 & 14 \\ 1 & -5 & 9 \end{array}\right)$ 　　　**22.** $\left(\begin{array}{cc|c} 9 & -6 & 3 \\ -12 & 8 & -4 \end{array}\right)$

23. $\left(\begin{array}{ccc|c} 1 & 1 & -1 & 1 \\ 1 & -2 & 3 & -3 \\ 4 & 1 & 0 & 2 \end{array}\right)$ 　　**24.** $\left(\begin{array}{ccc|c} -1 & 2 & 1 & 4 \\ 1 & 3 & 0 & 2 \\ 3 & -5 & -1 & 0 \end{array}\right)$

25. $\left(\begin{array}{ccc|c} 2 & 3 & -1 & 4 \\ 1 & -4 & 1 & 7 \end{array}\right)$ 　　**26.** $\left(\begin{array}{cc|c} 1 & 1 & 2 \\ 2 & -3 & 3 \\ 1 & -1 & 4 \end{array}\right)$

Section 12.3

In Exercises 27–30, perform the indicated matrix multiplication or state that the product is not defined.

$$A = \begin{pmatrix} -1 & 0 \\ 0 & -1 \end{pmatrix} \quad B = \begin{pmatrix} 2 & -3 \\ 4 & 1 \end{pmatrix} \quad C = \begin{pmatrix} 3 & 2 \\ 2 & 4 \end{pmatrix}$$

$$D = \begin{pmatrix} -3 & 1 & 2 \\ 1 & 0 & 4 \end{pmatrix} \quad E = \begin{pmatrix} 1 & 2 \\ -3 & 4 \\ 0 & 5 \end{pmatrix} \quad F = \begin{pmatrix} 2 & 3 \\ 6 & 3 \\ 6 & 1 \end{pmatrix}$$

27. AB 　　　**28.** CD 　　　**29.** AE 　　　**30.** DF

In Exercises 31–34, find the inverse of the matrix, if it exists.

31. $\begin{pmatrix} 3 & -7 \\ 4 & -9 \end{pmatrix}$ 　　　**32.** $\begin{pmatrix} 2 & 6 \\ 1 & 3 \end{pmatrix}$

33. $\begin{pmatrix} 3 & 2 & 6 \\ 1 & 1 & 2 \\ 2 & 2 & 5 \end{pmatrix}$ 　　**34.** $\begin{pmatrix} 1 & -1 & 1 \\ 2 & -3 & 2 \\ -4 & 6 & 1 \end{pmatrix}$

Section 12.4

In Exercises 35–38, use matrix inverses to solve the system.

35. $x - 2y + 3z = 4$
$2x + y - 4z = 3$
$-3x + 4y - z = -2$

36. $2x - y - 2z + 2u = 0$
$x + 3y - 2z + u = 0$
$-x + 4y + 2z - 3u = 0$
$x + y + z + u = 0$

37.
$$x \quad\quad + 2z + 6w = 2$$
$$3x + 4y - 2z - \quad w = 0$$
$$5x \quad\quad + 2z - 5w = -4$$
$$4x - 4y + 2z + 3w = 1$$

38.
$$2x + \quad y + 2z + \quad u \quad\quad = 2$$
$$x + 3y - 4z - 2u + 2v = -2$$
$$2x + 3y + 5z - 4u + \quad v = 1$$
$$x \quad\quad - 2z \quad\quad + 4v = 4$$
$$2x \quad\quad + 6z \quad\quad - 5v = 0$$

39. Find the equation of the parabola passing through the points $(-3, 52)$, $(2, 17)$, $(8, 305)$.

40. The table shows the number of hours spent per person per year on home video games. Find a quadratic equation that contains this data, with $x = 6$ corresponding to 1996.

Year	1996	2000	2004
Hours	25	76	161

[*Source: Statistical Abstract of the U.S.: 2001*]

Section 12.5

In Exercises 41–46, solve the system.

41.
$$x^2 - y = 0$$
$$y - 2x = 3$$

42.
$$x^2 + y^2 = 25$$
$$x^2 + y = 19$$

43.
$$x^2 + y^2 = 16$$
$$x + y = 2$$

44.
$$6x^2 + 4xy + 3y^2 = 36$$
$$x^2 - xy + y^2 = 9$$

45.
$$x^3 + y^3 = 26$$
$$x^2 + y = 6$$

46.
$$x^2 - 3xy + 2y^2 - y + x = 0$$
$$5x^2 - 10xy + 5y^2 = 8$$

Section 12.5.A

47. Minimize and maximize $F(x, y) = 30x + 10y$

$$\text{subject to } \begin{cases} 2x + 2y \geq 4 \\ x + y \leq 36 \\ 2x + y \leq 10 \\ x \geq 0 \\ y \geq 0 \end{cases}$$

48. Minimize and maximize $F(x, y) = 8x + 7y$

$$\text{subject to } \begin{cases} 4x + 3y \geq 24 \\ 3x + 4y \geq 8 \\ x \geq 0 \\ y \geq 0 \end{cases}$$

49. Animal feed is to be made from corn and soybeans. One pound of corn has 30 units of fat and 20 units of protein, and one pound of soybeans has 20 units of fat and 40 units of protein. What is the minimum total weight of feed to supply a daily requirement of 2800 units of fat and 2200 units of protein?

50. A home supply store sells two models of dehumidifiers, standard and deluxe. The standard model comes in a 10-ft³ box and weighs 10 lb, and the deluxe model comes in a 9-ft³ box and weighs 12 lb. The store's delivery van has 240 ft³ of space and can hold a maximum of 440 lb. If the store makes a profit of $20 on the standard model and $30 on the deluxe model, how many boxes of each model can the van carry to maximize the profit for each load?

37. $x = -\dfrac{1}{85}$, $y = -\dfrac{14}{85}$, $z = -\dfrac{21}{34}$, $w = \dfrac{46}{85}$

38. $x = \dfrac{130}{109}$, $y = -\dfrac{124}{109}$, $z = \dfrac{35}{109}$, $u = \dfrac{12}{109}$, $v = \dfrac{94}{109}$

39. $y = 5x^2 - 2x + 1$

40. $y = -1.0625x^2 \quad 4.25x + 12.25$

41. $x = 3$, $y = 9$ or $x = -1$, $y = 1$

42. $x = -\sqrt{21}$, $y = -2$ or $x = \sqrt{21}$, $y = -2$ or $x = -4$, $y = 3$ or $x = 4$, $y = 3$

43. $x = 1 - \sqrt{7}$, $y = 1 + \sqrt{7}$ or $x = 1 + \sqrt{7}$, $y = 1 - \sqrt{7}$

44. $x = 0.3851$, $y = 3.1739$ or $x = 2.6296$, $y = -0.6381$ or $x = -2.6296$, $y = 0.6381$ or $x = -0.3851$, $y = -3.1739$

45. $x = -1.692$, $y = 3.136$ or $x = 1.812$, $y = 2.717$

46. $x = -1.5298$, $y = -0.2649$ or $x = 3.5298$ $y = 2.2649$

47. maximum is 150 at $(5, 0)$; minimum is 20 at $(0, 2)$

48. minimum is 48 at $(6, 0)$; no maximum

49. minimum of 97.5 pounds at $(85, 12.5)$

50. 27 deluxe models and 0 standard models

Partial Fractions

Teaching Notes

Observe that for every other section in this chapter, a capital letter was used to represent a *matrix*. Here, it is used to represent a *number*.

Example Notes

In **Example 1,** make sure students understand how to get the first equation in the Solution.

$$\frac{(x+2)(x-3)}{1} \cdot \frac{7x-6}{x^2-x-6}$$

$$= \frac{(x+2)(x-3)}{1} \cdot \left(\frac{A}{x+2} + \frac{B}{x-3}\right)$$

$$7x - 6 = A(x-3) + B(x+2)$$

Show students that in **Example 2** we are solving the following equation:

$$\frac{2x^2+15x+10}{x^3+3x^2-4} = \frac{A}{x-1} + \frac{B}{x+2} + \frac{C}{(x+2)^2}$$

ADDITIONAL EXAMPLES

Example 1

Find the constants A and B such that $\frac{5x-5}{x^2-3x-4} = \frac{A}{x+1} + \frac{B}{x-4}$.

The common denominator is $x^2 - 3x - 4 = (x+1)(x-4)$. Multiply both sides by the common denominator.

$$5x - 5 = A(x-4) + B(x+1)$$
$$= Ax - 4A + Bx + B$$
$$= Ax + Bx - 4A + B$$
$$= (A+B)x + (-4A+B)$$

Therefore,

$$A + B = 5$$
$$-4A + B = -5$$

Solve the system by getting the augmented matrix into reduced row-echelon form:

```
[A]
    [[1   1  5 ]
     [-4  1  -5]]
rref([A])
        [[1 0 2]
         [0 1 3]]
```

Solving the system yields $A = 2$ and $B = 3$.

Therefore, $\frac{5x-5}{x^2-3x-4} = \frac{2}{x+1} + \frac{3}{x-4}$.

In calculus it is sometimes necessary to write a complicated rational expression as the sum of simpler ones. Two forms of rational expressions whose sum is a rational expression will be introduced in this section: denominators with nonrepeated factors and those with repeated factors.

Example 1   Denominators with Nonrepeated Factors

Find the constants A and B such that $\frac{7x-6}{x^2-x-6} = \frac{A}{x+2} + \frac{B}{x-3}$.

Solution

The denominators on the right side of the equation are linear factors of the denominator on the left side. Multiply both sides of the equation by the common denominator, $(x+2)(x-3)$, and collect like terms.

$$7x - 6 = A(x-3) + B(x+2)$$
$$= Ax - 3A + Bx + 2B$$
$$= Ax + Bx - 3A + 2B$$
$$= (A+B)x + (-3A+2B)$$

Because the polynomials on the left and right sides of the last equation are equal, their coefficients must be equal term by term.

$$A + B = 7 \qquad \text{\textit{Coefficient of x}}$$
$$-3A + 2B = -6 \qquad \text{\textit{Constant term}}$$

The two equations above form a system of equations with unknowns A and B. Solving the system yields $A = 4$ and $B = 3$. Therefore,

$$\frac{7x-6}{x^2-x-6} = \frac{4}{x+2} + \frac{3}{x-3}$$

◼

```
[A]
    [[1   1  7 ]
     [-3  2  -6]]
rref([A])
        [[1 0 4]
         [0 1 3]]
```

Figure 12.C-1

In Example 1, $\frac{4}{x+2} + \frac{3}{x-3}$ is called the **partial fraction decomposition,** or simply the partial fractions, of $\frac{7x-6}{x^2-x-6}$.

Nonrepeated Linear Factor Denominators

If the denominator of a rational expression can be expressed as a product of nonrepeated linear factors, each term of the decomposition has the form $\frac{A}{x-a}$.

838

When a factor of the denominator is repeated, every power less than or equal to the multiplicity of the factor must be considered.

Example 2 Repeated Linear Factors

Find the partial fraction decomposition of $\dfrac{2x^2 + 15x + 10}{x^3 + 3x^2 - 4}$.

Solution

The denominator can be factored into $(x - 1)(x + 2)^2$, as shown in Figure 12.C-2. Because $(x + 2)^2$ is a repeated factor, both $x + 2$ and $(x + 2)^2$ must be considered as possible denominators of the decomposition. The process of finding the numerators is the same as that shown in Example 1.

Multiply both sides of the equation by the common denominator, $(x - 1)(x + 2)^2$, and collect like terms on the right side.

$$
\begin{aligned}
2x^2 + 15x + 10 &= A(x + 2)^2 + B(x - 1)(x + 2) + C(x - 1) \\
&= A(x^2 + 4x + 4) + B(x^2 + x - 2) + C(x - 1) \\
&= Ax^2 + 4Ax + 4A + Bx^2 + Bx - 2B + Cx - C \\
&= (A + B)x^2 + (4A + B + C)x + (4A - 2B - C)
\end{aligned}
$$

The polynomials on the left and right sides are equal, so coefficients must be equal term by term.

$$
\begin{array}{lll}
A + B & = 2 & \textit{Coefficient of } x^2 \\
4A + B + C & = 15 & \textit{Coefficient of } x \\
4A - 2B - C & = 10 & \textit{Constant term}
\end{array}
$$

This is a system of equations with unknowns A, B, and C. The augmented matrix of the system and an equivalent reduced row echelon form matrix are shown in Figure 12.C-3.

Therefore, $A = 3$, $B = -1$, $C = 4$, and

$$
\frac{2x^2 + 15x + 10}{(x - 1)(x + 2)^2} = \frac{3}{x - 1} + \frac{-1}{x + 2} + \frac{4}{(x + 2)^2}
$$

∎

In theory, any polynomial with real coefficients can be written as a product of real linear factors and real quadratic factors. (See Section 4.2.)

Nonrepeated Quadratic Factor Denominators

> If the denominator contains a nonrepeated quadratic factor, then the decomposition will contain a term of the form $\dfrac{Ax + B}{ax^2 + bx + c}$, where $ax^2 + bx + c$ is irreducible over the set of real numbers.

Like repeated linear factors, if an irreducible quadratic factor is repeated, every power less than or equal to the multiplicity of the factor must be considered. The numerator of all quadratic factors has the form $Ax + B$.

839

Figure 12.C-2

Figure 12.C-3

ADDITIONAL EXAMPLES

Example 2

Find the partial fraction decomposition of $\dfrac{5x^2 + 3x + 1}{x^3 - 3x - 2}$.

The denominator can be factored into $(x - 2)(x + 1)^2$ as shown by the graph of $y = x^3 - 3x - 2$ below.

Because $(x + 1)^2$ represents a repeated factor, both $x + 1$ and $(x + 1)^2$ must be used as denominators.

Find constants A, B, and C such that

$$
\begin{aligned}
&\frac{5x^2 + 3x + 1}{x^3 - 3x - 2} \\
&= \frac{A}{x - 2} + \frac{B}{x + 1} + \frac{C}{(x + 1)^2}.
\end{aligned}
$$

Multiply both sides of the equation by the common denominator $(x - 2)(x + 1)^2$.

$$
\begin{aligned}
&5x^2 + 3x + 1 \\
&= A(x + 1)^2 + B(x - 2)(x + 1) + \\
&\qquad\qquad\qquad\qquad C(x - 2) \\
&= A(x^2 + 2x + 1) + \\
&\qquad B(x^2 - x - 2) + C(x - 2) \\
&= Ax^2 + 2Ax + A + \\
&\qquad Bx^2 - Bx - 2B + Cx - 2C \\
&= (A + B)x^2 + (2A - B + C)x + \\
&\qquad\qquad\qquad (A - 2B - 2C)
\end{aligned}
$$

Therefore,

$$
\begin{array}{lll}
A + B & = 5 \\
2A - B + C & = 3 \\
A - 2B - 2C & = 1
\end{array}
$$

Solve the system.

The solution of the system is $A = 3$, $B = 2$, and $C = -1$.

Partial fraction decomposition:

$$
\begin{aligned}
&\frac{5x^2 + 3x + 1}{x^3 - 3x - 2} \\
&= \frac{3}{x - 2} + \frac{2}{x + 1} + \frac{-1}{(x + 1)^2}
\end{aligned}
$$

can do calculus 839

Example Notes

Point out that $Bx + C$ in **Example 3** corresponds to $Ax + B$ in the box at the bottom of page 839.

In **Example 3**, have students show that $x^2 + 2x + 2$ is the other factor of $x^3 + 6x^2 + 10x + 8$ by using synthetic division (Section 4.1).

$$\begin{array}{r|rrrr} -4 & 1 & 6 & 10 & 8 \\ & & -4 & -8 & -8 \\ \hline & 1 & 2 & 2 & 0 \end{array}$$

ADDITIONAL EXAMPLES

Example 3

Find the partial fraction decomposition of $\dfrac{x - 3}{x^3 + 7x^2 + 13x + 15}$.

The denominator has the nonrepeated linear factor $x + 5$, as shown by the graph of $y = x^3 + 7x^2 + 13x + 15$ below, and the nonrepeated quadratic factor $x^2 + 2x + 3$, found by using synthetic division.

Find constants A, B, and C such that

$$\frac{x - 3}{x^3 + 7x^2 + 13x + 15}$$

$$= \frac{A}{x + 5} + \frac{Bx + C}{x^2 + 2x + 3}$$

Multiply both sides of the equation by the common denominator $(x + 5)(x^2 + 2x + 3)$.

$$x - 3 = A(x^2 + 2x + 3) +$$
$$(Bx + C)(x + 5)$$
$$= Ax^2 + 2Ax + 3A +$$
$$Bx^2 + Cx + 5Bx + 5C$$
$$= (A + B)x^2 +$$
$$(2A + 5B + C)x + (3A + 5C)$$

Therefore,

$$\begin{aligned} A + B &= 0 \\ 2A + 5B + C &= 1 \\ 3A + 5C &= -3 \end{aligned}$$

Solve the system.

Figure 12.C-4

Figure 12.C-5

$$\begin{array}{r} x - 1 \\ x^2 + x - 2 \overline{\smash{\big)}\, x^3 + 0x^2 - x + 3} \\ \underline{x^3 + x^2 - 2x} \\ -x^2 + x + 3 \\ \underline{-x^2 - x + 2} \\ 2x + 1 \end{array}$$

840

Example 3   Nonrepeated Quadratic Factor

Find the partial fraction decomposition of $\dfrac{x - 2}{x^3 + 6x^2 + 10x + 8}$.

Solution

The denominator has the nonrepeated linear factor $x + 4$, as shown in Figure 12.C-4, and the nonrepeated quadratic factor $x^2 + 2x + 2$ found by using synthetic division. Thus, the partial fraction decomposition has the form $\dfrac{x - 2}{x^3 + 6x^2 + 10x + 8} = \dfrac{A}{x + 4} + \dfrac{Bx + C}{x^2 + 2x + 2}$.

Multiplying both sides of the equation by the common denominator, $(x + 4)(x^2 + 2x + 2)$, and collecting like terms yields

$$\begin{aligned} x - 2 &= A(x^2 + 2x + 2) + (Bx + C)(x + 4) \\ &= Ax^2 + 2Ax + 2A + Bx^2 + Cx + 4Bx + 4C \\ &= (A + B)x^2 + (2A + 4B + C)x + (2A + 4C) \end{aligned}$$

Because there is no x^2 term in the original rational expression, the corresponding coefficient must be 0. Therefore,

$$\begin{aligned} A + B &= 0 & \text{\textit{Coefficient of } } x^2 \\ 2A + 4B + C &= 1 & \text{\textit{Coefficient of } } x \\ 2A + 4C &= -2 & \text{\textit{Constant term}} \end{aligned}$$

The solution of the system is $A = -\dfrac{3}{5}$, $B = \dfrac{3}{5}$, and $C = -\dfrac{1}{5}$, as shown in Figure 12.C-5.

$$\frac{x - 2}{x^3 + 6x^2 + 10x + 8} = \frac{-\dfrac{3}{5}}{x + 4} + \frac{\dfrac{3}{5}x - \dfrac{1}{5}}{x^2 + 2x + 2} = \frac{1}{5}\left(\frac{-3}{x + 4} + \frac{3x - 1}{x^2 + 2x + 2}\right)$$ ∎

All the rational expressions in the previous examples have been proper fractions, which means the degree of the numerator was less than the degree of the denominator. If the rational expression is improper, then divide the numerator by the denominator and decompose the remainder that is a proper fraction.

Example 4   Decomposing an Improper Rational Expression

Find the partial fraction decomposition of $\dfrac{x^3 - x + 3}{x^2 + x - 2}$.

Solution

The rational expression is an improper fraction because the degree of the numerator is greater than the degree of the denominator. Therefore, divide the numerator by the denominator (shown in the margin) and write the remainder as a fraction of the divisor.

The solution of the system is
$A = -\dfrac{4}{9}$, $B = \dfrac{4}{9}$, and $C = -\dfrac{1}{3}$.

Partial fraction decomposition:

$$\frac{x - 3}{x^3 + 7x^2 + 13x + 15}$$

$$= \frac{-\dfrac{4}{9}}{x + 5} + \frac{\dfrac{4}{9}x - \dfrac{1}{3}}{x^2 + 2x + 3}$$

$$= \frac{1}{9}\left(\frac{-4}{x + 5} + \frac{4x - 3}{x^2 + 2x + 3}\right)$$

$$\frac{x^3 - x + 3}{x^2 + x - 2} = x - 1 + \frac{2x + 1}{x^2 + x - 2}$$

Now decompose $\frac{2x + 1}{x^2 + x - 2}$ into $\frac{A}{x + 2} + \frac{B}{x - 1}$ by using the procedure discussed in Example 1.

$$2x + 1 = A(x - 1) + B(x + 2)$$
$$= Ax - A + Bx + 2B$$
$$= (A + B)x + (-A + 2B)$$

$$A + B = 2$$
$$-A + 2B = 1$$

As shown in Figure 12.C-6, $A = 1$ and $B = 1$.

$$\frac{x^3 - x + 3}{x^2 + x - 2} = x - 1 + \frac{1}{x + 2} + \frac{1}{x - 1}$$

[A]
```
      [[1   1 2]
       [-1  2 1]]
rref(Ans)
      [[1  0 1]
       [0  1 1]]
```

Figure 12.C-6

When the denominator contains a power of a linear or a quadratic factor, every integral power of that factor must be taken into consideration when finding partial fractions, as outlined below.

Decomposition into Partial Fractions

1. **Divide numerator by denominator if the fraction is improper, and find partial fractions of the remainder.**

2. **Factor the denominator into factors of the form $(px + q)^m$ and $(ax^2 + bx + c)^n$, where $ax^2 + bx + c$ is irreducible over the set of real numbers.**

3. **For each linear factor of the form $(px + q)^m$, the partial fraction must include the following sum:**
$$\frac{A_1}{px + q} + \frac{A_2}{(px + q)^2} + \cdots + \frac{A_m}{(px + q)^m}$$

4. **For each quadratic factor of the form $(ax^2 + bx + c)^n$, the partial fraction must include the following sum:**
$$\frac{B_1x + C_1}{ax^2 + bx + c} + \frac{B_2x + C_2}{(ax^2 + bx + c)^2} + \cdots + \frac{B_nx + C_n}{(ax^2 + bx + c)^n}$$

Exercises

In Exercises 1–7, find the partial fraction decomposition of each expression.

1. $\dfrac{x}{x^2 + 3x + 2}$

2. $\dfrac{1}{x^2 - 1}$

3. $\dfrac{2x + 1}{x^3 - 4x^2 - 3x + 18}$

4. $\dfrac{x^2 - x - 21}{2x^3 - x^2 + 8x - 4}$

5. $\dfrac{5x^2 + 1}{x^3 + 1}$

6. $\dfrac{x - 2}{x^3 + 6x^2 + 10x + 8}$

7. $\dfrac{2x^3 - 4x^2 - x - 3}{x^2 - 2x - 3}$

841

Exercises

ANSWERS

1. $\dfrac{-1}{x + 1} + \dfrac{2}{x + 2}$

2. $\dfrac{-\frac{1}{2}}{x + 1} + \dfrac{\frac{1}{2}}{x - 1}$

3. $\dfrac{-\frac{3}{25}}{x + 2} + \dfrac{\frac{3}{25}}{x - 3} + \dfrac{\frac{7}{5}}{(x - 3)^2}$

4. $\dfrac{-5}{2x - 1} + \dfrac{3x + 1}{x^2 + 4}$

5. $\dfrac{2}{x + 1} + \dfrac{3x - 1}{x^2 - x + 1}$

6. $\dfrac{-\frac{3}{5}}{x + 4} + \dfrac{\frac{3}{5}x - \frac{1}{5}}{x^2 + 2x + 2}$

7. $2x + \dfrac{2}{x + 1} + \dfrac{3}{x - 3}$

CHAPTER 13

Statistics and Probability

In this chapter, students will learn various ways of displaying statistical information and how to find various measures of center and spread, such as mean, median, mode, and standard deviation. They will study probability, probability density functions, and binomial experiments. Finally, they will study normal distributions, which are built on many of the topics in this chapter.

CHAPTER

13 Statistics and Probability

What are the odds?

Suppose a dart player can hit the bulls-eye about 25% of the time. How likely is the event shown above? The number of bulls-eyes in a given number of tries can be described as a *binomial experiment*, and the probabilities can be easily calculated. See Exercises 5–8 in Section 13.4.A.

842

Chapter Outline

Interdependence of Sections

13.1 → 13.2
      ↘
        13.5
      ↗
13.3 → 13.4

S tatistics and probability are essential tools for understanding the modern world. Both involve studying a group of individuals or objects, known as a **population,** and a subset of the population, known as a **sample.** In statistics, information from a sample is used to draw conclusions about the population. In probability, information from the population is used to draw conclusions about a sample.

 Basic Statistics

Objectives

- Identify data types
- Create displays of qualitative and quantitative data
- Describe the shape of a distribution

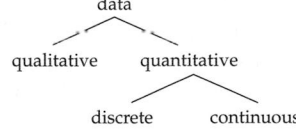

Statistics is used to make sense of information, or **data,** by using techniques to organize, summarize, and draw conclusions from the data. Most statistical data is gathered by taking a **random sample** of the population. In a random sample, all members of the population and all groups of members of a given size have an equal chance of being in the sample.

Data can be divided into two types: **qualitative** and **quantitative.** Quantitative data is numerical, such as "the number of hours spent studying each night" or "the distance from home to school." Qualitative data can be divided into categories, such as "liberal," "moderate," "conservative," or "blue eyes," "brown eyes."

Quantitative data can be further classified as either **discrete** or **continuous.** If the difference between two values can be arbitrarily small, the data is continuous. If there is a minimum increment between two different values, the data is discrete.

843

Real-World Application

Samples are used rather than entire populations in most statistical studies. Exercise 3 on page 851 describes how a sample of families is selected to determine the number of pets in a typical American family. The population represented by the sample consists of all American families. As described in the Math Background below, the sample in Exercise 3 is called a stratified sample.

COMMON ERROR ALERT

Some students might think that a **population** in statistics must be a group of people. Stress that in statistics, a population is a group of individuals or objects. For example, a population may be all the trees in a particular national park, or all the microwave ovens produced in a factory.

 ### Math Background

There are various methods of choosing a sample. A **random sample** is often best, but two other sampling methods are *systematic* and *stratified.* In systematic sampling, members are chosen according to a rule or formula (example: survey every tenth customer). In stratified sampling, members are chosen at random from randomly chosen subgroups (see Exercise 3 for an example). Both systematic and stratified samples can be representative of a population, if done under appropriate circumstances.

If for any reason a sample is not representative of the population, it is called a *biased sample.*

Teaching Notes

Students might benefit from a discussion of the **NOTE** on this page about continuous data and discrete data.

Height is continuous because the difference between any two values can be arbitrarily small. To explain, show that for any two heights, no matter how close in value, a height between them can be found (one way is to find the average). Ask students to find a height between each pair of heights given below. (Sample answers are shown.)

61 in. and 62 in.; 61.5 in.
61.3 in. and 61.4 in.; 61.35 in.
61.346 in. and 61.347 in.; 61.3465 in.

Now point out that height is usually rounded to the nearest inch for practical purposes, and therefore can be treated as discrete.

Money amounts, although actually discrete, are often treated as continuous. For example, suppose the amount in dollars earned by an employee is given by the function $f(x) = 12.65x$, where x is number of hours worked. This function would usually be graphed as a continuous, unbroken line, even though actual amounts earned must differ by at least $0.01.

Example Notes

In **Example 2,** have students find the sum of all the relative frequencies. Point out that if the frequency table is correct, the sum of the relative frequencies is 1, or 100%. For this example, $0.2 + 0.4 + 0.13 + 0.27 = 1$; however, there are cases in which the sum of the relative frequencies may be slightly less than (or greater than) 1, or 100%, due to rounding.

In **Example 3,** point out that the first step in creating a bar graph is to create a frequency table. If the frequency table had not already been created in Example 2, it would have to be done here.

Example 1 Types of Data

In each example, identify the data as either qualitative or quantitative. If quantitative, then identify it as discrete or continuous.

a. the height of each player on a basketball team
b. the style of shoes worn by each student in a classroom
c. the number of people in each household in the United States

Solution

a. The data is quantitative, because each value can be written as a number, such as 68.32 inches. It is continuous, because there is no minimum difference between two values; two players could have heights 68.32 inches and 68.33 inches, or 68.323 inches and 68.324 inches.

b. The data is qualitative, since it can be grouped into categories, such as tennis shoes, sandals, and high heels.

c. The data is quantitative, because each value is a number. It is discrete, because there is a minimum difference of 1 between two different values; two households could have 4 and 5 members, but not 4 and 4.1 members. ■

NOTE Continuous data is sometimes treated as discrete, and vice versa. For example, heights are usually rounded to the nearest inch, so there is a minimum difference of 1 inch between measurements. In the discrete case, for amounts of money, the minimum increment of $0.01 is so small that the data can often be treated as continuous.

Data Displays

One of the most important uses of statistics is to organize data and display it visually. Most displays show the data values or categories and some measure of how often each value or category occurs.

The number of times a value occurs is known as the **frequency** of that value. If the frequency is divided by the total number of responses, the result is the **relative frequency** of that value, which can be expressed as a fraction, a decimal, or a percent. A **frequency table** displays the categories with frequencies, relative frequencies, or both.

Example 2 Frequency Table

A group of 30 people were asked their favorite flavor of ice cream. Of these, 6 chose vanilla, 12 chose chocolate, 4 chose butter pecan, and 8 chose mint chocolate chip. Create a table with frequencies and relative frequencies for each flavor.

Solution

Flavor	Frequency	Relative frequency
Vanilla	6	$\frac{6}{30} = \frac{1}{5} = 0.2 = 20\%$
Chocolate	12	$\frac{12}{30} = \frac{2}{5} = 0.4 = 40\%$
Butter pecan	4	$\frac{4}{30} = \frac{2}{15} \approx 0.13 \approx 13\%$
Mint chocolate chip	8	$\frac{8}{30} = \frac{4}{15} \approx 0.27 \approx 27\%$

Displaying Qualitative Data

Two common ways of displaying qualitative data are *bar graphs* and *pie charts*. A **bar graph** displays the categories on a horizontal axis and the frequencies or relative frequencies on a vertical axis, or vice versa. The height or length of each bar shows the frequency of the value. All bars should have the same width.

Example 3 Bar Graph

Use the data in the frequency table from Example 2 to make a bar graph.

Solution

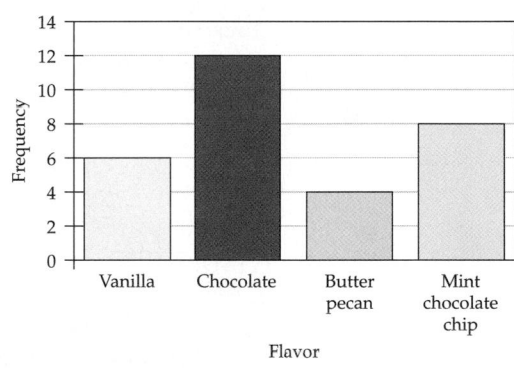

A **pie chart** displays the categories and their relative frequencies. The "pie" is divided into sectors whose central angle measure equals the fraction of 360° represented by the relative frequency of each category.

The central angle measure of the sector that represents a category with relative frequency r is $r \cdot 360°$.

Teaching Notes

As pointed out on page 845, two common ways of displaying qualitative data are bar graphs and pie charts. Examples 3 and 4 show the same qualitative data, which is divided into flavor categories.

Note that **Example 3** shows *frequencies*, and **Example 4** shows *relative frequencies*. Point out that both displays allow comparisons of categories. For example, you can see in both displays that mint chocolate chip was chosen more than vanilla, but less than chocolate. However, the pie chart in Example 4 shows important information that is not shown in the Example 3 bar graph. The pie chart gives a quick visual idea of how each category compares to the whole. For instance, you can see at a glance in Example 4 that mint chocolate chip represents approximately $\frac{1}{4}$ of all responses.

Math Background

An **outlier** is defined on page 847 as a data value that is far removed from the rest of the data. Students will learn later how to use quartiles and interquartile range to determine whether a data value is an outlier (see bottom of page 860).

COMMON ERROR ALERT

Students may confuse *skewed right* and *skewed left.* Suggest that they think of the following:

- A distribution is skewed right if it has a long tail to the right.
- A distribution is skewed left if it has a long tail to the left.

Example 4   Pie Chart

Create a pie chart using the data in the frequency table from Example 2. Label each sector with the category and its relative frequency.

Solution

The central angle measures of the categories of the sectors are:

Vanilla: $0.2 \cdot 360° = 72°$

Chocolate: $0.4 \cdot 360° = 144°$

Butter pecan: $0.13 \cdot 360° \approx 47°$

Mint chocolate chip: $0.27 \cdot 360° \approx 97°$

NOTE Before statistical analysis, numerical data is usually arranged in order from the lowest value to the highest value. An arrangement of numerical data is called a **distribution.**

Displaying Quantitative Data

Numerical data can also be displayed in a variety of ways to indicate each value and its frequency. The shape of a smooth curve over the display indicates characteristics of the data values. The most common distribution shapes are shown below.

Common Distribution Shapes

Uniform: All the data values have approximately the same frequency.

Symmetric: The right and left sides of the distribution have frequencies that are mirror images of each other.

Skewed right: The right side of the distribution has much lower frequencies than the left.

Skewed left: The left side of the distribution has much lower frequencies than the right.

NOTE If an outlier is caused by an error in measurement or other type of error, it is usually removed from the data set before further analysis. In general, an outlier should not be removed without justification.

An **outlier** is a data value that is far removed from the rest of the data, which usually indicates that the value needs investigation. Outliers may be caused by errors or by unusual members of the population.

Example 5 The Shape of Data

From the four given shapes, choose the best distribution for the data.

a. the last digit of each number in the phone book

b. the salaries of the employees of a corporation

c. the age of retirement for all people in the U.S.

d. the heights of all adult women in the U.S.

Solution

a. The last four digits of a phone number are assigned randomly, so all digits have about the same frequency. The distribution is uniform.

b. In a typical corporation, most employees earn relatively low salaries while a few executives make high salaries. The distribution is skewed right.

c. Few people make enough money to retire young, and most people retire in their 60's or later. The distribution is skewed left.

d. The average height of an adult woman is at the middle of the distribution, which is symmetric with respect to this value. ∎

Two common displays of quantitative data are the *stem plot* and the *histogram*. A **stem plot** is commonly used to display small data sets.

The data below shows 31 test scores for a class exam:

32, 67, 89, 90, 87, 72, 75, 88, 95, 83, 97, 72, 85, 93, 79, 63
70, 87, 74, 86, 98, 100, 97, 85, 77, 88, 92, 94, 81, 76, 64

The stem plot for the class test data is shown below:

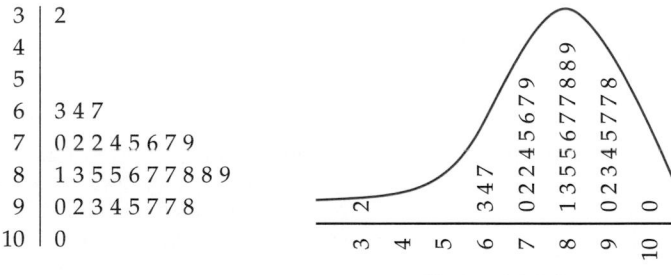

Figure 13.1-1

The entry 3 | 2 represents the score 32. Similarly, the row 6 | 3 4 7 represents the scores 63, 64, and 67. There are 31 scores represented.

ADDITIONAL EXAMPLES

Example 4

Create a pie chart using the data in the frequency table from **Additional Example 2.** Label each sector with the category and its relative frequency. The central angle measures of the categories of the sectors are:

A: $0.16 \cdot 360° \approx 58°$
B: $0.44 \cdot 360° \approx 158°$
C: $0.28 \cdot 360° \approx 101°$
D: $0.12 \cdot 360° \approx 43°$

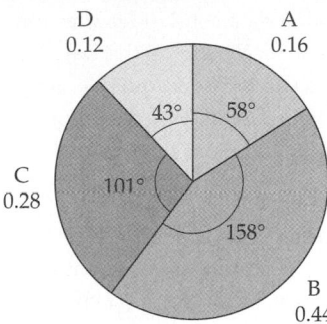

Example 5

From the four Common Distribution Shapes, choose the best distribution for the data.

a. the ages of people in an elementary school during a typical school day (including faculty and staff)   skewed right

b. the age at death for all people in the United States   skewed left

c. the day of the week of all students' birthdays in a school, where Sunday = 1, Monday = 2, and so on   uniform

d. the IQ scores of all the men living in the United States   symmetric

Math Background

A stem plot is sometimes called a stem-and-leaf plot. In the 1970's, American statistician John Tukey (1915–2000) used stem-and-leaf plots and box-and-whisker plots (box plots, pages 861–862) in his work on Exploratory Data Analysis (EDA). EDA is an approach for data analysis that relies heavily on statistical graphics, such as stem-and-leaf plots and box-and-whisker plots, to examine the structure of data before developing a model for the data.

Teaching Notes

The steps in **Creating a Stem Plot** will result in a configuration such as the one in the Solution of **Example 6,** that is:

```
0|2334555667778889
1|001223455889
2|1145889
3|00000
```

By "turning it on its side," we get Figure 13.1-2.

Figure 13.1-1 (page 847) and Figure 13.1-3 (page 849) are displays for the same data set. Notice that the stem plot actually shows the data. The histogram shows the frequency of the data in the intervals, but does not show the actual data. Both graphs show how the data is distributed.

A **histogram** (such as Figure 13.1-3) is commonly used to display quantitative data, whereas a bar graph (such as in Example 3, page 845) is used to display qualitative data. The width of a bar in a histogram (class interval) is based on the range of the data. The width of a bar in a bar graph is arbitrary. The height of a bar in a histogram is the frequency of data values in a class of values. The height of a bar in a bar graph is the frequency for a single data "value," or category.

For **Creating a Histogram,** the first step discusses forming the class intervals. Note that for a given data set, there is *not usually one correct* way to do this; often, there is more than one way that makes sense.

COMMON ERROR ALERT

For a **histogram,** some students may form classes such as 30–40 and 40–50. Point out that this is incorrect because these classes overlap; they both contain 40. The classes used in Figure 13.1-3 are 30–39, 40–49, and so on.

Note that the score of 32 is far below the remaining data and so it could be an outlier in this distribution. It may be the score of a student who didn't study for the test. However, it is most likely not an error in measurement, so the value cannot be removed from the data set. The distribution is skewed left (Figure 13.1-1).

Creating a Stem Plot

To create a stem plot:

1. Choose the leading digit or digits to be the *stems.* Arrange the stems vertically from lowest to highest value from top to bottom.

2. The last digit is the *leaf.* Record a leaf for each data value on the same horizontal line as its corresponding stem. Arrange the leaves from lowest to highest value from left to right.

3. Provide a key that indicates the total number of data elements and an interpretation of one stem and leaf indicating appropriate units.

Example 6   Stem Plot

A company uses a 3-minute recorded phone message to advertise its product. A random sample of 40 calls is used to determine how much of the message was heard before the listener hung up. Create a stem plot of the data below and discuss its shape.

> 2.4, 0.2, 3.0, 2.8, 1.5, 1.9, 0.7, 1.0, 2.5, 1.3,
> 0.8, 2.1, 3.0, 0.4, 1.2, 3.0, 1.1, 0.3, 0.7, 1.8,
> 0.3, 1.0, 2.1, 3.0, 2.9, 0.5, 1.4, 3.0, 2.8, 1.2,
> 0.5, 0.5, 1.5, 0.9, 1.8, 0.6, 0.6, 0.7, 0.8, 0.8

Solution

```
0|2334555667778889     Key: 2|8 represents a time of
1|001223455889              2.8 minutes.
2|1145889                   40 times are represented.
3|00000
```

The distribution is skewed right, as shown in Figure 13.1-2. The values on the right side have lower frequencies than the values on the left. Notice that the distribution is cut off at 3, because no phone calls last longer than 3 minutes, the length of the entire message.

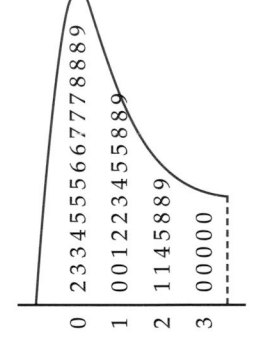

Figure 13.1-2

A **histogram,** which can be thought of as a bar graph with no gap between adjacent bars, is often used with large sets of quantitative data. First, the data is divided into a convenient number of intervals of equal width. The frequencies (or relative frequencies) of the data in the intervals are the heights of the rectangles. For example, the test scores given on page 847 can be represented by the histogram in Figure 13.1-3.

Figure 13.1-3

Here, the test scores have been divided into 10-point intervals, 0 through 9, 10 through 19, and so on. The histogram indicates, for example, that there are no scores between 50 and 59, eight scores between 70 and 79, and one score of 100. Each bar on the graph has width 10, so the **class interval** is said to be 10.

Creating a Histogram

Technology Tip

Most graphing calculators will produce histograms. Check the Xmin, Xmax, and Xscl to make sure the class intervals are relevant to the data. If you do not know how to create a histogram with a graphing calculator, refer to the Technology Appendix.

To create a histogram:

1. **Divide the range of the data into classes of equal width, so that each data value is in exactly one class. The width of these intervals is called the *class interval*.**

2. **Draw a horizontal axis and indicate the first value in each class interval.**

3. **Draw a vertical scale and label it with either frequencies or relative frequencies.**

4. **Draw rectangles with a width equal to the class interval and height equal to the frequency of the data within each interval.**

Example 7 Histogram

Create a histogram of the following scores.

580, 490, 590, 390, 410, 370, 470, 540, 490, 660, 500, 670, 430, 670, 490, 720, 580, 680, 590, 480, 560, 480, 400, 440, 560, 540, 330, 490, 540, 540, 520, 650, 540, 600, 630, 580, 540, 500, 270, 600, 390, 540, 300, 350, 600, 540, 510, 410, 370, 390, 160, 500, 740, 510, 540, 560, 510, 430, 440, 590, 560, 510, 600, 460, 450, 510, 420, 430, 560, 680, 610, 600, 600, 520, 480, 490, 320, 450, 500, 490

Class	60–69	70–79	80–89	90–99
Frequency	3	6	13	16

Class	100–109	110–119	120–129	130–139
Frequency	19	11	8	4

Example 6

A supermarket manager wants to know how long customers are waiting in the express lane. A random sample of 35 customers is taken, recording wait time in minutes. Create a stem plot of the data below and discuss its shape.

3.1, 1.1, 3.1, 3.2, 0.5, 3.2, 3.4, 2.8, 3.2, 3.4, 3.1, 2.3, 1.7, 2.1, 1.5, 2.7, 2.3, 3.6, 2.7, 2.5, 0.1, 2.4, 1.8, 3.3, 3.9, 1.6, 2.6, 3.9, 1.5, 3.8, 3.0, 2.3, 2.5, 2.4, 3.1

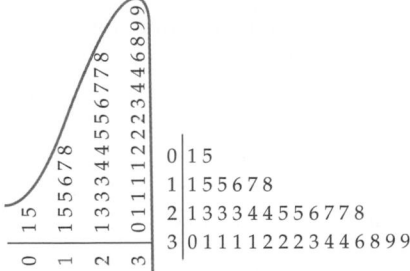

0	1 5
1	1 5 5 6 7 8
2	1 3 3 3 4 4 5 5 6 7 7 8
3	0 1 1 1 1 2 2 2 3 4 4 6 8 9 9

Key: 2|3 represents a time of 2.3 minutes. 35 times are represented.

The distribution is skewed left. The values on the left side have lower frequencies than the values on the right.

Example 7

Create a histogram of the following IQ scores.

75, 65, 121, 100, 101, 89, 114, 63, 123, 127, 100, 96, 116, 109, 92, 131, 134, 105, 108, 117, 90, 89, 101, 101, 87, 98, 104, 130, 104, 120, 73, 89, 115, 108, 108, 97, 78, 127, 117, 104, 123, 97, 116, 99, 100, 99, 119, 117, 79, 85, 87, 94, 101, 118, 106, 128, 90, 88, 84, 130, 94, 75, 94, 95, 91, 68, 81, 107, 70, 110, 98, 101, 80, 122, 85, 81, 102, 99, 116, 83

The smallest value is 63 and the largest value is 134, so the range is 71. A convenient choice for classes is 60–69, 70–79, 80–89, and so on—a class interval of 10. The frequency table is shown.

For the frequency table on this page, some students might think that the first class interval is 199 − 150 = 49, which is incorrect. The class interval includes both of the extreme values, so 150–199 *inclusive* includes 150, 199, and all values in between. One way to find the correct class interval is to subtract a lower class limit from the next lower class limit: 200 − 150 = 50.

Example Notes

Point out that a histogram does not show individual data values. For instance, by looking at Figure 13.1-4 for **Example 7,** you cannot determine whether 246 is a data value, or 584 is a data value, or any other particular number is a data value.

Remind students that if an endpoint of a class is an actual data value, it is represented in the adjacent bar to the right. For example, if 250 is a data value, it is included in the bar on the right side of 250.

In Figure 13.1-5, as the class interval (Xscl) increases, the number of classes decreases. Point out that Ymax is different in each graph. If the same value for Ymax had been used in each graph, the bar heights would be different. Ask students to estimate the height of the tallest bar in each histogram.   possible answers, left to right: 10, 20, 32

The best representation of the data is the graph in the middle. The graph on the left is cluttered with too much detail. The graph on the right does not have enough detail.

Math Background

To construct a histogram, you have to decide how many classes to use. The number of classes is usually between 5 and 15, inclusive. Using too many or too few classes can distort the presentation of the data.

Solution

The smallest value is 160 and the largest value is 740, so the range of the data is 580 points. A convenient choice for the classes is 150 through 199, 200 through 249, 250 through 299, and so on—a class interval of 50 points. The frequency table below shows how many data values are in each class.

Class	150–199	200–249	250–299	300–349	350–399	400–449	450–499	500–549	550–599	600–649	650–699	700–749
Frequency	1	0	1	3	6	9	13	20	11	8	6	2

The histogram is shown in Figure 13.1-4. The shape is approximately symmetric.

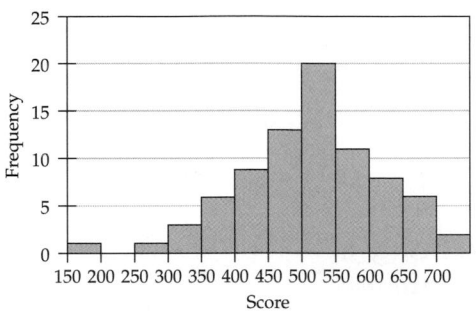

Figure 13.1-4

Figure 13.1-5 shows three histograms of the data in Example 7, created on a calculator. Notice that the choice of the scale on the *x*-axis determines the width of the class intervals. Which do you think is the best representation of the data?

Xscl = 25

Xscl = 50

Xscl = 100

Figure 13.1-5

Remember that it is more important to be able to interpret a distribution than it is to simply produce the display. Technology can easily produce a histogram, but the purpose of the display is to help interpret the data.

Exercises 13.1

ANSWERS

1. the entire student body; 50 students from each grade level

2. 10 shipments of 1000 cartons of eggs; every 50th carton in each shipment

3. all American families; 50 families in each of 10 counties in each of 5 states

4. all wild elephants; 400 elephants

5. qualitative; qualitative; quantitative and discrete; quantitative and continuous

10. Since a histogram records continuous lengths and a stem plot records discrete lengths, a histogram is more appropriate.

Exercises 13.1

In Exercises 1–4, identify the population and the sample.

1. There are three schedule options for classes at a high school: 90-minute classes every other day for a year, 90-minute classes every day for a semester, or 45-minute classes every day for a year. Out of 1200 students, 50 students from each grade level are chosen at random and asked their preference.

2. The manager of a convenience store wishes to determine how many cartons of eggs are damaged in shipment and delivery. For ten shipments of 1000 cartons of eggs, she examines every 50th carton to see how many cartons contain cracked eggs.

3. A survey is taken to determine the number of pets in the typical American family. A computer is used to randomly select 5 states, then 10 counties in each state, then 50 families in each county. Each of these families is asked how many pets they own.

4. A biologist tranquilizes 400 wild elephants and measures the lengths of their tusks to determine their ages.

Use the descriptions in Exercises 1–4 to answer Exercises 5–10.

5. Determine whether the data in each description is qualitative or quantitative. If the data is quantitative, determine whether it is continuous or discrete.

6. Describe two ways in which the data from Exercise 1 could be displayed.
   bar graph or pie chart
7. How large is the sample in Exercise 2?
   200 cartons
8. Describe two ways in which the data from Exercise 2 could be displayed.
   bar graph or pie chart
9. How large is the sample in Exercise 3?
   2500 families
10. Which would be more appropriate to display the data from Exercise 4: a stem plot or a histogram? Explain your reasoning.

The following frequency table gives the preferred type of exercise for 50 women at a local gym.

Exercise	Frequency	Relative frequency
Aerobics	20	**40%**
Kickboxing	8	**16%**
Tai chi	8	**16%**
Stationary bike	14	**28%**

11. Complete the table to show the relative frequency for each category.

12. Create a bar graph for the data with the vertical axis showing the frequencies.

13. Create a bar graph with the vertical axis showing the relative frequencies.

14. Create a pie chart for the data.

For Exercises 15–18, suppose 25 people are asked their favorite color. The results are: 6 red, 8 blue, 5 purple, 4 green, 1 yellow, and 1 orange.

15. Create a frequency table for the given data. Include relative frequencies.

16. Create a bar graph for the data with the vertical axis showing the frequencies.

17. Create a bar graph with the vertical axis showing the relative frequencies.

18. Create a pie chart for the data.

In Exercises 19–24, state whether the shape of the distribution is best described as uniform, symmetric, skewed right, or skewed left.

19. The scores of a national standardized test
   symmetric
20. The age at which students get a driver's license
   skewed right

21.
   skewed left

12.

13.

14.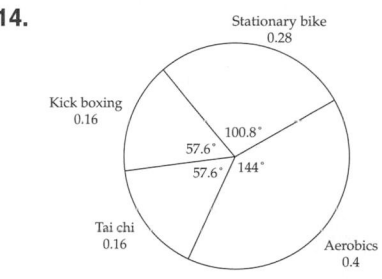

15.

Color	Frequency	Relative frequency
red	6	24%
blue	8	32%
purple	5	20%
green	4	16%
yellow	1	4%
orange	1	4%

16.

17.

18.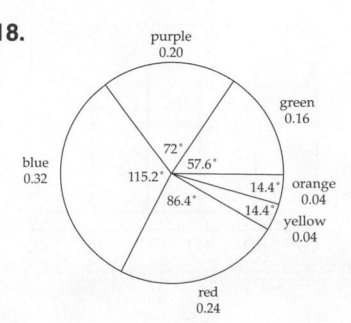

25.
```
2 | 3 4 7 9
3 | 3 3 6 8
4 | 1 1 2 3 5 6 7 7 9
5 | 1 4
6 | 7
```
Key: 2|3 represents 23

26.
```
0 | 4 5 7 8
1 | 1 1 3 4 4 5 6 8
2 | 0 6 6
3 |
4 |
5 | 6
```
Key: 0|8 represents 0.8

27.
```
5  | 6
6  |
7  | 0 2 6 8 9
8  | 1 2 3 4 5 6 6 6 7 8
9  | 0 1 1 2 3 8 9
10 | 0 0
```
Key: 5|6 represents 56

28.
```
0 | 6 8
1 | 2 2 5 7 8
2 | 2 5 5 7 8
3 | 0 2 5 5 7
4 | 0 0 2 2 5 5 8
5 | 5 5
6 | 0 5
7 | 5
8 |
9 | 0
```
Key: 1|2 represents 12

29. yes, 90; it is quite a distance from the rest of the data

30.
```
0  | 7 9
1  | 4 4 7
2  | 0 0 5 9 9
3  | 1 2 5 7
4  | 0 0 3 6 6 8 8
5  | 2 2 5
6  | 3 3 9
7  | 5
8  | 6
9  |
10 | 4
```
Key: 1|4 represents 14

31. The shape of the fall semester data is basically symmetric; the summer semester data is skewed right. It may be that summer students live closer to campus.

22.
```
1 | 0 2 5 6 8
2 | 3 5 6 9
3 | 1 4 7 8 8    uniform
4 | 2 3 5 5
5 | 4 6 7 9
```

23. The position of the second hand of a clock at 100 randomly chosen times in a 12-hour period **uniform**

24.
```
8  | 2
9  | 3 5
10 | 2 5 6 8    symmetric
11 | 0 1 4
12 | 7
```

In Exercises 25–28, create a stem plot for the given data.

25. 23, 45, 38, 41, 24, 67, 42, 46, 51, 33, 43, 47, 54, 49, 47, 36, 27, 33, 41, 29

26. 1.8, 2.0, 1.4, 5.6, 1.1, 2.6, 0.8, 1.5, 1.4, 2.6, 0.7, 1.6, 0.4, 1.1, 0.5, 1.3

27. 98, 87, 100, 86, 92, 78, 56, 100, 90, 88, 93, 99, 76, 83, 86, 91, 72, 85, 79, 81, 82, 91, 86, 70, 84

During summer semester, a community college surveyed its students to determine travel time to campus. A random sample of 30 students gave the following times in minutes:

12	25	48	45	6	90
15	55	75	60	27	30
32	40	18	35	22	8
42	65	17	25	35	40
12	28	42	37	45	55

During fall semester, the survey was repeated. The new times in minutes are:

63	52	43	48	32	14
46	40	29	20	75	48
9	25	40	20	46	37
35	31	69	86	63	17
104	7	52	55	29	14

28. Create a stem plot of the summer semester data.

29. Does the data set of the summer semester times contain any outliers? Explain.

30. Create a stem plot of the fall semester data.

31. Compare the shape of the two data sets. Which type of distribution do you think best describes these data sets? What might explain the differences in these data sets?

32. Create a histogram with a class interval of 10 for the data below.
68, 84, 59, 72, 62, 76, 61, 63, 68, 56, 70, 79, 54, 65, 66, 71, 70, 58, 63, 68, 84, 63, 53, 68, 63, 76, 66, 66, 70, 72, 88, 68, 75, 63, 76, 58, 86, 65, 66, 73, 53, 76, 59, 81, 59, 65, 67, 73, 62, 75, 89, 58

33. Create a histogram for the following ACT scores. Be sure to choose an appropriate class interval.
14, 25, 15, 18, 17, 11, 15, 10, 25, 6, 11, 4, 12, 24, 19, 14, 20, 13, 23, 19, 13, 20, 14, 24, 10, 18, 30, 22, 16, 26, 10, 23, 22, 19, 23, 21, 16, 18, 18, 20, 25, 14, 19, 7, 16, 18, 31, 14, 7, 10, 16, 13, 18, 10

34. Create a histogram with a class interval of 5 for the data in the stem plot below.

```
5 | 7 8 8 9 9 9
6 | 0 0 0 1 1 2 2 2 3 3 4 5 7 9
7 | 0 1 2 2 4 5 5 6 7 7 8
8 | 0 0 0 1 1
```

35. *Critical Thinking* How does the shape of the histogram you created in Exercise 34 compare to the shape of the data in the stem plot? Which do you think is a better representation of the data, and why?

possible answer: the histogram is not as symmetric as the stem plot. The histogram more accurately shows the distribution of the data due to the smaller class interval of 5.

32.

33.

13.2 Measures of Center and Spread

Objectives

- Calculate measures of center
- Calculate measures of spread
- Choose the most appropriate measure of center or spread
- Create and interpret a box plot

While the shape of a stem plot or a histogram gives a picture of a data set, numerical measures are more precise and can be calculated easily (using technology for large data sets). These measures help to further summarize and interpret data. Two quantities are commonly used to describe a data set: a measure of the "center" of the data and a measure of how spread out the data is.

Measures of Center

A sample may contain hundreds, or even thousands of data values. This information is often summarized by one value that represents the center, or central tendency, of the data. The three most common measures of center are *mean*, *median*, and *mode*.

Mean

The **mean** is more commonly known as the *average*. The mean is calculated by adding all values and dividing by the total number of values. Recall from Chapter 1, the symbol Σ is used to indicate the sum of a set of values.

$$\text{mean:} \qquad \overline{x} = \frac{x_1 + x_2 + \ldots + x_n}{n} = \frac{\Sigma x_i}{n}$$

The mean is represented by $\overline{x}$, read as "x bar." The x is used to represent the data variable, while each data value is represented as x_1, x_2, x_3, and so on. The sum is divided by n, the number of data elements.

> ### Example 1   Mean Number of Accidents
>
> A six-month study of a busy intersection reports the number of accidents per month as 3, 8, 5, 6, 6, 10. Find the mean number of accidents per month at the site.
>
> ### Solution
>
> $$x_1 = 3, x_2 = 8, x_3 = 5, x_4 = 6, x_5 = 6, x_6 = 10$$
> $$\overline{x} = \frac{\Sigma x_i}{n} = \frac{3 + 8 + 5 + 6 + 6 + 10}{6} = \frac{38}{6} \approx 6.3$$
>
> The data shows an average of 6.3 accidents per month at the given intersection. ∎

One problem with the mean as a measure of center is that it may be distorted by extreme values, as shown in the following example.

34.

13.2 Measures of Center and Spread

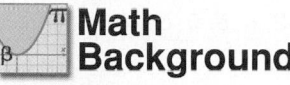

Math Background

The mean is also called the *average* or the *arithmetic* mean. Two other means are the *harmonic mean* and the *geometric mean*.

$$\text{harmonic mean} = \frac{n}{\Sigma \frac{1}{x_i}}$$

$$\text{geometric mean} = \sqrt[n]{x_1 \cdot x_2 \cdot \ldots \cdot x_n}$$

where n is the number of data elements and x_1, x_2, x_n, and x_i represent data values.

The harmonic mean is used to find average rates, e.g., the average speed of a car over a certain trip. The geometric mean is used to find average changes, e.g., the average annual change of a price.

Teaching Notes

Students may recall summation notation from their study of sequences (pages 25–28 and pages 61–64). Point out that the expression for **mean** could be written

$$\frac{\sum_{i=1}^{n} x_i}{n}, \text{ but that } \frac{\Sigma x_i}{n} \text{ is simpler and}$$

has the same meaning.

ADDITIONAL EXAMPLES

Example 1

The number of property crimes per month reported in a local suburb for the last seven months was 4, 5, 3, 6, 11, 8, 8. Find the mean number of property crimes reported per month.

$$\overline{x} = \frac{\Sigma x_i}{n} = \frac{4 + 5 + 3 + 6 + 11 + 8 + 8}{6}$$

$$= \frac{45}{7} \approx 6.4$$

The data shows an average of 6.4 property crimes reported per month.

Students sometimes forget to write a data set in order to determine a median. For instance, if you ask them to determine the median of the data in Example 1, they might calculate as follows.

data: 3, 8, 5, 6, 6, 10

$$\text{median} = \frac{5 + 6}{2} = 5.5$$

Remind them that the data must be ordered. The correct median is 6.

Teaching Notes

The **median** of a data set may or may not be one of the data values. Use the following activity to investigate this fact for the cases where n is even and n is odd.

Ask for the median of each data set below.

2, 5, 6, 11, 20   6
1, 5, 8, 8, 14, 20   8
1, 5, 8, 10, 14, 20   9

First, note that in every case, the number of data items less than the median equals the number of data items greater than the median. This fact is true for all data sets.

Next, ask students to describe when the median is one of the data values, using *even* and *odd*.
For an odd number of data values, the median is one of the data values.
For an even number of data values, the median is sometimes one of the data values.

Now focus on the case of an even number of data values. Have students use the expressions $\frac{n}{2}$ and $\frac{n}{2} + 1$ to describe when the median is one of the data values.
For an ordered data set of n values where n is even, the median is one of the data values when the values in the $\frac{n}{2}$ and $\frac{n}{2} + 1$ positions are equal.

To summarize all three measures of spread, make sure students understand that:
• The *mean* may or may not be an actual data value.
• The *median* may or may not be an actual data value.
• The *mode* is always an actual data value.

Example 2   Mean Home Prices

In the real-estate section of the Sunday paper, the following houses were listed:

2-bedroom fixer-upper:	$98,000
2-bedroom ranch:	$136,700
3-bedroom colonial:	$210,000
3-bedroom contemporary:	$289,900
4-bedroom contemporary:	$315,500
8-bedroom mansion:	$2,456,500

Find the mean price, and discuss how well it represents the center of the data.

Solution

$$\bar{x} = \frac{\Sigma x_i}{n} = \frac{98,000 + 136,700 + 210,000 + 289,900 + 315,500 + 2,456,500}{6}$$

$$= \frac{3,506,600}{6} \approx 584,433.33$$

In the data set, 5 out of the 6 values are below $350,000, but the mean is over $550,000, so the mean does not seem to be a very good representation of the center of the data set. Notice that the value $2,456,500 is more than twice the rest of the data combined. Thus, it has a very large effect on the mean, "pulling" it away from the other values. ∎

Median

As shown in Example 2, the mean is not always the best way to represent the center of a distribution. If the distribution is skewed or contains extreme values, the **median,** or middle value of the data set is often used. To determine the median, the data must be in order from smallest to largest (or largest to smallest).

If the number of values is odd, then one number will be the middle number, as shown below.

$$3, 4, 7, \textcircled{8}, 9, 11, 15$$

There are 7 values, and the median, which is in the 4th position, is 8. Notice that three values are less than the median and three values are greater than the median.

If the number of values is even, there are two middle numbers, as shown below.

$$17, 22, \textcircled{24, 30,} 35, 40$$

There are 6 values, and the median is the average of the middle numbers, which are in the 3rd and 4th positions. So the median is $\frac{24 + 30}{2} = 27$.

Notice that three values are less than the median and three values are greater than the median.

Median

> If $x_1, x_2, x_3 \ldots x_n$ are ordered from smallest to largest, then the median is the middle entry when n is odd and the average of the two middle entries when n is even.
>
> $$\text{median} = \begin{cases} \text{for } n \text{ odd, the value in the } \dfrac{n+1}{2} \text{ position} \\ \text{for } n \text{ even, the average of the values in} \\ \text{the } \dfrac{n}{2} \text{ and } \dfrac{n}{2} + 1 \text{ positions} \end{cases}$$

The median is said to be a more *resistant* measure of center than the mean, since it is less affected by a skewed distribution or extreme values in a data set.

Example 3   Median Home Prices

Find the median of the data in Example 2, and discuss how well it represents the center of the data.

Solution

The data is already in order from smallest to largest, with $n = 6$.

98,000	136,700	210,000	289,900	315,500	2,456,500
1st position	2nd position	3rd position	4th position	5th position	6th position

The median is the average of the values in positions $\dfrac{n}{2} = 3$ and $\dfrac{n}{2} + 1 = 4$, which are 210,000 and 289,900, so

$$\text{median} = \frac{210,000 + 289,900}{2} = \frac{499,900}{2} = 249,950$$

A price of \$249,950 is much more representative of the houses in this listing. The most expensive house does not have the same strong effect that it had in the calculation of the mean. ∎

Mode

The **mode** is the data value with the highest frequency. It is most often used for qualitative data, for which the mean and median are undefined. The mode can be thought of as the "most typical" value in the data set.

> **NOTE** If every value in a data set occurs the same number of times, there is no mode. If two or more scores have equal frequencies that are higher than those of all other values, the data set is called *bimodal* (two modes), *trimodal* (three modes), or *multimodal*.

ADDITIONAL EXAMPLES

Example 2

The 2003 population (to the nearest thousand) of selected western states is shown below:

Idaho	1,366,000
Nevada	2,241,000
Utah	2,351,000
Oregon	3,560,000
Washington	6,131,000
California	35,484,000

Find the mean population, and discuss how well it represents the center of the data.

$$\bar{x} = \frac{\sum x_i}{n} = \frac{51,133,000}{6}$$

$$\approx 8,522,000$$

In the data set, 5 out of the 6 values are below the mean. The mean is not a good representation of the center of the data set.

Example 3

Find the median of the data in **Additional Example 2,** and discuss how well it represents the center of the data.

The data is already in order from smallest to largest. The median is the average of the 3rd and 4th values of the ordered data set:

$$\text{median} = \frac{2,351,000 + 3,560,000}{6}$$

$$= 2,955,500$$

The median is a much better representation of the center.

Teaching Notes

Point out to students that although the mode is most often used for qualitative data, it is also used for quantitative data. In **Example 1,** the mode is 6.

You may want to give students some examples to illustrate the **NOTE** on the bottom of the page:
no mode: 2, 2, 3, 3, 5, 5
bimodal (2 and 6): 2, 2, 2, 4, 4, 6, 6, 6
trimodal (2, 4 and 6): 2, 2, 4, 4, 5, 6, 6
multimodal (2, 4, 5, and 6):
  2, 2, 4, 4, 5, 5, 6, 6, 7, 8

Some students might say that the mode of the data in **Example 4** is 12. Remind them that 12 is a frequency. That is, 12 people chose red as their favorite color. The mode is red.

ADDITIONAL EXAMPLES

Example 4

Find the mode of the data represented by the bar graph below.

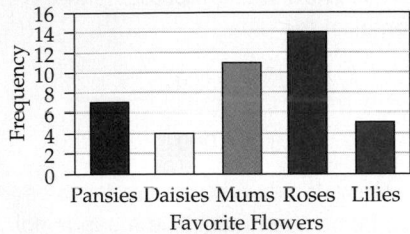

roses

Teaching Notes

Ask students to use the information in the bulleted statements under **Mean, Median, and Mode of a Distribution** to describe the skew of the data in **Example 1**. Have them justify their answers.

In Example 1, the data is skewed right because the mean is to the right of the median (mean ≈ 6.3, median = 6).

Math Background

Pearson's index of skewness *I* is sometimes used to determine if a distribution is skewed, or how much it is skewed.

$$I = \frac{3(\text{mean} - \text{median})}{\text{standard deviation}}$$

If $|I| \geq 1$, the distribution is considered to be skewed (or *significantly* skewed).

Example 4   Mode of a Data Set

Find the mode of the data represented by the bar graph below.

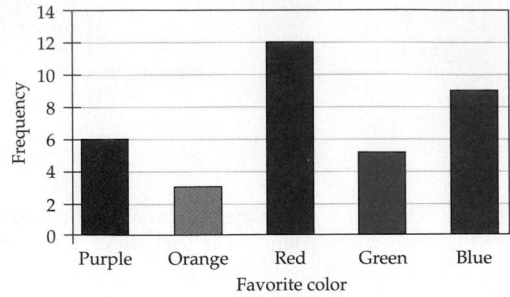

Solution

The height of each bar represents the frequency, so the mode is the category with the tallest bar, which is red. ∎

Mean, Median, and Mode of a Distribution

Recall the shapes of symmetric, skewed left, and skewed right distributions.

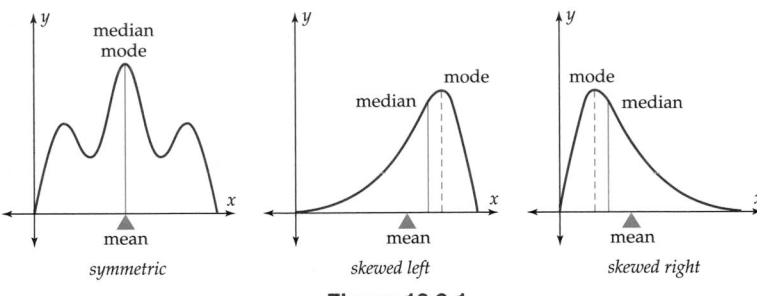

Figure 13.2-1

The mean is the balance point of a distribution. Notice that on a skewed distribution, the mean moves toward the tail to balance out the "weight" of the outlying data. The median divides the area under the distribution into 2 equal areas. The mode is the highest point on the distribution.

- **If a distribution is symmetric, then the mean and median are equal.**
- **If a distribution is skewed left, then the mean is to the left of the median.**
- **If a distribution is skewed right, then the mean is to the right of the median.**

Teaching Notes

Solution to the **Calculator Exploration**:

mean ≈ 81.44

median = 86

Technology Tip

If necessary, see the Technology Appendix to learn how to find the mean and median of a data set.

Calculator Exploration

Use the statistics functions of your calculator to find the mean and median of the data represented by the following stem plot.

```
 3 | 2
 4 | 8                 Key:  6|7 represents a score of 67 points.
 5 | 2 3                     43 scores are represented.
 6 | 3 5 6 7 9
 7 | 0 2 2 4 5 6 7 9
 8 | 1 3 5 5 6 7 7 8 8 9
 9 | 0 2 2 3 4 5 5 5 5 7 7 8
10 | 0 0 0 0
```

Measures of Spread

Finding the shape and center of a data set still gives an incomplete picture of the data. The following stem plots show three data sets with a symmetric distribution and center 105.

```
 6 |            6 | 5          6 |
 7 |            7 |            7 |
 8 | 5          8 | 1 9        8 |
 9 | 1 9        9 |            9 | 1 5
10 | 1 5 9     10 | 1 5 9     10 | 1 3 5 7 9
11 | 1 9       11 |           11 | 5 9
12 | 5         12 | 1 9       12 |
13 |           13 |           13 |
14 |           14 | 5         14 |
```

The data has a different spread in each stem plot. The spread of the data, or **variability,** is an important characteristic of a data set. The second plot has the most variability because the data is very spread out, while the third has the least because the date is clustered very near the center. The three most common measures of spread are the *standard deviation,* the *range,* and the *interquartile range.*

Standard Deviation

The **standard deviation** of a data set is the most common measure of variability. It is best used if the data is symmetric about a mean. Standard deviation measures the average distance of a data element from the mean.

The **deviation** of a data value x_i from the mean $\bar{x}$ is the difference, $x_i - \bar{x}$. Consider the following data set:

$$2, 5, 7, 8, 10$$

The mean of the data is $\dfrac{2 + 5 + 7 + 8 + 10}{5} = 6.4$. The points are shown with their deviations on a number line in Figure 13.2-2.

The three data sets under **Measures of Spread** all have 105 as both median and mean (same center), and they all have the same shape (symmetric distribution). However, the **spread,** or **variability,** is very different in the three data sets. Students can confirm that the second set has the most variability and the third set has the least variability by plotting the data sets on number lines as shown at the bottom of this page.

Point out that it is not always convenient or possible to plot the numbers in a data set on a number line. Therefore, we use *measures of spread* to describe the variability of data. Three measures of spread are discussed here and on following pages—standard deviation, range, and interquartile range.

Math Background

The average of the deviations shown in Figure 13.2-2 is 0 because the sum of the deviations is 0.

The sum of the deviations from the mean will be 0 in any data set, as shown below.

$$\sum (x_i - \bar{x}) = \sum x_i - \sum \bar{x}$$
$$= \sum x_i - n\bar{x}$$
$$= \sum x_i - n\left(\frac{\sum x_i}{n}\right)$$
$$= \sum x_i - \sum x_i = 0$$

There is another measure of variability (not often used) called the *mean absolute deviation.*

$$\text{mean absolute deviation} = \frac{\sum |x_i - \bar{x}|}{n}$$

For the same data set, the mean absolute deviation is:

$$\frac{|-4.4| + |-1.4| + |0.6| + |1.6| + |3.6|}{5}$$
$$= \frac{11.6}{5} = 2.32$$

This gives the average distance that a data element is from the mean.

An alternate formula for calculating the population standard deviation is

$$\sigma = \sqrt{\left(\frac{\sum x_i^2}{n}\right) - \left(\frac{\sum x_i}{n}\right)^2}.$$

Using the statistics from the left screen shot in Figure 13.2-3 (that is, $\sum x = 945$, $\sum x^2 = 104{,}121$, and $n = 9$):

$$\sigma = \sqrt{\left(\frac{104{,}121}{9}\right) - \left(\frac{945}{9}\right)^2}$$
$$= \sqrt{11{,}569 - 11{,}025} = \sqrt{544}$$
$$= 23.32380758$$

Teaching Notes

Note that if the **Standard Deviation** formulas are applied to both a **population** and a **sample** of that population, then the values of $\bar{x}$, n, and x_i are likely to be different in the two applications.

NOTE The *distance* from data value x_i to the mean $\bar{x}$ is the absolute value of the deviation.

Figure 13.2-2

The average of the deviations is $\dfrac{-4.4 + (-1.4) + 0.6 + 1.6 + 3.6}{5} = 0$, because the positive and negative values cancel each other out. To avoid this, each deviation is squared, then the average is found. This quantity is called the **variance.** The square root of the variance is the **standard deviation,** denoted by the Greek letter σ (sigma).

For the data set {2, 5, 7, 8, 10}, first square each deviation.

$$\{(-4.4)^2, (1.4)^2, 0.6^2, 1.6^2, 3.6^2\} = \{19.36, 1.96, 0.36, 2.56, 12.96\}$$

Average the squared deviations to find the variance, σ^2:

$$\sigma^2 = \frac{19.36 + 1.96 + 0.36 + 2.56 + 12.96}{5} = 7.44$$

Take the square root of the variance to find the standard deviation:

$$\sigma = \sqrt{7.44} \approx 2.73$$

Population versus Sample If data is taken from a sample instead of the entire population, it is common to divide by $n - 1$ instead of n when averaging the squared deviations. The result is called the **sample standard deviation** and is denoted by s. For large data sets, the sample standard deviation is very close to the population standard deviation.

Standard Deviation

To find the standard deviation of a data set with n values,

1. Subtract each value from the mean to find the deviation.
2. Square each deviation, and find the mean of the squared deviations. If the data is from a sample, divide by $n - 1$ instead of n. The result is called the *variance.*
3. Take the square root of the variance.

These steps are summarized in the following formulas:

Population standard deviation

$$\sigma = \sqrt{\frac{\sum(x_i - \bar{x})^2}{n}}$$

Sample standard deviation

$$s = \sqrt{\frac{\sum(x_i - \bar{x})^2}{n - 1}}$$

Example 5   Standard Deviation

Find the population standard deviation of the data in the first stem plot on page 857 using the formula. Then use a calculator to find the population standard deviations of the data in the other two plots.

Solution

For the first stem plot, $\bar{x} = 105$ and $n = 9$. The following table shows the squared deviations.

x_i	85	91	99	101	105	109	111	119	125
$x_i - \bar{x}$	−20	−14	−6	−4	0	4	6	14	20
$(x_i - \bar{x})^2$	400	196	36	16	0	16	36	196	400

$$\sigma = \sqrt{\frac{400 + 196 + 36 + 16 + 0 + 16 + 36 + 196 + 400}{9}} = \sqrt{\frac{1296}{9}} = 12$$

An informal interpretation is that the average distance from the data values to the mean is 12 units.

The population standard deviations of the data in the second and third stem plots are shown in Figure 13.2-3.

Figure 13.2-3

Notice that the second stem plot, which is the most spread out, has the largest standard deviation, and the third stem plot, which is the most clustered together, has the smallest standard deviation. ∎

Range

The **range** is the difference between the maximum and minimum data values. The main advantage of the range is that it is easy to compute.

Example 6   The Range

Find the range of the data in each stem plot on page 857.

Example 5

Find the population standard deviation of the data in the first stem plot below using the formula. Then use a calculator to find the population standard deviations of the data in the other two plots.

5		5	4	5	
6		6		6	
7		7	1 7	7	4
8	4 7	8		8	1 7
9	1 2 4 6 7	9	1 4 7	9	1 4 7
10	1 4	10		10	1 7
11		11	1 7	11	4
12		12		12	
13		13	4	13	

For the first stem plot, $\bar{x} = 94$ and $n = 9$.

x_i	84	87	91	92	94
$x_i - \bar{x}$	−10	−7	−3	−2	0
$(x_i - \bar{x})^2$	100	49	9	4	0

x_i	96	97	101	104
$x_i - \bar{x}$	2	3	7	10
$(x_i - \bar{x})^2$	4	9	49	100

$$\sigma = \sqrt{\frac{100 + 49 + 9 + 4 + 0 + 4 + 9 + 49 + 100}{9}}$$

$$= \sqrt{\frac{324}{9}} = 6$$

second stem plot:

third stem plot:

Example 6

Find the range of the data in each stem plot of **Additional Example 5**.

first stem plot: $104 - 84 = 20$

second stem plot: $134 - 54 = 80$

third stem plot: $114 - 74 = 40$

Teaching Notes

An outlier was described in Section 13.1 (page 847) as a data value that is far removed from the rest of the data. A numerical method for determining an outlier is given at the bottom of this page. Ask students if they think that $2,456,500 is an outlier in **Example 2,** page 854. The activity below, relating an **outlier,** a **five-number summary,** and a **box plot,** will show that it is an outlier.

Have students use their calculators to get a five-number summary of the data in Example 2.

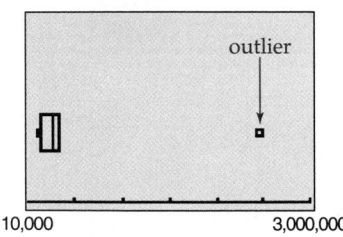

Next, have them find the interquartile range.

$IQR = Q_3 - Q_1 = 315{,}500 - 136{,}700$

$= 178{,}800$

Then, have them show that 2,456,500 is an outlier, using the rule on the bottom of page 860.

$Q_3 + 1.5(IQR) = 315{,}500 +$

$1.5(178{,}800)$

$= 315{,}500 + 268{,}200$

$= 583{,}700$

$2{,}456{,}500 > Q_3 + 1.5(IQR) = 583{,}700$

Lastly, have students construct a box plot with their calculators.

In a similar manner, students can use the data from the **Calculator Exploration** on page 857 to show that 32 is an outlier.

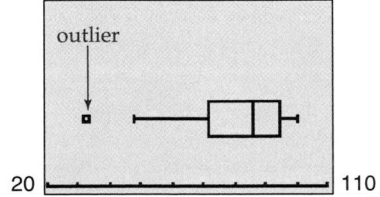

$IQR = Q_3 - Q_1 = 95 - 72 = 23$

$Q_1 - 1.5(IQR) = 72 - (1.5)(23)$

$= 72 - 34.5$

$= 37.5$

$32 < Q_1 - 1.5(IQR) = 37.5$

Solution

The range of the data in the first stem plot is $125 - 85 = 40$.
The range of the data in the second stem plot is $145 - 65 = 80$.
The range of the data in the third stem plot is $119 - 91 = 28$.   ∎

Interquartile Range

Like the mean, the standard deviation and range are strongly affected by extreme values in the data. The **interquartile range** is a measure of variability that is resistant to extreme values, yet gives a good indication of the spread of the data.

Recall that the median is the middle value of the data set. Thus, the median divides the data into two halves, the **lower half** and the **upper half.** The **quartiles** further divide the data into fourths. The **1st quartile,** Q_1, is the median of the lower half. The **3rd quartile,** Q_3, is the median of the upper half. (The median may be considered to be the 2nd quartile.)

Figure 13.2-4 shows the quartiles for n even or n odd.

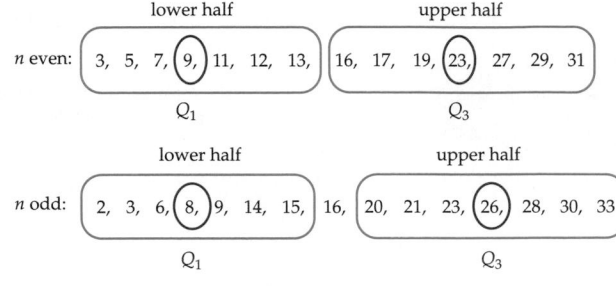

Figure 13.2-4

The **interquartile range** is the difference between the quartiles,

$$IQR = Q_3 - Q_1$$

which represents the spread of the middle 50% of the data.

A value that is less than $Q_1 - 1.5(IQR)$ or greater than $Q_3 + 1.5(IQR)$ is considered an outlier, as shown in Figure 13.2-5.

Figure 13.2-5

Example 7	Interquartile Range

Find the interquartile range of the data in the first stem plot on page 857.

Solution

The quartiles of the data in the first stem plot are shown below.

$$Q_1 = \frac{91 + 99}{2} = 95 \qquad Q_3 = \frac{111 + 119}{2} = 115$$

The interquartile range is $115 - 95 = 20$. ∎

— Calculator Exploration ●—

Use a graphing calculator to find the interquartile range of the data in each of the other two stem plots on page 857.

Five-Number Summary and Box Plots

The **five-number summary** of a data set is the following list:

$$\text{minimum}, Q_1, \text{median}, Q_3, \text{maximum}$$

These values are used to construct a display called a **box plot,** as follows:

1. Construct a number line and locate each value of the five-number summary.

2. Construct a rectangle whose length equals the interquartile range, with a vertical line to indicate the median.

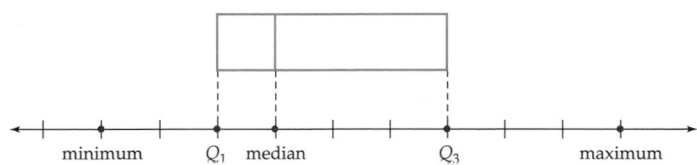

Math Background

Box plots are sometimes called box-and-whisker plots. See Math Background on page 847.

ADDITIONAL EXAMPLES

Example 7

Find the interquartile range of the data in the first stem plot of **Additional Example 5.**

$$Q_1 = \frac{87+91}{2} = 89 \qquad Q_3 = \frac{97+101}{2} = 99$$

interquartile range: $99 - 89 = 10$

Teaching Notes

Solution to the **Calculator Exploration:**

second stem plot:

$$IQR = Q_3 - Q_1 = 125 - 85 = 40$$

third stem plot:

```
1-Var Stats
↑n=9
 minX=91
 Q₁=98
 Med=105
 Q₃=112
 maxX=119
```

$$IQR = Q_3 - Q_1 = 112 - 98 = 14$$

Box plots provide a good method for comparing data sets. In **Example 8** and the **Calculator Exploration** on the next page, students will construct three separate box plots. As they construct those box plots, have them save the corresponding data lists on their calculators. Then, after completing the separate box plots, they can construct those box plots on the same calculator screen and compare them.

ADDITIONAL EXAMPLES

Example 8

Construct a box plot for the data in the first stem plot of **Additional Example 5.**

The five-number summary of the data is 84, 89, 94, 99, 104.

Teaching Notes

Solution to the **Calculator Exploration:**

second stem plot:

third stem plot:

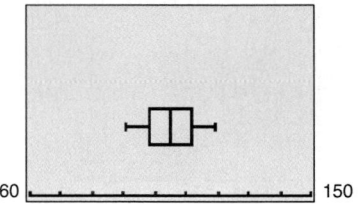

Technology Tip

See the technology appendix, if necessary, for instruction on constructing a box plot using a graphing calculator.

3. Construct horizontal whiskers to the minimum and maximum values.

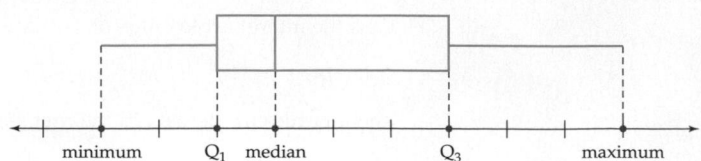

If a data element is an outlier, it may be marked with a ★ or other mark. The whiskers then extend to the farthest value on each side that is not an outlier.

Example 8   Constructing a Box Plot

Construct a box plot for the data in the first stem plot on page 857.

Solution

The five-number summary of the data is 85, 95, 105, 115, 125. The box plot is shown below.

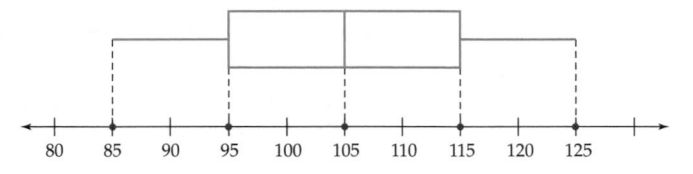

Calculator Exploration ●

Use a graphing calculator to construct a box plot for the data in each of the other two stem plots on page 857.

Exercises 13.2

In Exercises 1–4, find the mean of each data set.

1. 23, 25, 38, 42, 54, 57, 65
   ≈**43.429**
2. 3, 5, 6, 2, 10, 9, 7, 5, 11, 6, 4, 2, 5, 4
   ≈**5.643**
3. 3.6, 7.2, 5.9, 2.8, 21.6, 4.4
   ≈**7.583**
4. 78, 93, 87, 82, 90
   86
5. Find the median of the data set in Exercise 1.
   42

6. Find the median of the data set in Exercise 2.
   5
7. Find the median of the data set in Exercise 3.
   5.15
8. Find the median of the data set in Exercise 4.
   87
9. Find the mean, median, and mode of the following data set:
   13, 13, 12, 6, 14, 9, 11, 19, 13, 9, 7, 16, 11, 12, 15, 12, 11, 12, 14, 9, 11, 13, 17, 13, 13
   mean: 12.2
   median: 12
   mode: 13

In Exercises 10–13, find the mode of the data set represented by each display.

10.

C

11.

53

12. 3

13.

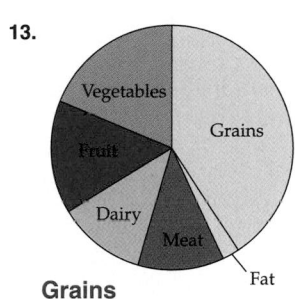

Grains

For each distribution shape, indicate whether the mean is larger, the median is larger, or the mean and median are equal.

14. symmetric **equal**   **15.** skewed left **median**

16. skewed right **mean**   **17.** uniform **equal**

Find the population standard deviation of the following data sets without using a calculator.

18. 8, 9, 10, 11, 12
≈1.414
19. 6, 8, 10, 12, 14
≈2.828
20. 10, 10, 10, 10, 10
0
21. 0, 5, 10, 15, 20
≈7.071

Use a calculator to find the population and sample standard deviations of the following data sets.

22. 3, 6, 3, 5, 7, 8, 2, 6, 3, 6, 8, 4, 8, 2, 6, 9
σ ≈ 2.233; s ≈ 2.306
23. 24, 17, 18, 18, 19, 26, 19, 8, 25, 15, 17, 11, 27, 20
σ ≈ 5.249; s ≈ 5.447

24. 6, 8, 4, 11, 8, 8, 9, 6, 6, 8, 8, 12, 10, 10, 7
σ ≈ 2.048; s ≈ 2.120
25. 50, 72, 86, 92, 86, 77, 57, 80, 93, 74, 53, 69, 65, 57, 73, 60, 66, 94, 81, 81
σ ≈ 13.176; s ≈ 13.518
26. Find the range of the data set in Exercise 22.
7
27. Find the range of the data set in Exercise 23.
19
28. Find the range of the data set in Exercise 24.
8
29. Find the range of the data set in Exercise 25.
44
30. Find the interquartile range of the data set in Exercise 22.
4.5
31. Find the interquartile range of the data set in Exercise 23.
7
32. Find the interquartile range of the data set in Exercise 24.
4
33. Find the interquartile range of the data set in Exercise 25.
21
34. Find the five-number summary of the data set in Exercise 22, and create a box plot for the data.

35. Find the five-number summary of the data set in Exercise 23, and create a box plot for the data.

36. Find the five-number summary of the data set in Exercise 24, and create a box plot for the data.

37. Find the five-number summary of the data set in Exercise 25, and create a box plot for the data.

For Exercises 38–43, the wait times of 30 people in a doctor's office are given below, rounded to the nearest five minutes:

40, 35, 65, 40, 40, 5, 50, 85, 30, 50, 60, 60, 10, 65, 15, 45, 20, 40, 45, 70, 70, 25, 40, 45, 70, 65, 45, 25, 15, 25

38. Construct a histogram of the data. Describe the shape of the data set. Based on the shape, discuss the relative positions of the mean and median.

39. Find the mean and median of the data set.

40. Which measure of central tendency is preferred for this data set? Why?

41. Find the sample standard deviation, range, and interquartile range of the data set.

42. Construct a box-plot of the data.

43. Explain why the sample standard deviation is or is not a good measure of dispersion for this data set.

34. 2, 3, 6, 7.5, 9

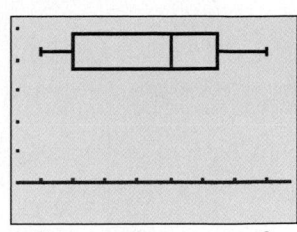

35. 8, 17, 18.5, 24, 27

36. 4, 6, 8, 10, 12

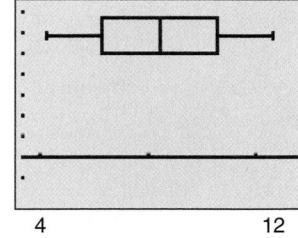

37. 50, 62.5, 73.5, 83.5, 94

38.

Since the histogram is nearly symmetric, the mean and the median should be approximately equal.

39. mean: ≈43.167   median: 42.5

40. Either the mean or median since they are close in value.

41. standard deviation: ≈20.3
range: 80
interquartile range: 35

42.

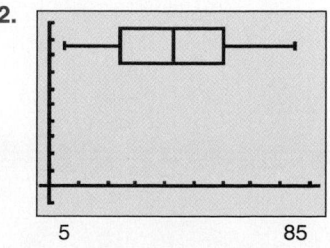

43. The sample standard deviation is a good measure of dispersion because the data set is relatively small.

46.

skewed left

78 · mean · 82 · median

47.

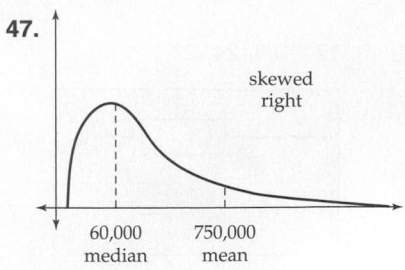

skewed right

60,000 · median · 750,000 · mean

49. The median more accurately describes the "typical" salary, since the outlier of 105,000 has a large effect on the mean.

51. Possible answer:

data	mean	standard deviation
26,28,30,32,34	30	3.162
20,25,30,35,40	30	7.906

52. Possible answer:

data	mean	standard deviation
26,28,30,32,34	30	3.162
46,48,50,52,54	50	3.162

Section 13.3 Basic Probability

Teaching Notes

Emphasize that an **experiment** in probability is not necessarily the same as an experiment in science or in everyday life. In probability, an experiment can be a simple toss of a coin or drawing a marble from a bag.

44. During a baseball game, 9 players had 1 hit each, 3 players had 2 hits each, and 6 players had no hits. Find the mean number of hits per player.
≈0.833

45. A teacher has two sections of the same course. The average on an exam was 94 for one class with 20 students, while the average was 88 for the other class with 30 students. Find the combined average exam score.
90.4

46. The mean score of a class exam was 78, and the median score was 82. Sketch a possible distribution of the scores.

47. Over the last year, 350 lawsuits for punitive damages were settled with a mean settlement of $750,000 and a median settlement of $60,000. Sketch a possible distribution of the settlements.

48. A restaurant employs six chefs with the salaries in dollars shown below:
25,000, 27,000, 35,000, 105,000, 40,000, 45,000
Determine the mean and median salaries.
mean: 46,167   median: 37,500

49. Which measure of center more accurately describes the "typical" salary at the restaurant in Exercise 48?

50. The speed of a computer is primarily determined by a chip in the CPU. A manufacturer tested 12 chips and reported the following speeds in megahertz units:
11.6, 11.9, 12.0, 12.0, 14.0, 15.2, 13.0, 14.3, 13.6, 13.8, 12.8, 12.9

$\sigma \approx 1.067$; $s \approx 1.114$; **The standard deviation is small because the data are clustered rather closely around the mean.**

Find the sample standard deviation and the population standard deviation of the data, and interpret your results.

51. Create two data sets of five numbers each that have the same mean but different standard deviations.

52. Create two data sets of five numbers each that have the same standard deviations but different means.

53. *Critical Thinking* How is the mean of a data set affected if a constant k is added to each value?
It will increase by the value of k.

54. *Critical Thinking* How is the standard deviation of a data set affected if a constant k is added to each value?
It will remain the same.

55. *Critical Thinking* How is the mean of a data set affected if each value is multiplied by a constant k?
It will be multiplied by k.

56. *Critical Thinking* How is the standard deviation of a data set affected if each value is multiplied by a constant k?
It will be multiplied by k.

57. *Critical Thinking* What must be true about a data set in order for the standard deviation to equal 0?
All data values must be the same.

13.3 Basic Probability

Objectives

- Define probability and use properties of probability
- Find the expected value of a random variable
- Use probability density functions to estimate probabilities

Definitions

In the study of probability, an **experiment** is any process that generates one or more observable outcomes. The set of all possible outcomes is called the **sample space** of the experiment. Some examples of experiments and their sample spaces are shown in the following table.

Figure 13.3-1

Experiment	Sample space
tossing a coin	heads and tails, written as {H, T}
rolling a number cube (Figure 13.3-1)	{1, 2, 3, 4, 5, 6}
choosing a name from the phone book	all the names in the phone book
counting the number of fish in a lake	the set of non-negative integers

An **event** is any outcome or set of outcomes in the sample space. For example, in the experiment of rolling a number cube, the set {1, 3, 5} is an event, which can be described as "rolling a 1, 3, or 5," or simply "rolling an odd number."

The **probability** of an event is a number from 0 to 1 (or 0% to 100%) inclusive that indicates how likely the event is to occur.

- A probability of 0 (or 0%) indicates that the event cannot occur.
- A probability of 1 (or 100%) indicates that the event must occur.

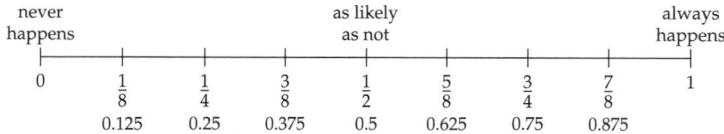

- The sum of the probabilities of all outcomes in the sample space is 1.
- The probability of an event is the sum of the probabilities of the outcomes in the event.

Probability Distributions

The probability of an event E can be described by a function P, where the domain of the function is the sample space and the range of the function is the closed interval [0, 1]. $P(X)$ denotes the probability of the outcome X, and $P(E)$ denotes the probability of the event E.

The rule of the function P can be described by a table, called a **probability distribution.**

Example 1 **Probability Distribution**

Suppose that 100 marbles are placed in a bag; 50 red, 30 blue, 10 yellow, and 10 green. An experiment consists of drawing one marble out of the bag and observing its color.

a. What is the sample space of the experiment?

The meanings of *experiment* and *event* in probability differ from the everyday meanings of these words, and this often leads to errors. Students might call the action of rolling a number cube an event, *which is incorrect.* An action, or process, in probability is an experiment. An event is simply an outcome or set of outcomes. Make the distinction as follows:

"Rolling a number cube" is an experiment.

"Rolling a 1, 3, or 5" is a description of the event {1, 3, 5}.

Teaching Notes

Remind students that the domain of a **Probability Distribution** is a sample space, and therefore need not consist of numbers.

- In **Example 1,** the domain is a set of *colors:* {red, blue, yellow, green}
- In **Example 2** (page 867), the domain is a set of *letters:* {A, S, C, E}
- In **Example 3** (page 868), the domain is the set {winning the game, losing the game}

Example Notes

In **Example 1,** if we assume that the marbles are all the same size and weight, then each of the 100 marbles has an equally likely chance of being selected. This assumption would lead to the probability distribution shown in part **b.**

ADDITIONAL EXAMPLES

Example 1

Suppose a box contains 50 candies. Twenty are strawberry, 15 are grape, 10 are lemon, and 5 are orange. An experiment consists of drawing one candy from the box and observing its flavor.

a. What is the sample space of the experiment?
{strawberry, grape, lemon, orange}

b. Write out a reasonable probability distribution for this experiment, and verify that the sum of the probabilities of the outcomes is 1.

continued from page 865

A reasonable probability distribution is shown below, based on the relative frequency of candies of each flavor.

Flavor of candy	Probability
Strawberry	$\frac{20}{50} = 0.4$
Grape	$\frac{15}{50} = 0.3$
Lemon	$\frac{10}{50} = 0.2$
Orange	$\frac{5}{50} = 0.1$

The sum of the probabilities of the outcomes is $0.4 + 0.3 + 0.2 + 0.1 = 1$.

c. What is the probability that a strawberry or orange candy will be drawn?

$P(\{\text{strawberry, orange}\})$
$= P(\text{strawberry}) + P(\text{orange})$
$= 0.4 + 0.1 = 0.5$

Example 2

An experiment consists of spinning the wheel shown below. The table lists the probability distribution for the experiment.

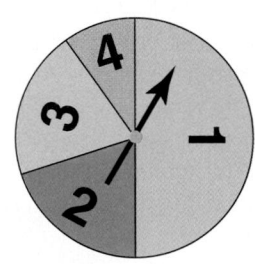

Outcome	Probability
1	0.5
2	0.2
3	0.2
4	0.1

a. Which of the following pairs of events E and F are mutually exclusive?
$E = \{1, 2, 4\}$ $F = \{1, 3\}$
not mutually exclusive;
common outcome, 1
$E = $ (an even number) $F = \{1\}$
mutually exclusive

b. Write out a reasonable probability distribution for this experiment, and verify that the sum of the probabilities of the outcomes is 1.

c. What is the probability that a blue or green marble will be drawn?

Solution

a. The sample space is all possible outcomes:

$$\{\text{red, blue, yellow, green}\}$$

b. A reasonable probability distribution is shown below, which is based on the relative frequency of marbles of each color.

Color of marble	Red	Blue	Yellow	Green
Probability	$\frac{50}{100} = 0.5$	$\frac{30}{100} = 0.3$	$\frac{10}{100} = 0.1$	$\frac{10}{100} = 0.1$

The sum of the probabilities of the outcomes is

$$0.5 + 0.3 + 0.1 + 0.1 = 1$$

c. The event "a blue or green marble will be drawn" can be written as the set of outcomes {blue, green}. The probability of the event is the sum of the probabilities for blue and green.

$$P(\{\text{blue, green}\}) = P(\text{blue}) + P(\text{green}) = 0.3 + 0.1 = 0.4$$

Mutually Exclusive Events

Two events are **mutually exclusive** if they have no outcomes in common. Two mutually exclusive events cannot both occur in the same trial of an experiment. If two events E and F are mutually exclusive, then the probability of the event (E or F) is the sum of the individual probabilities, $P(E) + P(F)$.

The **complement** of an event is the set of all outcomes that are *not* contained in the event. The complement of event E can be thought of as "the event that E does not occur." An event and its complement are always mutually exclusive, and together they contain all the outcomes in the sample space. Thus, the probability of an event and the probability of its complement must add to 1, which leads to the following fact.

Probability of a Complement

> If an event E has probability p, then the complement of the event has probability $1 - p$.

$E = $ (a number greater than 1)
$F = $ (an integer)
not mutually exclusive;
3 common outcomes, 2, 3, and 4

b. What is the complement of the event {1, 3}?
{2, 4}

c. What is the probability of the event "the spinner does not land on 4?"
$1 - P(4) = 1 - 0.1 = 0.9$

Example 2   Mutually Exclusive Events

An experiment consists of spinning the spinner in Figure 13.3-2. The following table shows the probability distribution for the experiment.

Outcome	A	S	C	E
Probability	0.4	0.3	0.2	0.1

a. Which of the following pairs of events E and F are mutually exclusive?

$E = \{A, C, E\}$ $F = \{C, S\}$

$E = $ (a vowel) $F = $ (in the first five letters of the alphabet)

$E = $ (a vowel) $F = \{C\}$

b. What is the complement of the event $\{A, S\}$?

c. What is the probability of the event "the spinner does not land on A?"

Figure 13.3-2

Solution

a. The events $E = \{A, C, E\}$ and $F = \{C, S\}$ are not mutually exclusive because they have a common outcome, C.

The events $E = $ (a vowel) and $F = $ (in the first five letters of the alphabet) are not mutually exclusive because they have two common outcomes, A and E.

The events $E = $ (a vowel) and $F = \{C\}$ are mutually exclusive because they have no common outcome.

b. The complement of the event $\{A, S\}$ is the set of outcomes that are not in the event, $\{C, E\}$.

c. The complement of the event "the spinner does not land on A" is $\{A\}$, which has a probability of 0.4. Thus, the probability of the event is $1 - 0.4 = 0.6$. ∎

Independent Events

Two events are **independent** if the occurrence or non-occurrence of one event has no effect on the probability of the other event. For example, if an experiment is repeated several times under exactly the same conditions, the outcomes of the individual trials are independent. If two events E and F are independent, then the probability of the event (E and F) is the product of the individual probabilities, $P(E) \cdot P(F)$.

Example Notes

In **Example 2c**, the solution can be confirmed by observing that the complement of "the spinner does not land on A" is "the spinner lands on S, C, or E."

$P(\{S, C, E\}) = P(S) + P(C) + P(E)$
$= 0.3 + 0.2 + 0.1$
$= 0.6$

Teaching Notes

For **Mutually Exclusive Events,** point out that a *trial* of an experiment is the action of performing the experiment one time. The probability of either of two mutually exclusive events occurring in a single trial is the sum of the probabilities of the individual events. For example, suppose a single number cube is rolled and E is the event that 5 is rolled and F is the event that 3 is rolled. The sample space is $\{1, 2, 3, 4, 5, 6\}$, so $P(E) = \frac{1}{6} = P(F)$. Events E and F are mutually exclusive since both cannot occur on the same roll. The event (E or F) is $\{5, 3\}$. So the probability of (E or F) is $\frac{2}{6}$. Therefore:

$$P(E \text{ or } F) = \frac{2}{6} = \frac{1}{6} + \frac{1}{6}$$
$$= P(E) + P(F)$$

You can use the experiment "toss a coin" to explain **Independent Events.** If a coin is tossed twice, then the event "head" on the first toss and the event "head" on the second toss are independent because the probability of getting a head on either toss is not affected by the other toss. The probability of two independent events occurring can be determined by multiplying the probabilities of the individual events. For example, suppose a coin is tossed twice. Let E be the event that heads comes up on the first toss and F the event that heads comes up on the second toss. Here, $P(E) = \frac{1}{2}$ and $P(F) = \frac{1}{2}$. There are four possible outcomes of tossing a coin twice: HH, HT, TH, and TT. So the probability of HH (heads on both tosses), that is, $P(E \text{ and } F)$, is $\frac{1}{4}$. Therefore:

$$P(E \text{ and } F) = \frac{1}{4} = \frac{1}{2} \cdot \frac{1}{2}$$
$$= P(E) \cdot P(F)$$

Example Notes

According to the table on this page, the term **mutually exclusive** often refers to two possible results for a *single trial* of a given experiment. In the Solution for **Example 3c**, it is noted that the events in parts **a** and **b**, winning both times and losing both times, are mutually exclusive. Students may be confused, reasoning that "winning both times" is not a result of a single trial, nor is "losing both times." Explain that:

• The statement in the table uses the word *often*, not *always*.

• The experiment in Example 3 can be considered to be "playing the game twice," so that either "winning both times" or "losing both times" *can be* considered to be the result of a single trial.

In **Example 3c**, help students understand that the complement of {winning once and losing once} is {winning both times and losing both times} as follows.

If W represents a win and L represents a loss, then the sample space for the experiment "playing the game twice" consists of the four outcomes WW, LL, WL, and LW. So,

• {winning once and losing once} is {WL, LW}.

• {winning both times and losing both times} is {WW, LL}.

 ## Math Background

An idea that is often used to illustrate **independent events** is replacement in an experiment (see page 879). Suppose that each letter of the alphabet is written on a piece of paper. One letter is chosen at random, and then another letter is chosen at random.

• If the first letter chosen is *replaced* before the second letter is chosen, then the events "choose an A on the first draw" and "choose an A on the second draw" are *independent*.

• If the first letter chosen is *not replaced* before the second letter is chosen, then the events "choose an A on the first draw" and "choose an A on the second draw" are *dependent*.

> **NOTE** The terms *mutually exclusive* and *independent* are often confused. Some important differences are detailed below.

Mutually exclusive	Independent
The term often refers to two possible results for a *single trial* of a given experiment.	The term often refers to the results from *two or more trials* of an experiment or from different experiments.
The word "or" is often used to describe a pair of mutually exclusive events.	The word "and" is often used to describe a pair of independent events.
For mutually exclusive events E and F, $$P(E \text{ or } F) = P(E) + P(F)$$	For independent events E and F, $$P(E \text{ and } F) = P(E) \cdot P(F)$$

If two events are mutually exclusive, they cannot be independent, because the occurrence of one would cause the other to have a probability of 0.

Example 3   Independent Events

The probability of winning a certain game is 0.1. Suppose the game is played on two different occasions. What is the probability of

a. winning both times?

b. losing both times?

c. winning once and losing once?

Solution

a. The results of the two different trials are independent, so the probability of winning both times can be found by multiplying the probability of winning each time.

$$P(\text{winning both games}) = 0.1 \cdot 0.1 = 0.01$$

b. Since losing is the complement of winning, the probability of losing is $1 - 0.1 = 0.9$. The probability of losing both times can be found by multiplying the probability of losing each time.

$$P(\text{losing both games}) = 0.9 \cdot 0.9 = 0.81$$

c. The complement of the event (winning once and losing once) is the set of the two events in parts **a** and **b**. The events in parts **a** and **b** are mutually exclusive, because it is impossible to win both times *and* lose both times, so their probabilities may be added.

$$P(\text{winning once and losing once}) = 1 - (0.01 + 0.81) = 0.18$$

Random Variables

In many cases, the characteristics of an experiment that are being studied are numerical, such as the total on a roll of two number cubes. In other cases, the outcomes of an experiment may be assigned numbers, such as heads = 1, tails = 0.

A **random variable** is a function that assigns a number to each outcome in the sample space of an experiment.

Example 4 **Random Variable**

An experiment consists of rolling two number cubes. A random variable assigns to each outcome the total of the faces shown.

a. Write out the sample space for the experiment.
b. Find the range of the random variable.
c. List the outcomes to which the value 7 is assigned.

Solution

a. The sample space may be written as a set of ordered pairs.

$$
\begin{array}{cccccc}
(1, 1) & (1, 2) & (1, 3) & (1, 4) & (1, 5) & (1, 6) \\
(2, 1) & (2, 2) & (2, 3) & (2, 4) & (2, 5) & (2, 6) \\
(3, 1) & (3, 2) & (3, 3) & (3, 4) & (3, 5) & (3, 6) \\
(4, 1) & (4, 2) & (4, 3) & (4, 4) & (4, 5) & (4, 6) \\
(5, 1) & (5, 2) & (5, 3) & (5, 4) & (5, 5) & (5, 6) \\
(6, 1) & (6, 2) & (6, 3) & (6, 4) & (6, 5) & (6, 6)
\end{array}
$$

b. The smallest possible value is 2, which is assigned to the outcome (1, 1). The largest possible value is 12, which is assigned to the outcome (6, 6). The range is the set of integers from 2 to 12.

c. The value 7 is assigned to the outcomes (1, 6), (2, 5), (3, 4), (4, 3), (5, 2), and (6, 1). ∎

Expected Value of a Random Variable

The **expected value,** or **mean,** of a random variable is the average value of the outcomes. In the experiment of rolling two number cubes, suppose the experiment was repeated 10 times, resulting in the following values for the random variable:

$$8, 5, 8, 6, 11, 11, 3, 9, 9, 7$$

The average value is $\dfrac{8 + 5 + 8 + 6 + 11 + 11 + 3 + 9 + 9 + 7}{10} = 7.7$. If the experiment is repeated a large number of times, the average approaches the expected value. A simulation was used to run a large number of trials, and the results are shown in Figure 13.3-3. The averages seem to be approaching 7, which is a reasonable estimate of the expected value.

Number of trials	Average sum of two number cubes
100	7.3
200	6.98
300	7.26
400	7.005
500	6.978

Figure 13.3-3

Teaching Notes

Review the definition of discrete and continuous on page 843.

Example 7 uses the random variable from Example 4 (page 869) whose range is the integer values 2 through 12. Because the integers 2 through 12 form a finite set, the probability density function in Example 7 is a **discrete probability density function.**

In **Example 8,** the random variable has infinitely many values in a certain interval, since, for any two values of time, it is possible to have another value in between them. Therefore, the probability density function in Example 8 is a **continuous probability density function.**

ADDITIONAL EXAMPLES

Example 5

The table below shows the probability distribution for the random variable in **Additional Example 4.** Find the expected value of the random variable.

Sum of spins	Probability
0	$\frac{1}{16}$
1	$\frac{1}{8}$
2	$\frac{3}{16}$
3	$\frac{1}{4}$
4	$\frac{3}{16}$
5	$\frac{1}{8}$
6	$\frac{1}{16}$

Multiply each value by its probability and add.

$$0\left(\frac{1}{16}\right) + 1\left(\frac{1}{8}\right) + 2\left(\frac{3}{16}\right) + 3\left(\frac{1}{4}\right) +$$
$$4\left(\frac{3}{16}\right) + 5\left(\frac{1}{8}\right) + 6\left(\frac{1}{16}\right) = 3$$

To calculate the expected value of a random variable from a probability distribution, multiply each value by its probability, and add the results.

Example 5   Expected Value

A probability distribution for the random variable in the experiment in Example 4 is given below. Find the expected value of the random variable.

Sum of faces	2	3	4	5	6	7	8	9	10	11	12
Probability	$\frac{1}{36}$	$\frac{1}{18}$	$\frac{1}{12}$	$\frac{1}{9}$	$\frac{5}{36}$	$\frac{1}{6}$	$\frac{5}{36}$	$\frac{1}{9}$	$\frac{1}{12}$	$\frac{1}{18}$	$\frac{1}{36}$

Solution

Multiply each value by its probability, and add.

$$2\left(\frac{1}{36}\right) + 3\left(\frac{1}{18}\right) + 4\left(\frac{1}{12}\right) + 5\left(\frac{1}{9}\right) + 6\left(\frac{5}{36}\right) + 7\left(\frac{1}{6}\right)$$
$$+ 8\left(\frac{5}{36}\right) + 9\left(\frac{1}{9}\right) + 10\left(\frac{1}{12}\right) + 11\left(\frac{1}{18}\right) + 12\left(\frac{1}{36}\right) = 7$$

The expected value is not always in the range of the random variable, as shown in the following example.

Example 6   Expected Value of a Lottery Ticket

The probability distribution for a $1 instant-win lottery ticket is given below. Find the expected value and interpret the result.

Solution

Win	$0	$3	$5	$10	$20	$40	$100	$400	$2500
Probability	0.882746	0.06	0.04	0.01	0.005	0.002	0.0002	0.00005	0.000004

$$0(0.882746) + 3(0.06) + 5(0.04) + 10(0.01) + 20(0.005) + 40(0.002)$$
$$+ 100(0.0002) + 400(0.00005) + 2500(0.000004) = 0.71$$

The *average* amount won is $0.71, though it is not possible to win exactly 71 cents on one ticket. However, since the ticket costs $1, there is an average net *loss* of $1 − $0.71 = $0.29 per play.

Real-World Application

Probability theory originated in the study of games of chance. **Example 6** is an application of probability to a familiar game of chance—playing the lottery.

Probability is used in many other ways. Exercises 9 and 10 on page 872 show an application of probability to the field of medicine.

Probability Density Functions

In Example 1, colored marbles were drawn from a bag and the probability of each color being drawn was determined by its relative frequency.

red: 0.5   blue: 0.3   yellow: 0.1   green: 0.1

This probability distribution is displayed in a bar graph in Figure 13.3-4, in which each bar is 1 unit wide. Thus the area of each rectangular bar represents the probability of the corresponding color. The sum of the areas of the bars is 1.

If rectangles in the bar graph have width 1 unit, then the area of each rectangle represents the probability of the corresponding category.

A function with the property that the area under the graph corresponds to a probability distribution is called a **probability density function.**

Figure 13.3-4

Example 7   Discrete Probability Density Functions

Draw a probability density function for the distribution in Example 5.

Solution

The probability density function is a piecewise-defined function, shown in Figure 13.3-5, where the height of each piece is the probability of the value on the left endpoint of the interval. The area of the shaded rectangle represents the probability that the sum is 9.

Figure 13.3-5 ∎

When a random variable has infinitely many values within a certain interval, the probability distribution can be represented by a continuous density function, as in the following example.

Example 8   Continuous Probability Density Function

The probability density function in Figure 13.3-6 can be used to estimate the probability that a customer calling a company's customer service line will have to wait for a given amount of time. The area of each square on the grid is $0.5 \cdot 0.05 = 0.025$, and the total area under the curve is 1. Estimate the probability that a customer will have to wait between 2 and 3 minutes.

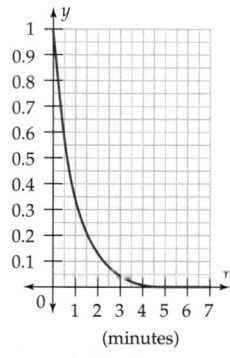

(minutes)

Figure 13.3-6

Example 6

The table below shows the probability distribution of the payoff on a $1 scratch-off lottery ticket. Find the expected value and interpret the result.

Payoff	Probability
$0	0.91176
$5	0.06
$10	0.02
$20	0.006
$50	0.002
$100	0.0002
$1000	0.00004

$0(0.91176) + 5(0.06) + 10(0.02) +$
$\qquad 20(0.006) + 50(0.002) +$
$100(0.0002) + 1000(0.00004) = 0.78$

The *average* amount won is $0.78, though it is not possible to win exactly $0.78 on one ticket. However, since the ticket costs $1, there is an average net *loss* of $1 − $0.78 = $0.22 per play.

Example 7

Draw a probability density function for the distribution in **Additional Example 5.**

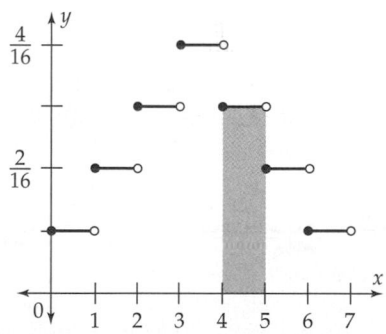

The area of the shaded rectangle represents the probability that the sum is 4.

872   Chapter 13   **Statistics and Probability**

Example 8

The probability density function shown below can used to estimate the probability that a student will receive a certain score on the SAT. The area of each square on the grid is $50 \cdot 0.0005 = 0.025$ and the total area under the curve is 1. Estimate the probability that a student will receive a score between 550 and 700.

The probability is the area under the curve between 550 and 700, which is shaded in the figure below.

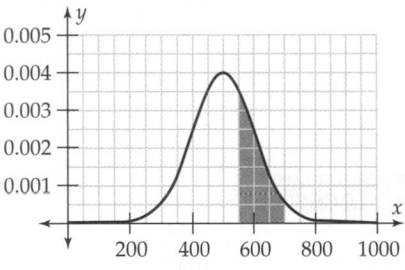

The area is approximately $11\frac{1}{2}$ squares on the grid, or

$$11\frac{1}{2}(0.025) = 0.2875$$

Thus, the probability that a student will receive a score between 550 and 700 is about 0.2875.

Exercises 13.3

ANSWERS

Solution

The probability is the area under the curve between 2 and 3, which is shaded in Figure 13.3-7. The area is approximately $3\frac{1}{2}$ squares on the grid, or

$$3\frac{1}{2}(0.025) = 0.0875$$

Thus, the probability that a customer will have to wait between 2 and 3 minutes is about 0.0875.

Figure 13.3-7

Exercises 13.3

Use the following probability distribution for Exercises 1–4.

Outcome	A	B	C	D
Probability	0.5	0.3	?	?

1. List the sample space for the probability distribution.
   {A, B, C, D}
2. Suppose that outcomes C and D have the same probability. Complete the probability distribution.
   probability of C = 0.1; probability of D = 0.1
3. What is the probability of the outcome (A or B)?
   0.8
4. What is the probability of the outcome (not A)?
   0.5

Exercises 5–8 refer to the spinner at the right. The probability of landing on black is $\frac{1}{2}$, and the probability of landing on red is $\frac{1}{3}$.

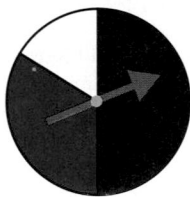

5. Create a probability distribution for the experiment of spinning the spinner.

Outcome	black	red	white
Probability	$\frac{1}{2}$	$\frac{1}{3}$	$\frac{1}{6}$

Suppose the experiment is repeated three times. Assume the trials are independent.

6. What is the probability it will land on black all three times? **$\frac{1}{8}$**
7. What is the probability it will land on white all three times? **$\frac{1}{216}$**
8. What is the probability of the outcome (black, white, red)? of the outcome (black, red, white)? What is the probability that it will land once on each color? **$\frac{1}{36}$; $\frac{1}{36}$; $\frac{1}{6}$**

A doctor has assigned the following chances to a medical procedure:

full recovery	55%
condition improves	24%
no change	17%
condition worsens	4%

Suppose the procedure is performed on 5 patients. Assume that the procedure is independent for each patient.

9. What is the probability that all five patients will recover completely?
   ≈0.05 or 5%
10. What is the probability that none of the patients will get worse?
    ≈0.815 or 81.5%

A bag contains red and blue marbles, such that the probability of drawing a blue marble is $\frac{3}{8}$. An experiment consists of drawing a marble, replacing it, and drawing another marble. The two draws are independent. A random variable assigns the number of blue marbles to each outcome.

11. What is the range of the random variable?
{0, 1, 2}

12. What is the probability that the random variable has an output of 2?
≈14%

13. What is the probability that the random variable has an outcome of 0?
≈39%

14. What is the probability that the random variable has an outcome of 3?
0

15. Create a probability distribution for the random variable.

16. Calculate the expected value of the random variable. $\frac{3}{4}$

In Exercises 17–20, find the expected value of the random variable with the given probability distribution.

17.

Outcome	0	1	5	10	1000
Probability	0.43	0.32	0.24	0.10	0.01

12.52

18.

Outcome	0	1	2	3
Probability	0.25	0.25	0.25	0.25

1.5

19.

Outcome	15	16	17	18	19	20
Probability	0.1	0.3	0.2	0.2	0.1	0.1

17.2

20.

Outcome	2	3	4
Probability	$\frac{1}{4}$	$\frac{1}{2}$	$\frac{1}{4}$

3

An office employs 5 people. A random variable is assigned to the number of people absent on a given day. The probability distribution is given below.

Absent	0	1	2	3	4	5
Probability	0.59	0.33	0.07	0.01	0	0

21. What is the probability that at least one person is absent? **0.41**

22. Find the expected value of the random variable, and interpret the result. **0.5; On average, one person is absent every two days.**

An experiment consists of planting four seeds. A random variable assigns the number of seeds that sprout to each outcome.

23. Complete the following probability distribution for the experiment. **0.026**

Sprouted	0	1	2	3	4
Probability	?	0.154	0.345	0.345	0.130

24. Find the expected value of the random variable, and interpret the result. **2.399; On average, 2.399 out of 4 seeds will sprout.**

25. Draw a probability density function for the random variable. Shade an area of the graph that corresponds to the probability that 3 or more seeds will sprout.

26. Use the probability distribution to determine the probability that each seed will sprout, assuming that they are independent. *Hint:* if the probability that one seed will sprout is p, what is the probability that all four seeds will sprout? **≈0.6**

A random variable with a *uniform* distribution has a probability density function that is constant over the range of the variable, and 0 everywhere else. Use the graph of the probability density function shown below for Exercises 27–30.

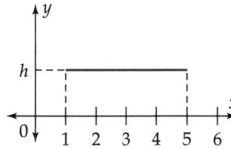

27. What is the range of the random variable? **1 to 5**

28. What is the height h of the probability density function? **h**

29. What is the probability that the random variable is between 2 and 4? $\frac{1}{2}$

30. What is the probability that the random variable is greater than 4? $\frac{1}{4}$

15.

Number of blue	0	1	2
Probability	$\frac{25}{64}$	$\frac{30}{64} = \frac{15}{32}$	$\frac{9}{64}$

25.

(inches)

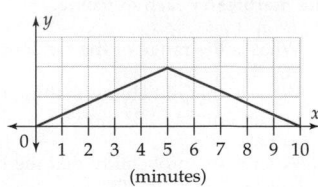

(minutes)

The probability density function at left above models the number of inches of rainfall per year for a certain location. The area of each square on the grid is 0.01.

31. Estimate the probability that the rainfall for a certain year is between 14 and 16 inches.
≈0.55

32. Estimate the probability that the rainfall for a certain year is greater than 17 inches.
≈0.02

33. The median of a probability density function is the point that divides the area under the curve into two equal areas. Estimate the median rainfall, based on the given probability density function.
The median appears to occur at 15 inches of rain.

In commuting to work, Joshua takes one bus, then transfers to another bus. The probability density function at right above models the total length of time that he has to wait for both buses.

34. What is the height of the probability density function at $t = 5$ minutes?   **2**

35. What is the probability that Joshua has to wait for less than 5 minutes? $\frac{5}{10}$ **or 50%**

36. What is the probability that Joshua has to wait for between 3 and 6 minutes? $\frac{5}{10}$ **or 50%**

13.4 Determining Probabilities

Teaching Notes

Refer students to the definition of probability on page 865: the probability of an event indicates how likely the event is to occur. So, we cannot know *exactly* how likely an event is to occur; we can only *estimate*.

Determining Probabilities

Objectives

• Estimate probability using experimental methods

• Estimate probability using theoretical methods

The exact probability of a real event can never be known. Probabilities are estimated in two ways: experimentally and theoretically.

Experimental Estimates of Probability

Suppose an outcome of an experiment has a probability of 0.3. If the experiment were repeated many times, that outcome would occur in approximately 30% of the trials. In 100 trials, for example, it might occur 30 times, or maybe 28 times or 34 times. Statistical analysis shows, however, that it is unlikely that it would occur fewer than 20 times or more than 40 times.

The basis for experimental estimates of probability may be summarized as follows:

As the number of trials of an experiment increases, the relative frequency of an outcome approaches the probability of the outcome.

Thus, if an experiment is repeated n times, the experimental estimate of the probability of an event is

$$P(E) \approx \frac{\text{number of trials with an outcome in } E}{n}$$

Example 1 **Experimental Estimate of Probability**

An experiment consists of throwing a dart at the target in Figure 13.4-1. Suppose the experiment is repeated 200 times, with the following results:

red	43
yellow	86
blue	71

Write a probability distribution for the experiment.

Figure 13.4-1

Solution

The probabilities may be estimated using the experimental formula.

Outcome	red	yellow	blue
Probability	$\frac{43}{200} \approx 0.2$	$\frac{86}{200} \approx 0.4$	$\frac{71}{200} \approx 0.4$

∎

Probability Simulations

In order to estimate probability using the experimental approach, a large number of trials is needed. Because this approach is often time-consuming, computer simulations that duplicate the conditions of a single trial are often used.

Most graphing calculators have random number generators that can be used to simulate simple probability experiments. To simulate an experiment with a large number of trials, it is easiest to use a program that can keep track of the frequency of each outcome.

Suppose an experiment consists of tossing three coins and counting the number of heads, and that the probability of heads for each coin is 0.5. The possible outcomes of the experiment are 0 heads, 1 head, 2 heads, or 3 heads. One trial can be simulated by a command that randomly generates three values, which can be either 0 or 1, and adds them (see the Technology Tip on page 876). The three random integers represent the three coins, where 1 represents heads and 0 represents tails.

Outcome	Probability
0 points	$\frac{102}{160} \approx 0.64$
2 points	$\frac{51}{160} \approx 0.32$
3 points	$\frac{7}{160} \approx 0.04$

Teaching Notes

The experiment described at the bottom of page 875 has four possible outcomes: 0, 1, 2, and 3. The tree diagram below shows all the ways to get those outcomes on any single trial.

1st coin	2nd coin	3rd coin	Outcome = number of heads

```
            H ── H    3
        H <
            T ── T    2
    H <
            T ── H    2
            T          1

            H ── H    2
        H <
            T ── T    1
    T <
            T ── H    1
            T          0
```

Note that there is one way to get the outcome 3 heads, three ways to get the outcome 2 heads, three ways to get the outcome 1 head, and one way to get the outcome 0 heads.
In the program on this page, T will be assigned 0, 1, 2, or 3 for each trial.

Solution to the **Calculator Exploration** (page 877):
> Answers will vary.

Yes, these results are similar to those in Example 2.

Consider applying the formula for **Probability for Equally Likely Outcomes** to Example 1 on pages 865–866. In Example 1, the outcomes red, blue, yellow, and green are *not* equally likely, so we cannot use the formula with $n = 4$. However, each of the 100 marbles is equally likely to be chosen, so we can use the formula with $n = 100$. For example,
$$P(\text{blue}) = \frac{30}{100}.$$

Technology Tip

To randomly generate three values that can be 0 or 1 and add them:

TI	sum (randInt (0, 1, 3))
Casio	Sum {Int 2Ran#, Int 2Ran#, Int 2Ran#}

The following is a sample program for running a simulation with n trials of the experiment. The program displays a list of the probabilities for 0 heads, 1 head, 2 heads, and 3 heads.

Prompt N	*N is the number of trials.*
0 → A: 0 → B: 0 → C: 0 → D	
For (K, 1, N, 1)	
sum (randInt (0, 1, 3)) → T	*T is the outcome of a single trial.*
If T = 0	
A + 1 → A	*A is the number of trials with 0 heads.*
If T = 1	
B + 1 → B	*B is the number of trials with 1 head.*
If T = 2	
C + 1 → C	*C is the number of trials with 2 heads.*
If T = 3	
D + 1 → D	*D is the number of trials with 3 heads.*
End	
{A/N, B/N, C/N, D/N}	

Example 2   Probability Simulation

Use the program to create a probability distribution for the experiment of tossing 3 coins and counting the number of heads. Assume that $P(\text{heads}) = P(\text{tails}) = 0.5$ for each coin.

Solution

The results will vary each time the program is run. Using the results from Figure 13.4-2, one approximate distribution is shown below.

Outcome	0 heads	1 head	2 heads	3 heads
Probability	0.14	0.38	0.36	0.12

```
N=?100
...14 .38 .36 .12}
```

Figure 13.4-2

Calculator Exploration

Run the probability simulation in Example 2, using 100 trials. Are your results similar to those in the example? Compare your results to those of your classmates.

NOTE The assumption that all outcomes are equally likely was used in the probability simulation in Example 2. If P(heads) = P(tails) = $\frac{1}{2}$, then heads and tails are equally likely. Also, for the given calculator commands, the outcomes 0 and 1 are equally likely each time.

Theoretical Estimates of Probability

In the theoretical approach, certain assumptions are made about the outcomes of the experiment. Then, the properties of probability are used to determine the probability of each outcome.

The most common assumption is that all outcomes are **equally likely,** that is, they have the same probability of occurring. For example, in tossing a coin it is usually assumed that heads and tails are equally likely. Since the probabilities must add to 1, the probability of each outcome must equal $\frac{1}{2}$. This idea is used to develop the following formula.

Probability for Equally Likely Outcomes

Suppose an experiment has a sample space of n outcomes, all of which are equally likely. Then the probability of each outcome is $\frac{1}{n}$, and the probability of an event E is given by

$$P(E) = \frac{\text{number of outcomes in } E}{n}$$

Example 3   **Rolling a Number Cube**

An experiment consists of rolling a number cube. Suppose that all outcomes are equally likely.

a. Write the probability distribution for the experiment.
b. Find the probability of the event that an even number is rolled.

Solution

a. The sample space consists of the 6 outcomes {1, 2, 3, 4, 5, 6}. If the outcomes are equally likely, then the probability of each is $\frac{1}{6}$. The probability distribution for the experiment is

Outcome	1	2	3	4	5	6
Probability	$\frac{1}{6}$	$\frac{1}{6}$	$\frac{1}{6}$	$\frac{1}{6}$	$\frac{1}{6}$	$\frac{1}{6}$

Example Notes

In **Example 2**, the program on page 876 was run with 100 trials specified. The results, partially displayed in Figure 13.4-2, were A/100 = 0.14, B/100 = 0.38, and so on. Therefore, there were A = 14 trials with 0 heads, B = 38 trials with 1 head, and so on.

Example 2 specifies that we assume P(heads) = P(tails) = 0.5 for each coin. Point out that this assumption is incorporated into the calculator program by appropriate use of the randInt command.

ADDITIONAL EXAMPLES

Example 2

Modify the program on page 876 to create a probability distribution for the experiment of tossing 4 coins and counting the number of heads. Assume that P(heads) = P(tails) = 0.5 for each coin.
The program should be modified as shown below (modifications are in magenta).
0 → A: 0 → B: 0 → C: 0 → D: 0 → E:
sum (randInt (0, 1, 4))
[Insert the next two lines after
D + 1 → D:]
If T = 4
E + 1 → E
{A/N, B/N, C/N, D/N, E/N}
Answers will vary.

```
N=?100
{.05 .22 .33 .3…
```

```
N=?100
…22 .33 .34 .06}
```

The probability distribution is shown below.

Outcome	Probability
0 heads	0.05
1 head	0.22
2 heads	0.33
3 heads	0.34
4 heads	0.06

Example 3

An experiment consists of spinning a spinner divided into 5 equal sections numbered from 1 to 5. Suppose that all outcomes are equally likely.

a. Write the probability distribution for the experiment.

Outcome	Probability
1	$\frac{1}{5}$
2	$\frac{1}{5}$
3	$\frac{1}{5}$
4	$\frac{1}{5}$
5	$\frac{1}{5}$

b. Find the probability of the event that the spinner lands on a prime number.

$P(\text{prime number}) = P(\{2, 3, 5\})$
$= \frac{3}{5}$

Example 4

Use properties of probability to write a theoretical probability distribution for the experiment in **Additional Example 2.**

Each outcome has a probability of $0.5(0.5)(0.5)(0.5) = 0.0625$

one outcome with 0 heads: TTTT
$P(0 \text{ heads}) = 0.0625$

four outcomes with 1 head: HTTT, THTT, TTHT, and TTTH.
$P(1 \text{ head}) = 0.25$

six outcomes with 2 heads: HHTT, HTHT, HTTH, THHT, THTH, and TTHH.
$P(2 \text{ heads}) = 0.375$

four outcomes with 3 heads: HHHT, HHTH, HTHH, and THHH.
$P(3 \text{ heads}) = 0.25$

one outcome with 4 heads: HHHH
$P(4 \text{ heads}) = 0.0625$

The probability distribution is shown below.

Outcome	Probability
0 heads	0.0625
1 head	0.25
2 heads	0.375
3 heads	0.25
4 heads	0.0625

b. The event that an even number is rolled consists of the 3 outcomes {2, 4, 6}. Thus, the probability that an even number is rolled is
$\frac{3}{6} = \frac{1}{2}$.

Of course, the outcomes of an experiment are not always equally likely. Based on the probability simulation of tossing 3 coins in Example 2, the outcomes 0, 1, 2, and 3 heads do not seem to be equally likely. However, it is possible to determine the probability theoretically by considering each coin separately.

Example 4   Theoretical Probability

Use properties of probability to write a theoretical probability distribution for the experiment in Example 2.

Solution

Each coin has no effect on the other coins, so the outcomes of the coins are independent. Thus, the probabilities can be multiplied.

The only outcome with 0 heads is TTT. The probability of tails for each coin is 0.5, so the probability of the outcome TTT is

T   T   T
$0.5(0.5)(0.5) = 0.125$

There are three outcomes with 1 head: HTT, THT, and TTH. Each outcome has a probability of 0.125. For example,

H   T   T
$0.5(0.5)(0.5) = 0.125$

The probabilities of the three outcomes can be added, so the probability of 1 head is $0.125 + 0.125 + 0.125 = 0.375$.

There are three outcomes with 2 heads: HHT, HTH, and THH. The probability of 2 heads is also $0.125 + 0.125 + 0.125 = 0.375$.

There is one outcome with 3 heads, HHH, which also has a probability of 0.125.

The probability distribution is shown below.

Outcome	0 heads	1 head	2 heads	3 heads
Probability	0.125	0.375	0.375	0.125

How do the theoretical probabilities obtained in Example 4 compare to the experimental ones you found in Example 2?

Counting Techniques

The probability formula for equally likely outcomes uses the size of the sample space. In simple experiments, this may be easily determined, but some experiments require more sophisticated counting techniques.

The basis of most counting techniques is the Fundamental Counting Principle, which is also known as the Multiplication Principle.

Fundamental Counting Principle

> Consider a set of k experiments. Suppose the first experiment has n_1 outcomes, the second has n_2 outcomes, and so on. Then the total number of outcomes is $n_1 \cdot n_2 \cdot \ldots \cdot n_k$ for all k experiments.

Example 5 Using the Fundamental Counting Principle

A catalog offers chairs in a choice of 2 heights, regular and tall. There are 10 colors available for the finish, and 12 choices of fabric for the seats. The chair back has 4 different possible designs. How many different chairs can be ordered?

Solution

Each option can be considered as an experiment. The number of choices for each option is the number of outcomes. According to the Fundamental Counting Principle, the number of different chairs is

$$2 \cdot 10 \cdot 12 \cdot 4 = 960$$

Consider the following experiment: Each letter of the alphabet is written on a piece of paper, and three letters are chosen at random. There are two important questions in determining the nature of the experiment:

1. Is each letter replaced before the next letter is chosen?

2. Does the order of the letters matter in the result?

If the answer to Question 1 is *yes*, the letters are said to be chosen **with replacement.** In this case, letters may be repeated in the result. Also, the number of letters to choose from is always the same. If the answer is *no*, then the letters are said to be chosen **without replacement.** In this case, there will be no repeated letters, and the number of letters to choose from decreases by 1 for each letter chosen.

If the answer to Question 2 is *yes*, the result is said to be **order important.** In this case, the outcome CAT is considered to be different from the outcome ACT. If the answer is *no*, the result is said to be in **any order.** In this case, the six outcomes CAT, CTA, TAC, TCA, ACT, ATC are considered to be the same.

NOTE Many times, it is necessary to use the context of the experiment to determine whether it is with replacement, or if order is important.

Teaching Notes

For the table at the top of this page, explain columns 2 and 3 as follows:

Column 2: Without replacement, there are 26 to choose from, then 25, then 24.

Column 3: For any 3 letters, there are $3 \cdot 2 \cdot 1 = 6$ arrangements if order is important, e.g, ACT, ATC, CAT, CTA, TAC, TCA. But for column 3, these are all the same outcome because order is not important. So, divide the column 2 expression by $3 \cdot 2 \cdot 1 = 6$.

Real-World Application

The roots of probability theory lie in gambling. In **Example 8,** on pages 881–882, probabilities of winning various lottery prizes are calculated. Discuss with students how these very low probabilities show that winning is very unlikely. You may want to have students research payoff amounts for winning certain state lottery prizes and compare those amounts to the probabilities of winning. For example, for a game to be "fair," winning on a $1 bet should result in a $100 payoff if the probability of winning is 0.01. However, because administrative expenses and state revenue are deducted, winning on that bet will result in a payoff substantially less than $100.

Exercises 27–29, on page 884 (see also the explanation paragraph at the bottom of page 883) illustrate how probability theory can be used to answer important questions that arise in science.

Example Notes

It may be instructive to have students calculate $_{54}C_6$ in Example 8 using the definition and cancellation.

$$_{54}C_6 = \frac{54!}{6!(54-6)!} = \frac{54!}{6! \cdot 48!}$$

$$= \frac{54 \cdot 53 \cdot 52 \cdot 51 \cdot 50 \cdot 49}{6 \cdot 5 \cdot 4 \cdot 3 \cdot 2 \cdot 1}$$

$$= 25,827,165$$

Three of the four possible cases are shown in the table below. The fourth case, with replacement and in any order, will not be discussed. Use the Fundamental Counting Principle to explain the number of outcomes in each case.

With replacement Order important	Without replacement Order important	Without replacement Any order
$26 \cdot 26 \cdot 26 = 17{,}576$	$26 \cdot 25 \cdot 24 = 15{,}600$	$\dfrac{26 \cdot 25 \cdot 24}{3 \cdot 2 \cdot 1} = 2600$

Example 6 3 Coin Toss

Use the Fundamental Counting Principle to verify the probability distribution in Example 4.

Solution

There are two possible outcomes for each coin: heads and tails. Thus, the number of outcomes for tossing three coins is $2 \cdot 2 \cdot 2 = 8$. To find the 8 different outcomes, it is helpful to use a tree diagram, as shown in Figure 13.4-3. The outcomes are given below.

HHH	HHT	HTH	HTT	THH	THT	TTH	TTT
3 heads	*2 heads*	*2 heads*	*1 head*	*2 heads*	*1 head*	*1 head*	*0 heads*

Each of these outcomes is equally likely, so the probability distribution is

Outcome	0 heads	1 head	2 heads	3 heads
Probability	$\frac{1}{8} = 0.125$	$\frac{3}{8} = 0.375$	$\frac{3}{8} = 0.375$	$\frac{1}{8} = 0.125$

■

Permutations and Combinations

The two cases without replacement are called **permutations** (order important) and **combinations** (any order). In order to write a formula for permutations and combinations, $n!$—read "n **factorial**"—is used to describe the product of all the integers from 1 to n.

$$n! = n(n-1)(n-2)\ldots(3)(2)(1)$$

In the example of drawing 3 letters without replacement where order is important, the number of permutations can be written using factorials as

$$26 \cdot 25 \cdot 24 = \frac{26 \cdot 25 \cdot 24 \cdot 23 \cdot 22 \cdot \ldots \cdot 3 \cdot 2 \cdot 1}{23 \cdot 22 \cdot \ldots \cdot 3 \cdot 2 \cdot 1} = \frac{26!}{23!}$$

In the case where order is not important, the number of combinations can be written as

$$\frac{26 \cdot 25 \cdot 24}{3 \cdot 2 \cdot 1} = \frac{26!}{(3 \cdot 2 \cdot 1)23!} = \frac{26!}{3! \cdot 23!}$$

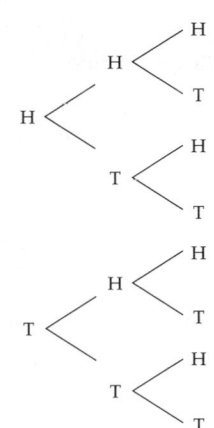

Figure 13.4-3

NOTE 0! is defined to equal 1.

Permutation and combination formulas are also written using factorials.

Permutations and Combinations

Technology Tip

Permutations and combinations are located on the PRB submenu of the MATH menu on TI and on the PROB submenu of the OPTN menu on Casio.

Permutations

If r items are chosen in order without replacement from n possible items, the number of permutations is

$$_nP_r = \frac{n!}{(n-r)!}$$

Combinations

If r items are chosen in any order without replacement from n possible items, the number of combinations is

$$_nC_r = \frac{n!}{r!(n-r)!}$$

If each item is equally likely to be chosen, the permutations and combinations are all equally likely for a given value of r.

Note: $_nP_r$ may also be written as $P_{n,r}$ or $P(n, r)$, and $_nC_r$ may be written as $C_{n,r}$, $C(n, r)$, or $\binom{n}{r}$.

Example 7 Matching Problem

Suppose you have four personalized letters and four addressed envelopes. If the letters are randomly placed in the envelopes, what is the probability that all four letters will go to the correct addresses?

Solution

For all four letters to go to the correct addresses, they must be chosen in the exact same order as the envelopes. The size of the sample space is the number of permutations, $_4P_4$.

$$_4P_4 = \frac{4!}{(4-4)!} = \frac{4!}{0!} = 24$$

Thus, the probability is $\frac{1}{24} \approx 0.04$.

Example 8 Pick-6 Lottery

In a "pick-6" lottery, 54 numbered balls are used. Out of these, 6 are randomly chosen. To win, at least 3 balls must be matched in any order. What is the probability of winning the jackpot (all 6 balls)? What is the probability of matching any 5 balls? any 4 balls? any 3 balls?

Example 6

Use the Fundamental Counting Principle to verify the probability distribution in **Additional Example 4**. There are a total of 2 possible outcomes for each coin. Thus, the number of outcomes for tossing four coins is $2 \cdot 2 \cdot 2 \cdot 2 = 16$.

The 16 outcomes are listed below.

HHHH	4 heads	THHH	3 heads
HHHT	3 heads	THHT	2 heads
HHTH	3 heads	THTH	2 heads
HHTT	2 heads	THTT	1 head
HTHH	3 heads	TTHH	2 heads
HTHT	2 heads	TTHT	1 head
HTTH	2 heads	TTTH	1 head
HTTT	1 head	TTTT	0 heads

Each outcome is equally likely, so the probability distribution is shown below.

Outcome	Probability
0 heads	$\frac{1}{16} = 0.0625$
1 head	$\frac{4}{16} = 0.25$
2 heads	$\frac{6}{16} = 0.375$
3 heads	$\frac{4}{16} = 0.25$
4 heads	$\frac{1}{16} = 0.0625$

Example 7

Suppose five tiles labeled with capital letters A, B, C, D, and E are placed randomly in slots a, b, c, d, and e. What is the probability that each capital letter is matched with its lowercase counterpart?

The size of the sample space is the number of permutations, $_5P_5$.

$$_5P_5 = \frac{5!}{(5-5)!} = \frac{5!}{0!} = \frac{5 \cdot 4 \cdot 3 \cdot 2 \cdot 1}{1}$$
$$= 120$$

Thus, the probability is $\frac{1}{120} \approx 0.008$.

Example 8

A bag contains 26 tiles, each labeled with a letter A through Z. Julie chooses 5 tiles at random from the bag. What is the probability that she chooses the letters of her name, in any order (matching all 5 letters)? What is the probability of matching 4 letters? 3 letters? 0 letters?

The size of the sample space is the number of combinations.

$$_{26}C_5 = 65{,}780$$

There is only one combination that contains the letters J, U, L, I, and E, so the probability of all 5 letters matching is:

$$P = \frac{1}{65{,}780} \approx 0.000015$$

There are $_5C_k$ ways to match k letters out of 5. The remaining $5 - k$ letters do *not* match any of the letters in her name, so there are 21 letters to choose from, giving $_{21}C_{5-k}$ ways to choose the remaining letters. By the Fundamental Counting Principle, there are $_5C_k \cdot {}_{21}C_{5-k}$ combinations that match k letters.

$$P(\text{matching } k \text{ letters}) = \frac{{}_5C_k \cdot {}_{21}C_{5-k}}{{}_{26}C_5}$$

Use the formula to verify the first answer and then find the other answers.

$P(\text{matching 5 letters})$

$$= \frac{{}_5C_5 \cdot {}_{21}C_0}{{}_{26}C_5} = \frac{1 \cdot 1}{65{,}780}$$

$$\approx 0.000015$$

$P(\text{matching 4 letters})$

$$= \frac{{}_5C_4 \cdot {}_{21}C_1}{{}_{26}C_5} = \frac{5 \cdot 21}{65{,}780}$$

$$\approx 0.0016$$

$P(\text{matching 3 letters})$

$$= \frac{{}_5C_3 \cdot {}_{21}C_2}{{}_{26}C_5} = \frac{10 \cdot 210}{65{,}780}$$

$$\approx 0.0319$$

$P(\text{matching 0 letters})$

$$= \frac{{}_5C_0 \cdot {}_{21}C_5}{{}_{26}C_5} = \frac{1 \cdot 20{,}349}{65{,}780}$$

$$\approx 0.3093$$

Figure 13.4-4

```
54 nCr 6
           25827165
Ans⁻¹
     3.87189225ᴇ-8
```

Solution

The size of the sample space is the number of combinations.

$$_{54}C_6 = 25{,}827{,}165$$

The probability of winning the jackpot is

$$\frac{1}{25{,}827{,}165} \approx 0.00000004$$

The event of matching 5, 4, or 3 numbers can be determined as follows:

$$P(\text{matching } k \text{ numbers}) = \frac{\text{number of combinations that match } k \text{ numbers}}{{}_{54}C_6}$$

There are $_6C_k$ ways to match k numbers out of 6. The remaining $6 - k$ numbers do *not* match any of the 6 winning numbers, so there are 48 numbers to choose from, giving $_{48}C_{6-k}$ ways to choose the remaining numbers. By the Fundamental Counting Principle, there are $_6C_k \cdot {}_{48}C_{6-k}$ combinations that match k numbers.

$$P(\text{matching } k \text{ numbers}) = \frac{{}_6C_k \cdot {}_{48}C_{6-k}}{{}_{54}C_6}$$

$$P(\text{matching 5 numbers}) = \frac{{}_6C_5 \cdot {}_{48}C_1}{{}_{54}C_6} = \frac{6 \cdot 48}{25{,}827{,}165} \approx 0.00001$$

$$P(\text{matching 4 numbers}) = \frac{{}_6C_4 \cdot {}_{48}C_2}{{}_{54}C_6} = \frac{15 \cdot 1128}{25{,}827{,}165} \approx 0.0007$$

$$P(\text{matching 3 numbers}) = \frac{{}_6C_3 \cdot {}_{48}C_3}{{}_{54}C_6} = \frac{20 \cdot 17296}{25{,}827{,}165} \approx 0.01$$

Exercises 13.4

For Exercises 1–4, an experiment consists of drawing a marble out of a bag, observing the color, and then placing it back in the bag. Suppose the experiment is repeated 75 times, with the following results:

red	38
blue	23
green	11
yellow	3

1. Write a probability distribution of the experiment using the experimental formula.

2. Based on your distribution from Exercise 1, what is the probability of drawing either a blue or green marble? **≈0.46**

3. Based on your distribution from Exercise 1, what is the probability of drawing two yellow marbles in a row? **0.0016**

4. Suppose it is known that there is a total of 300 marbles in the bag. Estimate the number of each color of marble.

A dreidel is a top with four sides, used in a Hanukah game. The sides are labeled with the Hebrew letters *nun, gimel, hay,* and *shin*. A dreidel is spun 100 times, with the following results:

nun	10
gimel	45
hay	24
shin	21

dreidel

5. Write a probability distribution for the dreidel.

Exercises 13.4
ANSWERS

1.
Outcome	red	blue	green	yellow
Probability	≈0.50	≈0.31	≈0.15	0.04

4.
Outcome	red	blue	green	yellow
Probability	150	93	45	12

5.
Outcome	nun	gimel	hay	shin
Probability	0.1	0.45	0.24	0.21

6. A player wins tokens if the dreidel lands on either *gimel* or *hay*. What is the probability of winning tokens? **0.69**

7. A player loses tokens if the dreidel lands on *nun*. What is the probability of losing four times in a row? **0.0001**

Exercises 8–11 refer to the following experiment: two number cubes are rolled, and a random variable assigns the sum of the faces to each outcome.

8. The following commands generate two random integers from 1 to 6 and add them.
TI-83/86: sum(randInt(1, 6, 2))
TI-89/92: sum({rand(6), rand(6)})
Sharp 9600: sum(int(6random(2)) + 1)
Casio 9850: Sum{Int 6Ran# + 1, Int 6Ran# + 1}
HP-38: ΣLIST({INT(6 RANDOM) + 1,
    INT(6 RANDOM) + 1})
Run 5 trials of the experiment and list your results.
Possible answers: 5, 7, 10, 8, 7

9. Run a simulation of the experiment with at least 50 trials, and create a probability distribution.

10. Use your probability distribution from Exercise 9 to find the probabilities for the following values of the random variable. **Possible answers:**
a. greater than 9 **0.2**
b. less than 6 **0.34**
c. at least 4 **0.9**

11. Use your probability distribution from Exercise 9 to find the expected value of the random variable.
Possible answer: 6.89

12. A bag contains 3 red marbles and 4 blue marbles. Suppose each marble is equally likely to be chosen. What is the probability of the event of drawing a red marble?
≈0.43

13. Suppose that a person's birthday is equally likely to be any day of the year. What is the probability that a randomly chosen person has the same birthday as you?
≈0.0027

A teacher writes the name of each of her 25 students on a slip of paper and places the papers in a box. To call on a student, she draws a slip of paper from the box. Each paper is equally likely to be drawn, and the papers are replaced in the box after each draw.

14. What is the probability of calling on a particular student?
0.04

15. What is the probability of calling on the same student twice in a row?
0.0016

16. If there are 9 students in the last row, what is the probability of calling on a student in the last row?
0.36

17. If the class contains 11 boys and 14 girls, what is the probability of calling on a girl? What is the probability of calling on 3 girls in a row?
0.56; ≈0.176

18. A clothing store offers a shirt in 5 colors, in long or short sleeves, with a choice of three different collars. How many ways can the shirt be designed?
30

19. A quiz has 5 true-false questions and 3 multiple choice questions with 4 options each. How many possible ways are there to answer the 8 questions?
2048

20. A license plate has 3 digits from 0 to 9, followed by 3 letters. How many different license plates are possible?
17,576,000

21. A gallery has 25 paintings in its permanent collection, with display space for 10 at one time. How many different collections can be shown?
3,268,760

22. A committee of 8 people randomly chooses 3 people in order to be president, vice president, and treasurer. In how many ways can the officers be chosen?
336

23. A baseball team has 9 players. How many different batting orders are there?
362,880

24. A small library contains 700 novels. In how many ways can you check out 3 novels?
56,921,900

25. A manufacturer is testing 4 brands of soda in a blind taste test. The participants know the brands being tested but do not know which is which. What is the probability that a participant will identify all 4 brands correctly by guessing?
≈0.04

26. A researcher is studying the abilities of people who claim to be able to read minds. He chooses 6 numbers between 1 and 50 (inclusive), and asks each participant to guess the numbers in order. What is the probability of guessing all 6 correctly?
≈8.7 × 10⁻¹¹

A botanist is testing two kinds of seeds. She divides a plot of land into 16 equal areas numbered from 1 to 16. She then randomly chooses 8 of these areas to plant seed A, and she plants seed B in the remaining areas.

1	2	3	4
5	6	7	8
9	10	11	12
13	14	15	16

9. Possible answer:

Outcome	Probability
2	$\frac{1}{50}$
3	$\frac{4}{50}$
4	$\frac{6}{50}$
5	$\frac{6}{50}$
6	$\frac{5}{50}$
7	$\frac{7}{50}$
8	$\frac{6}{50}$
9	$\frac{5}{50}$
10	$\frac{5}{50}$
11	$\frac{4}{50}$
12	$\frac{1}{50}$

33. probability $= 1 - \dfrac{_{365}P_n}{365^n}$

$n = 3$: ≈ 0.008

$n = 20$: ≈ 0.411

$n = 35$: ≈ 0.814

27. How many ways are there to choose 8 plots out of 16?

12,870

A	A	A	A
A	A	A	A
B	B	B	B
B	B	B	B

28. What is the probability of the event shown at right?

$\approx 7.77 \times 10^{-5}$

29. What is the probability that all of the areas with seed A will form a 4×2 rectangle on one side of the plot, and all of the areas with seed B will form a 4×2 rectangle on the other side?

$\approx 3.108 \times 10^{-4}$

Critical Thinking **Exercises 30–35 refer to a famous probability problem: suppose a certain number of people are in a room. What is the probability that two or more people in the room will have the same birthday?**

30. Suppose each day of the year is equally likely to be a person's birthday. How many ways are there to name one date per person (not necessarily all different) for each of 3 people? of 20 people? of n people?

365^3; 365^{20}; 365^n

31. The complement of the event "two or more people will have the same birthday" is

$48{,}228{,}180$; 1.03669×10^{51}; $\dfrac{365!}{(365-n)!}$

"everybody has a different birthday." How many ways are there to name a *different* date for each of 3 people? of 20 people? of n people?

32. The probability that everybody has a different birthday can be written as

$$\dfrac{\text{Number of ways to name } n \text{ different dates}}{\text{Number of ways to name } n \text{ dates}}$$

Use your results from Exercises 30 and 31 to write a formula in terms of n for the probability that everybody has a different birthday. $\dfrac{_{365}P_n}{365^n}$

33. Use your results from Exercise 32 to write a formula in terms of n for the probability that two or more people have the same birthday. Find the probability for $n = 3$, for $n = 20$, and for $n = 35$.

34. How many people must be in the room for the probability to be approximately $\dfrac{1}{2}$ that two or more have the same birthday?

23 people

35. How many people must be in the room for the probability to be 1 that two or more have the same birthday? *Hint:* do not use the formula.

366 people

Math Background

The Bernoulli family, including brothers Jacob and Johann, Johann's sons Nicolaus (II), Daniel, Johann (II), and other family members, made important contributions to mathematics and science in the 1600s and 1700s. Some of the areas of those contributions were probability theory, calculus, and mathematics relating to ship sails, optics, vibrating strings, and mechanics.

 13.4.A

Excursion: **Binomial Experiments**

Objectives

• Calculate the probability of a binomial experiment

Many experiments can be described in terms of just two outcomes, such as winning or losing, heads or tails, boy or girl. These experiments determine a group of problems called **binomial or Bernoulli experiments,** named after Jacob Bernoulli, a Swiss mathematician who studied these distributions extensively in the late 1600's.

Binomial Experiments

Here is a typical binomial experiment: in a basketball contest, each contestant is allowed 3 free-throws. If a certain individual has a 70% chance of making each free-throw, what is the probability of making exactly 2 out of 3?

The essential elements in a binomial experiment are given below.

Binomial Experiment

A set of n trials is called a binomial experiment if the following are true.

1. **The trials are independent.**
2. **Each trial has only 2 possible outcomes, which may be designated as** *success* **(S) and** *failure* **(F).**
3. **The probability of success p is the same for each trial. The probability of failure is $q = 1 - p$.**

In the example of the basketball contest, the outcome *SFS* indicates that the first free-throw is a success, the second a failure, and the third a success. The trials are independent, so the probability of the outcome *SFS* is the product of the probabilities for each trial.

$$P(SFS) = P(S) \cdot P(F) \cdot P(S) = (0.7)(0.3)(0.7) = 0.147$$

Example 1   Basketball Contest

Refer to the basketball contest described on page 884. Suppose that the probability of making each free-throw is 0.7. What is the probability of making exactly 2 free-throws in 3 tries?

Solution

The outcomes in the event "2 free-throws in 3 tries" are *SSF, SFS, FSS*. The probability of the event is the sum of the probabilities of the three outcomes.

$$P(SSF) = P(S) \cdot P(S) \cdot P(F) = (0.7)(0.7)(0.3) = 0.147$$
$$P(SFS) = P(S) \cdot P(F) \cdot P(S) = (0.7)(0.3)(0.7) = 0.147$$
$$P(FSS) = P(F) \cdot P(S) \cdot P(S) = (0.3)(0.7)(0.7) = 0.147$$
$$P(2 \text{ free-throws}) = P(SSF) + P(SFS) + P(FSS)$$
$$= 0.147 + 0.147 + 0.147 = 0.441$$

In Example 1, note that the probability of *SSF* is the same as the probability of *SFS* or *FSS*. In general, the probability of any outcome with r successes and $n-r$ failures in n trials is

$$\underbrace{(pp \dots p)}_{(r \text{ times})} \underbrace{(qq \dots q)}_{(n-r \text{ times})} = p^r q^{n-r}$$

To develop a general formula for the probability of r successes in n trials, it is necessary to determine how many different outcomes have r suc-

---

ADDITIONAL EXAMPLES

Example 1

A certain baseball player has a probability of 0.3 of getting a hit each time he is at bat. What is the probability he will get exactly 1 hit in 4 times at bat?

Letting S (success) represent getting a hit and F (failure) represent not getting a hit, the outcomes in the event "1 hit in 4 times at bat" are *SFFF, FSFF, FFSF,* and *FFFS.* The probability of the event is the sum of the probabilities of these four outcomes.

$$P(SFFF) = P(S) \cdot P(F) \cdot P(F) \cdot P(F)$$
$$= (0.3)(0.7)(0.7)(0.7)$$
$$= 0.1029$$
$$P(FSFF) = P(F) \cdot P(S) \cdot P(F) \cdot P(F)$$
$$= (0.7)(0.3)(0.7)(0.7)$$
$$= 0.1029$$
$$P(FFSF) = P(F) \cdot P(F) \cdot P(S) \cdot P(F)$$
$$= (0.7)(0.7)(0.3)(0.7)$$
$$= 0.1029$$
$$P(FFFS) = P(F) \cdot P(F) \cdot P(F) \cdot P(S)$$
$$= (0.7)(0.7)(0.7)(0.3)$$
$$= 0.1029$$
$$P(1 \text{ hit}) = P(SFFF) + P(FSFF) +$$
$$P(FFSF) + P(FFFS)$$
$$= 0.1029 + 0.1029 +$$
$$0.1029 + 0.1029$$
$$= 0.4116$$

Teaching Notes

Remind students that $_nC_r$, the first factor in the formula for calculating the **Probability of a Binomial Experiment**, represents the number of outcomes in n trials that have r successes. This factor is a number of combinations, not permutations, because the order of the successes is not important.

ADDITIONAL EXAMPLES

Example 2

A 4-digit lottery consists of choosing a number from 0000 to 9999. All digits of the number must be matched in order, so the probability of winning is $\frac{1}{10,000} = 0.0001$. A ticket costs $1, and the prize is $5000. Suppose you play the lottery 5000 times in a row.

a. Write a probability distribution for the number of wins.

The probabilities are calculated for $n = 5000$ and $p = 0.0001$.

$P(0 \text{ wins})$

$= _{5000}C_0(0.0001)^0(0.9999)^{5000} \approx 0.6065$

$P(1 \text{ wins})$

$= _{5000}C_1(0.0001)^1(0.9999)^{4999} \approx 0.3033$

$P(2 \text{ wins})$

$= _{5000}C_2(0.0001)^2(0.9999)^{4998} \approx 0.0758$

$P(3 \text{ wins})$

$= _{5000}C_3(0.0001)^3(0.9999)^{4997} \approx 0.0126$

$P(4 \text{ or more wins})$

$\approx 1 - 0.6065 - 0.3033 -$
$\qquad 0.0758 - 0.0126 \approx 0.0018$

Outcome	Probability
0 wins	0.6065
1 win	0.3033
2 wins	0.0758
3 wins	0.0126
4 or more wins	0.0018

b. What is the probability that you will break even or better?

To break even, you need to win 1 time because it costs $5000 to play 5000 times, and the prize is $5000. So,

$P(\text{break even or better})$

$\approx 0.3033 + 0.0758 +$
$\qquad 0.0126 + 0.0018$

$= 0.3935$

cesses. Consider the number of outcomes with 3 successes in 5 trials, as shown below. For clarity, the F's are left as blanks.

SSS _ _ SS _ S _ SS _ _ S S _ SS _ S _ S _ S

S _ _ SS _ SSS _   _ SS _ S _ S _ SS _ _ _ SSS

The number of outcomes is the same as the number of ways to choose 3 positions for the S out of 5 possible positions. The order of the S's does not matter, because they are all the same. This is the number of combinations, $_5C_3 = 10$.

Probability of a Binomial Experiment

> In a binomial experiment,
>
> $$P(r \text{ successes in } n \text{ trials}) = {_nC_r}p^rq^{n-r}$$
>
> where p is the probability of success, and $q = 1 - p$ is the probability of failure.

Example 2 Lottery Tickets

A lottery consists of choosing a number from 000 to 999. All digits of the number must be matched in order, so the probability of winning is $\frac{1}{1000} = 0.001$. A ticket costs $1, and the prize is $500. Suppose you play the lottery 1000 times in a row.

a. Write a probability distribution for the number of wins.

b. What is the probability that you will break even or better?

Solution

a. The number of wins could be anything from 0 to 1000. However, the probability of winning more than a few times is so small that it is essentially 0. Thus, the sample space will be considered as 0, 1, 2, 3, 4, and 5 or more wins. The probabilities are calculated using the binomial probability formula, with $n = 1000$ and $p = 0.001$.

$P(0 \text{ wins}) = {_{1000}C_0}(0.001)^0(0.999)^{1000} \approx 0.3677$
$P(1 \text{ win}) = {_{1000}C_1}(0.001)^1(0.999)^{999} \approx 0.3681$
$P(2 \text{ wins}) = {_{1000}C_2}(0.001)^2(0.999)^{998} \approx 0.1840$
$P(3 \text{ wins}) = {_{1000}C_3}(0.001)^3(0.999)^{997} \approx 0.0613$
$P(4 \text{ wins}) = {_{1000}C_4}(0.001)^4(0.999)^{996} \approx 0.0153$
$P(5 \text{ or more wins}) \approx 1 - 0.3677 - 0.3681 - 0.1840 - 0.0613 - 0.0153$
$\qquad \approx 0.0036$

Outcome	0 wins	1 win	2 wins	3 wins	4 wins	5 or more wins
Probability	0.3677	0.3681	0.1840	0.0613	0.0153	0.0036

b. In order to break even or better, you must win 2 or more times. The probability is the sum of the probabilities of winning 2, 3, 4, or 5 or more times.

$$P(\text{break even or better}) \approx 0.1840 + 0.0613 + 0.0153 + 0.0036 \approx 0.2642$$ ∎

Technology Tip

The command binom-pdf(in the DISTR menu of TI finds the probability for r successes in n trials of a binomial experiment, given n, p and r. The command binomcdf(finds the cumulative probability for r or fewer successes in n trials.

```
binompdf(10,0.25
,6)
      .0162220001
binomcdf(10,0.25
,4)
      .9218730926
```

Figure 13.4.A-1

Example 3   Multiple Choice Exam

Morgan is taking a 10-question multiple choice test but has not studied. Each question has 4 possible responses, only one of which is correct. Find the probability of getting the results below if he answers all questions randomly.

a. exactly 6 questions correct

b. 4 or fewer questions correct

c. 8 or more questions correct

Solution

The probability of getting each question correct is $p = \frac{1}{4} = 0.25$.

a. $P(6 \text{ correct}) = {}_{10}C_6(0.25)^6(0.75)^4 \approx 0.016$

b. $P(4 \text{ or fewer correct}) = {}_{10}C_0(0.25)^0(0.75)^{10} + {}_{10}C_1(0.25)^1(0.75)^9 + {}_{10}C_2(0.25)^2(0.75)^8 + {}_{10}C_3(0.25)^3(0.75)^7 + {}_{10}C_4(0.25)^4(0.75)^6 \approx 0.922$

c. $P(8 \text{ or more correct}) = {}_{10}C_8(0.25)^8(0.75)^2 + {}_{10}C_9(0.25)^9(0.75)^1 + {}_{10}C_{10}(0.25)^{10}(0.75)^0 \approx 0.0004$ ∎

Binomial Distributions

Consider the following binomial experiment: a coin is tossed 4 times, and the probability of heads on each toss is $\frac{1}{2}$. A probability distribution for the number of heads is shown below.

Number of heads	0	1	2	3	4
Probability	$\frac{1}{16}$	$\frac{1}{4}$	$\frac{3}{8}$	$\frac{1}{4}$	$\frac{1}{16}$

A probability density function that represents this distribution is shown in Figure 13.4.A-2. Notice that the shape of the graph is symmetric.

The expected value of this distribution is

$$0\left(\frac{1}{16}\right) + 1\left(\frac{1}{4}\right) + 2\left(\frac{3}{8}\right) + 3\left(\frac{1}{4}\right) + 4\left(\frac{1}{16}\right) = 2$$

which is the (approximate) center of the probability distribution.

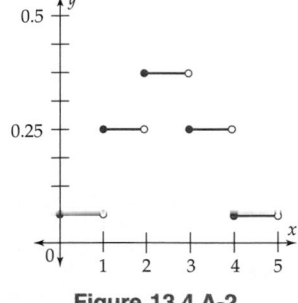

Figure 13.4.A-2

Each question on an 8-question multiple choice test has 5 possible responses, only one of which is correct. Find the probability of getting the results below by answering every question randomly.

a. exactly 5 questions correct

The probability of getting each question correct is $p = \frac{1}{5} = 0.2$.

$P(5 \text{ correct}) = {}_8C_5(0.2)^5(0.8)^3$
≈ 0.009

b. 3 or fewer questions correct

$P(3 \text{ or fewer correct})$
$= {}_8C_0(0.2)^0(0.8)^8 +$
$\quad {}_8C_1(0.2)^1(0.8)^7 + {}_8C_2(0.2)^2(0.8)^6 +$
$\quad\quad {}_8C_3(0.2)^3(0.8)^5$
≈ 0.944

c. 6 or more questions correct

$P(6 \text{ or more correct})$
$= {}_8C_6(0.2)^6(0.8)^2 +$
$\quad {}_8C_7(0.2)^7(0.8)^1 + {}_8C_8(0.2)^8(0.8)^0$
≈ 0.0012

Real-World Application

Examples 2 and **3** provide an excellent opportunity to show students how to apply their knowledge of probability theory to help them make choices in their daily lives.

Many states have lottery games like the one described in **Example 2.** Begin with a discussion of the following basic facts:

- It would cost $1000 to play 1000 times, and the prize is only $500.
- The probability of breaking even or better is 0.2642, only about $\frac{1}{4}$.

Encourage discussion about the probabilities found in the Example, and suggest that students research other lottery games.

Many students do not have a realistic idea of the low probability of getting a particular grade by guessing on a multiple choice test. Use **Example 3** as a basis for discussion.

Teaching Notes

An example of a binomial experiment is to randomly choose a card from 3 cards labeled S, F, and F. The probability of choosing S is $p = \frac{1}{3}$. If 3 trials of this experiment are conducted, then $n = 3$. The first graph in Figure 13.4.A-3 shows the probability distribution for this experiment, where $n = 3$. Have students confirm that the height of the first bar in the histogram is $\frac{8}{27} \approx 0.296$ by both methods shown below:

$P(r \text{ successes in } n \text{ trials}) = {}_nC_r p^r q^{n-r}$

$P(0 \text{ successes in } 3 \text{ trials}) =$

$${}_3C_0 \left(\frac{1}{3}\right)^0 \left(\frac{2}{3}\right)^{3-0} = \frac{3!}{0!3!}(1)\left(\frac{8}{27}\right) = \frac{8}{27}$$

```
binompdf(3,1/3,0
)
       .2962962963
```

Next, have students find the heights of the other bars and construct the histogram on their calculators by entering the heights in a list. (See Technology Appendix if necessary.)

ADDITIONAL EXAMPLES

Example 4

Find the expected value and standard deviation of the number of questions correct on the multiple choice test in **Additional Example 3.**

$n = 8$, $p = 0.2$, and $q = 0.8$.

expected value:

$np = 8(0.2) = 1.6$

standard deviation:

$\sqrt{npq} = \sqrt{8(0.2)(0.8)} \approx 1.1$

This means that if a large number of students guessed randomly on the test, the average number correct would be 1.6, with a standard deviation of 1.1. A graph of the distribution is shown below.

(histogram, y-axis labeled 0.35, x-axis from 0 to 9)

Characteristics of a Binomial Distribution

Figure 13.4.A-4

For large values of n or when p is near $\frac{1}{2}$, the shape of a binomial distribution is approximately symmetric, with its center at the expected value. For small values of n if p is different from $\frac{1}{2}$, the distribution will be skewed. However, as n increases, the distribution becomes more symmetric. The graphs in Figure 13.4.A-3 show the distributions of a binomial experiment with $p = \frac{1}{3}$ for $n = 3$, 10, and 30. The shape of the distribution approaches a special curve, called the *normal curve*, which is developed in the next section.

Figure 13.4.A-3

> The distribution of a binomial experiment with n trials and probability of success p is approximately symmetric for large values of n. The center of the distribution is the expected value.
>
> The expected value of the binomial distribution is np.
>
> The standard deviation of the binomial distribution is $\sqrt{npq}$.

Example 4   Multiple Choice Exam

Find the expected value and standard deviation of the number of questions correct on the multiple choice exam in Example 3.

Solution

In this case, $n = 10$, $p = 0.25$, and $q = 0.75$. The expected value is

$$np = 10(0.25) = 2.5$$

and the standard deviation is

$$\sqrt{npq} = \sqrt{10(0.25)(0.75)} \approx 1.4.$$

This means that if a large number of students guessed on the exam, the average number correct would be 2.5, with a standard deviation of 1.4. A graph of the distribution is shown in Figure 13.4.A-4. ∎

Exercises 13.4.A

For Exercises 1–4, a binomial experiment consists of planting 4 seeds. The probability of success (that a given seed will sprout) is $p = 0.65$. The sample outcome *SFSS* means that the first seed sprouted, the second seed did not sprout, and the third and fourth seeds sprouted.

1. What is the probability of failure? **0.35**

2. Write out the $_4C_2 = 6$ outcomes that have exactly two successes.
SSFF, SFSF, SFFS, FSFS, FSSF, FFSS

3. Complete the probability distribution below.

Sprouted	0	1	2	3	4
Probability	0.015	0.111	0.311	0.384	0.179

4. Find the expected value of the number of seeds that will sprout, and interpret the result. **≈2.6; 2 or 3 of any 4 seeds are expected to sprout.**

For Exercises 5–8, suppose the probability of a certain dart player hitting a bulls-eye is 0.25.

5. Write a probability distribution for the number of bulls-eyes in 4 tries.

6. What is the probability of hitting at least 3 bulls-eyes in 4 tries? **≈0.051**

7. What is the probability of hitting less than 2 bulls-eyes in 4 tries? **≈0.738**

8. What is the expected value of the number of bulls-eyes in 4 tries? **≈1**

A true-false exam has 100 questions, and for each question $P(\text{true}) = P(\text{false}) = 0.5$. What is the probability of answering

9. 50 questions correct? **≈0.0796**

10. 70 questions correct? **≈0.000023**

11. 30 questions correct? **≈0.000023**

12. 90 questions correct? **≈1.366 × 10⁻¹⁷**

13. Find the expected value and standard deviation of the number of correct answers. **50; 5**

An experiment consists of rolling a number cube 30 times. The outcome 6 is considered a success, and all other outcomes are considered failures. Assume all faces are equally likely, so that $p = P(\text{success}) = \frac{1}{6}$.

14. Find the expected value μ of the probability distribution. What is the probability of e successes?

15. What is the probability of $\mu + 1$ successes? What is the probability of $\mu - 1$ successes?
≈0.160; ≈0.185

16. Find the standard deviation σ of the probability distribution. What is the probability that the outcome is between $\mu + \sigma$ and $\mu - \sigma$?
σ ≈ 2.041; 0.784

5.

Bulls-eyes	Probability
0	0.316
1	0.422
2	0.211
3	0.047
4	0.004

14. $\mu = 5; P(e) = {}_{30}C_e \left(\dfrac{1}{6}\right)^e \left(\dfrac{5}{6}\right)^{30-e}$

13.5 **Normal Distributions**

Objectives
- Draw a normal distribution given its mean and standard deviation
- Use normal distributions to find probabilities

To statisticians, the most important probability density function is the **normal curve** (sometimes called the bell curve). **Normal distributions** are used to predict the outcomes of many events, such as the probability that a student scores a 750 on the SAT, or the probability that you will grow to be 67 inches tall. For statisticians, it is also a valuable tool for predicting if an outcome is statistically significant or just caused by chance.

Math Background

Using a normal distribution to make predictions does not take into account certain factors. For example, a prediction about a student's SAT score is valid, assuming we know nothing about that student. However, if we knew the student's IQ score and high school grade point average, then we might want to modify the prediction.

Teaching Notes

Discuss the **Properties of the Normal Curve** in the first paragraph. Students may need a review of inflection points. Refer them to page 154, and show the diagram below. Note that an inflection point is where the concavity changes. A portion of the curve is *concave up* if a segment connecting any two points on that portion lies *above* the curve. A portion of the curve is *concave down* if a segment connecting any two points on that portion lies *below* the curve.

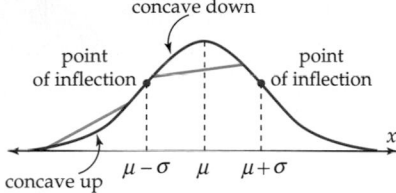

Solution to the **Graphing Exploration** (page 891):

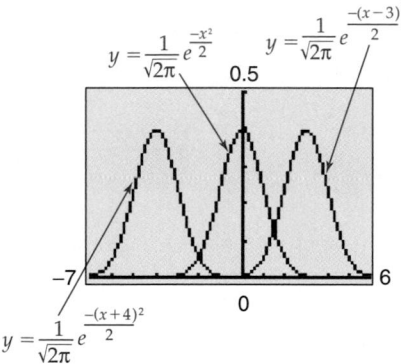

All 3 graphs have the same shape. The first equation is the standard normal curve. The second equation is a horizontal translation of the standard normal curve 3 units to the right. The third equation is a horizontal translation of the standard normal curve 4 units to the left.

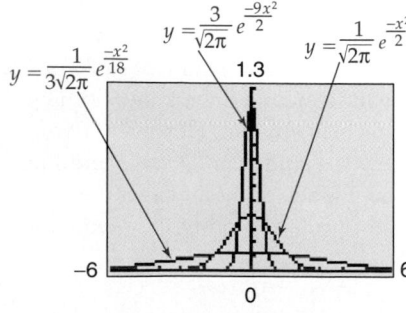

All 3 graphs have the same shape. The first equation is the standard normal curve. The second equation is the standard normal curve stretched horizontally by a factor of 3 and compressed vertically by a factor of $\frac{1}{3}$. The third equation is the standard normal curve compressed horizontally by a factor of $\frac{1}{3}$ and stretched vertically by a factor of 3.

Properties of the Normal Curve

A normal distribution is bell-shaped and symmetric about its mean. The *x*-axis is a horizontal asymptote, and the area under the curve and above the *x*-axis is 1. The maximum value occurs at the mean, and the curve has two points of inflection, at 1 standard deviation to the right and left of the mean.

Because a normal distribution is symmetric, the mean, median, and mode have the same value. This value is also called the *center*. The Greek letter μ (mu) is used to represent the mean of a normally distributed population. Also, the population standard deviation σ is used for the standard deviation.

Figure 13.5-1 shows three normal curves, with μ and σ labeled.

Figure 13.5-1

The normal curve with a mean of 0 and standard deviation of 1 is called the **standard normal curve.** The equation of the standard normal curve is

$$y = \frac{1}{\sqrt{2\pi}} e^{\frac{-x^2}{2}}$$

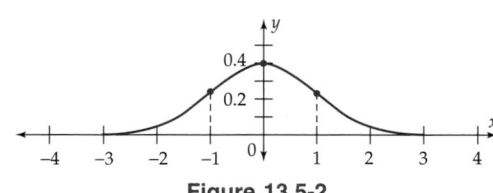

Figure 13.5-2

The standard normal curve can be thought of as a parent function for all normal curves.

- A change in μ results in a horizontal translation of the curve.
- A change in σ results in a horizontal stretch and vertical compression of the curve, or vice versa, so that the resulting area is still 1.

┌─ **Graphing Exploration** ●────────

The normal curves below have the same value of σ and different values of μ. Graph the curves in the same viewing window and describe the results.

$$y = \frac{1}{\sqrt{2\pi}}\,e^{\frac{-x^2}{2}} \qquad y = \frac{1}{\sqrt{2\pi}}\,e^{\frac{-(x-3)^2}{2}} \qquad y = \frac{1}{\sqrt{2\pi}}\,e^{\frac{-(x+4)^2}{2}}$$

The normal curves below have the same value of μ and different values of σ. Graph the curves below in the same viewing window and describe the results.

$$y = \frac{1}{\sqrt{2\pi}}\,e^{\frac{-x^2}{2}} \qquad y = \frac{1}{3\sqrt{2\pi}}\,e^{\frac{-x^2}{18}} \qquad y = \frac{3}{\sqrt{2\pi}}\,e^{\frac{-9x^2}{2}}$$

Equation of Normal Curve
○

A random variable is said to have a **normal distribution** with mean μ and standard deviation σ if its density function is given by the equation

$$y = \frac{1}{\sigma\sqrt{2\pi}}\,e^{\frac{-(x-\mu)^2}{2\sigma^2}}$$

Most of the time, the mean and standard deviation of an entire population cannot be measured. The population mean and standard deviation are often estimated by using a sample.

Example 1 Using Sample Information

A paper in *Animal Behavior* gives 11 sample distances, in cm, from which a bat can first detect a nearby insect. The bat does this by sending out high-pitched sounds and listening for the echoes. Assume the population is normally distributed.

$$62, 23, 27, 56, 52, 34, 42, 40, 68, 45, 83$$

a. Compute the mean and standard deviation of this sample.

b. Draw a normal curve to represent the distribution.

Solution

a. The mean is 48.36 and the sample standard deviation is 18.08, as shown in Figure 13.5-3.

b. The normal curve is shown in Figure 13.5-4.

```
1-Var Stats
x̄=48.36363636
Σx=532
Σx²=29000
Sx=18.08464944
σx=17.24303668
↓n=11
```

Figure 13.5-3

ADDITIONAL EXAMPLES

Example 1

The resting heart rates of 9 students, in beats per minute, are shown below. Assume that the resting heart rates of the student population are normally distributed.

$$65, 62, 60, 57, 66, 64, 63, 74, 71$$

a. Compute the mean and standard deviation of this sample.

```
1-Var Stats
x̄=64.66666667
Σx=582
Σx²=37856
Sx=5.244044241
σx=4.944132325
↓n=9
```

The mean is 64.67 and the sample standard deviation is 5.24.

b. Draw a normal curve to represent the distribution.

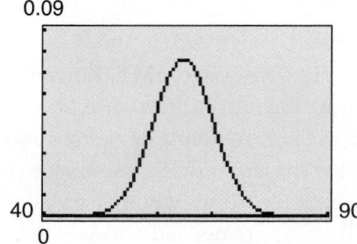

```
Plot1 Plot2 Plot3
\Y1◘1/(5.24√(2π)
)e^(-(X-64.67)²/
(2*5.24²)
\Y2=
\Y3=
\Y4=
\Y5=
```

0.09

40 ─────────────── 90
0

The **Empirical Rule** and the symmetric properties of a normal curve can be used to find areas under the curve. For example: The area under the curve from μ to $\mu + \sigma$ represents 34% of the data values $\left(\frac{1}{2} \text{ of } 68\%\right)$. Therefore, the entire area under the curve to the left of $\mu + \sigma$ represents 50% + 34% = 84% of the data.

Some students might think that the mean in a normal distribution has a 50% chance of occurring. For instance, in **Example 2,** the running shoes last an average (mean) of 450 miles, and thus a student might think that the probability of a pair of running shoes lasting exactly 450 miles is 50%. Emphasize that this is *incorrect.* A *correct* statement would be that there is a 50% probability that the shoes last *less than* (or more than) 450 miles.

Real-World Application

Some colleges require the SAT (Scholastic Aptitude Test) for admissions, and some colleges require the ACT (American College Test). The scales on these tests are very different; an SAT score can range from 200 to 800 while an ACT score can range from 0 to 36. But because scores on both tests are *normally distributed,* they can be compared by using the mean and standard deviation as shown in **Example 3** (page 894).

Example 5 (page 895) is about normally distributed EMT (Emergency Medical Technician) response times. Using mean, standard deviation, and probability, city officials can make decisions regarding whether more EMT teams are needed and where to locate them.

Figure 13.5-4

The Empirical Rule

Consider the intervals formed by one, two, and three standard deviations on either side of the mean, as shown below. The **empirical rule** describes the areas under the normal curve over these intervals.

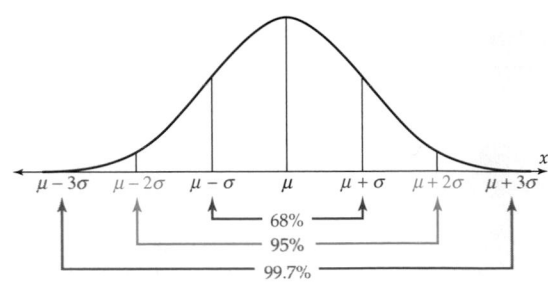

Empirical Rule

NOTE Each percentage in the empirical rule can also be interpreted as the probability that a data value chosen at random will lie within one, two, or three standard deviations of the mean.

In a normal distribution:

- about **68%** of the data values are within one standard deviation of the mean.
- about **95%** of the data values are within two standard deviations of the mean.
- about **99.7%** of the data values are within three standard deviations of the mean.

Example 2   **Running Shoes**

A pair of running shoes lasts an average of 450 miles, with a standard deviation of 50 miles. Use the empirical rule to find the probability that a new pair of shoes will have the following lifespans, in miles.

a. between 400 and 500 miles

b. more than 550 miles

Solution

Figure 13.5-5 shows the normal distribution with the intervals of one, two, and three standard deviations on either side of the mean.

Figure 13.5-5

a. The area under the curve between 400 and 500 miles is approximately 68% of the total area. Since the area under a density function corresponds to the probability, the probability that a pair of shoes will last between 400 and 500 miles is about 0.68.

b. The area under the curve between 350 and 550 miles is 95% of the total area, which leaves 5% for the area less than 350 and greater than 550. Since the normal curve is symmetric, the area greater than 550 is exactly half of this, or 2.5%. Thus, the probability that a pair of shoes will last more than 550 miles is about 0.025. ■

The Standard Normal Curve

In general, determining the area under a normal curve is very difficult. Because of this, it is common to **standardize** data to match the normal curve with a mean of 0 and standard deviation of 1, for which these areas are known.

Comparing Data Sets

Sarah and Megan are high school juniors. Sarah scored 660 on the SAT, and Megan scored 29 on the ACT. Who did better? Although the scores on both tests are normally distributed, the mean and standard deviation are very different. One way to compare the distributions is to adjust the scales of the axes, as shown in Figure 13.5-6.

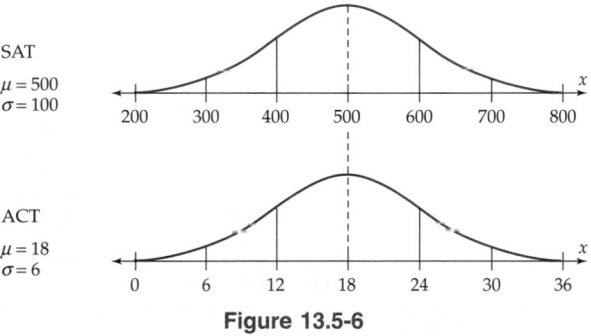

Figure 13.5-6

ADDITIONAL EXAMPLES

Example 2

Scores on a certain IQ test for people 16 and above are approximately normally distributed with $\mu = 100$ and $\sigma = 15$. Use the empirical rule to find the probability that a person will have the following scores on this IQ test.

a. between 85 and 100

The graph below shows the normal distribution of IQ scores, with intervals of one, two, and three standard deviations on either side of the mean.

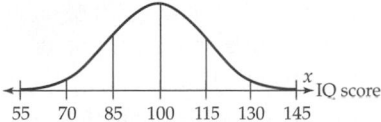

The area under the curve between 85 and 115 is approximately 68% of the total area. The area between 85 and 100 is one-half of the area between 85 and 115, or 34%. So, the probability that someone's IQ score is between 85 and 100 is about 0.34.

b. greater than 115

The area under the curve greater than 115 is equal to the entire area under the curve minus the area under the curve to the left of 115. The area to the left of 100 is 50% of the total area, and the area between 100 and 115 is about 34%. The area to the right of 115 is approximately $1 - (50\% + 34\%) = 16\%$. So, the probability of someone having an IQ greater than 115 is about 0.16.

Teaching Notes

Emphasize the importance of sketching the normal curve as in Figure 13.5-6 when solving problems. Each graph should show the mean and 1, 2, and 3 standard deviations on either side of the mean.

Teaching Notes

While discussing *z*-Values, have students relate the formula $z = \frac{x - \mu}{\sigma}$ to the two test scores in **Example 3.** In Sarah's case, $z = \frac{660 - 500}{100} = 1.6$ and in Megan's case, $z = \frac{29 - 18}{6} = 1.83$. Point out that this is the same method used in the Solution to Example 3.

To prepare students for **Examples 4** and **5**, have them use the table of *z*-values (page 895) to estimate the area of the shaded region in Figure 13.5-8.

z appears to be at about 0.5, so the area of the shaded region is approximately 0.19.

Next, have them estimate the area of the region underneath the curve *to the right* of the shaded region and explain how they found their answer. Because the normal curve is symmetric to the *y*-axis, the area of the region to the right of the *y*-axis is 0.5. So, the area of the region under the curve to the right of the shaded region is about $0.50 - 0.19 = 0.31$.

COMMON ERROR ALERT

Students may subtract in the wrong order when finding a *z*-value, resulting in a sign error. If a data value is less than the mean, then its *z*-value must be negative. If a data value is greater than the mean, then its *z*-value must be positive.

A more precise way to compare two scores from different data sets is to use the standard deviation as a unit of measurement. Each score is represented by the number of standard deviations above or below the mean.

Example 3   Comparing Scores

Use the standard deviation as a unit of measurement to compare the SAT and ACT scores for Sarah and Megan.

Solution

Sarah's score of 660 is 160 points above the mean, which is 500. The standard deviation is 100, so Sarah's score is $\frac{160}{100} = 1.6$ standard deviations above the mean.

Megan's score of 29 is 11 points above the mean, which is 18. The standard deviation is 6, so Megan's score is $\frac{11}{6} \approx 1.83$ standard deviations above the mean. Thus, Megan's score is better than Sarah's score. ■

The number of standard deviations that a data value is above the mean is called the *z*-**value.** In Example 3, Sarah's *z*-value is 1.6 and Megan's *z*-value is 1.83. For a normal distribution, the *z*-values correspond to values on the standard normal curve, as shown in Figure 13.5-7.

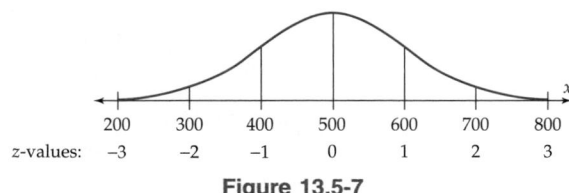

	200	300	400	500	600	700	800
z-values:	−3	−2	−1	0	1	2	3

Figure 13.5-7

z-Values

> The *z-value* of the value x in a data set with mean μ and standard deviation σ is
>
> $$z = \frac{x - \mu}{\sigma}$$
>
> The area under a normal curve between $x = a$ and $x = b$ is equal to the area under the standard normal curve between the *z*-value of a and the *z*-value of b.

Once *z*-values are determined, corresponding areas under the normal curve are often found using a table. Because of the symmetry of the normal curve, it is only necessary to include positive *z*-values in the table.

The following table gives the area under the normal curve between 0 and the given z-values, as shown in Figure 13.5-8.

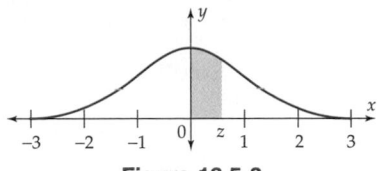

Figure 13.5-8

z	0.1	0.2	0.3	0.4	0.5	0.6	0.7	0.8	0.9	1
Area	0.04	0.08	0.12	0.16	0.19	0.23	0.26	0.29	0.32	0.34

Example 4   **Using z-Values to Determine Area**

A normally distributed data set has a mean of 25 and a standard deviation of 5. Find the probability that a data value chosen at random is between 23 and 28.

Solution

First, find the z-values for 23 and 28, given $\mu = 25$ and $\sigma = 5$.

$$z = \frac{23 - 25}{5} = -0.4 \qquad z = \frac{28 - 25}{5} = 0.6$$

Divide the area into two parts: the area from -0.4 to 0, and the area from 0 to 0.6, as shown in Figure 13.5-9. The areas are found in the table above. Because the normal curve is symmetric with respect to $x = 0$, the area from -0.4 to 0 is the same as the area from 0 to 0.4, or 0.16. The area from 0 to 0.6 is 0.23. The total area is the sum of the two areas, 0.39. Thus, the probability that a randomly chosen data value is between 23 and 28 is 0.39.

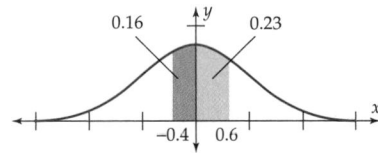

Figure 13.5-9

Example 5   **Response Times**

The EMT response time for an emergency is the difference between the time the call is received and the time the ambulance arrives on the scene. Suppose the response times for a given city have a normal distribution

So, the total area is $0.34 + 0.19 = 0.53$. Thus, the probability that a randomly chosen data value is between 66 and 78 is 0.53.

Technology Tip

Normalcdf under the DISTR menu of TI will calculate the area under the normal curve in a given interval. The parameters are Normalcdf (lower bound, upper bound, μ, σ).

ADDITIONAL EXAMPLES

Example 3

As the SAT is used for college admissions, the GRE is used for graduate school admissions. A sample of verbal scores and quantitative scores from the GRE are both normally distributed, with the values of μ and σ given below.

	Verbal	Quantitative
μ	470	550
σ	121	148

Kevin scored 610 on the verbal section and 700 on the quantitative section. Use the standard deviation as a unit of measurement to compare Kevin's verbal and quantitative scores on the GRE.

Kevin's verbal score of 610 is 140 points above the mean, which is 470. The standard deviation is 121, so his verbal score is $\frac{140}{121} \approx 1.16$ standard deviations above the mean.
Kevin's quantitative score of 700 is 150 points above the mean, which is 550. The standard deviation is 148, so his quantitative score is $\frac{150}{148} \approx 1.01$ standard deviations above the mean. Thus, Kevin's verbal score is better than his quantitative score.

Example 4

A normally distributed data set has a mean of 74 and a standard deviation of 8. Find the probability that a data value chosen at random is between 66 and 78.
With $\mu = 74$ and $\sigma = 8$, the z-values for 66 and 78 are

$$z = \frac{66 - 74}{8} = -1 \quad z = \frac{78 - 74}{8} = 0.5$$

Divide the area into two parts: the area from -1 to 0 and the area from 0 to 0.5. Use the table to find the area under the normal curve. Because the normal curve is symmetric with respect to $x = 0$, the area from -1 to 0 is the same as the area from 0 to 1, and the value from the table for $z = 1$ is 0.34. Therefore, the value for $z = -1$ is 0.34. The value for $z = 0.5$ is 0.19.

Example 5

Oxides of nitrogen (NO_x), which include nitrous oxide, nitric oxide, and nitrogen dioxide, contribute to smog and the depletion of the ozone layer. The concentrations of NO_x in a group of air samples collected from a certain automobile's exhaust at startup had a mean of 27.8 ppm (parts per million) with a standard deviation of 13.9 ppm. Assume the concentrations of NO_x at startup from this automobile have a normal distribution. Estimate the probability of each of the following concentrations of NO_x in a random sample from this automobile.

a. less than 41.7 ppm

$z = \dfrac{41.7 - 27.8}{13.9} = 1$

The area under a standard normal curve to the left of $z = 1$ is $0.5 + 0.34 = 0.84$. So, the probability of a concentration less than 41.7 ppm is 0.84.

b. more than 27.8 ppm

$z = \dfrac{27.8 - 27.8}{13.9} = 0.$

The area to the right of $z = 0$ is 0.5. So, the probability of a concentration more than 27.8 ppm is 0.5.

c. more than 19.5 ppm

$z = \dfrac{19.5 - 27.8}{13.9} \approx -0.6$

The area between $z = -0.6$ and $z = 0$ is 0.23. So, the probability of a concentration more than 19.5 ppm is $0.23 + 0.5 = 0.73$.

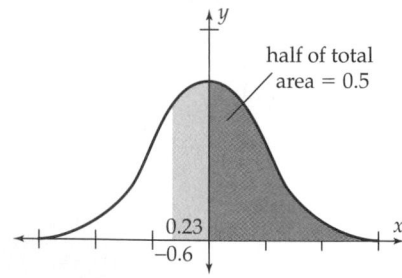

with $\mu = 6$ minutes and $\sigma = 1.2$ minutes. For a randomly received call, estimate the probability of the following response times.

a. between 6 and 7 minutes   **b.** less than 5 minutes

c. less than 7 minutes

Solution

a. The z-values are $z = \dfrac{6 - 6}{1.2} = 0$ and $z = \dfrac{7 - 6}{1.2} \approx 0.8$. The probability of a response time between 6 and 7 minutes is the area under the standard normal curve from 0 to 0.8, which is approximately 0.29.

b. The z-value is $z = \dfrac{5 - 6}{1.2} \approx -0.8$. The area from 0 to -0.8 is approximately 0.29, so the probability of a response time under 5 minutes is about $0.5 - 0.29 = 0.21$ (see Figure 13.5-10).

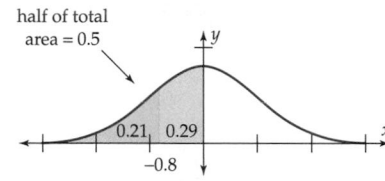

Figure 13.5-10

c. The area under the curve from 0 to 6 minutes is 0.5. From part **a**, the area under the curve from 6 to 7 minutes is 0.29. Thus, the probability of a response time under 7 minutes is $0.5 + 0.29 = 0.79$. ∎

Exercises 13.5

In Exercises 1–4, refer to the normal curve below. The area of each square of the grid is 0.01.

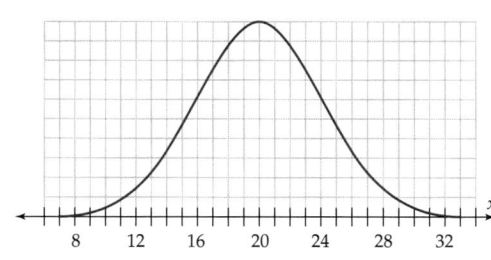

1. Find μ. **20**   **2.** Estimate σ. **≈4**

3. Estimate the area under the curve from 16 to 24.
≈0.68

4. Estimate the area under the curve from 12 to 28.
≈0.95

Graph the normal curves for the following values of μ and σ.

5. $\mu = 10, \sigma = 12$ **6.** $\mu = 40, \sigma = 12$

7. $\mu = 500, \sigma = 100$ **8.** $\mu = 3, \sigma = 5$

Suppose the heights of adult men are normally distributed. The heights of a sample of 30 men are shown below, in inches.

65, 83, 69, 67, 69, 67, 67, 72, 85, 68, 73, 65, 67, 65, 72, 71, 67, 73, 68, 72, 61, 75, 66, 78, 65, 71, 68, 76, 67, 68

Exercises 13.5

ANSWERS

5.

6.

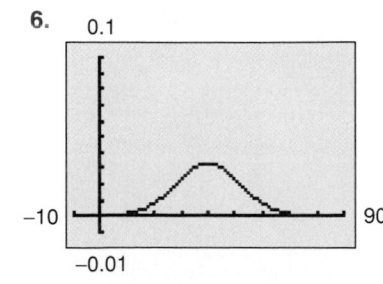

9. Compute the mean and standard deviation of this sample. **70; ≈5.228**

10. Draw a normal curve that represents the distribution of adult male heights, based on the sample.

Suppose that the heights of adult women are normally distributed with $\mu = 65$ inches and $\sigma = 2.5$ inches. Use the properties of the normal curve and the Empirical Rule to find the probability that a randomly chosen woman is within the given range.

11. taller than 65 inches **0.5**

12. shorter than 67.5 inches **0.84**

13. between 62.5 inches and 67.5 inches **0.68**

14. between 60 inches and 70 inches **0.95**

15. between 57.5 inches and 67.5 inches **0.8385**

16. A student took two national standardized tests while applying for college. On the first test, $\mu = 475$ and $\sigma = 75$, and on the second test, $\mu = 32$ and $\sigma = 6$. If he scored 630 on the first test and 45 on the second, on which test did he do better?
    second test

17. Four students took a national standardized test for which the mean was 500 and the standard deviation was 100. Their scores were 560, 450, 640, and 530. Determine the z-value for each student.

18. If a student's z-value was 1.75 on the test described in problem 17, what was the student's score?
    675

19. A sample of restaurants in a city showed that the average cost of a glass of iced tea is $1.25 with a standard deviation of 7¢. Three of the restaurants charge 95¢, $1.00, and $1.35. Determine the z-value for each restaurant.

20. If a new restaurant charges a price for iced tea that has a z-value of -1.25 (see Exercise 19), then what is the tea's actual cost? **$1.16**

At a certain restaurant, the wait time for a table is normally distributed with $\mu = 30$ minutes and $\sigma = 10$ minutes. Use the table on page 895 to estimate the following:

21. the probability that the wait time for a table is between 30 and 35 minutes **0.19**

22. the probability that the wait time for a table is between 24 and 30 minutes **0.23**

23. the probability that the wait time for a table is between 25 and 38 minutes
    0.48

24. the probability that the wait time for a table is less than 22 minutes
    0.21

Daytime high temperatures in New York in February are normally distributed with an average of 30.2° and a standard deviation of 8.5°.

25. Estimate the probability that the temperature on a given day in February is 39° or higher.
    0.16

26. Estimate the probability that the temperature on a given day in February is 22° or lower.
    0.16

27. Estimate the probability that the temperature on a given day in February is between 13° and 39°.
    0.815

28. Estimate the probability that the temperature on a given day in February is between 25° and 30°.
    0.23

29. Estimate the probability that the temperature on a given day in February is between 27° and 38°.
    0.48

The *quartiles* of a normal distribution are the values that divide the area under the curve into fourths.

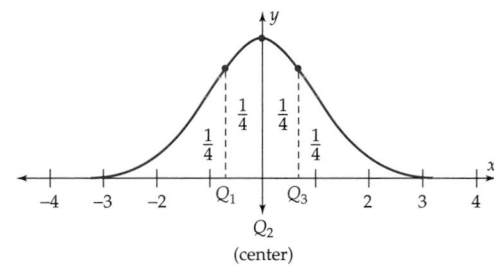
(center)

The 1ˢᵗ and 3ʳᵈ quartiles are approximately 0.675σ to the left and right of the mean, or

$$Q_1 = \mu - 0.675\sigma \quad \text{and} \quad Q_3 = \mu + 0.675\sigma$$

30. Find Q_1 and Q_3 for a distribution with $\mu = 20$ and $\sigma = 4$.
    $Q_1 = 17.3$; $Q_3 = 22.7$

31. Suppose the scores on an exam are normally distributed with $\mu = 70$ and $\sigma = 10$. Find Q_1 and Q_3, and interpret the result.

32. For the exam in Exercise 31, what exam score would place a student in the top 25% of the class?
    a score of 76.75 or above

7. 0.01

8.

10. 0.2
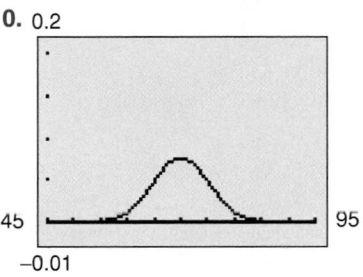

17. $560 \rightarrow 0.6$ z-value
    $450 \rightarrow -0.5$ z-value
    $640 \rightarrow 1.4$ z-value
    $530 \rightarrow 0.3$ z-value

19. $0.95 \rightarrow -4.29$ z-value
    $1.00 \rightarrow -3.57$ z-value
    $1.35 \rightarrow 1.43$ z-value

31. $Q_1 = 63.25$; $Q_3 = 76.75$;
    Fifty percent of the scores fall between 63.25 and 76.75.

CHAPTER 13

Review

CHAPTER
13
REVIEW

Important Concepts

898

Important Facts and Formulas

mean: $\bar{x} = \dfrac{\Sigma x_i}{n}$

If $x_1, x_2, x_3, \dots x_n$ are ordered from smallest to largest, then the median is the middle entry when n is odd and the average of the two middle entries when n is even.

$$\text{median} = \begin{cases} \text{for } n \text{ odd, the value in the } \dfrac{n+1}{2} \text{ position} \\ \text{for } n \text{ even, the average of the values in} \\ \quad \text{the } \dfrac{n}{2} \text{ and } \dfrac{n}{2} + 1 \text{ positions} \end{cases}$$

Population standard deviation

$$\sigma = \sqrt{\dfrac{\Sigma(x_i - \bar{x})^2}{n}}$$

Sample standard deviation

$$s = \sqrt{\dfrac{\Sigma(x_i - \bar{x})^2}{n-1}}$$

Suppose an experiment has a sample space of n outcomes, all of which are equally likely. Then the probability of each outcome is $\dfrac{1}{n}$, and the probability of an event E is given by

$$P(E) = \dfrac{\text{number of outcomes in } E}{n}$$

Fundamental Counting Principle

Consider a set of k experiments. Suppose the first experiment has n_1 outcomes, the second has n_2 outcomes, and so on. Then the total number of outcomes is $n_1 \cdot n_2 \cdot \dots \cdot n_k$ for all k experiments.

Permutations

If r items are chosen in order without replacement from n possible items, the number of permutations is

$$_nP_r = \dfrac{n!}{(n-r)!}$$

Combinations

If r items are chosen in any order without replacement from n possible items, the number of combinations is

$$_nC_r = \dfrac{n!}{r!(n-r)!}$$

In a binomial experiment, $P(r \text{ successes in } n \text{ trials}) = {}_nC_r p^r q^{n-r}$ where p is the probability of success, and $q = 1 - p$ is the probability of failure. The expected value of a binomial distribution is np, and the standard deviation is $\sqrt{npq}$.

A random variable is said to have a normal distribution with mean μ and standard deviation σ if its density function is given by the equation

$$y = \frac{1}{\sigma\sqrt{2\pi}}e^{-\frac{(x-\mu)^2}{2\sigma^2}}$$

Empirical Rule

In a normal distribution:

- about 68% of the data values are within one standard deviation of the mean.

- about 95% of the data values are within two standard deviations of the mean.

- about 99.7% of the data values are within three standard deviations of the mean.

The z-value of the value x in a data set with mean μ and standard deviation σ is $z = \dfrac{x - \mu}{\sigma}$.

Review Exercises

ANSWERS

2.

Type of bird	Frequency	Relative frequency
sparrow	12	39.6%
purple finch	15	28.3%
chickadee	10	18.9%
cardinal	5	9.4%
blue jay	2	3.8%

3.

4.

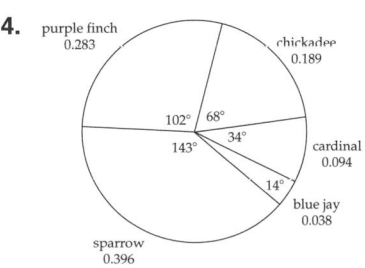

Review Exercises

Exercises 1–4 refer to the following description: A group of bird-watchers is trying to determine what types of birds are common to their area. The group observed 21 sparrows, 15 purple finches, 10 chickadees, 5 cardinals, and 2 blue jays.

Section **13.1**

1. Is the data qualitative or quantitative? **qualitative**

2. Create a frequency table for the data.

3. Create a bar graph for the data.

4. Create a pie chart for the data.

Exercises 5–17 refer to the following description: a study is done to determine the average commuting time of employees at a company. A total of 34 employees are surveyed, with the following results (in minutes).

31.9, 34, 30.7, 39, 33.1, 35.2, 30.5, 32.7, 29.4, 33.4, 22.3, 31.9, 32.3, 29.4, 33, 18.2, 29.1, 32.5, 22.2, 36.1, 27.7, 36, 31.9, 26, 31.7, 23.2, 30.7, 24.4, 33, 28.4, 28.8, 23.3, 32.2, 22.8

5. Is the data qualitative or quantitative? **quantitative**

6. Is the data discrete or continuous? **discrete with an interval of 0.1**

7. Create a stem plot for the data.

8. Create a histogram for the data with class intervals of 5 minutes.

9. Use your histogram from Exercise 8 to describe the shape of the data.
skewed left

Section **13.2**
10. Find the mean of the data.
≈29.9

11. Find the median of the data.
31.2

12. Find the mode of the data.
31.9

13. Find the sample standard deviation of the data.
≈4.72

14. Find the range of the data.
20.8

15. Find the first and third quartiles of the data.
$Q_1 = 27.7$; $Q_3 = 33$

16. Find the interquartile range of the data.
5.3

17. Create a box plot for the data.

Section **13.3**
Exercises 18–22 refer to the following probability distribution:

Outcome	1	2	3	4	5
Probability	0.1	**0.2**	0.4	**0.2**	0.1

18. List the sample space for the probability distribution. **{1, 2, 3, 4, 5}**

19. Suppose the probabilities are the same for outcomes 2 and 4. Complete the probability distribution. **see table above**

20. What is the probability that the outcome is an even number? **0.4**

21. What is the probability that the outcome is greater than 2? **0.7**

22. Suppose the experiment with the given probability distribution is repeated 3 times. Assuming the trials are independent, what is the probability of the outcome {1, 2, 3}? **0.048**

An experiment consists of spinning the spinner at left 3 times. A probability distribution for the outcomes is given below. (W = white, R = red)

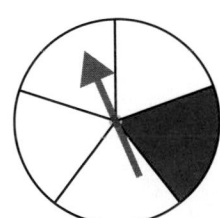

Outcome	WWW	WWR	WRW	RWW	WRR	RWR	RRW	RRR
Probability	0.512	0.128	0.128	0.128	0.032	0.032	0.032	0.008

A random variable is assigned to the number of times the spinner lands on red.

23. What is the range of the random variable? **0 to 3**

24. What is the probability that the value of the random variable is 2?
0.096

7.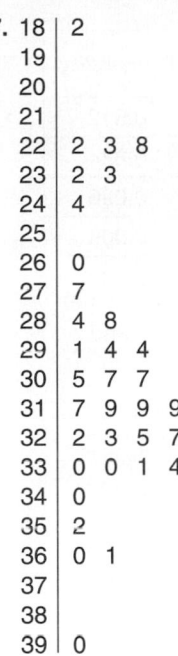

```
18 | 2
19 |
20 |
21 |
22 | 2  3  8
23 | 2  3
24 | 4
25 |
26 | 0
27 | 7
28 | 4  8
29 | 1  4  4
30 | 5  7  7
31 | 7  9  9  9
32 | 2  3  5  7
33 | 0  0  1  4
34 | 0
35 | 2
36 | 0  1
37 |
38 |
39 | 0
```

Key 18|2 represents 18.2

8.

17.

25.

Number of of red	Probability
0	0.512
1	0.384
2	0.096
3	0.008

26. 0.6; In 3 spins, the spinner can be expected to land on red 0.6 times.

27.

28.

Outcome	Probability
WWW	0.52
WWR	0.12
WRW	0.16
RWW	0.12
WRR	0
RWR	0.04
RRW	0.04
RRR	0

25. Create a probability distribution for the random variable.

26. Find the expected value of the random variable, and interpret the result.

27. Graph the probability density function of the random variable, and shade the area of the graph that corresponds to the probability that the spinner lands on white 3 times.

Section **13.4**

28. Suppose the experiment is repeated 25 times, with the following results: WRW, RRW, WWW, WWW, WWW, WWW, WWR, RWW, WWW, WRW, WWW, WWR, WWW, RWW, WWW, RWR, WWW, WRW, WWW, RWW, WWW, WWW, WRW, WWW, WWR
Write a probability distribution of the random variable, based on the experimental results. How do the probabilities compare to your results in Exercise 25?

Exercises 29–33 refer to the following experiment: A sock drawer contains 6 identical black socks, 8 identical white socks, and 1 blue sock. A sock is chosen randomly from the drawer. Assume all socks are equally likely to be chosen.

29. What is the probability of choosing a black sock? a white sock? a blue sock?
0.4; ≈0.53; ≈0.07

30. Suppose a black sock is chosen. What is the probability that the next sock chosen will also be black? *Hint*: how many of each color are left in the drawer?
≈0.36

31. Suppose a white sock is chosen. What is the probability that the next sock chosen will also be white? *Hint*: how many of each color are left in the drawer?
0.5

32. Suppose a blue sock is chosen. What is the probability that the next sock chosen will also be blue? *Hint*: how many of each color are left in the drawer?
0

33. Use your results from Exercises 30 – 32 to determine the probability of choosing a pair if two socks are chosen randomly from the drawer.
0.86

34. A lottery ticket involves matching 5 numbers between 1 and 50 in any order. What is the probability of matching all 5 numbers? What is the probability of matching any 4 numbers?
≈0.0000005; ≈0.000106

35. Suppose there are 4 people on a subcommittee, and you do not know their last names. If you have a list of 10 last names of all of the people in the committee, what is the probability of correctly guessing the last names of the people in the subcommittee?
≈0.0048

Section **13.4.A** A binomial experiment consists of randomly choosing 7 tiles imprinted with letters of the alphabet. An outcome of a vowel is considered a success, and a consonant is considered a failure. The probability of success is $p = 0.44$.

36. Complete the probability distribution below for the number of vowels.

Number of vowels	0	1	2	3	4	5	6	7
Probability	0.017	0.095	0.224	0.293	0.230	0.109	0.028	0.003

37. Find the expected value and standard deviation of the number of vowels.
   3.076; ≈1.3

Suppose the scores on an exam are normally distributed with $\mu = 75$ and $\sigma = 8$. Use properties of the normal curve, the empirical rule, and the table on page 895 to answer Exercises 38–46.

Section **13.5** **38.** Write the equation of the normal curve for the distribution of the scores.

39. Graph the normal curve for the distribution of the scores.

40. Estimate the probability that a randomly chosen score is greater than 75.
   0.50

41. Estimate the probability that a randomly chosen score is between 67 and 83.
   0.68

42. Estimate the probability that a randomly chosen score is greater than 59.
   0.975

43. Estimate the probability that a randomly chosen score is less than 99.
   0.9985

44. Estimate the probability that a randomly chosen score is between 75 and 78.
   0.16

45. Estimate the probability that a randomly chosen score is between 70 and 82.
   0.55

46. Estimate the probability that a randomly chosen score is less than 74.
   0.46

38. $y = \dfrac{1}{8\sqrt{2\pi}} e^{\frac{-(x-75)^2}{2 \cdot 8^2}}$

39. 0.1

40   110

−0.01

CHAPTER 13
can do calculus

Area Under a Curve

Math Background

Students will learn in calculus to find area by evaluating definite integrals. If the curve in Figure 13.C-1 is the graph of a function $f(x)$, then the area of the shaded region is given by

$$\int_a^b f(x)\,dx.$$

The **Area Under a Curve** means area *under* the curve and *above* the x-axis. So, if the curve is the graph of a function f and the x-axis is $g(x) = 0$, the area under the curve is the area *between* the graphs of f and g.

In general, the area from a to b between the graphs of two functions f and g is given by $\int_a^b [f(x) - g(x)]\,dx$ (if f and g are continuous and $g(x) \leq f(x)$ on $[a, b]$). The figure below shows one possible illustration.

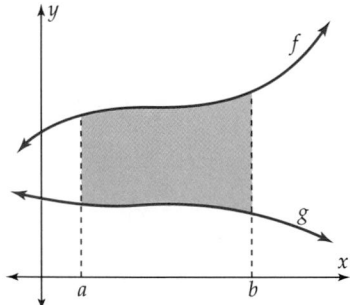

ADDITIONAL EXAMPLES

Example 1

Suppose that a point in the rectangle in Figure 13.C-1 is chosen at random. If A is the area of the shaded region, write a formula in terms of A, a, b, and h for the probability that the point is *not* in the shaded region.

CHAPTER 13
can do calculus

Area Under a Curve

Many applications of calculus involve finding the area under a curve. In probability, for example, it is often necessary to find areas under a normal curve or other probability density function. In other areas, such as physics, the area under a curve can be used to determine total distance traveled or the total amount of force on an object. In this section, properties of probability are used to estimate the area under a curve.

Example 1 Area Model for Probability

Consider the graph in Figure 13.C-1. Suppose a point in the rectangle is chosen randomly. If A is the area of the shaded region, write a formula in terms of A, a, b, and h for the probability that the point is in the shaded region.

Solution

If the point is chosen randomly, then all points in the sample space are equally likely to be chosen. The sample space is all points in the rectangle, and the event above can be described as the set of all points in the shaded area, both of which are infinite. Since it is impossible to divide the number of outcomes in the event by the number of outcomes in the sample space, the areas of the regions are used instead. The area of the rectangle is $h(b - a)$.

$$P(E) = \frac{\text{area of shaded region}}{\text{area of rectangle}} = \frac{A}{h(b - a)}$$

A probability simulation can also be used to find the probability in Example 1. Suppose $n = 1000$ points in the rectangle are chosen randomly, and 470 of them are in the shaded region. Recall that the experimental estimate of the probability of an event is

$$P(E) \approx \frac{\text{number of trials with an outcome in } E}{n} \approx \frac{470}{1000} \approx 0.47$$

By setting the two probability estimates equal to each other and solving, a formula can be found for the area A in terms of a, b, and h.

$$\frac{A}{h(b - a)} \approx 0.47$$
$$A \approx 0.47\,h(b - a)$$

The event that a point is not in the shaded region is the complement of the event that a point is in the shaded region. In **Example 1,** the probability that a randomly chosen point is in the shaded region is $\frac{A}{h(b - a)}$. Therefore, the probability that a randomly chosen point is not in the shaded region is $1 - \frac{A}{h(b - a)}$.

Figure 13.C-1

Area Under a Curve

In general, the area A under a curve between the x-values a and b with $a < b$ may be estimated as follows:

1. Draw a rectangle with a base of length $b - a$ that contains the desired area. Let h be the height of the rectangle.

2. Randomly choose n points in the rectangle, using a calculator or computer. Determine the number of points e that lie in the desired area.

3. The area is approximated by the formula below.

$$A \approx \frac{e}{n} h(b - a)$$

Using Probability Simulations

To generate a large number of points and determine the number of points that lie under a curve, a calculator or computer program is usually used. A sample program is given below. The equation of the graph must be entered in Y_1, and the calculator window should contain the desired region. Note: the choice of window will not affect the answer.

Prompt A	*A is the left bound of the rectangle.*
Prompt B	*B is the right bound of the rectangle.*
Prompt H	*H is the height of the rectangle.*
Prompt N	*N is the number of points in the rectangle.*
$0 \rightarrow E$	*E is the number of points in the shaded region.*
For (K, 1, N)	
$(B - A)$rand $+ A \rightarrow X$	*This command generates an x-coordinate, X.*
H rand $\rightarrow Y$	*This command generates a y-coordinate, Y.*
Pt-On (X, Y)	*This command displays the point (X, Y).*
If $Y \le Y_1(X)$	*The point is tested to determine whether it is*
$E + 1 \rightarrow E$	*under the curve.*
End	
Disp (E/N)H(B − A)	*This command displays the estimate of the area.*

Example 2   Area of a Quarter-Circle

Use a probability simulation to estimate the area under the curve with equation $y = \sqrt{1 - x^2}$ from 0 to 1. Since this region is one-fourth of a circle with radius 1, the area should be $\frac{\pi}{4} \approx 0.785$.

905

Example 2

Use a probability simulation to estimate the area under the graph of $y = 3x + 5$ from 0 to 1.

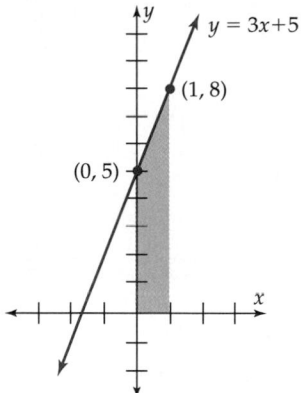

Since the region is a trapezoid with $h = 1$ and bases of 5 and 8, the estimated area should be close to the actual area, which is $\frac{1}{2}(1)(5 + 8) = 6.5$.

The result of a simulation with $n = 500$ points is shown in the figure below. The area estimate is 6.608, which is very close to the predicted area.

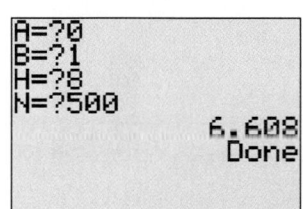

Example Notes

For **Example 3**, ask students to show that the equation $y = 0.03989e^{-0.005(x-70)^2}$ is indeed the equation of the normal curve with $\mu = 70$ and $\sigma = 10$.

$$y = \frac{1}{\sigma\sqrt{2\pi}}e^{\frac{-(x-\mu)^2}{2\sigma^2}}$$

$$= \frac{1}{10\sqrt{2\pi}}e^{\frac{-(x-70)^2}{2(10)^2}}$$

$$\approx 0.03989e^{-0.005(x-70)^2}$$

ADDITIONAL EXAMPLES

Example 3

a. Use a probability simulation to estimate the area under the normal curve with $\mu = 55$ and $\sigma = 15$ between $a = 70$ and $b = 80$. Find the equation of the normal curve with $\mu = 55$ and $\sigma = 15$:

$$y = \frac{1}{\sigma\sqrt{2\pi}}e^{\frac{-(x-\mu)^2}{2\sigma^2}}$$

$$= \frac{1}{15\sqrt{2\pi}}e^{\frac{-(x-55)^2}{2(15)^2}}$$

$$\approx 0.02660e^{-0.00222(x-55)^2}$$

The graph of this normal curve is shown below with h chosen as 0.016 for the interval from 70 to 80. The result of a simulation with $n = 500$ points is also shown. The area estimate is 0.11296.

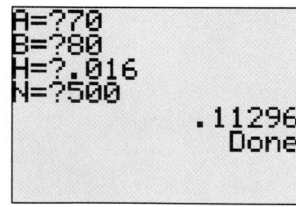

b. Suppose the scores on an exam are normally distributed with $\mu = 55$ and $\sigma = 15$. Estimate the probability that a randomly chosen score is between 70 and 80.

The probability that a randomly chosen score is between 70 and 80 is approximately the area under the normal curve, or about 0.11.

Solution

The result of a simulation with $n = 500$ points is shown in Figure 13.C-2. The area estimate is 0.782, which is very close to the predicted area.

Figure 13.C-2

This method can also be used to find areas under a normal curve.

Example 3   Area Under a Normal Curve

a. Use a probability simulation to estimate the area under the normal curve with $\mu = 70$ and $\sigma = 10$ between $a = 85$ and $b = 95$.

b. Suppose the scores on an exam are normally distributed with $\mu = 70$ and $\sigma = 10$. Estimate the probability that a randomly chosen score is between 85 and 95.

Solution

a. The normal curve has the equation $y = 0.03989e^{-0.005(x-70)^2}$. Trace to find a good value of h. The closer the value of h is to the maximum value of the function over the given interval, the better the estimate will be. A good choice of h is 0.014. The result of a simulation with $n = 500$ points is shown in Figure 13.C-3. The area estimate is 0.0616.

Figure 13.C-3

b. The probability that a randomly chosen score is between 85 and 95 is approximately the area under the normal curve, or about 0.06.

Exercises

In Exercises 1–6, estimate the area under the given curve between the given values of a and b.

1. $y = x^2 \approx \frac{1}{3}$ $a = 0, b = 1$

2. $y = \sin x \approx 2$ $a = 0, b = \pi$

3. $y = -x^2 + 5x - 4$ $a = 1, b = 4$
   ≈ 4.5

4. $y = e^{-x} \approx 0.14$ $a = 2, b = 10$

5. $y = \frac{1}{x} \approx 0.51$ $a = 3, b = 5$

6. $y = \sqrt{x} \approx 5.65$ $a = 7, b = 9$

7. Suppose the weights of apples from a certain tree are normally distributed with $\mu = 138$ g and $\sigma = 18$ g. Estimate the probability that a randomly chosen apple weighs between 100 g and 150 g.

The answer should be close to 0.7301. A sample is shown of the program using the normal curve with equation $y = \dfrac{1}{18\sqrt{2\pi}} e^{-\frac{(x-138)^2}{648}}$; $a = 100$, $b = 150$, and $h = 0.025$.

8. The function $y = \dfrac{1}{\sqrt{x}}$ is not defined at $x = 0$, and the graph has a vertical asymptote. However, calculus can be used to show that the area under the curve from 0 to 1 is finite. Use a probability simulation to estimate the area by letting $a = 0$ and $b = 1$. Compare the value of the area estimates for $h = 3, 4,$ and 5. Run the simulation at least twice for each value of h to be sure you have a good estimate.

9. Use a probability simulation to verify that the area under the standard normal curve is 1. *Hint*: according to the Empirical Rule, 99.7% of the area under a normal curve is within 3σ of the mean.

A sample is shown of the program using the equation of the standard normal curve with $a = -3$, $b = 3$, and $h = 0.5$. The estimate is very close to the expected area of 0.997, or 99.7% of the area under the curve.

8. Samples of the program are shown.

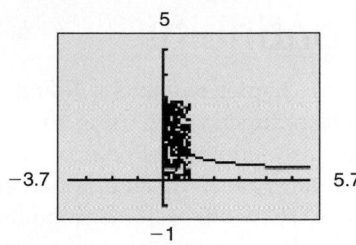

for $h = 3$; area ≈ 1.74

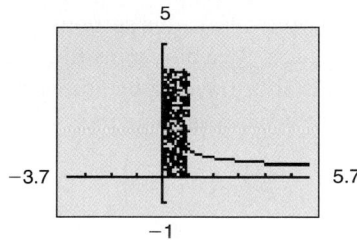

for $h = 4$; area ≈ 1.856

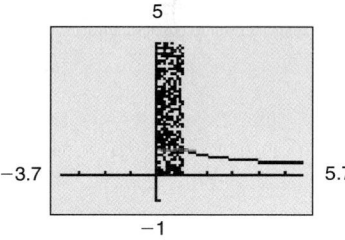

for $h = 5$; area ≈ 2.02

The area estimates get larger for larger values of h. The value for $h = 5$ is close to 2, which is the exact area under the curve from 0 to 1.

907

CHAPTER 14

Limits and Continuity

In this chapter, students will find limits of functions by using an informal definition of limit, a graphing calculator, and properties of limits. They will examine continuity of functions and find limits involving infinity. An optional section addresses the formal (ε-δ) definition of limit. The Can Do Calculus section introduces Riemann sums to estimate the distance traveled by an object whose velocity is changing.

CHAPTER

14 Limits and Continuity

Terminal Velocity

Parachutists have two forces acting on them, as does any free-falling body. One force is gravity, which causes the body to speed up as it falls, and the other is air resistance, which causes the body to slow down. As the body moves faster, the air resistance builds until it nearly balances the gravitational force. So the body speeds up very little after it has fallen some distance. Terminal velocity is achieved when the air resistance approaches the gravitational pull. See Exercise 43 in Section 14.5.

908

Chapter Outline

Interdependence of Sections

$$14.1 \longrightarrow 14.2 \begin{cases} \rightarrow 14.3 \\ \rightarrow 14.4 \\ \rightarrow 14.5 \end{cases}$$

The mathematics presented in previous chapters deals with static problems, such as

What is the size of the angle?

What is the average speed of a car between $t = 0$ and $t = 5$ minutes?

Calculus, on the other hand, deals with dynamic problems, such as

At what rate is the angle increasing in size?

How fast is the car going at time $t = 4.2$ minutes?

The key to dealing with such dynamic problems is the concept of limit, which is introduced in this chapter.

 14.1

Limits of Functions

Objectives

- Use the informal definition of limit

Many mathematical problems involve the behavior of a function at a particular value:

What is the value of the function $f(x)$ when $x = c$?

The underlying idea of **limit,** however, is the behavior of the function *near* $x = c$ rather than *at* $x = c$. You have dealt with limits informally in previous chapters, but this section will discuss limits in more detail and give the notation used when talking about them.

Suppose you want to describe the behavior of

$$f(x) = \frac{0.1x^4 - 0.8x^3 + 1.6x^2 + 2x - 8}{x - 4}$$

909

Teaching Notes

The introduction contrasts static problems (no movement or change) with dynamic problems (movement or change is occurring). Students may wonder why the average speed of a car is an example of a static problem. Explain that to compute an average speed, you use facts that have already been established—distance traveled and time elapsed—and that the movement has already occurred.

Remind students that the function f at the bottom of the page is a rational function because it is the quotient of two polynomials. Ask students for the domain of f.

all real numbers except $x = 4$

Math Background

The limit of the rational function f on this page is determined by its behavior near $x = 4$. It has a hole at $x = 4$ (rather than an asymptote), which is an important fact in determining its limit. The fact that there is a hole rather than an asymptote can be verified by synthetic division (page 241):

First express f as:

$$f(x) = \frac{0.1(x^4 - 8x^3 + 16x^2 + 20x - 80)}{x - 4}$$

Next, divide
$x^4 - 8x^3 + 16x^2 + 20x - 80$ by $x - 4$:

$$\begin{array}{r|rrrrr} 4 & 1 & -8 & 16 & 20 & -80 \\ & & 4 & -16 & 0 & 80 \\ \hline & 1 & -4 & 0 & 20 & 0 \end{array}$$

So, $f(x) = \dfrac{0.1(x - 4)(x^3 - 4x^2 + 20)}{x - 4}$,

and we can see that:
- 4 is a zero of the denominator of multiplicity 1.
- 4 is a zero of the numerator of multiplicity at least 1.

This establishes that f has a hole at $x = 4$ (see Holes, page 283).

Teaching Notes

Solution to the **Graphing Exploration**: As x approaches 4 from the left, the value of $f(x)$ when $x = 3.999$ is shown below.

As x approaches 4 from the right, the value of $f(x)$ when $x = 4.001$ is shown below.

The table below shows results consistent with the values in the **Graphing Exploration** box.

Math Background

There are two parts to the **Informal Definition of Limit**:

As x takes on values very close to but not equal to c (on both sides of c), the corresponding values of $f(x)$ get very close to (and possibly equal to) L.

The value of $f(x)$ can be made arbitrarily close to L by taking x sufficiently close (but not equal) to c.

when x is very close to 4. Notice that the function is not defined when $x = 4$. To see what happens to the values of $f(x)$ when x is very close to 4, observe the graph of the function in the viewing window shown in Figure 14.1-1. (See the Technology Tip about how to produce a graph that shows the hole.)

Figure 14.1-1

To further explore the behavior of the function near $x = 4$, perform the following Graphing Exploration.

Graphing Exploration

Graph $f(x)$ in the viewing window with $3.5 \le x \le 4.5$ and $0 \le y \le 3$. Use the trace feature to move along the graph, and examine the values of $f(x)$ when x takes values close to 4. Your results should be consistent with the following table of values.

	x approaches 4 from the left				x approaches 4 from the right		
x	3.9	3.99	3.999	4	4.001	4.01	4.1
$f(x)$	1.8479	1.9841	1.9984	*	2.0016	2.0161	2.168

The exploration and the table suggest that as x gets closer and closer to 4 from either side, the corresponding values of $f(x)$ get closer and closer to 2. Furthermore, by taking x close enough to 4, the corresponding values can be made *as close as you want* to 2.

For instance,

$$f(3.99999) = 1.999984 \quad \text{and} \quad f(4.00001) = 2.000016$$

Notation

The statement above is usually expressed by saying

"The limit of $f(x)$ as x approaches 4 is 2,"

which is written symbolically as

In the formal definition of limit in Section 14.3, inequalities are used to specify *how close* x is to c and *how close* $f(x)$ is to L:

- x taking on values very close to but not equal to c will be expressed as $0 < |x - c| < \delta$.
- Making $f(x)$ arbitrarily close to L, and possibly equal to L, will be expressed as $|f(x) - L| < \varepsilon$.

The limit in **Example 1**, $\lim\limits_{x \to 0} \dfrac{\sin x}{x} = 1$, is used in calculus to prove the rule for the derivative of the sine function: $\dfrac{d}{dx}\sin x = \cos x$. This is shown without using calculus on pages 614–615.

$$\lim_{x \to 4} f(x) = 2 \qquad \text{or} \qquad \lim_{x \to 4} \frac{0.1x^4 - 0.8x^3 + 1.6x^2 + 2x - 8}{x - 4} = 2$$

Informal Definition of Limit

The following definition of "limit" in the general case is similar to the situation previously described, but now f is any function, c and L are fixed real numbers, and the phrase "arbitrarily close" means "as close as you want." In the previous discussion, $c = 4$ and $L = 2$.

Informal Definition of Limit

Let f be a function and let c be a real number such that $f(x)$ is defined for all values of x near $x = c$, except possibly at $x = c$ itself. Suppose that

whenever x takes values closer and closer but not equal to c (on both sides of c), the corresponding values of $f(x)$ get very close to, and possibly equal, to the same real number L

and that

the values of $f(x)$ can be made arbitrarily close to L by taking values of x close enough to c, but not equal to c.

Then it is said that

The limit of the function $f(x)$ as x approaches c
is the number L,

which is written

$$\lim_{x \to c} f(x) = L$$

NOTE The limit in Example 1 is very important in calculus.

Example 1 Limit of a Function

If $f(x) = \dfrac{\sin x}{x}$, find $\lim_{x \to 0} f(x)$.

Solution

Although $f(x)$ is not defined when $x = 0$, a calculator's trace feature can be used with the graph of the function to examine the values of $f(x)$ when x is very close to 0. The table feature can also be used.

Calculator Exploration ●

Create a table of values for $f(x) = \dfrac{\sin x}{x}$ with values of x both smaller than and larger than $x = 0$. Are the function values approaching the same value as x approaches 0 from both sides?

Some students might think that $Y_1 = \dfrac{\sin x}{x}$ is equal to 1 at $x = \pm 0.001$ as shown in the table in the solution to the Calculator Exploration. Remind them that the values displayed in the table are rounded.

Have them calculate $\dfrac{\sin (0.001)}{0.001}$ as follows:

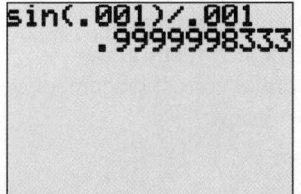

Example Notes

The **Calculator Exploration** at the bottom of this page is intended to be used to solve **Example 1.** The limit of $\dfrac{\sin x}{x}$ was also demonstrated in the Can Do Calculus on page 566.

Solution to the **Calculator Exploration:**

Yes, the function values are approaching the value 1 as x approaches 0 from both sides.

ADDITIONAL EXAMPLES

Example 1

If $f(x) = \dfrac{\sin 3x}{x}$, find $\lim_{x \to 0} f(x)$.

$f(x)$ is not defined for $x = 0$. Use a calculator's trace feature with the graph of the function to examine the values of $f(x)$ when x is very close to 0.

```
        4
  Y1=sin(3X)/X



 -2π                    2π



 X=-.001      Y=2.9999955
       -2
```

Then use the table feature to show function values for x-values close to 0 and on both sides of 0.

X	Y1
-.1	2.9552
-.01	2.9996
-.001	3
0	ERROR
.001	3
.01	2.9996
.1	2.9552

Y1■sin(3X)/X

Note that some of the values in the table are rounded—$f(x)$ never takes the value 3. The graph and the table suggest that $\lim_{x \to 0} f(x) = 3$ or equivalently, $\lim_{x \to 0} \dfrac{\sin 3x}{x} = 3$.

Teaching Notes

The **Limits and Function Values** box and the statement following the box tell us that if $\lim_{x \to c} f(x) = L$, then either $f(c) = L$, $f(c) \neq L$, or $f(c)$ is undefined. In **Example 1**, $f(c)$ is undefined. In **Example 2**, $f(c) \neq L$. In **Example 3**, $f(c) = L$.

Example Notes

In **Example 2**, students find that $\lim_{x \to 2} f(x) = 1$. Ask them to find $\lim_{x \to 3} f(x)$. 1 Ask them to state the limit of $f(x)$ as x approaches *any* integer. 1

To help them visualize these facts, tell them to imagine a particle moving along any of the red line segments in Figure 14.1-3. As the particle *approaches* any hole, it *stays on the red line segment.*

Note that 0 is not the limit of this function for *any* value that x approaches.

The **Graphing Exploration** on page 913 is intended to be used to solve **Example 3**.

Solution to the **Graphing Exploration** (page 913):

The figure below shows that when x is very close to 0.5, to the left of 0.5, $f(x)$ is very close to 1.

The figure below shows that when x is very close to 0.5, to the right of 0.5, $f(x)$ is very close to 1.

Figure 14.1-2

The exploration should suggest that

$$\lim_{x \to 0} f(x) = 1 \text{ or equivalently, } \lim_{x \to 0} \frac{\sin x}{x} = 1,$$

a fact that will be proved in calculus.

Example 2 Limit of a Function

Find $\lim_{x \to 2} f(x)$, where f is the function given by the following two-part rule.

$$f(x) = \begin{cases} 0 \text{ if } x \text{ is an integer} \\ 1 \text{ if } x \text{ is not an integer} \end{cases}$$

Solution

A calculator is not much help here, but the function is easily graphed by hand.

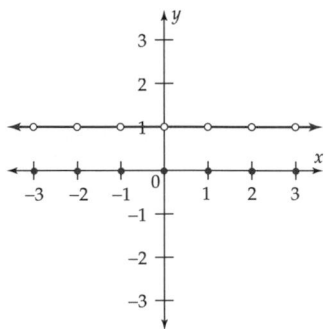

Figure 14.1-3

When x is a number very close but not equal to 2 (either greater than 2 or less than 2), the corresponding value of $f(x)$ is 1, and this is true no matter how close x is to 2. Thus,

$$\lim_{x \to 2} f(x) = 1.$$

Because $f(2) = 0$ by definition, the limit of f as x approaches 2 is *not* the same as the value of the function f at $x = 2$.

Limits and Function Values

> If the limit of a function f as x approaches c exists, this limit may *not* be equal to $f(c)$. In fact, $f(c)$ may not even be defined.

Very often the limit of a function as x approaches a point is equal to the value of the function at that point.

COMMON ERROR ALERT

Some students might enter the function $f(x) = \sin^2 \pi x - \cos \pi x$ incorrectly in the calculator. Remind them of correct placement of parentheses as shown below:

$$Y_1 = (\sin (\pi x))^2 - \cos (\pi x)$$

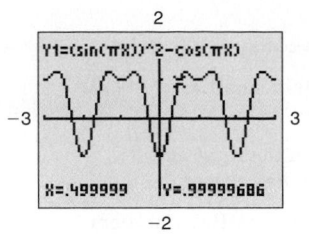

Figure 14.1-4

Example 3 Limit of a Function and a Function Value

If $f(x) = \sin^2 \pi x - \cos \pi x$, find $f(0.5)$ and $\lim_{x \to 0.5} f(x)$.

Solution

$$f(0.5) = f\left(\frac{1}{2}\right) = \sin^2 \frac{\pi}{2} - \cos \frac{\pi}{2} = 1^2 - 0 = 1.$$

Using the trace feature on the graph of $f(x)$, shown in Figure 14.1-4, suggests that the limit is a number near 1.

A much narrower viewing window is needed to determine the limit more precisely.

___

Graphing Exploration ●───────

Graph $f(x)$ in a viewing window with $0.49 \le x \le 0.51$ and $0.99 \le y \le 1.01$. Use the trace feature to move along the graph on both sides of $x = 0.5$ and confirm that as x gets closer and closer to 0.5, $f(x)$ gets closer and closer to 1.

___

The Exploration suggests that

$$\lim_{x \to 0.5} f(x) = 1 = f(0.5).$$

Thus, the value of the function at $x = 0.5$ is the same as the limit as x approaches 0.5. ■

___

NOTE Whenever a calculator was used in preceding examples, it was said that the information provided by the calculator *suggested* that the limit of the function was a particular number. Although such calculator explorations provide strong evidence, they do not constitute a proof and in some instances can be very misleading. (See Exercise 36.) Nevertheless, a calculator can help you develop an intuitive understanding for limits, which is needed for a rigorous treatment of the concept.

___

Nonexistence of Limits

Not every function has a limit at every number. Limits can fail to exist for several reasons.

For a value of x close to -1, to the left of -1, $f(x)$ is close to -1, as shown below.

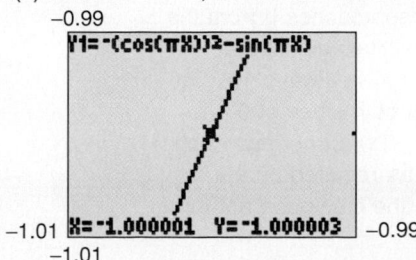

For a value of x close to -1, to the right of -1, $f(x)$ is close to -1, as shown below.

Example 2

Find $\lim_{x \to -1} f(x)$, where f is the function defined by the following two-part rule.

$$f(x) = \begin{cases} 1 & \text{if } x \text{ is an integer} \\ -2 & \text{if } x \text{ is not an integer} \end{cases}$$

The function, graphed by hand, is shown below.

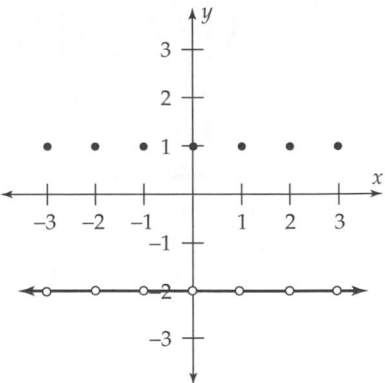

When x is a number very close but not equal to -1 (either greater than -1 or less than -1), the corresponding value of $f(x)$ is -2, and this is true no matter how close x is to -1.

So, $\lim_{x \to -1} f(x) = -2$.

Example 3

If $f(x) = -\cos^2 \pi x - \sin \pi x$, find $f(-1)$ and $\lim_{x \to -1} f(x)$.

$$\begin{aligned} f(-1) &= -\cos^2(-\pi) - \sin(-\pi) \\ &= -(-1)^2 - 0 = -1 \end{aligned}$$

Using the trace feature on the graph of $f(x)$, shown below, suggests that the limit is a number near -1.

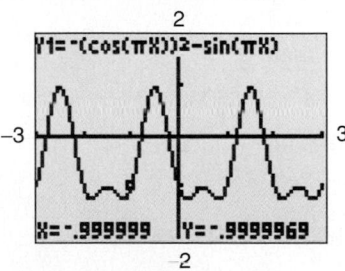

Using a much narrower viewing window (see graphs at left) determines the limit more precisely.

The graphs to the left suggest that $\lim_{x \to -1} f(x) = -1$. So, the value of the function at $x = -1$ is the same as the limit as x approaches -1.

ADDITIONAL EXAMPLES

Example 4

Discuss the existence of $\lim\limits_{x\to 0} -\dfrac{1}{x^2}$.

The figure below shows the graph of $f(x) = -\dfrac{1}{x^2}$ near $x = 0$.

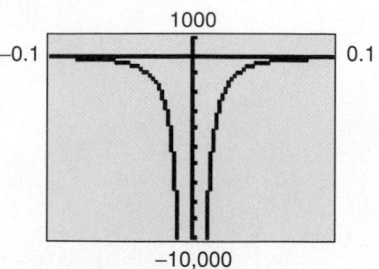

As x approaches 0 from the left or the right, the values of $f(x)$ get smaller and smaller without bound—rather than approaching one particular number—which can be verified using the trace feature.

So, $\lim\limits_{x\to 0} -\dfrac{1}{x^2}$ does not exist.

Example 5

Find $\lim\limits_{x\to 0} \dfrac{-|2x|}{x}$, if it exists.

The function $f(x) = \dfrac{-|2x|}{x}$ is not defined for $x = 0$. There are two possibilities.

If $x > 0$, then

$$f(x) = \frac{-|2x|}{x} = \frac{-2x}{x} = -2.$$

If $x < 0$, then

$$f(x) = \frac{-|2x|}{x} = \frac{-(-2x)}{x} = 2.$$

The graph of f is shown below.

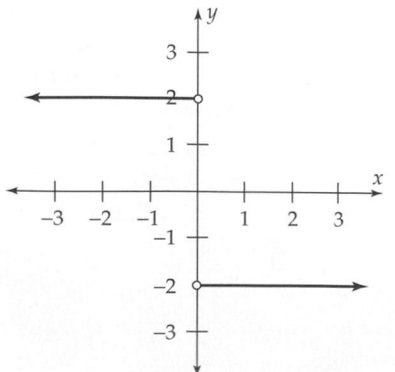

Nonexistence of Limits

The limit of a function f as x approaches c may fail to exist if:

1. $f(x)$ becomes infinitely large or infinitely small as x approaches c from either side

2. $f(x)$ approaches L as x approaches c from the right and $f(x)$ approaches M, with $M \neq L$, as x approaches c from the left

3. $f(x)$ oscillates infinitely many times between two numbers as x approaches c from either side

The examples that follow illustrate each of these possibilities.

Example 4 — A Function that Approaches Infinity

Discuss the existence of $\lim\limits_{x\to 0} \dfrac{1}{x^2}$.

Solution

Figure 14.1-5 shows the graph of $f(x) = \dfrac{1}{x^2}$ near $x = 0$. As x approaches 0 from the left or right, the corresponding values of $f(x)$ become larger and larger without bound—rather than approaching one particular number—which can be verified by using the trace feature. Therefore,

$\lim\limits_{x\to 0} \dfrac{1}{x^2}$ does not exist.

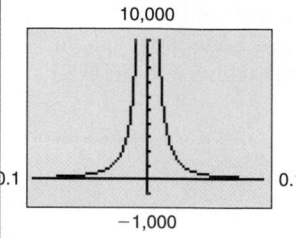

Figure 14.1-5

Example 5 — A Function that Approaches Two Values

Find $\lim\limits_{x\to 0} \dfrac{|x|}{x}$, if it exists.

Solution

The function $f(x) = \dfrac{|x|}{x}$ is not defined when $x = 0$.

According to the definition of absolute value, $|x| = x$ when $x > 0$ and $|x| = -x$ when $x < 0$. There are two possibilities.

$$\text{If } x > 0, \text{ then } f(x) = \frac{|x|}{x} = \frac{x}{x} = 1.$$

$$\text{If } x < 0, \text{ then } f(x) = \frac{|x|}{x} = \frac{-x}{x} = -1$$

Consequently, the graph of f looks like Figure 14.1-6a. A table of values for $f(x)$ is shown in Figure 14.1-6b.

If x approaches 0 from the right, that is, through positive values, then the

Figure 14.1-6a

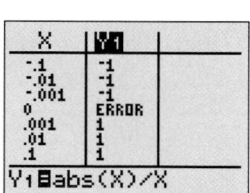

Figure 14.1-6b

A table of values is shown below.

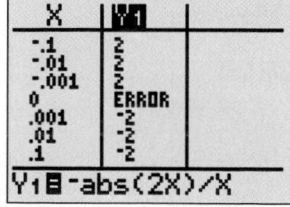

If x approaches 0 from the left, that is, through negative values, then the corresponding value of $f(x)$ is always 2. If x approaches 0 from the right, that is, through positive values, then the corresponding value of $f(x)$ is always -2. So, as x approaches 0 from both sides of 0, the corresponding values of $f(x)$ do not approach the same real number, as required by the definition of limit. Thus, the limit does not exist.

corresponding value of $f(x)$ is always 1. If x approaches 0 from the left, that is, from negative values, then the corresponding value of $f(x)$ is always -1. Thus, as x approaches 0 from both sides of 0, the corresponding values of $f(x)$ do not approach the same real number, as required by the definition of limit. Therefore, the limit does not exist. ∎

Example 6　An Oscillating Function

Find $\lim\limits_{x \to 0} \sin \dfrac{\pi}{x}$, if it exists.

Solution

To understand the behavior of $f(x) = \sin \dfrac{\pi}{x}$, consider what happens when x is close to 0.

As x takes values:	Then $\dfrac{\pi}{x}$ takes values:
from $\dfrac{1}{2}$ to $\dfrac{1}{4}$	2π to 4π
from $\dfrac{1}{4}$ to $\dfrac{1}{6}$	4π to 6π
from $\dfrac{1}{6}$ to $\dfrac{1}{8}$	6π to 8π

Thus, the graph of $\sin \dfrac{\pi}{x}$ completes one period of the sine function from $x = \dfrac{1}{2}$ to $x = \dfrac{1}{4}$, another from $x = \dfrac{1}{4}$ to $x = \dfrac{1}{6}$, and so on. A similar phenomenon occurs for negative values of x. Consequently, the graph of f oscillates infinitely often between -1 and 1, with the waves becoming more and more compressed as x approaches 0, as shown in Figure 14.1-7.

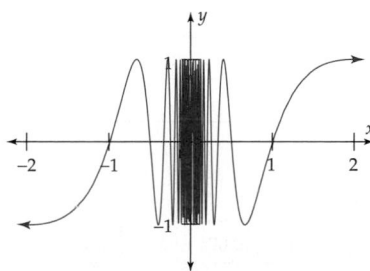

Figure 14.1-7

As x approaches 0, the function takes every value between -1 and 1 infinitely many times. In particular, $f(x)$ does not approach one particular real number. Therefore, $\lim\limits_{x \to 0} \sin \dfrac{\pi}{x}$ does not exist. ∎

Example 6

Find $\lim\limits_{x \to 0} \cos \dfrac{\pi}{x}$, if it exists.

As x takes on values from $\dfrac{1}{2}$ to $\dfrac{1}{4}$, $\dfrac{\pi}{x}$ takes on values from 2π to 4π. So, the graph of $\cos \dfrac{\pi}{x}$ completes one period of the cosine function from $x = \dfrac{1}{2}$ to $x = \dfrac{1}{4}$, as shown below.

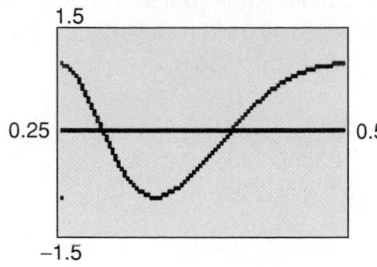

The graph of $\cos \dfrac{\pi}{x}$ completes one period of the cosine function from $x = \dfrac{1}{4}$ to $x = \dfrac{1}{6}$, another from $\dfrac{1}{6}$ to $\dfrac{1}{8}$, and so on. There are similar repetitions for negative values of x. Thus, the graph of f oscillates infinitely often between -1 and 1, with the waves becoming more and more compressed as x approaches 0, as shown in the figure below.

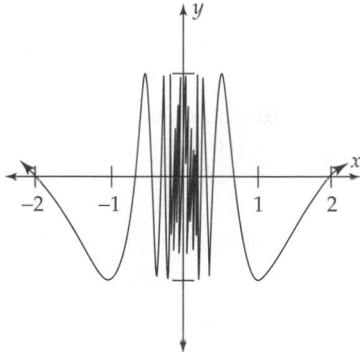

As x approaches 0, the function takes every value between -1 and 1 infinitely many times. So, $f(x)$ does not approach one particular number. Therefore, $\lim\limits_{x \to 0} \cos \dfrac{\pi}{x}$ does not exist.

Math Background

In **Example 4**, the function values increase without bound as x approaches 0 from either side. In **Additional Example 4**, the function values decrease without bound as x approaches 0 from either side.

In the function $f(x) = \dfrac{1}{x}$, the function values increase without bound as x approaches 0 from the right and decrease without bound as x approaches 0 from the left.

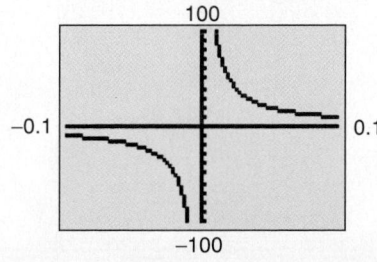

$\lim\limits_{x \to 0} \dfrac{1}{x}$ does not exist.

Exercises 14.1

ANSWERS

1. 0.25641; 0.25063; 0.25006;
0.24994; 0.24938; 0.2439;
$\lim_{x \to 3} f(x) = 0.25$

2. 0.1695; 0.1669; 0.1667;
0.1666; 0.1664; 0.1639;
$\lim_{x \to 3} f(x) = 0.1667$

3. 0.35809; 0.354; 0.3536;
0.35351; 0.35311; 0.34924;
$\lim_{x \to 0} f(x) = 0.3535$

4. 0.2247; 0.2237; 0.2236;
0.2236; 0.2235; 0.2225;
$\lim_{x \to 0} f(x) = 0.2236$

5. −0.1662; −0.1666; −0.1667;
−0.1667; −0.1667; −0.1671;
$\lim_{x \to -7} f(x) = -0.1667$

6. −0.4881; −0.4988; −0.4999;
−0.5001; −0.5013; −0.5132;
$\lim_{x \to 0} f(x) = -0.5$

7. −0.1149; −0.1115; −0.1111;
−0.1111; −0.1107; −0.1075;
$\lim_{x \to 1} f(x) = -0.1111$

8. −0.2632; −0.2513; −0.2501;
−0.2499; −0.2488; −0.2381;
$\lim_{x \to -1} f(x) = -0.25$

9. 0.04996; 0.005; 0.0005;
−0.0005; −0.005; −0.05;
$\lim_{x \to 0} f(x) = 0$

10. 1.9893; 1.9992; 1.9998;
2.0000; 2.0002; 2.0012;
$\lim_{x \to \frac{\pi}{4}} f(x) = 2$

Exercises 14.1

In Exercises 1–10, complete the table and use the result to estimate the given limit.

1. $\lim\limits_{x \to 3} \dfrac{x - 3}{x^2 - 2x - 3}$

x	2.9	2.99	2.999	3.001	3.01	3.1
$f(x)$						

2. $\lim\limits_{x \to 3} \dfrac{x - 3}{x^2 - 9}$

x	2.9	2.99	2.999	3.001	3.01	3.1
$f(x)$						

3. $\lim\limits_{x \to 0} \dfrac{\sqrt{x + 2} - \sqrt{2}}{x}$

x	−0.1	−0.01	−0.001	0.001	0.01	0.1
$f(x)$						

4. $\lim\limits_{x \to 0} \dfrac{\sqrt{x + 5} - \sqrt{5}}{x}$

x	−0.1	−0.01	−0.001	0.001	0.01	0.1
$f(x)$						

5. $\lim\limits_{x \to -7} \dfrac{\sqrt{2 - x} - 3}{x + 7}$

x	−7.1	−7.01	−7.001	−6.999	−6.99	−6.9
$f(x)$						

6. $\lim\limits_{x \to 0} \dfrac{\sqrt{1 - x} - 1}{x}$

x	−0.1	−0.01	−0.001	0.001	0.01	0.1
$f(x)$						

7. $\lim\limits_{x \to 1} \dfrac{\dfrac{1}{x + 2} - \dfrac{1}{3}}{x - 1}$

x	0.9	0.99	0.999	1.001	1.01	1.1
$f(x)$						

8. $\lim\limits_{x \to -1} \dfrac{\dfrac{1}{x + 3} - \dfrac{1}{2}}{x + 1}$

x	−1.1	−1.01	−1.001	−0.999	−0.99	−0.9
$f(x)$						

9. $\lim\limits_{x \to 0} \dfrac{\cos x - 1}{x}$

x	−0.1	−0.01	−0.001	0.001	0.01	0.1
$f(x)$						

10. $\lim\limits_{x \to \frac{\pi}{4}} \dfrac{\tan x - 1}{x - \dfrac{\pi}{4}}$

x	0.78	0.785	0.7853	0.7854	0.7855	0.786
$f(x)$						

In Exercises 11–26, use a calculator to find a reasonable estimate of the limit. If the limit does not exist, explain why.

11. $\lim\limits_{x \to -1} \dfrac{x^6 - 1}{x^4 - 1}$
1.5

12. $\lim\limits_{x \to 2} \dfrac{x^5 - 32}{x^3 - 8}$
6.6667

13. $\lim\limits_{x \to 3} \dfrac{x^2 - x - 6}{x^2 - 2x - 3}$
1.25

14. $\lim\limits_{x \to 1} \dfrac{x^2 - 1}{x^2 + x - 2}$
0.6667

15. $\lim\limits_{x \to 1} \dfrac{x^3 - 1}{x^2 - 1}$
1.5

16. $\lim\limits_{x \to -2} \dfrac{x^2 + 5x + 6}{x^2 - x - 6}$
−0.2

17. $\lim\limits_{x \to 0} \dfrac{\tan x - x}{x^3}$
0.3333

18. $\lim\limits_{x \to 0} \dfrac{\tan x}{x + \sin x}$
0.5

19. $\lim\limits_{x \to 0} \dfrac{x - \tan x}{x - \sin x}$
−2

20. $\lim\limits_{x \to 0} \dfrac{x + \sin 2x}{x - \sin 2x}$
−3

21. $\lim\limits_{x \to 3} \dfrac{\sqrt{x} - \sqrt{3}}{x - 3}$
0.2887

22. $\lim\limits_{x \to 25} \dfrac{\sqrt{x} - 5}{x - 25}$
0.1

23. $\lim\limits_{x \to 0} \dfrac{x}{\ln |x|}$
0

24. $\lim\limits_{x \to 0} \dfrac{e^{2x} - 1}{x}$
2

25. $\lim\limits_{x\to 0} \dfrac{e^x - 1}{\sin x}$ **1**

26. $\lim\limits_{x\to 0}\left(x \sin \dfrac{1}{x}\right)$ **0**

In Exercises 27–32, use the graph of the function f to determine the following:

$$\lim_{x\to -3} f(x) \qquad \lim_{x\to 0} f(x) \qquad \lim_{x\to 2} f(x)$$

27.

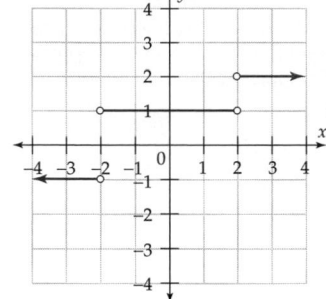

−1; 1; does not exist

28.

3; 0; −2

29.

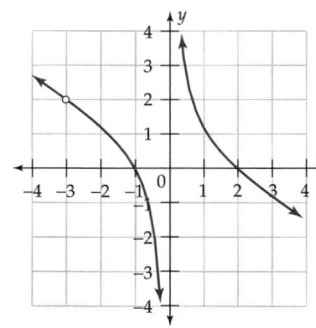

2; does not exist; 0

30.

0; 1; −1

31.

2; 1; 1

32.

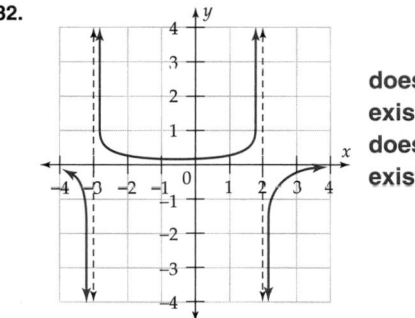

does not exist; 0.25; does not exist

33. a. Graph the function f whose rule is

$$f(x) = \begin{cases} 3 - x & \text{if } x < -2 \\ x + 2 & \text{if } -2 \le x < 2 \\ 1 & \text{if } x = 2 \\ 4 - x & \text{if } x > 2 \end{cases}$$

Use the graph in part **a** to evaluate the following limits.

b. $\lim\limits_{x\to -2} f(x)$ **c.** $\lim\limits_{x\to 1} f(x)$ **d.** $\lim\limits_{x\to 2} f(x)$

33. a.

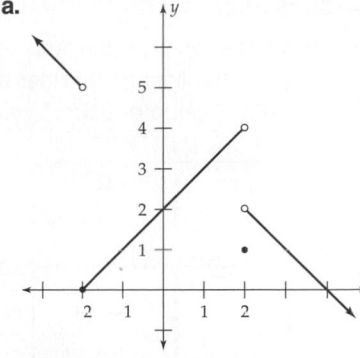

b. does not exist

c. 3

d. does not exist

34. a.

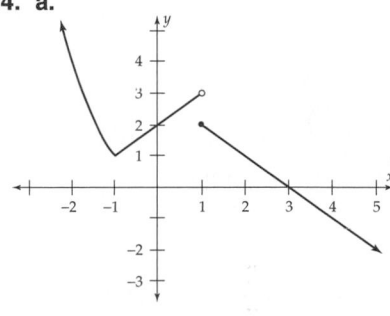

b. 1; 2; does not exist

35. No matter how close x gets to c, there are still an infinite number of both rational and irrational numbers between x and c, so $t(x)$ will take the values 0 and 1 an infinite number of times, but never get close to a *single* number for all values of x that are very close to c.

34–35. *See page 917.*

36. The trace function suggests a value of the limit as 0 rather than the actual value of 0.5.

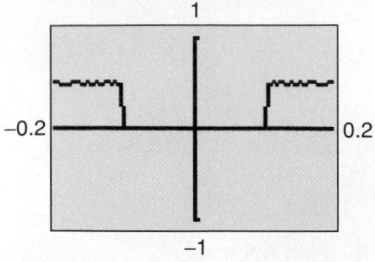

---

34. a. Graph the function g whose rule is

$$g(x) = \begin{cases} x^2 & \text{if } x < -1 \\ x + 2 & \text{if } -1 \le x < 1 \\ 2 & \text{if } x = 1 \\ 3 - x & \text{if } x > 1 \end{cases}$$

Use the graph in part **a** to evaluate the following limits.

b. $\lim\limits_{x \to -1} g(x)$　**c.** $\lim\limits_{x \to 0} g(x)$　**d.** $\lim\limits_{x \to 1} g(x)$

35. *Critical Thinking* Consider the function t whose rule is

$$t(x) = \begin{cases} 0 \text{ if } x \text{ is rational} \\ 1 \text{ if } x \text{ is irrational} \end{cases}$$

Explain why $\lim\limits_{x \to c} t(x)$ does not exist for every value of c.

36. *Critical Thinking* If $f(x) = \dfrac{1 - \cos x^6}{x^{12}}$, then $\lim\limits_{x \to 0} f(x) = \dfrac{1}{2}$, as is shown in calculus. A calculator or computer, however, may indicate otherwise. Graph $f(x)$ in a viewing window with $-0.1 \le x \le 0.1$, and use the trace feature to determine the values of $f(x)$ when x approaches 0. What does this suggest that the limit is?

Section

14.2 Properties of Limits

Math Background

All linear functions can be written in the form $f(x) = mx + b$, and the limit of a linear function can be stated as follows:

For every real number c,
$\lim\limits_{x \to c} mx + b = mc + b$. After the **Limit of a Constant**, the **Limit of the Identity Function**, and **Properties of Limits** are proved (not done here), they can be used to prove the limit of a linear function as follows.

$$\lim_{x \to c} (mx + b)$$

$= \lim\limits_{x \to c} (mx) + \lim\limits_{x \to c} b$　　*Property 1*

$= \lim\limits_{x \to c} m \cdot \lim\limits_{x \to c} x + \lim\limits_{x \to c} b$　*Property 3*

$= m \cdot \lim\limits_{x \to c} x + b$　　*Limit of a Constant*

$= mc + b$　　*Limit of the Identity Function*

Proofs of the Limit of a Constant, the Limit of the Identity Function, and Properties of Limits can be done using the formal ε-δ Definition of Limit (page 931).

14.2 Properties of Limits

Objectives

- Find the limit of
  the constant function
  the identity function
- Use the properties of limits
- Find the limit of
  polynomial functions
  rational functions
- Use the Limit Theorem

Most of the functions that appear in calculus are combinations of simpler functions, such as sums, products, quotients, and compositions. This section presents rules for finding limits of combinations of functions without a table or a graph.

There are two easy, but important, cases where the limit of a function may be found by evaluating the function. The first occurs with constant functions, such as $f(x) = 5$. To find $\lim\limits_{x \to 3} f(x)$, that is, $\lim\limits_{x \to 3} 5$, note that as x approaches 3, the corresponding value of $f(x)$ is *always* the number 5, so that $\lim\limits_{x \to 3} f(x) = \lim\limits_{x \to 3} 5 = 5$. Thus, $\lim\limits_{x \to 3} f(x)$ is the number $f(3) = 5$. The same thing is true for any constant function.

Limit of a Constant

If d is a constant, then $\lim\limits_{x \to c} d = d$.

The same phenomenon occurs with the identity function, which is given by the rule $I(x) = x$. If c is any real number, then the statement "x approaches c" is exactly the same as the statement "$I(x)$ approaches c" because $I(x) = x$ for every x. Thus,

Limit of the Identity Function

For every real number c, $\lim\limits_{x \to c} x = c$.

Teaching Notes

Ask students to state the **Properties of Limits** verbally. (State Property 1, and then have students state the others.)

1. The limit of the sum of two functions is equal to the sum of the limits.
2. The limit of the difference of two functions is equal to the difference of the limits.
3. The limit of the product of two functions is equal to the product of the limits.
4. The limit of the quotient of two functions is equal to the quotient of their limits, provided the limit of the denominator is not equal to zero.
5. The limit of the square root of a function is equal to the square root of the limit, provided that the function values near c are nonnegative.

Properties of Limits

There are a number of facts that greatly simplify the computation of limits. Rigorous proofs of these properties will not be given, knowing the central idea is more important now. For instance, suppose that as x approaches c, the values of a function f approach a number L and the values of a function g approach a number M. Then it is plausible that as x approaches c, the values of the function $f + g$ approach $L + M$ and that the values of the function $f \cdot g$ approach $L \cdot M$. Following is a formal statement in terms of limits.

Properties of Limits

If f and g are functions and c, L, and M are numbers such that

$$\lim_{x \to c} f(x) = L \quad \text{and} \quad \lim_{x \to c} g(x) = M,$$

then

1. $\lim_{x \to c} (f + g)(x) = \lim_{x \to c}[f(x) + g(x)]$
   $= L + M$

2. $\lim_{x \to c} (f - g)(x) = \lim_{x \to c}[f(x) - g(x)]$
   $= L - M$

3. $\lim_{x \to c} (f \cdot g)(x) = \lim_{x \to c}[f(x) \cdot g(x)]$
   $= L \cdot M$

4. $\lim_{x \to c} \left(\dfrac{f}{g}\right)(x) = \lim_{x \to c}\left(\dfrac{f(x)}{g(x)}\right)$
   $= \dfrac{L}{M} \quad$ (for $M \neq 0$)

5. $\lim_{x \to c} \sqrt{f(x)} = \sqrt{L} \quad$ (provided $f(x) \geq 0$ for all x near c)

NOTE In Property 4, $\lim_{x \to c} \left(\dfrac{f}{g}\right)(x)$ does not exist if $M = 0$ and $L \neq 0$. If $M = 0$ and $L = 0$, the limit may or may not exist.

These properties are often stated somewhat differently. For instance, because $\lim_{x \to c} f(x) = L$ and $\lim_{x \to c} g(x) = M$, Property 1 can be written as

$$\lim_{x \to c} (f + g)(x) = \lim_{x \to c} f(x) + \lim_{x \to c} g(x)$$

and similarly for the other properties.

Limits of Polynomial Functions

Properties 1–3, together with the facts about limits of constants and the identity function presented at the beginning of the section, now make it easy to find the limit of any polynomial function.

Example 1   **Limit of a Polynomial Function**

If $f(x) = x^2 - 2x + 3$, find $\lim_{x \to -4} f(x) = \lim_{x \to -4} (x^2 - 2x + 3)$.

Teaching Notes

The first line in property 1 of **Properties of Limits** is
$$\lim_{x \to c} (f + g)(x) = \lim_{x \to c}\big[f(x) + g(x)\big].$$
Point out that this statement is simply substituting $\big[f(x) + g(x)\big]$ for $(f + g)(x)$, using the rule for the sum of two functions (page 191). The actual limit property is in the statement
$$\lim_{x \to c}\big[f(x) + g(x)\big] = L + M.$$
Similar observations can be made about properties 2–4.

Math Background

The margin **NOTE** states that
$$\lim_{x \to c} \left(\dfrac{f}{g}\right)(x)$$
may or may not exist if $M = 0$ and $L = 0$. Students have already encountered an example of each case.

If $f(x) = \sin x$ and $g(x) = x$, then
$$\lim_{x \to 0} f(x) = \lim_{x \to 0} \sin x = 0,$$
$$\lim_{x \to 0} g(x) = \lim_{x \to 0} x = 0, \text{ and}$$
$$\lim_{x \to c} \left(\dfrac{f}{g}\right)(x) = \lim_{x \to c} \dfrac{\sin x}{x} = 1.$$
(See Example 1, pages 911–912.)

If $f(x) = |x|$ and $g(x) = x$, then
$$\lim_{x \to 0} f(x) = \lim_{x \to 0} |x| = 0,$$
$$\lim_{x \to 0} g(x) = \lim_{x \to 0} x = 0, \text{ and}$$
$$\lim_{x \to c} \left(\dfrac{f}{g}\right)(x) = \lim_{x \to c} \dfrac{|x|}{x} \text{ does not exist.}$$
(See Example 5, pages 914–915.)

ADDITIONAL EXAMPLES

Example 1

If $f(x) = x^2 + 3x - 6$, find
$$\lim_{x \to -2} f(x) = \lim_{x \to -2} (x^2 + 3x - 6).$$

$\lim_{x \to -2} (x^2 + 3x - 6)$
$= \lim_{x \to -2} x^2 + \lim_{x \to -2} 3x - \lim_{x \to -2} 6$
$= \lim_{x \to -2} x \cdot \lim_{x \to -2} x + \lim_{x \to -2} 3 \cdot \lim_{x \to -2} x - \lim_{x \to -2} 6$
$= (-2)(-2) \quad + 3(-2) \quad\quad - 6$
$= 4 + (-6) - 6$
$= -8$

Teaching Notes

Remind students that a rational function is a function whose rule is the quotient of two polynomials. Ask for the domain of:

- a polynomial function
  the set of all real numbers
- a rational function
  the set of all real numbers that are not zeros of its denominator

Now have students compare **Limits of Polynomial Functions** and **Limits of Rational Functions**. Ask how the statements differ.

In Limits of Polynomial Functions, the statement applies to every real number c, while in Limits of Rational Functions, the statement only applies when c is a real number such that $f(c)$ is defined.

Example Notes

For **Example 3**, you may want to have students graph $f(x) = \dfrac{x^2 - 2x - 3}{x - 3}$ with a viewing window such as $2.7 \le x \le 3.3$ and $3.8 \le y \le 4.2$, and use the TRACE feature to confirm that there is a hole at $x = 3$.

Math Background

The graph of every polynomial is continuous, that is, it is an unbroken curve, with no jumps, gaps, or holes (page 261). The graph of a rational function is continuous except at values of x for which $f(x)$ is not defined (Section 4.4). Section 14.4 discusses the concept of continuity in detail.

Solution

$$
\begin{aligned}
\lim_{x \to -4} (x^2 - 2x + 3) &= \lim_{x \to -4} x^2 - \lim_{x \to -4} 2x + \lim_{x \to -4} 3 & \textit{Properties 1 and 2} \\
&= \lim_{x \to -4} x \cdot \lim_{x \to -4} x - \lim_{x \to -4} 2 \cdot \lim_{x \to -4} x + \lim_{x \to -4} 3 & \textit{Property 3} \\
&= \lim_{x \to -4} x \cdot \lim_{x \to -4} x - 2 \lim_{x \to -4} x + 3 & \textit{Limit of a constant} \\
&= (-4)(-4) - \quad 2(-4) \quad + 3 & \textit{Limit of x} \\
&= 16 - (-8) + 3 \\
&= 27
\end{aligned}
$$

Note that the limit of $f(x) = x^2 - 2x + 3$ at $x = -4$ is the same as the value of the function at $x = -4$, namely, $f(-4) = (-4)^2 - 2(-4) + 3 = 27$. ∎

Because any polynomial function consists of sums and products of constants and x, the same argument used in Example 1 works for any polynomial function and leads to the following conclusion.

Limits of Polynomial Functions

> If $f(x)$ is a polynomial function and c is any real number, then
>
> $$\lim_{x \to c} f(x) = f(c).$$
>
> In other words, the limit is the value of the polynomial function f at $x = c$.

Limits of Rational Functions

The fact in the previous box and Property 4 of limits make it easy to compute limits of many rational functions.

Example 2 Limit of a Rational Function

If $f(x) = \dfrac{x^3 - 3x^2 + 10}{x^2 - 6x + 1}$, find $\lim_{x \to 2} f(x)$.

Solution

The graph of f near $x = 2$ suggests that the limit is a number near -0.86, as shown in Figure 14.2-1. You can determine the limit exactly by noting that $f(x)$ is the quotient of the two functions

$$g(x) = x^3 - 3x^2 + 10 \quad \text{and} \quad h(x) = x^2 - 6x + 1.$$

As x approaches 2, the limit of each can be found by evaluation of the functions at $x = 2$. Therefore,

Figure 14.2-1

$$\lim_{x \to 2} f(x) = \lim_{x \to 2} \left(\frac{x^3 - 3x^2 + 10}{x^2 - 6x + 1} \right)$$

$$= \frac{\lim_{x \to 2} (x^3 - 3x^2 + 10)}{\lim_{x \to 2} (x^2 - 6x + 1)} \qquad \textit{limit property 4}$$

$$= \frac{2^3 - 3 \cdot 2^2 + 10}{2^2 - 6 \cdot 2 + 1} \qquad \textit{limits of polynomial functions}$$

$$= \frac{6}{-7} = -\frac{6}{7} \approx -0.857$$

Note that the limit of $f(x)$ as x approaches 2 is the number $f(2)$. ∎

The procedure in Example 2 works for other rational functions as well.

Limits of Rational Functions

Let $f(x)$ be a rational function and let c be a real number such that $f(c)$ is defined. Then

$$\lim_{x \to c} f(x) = f(c).$$

In other words, the limit of a rational function as x approaches c is the value of the function at $x = c$, if the function is defined there.

When a rational function is not defined at a number, different techniques must be used to find its limit there—if it exists.

Example 3 Limit of a Rational Function

If $f(x) = \dfrac{x^2 - 2x - 3}{x - 3}$, find $\lim_{x \to 3} f(x)$.

Solution

Because $f(x)$ is not defined when $x = 3$, the limit cannot be found by evaluating the function. Although it could be estimated graphically, it can be found by using algebraic methods. Begin by factoring the numerator.

$$\frac{x^2 - 2x - 3}{x - 3} = \frac{(x + 1)(x - 3)}{x - 3}$$

Because the numerator and denominator have a common factor, the rational expression may be reduced.

$$\frac{(x + 1)(x - 3)}{x - 3} = x + 1, \text{ for all } x \neq 3.$$

The definition of the limit as x approaches 3 involves only the behavior of the function *near* $x = 3$ and not *at* $x = 3$. The preceding equation shows that both $f(x)$ and the function $g(x) = x + 1$ have exactly the same

X	Y1
-2.3	-6.3
-2.2	-6.2
-2.1	-6.1
-2	ERROR
-1.9	-5.9
-1.8	-5.8
-1.7	-5.7

Y1■(X²-2X-8)/(X...

ADDITIONAL EXAMPLES

Example 2

If $f(x) = \dfrac{x^3 + x^2 - 8x - 12}{x^2 - x - 2}$, find $\lim_{x \to -4} f(x)$.

The graph of f near $x = -4$ suggests that the limit is a number near -1.56, as shown in the figure below.

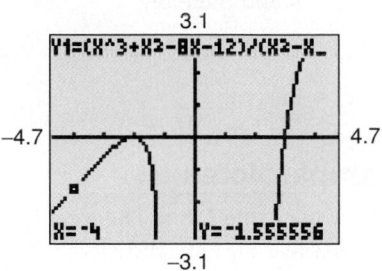

$f(x)$ is the quotient of the two functions $g(x) = x^3 + x^2 - 8x - 12$ and $h(x) = x^2 - x - 2$.

As x approaches -4, the limit can be found by evaluating the functions at $x = -4$. So,

$$\lim_{x \to -4} f(x)$$

$$= \lim_{x \to -4} \frac{x^3 + x^2 - 8x - 12}{x^2 - x - 2}$$

$$= \frac{\lim_{x \to -4} (x^3 + x^2 - 8x - 12)}{\lim_{x \to -4} (x^2 - x - 2)} \qquad \textit{limit property 4}$$

$$= \frac{(-4)^3 + (-4)^2 - 8(-4) - 12}{(-4)^2 - (-4) - 2} \qquad \textit{limits of polynomial functions}$$

$$= \frac{-28}{18} = -\frac{14}{9} \approx -1.556$$

Example 3

If $f(x) = \dfrac{x^2 - 2x - 8}{x + 2}$, find $\lim_{x \to -2} f(x)$.

Because $f(x)$ is not defined when $x = -2$, the limit cannot be found by evaluating the function.

$$\frac{x^2 - 2x - 8}{x + 2} = \frac{(x + 2)(x - 4)}{x + 2}$$

Reduce the rational expression.

$$\frac{(x + 2)(x - 4)}{x + 2} = x - 4 \text{ for all } x \neq -2.$$

The definition of limit as x approaches -2 involves only the behavior of the function near $x = -2$ and not at $x = -2$. Both $f(x)$ and the function $g(x) = x - 4$ have exactly the same values except at $x = -2$. So, they must have the same limit as x approaches -2.

$$\lim_{x \to -2} \frac{x^2 - 2x - 8}{x + 2} = \lim_{x \to -2} (x - 4)$$

$$= -2 - 4 = -6,$$

as illustrated.

Teaching Notes

Show students that the Limit Theorem is a generalization of the results found in **Example 3** as follows:

$$f(x) = \frac{x^2 - 2x - 3}{x - 3} = \frac{(x + 1)(x - 3)}{x - 3}$$

$$= x + 1,$$

for all $x \neq 3$

So, letting $g(x) = x + 1$, we find that:

$\lim\limits_{x \to 3} g(x) = 4$ and therefore

$\lim\limits_{x \to 3} f(x) = 4$ and we can state that

$\lim\limits_{x \to 3} f(x) = \lim\limits_{x \to 3} g(x).$

Example Notes

In **Example 4**, the Limit Theorem is used as a reason. Ask students to identify the functions $f(h)$ and $g(h)$ to which the Limit Theorem is applied.

$$f(h) = \frac{h(10 + h)}{h}, \; g(h) = (10 + h)$$

 Math Background

The **Limit of a Difference Quotient** is the slope of a tangent line (see pages 235–236). The limit found in **Example 4** shows that the slope of the tangent line to the graph of $f(x) = x^2$ at the point (5, 25) is 10.

ADDITIONAL EXAMPLES

Example 4

If $f(x) = 2x^2$, find

$\lim\limits_{h \to 0} \dfrac{f(-3 + h) - f(-3)}{h}.$

$\dfrac{f(-3 + h) - f(-3)}{h}$

$= \dfrac{2(-3 + h)^2 - 2(-3)^2}{h}$

$= \dfrac{2(9 - 6h + h^2) - 2(9)}{h}$

$= \dfrac{18 - 12h + 2h^2 - 18}{h}$

$= \dfrac{-12h + 2h^2}{h}$

$\lim\limits_{h \to 0} \dfrac{f(-3 + h) - f(-3)}{h}$

$= \lim\limits_{h \to 0} \dfrac{-12h + 2h^2}{h}$

$= \lim\limits_{h \to 0} \dfrac{h(-12 + 2h)}{h}$ *Factor the numerator.*

$= \lim\limits_{h \to 0} (-12 + 2h)$ *Limit Theorem*

$= -12 + 0 = -12$ *limit of a polynomial function*

Figure 14.2-2

values at all numbers except $x = 3$. So they must have the same limit as x approaches 3.

$$\lim\limits_{x \to 3} \frac{x^2 - 2x - 3}{x - 3} = \lim\limits_{x \to 3} (x + 1) = 3 + 1 = 4,$$

as illustrated in Figure 14.2-2.

■

The technique illustrated in Example 3 applies in many cases. When two functions have identical behavior, except possibly at $x = c$, they will have the same limit as x approaches c.

Limit Theorem

> If f and g are functions that have limits as x approaches c and
>
> $$f(x) = g(x) \qquad \text{for all } x \neq c,$$
>
> then
>
> $$\lim\limits_{x \to c} f(x) = \lim\limits_{x \to c} g(x).$$

Recall that the difference quotient of a function f is given by

$$\frac{f(x + h) - f(x)}{h}$$

The difference quotient can be evaluated for a specific value of x, say $x = c$, to obtain a new form.

$$\frac{f(c + h) - f(c)}{h}$$

Limits of the difference quotient of a function f play an important role in calculus. When computing such limits, the variable is often the quantity h, as in the following example.

NOTE Do not confuse the variable h with the function h. The meaning should be clear in context.

Example 4   Limit of a Difference Quotient

If $f(x) = x^2$, find $\lim\limits_{h \to 0} \dfrac{f(5 + h) - f(5)}{h}$.

Solution

Using algebra, write the difference quotient as follows:

$$\frac{f(5 + h) - f(5)}{h} = \frac{(5 + h)^2 - 5^2}{h}$$

$$= \frac{(25 + 10h + h^2) - 25}{h}$$

$$= \frac{10h + h^2}{h}$$

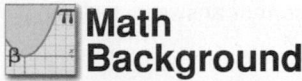

Math Background

The **Limit of a Difference Quotient** is used to find formulas for derivatives of functions. The derivative of $f(x) = x^2$ is $f'(x) = 2x$, as shown below.

Let $f(x) = x^2$.

$$f'(x) = \lim_{h \to 0} \frac{f(x + h) - f(x)}{h}$$

$$= \lim_{h \to 0} \frac{(x + h)^2 - x^2}{h}$$

$$= \lim_{h \to 0} \frac{x^2 + 2xh + h^2 - x^2}{h}$$

$$= \lim_{h \to 0} \frac{2xh + h^2}{h}$$

$$= \lim_{h \to 0} \frac{h(2x + h)}{h}$$

$$= \lim_{h \to 0} (2x + h)$$

$$= 2x + 0 = 2x$$

When the difference quotient is written this way, it is easy to see that it is a function of h, and the function is not defined when $h = 0$. Find the limit of the difference quotient as h approaches 0.

$$\lim_{h \to 0} \frac{f(5 + h) - f(5)}{5} = \lim_{h \to 0} \frac{10h + h^2}{h}$$

$$= \lim_{h \to 0} \frac{h(10 + h)}{h} \qquad \textit{Factor the numerator.}$$

$$= \lim_{h \to 0} (10 + h) \qquad \textit{Limit Theorem}$$

$$= 10 + 0 = 10 \qquad \textit{limit of a polynomial function}$$

Exercises 14.2

In Exercises 1–8, use the following facts about the functions f, g, and h to find the required limit.

$$\lim_{x \to 4} f(x) = 5 \quad \lim_{x \to 4} g(x) = 0 \quad \lim_{x \to 4} h(x) = -2$$

1. $\lim_{x \to 4} (f + g)(x)$ **5**

2. $\lim_{x \to 4} (g - h)(x)$ **2**

3. $\lim_{x \to 4} \frac{f}{g}(x)$ **does not exist**

4. $\lim_{x \to 4} \frac{g}{h}(x)$ **0**

5. $\lim_{x \to 4} (fg)(x)$ **0**

6. $\lim_{x \to 4} [h(x)]^2$ **4**

7. $\lim_{x \to 4} \left(\frac{3h}{2f + g}\right)(x)$ $-\frac{3}{5}$

8. $\lim_{x \to 4} \left(\frac{f - 2g}{4h}\right)(x)$ $-\frac{5}{8}$

In Exercises 9–23, find the limit, if it exists. If the limit does not exist, explain why.

9. $\lim_{x \to 2} (6x^3 - 2x^2 + 5x - 3)$ **47**

10. $\lim_{x \to -1} (x^7 + 2x^5 - x^4 + 3x + 4)$ **−3**

11. $\lim_{x \to -2} \frac{3x - 1}{2x + 3}$ **7**

12. $\lim_{x \to 3} \frac{x^2 + x + 1}{x^2 - 2x}$ $\frac{13}{3}$

13. $\lim_{x \to 1} \sqrt{x^3 + 6x^2 + 2x + 5}$ $\sqrt{14}$

14. $\lim_{x \to 2} \sqrt{x^2 + x + 3}$ **3**

15. $\lim_{x \to 0} \frac{\frac{1}{x + 5} - \frac{1}{5}}{x}$ $-\frac{1}{25}$

16. $\lim_{x \to 0} \frac{\frac{2}{x + 6} - \frac{1}{3}}{x}$ $-\frac{1}{18}$

17. $\lim_{x \to 1} \left(\frac{1}{x - 1} - \frac{2}{x^2 - 1}\right)$ $\frac{1}{2}$

18. $\lim_{x \to -2} \left[\frac{x^2}{x + 2} + \frac{2x}{x + 2}\right]$ **−2**

19. $\lim_{x \to 0} \frac{x^2}{|x|}$ **0**

20. $\lim_{x \to -2} |x + 2|$ **0**

21. $\lim_{x \to 0} \frac{\sqrt{2 - x} - \sqrt{2}}{x}$ $-\frac{1}{2\sqrt{2}}$

22. $\lim_{x \to 0} \left[\frac{|x|}{x} - \frac{x}{|x|}\right]$ **0**

23. $\lim_{x \to -3} \frac{|x + 3|}{x + 3}$

In Exercises 24–27, find

$$\lim_{h \to 0} \frac{f(2 + h) - f(2)}{h}.$$

24. $f(x) = x^2$ **4**

25. $f(x) = x^3$ **12**

26. $f(x) = x^2 + x + 1$ **5**

27. $f(x) = \sqrt{x}$ $\frac{1}{2\sqrt{2}}$

In Exercises 28–29, use a unit circle diagram to explain why the given statement is true.

28. $\lim_{t \to \frac{\pi}{2}} \sin t = 1$

29. $\lim_{t \to \frac{\pi}{2}} \cos t = 0$

Exercises 30–34 involve the greatest integer function, $f(x) = [x]$, which is defined to be the greatest integer that is less than or equal to a given number x. See Section 3.1. Use a calculator as an aid in analyzing these problems.

30. For $h(x) = [x] - [-x]$, find $\lim_{x \to 2} h(x)$, if the limit exists.

31. For $g(x) = x - [-x]$, find $\lim_{x \to 2} g(x)$, if the limit exists.

32. For $r(x) = \frac{[x] + [-x]}{x}$, find $\lim_{x \to 3} r(x)$, if the limit exists.

Exercises 14.2

ANSWERS

23. The limit does not exist. When x is less than -3, $f(x)$ is -1; when x is greater than -3, $f(x)$ is 1.

28. As the angle t in standard position gets closer to $\frac{\pi}{2}$, the y-coordinate of the point at which the terminal side of t crosses the unit circle gets closer to 1. Since this y-coordinate is the sine of the angle t, we have $\lim_{t \to \frac{\pi}{2}} \sin t = 1$.

29. As the angle t in standard position gets closer to $\frac{\pi}{2}$, the x-coordinate of the point at which the terminal side of t crosses the unit circle gets closer to 0. Since this x-coordinate is the cosine of the angle t, we have $\lim_{t \to \frac{\pi}{2}} \cos t = 0$.

30. Using the function $h(x) = [x] - [-x]$, when x is close to 2 but slightly greater than 2 we have $[x] = 2$ and $[-x] = -3$. When x is close to 2 but slightly less than 2 we have $[x] = 1$ and $[-x] = -2$. In either case $h(x) = -1$, so the limit has the value -1. Note that the limit is -1 even though $h(2) = 0$.

31. Using the function $g(x) = x + [-x]$, when x is close to 2 but slightly more than 2, we have $x \approx 2$, $[-x] = -3$. When x is close to 2 but slightly less than 2 we have $x \approx 2$, $[-x] = -2$. In this case, the difference is either 5 or 4 depending on whether x is more than 2 or less than 2 and so the limit doesn't exist.

32. Write $r(x) = \frac{h(x)}{x}$, where $h(x)$ is the function from Exercise 30.

Then $\lim_{x \to 3} r(x) = \frac{\lim_{x \to 3} h(x)}{\lim_{x \to 3} x} = -\frac{1}{3}$.

35. Many correct answers, including $f(x) = \frac{|x|}{x}$, $g(x) = \frac{-x}{|x|}$, and $c = 0$. In this case, $\lim\limits_{x \to 0} f(x)$ does not exist by Example 10; a similar argument shows that $\lim\limits_{x \to 0} g(x)$ does not exist. But $\lim\limits_{x \to 0} (f + g)(x) = 0$ by Exercise 22.

33. For $k(x) = \frac{x}{[x] + [-x]}$, find $\lim\limits_{x \to 1} k(x)$, if the limit exists.

−1

34. For $f(x) = x|x|$, find $\lim\limits_{h \to 0} \frac{f(0 + h) - f(0)}{h}$.

0

35. *Critical Thinking* Give an example of functions f and g and a number c such that neither $\lim\limits_{x \to c} f(x)$ nor $\lim\limits_{x \to c} g(x)$ exists, but $\lim\limits_{x \to c} (f + g)(x)$ does exist.

36. *Critical Thinking* Give an example of functions f and g and a number c such that neither $\lim\limits_{x \to c} f(x)$ nor $\lim\limits_{x \to c} g(x)$ exists, but $\lim\limits_{x \to c} (fg)(x)$ does exist.

Many correct answers including

$$f(x) = \begin{cases} 1 & x > 0 \\ -1 & x < 0 \end{cases}$$

$$g(x) = \begin{cases} -1 & x > 0 \\ 1 & x < 0 \end{cases}$$

using $c = 0$.

Section 14.2.A Excursion: One-Sided Limits

COMMON ERROR ALERT

Students sometimes misinterpret the meaning of the $+$ sign or the $-$ sign in one-sided limit expressions. For example, they might think that $\lim\limits_{x \to 4^+} f(x)$ represents the limit of $f(x)$ as x approaches 4 through positive values. Remind them that in this context, the $+$ sign means *from the right side*, not *positive*.

Show these examples to clarify the correct way to interpret one-sided limit notation:

* For $\lim\limits_{x \to 4^+} f(x)$, x approaches 4 from the right side of 4 (through positive values).

* For $\lim\limits_{x \to 4^-} f(x)$, x approaches 4 from the left side of 4 (through positive values).

Also show these examples (not pictured in Figure 14.2.A-1):

* For $\lim\limits_{x \to -4^+} f(x)$, x approaches -4 from the right side of -4 (through negative values).

* For $\lim\limits_{x \to -4^-} f(x)$, x approaches -4 from the left side of -4 (through negative values).

14.2.A Excursion: One-Sided Limits

Objectives

* Find one-sided limits

The function whose graph is shown in Figure 14.2.A-1 is defined for all values of x except $x = 4$.

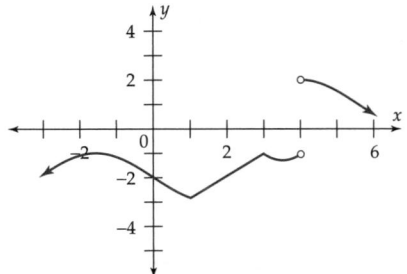

Figure 14.2.A-1

As x approaches 4 from the right, that is, takes values larger than but close to 4, the graph shows that the corresponding values of $f(x)$ get very close to 2. Consequently, "the limit of $f(x)$ as x approaches 4 from the right is 2."

$$\lim_{x \to 4^+} f(x) = 2$$

The small plus sign on 4 indicates that only the values of x with $x > 4$ are considered. Similarly, as x approaches 4 from the left, the graph shows that the corresponding values of $f(x)$ get very close to -1. Consequently, "the limit of $f(x)$ as x approaches 4 from the left is -1."

$$\lim_{x \to 4^-} f(x) = -1$$

The small minus sign indicates that only values of x with $x < 4$ are considered.

These "one-sided" limits are a bit different than the "two sided" limits discussed in Section 14.2. When x approaches 4 from the left and from the right, the corresponding values of $f(x)$ do not approach a single number, so the limit as x approaches 4, as defined in Section 14.1, does not exist.

The same notation and terminology are used in the general case, where f is any function and c and L are real numbers. The definition of the "right-hand limit,"

$$\lim_{x \to c^+} f(x) = L,$$

is obtained by inserting "$x > c$" in place of the phrase "on both sides of c" in the definition of limit in Section 14.2. The function f need not be defined when $x < c$.

Similarly, inserting "$x < c$" in place of "on both sides of c" in the same definition produces the definition of the "left-hand limit."

$$\lim_{x \to c^-} f(x) = L$$

Again, the function f need not be defined when $x > c$.

Example 1   One-Sided Limit

Find $\lim_{x \to 3^+} \left(\sqrt{x - 3} + 1 \right)$.

Solution

The function $f(x) = \sqrt{x - 3} + 1$ is defined only when $x \geq 3$, that is, for $x = 3$ and values of x to the right of 3. The graph of $f(x)$ is shown in Figure 14.2.A-2a, and a table of values is shown in 14.2.A-2b.

Figure 14.2.A-2a

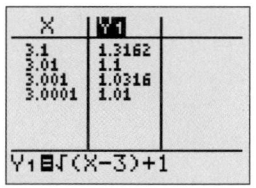

Figure 14.2.A-2b

The values of $f(x)$ approach 1 as x approaches 3 from the right. Therefore, $\lim_{x \to 3^+} \left(\sqrt{x - 3} + 1 \right) = 1$. ∎

Computing One-Sided Limits

The computation of one-sided limits is greatly facilitated by the following fact.

Example Notes

After finding the limit in **Example 2** by using the **Properties of Limits,** have students graph the function and then use the trace feature to confirm the limit.

Students may need some help in understanding how property 5 justifies the first step in the Solution for Example 2. Show the following details if necessary:

As stated at the top of the **Properties** box on page 919, $\lim\limits_{x\to c} f(x) = L$.

So, property 5 can be stated as:

$\lim\limits_{x\to c} \sqrt{f(x)} = \sqrt{L} = \sqrt{\lim\limits_{x\to c} f(x)}$; that is, $\lim\limits_{x\to c} \sqrt{f(x)} = \sqrt{\lim\limits_{x\to c} f(x)}$

Applying this to Example 2, replacing $f(x)$ with $\sqrt{9 - x^2}$ and $x\to c$ with $x\to 3^-$, we have:

$\lim\limits_{x\to 3^-} \sqrt{9 - x^2} = \sqrt{\lim\limits_{x\to 3^-}(9 - x^2)}$.

For **Example 3,** ask students to find $\lim\limits_{x\to 6} f(x)$, if it exists. If the limit does not exist, have them explain why.

The limit does not exist because $\lim\limits_{x\to 6^-} f(x) = 5$ and $\lim\limits_{x\to 6^+} f(x) = 4$, so $\lim\limits_{x\to 6^-} f(x) \neq \lim\limits_{x\to 6^+} f(x)$.

 Math Background

An alternate way to write the last statement in the **Two-sided Limits** box is:

$\lim\limits_{x\to c^-} f(x) - L$

if and only if

$\lim\limits_{x\to c^-} f(x) = L$ and $\lim\limits_{x\to c^+} f(x) = L$.

All the results about limits in Section 14.2, such as the properties of limits, limits of polynomial functions, and the Limit Theorem, remain valid if "$x \to c$" is replaced by either "$x \to c^+$" or "$x \to c^-$."

Example 2 Using Properties of Limits

Find $\lim\limits_{x\to 3^-} \sqrt{9 - x^2}$.

Solution

The function $f(x) = \sqrt{9 - x^2}$ is defined only when $-3 \le x \le 3$, because the quantity under the radical is negative for other values of x. Compute the limit of $f(x)$ as x approaches 3 from the left by using the properties of limits:

$$\lim\limits_{x\to 3^-} \sqrt{9 - x^2} = \sqrt{\lim\limits_{x\to 3^-}(9 - x^2)} \qquad \text{\textit{property 5}}$$
$$= \sqrt{\lim\limits_{x\to 3^-} 9 - \lim\limits_{x\to 3^-} x^2} \qquad \text{\textit{property 2}}$$
$$= \sqrt{\lim\limits_{x\to 3^-} 9 - \left(\lim\limits_{x\to 3^-} x\right)\left(\lim\limits_{x\to 3^-} x\right)} \qquad \text{\textit{property 3}}$$
$$= \sqrt{9 - 3^2} = 0 \qquad \begin{array}{l}\textit{limit of a constant} \\ \textit{limit of the identity function}\end{array}$$

■

Three Types of Limits

Notice that there are three kinds of limits: left-hand limits, right-hand limits, and "two-sided" limits as defined in Section 14.1. Example 1 exhibits a function that has a right-hand limit at $x = 3$, but no left-hand or two sided limit. Even when a function has both a left-hand and a right-hand limit at $x = c$, these limits may not be the same, as was shown in the introduction of this *Excursion*.

It is clear, however, that a function which has a two-sided limit L at $x = c$ necessarily has L as both its left-hand and right-hand limit at $x = c$. If the values of $f(x)$ can be made arbitrarily close to L by taking x close enough to c on both sides of c, then the same thing is true if you take only values of x on the left of c or on the right of c. Conversely, if a function has the same left-hand and right-hand limits at $x = c$, then this number must be a two-sided limit as well. In summary,

Two-sided Limits

Let f be a function and let c and L be real numbers. Then

$$\lim\limits_{x\to c} f(x) = L \quad \text{exactly when} \quad \lim\limits_{x\to c^-} f(x) = L \text{ and } \lim\limits_{x\to c^+} f(x) = L.$$

Example 3   Limits

From the following graph, find

a. $\lim\limits_{x \to 2} f(x)$ **b.** $\lim\limits_{x \to 2^-} f(x)$ **c.** $\lim\limits_{x \to 2^+} f(x)$

d. $\lim\limits_{x \to 6^-} f(x)$ **e.** $\lim\limits_{x \to 6^+} f(x)$

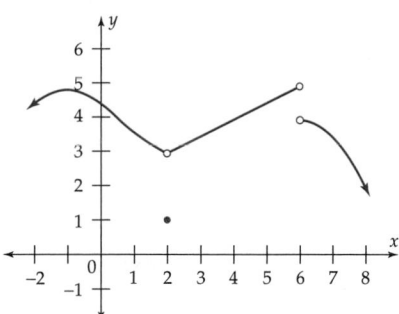

Figure 14.2.A-3

Solution

The graph shows that

a. $\lim\limits_{x \to 2} f(x) = 3$ **b.** $\lim\limits_{x \to 2^-} f(x) = 3$ **c.** $\lim\limits_{x \to 2^+} f(x) = 3$

d. $\lim\limits_{x \to 6^-} f(x) = 5$ **e.** $\lim\limits_{x \to 6^+} f(x) = 4$

Exercises 14.2.A

In Exercises 1–6, use a calculator to find a reasonable estimate of the limit.

1. $\lim\limits_{x \to \pi^-} \dfrac{\sin x}{1 - \cos x}$ **0**   **2.** $\lim\limits_{x \to \frac{\pi}{2}^-} (\sec x - \tan x)$ **0**

3. $\lim\limits_{x \to 0^+} \sqrt{x}\,(\ln x)$ **0**   **4.** $\lim\limits_{x \to 0^+} \left(\dfrac{1}{x}\right)^x$ **1**

5. $\lim\limits_{x \to 0^-} \dfrac{\sin 6x}{x}$ **6**   **6.** $\lim\limits_{x \to 0^+} \dfrac{\sin 3x}{1 + \sin 4x}$ **0**

In Exercises 7–10, use the graph of the function f to determine the required limits.

a. $\lim\limits_{x \to -2^-} f(x)$ **b.** $\lim\limits_{x \to 0^+} f(x)$

c. $\lim\limits_{x \to 3^-} f(x)$ **d.** $\lim\limits_{x \to 3^+} f(x)$

7.

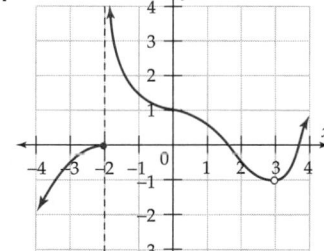

a. 0   **b. 1**

c. −1   **d. −1**

ADDITIONAL EXAMPLES

Example 2

Find $\lim\limits_{x \to -4^+} \sqrt{16 - x^2}$.

The function $f(x) = \sqrt{16 - x^2}$ is defined only when $-4 \le x \le 4$. Compute the limit as x approaches -4 from the right by using the properties of limits:

$$\lim_{x \to -4^+} f(x)$$
$$= \lim_{x \to -4^+} \sqrt{16 - x^2}$$
$$= \sqrt{\lim_{x \to -4^+}(16 - x^2)} \qquad \textit{property 5}$$
$$= \sqrt{\lim_{x \to -4^+} 16 - \lim_{x \to -4^+} x^2} \qquad \textit{property 2}$$
$$= \sqrt{\lim_{x \to -4^+} 16 - \left(\lim_{x \to -4^+} x\right)\left(\lim_{x \to -4^+} x\right)} \qquad \textit{property 3}$$
$$\qquad\qquad\qquad \textit{limit of a constant}$$
$$= \sqrt{16 - 4^2} = 0 \qquad \textit{limit of the identity function}$$

Example 3

From the graph below, find the following limits.

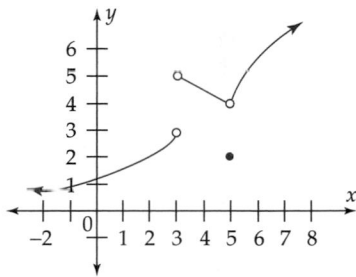

a. $\lim\limits_{x \to 5} f(x)$ **4**

b. $\lim\limits_{x \to 5^-} f(x)$ **4**

c. $\lim\limits_{x \to 5^+} f(x)$ **4**

d. $\lim\limits_{x \to 3^-} f(x)$ **3**

e. $\lim\limits_{x \to 3^+} f(x)$ **5**

Exercises 14.2.A

ANSWERS

8.

a. −3
b. 1
c. 1
d. 3

9.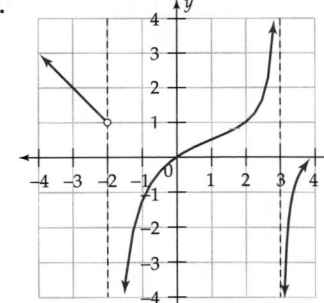

a. 1
b. 0
c. does not exist
d. does not exist

10.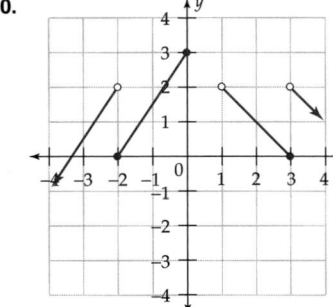

a. 2
b. does not exist
c. 0
d. 2

11. In Exercise 33a of Section 14.1, find
  a. $\lim_{x \to -2^-} f(x)$ **5**   b. $\lim_{x \to -2^+} f(x)$ **0**
  c. $\lim_{x \to 2^-} f(x)$ **4**   d. $\lim_{x \to 2^+} f(x)$ **2**

12. In Exercise 34a of Section 14.1, find
  a. $\lim_{x \to -1^-} g(x)$ **1**   b. $\lim_{x \to -1^+} g(x)$ **1**
  c. $\lim_{x \to 1^-} g(x)$ **3**   d. $\lim_{x \to 1^+} g(x)$ **2**

In Exercises 13–22, find the limit.

13. $\lim_{x \to 1^+} \left(\sqrt{x-1} + 3 \right)$ **3**   14. $\lim_{x \to 3^-} \sqrt{-3-x}$ **does not exist**

15. $\lim_{x \to 4^-} \dfrac{x-4}{x^2-16}$ **$\dfrac{1}{8}$**   16. $\lim_{x \to 2^+} \dfrac{|x-2|}{x-2}$ **1**

17. $\lim_{x \to 3^+} \dfrac{3}{x^2-9}$ **does not exist**   18. $\lim_{x \to 2^-} \dfrac{x+1}{x^2-x-2}$ **does not exist**

19. $\lim_{x \to -2.5^-} \left(\sqrt{5+2x} + x \right)$ **−2.5**

20. $\lim_{x \to 3^+} \left(\sqrt{x-3} + \sqrt{3x} \right)$ **3**

21. $\lim_{x \to -3^+} \left(\dfrac{|x+3|}{x+3} + \sqrt{x+3} + 1 \right)$ **2**

22. $\lim_{x \to -4^-} \left(\sqrt{|x|-4} + x^2 \right)$ **16**

Exercises 23 and 24 involve the greatest integer function, $f(x) = [x]$. See Exercise 30 in Section 14.2.

23. Find $\lim_{x \to 2^+} [x]$ and $\lim_{x \to 2^-} [x]$. **2; 1**

24. Find $\lim_{x \to 3^-} (x - [x])$ and $\lim_{x \to 3^+} (x - [x])$. **1; 0**

14.3 The Formal Definition of Limit (Optional)

Objectives

• Use the formal definition of limit

The informal definition of limit in Section 14.1 is quite adequate for understanding the basic properties of limits and for calculating the limits of many familiar functions. This definition, or one very much like it, was used for more than a century and played a crucial role in the development of calculus. Nevertheless, the informal definition is not entirely satisfactory; it is based on ideas that have been illustrated by examples but not precisely defined.

Mathematical intuition, as exemplified in the informal definition of limit, is a valuable guide; but it is not infallible. On several occasions in the history of mathematics, what first seemed intuitively plausible has turned out to be false. In the long run, the only way to guarantee the accuracy of mathematical results is to base them on rigorously precise definitions and theorems. This section takes the first step in building this rigorous foundation by developing a formal definition of limit.

In order to keep the discussion as concrete as possible, suppose f is a function such that $\lim_{x \to 5} f(x) = 12$. You do not need to know the rule of f or anything else about it to understand the following discussion.

The informal definition of the statement "$\lim_{x \to 5} f(x) = 12$" that was given in Section 14.1 has two components:

A. As x takes values very close to but not equal to 5, the corresponding values of $f(x)$ get very close—and possibly are equal—to 12.

B. The value of $f(x)$ can be made arbitrarily close (as close as you want) to 12 by taking x sufficiently close (but not equal) to 5.

In a sense, Component **A** is unnecessary because it is included in Component **B**: If the values of $f(x)$ can be made *arbitrarily close* to 12 by taking x close enough to 5, then presumably $f(x)$ can be made to get very close to 12 by taking values of x very close to 5.

Consequently, to obtain the formal definition of limit, begin with Component B of the informal definition.

$\lim_{x \to 5} f(x) = 12$ **means that the value of $f(x)$ can be made as close as you want to 12 by taking x close enough to 5.**   [1]

The definition above, referred to as Definition [1], will be modified step by step until the formal definition of limit is reached.

Definition [1] says, in effect, that there is a two-step process involved in finding a limit, if it exists:

1. Know how close you want $f(x)$ to be to 12,

2. Determine how close x must be to 5 to guarantee this.

Definition [1] can now be restated as Definition [2].

Teaching Notes

Remind students that the limits of functions found in Section 14.1 were based on calculator explorations that *suggested* a particular limit in each case. In Section 14.2, the Properties of Limits were used to find limits algebraically, but those properties were stated without proofs.

In this section, the **Formal Definition of Limit** will be used to *prove* that a limit is a particular number and to prove one of the limit properties.

Math Background

Historical research about prime numbers provides examples of mathematical intuition gone awry. For example, many mathematicians have tried to find polynomial functions that generate prime numbers. There are several polynomials that generate a finite number of prime numbers. For example, Euler's formula $p = n^2 + n + 41$ generates prime numbers for values of n from 0 to 39, and the polynomial $p = n^2 - 79n + 1601$ generates prime numbers for values of n from 0 to 79. However, there is no polynomial function that will generate prime numbers for *all* nonnegative integers n.

In 1640, French mathematician and statesman Pierre de Fermat (1601–1665) conjectured that all of the numbers

$$F_n = 2^{2^n} + 1, n = 0, 1, 2, \ldots$$

are prime. In his honor, these numbers are now called *Fermat numbers,* and the primes among them are called *Fermat primes.* The first five terms of the sequence ($F_0 = 3$, $F_1 = 5$, $F_2 = 17$, $F_3 = 257$, and $F_4 = 65{,}537$) are indeed prime, which can be verified by trial division. The next

Fermat number, $F_5 = 4{,}294{,}967{,}297$, however, is so large that it was not easy to check it with methods available in the 1600s. Therefore, the conjecture remained unresolved until 1731, when the great Swiss mathematician Leonhard Euler (1707–1783) refuted it by determining that 641 divides F_5. To this day, no Fermat primes past F_4 have been discovered, and the Fermat numbers from $n = 5$ to $n = 32$ are all known to be composite.

Teaching Notes

Show students these alternate ways to express the relationship between ε and δ in definition [4]:

- If $5 - \delta < x < 5 + \delta$ and $x \neq 5$, then $12 - \varepsilon < f(x) < 12 + \varepsilon$.
- If x is in the interval $(5 - \delta, 5 + \delta)$ and $x \neq 5$, then $f(x)$ is in the interval $(12 - \varepsilon, 12 + \varepsilon)$.

If a student asks how the **Definition of Limit** applies to a nonlinear function, the following explanation and diagrams may help.

To prove $\lim_{x \to c} f(x) = L$, decide how close you want $f(x)$ to be to L by choosing an ε-value. Use this ε-value to form an interval on the y-axis centered at L. This will determine a portion of the graph, shown below in red.

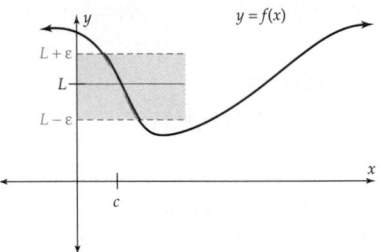

The next task is to show that for every x within δ of c, but not equal to c, the corresponding function value lies on the red portion of the graph. In the first diagram below, the choice of δ just barely works (that is, a larger δ would not work). In the second diagram, δ is smaller than necessary, and therefore also works.

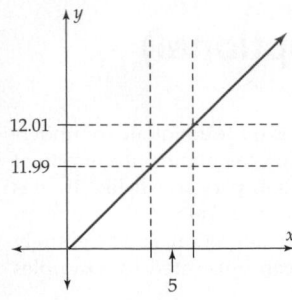

x is in this interval when
$11.99 < f(x) < 12.01$

Figure 14.3-1

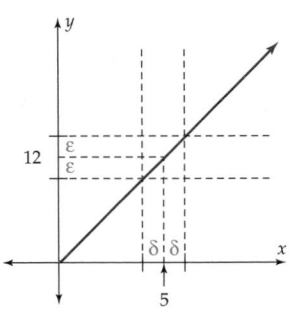

Figure 14.3-2

$\lim_{x \to 5} f(x) = 12$ means that whenever you specify how close $f(x)$ should be to 12, you know how close x must be to 5 to guarantee it. [2]

For example, if you want $f(x)$ to be within 0.01 of 12, that is, between 11.99 and 12.01, you can find how close x must be to 5 to guarantee that

$$11.99 < f(x) < 12.01.$$

Any value of x in the interval around 5 shown in Figure 14.3-1 will produce $11.99 < f(x) < 12.01$.

But "arbitrarily close" implies much more. You must be able to find how close x is to 5 regardless of how close you want $f(x)$ to be to 12. If you want $f(x)$ to be within 0.002 of 12, or 0.0001 of 12, or within any distance of 12, you must be able to find how close x must be to 5 in each case to accomplish this. So, Definition [2] can be restated as follows:

$\lim_{x \to 5} f(x) = 12$ means that no matter what positive number you specify in measuring how close you want $f(x)$ to be to 12, you must be able to find how close x must be to 5 in order to guarantee that $f(x)$ is that close to 12. [3]

Hereafter, the small positive number you specify in measuring how close $f(x)$ should be to 12 will be denoted by the Greek letter ε (epsilon). When you know how close x should be to 5 to accomplish this, denote the number by the Greek letter δ (delta). Presumably the number δ, which measures how close x must be to 5, will depend on the number ε, which measures how close you want $f(x)$ to be to 12. Using this language, Definition [3] becomes Definition [4].

$\lim_{x \to 5} f(x) = 12$ means that for every positive number ε there is a positive number δ that depends on ε with this property: [4]
If x is within δ of 5 but not equal to 5, then $f(x)$ is within ε of 12, and possibly equal to 12.

Although Definition [4] is essentially the formal definition, somewhat briefer notation is usually used.

If you think of $f(x)$ and 12 as numbers on the number line, then the statement

$$f(x) \text{ is within } \varepsilon \text{ of } 12$$

means that

the distance from $f(x)$ to 12 is less than ε.

Because distance on the number line is measured by absolute value (see Sections 2.4 and 2.5.A), the last statement can be written as

$$|f(x) - 12| < \varepsilon.$$

Similarly, saying that x is within δ of 5 and not equal to 5 means that the distance from x to 5 is less than δ but greater than 0, that is

$$0 < |x - 5| < \delta.$$

Example Notes

In **Example 1**, note that 0 is in the inequality $0 < |x - 5| < \delta$, but not in the inequality $|f(x) - 12| < \varepsilon$. Writing $0 < |x - 5|$ is another way of writing $x \neq 5$.

Figure 14.3-3 may be interpreted as saying if x is in the interval $(5 - \delta, 5 + \delta)$ and $x \neq 5$, then $f(x)$ is in the interval $(12 - \varepsilon, 12 + \varepsilon)$.

NOTE Epsilon, ε, and delta, δ, are Greek letters that are often used to represent small amounts.

Using this notation, Definition [4] becomes the desired formal definition.

$\lim\limits_{x\to 5} f(x) = 12$ **means that for each positive number ε, there is a number δ that depends on ε, such that if $0 < |x - 5| < \delta$, then $|f(x) - 12| < \varepsilon$.**   [5]

Definition [5] is sufficiently rigorous because the imprecise terms "arbitrarily close" and "close enough" in the informal definition have been replaced by a precise statement using inequalities that can be verified in specific cases, as will be shown in the examples that follow. There is nothing special about 5 and 12 in the preceding discussion; the entire analysis applies equally well in the general case and leads to the formal definition of limit, which is just Definition [5] with c in place of 5, L in place of 12, and f for any function.

Definition of Limit

Let f be a function and let c be a real number such that $f(x)$ is defined for all x, except possibly $x = c$, in some open interval containing c. The limit of $f(x)$ as x approaches c is L, which is written

$$\lim\limits_{x\to c} f(x) = L,$$

provided that for each positive number ε, there is a positive number δ that depends on ε with the property

if $0 < |x - c| < \delta$,   then $|f(x) - L| < \varepsilon$.

This definition is often called the ε-δ definition of limits.

Example 1   **Proving a Limit**

Let $f(x) = 4x - 8$ and prove that $\lim\limits_{x\to 5} f(x) = 12$.

Solution

Apply the definition of limit with $c = 5$, $L = 12$, and $f(x) = 4x - 8$. Figure 14.3-3 illustrates the situation. Suppose that ε is any positive number. Find a positive number δ with the property

If $0 < |x - 5| < \delta$,   then $|f(x) - 12| < \varepsilon$.

Let δ be the number $\frac{\varepsilon}{4}$, and show that this δ will work. For now, do not worry about how $\delta = \frac{\varepsilon}{4}$ was found; just verify that the following argument is valid.

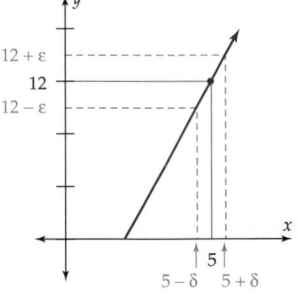

Figure 14.3-3

ADDITIONAL EXAMPLES

Example 1

Let $f(x) = 5x - 7$ and prove that

$\lim\limits_{x\to 3} f(x) = 8$.

Apply the definition of limit with $c = 3$, $L = 8$, and $f(x) = 5x - 7$. The figure below shows the situation.

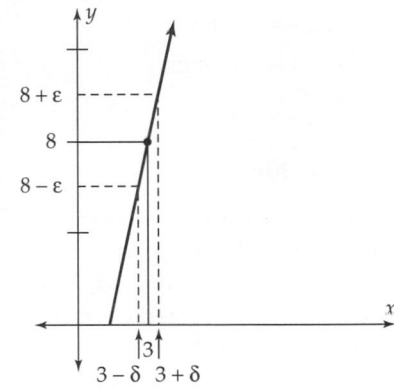

Suppose that ε is any positive number. Find a positive number δ with the property

If $0 < |x - 3| < \delta$, then
$\qquad |f(x) - 8| < \varepsilon$.

Let $\delta = \frac{\varepsilon}{5}$.

If $|x - 3| < \delta$, then

$\|x - 3\| < \frac{\varepsilon}{5}$	$\delta = \frac{\varepsilon}{5}$
$5\|x - 3\| < \varepsilon$	*Multiply both sides by 5.*
$\|5\|\|x - 3\| < \varepsilon$	$5 = \|5\|$
$\|5(x - 3)\| < \varepsilon$	$\|a\|\|b\| = \|ab\|$
$\|5x - 15\| < \varepsilon$	
$\|(5x - 7) - 8\| < \varepsilon$	*Rewrite -15 as $-7 - 8$.*
$\|f(x) - 8\| < \varepsilon$	$f(x) = 5x - 7$

This verifies that for each $\varepsilon > 0$, there is a positive number δ with the property

If $0 < |x - 3| < \delta$, then
$\qquad |f(x) - 8| < \varepsilon$.

Therefore, $\lim\limits_{x\to 3} f(x) = 8$.

![Math Background icon] **Math Background**

The proofs in **Examples 1** and **2** involve limits of linear functions. In both examples, the slope m is a positive integer, c is positive, and $\delta = \frac{1}{|m|}$ (see **Additional Example 3**).

In the limit statements discussed below, some other cases are shown for the slope and for c.

To prove $\lim\limits_{x\to 6}\left(\frac{1}{3}x + 5\right) = 7$, choose $\delta = 3\varepsilon$, and prove that If $0 < |x - 6| < 3\varepsilon$, then

$$\left|\left(\frac{1}{3}x + 5\right) - 7\right| < \varepsilon.$$

To prove $\lim\limits_{x\to -5}\left(-\frac{2}{5}x + 6\right) = 8$, choose $\delta = \frac{5}{2}\varepsilon$, and prove that If $0 < |x + 5| < \frac{5}{2}\varepsilon$, then

$$\left|\left(-\frac{2}{5}x + 6\right) - 8\right| < \varepsilon.$$

The last statement before **Example 2** is:

$|f(x) - 9| < \varepsilon$ whenever $0 < |x - 1| < \delta$. Students might misinterpret that statement to mean:

If $|f(x) - 9| < \varepsilon$, then $0 < |x - 1| < \delta$.

The correct interpretation is:

If $0 < |x - 1| < \delta$, then $|f(x) - 9| < \varepsilon$.

Example Notes

In **Example 2**, make sure students understand that the first part of the solution *is not the proof*. Instead, it is the "scratch work" (sometimes called the analysis) used to find a suitable expression for δ. You might want to comment that *working backwards* is a common strategy used in developing proofs in most areas of mathematics.

ADDITIONAL EXAMPLES

Example 2

Prove that $\lim\limits_{x \to 4}(3x - 2) = 10$.

$f(x) = 3x - 2, c = 4, L = 10$

Let ε be a positive number and find a δ with the property

If $0 < |x - 4| < \delta$, then $|(3x - 2) - 10| < \varepsilon$.

Work backwards from the desired conclusion $|(3x - 2) - 10| < \varepsilon$ to find a suitable δ.

"Scratch Work:"

$$|(3x - 2) - 10 < \varepsilon$$
$$|3x - 12| < \varepsilon$$
$$|3(x - 4)| < \varepsilon$$
$$|3||x - 4| < \varepsilon$$
$$3|x - 4| < \varepsilon$$
$$|x - 4| < \frac{\varepsilon}{3}$$

So, $\frac{\varepsilon}{3}$ would be a good choice for δ.

("End of Scratch Work")

If $|x - 5| < \delta$, then

$$|x - 5| < \frac{\varepsilon}{4} \qquad \delta = \frac{\varepsilon}{4}$$
$$4|x - 5| < \varepsilon \qquad \textit{Multiply both sides by 4.}$$
$$|4||x - 5| < \varepsilon \qquad 4 = |4|$$
$$|4(x - 5)| < \varepsilon \qquad |a||b| = |ab|$$
$$|4x - 20| < \varepsilon$$
$$|(4x - 8) - 12| < \varepsilon \qquad \textit{Rewrite } -20 \textit{ as } -8 - 12.$$
$$|f(x) - 12| < \varepsilon \qquad f(x) = 4x - 8$$

This verifies that for each $\varepsilon > 0$, there is a positive δ with the property

If $0 < |x - 5| < \delta$, then $|f(x) - 12| < \varepsilon$.

This completes the proof that $\lim\limits_{x \to 5} f(x) = 12$. ∎

Proofs like the one in Example 1 often seem mysterious to beginners. Although they can follow the argument after δ has been found, they do not see how to find δ. Example 2 gives a fuller picture of the processes used in proving statements about limits.

Example 2 proves that for any positive number ε, there exists δ such that

$$|f(x) - 9| < \varepsilon \text{ whenever } 0 < |x - 1| < \delta.$$

Example 2   Use the ε-δ Definition of Limit

Prove that $\lim\limits_{x \to 1}(2x + 7) = 9$.

Solution

In this case, $f(x) = 2x + 7, c = 1$, and $L = 9$. Let ε be a positive number and find a δ with the property

If $0 < |x - 1| < \delta$, then $|(2x + 7) - 9| < \varepsilon$.

In order to get some idea which δ might have this property, *work backwards* from the desired conclusion, namely,

$$|(2x + 7) - 9| < \varepsilon.$$

The last statement is equivalent to

$$|2x - 2| < \varepsilon,$$

which in turn is equivalent to each of the following statements.

$$|2(x - 1)| < \varepsilon$$
$$|2||x - 1| < \varepsilon$$
$$2|x - 1| < \varepsilon$$
$$|x - 1| < \frac{\varepsilon}{2}$$

continued from page 932

Now give the actual proof, written forwards.

When the conclusion is written this way, it suggests that the number $\frac{\varepsilon}{2}$ would be a good choice for δ.

Everything up to here has been "scratch work." Now give the actual proof, written forwards.

Given a positive number ε, let δ be the number $\frac{\varepsilon}{2}$. If $0 < |x - 1| < \delta$, then

$$
\begin{array}{ll}
|x - 1| < \frac{\varepsilon}{2} & \delta = \frac{\varepsilon}{2} \\
2|x - 1| < \varepsilon & \textit{Multiply both sides by 2.} \\
|2||x - 1| < \varepsilon & 2 = |2| \\
|2(x - 1)| < \varepsilon & |a||b| = |ab| \\
|2x - 2| < \varepsilon & \\
|(2x + 7) - 9| < \varepsilon & \textit{Rewrite } -2 \textit{ as } 7 - 9. \\
|f(x) - 9| < \varepsilon & f(x) = 2x + 7
\end{array}
$$

Therefore, $\delta = \frac{\varepsilon}{2}$ has the required property, and the proof is complete. ∎

Figure 14.3-4

Given a positive number ε, let $\delta = \frac{\varepsilon}{3}$. If $|x - 4| < \delta$, then

$$
\begin{array}{ll}
|x - 4| < \frac{\varepsilon}{3} & \delta = \frac{\varepsilon}{3} \\
3|x - 4| < \varepsilon & \textit{Multiply both sides by 3.} \\
|3||x - 4| < \varepsilon & 3 = |3| \\
|3(x - 4)| < \varepsilon & |a||b| = |ab| \\
|3x - 12| < \varepsilon & \\
|(3x - 2) - 10| < \varepsilon & \textit{Rewrite } -12 \textit{ as } -2 - 10. \\
|f(x) - 10| < \varepsilon & f(x) = 3x - 2
\end{array}
$$

Therefore, $\delta = \frac{\varepsilon}{3}$ has the required property.

Proving Limit Properties

Once the algebraic scratch work was done in Examples 1 and 2, the limit proofs were relatively easy. In most cases, however, a more involved argument is required. In fact, it can be quite difficult to prove directly from the definition, for example, that $\lim\limits_{x \to 3} \frac{x^2 - 4x + 1}{x^3 - 2x^2 - x} = -\frac{1}{3}$. Fortunately, such complicated calculations can often be avoided by using the various limit properties given in Section 14.2. Of course, these properties must first be proved using the definition. Surprisingly, the proofs are comparatively easy.

Example 3 ▸ Proving Limit Properties

Example 3

Prove that $\lim\limits_{x \to c}(mx + b) = mc + b$.

Let $\varepsilon > 0$. Find $\delta > 0$ such that

If $0 < |x - c| < \delta$, then
$|(mx + b) - (mc + b)| < \varepsilon$.

"Scratch Work:"

$$
\begin{array}{l}
|(mx + b) - (mc + b)| < \varepsilon \\
|mx + b - mc - b| < \varepsilon \\
|mx - mc| < \varepsilon \\
|m(x - c)| < \varepsilon \\
|m||(x - c)| < \varepsilon \\
|x - c| < \frac{\varepsilon}{|m|}
\end{array}
$$

So, choose $\delta = \frac{\varepsilon}{|m|}$.

(End of "Scratch Work")

Let f and g be functions such that

$$\lim_{x \to c} f(x) = L \quad \text{and} \quad \lim_{x \to c} g(x) = M.$$

Prove that $\lim\limits_{x \to c}(f(x) + g(x)) = L + M$.

Solution

Scratch Work: If ε is any positive number, find a positive δ with the property

If $0 < |x - c| < \delta$, then $|(f(x) + g(x)) - (L + M)| < \varepsilon$.

Given a positive number ε, let $\delta = \frac{\varepsilon}{|m|}$.

If $|x - c| < \delta$, then

$$
\begin{array}{l}
|x - c| < \frac{\varepsilon}{|m|} \\
|m||x - c| < \varepsilon \\
|m(x - c)| < \varepsilon \\
|mx - mc| < \varepsilon \\
|mx + b - mc + b| < \varepsilon \\
|(mx + b) - (mc + b)| < \varepsilon
\end{array}
$$

Therefore, $\lim\limits_{x \to c}(mx + b) = mc + b$.

Teaching Notes

The triangle inequality (page 109) is:
For any real numbers c and d,
$$|c + d| \leq |c| + |d|.$$
In the Solution for **Example 3** at the top of this page, the triangle inequality is used as follows:

$$|(f(x) - L) + (g(x) - M)| \leq |f(x) - L| + |g(x) - M|$$

$$\begin{array}{ccccccccc} | & c & + & d & | & \leq & |c| & + & |d| \end{array}$$

In the **Proof** on this page, students may wonder why it is permissible to use $\frac{\varepsilon}{2}$ in place of ε. Explain that if $\lim\limits_{x \to c} f(x) = L$, then, by the definition of limit, a suitable δ exists for *any* positive ε that is chosen. If a δ exists for a particular choice of ε, then another δ must exist for $\frac{\varepsilon}{2}$, or $\frac{\varepsilon}{100}$, or *any* other choice of ε.

Math Background

The limit proofs in this section involve linear functions. Below is an example of a limit proof for a nonlinear function.

Prove $\lim\limits_{x \to 3} (x^2 - 6x + 5) = -4$.

"Scratch Work:"
$$|(x^2 - 6x + 5) + 4| < \varepsilon$$
$$|x^2 - 6x + 9| < \varepsilon$$
$$|(x - 3)^2| < \varepsilon$$
$$|x - 3| < \sqrt{\varepsilon}$$

So, let $\delta = \sqrt{\varepsilon}$.

Proof :
Let $\varepsilon > 0$ and let $\delta = \sqrt{\varepsilon}$.
If $0 < |x - 3| < \delta$, then

$$|x - 3| < \sqrt{\varepsilon}$$
$$|x - 3|^2 < \varepsilon$$
$$|(x - 3)(x - 3)| < \varepsilon$$
$$|x^2 - 6x + 9| < \varepsilon$$
$$|(x^2 - 6x + 5) + 4| < \varepsilon$$
$$|f(x) + 4| < \varepsilon$$

Note the following result of the triangle inequality. (See Section 2.4.)
$$|(f(x) + g(x)) - (L + M)| = |(f(x) - L) + (g(x) - M)|$$
$$\leq |f(x) - L| + |g(x) - M|$$

If there is a δ with the property

If $0 < |x - c| < \delta$, then $|f(x) - L| + |g(x) - M| < \varepsilon$,

then the smaller quantity $|(f(x) + g(x)) - (L + M)|$ will also be less than ε when $0 < |x - c| < \delta$. Such a δ can be found as follows.

Proof Let ε be any positive number. Because $\lim\limits_{x \to c} f(x) = L$, apply the definition of limit with $\frac{\varepsilon}{2}$ in place of ε:

there is a positive number δ_1 with the property

If $0 < |x - c| < \delta_1$, then $|f(x) - L| < \frac{\varepsilon}{2}$.

Similarly, because $\lim\limits_{x \to c} g(x) = M$,

there is a positive number δ_2 with the property

If $0 < |x - c| < \delta_2$, then $|g(x) - M| < \frac{\varepsilon}{2}$.

Now let δ be the smaller of the two numbers δ_1 and δ_2, so that $\delta \leq \delta_1$ and $\delta \leq \delta_2$. Then if $0 < |x - c| < \delta$, it must be true that

$$0 < |x - c| < \delta_1 \quad \text{and} \quad 0 < |x - c| < \delta_2.$$

Therefore,

$$|f(x) - L| < \frac{\varepsilon}{2} \quad \text{and} \quad |g(x) - M| < \frac{\varepsilon}{2}.$$

Consequently, if $0 < |x - c| < \delta$, then

$$|(f(x) + g(x)) - (L + M)| = |(f(x) - L) + (g(x) - M)|$$
$$\leq |f(x) - L| + |g(x) - M|$$
$$< \frac{\varepsilon}{2} + \frac{\varepsilon}{2}$$
$$= \varepsilon$$

It has been shown that for any $\varepsilon > 0$, there is a $\delta > 0$ with the property:

If $0 < |x - c| < \delta$, then $|(f(x) + g(x)) - (L + M)| < \varepsilon$.

Therefore, $\lim\limits_{x \to c} (f(x) + g(x)) = L + M$.

The proofs of the other limit properties and theorems of Section 14.2 are introduced in calculus.

Teaching Notes

Have students write out the formal definitions of **One-Sided Limits** (or complete the definitions as shown below).

Let f be a function and let c be a real number such that $f(x)$ is defined for all x near c, with $x > c$.

The limit of $f(x)$ as x approaches c from the right is L, which is written

$$\lim_{x \to c^+} f(x) = L,$$

provided that for each positive number ε, there is a positive number δ that depends on ε with the property

if $c < x < c + \delta$ then $|f(x) - L| < \varepsilon.$

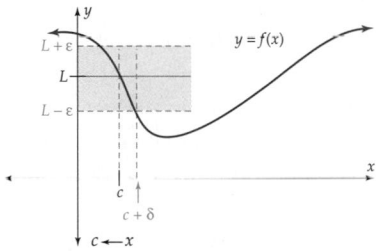

Let f be a function and let c be a real number such that $f(x)$ is defined for all x near c, with $x < c$.

The limit of $f(x)$ as x approaches c from the left is L, which is written

$$\lim_{x \to c^-} f(x) = L,$$

provided that for each positive number ε, there is a positive number δ that depends on ε with the property

if $c - \delta < x < c$ then $|f(x) - L| < \varepsilon.$

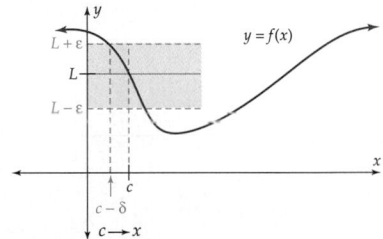

One-Sided Limits

The formal definition of limit may easily be carried over to one-sided limits, as defined informally in *Excursion* 14.2.A, by using the following fact:

$$|x - c| < \delta \qquad \text{exactly when} \qquad -\delta < x - c < \delta,$$

which is equivalent to

$$|x - c| < \delta \qquad \text{exactly when} \qquad c - \delta < x < c + \delta.$$

Thus, the numbers between c and $c + \delta$ lie to the right of c, within distance δ of c, and the numbers between $c - \delta$ and c lie to the left of c, within distance δ of c.

Consequently, the formal definition of right-hand limits can be obtained from the definition above by replacing the phrase "if $0 < |x - c| < \delta$" with "$c < x < c + \delta$." For a formal definition of the left-hand limits, replace the phrase "if $0 < |x - c| < \delta$" with "if $c - \delta < x < c$."

Exercises 14.3

In Exercises 1–12, use the formal definition of limit to prove the given statement, as in Example 1.

1. $\lim_{x \to 3} (3x - 2) = 7$

2. $\lim_{x \to 1} (4x + 2) = 6$

3. $\lim_{x \to 5} x = 5$

4. $\lim_{x \to 0} (x + 2) = 2$

5. $\lim_{x \to 2} (6x + 3) - 15$

6. $\lim_{x \to 7} (-2x + 19) = 5$

7. $\lim_{x \to 1} 4 = 4$

8. $\lim_{x \to 2} \pi = \pi$

9. $\lim_{x \to 4} (x - 6) = -2$

10. $\lim_{x \to 1} (2x - 7) = -5$

11. $\lim_{x \to -2} (2x + 5) - 1$

12. $\lim_{x \to -3} (2x - 4) = -10$

In Exercises 13 and 14, use the formal definition of limit to prove the statement.

13. $\lim_{x \to 0} x^2 = 0$

14. $\lim_{x \to 0} x^3 = 0$

In Exercises 15 and 16, let f and g be functions such that

$$\lim_{x \to c} f(x) = L \text{ and } \lim_{x \to c} g(x) = M.$$

15. *Critical Thinking* Prove that $\lim_{x \to c} (f(x) - g(x)) = L - M$. *Hint:* see Example 3.

16. *Critical Thinking* If k is a constant, prove that $\lim_{x \to c} kf(x) = kL$.

2. Given $\varepsilon > 0$, let $\delta = \frac{\varepsilon}{4}$. Then,
$|x - 1| < \delta \Rightarrow |4x - 4| < \varepsilon \Rightarrow$
$|4x + 2 - 6| < \varepsilon \Rightarrow |f(x) - 6| < \varepsilon.$

3. Given $\varepsilon > 0$, let $\delta = \varepsilon$.
Then, $0 < |x - 5| < \delta \Rightarrow$
$|x - 5| < \varepsilon \Rightarrow |f(x) - 5| < \varepsilon.$

4. Given $\varepsilon > 0$, let $\delta = \varepsilon$. Then,
$|x - 0| < \delta \Rightarrow |x + 2 - 2| < \varepsilon \Rightarrow$
$|f(x) - 2| < \varepsilon.$

5. Given $\varepsilon > 0$, let $\delta = \frac{\varepsilon}{6}$.
Then, $0 < |x - 2| < \delta \Rightarrow$
$|x - 2| < \frac{\varepsilon}{6} \Rightarrow 6|x - 2| < \varepsilon \Rightarrow$
$|6(x - 2)| < \varepsilon \Rightarrow |6x - 12| < \varepsilon \Rightarrow$
$|(6x + 3) - 15| < \varepsilon \Rightarrow |f(x) - 15| < \varepsilon.$

6–16. See pp. 1085–1086

Exercises 14.3

ANSWERS

1. Given $\varepsilon > 0$, let $\delta = \frac{\varepsilon}{3}$.
Then, $0 < |x - 3| < \delta \Rightarrow$
$|x - 3| < \frac{\varepsilon}{3} \Rightarrow 3|x - 3| < \varepsilon \Rightarrow$
$|3(x - 3)| < \varepsilon \Rightarrow |3x - 9| < \varepsilon \Rightarrow$
$|(3x - 2) - 7| < \varepsilon \Rightarrow$
$|f(x) - 7| < \varepsilon.$

Section
14.4 Continuity

Teaching Notes

Continuity was introduced in Section 4.3.

In Figure 14.4-1, the functions in the upper left and the lower right are continuous at all values of x that are shown. The functions in the upper right and the lower left each have one or more values of x where they are not continuous, although all four graphs are continuous at $x = c$.

Some other examples of function graphs that are continuous at $x = c$ are shown below. The first two graphs are also continuous at all values of x shown.

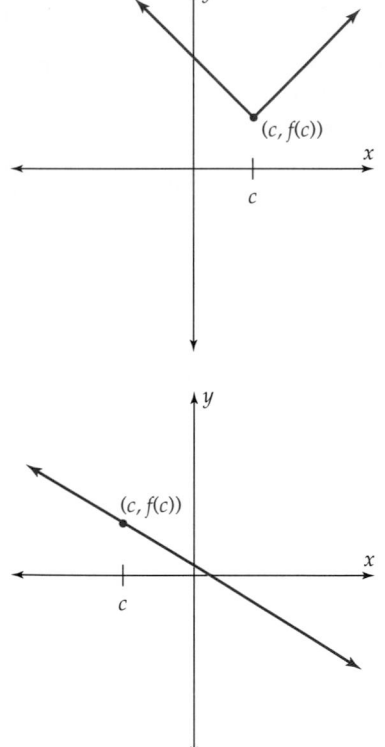

14.4 Continuity

Objectives

- Determine if a function is continuous at a point
- Determine if a function is continuous on an interval
- Apply properties of continuous functions

Calculus deals in large part with continuous functions, and the properties of continuous functions are essential for understanding many of the key theorems in calculus. This section presents the intuitive idea of continuity, its formal definition, and the various properties of continuity—which were used in the work with graphs in earlier chapters.

Continuity Informally

Let c be a real number in the domain of a function f. Informally, the function f is **continuous** at $x = c$ if you can draw the graph of f at and near the point $(c, f(c))$ without lifting your pencil from the paper. For example, each of the four graphs in Figure 14.4-1 is the graph of a function that is continuous at $x = c$.

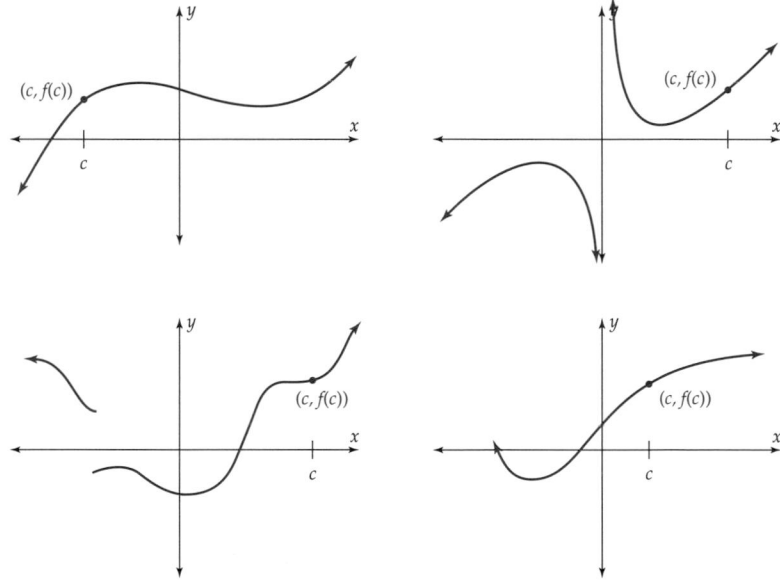

Figure 14.4-1

Thus, a function is continuous at $x = c$ if its graph around the point $(c, f(c))$ is connected and unbroken.

On the other hand, none of the functions whose graphs are shown in Figure 14.4-2 is continuous at $x = c$. Try to draw one of these graphs at and near $(c, f(c))$ without lifting your pencil from the paper.

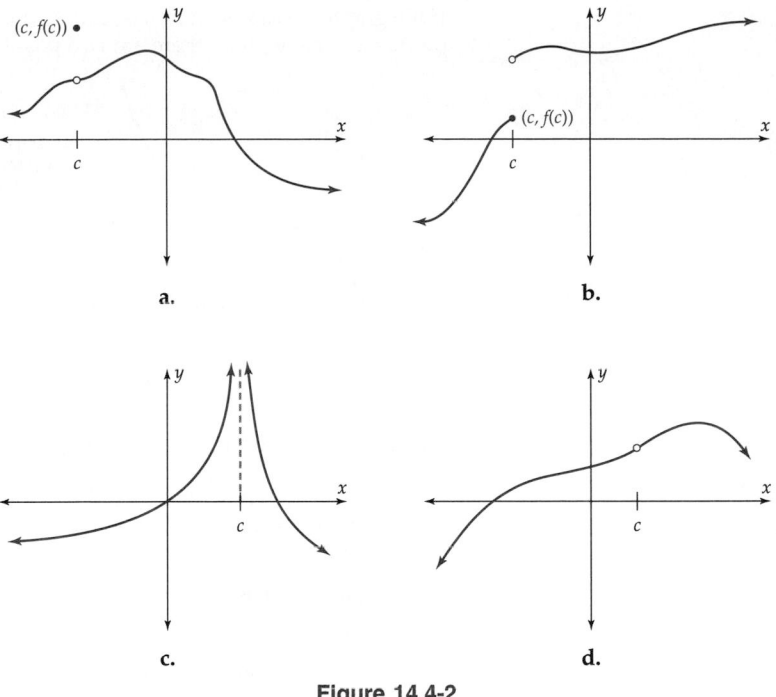

a.

b.

c.

d.

Figure 14.4-2

Figure 14.4-2 shows examples of different ways a function can be **discontinuous** at a number c. Point out that $f(c)$ may or may not be defined when f is discontinuous at $x = c$. Based on the graphs in Figure 14.4-2,

- $f(c)$ is defined in functions **a** and **b**.
- $f(c)$ is not defined in functions **c** and **d**.

Another example of a function graph that is discontinuous at $x = c$ is shown below.

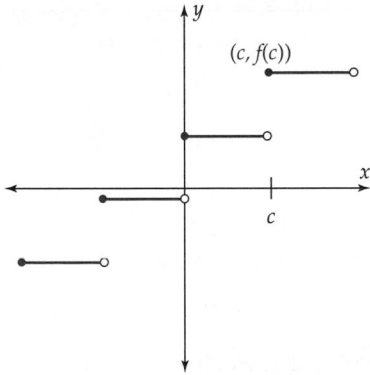

Figure 14.4-2 shows that a function is **discontinuous,** that is, not continuous, at $x - c$ if the graph has a break, gap, hole, or jump when $x = c$.

Calculators and Discontinuity

When a calculator uses "connected" mode to graph a function, it plots a number of points and then connects them with line segments to produce a curve. Thus, the calculator *assumes* that the function is continuous at any point it plots. For example, a calculator may not show the hole in graph **d** of Figure 14.4-2, or it may insert a vertical line segment where the graph jumps in graph **b** of Figure 14.4-2. Consequently, a calculator may present misleading information about the continuity of a function.

Analytic Description of Continuity

The goal is to find a mathematical description of continuity at a point that does not depend on having the graph given in advance. This is done by expressing in analytic terms the intuitive geometric idea of continuity given above.

For **Calculators and Discontinuity,** remind students that when graphing a function that is discontinuous at $x = c$, they may get a more accurate graph by setting a proper viewing window. If the graph has a hole at $x = c$, making c the center of the window will normally show the hole. If the hole is at an integer value, using a decimal window will normally show the hole (**Technology Tip,** page 910). If the graph has a vertical asymptote at $x = c$, either making a viewing window with c as its center or using a decimal window will usually produce a graph without an erroneous vertical line (**Technology Tips,** pages 283–284).

Teaching Notes

After discussing the **Definition of Continuity,** refer to Figure 14.4-4. Have students identify whether each condition of the definition is satisfied for $x = a$, $x = b$, and $x = c$ in the figure.

For $x = a$:

1. $f(a)$ is not defined.
2. $\lim\limits_{x \to a} f(x)$ does exist.
3. $\lim\limits_{x \to a} f(x) \neq f(a)$ (because $f(a)$ is not defined).

For $x = b$:

1. $f(b)$ is defined.
2. $\lim\limits_{x \to b} f(x)$ does not exist.
3. $\lim\limits_{x \to b} f(x) \neq f(b)$ (because $\lim\limits_{x \to b} f(x)$ does not exist).

For $x = c$:

1. $f(c)$ is defined.
2. $\lim\limits_{x \to c} f(x)$ does exist.
3. $\lim\limits_{x \to c} f(x) \neq f(c)$.

Point out that condition 3 fails in every case.

Note that condition 3 of the definition actually contains conditions 1 and 2. That is, if $\lim\limits_{x \to c} f(x) = f(c)$, then $f(c)$ must be defined and $\lim\limits_{x \to c} f(x)$ must exist.

Have students do a similar activity for the graph in Figure 14.4-2 on page 937 by completing the following table:

Graph	a	b	c	d
$f(c)$ defined?	yes	yes	no	no
$\lim\limits_{x \to c} f(x)$ exist?	yes	no	no	yes
$\lim\limits_{x \to c} f(x) = f(c)$?	no	no	no	no

Point out that a similar table for Figure 14.4-1 on page 936 would contain all *yes's*.

If the graph of f can be drawn at and near a point $(c, f(c))$ without lifting pencil from paper, then there are two possibilities:

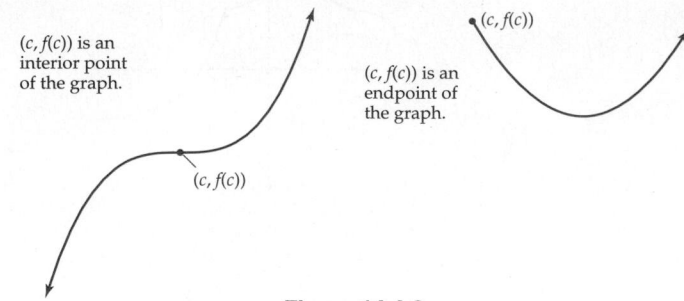

$(c, f(c))$ is an interior point of the graph.

$(c, f(c))$ is an endpoint of the graph.

$(c, f(c))$

Figure 14.4-3

Continuity at an Interior Point

If the point $(c, f(c))$ is an interior point of the graph, and the graph can be drawn around the point $(c, f(c))$ without lifting pencil from paper, then at the very least, the following two statments are true.

- $f(x)$ must be defined for $x = c$
- $f(x)$ must be defined for $x = t$, when t is any number near c

For if $f(t)$ is not defined for some t near c, there will be a hole in the graph at the point $(t, f(t))$, which would require lifting the pencil when drawing the graph. See graphs **c** and **d** of Figure 14.4-2 for functions that are not defined at $x = c$. The situation can be described more precisely by saying:

> $f(x)$ **is defined for all** x **in some open interval containing** c**. In other words, there are numbers** a **and** b [1]
> **with** $a < c < b$ **such that** $f(x)$ **is defined for all** x **with** $a < x < b$**. In particular,** $f(c)$ **is defined.**

Although condition [1] is necessary in order for f to be continuous at $x = c$, this condition by itself does not *guarantee* continuity. For instance, $x = c$ and the graphs **a** and **b** in Figure 14.4-2 show functions whose graphs are defined for all values of x near c, but are *not* continuous at $x = c$.

If $f(c)$ is defined, there are two conditions that can *prevent* a function from being continuous at $x = c$:

- There is a jump at $x = c$, that is, the limit of $f(x)$ as x approaches c does not exist.
- There is a hole in the graph at $x = c$, that is, limit of $f(x)$ exists at $x = c$, but it is not equal to $f(c)$.

The conditions that prevent a function from being continuous at a point are shown in Figure 14.4-4. Notice the reason that the graph is not continuous at $x = a$, at $x = b$, and at $x = c$.

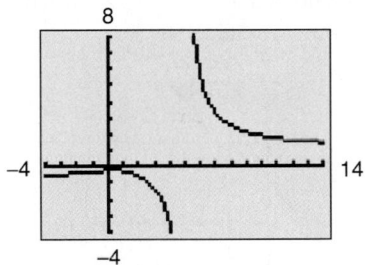

Figure 14.4-4

The preceding analysis leads to the following formal definition of continuity for interior points.

Definition of Continuity

Let f be a function that is defined for all x in some open interval containing c. Then f is said to be *continuous* at $x = c$ under the following conditions:

1. $f(c)$ is defined
2. $\lim\limits_{x \to c} f(x)$ exists
3. $\lim\limits_{x \to c} f(x) = f(c)$

Example 1   **Continuity at a Point**

Without graphing, show that the function

$$f(x) = \frac{\sqrt{x^2 - x + 1}}{x - 5}$$

is continuous at $x = -3$.

Solution

To show continuity of f at $x = -3$, show that

$$f(-3) = \lim_{x \to -3} \frac{\sqrt{x^2 - x + 1}}{x - 5}.$$

$$f(-3) = \frac{\sqrt{(-3)^2 - (-3) + 1}}{(-3) - 5}$$

$$= -\frac{\sqrt{13}}{8}$$

To show that f is continuous at $x = 3$,

show that $f(3) = \lim\limits_{x \to 3} \dfrac{\sqrt{2x}(2 - x)}{x^2}$.

$$f(3) = \frac{\sqrt{2(3)} \cdot (2 - 3)}{3^2} = \frac{\sqrt{6} \cdot (-1)}{9} = -\frac{\sqrt{6}}{9}$$

$$\lim_{x \to 3} f(x) = \lim_{x \to 3} \frac{\sqrt{2x}(2 - x)}{x^2}$$

$$= \frac{\lim\limits_{x \to 3} \sqrt{2x}(2 - x)}{\lim\limits_{x \to 3} x^2} \qquad \text{limit of a quotient}$$

$$= \frac{\lim\limits_{x \to 3} \sqrt{2x} \cdot \lim\limits_{x \to 3} (2 - x)}{\lim\limits_{x \to 3} x^2} \qquad \text{limit of a product}$$

$$= \frac{\sqrt{\lim\limits_{x \to 3} 2x} \cdot \lim\limits_{x \to 3} (2 - x)}{\lim\limits_{x \to 3} x^2} \qquad \text{limit of a root}$$

$$= \frac{\sqrt{6} \cdot (-1)}{9} \qquad \text{limit of a polynomial}$$

$$= -\frac{\sqrt{6}}{9}$$

So, $\lim\limits_{x \to 3} f(x) = f(3)$, and f is continuous at $x = 3$.

Example Notes

To show continuity of f at $x = -3$ in **Example 1**, we must show that

$$f(-3) = \lim_{x \to -3} \frac{\sqrt{x^2 - x + 1}}{x - 5}.$$

In other words, we must verify condition 3 of the definition. Note that if condition 3 is verified, then conditions 1 and 2 are automatically verified.

After discussing Example 1, ask students to find a value of x where the function is not continuous and why. $x = 5$; $f(5)$ is undefined Have students graph the function on their calculators with window $-4 \le x \le 14$, and use the table feature to confirm that:
- $x = -3$ is a point of continuity
- $x = 5$ is a point of discontinuity

ADDITIONAL EXAMPLES

Example 1

Without graphing, show that the function

$$f(x) = \frac{\sqrt{2x}(2 - x)}{x^2}$$

is continuous at $x = 3$.

Have students graph the following functions to show an example of each type mentioned in **Continuity of Special Functions**. Remind them that complete graphs cannot be displayed. The only purpose in this activity is to recall the shapes of the graphs.

$y = x^3 - 4x^2 + 1$ (polynomial; continuous at every real number)

$y = \dfrac{x^2 - 5}{x - 2}$ (rational; continuous at every value of x except $x = 2$, which is not in the domain)

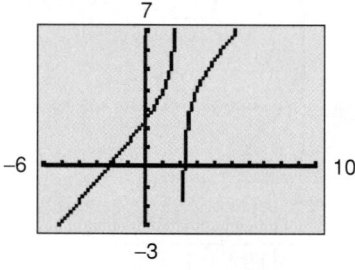

$y = 3^{0.4x}$ (exponential; continuous at every real number)

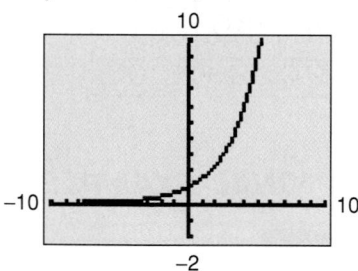

$y = 3\log x$ (logarithmic; continuous at every positive real number)

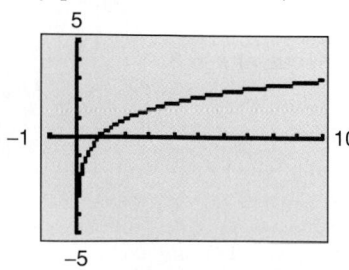

$y = \sin x$ (trigonometric; continuous at every real number)

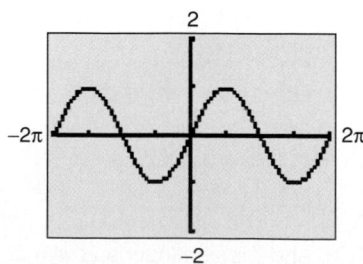

By the properties of limits given in Section 14.2,

$$\lim_{x \to -3} f(x) = \lim_{x \to -3} \frac{\sqrt{x^2 - x + 1}}{x - 5}$$

$$= \frac{\lim\limits_{x \to -3} \sqrt{x^2 - x + 1}}{\lim\limits_{x \to -3} (x - 5)} \qquad \textit{limit of a quotient}$$

$$= \frac{\sqrt{\lim\limits_{x \to -3} x^2 - x + 1}}{\lim\limits_{x \to -3} (x - 5)} \qquad \textit{limit of a root}$$

$$= \frac{\sqrt{(-3)^2 - (-3) + 1}}{(-3) - 5} \qquad \textit{limit of a polynomial}$$

$$= -\frac{\sqrt{13}}{8}$$

Therefore, $\lim\limits_{x \to -3} f(x) = f(-3)$ and f is continuous at $x = -3$. ∎

The facts about limits presented in Sections 14.1 and 14.2 and the definition of continuity provide justification for several assumptions about graphs that were made earlier in this book.

Continuity of Special Functions

> Every polynomial function is continuous at every real number.
>
> Every rational function is continuous at every real number in its domain.
>
> Every exponential function is continuous at every real number.
>
> Every logarithmic function is continuous at every *positive* real number.
>
> $f(x) = \sin x$ and $g(x) = \cos x$ are continuous at every real number.
>
> $h(x) = \tan x$ is continuous at every real number in its domain.

NOTE One-sided limits, which were discussed in Section 14.2.A, are a prerequisite for the material on continuity on an interval.

Continuity on an Interval

Consider continuity at an endpoint of the graph of a function f, such as $(a, f(a))$ or $(b, f(b))$ shown in Figure 14.4-5.

$y = \cos x$ (trigonometric; continuous at every real number)

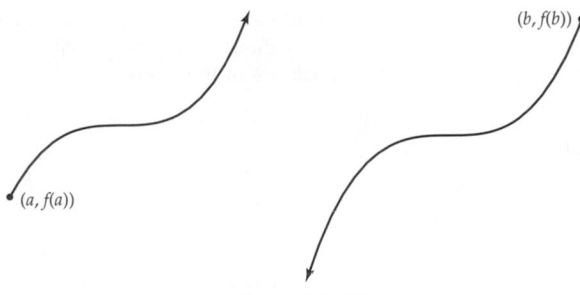

Figure 14.4-5

The intuitive idea of continuity at $(a, f(a))$ is that the graph of f can be drawn at $x = a$ and to the right of the point $(a, f(a))$ without lifting the pencil from the paper. Essentially the same analysis that was given above can be made here if we consider only values of x to the right of $x = a$. In short, continuity at the endpoint $(a, f(a))$ means that $\lim_{x \to a^+} f(x) = f(a)$. An analogous discussion applies to the endpoint $(b, f(b))$, which leads to the formal definition.

Continuity from the Left and Right

A function f is *continuous from the right* at $x = a$ provided that

$$\lim_{x \to a^+} f(x) = f(a).$$

A function f is *continuous from the left* at $x = b$ provided that

$$\lim_{x \to b^-} f(x) = f(b).$$

Example 2 **Continuity at an Endpoint**

Show that $f(x) = \sqrt{x}$ is continuous from the right at $x = 0$.

Solution

The function $f(x) = \sqrt{x}$, which is not defined when $x < 0$, is continuous from the right at $x = 0$ because $f(0) = \sqrt{0} = 0$, and

$$\lim_{x \to 0^+} f(x) = \lim_{x \to 0^+} \sqrt{x} = 0 = f(0).$$ ∎

The most useful functions are those that are continuous at every point in an interval. Consider the following three examples.

- $h(x) = \tan x$ is continuous at every number in the interval $\left(-\dfrac{\pi}{2}, \dfrac{\pi}{2}\right)$

- $g(x) = \ln x$ is continuous at every number in $(0, \infty)$
- $f(x) = \sin x$ is continuous at every number in $(-\infty, \infty)$

continued from page 940

$y = \tan x$ (trigonometric; continuous at every real number except odd multiples of $\frac{\pi}{2}$, which are not in the domain)

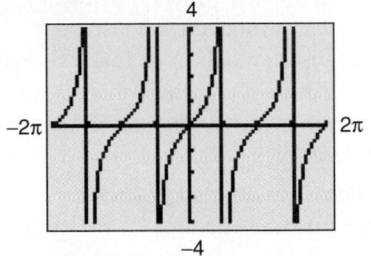

Example Notes

Have students graph $f(x) = \sqrt{x}$ in **Example 2** and use the table feature to confirm the continuity at 0 from the right.

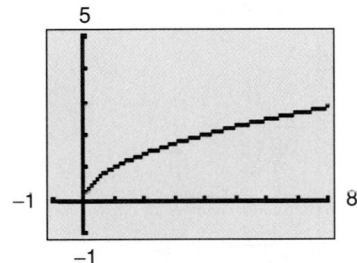

ADDITIONAL EXAMPLES

Example 2

Show that $f(x) = \sqrt{3 - x}$ is continuous from the left at $x = 3$.

$f(x) = \sqrt{3 - x}$ is not defined for x-values that make $3 - x < 0$.

Solve to find those x-values:

$$3 - x < 0$$
$$-x < -3$$
$$x > 3$$

So, $f(x) = \sqrt{3 - x}$ is not defined for $x > 3$.

$f(3) = \sqrt{3 - 3} = \sqrt{0} = 0$,

and $\lim_{x \to 3^-} f(x) = \lim_{x \to 3^-} \sqrt{3 - x}$

$$= \sqrt{0} = 0 = f(3).$$

Therefore, $f(x) = \sqrt{3 - x}$ is continuous from the left at $x = 3$.

Math Background

Continuity on an Interval describes continuity on both open and closed intervals, and **Example 3** illustrates both types. A function can also be continuous on a half-open interval and on an open interval where there is an asymptote at each end of the interval. Some examples are shown below.

The piecewise-defined greatest integer function (pages 147, 157, and shown below) is also discontinuous at certain values and continuous on certain intervals. It is discontinuous at all integer values and continuous on the half-open intervals $\cdots, [-1, 0), [0, 1), [1, 2), [2, 3) \cdots$, that is, on every half-open interval of the form $[n, n + 1)$, where n is any integer.

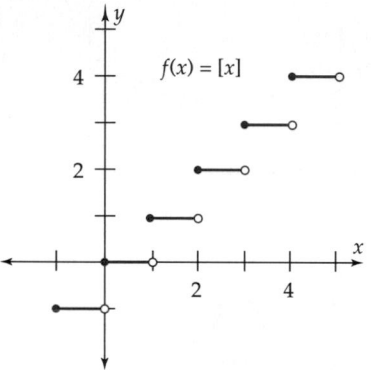

$f(x) = \dfrac{x}{(x^2 - 4)}$ is continuous on the open intervals $(-\infty, -2)$, $(-2, 2)$, and $(2, \infty)$.

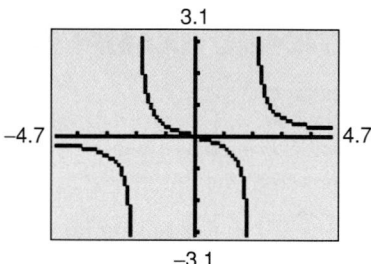

$f(x) = \sec x$ is continuous on every open interval $\left(\dfrac{k\pi}{2}, \dfrac{(k + 2)\pi}{2} \right)$, where k is any odd integer.

Continuity on an Interval

Intuitively, this means that their graphs can be drawn over the entire interval without lifting the pencil from the paper. Most of the functions in this book are of this type.

> A function f is said to be *continuous on an open interval* (a, b) provided that f is continuous at every value in the interval.
>
> A function f is said to be *continuous on a closed interval* $[a, b]$ provided that f is continuous from the right at $x = a$, continuous from the left at $x = b$, and continuous at every value in the open interval (a, b).

Analogous definitions may be given for continuity on intervals of the form $[a, b), (a, b], (a, \infty), [a, \infty), (-\infty, b), (-\infty, b],$ and $(-\infty, \infty)$.

Example 3   Continuity of a Function

Discuss the continuity of the function shown in Figure 14.4-6.

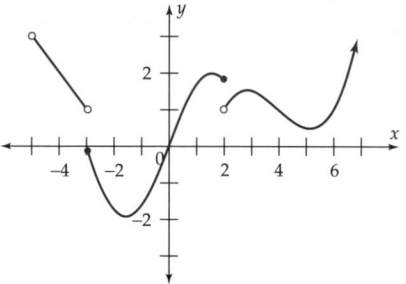

Figure 14.4-6

Solution

The function is discontinuous at $x = -3$ and $x = 2$, but it is continuous on each of the intervals $(-5, -3), [-3, 2], (2, \infty)$. ∎

Properties of Continuous Functions

Using the definition is not always the most convenient way to show that a particular function is continuous. It is often easier to establish continuity by using the following facts.

Properties of Continuous Functions

If the functions f and g are continuous at $x = c$, then each of the following functions is also continuous at $x = c$:

1. the sum function $f + g$
2. the difference function $f - g$
3. the product function fg
4. the quotient function $\dfrac{f}{g}$, $g(c) \neq 0$

Proof By the definition of the sum function, $(f + g)(x) = f(x) + g(x)$. Because f and g are continuous at $x = c$,

$$\lim_{x \to c} f(x) = f(c) \quad \text{and} \quad \lim_{x \to c} g(x) = g(c).$$

Therefore, by the first property of limits,

$$
\begin{aligned}
\lim_{x \to c} (f + g)(x) &= \lim_{x \to c} (f(x) + g(x)) \\
&= \lim_{x \to c} f(x) + \lim_{x \to c} g(x) \\
&= f(c) + g(c) \\
&= (f + g)(c)
\end{aligned}
$$

This says that $f + g$ is continuous at $x = c$.

The remaining statements are proved similarly, using limit properties 2, 3, and 4.

Example 4   Continuity of Functions

Assume that $f(x) = \sin x$ and $g(x) = x^3 + 5x - 2$ are continuous at $x = 0$. Prove that the following functions are continuous at $x = 0$.

a. $\sin x + (x^3 + 5x - 2)$ **b.** $\sin x - (x^3 + 5x - 2)$

c. $(\sin x)(x^3 + 5x - 2)$ **d.** $\dfrac{\sin x}{x^3 + 5x - 2}$

Solution

Because f an g are continuous at $x = 0$, each of the following functions are continuous at $x = 0$ by the listed property of continuous functions.

a. $\sin x + (x^3 + 5x - 2) = (f + g)(x)$ *sum of continuous functions*

b. $\sin x - (x^3 + 5x - 2) = (f - g)(x)$ *difference of continuous functions*

c. $(\sin x)(x^3 + 5x - 2) = fg(x)$ *product of continuous functions*

d. $\dfrac{\sin x}{x^3 + 5x - 2} = \left(\dfrac{f}{g}\right)(x)$ *quotient of continuous functions*   ∎

ADDITIONAL EXAMPLES

Example 3

Discuss the continuity of the function shown below.

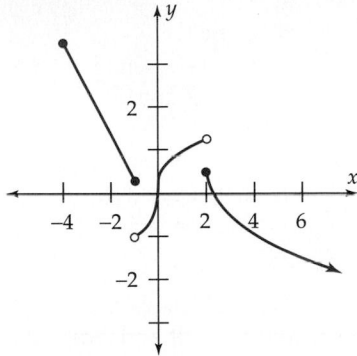

The function is discontinuous at $x = -1$ and $x = 2$, but it is continuous on each of the intervals $[-4, -1]$, $(-1, 2)$, $[2, \infty)$.

Example 4

Assume that $f(x) - \cos x$ and $g(x) = x^4 - 2x^2 + 4$ are continuous at $x = 1$. Prove that the following functions are continuous at $x = 1$.

a. $\cos x - (x^4 - 2x^2 + 4)$

$\cos x - (x^4 - 2x^2 + 4)$
$$= (f - g)(x)$$

difference of continuous functions

b. $(\cos x)(x^4 - 2x^2 + 4)$

$(\cos x)(x^4 - 2x^2 + 4) = fg(x)$

product of continuous functions

c. $\dfrac{\cos x}{x^4 - 2x^2 + 4}$

$\dfrac{\cos x}{x^4 - 2x^2 + 4} = \left(\dfrac{f}{g}\right)(x)$

quotient of continuous functions

d. $\cos x + (x^4 - 2x^2 + 4)$

$\cos x + (x^4 - 2x^2 + 4)$
$$= (f + g)(x)$$

sum of continuous functions

ADDITIONAL EXAMPLES

Example 5

Show that
$h(x) = \sqrt{x^3 + 2x^2 - 3x - 4}$ is continuous at -2.

The polynomial function
$f(x) = x^3 + 2x^2 - 3x - 4$ is continuous at $x = -2$ and
$f(-2) = (-2)^3 + 2(-2)^2 - 3(-2) - 4 = 2$. The function
$g(x) = \sqrt{x}$ is continuous at 2 because by limit property 5

$$\lim_{x \to 2} \sqrt{x} = \sqrt{\lim_{x \to 2} x} = \sqrt{2} = g(2).$$

By the Continuity of Composite Functions, with $c = -2$ and $f(c) = 2$, the composite function $g \circ f$, which is given by

$(g \circ f)(x)$
$= g(f(x))$
$= g(x^3 + 2x^2 - 3x - 4)$
$= \sqrt{x^3 + 2x^2 - 3x - 4}$

is also continuous at $x = -2$.

Teaching Notes

Explain the **Intermediate Value Theorem** as follows, referring to the diagram below.

- Assume that f is continuous on $[a, b]$.
- Form an interval on the y-axis using $f(a)$ and $f(b)$ as endpoints.
- Choose any number k on the y-axis between $f(a)$ and $f(b)$.

Then, the Intermediate Value Theorem guarantees that any horizontal line through k will intersect the graph. From that point of intersection, move vertically to the x-axis to get a number c guaranteed by the theorem.

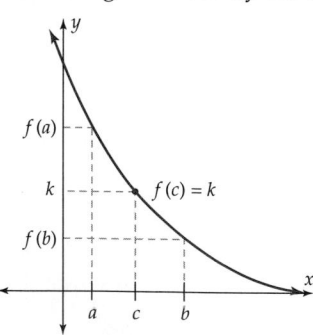

Now explain that the theorem guarantees the existence of at least one number c, but there may be more than one. The diagram shows a case where there are three numbers, c_1, c_2, and c_3, such that $f(c_1) = f(c_2) = f(c_3) = k$.

Composite Functions

Composition of functions is often used to construct new functions from given ones.

Continuity of Composite Functions

> If the function f is continuous at $x = c$ and the function g is continuous at $x = f(c)$, then the composite function $g \circ f$ is continuous at $x = c$.

Example 5   Continuity of Composite Functions

Show that $h(x) = \sqrt{x^3 - 3x^2 + x + 7}$ is continuous at $x = 2$.

Solution

The polynomial function $f(x) = x^3 - 3x^2 + x + 7$ is continuous at $x = 2$ and $f(2) = 2^3 - 3(2)^2 + 2 + 7 = 5$. The function $g(x) = \sqrt{x}$ is continuous at 5 because by limit property 5

$$\lim_{x \to 5} \sqrt{x} = \sqrt{\lim_{x \to 5} x} = \sqrt{5} = g(5).$$

By the box above, with $c = 2$ and $f(c) = 5$, the composite function $g \circ f$, which is given by

$$(g \circ f)(x) = g(f(x)) = g(x^3 - 3x^2 + x + 7) = \sqrt{x^3 - 3x^2 + x + 7}$$

is also continuous at $x = 2$.   ∎

The Intermediate Value Theorem

This section's introduction to continuity will close by mentioning, without proof, a very important property of continuous functions.

The Intermediate Value Theorem

> If the function f is continuous on the closed interval $[a, b]$ and k is any number between $f(a)$ and $f(b)$, then there exists at least one number c between a and b such that $f(c) = k$.

The truth of the Intermediate Value Theorem can be understood geometrically by remembering that since f is continuous on $[a, b]$, the graph of f can be drawn from the point $(a, f(a))$ to the point $(b, f(b))$ without lifting the pencil from the paper. As suggested in Figure 14.4-7, there is no way that this can be done unless the graph crosses the horizontal line $y = k$, where $f(a) < k < f(b)$.

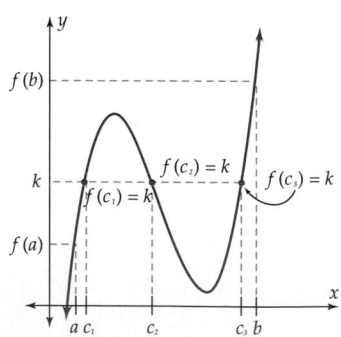

If f is not continuous on $[a, b]$, then there may not be a number c for every choice of k, as shown below.

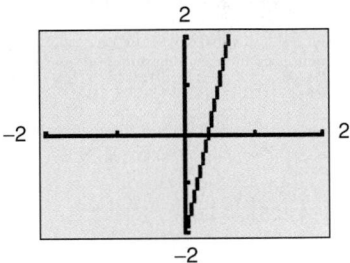

Math Background

An algorithm for finding zeros of a function that is based on the **Intermediate Value Theorem** is called the *bisection method*, described below.

If $f(x)$ is continuous on the closed interval $[a, b]$, $f(a) < 0$, and $f(b) > 0$, then by the Intermediate Value Theorem, with $k = 0$, there exists at least one number c between a and b such that $f(c) = 0$. In this case, the number c is a zero of the function.

The bisection method consists of finding an average of two numbers whose function values have different signs. This averaging is repeated until either the zero is found, or the desired level of accuracy is reached.

Suppose $f(x) = \sin x + (x^3 + 5x - 2)$. A graph shows that there is a zero between 0 and 1.

Some of the steps to find a zero of this function are shown below.

- Evaluate the function at 0 and 1.
  $f(0) = -2; f(1) = 4.8415$

- Find the average of 0 and 1.
  $\dfrac{0 + 1}{2} = 0.5$

- Evaluate the function at 0.5.
  $f(0.5) = 1.1044$

So, $f(0)$ and $f(0.5)$ have opposite signs, and there is a zero between 0 and 0.5.

- Find the average of 0 and 0.5.
  $\dfrac{0 + 0.5}{2} = 0.25$

- Evaluate the function at 0.25.
  $f(0.25) = -0.487$

So, $f(0.25)$ and $f(0.5)$ have opposite signs, and there is a zero between 0.25 and 0.5.

Figure 14.4-7

The first coordinate of the point where the graph crosses this line is some number c between a and b, and its second coordinate is $f(c)$ because the point is on the graph of f. But $(c, f(c))$ is also on the line $y = k$, so its second coordinate must be k; that is, $f(c) = k$.

The Intermediate Value Theorem further explains why the graph of a continuous function is connected and unbroken. If the function f is continuous on the interval $[a, b]$, then its graph cannot go from the point $(a, f(a))$ to the point $(b, f(b))$ without moving through all the y values between $f(a)$ and $f(b)$.

The graphical method of solving equations that has been used throughout this book is based on the Intermediate Value Theorem, as are some root-finding features on calculators. If f is continuous on the interval $[a, b]$ and $f(a)$ and $f(b)$ have opposite signs, then 0 is a number between $f(a)$ and $f(b)$. Consequently, by the Intermediate Value Theorem, with $k = 0$, there is at least one number c between a and b such that $f(c) = 0$. In other words, $x = c$ is a solution of the equation $f(x) = 0$.

So when a calculator shows that the graph of a continuous function f has points above and below the x-axis, there really is an x-intercept between these points, that is, a solution of $f(x) = 0$. Zoom-in uses this fact by looking at smaller and smaller viewing windows that contain points of the graph on both sides of the x-axis. The closer together the points are horizontally, the better the approximation of the x-intercept, or solution, that can be read from the graph.

The table below shows a few more iterations.

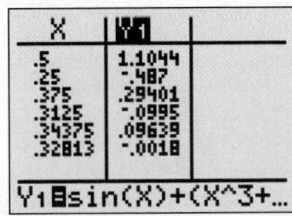

So, $x = 0.328125$ is an approximation of the zero.

ANSWERS

5. continuous at $x = 0$ and $x = 3$; discontinuous at $x = -2$

6. continuous at every real number except $x = 3$

7. $\lim\limits_{x \to 3} f(x)$

$= \lim\limits_{x \to 3} (x^2 + 5(x - 2)^7)$

$= \lim\limits_{x \to 3} x^2 + \lim\limits_{x \to 3} (5(x - 2)^7)$

$= \lim\limits_{x \to 3} x^2 + (\lim\limits_{x \to 3} 5)(\lim\limits_{x \to 3} (x - 2))^7$

$= 9 + 5(3 - 2)^7 = 14 = f(3)$

8. $\lim\limits_{x \to -1} g(x)$

$= \lim\limits_{x \to -1} (x^2 - 3x - 10) \cdot$

$\quad \lim\limits_{x \to -1} (x^2 + 2x^2 - 5x + 4)$

$= (-1^2 - 3(-1) - 10) \cdot$

$\quad (-1^2 + 2(-1)^2 - 5(-1) + 4)$

$= (-6)(12)$

$= -72 = g(-1)$

9. $\lim\limits_{x \to 2} f(x)$

$= \lim\limits_{x \to 2} \dfrac{x^2 - 9}{(x^2 - x - 6)(x^2 + 6x + 9)}$

$= \dfrac{\lim\limits_{x \to 2} (x^2 - 9)}{\lim\limits_{x \to 2} (x^2 - x - 6) \cdot \lim\limits_{x \to 2} (x^2 + 6x + 9)}$

$= \dfrac{2^2 - 9}{(2^2 - 2 - 6)(2^2 + 6 \cdot 2 + 9)}$

$= \dfrac{-5}{(-4)(25)} = \dfrac{1}{20} = f(2)$

10. $\lim\limits_{x \to -2} h(x)$

$= \dfrac{\lim\limits_{x \to -2} (x + 3)}{\lim\limits_{x \to -2} (x^2 - x - 1) \cdot \lim\limits_{x \to -2} (x^2 + 1)}$

$= \dfrac{-2 + 3}{(-2^2 - (-2) - 1)(-2^2 + 1)}$

$= \dfrac{1}{25} = h(-2)$

11. $\lim\limits_{x \to 36} f(x) = \dfrac{\lim\limits_{x \to 36} (x\sqrt{x})}{\lim\limits_{x \to 36} (x - 6)^2}$

$= \dfrac{\lim\limits_{x \to 36} x \cdot \lim\limits_{x \to 36} \sqrt{x}}{\lim\limits_{x \to 36} (x - 6) \cdot \lim\limits_{x \to 36} (x - 6)}$

$= \dfrac{36\sqrt{36}}{(36 - 6)(36 - 6)}$

$= \dfrac{36 \cdot 6}{30 \cdot 30} = \dfrac{216}{900} = \dfrac{6}{25} = f(36)$

12. $\lim\limits_{x \to -2} k(x) = \dfrac{\lim\limits_{x \to -2} \sqrt{8 - x^2}}{\lim\limits_{x \to -2} (2x^2 - 5)}$

$= \dfrac{\sqrt{8 - (-2)^2}}{(2(-2)^2 - 5)}$

$= \dfrac{2}{3} = k(-2)$

Exercises 14.4

In Exercises 1 and 2, use the graph to find all the numbers at which the function is not continuous.

1.

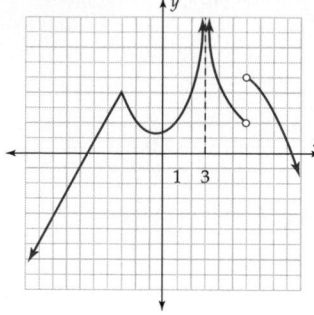

$x = 3, \ x = 6$

2.

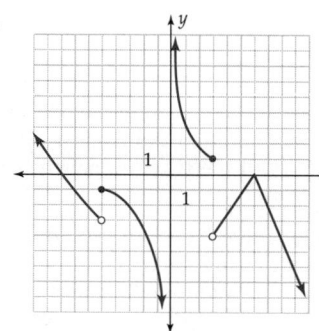

$x = -5, \ x = 0, \ x = 3$

In Exercises 3–6, determine whether the function whose graph is given is continuous at $x = -2$, at $x = 0$, and at $x = 3$.

3.

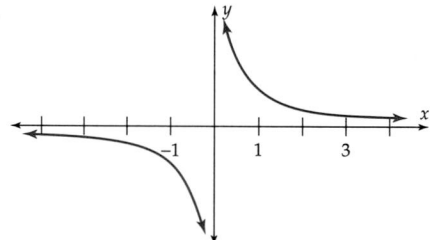

continuous at $x = -2$ and $x = 3$; discontinuous at $x = 0$

4.

continuous at every real number

5.

6.

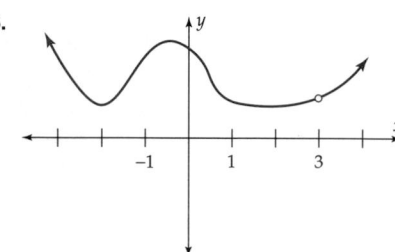

In Exercises 7–12, use the definition of continuity and the properties of limits to show that the function is continuous at the given number.

7. $f(x) = x^2 + 5(x - 2)^7, \ x = 3$

8. $g(x) = (x^2 - 3x - 10)(x^2 + 2x^2 - 5x + 4), \ x = -1$

9. $f(x) = \dfrac{x^2 - 9}{(x^2 - x - 6)(x^2 + 6x + 9)}, \ x = 2$

10. $h(x) = \dfrac{x + 3}{(x^2 - x - 1)(x^2 + 1)}, \ x = -2$

11. $f(x) = \dfrac{x\sqrt{x}}{(x - 6)^2}, \ x = 36$

12. $k(x) = \dfrac{\sqrt{8 - x^2}}{2x^2 - 5}, \ x = -2$

In Exercises 13–18, explain why the function is not continuous at the given number.

13. $f(x) = \dfrac{1}{(x-3)^3}$, $x = 3$

14. $h(x) = \dfrac{x^2 + 4}{x^2 - x - 2}$, $x = 2$

15. $f(x) = \dfrac{x^2 + 4x + 3}{x^2 - x - 2}$, $x = -1$

16. $g(x) = \begin{cases} \sin \dfrac{\pi}{x} & \text{if } x \neq 0 \\ 1 & \text{if } x = 0 \end{cases}$, $x = 0$

17. $f(x) = \begin{cases} x^2 & \text{if } x \neq 0 \\ 1 & \text{if } x = 0 \end{cases}$, $x = 0$

18. $f(x) = \dfrac{\sqrt{2+x} - \sqrt{2}}{x}$, $x = 0$

In Exercises 19–24, determine whether or not the function is continuous at the given number.

19. $f(x) = \begin{cases} -2x + 4 & \text{if } x \leq 2 \\ 2x - 4 & \text{if } x > 2 \end{cases}$, $x = 2$

20. $g(x) = \begin{cases} 2x + 5 & \text{if } x < -1 \\ -2x + 1 & \text{if } x \geq -1 \end{cases}$, $x = -1$

21. $f(x) = \begin{cases} x^2 - x & \text{if } x \leq 0 \\ 2x^2 & \text{if } x > 0 \end{cases}$, $x = 0$

22. $g(x) = \begin{cases} x^3 - x + 1 & \text{if } x < 2 \\ 3x^2 - 2x - 1 & \text{if } x \geq 2 \end{cases}$, $x = 2$

23. $f(x) = |x - 3|$, $x = 3$

24. $k(x) = -|x + 2| + 3$, $x = -2$

In Exercises 25–28, determine all numbers at which the function is continuous.

25. $f(x) = \begin{cases} \dfrac{x^2 + x - 2}{x^2 - 4x + 3} & \text{if } x \neq 1 \\ -\dfrac{3}{2} & \text{if } x = 1 \end{cases}$

26. $g(x) = \begin{cases} \dfrac{x^2 - x - 6}{x^2 - 4} & \text{if } x \neq -2 \\ \dfrac{4}{5} & \text{if } x = -2 \end{cases}$

27. $f(x) = \begin{cases} x^2 + 1 & \text{if } x < 0 \\ x & \text{if } 0 < x \leq 2 \\ -2x + 3 & \text{if } x > 2 \end{cases}$

28. $h(x) = \begin{cases} \dfrac{1}{x} & \text{if } x < 1 \text{ and } x \neq 0 \\ x^2 & \text{if } x \geq 1 \end{cases}$

29. *Critical Thinking* For what values of b is the following function continuous at $x = 3$?

$$f(x) = \begin{cases} bx + 4 & \text{if } x \leq 3 \\ bx^2 - 2 & \text{if } x > 3 \end{cases}$$

30. *Critical Thinking* Show that $f(x) = \sqrt{|x|}$ is continuous at $x = 0$.

A function f that is not defined at $x = c$ is said to have a **removable discontinuity** at $x = c$ if there is a function g such that $g(c)$ is defined, g is continuous at $x = c$, and $g(x) = f(x)$ for $x \neq c$. In Exercises 31–34, show that the function f has a removable discontinuity by finding an appropriate function g.

31. $f(x) = \dfrac{x - 1}{x^2 - 1}$

32. $f(x) = \dfrac{x^2}{|x|}$

33. $f(x) = \dfrac{2 - \sqrt{x}}{4 - x}$

34. $f(x) = \dfrac{\sin x}{x}$ *Hint:* See Example 1 of Section 14.1.

35. Show that the function $f(x) = \dfrac{|x|}{x}$ has a discontinuity at $x = 0$ that is *not* removable.

13. f is not defined at $x = 3$.

14. h is not defined at $x = 2$.

15. f is not defined at $x = -1$.

16. $\lim\limits_{x \to 0} g(x)$ does not exist.

17. $\lim\limits_{x \to 0} f(x) = 0$, but $f(0) = 1$; hence $\lim\limits_{x \to 0} f(x) \neq f(0)$.

18. f is not defined at $x = 0$.

19. continuous

20. continuous

21. continuous

22. continuous

23. continuous

24. continuous

25. continuous at every real number except $x = 3$

26. continuous at every real number except $x = 2$ and $x = -2$

27. continuous at every real number except $x = 0$ and $x = 2$

28. continuous at every real number except $x = 0$

29. $b = 1$

30. $\lim\limits_{x \to 0} \sqrt{|x|} = 0 = f(0)$

31. $g(x) = \dfrac{1}{x + 1}$; f has a removable discontinuity at $x = 1$.

32. $g(x) = |x|$; f has a removable discontinuity at $x = 0$.

33. $g(x) = \dfrac{1}{2 + \sqrt{x}}$; f has a removable discontinuity at $x = 4$.

34. $g(x) = \begin{cases} \dfrac{\sin x}{x} & x \neq 0 \\ 1 & x = 0 \end{cases}$;

f has a removable discontinuity at $x = 0$.

35. If $g(x) = f(x)$ for all $x \neq 0$, then $g(x) = 1$ for all $x > 0$ and $g(x) = -1$ for all $x < 0$.

Thus $\lim\limits_{x \to 0} g(x)$ does not exist. Hence the definition of continuity cannot be satisfied, no matter what $g(0)$ is.

Section 14.5 Limits Involving Infinity

Teaching Notes

Emphasize that when a numerical quantity gets smaller and smaller without bound, the meaning is that it can be made smaller than any given negative number. It does not mean that a physical quantity, like 0.0001 gram, gets smaller or closer to zero.

Explain how to make a number smaller than any given negative number as follows:
Given $-10,000,000,000$, you can subtract 1 to get $-10,000,000,001$, which is smaller.

Relate the idea of infinity to movement in the direction of the x-axis or y-axis:
- For the x-axis, associate ∞ with movement infinitely far right and $-\infty$ with movement infinitely far left.
- For the y-axis, associate ∞ with movement infinitely far up and $-\infty$ with movement infinitely far down.

Discuss the $=$ symbol in statements involving infinity. $\lim\limits_{x \to 3} f(x) = \infty$ is a symbolic way of writing that the function values are increasing without bound. The $=$ symbol in this case does *not* mean equal. This is *not* an equation.

In Figure 14.5-1, the function f has vertical asymptotes at 1, 3, and 5. For each of these values, the values of f(x) are approaching either positive infinity or negative infinity or both. When $\lim\limits_{x \to c} f(x) = \infty$ or $\lim\limits_{x \to c} f(x) = -\infty$ from both sides or from either the left or the right for a particular number c, there is a vertical asymptote at c. Horizontal asymptotes and limits will be discussed on pages 951–953.

 # Limits Involving Infinity

Objectives
- Define limits involving infinity
- Use properties of limits at infinity
- Use the Limit Theorem

In the discussion that follows, it is important to remember that

There is no real number called "infinity," and the symbol ∞, which is usually read "infinity," does not represent any real number.

Nevertheless, the word "infinity" and the symbol ∞ are often used as a convenient shorthand to describe the way some functions behave under certain circumstances. Generally speaking, "infinity" indicates a situation in which some numerical quantity gets larger and larger without bound, meaning that it can be made larger than any given number. Similarly, "negative infinity," $-\infty$, indicates a situation in which a numerical quantity gets smaller and smaller without bound, meaning that it can be made smaller than any given negative number.

In Section 14.1, several ways were discussed in which a function might fail to have a limit as x approaches a number c. The word "infinity" is often used to describe one such situation. Consider the function f whose graph is shown in Figure 14.5-1.

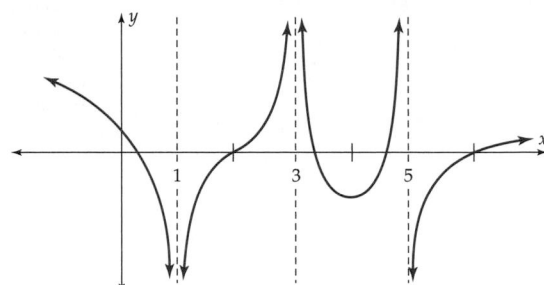

Figure 14.5-1

The graph shows that as x approaches 3 from the left or right, the corresponding values of $f(x)$ do not get closer and closer to a particular number. Instead, they become larger and larger without bound. Although there is no limit as defined in Section 14.1, it is convenient to describe this situation symbolically by writing

$$\lim_{x \to 3} f(x) = \infty,$$

which is read "the limit of $f(x)$ as x approaches 3 is infinity." Similarly, f does not have a limit as x approaches 1 from the left or right, because the corresponding values of $f(x)$ get smaller and smaller without bound. We say that "the limit of $f(x)$ as x approaches 1 is negative infinity" and write

$$\lim_{x \to 1} f(x) = -\infty.$$

NOTE *Excursion* 14.2.A is a prerequisite for some of the material that follows.

In Figure 14.5-1, point out that we can write $\lim\limits_{x \to 3} f(x) = \infty$ because
$$\lim_{x \to 3^-} f(x) = \infty \text{ and } \lim_{x \to 3^+} f(x) = \infty.$$
Likewise, $\lim\limits_{x \to 1} f(x) = -\infty$ because
$$\lim_{x \to 1^-} f(x) = -\infty \text{ and } \lim_{x \to 1^+} f(x) = -\infty.$$
However, there is no single statement for $\lim\limits_{x \to 5} f(x)$ because $\lim\limits_{x \to 5^-} f(x) = \infty$ and $\lim\limits_{x \to 5^+} f(x) = -\infty$.

Near $x = 5$, the values of $f(x)$ get very large on the left side of 5 and very small on the right side of 5, so we write

$$\lim_{x \to 5^-} f(x) = \infty \quad \text{and} \quad \lim_{x \to 5^+} f(x) = -\infty,$$

which are read "The limit as x approaches 5 from the left is infinity" and "the limit as x approaches 5 from the right is negative infinity."

There are many cases like the ones illustrated above in which the language of limits and the word "infinity" can be useful for describing the behavior of a function that actually does not have a limit in the sense of Section 14.1.

Example 1   Infinite Limits

Describe the behavior of $f(x) = -\dfrac{5}{x^4}$ near $x = 0$.

Solution

The graph of f is shown in Figure 14.5-2. The trace feature indicates that the values of $f(x)$ get small without bound as x approaches 0 from the left or from the right.

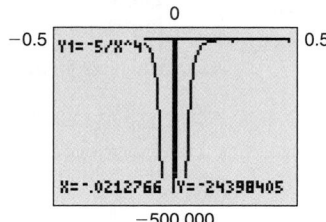

Figure 14.5-2

Therefore, $\lim\limits_{x \to 0} -\dfrac{5}{x^4} = -\infty$.

∎

Example 2   Infinite Limits

Describe the behavior of the function $g(x) = \dfrac{8}{x^2 - 2x - 8}$ near $x = -2$.

Solution

As shown in Figure 14.5-3, the graph of g is not continuous at $x = -2$. To the left of $x = -2$, the values of $g(x)$ get large without bound, and the values of $g(x)$ to the right of $x = -2$ get small without bound.

ADDITIONAL EXAMPLES

Example 1

Describe the behavior of $f(x) = \dfrac{9}{x^4}$ near $x = 0$.

The graph is shown below.

The trace feature indicates that the values of $f(x)$ get large without bound as x approaches 0 from the left or the right.

Therefore, $\lim\limits_{x \to 0} \dfrac{9}{x^4} = \infty$.

Example 2

Describe the behavior of the function $g(x) = \dfrac{-5}{x^2 - x - 6}$ near $x = 3$.

The figure below shows that the graph of g is not continuous at $x = 3$.

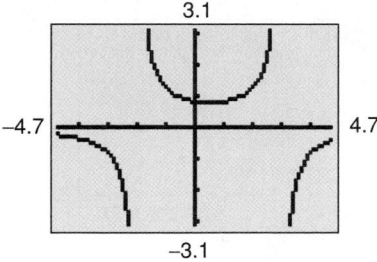

To the left of $x = 3$, the values of $g(x)$ get large without bound. To the right of $x = 3$, the values of $g(x)$ get small without bound.

So, $\lim\limits_{x \to 3^-} \dfrac{-5}{x^2 - x - 6} = \infty$ and

$\lim\limits_{x \to 3^+} \dfrac{-5}{x^2 - x - 6} = -\infty$.

Example Notes

In **Example 2,** have students write the function g in factored form.

$$g(x) = \frac{8}{(x + 2)(x - 4)}$$

Point out that the graph in Figure 14.5-3 (page 950) has erroneous vertical lines. Challenge students to find a window to graph g without erroneous vertical lines. One such window (obtained by using the ZDecimal and ZoomOut features) is shown.

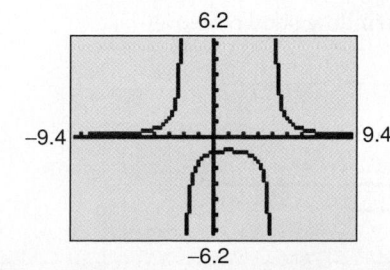

Teaching Notes

In the **Vertical Asymptotes** box, $\lim_{x \to c} f(x) = \infty$ is true if and only if $\lim_{x \to c^-} f(x) = \infty$ and $\lim_{x \to c^+} f(x) = \infty$ are both true.

A similar fact applies to the statements involving $-\infty$.

Remind students that in each case, there is no real number limit.

After the **Vertical Asymptotes** box, the topic changes from Infinite Limits to Limits at Infinity.

Infinite Limits focuses on the behavior of a function near a particular number c, using statements such as $\lim_{x \to 3} f(x) = \infty$ and $\lim_{x \to 3^+} f(x) = -\infty$.

Limits at Infinity focuses on the behavior of a function as x approaches ∞ or as x approaches $-\infty$, using statements such as $\lim_{x \to \infty} f(x) = 6$ and $\lim_{x \to -\infty} f(x) = 0$.

Solution to the **Graphing Exploration:**

Yes, the values of $f(x)$ are approaching 6.

Have students set Y_1 equal to the function from the **Graphing Exploration** and $Y_2 = 6$. Have them graph both functions on the same screen, using the same window as in the Graphing Exploration.

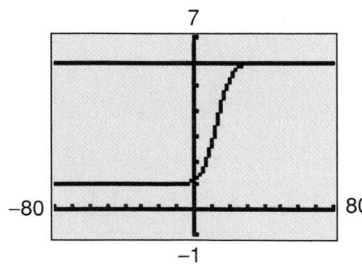

Then, use the window shown below.

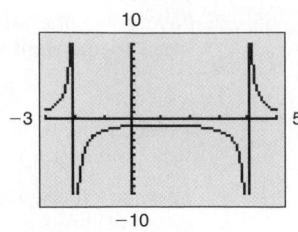

Figure 14.5-3

Therefore, $\lim_{x \to -2^-} \dfrac{8}{x^2 - 2x - 8} = \infty$ and $\lim_{x \to -2^+} \dfrac{8}{x^2 - 2x - 8} = -\infty$. ∎

Infinite Limits and Vertical Asymptotes

The "infinite limits" considered in Figure 14.5-1 and in Examples 1 and 2 can be interpreted geometrically: Each such limit corresponds to a vertical asymptote of the graph.

Vertical Asymptotes

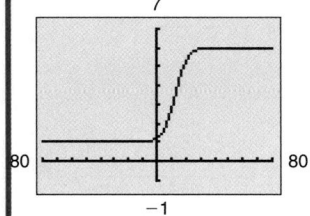

Figure 14.5-4

> The vertical line $x = c$ is a *vertical asymptote* of the graph of the function f if at least one of the following is true.
>
> $\lim_{x \to c^-} f(x) = \infty$ $\lim_{x \to c^+} f(x) = \infty$ $\lim_{x \to c} f(x) = \infty$
>
> $\lim_{x \to c^-} f(x) = -\infty$ $\lim_{x \to c^+} f(x) = -\infty$ $\lim_{x \to c} f(x) = -\infty$

Limits at Infinity

Whenever the word "limit" has been used up to now, it referred to the behavior of a function when x was near a particular number c. Now, the behavior of a function when x takes very large or very small values will be considered. That is, the end behavior of a function will be discussed.

The graph of $f(x) = \dfrac{5}{1 + 24e^{-\frac{x}{4}}} + 1$ is shown in Figure 14.5-4.

> **Graphing Exploration** ●
>
> Produce the graph shown in Figure 14.5-4 and use the trace feature to find values of $f(x)$ as x gets larger and larger. Are the values approaching a single value?

As you move to the right, the graph gets very close to the horizontal line $y = 6$. In other words, as x gets larger and larger, the corresponding

Use the last two graphs to reinforce the fact that because $\lim_{x \to \infty} f(x) = 6$, the graph of f approaches, but never touches, the horizontal asymptote $y = 6$.

values of $f(x)$ get closer and closer to 6, which can be expressed symbolically as

$$\lim_{x \to \infty} f(x) = 6.$$

The last statement is read "the limit of $f(x)$ as x approaches infinity is 6."

Toward the left the graph gets very close to the horizontal line $y = 1$; that is, as x gets smaller and smaller, the corresponding values of $f(x)$ get closer and closer to 1. (See note.) It is said that "the limit of $f(x)$ as x approaches negative infinity is 1," which is written

$$\lim_{x \to -\infty} f(x) = 1.$$

The types of limits when x gets large or small without bound are similar to those in Section 14.1 in that the values of the function do approach a fixed number. The definition in the general case is similar: f is any function, L is a real number, and the phrase "arbitrarily close" means "as close as you want."

NOTE Due to rounding, the trace feature on most calculators will display $y = 1$ when x is smaller than approximately -60. However, the value of the function is always greater than 1. Why?

Limits at Infinity

> Let f be a function that is defined for all $x > a$ for some number a. If
>
> > as x takes larger and larger positive values, increasing without bound, the corresponding values of $f(x)$ get very close, and possibly are equal, to a single real number L
>
> and
>
> > the values of $f(x)$ can be made arbitrarily close (as close as you want) to L by taking large enough values of x,
>
> then
>
> > the limit of $f(x)$ as x approaches infinity is L,
>
> which is written
>
> $$\lim_{x \to \infty} f(x) = L.$$

Limits as x approaches negative infinity are defined analogously by replacing "$x > a$" with "$x < a$", "increasing" with "decreasing", and "larger and larger positive" with "smaller and smaller negative" in the preceding definition. These definitions are informal because such phrases as "arbitrarily close" have not been precisely defined. Rigorous definitions, similar to those in Section 14.3 for ordinary limits, are discussed in Exercises 49–50.

Horizontal Asymptotes and Limits at Infinity

Limits as x approaches infinity or negative infinity correspond to horizontal asymptotes of the graph of the function.

ADDITIONAL EXAMPLES

Example 3

Describe the behavior of $f(x) = \frac{1}{x-3}$ as x approaches infinity and as x approaches negative infinity.

When x is a very large positive number, $\frac{1}{x-3}$ is a positive number that is close to zero. When x is a very small negative number, $\frac{1}{x-3}$ is a negative number that is close to zero. This suggests that $y = 0$ is a horizontal asymptote, or $\lim_{x\to\infty} f(x) = 0$ and $\lim_{x\to-\infty} f(x) = 0$, as confirmed in the figure shown below.

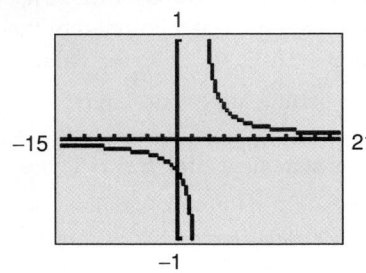

Example 4

Describe the behavior of $f(x) = -x^3 + 9x - 7$ as x approaches infinity and as x approaches negative infinity.

As shown in the figures below, $f(x)$ does not approach a single value as x approaches infinity or as x approaches negative infinity.

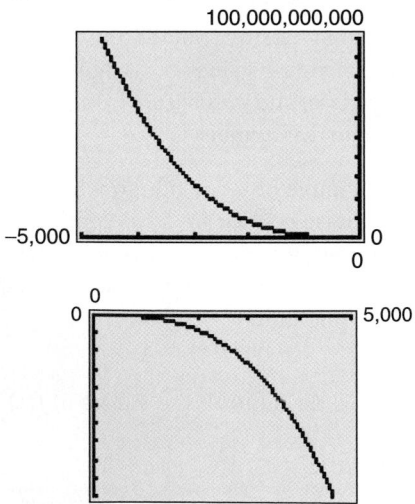

So, $\lim_{x\to\infty} f(x)$ and $\lim_{x\to-\infty} f(x)$ do not exist. However, the situations can be described by writing $\lim_{x\to\infty} f(x) = -\infty$ and $\lim_{x\to-\infty} f(x) = \infty$.

Horizontal Asymptotes

> The line $y = L$ is a *horizontal asymptote* of the graph of the function f if either
> $$\lim_{x\to\infty} f(x) = L \quad \text{or} \quad \lim_{x\to-\infty} f(x) = L.$$

Example 3 Limits at Infinity

Discuss the behavior of $f(x) = \frac{1}{x}$ as x approaches infinity and as x approaches negative infinity.

Solution

When x is a very large positive number, $\frac{1}{x}$ is a positive number that is very close to 0. Similarly, when x is a very small negative number—which is large in absolute value—such as $-5{,}000{,}000$, $\frac{1}{x}$ is a negative number that is very close to 0. These facts suggest that $y = 0$ is a horizontal asymptote, or

$$\lim_{x\to\infty} f(x) = 0 \quad \text{and} \quad \lim_{x\to-\infty} f(x) = 0,$$

as confirmed in Figure 14.5-5.

Figure 14.5-5

Example 4 Limits at Positive and Negative Infinity

Discuss the behavior of $f(x) = x^3 - 10x - 5$ as x approaches infinity and as x approaches negative infinity.

Solution

As shown in Figure 14.5-6, $f(x)$ does not approach a single value as x approaches infinity or as x approaches negative infinity.

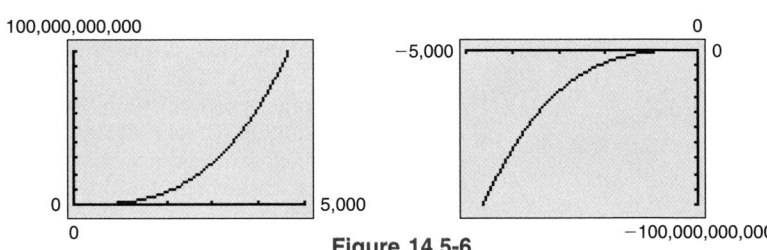

Figure 14.5-6

Thus, $\lim\limits_{x\to\infty} f(x)$ and $\lim\limits_{x\to-\infty} f(x)$, as defined in Section 14.1, do not exist. However, the situations are often described by writing

$$\lim_{x\to\infty} f(x) = \infty \quad \text{and} \quad \lim_{x\to-\infty} f(x) = -\infty$$

∎

In fact, no polynomial graph has a horizontal asymptote. That is, no polynomial function has a limit as x approaches infinity or negative infinity.

Limit of a Constant Function

The limits of constant functions are easily found. Consider, for example, the function $f(x) = 5$. As x approaches infinity or negative infinity, the corresponding value of $f(x)$ is *always* the number 5, so $\lim\limits_{x\to\infty} f(x) = 5$ and $\lim\limits_{x\to-\infty} f(x) = 5$. A similar argument works for any constant function.

Limit of a Constant

If c is a constant, then $\lim\limits_{x\to\infty} c = c$ and $\lim\limits_{x\to-\infty} c = c.$

Properties of Limits

Infinite limits have the same useful properties that ordinary limits have. For instance, suppose that as x approaches infinity, the values of a function f approach a number L, and the values of a function g approach a number M. Then it is plausible that the values of $(f + g)(x)$ approach $L + M$, the values of $(fg)(x)$ approach $L \cdot M$, and so forth. Similar remarks apply when x approaches negative infinity.

Properties of Limits at Infinity

If f and g are functions and L and M are numbers such that

$$\lim_{x\to\infty} f(x) = L \quad \text{and} \quad \lim_{x\to\infty} g(x) = M,$$

then

1. $\lim\limits_{x\to\infty} (f + g)(x) = \lim\limits_{x\to\infty} (f(x) + g(x)) = \lim\limits_{x\to\infty} f(x) + \lim\limits_{x\to\infty} g(x) = L + M$

2. $\lim\limits_{x\to\infty} (f - g)(x) = \lim\limits_{x\to\infty} (f(x) - g(x)) = \lim\limits_{x\to\infty} f(x) - \lim\limits_{x\to\infty} g(x) = L - M$

3. $\lim\limits_{x\to\infty} (fg)(x) = \lim\limits_{x\to\infty} (f(x) \cdot g(x)) = \left(\lim\limits_{x\to\infty} f(x)\right)\left(\lim\limits_{x\to\infty} g(x)\right) = L \cdot M$

4. $\lim\limits_{x\to\infty} \left(\dfrac{f}{g}\right)(x) = \lim\limits_{x\to\infty} \left(\dfrac{f(x)}{g(x)}\right) = \dfrac{\lim\limits_{x\to\infty} f(x)}{\lim\limits_{x\to\infty} g(x)} = \dfrac{L}{M}, \; M \neq 0$

5. $\lim\limits_{x\to\infty} \sqrt{f(x)} = \sqrt{L}$, provided $f(x) \geq 0$ for all large x

Properties 1–5 also hold with $-\infty$ in place of ∞, provided that for property 5, $f(x) \geq 0$ for all small x.

Example Notes

In **Example 4**, the limits do not exist as limits are previously defined, and the following notation is used:

$$\lim_{x\to\infty} f(x) = \infty \text{ and } \lim_{x\to-\infty} f(x) = -\infty$$

For statements of this type, there are no horizontal asymptotes as x approaches ∞ or as x approaches $-\infty$.

Teaching Notes

Refer students to the following statement near the top of this page: In fact, no polynomial graph has a horizontal asymptote.

Ask students if a polynomial graph can have a vertical asymptote, and to support their answer.
No. Every polynomial function is continuous at every real number (page 940), but a vertical asymptote could only occur where there is a discontinuity.

For **Example 4**, have students find a complete graph of $f(x)$.

Example 5

Describe the end behavior of

$f(x) = \dfrac{-4x^2 + 2x - 5}{5x^2 + 6x - 9}$ and justify your

conclusion.

As shown in the figure below, the

graph of $f(x) = \dfrac{-4x^2 + 2x - 5}{5x^2 + 6x - 9}$, to the

right of the y-axis, appears to have a horizontal asymptote that is slightly above $y = -1$.

To find the equation of the asymptote,

calculate $\displaystyle\lim_{x\to\infty} \dfrac{-4x^2 + 2x - 5}{5x^2 + 6x - 9}$:

$\displaystyle\lim_{x\to\infty} \dfrac{-4x^2 + 2x - 5}{5x^2 + 6x - 9}$

$= \displaystyle\lim_{x\to\infty} \dfrac{\dfrac{-4x^2 + 2x - 5}{x^2}}{\dfrac{5x^2 + 6x - 9}{x^2}}$

$= \displaystyle\lim_{x\to\infty} \dfrac{\dfrac{-4x^2}{x^2} + \dfrac{2x}{x^2} - \dfrac{5}{x^2}}{\dfrac{5x^2}{x^2} + \dfrac{6x}{x^2} - \dfrac{9}{x^2}}$

$= \displaystyle\lim_{x\to\infty} \dfrac{-4 + \dfrac{2}{x} - \dfrac{5}{x^2}}{5 + \dfrac{6}{x} - \dfrac{9}{x^2}}$

$= \dfrac{\displaystyle\lim_{x\to\infty}\left(-4 + \dfrac{2}{x} - \dfrac{5}{x^2}\right)}{\displaystyle\lim_{x\to\infty}\left(5 + \dfrac{6}{x} - \dfrac{9}{x^2}\right)}$ *property 4*

$= \dfrac{\displaystyle\lim_{x\to\infty}(-4) + \lim_{x\to\infty}\dfrac{2}{x} - \lim_{x\to\infty}\dfrac{5}{x^2}}{\displaystyle\lim_{x\to\infty}5 + \lim_{x\to\infty}\dfrac{6}{x} - \lim_{x\to\infty}\dfrac{9}{x^2}}$ *property 1, 2*

$= \dfrac{-4 + \displaystyle\lim_{x\to\infty}\dfrac{2}{x} - \lim_{x\to\infty}\dfrac{5}{x^2}}{5 + \displaystyle\lim_{x\to\infty}\dfrac{6}{x} - \lim_{x\to\infty}\dfrac{9}{x^2}}$ *limit of a constant*

$= \dfrac{-4 + 0 - 0}{5 + 0 - 0}$ *limit theorem*

$= -\dfrac{4}{5}$

By a similar procedure, we can find

that $\displaystyle\lim_{x\to-\infty} f(x) = -\dfrac{4}{5}$.

So, the graph approaches the

horizontal asymptote $y = -\dfrac{4}{5}$ as

x approaches infinity or as x approaches negative infinity.

Limit of $\dfrac{c}{x^n}$

If c is a constant, then Property 3 and Example 3 show that

$$\lim_{x\to\infty}\frac{c}{x} = \lim_{x\to\infty}\left(c\cdot\frac{1}{x}\right) = \left(\lim_{x\to\infty}c\right)\cdot\left(\lim_{x\to\infty}\frac{1}{x}\right) = c\cdot 0 = 0.$$

Repeatedly using Property 3 with this fact and Example 3, note that the result holds for any integer $n \ge 2$.

$$\lim_{x\to\infty}\frac{c}{x^n} = \lim_{x\to\infty}\left(\frac{c}{x}\cdot\frac{1}{x}\cdot\frac{1}{x}\cdot\,\cdots\,\cdot\frac{1}{x}\right)$$

$$= \left(\lim_{x\to\infty}\frac{c}{x}\right)\left(\lim_{x\to\infty}\frac{1}{x}\right)\left(\lim_{x\to\infty}\frac{1}{x}\right)\cdots\left(\lim_{x\to\infty}\frac{1}{x}\right)$$

$$= 0\cdot 0\cdot 0\cdot\,\cdots\,\cdot 0$$

$$= 0$$

A similar argument works with $-\infty$ in place of ∞ and produces this useful result, which is essentially a formal statement of half of the Big-Little Concept discussed in Section 4.4.

Limit Theorem ○——

> If c is a constant, then for each positive integer n,
>
> $$\lim_{x\to\infty}\frac{c}{x^n} = 0 \qquad \text{and} \qquad \lim_{x\to-\infty}\frac{c}{x^n} = 0$$

The Limit Theorem and the limit properties now make it possible to determine the limit, if it exists, of any rational function as x approaches infinity or negative infinity.

Example 5   **End Behavior of a Rational Function**

Describe the end behavior of $f(x) = \dfrac{3x^2 - 2x + 1}{2x^2 + 4x - 5}$ and justify your conclusion.

Solution

If you graph $f(x) = \dfrac{3x^2 - 2x + 1}{2x^2 + 4x - 5}$, to the right of the y-axis you will see that there appears to be a horizontal asymptote close to $y = 1.5$, as shown in Figure 14.5-7. This can be confirmed algebraically by computing

$$\lim_{x\to\infty}\frac{3x^2 - 2x + 1}{2x^2 + 4x - 5}.$$

Property 4 cannot be used directly because neither the numerator nor denominator have a finite limit as x approaches infinity, as discussed in Example 4. To rewrite the expression in an equivalent form, divide both

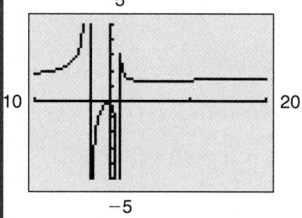

Figure 14.5-7

numerator and denominator by the highest power of x that appears, namely x^2. Dividing both by x^2 is the same as multiplying by $\dfrac{\frac{1}{x^2}}{\frac{1}{x^2}}$, a form of 1, so the value of the fraction is not changed.

$$\lim_{x\to\infty}\frac{3x^2-2x+1}{2x^2+4x-5}=\lim_{x\to\infty}\frac{\dfrac{3x^2-2x+1}{x^2}}{\dfrac{2x^2+4x-5}{x^2}}$$

$$=\lim_{x\to\infty}\frac{\dfrac{3x^2}{x^2}-\dfrac{2x}{x^2}+\dfrac{1}{x^2}}{\dfrac{2x^2}{x^2}+\dfrac{4x}{x^2}-\dfrac{5}{x^2}}$$

$$=\lim_{x\to\infty}\frac{3-\dfrac{2}{x}+\dfrac{1}{x^2}}{2+\dfrac{4}{x}-\dfrac{5}{x^2}}$$

$$=\frac{\lim\limits_{x\to\infty}\left(3-\dfrac{2}{x}+\dfrac{1}{x^2}\right)}{\lim\limits_{x\to\infty}\left(2+\dfrac{4}{x}-\dfrac{5}{x^2}\right)}\qquad\textit{property 4}$$

$$=\frac{\lim\limits_{x\to\infty}3-\lim\limits_{x\to\infty}\dfrac{2}{x}+\lim\limits_{x\to\infty}\dfrac{1}{x^2}}{\lim\limits_{x\to\infty}2+\lim\limits_{x\to\infty}\dfrac{4}{x}-\lim\limits_{x\to\infty}\dfrac{5}{x^2}}\qquad\textit{property 1, 2}$$

$$=\frac{3-\lim\limits_{x\to\infty}\dfrac{2}{x}+\lim\limits_{x\to\infty}\dfrac{1}{x^2}}{2+\lim\limits_{x\to\infty}\dfrac{4}{x}-\lim\limits_{x\to\infty}\dfrac{5}{x^2}}\qquad\textit{limit of constant}$$

$$=\frac{3-0+0}{2+0-0}\qquad\textit{limit theorem}$$

$$=\frac{3}{2}\qquad\blacksquare$$

A slight variation on the last example can be used to compute certain limits involving square roots.

Example 6　**Limits at Infinity**

Find each limit.

a. $\displaystyle\lim_{x\to\infty}\frac{\sqrt{3x^2+1}}{2x+3}$　　**b.** $\displaystyle\lim_{x\to-\infty}\frac{\sqrt{3x^2+1}}{2x+3}$

ADDITIONAL EXAMPLES

Example 6

Find each limit.

a. $\displaystyle\lim_{x\to\infty}\frac{\sqrt{2x^2-1}}{-5x+3}$

Only positive values of x need to be considered when finding the limit as x approaches infinity. When x is positive, $\sqrt{x^2}=x$.

Therefore,

$$\lim_{x\to\infty}\frac{\sqrt{2x^2-1}}{-5x+3}$$

$$=\lim_{x\to\infty}\frac{\dfrac{\sqrt{2x^2-1}}{x}}{\dfrac{-5x+3}{x}}\qquad\textit{multiply by }\dfrac{\frac{1}{x}}{\frac{1}{x}}$$

$$=\lim_{x\to\infty}\frac{\dfrac{\sqrt{2x^2-1}}{\sqrt{x^2}}}{\dfrac{-5x+3}{x}}\qquad\begin{array}{l}\sqrt{x^2}=x,\textit{ for}\\ x>0\end{array}$$

$$=\lim_{x\to\infty}\frac{\sqrt{\dfrac{2x^2-1}{x^2}}}{\dfrac{-5x+3}{x}}\qquad\dfrac{\sqrt{a}}{\sqrt{b}}=\sqrt{\dfrac{a}{b}}$$

$$=\lim_{x\to\infty}\frac{\sqrt{2-\dfrac{1}{x^2}}}{-5+\dfrac{3}{x}}$$

$$=\frac{\lim\limits_{x\to\infty}\sqrt{2-\dfrac{1}{x^2}}}{\lim\limits_{x\to\infty}\left(-5+\dfrac{3}{x}\right)}\qquad\textit{property 4}$$

$$=\frac{\sqrt{\lim\limits_{x\to\infty}\left(2-\dfrac{1}{x^2}\right)}}{\lim\limits_{x\to\infty}\left(-5+\dfrac{3}{x}\right)}\qquad\textit{property 5}$$

$$=\frac{\sqrt{\lim\limits_{x\to\infty}2-\lim\limits_{x\to\infty}\dfrac{1}{x^2}}}{\lim\limits_{x\to\infty}(-5)+\lim\limits_{x\to\infty}\dfrac{3}{x}}\qquad\textit{property 1}$$

$$=\frac{\sqrt{2-0}}{-5+0}\qquad\begin{array}{l}\textit{constant limit and}\\ \textit{limit theorem}\end{array}$$

$$=-\frac{\sqrt{2}}{5}$$

continued from page 955

b. $\lim\limits_{x\to-\infty} \dfrac{\sqrt{2x^2-1}}{-5x+3}$

Only negative values of x need to be considered.

$\lim\limits_{x\to-\infty} \dfrac{\sqrt{2x^2-1}}{-5x+3}$

$= \lim\limits_{x\to-\infty} \dfrac{\dfrac{\sqrt{2x^2-1}}{x}}{\dfrac{-5x+3}{x}}$ *multiply by* $\dfrac{\frac{1}{x}}{\frac{1}{x}}$

$= \lim\limits_{x\to-\infty} \dfrac{\dfrac{\sqrt{2x^2-1}}{-\sqrt{x^2}}}{\dfrac{-5x+3}{x}}$ $x = -\sqrt{x^2},$ *for* $x < 0$

$= \lim\limits_{x\to-\infty} \dfrac{\left(-\sqrt{\dfrac{2x^2-1}{x^2}}\right)}{\dfrac{-5x+3}{x}}$ $\dfrac{\sqrt{a}}{\sqrt{b}} = \sqrt{\dfrac{a}{b}}$

$= \lim\limits_{x\to-\infty} \dfrac{\left(-\sqrt{2-\dfrac{1}{x^2}}\right)}{-5+\dfrac{3}{x}}$

$= \dfrac{\lim\limits_{x\to-\infty}\left(-\sqrt{2-\dfrac{1}{x^2}}\right)}{\lim\limits_{x\to-\infty}\left(-5+\dfrac{3}{x}\right)}$ *property 4*

$= \dfrac{-\lim\limits_{x\to-\infty}\left(\sqrt{2-\dfrac{1}{x^2}}\right)}{\lim\limits_{x\to-\infty}\left(-5+\dfrac{3}{x}\right)}$ *property 3 and constant limit*

$= \dfrac{-\sqrt{\lim\limits_{x\to-\infty}\left(2-\dfrac{1}{x^2}\right)}}{\lim\limits_{x\to-\infty}\left(-5+\dfrac{3}{x}\right)}$ *property 5*

$= \dfrac{-\sqrt{\lim\limits_{x\to-\infty}2 - \lim\limits_{x\to-\infty}\dfrac{1}{x^2}}}{\lim\limits_{x\to-\infty}(-5) + \lim\limits_{x\to-\infty}\dfrac{3}{x}}$ *property 1*

$= \dfrac{-\sqrt{2-0}}{-5+0}$ *constant limit and limit theorem*

$= \dfrac{\sqrt{2}}{5}$

Solution

a. Only positive values of x need to be considered when finding the limit as x approaches infinity. When x is positive, $\sqrt{x^2} = x$. Therefore,

$\lim\limits_{x\to\infty} \dfrac{\sqrt{3x^2+1}}{2x+3} = \lim\limits_{x\to\infty} \dfrac{\dfrac{\sqrt{3x^2+1}}{x}}{\dfrac{2x+3}{x}}$ *multiply by* $\dfrac{\frac{1}{x}}{\frac{1}{x}}$

$= \lim\limits_{x\to\infty} \dfrac{\dfrac{\sqrt{3x^2+1}}{\sqrt{x^2}}}{\dfrac{2x+3}{x}}$ $\sqrt{x^2} = x,$ *for* $x > 0$

$= \lim\limits_{x\to\infty} \dfrac{\sqrt{\dfrac{3x^2+1}{x^2}}}{\dfrac{2x+3}{x}}$ $\dfrac{\sqrt{a}}{\sqrt{b}} = \sqrt{\dfrac{a}{b}}$

$= \lim\limits_{x\to\infty} \dfrac{\sqrt{3+\dfrac{1}{x^2}}}{2+\dfrac{3}{x}}$

$= \dfrac{\lim\limits_{x\to\infty}\sqrt{3+\dfrac{1}{x^2}}}{\lim\limits_{x\to\infty}\left(2+\dfrac{3}{x}\right)}$ *property 4*

$= \dfrac{\sqrt{\lim\limits_{x\to\infty}\left(3+\dfrac{1}{x^2}\right)}}{\lim\limits_{x\to\infty}\left(2+\dfrac{3}{x}\right)}$ *property 5*

$= \dfrac{\sqrt{\lim\limits_{x\to\infty}3 + \lim\limits_{x\to\infty}\dfrac{1}{x^2}}}{\lim\limits_{x\to\infty}2 + \lim\limits_{x\to\infty}\dfrac{3}{x}}$ *property 1*

$= \dfrac{\sqrt{3+0}}{2+0}$ *constant limit and limit theorem*

$= \dfrac{\sqrt{3}}{2}$

b. To compute the limit as x approaches negative infinity, you need only consider negative values of x and use the fact that when x is negative, $x = -\sqrt{x^2}$. For instance, $-2 = -\sqrt{(-2)^2} = -\sqrt{4}$. Then an argument similar to the one in part **a** shows that

$$\lim_{x\to-\infty} \frac{\sqrt{3x^2+1}}{2x+3} = -\frac{\sqrt{3}}{2}$$

∎

Although the properties of limits and some algebraic ingenuity can often by used to compute limits, as in the preceding examples, more sophisticated techniques are needed to determine certain limits. This is the case, for example, with the proof that $\lim\limits_{n\to\infty}\left(1+\dfrac{1}{n}\right)^n$ exists and is the number e.

Exercises 14.5

In Exercises 1–8, use a calculator to estimate the limit.

1. $\lim\limits_{x\to\infty}\left[\sqrt{x^2+1}-(x+1)\right]$ **−1**

2. $\lim\limits_{x\to\infty}\left[\sqrt{x^2+x+1}+x\right]$ **∞**

3. $\lim\limits_{x\to-\infty}\dfrac{x^{\frac{2}{3}}-x^{\frac{4}{3}}}{x^3}$ **0**

4. $\lim\limits_{x\to\infty}\dfrac{x^{\frac{5}{4}}+x}{2x-x^{\frac{5}{4}}}$ **−1**

5. $\lim\limits_{x\to-\infty}\sin\dfrac{1}{x}$ **0**

6. $\lim\limits_{x\to\infty}\dfrac{\sin x}{x}$ **0**

7. $\lim\limits_{x\to\infty}\dfrac{\ln x}{x}$ **0**

8. $\lim\limits_{x\to\infty}\dfrac{5}{1+(1.1)^{-\frac{x}{20}}}$ **5**

In Exercises 9–14, list the vertical asymptotes of the graph, if any exist. Then use the graph of the function to find

$$\lim\limits_{x\to\infty}f(x)\quad\text{and}\quad\lim\limits_{x\to-\infty}f(x).$$

9.

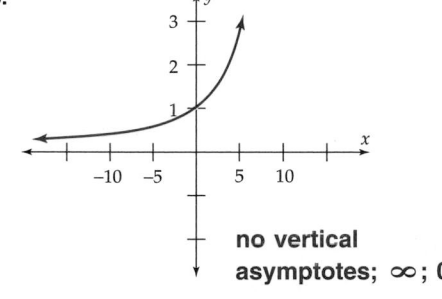

no vertical asymptotes; ∞; 0

10.

x = 10; 1; 1

11.

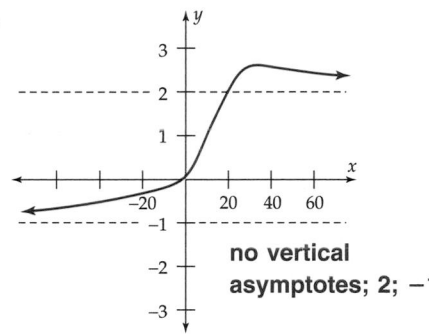

no vertical asymptotes; 2; −1

12.

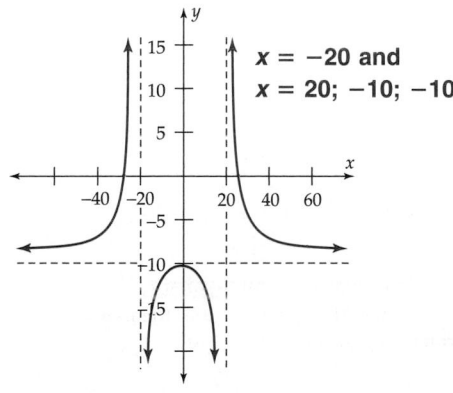

x = −20 and x = 20; −10; −10

Teaching Notes

To make sure that students understand the concepts of infinite limits and limits at infinity, ask them to identify the types of asymptotes, if any, that correspond to the following limits.

$\lim\limits_{x\to2}f(x)=\infty$	vertical asymptote
$\lim\limits_{x\to-\infty}f(x)=-3$	horizontal asymptote
$\lim\limits_{x\to-3^+}f(x)=-\infty$	vertical asymptote
$\lim\limits_{x\to2^-}f(x)=0$	no asymptote indicated
$\lim\limits_{x\to\infty}f(x)=\infty$	no asymptote indicated

Exercises 14.5

ANSWERS

48. a. Let n be the degree of $f(x)$ and m be the degree of $g(x)$. It is given that $m > n$. Let $p(x)$ be a polynomial with degree less than n and $q(x)$ be a polynomial with degree less than m such that $f(x) = ax^n + p(x)$ and $g(x) = cx^m + q(x)$.

Observe that

$$\lim_{x \to \infty} \frac{ax^n + p(x)}{cx^m + q(x)}$$

$$= \lim_{x \to \infty} \frac{\dfrac{ax^n + p(x)}{x^m}}{\dfrac{cx^m + q^x}{x^m}}$$

$$= \lim_{x \to \infty} \frac{\left(\dfrac{a}{x^{m-n}}\right) + \left(\dfrac{p(x)}{x^m}\right)}{c + \dfrac{q(x)}{x^m}}$$

$$= \frac{\lim_{x \to \infty}\left(\dfrac{a}{x^{m-n}}\right) + \lim_{x \to \infty}\left(\dfrac{p(x)}{x^m}\right)}{\lim_{x \to \infty} c + \lim_{x \to \infty} \dfrac{q(x)}{x^m}}$$

Since $m - n > 0$ and from

Example 5, $\lim_{x \to \infty}\left(\dfrac{p(x)}{x^m}\right) = 0$,

$\lim_{x \to \infty}\left(\dfrac{q(x)}{x^m}\right) = 0$ and

$\lim_{x \to \infty}\left(\dfrac{a}{x^{m-n}}\right) = 0.$

Also, since $\lim_{x \to \infty} c = c$, we get

$$\frac{\lim_{x \to \infty}\left(\dfrac{a}{x^{m-n}}\right) + \lim_{x \to \infty}\left(\dfrac{p(x)}{x^m}\right)}{\lim_{x \to \infty} c + \lim_{x \to \infty} \dfrac{q(x)}{x^m}} = 0$$

b. Let n be the degree of $f(x)$ and of $g(x)$. Proceed as in part (a) to obtain

$$\lim_{x \to \infty} \frac{ax^n + p(x)}{cx^n + q(x)}$$

$$= \lim_{x \to \infty} \frac{\dfrac{ax^n + p(x)}{x^n}}{\dfrac{cx^n + q(x)}{x^n}}$$

$$= \lim_{x \to \infty} \frac{a + \dfrac{p(x)}{x^n}}{c + \dfrac{q(x)}{x^n}}$$

$$= \frac{\lim_{x \to \infty} a + \lim_{x \to \infty}\left(\dfrac{p(x)}{x^n}\right)}{\lim_{x \to \infty} c + \lim_{x \to \infty}\left(\dfrac{q(x)}{x^n}\right)}$$

$$= \frac{a + 0}{c + 0} = \frac{a}{c}$$

13.

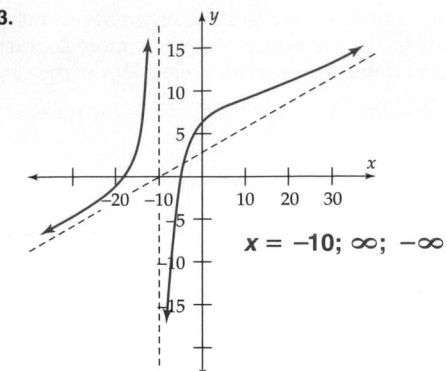

$x = -10;\ \infty;\ -\infty$

14.

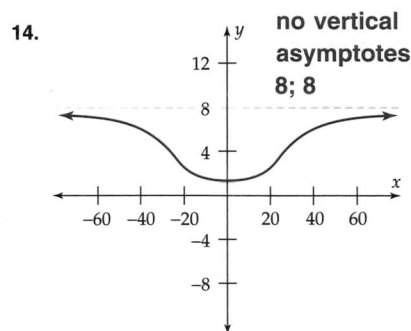

no vertical asymptotes; 8; 8

In Exercises 15–20, use the limit theorem and the properties of limits to find the horizontal asymptotes of the graph of the given function.

15. $f(x) = \dfrac{3x^2 + 5}{4x^2 - 6x + 2}$ $y = \dfrac{3}{4}$

16. $g(x) = \dfrac{x^2}{x^2 - 2x + 1}$ $y = 1$

17. $h(x) = \dfrac{2x^2 - 6x + 1}{2 + x - x^2}$ $y = -2$

18. $k(x) = \dfrac{3x + x^2 - 4}{2x - x^3 + x^2}$ $y = 0$

19. $f(x) = \dfrac{3x^4 - 2x^3 + 5x^2 - x + 1}{7x^3 - 4x^2 + 6x - 12}$
no horizontal asymptote

20. $g(x) = \dfrac{2x^5 - x^3 + 2x - 9}{5 - x^5}$
no horizontal asymptote

In Exercises 21–39, use the limit theorem and the properties of limits to find the limit.

c. Let n be the degree of $f(x)$ and let m be the degree of $g(x)$. Since $n > m$, it follows that $n - m > 0$. Proceed as in part (a) to obtain

$$\lim_{x \to \infty} \frac{ax^n + p(x)}{cx^m + q(x)} = \lim_{x \to \infty} \frac{\dfrac{ax^n + p(x)}{x^n}}{\dfrac{cx^m + q(x)}{x^n}}$$

$$= \lim_{x \to \infty} \frac{a + \dfrac{p(x)}{x^n}}{\dfrac{c}{x^{n-m}} + \dfrac{q(x)}{x^n}}$$

---

21. $\lim_{x \to -\infty} \dfrac{(x - 3)(x + 2)}{2x^2 + x + 1}$ $\dfrac{1}{2}$

22. $\lim_{x \to \infty} \dfrac{(2x + 1)(3x - 2)}{3x^2 + 2x - 5}$ 2

23. $\lim_{x \to \infty} \left(3x - \dfrac{1}{x^2}\right)$ ∞ **24.** $\lim_{x \to -\infty} (3x^2 + 1)^{-2}$ 0

25. $\lim_{x \to -\infty} \left(\dfrac{3x}{x + 2} + \dfrac{2x}{x - 1}\right)$ 5

26. $\lim_{x \to \infty} \left(\dfrac{x}{x^2 + 1} + \dfrac{2x^2}{x^3 + x}\right)$ 0

27. $\lim_{x \to \infty} \dfrac{2x}{\sqrt{x^2 - 2x}}$ 2 **28.** $\lim_{x \to -\infty} \dfrac{x}{\sqrt{x^2 - 1}}$ -1

29. $\lim_{x \to -\infty} \dfrac{3x - 2}{\sqrt{2x^2 + 1}}$ $-\dfrac{3}{\sqrt{2}}$ **30.** $\lim_{x \to \infty} \dfrac{3x - 2}{\sqrt{2x^2 + 1}}$ $\dfrac{3}{\sqrt{2}}$

31. $\lim_{x \to \infty} \dfrac{\sqrt{2x^2 + 1}}{3x - 5}$ $\dfrac{\sqrt{2}}{3}$ **32.** $\lim_{x \to -\infty} \dfrac{\sqrt{2x^2 + 1}}{3x - 5}$ $-\dfrac{2}{\sqrt{3}}$

33. $\lim_{x \to -\infty} \dfrac{\sqrt{3x^2 + 3}}{x + 3}$ $-\sqrt{3}$ **34.** $\lim_{x \to \infty} \dfrac{\sqrt{3x^2 + 2x}}{2x + 1}$ $\dfrac{\sqrt{3}}{2}$

35. $\lim_{x \to -\infty} \dfrac{x^2 + 2x + 1}{\sqrt{x^4 + 2x}}$ 1 **36.** $\lim_{x \to \infty} \dfrac{\sqrt{x^6 - x^2}}{2x^3}$ $\dfrac{1}{2}$

37. $\lim_{x \to \infty} \dfrac{1 - \sqrt{x}}{1 + \sqrt{x}}$ *Hint:* Rationalize the denominator.
-1

38. $\lim_{x \to \infty} \dfrac{\sqrt{x} + 2}{\sqrt{x} - 3}$ 1

39. $\lim_{x \to \infty} \left(\sqrt{x^2 + 1} - x\right)$ 0
Hint: Multiply by $\dfrac{\sqrt{x^2 + 1} + x}{\sqrt{x^2 + 1} + x}$.

In Exercises 40–42, find the limit by adapting the hint from Exercise 39.

40. $\lim_{x \to -\infty} \left(x + \sqrt{x^2 + 4}\right)$ 0

41. $\lim_{x \to \infty} \left(\sqrt{x^2 - 1} - \sqrt{x^2 + 1}\right)$ 0

42. $\lim_{x \to -\infty} \left(\sqrt{x^2 + 5x + 5} + x + 1\right)$ $-\dfrac{3}{2}$

43. A free-falling body has two forces acting on it: gravity, which causes the body to speed up as it falls, and air resistance, which causes the body to slow down. Assuming that a free-falling body has an initial velocity of zero and that its velocity is proportional to the force due to air resistance, the

---

$$= \frac{\lim_{x \to \infty} a + \lim_{x \to \infty}\left(\dfrac{p(x)}{x^n}\right)}{\lim_{x \to \infty} \dfrac{c}{x^{n-m}} + \lim_{x \to \infty}\left(\dfrac{q(x)}{x^n}\right)}$$

$$= \frac{a + 0}{0 + 0}$$

$$= \frac{a}{0}$$

Since division by 0 is undefined, the limit does not exist.

velocity of a falling object can be written as a function of the amount of elapsed time.

$$\text{velocity} = f(t) = \frac{mg}{k}\left(1 - e^{-\frac{k}{m}t}\right)$$

The variable m represents the mass of the body, g is acceleration due to gravity (≈ 32 feet per second per second), and k is the contant of proportionality. For a fall with a parachute, $k - 1.6m$; without a parachute, $k = 0.18m$.

When the air resistance has built until it nearly balances the gravitational force, the body speeds up very little. Upon reaching this condition, the body continues to move downward with a constant maximum speed called *terminal velocity*. Find the terminal velocity of falling bodies with a parachute and without a parachute by finding the limit as t approaches infinity.

with: 20 ft/sec; without: $\approx$177.78 ft/sec

In Exercises 44–45, find the limit.

44. *Critical Thinking* $\lim\limits_{x \to \infty} \dfrac{x}{|x|}$ **1**

45. *Critical Thinking* $\lim\limits_{x \to -\infty} \dfrac{|x|}{|x| + 1}$ **1**

46. *Critical Thinking* Let $[x]$ denote the greatest integer function and find

a. $\lim\limits_{x \to \infty} \dfrac{[x]}{x}$ **1** **b.** $\lim\limits_{x \to -\infty} \dfrac{[x]}{x}$ **1**

47. *Critical Thinking* Find $\lim\limits_{x \to \infty} \dfrac{\sqrt{x + \sqrt{x + \sqrt{x}}}}{\sqrt{x + 1}}$. **1**

48. *Critical Thinking* Let $f(x)$ be a nonzero polynomial with leading coefficient a, and let $g(x)$ be a nonzero polynomial with leading coefficient c. Prove that

a. if degree $f(x) <$ degree $g(x)$, then $\lim\limits_{x \to \infty} \dfrac{f(x)}{g(x)} = 0$.

b. if degree $f(x) =$ degree $g(x)$, then $\lim\limits_{x \to \infty} \dfrac{f(x)}{g(x)} = \dfrac{a}{c}$.

c. if degree $f(x) >$ degree $g(x)$, then $\lim\limits_{x \to \infty} \dfrac{f(x)}{g(x)}$

does not exist.

Formal definitions of limits at infinity and negative infinity are given in Exercises 49 and 50. Adapt the discussion in Section 14.3 to explain how these definitions are derived from the informal definitions in this section.

49. *Critical Thinking* Let f be a function and L be a real number. Then the statement $\lim\limits_{x \to \infty} f(x) = L$ means that for each positive number ε, there is a positive real number k that depends on ε with the following property:

If $x > k$, then $|f(x) - L| < \varepsilon$

Hint: Concentrate on the second part of the informal definition. The number k measures "large enough," that is, how large the values of x must be in order to guarantee that $f(x)$ is as close as you want to L.

50. *Critical Thinking* Let f be a function and L be a real number. Then the statement $\lim\limits_{x \to -\infty} f(x) = L$ means that for each positive number ε, there is a negative real number n that depends on ε with the following property:

If $x < n$, then $|f(x) - L| < \varepsilon$

49. The first part of the informal definition is included in the second part, which says "the values of $f(x)$ can be made arbitrarily close to L by taking large enough values of x." This means that whenever you specify how close $f(x)$ should be to L, we can tell you how large x must be to guarantee this. In other words, you specify how close you want $f(x)$ to be to L by giving a positive number ε and we tell you how large x must be to guarantee that $f(x)$ is within ε of L, that is, to guarantee that $|f(x) - L| < \varepsilon$. We do this by giving a positive number k such that $|f(x) - L| < \varepsilon$ whenever $x > k$. This can be reworded as follows: For every positive number ε, there is a positive number k (depending on ε) with this property:

If $x > k$, then $|f(x) - L| < \varepsilon$.

50. The informal definition "values of $f(x)$ can be made arbitrarily close to L by choosing negative values of x with large enough absolute value," means that when we specify how close to L we would like the function to be, we can find negative values for x with large enough absolute values for which $f(x)$ is within the desired distance of L. $|f(x) - L| < \varepsilon$ means that $f(x)$ is within ε of L. The value n is the x value such that all values of x less than n have large enough absolute values. That is, whenever x is less than n, $f(x)$ is within ε of L. Thus we have "for every $\varepsilon > 0$ there exists n such that if $x < n$, $|f(x) - L| < \varepsilon$.

CHAPTER 14 REVIEW

Important Concepts

960

Review Exercises

Section 14.1

In Exercises 1–2, use a calculator to estimate the limit.

1. $\lim\limits_{x \to 0} \dfrac{3x - \sin x}{x}$ **2**

2. $\lim\limits_{x \to \frac{\pi}{2}} \dfrac{1 - \sin x}{1 + \cos 2x}$ $\dfrac{1}{4}$

In Exercises 3–4, use the graph of the function to determine the limit.

3. $\lim\limits_{x \to 2} f(x)$

2

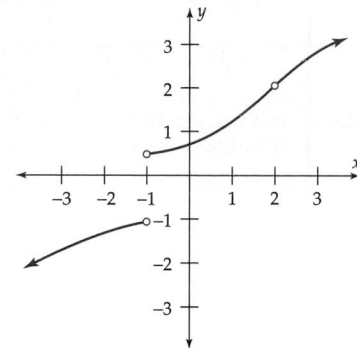

4. $\lim\limits_{x \to -1} f(x)$

does not exist

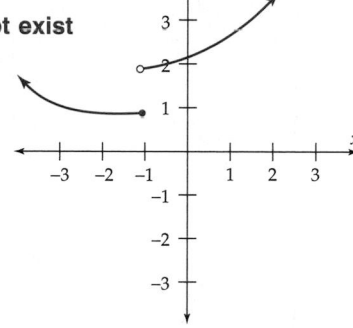

Section 14.2

In Exercises 5–6, assume that $\lim\limits_{x \to 3} f(x) = 5$ and $\lim\limits_{x \to 3} g(x) = -2$.

5. Find $\lim\limits_{x \to 3} \dfrac{f(x)g(x) - 2f(x)}{[g(x)]^2}$ **−5**   **6.** Find $\lim\limits_{x \to 3} \dfrac{\sqrt{f(x) - 2g(x)}}{f(x) + g(x)}$ **1**

In Exercises 7–10, find the limit if it exists. If the limit does not exist, explain why.

7. $\lim\limits_{x \to 1} \dfrac{x^2 - 1}{x^2 - 3x + 2}$ **−2**   **8.** $\lim\limits_{x \to -2} \dfrac{x^2 - x - 6}{x^2 + x - 2}$ $\dfrac{5}{3}$

9. $\lim\limits_{x \to 0} \dfrac{\sqrt{1 + x} - 1}{x}$ $\dfrac{1}{2}$ **10.** $\lim\limits_{x \to 2} \dfrac{x^2 - 2x - 3}{x^2 - 6x + 9}$ **−3**

15. Given $\varepsilon > 0$, let $\delta = \dfrac{\varepsilon}{2}$.

Then, $0 < |x - 3| < \delta \Rightarrow$

$|x - 3| < \dfrac{\varepsilon}{2} \Rightarrow 2|x - 3| < \varepsilon \Rightarrow$

$|2(x - 3)| < \varepsilon \Rightarrow |2x - 6| < \varepsilon \Rightarrow$

$|(2x + 1) - 7| < \varepsilon \Rightarrow$

$|f(x) - 7| < \varepsilon$.

16. Given $\varepsilon > 0$, let $\delta = 2\varepsilon$. Then,

$0 < |x - 2| < \delta \Rightarrow$

$\left| \dfrac{1}{2}x - 1 \right| < \varepsilon \Rightarrow$

$\left| \left(\dfrac{1}{2}x + 3 \right) - 4 \right| < \varepsilon \Rightarrow$

$|f(x) - 4| < \varepsilon$.

17. continuous at $x = -3$, discontinuous at $x = 2$

18. discontinuous at $x = -3$; continuous at $x = 2$

19. a. $\displaystyle\lim_{x \to 2} f(x) = \lim_{x \to 2} \dfrac{x^2 - x - 6}{x^2 - 9}$

$= \dfrac{\displaystyle\lim_{x \to 2}(x^2 - x - 6)}{\displaystyle\lim_{x \to 2}(x^2 - 9)}$

$= \dfrac{2^2 - 2 - 6}{2^2 - 9} = \dfrac{-4}{-5}$

$= \dfrac{4}{5} = f(2)$

b. f is not defined at $x = 3$ and hence is discontinuous there.

11. If $f(x) = x^2 + 1$, find $\displaystyle\lim_{h \to 0} \dfrac{f(2 + h) - f(2)}{h}$. **4**

12. If $f(x) = 3x - 2$ and c is a constant, find $\displaystyle\lim_{h \to 0} \dfrac{f(c + h) - f(c)}{h}$. **3**

Section 14.2.A

13. $\displaystyle\lim_{x \to -5^+} \dfrac{|x + 5|}{x + 5}$ **1**

14. $\displaystyle\lim_{x \to 7^-} \left(\sqrt{7 - x^2 + 6x} + 2 \right)$ **2**

Section 14.3

In Exercises 15–16, use the formal definition of limit to prove the statement.

15. $\displaystyle\lim_{x \to 3} (2x + 1) = 7$

16. $\displaystyle\lim_{x \to 2} \left(\dfrac{1}{2}x + 3 \right) = 4$

Section 14.4

In Exercises 17–18, determine whether the function whose graph is given is continuous at $x = -3$ and $x = 2$.

17.

18.

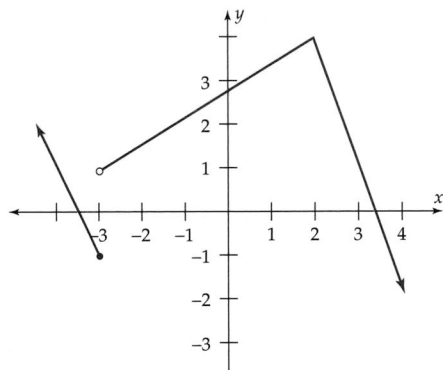

19. Show that $f(x) = \dfrac{x^2 - x - 6}{x^2 - 9}$ has the given traits.

a. continuous at $x = 2$ **b.** discontinuous at $x = 3$

20. Is the function given by

$$f(x) = \begin{cases} 3x - 2 & \text{if } x \le 3 \\ 10 - x & \text{if } x > 3 \end{cases}$$

continuous at $x = 3$? Justify your answer.

Section   14.5

In Exercises 21–22, find the vertical asymptotes of the graph of the given function, and state whether the graph moves upward or downward on each side of each asymptote.

21. $f(x) = \dfrac{x^2 + 1}{x^2 - x - 2}$

22. $g(x) = \dfrac{x^2 - 1}{x^2 - 3x + 2}$

In Exercises 23–26, find the limit.

23. $\lim\limits_{x \to \infty} \dfrac{2x^3 - 3x^2 + 5x - 1}{4x^3 + 2x^2 - x + 10}$ $\dfrac{1}{2}$

24. $\lim\limits_{x \to -\infty} \dfrac{4 - 3x - 2x^2}{x^3 + 2x + 5}$ **0**

25. $\lim\limits_{x \to -\infty} \left(\dfrac{2x + 1}{x - 3} + \dfrac{4x - 1}{3x} \right)$ $\dfrac{10}{3}$

26. $\lim\limits_{x \to \infty} \dfrac{\sqrt{3x^2 + 2}}{4x + 1}$ $\dfrac{\sqrt{3}}{4}$

In Exercises 27–28, find the horizontal asymptotes of the graph of the given function algebraically, and verify your results graphically with a calculator.

27. $f(x) = \dfrac{x^2 - x + 7}{2x^2 + 5x + 7}$ $y = \dfrac{1}{2}$

28. $f(x) = \dfrac{x - 9}{\sqrt{4x^2 + 3x + 2}}$ $y = -\dfrac{1}{2}$

20. $\lim\limits_{x \to 3} f(x) = 7 = f(3)$ so the function is continuous at $x = 3$.

21. There are vertical asymptotes at $x = -1$ and $x = 2$. The graph moves upward as x approaches -1 from the left and downward as x approaches -1 from the right. The graph moves downward as x approaches 2 from the left and upward as x approaches 2 from the right.

22. There is a vertical asymptote at $x = 2$ and a hole at $x = 1$. The graph moves downward as x approaches 2 from the left and upward as x approaches 2 from the right.

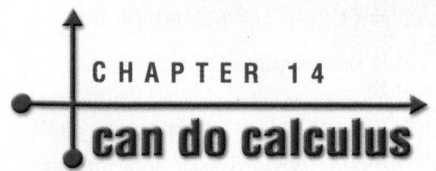

can do calculus

Riemann Sums

Math Background

German mathematician George Bernhard Riemann (1826–1866) made contributions of great depth and originality to several areas of mathematics, especially complex analysis, number theory, and mathematical physics. Riemann's work has had a substantial and lasting influence. For example, his ideas about differential geometry were important to the development of Albert Einstein's theory of general relativity.

ADDITIONAL EXAMPLES

Example 1

Suppose a self-propelled toy car is moving with increasing velocity. The velocity of the car at various times is given in the table. Estimate the total distance traveled in the 4-second interval.

Time (sec)	Velocity (cm/sec)
0	45
1	63
2	78
3	91
4	101

Because the velocity is increasing, the car has gone at least 45 cm during the first second, at least 63 cm during the second, at least 78 cm during the third second, and at least 91 cm during the fourth second. During the four-second interval, the car has traveled at least

$$45 + 63 + 78 + 91 = 277 \text{ cm}$$

underestimate

Therefore, 277 cm is an underestimate of the total distance traveled.

can do calculus

Riemann Sums

Calculus deals with rates of change, such as the speed of a car, and problems such as the following:

> If you know the continuously changing speed of a car at any instant, can you determine how far the car has traveled?

A special case of this question will be answered in this section by using Riemann sums.

Time (sec)	Velocity (ft/sec)
0	14
1	29
2	61
3	128
4	268

Example 1 Total Distance Given Velocities

Suppose a racecar is moving with increasing velocity. The velocity of the car at various times is given in the table. Estimate the total distance traveled in the 4-second interval.

Solution

Because the velocity is increasing, the car has gone at least 14 feet during the first second, at least 29 feet during the second, at least 61 feet during the third second, and at least 128 feet during the fourth second. During the four-second interval, the car has traveled at least

$$14 + 29 + 61 + 128 = 232 \text{ feet} \qquad \textit{underestimate}$$

Therefore, 232 feet is an underestimate of the total distance traveled.

An overestimate can be found by noting that the car travels no more than 29 feet in the first second, no more than 61 feet in the next second, no more than 128 in the third second, and no more than 268 feet in the last second. Altogether, the car traveled no more than

$$29 + 61 + 128 + 268 = 486 \text{ feet} \qquad \textit{overestimate}$$

Therefore, the total distance traveled is between 232 feet and 486 feet. ■

The lower and upper estimates can be represented on a graph, where the velocity is shown as a smooth curve passing through each point given in the table, and the estimates of the distance traveled each second are represented by the area of rectangles. See Figure 14.C-1. The darker rectangles represent the underestimate for each second and the darker and lighter rectangles stacked together represent the overestimate.

Because the time interval between each measurement is 1 second, each rectangle is 1 unit wide. Each height corresponds to how far the car could have traveled during each time interval. Therefore, the areas of the darker rectangles are 14, 29, 61, and 128, and the sum of the areas represents the total underestimate of 232.

Figure 14.C-1

An overestimate can be found by noting that the car travels no more than 63 cm during the first second, no more than 78 cm during the second, no more than 91 cm during the third second, and no more than 101 cm during the fourth second. During the four-second interval, the car has traveled no more than

$$63 + 78 + 91 + 101 = 333 \text{ cm}$$

overestimate

So, the total distance traveled is between 277 cm and 333 cm.

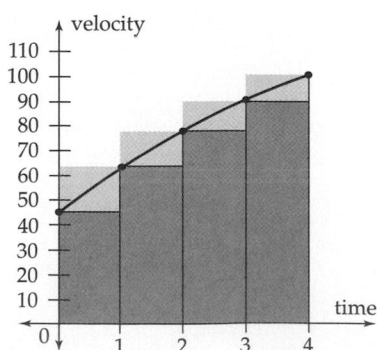

Similarly, the sum of the areas of the darker and lighter rectangles, which represents the overestimate, is 486.

There is a difference of $486 - 232 = 254$ feet between the estimates. This difference can also be found by adding the areas of the lighter rectangles.

A Better Estimate

Time (sec)	Velocity (ft/sec)
0	14
0.5	20
1	29
1.5	42
2	61
2.5	88
3	128
3.5	185
4	268

To get a better estimate of how far the car traveled during the 4-second interval, the velocity is measured for each half second, as shown in the table. The graph shown in Figure 14.C-2 displays the new data.

In the first half second, the car travels at least $14\left(\frac{1}{2}\right) = 7$ feet and at most $20\left(\frac{1}{2}\right) = 10$ feet. The distance traveled in each half second is calculated for both the underestimate and the overestimate as

$$v_i(\Delta t)$$

where v_i represents the velocity as measured at one end of the time interval and Δt represents length of each the time interval.

$$\text{Underestimate} = 14\left(\frac{1}{2}\right) + 20\left(\frac{1}{2}\right) + 29\left(\frac{1}{2}\right) + 42\left(\frac{1}{2}\right)$$
$$+ 61\left(\frac{1}{2}\right) + 88\left(\frac{1}{2}\right) + 128\left(\frac{1}{2}\right) + 185\left(\frac{1}{2}\right) = 283.5 \text{ feet}$$

$$\text{Overestimate} = 20\left(\frac{1}{2}\right) + 29\left(\frac{1}{2}\right) + 42\left(\frac{1}{2}\right) + 61\left(\frac{1}{2}\right)$$
$$+ 88\left(\frac{1}{2}\right) + 128\left(\frac{1}{2}\right) + 185\left(\frac{1}{2}\right) + 268\left(\frac{1}{2}\right) = 410.5 \text{ feet}$$

The difference between the estimates is again shown as the area of the lighter rectangles. This difference is

$$410.5 - 283.5 = 127.$$

Figure 14.C-2

Notice that the difference between the better estimates is half what it was in Example 1. By halving the intervals of measurement, the difference between the estimates is halved. Similarly, if the interval of measurement was given for every tenth of a second, the estimates would differ by $254(0.1) = 25.4$ feet, and if the interval of measurement was every thousandth of a second, the difference between the estimates would be $254(0.001) = 0.254$.

965

Teaching Notes

You might want to have students find the sum of the areas of the lighter rectangles in Figure 14.C-1. First, ask students how they would find the heights of the rectangles.

Subtract successive velocities. Then ask them for the width of each rectangle.   1

Finally, have them find the sum.

$(29 - 14) \cdot 1 + (61 - 29) \cdot 1 +$
$\quad (128 - 61) \cdot 1 + (268 - 128) \cdot 1$
$= 15 + 32 + 67 + 140$
$= 254$

The sum of the areas of the light rectangles in Figure 14.C-2 is shown below.

$(20 - 14) \cdot \left(\frac{1}{2}\right) + (29 - 20) \cdot \left(\frac{1}{2}\right) +$
$\quad (42 - 29) \cdot \left(\frac{1}{2}\right) + (61 - 42) \cdot \left(\frac{1}{2}\right) +$
$\quad (88 - 61) \cdot \left(\frac{1}{2}\right) + (128 - 88) \cdot \left(\frac{1}{2}\right) +$
$\quad (185 - 128) \cdot \left(\frac{1}{2}\right) + (268 - 185) \cdot \left(\frac{1}{2}\right)$

$= 6\left(\frac{1}{2}\right) + 9\left(\frac{1}{2}\right) + 13\left(\frac{1}{2}\right) + 19\left(\frac{1}{2}\right) +$
$\quad 27\left(\frac{1}{2}\right) + 40\left(\frac{1}{2}\right) + 57\left(\frac{1}{2}\right) + 83\left(\frac{1}{2}\right)$

$= 3 + 4.5 + 6.5 + 9.5 + 13.5 +$
$\quad\quad\quad 20 + 28.5 + 41.5$
$= 127$

COMMON ERROR ⫻ ALERT ⫼

Some students might use 1 as the width of the rectangles in Figure 14.C-2. Remind them that the width of the interval is the time between successive measurements.

Math Background

In the Can Do Calculus from Chapter 3, instantaneous rates of change were found. The concept of instantaneous rates of change is a central idea in differential calculus. In this Can Do Calculus, Riemann sums are used. The concept of Riemann sums is a central idea in integral calculus.

Example Notes

Students may need help interpreting the second statement in the Solution for **Example 2**: "If the time between each measurement is Δt, then the difference between the estimates is $254(\Delta t)$." Emphasize that the difference between the estimates refers to *distances*. Use the following table to summarize the information developed on pages 964 and 965:

	$\Delta t = 1$	$\Delta t = \frac{1}{2}$	$\Delta t = 0.1$
under-estimate	232	283.5	
over-estimate	486	410.5	
$254(\Delta t)$	$254(1)$ $= 254$	$254\left(\frac{1}{2}\right)$ $= 127$	$254(0.1)$ $= 25.4$

Have students verify that the difference between the overestimate and the underestimate is $254(\Delta t)$.

ADDITIONAL EXAMPLES

Example 2

How frequently must the velocity be measured to ensure that the estimated distances traveled by the toy car in Additional Example 1 are within 2 cm of each other?

The difference between the velocity at the beginning and the end of the measurements is $101 - 45 = 56$ cm. Let the time between successive measurements be Δt. Then the distance between successive measurements is $56\Delta t$. For the difference of the estimates to be within 2 cm, $56\Delta t < 2$, or $\Delta t < 0.0357142857$ seconds.

Teaching Notes

Each summation expression near the bottom of the page (labeled *overestimate* and *underestimate*) has n terms. The total distance traveled is calculated using the expression for the overestimate. Make sure students understand that total distance traveled can also be calculated using the expression for the underestimate. Make the point that these two expressions have the same limit, which is the exact area under the curve.

Example 2 **Accuracy of Estimates**

How frequently must the velocity be measured to ensure that the estimated distances traveled by the race car are within 5 feet of each other?

Solution

The difference between the velocity at the beginning and end of the measurements is $268 - 14 = 254$. If the time between each measurement is Δt, then the difference between the estimates is $254(\Delta t)$. For the differences of the estimates to be within 5 feet,

$$254(\Delta t) < 5 \qquad \text{or} \qquad \Delta t < 0.0196850394 \text{ seconds.} \qquad \blacksquare$$

As the length of the intervals of measurement become smaller and smaller, the underestimate and overestimate approach the same number—the area under the curve—which represents the total distance traveled.

Riemann Sums

Suppose that velocity is given as an increasing function of time: $v = f(t)$. To find the total distance traveled by a moving object over the time interval $a < t < b$, divide the interval into n equally spaced times $t_0 = a, t_1, \ldots, t_n = b$, where each time interval is $\Delta t = \dfrac{b - a}{n}$ in duration.

The velocity at the beginning or end of each time interval is given by $f(t_i)$, so the estimated distance traveled during each interval is velocity times the length of each time interval.

$$f(t_i)\Delta t \qquad \text{\small\textit{distance at each} } \Delta t$$

Both the underestimate and the overestimate of the total distance traveled can be written as the sum of the individual distances. The underestimate sum begins with $f(t_0)\Delta t$ and the overestimate sum begins with $f(t_1)\Delta t$.

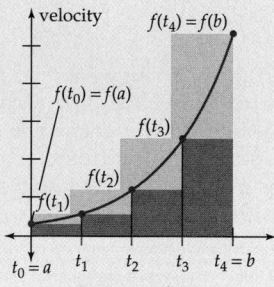

velocity

$f(t_4) = f(b)$

$f(t_0) = f(a)$

$f(t_3)$

$f(t_2)$

$f(t_1)$

$t_0 = a \quad t_1 \quad t_2 \quad t_3 \quad t_4 = b$

Figure 14.C-3

$$f(t_1)\Delta t + f(t_2)\Delta t + \cdots f(t_n)\Delta t = \sum_{i=1}^{n} f(t_i)\Delta t \qquad \text{\small\textit{overestimate}}$$

$$f(t_0)\Delta t + f(t_1)\Delta t + \cdots f(t_{n-1})\Delta t = \sum_{i=0}^{n-1} f(t_i)\Delta t \qquad \text{\small\textit{underestimate}}$$

$$\text{Total distance traveled} = \lim_{n \to \infty} f(t_1)\Delta t + f(t_2)\Delta t + \cdots + f(t_n)\Delta t$$

$$= \lim_{n \to \infty} \sum_{i=1}^{n} f(t_i)\Delta t$$

As Examples 1 and 2 show, these estimates will be very close to each other when n is very large and the correspoding Δt is very small. In fact, the actual total distance can be found by taking the limit of one of these sums as n gets very large without bound, written $n \to \infty$.

966

This limit can be interpreted geometrically as the area between the graph of f and the horizontal axis from $t = a$ to $t = b$. The sum $\sum_{i=1}^{n} f(t_i)\Delta t$ is called a **Riemann sum.** The limit of the Riemann sums

$$\lim_{n\to\infty} \sum_{i=1}^{n} f(t_i)\Delta t$$

is called the **definite integral** of f from a to b and is denoted by

$$\int_a^b f(t)dt.$$

Definite integrals are studied fully in calculus. They have a wide variety of other applications, including determining the lengths of curves and the volumes of irregularly shaped solids, finding the amount of work done by a force, and making sophisticated probability calculations.

Exercises

1. A driver slams on the brakes and comes to a stop in five seconds. The following velocities are recorded after the brakes are applied.

Time (sec)	0	1	2	3	4	5
Velocity (ft/sec)	102	70	46	29	12	0

a. Find an upper and lower estimate of the distance traveled by the car after the brakes were applied.
b. Sketch the graph of velocity versus time, and show the upper and lower estimates and the difference between them.
c. How often would the velocity need to be measured to assure that the estimates differ by less than 5 feet? by less than 1 foot?

2. Use the grid to estimate the area of the region bounded by the curve, the horizontal axis, and the lines $x = \pm 4$. Get an upper and a lower estimate that are within 4 square units of one another. Explain your procedure.

3. a. For the diagram below, estimate the shaded area with an error of at most 0.1.
b. How can the shaded area be approximated to any desired degree of accuracy?

4. Estimate the total distance an object travels between $t = 0$ and $t = 10$ if the graph below represents the velocity v of the object in ft/sec.

5. Suppose the velocity of an object is given by $v(t) = \cos t$ for $0 \le t \le 1.5$. Estimate the distance traveled during the 1.5-second interval, accurate to one decimal place.

6. A snail is crawling at a velocity given by $v(t) = \dfrac{1}{t}$, where $1 \le t \le 2$ hours and v is in feet per hour. Estimate the distance that the snail crawls during the second hour.

967

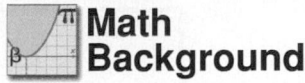
Math Background

A careful reading of the statements at the left suggests that there is more than one Riemann Sum for a particular function. This is in fact the case. The discussion in this section makes use of underestimates and overestimates, sometimes called lower sums and upper sums. A Riemann Sum is a sum of products of function values $f(t_i)$ and interval lengths Δt. In a Riemann Sum, each $f(t_i)$ can be *any* function value in the Δt-interval, and the Δt-intervals need not all be equal, as they are in this section.

Exercises

ANSWERS

1. a. upper estimate: 259 ft
lower estimate: 157 ft

b. 110

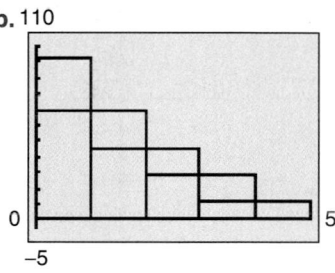

c. less than 5 ft:
$\Delta t < 0.04902$ sec
less than 1 ft:
$\Delta t < 0.0098$ sec

2. lower estimate: 21
upper estimate: 25
For the lower estimate, count all of the complete squares beneath the curve. For the upper estimate, count all of the complete squares below the curve and estimate the number of partial squares below the curve.

3. a. 1.798

b. The degree of accuracy can be increased by lowering the Δt.

4. between 15 and 17 ft

5. 1.0

6. between 0.67 and 0.72 ft

APPENDIX

ALGEBRA REVIEW

This appendix reviews the fundamental algebraic facts that are used frequently in this book. You must be able to handle these algebraic manipulations in order to succeed in this course and in calculus.

A.1 Integral Exponents

Exponents provide a convenient shorthand for certain products. If c is a real number, then c^2 denotes cc and c^3 denotes ccc. More generally, for any positive integer n

$$c^n \text{ denotes the product } ccc \cdots c \quad (n \text{ factors}).$$

In this notation c^1 is just c, so we usually omit the exponent 1.

Example 1

$3^4 = 3 \cdot 3 \cdot 3 \cdot 3 = 81$ and

$$(-2)^5 = (-2)(-2)(-2)(-2)(-2) = -32.$$

For every positive integer n, $0^n = 0 \cdots 0 = 0$. ∎

Example 2

To find $(2.4)^9$ use the $\wedge$ (or a^b or x^y) key on your calculator:*

$$2.4 \wedge 9 \text{ ENTER*}$$

which produces the (approximate) answer 2641.80754. ∎

Because exponents are just shorthand for multiplication, it is easy to determine the rules they obey. For instance,

$$c^3 c^5 = (ccc)(ccccc) = c^8, \quad \text{that is,} \quad c^3 c^5 = c^{3+5}.$$

$$\frac{c^7}{c^4} = \frac{ccccccc}{cccc} = \frac{\cancel{cccc}ccc}{\cancel{cccc}} = ccc = c^3, \quad \text{that is,} \quad \frac{c^7}{c^4} = c^{7-4}.$$

*The ENTER key is labeled EXE on Casio calculators.

Section A.1 Integral Exponents

Teaching Notes

A positive integer exponent tells how many times a number, the base, is used as a factor.

Example Notes

In **Example 1**, emphasize the need for parentheses in the expression $(-2)^5$. See **CAUTION** on page 972 for more explanation.

In **Example 2**, note that there are 9 decimal places in the exact value of $(2.4)^9$, 2641.807540224. Calculators display a limited number of digits based on screen size, settings, and memory.

ADDITIONAL EXAMPLES

Example 1

Evaluate 4^3 and $(-5)^3$.   64; −125

Example 2

Use a calculator to find $(3.6)^8$.
$\approx 28{,}211.09907$

Teaching Notes

Review meanings of *base*, *power*, and *exponent*. For 2^3, 2 is the base, 3 is the exponent, and 2^3, or 8, is the power. Illustrate several of the **Exponent Laws** as shown below.

1. $c^m \cdot c^n = c^{m+n}$

   $2^3 \cdot 2^2 = 8 \cdot 4 = 32 = 2^5 = 2^{3+2}$

2. $\dfrac{c^m}{c^n} = c^{m-n}$

   $\dfrac{2^5}{2^4} = \dfrac{32}{16} = 2 = 2^1 = 2^{5-4}$

5. $\left(\dfrac{c}{d}\right)^n = \dfrac{c^n}{d^n}$

   $\left(\dfrac{6}{2}\right)^2 = (3)^2 = 9$

   $\dfrac{6^2}{2^2} = \dfrac{36}{4} = 9$

Suggest that students illustrate other Exponent Laws in a similar way.

Have students attempt to find 0^0 and 0^{-2} on their calculators. Remind them that c^0 and c^{-2} are not defined if $c = 0$.

Emphasize to students that if n is a positive integer, $-n$ is a negative integer and c^{-n} is a base to a negative power.

For the **Exponent Laws,** c and d must be nonzero so that undefined expressions such as 0^0 are avoided.

Example Notes

In **Example 3,** point out that we may write 2^5 as 32 because it is easy to evaluate.

In **Example 7,** challenge students to simplify the expression by converting to positive exponents first.

Similar arguments work in the general case:

To multiply c^m by c^n, add the exponents: $c^m c^n = c^{m+n}$.

To divide c^m by c^n, subtract the exponents: $\dfrac{c^m}{c^n} = c^{m-n}$.

Example 3

$4^2 \cdot 4^7 = 4^{2+7} = 4^9$ and $\dfrac{2^8}{2^3} = 2^{8-3} = 2^5$. ∎

The notation c^n can be extended to the cases when n is zero or negative as follows:

If $c \neq 0$, then c^0 is defined to be the number 1.

If $c \neq 0$ and n is a positive integer, then

$$c^{-n} \text{ is defined to be the number } \dfrac{1}{c^n}.$$

Note that 0^0 and negative powers of 0 are *not* defined (negative powers of 0 would involve division by 0). The reason for choosing these definitions of c^{-n} for nonzero c is that the multiplication and division rules for exponents remain valid. For instance,

$$c^5 \cdot c^0 = c^5 \cdot 1 = c^5, \qquad \text{so that} \qquad c^5 c^0 = c^{5+0}.$$

$$c^7 c^{-7} = c^7\left(\dfrac{1}{c^7}\right) = 1 = c^0, \qquad \text{so that} \qquad c^7 c^{-7} = c^{7-7}.$$

Example 4

$6^{-3} = \dfrac{1}{6^3} = \dfrac{1}{216}$ and $(-2)^{-5} = \dfrac{1}{(-2)^5} = -\dfrac{1}{32}$. A calculator shows that $(0.287)^{-12} \approx 3{,}201{,}969.857.^*$ ∎

If c and d are nonzero real numbers and m and n are integers (positive, negative, or zero), then we have these

Exponent Laws

1. $c^m c^n = c^{m+n}$

2. $\dfrac{c^m}{c^n} = c^{m-n}$

3. $(c^m)^n = c^{mn}$

4. $(cd)^n = c^n d^n$

5. $\left(\dfrac{c}{d}\right)^n = \dfrac{c^n}{d^n}$

6. $c^{-n} = \dfrac{1}{c^n}$

$^* \approx$ means "approximately equal to."

Example 5

Here are examples of each of the six exponent laws.

1. $\pi^{-5}\pi^2 = \pi^{-5+2} = \pi^{-3} = \dfrac{1}{\pi^3}.$

4. $(2x)^5 = 2^5x^5 = 32x^5.$

2. $\dfrac{x^9}{x^4} = x^{9-4} = x^5.$

5. $\left(\dfrac{7}{3}\right)^{10} = \dfrac{7^{10}}{3^{10}}.$

3. $(5^{-3})^2 = 5^{(-3)2} = 5^{-6}.$

6. $\dfrac{1}{x^{-5}} = \dfrac{1}{\left(\frac{1}{x^5}\right)} = x^5.$

The exponent laws can often be used to simplify complicated expressions.

Example 6

a. $(2x^2y^3z)^4 = 2^4(x^2)^4(y^3)^4z^4 = 16x^8y^{12}z^4.$

$\quad\quad\quad\quad\quad\uparrow\quad\quad\quad\quad\quad\uparrow$

$\quad\quad\quad Law\ (4)\quad\quad\quad Law\ (3)$

b. $(r^{-3}s^2)^{-2} = (r^{-3})^{-2}(s^2)^{-2} = r^6s^{-4} = \dfrac{r^6}{s^4}.$

$\quad\quad\quad\quad\uparrow\quad\quad\quad\quad\uparrow$

$\quad\quad\quad Law\ (4)\quad\quad Law\ (3)$

c. $\dfrac{x^5(y^2)^3}{(x^2y)^2} = \dfrac{x^5y^6}{(x^2y)^2} = \dfrac{x^5y^6}{(x^2)^2y^2} = \dfrac{x^5y^6}{x^4y^2} = x^{5-4}y^{6-2} = xy^4.$

$\quad\quad\uparrow\quad\quad\quad\uparrow\quad\quad\quad\uparrow\quad\quad\uparrow$

$\quad Law\ (3)\quad Law\ (4)\quad Law\ (3)\ Law\ (2)$

It is usually more efficient to use the exponent laws with the negative exponents rather than first converting to positive exponents. If positive exponents are required, the conversion can be made in the last step.

Example 7

Simplify and express without negative exponents

$$\dfrac{a^{-2}(b^2c^3)^{-2}}{(a^{-3}b^{-5})^2c}.$$

Solution

$$\dfrac{a^{-2}(b^2c^3)^{-2}}{(a^{-3}b^{-5})^2c} = \dfrac{a^{-2}(b^2)^{-2}(c^3)^{-2}}{(a^{-3})^2(b^{-5})^2c} = \dfrac{a^{-2}b^{-4}c^{-6}}{a^{-6}b^{-10}c}$$

$$\quad\quad\quad\quad\quad\quad\uparrow\quad\quad\quad\quad\quad\quad\uparrow$$

$$\quad\quad\quad\quad\quad Law\ (4)\quad\quad\quad\quad Law\ (3)$$

$$= a^{-2-(-6)}b^{-4-(-10)}c^{-6-1} = a^4b^6c^{-7} = \dfrac{a^4b^6}{c^7}.$$

$$\uparrow$$

$$Law\ (2)$$

ADDITIONAL EXAMPLES

Example 3

Simplify $3^4 \cdot 3^5$ and $\dfrac{4^8}{4^6}$. 3^9; 4^2 or 16

Example 4

Simplify 7^{-2} and $(-3)^{-4}$. Use a calculator to approximate $(1.745)^{-7}$.

$\dfrac{1}{49}$; $\dfrac{1}{81}$; 0.020297006

Example 5

Apply the Exponent Laws to rewrite the expressions.

1. $e^6 \cdot e^{-9}$ e^{-3} or $\dfrac{1}{e^3}$

2. $\dfrac{t^6}{t^2}$ t^4

3. $(6^3)^{-5}$ 6^{-15}

4. $(7a)^3$ $343a^3$

5. $\left(\dfrac{4}{5}\right)^9$ $\dfrac{4^9}{5^9}$

6. $\dfrac{1}{c^{-4}}$ c^4

Example 6

Simplify.

a. $(3a^4bc^5)^3$ $27a^{12}b^3c^{15}$

b. $(m^4n^{-3})^{-5}$ $\dfrac{n^{15}}{m^{20}}$

c. $\dfrac{(r^2)^3s^5}{(r^3s^2)^2}$ s

Example 7

Simplify and express without negative exponents.

$\dfrac{(x^{-3}y^2)^{-2}z^{-3}}{x^5(y^2z^{-2})^{-5}}$ $\dfrac{xy^6}{z^{13}}$

Teaching Notes

In general, a negative number raised to an odd power is negative and a negative number raised to an even power is positive.

Remind students that if c is positive, $-c$ is negative.

COMMON ERROR ALERT

Students often make sign errors when simplifying expressions with exponents. Show the following examples to further illustrate the **CAUTION** note:

$$-2^4 = -(2 \cdot 2 \cdot 2 \cdot 2) = -16$$

$$(-2)^4 = (-2)(-2)(-2)(-2) = 16$$

$$-2^5 = -(2 \cdot 2 \cdot 2 \cdot 2 \cdot 2) = -32$$

$$(-2)^5 = (-2)(-2)(-2)(-2)(-2)$$

$$= -32$$

Note that $-2^4 \neq (-2)^4$. Note also that although $-2^5 = (-2)^5$, they do *not* represent the same expression.

ADDITIONAL EXAMPLES

Example 8

Simplify $(-2)^6$ and $(-4)^5$ **64; −1024**

Exercises A.1

ANSWERS

Since $(-1)(-1) = +1$, any even power of -1, such as $(-1)^4$ or $(-1)^{12}$, will be equal to 1. Every odd power of -1 is equal to -1; for instance $(-1)^5 = (-1)^4(-1) = 1(-1) = -1$. Consequently, for every positive number c

$$(-c)^n = [(-1)c]^n = (-1)^n c^n = \begin{cases} c^n & \text{if } n \text{ is even} \\ -c^n & \text{if } n \text{ is odd} \end{cases}.$$

Example 8

$(-3)^4 = 3^4 = 81$ and $(-5)^3 = -5^3 = -125$.

CAUTION

Be careful with negative bases. For instance, if you want to compute $(-12)^4$, which is a positive number, but you key in $(-)\ 12\ \wedge\ 4$ ENTER the calculator will interpret this as $-(12^4)$ and produce a negative answer. To get the correct answer, you must key in the parentheses:

$$(\ (-)\ 12\ )\ \wedge\ 4\ \text{ENTER}.$$

Exercises A.1

In Exercises 1–18, evaluate the expression.

1. $(-6)^2$ **36**

2. -6^2 **−36**

3. $5 + 4(3^2 + 2^3)$ **73**

4. $(-3)2^2 + 4^2 - 1$ **3**

5. $\dfrac{(-3)^2 + (-2)^4}{-2^2 - 1}$ **−5**

6. $\dfrac{(-4)^2 + 2}{(-4)^2 - 7} + 1$ **3**

7. $\left(\dfrac{-5}{4}\right)^3$ **$-\dfrac{125}{64}$**

8. $-\left(\dfrac{7}{4} + \dfrac{3}{4}\right)^2$ **$-\dfrac{25}{4}$**

9. $\left(\dfrac{1}{3}\right)^3 + \left(\dfrac{2}{3}\right)^3$ **$\dfrac{1}{3}$**

10. $\left(\dfrac{5}{7}\right)^2 + \left(\dfrac{2}{7}\right)^2$ **$\dfrac{29}{49}$**

11. $2^4 - 2^7$ **−112**

12. $3^3 - 3^{-7}$ **$26\dfrac{2186}{2187}$**

13. $(2^{-2} + 2)^2$ **$\dfrac{81}{16}$**

14. $(3^{-1} - 3^3)^2$ **$\dfrac{6400}{9}$**

15. $2^2 \cdot 3^{-3} - 3^2 \cdot 2^{-3}$ **$\dfrac{211}{216}$**

16. $4^3 \cdot 5^{-2} + 4^2 \cdot 5^{-1}$ **$\dfrac{144}{25}$**

17. $\dfrac{1}{2^3} + \dfrac{1}{2^{-4}}$ **$\dfrac{129}{8}$**

18. $3^2\left(\dfrac{1}{3} + \dfrac{1}{3^{-2}}\right)$ **84**

In Exercises 19–38, simplify the expression. Each letter represents a nonzero real number and should appear at most once in your answer.

19. $x^2 \cdot x^3 \cdot x^5$ **x^{10}**

20. $y \cdot y^4 \cdot y^6$ **y^{11}**

21. $(0.03)y^2 \cdot y^7$ **$0.03y^9$**

22. $(1.3)z^3 \cdot z^5$ **$1.3z^8$**

23. $(2x^2)^3 3x$ **$24x^7$**

24. $(3y^3)^4 5y^2$ **$405y^{14}$**

25. $(3x^2y)^2$ **$9x^4y^2$**

26. $(2xy^3)^3$ **$8x^3y^9$**

27. $(a^2)(7a)(-3a^3)$ **$-21a^6$**

28. $(b^3)(-b^2)(3b)$ **$-3b^6$**

29. $(2w)^3(3w)(4w)^2$ **$384w^6$**

30. $(3d)^4(2d)^2(5d)$ **$1620d^7$**

31. $a^{-2}b^3a^3$ **ab^3**

32. $c^4d^5c^{-3}$ **cd^5**

33. $(2x)^{-2}(2y)^3(4x)$ **$8x^{-1}y^3$**

34. $(3x)^{-3}(2y)^{-2}(2x)$ **$\dfrac{1}{54x^2y^2}$**

35. $(-3a^4)^2(9x^3)^{-1}$ **a^8x^{-3}**

36. $(2y^3)^3(3y^2)^{-2}$ **$\dfrac{8y^5}{9}$**

37. $(2x^2y)^0(3xy)$ **$3xy$**

38. $(3x^2y^4)^0$ **1**

In Exercises 39–42, express the given number as a power of 2.

39. $(64)^2$ **2^{12}**

40. $\left(\dfrac{1}{8}\right)^3$ **2^{-9}**

41. $(2^4 \cdot 16^{-2})^3$ **2^{-12}**

42. $\left(\dfrac{1}{2}\right)^{-8}\left(\dfrac{1}{4}\right)^4\left(\dfrac{1}{16}\right)^{-3}$ **2^{12}**

In Exercises 43–60, simplify and write the given expression without negative exponents. All letters represent nonzero real numbers.

43. $\dfrac{x^4(x^2)^3}{x^3}$ $\boldsymbol{x^7}$

44. $\left(\dfrac{z^2}{t^3}\right)^4 \cdot \left(\dfrac{z^3}{t}\right)^5$ $\dfrac{\boldsymbol{z^{23}}}{\boldsymbol{t^{17}}}$

45. $\left(\dfrac{e^6}{c^4}\right)^2 \cdot \left(\dfrac{c^3}{e}\right)^3$ $\boldsymbol{ce^9}$

46. $\left(\dfrac{x^7}{y^6}\right)^2 \cdot \left(\dfrac{y^2}{x}\right)^4$ $\dfrac{\boldsymbol{x^{10}}}{\boldsymbol{y^4}}$

47. $\left(\dfrac{ab^2c^3d^4}{abc^2d}\right)^2$ $\boldsymbol{b^2c^2d^6}$

48. $\dfrac{(3x)^2(y^2)^3x^2}{(2xy^2)^3}$ $\dfrac{\boldsymbol{9x}}{\boldsymbol{8}}$

49. $\left(\dfrac{a^6}{b^{-4}}\right)^2$ $\boldsymbol{a^{12}b^8}$

50. $\left(\dfrac{x^{-2}}{y^{-2}}\right)^2$ $\dfrac{\boldsymbol{y^4}}{\boldsymbol{x^4}}$

51. $\left(\dfrac{c^5}{d^{-3}}\right)^{-2}$ $\dfrac{\boldsymbol{1}}{\boldsymbol{c^{10}d^6}}$

52. $\left(\dfrac{x^{-1}}{2y^{-1}}\right)\left(\dfrac{2y}{x}\right)^{-2}$ $\dfrac{\boldsymbol{x}}{\boldsymbol{8y}}$

53. $\left(\dfrac{3x}{y^2}\right)^{-3}\left(\dfrac{-x}{2y^3}\right)^2$ $\dfrac{\boldsymbol{1}}{\boldsymbol{108x}}$

54. $\left(\dfrac{5u^2v}{2uv^2}\right)^2\left(\dfrac{-3uv}{2u^2v}\right)^{-3}$ $-\dfrac{\boldsymbol{50u^5}}{\boldsymbol{27v^2}}$

55. $\dfrac{(a^{-3}b^2c)^{-2}}{(ab^{-2}c^3)^{-1}}$ $\dfrac{\boldsymbol{a^7c}}{\boldsymbol{b^6}}$

56. $\dfrac{(-2cd^2e^{-1})^3}{(5c^{-3}de)^{-2}}$ $-\dfrac{\boldsymbol{200d^8}}{\boldsymbol{c^3e}}$

57. $(c^{-1}d^{-2})^{-3}$ $\boldsymbol{c^3d^6}$

58. $[(x^2y^{-1})^2]^{-3}$ $\dfrac{\boldsymbol{y^6}}{\boldsymbol{x^{12}}}$

59. $a^2(a^{-1} + a^{-3})$ $\boldsymbol{a} + \dfrac{\boldsymbol{1}}{\boldsymbol{a}}$

60. $\dfrac{a^{-2}}{b^{-2}} + \dfrac{b^2}{a^2}$ $\dfrac{\boldsymbol{2b^2}}{\boldsymbol{a^2}}$

In Exercises 61–66, determine the sign of the given number without calculating the product.

61. $(-2.6)^3(-4.3)^{-2}$
negative

62. $(4.1)^{-2}(2.5)^{-3}$
positive

63. $(-1)^9(6.7)^5$
negative

64. $(-4)^{12}6^9$
positive

65. $(-3.1)^{-3}(4.6)^{-6}(7.2)^7$
negative

66. $(45.8)^{-7}(-7.9)^{-9}(-8.5)^{-4}$
negative

In Exercises 67–72, r, s, and t are positive integers and a, b, and c are nonzero real numbers. Simplify and write the given expression without negative exponents.

67. $\dfrac{3^{-r}}{3^{-s-r}}$ $\boldsymbol{3^s}$

68. $\dfrac{4^{-(t+1)}}{4^{2-t}}$ $\dfrac{\boldsymbol{1}}{\boldsymbol{64}}$

69. $\left(\dfrac{a^6}{b^{-4}}\right)^t$ $\boldsymbol{a^{6t}b^{4t}}$

70. $\dfrac{c^{-t}}{(6b)^{-s}}$ $\dfrac{\boldsymbol{6^sb^s}}{\boldsymbol{c^t}}$

71. $\dfrac{(c^{-r}b^s)^t}{(c^tb^{-s})^r}$ $\dfrac{\boldsymbol{b^{rs+st}}}{\boldsymbol{c^{2rt}}}$

72. $\dfrac{(a^rb^{-s})^{-t}}{(b^tc^r)^{-s}}$ $\dfrac{\boldsymbol{b^{2st}c^{rs}}}{\boldsymbol{a^{rt}}}$

In Exercises 73–80, give an example to show that the statement may be false for some numbers.

73. $a^r + b^r = (a + b)^r$

74. $a^ra^s = a^{rs}$

75. $a^rb^s = (ab)^{r+s}$

76. $c^{-r} = -c^r$

77. $\dfrac{c^r}{c^s} = c^{\frac{r}{s}}$

78. $(a + 1)(b + 1) = ab + 1$

79. $(-a)^2 = -a^2$

80. $(-a)(-b) = -ab$

73. possible answer:
$3^2 + 4^2 = 9 + 16 = 25$,
but $(3 + 4)^2 = 7^2 = 49$

74. possible answer:
$2^3 \cdot 2^2 = 32$;
but $2^{3 \cdot 2} = 64$

75. possible answer:
$3^2 \cdot 2^3 = 9 \cdot 8 = 72$;
but $(3 \cdot 2)^{2+3} = 6^5 = 7776$

76. possible answer:
$1^{-1} = 1$;
but $-1^1 = -1$

77. possible answer:
$\dfrac{2^6}{2^3} = \dfrac{64}{8} = 8$,
but $2^{\frac{6}{3}} = 2^2 = 4$

78. possible answer:
$(1 + 1)(2 + 1) = 6$;
but $1 \cdot 2 + 1 = 3$

79. possible answer:
$(-3)^2 = (-3)(-3) = 9$,
but $-3^2 = -9$

80. possible answer:
$(-1)(-1) = 1$;
but $-(1)(1) = -1$

A.2 Arithmetic of Algebraic Expressions

Expressions such as

$$b + 3c^2, \qquad 3x^2 - 5x + 4, \qquad \sqrt{x^3 + z}, \qquad \dfrac{x^3 + 4xy - \pi}{x^2 + xy}$$

are called **algebraic expressions.** Each expression represents a number that is obtained by performing various algebraic operations (such as addition or taking roots) on one or more numbers, some of which may be denoted by letters.

A letter that denotes a particular real number is called a **constant;** its value remains unchanged throughout the discussion. For example, the Greek letter π has long been used to denote the number $3.14159 \cdots$. Sometimes a constant is a fixed but unspecified real number, as in "an angle of k degrees" or "a triangle with base of length b."

A letter that can represent *any* real number is called a **variable.** In the expression $2x + 5$, for example, the variable x can be any real

Section A.2 **Arithmetic of Algebraic Expressions** **973**

Section

A.2 Arithmetic of Algebraic Expressions

Teaching Notes

Remind students that not every letter is an appropriate choice for use as a variable. For example, e represents the number whose natural logarithm is 1 (Section 5.2, page 341) and the letter i represents $\sqrt{-1}$ (Section 4.5, page 294). These letters are typically not used as variables unless context makes the meaning of the variable clear (for example, when e is used to denote eccentricity—Chapter 11).

Teaching Notes

Remind students that like terms are terms that are *identical except for their coefficients*.

In **Example 1,** some students may have difficulty seeing how the distributive law is applied. They may only associate the distributive law with rewriting the expression $a(b + c)$ as $ab + ac$. Remind them that the law also works "in reverse," that is, it can be used to write an expression of the form $ab + ac$ as $a(b + c)$.

Students are more familiar with seeing the **left** distributive law, i.e., $a(b + c) = ab + ac$ than they are the **right** distributive law, $(b + c)a = ba + ca$. In **Example 3,** point out that the distributive law can also be applied "from the right" as shown below, yielding the same answer. Note, however, that this requires additional applications of the distributive property.

$$(y - 2)(3y^2 - 7y + 4)$$
$$= (y - 2)(3y^2) - (y - 2)(7y) + (y - 2)(4)$$
$$= 3y^3 \underbrace{- 6y^2 - 7y^2} + \underbrace{14y + 4y} - 8$$
$$= 3y^3 - \quad 13y^2 \quad + \quad 18y \quad - 8$$

Emphasize that the distributive law may be applied in either direction, yielding the same results, by having students multiply $(4x^2 + 2x - 3)(3x + 2)$ by using the left and right distributive laws.

left:
$$(4x^2 + 2x - 3)(3x + 2)$$
$$= 4x^2(3x + 2) + 2x(3x + 2) - 3(3x + 2)$$
$$= 12x^3 + \underbrace{8x^2 + 6x^2} + \underbrace{4x - 9x} - 6$$
$$= 12x^3 + \quad 14x^2 \quad - \quad 5x \quad - 6$$

right:
$$(4x^2 + 2x - 3)(3x + 2)$$
$$= (4x^2 + 2x - 3)3x + (4x^2 + 2x - 3)2$$
$$= 12x^3 + 6x^2 - 9x + 8x^2 + 4x - 6$$
$$= 12x^3 + \underbrace{6x^2 + 8x^2} \underbrace{- 9x + 4x} - 6$$
$$= 12x^3 + \quad 14x^2 \quad - \quad 5x \quad - 6$$

number. If $x = 3$, then $2x + 5 = 2 \cdot 3 + 5 = 11$. If $x = \frac{1}{2}$, then $2x + 5 = 2 \cdot \frac{1}{2} + 5 = 6$, and so on.*

Constants are usually denoted by letters near the beginning of the alphabet and variables by letters near the end of the alphabet. Consequently, in expressions such as $cx + d$ and $cy^2 + dy$, it is understood that c and d are constants and x and y are variables.

The usual rules of arithmetic are valid for algebraic expressions:

Commutative Laws:
$$a + b = b + a \quad \text{and} \quad ab = ba$$

Associative Laws:
$$(a + b) + c = a + (b + c) \quad \text{and} \quad (ab)c = a(bc)$$

Distributive Laws:
$$a(b + c) = ab + ac \quad \text{and} \quad (b + c)a = ba + ca.$$

Example 1

Use the distributive law to *combine like terms;* for instance,
$$3x + 5x + 4x = (3 + 5 + 4)x = 12x.$$

In practice, you do the middle part in your head and simply write $3x + 5x + 4x = 12x$. ∎

Example 2

In more complicated expressions, eliminate parentheses, use the commutative law to group like terms together, and then combine them.
$$\left(a^2b - 3\sqrt{c}\right) + \left(5ab + 7\sqrt{c}\right) + 7a^2b = a^2b - 3\sqrt{c} + 5ab + 7\sqrt{c} + 7a^2b$$

Regroup: $\quad = \underbrace{a^2b + 7a^2b} \; \underbrace{- 3\sqrt{c} + 7\sqrt{c}} + 5ab$

Combine like terms: $\quad = \quad 8a^2b \quad + \quad 4\sqrt{c} \quad + 5ab.$ ∎

CAUTION

Be careful when parentheses are preceded by a minus sign: $-(b + 3) = -b - 3$ and not $-b + 3$. Here's the reason: $-(b + 3)$ means $(-1)(b + 3)$, so that by the distributive law,
$$-(b + 3) = (-1)(b + 3) = (-1)b + (-1)3 = -b - 3.$$
Similarly, $-(7 - y) = -7 - (-y) = -7 + y$.

*We assume any conditions on the constants and variables necessary to guarantee that an algebraic expression does represent a real number. For instance, in $\sqrt{z}$ we assume $z \geq 0$ and in $\frac{1}{c}$ we assume $c \neq 0$.

The examples in the Caution Box illustrate the following.

Rules for Eliminating Parentheses

Parentheses preceded by a plus sign (or no sign) may be deleted.

Parentheses preceded by a minus sign may be deleted *if the sign of every term within the parentheses is changed.*

The usual method of multiplying algebraic expressions is to use the distributive laws repeatedly, as shown in the following examples. The net result is to *multiply every term in the first sum by every term in the second sum.*

Example 3

To compute $(y - 2)(3y^2 - 7y + 4)$, we first apply the distributive law, treating $(3y^2 - 7y + 4)$ as a single number:

$$(y - 2)(3y^2 - 7y + 4) = y(3y^2 - 7y + 4) - 2(3y^2 - 7y + 4)$$

Distributive law: $= 3y^3 - 7y^2 + 4y - 6y^2 + 14y - 8$

Regroup: $= 3y^3 - 7y^2 - 6y^2 + 4y + 14y - 8$

Combine like terms: $= 3y^3 - 13y^2 + 18y - 8.$

Example 4

We follow the same procedure with $(2x - 5y)(3x + 4y)$:

$$(2x - 5y)(3x + 4y) = 2x(3x + 4y) - 5y(3x + 4y)$$
$$= 2x \cdot 3x + 2x \cdot 4y + (-5y) \cdot 3x + (-5y) \cdot 4y$$
$$= 6x^2 + 8xy - 15xy - 20y^2$$
$$= 6x^2 - 7xy - 20y^2.$$

Observe the pattern in the second line of Example 4 and its relationship to the terms being multiplied:

$$(2x - 5y)(3x + 4y) = 2x \cdot 3x + 2x \cdot 4y + (-5y) \cdot 3x + (-5y) \cdot 4y$$

$(2x - 5y)(3x + 4y)$ First terms

$(2x - 5y)(3x + 4y)$ Outside terms

$(2x - 5y)(3x + 4y)$ Inside terms

$(2x - 5y)(3x + 4y)$ Last terms

Teaching Notes

Have students simplify the following expression by combining like terms to further illustrate the concepts presented in the **CAUTION** and **Rules for Eliminating Parentheses** boxes.

$(3x + 4y) - (2x + 6) - (10y - 4) + (4x + y)$

$= 3x + 4y - 2x - 6 - 10y + 4 + 4x + y$

$= 3x - 2x + 4x + 4y - 10y + y - 6 + 4$

$= 5x - 5y - 2$

ADDITIONAL EXAMPLES

Example 1

Use the distributive law to *combine like terms*:

$5x - 6x + 8x$
$= (5 - 6 + 8)x$
$= 7x$

Example 2

Combine like terms.

$10y + (4xy^2 - 2x) + (3y - xy^2) + 4x$

$= 10y + 4xy^2 - 2x + 3y - xy^2 + 4x$

$= 10y + 3y + 4xy^2 - xy^2 - 2x + 4x$

$= 13y + 3xy^2 + 2x$

Example 3

Multiply: $(x - 4)(2x^2 + 3x - 5)$

$= x(2x^2 + 3x - 5) - 4(2x^2 + 3x - 5)$
$= 2x^3 + 3x^2 - 5x - 8x^2 - 12x + 20$
$= 2x^3 + 3x^2 - 8x^2 - 5x - 12x + 20$
$= 2x^3 - 5x^2 - 17x + 20$

Example 4

Multiply: $(3x + 2y)(4x - 7y)$

$= 3x(4x - 7y) + 2y(4x - 7y)$
$= 3x \cdot 4x + 3x \cdot (-7y) + 2y \cdot 4x + 2y \cdot (-7y)$
$= 12x^2 - 21xy + 8xy - 14y^2$
$= 12x^2 - 13xy - 14y^2$

ADDITIONAL EXAMPLES

Example 5

Multiply: $(4x - 2)(3x + 5)$

$$= 12x^2 + 20x - 6x - 10$$
$$\uparrow \qquad \uparrow \qquad \uparrow \qquad \uparrow$$
$$F \qquad O \qquad I \qquad L$$
$$= 12x^2 + 14x - 10$$

Exercises A.2

ANSWERS

CAUTION

The FOIL method can be used only when multiplying two expressions that each have two terms.

This pattern is easy to remember by using the acronym FOIL (First, Outside, Inside, Last). The FOIL method makes it easy to find products such as this one mentally, without the necessity of writing out the intermediate steps.

Example 5

$$(3x + 2)(x + 5) = 3x^2 + 15x + 2x + 10 = 3x^2 + 17x + 10.$$
$$\uparrow \qquad \uparrow \qquad \uparrow \qquad \uparrow$$
$$\text{First Outside Inside Last}$$

Exercises A.2

In Exercises 1–54, perform the indicated operations and simplify your answer.

1. $x + 7x$ $\mathbf{8x}$

2. $5w + 7w - 3w$ $\mathbf{9w}$

3. $6a^2b + (-8b)a^2$ $\mathbf{-2a^2b}$

4. $-6x^3\sqrt{t} + 7x^3\sqrt{t} + 15x^3\sqrt{t}$ $\mathbf{16x^3\sqrt{t}}$

5. $(x^2 + 2x + 1) - (x^3 - 3x^2 + 4)$
$\mathbf{-x^3 + 4x^2 + 2x - 3}$

6. $\left[u^4 - (-3)u^3 + \dfrac{u}{2} + 1\right] + \left(u^4 - 2u^3 + 5 - \dfrac{u}{2}\right)$
$\mathbf{2u^4 + u^3 + 6}$

7. $\left[u^4 - (-3)u^3 + \dfrac{u}{2} + 1\right] - \left(u^4 - 2u^3 + 5 - \dfrac{u}{2}\right)$
$\mathbf{5u^3 + u - 4}$

8. $\left(6a^2b + 3a\sqrt{c} - 5ab\sqrt{c}\right) + \left(-6ab^2 - 3ab + 6ab\sqrt{c}\right)$
$\mathbf{6a^2b - 6ab^2 + 3a\sqrt{c} + ab\sqrt{c} - 3ab}$

9. $[4z - 6z^2w - (-2)z^3w^2] + (8 - 6z^2w - zw^3 + 4z^3w^2)$
$\mathbf{4z - 12z^2w + 6z^3w^2 - zw^3 + 8}$

10. $(x^5y - 2x + 3xy^3) - (-2x - x^5y + 2xy^3)$
$\mathbf{2x^5y + xy^3}$

11. $(9x - x^3 + 1) - [2x^3 + (-6)x + (-7)]$
$\mathbf{-3x^3 + 15x + 8}$

12. $\left(x - \sqrt{y} - z\right) - \left(x + \sqrt{y} - z\right) - \left(\sqrt{y} + z - x\right)$
$\mathbf{x - 3\sqrt{y} - z}$

13. $(x^2 - 3xy) - (x + xy) - (x^2 + xy)$
$\mathbf{-5xy - x}$

14. $2x(x^2 + 2)$
$\mathbf{2x^3 + 4x}$

15. $(-5y)(-3y^2 + 1)$
$\mathbf{15y^3 - 5y}$

16. $x^2y(xy - 6xy^2)$
$\mathbf{x^3y^2 - 6x^3y^3}$

17. $3ax(4ax - 2a^2y + 2ay)$
$\mathbf{12a^2x^2 - 6a^3xy + 6a^2xy}$

18. $2x(x^2 - 3xy + 2y^2)$
$\mathbf{2x^3 - 6x^2y + 4xy^2}$

19. $6z^3(2z + 5)$
$\mathbf{12z^4 + 30z^3}$

20. $-3x^2(12x^6 - 7x^5)$
$\mathbf{-36x^8 + 21x^7}$

21. $3ab(4a - 6b + 2a^2b)$
$\mathbf{12a^2b - 18ab^2 + 6a^3b^2}$

22. $(-3ay)(4ay - 5y)$
$\mathbf{-12a^2y^2 + 15ay^2}$

23. $(x + 1)(x - 2)$
$\mathbf{x^2 - x - 2}$

24. $(x + 2)(2x - 5)$
$\mathbf{2x^2 - x - 10}$

25. $(-2x + 4)(-x - 3)$
$\mathbf{2x^2 + 2x - 12}$

26. $(y - 6)(2y + 2)$
$\mathbf{2y^2 - 10y - 12}$

27. $(y + 3)(y + 4)$
$\mathbf{y^2 + 7y + 12}$

28. $(w - 2)(3w + 1)$
$\mathbf{3w^2 - 5w - 2}$

29. $(3x + 7)(-2x + 5)$
$\mathbf{-6x^2 + x + 35}$

30. $(ab + 1)(a - 2)$
$\mathbf{a^2b - 2ab + a - 2}$

31. $(y - 3)(3y^2 + 4)$
$\mathbf{3y^3 - 9y^2 + 4y - 12}$

32. $(y + 8)(y - 8)$
$\mathbf{y^2 - 64}$

33. $(x + 4)(x - 4)$
$\mathbf{x^2 - 16}$

34. $(3x - y)(3x + y)$
$\mathbf{9x^2 - y^2}$

35. $(4a + 5b)(4a - 5b)$
$\mathbf{16a^2 - 25b^2}$

36. $(x + 6)^2$
$\mathbf{x^2 + 12x + 36}$

37. $(y - 11)^2$
$\mathbf{y^2 - 22y + 121}$

38. $(2x + 3y)^2$
$\mathbf{4x^2 + 12xy + 9y^2}$

39. $(5x - b)^2$
$\mathbf{25x^2 - 10bx + b^2}$

40. $(2s^2 - 9y)(2s^2 + 9y)$
$\mathbf{4s^4 - 81y^2}$

41. $(4x^3 - y^4)^2$
$\mathbf{16x^6 - 8x^3y^4 + y^8}$

42. $(4x^3 - 5y^2)(4x^3 + 5y^2)$
$\mathbf{16x^6 - 25y^4}$

43. $(-3x^2 + 2y^4)^2$
$\mathbf{9x^4 - 12x^2y^4 + 4y^8}$

44. $(c - 2)(2c^2 - 3c + 1)$
$\mathbf{2c^3 - 7c^2 + 7c - 2}$

45. $(2y + 3)(y^2 + 3y - 1)$
$\mathbf{2y^3 + 9y^2 + 7y - 3}$

46. $(x + 2y)(2x^2 - xy + y^2)$
$\mathbf{2x^3 + 3x^2y - xy^2 + 2y^3}$

47. $(5w + 6)(-3w^2 + 4w - 3)$
$\mathbf{-15w^3 + 2w^2 + 9w - 18}$

48. $(5x - 2y)(x^2 - 2xy + 3y^2)$
$\mathbf{5x^3 - 12x^2y + 19xy^2 - 6y^3}$

49. $2x(3x + 1)(4x - 2)$
$\mathbf{24x^3 - 4x^2 - 4x}$

50. $3y(-y + 2)(3y + 1)$
$\mathbf{-9y^3 + 15y^2 + 6y}$

51. $(x - 1)(x - 2)(x - 3)$
$\mathbf{x^3 - 6x^2 + 11x - 6}$

52. $(y - 2)(3y + 2)(y + 2)$
$\mathbf{3y^3 + 2y^2 - 12y - 8}$

53. $(x + 4y)(2y - x)(3x - y)$
$\mathbf{-3x^3 - 5x^2y + 26xy^2 - 8y^3}$

54. $(2x - y)(3x + 2y)(y - x)$
$\mathbf{-6x^3 + 5x^2y + 3xy^2 - 2y^3}$

In Exercises 55–64, find the coefficient of x^2 in the given product. Avoid doing any more multiplying than necessary.

55. $(x^2 + 3x + 1)(2x - 3)$ **3**   **56.** $(x^2 - 1)(x + 1)$ **1**

57. $(x^3 + 2x - 6)(x^2 + 1)$ **−6**   **58.** $(\sqrt{3} + x)(\sqrt{3} - x)$ **−1**

59. $(x + 2)^3$ **6**   **60.** $(x^2 + x + 1)(x - 1)$ **0**

61. $(x^2 + x + 1)(x^2 - x + 1)$ **1**

62. $(2x^2 + 1)(2x^2 - 1)$ **0**

63. $(2x - 1)(x^2 + 3x + 2)$ **5**

64. $(1 - 2x)(4x^2 + x - 1)$ **2**

In Exercises 65–70, perform the indicated multiplication and simplify your answer if possible.

65. $(\sqrt{x} + 5)(\sqrt{x} - 5)$
$x - 25$

66. $(2\sqrt{x} + \sqrt{2y})(2\sqrt{x} - \sqrt{2y})$
$4x - 2y$

67. $(3 + \sqrt{y})^2$ **68.** $(7w - \sqrt{2x})^2$
$9 + 6\sqrt{y} + y$ **$49w^2 - 14w\sqrt{2x} + 2x$**

69. $(1 + \sqrt{3}x)(x + \sqrt{3})$ **70.** $(2y + \sqrt{3})(\sqrt{5}y - 1)$
$\sqrt{3}x^2 + 4x + \sqrt{3}$ **$2\sqrt{5}y^2 + (\sqrt{15} - 2)y - \sqrt{3}$**

In Exercises 71–76, compute the product and arrange the terms of your answer according to decreasing powers of x, with each power of x appearing at most once.

Example: $(ax + b)(4x - c) = 4ax^2 + (4b - ac)x - bc$.

71. $(ax + b)(3x + 2)$ **72.** $(4x - c)(dx + c)$

73. $(ax + b)(bx + a)$ **74.** $rx(3rx + 1)(4x - r)$

75. $(x - a)(x - b)(x - c)$ **76.** $(2dx - c)(3cx + d)$

In Exercises 77–82, assume that all exponents are nonnegative integers and find the product.

Example: $2x^k(3x + x^{n+1}) = (2x^k)(3x) + (2x^k)(x^{n+1})$
$= 6x^{k+1} + 2x^{k+n+1}$.

77. $3^r 3^4 3^t$ **78.** $(2x^n)(8x^k)$

79. $(x^m + 2)(x^n - 3)$ **80.** $(y^r + 1)(y^s - 4)$

81. $(2x^n - 5)(x^{3n} + 4x^n + 1)$

82. $(3y^{2k} + y^k + 1)(y^k - 3)$

In Exercises 83–92, find a numerical example to show that the given statement is false. Then find the mistake in the statement and correct it.

Example: *The statement* $-(b + 2) = -b + 2$ *is false when* $b = 5$, *since* $-(5 + 2) = -7$ *but* $-5 + 2 = -3$. *The mistake is the sign on the 2. The correct statement is* $-(b + 2) = -b - 2$.

83. $3(y + 2) = 3y + 2$

84. $x - (3y + 4) = x - 3y + 4$

85. $(x + y)^2 = x + y^2$ **86.** $(2x)^3 = 2x^3$

87. $(7x)(7y) = 7xy$ **88.** $(x + y)^2 = x^2 + y^2$

89. $y + y + y = y^3$ **90.** $(a - b)^2 = a^2 - b^2$

91. $(x - 3)(x - 2) = x^2 - 5x - 6$

92. $(a + b)(a^2 + b^2) = a^3 + b^3$

In Exercises 93 and 94, explain algebraically why each of these parlor tricks always works.

93. *Critical Thinking* Write down a nonzero number. Add 1 to it and square the result. Subtract 1 from the original number and square the result. Subtract this second square from the first one. Divide by the number with which you started. The answer is 4.

94. *Critical Thinking* Write down a positive number. Add 4 to it. Multiply the result by the original number. Add 4 to this result and then take the square root. Subtract the number with which you started. The answer is 2.

95. *Critical Thinking* Invent a similar parlor trick in which the answer is always the number with which you started.

71. $3ax^2 + (3b + 2a)x + 2b$

72. $4dx^2 + (4c - dc)x - c^2$

73. $abx^2 + (a^2 + b^2)x + ab$

74. $12r^2x^3 + (4r - 3r^3)x^2 - r^2x$

75. $x^3 - (a + b + c)x^2 +$
$(ab + ac + bc)x - abc$

76. $6cdx^2 + (2d^2 - 3c^2)x - cd$

77. 3^{4+r+t}

78. $16x^{n+k}$

79. $x^{m+n} + 2x^n - 3x^m - 6$

80. $y^{r+s} - 4y^r + y^s - 4$

81. $2x^{4n} - 5x^{3n} + 8x^{2n} - 18x^n - 5$

82. $3y^{3k} - 8y^{2k} - 2y^k - 3$

83. example: if $y = 4$, then
$3(4 + 2) \neq (3 \cdot 4) + 2$;
correct statement:
$3(y + 2) = 3y + 6$

84. example: if $x = 0$, $y = 0$, then
$0 - (3(0) + 4) \neq 0 - 3(0) + 4$;
correct statement:
$x - (3y + 4) = x - 3y - 4$

85. example: if $x = 2$, $y = 3$,
then $(2 + 3)^2 \neq 2 + 3^2$;
correct statement:
$(x + y)^2 = x^2 + 2xy + y^2$

86. example: if $x = 5$,
then $(2(5))^3 \neq 2(5)^3$;
correct statement:
$(2x)^3 = 8x^3$

87. example: if $x = 2$, $y = 3$,
then $(7 \cdot 2)(7 \cdot 3) \neq 7 \cdot 2 \cdot 3$;
correct statement:
$(7x)(7y) = 49xy$

88. example: if $x = 2$, $y = 1$,
then $(2 + 1)^2 \neq 2^2 + 1^2$;
correct statement:
$(x + y)^2 = x^2 + 2xy + y^2$

89. example: if $y = 2$,
then $2 + 2 + 2 \neq 2^3$;
correct statement: $y + y + y = 3y$

90. example: if $a = 2$, $b = 1$,
then $(2 - 1)^2 \neq 2^2 - 1^2$;
correct statement:
$(a - b)^2 = a^2 - 2ab + b^2$

91. example: if $x = 4$, then
$(4 - 3)(4 - 2) \neq 4^2 - 5 \cdot 4 - 6$;
correct statement:
$(x - 3)(x - 2) = x^2 - 5x + 6$

92. example: if $a = 1$, $b = 1$,
then $(1 + 1)(1^2 + 1^2) \neq 1^3 + 1^3$;
correct statement:
$(a + b)(a^2 + b^2)$
$= a^3 + a^2b + ab^2 + b^3$

93. If x is the chosen number, then adding 1 and squaring the result gives $(x + 1)^2$. Subtracting 1 from the original number x and squaring the result gives $(x - 1)^2$. Subtracting the second of these squares from the first yields: $(x + 1)^2 - (x - 1)^2 = (x^2 + 2x + 1) - (x^2 - 2x + 1) = 4x$. Dividing by the original number x now gives $\frac{4x}{x} = 4$. So the answer is always 4, no matter what number x is chosen.

94. If x is the chosen positive number, then adding 4 and then multiplying the original number by this one gives $x(x + 4) = x^2 + 4x$. Adding 4 and then taking the square root gives $x + 2$. Subtracting x now gives 2.

95. many correct answers

Section A.3 Factoring

Students often factor a difference of squares incorrectly. In **Example 2a,** some students may incorrectly write $x^2 - (3y)^2$ as $(x - 3y)^2$. Encourage students to check their answers by multiplying. Have them use the third property in the **Quadratic Factoring Patterns** box to see that $(x - 3y)^2$ is incorrect:
$(x - 3y)^2 = x^2 - 6xy + 9y^2 \neq x^2 - 9y^2$

Example Notes

After completing **Example 2c,** have students observe that they can obtain the same answer by first factoring out the common factor and then applying the Difference of Squares:

$$36r^2 - 64s^2 = 4(9r^2 - 16s^2)$$
$$= 4((3r)^2 - (4s)^2)$$
$$= 4(3r + 4s)(3r - 4s)$$

Teaching Notes

When using trial and error to factor quadratic polynomials whose x^2 coefficient is 1, encourage students to rule out possibilities by using the following method:
Consider the polynomial $x^2 + 7x + 12$ and refer to the paragraph preceding Example 5.
Since $ac = 1$, let $a = c = 1$.
Then $(ax + b)(cx + d)$
$$= 1 \cdot x^2 + (1 \cdot d + b \cdot 1)x + bd$$
$$= x^2 + (b + d)x + bd$$
where $b + d = 7$ and $bd = 12$. Therefore, we are looking for two factors of 12 whose sum is 7. The factors of 12 are $\pm 1, \pm 12$ or $\pm 2, \pm 6$ or $\pm 3, \pm 4$. Of these, it is easy to see that the pair that sums to 7 is 3 and 4, so it is unnecessary to go through all possible pairs.
$$x^2 + 7x + 12 = (x + 3)(x + 4).$$

A.3 Factoring

Factoring is the reverse of multiplication: We begin with a product and find the factors that multiply together to produce this product. Factoring skills are necessary to simplify expressions, to do arithmetic with fractional expressions, and to solve equations and inequalities.

The first general rule for factoring is

Common Factors

> If there is a common factor in every term of the expression, factor out the common factor of highest degree.

Example 1

In $4x^6 - 8x$, for example, each term contains a factor of $4x$, so that $4x^6 - 8x = 4x(x^5 - 2)$. Similarly, the common factor of highest degree in $x^3y^2 + 2xy^3 - 3x^2y^4$ is xy^2 and

$$x^3y^2 + 2xy^3 - 3x^2y^4 = xy^2(x^2 + 2y - 3xy^2).$$

You can greatly increase your factoring proficiency by learning to recognize multiplication patterns that appear frequently. Here are the most common ones.

Quadratic Factoring Patterns

Difference of Squares	$u^2 - v^2 = (u + v)(u - v)$
Perfect Squares	$u^2 + 2uv + v^2 = (u + v)^2$
	$u^2 - 2uv + v^2 = (u - v)^2$

Example 2

a. $x^2 - 9y^2$ can be written $x^2 - (3y)^2$, a difference of squares. Therefore, $x^2 - 9y^2 = (x + 3y)(x - 3y)$.

b. $y^2 - 7 = y^2 - (\sqrt{7})^2 = (y + \sqrt{7})(y - \sqrt{7})$.*

c. $36r^2 - 64s^2 = (6r)^2 - (8s)^2 = (6r + 8s)(6r - 8s)$
$$= 2(3r + 4s)2(3r - 4s) = 4(3r + 4s)(3r - 4s).$$

---

*When a polynomial has integer coefficients, we normally look only for factors with integer coefficients. But when it is easy to find other factors, as here, we shall do so.

Example 3

Since the first and last terms of $4x^2 - 36x + 81$ are perfect squares, we try to use the perfect square pattern with $u = 2x$ and $v = 9$:

$$4x^2 - 36x + 81 = (2x)^2 - 36x + 9^2$$
$$= (2x)^2 - 2 \cdot 2x \cdot 9 + 9^2 = (2x - 9)^2. \blacksquare$$

Cubic Factoring Patterns

Difference of Cubes	$u^3 - v^3 = (u - v)(u^2 + uv + v^2)$
Sum of Cubes	$u^3 + v^3 = (u + v)(u^2 - uv + v^2)$
Perfect Cubes	$u^3 + 3u^2v + 3uv^2 + v^3 = (u + v)^3$
	$u^3 - 3u^2v + 3uv^2 - v^3 = (u - v)^3$

Example 4

a. $x^3 - 125 = x^3 - 5^3 = (x - 5)(x^2 + 5x + 5^2)$
$\qquad = (x - 5)(x^2 + 5x + 25).$

b. $x^3 + 8y^3 = x^3 + (2y)^3 = (x + 2y)[x^2 - x \cdot 2y + (2y)^2]$
$\qquad = (x + 2y)(x^2 - 2xy + 4y^2).$

c. $x^3 - 12x^2 + 48x - 64 = x^3 - 12x^2 + 48x - 4^3$
$\qquad = x^3 - 3x^2 \cdot 4 + 3x \cdot 4^2 - 4^3$
$\qquad = (x - 4)^3. \blacksquare$

When none of the multiplication patterns applies, use trial and error to factor quadratic polynomials. If a quadratic has two first-degree factors, then the factors must be of the form $ax + b$ and $cx + d$ for some constants a, b, c, d. The product of such factors is

$$(ax + b)(cx + d) = acx^2 + adx + bcx + bd$$
$$= acx^2 + (ad + bc)x + bd.$$

Note that *ac is the coefficient of x^2* and *bd is the constant term* of the product polynomial. This pattern can be used to factor quadratics by reversing the FOIL process.

Example 5

If $x^2 + 9x + 18$ factors as $(ax + b)(cx + d)$, then we must have $ac = 1$ (coefficient of x^2) and $bd = 18$ (constant term). Thus, $a = \pm 1$ and $c = \pm 1$ (the only integer factors of 1). The only possibilities for b and d are

$$\pm 1, \pm 18 \quad \text{or} \quad \pm 2, \pm 9 \quad \text{or} \quad \pm 3, \pm 6.$$

We mentally try the various possibilities, using FOIL as our guide. For example, we try $b = 2$, $d = 9$ and check this factorization: $(x + 2)(x + 9)$. The sum of the outside and inside terms is $9x + 2x = 11x$, so this prod-

ADDITIONAL EXAMPLES

Example 1

Factor $3x^4 - 6x^2$. $3x^2(x^2 - 2)$

Factor $4x^2y^4 - 2xy^3 + 6x^2y^2$.
$2xy^2(2xy^2 - y + 3x)$

Example 2

Factor each expression.

a. $25x^2 - y^2$
$\qquad = (5x)^2 - y^2$
$\qquad = (5x + y)(5x - y)$

b. $z^2 - 10$
$\qquad = z^2 - \left(\sqrt{10}\right)^2$
$\qquad = \left(z + \sqrt{10}\right)\left(z - \sqrt{10}\right)$

c. $100x^2 - 36y^2$
$\qquad = (10x)^2 - (6y)^2$
$\qquad = (10x + 6y)(10x - 6y)$
$\qquad = 2(5x + 3y)2(5x - 3y)$
$\qquad = 4(5x + 3y)(5x - 3y)$

Example 3

Factor $16x^2 + 40x + 25$.
$\qquad = (4x)^2 + 40x + 5^2$
$\qquad = (4x)^2 + 2(4x)(5) + 5^2$
$\qquad = (4x + 5)^2$

Example 4

Factor each expression.

a. $y^3 - 64$
$\qquad = y^3 - 4^3$
$\qquad = (y - 4)(y^2 + 4y + 16)$

b. $27x^3 + y^3$
$\qquad = (3x)^3 + y^3$
$\qquad = (3x + y)(9x^2 - 3xy + y^2)$

c. $x^3 - 15x^2 + 75x - 125$
$\qquad = x^3 - 3 \cdot 5x^2 + 3 \cdot 5^2x - 5^3$
$\qquad = (x - 5)^3$

Example 5

Factor $x^2 - 8x + 12$.
If $x^2 - 8x + 12 = (ax + b)(cx + d)$, then $ac = 1$ and $bd = 12$. Thus, $a = \pm 1$ and $c = \pm 1$, and the possibilities for b and d are:

$\pm 1, \pm 12$ or $\pm 2, \pm 6$ or $\pm 3, \pm 4$

Trying the possibilities gives the correct factorization
$x^2 - 8x + 12 = (x - 2)(x - 6)$.

ADDITIONAL EXAMPLES

Example 6

Factor $8x^2 + 10x + 3$.

If $8x^2 + 10x + 3 = (ax + b)(cx + d)$, then $ac = 8$ and $bd = 3$. The possibilities are:

$ac = 8$		$bd = 3$	
a	**c**	**b**	**d**
±1	±8	±1	±3
±2	±4	±3	±1
±4	±2		
±8	±1		

Trial and error shows that
$8x^2 + 10x + 3 = (2x + 1)(4x + 3)$.

Example 7

Factor each expression.

a. $x^6 - 64$
$= (x^3)^2 - (8)^2$
$= (x^3 + 8)(x^3 - 8)$
$= (x^3 + 2^3)(x^3 - 2^3)$
$= (x + 2)(x^2 - 2x + 4) \cdot$
$\qquad (x - 2)(x^2 + 2x + 4)$

b. $x^{16} - 256$
$= (x^8)^2 - 16^2$
$= (x^8 + 16)(x^8 - 16)$
$= (x^8 + 16)((x^4)^2 - 4^2)$
$= (x^8 + 16)(x^4 + 4)(x^4 - 4)$
$= (x^8 + 16)(x^4 + 4)((x^2)^2 - 2^2)$
$= (x^8 + 16)(x^4 + 4)(x^2 + 2)(x^2 - 2)$
$= (x^8 + 16)(x^4 + 4)(x^2 + 2)(x + \sqrt{2})(x - \sqrt{2})$

Example 8

Factor $x^4 - 5x^2 + 4$.

Let $u = x^2$, so
$x^4 - 5x^2 + 4$
$= (x^2)^2 - 5x^2 + 4$
$= u^2 - 5u + 4$
$= (u - 1)(u - 4)$
$= (x^2 - 1)(x^2 - 4)$
$= (x + 1)(x - 1)(x + 2)(x - 2)$

Example 9

Factor $2x^3 - 6x^2 + 4x - 12$.

$= (2x^3 - 6x^2) + (4x - 12)$
$= 2x^2(x - 3) + 4(x - 3)$
$= (2x^2 + 4)(x - 3)$

uct can't be $x^2 + 9x + 18$. By trying other possibilities we find that $b = 3$, $d = 6$ leads to the correct factorization: $x^2 + 9x + 18 = (x + 3)(x + 6)$. ∎

Example 6

To factor $6x^2 + 11x + 4$ as $(ax + b)(cx + d)$, we must find numbers a and c whose product is 6, the coefficient of x^2, and numbers b and d whose product is the constant term 4. Some possibilities are

$ac = 6$	a	±1	±2	±3	±6
	c	±6	±3	±2	±1

$bd = 4$	b	±1	±2	±4
	d	±4	±2	±1

Trial and error shows that $(2x + 1)(3x + 4) = 6x^2 + 11x + 4$. ∎

Occasionally the patterns above can be used to factor expressions involving larger exponents than 2.

Example 7

a. $x^6 - y^6 = (x^3)^2 - (y^3)^2 = (x^3 + y^3)(x^3 - y^3)$
$\qquad = (x + y)(x^2 - xy + y^2)(x - y)(x^2 + xy + y^2)$.
b. $x^8 - 1 = (x^4)^2 - 1 = (x^4 + 1)(x^4 - 1)$
$\qquad = (x^4 + 1)(x^2 + 1)(x^2 - 1)$
$\qquad = (x^4 + 1)(x^2 + 1)(x + 1)(x - 1)$. ∎

Example 8

To factor $x^4 - 2x^2 - 3$, let $u = x^2$. Then,

$x^4 - 2x^2 - 3 = (x^2)^2 - 2x^2 - 3$
$\qquad = u^2 - 2u - 3 = (u + 1)(u - 3)$
$\qquad = (x^2 + 1)(x^2 - 3)$
$\qquad = (x^2 + 1)(x + \sqrt{3})(x - \sqrt{3})$. ∎

Example 9

$3x^3 + 3x^2 + 2x + 2$ can be factored by regrouping and using the distributive law to factor out a common factor:

$(3x^3 + 3x^2) + (2x + 2) = 3x^2(x + 1) + 2(x + 1)$
$\qquad = (3x^2 + 2)(x + 1)$. ∎

Exercises A.3

In Exercises 1–58, factor the expression.

1. $x^2 - 4$
$(x + 2)(x - 2)$

2. $x^2 + 6x + 9$
$(x + 3)^2$

3. $9y^2 - 25$
$(3y + 5)(3y - 5)$

4. $y^2 - 4y + 4$
$(y - 2)^2$

5. $81x^2 + 36x + 4$
$(9x + 2)^2$

6. $4x^2 - 12x + 9$
$(2x - 3)^2$

7. $5 - x^2$
$(\sqrt{5} + x)(\sqrt{5} - x)$

8. $1 - 36u^2$
$(1 - 6u)(1 + 6u)$

9. $49 + 28z + 4z^2$
$(7 + 2z)^2$

10. $25u^2 - 20uv + 4v^2$
$(5u - 2v)^2$

11. $x^4 - y^4$
$(x^2 + y^2)(x + y)(x - y)$

12. $x^2 - \dfrac{1}{9}$
$\left(x - \dfrac{1}{3}\right)\left(x + \dfrac{1}{3}\right)$

13. $x^2 + x - 6$
$(x + 3)(x - 2)$

14. $y^2 + 11y + 30$
$(y + 5)(y + 6)$

15. $z^2 + 4z + 3$
$(z + 3)(z + 1)$

16. $x^2 - 8x + 15$
$(x - 3)(x - 5)$

17. $y^2 + 5y - 36$
$(y + 9)(y - 4)$

18. $z^2 - 9z + 14$
$(z - 7)(z - 2)$

19. $x^2 - 6x + 9$
$(x - 3)^2$

20. $4y^2 - 81$
$(2y - 9)(2y + 9)$

21. $x^2 + 7x + 10$
$(x + 5)(x + 2)$

22. $w^2 - 6w - 16$
$(w - 8)(w + 2)$

23. $x^2 + 11x + 18$
$(x + 9)(x + 2)$

24. $x^2 + 3xy - 28y^2$
$(x + 7y)(x - 4y)$

25. $3x^2 + 4x + 1$
$(3x + 1)(x + 1)$

26. $4y^2 + 4y + 1$
$(2y + 1)^2$

27. $2z^2 + 11z + 12$
$(2z + 3)(z + 4)$

28. $10x^2 - 17x + 3$
$(5x - 1)(2x - 3)$

29. $9x^2 - 72x$
$9x(x - 8)$

30. $4x^2 - 4x - 3$
$(2x + 1)(2x - 3)$

31. $10x^2 - 8x - 2$
$2(x - 1)(5x + 1)$

32. $7z^2 + 23z + 6$
$(7z + 2)(z + 3)$

33. $8u^2 + 6u - 9$
$(4u - 3)(2u + 3)$

34. $2y^2 - 4y + 2$
$2(y - 1)^2$

35. $4x^2 + 20xy + 25y^2$
$(2x + 5y)^2$

36. $63u^2 - 46uv + 8v^2$
$(7u - 2v)(9u - 4v)$

37. $x^3 - 125$

38. $y^3 + 64$

39. $x^3 + 6x^2 + 12x + 8$

40. $y^3 - 3y^2 + 3y - 1$

41. $8 + x^3$

42. $z^3 - 9z^2 + 27z - 27$

43. $-x^3 + 15x^2 - 75x + 125$

44. $27 - t^3$

45. $x^3 + 1$

46. $x^3 - 1$

47. $8x^3 - y^3$

48. $(x - 1)^3 + 1$

49. $x^6 - 64$

50. $x^5 - 8x^2$

51. $y^4 + 7y^2 + 10$

52. $z^4 - 5z^2 + 6$

53. $81 - y^4$

54. $x^6 + 16x^3 + 64$

55. $z^6 - 1$

56. $y^6 + 26y^3 - 27$

57. $x^4 + 2x^2y - 3y^2$

58. $x^8 - 17x^4 + 16$

In Exercises 59–64, factor by regrouping and using the distributive law (as in Example 9).

59. $x^2 - yz + xz - xy$

60. $x^6 - 2x^4 - 8x^2 + 16$

61. $a^3 - 2b^2 + 2a^2b - ab$

62. $u^2v - 2w^2 - 2uvw + uw$

63. $x^3 + 4x^2 - 8x - 32$

64. $z^8 - 5z^7 + 2z - 10$

65. *Critical Thinking* Show that there do *not* exist real numbers c and d such that $x^2 + 1 = (x + c)(x + d)$.

Exercises A.3

ANSWERS

37. $(x - 5)(x^2 + 5x + 25)$

38. $(y + 4)(y^2 - 4y + 16)$

39. $(x + 2)^3$

40. $(y - 1)^3$

41. $(2 + x)(4 - 2x + x^2)$

42. $(z - 3)^3$

43. $(-x + 5)^3$

44. $(3 - t)(9 + 3t + t^2)$

45. $(x + 1)(x^2 - x + 1)$

46. $(x - 1)(x^2 + x + 1)$

47. $(2x - y)(4x^2 + 2xy + y^2)$

48. $x(x^2 - 3x + 3)$

49. $(x^3 + 2^3)(x^3 - 2^3)$
$= (x + 2)(x^2 - 2x + 4)(x - 2) \cdot$
$(x^2 + 2x + 4)$

50. $x^2(x - 2)(x^2 + 2x + 4)$

51. $(y^2 + 5)(y^2 + 2)$

52. $(z - \sqrt{3})(z + \sqrt{3})(z - \sqrt{2})(z + \sqrt{2})$

53. $(9 + y^2)(3 + y)(3 - y)$

54. $(x + 2)^2(x^2 - 2x + 4)^2$

55. $(z + 1)(z^2 - z + 1)(z - 1)(z^2 + z + 1)$

56. $(y + 3)(y^2 - 3y + 9)(y - 1)(y^2 + y + 1)$

57. $(x^2 + 3y)(x^2 - y)$

Section
A.4 Fractional Expressions

A.4 Fractional Expressions

Quotients of algebraic expressions are called **fractional expressions**. A quotient of two polynomials is sometimes called a **rational expression**. The basic rules for dealing with fractional expressions are essentially the same as those for ordinary numerical fractions. For instance, $\dfrac{2}{4} = \dfrac{3}{6}$ and the "cross products" are equal: $2 \cdot 6 = 4 \cdot 3$. In the general case we have

Section A.4 **Fractional Expressions** 981

Section A.4 Fractional Expressions

Teaching Notes

This section relies heavily on the factoring techniques discussed in Section A.3 in order to simplify and perform calculations on rational expressions. It is highly encouraged to have students review the formulas in the boxes on pages 978–979 and do several of the exercises at the top of this page before continuing.

---

58. $(x + 2)(x - 2)(x^2 + 4)(x - 1)(x + 1)(x^2 + 1)$

59. $(x + z)(x - y)$

60. $(x - \sqrt{2})(x + \sqrt{2})(x^2 - \sqrt{8})(x^2 + \sqrt{8})$

61. $(a + 2b)(a^2 - b)$

62. $(uv + w)(u - 2w)$

63. $(x^2 - 8)(x + 4) = (x + \sqrt{8})(x - \sqrt{8})(x + 4)$

64. $(z^7 + 2)(z - 5)$

65. If $x^2 + 1 = (x + c)(x + d)$
$= x^2 + (c + d)x + cd$, then
$c + d = 0$ and $cd = 1$. But $c + d = 0$
implies that $c = -d$ and hence that
$1 = cd = (-d)d = -d^2$, or equivalently,
that $d^2 = -1$. Since there is no real number with this property, $x^2 + 1$ cannot possibly factor in this way.

COMMON ERROR ALERT

In **Example 3**, students may forget to distribute the negative sign across the second expression; getting the incorrect answer below:

$$\frac{(7x^2 + 2) - (4x^2 + 2x - 5)}{x^2 + 3}$$

$$= \frac{7x^2 + 2 - 4x^2 + 2x - 5}{x^2 + 3} = \frac{3x^2 + 2x - 3}{x^2 + 3}$$

Refer students to Section A.2 if they need to refresh the rules for eliminating parentheses.

Example Notes

Example 4 shows how to subtract fractional expressions with different denominators by using a common denominator equal to the product of the denominators, while **Examples 5–8** develop the use of the *least* common denominator. Point out to students that in Example 4, the product $3x(x - 1)$ is, in fact, the least common denominator because $3x$ and $x - 1$ have no common factors.

Teaching Notes

Provide students with the following simple numerical example to show how using the least common denominator can be more efficient than the product of the denominators.

Using the product $2 \cdot 4 \cdot 8 \cdot 16 = 1024$:

$$\frac{1}{2} + \frac{3}{4} + \frac{7}{8} + \frac{5}{16}$$

$$= \frac{512}{1024} + \frac{768}{1024} + \frac{896}{1024} + \frac{320}{1024}$$

$$= \frac{2496}{1024}$$

$$= \frac{39 \cdot 64}{16 \cdot 64}$$

$$= \frac{39}{16}$$

$$= 2\frac{7}{16}$$

Using LCD = 16:

$$\frac{1}{2} + \frac{3}{4} + \frac{7}{8} + \frac{5}{16}$$

$$= \frac{8}{16} + \frac{12}{16} + \frac{14}{16} + \frac{5}{16}$$

$$= \frac{39}{16}$$

$$= 2\frac{7}{16}$$

Properties of Fractions

1. **Equality rule:** $\frac{a}{b} = \frac{c}{d}$ exactly when $ad = bc$.*

2. **Cancellation property:** If $k \neq 0$, then $\frac{ka}{kb} = \frac{a}{b}$.

The cancellation property follows directly from the equality rule because $(ka)b = (kb)a$.

Example 1

Here are examples of the two properties:

1. $\dfrac{x^2 + 2x}{x^2 + x - 2} = \dfrac{x}{x - 1}$ because the cross products are equal:

$$(x^2 + 2x)(x - 1) = x^3 + x^2 - 2x = (x^2 + x - 2)x.$$

2. $\dfrac{x^4 - 1}{x^2 + 1} = \dfrac{(x^2 + 1)(x^2 - 1)}{(x^2 + 1)} = \dfrac{x^2 - 1}{1} = x^2 - 1.$

A fraction is in **lowest terms** if its **numerator** (top) and **denominator** (bottom) have no common factors except ± 1. To express a fraction in lowest terms, factor numerator and denominator and cancel common factors.

Example 2

$$\frac{x^2 + x - 6}{x^2 - 3x + 2} = \frac{(x - 2)(x + 3)}{(x - 2)(x - 1)} = \frac{x + 3}{x - 1}.$$

To add two fractions with the same denominator, simply add the numerators as in ordinary arithmetic: $\dfrac{a}{b} + \dfrac{c}{b} = \dfrac{a + c}{b}$. Subtraction is done similarly.

Example 3

$$\frac{7x^2 + 2}{x^2 + 3} - \frac{4x^2 + 2x - 5}{x^2 + 3} = \frac{(7x^2 + 2) - (4x^2 + 2x - 5)}{x^2 + 3}$$

$$= \frac{7x^2 + 2 - 4x^2 - 2x + 5}{x^2 + 3}$$

$$= \frac{3x^2 - 2x + 7}{x^2 + 3}.$$

*Throughout this section we assume that all denominators are nonzero.

To add or subtract fractions with different denominators, you must first find a common denominator. One common denominator for a/b and c/d is the product of the two denominators bd because both fractions can be expressed with this denominator:

$$\frac{a}{b} = \frac{ad}{bd} \quad \text{and} \quad \frac{c}{d} = \frac{bc}{bd}.$$

Consequently,

$$\frac{a}{b} + \frac{c}{d} = \frac{ad}{bd} + \frac{bc}{bd} = \frac{ad + bc}{bd} \quad \text{and} \quad \frac{a}{b} - \frac{c}{d} = \frac{ad}{bd} - \frac{bc}{bd} = \frac{ad - bc}{bd}.$$

Example 4

$$\frac{2x + 1}{3x} - \frac{x^2 - 2}{x - 1} = \frac{(2x + 1)(x - 1)}{3x(x - 1)} - \frac{3x(x^2 - 2)}{3x(x - 1)}$$

$$= \frac{(2x + 1)(x - 1) - 3x(x^2 - 2)}{3x(x - 1)}$$

$$= \frac{2x^2 - x - 1 - 3x^3 + 6x}{3x^2 - 3x}$$

$$= \frac{-3x^3 + 2x^2 + 5x - 1}{3x^2 - 3x}.$$

Although the product of the denominators can always be used as a common denominator, it's often more efficient to use the *least common denominator*. The least common denominator can be found by factoring each denominator completely (with integer coefficients) and then taking the product of the highest power of each of the distinct factors.

Example 5

In the sum $\frac{1}{100} + \frac{1}{120}$, the denominators are $100 = 2^2 \cdot 5^2$ and $120 = 2^3 \cdot 3 \cdot 5$. The distinct factors are 2, 3, 5. The highest exponent of 2 in either denominator is 3, the highest of 3 is 1, and the highest of 5 is 2. So the least common denominator is $2^3 \cdot 3 \cdot 5^2 = 600$

$$\frac{1}{100} + \frac{1}{120} = \frac{6}{600} + \frac{5}{600} = \frac{11}{600}.$$

Example 6

To find the least common denominator of $\frac{1}{x^2 + 2x + 1}$, $\frac{5x}{x^2 - x}$, and $\frac{3x - 7}{x^4 + x^3}$, factor each of the denominators completely:

$$(x + 1)^2, \quad x(x - 1), \quad x^3(x + 1),$$

Example 1

1. Use the Equality Rule to show that
$$\frac{x^2 + 3x}{x} = \frac{x^2 - x - 12}{x - 4}.$$
$$(x^2 + 3x)(x - 4) = x^3 - x^2 - 12x$$
$$= (x^2 - x - 12)x \; \checkmark$$

2. Use the Cancellation Property to simplify $\frac{x^2 - 4}{x + 2}$.
$$= \frac{(x - 2)(x + 2)}{x + 2} = \frac{x - 2}{1}$$
$$= x - 2$$

Example 2

Write $\frac{x^2 - x - 2}{x^2 + 5x + 4}$ in lowest terms.
$$\frac{x^2 - x - 2}{x^2 + 5x + 4} = \frac{(x - 2)(x + 1)}{(x + 4)(x + 1)} = \frac{x - 2}{x + 4}$$

Example 3

Subtract: $\frac{3x - 4}{x^2 - 5} - \frac{3x^2 - 4x + 2}{x^2 - 5}$
$$= \frac{(3x - 4) - (3x^2 - 4x + 2)}{x^2 - 5}$$
$$= \frac{3x - 4 - 3x^2 + 4x - 2}{x^2 - 5}$$
$$= \frac{-3x^2 + 7x - 6}{x^2 - 5}$$

Example 4

Add: $\frac{5x - 2}{x + 3} + \frac{x^2 - 1}{2x}$
$$= \frac{(5x - 2)2x}{(x + 3)2x} + \frac{(x + 3)(x^2 - 1)}{(x + 3)2x}$$
$$= \frac{(5x - 2)2x + (x + 3)(x^2 - 1)}{(x + 3)2x}$$
$$= \frac{10x^2 - 4x + x^3 - x + 3x^2 - 3}{2x^2 + 6x}$$
$$= \frac{x^3 + 13x^2 - 5x - 3}{2x^2 + 6x}$$

Example 5

Add: $\frac{1}{60} + \frac{1}{80}$

$60 = 2^2 \cdot 3 \cdot 5 \qquad 80 = 2^4 \cdot 5$

least common denominator:
$$2^4 \cdot 3 \cdot 5 = 240$$

$$\frac{1}{60} + \frac{1}{80} = \frac{4}{240} + \frac{3}{240} = \frac{7}{240}$$

ADDITIONAL EXAMPLES

Example 6

Find the least common denominator

of $\dfrac{1}{x^2 - 4x + 4}$, $\dfrac{2x}{x^2 + x - 6}$, and

$\dfrac{2x - 3}{x^3 + 3x^2}$.

factor each denominator:

$$x^2 - 4x + 4 = (x - 2)^2$$
$$x^2 + x - 6 = (x - 2)(x + 3)$$
$$x^3 + 3x^2 = x^2(x + 3)$$

least common denominator:

$$x^2(x - 2)^2(x + 3)$$

Example 7

Express each of the fractions from **Additional Example 6** in terms of their least common denominator.

$$\frac{1}{x^2 - 4x + 4} = \frac{1}{(x - 2)^2} \cdot \frac{x^2(x + 3)}{x^2(x + 3)}$$

$$= \frac{x^2(x + 3)}{x^2(x - 2)^2(x + 3)}$$

$$\frac{2x}{x^2 + x - 6} = \frac{2x}{(x - 2)(x + 3)} \cdot \frac{x^2(x - 2)}{x^2(x - 2)}$$

$$= \frac{2x^3(x - 2)}{x^2(x - 2)^2(x + 3)}$$

$$\frac{2x - 3}{x^3 + 3x^2} = \frac{2x - 3}{x^2(x + 3)} \cdot \frac{(x - 2)^2}{(x - 2)^2}$$

$$= \frac{(2x - 3)(x - 2)^2}{x^2(x - 2)^2(x + 3)}$$

Example 8

Simplify: $\dfrac{2}{x} - \dfrac{2x}{x - 2} + \dfrac{4x^2}{(x - 2)^2}$

Use the LCD $x(x - 2)^2$:

$$\frac{2}{x} - \frac{2x}{x - 2} + \frac{4x^2}{(x - 2)^2}$$

$$= \frac{2(x - 2)^2}{x(x - 2)^2} - \frac{2x^2(x - 2)}{x(x - 2)^2} + \frac{4x^3}{x(x - 2)^2}$$

$$= \frac{2(x - 2)^2 - 2x^2(x - 2) + 4x^3}{x(x - 2)^2}$$

$$= \frac{2x^2 - 8x + 8 - 2x^3 + 4x^2 + 4x^3}{x(x + 4)^2}$$

$$= \frac{2x^3 + 6x^2 - 8x + 8}{x(x + 4)^2}$$

The distinct factors are x, $x + 1$, and $x - 1$. The least common denominator is determined by the highest power of each factor:

$$x^3(x + 1)^2(x - 1).$$

To express one of several fractions in terms of the least common denominator, multiply its numerator and denominator by those factors in the common denominator that *don't* appear in the denominator of the fraction.

Example 7

The preceding example shows the least common denominator (LCD) of

$\dfrac{1}{(x + 1)^2}$, $\dfrac{5x}{x(x - 1)}$, and $\dfrac{3x - 7}{x^3(x + 1)}$ to be $x^3(x + 1)^2(x - 1)$. Therefore,

$$\frac{1}{(x + 1)^2} = \frac{1}{(x + 1)^2} \cdot \frac{x^3(x - 1)}{x^3(x - 1)} = \frac{x^3(x - 1)}{x^3(x + 1)^2(x - 1)}$$

$$\frac{5x}{x(x - 1)} = \frac{5x}{x(x - 1)} \cdot \frac{x^2(x + 1)^2}{x^2(x + 1)^2} = \frac{5x^3(x + 1)^2}{x^3(x + 1)^2(x - 1)}$$

$$\frac{3x - 7}{x^3(x + 1)} = \frac{3x - 7}{x^3(x + 1)} \cdot \frac{(x + 1)(x - 1)}{(x + 1)(x - 1)} = \frac{(3x - 7)(x + 1)(x - 1)}{x^3(x + 1)^2(x - 1)}.$$

Example 8

To find $\dfrac{1}{z} + \dfrac{3z}{z + 1} - \dfrac{z^2}{(z + 1)^2}$ we use the LCD $z(z + 1)^2$:

$$\frac{1}{z} + \frac{3z}{z + 1} - \frac{z^2}{(z + 1)^2} = \frac{(z + 1)^2}{z(z + 1)^2} + \frac{3z^2(z + 1)}{z(z + 1)^2} - \frac{z^3}{z(z + 1)^2}$$

$$= \frac{(z + 1)^2 + 3z^2(z + 1) - z^3}{z(z + 1)^2}$$

$$= \frac{z^2 + 2z + 1 + 3z^3 + 3z^2 - z^3}{z(z + 1)^2}$$

$$= \frac{2z^3 + 4z^2 + 2z + 1}{z(z + 1)^2}.$$

Multiplication of fractions is easy: Multiply corresponding numerators and denominators, then simplify your answer.

Example 9

$$\frac{x^2 - 1}{x^2 + 2} \cdot \frac{3x - 4}{x + 1} = \frac{(x^2 - 1)(3x - 4)}{(x^2 + 2)(x + 1)}$$

$$= \frac{(x - 1)(x + 1)(3x - 4)}{(x^2 + 2)(x + 1)} = \frac{(x - 1)(3x - 4)}{x^2 + 2}.$$

Division of fractions is given by the rule:

Invert the divisor and multiply: $\quad \dfrac{a}{b} \div \dfrac{c}{d} = \dfrac{a}{b} \cdot \dfrac{d}{c} = \dfrac{ad}{bc}.$

Example 10

$$\frac{x^2 + x - 2}{x^2 - 6x + 9} \div \frac{x^2 - 1}{x - 3} = \frac{x^2 + x - 2}{x^2 - 6x + 9} \cdot \frac{x - 3}{x^2 - 1}$$

$$= \frac{(x + 2)(x - 1)}{(x - 3)^2} \cdot \frac{x - 3}{(x - 1)(x + 1)}$$

$$= \frac{x + 2}{(x - 3)(x + 1)}.$$

∎

Division problems can also be written as fractions. For instance, $\dfrac{8}{2}$ means

$8 \div 2 = 4$. Similarly, the compound fraction $\dfrac{\dfrac{a}{b}}{\dfrac{c}{d}}$ means $\dfrac{a}{b} \div \dfrac{c}{d}.$ So,

the basic rule for simplifying compound fractions is: *Invert the denominator and multiply it by the numerator.*

Example 11

a. $\quad \dfrac{\dfrac{16y^2z}{8yz^2}}{\dfrac{yz}{6y^3z^3}} = \dfrac{16y^2z}{8yz^2} \cdot \dfrac{6y^3z^3}{yz} = \dfrac{16 \cdot 6 \cdot y^5z^4}{8y^2z^3}$

$$= 2 \cdot 6 \cdot y^{5-2}z^{4-3} = 12y^3z.$$

b. $\quad \dfrac{\dfrac{y^2}{y + 2}}{y^3 + y} = \dfrac{y^2}{y + 2} \cdot \dfrac{1}{y^3 + y} = \dfrac{y^2}{(y + 2)(y^3 + y)}$

$$= \frac{y^2}{(y + 2)y(y^2 + 1)}$$

$$= \frac{y}{(y + 2)(y^2 + 1)}.$$

∎

Exercises A.4

In Exercises 1–10, express the fraction in lowest terms.

1. $\dfrac{63}{49}\quad \dfrac{9}{7}$ **2.** $\dfrac{121}{33}\quad \dfrac{11}{3}$ **3.** $\dfrac{13 \cdot 27 \cdot 22 \cdot 10}{6 \cdot 4 \cdot 11 \cdot 12}\quad \dfrac{195}{8}$

4. $\dfrac{x^2 - 4}{x + 2}$ **5.** $\dfrac{x^2 - x - 2}{x^2 + 2x + 1}$ **6.** $\dfrac{z + 1}{z^3 + 1}$

$\quad x - 2 \qquad\qquad \dfrac{x - 2}{x + 1} \qquad\qquad \dfrac{1}{z^2 - z + 1}$

7. $\dfrac{a^2 - b^2}{a^3 - b^3}\quad \dfrac{a + b}{a^2 + ab + b^2}$ **8.** $\dfrac{x^4 - 3x^2}{x^3}\quad \dfrac{x^2 - 3}{x}$

9. $\dfrac{(x + c)(x^2 - cx + c^2)}{x^4 + c^3x}$

$\quad \dfrac{1}{x}$

10. $\dfrac{x^4 - y^4}{(x^2 + y^2)(x^2 - xy)}$

$\quad \dfrac{x + y}{x}$

Section A.4 **Fractional Expressions** 985

ADDITIONAL EXAMPLES

Example 9

Multiply: $\dfrac{5x + 6}{x - 2} \cdot \dfrac{x^2 - 4}{x^2 + 3}$

$$= \frac{(5x + 6)(x^2 - 4)}{(x - 2)(x^2 + 3)}$$

$$= \frac{(5x + 6)(x + 2)(x - 2)}{(x - 2)(x^2 + 3)}$$

$$= \frac{(5x + 6)(x + 2)}{x^2 + 3}$$

Example 10

Divide: $\dfrac{x^2 - 4x + 4}{x^2 - 25} \div \dfrac{x^2 + 4x - 12}{x - 5}$

$$= \frac{x^2 - 4x + 4}{x^2 - 25} \cdot \frac{x - 5}{x^2 + 4x - 12}$$

$$= \frac{(x - 2)^2}{(x + 5)(x - 5)} \cdot \frac{x - 5}{(x - 2)(x + 6)}$$

$$= \frac{x - 2}{(x + 5)(x + 6)}$$

Example 11

Simplify:

a. $\dfrac{\dfrac{24a^4b}{ab^2}}{\dfrac{8a^2b^2}{2a^3b^4}}$

$$= \frac{24a^4b}{ab^2} \cdot \frac{2a^3b^4}{8a^2b^2}$$

$$= \frac{24 \cdot 2 \cdot a^7b^5}{8 \cdot a^3b^4}$$

$$= 3 \cdot 2 \cdot a^{7-3}b^{5-4}$$

$$= 6a^4b$$

b. $\dfrac{\dfrac{x^3}{x - 3}}{x^2 - x}$

$$= \frac{x^3}{x - 3} \cdot \frac{1}{x^2 - x}$$

$$= \frac{x^3}{(x - 3)(x^2 - x)}$$

$$= \frac{x^3}{(x - 3)x(x - 1)}$$

$$= \frac{x^2}{(x - 3)(x - 1)}$$

Exercises A.4

ANSWERS

14. $\dfrac{b - 2a^2}{ab}$

15. $\dfrac{ce + 3cd}{de}$

16. $\dfrac{r^2t + s^2r + st^2}{rst}$

17. $\dfrac{b^2 - c^2}{bc}$

18. $\dfrac{ab^2 + 2ab + 3a}{b^3}$

19. $\dfrac{-1}{x(x+1)}$

22. $\dfrac{y^2 + y + 1}{xy^2}$

23. $\dfrac{2x - 4}{x(3x - 4)}$

24. $\dfrac{7x - 1}{(x-1)(x+1)}$

25. $\dfrac{x^2 - xy + y^2 + x + y}{x^3 + y^3}$

27. $\dfrac{-6x^5 - 38x^4 - 84x^3 - 71x^2 - 14x + 1}{4x(x+1)^3(x+2)^3}$

28. $\dfrac{(x+y)^3 - 2x(x-y)}{x(x-y)^3(x+y)^2}$

51. $\dfrac{cd(c+d)}{c-d}$

52. $\dfrac{-3x^2 + 8x - 4}{14x - 20}$

53. $\dfrac{y - x}{xy}$

61. example: if $a = 1$, $b = 2$, then
$\dfrac{1}{1} + \dfrac{1}{2} \neq \dfrac{1}{1+2}$; correct statement:
$\dfrac{1}{a} + \dfrac{1}{b} = \dfrac{b + a}{ab}$

62. example: if $x = 1$, then
$\dfrac{1^2}{1^2 + 1^6} \neq 1 + 1^3$;
correct statement:
$\dfrac{x^2}{x^2 + x^6} = \dfrac{1}{1 + x^4}$

63. example: if $a = 4$, $b = 9$, then
$\left(\dfrac{1}{\sqrt{4} + \sqrt{9}}\right)^2 \neq \dfrac{1}{4 + 9}$;
correct statement:
$\left(\dfrac{1}{\sqrt{a} + \sqrt{b}}\right)^2 = \dfrac{1}{a + 2\sqrt{ab} + b}$

64. example: if $r = 1$, $s = 1$, $t = 1$,
then $\dfrac{1 + 1}{1 + 1} \neq 1 + \dfrac{1}{1}$.
correct statement: fraction cannot be reduced

65. example: if $u = 1$, $v = 2$,
then $\dfrac{1}{2} + \dfrac{2}{1} \neq 1$;
correct statement:
$\dfrac{u}{v} + \dfrac{v}{u} = \dfrac{u^2 + v^2}{vu}$

In Exercises 11–28, perform the indicated operations.

11. $\dfrac{3}{7} + \dfrac{2}{5}$ **$\dfrac{29}{35}$** **12.** $\dfrac{7}{8} - \dfrac{5}{6}$ **$\dfrac{1}{24}$** **13.** $\left(\dfrac{19}{7} + \dfrac{1}{2}\right) - \dfrac{1}{3}$ **$\dfrac{121}{42}$**

14. $\dfrac{1}{a} - \dfrac{2a}{b}$ **15.** $\dfrac{c}{d} + \dfrac{3c}{e}$ **16.** $\dfrac{r}{s} + \dfrac{s}{t} + \dfrac{t}{r}$

17. $\dfrac{b}{c} - \dfrac{c}{b}$ **18.** $\dfrac{a}{b} + \dfrac{2a}{b^2} + \dfrac{3a}{b^3}$ **19.** $\dfrac{1}{x+1} - \dfrac{1}{x}$

20. $\dfrac{1}{2x+1} + \dfrac{1}{2x-1}$ **$\dfrac{4x}{(2x-1)(2x+1)}$**

21. $\dfrac{1}{x+4} + \dfrac{2}{(x+4)^2} - \dfrac{3}{x^2 + 8x + 16}$ **$\dfrac{x+3}{(x+4)^2}$**

22. $\dfrac{1}{x} + \dfrac{1}{xy} + \dfrac{1}{xy^2}$ **23.** $\dfrac{1}{x} - \dfrac{1}{3x-4}$

24. $\dfrac{3}{x-1} + \dfrac{4}{x+1}$ **25.** $\dfrac{1}{x+y} + \dfrac{x+y}{x^3 + y^3}$

26. $\dfrac{6}{5(x-1)(x-2)^2} + \dfrac{x}{3(x-1)^2(x-2)}$ **$\dfrac{5x^2 + 8x - 18}{15(x-1)^2(x-2)^2}$**

27. $\dfrac{1}{4x(x+1)(x+2)^3} - \dfrac{6x+2}{4(x+1)^3}$

28. $\dfrac{x+y}{(x^2 - xy)(x-y)^2} - \dfrac{2}{(x^2 - y^2)^2}$

In Exercises 29–42, express in lowest terms.

29. $\dfrac{3}{4} \cdot \dfrac{12}{5} \cdot \dfrac{10}{9}$ **2** **30.** $\dfrac{10}{45} \cdot \dfrac{6}{14} \cdot \dfrac{1}{2}$ **$\dfrac{1}{21}$**

31. $\dfrac{3a^2c}{4ac} \cdot \dfrac{8ac^3}{9a^2c^4}$ **$\dfrac{2}{3c}$** **32.** $\dfrac{6x^2y}{2x} \cdot \dfrac{y}{21xy}$ **$\dfrac{y}{7}$**

33. $\dfrac{7x}{11y} \cdot \dfrac{66y^2}{14x^3}$ **$\dfrac{3y}{x^2}$** **34.** $\dfrac{ab}{c^2} \cdot \dfrac{cd}{a^2b} \cdot \dfrac{ad}{bc^2}$ **$\dfrac{d^2}{bc^3}$**

35. $\dfrac{3x+9}{2x} \cdot \dfrac{8x^2}{x^2 - 9}$ **$\dfrac{12x}{x-3}$** **36.** $\dfrac{4x+16}{3x+15} \cdot \dfrac{2x+10}{x+4}$ **$\dfrac{8}{3}$**

37. $\dfrac{5y-25}{3} \cdot \dfrac{y^2}{y^2 - 25}$ **$\dfrac{5y^2}{3(y+5)}$** **38.** $\dfrac{6x-12}{6x} \cdot \dfrac{8x^2}{x-2}$ **$8x$**

39. $\dfrac{u}{u-1} \cdot \dfrac{u^2 - 1}{u^2}$ **$\dfrac{u+1}{u}$**

40. $\dfrac{t^2 - t - 6}{t^2 - 6t + 9} \cdot \dfrac{t^2 + 4t - 5}{t^2 - 25}$ **$\dfrac{(t+2)(t-1)}{(t-3)(t-5)}$**

41. $\dfrac{2u^2 + uv - v^2}{4u^2 - 4uv + v^2} \cdot \dfrac{8u^2 + 6uv - 9v^2}{4u^2 - 9v^2}$ **$\dfrac{(u+v)(4u-3v)}{(2u-v)(2u-3v)}$**

42. $\dfrac{2x^2 - 3xy - 2y^2}{6x^2 - 5xy - 4y^2} \cdot \dfrac{6x^2 + 6xy}{x^2 - xy - 2y^2}$ **$\dfrac{6x}{3x - 4y}$**

In Exercises 43–60, compute the quotient and express in lowest terms.

43. $\dfrac{5}{12} \div \dfrac{4}{14}$ **$\dfrac{35}{24}$** **44.** $\dfrac{\frac{100}{52}}{\frac{27}{26}}$ **$\dfrac{50}{27}$** **45.** $\dfrac{uv}{v^2w} \div \dfrac{uv}{u^2v}$ **$\dfrac{u^2}{vw}$**

46. $\dfrac{3x^2y}{(xy)^2} \div \dfrac{3xyz}{x^2y}$ **$\dfrac{x}{yz}$** **47.** $\dfrac{\frac{x+3}{x+4}}{\frac{2x}{x+4}}$ **$\dfrac{x+3}{2x}$** **48.** $\dfrac{\frac{(x+2)^2}{(x-2)^2}}{\frac{x^2+2x}{x^2-4}}$ **$\dfrac{(x+2)^2}{x(x-2)}$**

49. $\dfrac{x+y}{x+2y} \div \left(\dfrac{x+y}{xy}\right)^2$ **$\dfrac{x^2y^2}{(x+y)(x+2y)}$**

50. $\dfrac{\frac{u^3+v^3}{u^2-v^2}}{\frac{u^2-uv+v^2}{u+v}}$ **$\dfrac{u+v}{u-v}$**

51. $\dfrac{\frac{(c+d)^2}{c^2-d^2}}{cd}$ **52.** $\dfrac{\frac{1}{x}-\frac{3}{2}}{\frac{2}{x-2}+\frac{5}{x}}$ **53.** $\dfrac{\frac{1}{x^2}-\frac{1}{y^2}}{\frac{1}{x}+\frac{1}{y}}$

54. $\dfrac{\frac{x}{x+1}+\frac{1}{x}}{\frac{1}{x}+\frac{1}{x+1}}$ **$\dfrac{x^2+x+1}{2x+1}$** **55.** $\dfrac{\frac{6}{y}-3}{1-\frac{1}{y-1}}$ **$\dfrac{-3y+3}{y}$**

56. $\dfrac{\frac{1}{3x}-\frac{1}{4y}}{\frac{5}{6x^2}+\frac{1}{y}}$ **$\dfrac{4xy-3x^2}{10y+12x^2}$** **57.** $\dfrac{\frac{1}{x+h}-\frac{1}{x}}{h}$ **$\dfrac{-1}{x(x+h)}$**

58. $\dfrac{\frac{1}{(x+h)^2}-\frac{1}{x^2}}{h}$ **$\dfrac{-h-2x}{x^2(x+h)^2}$** **59.** $(x^{-1} + y^{-1})^{-1}$ **$\dfrac{xy}{x+y}$**

60. $\dfrac{(x+y)^{-1}}{x^{-1}+y^{-1}}$ **$\dfrac{xy}{(x+y)^2}$**

In Exercises 61–67, find a numerical example to show that the given statement is false. Then find the mistake in the statement and correct it.

61. $\dfrac{1}{a} + \dfrac{1}{b} = \dfrac{1}{a+b}$ **62.** $\dfrac{x^2}{x^2 + x^6} = 1 + x^3$

63. $\left(\dfrac{1}{\sqrt{a} + \sqrt{b}}\right)^2 = \dfrac{1}{a+b}$ **64.** $\dfrac{r+s}{r+t} = 1 + \dfrac{s}{t}$

65. $\dfrac{u}{v} + \dfrac{v}{u} = 1$ **66.** $\dfrac{\frac{1}{x}}{\frac{1}{y}} = \dfrac{1}{xy}$

67. $(\sqrt{x} + \sqrt{y}) \dfrac{1}{\sqrt{x} + \sqrt{y}} = x + y$

66. example: if $x = 1$, $y = 2$, then $\dfrac{\frac{1}{1}}{\frac{1}{2}} \neq \dfrac{1}{1(2)}$;
correct statement: $\dfrac{\frac{1}{x}}{\frac{1}{y}} = \dfrac{y}{x}$

67. example: if $x = 4$, $y = 9$, then
$(\sqrt{4} + \sqrt{9}) \cdot \dfrac{1}{\sqrt{4} + \sqrt{9}} \neq 4 + 9$;
correct statement:
$(\sqrt{x} + \sqrt{y}) \cdot \dfrac{1}{\sqrt{x} + \sqrt{y}} = 1$

A.5 The Coordinate Plane

The Distance Formula

We shall often identify a point with its coordinates and refer, for example, to the point (2, 3). When dealing with several points simultaneously, it is customary to label the coordinates of the first point (x_1, y_1), the second point (x_2, y_2), the third point (x_3, y_3), and so on.* Once the plane is coordinatized, it's easy to compute the distance between any two points:

The Distance Formula

> The distance between points (x_1, y_1) and (x_2, y_2) is
> $$\sqrt{(x_1 - x_2)^2 + (y_1 - y_2)^2}.$$

Before proving the distance formula, we shall see how it is used.

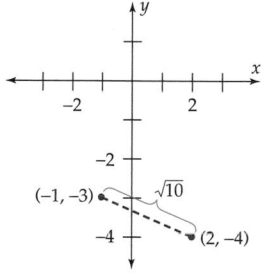

Figure A.5-1

Example 1

To find the distance between the points $(-1, -3)$ and $(2, -4)$ in Figure A.5–1, substitute $(-1, -3)$ for (x_1, y_1) and $(2, -4)$ for (x_2, y_2) in the distance formula.

Distance formula: $\quad$ distance $= \sqrt{(x_1 - x_2)^2 + (y_1 - y_2)^2}$

Substitute: $\qquad\qquad = \sqrt{(-1 - 2)^2 + (-3 - (-4))^2}$

Simplify: $\qquad\qquad = \sqrt{(-3)^2 + (-3 + 4)^2}$

$\qquad\qquad\qquad\quad = \sqrt{9 + 1} = \sqrt{10}$

The order in which the points are used in the distance formula doesn't make a difference. If we substitute $(2, -4)$ for (x_1, y_1) and $(-1, -3)$ for (x_2, y_2), we get the same answer:

$$\sqrt{[2 - (-1)]^2 + [-4 - (-3)]^2} = \sqrt{3^2 + (-1)^2} = \sqrt{10}.$$

CAUTION

$\sqrt{a^2 + 4b^2}$ cannot be simplified. In particular, it is *not* equal to $a + 2b$.

Example 2

To find the distance from (a, b) to $(2a, -b)$, where a and b are fixed real numbers, substitute a for x_1, b for y_1, $2a$ for x_2, and $-b$ for y_2 in the distance formula:

$$\sqrt{(x_1 - x_2)^2 + (y_1 - y_2)^2} = \sqrt{(a - 2a)^2 + (b - (-b))^2}$$
$$= \sqrt{(-a)^2 + (b + b)^2} = \sqrt{a^2 + (2b)^2}$$
$$= \sqrt{a^2 + 4b^2}$$

*"x_1" is read "x-one" or "x-sub-one"; it is a *single symbol* denoting the first coordinate of the first point, just as c denotes the first coordinate of (c, d). Analogous remarks apply to y_1, x_2, and so on.

Section A.5 **The Coordinate Plane** **987**

Section A.5 The Coordinate Plane

COMMON ERROR ALERT

For **Example 1,** students might incorrectly substitute -4 in for y_2 in the distance formula as shown below:

$$\sqrt{(x_1 - x_2)^2 + (y_1 - y_2)^2}$$
$$= \sqrt{(-1 - 2)^2 + (-3 - 4)^2}$$
$$= \sqrt{(-3)^2 + (-7)^2} = \sqrt{9 + 49}$$
$$= \sqrt{58}$$

Emphasize that you need to *subtract* -4 and that *subtracting a negative* is the same as *adding a positive*, so that $(-3 - (-4)) = (-3 + 4) = 1$.

ADDITIONAL EXAMPLES

Example 1

Find the distance between the points (3, 1) and $(-2, 5)$.

$$d = \sqrt{(x_1 - x_2)^2 + (y_1 - y_2)^2}$$
$$= \sqrt{(3 - (-2))^2 + (1 - 5)^2}$$
$$= \sqrt{(5)^2 + (-4)^2}$$
$$= \sqrt{25 + 16}$$
$$= \sqrt{41}$$

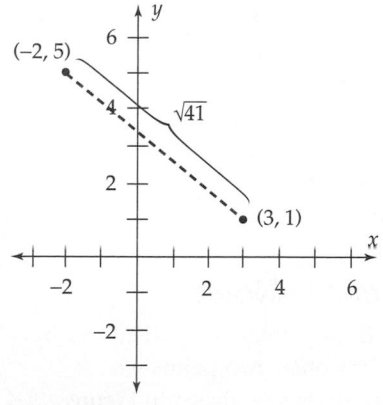

Example 2

Find the distance between the points (a, b) and $(-3a, 4b)$.

$$d = \sqrt{(x_1 - x_2)^2 + (y_1 - y_2)^2}$$
$$= \sqrt{(a - (-3a))^2 + (b - 4b)^2}$$
$$= \sqrt{(4a)^2 + (-3b)^2}$$
$$= \sqrt{16a^2 + 9b^2}$$

Algebra Review

Teaching Notes

After completing **Example 1**, point out to students that **The Midpoint Formula** can be expressed verbally as:

The *x*-coordinate of the midpoint is the average of the *x*-coordinates and the *y*-coordinate of the midpoint is the average of the *y*-coordinates.

Then have students find the midpoint of $(-1, 4)$ and $(3, 1)$ from Example 1 with that reasoning:

average of *x*-coordinates, -1 and 3:

$$\frac{-1 + 3}{2} = 1$$

average of *y*-coordinates, 4 and 1:

$$\frac{4 + 1}{2} = \frac{5}{2}$$

coordinate of midpoint: $\left(1, \frac{5}{2}\right)$

COMMON ERROR ALERT

Because the expressions $x_1 - x_2$ and $y_1 - y_2$ appear in the distance formula, some students might be tempted to use them in **The Midpoint Formula**. For instance, in **Example 3**, they might incorrectly try to find the midpoint of the segment joining $(-1, 4)$ and $(3, 1)$ by doing the following:

$$\left(\frac{x_1 - x_2}{2}, \frac{y_1 - y_2}{2}\right)$$

$$= \left(\frac{-1 - 3}{2}, \frac{4 - 1}{2}\right) = \left(-2, \frac{3}{2}\right)$$

Remind them that the midpoint is found by *averaging* the *x*- and *y*-coordinates of the endpoints, so the operation that should be used is *addition*.

Example Notes

For **Example 4**, have students verify that the other two points whose coordinates are labeled in Figure A.5-4 are also solutions of the equation $y = x^2 - 2x - 1$.

$(-1, 2)$:

$$(-1)^2 - 2(-1) - 1 = 1 + 2 - 1$$
$$= 2$$

$(1.5, -1.75)$:

$$1.5^2 - 2(1.5) - 1 = 2.25 - 3 - 1$$
$$= -1.75$$

The Midpoint Formula

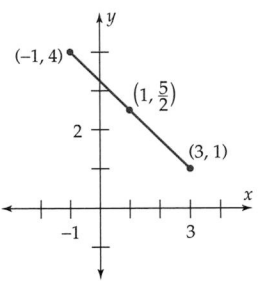

Figure A.5-3

Proof of the Distance Formula Figure A.5-2 shows typical points *P* and *Q* in the plane. We must find length *d* of line segment *PQ*.

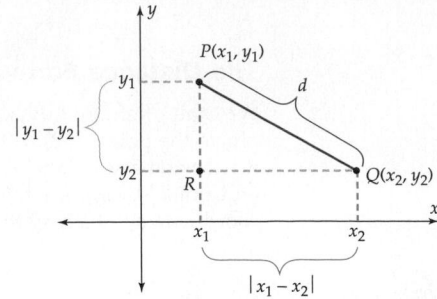

Figure A.5-2

As shown in Figure A.5-2, the length of *RQ* is the same as the distance from x_1 to x_2 on the *x*-axis (number line), namely, $|x_1 - x_2|$. Similarly, the length of *PR* is the same as the distance from y_1 to y_2 on the *y*-axis, namely, $|y_1 - y_2|$. According to the Pythagorean Theorem* the length *d* of *PQ* is given by:

$$(\text{Length } PQ)^2 = (\text{length } RQ)^2 + (\text{length } PR)^2$$

$$d^2 = |x_1 - x_2|^2 + |y_1 - y_2|^2$$

Since $|c|^2 = |c| \cdot |c| = |c^2| = c^2$ (because $c^2 \geq 0$), this equation becomes:

$$d^2 = (x_1 - x_2)^2 + (y_1 - y_2)^2$$

Since the length *d* is nonnegative, we must have

$$d = \sqrt{(x_1 - x_2)^2 + (y_1 - y_2)^2}$$

The distance formula can be used to prove the following useful fact (see Exercise 54).

> **The midpoint of the line segment from (x_1, y_1) to (x_2, y_2) is**
> $$\left(\frac{x_1 + x_2}{2}, \frac{y_1 + y_2}{2}\right)$$

Example 3

To find the midpoint of the segment joining $(-1, 4)$ and $(3, 1)$, use the formula in the box with $x_1 = -1$, $y_1 = 4$, $x_2 = 3$, and $y_2 = 1$. The midpoint is

$$\left(\frac{x_1 + x_2}{2}, \frac{y_1 + y_2}{2}\right) = \left(\frac{-1 + 3}{2}, \frac{4 + 1}{2}\right) = \left(1, \frac{5}{2}\right)$$

as shown in Figure A.5-3. ∎

*See the Geometry Review Appendix.

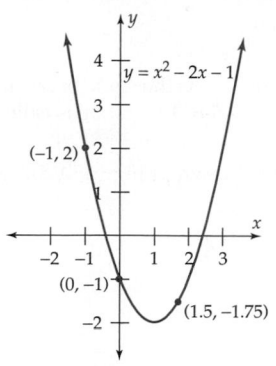

Figure A.5-4

Graphs

A **graph** is a set of points in the plane. Some graphs are based on data points. Other graphs arise from equations, as follows. A **solution** of an equation in variables x and y is a pair of numbers such that the substitution of the first number for x and the second for y produces a true statement. For instance, $(3, -2)$ is a solution of $5x + 7y = 1$ because

$$5 \cdot 3 + 7(-2) = 1$$

and $(-2, 3)$ is *not* a solution because $5(-2) + 7 \cdot 3 \neq 1$. The **graph of an equation** in two variables is the set of points in the plane whose coordinates are solutions of the equation. Thus the graph is a *geometric picture of the solutions.*

Example 4

The graph of $y = x^2 - 2x - 1$ is shown in Figure A.5-4. You can readily verify that each of the points whose coordinates are labeled is a solution of the equation. For instance, $(0, -1)$ is a solution because $-1 = 0^2 - 2(0) - 1$. ∎

Circles If (c, d) is a point in the plane and r a positive number, then the **circle with center (c, d) and radius r** consists of all points (x, y) that lie r units from (c, d), as shown in Figure A.5-5. According to the distance formula, the statement that "the distance from (x, y) to (c, d) is r units" is equivalent to:

$$\sqrt{(x - c)^2 + (y - d)^2} = r$$

Squaring both sides shows that (x, y) satisfies this equation:

$$(x - c)^2 + (y - d)^2 = r^2$$

Reversing the procedure shows that any solution (x, y) of this equation is a point on the circle. Therefore,

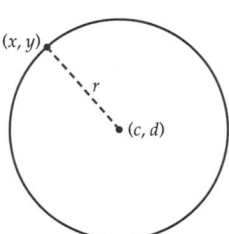

Figure A.5-5

Circle Equation

The circle with center (c, d) and radius r is the graph of

$$(x - c)^2 + (y - d)^2 = r^2.$$

We say that $(x - c)^2 + (y - d)^2 = r^2$ is the **equation of the circle** with center (c, d) and radius r. If the center is at the origin, then $(c, d) = (0, 0)$ and the equation has a simpler form:

Circle at the Origin

The circle with center $(0, 0)$ and radius r is the graph of

$$x^2 + y^2 = r^2.$$

Section A.5 **The Coordinate Plane**   **989**

Example 3

Find the midpoint of the segment joining $(-6, -3)$ and $(4, 6)$.

$$\left(\frac{x_1 + x_2}{2}, \frac{y_1 + y_2}{2} \right)$$

$$= \left(\frac{-6 + 4}{2}, \frac{-3 + 6}{2} \right)$$

$$= \left(-1, \frac{3}{2} \right)$$

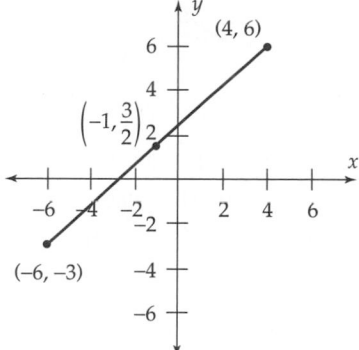

Example 4

The graph of $y = x^2 - 3x - 10$ is shown below. Verify that each of the points whose coordinates are labeled is a solution of the equation.

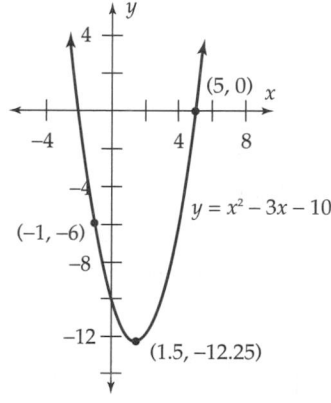

$(-1, -6)$:
$$(-1)^2 - 3(-1) - 10 = 1 + 3 - 10$$
$$= -6$$

$(1.5, -12.25)$:
$$1.5^2 - 3(1.5) - 10 = 2.25 - 4.5 - 10$$
$$= -12.25$$

$(5, 0)$:
$$5^2 - 3(5) - 10 = 25 - 15 - 10$$
$$= 0$$

Teaching Notes

In the discussion of circles, the word *radius* refers not only to a segment with one endpoint at the center and the other on the circle, but also to the segment's *length*.

ADDITIONAL EXAMPLES

Example 5

a. Graph and describe the circle whose equation is $x^2 + y^2 = 4$.

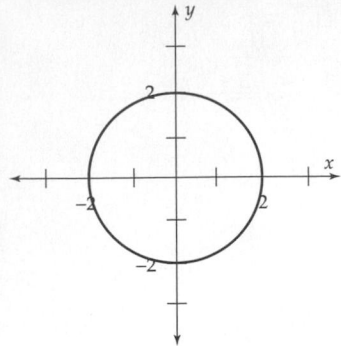

radius 2; centered at the origin

b. Graph the circle with center $(1, -3)$ and radius 4, and find its equation.

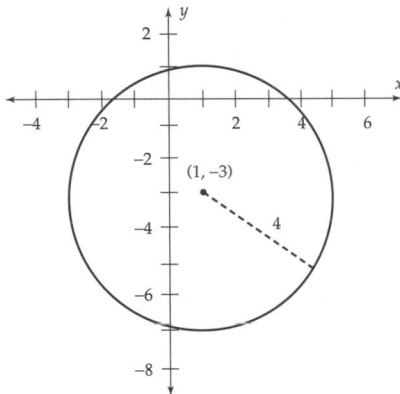

$(x - 1)^2 + (y - (-3))^2 = 16$ or
$(x - 1)^2 + (y + 3)^2 = 16$

Example 6

Find the equation of the circle with center $(4, -2)$ that passes through $(3, 5)$.

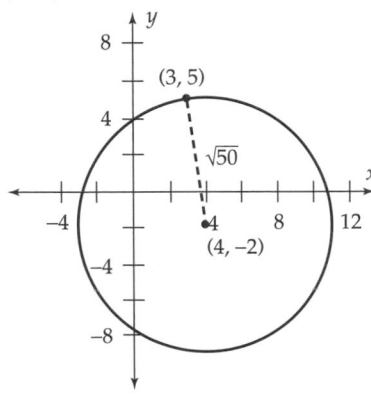

Example 5

a. Letting $r = 1$ shows that the graph of $x^2 + y^2 = 1$ is the circle of radius 1 centered at the origin, as shown in Figure A.5-6. This circle is called the **unit circle**.

b. The circle with center $(-3, 2)$ and radius 2, shown in Figure A.5-7, is the graph of the equation

$$((x - (-3))^2 + (y - 2)^2 = 2^2$$

or equivalently,

$$(x + 3)^2 + (y - 2)^2 = 4.$$

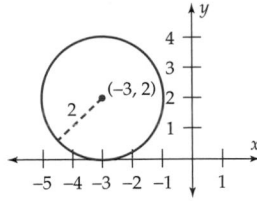

Figure A.5-6   **Figure A.5-7**

Example 6

Find the equation of the circle with center $(3, -1)$ that passes through $(2, 4)$.

Solution

We must first find the radius. Since $(2, 4)$ is on the circle, the radius is the distance from $(2, 4)$ to $(3, -1)$ as shown in Figure A.5-8, namely,

$$\sqrt{(2 - 3)^2 + (4 - (-1))^2} = \sqrt{1 + 25} = \sqrt{26}$$

The equation of the circle with center at $(3, -1)$ and radius $\sqrt{26}$ is

$$(x - 3)^2 + (y - (-1))^2 = \left(\sqrt{26}\right)^2$$
$$(x - 3)^2 + (y + 1)^2 = 26$$
$$x^2 - 6x + 9 + y^2 + 2y + 1 = 26$$
$$x^2 + y^2 - 6x + 2y - 16 = 0.$$

The equation of any circle can always be written in the form

$$x^2 + y^2 + Bx + Cy + D = 0$$

for some constants B, C, D, as in Example 6 (where $B = -6$, $C = 2$, $D = -16$). Conversely, the graph of such an equation can always be determined.

Figure A.5-8

Use the distance formula to find r, the distance between the points $(4, -2)$ and $(3, 5)$.

$$r = \sqrt{(4 - 3)^2 + ((-2) - 5)^2}$$
$$= \sqrt{1 + 49}$$
$$= \sqrt{50}$$

The equation of the circle is:
$$(x - 4)^2 + (y - (-2))^2 = \left(\sqrt{50}\right)^2$$
$$(x - 4)^2 + (y + 2)^2 = 50$$
$$x^2 - 8x + 16 + y^2 + 4y + 4 = 50$$
$$x^2 + y^2 - 8x + 4y - 30 = 0$$

Example 7

Find the graph of $4x^2 + 4y^2 - 8x + 32y + 32 = 0$.

$$\frac{4x^2 + 4y^2 - 8x + 32y + 32}{4} = \frac{0}{4}$$
$$x^2 + y^2 - 2x + 8y + 8 = 0$$
$$(x^2 - 2x) + (y^2 + 8y) = -8$$
$$(x^2 - 2x + 1) + (y^2 + 8y + 16) = -8 + 1 + 16$$
$$(x - 1)^2 + (y + 4)^2 = 9$$

The graph of the equation is a circle with center $(1, -4)$ and radius 3.

Example 7

To find the graph of $3x^2 + 3y^2 - 12x - 30y + 45 = 0$, we divide both sides by 3 and rewrite the equation as

$$(x^2 - 4x) + (y^2 - 10y) = -15.$$

Next we complete the square in both expressions in parentheses (see page 91). To complete the square in $x^2 - 4x$, we add 4 (the square of half the coefficient of x) and to complete the square in $y^2 - 10y$ we add 25 (why?). In order to have an equivalent equation we must add these numbers to *both* sides:

$$(x^2 - 4x + 4) + (y^2 - 10y + 25) = -15 + 4 + 25$$
$$(x - 2)^2 + (y - 5)^2 = 14$$

Since $14 = (\sqrt{14})^2$, this is the equation of the circle with center $(2, 5)$ and radius $\sqrt{14}$.

Exercises A.5

In Exercises 1–8, find the distance between the two points and the midpoint of the segment joining them.

1. $(-3, 5), (2, -7)$ **2.** $(2, 4), (1, 5)$

3. $(1, -5), (2, -1)$ **4.** $(-2, 3), (-3, 2)$

5. $(\sqrt{2}, 1), (\sqrt{3}, 2)$ **6.** $(-1, \sqrt{5}), (\sqrt{2}, -\sqrt{3})$

7. $(a, b), (b, a)$ **8.** $(s, t), (0, 0)$

9. According to the Information Technology Industry Council, there were about 12 million personal computers sold in the United States in 1992 and about 36 million in 1998.
 a. Represent the data graphically by two points.
 b. Find the midpoint of the line segment joining these points.
 c. How might this midpoint be interpreted? What assumptions, if any, are needed to make this interpretation?

10. A standard baseball diamond (which is actually a square) is shown in the figure at right. Suppose it is placed on a coordinate plane with home plate at the origin, first base on the positive x-axis, and third base on the positive y-axis. The unit of measurement is feet.
 a. Find the coordinates of first, second, and third base. **(90, 0); (90, 90); (0, 90)**
 b. If the left fielder is at the point $(50, 325)$, how far is he from first base? **$\approx$327.5 ft**
 c. How far is the left fielder in part **b** from the right fielder, who is at the point $(280, 20)$? **$\approx$382 ft**

In Exercises 11–14, find the equation of the circle with given center and radius r.

11. $(-3, 4)$; $r = 2$
$(x + 3)^2 + (y - 4)^2 = 4$
12. $(-2, -1)$; $r = 3$
$(x + 2)^2 + (y + 1)^2 = 9$
13. $(0, 0)$; $r = \sqrt{2}$
$x^2 + y^2 = 2$
14. $(5, -2)$; $r = 1$
$(x - 5)^2 + (y + 2)^2 = 1$

In Exercises 15–18, sketch the graph of the equation.

15. $(x - 2)^2 + (y - 4)^2 = 1$

16. $(x + 1)^2 + (y - 3)^2 = 9$

17. $(x - 5)^2 + (y + 2)^2 = 5$

18. $(x + 6)^2 + y^2 = 4$

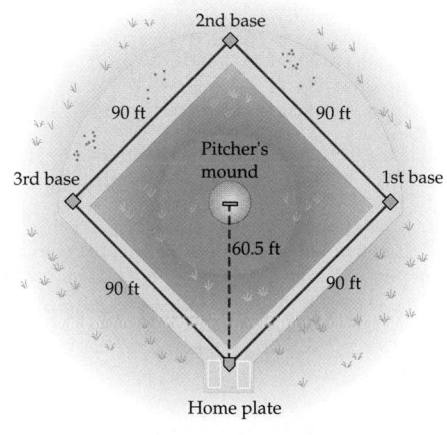

Home plate

When completing the square, students may fail to add the newly created constant term(s) to the other side of the equation. Remind them that they must always maintain the balance of the equation by performing the same operation on *both* sides.

Refer students to pages 90–91 for more detail on completing the square.

Exercises A.5

ANSWERS

1. $13; \left(-\dfrac{1}{2}, -1\right)$

2. $\sqrt{2}; \left(\dfrac{3}{2}, \dfrac{9}{2}\right)$

3. $\sqrt{17}; \left(\dfrac{3}{2}, -3\right)$

4. $\sqrt{2}; \left(-\dfrac{5}{2}, \dfrac{5}{2}\right)$

5. $\sqrt{6 - 2\sqrt{6}} \approx 1.05; \left(\dfrac{\sqrt{2} + \sqrt{3}}{2}, \dfrac{3}{2}\right)$

6. $4.6448; \left(\dfrac{-1 + \sqrt{2}}{2}, \dfrac{\sqrt{5} - \sqrt{3}}{2}\right)$

7. $\sqrt{2}\, |a - b|; \left(\dfrac{a + b}{2}, \dfrac{a + b}{2}\right)$

8. $\sqrt{s^2 + t^2}; \left(\dfrac{s}{2}, \dfrac{t}{2}\right)$

9. a.

b.

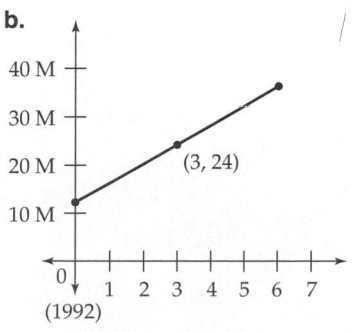

c. In 1995, about 24 million personal computers were sold. We must assume that sales increased steadily.

15.

16.

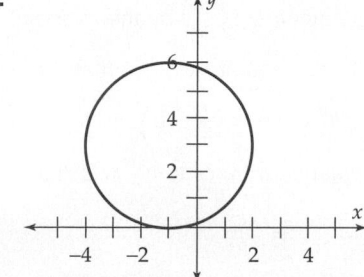

17–18. See p. 992.

17.

18.

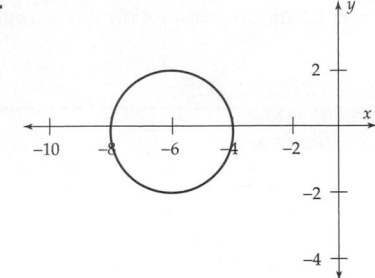

25. Hypotenuse from $(1, 1)$ to $(2, -2)$ has length $\sqrt{10}$; other sides have lengths $\sqrt{2}$ and $\sqrt{8}$. Since $(\sqrt{2})^2 + (\sqrt{8})^2 = (\sqrt{10})^2$, this is a right triangle.

26. Hypotenuse from $(0, 0)$ to $\left(\dfrac{\sqrt{2}}{2}, \dfrac{\sqrt{2}}{2}\right)$ has length 1; other sides have lengths $\sqrt{\dfrac{1}{2}}$ and $\sqrt{\dfrac{1}{2}}$. Since $\left(\sqrt{\dfrac{1}{2}}\right)^2 + \left(\sqrt{\dfrac{1}{2}}\right)^2 = 1$, this is a right triangle.

27. Hypotenuse from $(-2, 3)$ to $(3, -2)$ has length $\sqrt{50}$; other sides have lengths $\sqrt{5}$ and $\sqrt{45}$. Since $(\sqrt{5})^2 + (\sqrt{45})^2 = (\sqrt{50})^2$, this is a right triangle.

39. Assume $k > d$. The other two vertices of one possible square are $(c + k - d, d)$, $(c + k - d, k)$; those of another square are $(c - (k - d), d)$, $(c - (k - d), k)$; those of a third square are $\left(c + \dfrac{k - d}{2}, \dfrac{k + d}{2}\right)$, $\left(\dfrac{k - d}{2}, \dfrac{k + d}{2}\right)$.

In Exercises 19–24, find the center and radius of the circle whose equation is given.

19. $x^2 + y^2 + 8x - 6y - 15 = 0$ **$(-4, 3)$; $2\sqrt{10}$**

20. $15x^2 + 15y^2 = 10$ **$(0, 0)$; $\sqrt{\dfrac{2}{3}}$**

21. $x^2 + y^2 + 6x - 4y - 15 = 0$ **$(-3, 2)$; $2\sqrt{7}$**

22. $x^2 + y^2 + 10x - 75 = 0$ **$(-5, 0)$; 10**

23. $x^2 + y^2 + 25x + 10y = -12$ **$(-12.5, -5)$; $\sqrt{169.25}$**

24. $3x^2 + 3y^2 + 12x + 12 = 18y$ **$(-2, 3)$; $3\sqrt{3}$**

In Exercises 25–27, show that the three points are the vertices of a right triangle, and state the length of the hypotenuse. [You may assume that a triangle with sides of lengths a, b, c is a right triangle with hypotenuse c provided that $a^2 + b^2 = c^2$.]

25. $(0, 0)$, $(1, 1)$, $(2, -2)$

26. $\left(\dfrac{\sqrt{2}}{2}, 0\right)$, $\left(\dfrac{\sqrt{2}}{2}, \dfrac{\sqrt{2}}{2}\right)$, $(0, 0)$

27. $(3, -2)$, $(0, 4)$, $(-2, 3)$

28. What is the perimeter of the triangle with vertices $(1, 1)$, $(5, 4)$, and $(-2, 5)$? **$10 + 5\sqrt{2}$**

In Exercises 29–36, find the equation of the circle.

29. Center $(2, 2)$; passes through the origin. **$(x - 2)^2 + (y - 2)^2 = 8$**

30. Center $(-1, -3)$; passes through $(-4, -2)$. **$(x + 1)^2 + (y + 3)^2 = 10$**

31. Center $(1, 2)$; intersects x-axis at -1 and 3. **$(x - 1)^2 + (y - 2)^2 = 8$**

32. Center $(3, 1)$; diameter 2. **$(x - 3)^2 + (y - 1)^2 = 1$**

33. Center $(-5, 4)$; tangent (touching at one point) to the x-axis. **$(x + 5)^2 + (y - 4)^2 = 16$**

34. Center $(2, -6)$; tangent to the y-axis. **$(x - 2)^2 + (y + 6)^2 = 4$**

35. Endpoints of diameter are $(3, 3)$ and $(1, -1)$. **$x^2 + y^2 - 4x - 2y = 0$**

36. Endpoints of diameter are $(-3, 5)$ and $(7, -5)$. **$(x - 2)^2 + y^2 = 50$**

37. One diagonal of a square has endpoints $(-3, 1)$ and $(2, -4)$. Find the endpoints of the other diagonal. **$(-3, -4)$ and $(2, 1)$**

38. Find the vertices of all possible squares with this property: Two of the vertices are $(2, 1)$ and $(2, 5)$. *Hint:* There are three such squares. **$(-2, 1)$, $(-2, 5)$, $(0, 3)$, $(4, 3)$, $(6, 1)$ and $(6, 5)$**

39. Do Exercise 38 with (c, d) and (c, k) in place of $(2, 1)$ and $(2, 5)$.

---

40. Find the three points that divide the line segment from $(-4, 7)$ to $(10, -9)$ into four parts of equal length. **$(3, -1)$, $\left(-\dfrac{1}{2}, 3\right)$ and $\left(\dfrac{13}{2}, -5\right)$**

41. Find all points P on the x-axis that are 5 units from $(3, 4)$. *Hint:* P must have coordinates $(x, 0)$ for some x and the distance from P to $(3, 4)$ is 5. **$(0, 0)$, $(6, 0)$**

42. Find all points on the y-axis that are 8 units from $(-2, 4)$. **$\left(0, 4 + 2\sqrt{15}\right)$ and $\left(0, 4 - 2\sqrt{15}\right)$**

43. Find all points with first coordinate 3 that are 6 units from $(-2, -5)$. **$\left(3, -5 + \sqrt{11}\right)$, $\left(3, -5 - \sqrt{11}\right)$**

44. Find all points with second coordinate -1 that are 4 units from $(2, 3)$. **$(2, -1)$**

45. Find a number x such that $(0, 0)$, $(3, 2)$, and $(x, 0)$ are the vertices of an isosceles triangle, neither of whose two equal sides lie on the x-axis. **$x = 6$**

46. Do Exercise 45 if one of the two equal sides lies on the positive x-axis. **$x = \dfrac{13}{6}$ or $x = \sqrt{13}$**

47. Show that the midpoint M of the hypotenuse of a right triangle is equidistant from the vertices of the triangle. *Hint:* Place the triangle in the first quadrant of the plane, with right angle at the origin so that the situation looks like the figure.

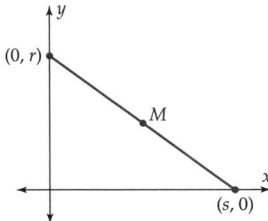

48. Show that the diagonals of a parallelogram bisect each other. *Hint:* Place the parallelogram in the first quadrant with a vertex at the origin and one side along the x-axis, so that the situation looks like the figure.

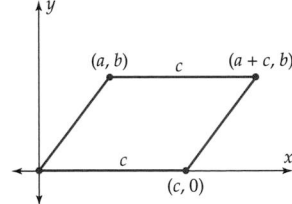

---

47. M has coordinates $\left(\dfrac{s}{2}, \dfrac{r}{2}\right)$ by the midpoint formula. Hence the distance from M to $(0, 0)$ is $\sqrt{\left(\dfrac{s}{2} - 0\right)^2 + \left(\dfrac{r}{2} - 0\right)^2} = \sqrt{\dfrac{s^2}{4} + \dfrac{r^2}{4}}$, and the distance from M to $(0, r)$ is the

same: $\sqrt{\left(\dfrac{s}{2} - 0\right)^2 + \left(\dfrac{r}{2} - r\right)^2} = \sqrt{\left(\dfrac{s}{2}\right)^2 + \left(-\dfrac{r}{2}\right)^2}$

$= \sqrt{\dfrac{s^2}{4} + \dfrac{r^2}{4}}$

as is the distance from M to $(s, 0)$:

$\sqrt{\left(\dfrac{s}{2} - s\right)^2 + \left(\dfrac{r}{2} - 0\right)^2} = \sqrt{\left(-\dfrac{s}{2}\right)^2 + \left(\dfrac{r}{2}\right)^2}$

$= \sqrt{\dfrac{s^2}{4} + \dfrac{r^2}{4}}$

49. Show that the diagonals of a rectangle have the same length. *Hint:* Place the rectangle in the first quadrant of the plane and label its vertices appropriately, as in Exercises 47–48.

50. If the diagonals of a parallelogram have the same length, show that the parallelogram is actually a rectangle. *Hint:* See Exercise 48.

51. *Critical Thinking* For each nonzero real number k, the graph of $(x - k)^2 + y^2 = k^2$ is a circle. Describe all possible such circles.

52. *Critical Thinking* Suppose every point in the coordinate plane is moved 5 units straight up.
  a. To what point does each of these points go: $(0, -5), (2, 2), (5, 0), (5, 5), (4, 1)$?
  b. Which points go to each of the points in part **a**?
  c. To what point does (a, b) go?
  d. To what point does $(a, b - 5)$ go?
  e. What point goes to $(-4a, b)$?
  f. What points go to themselves?

  a. $(0, 0), (2, 7), (5, 5), (5, 10), (4, 6)$

  b. $(0, -10), (2, -3), (5, -5), (5, 0), (4, -4)$

  c. $(a, b + 5)$

  d. (a, b)

  e. $(-4a, b - 5)$

  f. none

53. *Critical Thinking* Let (c, d) be any point in the plane with $c \neq 0$. Prove that (c, d) and $(-c, -d)$ lie on the same straight line through the origin, on opposite sides of the origin, the same distance from the origin. *Hint:* Find the midpoint of the line segment joining (c, d) and $(-c, -d)$.

54. *Critical Thinking* *Proof of the Midpoint Formula* Let P and Q be the points (x_1, y_1) and (x_2, y_2) respectively and let M be the point with coordinates

$$\left(\frac{x_1 + x_2}{2}, \frac{y_1 + y_2}{2} \right).$$

Use the distance formula to compute the following:
  a. the distance d from P to Q;
  b. the distance d_1 from M to P;
  c. the distance d_2 from M to Q.
  d. Verify that $d_1 = d_2$.
  e. Show that $d_1 + d_2 = d$. *Hint:* Verify that

$$d_1 = \frac{1}{2}d \text{ and } d_2 = \frac{1}{2}d.$$

  f. Explain why parts **d** and **e** show that M is the midpoint of PQ.

  a. $d = \sqrt{(x_1 - x_2)^2 + (y_1 - y_2)^2}$

  b. $d_1 = \sqrt{\left(\dfrac{x_2 - x_1}{2}\right)^2 + \left(\dfrac{y_2 - y_1}{2}\right)^2}$

  c. $d_2 = \sqrt{\left(\dfrac{x_1 - x_2}{2}\right)^2 + \left(\dfrac{y_1 - y_2}{2}\right)^2}$

  d. Since $(a - b)^2 = (b - a)^2$ for any a and b, the two distances are equal.

  e. $d_1 = \sqrt{\left(\dfrac{x_2 - x_1}{2}\right)^2 + \left(\dfrac{y_2 - y_1}{2}\right)^2} = \dfrac{1}{2}d$

  and since $d_2 = d_1$, $d_1 + d_2 = d$.

  f. Since the distances are the same, the point M is the same distance from P as from Q. Also, since they add to d, the point M lies on the shortest route from P to Q, a straight line. Therefore, M is the midpoint of the line segment joining P and Q.

48. With the vertices labeled as in the text use the midpoint formula to find the midpoint of each diagonal.
The midpoint of each diagonal is
$$\left(\frac{a + c}{2}, \frac{b}{2} \right).$$

49. Place one vertex of the rectangle at the origin, with one side on the positive x-axis and another on the positive y-axis. Let $(a, 0)$ be the coordinates of the vertex on the x-axis and $(0, b)$ the coordinates of the vertex on the y-axis. Then the fourth vertex has coordinates (a, b). One diagonal has endpoints $(0, b)$ and $(a, 0)$, so that its length is
$\sqrt{(0 - a)^2 + (b - 0)^2} = \sqrt{a^2 + b^2}$.
The other diagonal has endpoints $(0, 0)$ and (a, b) and hence has the same length:
$\sqrt{(0 - a)^2 + (0 - b)^2} = \sqrt{a^2 + b^2}$.

50. With the vertices labeled as in exercise 48, the lengths of the diagonals are
$$d_1 = \sqrt{(a - c)^2 + (b - 0)^2}$$
$$= \sqrt{(a - c)^2 + b^2},$$
$$d_2 = \sqrt{(a + c - 0)^2 + (b - 0)^2}$$
$$= \sqrt{(a + c)^2 + b^2}$$
Set these two equal to each other and find that $a = 0$. This means that the figure is a rectangle.

51. The circle $(x - k)^2 + y^2 = k^2$ has center $(k, 0)$ and radius $|k|$ (the distance from $(k, 0)$ to $(0, 0)$). So the family consists of every circle that is tangent to the y-axis *and* has center on the x-axis.

53. The points are on opposite sides of the origin because one first coordinate is positive and one is negative. They are equidistant from the origin because the midpoint on the line segment joining them is
$$\left[\frac{c + (-c)}{2}, \frac{d + (-d)}{2} \right] = (0, 0).$$

ADVANCED TOPICS

Section
B.1 The Binomial Theorem

Teaching Notes

When discussing *n* **Factorial,** students might be more familiar with the product being written with terms in *decreasing* order. For example,

$2! = 2 \cdot 1 = 2,$

$3! = 3 \cdot 2 \cdot 1 = 6$

$4! = 4 \cdot 3 \cdot 2 \cdot 1 = 24$

$5! = 5 \cdot 4 \cdot 3 \cdot 2 \cdot 1 = 120$

$10! = 10 \cdot 9 \cdot 8 \cdot 7 \cdot 6 \cdot 5 \cdot 4 \cdot 3 \cdot 2 \cdot 1$
$= 3,628,800$

Remind them that both ways are equivalent because multiplication of integers is commutative.

Be sure to draw attention to the fact that $0! \neq 0$, as one might be inclined to think. Note that if $0!$ had been defined to be 0, both of the binomial coefficients $\binom{n}{0}$ and $\binom{n}{n}$ would be undefined due to a zero in the denominator.

Solution to the **Calculator Exploration:**

```
15!
     1.307674368E12
69!
     1.711224524E98
```

Answers may vary.
The TI-83 gives an error message for factorials larger than 69!

B.1 The Binomial Theorem

The Binomial Theorem provides a formula for calculating the product $(x + y)^n$ for any positive integer n. Before we state the theorem, some preliminaries are needed.

Let n be a positive integer. The symbol $n!$ (read *n* **factorial**) denotes the product of all the integers from 1 to n. For example,

$$2! = 1 \cdot 2 = 2, \quad 3! = 1 \cdot 2 \cdot 3 = 6, \quad 4! = 1 \cdot 2 \cdot 3 \cdot 4 = 24,$$
$$5! = 1 \cdot 2 \cdot 3 \cdot 4 \cdot 5 = 120,$$
$$10! = 1 \cdot 2 \cdot 3 \cdot 4 \cdot 5 \cdot 6 \cdot 7 \cdot 8 \cdot 9 \cdot 10 = 3,628,800.$$

In general, we have this result:

n **Factorial**

> **Let n be a positive integer. Then**
>
> $$n! = 1 \cdot 2 \cdot 3 \cdot 4 \cdots (n - 2)(n - 1)n.$$
>
> **$0!$ is defined to be the number 1.**

Learn to use your calculator to compute factorials. You will find ! in the PROB (or PRB) submenu of the MATH or OPTN menu.

Calculator Exploration

15! is such a large number your calculator will switch to scientific notation to express it. Many calculators cannot compute factorials larger than 69! If yours does compute larger ones, what is the largest factorial that you can compute without getting an error message?

Binomial Coefficients

If r and n are integers with $0 \leq r \leq n$, then

Either of the symbols $\binom{n}{r}$ or $_nC_r$ denotes the number $\dfrac{n!}{r!(n-r)!}$.

$\binom{n}{r}$ is called a *binomial coefficient*.

For example,

$$_5C_3 = \binom{5}{3} = \frac{5!}{3!(5-3)!} = \frac{5!}{3!2!} = \frac{1 \cdot 2 \cdot 3 \cdot 4 \cdot 5}{(1 \cdot 2 \cdot 3)(1 \cdot 2)} = \frac{4 \cdot 5}{2} = 10$$

$$_4C_2 = \binom{4}{2} = \frac{4!}{2!(4-2)!} = \frac{4!}{2!2!} = \frac{1 \cdot 2 \cdot 3 \cdot 4}{(1 \cdot 2)(1 \cdot 2)} = \frac{3 \cdot 4}{2} = 6.$$

Binomial coefficients can be computed on a calculator by using $_nC_r$ or Comb in the PROB (or PRB) submenu of the MATH or OPTN menu.

Calculator Exploration

Compute $_{56}C_{47} = \binom{56}{47}$. Although calculators cannot compute 475!, they can compute many binomial coefficients, such as $\binom{475}{400}$, because most of the factors cancel out (as in the previous example). Check yours. Will it also compute $\binom{475}{200}$?

The preceding examples illustrate a fact whose proof will be omitted: *Every binomial coefficient is an integer.* Furthermore, for every nonnegative integer n,

$$\binom{n}{0} = 1 \qquad \text{and} \qquad \binom{n}{n} = 1$$

because

$$\binom{n}{0} = \frac{n!}{0!(n-0)!} + \frac{n!}{0!n!} = \frac{n!}{n!} = 1 \qquad \text{and}$$

$$\binom{n}{n} = \frac{n!}{n!(n-n)!} = \frac{n!}{n!0!} = \frac{n!}{n!} = 1.$$

If we list the binomial coefficients for each value of n in this manner, we find that they form a rectangular array.

Teaching Notes

Remind students that they have encountered the **Binomial Coefficients** when determining probabilities in Chapter 12. In particular, have them recall that $\binom{n}{r} = {}_nC_r = \dfrac{n!}{r!(n-r)!}$ represents the number of combinations of r items chosen in any order without replacement from n possible items (page 881).

Point out that in this section, the conditions that r and n are both integers with $0 \leq r \leq n$ must be explicitly stated, as it is at the top of the page. It was not necessary to include this condition in Chapter 12 because the context of choosing r items out of n possible items implicitly does so.

Encourage students to observe that 5! can be written as $5 \cdot 4 \cdot 3!$ because

$$5! = 5 \cdot 4 \cdot 3 \cdot 2 \cdot 1$$
$$= 5 \cdot 4 \cdot (3 \cdot 2 \cdot 1)$$
$$= 5 \cdot 4 \cdot 3!$$

Then, when they use the $\dfrac{n!}{r!(n-r)!}$ definition to evaluate binomial coefficients by hand, encourage them to "cancel out" factorial expressions from the numerator and denominator that are equal (instead of writing out every term):

$$_5C_3 = \binom{5}{3} = \frac{5!}{3!\,2!} = \frac{5 \cdot 4 \cdot \cancel{3!}}{\cancel{3!}\,(2 \cdot 1)} = \frac{20}{2} = 10$$

Have students use this cancellation method to evaluate $_{74}C_{72}$ by hand.

$$_{74}C_{72} = \binom{74}{72} = \frac{74!}{72!\,2!} = \frac{74 \cdot 73 \cdot \cancel{72!}}{\cancel{72!}\,(2 \cdot 1)}$$
$$= 37 \cdot 73 = 2701$$

Solution to the Calculator Exploration:

```
56 nCr 47
            7575968400
475 nCr 400
      4.743213757E88
475 nCr 200
```

In the Calculator Exploration, students will find that $\binom{475}{400}$ can be computed, whereas $\binom{475}{200}$ cannot be computed on most calculators. Have students make a table on their calculators with $Y_1 = {}_{475}C_x$ and determine if all values of x can be computed. They will find that values of x such that $92 \leq x \leq 383$ will result in an overflow error.

Teaching Notes

You may want to have students extend Pascal's triangle to at least row 8 by hand. Having these first 8 rows of binomial coefficients will be beneficial to them when they get to the exercises on pages 1000–1001, which will require they calculate many coefficients. It will be easier for them to refer to Pascal's triangle than to calculate each coefficient repeatedly.

row 5: 1; 5; 10; 10; 5; 1
row 6: 1; 6; 15; 20; 15; 6; 1
row 7: 1; 7; 21; 35; 35; 21; 7; 1
row 8: 1; 8; 28; 56; 70; 56; 28; 8; 1

Also, encourage them to notice the symmetry that appears in Pascal's triangle. Challenge them to explain it symbolically by completing the following:

$$\binom{n}{r} = \binom{n}{n-r}$$

COMMON ERROR ALERT

In **Example 1,** some students might incorrectly cancel out factors in the numerator and denominator while calculating $_8C_2$ as follows:

$$_8C_2 = \frac{8!}{2!\,6!} = \frac{4!}{6!}$$

Remind them of the correct way to compute $_8C_2$:

$$_8C_2 = \frac{8!}{2!\,6!} = \frac{8 \cdot 7 \cdot 6!}{(2 \cdot 1)6!} = \frac{56}{2} = 28$$

In **Example 2** on page 998, some students might overlook the minus sign, obtaining the incorrect expansion $1 + 6z + 15z^2 + 20z^3 + 15z^4 + 6z^5 + z^6$ (which is actually the correct expansion of $(1 + z)^6$).

Point out that you first need to write $(1 - z)^6$ as $(1 + (-z))^6$, and then, when expanding, you must pay attention to the exponents of $-z$. Encourage them to recall that a negative raised to an *odd* power is *negative*, while a negative raised to an *even* power is *positive*. Because the exponents of $-z$ alternate between even and odd integers, the signs of terms in the expansion will alternate between positive and negative, with a negative term appearing when $-z$ is raised to an odd power.

$$
\begin{array}{llcccc}
n = 0 & & & \binom{0}{0} & & \\
n = 1 & & \binom{1}{0} & & \binom{1}{1} & \\
n = 2 & \binom{2}{0} & & \binom{2}{1} & & \binom{2}{2} \\
n = 3 & \binom{3}{0} & \binom{3}{1} & & \binom{3}{2} & \binom{3}{3} \\
n = 4 & \binom{4}{0} & \binom{4}{1} & \binom{4}{2} & \binom{4}{3} & \binom{4}{4} \\
\end{array}
$$

Calculating each binomial coefficient, we obtain the following array of numbers:

row 0					1			
row 1				1		1		
row 2			1		2		1	
row 3		1		3		3		1
row 4	1		4		6		4		1

This array is called **Pascal's triangle.** Its pattern is easy to remember. Each entry (except the 1's at the beginning or end of a row) is the sum of the two closest entries in the row above it. In the fourth row, for instance, 6 is the sum of the two 3's above it, and each 4 is the sum of the 1 and 3 above it. See Exercise 47 for a proof.

In order to develop a formula for calculating $(x + y)^n$, we first calculate these products for small values of n to see if we can find some kind of pattern:

$$
\begin{array}{lll}
 & n = 0 & (x + y)^0 = \quad\quad\quad\quad 1 \\
 & n = 1 & (x + y)^1 = \quad\quad\quad 1x + 1y \\
(*) & n = 2 & (x + y)^2 = \quad\quad 1x^2 + 2xy + 1y^2 \\
 & n = 3 & (x + y)^3 = \quad 1x^3 + 3x^2y + 3xy^2 + 1y^3 \\
 & n = 4 & (x + y)^4 = 1x^4 + 4x^3y + 6x^2y^2 + 4xy^3 + 1y^4 \\
\end{array}
$$

One pattern is immediately obvious: the coefficients here (shown in color) are the top part of Pascal's triangle! In the case $n = 4$, for example, this means that the coefficients are the numbers

$$
\begin{array}{ccccc}
1 & 4 & 6 & 4 & 1 \\
\binom{4}{0}, & \binom{4}{1}, & \binom{4}{2}, & \binom{4}{3}, & \binom{4}{4}.
\end{array}
$$

If this pattern holds for larger n, then the coefficients in the expansion of $(x + y)^n$ are

$$\binom{n}{0}, \binom{n}{1}, \binom{n}{2}, \binom{n}{3}, \ldots, \binom{n}{n-1}, \binom{n}{n}.$$

As for the xy-terms associated with each of these coefficients, look at the pattern in (∗) above: the exponent of x goes down by 1 and the exponent of y goes up by 1 as you go from term to term, which suggests that the terms of the expansion of $(x + y)^n$ (without the coefficients) are:

$$x^n, \quad x^{n-1}y, \quad x^{n-2}y^2, \quad x^{n-3}y^3, \ldots, xy^{n-1}, \quad y^n.$$

Combining the patterns of coefficients and xy-terms and using the fact that $\binom{n}{0} = 1$ and $\binom{n}{n} = 1$ suggests that the following result is true about the expansion of $(x + y)^n$.

The Binomial Theorem

For each positive integer n,

$$(x + y)^n = x^n + \binom{n}{1}x^{n-1}y + \binom{n}{2}x^{n-2}y^2 +$$
$$\binom{n}{3}x^{n-3}y^3 + \cdots + \binom{n}{n-1}xy^{n-1} + y^n.$$

Using summation notation and the fact that $\binom{n}{0} = 1 = \binom{n}{n}$, we can write the Binomial Theorem compactly as

$$(x + y)^n = \sum_{j=0}^{n} \binom{n}{j} x^{n-j}y^j.$$

The Binomial Theorem will be proved in Section B.2 by means of mathematical induction. We shall assume its truth for now and illustrate some of its uses.

Example 1

Expand $(x + y)^8$.

Solution

We apply the Binomial Theorem in the case $n = 8$:

$$(x + y)^8 = x^8 + \binom{8}{1}x^7y + \binom{8}{2}x^6y^2 + \binom{8}{3}x^5y^3$$
$$+ \binom{8}{4}x^4y^4 + \binom{8}{5}x^3y^5 + \binom{8}{6}x^2y^6 + \binom{8}{7}xy^7 + y^8.$$

The coefficients can be computed individually by hand or by using $_nC_r$ (or COMB) on a calculator; for instance,

$$_8C_2 = \binom{8}{2} = \frac{8!}{2!6!} = 28 \quad \text{or} \quad _8C_3 = \binom{8}{3} = \frac{8!}{3!5!} = 56.$$

Section B.1   **The Binomial Theorem**   **997**

Section B.1   **The Binomial Theorem**   **997**

ADDITIONAL EXAMPLES

Example 1

Expand $(x + y)^{10}$.

$$(x + y)^{10} = x^{10}$$
$$+ \binom{10}{1}x^9y + \binom{10}{2}x^8y^2$$
$$+ \binom{10}{3}x^7y^3 + \binom{10}{4}x^6y^4$$
$$+ \binom{10}{5}x^5y^5 + \binom{10}{6}x^4y^6$$
$$+ \binom{10}{7}x^3y^7 + \binom{10}{8}x^2y^8$$
$$+ \binom{10}{9}xy^9 + y^{10}$$

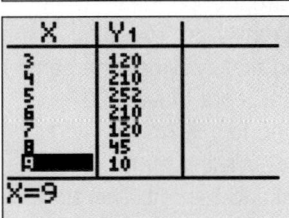

Substituting these values into the expansion:

$$(x + y)^{10} = x^{10} + 10x^9y + 45x^8y^2$$
$$+ 120x^7y^3 + 210x^6y^4$$
$$+ 252x^5y^5 + 210x^4y^6$$
$$+ 120x^3y^7 + 45x^2y^8$$
$$+ 10xy^9 + y^{10}$$

Advanced Topics

ADDITIONAL EXAMPLES

Example 2

Expand $(2 - q)^7$.

$2 - q = 2 + (-q)$

Apply the Binomial Theorem with $x = 2$, $y = -q$, and $n = 7$.

$(2 + q)^7 = 2^7$

$$+ \binom{7}{1}2^6(-q) + \binom{7}{2}2^5(-q)^2$$

$$+ \binom{7}{3}2^4(-q)^3 + \binom{7}{4}2^3(-q)^4$$

$$+ \binom{7}{5}2^2(-q)^5 + \binom{7}{6}2(-q)^6$$

$$+ (-q)^7$$

$$= 128 - 64(7)q + 32(21)q^2$$

$$- 16(35)q^3 + 8(35)q^4$$

$$- 4(21)q^5 + 2(7)q^6 - q^7$$

$$= 128 - 448q + 672q^2 - 560q^3$$

$$+ 280q^4 - 84q^5 + 14q^6 - q^7$$

Example 3

The unemployment rate in the state of Indiana can be modeled by

$$f(x) = -0.0042x^4 + 0.1380x^3$$
$$-1.5207x^2 + 6.2463x$$
$$-3.1928 \quad (3 \le x \le 13)$$

where $x = 3$ corresponds to 1993. Write and simplify the rule of a function $g(x)$ that provides the same information as f but has $x = 0$ corresponding to 1993.

The graph of g is the graph of f shifted 3 units to the left. Therefore, $g(x) = f(x + 3)$.

$g(x) =$
$$-0.0042(x + 3)^4 + 0.1380(x + 3)^3$$
$$-1.5207(x + 3)^2 + 6.2463(x + 3)$$
$$-3.1928$$

$$g(x) = -0.0042[x^4 + 4x^3(3) + 6x^2(3)^2 + 4x(3)^3 + (3)^4]$$
$$+ 0.1380[x^3 + 3x^2(3) + 3x(3)^2 + (3)^3]$$
$$-1.5207[x^2 + 2x(3) + (3)^2]$$
$$+ 6.2463(x + 3)$$
$$-3.1928$$

$$g(x) = -0.0042x^4 + 0.0876x^3$$
$$-0.5055x^2 + 0.3945x$$
$$+ 5.2456$$

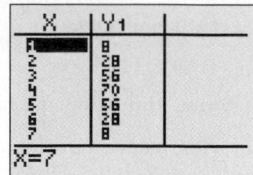

Figure B.1-1

Alternatively, you can display all the coefficients at once by making a table of values for the function $f(x) = {}_8C_x$, as shown in Figure B.1-1 at left.

Substituting these values in the preceding expansion, we have

$$(x + y)^8 = x^8 + 8x^7y + 28x^6y^2$$
$$+ 56x^5y^3 + 70x^4y^4 + 56x^3y^5 + 28x^2y^6 + 8xy^7 + y^8.$$

Example 2

Expand $(1 - z)^6$.

Solution

Note that $1 - z = 1 + (-z)$ and apply the Binomial Theorem with $x = 1$, $y = -z$, and $n = 6$:

$$(1 - z)^6 = 1^6 + \binom{6}{1}1^5(-z) + \binom{6}{2}1^4(-z)^2 + \binom{6}{3}1^3(-z)^3$$

$$+ \binom{6}{4}1^2(-z)^4 + \binom{6}{5}1(-z)^5 + (-z)^6$$

$$= 1 - \binom{6}{1}z + \binom{6}{2}z^2 - \binom{6}{3}z^3 + \binom{6}{4}z^4 - \binom{6}{5}z^5 + z^6$$

$$= 1 - 6z + 15z^2 - 20z^3 + 15z^4 - 6z^5 + z^6.$$

Example 3

The unemployment rate in the United States can be modeled by

$$f(x) = -.0051x^4 + .1813x^3 - 2.2202x^2 + 10.8212x - 12.1394 \quad (4 \le x \le 14)$$

where $x = 4$ corresponds to 1994.* Write and simplify the rule of a function $g(x)$ that provides the same information as f but has $x = 0$ corresponding to 1994.

*Source: Bureau of Labor Statistics

Solution

The graph of g will be the graph of f shifted 4 units to the left, which means that $g(x) = f(x + 4)$.

$$g(x) = -.0051(x+4)^4 + .1813(x+4)^3 - 2.2202(x+4)^2 + 10.8212(x+4) - 12.1394$$

$$g(x) = -.0051[x^4 + 4x^3(4) + 6x^2(4)^2 + 4x(4)^3 + (4)^4]$$
$$+.1813[x^3 + 3x^2(4) + 3x(4)^2 + (4)^3]$$
$$-2.2202[x^2 + 2x(4) + (4)^2]$$
$$+10.8212(x + 4)$$
$$-12.1394$$

$$g(x) = -.0051x^4 + .099x^3 - .534x^2 + .455x + 5.92$$

Example 4

Show that $(1.001)^{1000} > 2$ without using a calculator.

Solution

We write 1.001 as $1 + .001$ and apply the Binomial Theorem with $x = 1$, $y = .001$, and $n = 1000$:

$$(1.001)^{1000} = (1 + .001)^{1000}$$

$$= 1^{1000} + \binom{1000}{1}1^{999}(.001) + \text{other positive terms}$$

$$= 1 + \binom{1000}{1}(.001) + \text{other positive terms}.$$

But $\binom{1000}{1} = \dfrac{1000!}{1!999!} = \dfrac{1000 \cdot 999!}{999!} = 1000$. Therefore, $\binom{1000}{1}(.001) = 1,000(.001) = 1$ and $(1.001)^{1000} = 1 + 1 + \text{other positive terms} = 2 + \text{other positive terms}$.

Hence, $(1.001)^{1000} > 2$. ∎

Sometimes we need to know only one term in the expansion of $(x + y)^n$. If you examine the expansion given by the Binomial Theorem, you will see that in the second term y has exponent 1, in the third term y has exponent 2, and so on. Thus,

Properties of the Binomial Expansion

> In the binomial expansion of $(x + y)^n$,
>
> The exponent of y is always one less than the number of the term.
>
> Furthermore, in each of the middle terms of the expansion,
>
> The coefficient of the term containing y^r is $\binom{n}{r}$.
>
> The sum of the x exponent and the y exponent is n.

For instance, in the *ninth* term of the expansion of $(x + y)^{13}$, y has exponent 8, the coefficient is $\binom{13}{8}$, and x must have exponent 5 (since $8 + 5 = 13$). Thus, the ninth term is $\binom{13}{8}x^5y^8$.

ADDITIONAL EXAMPLES

Example 4

Show that $(1.0001)^{10,000} > 2$ without using a calculator.

Write 1.0001 as $1 + 0.0001$ and apply the Binomial Theorem with $x = 1$, $y = 0.0001$, and $n = 10,000$:

$$(1.0001)^{10,000}$$

$$= (1 + 0.0001)^{10,000}$$

$$= 1^{10,000} + \binom{10,000}{1}1^{9999}(0.0001)$$

$$+ \text{ other positive terms}$$

$$= 1 + \binom{10,000}{1}(0.0001)$$

$$+ \text{ other positive terms}$$

$$= 1 + 10,000(0.0001)$$

$$+ \text{ other positive terms}$$

$$= 1 + 1 + \text{ other positive terms}$$

$$= 2 + \text{ other positive terms}$$

Hence, $(1.0001)^{10,000} > 2$.

Example Notes

You may want to have students verify the solutions to **Example 4** and **Additional Example 4** on a calculator:

```
1.001^1000
          2.716923932
1.0001^10000
          2.718145927
```

Teaching Notes

It may be helpful to give students the following formula to summarize how the **Properties of the Binomial Expansion** can be used to find the kth term in a binomial expansion:

The kth term in the binomial expansion of $(x + y)^n$ is given by

$$\binom{n}{k-1}x^{n-(k-1)}y^{k-1}$$

or equivalently, $\binom{n}{k-1}x^{n-k+1}y^{k-1}$.

Ask them to verify that conditions in the Properties box hold true.

- The exponent of y is $k - 1$, which is one less than the number of terms, k. ✓
- If the kth term contains y^r, then $k - 1 = r$, so that $k = r + 1$. Therefore, the coefficient of the kth term is $\binom{n}{(r+1)-1} = \binom{n}{r}$. ✓
- The sum of the x exponent and the y exponent is $(n - k + 1) + (k - 1) = n$. ✓

ADDITIONAL EXAMPLES

Example 5

Find the seventh term of
$$\left(3x^2 + \frac{\sqrt[3]{y}}{\sqrt{3}}\right)^{14}.$$

Use the Binomial Theorem with
$n = 14$, $3x^2$ in place of x, and $\dfrac{\sqrt[3]{y}}{\sqrt{3}}$ in place of y.

From the Properties of the Binomial Expansion box on page 999, the seventh term is:
$$\binom{14}{6}(3x^2)^8\left(\frac{\sqrt[3]{y}}{\sqrt{3}}\right)^6$$

Simplify:
$$\binom{14}{6}(3x^2)^8\left(\frac{\sqrt[3]{y}}{\sqrt{3}}\right)^6$$

$$= \binom{14}{6}3^8(x^2)^8\frac{\left(y^{\frac{1}{3}}\right)^6}{\left(3^{\frac{1}{2}}\right)^6}$$

$$= \binom{14}{6}3^8 x^{16}\frac{y^2}{3^3}$$

$$= \binom{14}{6}\frac{3^8}{3^3}x^{16}y^2$$

$$= \frac{14 \cdot 13 \cdot 12 \cdot 11 \cdot 10 \cdot 9 \cdot 8 \cdot 7}{8 \cdot 7 \cdot 6 \cdot 5 \cdot 4 \cdot 3 \cdot 2} \cdot 3^5 x^{16}y^2$$

$$= 729,729x^{16}y^2$$

Exercises B.1

ANSWERS

11. $x^5 + 5x^4y + 10x^3y^2 + 10x^2y^3 + 5xy^4 + y^5$

12. $a^7 + 7a^6b + 21a^5b^2 + 35a^4b^3 + 35a^3b^4 + 21a^2b^5 + 7ab^6 + b^7$

13. $a^5 - 5a^4b + 10a^3b^2 - 10a^2b^3 + 5ab^4 - b^5$

14. $c^8 - 8c^7d + 28c^6d^2 - 56c^5d^3 + 70c^4d^4 - 56c^3d^5 + 28c^2d^6 - 8cd^7 + d^8$

15. $32x^5 + 80x^4y^2 + 80x^3y^4 + 40x^2y^6 + 10xy^8 + y^{10}$

16. $729u^6 - 1458u^5v^3 + 1215u^4v^6 - 540u^3v^9 + 135u^2v^{12} - 18uv^{15} + v^{18}$

17. $x^3 + 6x^2\sqrt{x} + 15x^2 + 20x\sqrt{x} + 15x + 6\sqrt{x} + 1$

18. $32 - 80\sqrt{y} + 80y - 40y^{\frac{3}{2}} + 10y^2 - y^{\frac{5}{2}}$

Example 5

Find the ninth term of the expansion of $\left(2x^2 + \dfrac{\sqrt[4]{y}}{\sqrt{6}}\right)^{13}$.

Solution

We shall use the Binomial Theorem with $n = 13$ and with $2x^2$ in place of x and $\dfrac{\sqrt[4]{y}}{\sqrt{6}}$ in place of y. The remarks on the previous page show that the ninth term is

$$\binom{13}{8}(2x^2)^5\left(\frac{\sqrt[4]{y}}{\sqrt{6}}\right)^8.$$

Since $\sqrt[4]{y} = y^{\frac{1}{4}}$ and $\sqrt{6} = \sqrt{3}\sqrt{2} = 3^{\frac{1}{2}}2^{\frac{1}{2}}$, we can simplify as follows:

$$\binom{13}{8}(2x^2)^5\left(\frac{\sqrt[4]{y}}{\sqrt{6}}\right)^8 = \binom{13}{8}2^5(x^2)^5\frac{\left(y^{\frac{1}{4}}\right)^8}{\left(3^{\frac{1}{2}}\right)^8\left(2^{\frac{1}{2}}\right)^8} = \binom{13}{8}2^5x^{10}\frac{y^2}{3^4 \cdot 2^4}$$

$$= \binom{13}{8}\frac{2}{3^4}x^{10}y^2 = \frac{13 \cdot 12 \cdot 11 \cdot 10 \cdot 9}{5 \cdot 4 \cdot 3 \cdot 2} \cdot \frac{2}{3^4}x^{10}y^2$$

$$= \frac{286}{9}x^{10}y^2. \blacksquare$$

Exercises B.1

In Exercises 1–10, evaluate the expression.

1. $6!$ **720** **2.** $\dfrac{11!}{8!}$ **990** **3.** $\dfrac{12!}{9!3!}$ **220** **4.** $\dfrac{9! - 8!}{7!}$ **64**

5. $\binom{5}{3} + \binom{5}{2} - \binom{6}{3}$ **0** **6.** $\binom{12}{11} - \binom{11}{10} + \binom{7}{0}$ **2**

7. $\binom{6}{0} + \binom{6}{1} + \binom{6}{2} + \binom{6}{3} + \binom{6}{4} + \binom{6}{5} + \binom{6}{6}$ **64**

8. $\binom{6}{0} - \binom{6}{1} + \binom{6}{2} - \binom{6}{3} + \binom{6}{4} - \binom{6}{5} + \binom{6}{6}$ **0**

9. $\binom{100}{96}$ **3,921,225** **10.** $\binom{75}{72}$ **67,525**

In Exercises 11–16, expand the expression.

11. $(x + y)^5$ **12.** $(a + b)^7$ **13.** $(a - b)^5$

14. $(c - d)^8$ **15.** $(2x + y^2)^5$ **16.** $(3u - v^3)^6$

In Exercises 17–26, use the Binomial Theorem to expand and (where possible) simplify the expression.

17. $(\sqrt{x} + 1)^6$ **18.** $(2 - \sqrt{y})^5$

19. $(1 - c)^{10}$ **20.** $\left(\sqrt{c} + \dfrac{1}{\sqrt{c}}\right)^7$

21. $(x^{-3} + x)^4$ **22.** $(3x^{-2} - x^2)^6$

23. $(1 + \sqrt{3})^4 + (1 - \sqrt{3})^4$ **56**

24. $(\sqrt{3} + 1)^6 - (\sqrt{3} - 1)^6$ **240$\sqrt{3}$**

25. $(1 + i)^6$, where $i^2 = -1$ **−8i**

26. The median income of U.S. households (in thousands of dollars) from 1992 through 2002 can be modeled by

$$f(x) = -.001x^4 + .003x^3 + .211x^2 - .322x + 30.345 \quad (2 \le x \le 12)$$

where $x = 2$ corresponds to 1992.* Write and simplify the rule of a function $g(x)$ that provides the same information as f but has $x = 0$ corresponding to 2000.

Source: U.S. Census Bureau

19. $1 - 10c + 45c^2 - 120c^3 + 210c^4 - 252c^5 + 210c^6 - 120c^7 + 45c^8 - 10c^9 + c^{10}$

20. $c^{\frac{7}{2}} + 7c^{\frac{5}{2}} + 21c^{\frac{3}{2}} + 35c^{\frac{1}{2}} + 35c^{-\frac{1}{2}} + 21c^{-\frac{3}{2}} + 7c^{-\frac{5}{2}} + c^{-\frac{7}{2}}$

21. $x^{-12} + 4x^{-8} + 6x^{-4} + 4 + x^4$

22. $729x^{-12} - 1458x^{-8} + 1215x^{-4} - 540 + 135x^4 - 18x^8 + x^{12}$

26. $g(x) = f(x + 8) = -0.001(x + 8)^4 + 0.003(x + 8)^3 + 0.211(x + 8)^2 - 0.322(x + 8) + 30.345$
$= -0.001x^4 - 0.029x^3 - 0.101x^2 + 1.582x + 38.713$

37. a. $\binom{9}{1} = \dfrac{9!}{1!8!} = 9$; $\binom{9}{8} = \dfrac{9!}{8!1!} = 9$

b. $\binom{n}{1} = \binom{n}{n-1} = \dfrac{n!}{1!(n-1)!}$
$= \dfrac{n(n-1)!}{(n-1)!} = n$

In Exercises 27–32, find the indicated term of the expansion of the given expression.

27. third, $(x + y)^5$
$10x^3y^2$

28. fourth, $(a + b)^6$
$20a^3b^3$

29. fifth, $(c - d)^7$
$35c^3d^4$

30. third, $(a + 2)^8$
$112a^6$

31. fourth, $\left(\dfrac{u^{-2}}{35} + \dfrac{u}{2}\right)^7$
$\dfrac{35}{8}u^{-\frac{5}{2}}$

32. fifth, $(\sqrt{x} - \sqrt{2})^7$
$140x^{\frac{3}{2}}$

33. Find the coefficient of x^5y^8 in the expansion of $(2x - y^2)^9$.
4032

34. Find the coefficient of $x^{12}y^6$ in the expansion of $(x^3 - 3y)^{10}$.
153,090

35. Find the coefficient of $\dfrac{1}{x^3}$ in the expansion of $\left(2x + \dfrac{1}{x^2}\right)^6$.
160

36. Find the constant term in the expansion of $\left(y - \dfrac{1}{2y}\right)^{10}$.
$-\dfrac{63}{8}$

37. a. Verify that $\dbinom{9}{1} = 9$ and $\dbinom{9}{8} = 9$.

b. Prove that for each positive integer n, $\dbinom{n}{1} = n$ and $\dbinom{n}{n-1} = n$. *Note:* Part **a** is just the case when $n = 9$ and $n - 1 = 8$.

38. a. Verify that $\dbinom{7}{2} = \dbinom{7}{5}$.

b. Let r and n be integers with $0 \le r \le n$. Prove that $\dbinom{n}{r} = \dbinom{n}{n-r}$. *Note:* Part **a** is just the case when $n = 7$ and $r = 2$.

39. Prove that for any positive integer n,
$$2^n = \binom{n}{0} + \binom{n}{1} + \binom{n}{2} + \cdots + \binom{n}{n}.$$
Hint: $2 = 1 + 1$.

40. Prove that for any positive integer n,
$$\binom{n}{0} - \binom{n}{1} + \binom{n}{2} - \binom{n}{3} + \binom{n}{4} - \cdots$$
$$+ (-1)^k\binom{n}{k} + \cdots + (-1)^n\binom{n}{n} = 0.$$

41. Use the Binomial Theorem with $x = \sin\theta$ and $y = \cos\theta$ to find $(\cos\theta + i\sin\theta)^4$ where $i^2 = -1$.

42. a. Use DeMoivre's Theorem on page 441 to find
$$(\cos\theta + i\sin\theta)^4.$$

b. Use the fact that the two expressions obtained in part **a** and in Exercise 41 must be equal to express $\cos 4\theta$ and $\sin 4\theta$ in terms of $\sin\theta$ and $\cos\theta$.

43. a. Let f be the function given by $f(x) = x^5$. Let h be a nonzero number and compute $f(x + h) - f(x)$ (but leave all binomial coefficients in the form $\dbinom{5}{r}$ here and below).

b. Use part **a** to show that h is a factor of $f(x + h) - f(x)$ and find $\dfrac{f(x + h) - f(x)}{h}$.

c. If h is *very* close to 0, find a simple approximation of the quantity $\dfrac{f(x + h) - f(x)}{h}$. See part **b**.

44. Do Exercise 43 with $f(x) = x^8$ in place of $f(x) = x^5$.

45. Do Exercise 43 with $f(x) = x^{12}$ in place of $f(x) = x^5$.

46. Let n be a fixed positive integer. Do Exercise 43 with $f(x) = x^n$ in place of $f(x) = x^5$.

47. Let r and n be integers such that $0 \le r \le n$.
a. Verify that $(n - r)! = (n - r)[n - (r + 1)]!$
b. Verify that $(n - r)! = [(n + 1) - (r + 1)]!$
c. Prove that $\dbinom{n}{r+1} + \dbinom{n}{r} = \dbinom{n+1}{r+1}$ for any $r \le n - 1$. *Hint:* Write out the terms on the left side and use parts **a** and **b** to express each of them as a fraction with denominator $(r + 1)!(n - r)!$. Then add these two fractions, simplify the numerator, and compare the result with $\dbinom{n+1}{r+1}$.

d. Use part **c** to explain why each entry in Pascal's triangle (except the 1's at the beginning or end of a row) is the sum of the two closest entries in the row above it.

48. a. Find these numbers and write them one *below* the next: 11^0, 11^1, 11^2, 11^3, 11^4.
b. Compare the list in part **a** with rows 0 to 4 of Pascal's triangle. What's the explanation?
c. What can be said about 11^5 and row 5 of Pascal's triangle?
d. Calculate all integer powers of 101 from 101^0 to 101^8, list the results one under the other, and compare the list with rows 0 to 8 of Pascal's triangle. What's the explanation? What happens with 101^9?

38. a. $\dbinom{7}{2} = \dfrac{7!}{5!2!} = 21$; $\dbinom{7}{5} = \dfrac{7!}{2!5!} = 21$

b. $\dbinom{n}{r} = \dfrac{n!}{r!(n-r)!} = \dfrac{n!}{(n-r)!r!}$
$= \dbinom{n}{n-r}$

39. $2^n = (1 + 1)^n = 1^n + \dbinom{n}{1}1^{n-1}\cdot 1 +$
$\dbinom{n}{2}1^{n-2}\cdot 1^2 + \dbinom{n}{3}1^{n-3}\cdot 1^3 + \cdots +$
$\dbinom{n}{n-1}1^1\cdot 1^{n-1} + 1^n = \dbinom{n}{0} + \dbinom{n}{1} +$
$\dbinom{n}{2} + \dbinom{n}{3} + \cdots + \dbinom{n}{n-1} + \dbinom{n}{n}$

40. $0 = 0^n = (1 - 1)^n = \dbinom{n}{0}(-1)^0 +$
$\dbinom{n}{1}(-1)^1 + \dbinom{n}{2}(-1)^2 + \cdots +$
$\dbinom{n}{k}(-1)^k + \cdots + \dbinom{n}{n}(-1)^n$
$= \dbinom{n}{0} - \dbinom{n}{1} + \dbinom{n}{2} -$
$\dbinom{n}{3} + \cdots + \dbinom{n}{n}$

41. $\cos^4\theta + 4i\cos^3\theta\sin\theta -$
$6\cos^2\theta\sin^2\theta -$
$4i\cos\theta\sin^3\theta + \sin^4\theta$

42. a. $\cos(4\theta) + i\sin(4\theta)$

b. $\cos(4\theta) = \cos^4\theta -$
$6\cos^2\theta\sin^2\theta + \sin^4\theta$
$\sin(4\theta) = 4\cos^3\theta\sin\theta -$
$4\cos\theta\sin^3\theta$

43. a. $f(x + h) - f(x) = (x + h)^5 - x^5$
$= \left[x^5 + \dbinom{5}{1}x^4h +\right.$
$\dbinom{5}{2}x^3h^2 + \dbinom{5}{3}x^2h^3 +$
$\left.\dbinom{5}{4}xh^4 + h^5\right] - x^5$
$= \dbinom{5}{1}x^4h + \dbinom{5}{2}x^3h^2 +$
$\dbinom{5}{3}x^2h^3 + \dbinom{5}{4}xh^4 + h^5$

b. $\dfrac{f(x + h) - f(x)}{h} = \dbinom{5}{1}x^4 +$
$\dbinom{5}{2}x^3h + \dbinom{5}{3}x^2h^2 +$
$\dbinom{5}{4}xh^3 + h^4$

c. When h is *very* close to 0, so are the last four terms in part **b**, so $\dfrac{f(x + h) - f(x)}{h}$
$\approx \dbinom{5}{1}x^4 = 5x^4.$

44. a. $f(x + h) - f(x) = (x + h)^8 - x^8 = \displaystyle\sum_{k=1}^{8}\binom{8}{k}x^kh^{8-k} - x^8$

b. $\dbinom{8}{1}x^7 + \dbinom{8}{2}x^6h + \dbinom{8}{3}x^5h^2 + \dbinom{8}{4}x^4h^3 + \dbinom{8}{5}x^3h^4 + \dbinom{8}{6}x^2h^5 + \dbinom{8}{7}xh^6 + h^7$

c. When h is very close to 0, so are the last 7 terms in part **b**, so $\dfrac{f(x + h) - f(x)}{h} \approx \dbinom{8}{1}x^7 = 8x^7.$

45–48. *See p. 1086.*

Teaching Notes

The opening paragraph of this section gives several examples of mathematical facts that can be proved using mathematical induction. The proofs of these facts are given in the following pages of this section:

- Binomial Theorem: pages 1007–1009
- The sum of the first n positive integers is the number $\dfrac{n(n + 1)}{2}$: pages 1002–1004.

- $2^n > n$ for every positive integer n: **Example 1,** page 1005
- For each positive integer n, 4 is a factor of $7^n - 3^n$: **Example 2,** page 1006

The proof of DeMoivre's Theorem (Section 10.4) is left to the student in Exercise 37, page 1010.

Have students review the **Exponent Laws** on page 970. The first law, $c^m c^n = c^{m+n}$, is used to rewrite $c^{k+1} = c^k c^1 = c^k \cdot c$ extensively throughout this lesson and the exercises.

A common way to describe the **Principle of Mathematical Induction** is to make a visual analogy to dominoes. If a series of dominos is arranged so that a domino falling ensures that the next domino falls, then making the first domino fall will make the second domino fall, which will make the third domino fall, and so on down the line.

Mathematical induction is a method of proof that can be used to prove a wide variety of mathematical facts, including the Binomial Theorem, DeMoivre's Theorem, and statements such as:

The sum of the first n positive integers is the number $\dfrac{n(n + 1)}{2}$.

$2^n > n$ for every positive integer n.

For each positive integer n, 4 is a factor of $7^n - 3^n$.

All of the preceding statements have a common property. For example, a statement such as

The sum of the first n positive integers is the number $\dfrac{n(n + 1)}{2}$

or, in symbols,

$$1 + 2 + 3 + \cdots + n = \frac{n(n + 1)}{2}$$

is really an infinite sequence of statements, one for each possible value of n:

$$n = 1: \qquad 1 = \frac{1(2)}{2}$$

$$n = 2: \qquad 1 + 2 = \frac{2(3)}{2}$$

$$n = 3: \qquad 1 + 2 + 3 = \frac{3(4)}{2}$$

and so on. Obviously, there isn't time enough to verify every one of the statements on this list, one at a time. But we can find a workable method of proof by examining how each statement on the list is *related* to the *next* statement on the list.

For example, for $n = 50$, the statement is

$$1 + 2 + 3 + \cdots + 50 = \frac{50(51)}{2}.$$

At the moment, we don't know whether or not this statement is true. But just *suppose* that it were true. What could then be said about the next statement, the one for $n = 51$:

$$1 + 2 + 3 + \cdots + 50 + 51 = \frac{51(52)}{2}?$$

Well, *if* it is true that

$$1 + 2 + 3 + \cdots + 50 = \frac{50(51)}{2}$$

then adding 51 to both sides and simplifying the right side would yield these equalities:

$$1 + 2 + 3 + \cdots + 50 + 51 = \frac{50(51)}{2} + 51$$

$$1 + 2 + 3 + \cdots + 50 + 51 = \frac{50(51)}{2} + \frac{2(51)}{2} = \frac{50(51) + 2(51)}{2}$$

$$1 + 2 + 3 + \cdots + 50 + 51 = \frac{(50 + 2)51}{2}$$

$$1 + 2 + 3 + \cdots + 50 + 51 = \frac{51(52)}{2}.$$

Since this last equality is just the original statement for $n = 51$, we conclude that

If the statement is true for $n = 50$, then it is also true for $n = 51$.

We have *not* proved that the statement actually *is* true for $n = 50$, but only that *if* it is, then it is also true for $n = 51$.

We claim that this same conditional relationship holds for any two consecutive values of n. In other words, we claim that for any positive integer k,

① **If the statement is true for $n = k$, then it is also true for $n = k + 1$.**

The proof of this claim is the same argument used earlier (with k and $k + 1$ in place of 50 and 51): *If* it is true that

$$1 + 2 + 3 + \cdots + k = \frac{k(k + 1)}{2} \qquad \textit{[Original statement for $n = k$]}$$

then adding $k + 1$ to both sides and simplifying the right side produces these equalities:

$$1 + 2 + 3 + \cdots + k + (k + 1) = \frac{k(k + 1)}{2} + (k + 1)$$

$$1 + 2 + 3 + \cdots + k + (k + 1) = \frac{k(k + 1)}{2} + \frac{2(k + 1)}{2} = \frac{k(k + 1) + 2(k + 1)}{2}$$

$$1 + 2 + 3 + \cdots + k + (k + 1) = \frac{(k + 2)(k + 1)}{2}$$

$$1 + 2 + 3 + \cdots + k + (k + 1) = \frac{(k + 1)[(k + 1) + 1]}{2}.$$

[Original statement for $n = k + 1$]

We have proved that claim ① is valid for each positive integer k. We have *not* proved that the original statement is true for any value of n, but only that *if* it is true for $n = k$, then it is also true for $n = k + 1$. Applying this fact when $k = 1, 2, 3, \ldots$, we see that a recursive pattern emerges. Beginning with the smallest positive integer, 1,

Teaching Notes

The discussion on pages 1002–1004 provides the motivation behind the **Principle of Mathematical Induction** and the "scratch work" for proving the statement "The sum of the first n positive integers is $\frac{n(n + 1)}{2}$."

A more concise "finished proof" of the statement

"$1 + 2 + 3 + \cdots + n = \frac{n(n + 1)}{2}$

for any positive integer n" using the two-step method shown at the top of page 1005 is shown below:

Step 1

When $n = 1$, the statement is

$1 = \frac{1(1 + 1)}{2}$. Since

$\frac{1(1 + 1)}{2} = \frac{1 \cdot 2}{2} = \frac{2}{2} = 1$,

the statement is true for $n = 1$.

Step 2

Let k be a positive integer and assume that the statement is true for $n = k$, that is,

$1 + 2 + 3 + \cdots + k = \frac{k(k + 1)}{2}$.

We must use this assumption to prove that the statement is true for $n = k + 1$, that is,

$1 + 2 + 3 + \cdots + (k + 1)$

$= \frac{(k + 1)[(k + 1) + 1]}{2}.$

Proof:

$1 + 2 + 3 + \cdots + (k + 1)$

$= 1 + 2 + 3 + \cdots + k + (k + 1)$

$= [1 + 2 + 3 + \cdots + k] + (k + 1)$

$= \frac{k(k + 1)}{2} + (k + 1)$ *Induction hypothesis*

$= \frac{k(k + 1)}{2} + \frac{2(k + 1)}{2}$

$= \frac{k(k + 1) + 2(k + 1)}{2}$

$= \frac{(k + 1)(k + 2)}{2}$

$= \frac{(k + 1)[(k + 1) + 1]}{2}$

Thus, the statement is true for $n = k + 1$, and by the Principle of Mathematical Induction,

$1 + 2 + 3 + \cdots + n = \frac{n(n + 1)}{2}$

for any positive integer n.

In the Solution to **Example 1,** some students may conclude from the string of inequalities at the bottom of page 1005 that $2^{k+1} \geq k + 1$. While this is technically still correct, explain that we can make the stronger statement that 2^{k+1} is *strictly* greater than $k + 1$, that is, $2^{k+1} > k + 1$ because 2^{k+1} is *strictly* greater than $2k$.

In general, explain that we can claim a strict inequality between the first and last expression in a string of inequalities if it contains at least one greater than (or less than) sign.

Teaching Notes

It is crucial that students understand the need for *both* steps of **Mathematical Induction.** Using the domino analogy, **Step 2** guarantees that the dominoes are set up in such a way that a domino falling ensures the next domino will fall, while **Step 1** guarantees that the *first domino will actually fall.* Without verifying Step 1, it is unknown whether *any* dominos will fall.

Stress the importance of **Step 1** by going through the example under the Teaching Notes on TE page 1006.

$$\text{②} \begin{cases} \textit{If} \text{ the statement is true for } n = 1, \quad \textit{then} \text{ it is also true for} \\ n = 1 + 1 = 2; \\[4pt] \textit{If} \text{ the statement is true for } n = 2, \quad \textit{then} \text{ it is also true for} \\ n = 2 + 1 = 3; \\[4pt] \textit{If} \text{ the statement is true for } n = 3, \quad \textit{then} \text{ it is also true for} \\ n = 3 + 1 = 4; \\ \quad \vdots \\ \textit{If} \text{ the statement is true for } n = 50, \quad \textit{then} \text{ it is also true for} \\ n = 50 + 1 = 51; \\[4pt] \textit{If} \text{ the statement is true for } n = 51, \quad \textit{then} \text{ it is also true for} \\ n = 51 + 1 = 52; \\ \quad \vdots \end{cases}$$

and so on.

We are finally in a position to *prove* the original statement: $1 + 2 + 3 + \cdots + n = n(n + 1)/2$. Obviously, it *is true* for $n = 1$ since $1 = 1(2)/2$. Now apply in turn each of the propositions on list ②. Since the statement *is* true for $n = 1$, it must also be true for $n = 2$, and hence for $n = 3$, and hence for $n = 4$, and so on, for every value of n. Therefore, the original statement is true for *every* positive integer n.

The preceding proof is an illustration of the following principle:

Principle of Mathematical Induction

> Suppose there is given a statement involving the positive integer n and that:
>
> **(i)** The statement is true for $n = 1$.
>
> **(ii)** If the statement is true for $n = k$ (where k is any positive integer), then the statement is also true for $n = k + 1$.
>
> Then the statement is true for every positive integer n.

Property (i) is simply a statement of fact. To verify that it holds, you must prove the given statement is true for $n = 1$. This is usually easy, as in the preceding example.

Property (ii) is a *conditional* property. It does not assert that the given statement *is* true for $n = k$, but only that *if* it is true for $n = k$, then it is also true for $n = k + 1$. So to verify that property (ii) holds, you need only prove this conditional proposition:

> *If* the statement is true for $n = k$, *then* it is also true for $n = k + 1$.

In order to prove this, or any conditional proposition, you must proceed as in the previous example: Assume the "if" part and use this assumption to prove the "then" part. As we saw earlier, the same argument will usually work for any possible k. Once this conditional proposition has been proved, you can use it *together* with property (i) to conclude that the given statement is necessarily true for every n, just as in the preceding example.

Thus proof by mathematical induction reduces to two steps:

Step 1

Prove that the given statement is true for $n = 1$.

Step 2

Let k be a positive integer. Assume that the given statement is true for $n = k$. Use this assumption to prove that the statement is true for $n = k + 1$.

Step 2 may be performed before step 1 if you wish. Step 2 is sometimes referred to as the **inductive step.** The assumption that the given statement is true for $n = k$ in this inductive step is called the **induction hypothesis.**

Example 1

Prove that $2^n > n$ for every positive integer n.

Solution

Here the statement involving n is $2^n > n$.

Step 1

When $n = 1$, we have the statement $2^1 > 1$. This is obviously true.

Step 2

Let k be any positive integer. We assume that the statement is true for $n = k$, that is, we assume that $2^k > k$. We shall use this assumption to prove that the statement is true for $n = k + 1$, that is, that $2^{k+1} > k + 1$.

We begin with the induction hypothesis:* $2^k > k$. Multiplying both sides of this inequality by 2 yields:

$$2 \cdot 2^k > 2k$$
$$③ \qquad 2^{k+1} > 2k.$$

Since k is a positive integer, we know that $k \geq 1$. Adding k to each side of the inequality $k \geq 1$, we have

$$k + k \geq k + 1$$
$$2k \geq k + 1.$$

Combining this result with inequality ③, we see that

$$2^{k+1} > 2k \geq k + 1.$$

---

*This is the point at which you usually must do some work. Remember that what follows is the "finished proof." It does not include all the thought, scratch work, false starts, and so on that were done before this proof was actually found.

Example 1

Prove that $3^n > 2n$ for every positive integer n.

Step 1

When $n = 1$, we have $3^1 > 2 \cdot 1$, which is true.

Step 2

Let k be any positive integer. We assume the statement is true for $n = k$, that is, we assume that $3^k > 2k$. We shall use this assumption to prove that the statement is true for $n = k + 1$, that is, $3^{k+1} > 2(k + 1)$.

Begin with the induction hypothesis: $3^k > 2k$. Multiplying both sides of this inequality by 3 yields:

$$3 \cdot 3^k > 3 \cdot 2k$$
$$3^{k+1} > 6k \qquad \textbf{(1)}$$

Since k is a positive integer, we know that $k \geq 1$. From this inequality, we can obtain:

$$k \geq 1$$
$$k + k \geq k + 1$$
$$2k \geq k + 1$$
$$2 \cdot 2k \geq 2(k + 1)$$
$$4k \geq 2(k + 1) \qquad \textbf{(2)}$$

Also, since k is a positive integer and $6 > 4$, we can multiply both sides of the inequality $6 > 4$ by k, yielding:

$$6 > 4$$
$$6k > 4k \qquad \textbf{(3)}$$

Combining inequalities **(1)**, **(3)**, and **(2)**, we see that

$$3^{k+1} > 6k > 4k \geq 2(k + 1).$$

The first and last terms of this inequality show that $3^{k+1} > 2(k + 1)$. Therefore, the statement is true for $n = k + 1$, for any positive integer k. By the Principle of Mathematical Induction, we conclude that $3^n > 2n$ for every positive integer n.

Example Notes

In **Example 2**, it is first necessary to translate the verbal statement into a mathematical statement. Remind students that for integers x and y, x is a factor of y if $y = xc$ for some integer c. Thus, 4 is a factor of $7^n - 3^n$ if $7^n - 3^n = 4D$ for some integer D. The statement "$7^n - 3^n = 4D$, for some integer D" becomes the induction hypothesis in the argument.

Note that when students obtain the statement $7^{k+1} - 3^{k+1} = 4(7D + 3^k)$, it can be written as $7^{k+1} - 3^{k+1} = 4C$ (for integer $C = 7D + 3^k$), so that 4 is indeed a factor of $7^{k+1} - 3^{k+1}$.

It is important to note that we can be sure $C = 7D + 3^k$ is an integer when D and k are integers due to the closure of the set of integers under addition and multiplication.

Teaching Notes

The first sentence in the paragraph at the bottom of the page illustrates the need to verify that the statement is true for $n = 1$. Omitting Step 1 could lead students to believe that something is true for all positive integers, even if it is not. For example, ask students to complete the following:

Let k be a positive integer and assume that $2k^2 > 2k$ (induction hypothesis). Show that $2(k + 1)^2 > 2(k + 1)$.

$2(k + 1)^2$
$= 2(k^2 + 2k + 1)$
$= 2k^2 + 4k + 2$
$> 2k + 4k + 2$ *Induction hypothesis*
$> 2k + 2$
$= 2(k + 1)$

Since assuming $2k^2 > 2k$ was true led to $2(k + 1)^2 > 2(k + 1)$ being true, some students might jump to the conclusion that $2n^2 > 2n$ for all positive integers n. However, when $n = 1$, we get the clearly incorrect statement $2(1)^2 > 2(1)$, or $2 > 2$.

Using the *Extended Principle of Mathematical Induction* (page 1010, Exercise 28), it can be shown that $2n^2 > 2n$ for all integers $n \geq 2$.

The first and last terms of this inequality show that $2^{k+1} > k + 1$. Therefore, the statement is true for $n = k + 1$. This argument works for any positive integer k. Thus, we have completed the inductive step. By the Principle of Mathematical Induction, we conclude that $2^n > n$ for every positive integer n. ∎

Example 2

Simple arithmetic shows that

$$7^2 - 3^2 = 49 - 9 = 40 = 4 \cdot 10$$

and

$$7^3 - 3^3 = 343 - 27 = 316 = 4 \cdot 79.$$

In each case, 4 is a factor. These examples suggest that

For each positive integer n, 4 is a factor of $7^n - 3^n$.
This conjecture can be proved by induction as follows.

Step 1

When $n = 1$, the statement is "4 is a factor of $7^1 - 3^1$." Since $7^1 - 3^1 = 4 = 4 \cdot 1$, the statement is true for $n = 1$.

Step 2

Let k be a positive integer and assume that the statement is true for $n = k$, that is, that 4 is a factor of $7^k - 3^k$. Let us denote the other factor by D, so that the induction hypothesis is: $7^k - 3^k = 4D$. We must use this assumption to prove that the statement is true for $n = k + 1$, that is, that 4 is a factor of $7^{k+1} - 3^{k+1}$. Here is the proof:

$7^{k+1} - 3^{k+1} = 7^{k+1} - 7 \cdot 3^k + 7 \cdot 3^k - 3^{k+1}$ [*Since $-7 \cdot 3^k + 7 \cdot 3^k = 0$*]
$= 7(7^k - 3^k) + (7 - 3)3^k$ [*Factor*]
$= 7(4D) + (7 - 3)3^k$ [*Induction hypothesis*]
$= 7(4D) + 4 \cdot 3^k$ [*$7 - 3 = 4$*]
$= 4(7D + 3^k)$.   [*Factor out 4*]

From this last line, we see that 4 is a factor of $7^{k+1} - 3^{k+1}$. Thus, the statement is true for $n = k + 1$, and the inductive step is complete. Therefore, by the Principle of Mathematical Induction the conjecture is actually true for every positive integer n. ∎

Another example of mathematical induction, the proof of the Binomial Theorem, is given at the end of this section.

Sometimes a statement involving the integer n may be false for $n = 1$ and (possibly) other small values of n, but true for all values of n beyond a particular number. For instance, the statement $2^n > n^2$ is false for $n = 1$, 2, 3, 4. But it is true for $n = 5$ and all larger values of n. A variation on the Principle of Mathematical Induction can be used to prove this fact and similar statements. See Exercise 28 for details.

A Common Mistake with Induction

It is sometimes tempting to omit step 2 of an inductive proof when the given statement can easily be verified for small values of n, especially if a clear pattern seems to be developing. As the next example shows, however, *omitting step 2 may lead to error.*

Example 3

An integer (>1) is said to be *prime* if its only positive integer factors are itself and 1. For instance, 11 is prime since its only positive integer factors are 11 and 1. But 15 is not prime because it has factors other than 15 and 1 (namely, 3 and 5). For each positive integer n, consider the number

$$f(n) = n^2 - n + 11.$$

You can readily verify that

$$f(1) = 11, \quad f(2) = 13, \quad f(3) = 17, \quad f(4) = 23, \quad f(5) = 31$$

and that *each of these numbers is prime.* Furthermore, there is a clear pattern: The first two numbers (11 and 13) differ by 2; the next two (13 and 17) differ by 4; the next two (17 and 23) differ by 6; and so on. On the basis of this evidence, we might conjecture:

For each positive integer n, the number $f(n) = n^2 - n + 11$ is prime.

We have seen that this conjecture is true for $n = 1, 2, 3, 4, 5$. Unfortunately, however, it is *false* for some values of n. For instance, when $n = 11$,

$$f(11) = 11^2 - 11 + 11 = 11^2 = 121.$$

But 121 is obviously *not* prime since it has a factor other than 121 and 1, namely, 11. You can verify that the statement is also false for $n = 12$ but true for $n = 13$. ∎

In the preceding example, the proposition

If the statement is true for $n = k$, then it is true for $n = k + 1$

is false when $k = 10$ and $k + 1 = 11$. If you were not aware of this and tried to complete step 2 of an inductive proof, you would not have been able to find a valid proof for it. Of course, the fact that you can't find a proof of a proposition doesn't always mean that no proof exists. But when you are unable to complete step 2, you are warned that there is a possibility that the given statement may be false for some values of n. This warning should prevent you from drawing any wrong conclusions.

Proof of the Binomial Theorem

We shall use induction to prove that for every positive integer n,

$$(x + y)^n = x^n + \binom{n}{1} x^{n-1} y$$

$$+ \binom{n}{2} x^{n-2} y^2 + \binom{n}{3} x^{n-3} y^3 + \cdots + \binom{n}{n-1} xy^{n-1} + y^n.$$

Example 2

Prove 3 is a factor of $8^n - 5^n$ for every positive integer n.

Step 1

When $n = 1$, the statement is "3 is a factor of $8^1 - 5^1$." Since

$$8^1 - 5^1 = 8 - 5 = 3 = 3 \cdot 1,$$

the statement is true for $n = 1$.

Step 2

Let k be a positive integer and assume that the statement is true for $n = k$, that is, that 3 is a factor of $8^k - 5^k$. Let us denote the other factor by D, so that the induction hypothesis is: $8^k - 5^k = 3D$. We must use this assumption to prove that the statement is true for $n = k + 1$, that is, that 3 is a factor of $8^{k+1} - 5^{k+1}$.

Proof:

$$8^{k+1} - 5^{k+1}$$

$$= 8^{k+1} - 8 \cdot 5^k + 8 \cdot 5^k - 5^{k+1}$$

Since $-8 \cdot 5^k + 8 \cdot 5^k = 0$

$$= 8(8^k - 5^k) + (8 - 5)5^k$$

Factor

$$= 8(3D) + (8 - 5)5^k$$

Induction hypothesis

$$= 8(3D) + 3 \cdot 5^k$$

$8 - 5 = 3$

$$= 3(8D + 5^k)$$

Factor out 3

Thus, 3 is a factor of $8^{k+1} - 5^{k+1}$, the statement is true for $n = k + 1$, and the inductive step is complete. By the Principle of Mathematical Induction, 3 is a factor of $8^n - 5^n$ for every positive integer n.

ADDITIONAL EXAMPLES

Example 3

Find a counterexample for the following statement:

For any positive integer n, $5n^2 + 1$ is not a perfect square.

Consider $f(n) = 5n^2 + 1$. Try several values of n:

$f(1) = 5 + 1 = 6$;
  not a perfect square

$f(2) = 20 + 1 = 21$;
  not a perfect square

$f(3) = 45 + 1 = 46$;
  not a perfect square

$f(4) = 80 + 1 = 81 = 9^2$;
  a perfect square

Since the statement is false for $n = 4$, 4 is a counterexample.

Teaching Notes

In the proof of the Binomial Theorem, you may want to have students supply the missing steps (denoted below by **[1]**) in writing the equation for $n = k + 1$, the equation we are trying to show is true, thereby showing that the equation presented in the text (denoted below by **[2]**) is indeed the correct statement for $n = k + 1$.

$(x + y)^{k+1}$

$$= x^{k+1} + \binom{k+1}{1}x^{(k+1)-1}y$$
$$+ \binom{k+1}{2}x^{(k+1)-2}y^2 + \cdots$$
$$+ \binom{k+1}{r+1}x^{(k+1)-(r+1)}y^{r+1} + \cdots \Bigg\}\ [1]$$
$$+ \binom{k+1}{k}xy^k + y^{k+1}$$

$$= x^{k+1} + \binom{k+1}{1}x^k y$$
$$+ \binom{k+1}{2}x^{k-1}y^2 + \cdots$$
$$+ \binom{k+1}{r+1}x^{k-r}y^{r+1} + \cdots \Bigg\}\ [2]$$
$$+ \binom{k+1}{k}xy^k + y^{k+1}$$

This theorem was discussed and its notation explained in Section B.1.

Step 1

When $n = 1$, there are only two terms on the right side of the preceding equation, and the statement reads $(x + y)^1 = x^1 + y^1$. This is certainly true.

Step 2

Let k be any positive integer and assume that the theorem is true for $n = k$, that is, that

$$(x + y)^k = x^k + \binom{k}{1}x^{k-1}y + \binom{k}{2}x^{k-2}y^2 + \cdots$$
$$+ \binom{k}{r}x^{k-r}y^r + \cdots + \binom{k}{k-1}xy^{k-1} + y^k.$$

[On the right side of this equation, we have included a typical middle term $\binom{k}{r}x^{k-r}y^r$. The sum of the exponents is k, and the bottom part of the binomial coefficient is the same as the y exponent.] We shall use this assumption to prove that the theorem is true for $n = k + 1$, that is, that

$$(x + y)^{k+1} = x^{k+1} + \binom{k+1}{1}x^k y + \binom{k+1}{2}x^{k-1}y^2 + \cdots$$
$$+ \binom{k+1}{r+1}x^{k-r}y^{r+1} + \cdots + \binom{k+1}{k}xy^k + y^{k+1}.$$

We have simplified some of the terms on the right side; for instance, $(k + 1) - 1 = k$ and $(k + 1) - (r + 1) = k - r$. But this is the correct statement for $n = k + 1$: The coefficients of the middle terms are $\binom{k+1}{1}$, $\binom{k+1}{2}$, $\binom{k+1}{3}$, and so on; the sum of the exponents of each middle term is $k + 1$, and the bottom part of each binomial coefficient is the same as the y exponent.

In order to prove the theorem for $n = k + 1$, we shall need this fact about binomial coefficients: For any integers r and k with $0 \le r < k$,

④
$$\binom{k}{r+1} + \binom{k}{r} = \binom{k+1}{r+1}.$$

A proof of this fact is outlined in Exercise 47 on page 1001.

To prove the theorem for $n = k + 1$, we first note that

$$(x + y)^{k+1} = (x + y)(x + y)^k.$$

Applying the induction hypothesis to $(x + y)^k$, we see that

$$(x + y)^{k+1} = (x + y)\left[x^k + \binom{k}{1}x^{k-1}y + \binom{k}{2}x^{k-2}y^2 + \cdots + \binom{k}{r}x^{k-r}y^r\right.$$
$$\left. + \binom{k}{r+1}x^{k-(r+1)}y^{r+1} + \cdots + \binom{k}{k-1}xy^{k-1} + y^k\right]$$
$$= x\left[x^k + \binom{k}{1}x^{k-1}y + \cdots + y^k\right] + y\left[x^k + \binom{k}{1}x^{k-1}y + \cdots + y^k\right].$$

1008   **Advanced Topics**

Next we multiply out the right-hand side. Remember that multiplying by x increases the x exponent by 1 and multiplying by y increases the y exponent by 1.

$$(x + y)^{k+1} = \left[x^{k+1} + \binom{k}{1}x^k y + \binom{k}{2}x^{k-1}y^2 + \cdots + \binom{k}{r}x^{k-r+1}y^r \right.$$
$$\left. + \binom{k}{r+1}x^{k-r}y^{r+1} + \cdots + \binom{k}{k-1}x^2 y^{k-1} + xy^k \right]$$
$$+ \left[x^k y + \binom{k}{1}x^{k-1}y^2 + \binom{k}{2}x^{k-2}y^3 + \cdots + \binom{k}{r}x^{k-r}y^{r+1} \right.$$
$$\left. + \binom{k}{r+1}x^{k-(r+1)}y^{r+2} + \cdots + \binom{k}{k-1}xy^k + y^{k+1} \right]$$
$$= x^{k+1} + \left[\binom{k}{1} + 1 \right]x^k y + \left[\binom{k}{2} + \binom{k}{1} \right]x^{k-1}y^2 + \cdots$$
$$+ \left[\binom{k}{r+1} + \binom{k}{r} \right]x^{k-r}y^{r+1} + \cdots + \left[1 + \binom{k}{k-1} \right]xy^k + y^{k+1}.$$

Now apply statement ④ to each of the coefficients of the middle terms.

For instance, with $r = 1$, statement ④ shows that $\binom{k}{2} + \binom{k}{1} = \binom{k+1}{2}$.

Similarly, with $r = 0$, $\binom{k}{1} + 1 = \binom{k}{1} + \binom{k}{0} = \binom{k+1}{1}$, and so on. Then the expression above for $(x + y)^{k+1}$ becomes

$$(x + y)^{k+1} = x^{k+1} + \binom{k+1}{1}x^k y + \binom{k+1}{2}x^{k-1}y^2 + \cdots$$
$$+ \binom{k+1}{r+1}x^{k-r}y^{r+1} + \cdots + \binom{k+1}{k}xy^k + y^{k+1}.$$

Since this last statement says the theorem is true for $n = k + 1$, the inductive step is complete. By the Principle of Mathematical Induction the theorem is true for every positive integer n.

Teaching Notes

It may also be helpful for students to see the following, which is exactly the same as the manipulation at the top of page 1009, but with coloring added, to allow students to more easily see which terms are being factored and where.

$$\left[x^{k+1} + \binom{k}{1}x^k y + \binom{k}{2}x^{k-1}y^2 + \cdots \right.$$
$$+ \binom{k}{r}x^{k-r+1}y^r + \binom{k}{r+1}x^{k-r}y^{r+1} + \cdots$$
$$\left. + \binom{k}{k-1}x^2 y^{k-1} + xy^k \right]$$
$$+ \left[x^k y + \binom{k}{1}x^{k-1}y^2 + \binom{k}{2}x^{k-2}y^3 + \cdots \right.$$
$$+ \binom{k}{r}x^{k-r}y^{r+1}$$
$$+ \binom{k}{r+1}x^{k-(r+1)}y^{r+2} + \cdots$$
$$\left. + \binom{k}{k-1}xy^k + y^{k+1} \right]$$
$$= x^{k+1} + \left[\binom{k}{1} + 1 \right]x^k y$$
$$+ \left[\binom{k}{2} + \binom{k}{1} \right]x^{k-1}y^2 + \cdots$$
$$+ \left[\binom{k}{r+1} + \binom{k}{r} \right]x^{k-r}y^{r+1} + \cdots$$
$$+ \left[1 + \binom{k}{k-1} \right]xy^k + y^{k+1}$$

Exercises B.2

In Exercises 1–18, use mathematical induction to prove that each of the given statements is true for every positive integer n.

1. $1 + 2 + 2^2 + 2^3 + 2^4 + \cdots + 2^{n-1} = 2^n - 1$

2. $1 + 3 + 3^2 + 3^3 + 3^4 + \cdots + 3^{n-1} = \dfrac{3^n - 1}{2}$

3. $1 + 3 + 5 + 7 + \cdots + (2n - 1) = n^2$

4. $2 + 4 + 6 + 8 + \cdots + 2n = n^2 + n$

5. $1^2 + 2^2 + 3^2 + \cdots + n^2 = \dfrac{n(n + 1)(2n + 1)}{6}$

6. $\dfrac{1}{2} + \dfrac{1}{4} + \dfrac{1}{8} + \cdots + \dfrac{1}{2^n} = 1 - \dfrac{1}{2^n}$

7. $\dfrac{1}{1 \cdot 2} + \dfrac{1}{2 \cdot 3} + \dfrac{1}{3 \cdot 4} + \cdots + \dfrac{1}{n(n + 1)} = \dfrac{n}{n + 1}$

8. $\left(1 + \dfrac{1}{1}\right)\left(1 + \dfrac{1}{2}\right)\left(1 + \dfrac{1}{3}\right) \cdots \left(1 + \dfrac{1}{n}\right) = n + 1$

9. $n + 2 > n$ **10.** $2n + 2 > n$

11. $3^n \geq 3n$ **12.** $3^n \geq 1 + 2n$

13. $3n > n + 1$ **14.** $\left(\dfrac{3}{2}\right)^n > n$

15. 3 is a factor of $2^{2n+1} + 1$

Section B.2   **Mathematical Induction**   **1009**

Note: Hereafter, in these answers, step 1 will be omitted if it is trivial (as in Exercise 1), and only the essential parts of step 2 will be given.

2. Assume that the statement is true for $n = k$:
$$1 + 3 + 3^2 + 3^3 + \cdots + 3^{k-1} = \dfrac{3^k - 1}{2}.$$

Add 3^k to both sides to get
$$1 + 3 + 3^2 + 3^3 + \cdots + 3^{k-1} + 3^k$$
$$= \dfrac{3^k - 1}{2} + 3^k = \dfrac{3^{k+1} - 1}{2}.$$

Therefore the statement is true for $n = k + 1$. By the Principle of Mathematical Induction, the statement is true for all positive integers n.

3–15. *See pp. 1086–88.*

Exercises B.2 Answers sidebar

Exercises B.2

ANSWERS

1. *Step 1:* For $n = 1$ the statement is $1 = 2^1 - 1$, which is true.

Step 2: Assume that the statement is true for $n = k$: that is, $1 + 2 + 2^2 + 2^3 + \cdots + 2^{k-1} = 2^k - 1$. Add 2^k to both sides, and rearrange terms:

$$1 + 2 + 2^2 + 2^3 + \cdots + 2^{k-1} + 2^k$$
$$= 2^k - 1 + 2^k$$
$$1 + 2 + 2^2 + 2^3 + \cdots + 2^{k-1} + 2^{(k+1)-1} = 2(2^k) - 1$$
$$1 + 2 + 2^2 + 2^3 + \cdots + 2^{k-1} + 2^{(k+1)-1} = 2^{k+1} - 1$$

But this last line says that the statement is true for $n = k + 1$. Therefore, by the Principle of Mathematical Induction the statement is true for every positive integer n.

Section B.2   **Mathematical Induction**   **1009**

16. Assume the statement is true for $n = k$; then 5 is a factor of $2^{4k-2} + 1$; that is, there is an integer P for which $5P = 2^{4k-2} + 1$. Consider

$$2^{4(k+1)-2} + 1$$
$$= 2^{4k-2+4} + 1$$
$$= 2^{4k-2}2^4 + 1$$
$$= (5P - 1)(16) + 1$$
$$= 80P - 15$$
$$= 5(16P - 3).$$

Therefore, 5 is a factor of $2^{4(k+1)-2} + 1$ and the statement is true for $n = k + 1$. Therefore, the statement is true for all positive integers n.

17. Assume the statement is true for $n = k$: 64 is a factor of $3^{2k+2} - 8k - 9$. Then $3^{2k+2} - 8k - 9 = 64N$ for some integer N so that $3^{2k+2} = 8k + 9 + 64N$. Now $3^{2(k+1)+2} = 3^{2k+2+2} = 3^{2+(2k+2)} = 3^2 \cdot 3^{2k+2} = 9(8k + 9 + 64N)$. Consequently,

$$3^{2(k+1)+2} - 8(k + 1) - 9$$
$$= 3^{2(k+1)+2} - 8k - 8 - 9$$
$$= 3^{2(k+1)+2} - 8k - 17$$
$$= [9(8k + 9 + 64N)] - 8k - 17$$
$$= 72K + 81 + 9 \cdot 64N - 8k - 17$$
$$= 64k + 64 + 9 \cdot 64N$$
$$= 64(k + 1 + 9N).$$

From the first and last parts of this equation we see that 64 is a factor of $3^{2(k+1)+2} - 8(k + 1) - 9$. Therefore, the statement is true for $n = k + 1$.

18. Assume the statement is true for $n = k$: 64 is a factor of $9^k - 8k - 1$; that is, there is an integer P such that $64P = 9^k - 8k - 1$. Consider $9^{k+1} - 8(k + 1) - 1$

$$= 9(9^k) - 8k - 9$$
$$= 9(64P + 8k + 1) - 8k - 9$$
$$= 64(9P + k).$$

Therefore, 64 is a factor of $9^{k+1} - 8(k + 1) - 1$ and the statement is true for $n = k + 1$. Therefore, by The Principle of Mathematical Induction, the statement is true for all positive integers n.

19–37. *See pp.* 1088–89.

16. 5 is a factor of $2^{4n-2} + 1$

17. 64 is a factor of $3^{2n+2} - 8n - 9$

18. 64 is a factor of $9^n - 8n - 1$

19. Let c and d be fixed real numbers. Prove that
$$c + (c + d) + (c + 2d) + (c + 3d) + \cdots$$
$$+ [c + (n - 1)d] = \frac{n[2c + (n - 1)d]}{2}.$$

20. Let r be a fixed real number with $r \neq 1$. Prove that
$$1 + r + r^2 + r^3 + \cdots + r^{n-1} = \frac{r^n - 1}{r - 1}.$$

Remember: $1 = r^0$; so when $n = 1$ the left side reduces to $r^0 = 1$.

21. a. Write *each* of $x^2 - y^2$, $x^3 - y^3$, and $x^4 - y^4$ as a product of $x - y$ and another factor.
b. Make a conjecture as to how $x^n - y^n$ can be written as a product of $x - y$ and another factor. Use induction to prove your conjecture.

22. Let $x_1 = \sqrt{2}$; $x_2 = \sqrt{2 + \sqrt{2}}$;
$x_3 = \sqrt{2 + \sqrt{2 + \sqrt{2}}}$; and so on. Prove that $x_n < 2$ for every positive integer n.

In Exercises 23–27, if the given statement is true, prove it. If it is false, give a counterexample.

23. Every odd positive integer is prime.

24. The number $n^2 + n + 17$ is prime for every positive integer n.

25. $(n + 1)^2 > n^2 + 1$ for every positive integer n.

26. 3 is a factor of the number $n^3 - n + 3$ for every positive integer n.

27. 4 is a factor of the number $n^4 - n + 4$ for every positive integer n.

28. Let q be a *fixed* integer. Suppose a statement involving the integer n has these two properties:
  i. The statement is true for $n = q$.
  ii. If the statement is true for $n = k$ (where k is any integer with $k \geq q$), then the statement is also true for $n = k + 1$.
Then we claim that the statement is true for every integer n greater than or equal to q.
  a. Give an informal explanation that shows why this claim should be valid. Note that when $q = 1$, this claim is precisely the Principle of Mathematical Induction.
  b. The claim made before part **a** will be called the *Extended Principle of Mathematical Induction*.

State the two steps necessary to use this principle to prove that a given statement is true for all $n \geq q$. (See discussion on page 1005.)

In Exercises 29–34, use the Extended Principle of Mathematical Induction (Exercise 28) to prove the given statement.

29. $2n - 4 > n$ for every $n \geq 5$. (Use 5 for q here.)

30. Let r be a fixed real number with $r > 1$. Then $(1 + r)^n > 1 + nr$ for every integer $n \geq 2$. (Use 2 for q here.)

31. $n^2 > n$ for all $n \geq 2$

32. $2^n > n^2$ for all $n \geq 5$

33. $3^n > 2^n + 10n$ for all $n \geq 4$

34. $2n < n!$ for all $n \geq 4$

35. Let n be a positive integer. Suppose that there are three pegs and on one of them n rings are stacked, with each ring being smaller in diameter than the one below it (see the figure). We want to transfer the stack of rings to another peg according to these rules: (i) Only one ring may be moved at a time; (ii) a ring can be moved to any peg, provided it is never placed on top of a smaller ring; (iii) the final order of the rings on the new peg must be the same as the original order on the first peg.

a. What is the smallest possible number of moves when $n = 2$? $n = 3$? $n = 4$?
b. Make a conjecture as to the smallest possible number of moves required for any n. Prove your conjecture by induction.

36. The basic formula for compound interest $T(x) = P(1 + r)^x$ was discussed in Chapter 5. Prove by induction that the formula is valid whenever x is a positive integer. [*Note: P* and *r* are assumed to be constant.]

37. Use induction to prove DeMoivre's Theorem: For any complex number $z = r(\cos \theta + i \sin \theta)$ and any positive integer n,
$$z^n = r^n[\cos(n\theta) + i \sin(n\theta)].$$

GEOMETRY REVIEW

G.1   Geometry Concepts

An **angle** consists of two half-lines that begin at the same point P, as in Figure G.1-1. The point P is called the **vertex** of the angle and the half-lines the **sides** of the angle.

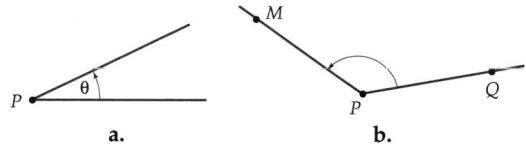

Figure G.1-1

An angle may be labeled by a Greek letter, such as angle θ in Figure G.1-1**a**, or by listing three points (a point on one side, the vertex, a point on the other side), such as angle QPM in Figure G.1-1**b**.

In order to measure the size of an angle, we must assign a number to each angle. Here is the classical method for doing this:

1. Construct a circle whose center is the vertex of the angle.

2. Divide the circumference of the circle into 360 equal parts (called **degrees**) by marking 360 points on the circumference, beginning with the point where one side of the angle intersects the circle. Label these points $0°$, $1°$, $2°$, $3°$, and so on.

3. The label of the point where the second side of the angle intersects the circle is the degree measure of the angle.

For example, Figure G.1-2 on the next page shows an angle θ of measure 25 degrees (in symbols, $25°$) and an angle β of measure $135°$.

Figure G.1-2

An **acute angle** is an angle whose measure is strictly between 0° and 90°, such as angle θ in Figure G.1-2. A **right angle** is an angle that measures 90°. An **obtuse angle** is an angle whose measure is strictly between 90° and 180°, such as angle β in Figure G.1-2.

A **triangle** has three sides (straight line segments) and three angles, formed at the points where the various sides meet. When angles are measured in degrees,

> the sum of the measures of all three angles of a triangle is *always* 180°.

For instance, see Figure G.1-3.

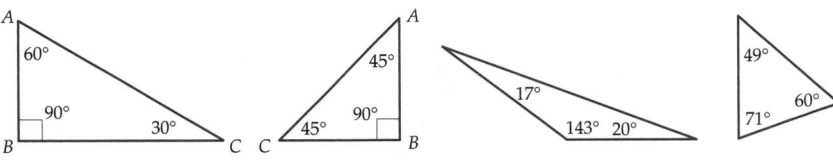

Figure G.1-3

A **right triangle** is a triangle, one of whose angles is a right angle, such as the first two triangles shown in Figure G.1-3. The side of a right triangle that lies opposite the right angle is called the **hypotenuse.** In each of the right triangles in Figure G.1-3, side AC is the hypotenuse.

Pythagorean Theorem

If the sides of a right triangle have lengths a and b and the hypotenuse has length c, then

$$c^2 = a^2 + b^2.$$

Example 1

Consider the right triangle with sides of lengths 5 and 12, as shown in Figure G.1-4.

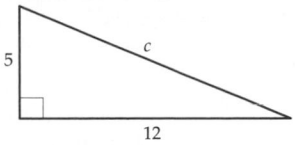

Figure G.1-4

According to the Pythagorean Theorem the length c of the hypotenuse satisfies the equation: $c^2 = 5^2 + 12^2 = 25 + 144 = 169$. Since $169 = 13^2$, we see that c must be 13.

∎

Theorem I

> If two angles of a triangle are equal, then the two sides opposite these angles have the same length.

Example 2

Suppose the hypotenuse of the right triangle shown in Figure G.1-5 has length 1 and that angles B and C measure $45°$ each.

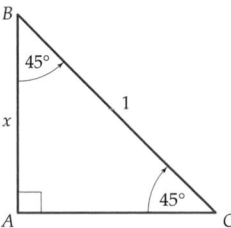

Figure G.1-5

Then by Theorem I, sides AB and AC have the same length. If x is the length of side AB, then by the Pythagorean Theorem:

$$x^2 + x^2 = 1^2$$
$$2x^2 = 1$$
$$x^2 = \frac{1}{2}$$
$$x = \sqrt{\frac{1}{2}} = \frac{1}{\sqrt{2}} = \frac{\sqrt{2}}{2}.$$

Section G.1　**Geometry Concepts**　**1013**

(We ignore the other solution of this equation, namely, $x = -\sqrt{\frac{1}{2}}$, since x represents a length here and thus must be nonnegative.) Therefore, the sides of a $90° - 45° - 45°$ triangle with hypotenuse 1 are each of length $\frac{\sqrt{2}}{2}$. ■

Theorem II

> In a right triangle that has an angle of 30°, the length of the side opposite the 30° angle is one-half the length of the hypotenuse.

Example 3

Suppose that in the right triangle shown in Figure G.1-6 angle B is 30° and the length of hypotenuse BC is 2.

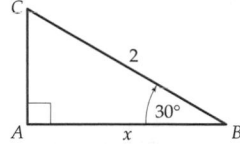

Figure G.1-6

By Theorem II the side opposite the 30° angle, namely, side AC, has length 1. If x denotes the length of side AB, then by the Pythagorean Theorem:

$$1^2 + x^2 = 2^2$$
$$x^2 = 3$$
$$x = \sqrt{3}.$$
■

Example 4

The right triangle shown in Figure G.1-7 has a 30° angle at C, and side AC has length $\frac{\sqrt{3}}{2}$.

Figure G.1-7

Let x denote the length of the hypotenuse BC. By Theorem II, side AB has length $\frac{1}{2}x$. By the Pythagorean Theorem:

$$\left(\frac{1}{2}x\right)^2 + \left(\frac{\sqrt{3}}{2}\right)^2 = x^2$$

$$\frac{x^2}{4} + \frac{3}{4} = x^2$$

$$\frac{3}{4} = \frac{3}{4}x^2$$

$$x^2 = 1$$

$$x = 1.$$

Therefore, the triangle has hypotenuse of length 1 and sides of lengths $\frac{1}{2}$ and $\frac{\sqrt{3}}{2}$.

∎

Two triangles, as in Figure G.1-8, are said to be **similar** if their corresponding angles are equal (that is, $\angle A = \angle D$; $\angle B = \angle E$; and $\angle C = \angle F$). Thus, similar triangles have the same *shape* but not necessarily the same *size*.

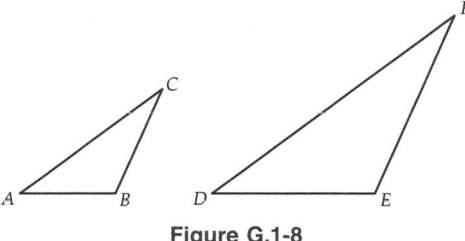

Figure G.1-8

Theorem III

Suppose triangle *ABC* with sides *a*, *b*, *c* is similar to triangle *DEF* with sides *d*, *e*, *f* (that is, ∡*A* = ∡*D*; ∡*B* = ∡*E*; ∡*C* = ∡*F*).

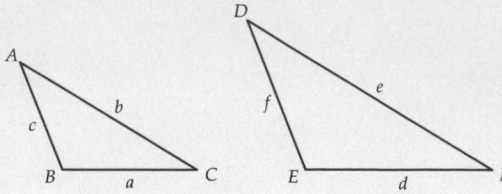

Then

$$\frac{a}{d} = \frac{b}{e} = \frac{c}{f}.$$

These equalities are equivalent to:

$$\frac{a}{b} = \frac{d}{e}, \qquad \frac{b}{c} = \frac{e}{f}, \qquad \frac{a}{c} = \frac{d}{f}.$$

The equivalence of the equalities in the conclusion of the theorem is easily verified. For example, since

$$\frac{a}{d} = \frac{b}{e}$$

we have

$$ae = db.$$

Dividing both sides of this equation by *be* yields:

$$\frac{ae}{be} = \frac{db}{be}$$

$$\frac{a}{b} = \frac{d}{e}.$$

The other equivalences are proved similarly.

Example 5

Suppose the triangles in Figure G.1-9 are similar and that the sides have the lengths indicated.

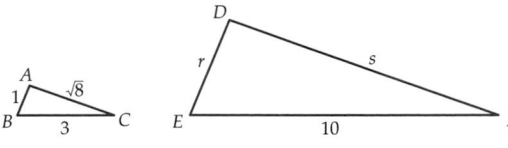

Figure G.1-9

Then by Theorem III,

$$\frac{\text{length } AC}{\text{length } DF} = \frac{\text{length } BC}{\text{length } EF}$$

In other words,

$$\frac{\sqrt{8}}{s} = \frac{3}{10}$$

so that

$$3s = 10\sqrt{8}$$
$$s = \left(\frac{10}{3}\right)\sqrt{8}.$$

Similarly, by Theorem III,

$$\frac{\text{length } AB}{\text{length } DE} = \frac{\text{length } BC}{\text{length } EF}$$

so that

$$\frac{1}{r} = \frac{3}{10}$$
$$3r = 10$$
$$r = \frac{10}{3}.$$

Therefore the sides of triangle DEF are of lengths 10, $\frac{10}{3}$, and $\frac{10}{3}\sqrt{8}$. ■

Section G.1   **Geometry Concepts**   **1017**

Technology

This appendix describes calculator features used throughout the book. The first section focuses on graphing functions and sequences; the second section presents procedures for creating lists, statistics, statistical plots, and regression equations. Students who are unfamiliar with a graphing calculator should complete the entire appendix; all students may use it as a reference to specific features seen in the text.

Graphs and Tables

Graphing calculators have a MODE or SET UP feature that allows you to set different modes for number format, type of angle measure, graph type, and drawing mode. Select the following modes by using the procedures explained in detail below for TI-84 Plus/TI-83 and Casio 9850GB-Plus.

Number format:	Float or Standard
Angle measure:	Degree
Graph type:	Function or Rect
Drawing mode:	Connected or Connect

TI-84/TI-83 Press MODE, then use the up/down arrow keys to move from one row to another and the left/right arrow keys to move to a desired selection. When the cursor is on a desired selection, press ENTER to choose that option. After all selections have been made, press 2nd QUIT to return to the home screen.

Casio 9850 From the MAIN MENU, select RUN EXE. Then press SHIFT SET UP. Use the up/down arrow key to select the different mode types. Use the F1 through F6 buttons to select the desired setting for each mode.

Solutions and Graphs

The **graph of an equation** in two variables is the set of points in the plane whose coordinates are solutions of the equation. Thus, the graph is a *geometric picture of the solutions.*

The graph of $y = x^2$ consists of all points (x, x^2), where x is a real number. A table of values for this function is shown below along with the graphical representation of the points. See Figure T1-1a. The points suggest that the graph looks like Figure T1-1b, which is obtained by connecting the plotted points and extending the graph.

x	$y = x^2$
-2	4
-1.5	2.25
-1	1
-0.5	0.25
0	0
0.5	0.25
1	1
1.5	2.25
2	4

Figure T1-1a

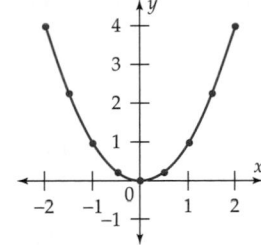

Figure T1-1b

Using Technology to Graph Functions

Technology improves graphing speed and accuracy by plotting a large number of points quickly. A graphing calculator graphs in the same way you would graph by hand, but it uses many more points.

Viewing Windows

The first step in graphing with technology is to choose a preliminary **viewing window,** which is the portion of the coordinate plane that will appear on the screen. Using an inappropriate viewing window may display no portion of a graph or may misrepresent its important characteristics.

The viewing window for the graph in Figure T1-2a is the rectangular region indicated by the dashed blue lines. It includes all points (x, y) whose coordinates satisfy $-4 \leq x \leq 5$ and $-3 \leq y \leq 6$. To display this viewing window on a calculator, press the WINDOW (or SHIFT V-Window) key, and enter the appropriate numbers, as shown in Figure T1-2b for the TI-84/TI-83. Other calculators are similar. The settings Xscl = 1 and Yscl = 1 put the tick marks 1 unit apart on the respective axes. This is usually the best setting for small viewing windows but not for large ones.

Figure T1-2a

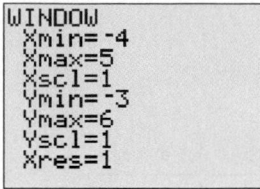

Figure T1-2b

Resolution   Xres sets the pixel resolution for function graphs. When Xres is 1, functions are evaluated and graphed at each **pixel** (point) along the *x*-axis. At 10, functions are evaluated and graphed at every 10th pixel along the *x*-axis. Some calculators do not have a Xres setting, and on those that do, it should normally be set at 1.

Graphing Functions

The following example outlines the procedure for graphing an equation.

Example 1   Using Technology to Graph a Function

Use technology to graph the relation $2u^3 - 8u - 2v + 4 = 0$.

Solution

Step 1

Choose a preliminary viewing window.

If it is unknown where the graph lies in the plane, start with a viewing window with $-10 \le x \le 10$ and $-10 \le y \le 10$. This window setting is called the **standard window** on most calculators. The window may be adjusted to fit the functions after graphing.

To display the viewing **window editor** on a calculator, press WINDOW (or SHIFT V-Window) and enter the appropriate numbers, as shown in Figure T1-3a.

Xscl and Yscl determine where the tick marks will be displayed on the axes. Setting both to 1 is usually best for small viewing windows but not for large ones.

Figure T1-3a

Step 2

Solve for the output variable, if necessary.

Calculators can only graph *functions* in a form where the output variable is expressed as a function of the input variable. In this example, assume that the output variable is *v* and solve the given equation for *v*:

$$2u^3 - 8u - 2v + 4 = 0$$
$$-2v = -2u^3 + 8u - 4 \qquad \text{\textit{Rearrange terms.}}$$

Figure T1-3b

Figure T1-3c

Figure T1-3d

Because the calculator graphs functions of the form $y = f(x)$, replace v with y and replace u with x. The function can be represented as the following.

$$y = x^3 - 4x + 2$$

Step 3

Enter the function by selecting the following.

> **TI-84/TI-83**   Y=
>
> **Casio 9850**   GRAPH from the MAIN MENU

Key in the function, as shown in Figure T1-3b.

Display the graph by pressing GRAPH (or DRAW). The graph of the function is shown in Figure T1-3c.

Step 4

If necessary, adjust the viewing window for a better view.

Notice that the point where the graph crosses the y-axis is not clear in the standard window. Changing the viewing window and displaying the graph again shows that the graph crosses the y-axis at 2. Figure T1-3d shows the graph after TRACE—which is discussed below—was pressed and the arrow keys were used to move the cursor to the y-intercept. ∎

Graphing Relations

Some relations must be written as two separate functions before they can be graphed. The method used to graph the function in Example 1 can be used to graph any equation that can be solved for y.

Example 2   Graphing a Relation

Graph the relation given by the equation $12x^2 - 4y^2 + 16x + 12 = 0$.

Solution

Solve the equation $12x^2 - 4y^2 + 16x + 12 = 0$ for y:

$$4y^2 = 12x^2 + 16x + 12$$
$$y^2 = 3x^2 + 4x + 3$$
$$y = \pm\sqrt{3x^2 + 4x + 3}$$

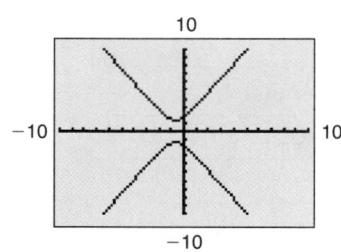

Figure T1-4

The graph is shown in Figure T1-4, where $y = \sqrt{3x^2 + 4x + 3}$ represents the upper portion of the graph and $y = -\sqrt{3x^2 + 4x + 3}$ represents the lower portion. ∎

Other Graphing Calculator Features

Trace

The trace feature allows you to display the coordinates of points on a graph of a function by using the left/right arrow keys, as illustrated in

Technology Tip

• When you get a blank screen, press TRACE and use the left/right arrow keys. The coordinates of the points on the graph will be displayed at the bottom of the screen, even though they are not in the current window. Use these coordinates as a guide for selecting a viewing window in which the graph does appear.

Figure T1-3d. The TRACE feature is located on the different calculators as follows.

TI-84/TI-83	Trace is on the keyboard.
Casio 9850	Trace is the 2nd function above F1.

Zoom

Using the ZOOM feature of a graphing calculator will change the viewing window. ZOOM IN may be used to obtain better approximations for the coordinates of a point, while ZOOM OUT may be used to view a larger portion of the graph.

TI-84/TI-83	ZOOM is on the keyboard.
Casio 9850	ZOOM is the 2nd function above F2.

To use the ZOOM feature, select Zoom In (or IN) from the ZOOM menu, move the cursor to the desired point, and press ENTER. The coordinates of the cursor's position are shown at the bottom of the screen. Repeatedly using Zoom In will give better approximations of the coordinates of points.

The **scaling factors** used to Zoom In or Zoom Out may be adjusted on most calculators. To set the ZOOM factors, look for Set Factors or FACT in the Zoom menu or in the MEMORY submenu of ZOOM of TI-84/TI-83.

Maximums and Minimums

There are several ways to approximate the coordinates of a high point or a low point: using the TRACE feature as discussed in Example 1, using the ZOOM feature, and using the **maximum finder.** The maximum/minimum finder automatically finds the highest/lowest point with the calculator's greatest degree of accuracy. On some calculators, left and right bounds and an initial guess must be indicated. On other calculators, the cursor must be placed near the maximum point. The maximum finder is referenced by the term in the second column of the chart following this paragraph; it can be found in the menu referred to in the third column. The **minimum finder** works in a similar way. Minimum finders are found in the same menu.

Model	Reference	Menu(s)
TI-84/TI-83	maximum	CALC (2nd TRACE)
Casio 9850	MAX	G-Solv

Technology Tip

To use a square viewing window, use **ZSquare**, or **SQR** in the **ZOOM** menu. This will adjust the x scale while keeping the y scale fixed.

Square Windows

Another useful screen is one in which one-unit segments on the x-axis are the same one-unit segments on the y-axis. This type of window is called a **square window**. Because calculator screens are wider than they are high, the y-axis in a square window must be shorter than the x-axis. On many calculators, such as the TI-84/TI-83, the ratio of height to width is about $\dfrac{2}{3}$, so an x-axis with 20 units will have on its y-axis about $\dfrac{2}{3}(20) = 13$ units when square. Therefore, a square window with $-10 \le x \le 10$ could have $-6 \le y \le 7$, or $0 \le y \le 13$, on a screen that has a $2:3$ height-to-width ratio. Check your calculator's height-to-width ratio by looking at the scales after producing a square window. A square window should be used to display circles and perpendicular lines.

Technology Tip

For a decimal window that is also square, use **ZDecimal** in the TI-84/TI-83 **ZOOM** menu and **INIT** in the Casio 9850 **V-Window** menu.

Graphing Exploration ●

The lines $y = 0.5x$ and $y = -2x + 2$ are perpendicular because the product of their slopes is -1. Graph both in the standard viewing window, and then graph them in a square window. Describe the different appearances of the lines in both window types.

Decimal Window

When using the **TRACE** feature, a calculator typically displays points as 2.34042519, for example, rather than as 2.3 or 2.34. A screen in which the points represent values with one or two decimal places is called a **decimal window**. A decimal window is appropriate when accuracy to one or two decimal places is desired.

Choosing a viewing window carefully can make the trace feature much more convenient, as the following Exploration demonstrates.

Technology Tip

The screen widths, in pixels, of commonly used calculators:

TI-84/TI-83 and Casio 9800: 95

TI-86, Sharp 9600, Casio 9850: 127

HP-38: 131

TI-89: 159

TI-92: 239

Graphing Exploration

- Graph $y = \frac{5}{9}(x - 32)$, which relates the temperature x in degrees Fahrenheit and the temperature y in degrees Celsius.
- Use a viewing window with $-40 \leq y \leq 40$ and $0 \leq x \leq k$, where k is one less than the number of pixels, or points, on your calculator screen divided by 10. On a TI-84/TI-83, for example, $k = \frac{95 - 1}{10} = 9.4$. (See Technology Tip at left.)
- Use the TRACE feature to determine the Celsius temperatures corresponding to 20°F and 77°F.
- Set the window to $32 - \frac{k}{20} \leq x \leq 32 + \frac{k}{20}$, where k is the same as above. This is a decimal window with $(32, 0)$ at its center.
- Graph the equation again, and use TRACE to determine the Celsius equivalent of 33.8°F.

Figure T1-5a

Figure T1-5b

Function Tables

Table of Function Values

The **table feature** of a calculator is a convenient way to display points and evaluate functions. By setting the initial input value and the increment value, a table of values may be displayed for functions stored in the memory, as shown in Figure T1-5a. If more than one function is in the function memory, the output values for each are stored in separate columns of a table. To access the table setup screen, select the following.

TI-84/TI-83	TBLSET on the keyboard
Casio 9850	RANG in the TABLE menu

The increment is labeled ΔTbl on TI-84/TI-83 and Pitch on Casio 9850.

Figure T1-5b shows a table of values for the function $y = x^3 - 4x + 2$, which is stored as Y1.

Select the following to view the table of values.

TI-84/TI-83	TABLE on the keyboard
Casio 9850	Press TABL.

Graphs On and Off

An equation stays in the equation memory until you delete it. If there are several equations in memory and you want to graph only some of them, turn those equations "on" and the others "off." On most calculators an equation is "on" if its equal sign is shaded and "off" if its equal sign is clear.

Graphing Conventions

1. Unless directed otherwise, use a calculator for graphing.

2. Complete graphs are required unless a viewing window is specified or the context of a problem indicates that a partial graph is acceptable.

3. If the directions say "obtain the graph," "find the graph," or "graph the equation," you need not actually draw the graph on paper. For review purposes, however, it may be helpful to record the viewing window used.

4. The directions "sketch the graph" mean to draw the graph on paper, indicating the scale on each axis. This may involve simply copying the display that is on the calculator screen, or it may require graphing if the calculator display is misleading.

Calculator Exploration

1. Tick Marks
   a. Set Xscl = 1 so that adjacent tick marks on the x-axis are one unit apart. Find the largest range of x values such that the tick marks on the x-axis are clearly distinguishable and appear to be equally spaced.
   b. Do part **a** with y in place of x.

2. Viewing Window Look in the ZOOM menu to find out how many built-in viewing windows your calculator has. Take a look at each one.

3. Maximum/Minimum Finders Use your minimum finder to approximate the x-coordinates of the lowest point on the graph of $y = x^3 - 2x + 5$ in the window with $0 \le x \le 5$ and $-3 \le y \le 8$.

   The correct answer is $x = \sqrt{\dfrac{2}{3}} \approx 0.81649658$.

   How good is your approximation?

4. Square Windows Find a square viewing window on your calculator that has $-4 \le x \le 4$.

5. Dot Graphing Mode To see the points plotted by a calculator without the connecting segments, set your calculator to DOT mode, then graph $y = 0.5x^3 - 2x^2 + 1$ in the standard window. Try some other equations as well.

Sequence Graphing

Many calculators can produce a table of values and graph functions that are defined by recursive and nonrecursive sequences. In a recursive sequence, the nth term is defined in relation to a previous term or terms, such as $u(n) = u(n-1) - 6$ or $u(n) = 3u(n-2) - u(n-1) + 4$. In a nonrecursive sequence, the nth term is a function of the variable n, such as $u(n) = 2n - 5$.

To enter, display a table of values for, and graph a sequence, select the following. In general, first set the mode to sequence and enter the sequence rule.

- Set the window parameters, set the drawing mode (dot or connected), and graph the sequence.
- Choose the table settings, and display the table.

TI-84/TI-83 MODE SEQ

Y= access the sequence editor screen
nMin	the minimum n value evaluated
u(n)	the rule of the sequence
u(nMin)	the value of the sequence at the minimum n value (recursive sequence only)

WINDOW
nMin	the smallest n value evaluated; must be an integer
nMax	the largest n value evaluated
PlotStart	first term plotted
PlotStep	incremental n value (graphing only); designates which points are plotted; does not affect sequence evaluation

Xmin, Xmax, Xscl, Ymin, Ymax, Yscl same as function graphing values

GRAPH	displays the graph of sequences stored in memory
TBLSET	table settings
	TblStart smallest n value
	ΔTbl increment
TABLE	displays a table of values of sequences stored in memory

Casio 9850 RECUR TYPE

a_n general term of the sequence $\{u_n\}$
a_{n+1} linear recursion between two terms
a_{n+2} linear recursion between three terms

RANG displays table range settings

Start	starting value of n
End	ending value of n
a_1, b_1	value of first term

(the value of n increments by 1)

TABL displays a table of values

G-PLT displays a graph of the data in the table

Press **EXIT** to return to the table and **EXIT** again to return to the sequence editor.

NOTE In the TI-84/TI-83, nMax, PlotStart, and PlotStep must be integers greater than 1.

NOTE In the TI-84/TI-83, both Indpnt (independent) and Depend (dependent) values may be set by the user or the calculator.

Sharp 9600 Input can be set by the user or the calculator.

Auto: Calculator enters values.
Ask: User enters values.

Technology

T.2   Lists, Statistics, Plots, and Regression

Most calculators allow you to store one or more lists that can be used with statistical operations and graphs. Although the procedures needed to create the statistical values seen in this book are shown below, refer to your calculator's manual for a complete guide.

This section outlines the procedures to create the following items:

- statistical lists for 1-variable and 2-variable data
- statistics for 1-variable and 2-variable data
- histograms and box plots for 1-variable data
- scatter plots of 2-variable data
- regression equations of 2-variable data

Refer to Sections 1.5, 4.3.A, 5.7, and 13.1 for examples that involve lists and regression.

Lists

Call up the **list editor** to enter data into lists by using the commands below.

TI-84/TI-83	STAT	EDIT
	Lists are L1, L2, . . ., L6.	
Casio 9850	STAT	
	Lists are List 1, List 2, . . ., List 6.	

Press ENTER (or EXE) after each entry in a list to proceed to the next position. Use the left/right arrow keys to move among lists and the up/down arrow keys to move within a list.

One-Variable Statistics

Data for 1-variable statistics can be entered into the list editor in two ways:

- Each value is entered into a single list.
- Each value is entered into one list and its frequency into the corresponding position of a second list to create a frequency table.

The symbols commonly used to represent the statistics for 1-variable data are as follows:

n	sample number
$\overline{x}$	mean
Sx, $x\sigma n - 1$	standard deviation from the sample
σx, $x\sigma n$	population standard deviation from the sample
Σx	sum of the data
Σx^2	sum of squares of the data
minX	smallest value of the data
Q_1	value of the first quartile
Med	median of the data
Q_3	value of the third quartile
maxX	largest value of the data

> **NOTE** Words printed in all caps refer to buttons to be pressed or menu choices to be selected. For example,
> STAT   EDIT
> directs you to press the STAT button and then to select EDIT from the options shown.

To compute 1-variable statistics, use the following procedures.

TI-84/TI-83   STAT   CALC   1: 1-Var Stats

- If the data is contained in one list, enter the list name by pressing the list name shown above the number keys 1 through 6.

- If the data was entered as a frequency table, enter the list name of the data, press [,] (comma), and enter the name of the list that contains the frequency.

Casio 9850   STAT   EXE   CALC   SET

NOTE Directions for Casio 9850 begin from the main menu screen.

- If the data is contained in one list:
  1. Set XList to the list that contains the data by pressing the key below the appropriate list name.
  2. Use the down arrow key to highlight 1Var Freq and set 1Var Freq to 1 by pressing F1.

- If the data is contained in a frequency table.
  1. Set 1Var XList to the list that contains the data by pressing the key below the appropriate list name.
  2. Set 1Var Freq to the list that contains the frequency of the data.

Press EXIT to return to the list editor.
Press 1VAR to display the statistics.

Histograms and Box Plots (1-Variable Graphs)

A histogram is a bar graph that displays 1-variable data values on the x-axis and represents each corresponding frequency as the height of the box above the x-axis. A box plot and a modified box plot display the values Q1 to Q3 as a box with a vertical line at the median. A box plot displays the values of xMin to Q1 and of Q3 to xMax as whiskers at either end of the box, and a modified box plot displays outliers (values at least $1.5 * (Q3–Q1)$ below Q1 and above Q3) as points beyond the whiskers.

To create a graph of 1-variable data, enter the data into a single list or into a frequency table, and use the procedures to create a histogram or a box plot.

TI-84/TI-83

- STAT PLOT   Plot1

- Highlight On and press ENTER.

- Highlight the desired graph type by using the arrow keys, and press ENTER.

- Use the down arrow key to select Xlist. Enter the name of the list that contains the data by using the keys L1 through L6, which are the 2nd functions above the number keys 1 through 6.

- Move the cursor to Freq and enter 1 if the data is contained in a single list, or enter the name of the list that contains the frequency.

- If a modified box plot is selected, select the type of symbol that will denote outliers.
- Set the window values for xMin and xMax, and if creating a histogram, set the yMin and yMax values. Box plots ignore yMin and yMax values.
- GRAPH

Casio 9850   STAT   EXE

- GRPH SET
- Select the StatGraph area desired by choosing GPH1, GPH2, or GPH3.
- Use the down arrow key to highlight Graph Type. Press $\triangleright$ to display the graph type options. Choose Hist, Box (MedBox), or Box (MeanBox). MedBox shows the distribution of the data items that are grouped within Q1, Med, and Q3. MeanBox shows the distribution of the data around the mean when there is a large number of data items, and a vertical line is drawn at the mean.
- Select XList and enter the name of the list that contains the data.
- Select Frequency and enter 1 if the data is in one list or the name of the list that contains the frequency of the data.
- Choose the graph color.
- Press EXIT.
- Press GPH1 (GRPH2 or GRPH3) to display the StatGraph area. Press EXIT to return to the previous screen.

Two-Variable Statistics and Graphs

Two-variable statistics for both the x-variable and the y-variable include all the statistics listed for 1-variable statistics; that is, the mean of the y-variable data is denoted as $\bar{y}$, the minimum value of the y-variable data is denoted by minY or yMin, and so forth. Additionally, Σxy, the sum of the product of corresponding data pairs, is also given.

To compute 2-variable statistics, use the following procedure after entering the data pairs into two lists.

TI-84/TI-83   STAT   CALC   2–Var Stats

- Enter the list names that contain the data pairs separated by a comma, and press ENTER. The first named list is the x-list, and the second named list is the y-list.

Casio 9850   STAT   EXE   CALC   SET

- Use the down arrow key to select 2Var XList, and enter the name of the list that contains the x-data. Similarly, enter the name of the list that contains the y-data. 2Var Freq specifies the list where paired-variable frequency values are located. Enter 1 if the data pairs are entered separately in the XList, and set 2Var Freq to 1 if the data pairs are entered separately in the XList and the Ylist.
- EXIT 2VAR

Scatter Plots

Scatter plots graph the data points from Xlist and Ylist as coordinate pairs. The general procedure for graphing 2-variable data contained in two lists is as follows.

- Define the statistical plot.
- Define the viewing window.
- Display the graph.

TI-84/TI-83

- STAT PLOT, select the desired stat plot editor, highlight On, and press ENTER.
- Select the icon that represents the type of graph desired and press ENTER.
- Enter the names of the lists that contain the x-data and the y-data.
  Choose the graph type and Mark symbol.
  Option GS.D. represents a scatter plot.
- GRAPH

Casio 9850   STAT   EXE   GPH   SET

- Select the graph number: GPH1, GPH2, or GPH3.
- Highlight Graph Type and choose Scat.
- Enter the names of the lists that contain the x-data and the y-data, enter the frequency of the data pairs, choose the mark type and the graph color. EXIT
- V-Window, enter the viewing window values, EXIT
- GPH, select the graph number that contains the desired settings

Regression Equations

Most graphing calculators can compute the following types of regression equations.

Regression Type	Model	Reference
linear	$y = ax + b$	LinReg or LinearReg
quadratic	$y = ax^2 + bx + c$	QuadReg
cubic	$y = ax^3 + bx^2 + cx + d$	CubicReg
quartic	$y = ax^4 + bx^3 + cx^2 + dx + e$	QuartReg
logarithmic	$y = a \ln x$	LnReg or LogReg
exponential	$y = ae^{bx}$	ExpReg
power	$y = ax^n$	PwrReg or PowerReg
logistic	$y = \dfrac{c}{1 + ae^{-bx}}$	Logistic or LogisticReg
sinusoidal	$y = a \sin(bx + c) + d$	SinReg

The procedure to compute regression equations follows. Enter the data into two lists.

TI-84/TI-83   STAT   CALC

Select the regression model by using the up/down arrow keys. Enter the names of the lists separated by a comma by using the L1 through L6 keys, which are the 2nd functions for the numerals 1 through 6. The default is L1, L2.

Casio 9850   While viewing the lists, press CALC REG.

Select the regression model by pressing the corresponding F key. Additional models are accessed by pressing F6.

Displaying a Regression Equation's Graph

Set the bounds of the display window by selecting the following.

TI-84/TI-83   WINDOW

Casio 9850   V-Window

TI-84/TI-83 There are two methods for entering a regression equation into the Y= editor for display: automatic and manual. Note that each time a regression equation is found, the contents of RegEQ are overwritten with the new regression equation.

- *Automatic* The calculator can automatically place the regression equation into the Y= editor as Y3 when computing a regression equation. The following entry places the linear regression equation for the lists L1 and L2 into Y3 in the Y= editor.

  LinReg L1,L2,Y3

- *Manual* Whenever a regression model is found, the calculator places the regression equation into the variable RegEQ (or RegEqn), which can be entered into the Y= editor.

  Press VARS Statistics EQ RegEQ from the Y= editor screen.

  A regression equation is displayed using the procedure to graph any type of equation.

Casio 9850

- While viewing the data lists, press GRPH.
- Select GPH1, GPH2, or GPH3 to view the desired graph type. (Press SET to change the options.)
- Choose the type of regression model desired (X represents linear regression.)

  COPY   lets you store the displayed regression equation as a function in the Y= editor. Use the up/down arrow keys to select the desired Y variable.

  DRAW   graphs the displayed regression equation

Regression Coefficients

When some regression models are created, values of r, the correlation coefficient, and r^2 (or R^2), the coefficient of determination, are computed and stored as values. Values of r and r^2 are computed for the following regression models: linear, logarithmic, power, and exponential. The value of R^2 is computed for the following regression models: quadratic, cubic, and quartic. No correlation coefficient or coefficient of determination is given for logistic and sinusoidal regression models.

TI-84/TI-83   The variables r, r^2, and R^2 are displayed when a regression equation is computed by executing the DiagnosticOn instruction, which is found in the CATALOG menu. When DiagnosticOff is set, the values for r, r^2, and R^2 are not displayed.

Casio 9850   Neither form of a coefficient of determination is computed on a Casio.

Scatter Plots of Residuals

Residuals, also called relative error, are stored as a list of values in a variable named Resid or RelErr on some calculators. Scatter plots of the residuals can be graphed but may not be visible in the same viewing window as the data. Adjust the window to view the scatter plot of the residuals.

TI-84/TI-83   From a STAT PLOT menu set the following:

    ON

    Type Scatter Plot

    XList   Ln (the list that contains the input data)

    Ylist   RESID (which is found in LIST NAMES)

    Mark   as desired

    GRAPH

Casio 9850   Residuals are not automatically computed when a regression equation is found.

T.3 Programs

The programs listed here are of two types: programs to give older calculators some of the features that are built-in on newer ones and programs to do specific tasks discussed in this book (such as synthetic division). Each program is preceded by a *Description,* which describes, in general terms, how the program operates and what it does. Some programs require that certain things be done before the program is run (such as entering a function in the function memory); these requirements are listed as *Preliminaries.* Occasionally, italic remarks appear in brackets after a program step; they are *not* part of the program, but are intended to provide assistance when you are entering the program into your calculator. A remark such as "[*MATH NUM menu*]" means that the symbols or commands needed for that step of the program are in the NUM submenu of the MATH menu.

Fraction Conversion
(Built-in on TI-82/83/84/85/86)

Description: Enter a repeating decimal; the program converts it into a fraction. The denominator is displayed on the last line and the numerator on the line above.

Casio 9850

Fix 7	Rnd [*MATH NUM menu*]
"N = "? → N	(Frac Ans) ≠ 0 ⇒ Goto 1 [*MATH NUM menu*]
0 → D	(Ans + .5) → N
Lbl 1	Norm [*DISP menu*]
D + 1 → D	(Int N)◢
N × D	D

TI-82/83/84 Quadratic Formula
(Built-in on other calculators)

Description: Enter the coefficients of the quadratic equation $ax^2 + bx + c = 0$; the program finds all real solutions.

:ClrHome [*Optional*]	:Goto 1
:Disp "AX² + BX + C = 0" [*Optional*]	:Disp $(-B + \sqrt{S})/2A$
:Prompt A	:Disp $(-B - \sqrt{S})/2A$
:Prompt B	:Stop
:Prompt C	:Lbl 1
:(B² − 4AC) → S	:Disp "NO REAL ROOTS"
:If S < 0	

Synthetic Division
(Built-in on TI-89/92)

Preliminaries: Enter the coefficients of the dividend $F(x)$ (in order of decreasing powers of x, putting in zeros for missing coefficients) as list L_1 (or List 1). If the coefficients are 1, 2, 3, for example, key in {1, 2, 3,} and store it in L_1. The symbols { } are on the keyboard or in the LIST menu. The list name L_1 is on the keyboard of TI-82/83 and Sharp 9600. On TI-85/86 and HP-38, type in L1. On Casio 9850, use "List" in the LIST submenu of the OPTN menu to type in List 1.

Description: Write the divisor in the form $x - a$ and enter a. The program displays the degree of the quotient $Q(x)$, the coefficients of $Q(x)$ (in order of decreasing powers of x), and the remainder. If the program pauses before it has displayed all these items, you can use the arrow keys to scroll through the display; then press ENTER (or OK) to continue.

TI-82/83/84/85/86

:ClrHome [ClLCD on TI-85/86]
:Disp "DIVISOR IS X − A"
:Prompt A
:$L_1 \to L_2$ [*See Preliminaries for how to enter list names*]
:dim $L_1 \to N$ [dimL L_1 on TI-85/86]   [*LIST OPS menu*]
:For (K, 2, N)
:$(L_1(K) + A \times L_2(K - 1)) \to L_2(K)$
:End

:round($L_2(N)$,9) $\to R$ [*MATH NUM menu*]
:$(N - 1) \to$ dim L_2
:Disp "DEGREE OF QUOTIENT"
:Disp dim $L_2 - 1$
:Disp "COEFFICIENTS"
:Pause L_2
:Disp "REMAINDER"
:Disp R

Casio 9850

"DIVISOR IS X − A"
"A = "? $\to A$
List 1 $\to$ List 2   [*See Preliminaries for how to enter list names*]
dim List 1 $\to N$ [*OPTN LIST menu*]
2 $\to K$
Lbl 1
(List 1[K] + A × List 2 [K − 1]) $\to$ List 2 [K]
K + 1 $\to K$
K ≤ N ⇒ Goto 1
Fix 9   [*SETUP DISP menu*]
List 2 [N]

Rnd   [*OPTN MATH NUM menu*]
Ans $\to R$
Norm   [*SETUP DISP menu*]
Seq(List 2 [X], X, 1, N − 1, 1) $\to$ List 2
    [*OPTN LIST menu*]
"DEGREE OF QUOTIENT"
dim List 2 − 1◢
"COEFFICIENTS"
List 2◢
"REMAINDER"
R

Glossary

A

absolute value (of a complex number)
$|a + bi| = \sqrt{a^2 + b^2}$ (p. 638)

absolute value of a number   For any real number c, if $c \geq 0$, then $|c| = c$ and if $c < 0$, then $|c| = -c$ (algebraic definition). $|c|$ is the distance from c to 0 on the number line (geometric definition). (p. 107, 108)

absolute-value inequalities   For a positive number k and any real number r, $|r| \leq k$ is equivalent to $-k \leq r \leq k$ and $|r| \geq k$ is equivalent to $r \leq -k$ or $r \geq k$. (p. 129)

acute angle   an angle with a degree measure of less than $90°$ (p. 414)

addition and subtraction identities   trigonometric identities involving a function of the sum or difference of two angle measures (p. 582)

adjacency matrix   a matrix used to represent the connections between vertices in a directed network (p. 809)

adjacent side (of a right triangle)   abbreviated adj, the side of a given acute angle in a right triangle that is *not* the hypotenuse (p. 415)

ambiguous case   When the measures of two sides of a triangle and the angle opposite one of them are known, there may be one, two, or no triangles that satisfy the given measures. (p. 627)

amplitude   The amplitude of a sinusoidal function is one-half of the difference between the maximum and minimum function values and is always positive. (p. 497) See also *sinusoidal function.*

analytic geometry   the study of geometric properties of objects using a coordinate system (p. 691)

angle   a figure formed by two rays and a common endpoint (p. 413)

angle of depression   the angle formed by a horizontal line and a line below it (p. 427)

angle of elevation   the angle formed by a horizontal line and a line above it (p. 426)

angle of inclination   If L is a nonhorizontal straight line in a coordinate plane, then the angle of inclination of L is the angle formed by the part of L above the x-axis and the x-axis in the positive direction. (p. 589)

Angle of Inclination Theorem   If L is a nonvertical line with angle of inclination θ, then $\tan \theta = $ slope of L. (p. 589)

Angle Theorem   If θ is the angle between nonzero vectors $\mathbf{u}$ and $\mathbf{v}$, then $\mathbf{u} \cdot \mathbf{v} = \|\mathbf{u}\| \|\mathbf{v}\| \cos \theta$ and $\cos \theta = \dfrac{\mathbf{u} \cdot \mathbf{v}}{\|\mathbf{u}\| \|\mathbf{v}\|}$. (p. 672)

angular speed   a measure of speed of a point rotating at a constant rate around the center of a circle, given as the angle through which the point rotates over time (p. 440)

approach infinity   Output values of a function that get larger and larger without bound as input values increase are said to approach infinity. (p. 201)

arc   an unbroken part of a circle (p. 434)

arc length   the length of an arc, which is equal to the radius times the radian measure of the central angle of the arc (p. 435, 439)

arccosine function   the inverse cosine function, denoted by $g(x) = \arccos x$ (p. 533)

arcsine function   the inverse sine function, denoted by $g(x) = \arcsin x$ (p. 530)

arctangent function   the inverse tangent function, denoted by $g(x) = \arctan x$ (p. 535)

area of a triangle formula   The area of any triangle ABC in standard notation is $\dfrac{1}{2}ab \sin C$. (p. 632)

argument   the angle θ in a trigonometric expression (p. 639)

arithmetic progression   See *arithmetic sequence*.

arithmetic sequence   a sequence in which the difference between each term and the preceding term is always constant (p. 22)

asymptotes of a hyperbola   two lines intersecting at the center of a hyperbola which the hyperbola approaches but never touches (p. 701)

augmented matrix   a matrix in which each row represents an equation of a system and contains the coefficients of the variables in the equation (p. 795)

average   See *mean*.

average rate of change   For any function f, the average rate of change of $f(x)$ with respect to x as x changes from a to b is the value $\dfrac{\text{change in } f(x)}{\text{change in } x} = \dfrac{f(b) - f(a)}{b - a}$. (p. 216)

axes (singular: axis)   the number lines in a coordinate system (p. 5)

axis of a parabola   the line through the focus of a parabola perpendicular to the directrix of the parabola (p. 709)

bar graph   a visual display of qualitative data in which categories are displayed on the horizontal axis and frequencies or relative frequencies on the vertical axis (p. 845)

Basic Properties of Logarithms $\log_b x$ is defined only for $x > 0$; $\log_b 1 = 0$ and $\log_b b = 1$; $\log_b b^k = k$ for all real k; and $b^{\log_b x} = x$ for all $x > 0$. (p. 364, 372)

bell curve   See *normal curve*.

Bernoulli experiment   See *binomial experiment*.

Big-Little Concept   If c is a number far from 0, then $\dfrac{1}{c}$ is a number close to 0. Conversely, if c is a number close to 0, then $\dfrac{1}{c}$ is a number far from 0. (p. 280)

binomial distribution   the probability distribution for a binomial experiment (p. 888)

binomial experiment   A probability experiment that can be described in terms of just two outcomes is a binomial experiment, also known as a *Bernoulli experiment*. It must meet the following conditions: the experiment consists of n trials whose outcomes are either

successes or failures, and the trials are identical and independent with a constant probability of success, p, and a constant probability of failure, $q = 1 - p$. (p. 885)

bounds test   a test used to determine the lower and upper bounds for the real zeros of a polynomial function (p. 256)

Cartesian coordinate system   a two-dimensional coordinate system that corresponds ordered pairs of real numbers with locations in a coordinate plane (p. 5)

center of a hyperbola   the midpoint of the segment that has the foci of the hyperbola as endpoints (p. 701)

center of an ellipse   the midpoint of the segment that has the foci of the ellipse as endpoints (p. 692)

central angle   an angle whose vertex is at the center of a circle (p. 434)

central tendency   a value that is used to represent the center of an entire data set (p. 853)

change in x   the horizontal distance moved from one point to another point in a coordinate plane; sometimes denoted Δx, and read "delta x" (p. 31)

change in y   the vertical distance moved from one point to another point in a coordinate plane; sometimes denoted Δy, and read "delta y" (p. 31)

Change-of-Base Formula   For any positive number x, $\log_b x = \dfrac{\log x}{\log b}$ and $\log_b x = \dfrac{\ln x}{\ln b}$. (p. 374)

closed interval   an interval of numbers in which both endpoints of the interval are included in the set; denoted with two brackets (p. 118)

coefficient   the numerical factor of a term in a polynomial (p. 239)

coefficient of determination   a statistical measure, often denoted by r^2, that is the proportion of variation in y that can be attributed to a linear relationship between x and y in a data set (p. 47)

Cofunction Identities   trigonometric identities that relate the sine, secant, and tangent functions to the cosine, cosecant, and cotangent functions, respectively (p. 586)

combination   an arrangement of objects in which order is *not* important; a collection of objects (p. 880)

common difference   the constant number, usually denoted by d, that is the difference between each term and the preceding term in an arithmetic sequence (p. 22)

common logarithm (of x) the value of $g(x) = \log x$ at the number x, denoted $\log x$ (p. 356)

common logarithmic function the inverse of the exponential function $f(x) = 10^x$, denoted $g(x) = \log x$ (p. 356)

common ratio the constant value, denoted by r, given by the quotient of consecutive terms in a geometric sequence (p. 58)

complement of an event the set of all outcomes that are not contained in the event (p. 866)

complete graph a graph that shows all of its important features, including all peaks and valleys, points where it touches an axis, and suggests the general shape of the portions of the graph that are not in view (p. 82)

completely factored (over the set of real numbers) a polynomial written as the product of irreducible factors with real coefficients (p. 253)

completing the square a process used to change an expression of the form $x^2 + bx$ into a perfect square by adding a suitable constant (p. 92)

complex number system the number system that consists of real and nonreal numbers (p. 293)

complex numbers numbers of the form $a + bi$, where a is a real number and bi is an imaginary number (p. 294)

complex plane a coordinate plane with the horizontal axis labeled for real numbers and the vertical axis labeled for imaginary numbers (p. 301, 638)

components (of a vector) the numbers a and b in the vector $\mathbf{u} = \langle a, b \rangle$, where $\mathbf{u}$ is a vector with initial point at the origin and terminal point at (a, b) (p. 655)

composite functions If f and g are functions, then the composite function of f and g is $(g \circ f)(x) = g(f(x))$, read "g circle f" or "f followed by g." (p. 193)

composition of functions a way of combining functions in which the output of one function is used as the input of another function (p. 193)

compound inequality an inequality that compares more than two quantities and contains more than one inequality symbol (p. 118)

compound interest This interest on an investment is compounded, or becomes part of the investment, at a particular interest rate per time period. If P dollars is invested at annual interest rate r per time period (expressed as a decimal), then the amount A after t time periods is $A = P(1 + r)t$. (p. 345)

concave down a description of the way a curve bends if for any two points in a given interval that lie on the curve, the segment that connects them is *below* the curve (p. 154)

concave up a description of the way a curve bends if for any two points in a given interval that lie on the curve, the segment that connects them is *above* the curve (p. 154)

concavity a description of the way that a curve bends, such as *concave up* or *concave down* (p. 154)

conic section a curve that is formed by the intersection of a plane and a double-napped right circular cone (p. 691); Let L be a fixed line, called a directrix, P a fixed point not on L, and e a positive constant. The set of all points X in the plane such that

$$\frac{\text{distance between } X \text{ and the fixed point}}{\text{distance between } X \text{ and the fixed line}} = \frac{XP}{XL} = e \text{ is a}$$

conic section with P as one of its foci. (p. 747)

conjugate The *conjugate* of the complex number $a + bi$ is the number $a - bi$, and the *conjugate* of $a - bi$ is $a + bi$. (p. 296, 309)

conjugate pairs complex numbers $a + bi$ and $a - bi$ (p. 296)

Conjugate Zero Theorem For every polynomial function f, if the complex number z is a zero of f, then its conjugate, $\bar{z}$, is also a zero of f. (p. 309)

consistent system a system of equations with at least one solution (p. 781)

constant function A function is said to be constant on an interval if its graph is a horizontal line over the interval; that is, if its output values are always constant as the input values are increasing. (p. 152)

constant polynomial a polynomial that consists of only a constant term (p. 240)

constant term the coefficient a_0 in a polynomial that is written in the form $a_n x^n + a_{n-1} x^{n-1} + \cdots + a_1 x + a_0$ (p. 239)

constraints restrictions, represented by inequalities, that exist in linear programming (p. 829)

continuous compounding This compound interest is compounded infinitely many times during a time period. If P dollars is invested at annual interest rate r and compounded continuously, then the amount A after t years is $A = Pe^{rt}$. (p. 348)

continuous function a function whose graph is an unbroken curve with no jumps, gaps, or holes (p. 261, 939)

convergent series a geometric series in which the terms $S_1, S_2, S_3, \ldots$ of the sequence of partial sums get closer and closer to a particular real number S in such a way that the partial sum S_k is arbitrarily close to S when k is large enough; a geometric series with common ratio r such that $|r| < 1$ (p. 77)

coordinate plane See *Cartesian coordinate system.*

coordinate system a system of locating points in a plane or in space by using ordered pairs or ordered triples, respectively, of real numbers (p. 5)

corner point any point of a feasible region where at least two of the graphs of the constraints intersect (p. 829)

correlation coefficient a statistical measure, often denoted by r, of how well the least squares regression line fits the data points that it models (p. 47)

cosecant ratio For a given acute angle θ in a right triangle, the cosecant of θ is written as csc θ and is equal to the reciprocal of the sine ratio of the given angle. (p. 416)

cosine ratio For a given acute angle θ in a right triangle, the cosine of θ is written as cos θ and is equal to the ratio of the adjacent side length to the length of the hypotenuse. (p. 416)

cotangent ratio For a given acute angle θ in a right triangle, the cotangent of θ is written as cot θ and is equal to the reciprocal of the tangent ratio of the given angle. (p. 416)

coterminal angles angles formed by different rotations that have the same initial and terminal sides (p. 434)

cubic function a third-degree polynomial function (p. 240)

cycle (of a periodic function) a portion of the graph of a periodic function in which the function goes through one period (p. 493)

data information gathered in a statistical experiment (p. 843)

decreasing function A function is said to be decreasing on an interval if its graph always falls as you move from left to right over the interval; that is, its output values are always decreasing as the input values are increasing. (p. 152)

degenerate conic section a point, line, or intersecting lines formed by the intersection of a plane and a double-napped right circular cone (p. 691)

degree (measure) a unit of angle measure that equals $\frac{1}{360}$ of a circle, denoted with the degree symbol (°) (p. 414)

degree (of a polynomial) the exponent of the highest power of the variable that appears with a nonzero coefficient in a polynomial (p. 240)

delta See *change in x* or *change in y*.

DeMoivre's Theorem For any complex number, $z = r(\cos \theta + i \sin \theta)$, and for any positive integer n, $z^n = r^n (\cos n\theta + i \sin n\theta)$. (p. 644)

denominator the expression in a fraction that lies below the fraction bar (p. 4)

deviation (of a data value) the difference of a data value from the mean of the data set (p. 857)

difference function For any functions $f(x)$ and $g(x)$, their difference function is the new function $(f - g)(x) = f(x) - g(x)$. (p. 191)

difference quotient the quantity $\frac{f(x + h) - f(x)}{h}$ for a function f (p. 219)

differential calculus a method of calculating the changes in one variable produced by changes in a related variable (p. 138)

dimensions of a matrix used to indicate the number of rows and columns in a matrix (Example: an $m \times n$ matrix has m rows and n columns) (p. 804)

directed network a finite set of connected points in which permissible directions of travel between the points are indicated (p. 809)

direction (of a vector) the angle that the directed line segment representing a vector $\langle a, b \rangle$ makes with the positive x-axis (p. 662)

directrix of a parabola the line in the formation of a parabola such that its distance from any point on the parabola is equal to the distance from that point to the focus of the parabola (p. 709)

discontinuous function a function that has one or more jumps, gaps, or holes (p. 937)

discriminant the expression $b^2 - 4ac$ in the quadratic formula, used to determine the number of real solutions of a quadratic equation $ax^2 + bx + c = 0$ (p. 93)

distance (between real numbers) The distance on the number line between real numbers c and d is $|c - d|$. (p. 108)

distance difference the constant difference between the distances from each focus of a hyperbola to a point on the hyperbola (p. 700)

distribution an arrangement of numerical data in order (usually ascending) (p. 846)

divergent series a geometric series that is not convergent; a geometric series with common ratio r such that $|r| \geq 1$ (p. 77)

Division Algorithm   If a polynomial $f(x)$ is divided by a nonzero polynomial $h(x)$, then there is a quotient polynomial $q(x)$ and a remainder polynomial $r(x)$ such that $f(x) = h(x) \cdot q(x) + r(x)$, where either $r(x) = 0$ or $r(x)$ has a degree less than the degree of the divisor, $h(x)$. (p. 243)

DMS form   a form of degree measure expression which includes degrees, minutes, and seconds (p. 414)

domain   the set of first numbers in the ordered pairs of a relation (p. 6, 142)

domain convention   Unless information to the contrary is given, the domain of a function f includes every real number input for which the function rule produces a real number output. (p. 145)

dot product   a real number produced by multiplying corresponding components of two vectors and adding the products (p. 670)

Double-Angle Identities   trigonometric identities involving a function of an angle multiplied by 2 (p. 593)

eccentricity (of an ellipse or hyperbola)   the ratio $e = \dfrac{\text{distance between the foci}}{\text{distance between the vertices}}$, where $0 < e < 1$ for all ellipses and $e > 1$ for all hyperbolas (p. 745)

elementary row operations   operations used on an augmented matrix that produce an augmented matrix of an equivalent system (p. 796)

eliminating the parameter   expressing a curve that is given by parametric equations as part of the graph of an equation in x and y (p. 757)

ellipse   For any points P and Q in the plane and any number k greater than the distance from P to Q, an ellipse, with foci P and Q, is the set of all points (x, y) such that the sum of the distance from (x, y) to P and the distance from (x, y) to Q is k. (p. 692) a conic section with eccentricity between 0 and 1, not inclusive (p. 747)

empirical rule   a rule that describes the areas under the normal curve over intervals of one, two, and three standard deviations on either side of the mean in terms of percentages of the number of data values (p. 892)

end behavior   the shape of the graph of a function at the far left and far right of the coordinate plane when $|x|$ is large (p. 262, 287)

endpoints (of an interval)   the numbers c and d in a set of numbers that can be expressed as an interval from c to d (p. 118)

equal matrices   two or more matrices that have the same dimensions and equal corresponding entries (p. 804)

equivalent equations   equations that have the same solutions (p. 81)

equivalent inequalities   inequalities that have the same solutions (p. 119)

equivalent systems   systems of equations with the same solutions (p. 795)

equivalent vectors   vectors, such as $\mathbf{u}$ and $\mathbf{v}$, that have the same magnitude and direction, denoted $\mathbf{u} = \mathbf{v}$ (p. 654)

Euler's Formula   the identity $e^{ix} = \cos x + i \sin x$ (p. 688)

even function   a function f for which $f(-x) = f(x)$ for all x in its domain, its graph symmetric with respect to the y-axis (p. 188, 482)

event   any outcome or collection of outcomes in the sample space of an experiment (p. 865)

eventually fixed point   the number c for which the orbit of c for a given function eventually produces constant output values (p. 202)

eventually periodic point   the number c for which the orbit of c for a given function eventually produces repeating output values (p. 202)

expected value of a random variable   the average value of the outcome values for a random variable (p. 869)

experiment   in probability, any process that generates one or more observable outcomes (p. 864)

explicit form of a geometric sequence   In a geometric sequence $\{u_n\}$ with common ratio r, $u_n = r^{n-1}u_1$ for all $n \geq 1$. (p. 60)

explicit form of an arithmetic sequence   In an arithmetic sequence $\{u_n\}$ with common difference d, $u_n = u_1 + (n - 1)d$ for all $n \geq 2$. (p. 23)

exponential decay   decay that can be represented by a function of the form $f(x) = Pa^x$, where $f(x)$ is the quantity at time x, P is the initial quantity when $x = 0$, and $0 < a < 1$ is the factor by which the quantity decreases when x increases by 1 (p. 351)

exponential function (with base a)   a function whose rule is $f(x) = a^x$, where a is any positive real number, and whose domain is all real numbers (p. 336)

exponential growth   growth that can be represented by a function of the form $f(x) = Pa^x$, where $f(x)$ is the quantity at time x, P is the initial quantity when $x = 0$, and $a > 1$ is the factor by which the quantity increases when x increases by 1 (p. 349)

exponential model an exponential function used to represent the trend in a data set (p. 389)

extraneous roots See *extraneous solutions*.

extraneous solutions solutions of a derived equation that are not solutions of the original equation (p. 110)

Factor Theorem A polynomial $f(x)$ has a linear factor $(x - a)$ if and only if $f(a) = 0$. (p. 245)

factorial The notation $n!$ is read "n factorial" and describes the product of all the integers from 1 through n. (p. 520, 880)

feasible region the region of the coordinate plane that is the intersection of the graphs of the constraints in linear programming (p. 829)

Fibonacci sequence the sequence $\{a_n\}$ discovered by Leonardo Fibonacci in the thirteenth century in which $a_1 = 1$, $a_2 = 1$, and for $n \geq 3$, a_n is the sum of the two preceding terms; $a_n = a_{n-1} + a_{n-2}$ (p. 21)

finite differences the differences between each y-value and the preceding one in a table of values (p. 43)

first octant the octant of a three-dimensional coordinate system in which all coordinates are positive (p. 790)

first quartile See *quartiles*.

five-number summary (of a data set) the following list of values: minimum, first quartile, second quartile, third quartile, and maximum (p. 861)

fixed point (of an orbit) the number c for which the orbit of c for a given function produces constant output values (p. 202)

focal axis of a hyperbola the line through the foci of a hyperbola (p. 701)

foci (singular, focus) of a hyperbola the points in the formation of hyperbola such that the difference of the distances from each focus to a point on the hyperbola is constant (p. 701)

foci (singular, focus) of an ellipse the points in the formation of an ellipse such that the sum of the distances from each focus to a point on the ellipse is constant (p. 692)

focus of a parabola the point in the formation of a parabola such that its distance from any point on the

parabola is equal to the distance from that point to the directrix (p. 709)

Formula for Roots of Unity For each positive integer n, the n distinct nth roots of unity are
$$\cos \frac{2k\theta}{n} + i \sin \frac{2k\theta}{n} \text{ for } k = 0, 1, 2, \ldots, \text{ and } n - 1.$$
(p. 648)

fractional equation an equation formed by a fractional expression equal to 0 (p. 114)

fractional expression the quotient $\dfrac{f(x)}{g(x)}$, where $f(x)$ and $g(x)$ are algebraic expressions and $g(x) \neq 0$ (p. 114)

frequency (of a sound wave) the reciprocal of the period of the sinusoidal function that represents a sound wave (p. 558)

function a special type of relation in which each member of the domain corresponds to one and only one member of the range (p. 7) A function consists of a set of inputs called the domain, a rule by which each input determines one and only one output, and a set of outputs called the range. (p. 142)

function notation There is a customary method of denoting a function in abbreviated form. If f denotes a function and a denotes a number in the domain, then $f(a)$ denotes the output of the function f produced by input a. (p. 9)

function rule a set of operations that defines a function (p. 7)

Fundamental Counting Principle In a set of k experiments, if the first experiment has n_1 outcomes, the second has n_2 outcomes, $\ldots$, and the kth has n_k outcomes, then the total number of outcomes for all k experiments is $n_1 \cdot n_2 \cdot \ldots \cdot n_k$. (p. 879)

Fundamental Theorem of Algebra Every nonconstant polynomial has a zero in the complex number system. (p. 307)

Fundamental Theorem of Linear Programming The maximum or minimum of the objective function (if it exists) always occurs at one or more of the corner points of the feasible region. (p. 829)

Gauss-Jordan elimination the method of using elementary row operations on an augmented matrix to produce a matrix in reduced row-echelon form that represents an equivalent system (p. 797)

general form (of a line)   a linear equation in the form $Ax + By - C = 0$, where A and B are not both equal to zero (p. 39)

geometric progression   See *geometric sequence*.

geometric sequence   a sequence in which terms are formed by multiplying a preceding term by a nonzero constant (p. 58)

graph   a visual display of a set of points (p. 30)

graph of an equation   the set of points whose coordinates are solutions of the equation (p. 30)

graphical zero finder   the calculation performed by a graphics calculator in which the x-intercepts of the graph of a function are identified; labeled ROOT, ZERO, or X-INCPT in the TI-83 and Sharp 9600 CALC menu, the Casio 9850 G-SOLVE menu, the MATH submenu of TI-86/89 GRAPH menu, and the FCN submenu of the HP-38 PLOT menu (p. 84)

greatest integer function   a piecewise-defined function denoted as $f(x) = [x]$ that converts a real number x into the largest integer that is less than or equal to x (p. 147)

Half-Angle Identities   trigonometric identities involving a function of an angle divided by 2 (p. 596)

half-open interval   an interval of numbers in which one endpoint of the interval is included in the set and the other endpoint of the interval is not included; denoted with one bracket and one parenthesis, respectively (p. 118)

Heron's Formula   The area of any triangle ABC in standard notation is $\sqrt{s(s-a)(s-b)(s-c)}$, where $s = \frac{1}{2}(a + b + c)$. (p. 633)

Hertz   the unit of measure for the frequency of a sound wave, where one Hertz is one cycle per second (p. 559)

histogram   a display of quantitative data in which the data is divided into classes of equal size and displayed along the horizontal axis and frequencies or relative frequencies on the vertical axis (p. 848)

hole in a graph   A point is omitted in the graph of a function and is not contained by an asymptote. For any rational function $f(x) = \dfrac{g(x)}{h(x)}$ and number d that produces both a zero numerator and a zero denominator, if the multiplicity of d as a zero of the related function g is greater than or equal to the multiplicity of d as a zero of the related function h, then the graph of f has a hole at $x = d$. (p. 283)

horizontal asymptote   a horizontal line that the graph of a function approaches but never touches or crosses as $|x|$ gets large (p. 284, 952)

horizontal compression   For any positive number $c > 1$, the graph of $y = f(cx)$ is the graph of f compressed horizontally, toward the y-axis, by a factor of $\frac{1}{c}$. (p. 179)

horizontal line   a line that has a slope of zero and an equation of the form $y = b$, where b is the y-intercept (p. 37)

horizontal shifts   For any positive number c, the graph of $y = f(x + c)$ is the graph of f shifted c units to the left, and the graph of $y = f(x - c)$ is the graph of f shifted c units to the right. (p. 175)

horizontal stretch   For any positive number $c < 1$, the graph of $y = f(cx)$ is the graph of f stretched horizontally, away from the y-axis, by a factor of $\frac{1}{c}$. (p. 179)

horizontal line test   A function f is one-to-one if and only if no horizontal line intersects the graph of f more than once. (p. 209)

hyperbola   For any points P and Q in the plane and any positive number k, a hyperbola with foci P and Q is the set of all points (x, y) such that the absolute value of the difference of the distance from (x, y) to P and the distance from (x, y) to Q is k. (p. 700) a conic section with eccentricity greater than 1 (p. 700)

hypotenuse   abbreviated hyp, the side of a right triangle that is across from the right angle (p. 415)

identities involving $\pi - t$ $\cos(\pi - t) = -\cos t$, $\sin(\pi - t) = \sin t$, $\tan(\pi - t) = -\tan t$ (p. 459)

identity   an equation that is true for all values of the variable for which every term of the equation is defined (p. 454)

identity matrix   The $n \times n$ matrix, denoted I_n, has 1s on the diagonal from the top left to the bottom right and 0s in all other entries. For any $n \times n$ matrix A, $AI_n = I_nA = A$. (p. 815)

imaginary axis   the vertical axis in the complex plane where each imaginary number $0 + bi$ corresponds to the point $(0, b)$ (p. 638)

imaginary numbers   a number of the form bi, where b is a real number and i is the imaginary unit (p. 294) The number $i = \sqrt{-1}$. (p. 294, 297)

inconsistent system   a system of equations with no solutions (p. 781)

increasing function A function is said to be increasing on an interval if its graph always rises as you move from left to right over the interval, that is, if its output values are always increasing as the input values are increasing. (p. 152)

independent events two events such that the occurrence or non-occurrence of one event has no effect on the probability of the other event (p. 867)

infinite geometric series the infinite series $a_1 + a_2 + a_3 + \cdots$, where $\{a_n\}$ is a geometric sequence with common ratio r (p. 77)

infinite limit a limit of infinity as x approaches some constant c; corresponds to a vertical asymptote (p. 949)

infinite sequence a sequence with an infinite number of terms (p. 13)

infinite series the sum of terms of a sequence that continues without end, or an infinite sequence; an expression of the form $a_1 + a_2 + a_3 + \cdots$, in which a_n is a real number; also denoted by $\sum_{n=1}^{\infty} a_n$ (p. 76)

inflection point a point where the graph of a function changes concavity (p. 154, 266)

initial point (of a vector) the point P in a vector that extends from point P to point Q (p. 653)

initial side the starting position of a ray that is rotated around its vertex (p. 433)

input (of a relation) the values denoted by the first numbers in the ordered pairs of a relation (p. 7)

instantaneous rate of change the rate of change of a function at a particular point (p. 234)

integers the set of numbers that consists of whole numbers and their opposites: $\ldots, -3, -2, -1, 0, 1, 2, 3, \ldots$ (p. 3)

integral calculus a method of calculating quantities such as distance, area, and volume (p. 138)

intercepts (of a rational function) If the graph of a rational function, f, has a y-intercept, it occurs at $f(0)$, and the x-intercepts occur at the numbers that are zeros of the numerator and *not* zeros of the denominator. (p. 279)

intercepts (of polynomial functions) The graph of a polynomial function of degree n has one y-intercept, which is equal to the constant term, and at most n x-intercepts. (p. 264)

interest a fee paid for the use of borrowed money; calculated as a percentage of the principal (p. 100)

Intermediate Value Theorem If the function f is continuous on the closed interval $[a, b]$ and k is any number between $f(a)$ and $f(b)$, then there exists at least

one number c between a and b such that $f(c) = k$. (p. 944)

interquartile range a measure of variability resistant to outliers; the difference between the first and third quartiles (p. 860)

intersection method a method of solving an equation of the form $f(x) = g(x)$ by graphing $y_1 = f(x)$ and $y_2 = g(x)$ on the same screen of a graphics calculator and finding the x-coordinate of each point of intersection (p. 82)

interval (of numbers) the set of all numbers lying between two fixed numbers (p. 118)

interval notation There is a customary method of denoting an interval of numbers. For real numbers c and d with $c < d$: $[c, d]$ denotes all real numbers x such that $c \leq x \leq d$; (c, d) denotes all real numbers x such that $c < x < d$; $[c, d)$ denotes all real numbers x such that $c \leq x < d$; and $(c, d]$ denotes all real numbers x such that $c < x \leq d$. (p. 118)

interval of convergence the set of values of x for which an infinite series converges to a function (p. 520)

inverse cosine function the inverse of the cosine function with a domain restricted to $[-1, 1]$, denoted by $g(x) = \cos^{-1} x$ (p. 533)

inverse function an inverse relation that is a function (p. 205)

inverse of a matrix For an $n \times n$ matrix A, the inverse of A is an $n \times n$ matrix B, also denoted A^{-1}, such that $AB = I_n$ and $BA = I_n$, or equivalently, $AA^{-1} = I_n$ and $A^{-1}A = I_n$. (p. 816)

inverse relation the result of exchanging the input and output values of a function or relation (p. 205)

inverse sine function the inverse of the sine function with a domain restricted to $\left[-\dfrac{\pi}{2}, \dfrac{\pi}{2}\right]$, denoted by $g(x) = \sin^{-1} x$ (p. 530)

inverse tangent function the inverse of the tangent function with a domain restricted to $\left[-\dfrac{\pi}{2}, \dfrac{\pi}{2}\right]$, denoted by $g(x) = \tan^{-1} x$ (p. 535)

invertible matrix an $n \times n$ matrix for which there exists an inverse matrix (p. 815)

irrational number the set of real numbers that cannot be expressed as a fraction of integers (p. 4)

irreducible (polynomial) a polynomial that cannot be written as the product of polynomials of lesser degree (p. 253)

iterations (of a function) the repeated compositions of a function with itself (p. 199)

kth partial sum the sum of the first k terms of a sequence $\{u_n\}$, where k is a positive integer (p. 26)

Law of Cosines For any triangle ABC in standard notation, $a^2 = b^2 + c^2 - 2bc \cos A$, $b^2 = a^2 + c^2 - 2ac \cos B$, and $c^2 = a^2 + b^2 - 2ab \cos C$. (p. 617)

Law of Sines For any triangle ABC in standard notation, $\dfrac{a}{\sin A} = \dfrac{b}{\sin B} = \dfrac{c}{\sin C}$. (p. 625)

Laws of Exponents For any nonnegative real numbers c and d and any rational numbers r and s,
$c^r c^s = c^{r+s}$, $\dfrac{c^r}{c^s} = c^{r-s}$ $(c \neq 0)$, $(c^r)^s = c^{rs}$, $(cd)^r = c^r d^r$, $\left(\dfrac{c}{d}\right)^r = \dfrac{c^r}{d^r}$ $(d \neq 0)$, and $c^{-r} = \dfrac{1}{c^r}$ $(c \neq 0)$. (p. 330)

leading coefficient the nonzero coefficient of the highest power of the variable in a polynomial (p. 240)

least-squares regression line the one and only one line for which the sum of the squares of the residuals for a set of data is as small as possible (p. 47)

length (of a vector) the distance from point P to point Q in a vector that extends from point P to point Q, denoted $\|\overrightarrow{PQ}\|$ (p. 653)

limit a number (or infinity) that a function value approaches but never reaches as the domain values of that function approach a particular value or infinity (p. 909, 931)

limit at infinity a real number limit as x gets large or small without bound; corresponds to a horizontal asymptote (p. 951)

limit of a constant If d is a constant, then $\lim\limits_{x \to c} d = d$. (p. 918)

limit of a constant at infinity If c is a constant, then $\lim\limits_{x \to \infty} c = c$ and $\lim\limits_{x \to -\infty} c = c$. (p. 953)

limit of a polynomial function If $f(x)$ is a polynomial function and c is any real number, then $\lim\limits_{x \to c} f(x) = f(c)$. (p. 920)

limit of a rational function If $f(x)$ is a rational function and c is any real number such that $f(c)$ is defined, then $\lim\limits_{x \to c} f(x) = f(c)$. (p. 921)

limit of the identity function For every real number c, $\lim\limits_{x \to c} x = c$. (p. 918)

Limit Theorem If f and g are functions that have limits as x approaches c and $f(x) = g(x)$ for all $x \neq c$, then $\lim\limits_{x \to c} f(x) = \lim\limits_{x \to c} g(x)$. (p. 922, 954)

linear combination The vector $\mathbf{v} = a\mathbf{i} + b\mathbf{j}$ is said to be a linear combination of $\mathbf{i}$ and $\mathbf{j}$, where $\mathbf{i} = \langle 1, 0 \rangle$ and $\mathbf{j} = \langle 0, 1 \rangle$ are unit vectors. (p. 662)

linear function a first-degree polynomial function (p. 240)

linear programming a process that involves finding the maximum or minimum output of a linear function, called the objective function, subject to certain restrictions called constraints (p. 829)

linear regression the computational process for finding the least-squares regression line for a set of data (p. 47)

linear speed a measure of speed of a point rotating at a constant rate around the center of a circle, given as the distance that the point travels over time (p. 440)

linear system a system of equations in which all equations are linear (p. 779)

local extremum (plural: extrema) either a local maximum or a local minimum (p. 266)

local maximum (plural: local maxima) A function is said to have a local maximum of $f(c)$ at $x = c$ if the graph of f has a peak at the point $(c, f(c))$; that is, $f(x) < f(c)$ for all x near c. (p. 153)

local minimum (plural: local minima) A function is said to have a local minimum of $f(d)$ at $x = d$ if the graph of f has a valley at the point $(d, f(d))$; that is, $f(x) > f(d)$ for all x near d. (p. 153)

logarithm to the base b (of x) the value of $g(x) = \log_b x$ at the number x, denoted $\log_b x$ (p. 371)

logarithmic function to the base b the inverse of the exponential function $f(x) = b^x$, denoted $g(x) = \log_b x$, where b is a fixed positive number and $b > 1$ (p. 371)

logarithmic model a logarithmic function used to represent the trend in a data set (p. 389)

logarithmic scale a scale of numbers, such as the Richter scale, that is determined by a logarithmic function to measure logarithmic growth, which is very gradual and slow (p. 368)

logistic model a logistic function of the form $y = \dfrac{a}{1 + be^{-kx}}$, where a, b, and k are constant, used to represent the trend in a data set (p. 389)

lower bound (for the real zeros of a polynomial function) the number r such that all the real zeros of a polynomial function $f(x)$ are between r and s, where r and s are real numbers and $r < s$ (p. 255)

magnitude (of a vector)   The length of a vector $\mathbf{v} = \langle a, b \rangle$ is $\|\mathbf{v}\| = \sqrt{a^2 + b^2}$. (p. 653)

major axis of an ellipse   the segment connecting the vertices of an ellipse (p. 692)

Mandelbrot Set   the set of complex numbers c such that the orbit of 0 under the function $f(x) = z^2 + c$ does not approach infinity (p. 304)

mathematical model   a mathematical description or structure, such as an equation or graph, which illustrates a relationship between real-world quantities and which is often used to predict the likely value of an unknown quantity (p. 43)

matrix   an array of numbers often used to represent a system of equations (p. 795)

matrix addition   addition of corresponding entries of matrices that have the same dimensions (p. 804)

matrix equation   a matrix equation in the form $AX = B$ that represents a system of equations, where A contains the coefficients of the equations in the system, X contains the variables of the system, and B contains the constants of the equations (p. 814)

matrix multiplication   a method of multiplying two compatible matrices to produce a product matrix (p. 806)

matrix subtraction   subtraction of corresponding entries of matrices that have the same dimensions (p. 804)

mean   a measure of central tendency—also known as the *average*, denoted by $\bar{x}$ and read "x bar"—that is calculated by adding the data values and then dividing the sum by the number of data values (p. 853)

mean of a random variable   See *expected value of a random variable.*

median   a measure of central tendency that is, or indicates, the middle of a data set when the data values are arranged in ascending order (p. 855)

minor axis of an ellipse   the segment through the center of the ellipse, perpendicular to the major axis, and with points of the ellipse as endpoints (p. 692)

minute   a unit of degree measure equal to $\frac{1}{60}$ of a degree (p. 414)

mode   a measure of central tendency that is given by the data value that occurs most frequently in a data set (p. 855)

modulus   See *absolute value of a complex number.*

Multiplication Principle   See *Fundamental Counting Principle.*

multiplicity (of a zero)   If $x - a$ is a factor that occurs m times in the complete factorization of a polynomial, then a is called a zero with multiplicity m of the related polynomial function. (p. 265)

mutually exclusive events   two events in a sample space that do not have outcomes in common (p. 866)

natural logarithm (of x)   the value of $g(x) = \ln x$ at the number x, denoted $\ln x$ (p. 358)

natural logarithmic function   the inverse of the natural exponential function $f(x) = e^x$, denoted $g(x) = \ln x$ (p. 358)

natural numbers   The set of numbers that consists of counting numbers: 1, 2, 3, … (p. 3)

Negative Angle Identities $\cos(-t) = \cos t$, $\sin(-t) = -\sin t$, $\tan(-t) = -\tan t$ (p. 459)

negative correlation   the relationship between two real-world quantities when the slope of the least-squares regression line that represents the relationship is negative, that is, as one quantity increases, the other quantity decreases (p. 52)

no correlation   the relationship between two real-world quantities when the correlation coefficient, r, for a least-squares regression line that represents the relationship is close to zero; no apparent trend in the data (p. 52)

nonlinear system   a system of equations in which at least one equation is nonlinear (p. 779)

nonnegative integers   the set of whole numbers: 0, 1, 2, 3, … (p. 3)

nonsingular matrix   See *invertible matrix.*

norm (of a vector)   See *magnitude.*

normal curve   the graph of a probability density function that corresponds to a normal distribution: bell-shaped and symmetric about the mean, with the x-axis as a horizontal asymptote (p. 889)

normal distribution   a distribution of data that varies about the mean in such a way that the graph of its probability density function is a normal curve (p. 889)

nth root of a complex number   The nth root of $a + bi$ is any of the n solutions of the equation $z^n = a + bi$. (p. 645)

nth roots   For any real number c and any positive integer n, the nth root of c is denoted by either $\sqrt[n]{c}$ or

$c^{\frac{1}{n}}$ and is defined to be the solution of $x^n = c$ when n is odd or the nonnegative solution of $x^n = c$ when n is even and nonnegative. (p. 328)

numerator   the expression in a fraction that lies above the fraction bar (p. 4)

numerical derivative   A calculator term for the instantaneous rate of change at a given input value; denoted nDeriv, nDer, d/dx, dY/dX, or ∂. (p. 237)

objective function   a linear function of which a minimum or maximum is obtained in linear programming (p. 829)

oblique asymptote   See *slant asymptote.*

oblique triangle   a triangle that does not contain a right angle (p. 617)

octant   one of eight regions into which a three-dimensional coordinate system is divided by the intersection of the three coordinate planes (p. 790)

odd function   a function f for which $f(-x) = -f(x)$ for all x in its domain, its graph symmetric with respect to the origin (p. 189, 483)

one-stage path (of a network)   a direct path from one vertex to another in a directed network (p. 809)

one-to-one function   a function f in which $f(a) = f(b)$ only when $a = b$; a function whose inverse relation is a function (p. 208)

open interval   an interval of numbers in which neither endpoint of the interval is included in the set; denoted with two parentheses (p. 118)

opposite side (of a right triangle)   abbreviated opp, the side of a right triangle that is across from a given acute angle of the triangle (p. 415)

orbit (of a number)   the sequence of output values produced by iterating a given function with that number; the orbit of a number c for a given function is c, $f(c)$, $f^2(c)$, $f^3(c)$, $f^4(c)$, ... (p. 200)

ordered pair   A pair of real numbers in parentheses, separated by a comma, is used to locate or represent a point in a coordinate plane. The first number represents the horizontal distance from the origin and the second number represents the vertical distance from the x-axis. (p. 5)

ordered set of numbers   a set of numbers such that for any two numbers a and b in the set, exactly one of the following statements is true: $a < b$, $a = b$, or $a > b$ (p. 118)

orientation (of a parametric curve)   the direction that a parametric curve is traced out (p. 757)

origin   the point of intersection of the axes in a coordinate system (p. 5)

origin symmetry   A graph is symmetric with respect to the origin if whenever (x, y) is on the graph, then $(-x, -y)$ is also on it. (p. 187)

orthogonal vectors   perpendicular vectors; vectors **u** and **v** such that $\mathbf{u} \cdot \mathbf{v} = 0$ (p. 673)

outlier   a data value that shows a strong deviation from the general trend of the distribution (p. 847)

output (of a relation)   the values denoted by the second numbers in the ordered pairs of a relation (p. 7)

parabola   the shape of the graph of a quadratic function (p. 165) For any line L in the plane and any point P not on line L, a parabola with focus P and directrix L is the set of points such that the distance from X to P is equal to the distance from X to line L. (p. 709) a conic section with eccentricity equal to 1 (p. 709)

parabolic asymptote   a parabolic curve that the graph of a function approaches as $|x|$ gets large (p. 286)

parallel lines   In a plane, these lines have the same slope. All vertical lines are also parallel. (p. 38)

parallel vectors   vectors that are scalar multiples of each other (p. 671)

parameter   the third variable used as input for the two functions that form a pair of parametric equations (p. 157, 785)

parameterization   a pair of parametric equations that describe a given curve (p. 755)

parametric equations   a pair of continuous functions that define the x- and y-coordinates of points in a coordinate plane in terms of a third variable, the parameter (p. 157)

parametric graphing   graphing parametric equations (p. 157)

parent function   a function with a certain shape that has the simplest algebraic rule for that shape (p. 172)

partial fraction decomposition   See *partial fractions.*

partial fractions   When a fraction is decomposed (broken down) and written as the sum of fractions, the terms of the sum are called partial fractions, and the sum is called the partial fraction decomposition of the original fraction. (p. 838)

partial sums of a geometric sequence For each positive integer k, the kth partial sum of a geometric sequence $\{u_n\}$ with common ratio $r \neq 1$ is
$$\sum_{n=1}^{k} u_n = u_1\left(\frac{1 - r^k}{1 - r}\right). \text{ (p. 61)}$$

partial sums of an arithmetic sequence For each positive integer k, the kth partial sum of an arithmetic sequence $\{u_n\}$ with common difference d is
$$\sum_{n=1}^{k} u_n = ku_1 + \frac{k(k - 1)}{2}d \text{ or } \sum_{n=1}^{k} u_n = \frac{k}{2}(u_1 + u_k). \text{ (p. 27)}$$

period (of a function) the smallest value of k in a function f for which there exists some constant k such that $f(t) = f(t + k)$ for every number t in the domain of f (p. 457, 498) See also *sinusoidal function*.

periodic function a nonconstant function that repeats its values at regular intervals; a function f for which there exists some constant k such that $f(t) = f(t + k)$ for every number t in the domain of f (p. 457)

periodic orbit an orbit for a given function that produces repeating output values (p. 202)

periodic point (of an orbit) the number c for which the orbit of c for a given function produces repeating output values (p. 202)

periodicity identities $\sin t = \sin(t \pm 2\pi)$, $\cos t = \cos(t \pm 2\pi)$, $\tan t = \tan(t \pm \pi)$ (p. 458)

permutation an arrangement of objects in a specific order (p. 880)

perpendicular lines In a plane, two lines are perpendicular when their slopes are negative reciprocals (having a product of -1). Vertical lines and horizontal lines are perpendicular to each other. (p. 38)

phase shift a number representing the horizontal translation of a sinusoidal graph (p. 502) See also *sinusoidal function*.

pie chart a visual display of qualitative data in which categories are displayed in sectors of a circle, where the central angle of each sector is the product of the relative frequency of that category and $360°$ (p. 845)

piecewise-defined function a function whose rule includes several formulas, each of which is applied to certain values of the domain, as specified in the definition of the function (p. 146)

plane curve the set of all points (x, y) such that $x = f(t)$ and $y = g(t)$ and that f and g are continuous functions of t on an interval I (p. 755)

point-slope form a linear equation in the form $y - y_1 = m(x - x_1)$, where m represents the slope and (x_1, y_1) is a point on the line (p. 36)

polar axis the horizontal ray extending to the right from the pole in a polar coordinate system (p. 734)

polar coordinates coordinates (r, θ) of a point in the polar coordinate system, where r gives the distance from the point to the pole, and θ is the measure of the angle with the polar axis as its initial side and the segment from the pole to the point as its terminal side (p. 734)

polar form of a complex number For the complex number $a + bi$, the polar form is $r(\cos\theta + i\sin\theta)$, where $r = |a + bi|$, $a = r\cos\theta$, and $b = r\sin\theta$. (p. 639)

pole the origin of a polar coordinate system (p. 734)

polynomial an algebraic expression that can be written in the form $a_nx^n + a_{n-1}x^{n-1} + \cdots + a_3x^3 + a_2x^2 + a_1x + a_0$, where n is a nonnegative integer, x is a variable, and each of $a_0, a_1, \ldots, a_n$ is a constant (p. 239)

polynomial equation (of degree *n*) an equation that can be written in the form $a_nx^n + a_{n-1}x^{n-1} + \cdots + a_1x + a_0 = 0$, where n is a nonnegative integer, x is a variable, and each of $a_0, a_1, \ldots, a_n$ is a constant (p. 94)

polynomial form of a quadratic function a quadratic function in the form $f(x) = ax^2 + bx + c$, where a, b, and c are real numbers and $a \neq 0$ (p. 164)

polynomial function a function whose rule is given by a polynomial (p. 240)

polynomial model a polynomial function used to represent the trend in a data set (p. 273)

population a group of individuals or objects studied in a statistical experiment (p. 843)

positive correlation the relationship between two real-world quantities when the slope of the least-squares regression line that represents the relationship is positive, that is, as one quantity increases, the other quantity increases (p. 52)

positive integers the set of natural numbers: 1, 2, 3, … (p. 3)

Power Law of Logarithms For all positive b and v, and all k, and $b \neq 1$, $\log_b(v^k) = k(\log_b v)$. (p. 366, 373)

power model a power function of the form $y = ax^r$, where a and r are constant, used to represent the trend in a data set (p. 389)

Power Principal If both sides of an equation are raised to the same positive integer power, then every solution of the original equation is a solution of the derived equation. However, the derived equation may have solutions that are not solutions of the original equation. (p. 112)

power-reducing identities trigonometric identities that relate second-degree expressions to first-degree expressions (p. 595)

prime number　an integer greater than 1 whose only factors are itself and 1 (p. 20)

principal　an amount of money that is deposited or borrowed (p. 100)

probability (of an event)　a number from 0 to 1 (or 0% to 100%) that indicates how likely an event is to occur; calculated by dividing the number of elements in the event by the number of elements in the sample space (p. 865)

probability density function　A function with the property that the area under the graph corresponds to a probability distribution. (p. 871)

probability distribution　a table that describes the rule of a function $P(E)$ that gives the probability of an event, where the domain of the function is the sample space and the range of the function is the closed interval $[0, 1]$ (p. 865)

probability of a binomial experiment　$P(r$ successes in n trials$) = {}_nC_r p^r q^{n-r}$, where p is the probability of success, and $q = 1 - p$ is the probability of failure. (p. 886)

probability of a complement　If an event E has probability p, then the complement of the event has probability $1 - p$. (p. 866)

product function　For any functions $f(x)$ and $g(x)$, their product function is the new function $(fg)(x) = f(x) \cdot g(x)$. (p. 192)

Product Law of Logarithms　For all positive b, v, and w, and $b \neq 1$, $\log_b(vw) = \log_b v + \log_b w$. (p. 365, 373)

product-to-sum　trigonometric identities involving the product of two functions (p. 599)

projection vector　A vector $\overrightarrow{OQ}$, called the projection of **u** on v, determined by constructing a segment from the terminal point of a vector **u** perpendicular to another vector **v** at a point Q on the vector, where point O is the initial point of both vectors, denoted proj_v **u**. (p. 674)

Pythagorean identities　the identity $\sin^2 t + \cos^2 t = 1$ and the identities derived from it (p. 456)

Pythagorean Theorem　In a right triangle with legs a and b and hypotenuse c, $a^2 + b^2 = c^2$. (p. 421)

quadrants　the four regions into which a coordinate plane is divided by its axes, usually indicated by Roman numerals I, II, III, and IV (p. 5)

quadratic equation　an equation that can be written in the form $ax^2 + bx + c = 0$, where a, b, and c are real constants and $a \neq 0$ (p. 88)

quadratic formula　The solutions of a quadratic equation $ax^2 + bx + c = 0$ are $x = \dfrac{-b \pm \sqrt{b^2 - 4ac}}{2a}$. (p. 92)

quadratic function　a function whose rule is a second-degree polynomial (p. 163, 240)

qualitative data　data that is categorical in nature, such as "liberal," "moderate," and "conservative" (p. 843)

quantitative data　numerical data (p. 843)

quartic function　a fourth-degree polynomial function (p. 240)

quartiles　These values divide a data set into fourths. The median, or *second quartile* Q_2, divides the data into a *lower half* and an *upper half*; the *first quartile* Q_1 is the median of the lower half; and the third quartile Q_3 is the median of the upper half. (p. 860)

quotient function　For any functions $f(x)$ and $g(x)$, their quotient function is the new function $\left(\dfrac{f}{g}\right)(x) = \dfrac{f(x)}{g(x)}$. (p. 192)

quotient identities　$\tan t = \dfrac{\sin t}{\cos t}$ and $\cot t = \dfrac{\cos t}{\sin t}$ (p. 455)

Quotient Law of Logarithms　For all positive b, v, and w, and $b \neq 1$, $\log_b\left(\dfrac{v}{w}\right) = \log_b v - \log_b w$. (p. 366, 373)

radian measure　The radian measure of an angle in standard position is the length of the arc along the unit circle from the point $(1, 0)$ on the initial side to the point P where the terminal side intersects the unit circle. (p. 436)

radical equations　equations that contain roots (such as square roots, cube roots, etc.) of expressions that contain variables (p. 111)

radioactive decay　decay in the amount of a radioactive substance that can be modeled by the function $f(x) = P(0.5)^{\frac{x}{h}}$, where P is the initial amount of the substance, $x = 0$ corresponds to when the decay began, and h is the half-life of the substance (p. 352)

radiocarbon dating　a process of determining the age of an organic object by using the amount of carbon-14 remaining in the object (p. 352)

random sample a sample in which all members of the population and all groups of members of a given size have an equal chance of being in the sample (p. 843)

random variable a function that assigns a number to each element in the sample space of an experiment (p. 869)

range (of a data set) the difference between the maximum and minimum data values in a data set (p. 859)

range (of a function) the set of second numbers in the ordered pairs of a relation (p. 6, 142, 447)

rational exponent A rational exponent is a rational number with a nonzero denominator; for any positive real number c and rational number $\frac{t}{k}$ with positive denominator, $c^{\frac{t}{k}} = (c^t)^{\frac{1}{k}} = (c^{\frac{1}{k}})^t$ or $c^{\frac{t}{k}} = \sqrt[k]{c^t} = (\sqrt[k]{c})^t$. (p. 330)

rational function a function whose rule is the quotient of two polynomials, defined only for input values that produce a nonzero denominator (p. 278)

rational number the set of real numbers that can be expressed as a fraction of an integer numerator and an integer denominator, where the denominator is not equal to zero (p. 4)

Rational Zero Test If a rational number $\frac{r}{s}$, written in lowest terms, is a zero of the polynomial function $f(x) = a_n x^n + \cdots + a_1 x + a_0$, where the coefficients $a_n, \ldots, a_1$ are integers with $a_n \neq 0$ and $a_0 \neq 0$, then r is a factor of the constant term, a_0, and s is a factor of the leading coefficient, a_n. (p. 251)

rational zeros zeros of a function that are rational numbers (p. 250)

rationalizing (a denominator) writing equivalent fractions with no radicals in the denominator (p. 332)

real axis the horizontal axis in the complex plane where each real number $a + 0i$ corresponds to the point $(a, 0)$ (p. 638)

real numbers the set of numbers that consists of rational numbers and irrational numbers (p. 3)

real solutions solutions of an equation that are real numbers (p. 88)

real zeros solutions of an equation of the form $f(x) = 0$ that are real numbers (p. 245)

reciprocal identities identities that relate trigonometric functions and their reciprocals (p. 455)

rectangular coordinate system See *Cartesian coordinate system.*

recursive form of a geometric sequence In a geometric sequence $\{u_n\}$, $u_n = ru_{n-1}$ for some nonzero constant r and all $n \geq 2$. (p. 59)

recursive form of a sequence a method of defining a sequence when given the first term and the procedure for determining each term by using the preceding term (p. 15)

recursive form of an arithmetic sequence In an arithmetic sequence $\{u_n\}$, $u_n = u_{n-1} + d$ for some constant d and all $n \geq 2$. (p. 22)

reduced row-echelon form This form of an augmented matrix satisfies the following conditions: all rows consisting entirely of zeros (if any) are at the bottom; the first nonzero entry in each nonzero row is a 1 (called *leading 1*); any column containing a leading 1 has zeros in all other entries; and each leading 1 appears to the right of leading 1s in any preceding row. (p. 797)

reference angle the positive acute angle formed by the terminal side of θ in standard position and the x-axis (p. 449)

reflections The graph of $y = -f(x)$ is the graph of f reflected across the x-axis, and the graph of $y = f(-x)$ is the graph of f reflected across the y-axis. (p. 177)

relation a correspondence between two sets; a set of ordered pairs (p. 6)

Remainder Theorem If a polynomial $f(x)$ is divided by $(x - c)$, then the remainder is $f(c)$. (p. 244)

residual a measure of the error between an actual data value and the corresponding value given by a model; $r - y$, where (x, r) is a data point and (x, y) is a point contained by the model (p. 44)

Richter scale a logarithmic scale used to measure the magnitude of an earthquake (p. 368)

right angle an angle with a degree measure of 90° (p. 414)

roots solutions of an equation of the form $f(x) = 0$ and equal to the zeros of f (p. 83)

roots of unity the n distinct nth roots of 1 (the solutions of $z^n = 1$) (p. 648)

rotation equations equations that relate a point in a coordinate plane to the corresponding point in the plane after a rotation (p. 729)

rule of the function See *function rule.*

sample a subset of the population studied in a statistical experiment, whose information is used to draw conclusions about the population (p. 843)

Glossary

sample space   the set of all possible outcomes in an experiment (p. 864)

scalar   a real number, often denoted by k, used in scalar multiplication (p. 655)

scalar multiplication (with vectors)   an operation in which a scalar k is multiplied by a vector $\mathbf{v}$ to produce another vector, denoted by $k\mathbf{v}$ (p. 655)

scalar multiplication with matrices   multiplication of each entry in a matrix by a real number (p. 805)

scatter plot   a graphical display of statistical data plotted as points on a coordinate plane to show the relationship between two quantities (p. 5)

Schwartz Inequality   For any vectors $\mathbf{u}$ and $\mathbf{v}$, $|\mathbf{u} \cdot \mathbf{v}| \leq \|\mathbf{u}\| \|\mathbf{v}\|$. (p. 673)

secant line (of a function)   the straight line determined by two points on the graph of a function; the slope of the secant line joining points $(a, f(a))$ and $(b, f(b))$ on the graph of a function, equal to the average rate of change of the function from a to b (p. 218)

secant ratio   For a given acute angle θ in a right triangle, the secant of θ is written as $\sec \theta$ and is equal to the reciprocal of the cosine ratio of the given angle. (p. 416)

second   a unit of degree measure equal to $\frac{1}{60}$ of a minute, or $\frac{1}{3600}$ of a degree (p. 414)

second quartile   See *quartiles*.

second-degree equation   See *quadratic equation*.

self-similar   the property possessed by fractals that every subdivision of the fractal has a structure similar to the structure of the whole (p. 305)

sequence   an ordered list of numbers (p. 13)

sequence notation   a customary method of denoting a sequence or terms of a sequence in abbreviated form: $u_1, u_2, u_3, \ldots, u_n$ (p. 14)

series   the sum of the terms of a sequence (p. 76)

sides (of an angle)   the two rays, segments, or lines that form an angle (p. 413)

Sigma notation   See *summation notation*.

simple harmonic motion   motion that can be described by a function of the form $f(x) = a \sin(bt + c) + d$ or $f(x) = a \cos(bt + c) + d$ (p. 549)

simple interest   interest that is generally used when a loan or a bank balance is less than 1 year; calculated by $I = Prt$, where I is the simple interest, P is the principal, r is the annual interest, and t is time in years (p. 100)

sine ratio   For a given acute angle θ in a right triangle, the sine of θ is written as $\sin \theta$ and is equal to the ratio of the opposite side length to the length of the hypotenuse. (p. 416)

sinusoid   the wave shape of the graph of a sine or cosine function (p. 510, 548)

sinusoidal function   A function whose graph is the shape of a sinusoid and can be expressed in the form $f(x) = a \sin(bt + c) + d$ or $f(x) = a \cos(bt + c) + d$, where $|a|$ is the amplitude, $\frac{2\pi}{b}$ is the period, $-\frac{c}{b}$ is the phase shift, and d is the vertical shift. (p. 548)

skewed distribution   a type of distribution in which the right or left side of its display indicate frequencies that are much greater than those of the other side (p. 846)

slant asymptote   a nonvertical and nonhorizontal line that the graph of a function approaches as $|x|$ gets large (p. 286)

slope of a line   The value of the ratio $\frac{\Delta y}{\Delta x} = \frac{y_2 - y_1}{x_2 - x_1}$, where (x_1, y_1) and (x_2, y_2) are points contained by the line and $x_1 \neq x_2$. (p. 32)

slope-intercept form   a linear equation in the form $y = mx + b$, where m represents the slope and b represents the y-intercept (p. 33)

solution of a system of equations   a set of values that satisfy all the equations in the system (p. 780)

solution of an equation   the value(s) of the variable(s) that make the equation true (p. 30)

solution to an inequality (in two variables)   the region in the coordinate plane consisting of all points whose coordinates satisfy the inequality (p. 827)

solving a triangle   finding the lengths of all three sides and the measures of all three angles in a triangle when only some of these measures are known (p. 424)

sound waves   periodic air pressure waves created by vibrations (p. 558)

special angles   angles of degree measure 30°, 45°, or 60° (p. 418)

square root of squares   For every real number c, $\sqrt{c^2} = |c|$. (p. 109)

square system   a system of equations that has the same number of equations as variables (p. 814)

standard deviation   a measure of variability that describes the average distance of data values from the mean, given by the square root of the variance (p. 857)

standard equation of a hyperbola   For any point (h, k) in the plane and positive real numbers a and b,

$$\frac{(x-h)^2}{a^2} - \frac{(y-k)^2}{b^2} = 1 \text{ or } \frac{(x-h)^2}{b^2} - \frac{(y-k)^2}{a^2} = 1.$$
(p. 701, 720)

standard equation of a parabola　For any point (h, k) in the plane and nonzero real number p, $(x-h)^2 = 4p(y-k)$ or $(y-k)^2 = 4p(x-h)$. (p. 710, 720)

standard equation of an ellipse　For any point (h, k) in the plane and real numbers a and b with $a > b > 0$, $\frac{(x-h)^2}{a^2} + \frac{(y-k)^2}{b^2} = 1$ or $\frac{(x-h)^2}{b^2} + \frac{(y-k)^2}{a^2} = 1.$ (p. 693, 720)

standard form (of a line)　used to display the equation of a line without fractions, a linear equation in the form $Ax + By = C$, where A and B are not both equal to zero (p. 39)

standard normal curve　a normal curve with a mean of 0 and a standard deviation of 1 (p. 890)

standard notation (of triangles)　a method of labeling triangles in which each vertex is labeled with a capital letter to denote the angle at that vertex, and the length of the side opposite that vertex is denoted by the same letter in lower case (p. 617)

standard position (of an angle)　an angle in the coordinate plane with its vertex at the origin and its initial side on the positive x-axis (p. 434)

standard viewing window　the window or screen of a graphics calculator that displays $-10 \le x \le 10$ and $-10 \le y \le 10$, listed in the ZOOM menu of most graphics calculators (p. 84)

standardize (data)　to adjust the scale of data that is normally distributed in order to match the standard normal curve (p. 893)

stem plot　a display of quantitative data in a tabular format consisting of the initial digit(s) of the data values, called *stems*, on the left and the remaining digits of the data values, called *leaves*, on the right; commonly used to display small data sets (p. 847)

step function　a function, such as the greatest-integer function, whose graph consists of horizontal line segments resembling steps (p. 157)

sum function　For any functions $f(x)$ and $g(x)$, their sum function is the new function $(f+g)(x) = f(x) + g(x)$. (p. 191)

sum of an infinite geometric series　The sum $S = \frac{a_1}{1-r}$, where $a_1 + ra_1 + r^2a_1 + r^3a_1 + \cdots$ is a convergent geometric series with common ratio r such that $|r| < 1$. (p. 77)

sum-to-product　trigonometric identities involving $\sin x \pm \sin y$ or $\cos x \pm \cos y$ (p. 599)

summation notation　a customary method of denoting the sum of terms by using the Greek letter Sigma (Σ) as follows: $\sum_{k=1}^{m} c_k = c_1 + c_2 + c_3 + \cdots + c_m$ (p. 25)

supplementary angle identity　For any acute angle θ, $\sin \theta = \sin(180° - \theta)$. (p. 628)

symmetric distribution　a type of distribution in which the right and left sides of its display indicate frequencies that are mirror images of each other (p. 846)

synthetic division　an abbreviated notation for performing polynomial division when the divisor is a first-degree polynomial (p. 241)

system of equations　a set of two or more equations in two or more variables (p. 779)

tangent line (of a function)　a line that touches the graph of a function at exactly one point; the slope of the tangent line to a curve at a point, equal to the instantaneous rate of change of the function at that point (p. 235)

tangent ratio　For a given acute angle θ in a right triangle, the tangent of θ is written as $\tan \theta$ and is equal to the ratio of the opposite side length to the adjacent side length. (p. 416)

term (of a sequence)　a number in a sequence (p. 13)

terminal point (of a vector)　the point Q in a vector that extends from point P to point Q (p. 653)

terminal side　the final position of a ray that is rotated around its vertex (p. 433)

third quartile　See *quartiles.*

transformation form of a quadratic function　a quadratic function in the form $f(x) = a(x-h)^2 + k$, where a, h, and k are real numbers and $a \ne 0$ (p. 164)

Triangle Sum Theorem　The sum of the measures of the angles in a triangle is 180°. (p. 421)

trigonometric form of a complex number　See *polar form of a complex number.*

trigonometric functions of a real variable　a function whose rule is a trigonometric ratio in the coordinate plane with domain values in radian measure (p. 445)

trigonometric ratios (in a triangle)　the six possible combinations of side length ratios of a right triangle (p. 415)

trigonometric ratios (in the coordinate plane) the six trigonometric ratios defined in terms of a triangle determined by the coordinates of a point on the terminal side of an angle in standard position and the origin (p. 444)

two-stage path (of a network) a path in a directed network from one vertex to another with exactly one intermediate vertex (p. 810)

uniform distribution a type of distribution in which all of the data values have approximately the same frequency; its display is level (p. 846)

unit circle the circle of radius 1 centered at the origin of the coordinate plane (p. 435)

unit vector a vector with a length of 1 (p. 661)

upper bound (for the real zeros of a polynomial function) the number s such that all the real zeros of a polynomial function $f(x)$ are between r and s, where r and s are real numbers and $r < s$ (p. 255)

variability the spread of a data set (p. 857)

variance a measure of variability given by the average of squared deviations (p. 858)

vector a quantity that involves both magnitude and direction; represented geometrically by a directed line segment or arrow and denoted by using its endpoints, such as $\overrightarrow{PQ}$, or by a boldface lowercase letter, such as $\mathbf{u}$ (p. 653)

vector addition If $\mathbf{u} = \langle a, b \rangle$ and $\mathbf{v} = \langle c, d \rangle$, then $\mathbf{u} + \mathbf{v} = \langle a + c, b + d \rangle$. (p. 657)

vector subtraction If $\mathbf{u} = \langle a, b \rangle$ and $\mathbf{v} = \langle c, d \rangle$, then $\mathbf{u} - \mathbf{v} = \langle a - c, b - d \rangle$. (p. 658)

vertex (of an angle) the common endpoint of the two rays, segments, or lines that form an angle (p. 413)

vertex of a parabola the intersection of the axis of a parabola and the parabola; the midpoint of the segment from the focus of the parabola to the directrix (p. 709)

vertical asymptotes a vertical line that the graph of a function approaches but never touches or crosses because it is not defined there (p. 284, 950)

vertical compression For any positive number $c < 1$, the graph of $y = c \cdot f(x)$ is the graph of f compressed vertically, toward the x-axis, by a factor of c. (p. 179)

vertical line a line that has an undefined slope and an equation of the form $x = c$, where c is a constant real number (p. 37)

vertical shifts For any positive number c, the graph of $y = f(x) + c$ is the graph of f shifted upward c units, and the graph of $y = f(x) - c$ is the graph of f shifted downward c units. (p. 174) See also *sinusoidal function*.

vertical stretch For any positive number $c > 1$, the graph of $y = c \cdot f(x)$ is the graph of f stretched vertically, away from the x-axis, by a factor of c. (p. 179)

vertical line test A graph in a coordinate plane represents a function if and only if no vertical line intersects the graph more than once. (p. 151)

vertices of a hyperbola the points where the line through the foci intercepts the hyperbola (p. 701)

vertices of a network the points that are connected in a network (p. 809)

vertices of an ellipse the points where the line through the foci intercepts the ellipse (p. 692)

whole numbers the set of numbers that consists of natural numbers and zero: 0, 1, 2, … (p. 3)

work The work W done by a constant force $\mathbf{F}$ as its point of application moves along the vector $\mathbf{d}$ is $W = \mathbf{F} \cdot \mathbf{d}$. (p. 678)

x-axis often the name of the horizontal axis of a coordinate plane with the positive direction to the right and the negative direction to the left (p. 5)

x-axis symmetry A graph is symmetric with respect to the x-axis if whenever (x, y) is on the graph, then $(x, -y)$ is also on it. (p. 185)

x-coordinate usually the first real number in an ordered pair (p. 5)

x-intercept the x-coordinate of a point where a graph crosses the x-axis; the x-intercepts of the graph of f, equal to the zeros of f and the solutions of $f(x) = 0$ (p. 83)

x-intercept form of a quadratic function a quadratic function in the form $f(x) = a(x - s)(x - t)$, where $a, x, s,$ and t are real numbers and $a \neq 0$ (p. 164)

x-intercept method   a method of solving an equation of the form $f(x) = 0$ by graphing $y = f(x)$ and finding the x-intercepts (p. 84)

y-axis   often the name of the vertical axis of a coordinate plane with the positive direction up and the negative direction down (p. 5)

y-axis symmetry   A graph is symmetric with respect to the y-axis if whenever (x, y) is on the graph, then $(-x, y)$ is also on it. (p. 184)

y-coordinate   usually the second real number in an ordered pair (p. 5)

z-axis   the vertical axis in a three-dimensional coordinate system with positive direction upward (p. 790)

zero polynomial   the constant polynomial 0 (p. 240)

Zero Product Property   If a product of real numbers is zero, then at least one of the factors is zero; if $ab = 0$, then $a = 0$ or $b = 0$. (p. 89)

zeros of a function   inputs of the function that produce an output of zero (p. 83)

z-value   a value that gives the number of standard deviations that a data value in a normal distribution is located above the mean (p. 894)

Acknowledgments

Photo Credits: page 2, Ron Behrmann/International Stock Photography; page 80, Orion Press/Natural Selection; page 140, Peter Van Steen/HRW Photo; page 326, Laurence Parent; page 412, Todd Gipstein/National Geographic Society Image Collection; page 472, Peter Van Steen/HRW Photo/Courtesy Jim Reese at KVET, Austin, Tx; page 522, Coco McCoy/Rainbow/PictureQuest; page 570, Telegraph Color Library/FPG International; page 616, Scott Barrow/International Stock Photography; page 690, Stone; page 778, Tom McHugh/Photo Researchers, Inc.; page 842, SuperStock; page 908, Tom Sanders/Photri/The Stock Market

Illustration Credits: Abbreviations used: (t) top, (c) center, (b) bottom, (l) left, (r) right, (bkgd) background

All work, unless otherwise noted, contributed by Holt, Rinehart and Winston.

Chapter Four: page 306 (tc), Pronk&Associates;
Chapter Six: page 470 (cl), NETS; page 471 (br), NETS. Chapter Eleven: page 713 (b), NETS. Chapter Thirteen: page 882 (br), NETS.

Additional Answers

Chapter 1

Section 1.2, page 19

5.

6.

7.

8.

14.

15.

$u_{25} = 300$

Chapter 2

Chapter 2 can do calculus, page 139

1. *Numerical Method*

a. Each base must be greater than 0 and less than 10 yards. The *nr* in the chart indicates that no rectangle can be formed with a base length of 5 yards or more because the opposite bases of a rectangle are the same length, and, since $5 + 5 = 10$, there would be no wire left to make the sides of a rectangle.

b.

length	1 yd	1.5 yd	2 yd	2.5 yd	3 yd	3.5 yd	4 yd	4.5 yd	5 yd	5.5 yd
height	4 yd	3.5 yd	3 yd	2.5 yd	2 yd	1.5 yd	1 yd	0.5 yd	*nr*	*nr*
area	4 yd²	5.25 yd²	6 yd²	6.25 yd²	6 yd²	5.25 yd²	4 yd²	2.25 yd²	—	—

c.

d. The maximum area 6.25 yd² appears to occur when the base length is 2.5 yd.

Analytical and Graphical Method

$$2l + 2w = 10$$
$$2w = 10 - 2l$$
$$w = 5 - l$$

$$A = l \times w$$
$$A = l(5 - l)$$
$$A = 5l - l^2$$
$$A = -l^2 + 5l$$

Using the maximum finder on a graphing calculator indicates that the maximum area of 6.25 yd² occurs at approximately 2.5 yd.

2. *Numerical Method*

a. The base must be greater than 0 and less than 6 units. The *nr* in the table indicates that no rectangle can be formed with a base of 6 or more units because $y = \sqrt{36 - x^2}$ would not exist if $x > 6$.

b.

x	1	2	3	4	5	6
y	5.92	5.66	5.20	4.47	3.32	nr
area	5.92	11.32	15.6	17.88	16.6	—

c.

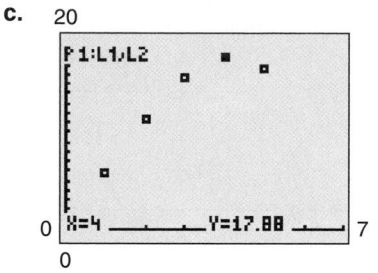

d. A maximum area of 17.88 square units appears to occur when *x* is 4.

Analytical and Graphical Method

$$A = x \times y$$
$$y = \sqrt{36 - x^2}$$
$$A = x \times \sqrt{36 - x^2}$$

Using the maximum finder on a graphing calculator indicates that the maximum area of 18 square units occurs when *x* is approximately 4.24.

3. *Numerical Method*

a. The base must be greater than 0 and less than 4 units. The *nr* in the table indicates that no rectangle with a base of 4 or more units because $y \leq 0$ if $x \geq 4$.

b.

x	0.5	1.0	1.5	2.0	2.5	3.0	3.5	4.0
y	1.75	1.5	1.25	1	0.75	0.5	0.25	nr
area	0.875	1.5	1.875	2.0	1.875	1.5	0.875	—

c.

d. A maximum area of 2 square units appears to occur at *x* = 2.

Analytical and Graphical Method

$$A = x \times y$$
$$y = \frac{(4 - x)}{2}$$
$$A = x \times \frac{(4 - x)}{2}$$
$$A = \frac{4x - x^2}{2}$$

Using the maximum finder on a graphing calculator indicates that the maximum area is 2 when *x* is approximately 2.

Chapter 3

Section 3.2, page 161

33.

34.

35.

36.

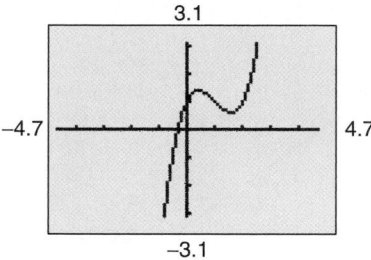

Section 3.2, page 162

37. a.

38. a.

39. a.

40. a.

41.

42.

43.

44.

45. b.

46. b.

47. b.

48. b.

49. b.

50.

51.

$y = [-x]$

52.

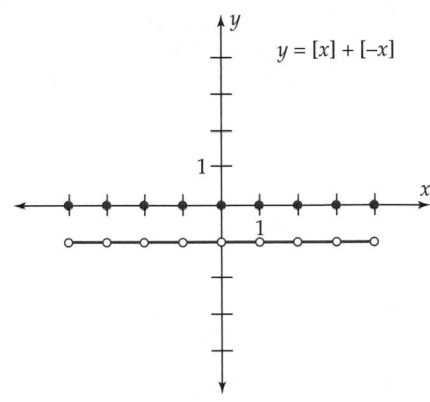

$y = [x] + [-x]$

53.

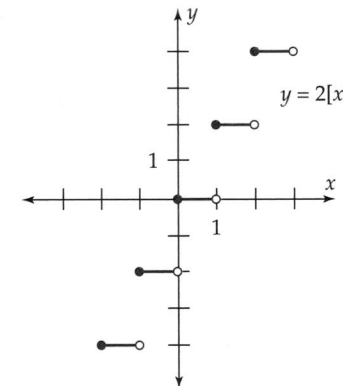

$y = 2[x]$

Section 3.2, page 163

60. Many correct answers, including

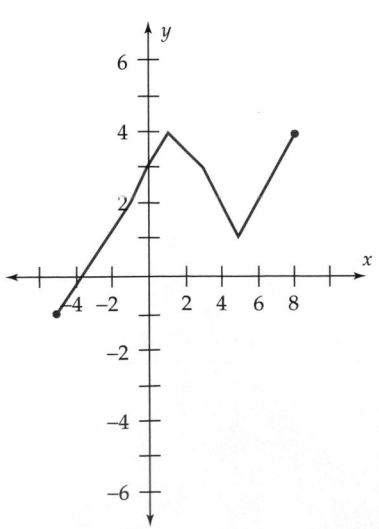

61. Many correct answers, including

62.

63. Entire graph:

near the origin:

64.

65. Entire graph:

near the origin:

66.

67.

68.

69.

70.

71.

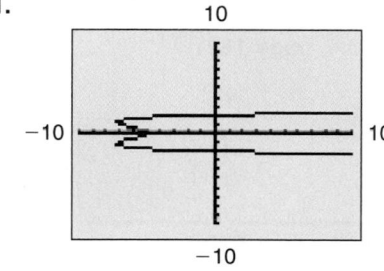

Section 3.3, page 171

17.

18.

19.

20.

21.

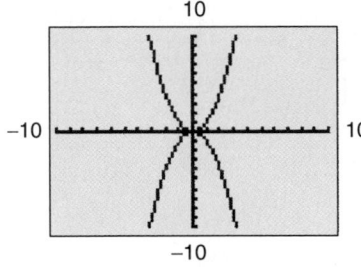

Section 3.4, page 182

10.

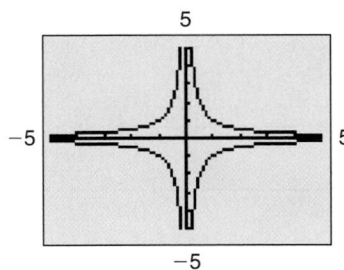

$$f(x) = -x^2, f(x) = x^2$$

11.

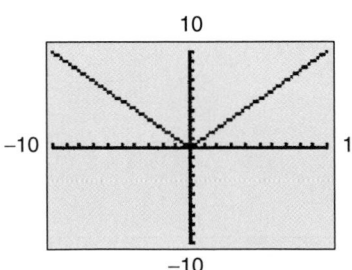

$$h(x) = -\frac{1}{x}, h(x) = \frac{1}{x}$$

12.

$$g(x) = |-x|, g(x) = |x|$$

13.

$$h(x) = \sqrt[3]{-x}, h(x) = \sqrt[3]{x}$$

14.

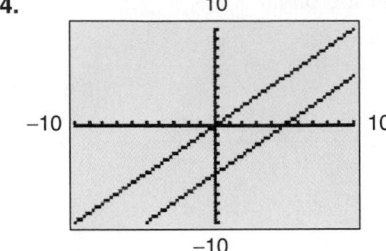

$$f(x) = x - 5, f(x) = x$$

15.

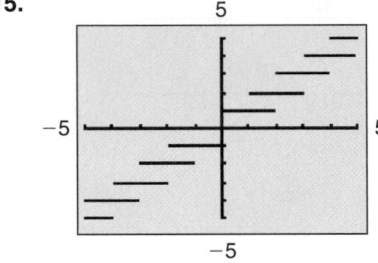

$$g(x) = [x] + 1, g(x) = [x]$$

16.

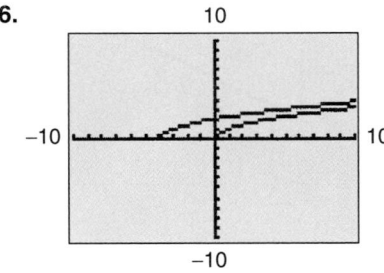

$$f(x) = \sqrt{x + 4}, f(x) = \sqrt{x}$$

17.

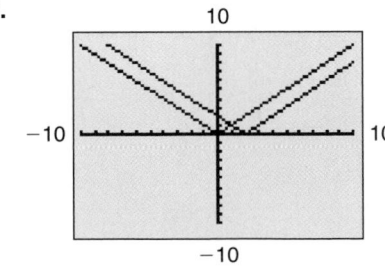

$$h(x) = |x - 2|, h(x) = |x|$$

18.

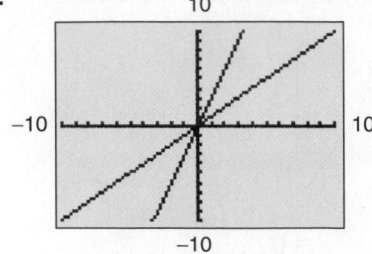

$$g(x) = 3x, g(x) = x$$

19.

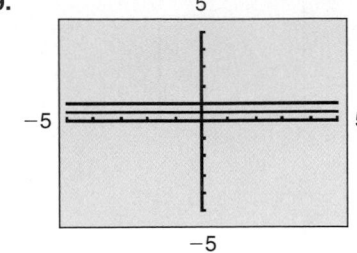

$$f(x) = \frac{1}{2}, f(x) = 1$$

20.

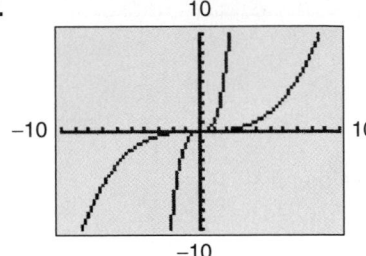

$$g(x) = \left(\frac{1}{4}x\right)^3, g(x) = x^3$$

21.

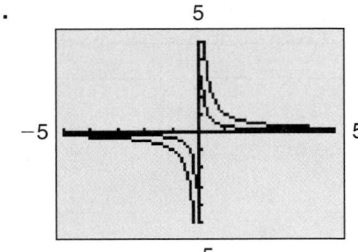

$$h(x) = \frac{1}{3x}, h(x) = \frac{1}{x}$$

34.

$$f(x) = -2(x + 1)^2 + 3, f(x) = x^2$$

35.

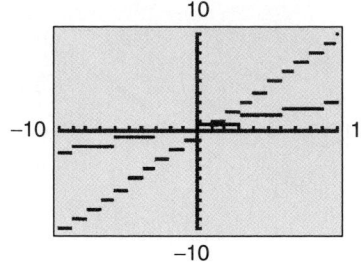

$g(x) = \frac{1}{4}\sqrt[3]{x+3} - 1, g(x) = \sqrt[3]{x}$

36.

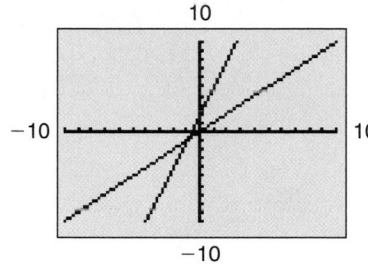

$f(x) = -\frac{3}{4}\left[-\frac{1}{3}x\right], f(x) = [x]$

37.

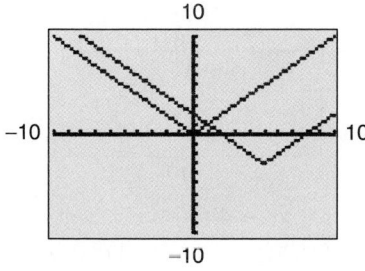

$h(x) = 3(x-1) + 5, y = x$

38.

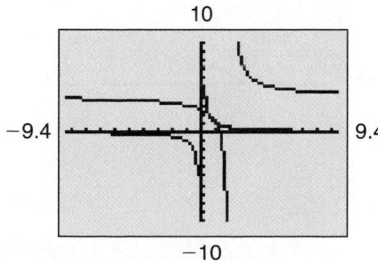

$g(x) = |-x+5| - 3, g(x) = |x|$

39.

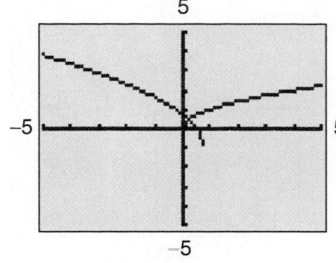

$f(x) = \frac{-3}{2-x} + 4, f(x) = \frac{1}{x}$

40.

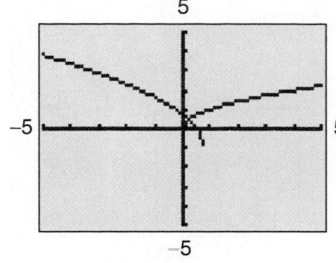

$h(x) = \sqrt{-4x+3} - 1, h(x) = \sqrt{x}$

41.

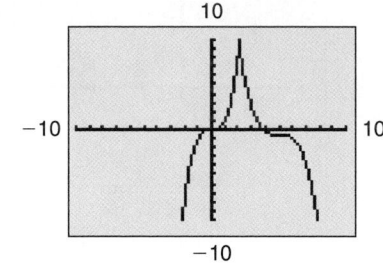

$g(x) = \frac{2}{5}(5-x)^3 - \frac{3}{5}, g(x) = x^3$

Section 3.4, page 183

46.

47.

48.

49.

50.

51.

52.

53.

54.

55.

56.

57.

58.

59.

60.

61.

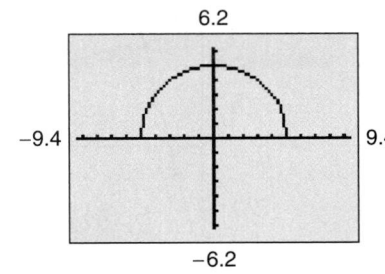

62. a. $c(x) = 37 + 23[x]$

b.

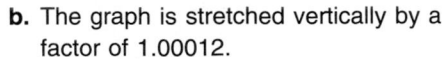

The parent function of $c(x)$ is $f(x) = [x]$. The parent function is stretched vertically by a factor of 23 and then shifted upward 37 units.

63. a. Shifts upward by 28 units

b. The graph is stretched vertically by a factor of 1.00012.

Section 3.5, page 197

37.

38.

43.

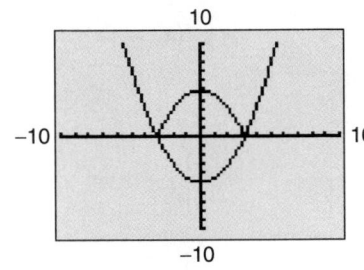

$f(x) = 0.5x^2 - 5$,
$g \circ f = |f(x)| = |0.5x^2 - 5|$

44.

$f(x) = x^3 - 4x^2 + x + 3$,
$g \circ f = |f(x)| = |x^3 - 4x^2 + x + 3|$

45.

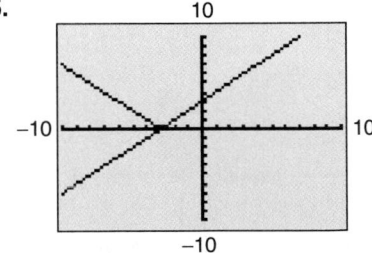

$f(x) = x + 3$, $g \circ f = |f(x)| = |x + 3|$

46.

$f(x) = |x| - 2$,
$g \circ f = |f(x)| = ||x| - 2|$

Section 3.6, page 213

31.

32.

33.

34.

35.

36.

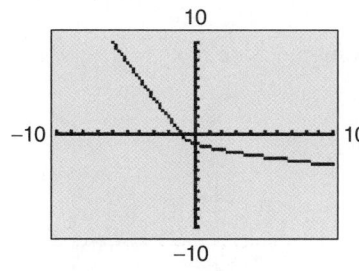

37. One restricted function is $h(x) = |x|$ with $x \geq 0$ (so that $h(x) = x$); inverse function $g(x) = x$.

38. One restricted function is $f(x) = |x - 3|$ with $x \geq 3$; inverse function is $g(x) = x + 3$.

39. One restricted function is $h(x) = -x^2$ with $x \leq 0$; inverse function $g(x) = -\sqrt{-x}$. Another restricted function is $h(x) = -x^2$ with $x \geq 0$; inverse function $g(x) = \sqrt{-x}$.

40. One restricted function is $f(x) = x^2 + 4$ with $x \geq 0$; inverse function is $g(x) = \sqrt{x - 4}$.

41. One restricted function is $h(x) = \dfrac{x^2 + 6}{2}$ with $x \geq 0$; inverse function $g(x) = \sqrt{2x - 6}$.

42. One restricted function is $f(x) = \sqrt{4 - x^2}$ with $x \geq 0$; inverse function is $g(x) = \sqrt{4 - x^2}$.

43. One restricted function is $f(x) = \dfrac{1}{x^2 + 1}$ with $x \leq 0$, inverse function $g(x) = -\sqrt{\dfrac{1}{x} - 1} = -\sqrt{\dfrac{1 - x}{x}}$.

44. One restricted function is $f(x) = 3(x + 5)^2 + 2$ with $x \geq -5$; inverse function is $g(x) = -5 + \sqrt{\dfrac{x - 2}{3}}$.

45. $(f \circ g)(x) = f(g(x)) = f(x - 1)$
$= (x - 1) + 1 = x$ and
$(g \circ f)(x) = g(f(x)) = g(x + 1)$
$= (x + 1) - 1 = x$

46. $(f \circ g)(x) = f(g(x)) = f\left(\dfrac{x}{2} + 3\right)$
$= 2\left(\dfrac{x}{2} + 3\right) - 6 = x$ and
$(g \circ f)(x) = g(f(x))$
$= g(2x - 6) = \dfrac{2x - 6}{2} + 3 = x$

47. $(f \circ g)(x) = f\left(\dfrac{1 - x}{x}\right) = \dfrac{1}{\left(\dfrac{1 - x}{x}\right) + 1}$
$= \dfrac{1}{\dfrac{(1 - x) + x}{x}} = x$ and

$(g \circ f)(x) = g\left(\dfrac{1}{x + 1}\right)$
$= \dfrac{1 - \dfrac{1}{x + 1}}{\dfrac{1}{x + 1}}$
$= \dfrac{\dfrac{(x + 1) - 1}{x + 1}}{\dfrac{1}{x + 1}} = x$

48. $(f \circ g)(x) = f\left(\dfrac{-3 - 5x}{2x}\right)$
$= \dfrac{-3}{2\left(\dfrac{-3 - 5x}{2x}\right) + 5} = \dfrac{-3}{\dfrac{-3 - 5x}{x} + 5}$
$= \dfrac{-3}{\dfrac{-3 - 5x + 5x}{x}} = \dfrac{-3}{\dfrac{-3}{x}} = x$ and

$(g \circ f)(x) = g\left(\dfrac{-3}{2x + 5}\right)$
$= \dfrac{-3 - 5\left(\dfrac{-3}{2x + 5}\right)}{2\left(\dfrac{-3}{2x + 5}\right)}$
$= \dfrac{-3(2x + 5) + 15}{-6}$
$= \dfrac{-6x}{-6} = x$

49. $(f \circ g)(x) = f(\sqrt[5]{x}) = (\sqrt[5]{x})^5 = x$ and
$(g \circ f)(x) = g(x^5) = \sqrt[5]{x^5} = x$

50. $(f \circ g)(x) = f(\sqrt[3]{x + 1}) =$
$= (\sqrt[3]{x + 1})^3 - 1$
$= x + 1 - 1 = x$ and
$(g \circ f)(x) = g(x^3 - 1)$
$= \sqrt[3]{(x^3 - 1) + 1} = x$

51. $(f \circ f)(x) = f(f(x)) = \dfrac{2f(x) + 1}{3f(x) - 2}$
$= \dfrac{2\left[\dfrac{2x + 1}{3x - 2}\right] + 1}{3\left[\dfrac{2x + 1}{3x - 2}\right] - 2} = \dfrac{\dfrac{2(2x + 1) + (3x - 2)}{3x - 2}}{\dfrac{3(2x + 1) - 2(3x - 2)}{3x - 2}}$
$= \dfrac{\dfrac{7x}{3x - 2}}{\dfrac{7}{3x - 2}} = x$

22.

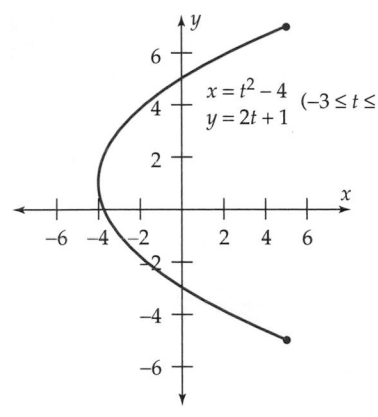

$$x = t^3 + 3t^2 - 1$$
$$y = t^2 + 1$$ $(-3 \le t \le 2)$

23.

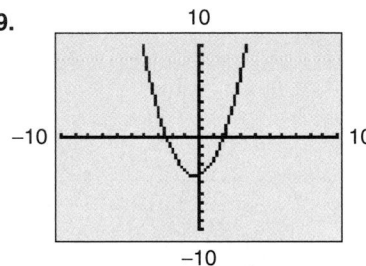

$$x = t^2 - 4$$ $(-3 \le t \le 3)$
$$y = 2t + 1$$

Chapter 3 Review, page 229

29.

Vertex is $(-0.35, -4.2025)$.

The y-intercept is -4.08.

The x-intercepts are -2.4 and 1.7.

30. $f(x) = x^2 - 2x$ (polynomial form)

$f(x) = x(x - 2)$ (x-intercept form)

31. $f(x) = \left(x - \dfrac{3}{2}\right)^2 - \dfrac{25}{4}$
(transformation form)

$f(x) = (x - 4)(x + 1)$
(x-intercept form)

32. $f(x) = -2(x - 1)^2 + 8$
(transformation form)

$f(x) = -2x^2 + 4x + 6$
(polynomial form)

33. parent function: $f(x) = \sqrt{x}$

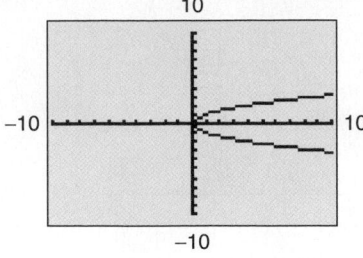

34. parent function: $h(x) = \dfrac{1}{x}$

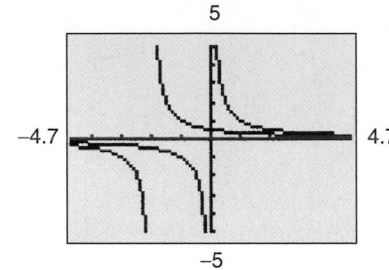

35. parent function: $g(x) = |x|$

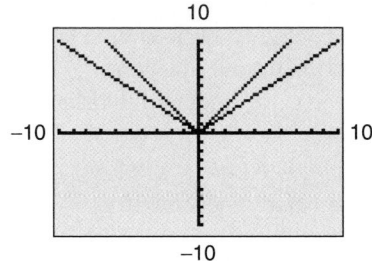

36. parent function: $h(x) = [x]$

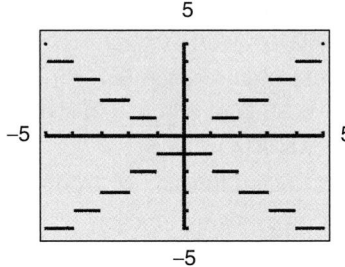

37. parent function: $f(x) = x^2$

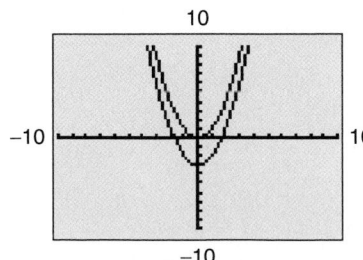

38. parent function: $g(x) = \sqrt[3]{x}$

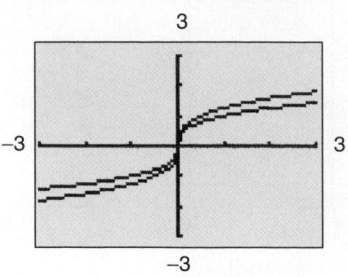

39. Compress the graph of g toward the x-axis by a factor of 0.25, then shift the graph vertically 2 units upward.

40. Shift 4 units left, then reflect across the x-axis, then shift 5 units down.

41. Shift the graph of g horizontally 7 units to the right; then stretch it away from the x-axis by a factor of 3; then reflect it across the x-axis; finally, shift the graph vertically 2 units upward.

42. A horizontal shift of 2 units to the right.

43. e

Chapter 3 Review, page 232

79. $(g \circ f)(x) = \dfrac{3\left(\dfrac{2x + 1}{x - 3}\right) + 1}{\left(\dfrac{2x + 1}{x - 3}\right) - 2}$

$= \dfrac{\dfrac{3(2x + 1) + 1(x - 3)}{x - 3}}{\dfrac{2x + 1 - 2(x - 3)}{x - 3}} = \dfrac{\dfrac{7x}{x - 3}}{\dfrac{7}{x - 3}}$

$= \dfrac{7x}{x - 3} \cdot \dfrac{x - 3}{7} = x$

$(f \circ g)(x) = \dfrac{2\left(\dfrac{3x + 1}{x - 2}\right) + 1}{\left(\dfrac{3x + 1}{x - 2}\right) - 3}$

$= \dfrac{\dfrac{2(3x + 1) + 1(x - 2)}{x - 2}}{\dfrac{3x + 1 - 3(x - 2)}{x - 2}} = \dfrac{\dfrac{7x}{x - 2}}{\dfrac{7}{x - 2}}$

$= \dfrac{7x}{x - 2} \cdot \dfrac{x - 2}{7} = x$

80. $(g \circ f)(x) = (f \circ g)(x)$

$= \dfrac{\dfrac{x + 1}{x - 1} + 1}{\dfrac{x + 1}{x - 1} - 1} = \dfrac{\dfrac{x + 1 + x - 1}{x - 1}}{\dfrac{x + 1 - (x - 1)}{x - 1}}$

$= \dfrac{\dfrac{2x}{x - 1}}{\dfrac{2}{x - 1}} = x$

82. a. $\dfrac{1 - \sqrt{13}}{3}$

b. $\dfrac{\sqrt{9.75} - \sqrt{13}}{6.5}$

c. $\dfrac{\sqrt{21} - \sqrt{13}}{8}$

Chapter 4

Section 4.3, page 272

52.

53.

54.

55.

56.

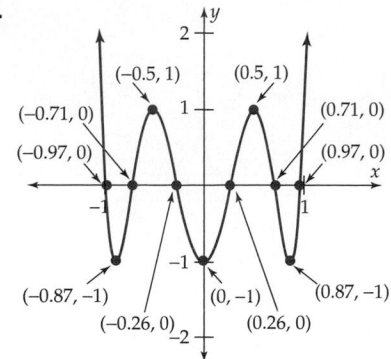

Section 4.3, page 273

58. a. A polynomial of odd degree is continuous and has ends pointing in opposite directions. Therefore, it has to cross the x-axis at least once and so will have at least one zero.

b. Since the constant term is positive, the y-intercept of the function is positive. Since the leading coefficient is negative, the ends both point down. Therefore, there must be at least two places where the function crosses the x-axis, one to the right and one to the left of the y-axis. Therefore, there must be at least one positive and one negative real zero.

59. a. The general shape of the graph should be as shown here. The graph should cross the x-axis at the points specified, and bounce off the axis at 2.

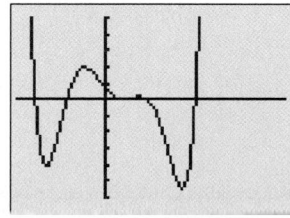

b. Only 3 of the roots are shown. 2 is skipped over entirely.

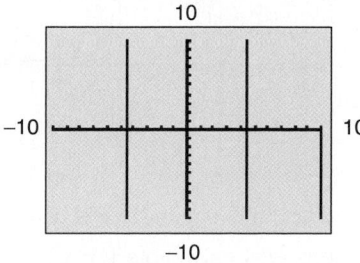

c. Again, x = 2 is missed.

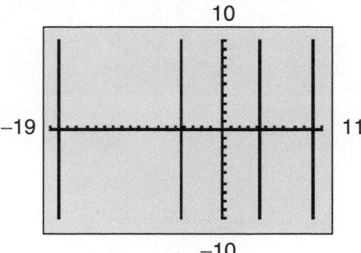

d. Try the windows $-20 \le x \le -3$, $-5{,}000{,}000 \le y \le 1{,}000{,}000$. Then try $-3 \le x \le 2$, $-5000 \le y \le 60{,}000$. For the third part $1 \le x \le 5$, $-5000 \le y \le 5000$ and lastly $5 \le x \le 11$, $-100{,}000 \le y \le 100{,}000$.

Section 4.4, page 290

24.

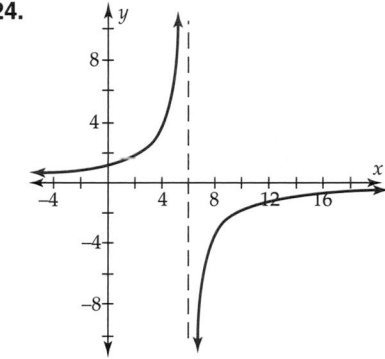

vertical asymptote $x = 6$
horizontal asymptote $y = 0$

25.

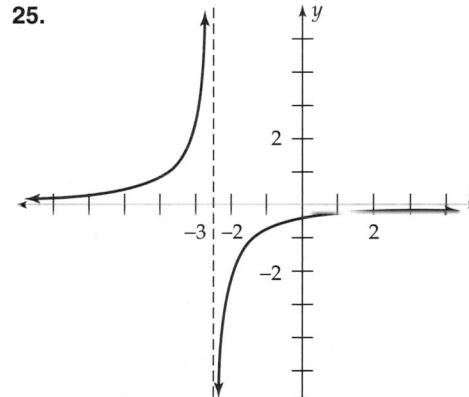

vertical asymptote $x = -2.5$
horizontal asymptote $y = 0$

26.

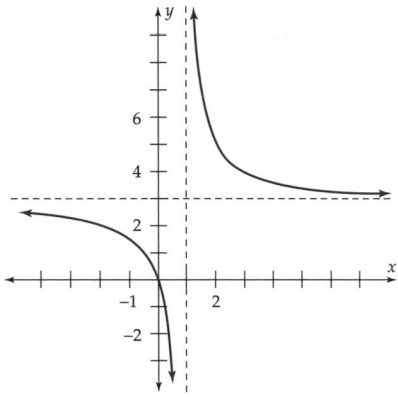

vertical asymptote $x = 2$

horizontal asymptote $y = 0$

27.

vertical asymptote $x = 1$

horizontal asymptote $y = 3$

28.

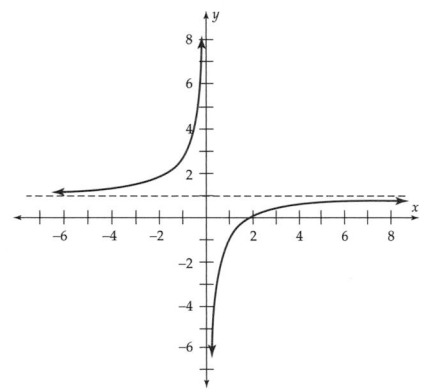

vertical asymptote $x = 0$

horizontal asymptote $y = 1$

29.

vertical asymptote $x = 3$

horizontal asymptote $y = -1$

30.

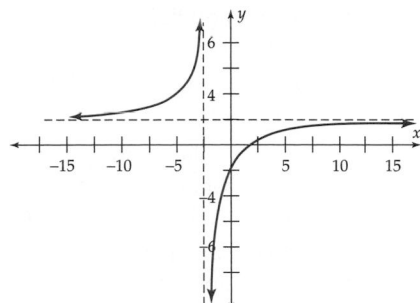

vertical asymptote $x = -3$

horizontal asymptote $y = 3$

31.

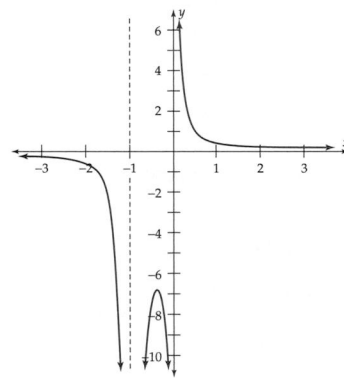

vertical asymptotes $x = -1$, $x = 0$

horizontal asymptote $y = 0$

32.

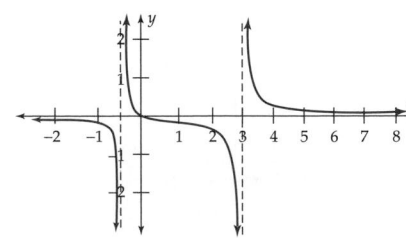

vertical asymptotes $x = 3$, $x = -\dfrac{1}{2}$

horizontal asymptote $y = 0$

33.

vertical asymptotes $x = -2$, $x = 1$

horizontal asymptote $y = 0$

34.

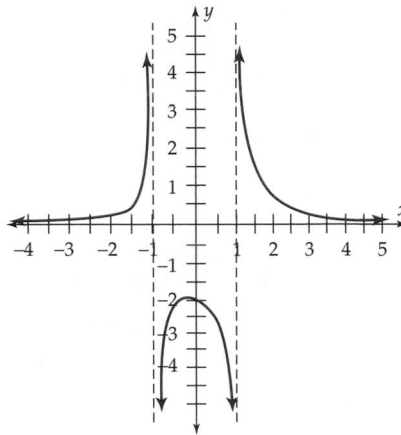

vertical asymptotes $x = \pm 1$

horizontal asmptote $y = 0$

35.

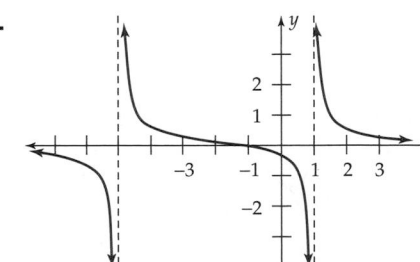

vertical asymptotes $x = -5$, $x = 1$

horizontal asymptote $y = 0$

36.

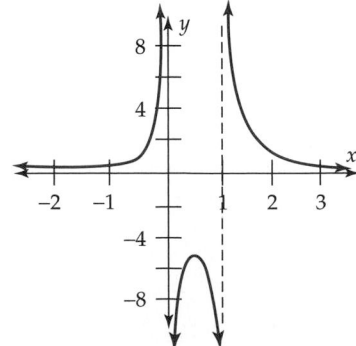

vertical asymptotes $x = 0$, $x = 1$

horizontal asymptote $y = 0$

37.

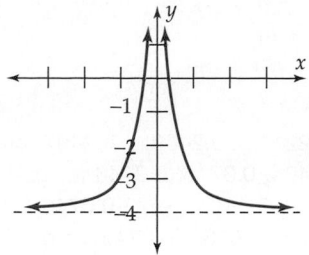

vertical asymptotes $x = 0$

horizontal asymptote $y = -4$

38.

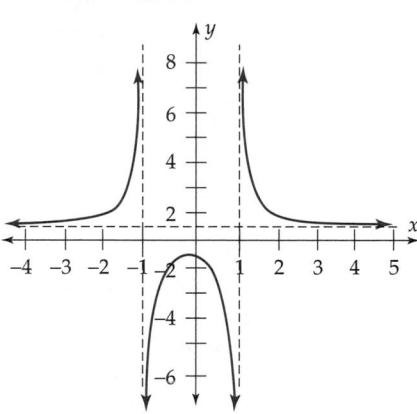

vertical asymptotes $x = \pm 1$

horizontal asymptote $y = 1$

39.

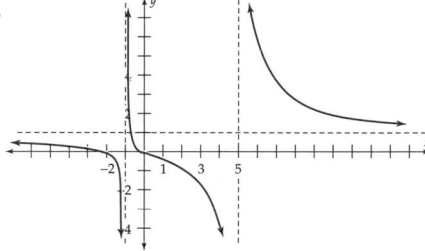

vertical asymptotes $x = -1$, $x = 5$

horizontal asymptote $y = 1$

40.

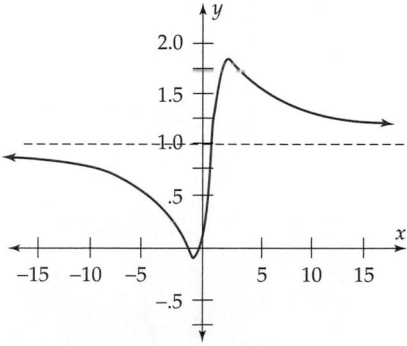

no vertical asymptote

horizontal asymptote $y = 1$

41.

vertical asymptotes $x = -4$, $x = 5$

hole at $x = -3$

horizontal asymptote $y = 0$

42.

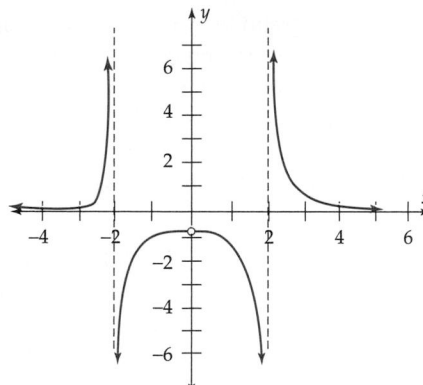

hole $x = 0$

vertical asymptotes $x = \pm 2$

horizontal asymptote $y = 0$

43.

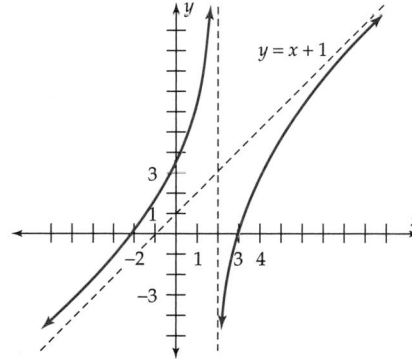

vertical asymptote $x = 2$

oblique asymptote $y = x + 1$

44.

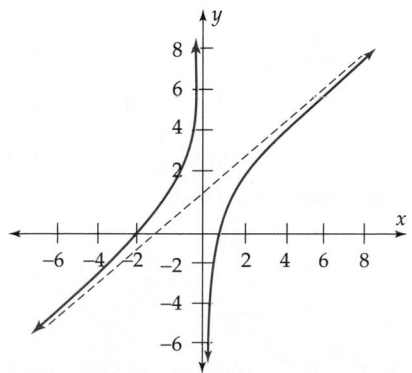

vertical asymptote $x = 0$

oblique asymptote $y = x + 1$

45.

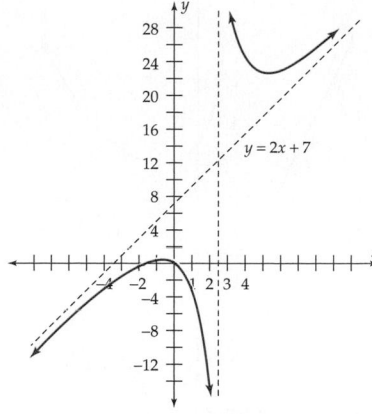

vertical asymptote $x = \dfrac{5}{2}$

oblique asymptote $y = 2x + 7$

46.

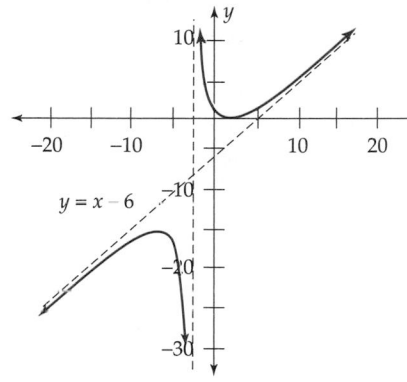

vertical asymptote $x = -2$

oblique asymptote $y = x - 6$

47.

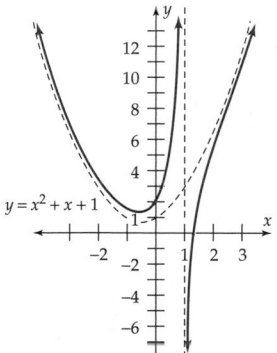

vertical asymptote $x = 1$

parabolic asymptote $y = x^2 + x + 1$

Additional Answers

Additional Answers **1065**

48.

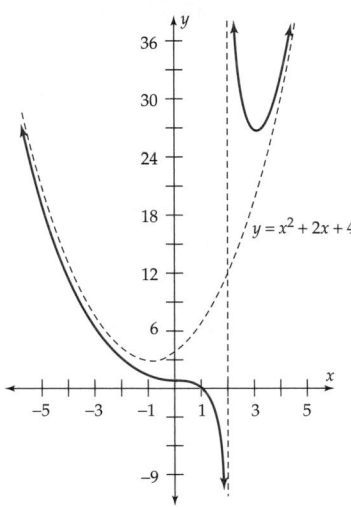

vertical asymptote $x = -1$

parabolic asymptote $y = x^2 - x + 1$

49.

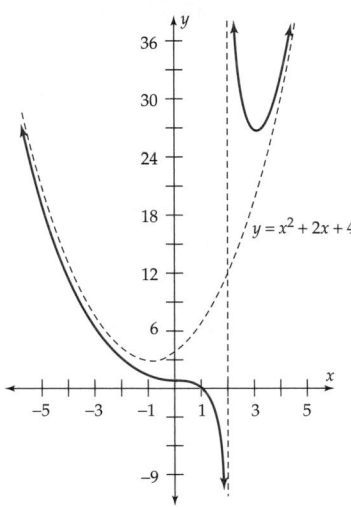

vertical asymptote $x = 2$

parabolic asymptote $y = x^2 + 2x + 4$

50.

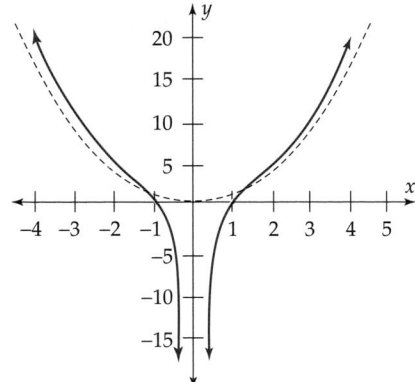

vertical asymptote $x = 0$

parabolic asymptote $y = x^2$

Section 4.4, page 291

67. a.

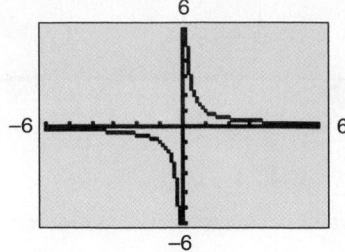

b. Stretch the graph of $f(x)$ away from the x-axis by a factor of 2.

c. The graph of $h(x)$ is the graph of $f(x)$ shifted vertically 4 units upward; the graph of $k(x)$ is the graph of $f(x)$ shifted horizontally 3 units to the right; the graph of $t(x)$ is the graph of $f(x)$ shifted horizontally 2 units to the left.

d. Shift the graph of $f(x)$ horizontally 3 units to the right, stretch vertically by a factor of 2, then shift vertically 4 units upward.

e. $p(x) = \dfrac{4x - 10}{x - 3}$

f. Shift the graph of $f(x)$ horizontally $|s|$ units (to the left if $s > 0$; to the right if $s < 0$); stretch (or shrink) the graph by a factor of $|r|$ (away from the x-axis if $|r| > 1$, toward the x-axis if $0 < |r| < 1$); also if $r < 0$, reflect the graph in the x-axis; then shift vertically $|t|$ units (upward if $t > 0$; downward if $t < 0$).

g. $q(x) = \dfrac{tx + (r + ts)}{x + s}$

68. $-1 \le x \le 1$ and $-1 \le y \le 1$

69. a. $\dfrac{-1}{x(x + h)}$

b. $-\dfrac{1}{4.2} \approx -0.2381$; $-\dfrac{1}{4.02} \approx -0.2488$;

$-\dfrac{1}{4.002} \approx -0.2499$; instantaneous

rate of change $-\dfrac{1}{4} = -0.25$

c. $-\dfrac{1}{9.3} \approx -0.1075$; $-\dfrac{1}{9.03} \approx -0.1107$;

$-\dfrac{1}{9.003} \approx -0.1111$; instantaneous

rate of change $-\dfrac{1}{9} = -0.1111\cdots$

d. They are the same.

70. a. $\dfrac{-2x + h}{x^2(x + h)^2}$ for f;

$\dfrac{6x^2 + 6xh + 2h^2}{x^3(x + h)^3}$ for g

b. $-0.2211, -0.2469, -0.2497$ for f; $-.3404, 0.3713, 0.3746$ for g;

c. $-0.0682, -0.0735, -0.0740$ for f; $0.0694, 0.0736, 0.0740$ for g

d. The estimated rates of change for $f(x)$ and $x = 2$ and $x = 3$ are the same as the values of $h(x) = \dfrac{-2}{x^3}$ at $x = 2$ and $x = 3$; the estimated rates of change for $g(x)$ at $x = 2$ and $x = 3$ are the same as the values of $h(x) = \dfrac{6}{x^4}$ at $x = 2$ and $x = 3$

71. a. $y = \dfrac{x - 1}{x - 2}$

b. $y = \dfrac{x - 1}{-x - 2}$

c. Graph (a) has a vertical asymptote at $x = 2$ and graph (b) has a vertical asymptote at $x = -2$.

Chapter 5

Section 5.2, page 343

14.

15.

16.

17.

18.

19.

Section 5.4, page 362

49.

50.

51.

52.

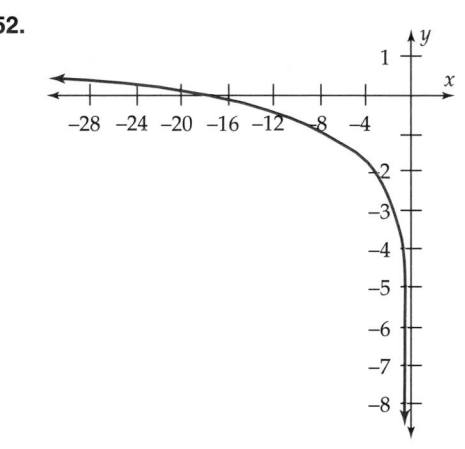

Chapter 5 can do calculus, page 411

1.

2.

3.

4.

5.

6.

7.

8.

9.

10.

11.

12.

Chapter 6

Section 6.4, page 452

24.

25.

26.

27.

28.

29.

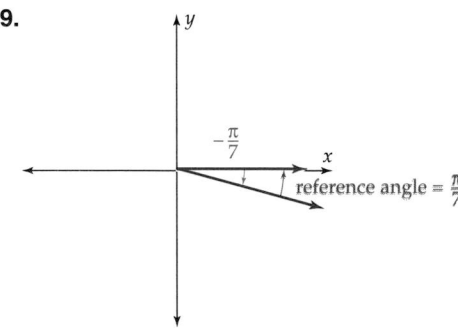

30. $-\dfrac{1}{2}$; $-\dfrac{\sqrt{3}}{2}$; $\dfrac{1}{\sqrt{3}}$

31. $\dfrac{\sqrt{3}}{2}$; $\dfrac{1}{2}$; $\sqrt{3}$

32. $-\dfrac{\sqrt{3}}{2}$; $\dfrac{1}{2}$; $-\sqrt{3}$

33. $\dfrac{\sqrt{2}}{2}$; $-\dfrac{\sqrt{2}}{2}$; -1

34. $-\dfrac{\sqrt{2}}{2}$; $-\dfrac{\sqrt{2}}{2}$; 1

35. 1; 0; undefined

36. 0; -1; 0

37. $\dfrac{1}{2}$; $\dfrac{\sqrt{3}}{2}$; $\dfrac{\sqrt{3}}{3}$

38. $-\dfrac{1}{2}$; $\dfrac{\sqrt{3}}{2}$; $-\dfrac{1}{\sqrt{3}}$

39. $-\dfrac{\sqrt{3}}{2}$; $\dfrac{1}{2}$; $-\sqrt{3}$

40. $\dfrac{\sqrt{3}}{2}$; $-\dfrac{1}{2}$; $-\sqrt{3}$

41. $\dfrac{\sqrt{2}}{2}$; $\dfrac{\sqrt{2}}{2}$; 1

42. $-\dfrac{\sqrt{2}}{2}$; $\dfrac{\sqrt{2}}{2}$; -1

43. $\dfrac{1}{2}$; $-\dfrac{\sqrt{3}}{2}$; $-\dfrac{\sqrt{3}}{3}$

44. -1; 0; undefined

45. 1; 0; undefined

46. 0; -1; 0

47. 0; 1; 0

48. $-\dfrac{\sqrt{3}}{2}$

49. $\dfrac{-\sqrt{2}}{2}$

50. $\dfrac{1}{2}$

51. $\dfrac{\sqrt{2}}{4}(1-\sqrt{3})$

52. $\dfrac{\sqrt{6}-\sqrt{2}}{4}$

53. $\dfrac{-\sqrt{3}}{2}$

54. $-\dfrac{2}{\sqrt{5}}$; $-\dfrac{1}{\sqrt{5}}$; 2

55. $-\dfrac{5}{\sqrt{34}}$; $\dfrac{3}{\sqrt{34}}$; $-\dfrac{5}{3}$

56. $-\dfrac{7}{\sqrt{53}}$; $-\dfrac{2}{\sqrt{53}}$; $\dfrac{7}{2}$

Chapter 6 can do calculus, page 471

1. $\dfrac{\pi}{12}$

X	Y1
0	0
.2618	.25
.5236	.43301
.7854	.5
1.0472	.43301
1.309	.25
1.5708	0

Y1=sin(X)cos(X)

$\dfrac{\pi}{144}$

X	Y1
.71993	.49572
.74175	.4981
.76356	.49952
.78538	.5
.8072	.49952
.82901	.4981
.85083	.49572

Y1=sin(X)cos(X)

2. $\dfrac{\pi}{12}$

```
    X       Y1
 0        2
 .2618    2.1907
 .5236    2.2321
 .7854    2.1213
 1.0472   1.866
 1.309    1.4836
 1.5708   1
Y1■sin(X)+2cos(…
```

$\dfrac{\pi}{144}$

```
    X       Y1
 .3927    2.2304
 .41452   2.2334
 .43633   2.2352
 .45815   2.236
 .47997   2.2358
 .50178   2.2344
 .5236    2.2321
Y1■sin(X)+2cos(…
```

3. $\dfrac{\pi}{12}$

```
    X       Y1
 0        1
 .2618    1.7424
 .5236    2.366
 .7854    2.8284
 1.0472   3.0981
 1.309    3.1566
 1.5708   3
Y1■3sin(X)+sin(…
```

$\dfrac{\pi}{144}$

```
    X       Y1
 1.1781   3.1543
 1.1999   3.1585
 1.2217   3.1611
 1.2435   3.1622
 1.2653   3.1619
 1.2872   3.16
 1.309    3.1566
Y1■3sin(X)+sin(…
```

4. $\dfrac{\pi}{12}$

```
    X       Y1
 0        1
 .2618    1.1375
 .5236    1.0654
 .7854    .82843
 1.0472   .4641
 1.309    .00897
 1.5708   -.5
Y1■2cos(X)-1/(1…
```

$\dfrac{\pi}{144}$

```
    X       Y1
 .21817   1.1305
 .23998   1.1347
 .2618    1.1375
 .28362   1.1387
 .30543   1.1386
 .32725   1.1371
 .34907   1.1342
Y1■2cos(X)-1/(1…
```

Chapter 7

Section 7.4, page 509

47.

48.

49.

50.

51.

52.

58.

59.

60.

61.

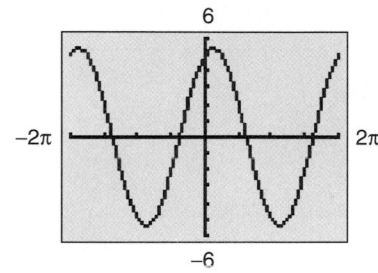

Chapter 8

Section 8.1, page 528

1.

2.

3.

4.

5.

6.

7.

8.

9.

10.

11.

12.

13.

14.

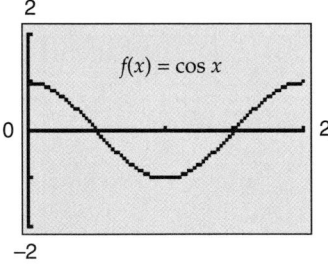

Chapter 9

Section 9.1, page 581

29. $\sin^2 x(\cot x + 1)^2$
$= [\sin x(\cot x + 1)]^2$
$= (\cos x + \sin x)^2$
$= [\cos x(1 + \tan x)]^2$
$= \cos^2 x(\tan x + 1)^2$

30. $\cos^2 x(\sec x + 1)^2$
$= \cos^2 x(\sec^2 x + 2\sec x + 1)$
$= \cos^2 x\left(\dfrac{1}{\cos^2 x} + \dfrac{2}{\cos x} + 1\right)$
$= 1 + 2\cos x + \cos^2 x$
$= (1 + \cos x)^2$

31. $\sin^2 x - \tan^2 x = \sin^2 x - \dfrac{\sin^2 x}{\cos^2 x}$
$= \sin^2 x\left(1 - \dfrac{1}{\cos^2 x}\right)$
$= \sin^2 x(1 - \sec^2 x)$
$= \sin^2 x(-\tan^2 x)$
$= -\sin^2 x \tan^2 x$

32. not an identity

33. $(\cos^2 x - 1)(\tan^2 x + 1)$
$= (-\sin^2 x)(\sec^2 x)$
$= (-\sin^2 x)\left(\dfrac{1}{\cos^2 x}\right) = -\tan^2 x$

34. $(1 - \cos^2 x)\csc x$
$= (1 - \cos^2 x)\left(\dfrac{1}{\sin x}\right)$
$= \sin^2 x\left(\dfrac{1}{\sin x}\right) = \sin x$

35. $\dfrac{\sec x}{\csc x} = \dfrac{\dfrac{1}{\cos x}}{\dfrac{1}{\sin x}} = \dfrac{\sin x}{\cos x} = \tan x$

36. $\dfrac{\cos(-x)}{\sin(-x)} = \dfrac{\cos x}{-\sin x} = -\cot x$

37. $\cos^4 x - \sin^4 x$
$= (\cos^2 x - \sin^2 x)(\cos^2 x + \sin^2 x)$
$= \cos^2 x - \sin^2 x$

38. $\cot^2 x - \cos^2 x = \dfrac{\cos^2 x}{\sin^2 x} - \cos^2 x$
$= \dfrac{\cos^2 x - \cos^2 x \sin^2 x}{\sin^2 x}$
$= \dfrac{(\cos^2 x)(1 - \sin^2 x)}{\sin^2 x}$
$= \cos^2 x\left(\dfrac{\cos^2 x}{\sin^2 x}\right) = \cos^2 x \cot^2 x$

39. not an identity

40. not an identity

41. $\dfrac{\sec x}{\csc x} + \dfrac{\sin x}{\cos x}$

$= \dfrac{\frac{1}{\cos x}}{\frac{1}{\sin x}} + \tan x = \dfrac{\sin x}{\cos x} + \tan x$

$= \tan x + \tan x = 2 \tan x$

42. $\dfrac{1 + \cos x}{\sin x} + \dfrac{\sin x}{1 + \cos x}$

$= \dfrac{(1 + \cos x)^2 + \sin^2 x}{\sin x(1 + \cos x)}$

$= \dfrac{1 + 2\cos x + \cos^2 x + \sin^2 x}{\sin x(1 + \cos x)}$

$= \dfrac{2 + 2\cos x}{\sin x(1 + \cos x)}$

$= \dfrac{2(1 + \cos x)}{\sin x(1 + \cos x)}$

$= \dfrac{2}{\sin x} = 2\csc x$

43. $\dfrac{\sec x + \csc x}{1 + \tan x}$

$= \dfrac{\frac{1}{\cos x} + \frac{1}{\sin x}}{1 + \frac{\sin x}{\cos x}} \cdot \dfrac{\sin x \cos x}{\sin x \cos x}$

$= \dfrac{\sin x + \cos x}{\sin x \cos x + \sin^2 x}$

$= \dfrac{\sin x + \cos x}{\sin x(\cos x + \sin x)}$

$= \dfrac{1}{\sin x} = \csc x$

44. $\dfrac{\cot x - 1}{1 - \tan x} = \dfrac{\frac{\cos x}{\sin x} - 1}{1 - \frac{\sin x}{\cos x}}$

$= \dfrac{\frac{\cos x - \sin x}{\sin x}}{\frac{\cos x - \sin x}{\cos x}}$

$= \dfrac{\cos x - \sin x}{\sin x} \cdot \dfrac{\cos x}{\cos x - \sin x}$

$= \dfrac{\cos x}{\sin x} = \dfrac{\frac{1}{\sin x}}{\frac{1}{\cos x}} = \dfrac{\csc x}{\sec x}$

45. $\dfrac{1}{\csc x - \sin x} = \dfrac{1}{\frac{1}{\sin x} - \sin x} \cdot \dfrac{\sin x}{\sin x}$

$= \dfrac{\sin x}{1 - \sin^2 x} = \dfrac{\sin x}{\cos^2 x}$

$= \left(\dfrac{1}{\cos x}\right)\left(\dfrac{\sin x}{\cos x}\right)$

$= \sec x \tan x$

46. $\dfrac{1 + \csc x}{\csc x} = \dfrac{1}{\csc x} + \dfrac{\csc x}{\csc x}$

$= \sin x + 1$

$= \sin x + 1 \cdot \dfrac{1 - \sin x}{1 - \sin x}$

$= \dfrac{1 - \sin^2 x}{1 - \sin x} = \dfrac{\cos^2 x}{1 - \sin x}$

47. not an identity

48. $\dfrac{\cot x}{\csc x - 1} = \dfrac{\cot x}{\csc x - 1} \cdot \dfrac{\csc x + 1}{\csc x + 1}$

$= \dfrac{\cot x(\csc x + 1)}{\csc^2 x - 1}$

$= \dfrac{\cot x(\csc x + 1)}{\cot^2 x}$

$= \dfrac{\csc x + 1}{\cot x}$

49. Conjecture: $\cos x$. Proof:

$1 - \dfrac{\sin^2 x}{1 + \cos x}$

$= \dfrac{1 + \cos x - \sin^2 x}{1 + \cos x}$

$= \dfrac{\cos x + (1 - \sin^2 x)}{1 + \cos x}$

$= \dfrac{\cos x + \cos^2 x}{1 + \cos x}$

$= \dfrac{\cos x(1 + \cos x)}{1 + \cos x} = \cos x$

50. Conjecture: $\sin x$. Proof:

$\dfrac{1 + \cos x - \cos^2 x}{\sin x} - \cot x$

$= \dfrac{(1 - \cos^2 x) + \cos x - \cos x}{\sin x}$

$= \dfrac{\sin^2 x}{\sin x} = \sin x$

51. Conjecture: $\tan x$. Proof:

$(\sin x + \cos x)(\sec x + \csc x) - \cot x - 2$

$= \sin x \sec x + \sin x \csc x + \cos x \sec x + \cos x \csc x - \cot x - 2$

$= \sin x \cdot \dfrac{1}{\cos x} + \sin x \cdot \dfrac{1}{\sin x} + \cos x \cdot \dfrac{1}{\cos x} + \cos x \cdot \dfrac{1}{\sin x} - \cot x - 2$

$= \dfrac{\sin x}{\cos x} + 1 + 1 + \dfrac{\cos x}{\sin x} - \cot x - 2$

$= \tan x + \cot x - \cot x = \tan x$

52. Conjecture: $2\cos x$. Proof:

$\cos^3 x(1 - \tan^4 x + \sec^4 x)$

$= \cos^3 x - \dfrac{\sin^4 x}{\cos x} + \dfrac{1}{\cos x}$

$= \dfrac{\cos^4 x - \sin^4 x + 1}{\cos x}$

$= \dfrac{(\cos^2 x - \sin^2 x)(\cos^2 x + \sin^2 x) + 1}{\cos x}$

$= \dfrac{\cos^2 x - \sin^2 x + 1}{\cos x}$

$= \dfrac{\cos^2 x - \sin^2 x + \cos^2 x + \sin^2 x}{\cos x}$

$= \dfrac{2\cos^2 x}{\cos x} = 2\cos x$

53. $\dfrac{1 - \sin x}{\sec x} = \dfrac{1 - \sin x}{\sec x} \cdot \dfrac{1 + \sin x}{1 + \sin x}$

$= \dfrac{1 - \sin^2 x}{\sec x(1 + \sin x)} \quad \dfrac{\cos^2 x}{\frac{1}{\cos x}(1 + \sin x)}$

$= \dfrac{\cos^3 x}{1 + \sin x}$

54. $\dfrac{\sin x}{1 - \cot x} + \dfrac{\cos x}{1 - \tan x}$

$= \dfrac{\sin^2 x}{\sin x - \cos x} + \dfrac{\cos^2 x}{\cos x - \sin x}$

$= \dfrac{\sin^2 x - \cos^2 x}{\sin x - \cos x}$

$= \dfrac{(\sin x - \cos x)(\sin x + \cos x)}{\sin x - \cos x}$

$= \sin x + \cos x$

55. $\dfrac{\cos x}{1 - \sin x} \cdot \dfrac{1 + \sin x}{1 + \sin x}$

$= \dfrac{\cos x(1 + \sin x)}{1 - \sin^2 x}$

$= \dfrac{\cos x(1 + \sin x)}{\cos^2 x}$

$= \dfrac{1 + \sin x}{\cos x} = \dfrac{1}{\cos x} + \dfrac{\sin x}{\cos x}$

$= \sec x + \tan x$

56. $\dfrac{1 + \sec x}{\tan x + \sin x} = \dfrac{\cos x + 1}{\sin x + \sin x \cos x}$

$= \dfrac{1 + \cos x}{\sin x(1 + \cos x)} = \dfrac{1}{\sin x} = \csc x$

57. $\dfrac{\cos x \cot x}{\cot x - \cos x} \cdot \dfrac{\sin x}{\sin x}$

$= \dfrac{\cos x \cos x}{\cos x - \cos x \sin x}$

$= \dfrac{\cos^2 x}{\cos x(1 - \sin x)}$

$= \dfrac{\cos x}{1 - \sin x} \cdot \dfrac{1 + \sin x}{1 + \sin x}$

$= \dfrac{\cos x(1 + \sin x)}{1 - \sin^2 x}$

$= \dfrac{\cos x + \sin x \cos x}{\cos^2 x} \cdot \dfrac{\frac{1}{\sin x}}{\frac{1}{\sin x}}$

$= \dfrac{\frac{\cos x}{\sin x} + \cos x}{\cos x\left(\frac{\cos x}{\sin x}\right)} = \dfrac{\cot x + \cos x}{\cos x \cot x}$

58. $\dfrac{\cos^3 x - \sin^3 x}{\cos x - \sin x}$

$= \dfrac{(\cos x - \sin x)(\cos^2 x + \sin x \cos x + \sin^2 x)}{\cos x - \sin x}$

$= \cos^2 x + \sin x \cos x + \sin^2 x$

$= 1 + \sin x \cos x$

59. $\log_{10}(\cot x) = \log_{10}(\tan x)^{-1}$

$= -\log_{10}(\tan x)$

60. $\log_{10}(\sec x) = \log_{10}(\cos x)^{-1}$

$= -\log_{10}\cos x$

61. $\csc x + \cot x$

$= (\csc x + \cot x) \cdot \dfrac{(\csc x - \cot x)}{(\csc x - \cot x)}$

$= \dfrac{\csc^2 x - \cot^2 x}{\csc x - \cot x} = \dfrac{1}{\csc x - \cot x};$

so, $\log_{10}(\csc x + \cot x)$

$= \log_{10}\left(\dfrac{1}{\csc x - \cot x}\right)$

$= \log_{10}(\csc x - \cot x)^{-1}$

$= -\log_{10}(\csc x - \cot x)$

62. $\log_{10}(\sec x + \tan x)$

$= \log_{10}\left(\dfrac{1}{\cos x} + \dfrac{\sin x}{\cos x}\right)$

$= \log_{10}\left(\dfrac{1 + \sin x}{\cos x}\right)$

$= \log_{10}\left(\dfrac{\cos x}{1 - \sin x}\right)$

$= \log_{10}\left(\dfrac{1}{\dfrac{1}{\cos x} - \dfrac{\sin x}{\cos x}}\right)$

$= \log_{10}\left(\dfrac{1}{\sec x - \tan x}\right)$

$= -\log_{10}(\sec x - \tan x)$

63. $-\tan x \tan y (\cot x - \cot y)$

$= -\tan y (\tan x \cot x) +$

$\qquad\qquad \tan x(\tan y \cot y)$

$= -\tan y + \tan x = \tan x - \tan y$

64. $\dfrac{\tan x - \tan y}{\cot x - \cot y}$

$= \dfrac{\tan x - \tan y}{\dfrac{1}{\tan x} - \dfrac{1}{\tan y}}$

$= \dfrac{\tan x - \tan y}{\dfrac{\tan y - \tan x}{\tan x \tan y}}$

$= -\tan x \tan y$

65. $\dfrac{\cos x - \sin y}{\cos y - \sin x} \cdot \dfrac{\cos x + \sin y}{\cos x + \sin y}$

$= \dfrac{\cos^2 x - \sin^2 y}{(\cos y - \sin x)(\cos x + \sin y)}$

$= \dfrac{(1 - \sin^2 x) - (1 - \cos^2 y)}{(\cos y - \sin x)(\cos x + \sin y)}$

$= \dfrac{\cos^2 y - \sin^2 x}{(\cos y - \sin x)(\cos x + \sin y)}$

$= \dfrac{(\cos y - \sin x)(\cos y + \sin x)}{(\cos y - \sin x)(\cos x + \sin y)}$

$= \dfrac{\cos y + \sin x}{\cos x + \sin y}$

66. $\dfrac{\tan x + \tan y}{\cot x + \cot y} = \dfrac{\tan x + \tan y}{\dfrac{1}{\tan x} + \dfrac{1}{\tan y}}$

$= \dfrac{\tan x + \tan y}{\dfrac{\tan y + \tan x}{\tan x \tan y}}$

$= \tan x \tan y$

Also, $\dfrac{\tan x \tan y - 1}{1 - \cot x \cot y}$

$= \dfrac{\tan x \tan y - 1}{1 - \dfrac{1}{\tan x \tan y}}$

$= \dfrac{\tan x \tan y(\tan x \tan y - 1)}{\tan x \tan y - 1}$

$= \tan x \tan y$

Section 9.2, page 588

59. not an identity; The graph shows the function with $y = \frac{\pi}{2}$.

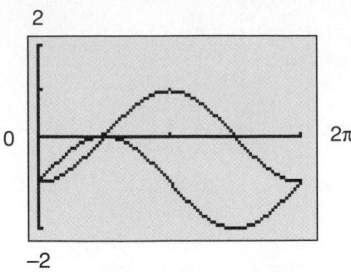

60. not an identity; The graph shows the function with $y = \frac{\pi}{4}$.

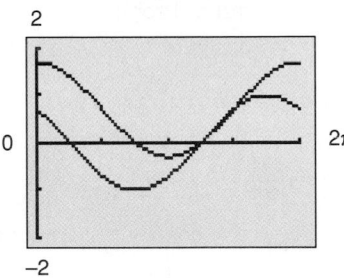

61. $\dfrac{\sin(x + y)}{\sin(x - y)}$

$= \dfrac{\sin x \cos y + \cos x \sin y}{\sin x \cos y - \cos x \sin y} \cdot \dfrac{\dfrac{1}{\cos x \cos y}}{\dfrac{1}{\cos x \cos y}}$

$= \dfrac{\dfrac{\sin x}{\cos x} + \dfrac{\sin y}{\cos y}}{\dfrac{\sin x}{\cos x} - \dfrac{\sin y}{\cos y}}$

$= \dfrac{\tan x + \tan y}{\tan x - \tan y}$

62. $\dfrac{\sin(x + y)}{\sin(x - y)}$

$= \dfrac{\sin x \cos y + \sin y \cos x}{\sin x \cos y - \sin y \cos x}$

$= \dfrac{\dfrac{\sin x \cos y + \sin y \cos x}{\sin x \sin y}}{\dfrac{\sin x \cos y - \sin y \cos x}{\sin x \sin y}}$

$= \dfrac{\cot y + \cot x}{\cot y - \cot x}$

63. not an identity; The graph shows the function with $y = \frac{\pi}{4}$.

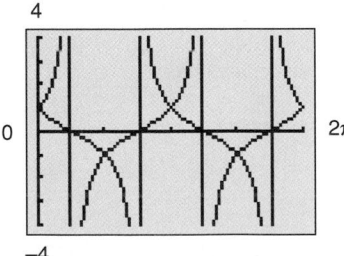

---

64. $\dfrac{\cos(x - y)}{\cos(x + y)}$

$= \dfrac{\cos x \cos y + \sin x \sin y}{\cos x \cos y - \sin x \sin y}$

$= \dfrac{\dfrac{\cos x \cos y + \sin x \sin y}{\cos x \sin y}}{\dfrac{\cos x \cos y - \sin x \sin y}{\cos x \sin y}}$

$= \dfrac{\cot y + \tan x}{\cot y - \tan x}$

65. not an identity; The graph shows the function with $y = \frac{\pi}{4}$.

66. not an identity; The graph shows the function with $y = \frac{\pi}{4}$.

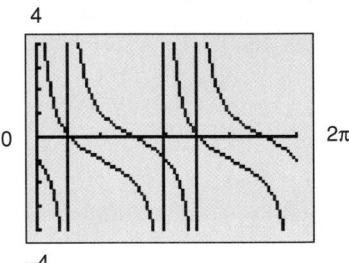

Section 9.3, page 601

65. $\dfrac{\sin x - \sin 3x}{\cos x + \cos 3x}$

$= \dfrac{2 \cos 2x \sin(-x)}{2 \cos 2x \cos(-x)} = \dfrac{-\sin x}{\cos x}$

$= -\tan x$

66. $\dfrac{\sin x - \sin 3x}{\cos x - \cos 3x}$

$= \dfrac{2 \cos\left(\dfrac{x + 3x}{2}\right)\sin\left(\dfrac{x - 3x}{2}\right)}{-2 \sin\left(\dfrac{x + 3x}{2}\right)\sin\left(\dfrac{x - 3x}{2}\right)}$

$= \dfrac{2 \cos 2x \sin(-x)}{-2 \sin 2x \sin(-x)}$

$= \cot 2x$

67. $\dfrac{\sin 4x + \sin 6x}{\cos 4x - \cos 6x}$

$= \dfrac{2 \sin 5x \cos(-x)}{-2 \sin 5x \sin(-x)} = \dfrac{\cos x}{\sin x}$

$= \cot x$

1072   Additional Answers

68. $\dfrac{\cos 8x + \cos 4x}{\cos 8x - \cos 4x}$

$= \dfrac{2\cos\left(\dfrac{8x + 4x}{2}\right)\cos\left(\dfrac{8x - 4x}{2}\right)}{-2\sin\left(\dfrac{8x + 4x}{2}\right)\sin\left(\dfrac{8x - 4x}{2}\right)}$

$= \dfrac{2\cos 6x \cos 2x}{-2\sin 6x \sin 2x} = -\cot 6x \cot 2x$

69. $\dfrac{\sin x + \sin y}{\cos x - \cos y}$

$= \dfrac{2\sin\left(\dfrac{x + y}{2}\right)\cos\left(\dfrac{x - y}{2}\right)}{-2\sin\left(\dfrac{x + y}{2}\right)\sin\left(\dfrac{x - y}{2}\right)}$

$= \dfrac{-\cos\left(\dfrac{x - y}{2}\right)}{\sin\left(\dfrac{x - y}{2}\right)} = -\cot\left(\dfrac{x - y}{2}\right)$

70. $\dfrac{\sin x - \sin y}{\cos x + \cos y}$

$= \dfrac{2\cos\left(\dfrac{x + y}{2}\right)\sin\left(\dfrac{x - y}{2}\right)}{2\cos\left(\dfrac{x + y}{2}\right)\cos\left(\dfrac{x - y}{2}\right)}$

$= \tan\left(\dfrac{x - y}{2}\right)$

71. a. $\dfrac{1 - \cos x}{\sin x}$

$= \dfrac{(1 - \cos x)(1 + \cos x)}{\sin x(1 + \cos x)}$

$= \dfrac{1 - \cos^2 x}{\sin x(1 + \cos x)}$

$= \dfrac{\sin^2 x}{\sin x(1 + \cos x)} = \dfrac{\sin x}{1 + \cos x}$

b. By the half-angle identity proved in the text and part (a),
$\tan \dfrac{x}{2} = \dfrac{1 - \cos x}{\sin x} = \dfrac{\sin x}{1 + \cos x}$

72. $x = 2\cos^2 t - 1 \qquad y^2 = \sin^2 t$

$y^2 + \dfrac{x + 1}{2} = \sin^2 t + \cos^2 t$

$y^2 + \dfrac{x + 1}{2} = 1$

$y^2 = -\dfrac{x}{2} + \dfrac{1}{2} = \dfrac{1 - x}{2}$

Chapter 10

Section 10.3, page 642

1, 3, 5, 7

2, 4, 6, 8

17.

18.

19.

20.

21.

22.

23.

24.

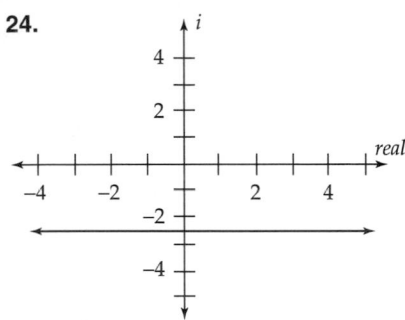

Section 10.4, page 652

23. $\dfrac{\sqrt{3}}{2} + \dfrac{1}{2}i$ or $\dfrac{\sqrt{3}}{2} - \dfrac{1}{2}i$ or

$-\dfrac{\sqrt{3}}{2} + \dfrac{1}{2}i$ or $-\dfrac{\sqrt{3}}{2} - \dfrac{1}{2}i$ or i or $-i$

24. $\sqrt{3} + i$, $\sqrt{3} - i$, $-\sqrt{3} + i$, $-\sqrt{3} - i$
or $2i$ or $-2i$

25. $\dfrac{\sqrt{3}}{2} + \dfrac{1}{2}i$ or $-\dfrac{\sqrt{3}}{2} + \dfrac{1}{2}i$ or $-i$

26. $0.9239 + 0.3827i$ or $-0.3827 + 0.9239i$
or $-0.9239 - 0.3827i$ or
$0.3827 - 0.9239i$

27. $3i$ or $\dfrac{3\sqrt{3}}{2} - \dfrac{3}{2}i$ or $-\dfrac{3\sqrt{3}}{2} - \dfrac{3}{2}i$

28. $3i$ or $-3i$ or $\dfrac{3\sqrt{3}}{2} + \dfrac{3}{2}i$ or $\dfrac{3\sqrt{3}}{2} - \dfrac{3}{2}i$ or

$-\dfrac{3\sqrt{3}}{2} + \dfrac{3}{2}i$ or $-\dfrac{3\sqrt{3}}{2} - \dfrac{3}{2}i$

29. $\sqrt[4]{2}\left(\dfrac{\sqrt{3}}{2} + \dfrac{1}{2}i\right)$

or $\sqrt[4]{2}\left(-\dfrac{1}{2} + \dfrac{\sqrt{3}}{2}i\right)$

or $\sqrt[4]{2}\left(-\dfrac{\sqrt{3}}{2} - \dfrac{1}{2}i\right)$

or $\sqrt[4]{2}\left(\dfrac{1}{2} - \dfrac{\sqrt{3}}{2}i\right)$

30. $1 + i\sqrt{3}$ or $-\sqrt{3} + i$ or $-1 - i\sqrt{3}$ or
$\sqrt{3} - i$

31. 1, $0.6235 \pm 0.7818i$,
$-0.2225 \pm 0.9749i$,
$-0.9010 \pm 0.4339i$

32. 1, $0.3090 \pm 0.9511i$, $-0.8090 \pm 0.5878i$

33. ± 1, $\pm i$, $0.7071 \pm 0.7071i$,
$-0.7071 \pm 0.7071i$

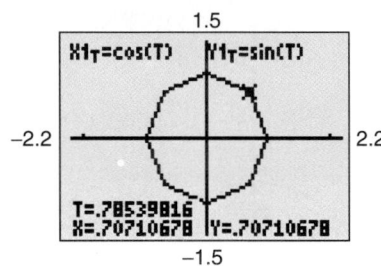

34. ± 1, $\pm i$, $0.8660 \pm 0.5i$, $0.5 \pm 0.8660i$,
$-0.5 \pm 0.8660i$, $-0.8660 \pm 0.5i$

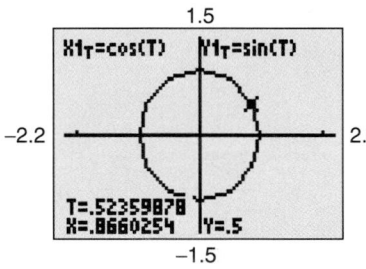

35. 1, $0.7660 \pm 0.6428i$,
$0.1736 \pm 0.9848i$, $-0.5 \pm 0.8660i$,
$-0.9397 \pm 0.3420i$

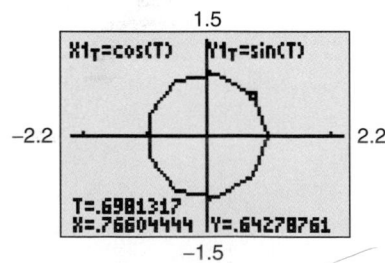

36. -1, $-i$, i

37. $x^6 - 1 = (x - 1) \cdot$
$\qquad (x^5 + x^4 + x^3 + x^2 + x + 1)$,
so the solutions of
$x^5 + x^4 + x^3 + x^2 + x + 1 = 0$
are the sixth roots of unity
other than 1; namely,

$-1, \dfrac{1}{2} + \dfrac{\sqrt{3}}{2}i, \dfrac{1}{2} - \dfrac{\sqrt{3}}{2}i$,

$-\dfrac{1}{2} + \dfrac{\sqrt{3}}{2}i, -\dfrac{1}{2} - \dfrac{\sqrt{3}}{2}i$.

38. The solutions are the nth roots of
unity except for $x = 1$.

39. 12

40. If u is an nth root of unity, then $u^n = 1$.

Then we have $\left(\dfrac{1}{u}\right)^n = \dfrac{1^n}{u^n} = \dfrac{1}{1} = 1$

and $\dfrac{1}{u}$ is also a root of unity.

41. For each i, u_i is an nth root of
unity, so $(u_1)^n = 1$. Hence
$(vu_i)^n = (v^n)(u_i)^n = v^n \cdot 1$
$= r(\cos \theta + i \sin \theta)$ and vu_i
is a solution of the equation.
If $vu_i = vu_j$, then multiplying
both sides by $\dfrac{1}{v}$ shows that
$u_i = u_j$. In other words, if u_i is
not equal to u_j, then $vu_i \neq vu_j$.
Thus, the solution $vu_1, \dots, vu_n$
are all distinct.

42. $\sqrt{r(\cos \theta + i \sin \theta)}$

$= \sqrt{r}\left(\cos\left(\dfrac{\theta + 2k\pi}{2}\right) + i \sin\left(\dfrac{\theta + 2k\pi}{2}\right)\right)$

for $k = 0, 1$. When $k = 0$, we have

$\sqrt{r}\left(\cos\dfrac{\theta}{2} + i \sin\dfrac{\theta}{2}\right)$ and when $k = 1$,

$\sqrt{r}\left(\cos\left(\dfrac{\theta}{2} + \pi\right) + i \sin\left(\dfrac{\theta}{2} + \pi\right)\right)$

$= -\sqrt{r}\left(\cos\dfrac{\theta}{2} + i \sin\dfrac{\theta}{2}\right)$

Chapter 11

Section 11.2, page 708

26. The two branches of the hyperbola are
very "flat" when a is small, With very
small a and a small viewing window,
the hyperbola may look like two
horizontal lines, but it isn't because its
asymptotes $y = \pm\dfrac{a}{4}x$ are not

horizontal (their slopes, $\pm\dfrac{a}{4}$, are close
to, but not equal to, 0 when a is small).

27.

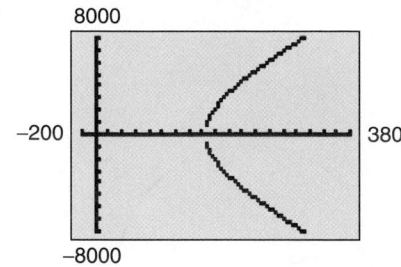

28.

8000

-200 ⎯⎯⎯⎯⎯ 3800

-8000

31. The distance between the vertices is 2*a*. One point on the hyperbola is the vertex at (*a*, 0). This point is the distance *c* − *a* from the closest focus and a distance *c* + *a* from the other focus. The differences of these distances is *c* + *a* − (*c* − *a*) = 2*a*. Therefore, by the definition of a hyperbola, when the difference of the distances from any point on the hyperbola to the two foci is constant, this constant difference is 2*a*; this is the distance between the two vertices.

32. a. $\sqrt{(x + c)^2 + y^2} - \sqrt{(x - c)^2 + y^2}$
$$= 2a$$

$$\left(\sqrt{(x + c)^2 + y^2}\right)^2$$
$$= \left(2a + \sqrt{(x - c)^2 + y^2}\right)^2$$

$x^2 + 2cx + c^2 + y^2$
$$= 4a^2 + 4a\sqrt{(x - c)^2 + y^2} + x^2 - 2cx + c^2 + y^2$$

$4cx - 4a^2 = 4a\sqrt{(x - c)^2 + y^2}$

$cx - a^2 = a\sqrt{(x - c)^2 + y^2}$

b. $(cx - a^2)^2 = \left(a\sqrt{(x - c)^2 + y^2}\right)^2$

$c^2x^2 - 2a^2cx + a^4$
$$= a^2x^2 - 2a^2cx + a^2c^2 + a^2y^2$$

$c^2x^2 - a^2x^2 - a^2y^2 = a^2c^2 - a^4$

$x^2(c^2 - a^2) - a^2y^2 = a^2(c^2 - a^2)$

c. if $b^2 = c^2 - a^2$

$x^2b^2 - a^2y^2 = a^2b^2$

$\dfrac{x^2b^2}{a^2b^2} - \dfrac{a^2y^2}{a^2b^2} = \dfrac{a^2b^2}{a^2b^2}$

$\dfrac{x^2}{a^2} - \dfrac{y^2}{b^2} = 1$

Section 11.4, page 726

29.

30.

31.

32.

33.

34.

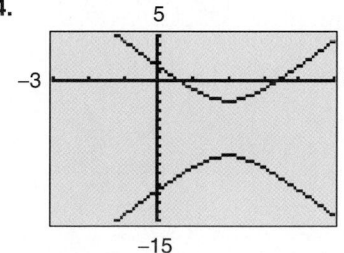

Section 11.5, page 744

22.

23.

24.

25.

26.

30.

34.

27.

31.

35.

28.

32.

36.

29.

33.

37.

38.

42.

46.

39.

43.

47. a.

b.

40.

44.

c.

41.

45.

48. a.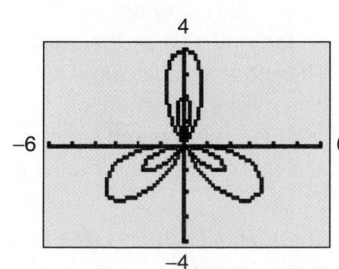

b.

Additional Answers

48. c.

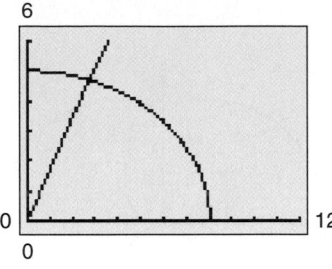

49. $r = a \sin \theta + b \cos \theta \Rightarrow$

$r^2 = ar \sin \theta + br \cos \theta \Rightarrow$

$x^2 + y^2 = ay + bx \Rightarrow$

$x^2 - bx + y^2 - ay = 0 \Rightarrow$

$\left(x^2 - bx + \dfrac{b^2}{4}\right) + \left(y^2 - ay + \dfrac{a^2}{4}\right)$

$= \dfrac{(a^2 + b^2)}{4} \Rightarrow$

$\left(x - \dfrac{b}{2}\right)^2 + \left(y - \dfrac{a}{2}\right)^2 = \dfrac{(a^2 + b^2)}{4}$,

a circle with center $\left(\dfrac{b}{2}, \dfrac{a}{2}\right)$ and radius

$\dfrac{\sqrt{a^2 + b^2}}{2}$.

50. Let $r > 0$. Then $-r < 0$. Let the point P have the rectangular coordinates (x, y) and polar coordinates, (r, θ). Let the point Q have rectangular coordinates $(-x, -y)$. Its polar coordinates are $(-r, \theta)$ so that $-r = -x \cos \theta$, $-r = -y \sin \theta$ and $x = r \cos \theta$, $y = r \sin \theta$.

51. Using the Law of Cosines in the following diagram,
$d^2 = r^2 + s^2 - 2rs \cos(\theta - \beta)$, so $d = \sqrt{r^2 + s^2 - 2rs \cos(\theta - \beta)}$.

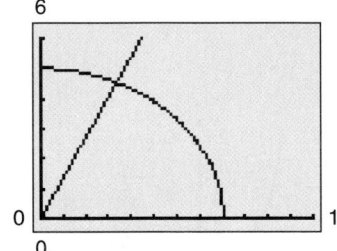

52. a. (r, θ) and $(r, -\theta)$ are mirror images of each other over the x-axis. Therefore, If replacing θ with $-\theta$ gives the same equation, whenever (r, θ) is on the graph so is $(r, -\theta)$ and the graph is symmetric around the x-axis.

b. The points (r, θ) and $(r, \pi - \theta)$ are mirror images of each other over the y-axis.

c. The points (r, θ) and $(-r, \theta)$ are mirror images of each other with respect to the origin. Therefore, if replacing r with $-r$ gives the same equation, whenever (r, θ) is on the graph $(-r, \theta)$ will also be on the graph and the graph will be symmetric with respect to the origin.

Section 11.7, page 765

45. a. Since $\angle TCQ = \dfrac{3\pi}{2}$, $t = \dfrac{3\pi}{2} + \theta$.

Therefore, $\theta = t - \dfrac{3\pi}{2}$.

Then $x = OT + CQ$

$= 3t + 3 \cos \theta$

$= 3t + 3 \cos \left(t - \dfrac{3\pi}{2}\right)$.

and $y = CT - PQ = 3 - 3 \sin \theta$

$= 3 - 3 \sin \left(t - \dfrac{3\pi}{2}\right)$.

b. $\cos\left(t - \dfrac{3\pi}{2}\right) = \cos t \cos \dfrac{3\pi}{2} +$

$\sin t \sin \dfrac{3\pi}{2}$

$= (\cos t)(0) + (\sin t)(-1) = -\sin t.$

Therefore,

$3t + 3 \cos \left(t - \dfrac{3\pi}{2}\right)$

$= 3t - 3 \sin t = 3(t - \sin t).$

$\sin\left(t - \dfrac{3\pi}{2}\right) = \sin t \cos \dfrac{3\pi}{2} -$

$\cos t \sin \dfrac{3\pi}{2} = (\sin t)(0) -$

$(\cos t)(-1) = \cos t.$

Therefore, $3 - 3 \sin \left(t - \dfrac{3\pi}{2}\right)$

$= 3 - 3 \cos t = 3(1 - \cos t).$

46. a. If $\pi < t < \dfrac{3\pi}{2}$, $t = \dfrac{3\pi}{2} - \theta$,

$\theta = \dfrac{3\pi}{2} - t$, $\cos \theta = \dfrac{CQ}{3}$, and

$CQ = 3 \cos \left(\dfrac{3\pi}{2} - t\right)$.

Also, since $\sin \theta = \dfrac{PQ}{3}$,

$PQ = 3 \sin \left(\dfrac{3\pi}{2} - t\right)$

Therefore, $x = OT + CQ$

$= 3t + 3 \cos \left(\dfrac{3\pi}{2} - t\right)$ and

$y = CT + PQ$

$= 3 + 3 \sin \left(\dfrac{3\pi}{2} - t\right)$

b. $x = 3t + 3 \cos \left(\dfrac{3\pi}{2} - t\right)$

$= 3t + 3 \left(\cos \dfrac{3\pi}{2} \cos t + \sin \dfrac{3\pi}{2} \sin t\right)$

$= 3(t - \sin t)$

$y = 3 + 3 \sin \left(\dfrac{3\pi}{2} - t\right)$

$= 3 + 3((-1)\cos t)$

$= 3(1 - \cos t)$

47. a.

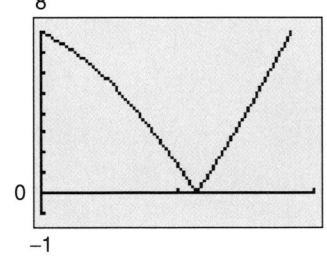

The particles do not collide.

b. $t \approx 1.1$

c.

6

The particles do not collide; they are closest when $t \approx 1.13$.

d.

8

d is smallest when $t \approx 1.1322$.

48. a. Use the parametric equations
$x = 2t^3 - 13t^2 + 23t - 8$, $y = 3$.

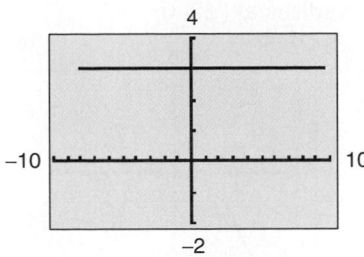

The graph is a horizontal line. Note how the line is traced by a point moving back and forth on the line. If you want the graph to slow down use a smaller value for *t*-step.

b. The point moves from left to right until about $t = 1.25$ when it moves back left. Then at about $t = 3.1$ it moves back to the right. It appears to move fastest as *t* approaches 4.3.

c. As noted in part b, the changes occur at about $t = 1.25$ and $t = 3.1$. The *x* coordinates at these times are about 4.34 and -2.05.

Section 11.7.A, page 769

6. $x = 9 \cos t$, $y = 7 \sin t$ $(0 \le t \le 2\pi)$

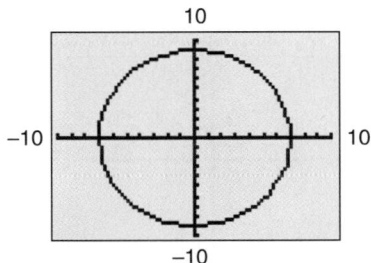

7. $x = \frac{1}{2} \cos t$, $y = \frac{1}{2} \sin t$ $(0 \le t \le 2\pi)$

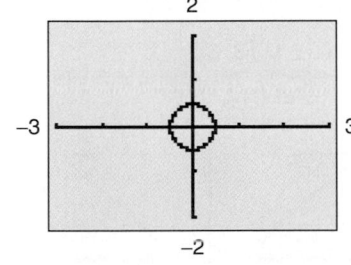

8. $x = \cos t$, $y = \frac{1}{2} \sin t$ $(0 \le t \le 2\pi)$

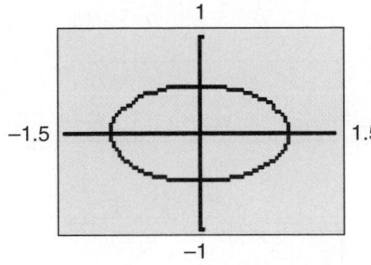

9. $x = \frac{\sqrt{10}}{\cos t}$, $y = 6 \tan t$ $(0 \le t \le 2\pi)$

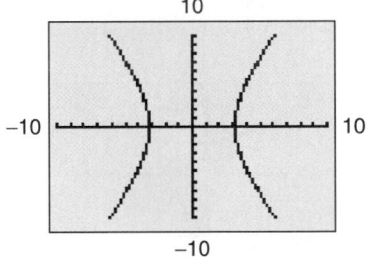

10. $x = 4 \tan t$, $y = 3 \sec t$ $\left(0 < t < \frac{\pi}{2}\right)$

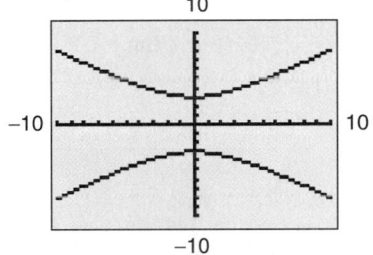

11. $x = \frac{1}{\cos t}$, $y = \frac{1}{2} \tan t$ $(0 \le t \le 2\pi)$

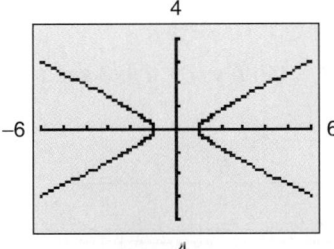

12. $x = \sqrt{2} \sec t$, $y = 2 \tan t$ $\left(0 < t < \frac{\pi}{2}\right)$

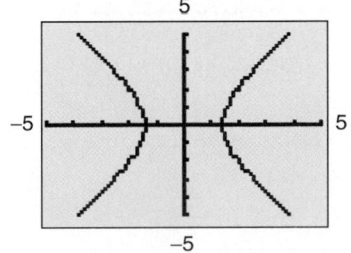

13. $x = \frac{t^2}{4}$, $y = t$ (any real number *t*)

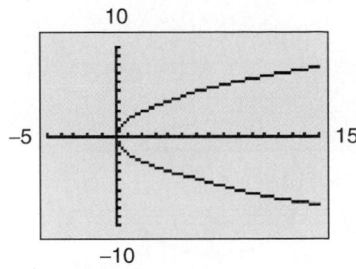

14. $x = t$, $y = \frac{t^2}{4}$ $(-5 \le t \le 5)$

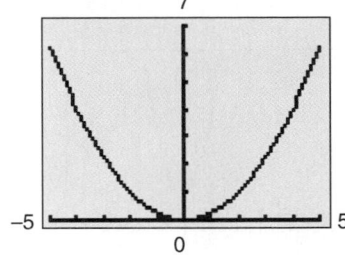

15. $x = 2 \cos t + 1$, $y = 3 \sin t + 5$ $(0 \le t \le 2\pi)$

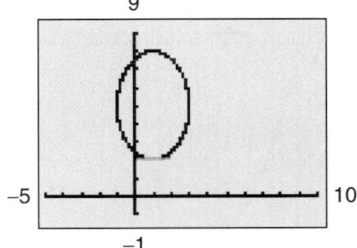

16. $x = 2 + 4 \cos t$, $y = -3 + \sqrt{12} \sin t$ $(0 \le t \le 2\pi)$

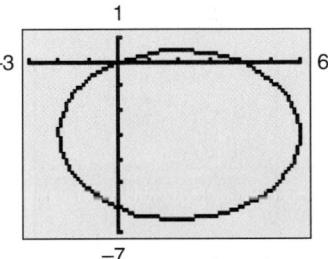

17. $x = 4 \cos t - 1$, $y = \sqrt{8} \sin t + 4$ $(0 \le t \le 2\pi)$

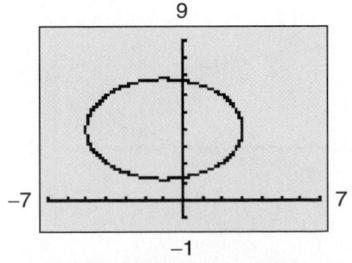

18. $x = -5 + 2 \cos t$, $y = -2 + \sqrt{12} \sin t$
$(0 \le t \le 2\pi)$

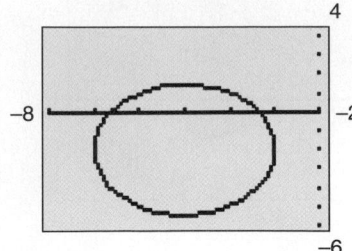

19. $x = t$, $y = 4(t - 1)^2 + 2$
(any real number t)

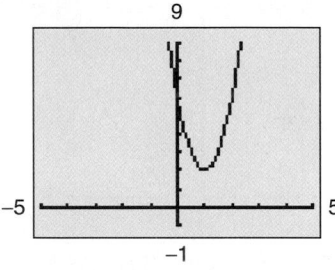

20. $x = t$, $y = 3(t - 2)^2 - 3$ $(-1 \le t \le 5)$

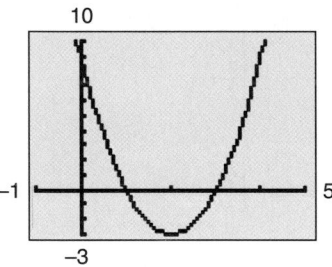

21. $x = 2(t - 2)^2$, $y = t$ (any real number t)

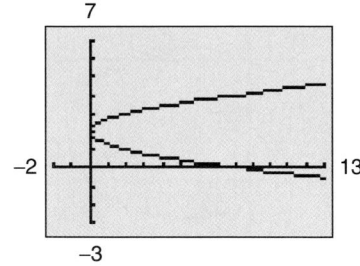

22. $y = t$, $x = -3(t - 1)^2 - 2$
$(-10 \le t \le 0)$

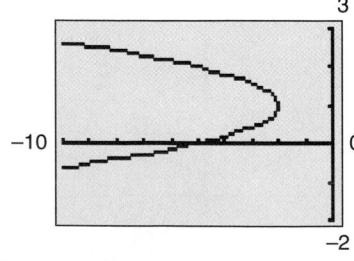

23. $x = 4 \tan t - 1$, $y = \dfrac{5}{\cos t} - 3$
$(0 \le t \le 2\pi)$

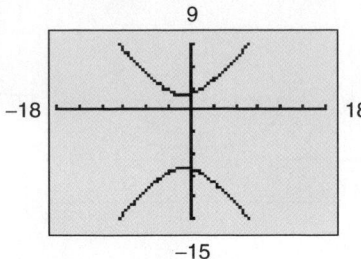

24. $x = 1 + 5 \tan t$, $y = -1 + 3 \sec t$
$\left(0 < t < \dfrac{\pi}{2}\right)$

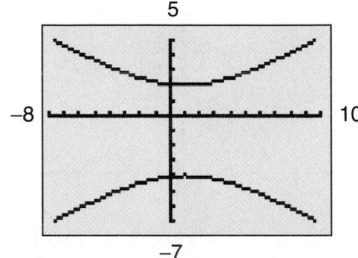

25. $x = \dfrac{1}{\cos t} - 3$, $y = 2 \tan t + 2$
$(0 \le t \le 2\pi)$

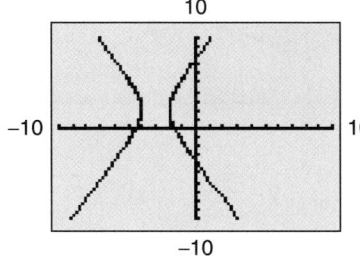

26. $x = 2 + \tan t$, $y = -5 + 3 \sec t$
$\left(0 < t < \dfrac{\pi}{2}\right)$

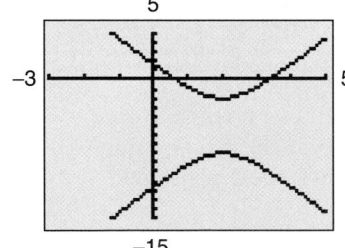

Chapter 11 Review, page 772

7. hyperbola; foci at $(\pm 5, 0)$;
vertices at $(\pm 3, 0)$

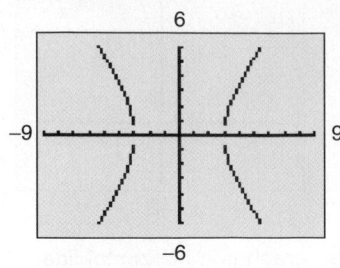

8. hyperbola; foci at $\left(\pm \sqrt{20}, 0\right)$;
vertices at $(\pm 4, 0)$

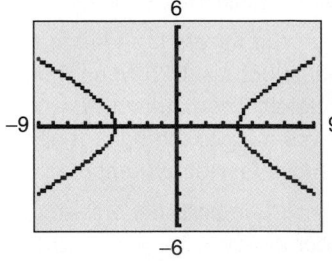

9. $\dfrac{y^2}{4} - \dfrac{x^2}{1} = 1$; hyperbola;
foci at $\left(0, \pm \sqrt{5}\right)$;
vertices at $(0, \pm 2)$

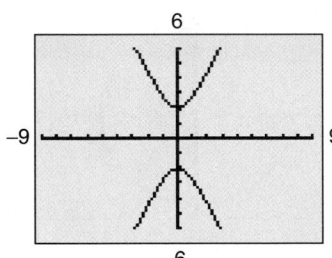

10. $\dfrac{x^2}{9} - \dfrac{y^2}{4} = 1$; hyperbola;
foci at $\left(\pm \sqrt{13}, 0\right)$;
vertices at $(\pm 3, 0)$

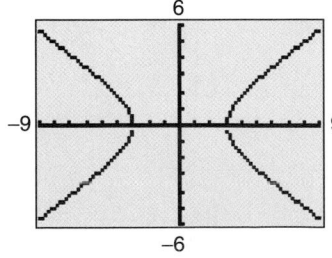

22. hyperbola, center: $(1, -4)$,
vertices: $(1, 1)$ and $(1, -9)$,
foci: $\left(1, -4 \pm \sqrt{29}\right)$,
asymptotes: $y + 4 = \pm\frac{5}{2}(x - 1)$

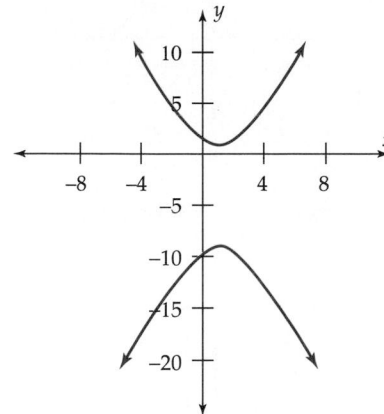

23. hyperbola, center: $(0, 0)$,
vertices: $(6, 0)$ and $(-6, 0)$,
foci: $\left(\pm\sqrt{52}, 0\right)$,
asymptotes: $y = \pm\frac{2}{3}x$

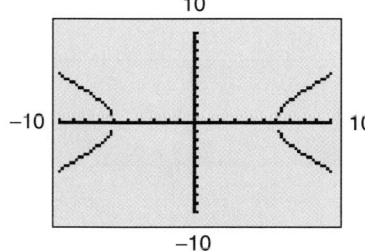

24. ellipse, center: $(5, 0)$,
vertices: $(1, 0)$ and $(9, 0)$,
foci: $\left(5 \pm \sqrt{12}, 0\right)$

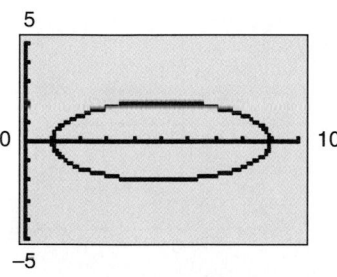

25. parabola, vertex: $(3, 3)$,
focus: $\left(3, \frac{25}{8}\right)$, directrix: $y = \frac{23}{8}$

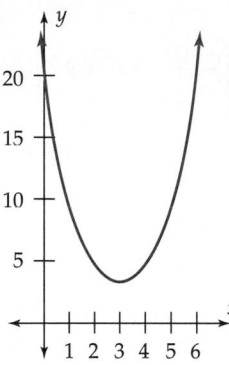

26. parabola, vertex: $(-1, -3)$,
focus: $\left(-1, -\frac{23}{8}\right)$,
directrix: $y = -\frac{25}{8}$

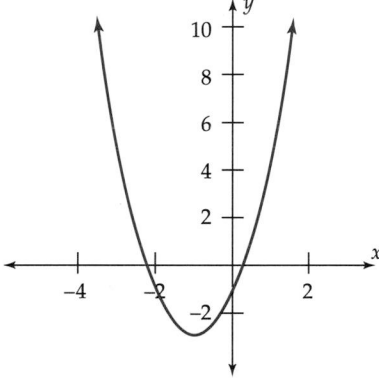

27. parabola, vertex: $(1, -1)$,
focus: $\left(\frac{5}{4}, -1\right)$, directrix: $x = \frac{3}{4}$

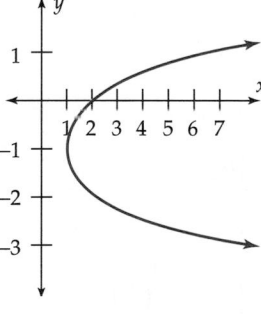

28. parabola, vertex: $(1, 2)$,
focus: point $\left(1, \frac{9}{4}\right)$, directrix: $y = \frac{7}{4}$

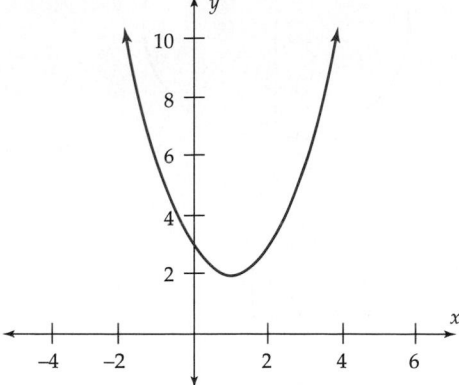

Chapter 11 Review, page 774

54.

55.

56.

57.

58.

59.

60.

61.

66. Parabola

67. Hyperbola

68. Hyperbola

69. Ellipse

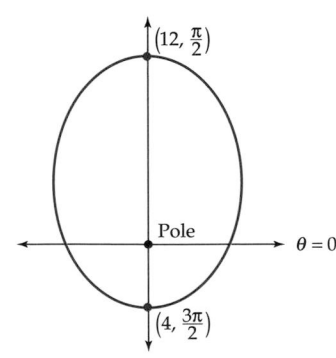

84. $x = 4 \cos t + 3$, $y = 4 \sin t - 2$,
$0 \le t \le 2\pi$

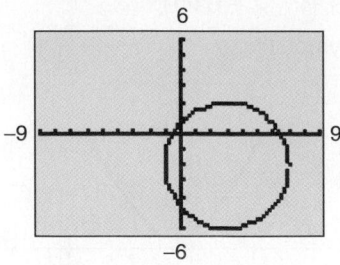

85. $x = 5 \cos t - 3$, $y = 5 \sin t + 5$,
$0 \le t \le 2\pi$

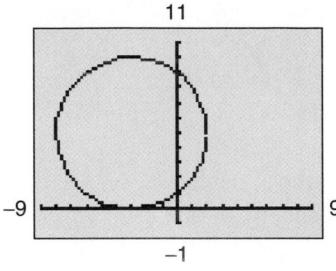

86. $x = 2 \cos t + 3$, $y = 3 \sin t - 2$,
$0 \le t \le 2\pi$

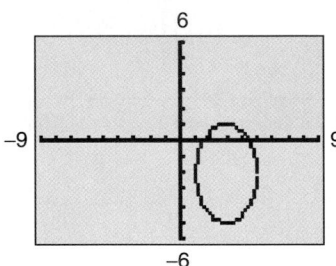

87. $x = \cos t - 2$, $y = 2 \sin t + 3$,
$0 \le t \le 2\pi$

Additional Answers

88. $x = \frac{1}{3} \cos t$, $y = \frac{1}{3} \sin t$, $0 \le t \le 2\pi$

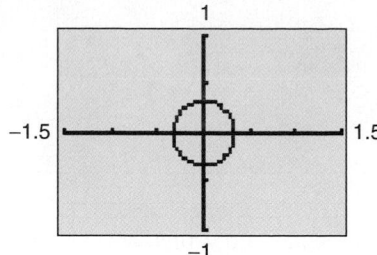

89. $x = \frac{1}{2} \cos t$, $y = \frac{1}{3} \sin t$, $0 \le t \le 2\pi$

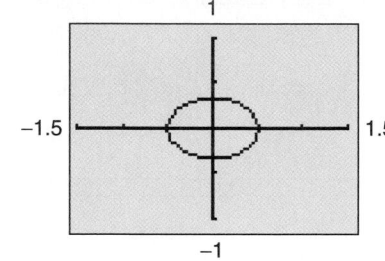

90. $x = \frac{1}{4} \sec t$, $y = \tan t$, $0 \le t \le 2\pi$

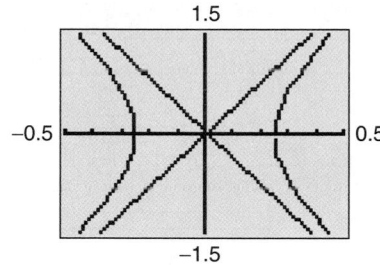

91. $x = \sec t$, $y = \frac{1}{6} \tan t$, $0 \le t \le 2\pi$

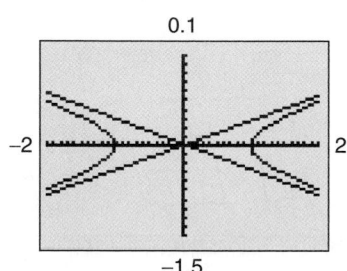

92. $x = 3 \cos t + 3$, $y = 5 \sin t - 4$, $0 \le t \le 2\pi$

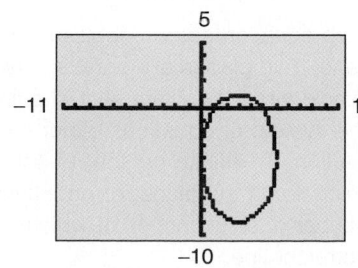

93. $x = 7 \cos t - 2$, $y = 8 \sin t + 5$, $0 \le t \le 2\pi$

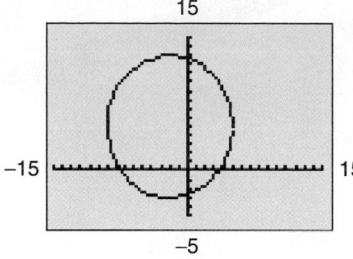

94. $x = 9 \sec t + 2$, $y = 10 \tan t + 5$, $0 \le t \le 2\pi$

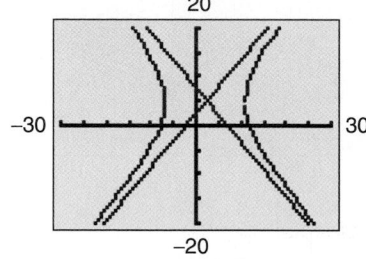

95. $x = \sqrt{12} \tan t + 2$, $y = 2 \sec t - 3$, $0 \le t \le 2\pi$

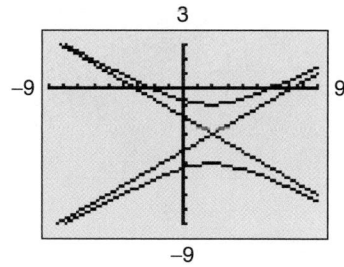

96. $x = t$, $= 3(t + 2)^2 - 5$, $-10 \le t \le 10$

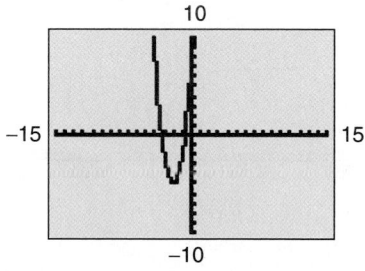

97. $x = -32(t + 4)^2 - 5$, $y = t$, $-10 \le t \le 10$

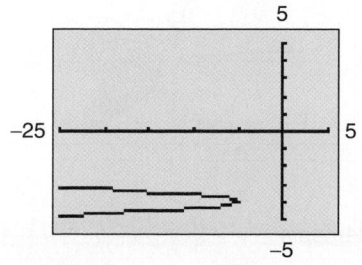

Chapter 12

Section 12.1.A, page 794

3.

4.

5.

6.

7.

8.

9.

intercepts:
$x = 6$
$y = 2$
$z = -6$

10.

intercepts:
$x = 2$
$y = 5$
$z = -2.5$

11.

intercepts:
$x = 3$
$y = -\dfrac{9}{4}$
$z = \dfrac{3}{2}$

12.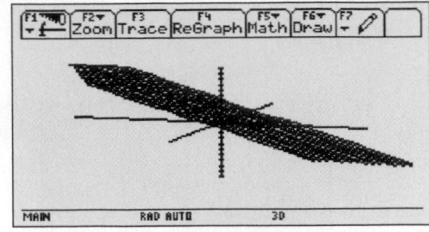

intercepts:
$x = -4$
$y = 2$
$z = \dfrac{8}{5}$

13.

intercepts:
$x = 3$
$y = 3$
$z = -3$

14.

intercepts:
$x = -3$
$y = 6$
$z = 6$

15.

intercepts:
$x = 4$
$y = 2$
$z = -8$

16.

intercepts:
$x = -3$
$y = \dfrac{9}{5}$
$z = 9$

17.

intercepts:
$x = 4$
no y-intercept
$z = -12$

18.

intercepts:
no x-intercept
$y = 1$
$z = -4$

19.

intercepts:
$x = -2$
no y-intercept
$z = -3$

20.

intercepts:
$x = \dfrac{1}{2}$
no y-intercept
$z = 2$

21. Each equation can be represented by a plane. Two planes are parallel, are coincident, or they intersect in a line. The system of equations either has no solution, an infinite number of solutions which lie on the plane, or an infinite number of solutions, all of which lie on a straight line.

9.

10.

11.

12.

13.

corner points: $(0,0), (0,6), \left(3\frac{1}{3},0\right)(4,3)$

14.

corner points: $(0,0), (0,7), \left(3\frac{3}{7},0\right), (2,5)$

15.

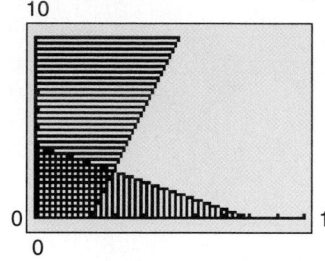

corner points: $(0,0), (0,4), (2,0), \left(\frac{20}{7},\frac{18}{7}\right)$

16.

corner points: $(0,0), (0,4), (2,0), \left(\frac{6}{11},\frac{40}{11}\right)$

17. At $(0, 6)$, the objective function has a value of 30.

18. At $(4, 7)$, the objective function has a value of 61.

19. At $(0, 0)$, the objective function has a value of 0.

20. At $(0, 0)$, the objective function has a value of 0.

21. 24 roast beef sandwiches for a profit of $72.

22. 20 model A cars and 10 model B cars for a profit of $43,000.

23. 3000 peach trees and 27,000 almond trees for a profit of $633,600.

24. $4000 invested in Fund A and $8000 invested in Fund B for a maximum return of $1040.

Chapter 14

Section 14.3, page 935

6. Given $\varepsilon > 0$, let $\delta = \frac{\varepsilon}{|-2|}$. Then,
$|x - 7| < \delta \Rightarrow |-2||x - 7| < \varepsilon \Rightarrow$
$|-2x + 14| < \varepsilon \Rightarrow$
$|-2x + 19 - 5| < \varepsilon \Rightarrow$
$|f(x) - 5| < \varepsilon$.

7. Given $\varepsilon > 0$, let δ be any positive number. Then, for every number x (including those satisfying $0 < |x - 1| < \delta$), $|f(x) - 4| = |4 - 4| = 0 < \varepsilon$.

8. Given $\varepsilon > 0$, let $\delta = 1$. Then,
$|x - 2| < \delta \Rightarrow |f(x) - \pi| = 0 < \varepsilon$.

9. Given $\varepsilon > 0$, let $\delta = \varepsilon$. Then,
$0 < |x - 4| < \delta \Rightarrow |x - 4| < \varepsilon \Rightarrow$
$|(x - 6) - (-2)| < \varepsilon \Rightarrow$
$|f(x) - (-2)| < \varepsilon$.

10. Given $\varepsilon > 0$, let $\delta = \frac{\varepsilon}{2}$. Then,
$|x - 1| < \delta \Rightarrow |2x - 2| < \varepsilon \Rightarrow$
$|2x - 7 - (-5)| < \varepsilon \Rightarrow$
$|f(x) - (-5)| < \varepsilon$.

11. Given $\varepsilon > 0$, let $\delta = \frac{\varepsilon}{2}$.
Then, $0 < |x - (-2)| < \delta \Rightarrow$
$|x - (-2)| < \frac{\varepsilon}{2} \Rightarrow$
$2|x - (-2)| < \varepsilon \Rightarrow$
$|2(x - (-2))| < \varepsilon \Rightarrow$
$|2x + 4| < \varepsilon \Rightarrow$
$|(2x + 5) - 1| < \varepsilon \Rightarrow$
$|f(x) - 1| < \varepsilon$.

12. Given $\varepsilon > 0$, let $\delta = \frac{\varepsilon}{2}$. Then,
$|x - (-3)| < \delta \Rightarrow |2x + 6| < \varepsilon \Rightarrow$
$|2x - 4 - (-10)| < \varepsilon \Rightarrow$
$|f(x) - (-10)| < \varepsilon$.

13. Given $\varepsilon > 0$, let $\delta = \sqrt{\varepsilon}$.
Then, $0 < |x - 0| < \delta \Rightarrow$
$0 < |x| < \sqrt{\varepsilon} \Rightarrow |x|^2 < \varepsilon \Rightarrow$
$|x^2| < \varepsilon \Rightarrow |x^2 - 0| < \varepsilon \Rightarrow$
$|f(x) - 0| < \varepsilon$.

14. Given $\varepsilon > 0$, let $\delta = \sqrt[3]{\varepsilon}$. Then,
$|x - 0| < \delta \Rightarrow |x - 0| < \sqrt[3]{\varepsilon} \Rightarrow$
$|x - 0|^3 < \varepsilon \Rightarrow |x|^3 < \varepsilon$.
Since $|x|^3 = |x^3| = |x^3 - 0|$,
we have $|x^3 - 0| < \varepsilon$.

15. Let $\varepsilon > 0$. Then there exist positive numbers δ_1, δ_2 such that if $0 < |x - c| < \delta_1$, then $|f(x) - L| < \frac{\varepsilon}{2}$ and if $0 < |x - c| < \delta_2$, then $|g(x) - M| < \frac{\varepsilon}{2}$. Choose δ to be the smaller of δ_1, δ_2. Then if $0 < |x - c| < \delta$, we have both $|f(x) - L| < \frac{\varepsilon}{2}$ and $|g(x) - M| < \frac{\varepsilon}{2}$. Then

$|f(x) - L| + |g(x) - M| < \frac{\varepsilon}{2} + \frac{\varepsilon}{2} = \varepsilon$.

This can be rewritten as $|f(x) - L| + |M - g(x)| < \varepsilon$.

Now using the triangle inequality we have $|f(x) - g(x) - (L - M)| < \varepsilon$.

Therefore, $\lim_{x \to c}(f(x) - g(x)) = L - M$.

16. Let $\varepsilon > 0$. Then there exists a positive number δ such that if $0 < |x - c| < \delta$, then $|f(x) - L| < \varepsilon$. Choose $\delta = \frac{\varepsilon}{|k|}$.

Then $|x - c| < \delta \Rightarrow |x - c| < \frac{\varepsilon}{|k|} \Rightarrow$
$|k||f(x) - L| < \varepsilon$ and $|kf(x) - kL| < \varepsilon$, and we have $\lim_{x \to c} kf(x) = kL$.

Advanced Topics

Section B.1, page 1001

45. $\dfrac{f(x + h) - f(x)}{h} = \dfrac{(x + h)^{12} - x^{12}}{h}$

$= \binom{12}{1}x^{11} + \binom{12}{2}x^{10}h + \binom{12}{3}x^9h^2 +$

$\quad \binom{12}{4}x^8h^3 + \cdots + \binom{12}{10}x^2h^9 +$

$\quad \binom{12}{11}xh^{10} + h^{11} \approx \binom{12}{1}x^{11} = 12x^{11}$,

when h is very close to 0.

46. $\dfrac{f(x + h) - f(x)}{h} = \dfrac{(x + h)^n - x^n}{h}$

$= \dfrac{\sum_{k=0}^{n} x^k h^{n-k} - x^n}{h} = \sum_{k=1}^{n}\binom{n}{k}x^{n-k}h^{k-1}$

When h is very close to 0, so are the last $n - 1$ terms, so

$\dfrac{f(x + h) - f(x)}{h} \approx \binom{n}{1}x^{n-1} = nx^{n-1}$

47. a. $(n - r)! = (n - r)(n - r - 1) \cdot$
$\quad (n - r - 2)(n - r - 3)\cdots 2 \cdot 1$
$\quad = (n - r)[n - (r + 1)] \cdot$
$\quad\quad (n - (r + 1) - 1)\cdots 2 \cdot 1$
$\quad = (n - r)[n - (r + 1)]!$

b. Since $(n + 1) - (r + 1) = n - r$,
$\quad [(n + 1) - (r + 1)]! = (n - r)!$

c. $\binom{n}{r + 1} + \binom{n}{r}$

$= \dfrac{n!}{(r + 1)![n - (r + 1)]!} +$

$\quad \dfrac{n!}{r!(n - r)!} = \dfrac{n!(n - r) + n!(r + 1)}{(r + 1)!(n - r)!}$

$= \dfrac{n!(n + 1)}{(r + 1)!(n - r)!}$

$= \dfrac{(n + 1)!}{(r + 1)![(n + 1) - (r + 1)]!}$

$= \binom{n + 1}{r + 1}$

d. For example, rows 2 and 3 of Pascal's triangle are

$$\begin{array}{ccccc} & 1 & & 2 & & 1 \\ 1 & & ③ & & 3 & & 1 \end{array}$$

that is,

$$\binom{2}{0} \quad \binom{2}{1} \quad \binom{2}{2}$$
$$\binom{3}{0} \quad \binom{3}{1} \quad \binom{3}{2} \quad \binom{3}{3}$$

The circled 3 is the sum of the two closest entries in the row above: $1 + 2$. But this just says that $\binom{3}{1} = \binom{2}{0} + \binom{2}{1}$, which is part **c** with $n = 2$ and $r = 0$. Similarly, in the general case, verify that the two closest entries in the row above $\binom{n + 1}{r + 1}$ are $\binom{n}{r}$ and $\binom{n}{r + 1}$ and use part **c**.

48. a.
$$\begin{array}{c} 1 \\ 1\ 1 \\ 1\ 2\ 1 \\ 1\ 3\ 3\ 1 \\ 1\ 4\ 6\ 4\ 1 \end{array}$$

b. These are identical with the first 5 rows of Pascal's triangle.

$11^4 = (10 + 1)^4$

$= \binom{4}{0}10^4 + \binom{4}{1}10^3 + \binom{4}{2}10^2 +$

$\quad \binom{4}{3}10^1 + \binom{4}{4}10^0$

$= 14{,}461$

c. As long as the numbers $\binom{n}{r}$ are less than 10 the pattern will hold. Note that it blows up for the fifth row.

d.
$$\begin{array}{l} 1 \\ 101 \\ 10201 \\ 1030301 \\ 104060401 \\ 10510100501 \\ 1061520150601 \\ 107213535210701 \\ 10828567056280801 \end{array}$$

If the numbers less than ten in Pascal's Triangle have a leading zero attached to them, these are the same as the first eight rows of Pascal's Triangle. It fails on 101^9 since the ninth row of Pascal's Triangle includes the number 126.

Section B.2, page 1009

3. Assume that the statement is true for $n = k$:
$1 + 3 + 5 + \cdots + (2k - 1) = k^2$.
Add $2(k + 1) - 1$ to both sides:
$1 + 3 + 5 + \cdots + (2k - 1) +$
$\quad\quad\quad [2(k + 1) - 1]$
$= k^2 + 2(k + 1) - 1$
$= k^2 + 2k + 1 = (k + 1)^2$.
The first and last parts of this equation say that the statement is true for $n = k + 1$.

4. Assume that the statement is true for $n = k$:

$2 + 4 + 6 + \cdots + 2k = k^2 + k$.

Add $2(k + 1)$ to both sides of the equation to get

$2 + 4 + 6 + \cdots + 2k + 2(k + 1)$
$= k^2 + k + 2(k + 1)$
$= k^2 + 2k + k + 1$
$= (k + 1)^2 + (k + 1)$.

Therefore, the statement is true for $n = k + 1$. By The Principle of Mathematical Induction, the statement is true for all positive integers n.

5. Assume that the statement is true for $n = k$:

$1^2 + 2^2 + 3^2 + \cdots + k^2$
$$= \frac{k(k + 1)(2k + 1)}{6}$$

Add $(k + 1)^2$ to both sides:

$1^2 + 2^2 + 3^2 + \cdots + k^2 + (k + 1)^2$
$$= \frac{k(k + 1)(2k + 1)}{6} + (k + 1)^2$$
$$= \frac{k(k + 1)(2k + 1) + 6(k + 1)^2}{6}$$
$$= \frac{(k + 1)[k(2k + 1) + 6(k + 1)]}{6}$$
$$= \frac{(k + 1)(2k^2 + 7k + 6)}{6}$$
$$= \frac{(k + 1)(k + 2)(2k + 3)}{6}$$
$$= \frac{(k + 1)[(k + 1) + 1][2(k + 1) + 1]}{6}$$

The first and last parts of this equation say that the statement is true for $n = k + 1$.

6. Assume that the statement is true for $n = k$:

$\frac{1}{2} + \frac{1}{4} + \frac{1}{8} + \cdots + \frac{1}{2^k} = 1 - \frac{1}{2^k}$.

Add $\frac{1}{2^{k+1}}$ to both sides of the equation

to get

$\frac{1}{2} + \frac{1}{4} + \frac{1}{8} + \cdots + \frac{1}{2^k} + \frac{1}{2^{k+1}}$
$$= 1 - \frac{1}{2^k} + \frac{1}{2^{k+1}}$$
$$= 1 + \frac{-2 + 1}{2^{k+1}}$$
$$= 1 - \frac{1}{2^{k+1}}$$

and the statement is true for $n = k + 1$. Therefore, by The Principle of Mathematical Induction, the statement is true for all positive integers n.

7. Assume that the statement is true for $n = k$:

$\frac{1}{1 \cdot 2} + \frac{1}{2 \cdot 3} + \cdots + \frac{1}{k(k + 1)} = \frac{k}{k + 1}$.

Adding $\frac{1}{(k + 1)[(k + 1) + 1]}$

$= \frac{1}{(k + 1)(k + 2)}$ to both sides yields:

$\frac{1}{1 \cdot 2} + \frac{1}{2 \cdot 3} + \cdots + \frac{1}{k(k + 1)} +$

$$\frac{1}{(k + 1)(k + 2)}$$
$$= \frac{k}{k + 1} + \frac{1}{(k + 1)(k + 2)}$$
$$= \frac{k(k + 2) + 1}{(k + 1)(k + 2)}$$
$$= \frac{k^2 + 2k + 1}{(k + 1)(k + 2)}$$
$$= \frac{(k + 1)^2}{(k + 1)(k + 2)} = \frac{k + 1}{k + 2}$$
$$= \frac{k + 1}{(k + 1) + 1}$$

The first and last parts of this equation show that the statement is true for $n = k + 1$.

8. Assume that the statement is true for $n = k$:

$$\left(1 + \frac{1}{1}\right)\left(1 + \frac{1}{2}\right)\left(1 + \frac{1}{3}\right)\cdots\left(1 + \frac{1}{k}\right)$$
$$= k + 1.$$

Multiply both sides by $\left(1 + \frac{1}{k + 1}\right)$ to get

$$\left(1 + \frac{1}{1}\right)\left(1 + \frac{1}{2}\right)\left(1 + \frac{1}{3}\right)\cdots$$
$$\left(1 + \frac{1}{k}\right)\left(1 + \frac{1}{k + 1}\right)$$
$$= (k + 1)\left(1 + \frac{1}{k + 1}\right)$$
$$= 1 + k + 1$$
$$= k + 2$$

and the statement is true for $n = k + 1$. Therefore, by The Principle of Mathematical Induction, the statement is true for all positive integers n.

9. Assume the statement is true for $n = k$: $k + 2 > k$. Adding 1 to both sides, we have: $k + 2 + 1 > k + 1$, or equivalently, $(k + 1) + 2 > (k + 1)$. Therefore, the statement is true for $n = k + 1$.

10. Assume that the statement is true for $n = k$: $2k + 2 > k$. Add 1 to both sides to get $2k + 2 + 1 > k + 1$. Now we have

$2(k + 1) + 2 > 2(k + 1) + 1$
$= 2k + 2 + 1$
$> k + 1$

and the statement is true for $n = k + 1$. Therefore, by The Principle of Mathematical Induction, the statement is true for all positive integers n.

11. Assume the statement is true for $n = k$: $3^k \geq 3k$. Multiplying both sides by 3 yields: $3 \cdot 3^k \geq 3 \cdot 3k$, or equivalently, $3^{k+1} \geq 3 \cdot 3k$. Now since $k \geq 1$, we know that $3k \geq 3$ and hence that $2 \cdot 3k \geq 3$. Therefore, $2 \cdot 3k + 3k \geq 3 + 3k$, or equivalently, $3 \cdot 3k \geq 3k + 3$. Combining this last inequality with the fact that $3^{k+1} \geq 3 \cdot 3k$, we see that $3^{k+1} \geq 3k + 3$, or equivalently, $3^{k+1} \geq 3(k + 1)$. Therefore, the statement is true for $n = k + 1$.

12. Assume that the statement is true for $n = k$: $3^k \geq 1 + 2k$. Multiply both sides by 3 to get

$3^{k+1} \geq 3(1 + 2k)$
$= 3 + 6k$
$> 3 + 2k$
$= 1 + 2k + 2$
$= 1 + 2(k + 1)$

and the statement is true for $n = k + 1$. Therefore, by The Principle of Mathematical Induction, the statement is true for all positive integers n.

13. Assume the statement is true for $n = k$: $3k > k + 1$. Adding 3 to both sides yields: $3k + 3 > k + 1 + 3$, or equivalently, $3(k + 1) > (k + 1) + 3$. Since $(k + 1) + 3$ is certainly greater than $(k + 1) + 1$, we conclude that $3(k + 1) > (k + 1) + 1$. Therefore, the statement is true for $n = k + 1$.

14. Assume that the statement is true for $n = k$: $\left(\frac{3}{2}\right)^k > k$.

Multiply both sides of this inequality by $\frac{3}{2}$ to get

$$\left(\frac{3}{2}\right)^{k+1} > \frac{3}{2}k = k + \frac{k}{2} \geq k + 1$$

provided k is at least 2. Therefore, the statement is true for $n = k + 1$. Therefore, the statement is true for all positive integers n.

15. Assume the statement is true for $n = k$; then 3 is a factor of $2^{2k+1} + 1$; that is, $2^{2k+1} + 1 = 3M$ for some integer M. Thus, $2^{2k+1} = 3M - 1$. Now $2^{2(k+1)+1} = 2^{2k+2+1} = 2^{2+2k+1} = 2^2 \cdot 2^{2k+1} = 4(3M - 1) = 12M - 4 = 3(4M) - 3 - 1 = 3(4M - 1) - 1$. From the first and last terms of this equation we see that $2^{2(k+1)+1} + 1 = 3(4M - 1)$.

Hence, 3 is a factor of $2^{2(k+1)+1} + 1$. Therefore, the statement is true for $n = k + 1$.

Section B.2, page 1010

19. Assuming that the statement is true for $n = k$: $c + (c + d) + (c + 2d) + \cdots$

$$+ [c + (k - 1)d] = \frac{k[2c + (k - 1)d]}{2}.$$

Adding $c + kd$ to both sides, we have

$c + (c + d) + (c + 2d) + \cdots + [c + (k - 1)d] + (c + kd)$

$= \dfrac{k[2c + (k - 1)d]}{2} + c + kd$

$= \dfrac{k[2c + (k - 1)d] + 2(c + kd)}{2}$

$= \dfrac{2ck + k(k - 1)d + 2c + 2kd}{2}$

$= \dfrac{2ck + 2c + kd(k - 1) + 2kd}{2}$

$= \dfrac{(k + 1)2c + kd(k - 1 + 2)}{2}$

$= \dfrac{(k + 1)2c + kd(k + 1)}{2}$

$= \dfrac{(k + 1)(2c + kd)}{2}$

$= \dfrac{(k + 1)(2c + [(k + 1) - 1]d)}{2}$

Therefore, the statement is true for $n = k + 1$.

20. Assume the statement is true for $n = k$: $1 + r + r^2 + \cdots + r^{k-1} = \dfrac{r^k - 1}{r - 1}$.

Add r^k to both sides to get $1 + r + r^2 + \cdots + r^{k-1} + r^k$

$= \dfrac{r^k - 1}{r - 1} + r^k$

$= \dfrac{r^k - 1 + r^k(r - 1)}{r - 1} = \dfrac{r^{k+1} - 1}{r - 1}$

and the statement is true for $n = k + 1$. Therefore, by The Principle of Mathematical Induction, the statement is true for all positive integers n.

21. a. $x^2 - y^2 = (x - y)(x + y)$;
$x^3 - y^3 = (x - y)(x^2 + xy + y^2)$;
$x^4 - y^4 = (x - y)(x^3 + x^2y + xy^2 + y^3)$

b. *Conjecture:* $x^n - y^n =$

$(x - y)(x^{n-1} + x^{n-2}y + x^{n-3}y^2 + \cdots + x^2y^{n-3} + xy^{n-2} + y^{n-1}).$

Proof: The statement is true for $n = 2, 3, 4$, by part **a**. Assume that the statement is true for $n = k$:

$x^k - y^k = (x - y)(x^{k-1} + x^{k-2}y + \cdots + xy^{k-2} + y^{k-1}).$

Now use the fact that $-yx^k + yx^k = 0$ to write $x^{k+1} - y^{k+1}$ as follows:

$x^{k+1} - y^{k+1}$

$= x^{k+1} - yx^k + yx^k - y^{k+1}$

$= (x^{k+1} - yx^k) + (yx^k - y^{k+1})$

$= (x - y)x^k + y(x^k - y^k)$

$= (x - y)x^k +$

$\quad + y(x - y)(x^{k-1} + x^{k-2}y + x^{k-3}y^2 + \cdots + xy^{k-2} + y^{k-1})$

$= (x - y)x^k + (x - y)(x^{k-1}y + x^{k-2}y^2 + x^{k-3}y^3 + \cdots + xy^{k-1} + y^k)$

$= (x - y)[x^k + x^{k-1}y + x^{k-2}y^2 + x^{k-3}y^3 + \cdots + xy^{k-1} + y^k]$

The first and last parts of this equation show that the conjecture is true for $n = k + 1$. Therefore, by mathematical induction, the conjecture is true for every integer $n \geq 2$.

22. Assume that x^k is less than 2: that is,

$$\sqrt{2 + \sqrt{2 + \sqrt{2 + \cdots + \sqrt{2}}}} < 2.$$

Consider the next term in the sequence.

$x_{k+1} = \sqrt{2 + x_k} < \sqrt{2 + 2} = 2$

and so $x_{k+1} < 2$. Therefore, by the Principle of Mathematical Induction, all terms in the sequence are less than 2.

23. False; counterexample: $n = 9$

24. False; counterexample: $n = 16$

25. True: *Proof:* Since $(1 + 1)^2 > 1^2 + 1$, the statement is true for $n = 1$. Assume the statement is true for $n = k$: $(k + 1)^2 > k^2 + 1$.

Then $[(k + 1) + 1]^2$

$= (k + 1)^2 + 2(k + 1) + 1$

$> k^2 + 1 + 2(k + 1) + 1$

$= k^2 + 2k + 2 + 2$

$> k^2 + 2k + 2$

$= k^2 + 2k + 1 + 1$

$= (k + 1)^2 + 1.$

The first and last terms of this inequality say that the statement is true for $n = k + 1$. Therefore, by induction the statement is true for every positive integer n.

26. True: *Proof:* Since $1^3 - 1 + 3 = 3$ and since 3 is a factor of 3, the statement is true for $n = 1$. Assume that 3 is a factor of $k^3 - k + 3$: That is, there is a positive integer P such that $3P = k^3 - k + 3$. Consider $(k + 1)^3 - (k + 1) + 3$

$= k^3 + 3k^2 + 2k + 3$

$= (3P + k - 3) + 3k^2 + 2k + 3$

$= 3P + 3k^2 + 3k$

$= 3(P + k^2 + k)$

and so 3 is a factor of $(k + 1)^3 - (k + 1) + 3$. Therefore, 3 is a factor of $n^3 - n + 3$ for all positive integers n. Therefore, by The Principle of Mathematical Induction, the statement is true for all positive integers n.

27. False; counterexample: $n = 2$

28. a. If the statement is true for $n = q$ and whenever it is true for $n = k$ it is true for $n = k + 1$, then it will be true for all positive integers greater than or equal to q.

b. Step 1: Show that the statement is true for $n = q$.
Step 2: Show that if the statement is true for $n = k$ then it is true for $n = k + 1$.

29. Since $2 \cdot 5 - 4 > 5$, the statement is true for $n = 5$. Assume the statement is true for $n = k$ (with $k \geq 5$): $2k - 4 > k$. Adding 2 to both sides shows that $2k - 4 + 2 > k + 2$, or equivalently, $2(k + 1) - 4 > k + 2$. Since $k + 2 > k + 1$, we see that $2(k + 1) - 4 > k + 1$. So the statement is true for $n = k + 1$. Therefore, by the Extended Principle of Mathematical Induction, the statement is true for all $n \geq 5$.

30. Since $(1 + r)^2 = 1 + 2r + r^2 > 1 + 2r$, the statement is true for $n = 2$. Assume that $k \geq 2$ and that the statement is true for $n = k$: $(1 + r)^k > 1 + kr$. Multiply both sides by $1 + r$ to get
$$(1 + r)^{k+1} > (1 + kr)(1 + r)$$
$$= 1 + (k+1)r + kr^2$$
$$> 1 + (k+1)r$$
and the statement is true for $n = k + 1$. Therefore, by induction, the statement is true for all $n \geq 2$.

31. Since $2^2 > 2$, the statement is true for $n = 2$. Assume that $k \geq 2$ and that the statement is true for $n = k$: $k^2 > k$. Then $(k + 1)^2 = k^2 + 2k + 1$
$$> k^2 + 1$$
$$> k + 1.$$
The first and last terms of this inequality show that the statement is true for $n = k + 1$. Therefore, by induction, the statement is true for all $n \geq 2$.

32. Since $2^5 > 5^2$, the statement is true for $n = 5$. Assume that $k \geq 5$ and that the statement is true for $n = k$:
$k - 1 \geq 4$, so $(k - 1)^2 \geq 16$,
$k^2 \geq 2k + 15 > 2k + 1$. We have $2^k > k^2$ by assumption. Multiply both sides by 2 to get
$$2^{k+1} > 2k^2$$
$$= k^2 + k^2$$
$$> k^2 + 2k + 1$$
$$= (k + 1)^2$$
and the statement is true for $n = k + 1$. Therefore, by induction, the statement is true for all $n \geq 5$.

33. Since $3^4 = 81$ and
$2^4 + 10 \cdot 4 = 16 + 40 = 56$, we see that $3^4 > 2^4 + 10 \cdot 4$. So the statement is true for $n = 4$. Assume that $k \geq 4$ and that the statement is true for $n = k$:
$3^k > 2^k + 10k$. Multiplying both sides by 3 yields: $3 \cdot 3^k > 3(2^k + 10k)$, or equivalently, $3^{k+1} > 3 \cdot 2^k + 30k$. But
$$3 \cdot 2^k + 30k > 2 \cdot 2^k + 30k$$
$$= 2^{k+1} + 30k.$$
Therefore, $3^{k+1} > 2^{k+1} + 30k$. Now we shall show that $30k > 10(k + 1)$. Since $k \geq 4$, we have $20k \geq 20 \cdot 4$, so that $20k > 80 > 10$. Adding $10k$ to both sides of $20k > 10$ yields:
$30k > 10k + 10$, or equivalently,
$30k > 10(k + 1)$. Consequently,
$$3^{k+1} > 2^{k+1} + 30k > 2^{k+1} + 10(k + 1).$$
The first and last terms of this inequality show that the statement is true for $n = k + 1$. Therefore, the statement is true for all $n \geq 4$ by induction.

34. Since $2(4) < 4!$, the statement is true for $n = 4$. Assume that $k \geq 4$ and that the statement is true for $n = k$:
$2k < k!$.
Multiply both sides by $k + 1$ to get $2k(k + 1) < (k + 1)!$
Then $2(k + 1) < 2k(k + 1) < (k + 1)!$ and the statement is true for $n = k + 1$. Therefore, by induction, the statement is true for all $n \geq 4$.

35. a. 3 (that is, $2^2 - 1$) for $n = 2$; 7 (that is, $2^3 - 1$) for $n = 3$; 15 (that is, $2^4 - 1$) for $n = 4$.

b. *Conjecture:* The smallest possible number of moves for n rings is $2^n - 1$. *Proof:* This conjecture is easily seen to be true for $n = 1$ or $n = 2$. Assume it is true for $n = k$ and that we have $k + 1$ rings to move. In order to move the *bottom* ring from the first peg to another peg (say, the second one), it is first necessary to move the top k rings off the first peg *and* leave the second peg vacant at the end (the second peg will have to be used *during* this moving process). If this is to be done according to the rules, we will end up with the top k rings on the third peg in the *same* order they were on the first peg. According to the induction assumption, the least possible number of moves needed to do this is $2^k - 1$. It now takes one move to transfer the bottom ring [the $(k + 1)$st] from the first to the second peg. Finally, the top k rings now on the third peg must be moved to the second peg. Once again by the induction hypothesis, the least number of moves for doing this is $2^k - 1$. Therefore, the smallest total number of moves needed to transfer all $k + 1$ rings from the first to the second peg is
$$(2^k - 1) + 1 + (2^k - 1)$$
$$= (2^k + 2^k) - 1$$
$$= 2 \cdot 2^k - 1$$
$$= 2^{k+1} - 1.$$
Hence, the conjecture is true for $n = k + 1$. Therefore, by induction, it is true for all positive integers n.

36. At the end of each period the amount of money you have is the amount of interest you have plus the interest earned in the period. Our claim is that after n years we will have accumulated $P(1 + r)^n$. When $n = 1$, we begin the period with the initial amount P and end with the amount
$P + rP = P(1 + r) = P(1 + r)^1$
so that the claim is true for $n = 1$. Assume that the claim is true for $n = k$. Then after k periods we have accumulated $P(1 + r)^k$. We begin the next period with this amount and during the period earn $rP(1 + r)^k$ in interest so that at the end of the $(k + 1)$st period we have $P(1 + r)^k + rP(1 + r)^k$
$= P(1 + r)^k(1 + r) = P(1 + r)^{k+1}$
and the claim is true for $n = k + 1$. Therefore, the accumulated value at the end of n periods is $P(1 + r)^n$.

37. *De Moivre's Theorem:* For any complex number $z = r(\cos\theta + i\sin\theta)$ and any positive integer n,
$z^n = r^n[\cos(n\theta) + i\sin(n\theta)]$.
Proof: The theorem is obviously true when $n = 1$. Assume that the theorem is true for $n = k$, that is,
$x^k = r^k[\cos(k\theta) + i\sin(k\theta)]$. Then
$z^{k+1} = z \cdot z^k = [r(\cos\theta + i\sin\theta)] \cdot$
$$(r^k[\cos(k\theta) + i\sin(k\theta)].$$
According to the multiplication rule for complex numbers in polar form (multiply the moduli and add the arguments) we have:
$z^{k+1} = r \cdot r^k[\cos(\theta + k\theta) +$
$$i\sin(\theta + k\theta)]$$
$$= r^{k+1}\{\cos[(k + 1)\theta] +$$
$$i\sin[(k + 1)\theta]\}.$$
This statement says the theorem is true for $n = k + 1$. Therefore, by induction, the theorem is true for every positive integer n.

Index

Index

Index

relative frequency, 844–845
remainders, 244–245
Remainder Theorem, 244
removable discontinuities, 947
repeating decimals, 78–79
replacement, in counting, 879–880
residuals, 44–46, 48, 50–51, 66
response times, 895–896
restricted domains, 210–211, 529, 532, 534
resultant force, 664–667
Richter magnitudes, 368–369
Riemann sums, 964–967
right triangles, 415–418, 421–426
roots
    absolute value, 109
    of complex numbers, 646–648
    cube root of one, 299
    extraneous, 110–111
    graphical root finder, 84–85, 122
    limits at infinity, 955–957
    nth, 327–329, 645–651
    square, 90, 109, 297, 955–956
    of unity, 648–651, 682
roots of unity, 648–651, 682
rose graphs, 742
rotation angles, 730–731, 771
rotations, 722–723, 728–732, 771
rounding, 426, 525
rule of a relation, 7
rule of the function, 7

samples, definition, 843
sample space, definition, 864–865
sample standard deviation, 858, 899
scalar multiplication, 655–656, 659, 661, 683, 805–806
scatter plots, 5–7, 48, 50–51
Schwarz inequality, 673, 683
secant lines, 218–219, 408
secants, 408, 416–418, 444–445, 486–487, 489
second-degree equations, 722–724. see also quadratic equations
self-similar under magnification, 305
sequences
    applications, 17–19, 28–29
    arithmetic, 21–29, 34, 66
    definition, 13, 66
    explicit forms, 34, 66
    geometric, 58–63, 76–79
    graphs, 14–16

sequences (continued)
    limits, 76–77
    notation, 14, 16–17
    partial sums, 26–29
    recursive forms, 15–16, 22, 66
    summation notation, 25
series
    arithmetic, 25–29
    infinite geometric, 76–79, 520–521
shading on graphs, 827–828
side-angle-side (SAS) information, 618–621
side-side-angle (SSA) information, 627–631
side-side-side (SSS) information, 619, 633
sides of angles, 413, 422, 424
simple harmonic motion. see also sinusoidal functions
    bouncing springs, 551–553
    characteristics, 547
    definition, 549
    examples of, 522, 550–553
    rotating wheel, 550–551
simple interest, 100
sines
    addition and subtraction identities, 582–583, 604, 610
    amplitude, 497–498, 516
    basic equations, 539–540, 542
    calculators, 423
    coterminal angles, 451
    damping, 512–513
    definition, 416, 444
    domain and range, 446, 476, 482
    double-angle identities, 593–594, 602–603, 611
    exact values, 448–450
    finding values, 449–450
    graphical transformations, 481–482, 503–504
    graph of, 473–475, 497–498, 510–511
    half-angle identities, 596–597, 604, 611
    instantaneous rates of change, 614–615
    inverse function, 529–532, 539, 563
    law of, 625–633, 682
    oscillating behavior, 514–515
    periodicity, 456–457, 493–494, 496–497, 516
    phase shifts, 501–503, 516, 549
    polar graphs, 740–741
    power-reducing identities, 595–596
    product-to-sum identities, 599

sines (continued)
    restricted, 529, 531
    roots of unity, 648–651, 682
    sinusoidal graphs, 510–511
    special angles, 418, 462
    summary of properties, 483
    sum-to-product identities, 599–600
    trigonometric identities, 454–460, 463
    unit circle, 445
SIN^{-1} key, 423
sinusoidal functions
    amplitude, 547–549
    constructing, 548–549
    examples, 522
    graphs, 510–511, 548
    modeling, 553–555
    rotating wheels, 550–551
    sound waves, 560–561
    spring motion, 551–553
skewed distributions, 846
skid mark length, 335
slant asymptotes, 285–286, 289
slope
    correlation and, 52, 66
    definition, 31–32, 66
    from a graph, 32
    horizontal and vertical lines, 37–38
    parallel and perpendicular lines, 38–39
    point-slope form, 36–37, 39, 66, 792
    properties, 33
    secant lines, 408, 410
    slope-intercept form, 33–36, 39, 66, 792–793
    tangent lines, 235–237, 408–409
Snell's Law of Refraction, 545
solutions, definition, 81
solving a triangle, 421
sound, speed of, 705
sound waves, 558–562, 696–697
special angles, 418–419, 437, 462
speed
    angular, 439–440
    average, 215–216, 219–220
    instantaneous, 234–236
    linear, 439–440
    skid mark length, 335
    sound, 705
spring motion, 551–553
square roots, 90, 109, 173, 297, 955–956
square systems, 814–818
standard deviation, 857–859, 888, 894, 899
standard form, of a line, 39, 66
standard normal curve, 890, 893–896

standard position, of angles, 434
standard viewing window, 84
statistics. see also data
    box plots, 861–862
    data displays, 844–850
    five-number summary, 861–862
    interquartile range, 860–861
    mean, 853–854, 856–857, 869, 899
    median, 854–856, 861
    mode, 855–856, 898
    range, 859–860
    standard deviation, 857–859, 888, 894, 899
    variance, 858
    z-values, 894–896, 900
stem plots, 847–848
step functions, 157
substitution method, 782, 821–822
subtraction
    identities, 582–585, 593–600
    matrix, 804–805
    vector, 658–659
sum functions, 191, 943
summation notation, 25–26, 61
sum of the convergent series, 77
sum-to-product identities, 599–600
surface area of a cylinder, 149, 324
symmetric distributions, 846
symmetry, 184–189, 482–483
synthetic division, 241–242
systems of equations. see also matrices
    algebraic solutions, 782–786
    applications, 786–787
    augmented matrices and, 795–798
    definition, 779
    elimination method, 783–786, 797–798, 821
    equivalent, 795
    graphs of, 780–781, 783–785, 822–824
    inconsistent and consistent, 781, 784–785, 799
    linear, 779, 781–782, 796–797
    nonlinear, 779, 821–824
    number of solutions, 781–782, 821
    square, 814–818
    substitution method, 782, 821–822
systems of inequalities, 826, 828–832

Index

velocity
average, 235
free-fall, 958–959
instantaneous, 234–236
terminal, 908, 959
total distance from, 964–965
vectors, 663
vertical asymptotes, 281–282, 288–289, 950
vertical lines, 37–38, 66, 792
vertical line test, 151–152, 186, 225
vertical shifts, 174, 481–482, 501, 504, 516
vertical stretches and compressions, 177–180, 339, 481, 487, 501
vertices (singular: vertex)
directed matrices, 809–810
ellipse, 692, 720
hyperbolas, 701, 720
parabolas, 709, 720
quadratic functions, 163–166, 169, 225
triangle, 415
Very Large Array (Socorro, New Mexico), 713–714
volume, 216, 323

waves, 493–498, 558–562
whole numbers, 3–4
wind chill, 335
work, 677–678

x-axis symmetry, 185–186, 188
x-coordinates, 5
x-coordinate transformations, 180–181
x-intercept form of quadratic functions, 164, 166–169, 225
x-intercept method, 84–86, 94, 112, 127–128, 134, 525–528
x-intercepts
ellipses, 694
hyperbolas, 702
parabolas, 163
polynomial functions, 264–265

x-intercepts (*continued*)
quadratic functions, 163–165, 169, 225
rational functions, 279–280, 288–289
x-variables, 6

y-axis symmetry, 184–185, 188
y-coordinates, 5, 166
y-coordinate transformations, 178–179
y-intercepts
ellipses, 694
hyperbolas, 702
parabolas, 163
polynomial functions, 264
quadratic functions, 163–166, 169
rational functions, 279, 288–289
in three dimensions, 792
y-variables, 6

z-axis, 790
Zero Product Property, 89
zeros
bounds, 254–256
complex, 310–313, 317
complex polynomials, 307–313
conjugate, 309–313
Factor Theorem and, 252–253
multiplicity, 265, 283, 308–309
orbits, 302–304
polynomials, 240, 245–248, 250–257, 265, 308–313, 316–317
rational, 250–254, 316
of unity, 298–299
zero vectors, 658
z-values, 894–896, 900

Trigonometry

If t is a real number and P is the point where the terminal side of an angle of t radians in standard position meets the unit circle, then

$$\cos t = x\text{-coordinate of } P \qquad \sin t = y\text{-coordinate of } P$$

$$\tan t = \frac{\sin t}{\cos t} \qquad \csc t = \frac{1}{\sin t} \qquad \sec t = \frac{1}{\cos t} \qquad \cot t = \frac{\cos t}{\sin t}$$

Trigonometric Ratios in the Coordinate Plane

For any real number t and point (x, y) on the terminal side of an angle of t radians in standard position:

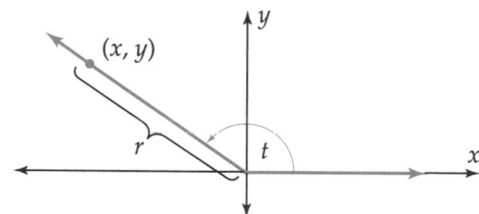

$$\sin t = \frac{y}{r} \qquad \cos t = \frac{x}{r} \qquad \tan t = \frac{y}{x} \quad (x \neq 0)$$

$$\csc t = \frac{r}{y} \quad (y \neq 0) \qquad \sec t = \frac{r}{x} \quad (x \neq 0) \qquad \cot t = \frac{x}{y} \quad (y \neq 0)$$

Periodic Graphs

If $a \neq 0$ and $b > 0$, then each of $f(t) = a \sin(bt + c)$ and $g(t) = a \sin(bt + c)$ has

- amplitude $|a|$
- period $\dfrac{2\pi}{b}$
- phase shift $-\dfrac{c}{b}$

Right Triangle Trigonometry

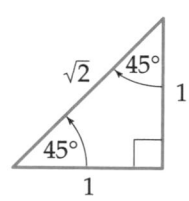

$$\sin \theta = \frac{\text{opposite}}{\text{hypotenuse}}$$

$$\tan \theta = \frac{\text{opposite}}{\text{adjacent}}$$

$$\cos \theta = \frac{\text{adjacent}}{\text{hypotenuse}}$$

Special Right Triangles

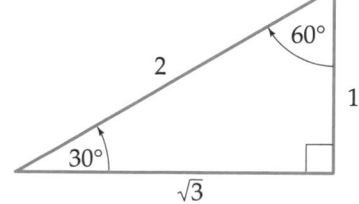

Special Values

θ				
Degrees	Radians	$\sin \theta$	$\cos \theta$	$\tan \theta$
0°	0	0	1	0
30°	$\dfrac{\pi}{6}$	$\dfrac{1}{2}$	$\dfrac{\sqrt{3}}{2}$	$\dfrac{\sqrt{3}}{3}$
45°	$\dfrac{\pi}{4}$	$\dfrac{\sqrt{2}}{2}$	$\dfrac{\sqrt{2}}{2}$	1
60°	$\dfrac{\pi}{3}$	$\dfrac{\sqrt{3}}{2}$	$\dfrac{1}{2}$	$\sqrt{3}$
90°	$\dfrac{\pi}{2}$	1	0	undefined

Law of Cosines

$$a^2 = b^2 + c^2 - 2bc \cos A$$

$$b^2 = a^2 + c^2 - 2ac \cos B$$

$$c^2 = a^2 + b^2 - 2ab \cos C$$

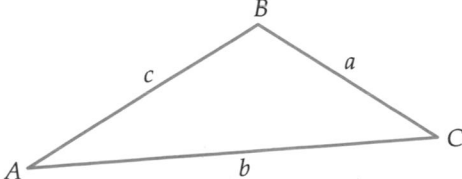

Law of Sines

$$\frac{a}{\sin A} = \frac{b}{\sin B} = \frac{c}{\sin C}$$

Area Formulas for Triangles

$$\text{Area} = \frac{1}{2}ab \sin C \qquad \textit{Heron's Formula: } \text{Area} = \sqrt{s(s - a)(s - b)(s - c)}, \text{ where } s = \frac{1}{2}(a + b + c)$$